The Elements

Name	Symbol	Atomic Number	Relative Atomic Mass	Name	Symbol	Atomic Number	Relative Atomic Mass
Actinium	Ac	89	227.028	Mendelevium	Md	101	(258)
Aluminum	Al	13	26.9815	Mercury	Hg	80	200.59
Americium	Am	95	(243)	Molybdenum	Mo	42	95.94
Antimony	Sb	51	121.757	Neodymium	Nd	60	144.24
Argon	Ar	18	39.948	Neon	Ne	10	20.1797
Arsenic	As	33	74.9216	Neptunium	Np	93	237.048
Astatine	At	85	(210)	Nickel	Ni	28	58.693
Barium	Ba	56	137.327	Niobium	Nb	41	92.9064
Berkelium	Bk	97	(247)	Nitrogen	N	7	14.0067
Beryllium	Be	4	9.01218	Nobelium	No	102	(259)
Bismuth	Bi	83	208.980	Osmium	Os	76	190.23
Bohrium	Bh	107	(262)	Oxygen	O	8	15.9994
Boron	B	5	10.811	Palladium	Pd	46	106.42
Bromine	Br	35	79.904	Phosphorus	P	15	30.9738
Cadmium	Cd	48	112.411	Platinum	Pt	78	195.08
Calcium	Ca	20	40.078	Plutonium	Pu	94	(244)
Californium	Cf	98	(251)	Polonium	Po	84	(209)
Carbon	C	6	12.011	Potassium	K	19	39.0983
Cerium	Ce	58	140.115	Praseodymium	Pr	59	140.908
Cesium	Cs	55	132.905	Promethium	Pm	61	(145)
Chlorine	Cl	17	35.4527	Protactinium	Pa	91	231.036
Chromium	Cr	24	51.9961	Radium	Ra	88	226.025
Cobalt	Co	27	58.9332	Radon	Rn	86	(222)
Copper	Cu	29	63.546	Rhenium	Re	75	186.207
Curium	Cm	96	(247)	Rhodium	Rh	45	102.906
Darmstadtium	Ds	110	(271)	Roentgenium	Rg	111	(272)
Dubnium	Db	105	(262)	Rubidium	Rb	37	85.4678
Dysprosium	Dy	66	162.50	Ruthenium	Ru	44	101.07
Einsteinium	Es	99	(252)	Rutherfordium	Rf	104	(261)
Erbium	Er	68	167.26	Samarium	Sm	62	150.36
Europium	Eu	63	151.965	Scandium	Sc	21	44.9559
Fermium	Fm	100	(257)	Seaborgium	Sg	106	(263)
Fluorine	F	9	18.9984	Selenium	Se	34	78.96
Francium	Fr	87	(223)	Silicon	Si	14	28.0855
Gadolinium	Gd	64	157.25	Silver	Ag	47	107.868
Gallium	Ga	31	69.723	Sodium	Na	11	22.9898
Germanium	Ge	32	72.61	Strontium	Sr	38	87.62
Gold	Au	79	196.967	Sulfur	S	16	32.066
Hafnium	Hf	72	178.49	Tantalum	Ta	73	180.948
Hassium	Hs	108	(265)	Technetium	Tc	43	(98)
Helium	He	2	4.00260	Tellurium	Te	52	127.60
Holmium	Ho	67	164.930	Terbium	Tb	65	158.925
Hydrogen	H	1	1.00794	Thallium	Tl	81	204.383
Indium	In	49	114.818	Thorium	Th	90	232.038
Iodine	I	53	126.904	Thulium	Tm	69	168.934
Iridium	Ir	77	192.22	Tin	Sn	50	118.710
Iron	Fe	26	55.847	Titanium	Ti	22	47.88
Krypton	Kr	36	83.80	Tungsten	W	74	183.84
Lanthanum	La	57	138.906	Uranium	U	92	238.029
Lawrencium	Lr	103	(260)	Vanadium	V	23	50.9415
Lead	Pb	82	207.2	Xenon	Xe	54	131.29
Lithium	Li	3	6.941	Ytterbium	Yb	70	173.04
Lutetium	Lu	71	174.967	Yttrium	Y	39	88.9059
Magnesium	Mg	12	24.3050	Zinc	Zn		
Manganese	Mn	25	54.9381	Zirconium			
Meitnerium	Mt	109	(266)				

Atomic masses in this table are relative to carbon-12 and limited to six significant figures, although some
For certain radioactive elements the numbers listed (in parentheses) are the mass numbers of the most stab

How to Use This Annotated Instructor's Edition

This Annotated Instructor's Edition (AIE) is a specially created version of this text. In addition to the complete student edition, it references all the print and media resources available to instructors teaching the course using Petrucci/Harwood/Herring/Madura, *General Chemistry*, Ninth Edition.

This AIE is designed to reduce the amount of time you need to prepare for lectures. It also enables you to maximize the effective integration of the many resources available to you. Prentice Hall provides a comprehensive package of supplements, including several newly developed multimedia tools, which are described on page xx.

Throughout the text, blue marginal notes indicate specific instructor resources:

This icon indicates a figure or table that is available in the acetate transparency set.

This icon references demonstrations you can perform live in class to illustrate the point being made in the text.

This icon indicates a reference to the primary literature for a point being made in the text.

This icon indicates a teaching tip. These include points to emphasize and common student misconceptions. Some experienced professors of general chemistry will find the information provided to be thoroughly familiar. But we hope instructors rotating into general chemistry once every 3 or 4 years, those teaching the course for the first time, and graduate assistants will find these helpful.

You may also find it useful to consult the Instructor's Resource Manual (IRM). The IRM offers a summary of each section, suggested lecture outlines, references to the published laboratory manual, and notes. It also suggests where certain ancillary resources can best be employed.

GENERAL CHEMISTRY

Principles and Modern Applications

Ninth Edition

Ralph H. Petrucci

California State University, San Bernardino

William S. Harwood

Indiana University, Bloomington

F. Geoffrey Herring

University of British Columbia, Vancouver

Jeffry D. Madura

Duquesne University

Annotations by
Marc D. Lord, Columbus State Community College,
Gardiner H. Myers, University of Florida, and
Bryan Sanctuary, McGill University

PEARSON

Prentice Hall

Upper Saddle River, New Jersey 07458

Editor in Chief, Science: Daniel Kaveney
Acquisitions Editor: Kent Porter Hamann
Editor in Chief, Development: Ray Mullaney
Development Editor: Deena Cloud
Production Editor: Rosaria Cassinese/Prepare Inc.
Executive Managing Editor: Kathleen Schiaparelli
Assistant Managing Editor: Beth Sweeten
Project Manager: Kristen Kaiser
Editorial Assistant: Joya Carlton
Production Assistant: Nancy Bauer
Media Editor: Margaret Trombley
Managing Editor, Science and Math Media: Nicole M. Jackson
Director of Marketing: Patrick Lynch
Manufacturing Buyer: Alan Fisher
Manufacturing Manager: Alexis Heydt-Long
Director of Creative Services: Paul Belfanti
Director of Design: Juan López
Art Director: Jonathan Boylan
Interior Designer: James Sullivan
Cover Designer: James Sullivan

Director, Image Resource Center: Melinda Patelli-Reo
Manager, Rights and Permissions: Zina Arabia
Manager, Visual Research: Beth Brenzel
Manager, Cover Visual Research & Permissions: Karen Sanatar
Image Permission Coordinator: Debbie Latronica
Photo Researcher: Sheila Norman
Senior Managing Editor, Art Production and Management: Patricia Burns
Manager, Production Technologies: Matthew Haas
Managing Editor, Art Management: Abigail Bass
AV Editor: Rhonda Aversa
Manager, Art Production: Sean Hogan
Assistant Manager, Art Production: Ronda Whitson
Illustrations: ESM Art Production, Lead Illustrators: Royce Copenhaver; Daniel Knopsnyder
EPM Artist: Richard Johnson
Mathematical Rendering Artist: Teresa Smolenski
Cover Image Artist: Daniel Knopsnyder
Composition: Prepare Inc.

BRIEF CONTENTS

APPENDIXES

CONTENTS

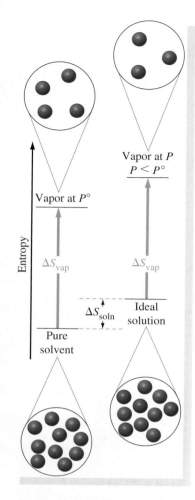

19 SPONTANEOUS CHANGE:
ENTROPY AND FREE ENERGY 780

20 ELECTROCHEMISTRY 822

21 CHEMISTRY OF THE MAIN-GROUP ELEMENTS I:
GROUPS 1, 2, 13, AND 14 870

22 CHEMISTRY OF THE MAIN-GROUP ELEMENTS II: GROUPS 18, 17, 16, 15, AND HYDROGEN   917

23 THE TRANSITION ELEMENTS   964

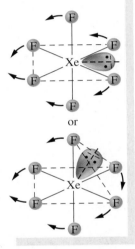

24 COMPLEX IONS AND COORDINATION COMPOUNDS   1001

25 NUCLEAR CHEMISTRY   1040

Appendixes

A   Mathematical Operations   A1

ABOUT THE AUTHORS

Ralph H. Petrucci

Ralph Petrucci received his B.S. in Chemistry from Union College, Schenectady, NY, and his Ph.D. from the University of Wisconsin–Madison. Following ten years of teaching, research, consulting, and directing the NSF Institutes for Secondary School Science Teachers at Case Western Reserve University, Cleveland, OH, Dr. Petrucci joined the planning staff of the new California State University campus at San Bernardino in 1964. There, in addition to his faculty appointment, he served as Chairman of the Natural Sciences Division and Dean of Academic Planning. Professor Petrucci, now retired from teaching, is also a coauthor of *General Chemistry* with John W. Hill, Terry W. McCreary, and Scott S. Perry.

William S. Harwood

Bill Harwood received his B.S. from the University of Massachusetts, Amherst, and his Ph.D. in Inorganic Chemistry from Purdue University in 1986. He has taught at several large universities, where he has won awards for his excellence in teaching chemistry. Beginning in summer 2006, Dr. Harwood will be Professor and Head of the Chemistry & Biochemistry Department at the University of Northern Iowa. Dr. Harwood's research in Chemistry Education involves exploring how students develop from novices toward experts as well as continuing his interests in inquiry teaching. He was co-chair of the 18th Biennial Conference on Chemical Education and continues to be active in the Chemistry Education division of the American Chemistry Society.

F. Geoffrey Herring

Geoff Herring received his B.Sc. and his Ph.D. in Physical Chemistry, both from the University of London. He is currently a Professor Emeritus in the Department of Chemistry of the University of British Columbia, Vancouver. Dr. Herring has research interests in the area of biophysical chemistry and has published over 100 papers in the area of physical chemistry and chemical physics. Recently, Dr. Herring has undertaken studies in the use of information technology and interactive engagement methods in teaching general chemistry with a view to improving student comprehension and learning. Dr. Herring has taught chemistry from undergraduate to graduate levels for 30 years and has twice been the recipient of the Killam Prize for Excellence in Teaching.

Jeffry D. Madura

Jeffry D. Madura received his B.A. from Thiel College and his Ph.D. in Physical Chemistry from Purdue University. He is currently Professor and Chair in the Department of Chemistry and Biochemistry at Duquesne University in Pittsburgh, PA. Dr. Madura's research interests are in the area of computational chemistry and biophysical chemistry, and he has published over 70 papers in the area of physical chemistry and chemical physics. Recently, Dr. Madura has undertaken studies in the use of technology and interactive personal response systems in teaching general and physical chemistry with the goal of improving student comprehension and learning. Dr. Madura has taught chemistry from undergraduate to graduate levels for 15 years and has been the recipient of a Dreyfus Teacher-Scholar Award.

PREFACE

"Know your audience." For this new edition, we have tried to follow this important advice to writers by attending more to the needs of those students who are taking a serious journey through the material. We also know that most general chemistry students have career interests not in chemistry, but in biology, medicine, engineering, environmental and agricultural sciences, and so on. And we understand that general chemistry will be the only college chemistry course for some students, and thus their only opportunity to learn some practical applications of chemistry. We have designed this book for all these students.

Students of this text should have already studied some chemistry. But those with no prior background and those who could use a refresher will find that the early chapters develop fundamental concepts from the most elementary ideas. Students who do plan to become professional chemists will also find opportunities in the text to pursue their own special interests.

The typical student may need help identifying and applying principles and visualizing their physical significance. The pedagogical features of this text are designed to provide this help. At the same time, we hope the text serves to sharpen student skills in problem solving and critical thinking. Thus, we have tried to strike the proper balances between principles and applications, qualitative and quantitative discussions, and rigor and simplification.

Throughout the text we provide real-world examples to enhance the discussion. Examples relevant to the biological sciences, engineering, and the environmental sciences will be found in numerous places. This should help to bring the chemistry alive for these students, and help them understand its relevance to their career interests. It also, in most cases, should help them master core concepts.

ORGANIZATION

In this edition we retain the core organization of the eighth edition of this text, but with additional depth and breadth of coverage of material in several chapters. After a brief overview of core concepts in Chapter 1, we introduce atomic theory, including the periodic table, in Chapter 2. The periodic table is an extraordinarily useful tool, and presenting it early allows us to use the periodic table in new ways throughout the early chapters of the text. In Chapter 3 we introduce chemical compounds and their stoichiometry. Organic compounds are included in this presentation. The early introduction of organic compounds allows us to use organic examples throughout the book. Chapters 4 and 5 introduce chemical reactions. We discuss gases in Chapter 6, partly because they are familiar to students (which helps them build confidence), but also because some instructors prefer to cover this material early to better integrate their lecture and lab programs. Note that Chapter 6 can easily be deferred for coverage with the other states of matter, in Chapter 12. In Chapter 8 we delve more deeply into wave mechanics, although we do so in a way that allows excision of this material at the instructor's discretion. As with previous editions, we have emphasized real-world chemistry in the final chapters that cover descriptive chemistry (Chapters 21–24), and we have tried to make this material easy to bring forward into earlier parts of the text. Moreover, many topics in these chapters can be covered selectively, without requiring the study of entire chapters. The text ends with comprehensive chapters on organic chemistry (Chapter 26) and biochemistry (Chapter 27).

CHANGES TO THIS EDITION

To improve the flow of information to the student and to reflect contemporary thoughts about how best to teach general chemistry a number of improvements have been made throughout the book.

- Major changes in this edition have focused on increasing the depth of coverage and adding some more challenging end-of-chapter exercises. In Chapter 3 (Chemical Compounds), we have retained the section introducing organic compounds, including nomenclature. This allows more reference to organic compounds throughout the book and also suits those who chose to introduce organic chemistry earlier in the course.
- In Chapter 6 (Gases), there is greater emphasis on the use of SI units and more detail on the kinetic-molecular theory of gases.
- A major change was the elimination of the early descriptive chapter on "Atmospheric Gases and Hydrogen," which was Chapter 8 in the eighth edition. The material from this chapter has been integrated into other chapters, specifically Chapters 6, 14, 15, 21, and 22.
- In Chapter 7, "Thermochemistry," the discussion of pressure–volume work has been completely revised and includes moving the discussion of reversible processes from Chapter 20 of the eighth edition to Chapter 7.
- Chapter 8, "Electrons in Atoms," includes a revised presentation of the Heisenberg uncertainty principle and now treats in much more detail the phases and contour maps of atomic orbitals.
- Chapter 10, "Chemical Bonding I: Basic Concepts," provides additional background on the concept of electronegativity and an in-depth introduction of electrostatic potential maps, which are employed extensively in Chapters 10, 11, and 12, and elsewhere in the text.
- Greater emphasis has been placed on the use of activities in Chapters 15 and 19 by writing equilibrium constant expressions in terms of activities.
- In Chapter 19, "Thermodynamics," the connection between statistical entropy and Clausius's entropy is introduced using a particle-in-a-box approach and the Boltzmann distribution.
- The chapters on descriptive inorganic chemistry (Chapters 21–23) are organized as groups.
- The subjects of rotational spectroscopy (Chapter 10), nanotechnology (Chapter 23), and green chemistry (Chapter 26) are introduced as new Focus On topics.

We have made a number of smaller organizational changes to improve the flow of information to the student and to reflect contemporary thoughts about how best to teach general chemistry. Minor changes throughout the textbook include revised end-of-chapter integrative examples, a two-column style for in-chapter examples, where appropriate, and the replacement of the end-of-chapter review questions by a section of self-assessment exercises.

IN-TEXT LEARNING AIDS FOR STUDENTS

As with previous editions, we have tried to create the most useful possible text for students. Here are some of the things that should make this so:

Concept Assessment Questions.   The purpose of these new, in-text, mostly qualitative questions is to assess a student's understanding of basic concepts as they are presented. Students who successfully answer these questions can proceed with some confidence that they have mastered the concepts. Those who have difficulty with a particular question may need to re-read or re-think the relevant material in the text. These questions are fully answered in Appendix H.

Important Expressions. The most significant equations, concepts, and rules are highlighted with colored panels so that students can readily find them.

Summary/Key Terms/Glossary. Each chapter concludes with a comprehensive, section-by-section verbal *Summary* in which *Key Terms* appearing in boldface type in the text are used in context. These key terms appear again in the *Glossary* (Appendix F).

Are You Wondering...? To help clarify matters that often puzzle students, we pose and then answer questions under this special heading. For obvious pedagogical reasons, these questions are cast in the form in which students typically ask them. Some are designed to help students avoid common misconceptions; others provide analogies or alternative explanations of a concept; still others address apparent inconsistencies in the material they are learning. The *Are You Wondering...?* format is also used in several instances to introduce material directed at the better-prepared students. Some of these topics are pursued further in end-of-chapter exercises. These topics can be assigned or omitted at the discretion of the instructor.

Keep in Mind margin notes. To help students appreciate the significance of earlier ideas, or to warn them about common pitfalls, we have retained in this edition *Keep in Mind* margin notes. As the name suggests, these notes ask students to recall key information about concepts and problem-solving skills. At times, we use these in conjunction with worked examples to forewarn students about common mistakes.

Focus On boxes. We believe that relevant applications should be an integral part of the text and that asides should be limited to margin notes and *Are You Wondering...?* features. With this in mind, we have concluded the text of each chapter with a short essay on a practical topic appropriate to the chapter content. These essays, which may be considered optional reading, focus on ideas introduced in the chapter.

THE STRONGEST AVAILABLE PROBLEM-SOLVING FOCUS

One probably will not become a better golfer just by watching tournaments on TV; one has to get onto the course and practice and play often. To give students the support they need to develop strong problem-solving skills, we offer extensive in-text examples that cover all the key concepts introduced in the book, each accompanied by two practice examples. We also provide integrative problems as concluding in-text examples in each chapter and a very large selection of end-of-chapter exercises, including a set that integrates the student media:

In-Text Illustrative Examples. In each chapter, most concepts—especially those that students will be expected to apply in homework assignments and examinations—are illustrated with worked-out examples. To aid visual learners and to emphasize abstract concepts, in many cases a line drawing or photograph accompanies an example to help students visualize what is going on in the problem.

Practice Examples. These are designed to give students immediate practice in applying the principle(s) illustrated in the example. We offer two for every illustrative example. The first, Practice Example A, provides immediate practice in a problem very similar to the illustrative example. The second, Practice Example B, generally takes the student one step farther than the illustrative example. This combination helps students to integrate and extend their knowledge and problem-solving skills. Answers to all Practice Examples are given in Appendix G. Complete solutions are given in the *Selected Solutions Manual*.

Integrative Examples. The text includes a special category of problems that requires students to link various important problem types introduced in the chapter—with each other and with problem types from earlier chapters. These problems are meant to be challenging for students, and to help them learn how to solve such problems. Each chapter concludes with an *Integrative Example*, sometimes of a practical nature. In each case, a strategy is outlined, followed by a step-wise solution leading to an answer. An assessment section comments on salient features of the problem.

End-of-Chapter Exercises.   Each chapter ends with six categories of exercises.

- *Exercises* are presented in pairs and grouped by categories related to the text sections.

- The *Integrative and Advanced Exercises* are not grouped by type and are generally more difficult than the *Exercises*. They integrate material from multiple sections, or multiple chapters, and they may introduce new ideas or pursue certain ideas further than is done in the text.

- *Feature Problems* are of special interest. Some of these problems require the highest level of cognitive skill on the part of students to solve. Some retrace aspects of the history of chemistry; a few deal with classic experiments; others require students to interpret data or graphs; some present new material; some suggest alternative techniques for problem solving; and a few summarize main points of the chapter in a comprehensive manner. The *Feature Problems* are a resource that can be used in several ways: as discussion points in class, as assigned homework for individuals, or for collaborative group work.

- New to this edition is a set of *Self-Assessment Exercises*, many of which may resemble typical quiz or examination questions.

- The *eMedia Exercises* are questions that can only be answered using the interactive media accompanying this text. This permits the instructor to mandate the use of the media by simply assigning one or more of these problems.

- New to this edition are the *eLaboratory Exercises* that enable a student to apply the concepts and skills of a particular chapter in a virtual chemistry laboratory setting called Virtual ChemLab.

We have also encouraged the use of concept mapping by suggesting that the student construct a concept map to connect the most significant ideas in the chapter. We have provided a discussion of how to construct a concept map in Appendix E.

Answers to all red-numbered *Exercises*, *Integrative and Advanced Exercises*, and *Feature Problems* are given in Appendix G. Full solutions to all red-numbered problems are found in the *Selected Solutions Manual* supplement. Answers to red-numbered *Self-Assessment Exercises* are given in Appendix H.

SUPPLEMENTS

FOR THE INSTRUCTOR

Instructor MediaPak (0-13-199525-1) Every new copy of the Annotated Instructor's Edition comes with an Instructor's MediaPak, which includes (1) access to the Companion Website with GradeTracker available at <u>http://www.prenhall.com/petrucci</u>, (2) a copy of the Student Accelerator CD, and (3) the Instructor's Edition of the Virtual ChemLab Workbook and the Virtual ChemLab CD.

Annotated Instructor's Edition (0-13-149364-7) Prepared by Marc Lord of Columbus State Community College. This special instructor's edition provides marginal notes and information for instructors and TAs, including teaching tips, suggested lecture demonstrations, and background references from the chemical education literature for key topics.

Instructor's Resource Center on CD/DVD (0-13-149365-5) Prepared by Philip Dutton of University of Windsor, Travis Fridgen of Memorial University of Newfoundland, and Darcy Gentleman of University of Toronto. This fully searchable and integrated collection of resources includes everything you need organized in one easy-to-access place designed to help you make efficient and effective use of your lecture preparation time as well as to enhance your classroom presentations and assessment efforts. This package features nearly all the art from the text, including tables; three pre-built PowerPoint™ presentations; PDF files of the art for high-resolution printing; all the interactive and dynamic media objects from the Companion Website; the Instructor's Resource Manual and Test Item File Word™ files; and one set of "clicker" questions for use with Classroom Response Systems. This CD/DVD set also features a search engine tool that enables you to find relevant resources via a number of different parameters, such as key terms, learning objectives, figure numbers, and resource type. Also included is the TestGen test-generation software and a TestGen version of the Test Item File that enables professors to create and tailor exams to their needs, or to create online quizzes for delivery in WebCT, Blackboard, or CourseCompass.

Test Item File (0-13-149380-9) Prepared by Alton Hassell of Baylor University and Bob Balahura of University of Guelph. This printed test bank contains more than 2250 questions, each checked for accuracy in this new edition. These questions are also available in OneKey and on the Instructor's Resource Center in the online catalog (http://www.prenhall.com/chemistry) for adopting institutions.

Instructor's Resource Manual (0-13-149366-3) Prepared by Pamela Kerrigan of Manhattan College. This useful guide describes all the different resources available to instructors and demonstrates how to integrate them into your course. Organized by chapter, this manual offers detailed lecture outlines and complete descriptions of all available lecture demonstrations, the interactive media assets, common student misconceptions, and much more.

Full Solutions Manual (0-13-199734-3) Prepared by Lucio Gelmini and Robert Hilts, both of Grant MacEwan College. This manual contains step-by-step solutions to all end-of-chapter exercises, including the Integrative and Advanced Problems. With instructor permission, this manual may be made available to students.

Instructor's Manual for Experiments in General Chemistry (0-13-149377-9) Prepared by Thomas G. Greco, Lyman H. Rickard, and Gerald S. Weiss, all of Millersville University. This manual covers the descriptions of standard lab equipment and materials, safety instructions for the lab, proper disposal of chemical waste, answers to questions, and more. This laboratory book, as well as a wealth of other Prentice Hall lab experiments, is available in a fully customizable format. *Catalyst* enables you to view, select, and organize lab experiments from all of our lab offerings, and add your own content as well. Visit http://www.prenhall.com/catalyst or contact your Prentice Hall representative for more information.

Instructor's Manual for Virtual ChemLab (0-13-221076-2) Prepared by Brian F. Woodfield of Brigham Young University. This AIE combines the full student Virtual ChemLab manual with answers, and more.

Transparency Pack (0-13-149384-1) Prepared by Jeffry Madura of Duquesne University. This set contains 350 full-color transparencies from the text. Chosen specifically to put key principles into a visual perspective, it is designed to save you time while you are preparing your lectures.

FOR THE LABORATORY

Experiments in General Chemistry (0-13-149391-4) by Gerald S. Weiss, Thomas G. Greco and Lyman H. Rickard, all of Millersville University. A comprehensive laboratory manual containing 39 experiments that parallel the text, including a final group of six experiments on qualitative cation analysis.

COURSE MANAGEMENT

Prentice Hall Course Management Solutions. Prentice Hall offers pre-built courses in a variety of Course Management systems, each of which lets you easily post your syllabus, communicate with students online or offline, administer quizzes, and record student results and track their progress. Conveniently organized by textbook chapter, these compiled resources help you save time and help your students reinforce and apply what they have learned in class.

Course Compass™—the easiest way to get your course online! Three clicks and you're up. The course includes all media resources from the instructor CD, the student Activebook, and over 5000 quiz questions.

BlackBoard®—for campuses that use the user-friendly system BlackBoard, consider a pre-built course that includes all media resources from the instructor CD, the student Activebook, and over 5000 quiz questions.

WebCT®—for campuses that use the sophisticated course management tools of WebCT, the pre-built course offers everything above as well as algorithmic questions developed in WebCT's calculation format.

OneKey content—along with all the material from the Companion Website (http://www.prenhall.com/petrucci), OneKey includes:

- Resources from the **Instructor's Resource Center on CD/DVD**.
- Test bank questions, converted from our **TestGen** test item file.

PH GradeAssist—PH GradeAssist is a text-specific homework and assessment system that allows students unlimited practice with algorithmically generated and media-enhanced problems in an online environment. Instructors can easily customize quizzes and assignments, control the content and assignment parameters, and receive assignments and view performance statistics with the built-in time-saving gradebook. Content includes select end-of-chapter questions, MCAT study guide questions, and multiple-choice quiz questions with detailed feedback to assists students in mastering key chemistry concepts. Continual, seamless upgrades to the PH GradeAssist platform offer increasing options for instructors and students.

Ask your Prentice Hall representative or visit http://cms.prenhall.com for details about any of these options.

FOR THE STUDENT

Student MediaPak (0-13-228695-5) Every new copy of the text comes with a Student MediaPak, which includes access to the Companion Website with GradeTracker available at http://www.prenhall.com/petrucci, the Student Accelerator CD, and the Virtual ChemLab Workbook and CD.

Student MediaPak for OneKey Assigned by an instructor who prefers more robust, customizable Web resources, this version of the Student MediaPak includes access to a OneKey course; *WebCT (0-13-228696-3)*, *BlackBoard (0-13-228697-1)*, and *CourseCompass (0-13-228698-X)*, and access to the PH GradeAssist online homework system. It also contains the Accelerator CD and the Virtual ChemLab Workbook and CD.

The Petrucci/Harwood/Herrring/Madura Companion Website http://www.prenhall.com/petrucci This innovative online resource center is designed to specifically support and enhance Petrucci/Harwood/Herring/Madura 9/e. Each chapter features:

- Media Gallery: Animated tutorials and videos highlight important chemistry concepts.
- 3-D Molecule Gallery: Students may access Chime models of important molecules introduced throughout the course.
- Quizzes: Multiple-choice questions are available as a self-assessment tool for students to evaluate their chemistry knowledge.

With contributions by Philip J. Dutton, University of Windsor, Jason S. Overby, College of Charleston, and Rashmi Venkateswaran, University of Ottawa.

Virtual ChemLab Workbook and CD Prepared by Brian F. Woodfield of Brigham Young University. This virtual laboratory is a realistic, simulated laboratory environment where students can get a feel for what to expect in a real wet lab, or conduct experiments that are not included in the department's lab program. Students may experiment on their own in the full virtual lab environment, or choose pre-arranged labs that are referenced in the workbook and at the end of the chapter in the textbook. Virtual ChemLab, available in the MediaPak, can be run directly from the CD or installed on the student's computer.

Student Accelerator CD-ROM Prepared by Philip J. Dutton of University of Windsor. This student CD, which contains animations, videos, and molecules from the Companion Website, accelerates the performance of the website when students download high-bandwidth media to prevent restriction by slow connections. It can also be used apart from the Companion Website if a student doesn't have a live Internet connection. The media objects referenced throughout the textbook and molecular models conveniently sorted by chapter are easily accessed with this resource. The General Chemistry: 9th Edition Accelerator CD comes packaged with every copy of the textbook's MediaPak.

Selected Solutions Manual (0-13-149385-X) Prepared by Lucio Gelmini and Robert Hilts, both of Grant MacEwan College. This manual contains completely revised step-by-step solutions to the odd-numbered end-of-chapter exercises, including the Integrative and Advanced Problems.

Student Study Guide (0-13-149387-6) Prepared by Dixie Goss of Hunter College. This guide brings students through the material of the text with discussion of chapter learning objectives, drill problems, self-quizzes, and sample tests.

Experiments in General Chemistry (0-13-149391-4) Prepared by Thomas G. Greco, Lyman H. Rickard, and Gerald S. Weiss, all of Millersville University. A comprehensive laboratory manual containing 39 experiments that parallel the text, including a final group of six experiments on qualitative cation analysis.

Student Lecture Notebook (0-13-149388-4) This lecture notebook contains the art from the text with designated note-taking sections to obviate the need for students to spend time re-drawing figures in lecture, and instead lets them concentrate on taking notes.

Study Card (0-13-222711-8) Prepared by Noel George of Ryerson University. This card is a concise, quick-reference card covering key topics in each chapter of the text. Presented in an easy-to-read format, the Ninth Edition Study Card enables students to master concepts, theories and facts for exams and review on the go.

Math Review Toolkit (0-13-149383-3) Prepared by Gary Long of Virginia Tech University. This toolkit contains a chapter-by-chapter review of the essential math skills required for each chapter, as well as a brief review of writing in chemistry. It is ideal for students for whom math is a major obstacle to success in the course and available free with a new book; please see your Prentice Hall representative for details.

Activebook This interactive version of the textbook includes animations, key glossary terms, manipulable molecular models and videos all integrated in context within an electronic version of the book. Accessed easily using a Web browser and available for purchase online, this product allows students to interact with the text and highlight important chemistry passages. Available at http://www.prenhall.com/petrucci.

ACKNOWLEDGMENTS

Many people have given of their time, creativity, and support during the preparation of this edition. Numerous colleagues from many places have offered helpful suggestions through the several editions of this text. Some are cited specifically in these acknowledgments, but many others are not. To all, however, we are deeply grateful.

We are especially grateful for the patience and encouragement of our wives, Ruth Petrucci, Jeanie Herring, and Colleen Madura. They have been willing to give up precious family time so that we could produce this textbook. Without their love and support, this book would not have been possible.

We extend our sincere thanks and acknowledgments to those of our colleagues, in both the U.S. and Canada, who gave us their advice and counsel during the preparation of this edition, either as commentators on the 8th edition, or reviewers of the 9th edition manuscript or page proofs, or as technical reviewers of 9th edition page proofs. We appreciate your time, thoughtfulness, and creativity:

Randy Alex, *Douglas College*
Raymond J. Batchelor, *Simon Fraser University*
Carey Bissonnette, *University of Waterloo*
Phillip J. Dutton, *University of Windsor*
Major Joseph W. Ellison III, *United States Military Academy*
Ken Friesen, *University of Winnipeg*
Keith Griffiths, *University of Western Ontario*
Michael Hempstead, *York University*
Richard H. Jarman, *College of DuPage*
Kirk Kawagoe, *Fresno City College*
Logan S. McCarty, *Harvard University*
Claude R. Lassigne, *Kwantlen University*
William T. Lavell, *Camden Community College*
Robert Perkins, *Kwantlen University*
Kerry Reimer, *University of Northern British Columbia*
Robert Singer, *St. Mary's University*
Alan Storr, *University of British Columbia*
Rashmi Venkateswaran, *University of Ottawa*
Thomas R. Webb, *Auburn University*
Peter M. Weber, *Brown University*

We extend thanks to the staff at Prentice Hall who took the last edition, paper, files, and sketches and turned them into this beautiful book: Joya Carlton, editorial assistant, was instrumental in coordinating the reviewing process. Rosaria Cassinese, our production editor, worked diligently and with great patience. We appreciate her careful attention to detail and her overall professionalism. Deena Cloud, our development editor, has kept us on track, handling the myriad details while maintaining a sense of humor. Finally, we give special thanks to two people: Kent Porter-Hamann, our acquisitions editor, and Ray Mullaney, editor in chief of development. Kent assembled the author team and coordinated numerous activities in the production of this book and its supplements. Ray was our chief advisor on editorial matters, our liaison with other production team members, and our rescuer in some critical predicaments. Both Kent and Ray kept up our spirits with their unbounded enthusiasm.

Responding to feedback from our colleagues and students is the most important element in keeping this book on target from one revision to the next. Your comments are most welcome.

RALPH H. PETRUCCI
rhpetrucci@earthlink.net

F. GEOFFREY HERRING
fgh@chem.ubc.ca

JEFFRY D. MADURA
madura@duq.edu

WARNING: Many of the compounds described or pictured in this text are hazardous, as are many of the chemical reactions. Do not attempt any experiment pictured or implied in the text except with permission, in an authorized laboratory setting, and under adequate supervision.

STUDENT'S GUIDE TO USING THIS TEXT

The following pages walk you through some of the main features of this text and its integrated media resources. Using this text as designed will help you develop the essential knowledge and skills you need to succeed in chemistry. Good luck!

Keep in Mind Margin Notes

These will help to remind you of ideas introduced earlier in the text that are important to your understanding of what's currently being discussed.

KEEP IN MIND ▶

that the particle in Figure 8-21 exhibits wave–particle duality, rendering inappropriate a question about how it gets from one side of the node to the other (but an appropriate question for a *classical* particle). All we know is that in the state $n = 2$, for example, the particle is in the box somewhere. When we make a measurement, we'll find the particle on one side of the node or the other!

CONCEPT ASSESSMENT ✓

For a particle in a one-dimensional box, in which state (value of n) is the greatest probability of finding the particle at one-quarter the length of the box from either end?

WAVE FUNCTIONS OF THE HYDROGEN ATOM

In 1927, Schrödinger showed that the wave functions of a quantum mechanical system can be obtained by solving a wave equation that has since become known as the **Schrödinger equation**. We shall not go into the details of its solution but just describe and interpret the solution using ideas introduced in the previous discussion.

Solutions of the Schrödinger equation for the hydrogen atom give the wave functions for the electron in the hydrogen atom. These wave functions are called **orbitals** to distinguish them from the orbits of the Bohr theory. The

Concept Assessment Questions

These NEW, informal, mostly qualitative questions are designed to provide you opportunities to test your understanding of the basic concepts as they are presented in the text. Give these questions some real thought before you check your responses against the answers at the back of the book.

Are You Wondering?

Always ask questions about what you're learning. As you read the text, new ideas may prompt you to raise important queries. The "Are You Wondering?" boxes answer good questions that students frequently ask.

Are You Wondering . . .

Why ΔH depends on temperature?

The difference in ΔH for a reaction at two different temperatures is determined by the amount of heat involved in changing the reactants and products from one temperature to the other under constant pressure. These quantities of heat can be calculated with the help of equation (7.5): q_P = heat capacity × temperature change = $C_P \times \Delta T$. We write an expression of this type for each reactant and product and combine these expressions with the measured ΔH value at one temperature to obtain the value of ΔH at another. This method is illustrated in Figure 7-16 and applied in Exercise 101.

▲ FIGURE 7-16
Conceptualizing ΔH as a function of temperature
In the three-step process outlined here, **(a)** the reactants are cooled from the temperature T_2 to T_1. **(b)** The reaction is carried out at T_1, and **(c)** the products are warmed from T_1 to T_2. When the quantities of heat associated with each step are combined, the result is the same as if the reaction had been carried out at T_2, that is, ΔH_{T_2}.

Molecular Art

It is sometimes difficult to visualize molecules and processes that can't be seen directly. To help you understand what's going on at the molecular level, carefully review and make sure you understand the molecular depictions provided in the text.

▲ **FIGURE 5-1**
Molecular view of water and an aqueous solution of air
(a) Water molecules (red and white) are in close proximity in liquid water. **(b)** Dissolved oxygen (red) and nitrogen (blue) molecules are far apart, separated by water molecules.

"Focus On" Boxes

You'll find one of these at the end of each chapter. They detail interesting, real-world applications of the chemistry you're learning. This will help you appreciate the enormous importance of chemistry in all aspects of your daily life.

FOCUS ON   HELIUM–NEON LASERS

◀ Helium–neon laser device for use as a bar-code scanner.

Laser devices are in use everywhere—from reading bar codes at supermarket checkout counters to maintaining quality control in factory assembly lines, in compact disc players, laboratory instruments, and, increasingly, as tools in surgery. The word *laser* is an acronym for *light amplification by stimulated emission of radiation*.

Consider a neon sign. An electric discharge produces high-energy electrons that strike Ne atoms and excite certain Ne electrons to a higher energy state. When an excited electron in the neon atom returns to a lower-energy orbital, a photon of light is emitted. Although we know how long Ne atoms remain in an excited state *on average*, we do not know precisely when an atom will emit a photon, nor

A He–Ne laser consists of a tube containing a helium–neon mixture at a pressure of about 1 mmHg. One end of the tube is a totally reflecting mirror, and the other end is a mirror that allows about 1% of the light to leave. An electric discharge is used to produce excited He atoms. These atoms transfer their excitation energy to Ne atoms through collisions. The Ne atoms enter a *metastable* state, an excited state that is stable for a relatively long time before the spontaneous emission of a photon occurs. Most of the Ne atoms must remain "pumped up" to this metastable state during the operation of the laser.

Following the first spontaneous release of a photon, other excited atoms release photons of the same frequency and in phase with the stimulating photon. This is rather like lining up a row of dominoes and knocking over the first one. This is the beginning of the laser beam. As shown in Figure 8-40, the beam is *amplified* as it bounces back and forth between the two mirrors. The output is the portion of the laser beam that escapes through the partially reflecting mirror. Because the photons of light travel in phase and in the same direction, laser light can be produced at a much higher intensity than would normally be achieved with spontaneous light emission.

Shown below are the transitions that produce (1) excited He atoms, (2) Ne atoms in the metastable state, and (3) laser light. After the laser light emission, (4) Ne atoms return to the ground state by way of two additional transitions. Ground-state Ne atoms are then pumped

Problem Solving

Worked Examples are followed by A & B Practice Exercises. These examples are designed help you understand how to solve important types of problems. To help you practice, two Practice Examples follow each worked example. Practice Example A is another problem very similar to the worked example. Practice Example B is more difficult, closer to the end-of-chapter problems and those you'll find on an exam.

EXAMPLE 6-6

Using the Molar Volume of a Gas at STP as a Conversion Factor. What is the mass of 1.00 L of cyclopropane gas, C_3H_6 (used as an anesthetic), when measured at STP?

Solution

Expression (6.10) makes it possible to convert directly from volume at STP to number of moles of gas. The conversion from moles of gas to mass of gas requires the molar mass.

$$? \text{ g } C_3H_6 = 1.00 \text{ L} \times \frac{1 \text{ mol } C_3H_6}{22.4 \text{ L}} \times \frac{42.08 \text{ g } C_3H_6}{1 \text{ mol } C_3H_6} = 1.88 \text{ g } C_3H_6$$

◀ If a gas is *not* at STP, relating the amount of gas and its volume is best done with the ideal gas equation (Section 6-3).

Practice Example A: Propane, C_3H_8, is stored as a liquid under pressure for use in backyard barbecue units. The liquid vaporizes to a gas when the pressure is released. A small tank of propane is opened and releases 30.0 L of gas at STP. What mass of gas was released?

Practice Example B: A 128-g piece of solid carbon dioxide (dry ice) sublimes (evaporates without first melting) into $CO_2(g)$. How many liters of gas are formed at STP?

Problem-Solving Notes

These marginal reminders warn you of common mistakes and highlight key strategies for solving particular types of problems.

Integrative Examples

These conclude each chapter and serve two purposes: they summarize many of the key concepts in the chapter, and they show you how to approach more complicated, integrative exercises (like those at the end of the chapter).

Integrative Example

A stainless steel ball bearing has a radius of 6.35 mm and a density of 7.75 g/cm³. Iron is the principal element in steel. Carbon is a key minor element. The ball bearing contains 0.25% carbon, by mass. Given that the percent natural abundance of ${}^{13}C$ is 1.108%, how many ${}^{13}C$ atoms are present in the ball bearing?

Strategy

The goal is to determine the number of carbon-13 atoms found in a ball bearing with a particular composition. The critical point in this problem is recognizing that we can relate number of atoms to mass by using molar mass and Avogadro's constant. The first step is to use the radius of the ball bearing to determine its volume. The second step is to determine the mass of carbon present by using the density of steel along with the percent composition. The third step uses the molar mass of carbon to convert grams of carbon to moles of carbon; Avogadro's constant is then used to convert moles of carbon to the number of carbon atoms. In the final step, the natural abundance of carbon-13 atoms is used to find the number of carbon-13 atoms in the total number of carbon atoms in the ball bearing.

Solution

The ball-bearing volume in cubic centimeters is found by applying the formula for the volume of a sphere, $V = 4/3 \, \pi r^3$. Remember to convert the given radius from millimeters to centimeters, so that the volume will be in cubic centimeters.

$$V = \frac{4\pi}{3}\left[6.35 \text{ mm} \times \frac{1 \text{ cm}}{10 \text{ mm}}\right]^3 = 1.07 \text{ cm}^3$$

Self-Assessment Exercises

NEW to this edition, these end-of-chapter exercises are designed to help you prepare for the types of questions you will most commonly see on quizzes and on exams.

Self-Assessment Exercises

119. In your own words, define the following terms or symbols: **(a)** λ; **(b)** ν; **(c)** h; **(d)** ψ; **(e)** principal quantum number, n.
120. Briefly describe each of the following ideas or phenomena: **(a)** atomic (line) spectrum; **(b)** photoelectric effect; **(c)** matter wave; **(d)** Heisenberg uncertainty principle; **(e)** electron spin; **(f)** Pauli exclusion principle; **(g)** Hund's rule; **(h)** orbital diagram; **(i)** electron charge density; **(j)** radial electron density.
121. Explain the important distinctions between each pair of terms: **(a)** frequency and wavelength; **(b)** ultraviolet and infrared light; **(c)** continuous and discontinuous spectra; **(d)** traveling and standing

123. Explain the phrase *effective nuclear charge*. How is this related to the shielding effect?
124. With the help of sketches, explain the difference between a p_x, p_y, and p_z orbital.
125. With the help of sketches, explain the difference between a $2p_z$ and $3p_z$ orbital.
126. If traveling at equal speeds, which of the following matter waves has the longest wavelength? Explain. **(a)** electron; **(b)** proton; **(c)** neutron; **(d)** α particle (He^{2+}).
127. For electromagnetic radiation transmitted through a vacuum, state whether each of the following properties is directly proportional to, inversely proportional to, or independent of the frequency: **(a)** velocity;

Integrative and Advanced Exercises

These Exercises are not grouped by type and are generally more difficult than the Exercises. They integrate material from multiple sections, or multiple chapters, and they may introduce new ideas or pursue certain ideas further than done in the text.

Integrative and Advanced Exercises

89. Derive the Balmer equation from equation (8.6).
90. Electromagnetic radiation can be transmitted through a vacuum or empty space. Can heat be similarly transferred? Explain.
91. The *work function* is the energy that must be supplied to cause the release of an electron from a photoelectric material. The corresponding photon frequency is the threshold frequency. The higher the energy of the incident light, the more kinetic energy the electrons have in moving away from the surface. The work function for mercury is equivalent to 435 kJ/mol photons.
    (a) Can the photoelectric effect be obtained with

$O_2 + O$. A 1.00-L sample of air at 22 °C and 748 mmHg contains 0.25 ppm of O_3. How much energy, in joules, must be absorbed if all the O_3 molecules in the sample of air are to dissociate? Assume that each photon absorbed causes one O_3 molecule to dissociate, and that the wavelength of the radiation is 254 nm.
102. Radio signals from *Voyager 1* in the 1970s were broadcast at a frequency of 8.4 GHz. On Earth, this radiation was received by an antenna able to detect signals as weak as 4×10^{-21} W. How many photons per second does this detection limit represent?

Feature Problems

To solve these problems the highest level of cognitive skills is required on the part of the students. These problems are a resource that can be used in several ways: as discussion points in class, as assigned homework for individuals, or for collaborative group work.

Feature Problems

113. We have noted that an emission spectrum is a kind of "atomic fingerprint." The various steels are alloys of iron and carbon, usually containing one or more other metals. Based on the principal lines of their atomic

spectra, which of the metals in the table below are likely to be present in a steel sample whose hypothetical emission spectrum is pictured? Is it likely that still other metals are present in the sample? Explain.

eMedia Exercises

These exercises can only be solved by using the interactive media available in your student MediaPak. These exercises foster your understanding through visual and interactive learning styles.

 eMedia Exercises

131. Using the **Electromagnetic Spectrum** activity (*Activebook 8-1*), establish the mathematical relationship between the *energy* of radiation and the *wavelength* of radiation.
[*Hint:* You should have three to five data points to determine a relationship between two variables. Consider whether there is a linear or inversely linear relationship.]

133. View the **Quantum Number** activity (*Activebook 8-7*). This illustration demonstrates that the total number of populated orbitals in an energy level is equal to n^2, where n is the principal quantum number. At what value of n does this calculation no longer provide physically applicable information?
[*Hint:* See the periodic table and refer to the number of known elements.]

eLaboratory Exercises

These exercises are answered by using the Virtual ChemLab software in your student MediaPak. These are chemistry questions posed in a simulated laboratory setting.

 eLaboratory Exercises

These exercises allow students to apply the concepts and skills for this chapter in the simulated laboratory of Virtual ChemLab. Worksheets for each of these exercises are found in the Virtual ChemLab Workbook in your MediaPak.

131. *(VCL 6-1) Boyle's Law: Pressure and Volume*
Robert Boyle, a philosopher and theologian, studied the properties of gases in the seventeenth century. He noticed that gases behave similarly to springs; when compressed or expanded, they tend to spring back to their original volume. He published his findings in 1662 in a monograph entitled *The Spring of the Air and Its Effects*. You will make observations similar to those of Robert Boyle and learn about the relationship between the pressure and volume of an ideal gas.

132. *(VCL 6-2) Charles's Law: Temperature and Volume*
Charles's law was discovered by Joseph Louis Gay-Lussac in 1802, based on unpublished work done by Jacques Charles in about 1787. Charles had found that a number of gases expand to the same extent over the same 80° temperature interval. You will be observing the relationship between the temperature and volume of a gas similar to that studied by Charles.

1

MATTER—ITS PROPERTIES AND MEASUREMENT

CONTENTS

A Hubble Space Telescope image of a cloud of hydrogen gas and dust (lower right half of the image) that is part of the Swan Nebula (M17). The colors correspond to light emitted by hydrogen (green), sulfur (red), and oxygen (blue). The chemical elements discussed in this text are those found on Earth and, presumably, throughout the universe.

From the clinic that treats "chemical dependency" to a theatrical performance with "good chemistry" to the food label stating "no chemicals added," chemistry and chemicals seem an integral part of life, even if everyday references to them are often misleading. A label implying the absence of chemicals in a food makes no sense. All foods consist entirely of chemicals, even if "organically grown." In fact, all material objects—whether living or inanimate—are made up only of chemicals, and we should begin our study with that thought clearly in mind.

By manipulating materials in their environment, people have always practiced chemistry. Among the earliest applications were the glazing of pottery, the smelting of ores to produce metals, the tanning of hides, the dyeing of fabrics, and the making of cheese, wine, beer, and soap. With modern knowledge, though, chemists can literally decompose matter into its smallest components (atoms) and reassemble those components into materials that do not exist naturally, often exhibiting unusual properties. Thus, motor fuels and thousands of chemicals used in the manufacture of plastics, synthetic fabrics, pharmaceuticals, and pesticides can all be made from petroleum. Modern chemical knowledge is also needed to understand the processes that sustain life, and to understand and control processes that are detrimental to the environment, such as the formation of smog and the destruction of stratospheric ozone. Because it relates to so many areas of human endeavor, chemistry is sometimes called the central science.

Early chemical knowledge consisted of the "how to" of chemistry, discovered through trial and error. Modern chemical knowledge answers the "why" as well as the "how to" of chemical change. It is grounded in principles and theory, and mastering the principles of chemistry requires a systematic approach to the subject. Scientific progress depends on the way scientists do their work—asking the right questions, designing the right experiments to supply the answers, and formulating plausible explanations of their findings. We begin with a closer look into the scientific method.

1-1 THE SCIENTIFIC METHOD

Science differs from other fields of study in the *method* that scientists use to acquire knowledge and the special significance of this knowledge. Scientific knowledge can be used to explain natural phenomena and, at times, to *predict* future events.

The ancient Greeks developed some powerful methods of acquiring knowledge, particularly in mathematics. The Greek approach was to start with certain basic assumptions, or premises. Then, by the method known as *deduction*, certain conclusions must logically follow. For example, if $a = b$ and $b = c$, then $a = c$. Deduction alone is not enough for obtaining scientific knowledge, however. The Greek philosopher Aristotle *assumed* four fundamental substances: air, earth, water, and fire. All other materials, he believed, were formed by combinations of these four elements. Chemists of several centuries ago (more commonly referred to as alchemists) tried, in vain, to apply the four-element idea to turn lead into gold. They failed for many reasons, one being that the four-element assumption is false.

The scientific method originated in the seventeenth century with such people as Galileo, Francis Bacon, Robert Boyle, and Isaac Newton. The key to the method is to make no initial assumptions, but rather to make careful observations of natural phenomena. When enough observations have been made so that a pattern begins to emerge, a generalization or natural law can be formulated describing the phenomenon. **Natural laws** are concise statements, often in mathematical form, about natural phenomena. The form of reasoning in which a general statement or natural law is inferred from a set of observations is called *induction*. For example, early in the sixteenth century, the Polish astronomer Nicolas Copernicus (1473–1543), through careful study of astronomical observations, concluded that Earth revolves around the sun in a circular orbit, although the general teaching of the time, not based on scientific study, was that the sun and other heavenly bodies revolved around Earth. We can think of Copernicus's statement as a natural law. Another example of a natural law is the radioactive decay law, which dictates how long it takes for a radioactive substance to lose its radioactivity.

The success of a natural law depends on its ability to explain, or account for, observations and to predict new phenomena. Copernicus's work was a great success because he was able to predict future positions of the planets more accurately than his contemporaries. We should not think of a natural law as an *absolute* truth, however. Future experiments may require us to modify the law. For example, Copernicus's ideas were refined a half-century later by Johannes Kepler, who showed that planets travel in elliptical, not circular, orbits. To verify a natural law, a scientist designs *experiments* that show whether the conclusions deduced from the natural law are supported by experimental results.

The development of *Dalton's atomic theory* (Section 2-1) is an excellent example of the application of the *scientific method*. This topic is suitable for discussion or quiz questions.

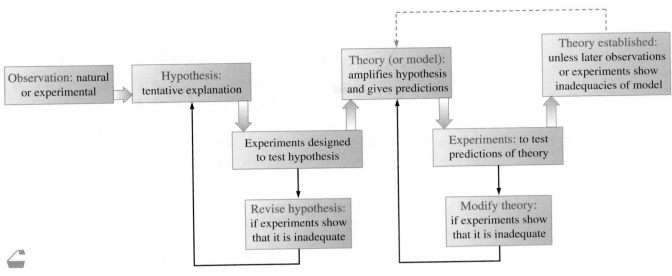

▲ **FIGURE 1-1**
The scientific method illustrated

A **hypothesis** is a tentative explanation of a natural law. If a hypothesis survives testing by experiments, it is often referred to as a theory. In a broader sense, a **theory** is a model or way of looking at nature that can be used to explain natural laws and make further predictions about natural phenomena. When differing or conflicting theories are proposed, the one that is most successful in its predictions is generally chosen. Also, the theory that involves the smallest number of assumptions—the simplest theory—is preferred. Over time, as new evidence accumulates, most scientific theories undergo modification, and some are discarded.

The **scientific method** is the combination of observation, experimentation, and the formulation of laws, hypotheses, and theories. The method is illustrated by the flow diagram in Figure 1-1. Scientists may develop a pattern of thinking about their field, known as a *paradigm*. Some paradigms may be successful at first, but then become less so. When that happens, a new paradigm may be needed or, as is sometimes said, a "paradigm shift" occurs. In a way, the method of inquiry that we call the scientific method is itself a paradigm, and there are some who feel that it, too, is in need of change. That is, the varied activities of modern scientists are more complex than the simplified description of the scientific method presented here.* In any case, merely following a set of procedures, rather like using a cookbook, will not guarantee scientific success.

Another factor in scientific discovery is chance, or serendipity. Many discoveries have been made by accident. For example, in 1839, the American inventor Charles Goodyear was searching for a treatment of natural rubber that would make it less brittle when cold and less tacky when warm. In the course of this work, he accidentally spilled a rubber–sulfur mixture on a hot stove and found that the resulting product had exactly the properties he was seeking. Other chance discoveries include X-rays, radioactivity, and penicillin. So scientists and inventors always need to be alert to unexpected observations. Perhaps no one was more aware of this than Louis Pasteur, who wrote, "Chance favors the prepared mind."

Paradigms that are based on untested assumptions have historically confused the development of science. We no longer think that the Earth is flat nor that the stars rotate around it. The debate about evolution continues to include matters of belief.

▲ Louis Pasteur (1822–1895). This great practitioner of the scientific method was the developer of the germ theory of disease, the sterilization of milk by pasteurization, and vaccination against rabies. He has been called the greatest physician of all time by some. He was, in fact, not a physician at all, but a chemist—by training and by profession.

CONCEPT ASSESSMENT ✓

Is the common saying, "The exception proves the rule," a good statement of the scientific method? Explain.

1-2　PROPERTIES OF MATTER

Dictionary definitions of chemistry usually include the terms *matter*, *composition*, and *properties*, as in the statement that "chemistry is the science that deals with the composition and properties of matter." In this and the next section, we will consider some basic ideas relating to these three terms in hopes of gaining a better understanding of what chemistry is all about.

Matter is anything that occupies space and displays the properties of *mass* and inertia. Every human being is a collection of matter. We all occupy space, and we describe our mass in terms of weight, a related property. (Mass and weight are described in more detail in Section 1-4. Inertia is described in Appendix B.) All the objects that we see around us consist of matter. The gases of the atmosphere, even though they are invisible, are matter—they occupy space and have mass. Sunlight is *not* matter; rather, it is a form of energy. Energy is discussed in later chapters.

Composition refers to the parts or components of a sample of matter and their relative proportions. Ordinary water is made up of two simpler substances—hydrogen and oxygen—present in certain fixed proportions. A chemist would say that the composition of water is 11.19% hydrogen and 88.81% oxygen by mass. Hydrogen peroxide, a substance used in bleaches and antiseptics, is also made up of hydrogen and oxygen, but it has a different composition. Hydrogen peroxide is 5.93% hydrogen and 94.07% oxygen by mass.

Properties are those qualities or attributes that we can use to distinguish one sample of matter from others; and as we consider next, the properties of matter are generally grouped into two broad categories: physical and chemical.

PHYSICAL PROPERTIES AND PHYSICAL CHANGES

A **physical property** is one that a sample of matter displays without changing its composition. Thus, we can distinguish between the reddish brown solid, copper, and the yellow solid, sulfur, by the physical property of *color* (Fig. 1-2).

Another physical property of copper is that it can be hammered into a thin sheet of foil (see Figure 1-2). Solids having this ability are said to be *malleable*. Sulfur is not malleable. If we strike a chunk of sulfur with a hammer, it crumbles into a powder. Sulfur is *brittle*. One physical property of copper that sulfur does not share is the ability to be drawn into a fine wire (ductility). Also, sulfur is a far poorer conductor of heat and electricity than is copper.

Sometimes a sample of matter undergoes a change in its physical appearance. In such a **physical change**, some of the physical properties of the sample may change, but its composition remains unchanged. When liquid water freezes into solid water (ice), it certainly looks different and, in many ways, it is different. Yet, the water remains 11.19% hydrogen and 88.81% oxygen by mass.

Changes of State animation

☑ Mention that matter exists in three states of matter: solid, liquid and gas.

☑ Some prefer to define chemical change as a process *forming a new substance*. A precipitation reaction, such as $Ag^+ + Cl^- \longrightarrow AgCl(s)$, is certainly chemical. How about the opposite, forming a solution, such as $NaCl(s) \longrightarrow Na^+(aq) + Cl^-(aq)$? The change in structure and bonding here is just as substantial as in any other chemical reaction. Is $Na^+(aq)$ a new substance? A definition based on composition change is probably the safest. How about, however, the $S_8 \longrightarrow S_n$ transformation?

▶ **FIGURE 1-2**
Physical properties of sulfur and copper
A lump of sulfur (left) crumbles into a yellow powder when hammered. Copper (right) can be obtained as large lumps of native copper, formed into pellets, hammered into a thin foil, or drawn into a wire.

CHEMICAL PROPERTIES AND CHEMICAL CHANGE

In a **chemical change**, or **chemical reaction**, one or more kinds of matter are converted to new kinds of matter with different compositions. The key to identifying chemical change, then, comes in observing a *change in composition*. The burning of paper involves a chemical change. Paper is a complex material, but its principal constituents are carbon, hydrogen, and oxygen. The chief products of the combustion are two gases, one consisting of carbon and oxygen (carbon dioxide) and the other consisting of hydrogen and oxygen (water, as steam). The ability of paper to burn is an example of a chemical property. A **chemical property** is the ability (or inability) of a sample of matter to undergo a change in composition under stated conditions.

Zinc reacts with hydrochloric acid solution to produce hydrogen gas and a solution of zinc chloride in water (Fig. 1-3). This reaction is one of zinc's distinctive chemical properties, just as the inability of gold to react with hydrochloric acid is one of gold's chemical properties. Sodium reacts not only with hydrochloric acid but also with water. In some of their physical properties, zinc, gold, and sodium are similar. For example, each is malleable and a good conductor of heat and electricity. In most of their chemical properties, though, zinc, gold, and sodium are quite different. Knowing these differences helps us to understand why zinc, which does not react with water, is used in roofing nails, roof flashings, and rain gutters, and sodium is not. Also, we can appreciate why gold, because of its chemical inertness, is prized for jewelry and coins: It does not tarnish or rust. In our study of chemistry, we shall see why substances differ in properties and how these differences determine the ways in which we use them.

▲ **FIGURE 1-3**
A chemical property of zinc and gold: reaction with hydrochloric acid
The zinc-plated (galvanized) nail reacts with hydrochloric acid, producing the bubbles of hydrogen gas seen on its surface. The gold bracelet is unaffected by hydrochloric acid. In this photograph, the zinc plating has been consumed, exposing the underlying iron nail. The reaction of iron with hydrochloric acid imparts some color to the acid solution.

1-3 CLASSIFICATION OF MATTER

Matter is made up of very tiny units called **atoms**. Presently we know of about 114 different types of atoms, and *all* matter is made up of just these types! Each different type of atom is the building block of a different chemical **element**. The known elements range from common substances, such as carbon, iron, and silver, to uncommon ones, such as lutetium and thulium. About 90 of the elements can be obtained from natural sources. The remainder do not occur naturally and have been created only in laboratories. On the inside front cover you will find a complete listing of the elements and also a special tabular arrangement of the elements known as the *periodic table*. The periodic table is the chemist's directory of the elements. We will describe it in Chapter 2 and use it throughout most of the text.

Chemical **compounds** are substances comprised of atoms of two or more elements joined together. Scientists have identified millions of different chemical compounds. In some cases, we can isolate a molecule of a compound. A **molecule** is the smallest entity having the same proportions of the constituent atoms as does the compound as a whole. A molecule of water consists of three atoms: two hydrogen atoms joined to a single oxygen atom. A molecule of hydrogen peroxide has two hydrogen atoms and two oxygen atoms; the two oxygen atoms are joined together and one hydrogen atom is attached to each oxygen atom. By contrast, a molecule of the blood protein gamma globulin is made up of 19,996 atoms, but they are of just four types: carbon, hydrogen, oxygen, and nitrogen.

◄ The identity of an atom is established by a feature called its atomic number (see Section 2-3). In recent years, a number of new elements have been synthesized, such as those with atomic numbers 110 and 111 first reported in 1994 and whose discoveries have been confirmed. Reports of other new elements await confirmation. Characterizing "superheavy" elements is a daunting challenge; they are produced only a few atoms at a time and the atoms disintegrate almost instantaneously.

Gamma globulin

Mixtures and Compounds movie

▲ Is it homogeneous or heterogeneous? When viewed through a microscope, homogenized milk is seen to consist of globules of fat dispersed in a watery medium. Homogenized milk is a *heterogeneous* mixture.

 Again, it is composition, particularly its variability, that helps us distinguish the several classifications of matter.

☑ Solutions can be gaseous and liquids as described here, but they can also be solids. Alloys are examples of solid solutions.

The composition and properties of an element or compound are uniform throughout a given sample and from one sample to another. Elements and compounds are called **substances**. (In the chemical sense, the term *substance* should be used only for elements and compounds.) A *mixture* of substances can vary in composition and properties from one sample to another. One that is uniform in composition and properties throughout is said to be a **homogeneous mixture** or a *solution*. A given solution of sucrose (cane sugar) in water is uniformly sweet throughout the solution, but the sweetness of another sucrose solution may be rather different if the sugar and water are present in different proportions. Ordinary air is a homogeneous mixture of several gases, principally the *elements* nitrogen and oxygen. Seawater is a solution of the *compounds* water, sodium chloride (salt), and a host of others. Gasoline is a homogeneous mixture or solution of dozens of compounds.

In **heterogeneous mixtures**—sand and water, for example—the components separate into distinct regions. Thus, the composition and physical properties vary from one part of the mixture to another. Salad dressing, a slab of concrete, and the leaf of a plant are all heterogeneous. It is usually easy to distinguish heterogeneous from homogeneous mixtures. A scheme for classifying matter into elements and compounds and homogeneous and heterogeneous mixtures is summarized in Figure 1-4.

SEPARATING MIXTURES

A mixture can be separated into its components by appropriate physical means. Consider again the heterogeneous mixture of sand in water. When we pour this mixture into a funnel lined with porous filter paper, the water passes through and sand is retained on the paper. This process of separating a solid from the liquid in which it is suspended is called *filtration* (Fig. 1-5a). You will probably use this procedure in the laboratory. On the other hand, we cannot separate a homogeneous mixture (solution) of copper(II) sulfate in water by filtration because all components pass through the paper. We can, however, boil the solution of copper(II) sulfate and water. In the process of *distillation*, a pure liquid is condensed from the vapor given off by a boiling solution. When all the water has been removed by boiling a solution of copper(II) sulfate in water, solid copper(II) sulfate remains behind (Fig. 1-5b).

📖 Classification of Matter activity

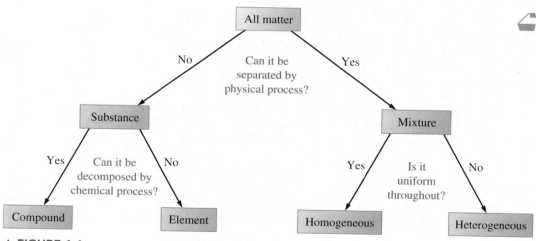

▲ **FIGURE 1-4**
A classification scheme for matter
Every sample of matter is either a single substance (an element or compound) or a mixture of substances. At the molecular level, an element consists of atoms of a single type and a compound consists of two or more different types of atoms, usually joined into molecules. In a homogeneous mixture, atoms or molecules are randomly mixed at the molecular level. In heterogeneous mixtures, the components are physically separated, as in a layer of octane molecules (a constituent of gasoline) floating on a layer of water molecules.

(a)   (b)

(c)   (d)

The distinction of a method or means as either *physical* or *chemical* is more a matter of results than the technique employed. Differential thermal analysis or simply heating a sample can result in both chemical and physical changes, and it often requires careful interpretation to distinguish between these alternatives.

Decomposition of Ammonium Dichromate. Perform as shown in Figure 1-6, using a Mg ribbon fuse. This is less messy if performed in a large test tube. Use a loose cotton plug to stop the bits of flying product. Heat with a burner near the top of the solid sample. Once started, this is self-sustaining.

◀ **FIGURE 1-5**
Separating mixtures: a physical process
(a) Separation of a heterogeneous mixture by filtration: Solid copper(II) sulfate is retained on the filter paper, while liquid hexane passes through. **(b)** Separation of a homogeneous mixture by distillation: Copper(II) sulfate remains in the flask on the left as water passes to the flask on the right, by first evaporating and then condensing back to a liquid. **(c)** Separation of the components of ink using chromatography: A dark spot of black ink can be seen just above the water line as water moves up the paper. **(d)** Water has dissolved the colored components of the ink, and these components are retained in different regions on the paper according to their differing tendencies to adhere to the paper.

Another method of separation available to modern chemists depends on the differing abilities of compounds to adhere to the surfaces of various solid substances, such as paper and starch. The technique of *chromatography* relies on this principle. The dramatic results that can be obtained with chromatography are illustrated by the separation of ink on a filter paper (Fig. 1-5c–d).

Paper Chromatography of Ink movie

DECOMPOSING COMPOUNDS

A chemical compound retains its identity during physical changes, but it can be decomposed into its constituent elements by *chemical changes*. The decomposition of compounds into their constituent elements is a more difficult matter than the mere physical separation of mixtures. The extraction of iron from iron oxide ores requires a blast furnace. The industrial production of pure magnesium from magnesium chloride requires electricity. It is generally easier to convert a compound into other compounds by a chemical reaction than it is to separate a compound into its constituent elements. For example, when heated, ammonium dichromate decomposes into the substances chromium(III) oxide, nitrogen, and water. This reaction, once used in movies to simulate a volcano, is illustrated in Figure 1-6.

STATES OF MATTER

Matter is generally found in one of three *states*—solid, liquid, or gas. In a **solid**, atoms or molecules are in close contact, sometimes in a highly organized arrangement called a *crystal*. A solid has a definite shape. In a **liquid**, the atoms or molecules are usually separated by somewhat greater distances than in a solid. Movement of these atoms or molecules gives a liquid its most distinctive property—the ability to flow, covering the bottom and assuming the shape of its container. In a **gas**, distances between atoms or molecules are much greater than in a liquid. A gas always expands to fill its container.

▲ **FIGURE 1-6**
A chemical change: decomposition of ammonium dichromate

► **FIGURE 1-7**
Macroscopic and microscopic views of matter
The picture shows a block of ice on a heated surface and the three states of water. The circular insets show how chemists conceive of these states microscopically, in terms of molecules with two hydrogen atoms joined to one of oxygen. In ice **(a)**, the molecules are joined together in a regular pattern in a rigid framework. In liquid water **(b)**, the molecules are rather closely packed but move freely. In gaseous water **(c)**, the molecules are widely separated.

 Phases of Water activity

 Phases of the Elements activity

 Students might find it interesting at this point to learn about the six types of changes of state: Conversion of a

1. solid to a liquid is *melting*.
2. liquid to a solid is *freezing*.
3. liquid to a gas is *evaporation*.
4. gas to a liquid is *condensation*.
5. solid to a gas is *sublimation*.
6. gas to a solid is *deposition*.

► Nonnumerical information is *qualitative*, such as the color blue.

The *definition of the meter*, formerly based on an atomic line of ^{86}Kr, was changed to the speed of light in 1983. Effectively, the speed of light is now defined as 2.99792458×10^8 m/s.

Depending on conditions, a substance may exist in only one state of matter, or it may be present in two or three states. Thus, as the ice in a small pond begins to melt in the spring, water is in two states: solid and liquid (actually, three states if we also consider water vapor in the air above the pond). The three states of water are illustrated at two levels in Figure 1-7.

The *macroscopic level* refers to how we perceive matter with our eyes, through the outward appearance of objects. The *microscopic level* describes matter as chemists conceive of it—in terms of atoms and molecules and their behavior. In this text, we will describe many macroscopic, observable properties of matter, but to explain these properties, we will often shift our view to the atomic or molecular level—the microscopic level.

1-4   MEASUREMENT OF MATTER: SI (METRIC) UNITS

Chemistry is a *quantitative* science, which means that in many cases we can measure a property of a substance and compare it with a standard having a known value of the property. We express the measurement as the product of a *number* and a *unit*. The unit indicates the standard against which the measured quantity is being compared. When we say that the length of the playing field in football is 100 yd, we mean that the field is 100 times longer than a standard of length called the yard (yd). In this section, we will introduce some basic units of measurement that are important to chemists.

The scientific system of measurement is called the *Système Internationale d'Unités* (International System of Units) and is abbreviated **SI**. It is a modern version of the metric system, a system based on the unit of length called a *meter* (m). The meter was originally defined as 1/10,000,000 of the distance from the equator to the North Pole and translated into the length of a metal bar kept in Paris. Unfortunately, this length is subject to change with temperature, and it cannot be exactly reproduced. The SI system substitutes for the standard meter bar an unchanging, reproducible quantity: 1 meter is the distance traveled by light in a vacuum in 1/299,792,458 of a second. Length is one of the seven fundamental quantities in the SI system (see Table 1.1). All other physical

TABLE 1.1 SI Base Quantities		
Physical Quantity	Unit	Abbreviation
Length	meter[a]	m
Mass	kilogram	kg
Time	second	s
Temperature	kelvin	K
Amount of substance[b]	mole	mol
Electric current[c]	ampere	A
Luminous intensity[d]	candela	cd

[a] The official spelling of this unit is "metre," but we will use the American spelling.
[b] The mole is introduced in Section 2-7.
[c] Electric current is described in Appendix B and in Chapter 20.
[d] Luminous intensity is not discussed in this text.

TABLE 1.2 SI Prefixes	
Multiple	Prefix
10^{18}	exa (E)
10^{15}	peta (P)
10^{12}	tera (T)
10^{9}	giga (G)
10^{6}	mega (M)
10^{3}	kilo (k)
10^{2}	hecto (h)
10^{1}	deca (da)
10^{-1}	deci (d)
10^{-2}	centi (c)
10^{-3}	milli (m)
10^{-6}	micro (μ)[a]
10^{-9}	nano (n)
10^{-12}	pico (p)
10^{-15}	femto (f)
10^{-18}	atto (a)

[a] The Greek letter μ (pronounced "mew").

quantities have units that can be derived from these seven. SI is a *decimal* system. Quantities differing from the base unit by powers of ten are noted by the use of prefixes. For example, the prefix *kilo* means *one thousand* (10^3) times the base unit; it is abbreviated as k. Thus 1 *kilometer = 1000* meters, or 1 km = 1000 m. The SI prefixes are listed in Table 1.2.

Most measurements in chemistry are made in SI units. Sometimes we must convert between SI units, as when converting kilometers to meters. At other times we must convert measurements expressed in non-SI units into SI units, or from SI units into non-SI units. In all of these cases we can use a *conversion factor* or a series of conversion factors in a scheme called a conversion pathway. Later in this chapter, we will apply conversion pathways in a method of problem solving known as *dimensional analysis*. The method itself is described in some detail in Appendix A.

MASS

Mass describes the quantity of matter in an object. In SI the standard of mass is 1 *kilogram* (kg), which is a fairly large unit for most applications in chemistry. More commonly we use the unit *gram* (g) (about the mass of three aspirin tablets).

Weight is the force of gravity on an object. It is directly proportional to mass, as shown in the following mathematical expressions.

$$W \propto m \text{ and } W = g \cdot m \tag{1.1}$$

An object has a fixed mass (m), which is independent of where or how the mass is measured. Its weight (W), on the other hand, may vary because the acceleration due to gravity (g) varies slightly from one point on Earth to another. Thus, an object that weighs 100.0 kg in St. Petersburg, Russia, weighs only 99.6 kg in Panama (about 0.4% less). The same object would weigh only about 17 kg on the moon. Although the weight of an object varies from place to place, its mass is the same in all locations. The terms *weight* and *mass* are often used interchangeably, but only mass is a measure of the quantity of matter. A common laboratory device for measuring mass is called a balance. A balance is often called, incorrectly, a scale.

The principle used in a balance is that of counteracting the force of gravity on an unknown mass with a force of equal magnitude that can be precisely measured. In older two-pan beam balances, the object whose mass is being determined is placed on one pan and counterbalancing is achieved through the force of gravity acting on *weights*, objects of precisely known mass, placed on the other pan. In the type of balance most commonly seen in laboratories today—the electronic balance—the counterbalancing force is a magnetic force produced by passing an electric current through an electromagnet. First, an initial balance condition is achieved when no object is present on the balance pan.

It is suggested that students be asked to *memorize the most common SI prefixes* (such as G, M, k, d, c, m, μ, n, and p) and that these be tested on the first quiz. You can't survive in a world of science without knowing the SI Prefixes.

SI Prefix activity

 Measuring Mass

◀ The symbol $\propto$ means "proportional to." It can be replaced by an equality sign and a proportionality constant. In expression (1.1), the constant is the acceleration due to gravity, g. (See Appendix B.)

 Measuring Mass. Display a spring scale, a triple-beam balance, and an electronic balance. Discuss their relative accuracy and ease of use. Which would give the correct reading on the surface of the moon? Possibly combine this with the demonstration, Conservation of Mass (Section 2-1).

▲ An electronic balance.

 A *beam balance* requires some gravity in order to function, but would yield the same result if used on the surface of the moon. A modern *electronic balance* opposes the force of gravity with an electromagnetic force. The result is highly accurate, but what is measured is weight, not mass.

▶ Electromagnetic radiation is discussed in Section 8-1.

VCL *Measuring Temperature*

Under SI, the *Kelvin temperature scale* is defined based on absolute zero and 273.16 K as the triple point of water.

▶ We introduce and use Kelvin temperature in Chapter 6.

▶ The SI symbol for Kelvin temperature is T and that for Celsius temperature is t, but shown here as $t(^\circ C)$. The Fahrenheit temperature, shown here as $t(^\circ F)$, is not recognized in SI.

When the object to be weighed is placed on the pan, the initial balance condition is upset. To restore the balance condition, additional electric current must be passed through the electromagnet. The magnitude of this additional current is proportional to the mass of the object being weighed and is translated into a mass reading that is displayed on the balance.

CONCEPT ASSESSMENT ✔

Would either the two-pan beam balance or the electronic balance yield the same result for the mass of an object measured on the moon as that measured for the same object on Earth? Explain.

TIME

In daily use we measure time in seconds, minutes, hours, and years, depending on whether we are dealing with short intervals (such as the time for a 100-m race) or long ones (such as the time before the next appearance of Halley's comet in 2062). We can use all these units in scientific work also, although in SI the standard of time is the *second* (s). A time interval of 1 second is not easily established. At one time it was based on the length of a day, but this is not constant because the rate of Earth's rotation undergoes slight variations. In 1956, the second was defined as 1/31,556,925.9747 of the length of the year 1900. With the advent of atomic clocks, a more precise definition became possible. The second is now defined as the duration of 9,192,631,770 cycles of a particular radiation emitted by certain atoms of the element cesium (cesium-133).

TEMPERATURE

To establish a temperature scale, we arbitrarily set certain fixed points and temperature increments called degrees. Two commonly used fixed points are the temperature at which ice melts and the temperature at which water boils, both at standard atmospheric pressure.*

On the **Celsius** (centigrade) scale, the melting point of ice is 0 °C, the boiling point of water is 100 °C, and the interval between is divided into 100 equal parts called Celsius degrees. On the **Fahrenheit** temperature scale, the melting point of ice is 32 °F, the boiling point of water is 212 °F, and the interval between is divided into 180 equal parts called Fahrenheit degrees. Figure 1-8 compares the Fahrenheit and Celsius temperature scales.

The SI temperature scale, called the **Kelvin** scale, assigns a value of zero to the lowest possible temperature. This zero—0 K—comes at −273.15 °C. The Kelvin scale is an absolute temperature scale; there are no negative Kelvin temperatures. The interval on the Kelvin scale, called a *kelvin*, is the same size as the Celsius degree, but the degree symbol is not used with Kelvin temperatures. In the laboratory, temperature is most commonly measured in Celsius degrees; however, these temperatures must often be converted to the Kelvin scale (in describing the behavior of gases, for example). Occasionally, particularly in some engineering applications, temperatures must be converted between the Celsius and Fahrenheit scales. Temperature conversions can be made in a straightforward way by using the algebraic equations shown below.

$$\text{Kelvin from Celsius} \quad T(K) = t(^\circ C) + 273.15$$

$$\text{Fahrenheit from Celsius} \quad t(^\circ F) = \frac{9}{5} t(^\circ C) + 32$$

$$\text{Celsius from Fahrenheit} \quad t(^\circ C) = \frac{5}{9} [t(^\circ F) - 32]$$

*Standard atmospheric pressure is defined in Section 6-1. The effect of pressure on melting and boiling points is described in Chapter 12.

bp of water

| 373 K | 100 °C | 212 °F |

hot day

303 K — 30 °C — 86 °F

mp of ice

273 K — 0 °C — 32 °F

very cold day

238 K — −35 °C — −31 °F

bp of liquid nitrogen

77 K — −196 °C — −321 °F

0 K   −273.15 °C −459.67 °F
Absolute zero

▲ **FIGURE 1-8**
A comparison of temperature scales
(a) The melting point of ice. **(b)** The boiling point of water.

The factors $\frac{9}{5}$ and $\frac{5}{9}$ arise because the Celsius scale uses 100 degrees between the two chosen reference points and the Fahrenheit scale uses 180 degrees: $180/100 = \frac{9}{5}$ and $100/180 = \frac{5}{9}$. The diagram in Figure 1-8 illustrates the relationship between the three scales for several temperatures.

EXAMPLE 1-1

Temperature activity

Converting Between Fahrenheit and Celsius Temperatures. The predicted high temperature for New Delhi on a given day is 41 °C. Is this temperature higher or lower than the predicted daytime high of 103 °F for the same day in Phoenix, Arizona reported by a newscaster?

Solution

We are given a Celsius temperature and seek a comparison with a Fahrenheit temperature.

We need the algebraic equation given previously that expresses $t(°F)$ as a function of $t(°C)$.

$$t(°F) = \frac{9}{5}t(°C) + 32 = \frac{9}{5}(41) + 32 = 106 °F$$

The predicted temperature for New Delhi, 106 °F, is 3 °F higher than for Phoenix, 103 °F.

Practice Example A: A recipe in an American cookbook calls for roasting a cut of meat at 350 °F. What is this temperature on the Celsius scale?

Practice Example B: A particular automobile engine coolant has antifreeze protection to a temperature of −22 °C. Will this coolant offer protection at temperatures as low as −15 °F?

◀ Answers to Practice Examples are given in Appendix G.

CONCEPT ASSESSMENT ✓

Can there be a temperature at which °C and °F have the same value? Can there be more than one such temperature? Explain.

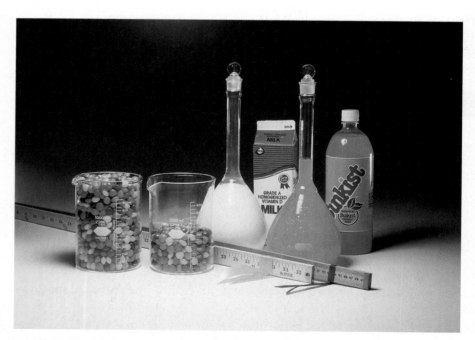

FIGURE 1-9
Some metric volume units compared
The largest volume, shown in part, is the SI standard of 1 cubic meter (m^3). A cube with a length of 10 cm (1 dm) on edge (in blue) has a volume of 1000 cm^3 (1 dm^3) and is called 1 liter (1 L). The smallest cube is 1 cm on edge (red) and has a volume of 1 cm^3 = 1 mL.

An *SI derived unit* is any combination of the base units. Some derived units have special names, such as the joule ($J = 1 \text{ kg} \cdot m^2 \cdot s^{-2}$).

Measuring Volume. Display graduated cylinders and volumetric flasks in several sizes. Discuss their relative accuracy and ease of use, and the difference between "to deliver" and "to contain." Discuss why the proper reading is at the bottom of the meniscus.

The use of *special names and symbols* for fractions and multiples of SI units is progressively and selectively discouraged. The erg and angstrom are largely obsolete. The liter will probably be with us for some time.

Under SI, the use of *non-SI units* is progressively discouraged, with the expectation that these will eventually be abandoned. Any non-SI units used should be defined in terms of SI units, such as 1 in = 2.54 cm (not 1 cm = 0.3937 in).

Students should be clearly assured that on exams, all needed *unit equivalences will be given*.

DERIVED UNITS

The seven units listed in Table 1.1 are the SI units for the fundamental quantities of length, mass, time, and so on. Many measured properties are expressed as combinations of these fundamental, or base, quantities. We refer to the units of such properties as *derived units*. For example, velocity is a distance divided by the time required to travel that distance. The unit of velocity is length divided by time, such as m/s or m s^{-1}.

An important measurement that uses derived units is *volume*. Volume has the unit (length)^3, and the SI standard unit of volume is the *cubic meter* (m^3). More commonly used volume units are the *cubic centimeter* (cm^3) and the *liter* (L). One liter is defined as a volume of 1000 cm^3, which means that one *milliliter* (1 mL) is equal to 1 cm^3. The liter is also equal to one *cubic decimeter* (1 dm^3). Several volume units are depicted in Figure 1-9.

NON-SI UNITS

Although its citizens are growing more accustomed to expressing distances in kilometers and volumes in liters, the United States is one of the few countries where most units used in everyday life are still non-SI. Masses are given in pounds, room dimensions in feet, and so on. In this book, we will not routinely use these non-SI units, but we will occasionally introduce them in examples and end-of-chapter exercises. In such cases, any necessary relationships between non-SI and SI units will be given or can be found on the inside back cover. Figure 1-10 may help you to develop a frame of reference between some non-SI and SI units.

FIGURE 1-10
Some familiar non-SI and SI units compared
The green ribbon is 1 cm wide and is wrapped around a stick that is 1 m long. The yellow ribbon is 1 inch (in) wide and is wrapped around a stick 1 yard (yd) long. The meterstick is about 10% longer than the yardstick (1 in = 2.54 cm, *exactly*). Of the two identical beakers, the beaker on the left contains 1 kg of candy and the one on the right, 1 pound (lb) (1 lb = 0.4536 kg = 453.6 g). The two identical volumetric flasks hold 1 L when filled to the mark. The flask on the left and the carton behind it each contain 1 quart (qt) of milk. The flask on the right and the bottle behind it each contain 1 L of orange soda (1 qt = 0.9464 L).

Are You Wondering . . .

Why attaching the units to a number is so important?

In 1993, NASA started the Mars Surveyor program to conduct an ongoing series of missions to explore Mars. In 1995, two missions were scheduled that would be launched in late 1998 and early 1999. The missions were the Mars Climate Orbiter (MCO) and the Mars Polar Lander (MPL). The MCO was launched December 11, 1998, and the MPL, January 3, 1999.

Nine and a half months after launch, the MCO was to fire its main engine to achieve an elliptical orbit around Mars. The MCO engine start occurred on September 23, 1999, but the MCO mission was lost when the orbiter entered the Martian atmosphere on a lower-than-expected trajectory. The MCO entered the low orbit because the computer on Earth used British Engineering units, whereas the MCO computer used SI units.

This error in units brought the MCO 56 km above the surface of Mars instead of the desired 250 km. At 250 km, the MCO would have successfully entered the desired elliptical orbit, and the $168 million orbiter would probably not have been lost.

The *current paradigm* is that the development of science requires careful, *quantitative measurement*. Theories have stood or fallen based on their agreement or otherwise with experiments in the fourth significant figure or beyond. Hence this material on problem solving, handling units, and significant figures occurs as early as this first chapter.

1-5   DENSITY AND PERCENT COMPOSITION: THEIR USE IN PROBLEM SOLVING

Throughout this text, we will encounter new concepts about the structure and behavior of matter. One means of firming up our understanding of these new concepts is to work problems that relate concepts that we already know to those we are trying to understand. In this section, we will introduce two quantities frequently required in problem solving: density and percent composition.

This paper presents non-mathematical illustrations of the concept of density: Hawkes, Stephen J. *J. Chem. Educ.* **2004**: *81*, 14.

DENSITY

Here is an old riddle: "What weighs more, a ton of bricks or a ton of cotton?" If you answer that they weigh the same, you demonstrate a clear understanding of the meaning of weight and, indirectly, of the quantity of matter to which weight is proportional, that is, mass. Anyone who answers that the bricks weigh more than the cotton has confused the concepts of weight and density. Matter in a brick is more concentrated than in cotton—that is, the matter in a brick is confined to a smaller volume. Bricks are more dense than cotton. **Density** is the ratio of mass to volume.

 Calculating Density

Recognizing properties as either *intensive* or *extensive* is particularly useful in solving problems. Intensive properties serve as conversion relationships. If the answer sought is extensive, start with something extensive and then convert units.

$$\text{density } (d) = \frac{\text{mass } (m)}{\text{volume } (V)} \tag{1.2}$$

Mass and volume are both extensive properties. An **extensive property** is *dependent* on the quantity of matter observed. However, if we divide the mass of a substance by its volume, we obtain density, an intensive property. An **intensive property** is *independent* of the amount of matter observed. Thus, the density of pure water at 25 °C (mass/volume) has a unique value, whether the sample fills a small beaker (small mass/small volume) or a swimming pool (large mass/large volume). Intensive properties are especially useful in chemical studies because they can often be used to identify substances.

The SI base units of mass and volume are kilograms and cubic meters, respectively, but chemists generally express mass in grams, and volume in cubic centimeters or milliliters. Thus, the most commonly encountered density unit is grams per cubic centimeter (g/cm^3) or the identical unit grams per milliliter (g/mL).

The mass of 1.000 L of water at 4 °C is 1.000 kg. The density of water at 4 °C is 1000 g/1000 mL, or 1.000 g/mL. At 20 °C, the density of water is 0.9982 g/mL. Density is a function of temperature because volume varies with temperature, whereas mass remains constant. One reason that global warming is a concern is

Density of Liquids and Solids. Pour into a large cylinder or tall form beaker: Hg (optional), then $CHCl_3$, then water, and then C_7H_8 (toluene). The organics may first be colored with a trace of I_2. Then add solid samples such as cork, rubber stoppers, Fe, Pb, and (if Hg is used) Ta or W. Provide a table of density data. Note how liquid densities are known to as many as six significant figures. Solid metals, which have imperfections, are only listed to three to four significant figures. Samples that have variable composition are given to only two significant figures.

because as the average temperature of seawater increases, the seawater will become less dense, its volume will increase, and sea level will rise—*even if no continental ice melts.*

Like temperature, the state of matter affects the density of a substance. In general, solids are denser than liquids and both are denser than gases, but there are notable overlaps in densities between solids and liquids. Following are the ranges of values generally observed for densities; this information should prove useful in solving problems.

- Solid densities: from about 0.2 g/cm^3 to 20 g/cm^3
- Liquid densities: from about 0.5 g/mL to $3–4 \text{ g/mL}$
- Gas densities: mostly in the range of a few grams per liter

In general, densities of liquids are known more precisely than those of solids (which may have imperfections in their microscopic structures). Also, densities of elements and compounds are known more precisely than densities of materials with variable compositions (such as wood or rubber).

There are several important consequences of the differing densities of solids and liquids. A solid that is insoluble and floats on a liquid is *less* dense than the liquid, and it displaces a *mass* of liquid equal to its own mass. An insoluble solid that sinks to the bottom of a liquid is *more* dense than the liquid and displaces a *volume* of liquid equal to its own volume. Liquids that are immiscible in each other separate into distinct layers, with the most dense liquid at the bottom and the least dense liquid at the top.

> ✓ Recognizing the *scale of things* is one important step in avoiding "silly mistakes." If a solid density calculates out as 0.05 g/cm^3, or a gas density as 5.0 g/cm^3, one needs to review the work done up to that point!

CONCEPT ASSESSMENT ✓

Approximately what fraction of its volume is submerged when a 1.00-kg block of wood ($d = 0.68 \text{ g/cm}^3$) floats on water?

KEEP IN MIND ▶
that in a conversion pathway, all units must cancel except for the desired unit in the final result (see Appendix A-5). Also, note that the quantities given and sought are typically *extensive* properties and the conversion factor(s) are often *intensive* properties (here, density).

> ✓ *Conversion relationships* can be constructed from either intensive properties or unit equivalences. Emphasize that a conversion relationship is equal to the number 1. For units, this is strictly so, as in 1 = 2.54 cm/in. With intensive properties, this is a matter of practicality: 1 = 0.9982 g/mL only for water at 20 °C.

DENSITY IN CONVERSION PATHWAYS

If we measure the mass of an object and its volume, simple division gives us its density. On the other hand, if we know the density of an object, we can use density as a conversion factor to determine the object's mass or volume. For example, a cube of osmium 1.000 cm on edge weighs 22.48 g. The density of osmium (the densest of the elements) is 22.48 g/cm^3. What would be the mass of a cube of osmium that is 1.25 in on edge (1 in = 2.54 cm)? To solve this problem, we begin by relating the volume of a cube to its length, that is, $V = l^3$. Then we can map out the *conversion pathway*:

$$\text{in osmium} \longrightarrow \text{cm osmium} \longrightarrow \text{cm}^3 \text{ osmium} \longrightarrow \text{g osmium}$$

(converts in to cm)   (converts cm to cm³)   (converts cm³ to g osmium)

$$? \text{ g osmium} = \left[1.25 \text{ in} \times \frac{2.54 \text{ cm}}{1 \text{ in}} \right]^3 \times \frac{22.48 \text{ g osmium}}{1 \text{ cm}^3} = 719 \text{ g osmium}$$

At 25 °C the density of mercury, the only metal that is liquid at this temperature, is 13.5 g/mL. Suppose we wish to know the volume, in mL, of 1.000 kg of mercury at 25 °C. We proceed by (1) identifying the known information: 1.000 kg of mercury and $d = 13.5 \text{ g/mL}$ (at 25 °C); (2) noting what we are trying to determine—a volume in milliliters (which we designate mL mercury); and (3) looking for the relevant conversion factors. Outlining the conversion pathway will help us find these conversion factors:

$$\text{kg mercury} \longrightarrow \text{g mercury} \longrightarrow \text{mL mercury}$$

Conversion Example activity

We need the factor 1000 g/kg to convert from kilograms to grams. Density provides the factor to convert from mass to volume. But in this instance, we need to use density in the *inverted* form. That is,

$$? \text{ mL mercury} = 1.000 \text{ kg} \times \frac{1000 \text{ g}}{1 \text{ kg}} \times \frac{1 \text{ mL mercury}}{13.5 \text{ g}} = 74.1 \text{ mL mercury}$$

Examples 1-2 and 1-3 further illustrate that numerical calculations involving density are generally of two types: determining density from mass and volume measurements and using density as a conversion factor to relate mass and volume.

EXAMPLE 1-2

Relating Mass, Volume, and Density. The stainless steel in the solid cylindrical rod pictured below has a density of 7.75 g/cm³. If we want a 1.00-kg mass of this rod, how long a section must we cut off?

1.000 in

Solution

Because we know the density of the steel, we can solve equation (1.2) to find the volume of the rod that will have a 1.00-kg mass

$$V = \frac{m}{d} = m \times \frac{1}{d}$$

Density activity

The density is 7.75 g/cm³, and its reciprocal is

$$\frac{1}{d} = \frac{1 \text{ cm}^3}{7.75 \text{ g}}$$

Converting the mass from kilograms to grams and using the reciprocal of the density as a conversion factor between mass and volume, we obtain

$$V = 1.00 \text{ kg} \times \frac{1000 \text{ g}}{1 \text{ kg}} \times \frac{1 \text{ cm}^3}{7.75 \text{ g}} = 129 \text{ cm}^3$$

At this point we can use data from the inside back cover to relate the volume of a cylinder to its height and area at the base, $V = \pi r^2 h$, which rearranges to

$$h = \frac{V}{\pi r^2}$$

The height, h, is the length of rod that we seek. In this final step, we must be certain to use the radius of the rod (one-half the diameter) and to express this radius in centimeters.

$$h = \frac{129 \text{ cm}^3}{3.1416 \times (0.500 \text{ in} \times 2.54 \text{ cm}/1 \text{ in})^2} = 25.5 \text{ cm}$$

Practice Example A: To determine the density of trichloroethylene, a liquid used to degrease electronic components, a flask is first weighed empty (108.6 g). It is then filled with 125 mL of the trichloroethylene to give a total mass of 291.4 g. What is the density of trichloroethylene in grams per milliliter?

Practice Example B: Suppose that instead of using the cylindrical rod of Example 1-2 to prepare a 1.000-kg mass we were to use a solid spherical ball of copper ($d = 8.96$ g/cm³). What must be the radius of this ball?

EXAMPLE 1-3

Determining the Density of an Irregularly Shaped Solid. A chunk of coal is weighed twice while suspended from a spring scale (see Figure 1-11).

When the coal is suspended in air, the scale registers 156 g; when the coal is suspended underwater at 20 °C, the scale registers 59 g. What is the density of the coal?

▶ **FIGURE 1-11**
Measuring the volume of an irregularly shaped solid
When submerged in a liquid, an irregularly shaped solid displaces a volume of liquid equal to its own. The necessary data can be obtained by two mass measurements of the type illustrated here; the required calculations are like those in Example 1-3.

Solution

As in other density determinations, we need the ratio of mass to volume of the chunk of coal. The mass of the coal is easily obtained; it is what is registered on the scale when the coal is suspended in air—156 g. But what is the volume of this chunk of coal? Key to this calculation is the weight measurement under water. The coal weighs less than 156 g when submerged in water because the water exerts a buoyant force on the coal, thus partially overcoming the force of gravity on the coal. This buoyant force is the difference between the two weight measurements: 156 g − 59 g = 97 g. Recall the statement on page 14 that a submerged solid displaces its *volume* of water. We don't know this volume of water directly, but we do know that the displaced water has a mass of 97 g. Moreover we can easily find the density of water in a handbook (on page 13 we cited a density of 0.9982 g/cm^3 at 20 °C). Thus the volume of displaced water, which is the same as the volume of the coal, is

$$V = \frac{m}{d} = \frac{97 \text{ g}}{0.9982 \text{ g/cm}^3} = 97 \text{ cm}^3$$

Our final result for the density of the coal becomes

$$d = \frac{156 \text{ g}}{97 \text{ cm}^3} = 1.6 \text{ g/cm}^3$$

Practice Example A: A graduated cylinder contains 33.8 mL of water. A stone with a mass of 28.4 g is placed in the cylinder and the water level rises to 44.1 mL. What is the density of the stone?

Practice Example B: In the situation shown in the photograph, when the ice cube melts completely will the water overflow the container, will the water level in the container drop, or will the water level remain unchanged? Explain.

PERCENT COMPOSITION AS A CONVERSION FACTOR

In Section 1-2, we described composition as an identifying characteristic of a sample of matter. A common way of referring to composition is through percentages. Percent (*per centum*) is the Latin for *per* (meaning "for each") and *centum* (meaning "100"). Thus, percent is the number of parts of a constituent in 100 parts of the whole. To say that a seawater sample contains 3.5% sodium chloride by mass means that there are 3.5 g of sodium chloride in every 100 g of the seawater. We make the statement in terms of grams because we are talking about percent *by mass*. We can express this percent by writing the following ratios:

$$\frac{3.5 \text{ g sodium chloride}}{100 \text{ g seawater}} \quad \text{and} \quad \frac{100 \text{ g seawater}}{3.5 \text{ g sodium chloride}} \tag{1.3}$$

In Example 1-4, we will use one of these ratios as a conversion factor.

Students have a surprisingly large amount of difficulty with *mass percent* problems, particularly with "g of solution" versus "g of solvent." It is important to include the use of mass percent as a component of problems on topics occurring later in the text.

EXAMPLE 1-4

Using Percent Composition as a Conversion Factor. A 75-g sample of sodium chloride (table salt) is to be produced by evaporating to dryness a quantity of seawater containing 3.5% sodium chloride by mass. How many liters of seawater must be taken for this purpose? Assume a density of 1.03 g/mL for seawater.

Solution

To convert from grams of sodium chloride to grams of seawater, we need the conversion factor in expression (1.3) having grams of seawater in the numerator and grams of sodium chloride in the denominator. In addition, we need to make the conversions g seawater $\longrightarrow$ mL seawater $\longrightarrow$ L seawater.

$$? \text{ L seawater} = 75 \text{ g sodium chloride} \times \frac{100 \text{ g seawater}}{3.5 \text{ g sodium chloride}}$$

$$\times \frac{1 \text{ mL seawater}}{1.03 \text{ g seawater}} \times \frac{1 \text{ L seawater}}{1000 \text{ mL seawater}}$$

$$= 2.1 \text{ L seawater}$$

Practice Example A: How many kilograms of ethanol are present in 25 L of a gasohol solution that is 90% gasoline to 10% ethanol by mass? The density of gasohol is 0.71 g/mL.

Practice Example B: Common rubbing alcohol is a solution of 70.0% isopropyl alcohol by mass in water. If a 25.0-mL sample of rubbing alcohol contains 15.0 g of isopropyl alcohol, what is the density of the rubbing alcohol?

Are You Wondering . . .

When to multiply and when to divide in doing problems with percentages?

A common way of dealing with a percentage is to convert it to decimal form (3.5% becomes 0.035) and then to multiply or divide by this decimal, but students sometimes can't decide which to do. Expressing percentage as a conversion factor and using it to produce a necessary cancellation of units gets around this difficulty. Also, remember that

The quantity of a *component* must always be less than the quantity of the entire mixture. (*Multiply* by percentage.)

The quantity of the entire *mixture* must always be greater than the quantity of any of the components. (*Divide* by percentage.)

If, in Example 1-4, we had not been careful about the cancellation of units and had multiplied by percentage (3.5/100) instead of dividing by it (100/3.5), we would have obtained the numerical answer 2.5×10^{-3}. This would be a 2.5-mL sample of seawater, weighing about 2.5 g. Clearly, a sample of seawater that *contains* 75 g of sodium chloride must have a mass *greater than* 75 g.

◀ **KEEP IN MIND**
that a numerical answer that defies common sense is probably wrong.

1-6   UNCERTAINTIES IN SCIENTIFIC MEASUREMENTS

All measurements are subject to error. To some extent, measuring instruments have built-in, or inherent, errors, called **systematic errors**. (For example, a kitchen scale might consistently yield results that are 25 g too high or a

Random errors are observed by scatter in the data and can be dealt with effectively by taking the average of many measurements.

 Systematic errors, on the other hand, are the bane of the experimental scientist. They are not readily apparent and must be avoided by carefully calibrating a method against a known sample or result. Systematic errors influence the *accuracy* of a measurement, whereas random errors are linked to the *precision* of measurements.

 Students commonly think that a single measurement can be said to be precise. Students should understand that *precision* requires the comparison of more than one measurement.

thermometer a reading that is 2° too low.) Limitations in an experimenter's skill or ability to read a scientific instrument also lead to errors and give results that may be either too high or too low. Such errors are called **random errors**.

Precision refers to the degree of reproducibility of a measured quantity— that is, the closeness of agreement when the same quantity is measured several times. The precision of a series of measurements is *high* (or good) if each of a series of measurements deviates by only a small amount from the average. Conversely, if there is wide deviation among the measurements, the precision is *poor* (or low). **Accuracy** refers to how close a measured value is to the accepted, or actual, value. High-precision measurements are not always accurate— a large systematic error could be present. (A tight cluster of three darts near the edge of a dart board can be considered precise, but not very accurate if the intention was to strike the center of the board.) Still, scientists generally strive for high precision in measurements.

To illustrate these ideas, consider the mass of an object measured on two different balances. One is a relatively low-precision single-pan balance, and the other is a sophisticated analytical balance.

	Pan Balance	Analytical Balance
Three measurements	10.6, 10.4, 10.5 g	10.4978, 10.4979, 10.4977 g
Their average	10.5 g	10.4978 g
Reproducibility	±0.1 g	±0.0001 g
Precision	low or poor	high or good

CONCEPT ASSESSMENT ✓

Can a set of measurements be precise without being accurate? Can the average of a set of measurements be accurate and the individual measurements be imprecise? Explain.

 An uncertainty of ±1 to ±3 is typically implied in the last significant digit of a reported property.

Significant Figures Calculations activity

1-7 Significant Figures

Consider these measurements made on a low-precision balance: 10.4, 10.2, and 10.3 g. The reported result is best expressed as their average, that is, 10.3 g. A scientist would interpret these results to mean that the first two digits—10— are known with certainty and the last digit—3—is uncertain because it was estimated. That is, the mass is known only to the nearest 0.1 g, a fact that we could also express by writing 10.3 ± 0.1 g. To a scientist, the measurement 10.3 g is said to have *three* **significant figures**. If this mass is reported in kilograms rather than in grams, 10.3 g = 0.0103 kg, the measurement is still

Not significant:
zero for
"cosmetic"
purpose

Not significant:
zeros used only
to locate the
decimal point

Significant:
all zeros between
nonzero numbers

0 . 0 0 4 0 0 4 5 0 0

Significant:
all nonzero
integers

Significant:
zeros at the end of
a number to the right
of decimal point

◀ **FIGURE 1-12**
**Determining the number
of significant figures in a
quantity**
The quantity shown here,
0.004004500, has *seven*
significant figures. All
nonzero digits are significant,
as are the indicated zeros.

expressed to *three* significant figures even though more than three digits are shown. When measured on an analytical balance, the corresponding reported value might be 10.3107 g—a value with *six* significant figures. The number of significant figures in a measured quantity gives an indication of the capabilities of the measuring device and the precision of the measurements.

We will frequently need to determine the number of significant figures in a numerical quantity. The rules for doing this, outlined in Figure 1-12, are as follows:

- All nonzero digits are significant
- Zeros are also significant, but with two important *exceptions* for quantities less than one. Any zeros (1) preceding the decimal point, or (2) following the decimal point and preceding the first nonzero digit are *not* significant.
- The case of terminal zeros that precede the decimal point in quantities greater than one is *ambiguous*.

The quantity 7500 m is an example of an ambiguous case.

Do we mean 7500 m, measured to the nearest meter? nearest 10 meters? If all the zeros are significant—if the value has *four* significant figures—we can write 7500. m. That is, by writing a decimal point that is not otherwise needed, we show that all zeros preceding the decimal point are significant. This technique does not help if only one of the zeros, or if neither zero, is significant. The best approach here is to use exponential notation. (Review Appendix A if necessary.) The coefficient establishes the number of significant figures, and the power of ten locates the decimal point.

2 significant figures	*3 significant figures*	*4 significant figures*
7.5×10^3 m	7.50×10^3 m	7.500×10^3 m

SIGNIFICANT FIGURES IN NUMERICAL CALCULATIONS

Precision must neither be gained nor lost in calculations involving measured quantities. There are several methods for determining how precisely to express the result of a calculation, but it is usually sufficient just to observe some simple rules involving significant figures.

> The result of multiplication or division may contain only as many significant figures as the *least* precisely known quantity in the calculation.

In the following chain multiplication to determine the volume of a rectangular block of wood, we should round off the result to *three* significant figures. Figure 1-13 may help you to understand this.

$$14.79 \text{ cm} \times 12.11 \text{ cm} \times 5.05 \text{ cm} = 904 \text{ cm}^3$$

(*4 sig. fig.*)   (*4 sig. fig.*)   (*3 sig. fig.*)   (*3 sig. fig.*)

◀ A more exact rule on multiplication/division is that the result should have about the same relative error—for example, expressed as parts per hundred (percent) or parts per thousand—as the least precisely known quantity. Usually the significant figure rule conforms to this requirement; occasionally, it does not (see Exercise 67).

Significant Figures in Volume Measurement. Fill a graduated cylinder, the largest available, about $\frac{3}{4}$ full of colored water. Read the volume and estimate the error. Repeat with the smallest cylinder available. Pour the latter into the former. Compare the value and estimated error of the calculated and observed total volumes.

Density of Aluminum by Displacement. Fill a 100-mL cylinder half-full of water and record the volume. Also measure the mass of cylinder + water, preferably using a spring scale or low-accuracy balance so as to provide some error. Add Al pellets to just below the full capacity of the cylinder. Measure the total mass and volume. Calculate the mass, volume, and density. Perform a significant figure analysis. Based on this analysis, discuss which measurement (volume or mass) first needs to be improved.

▲ **FIGURE 1-13**
Significant-figure rule in multiplication
In forming the product 14.79 cm × 12.11 cm × 5.05 cm, the least precisely known quantity is 5.05 cm. Shown on the calculators are the products of 14.79 and 12.11 with 5.04, 5.05, and 5.06, respectively. In the three results, only the first two digits, 90..., are identical; variations begin in the third digit. We are certainly not justified in carrying digits beyond the third. We express the volume as 904 cm³. Usually, instead of a detailed analysis of the type done here, we can use a simpler idea: *The result of a multiplication may contain only as many significant figures as does the least precisely known quantity.*

In adding and subtracting numbers, the applicable rule is that

> the result must be expressed with the same number of digits beyond the decimal point as the quantity carrying the *smallest* number of such digits.

Consider the following sum of masses.

$$
\begin{array}{r}
15.02 \ \text{g} \\
9986.0 \ \ \text{g} \\
\underline{3.518 \ \text{g}} \\
10{,}004.538 \ \text{g}
\end{array}
$$

▶ In addition/subtraction the *absolute* error in the result can be no less than the absolute error in the least precisely known quantity. In the summation at the right, the absolute error in one quantity is ±0.1 g; in another, ±0.01 g; and in the third, ±0.001 g. The sum *must* be expressed with an absolute error of ±0.1 g.

The sum has the same uncertainty, ±0.1 g, as does the term with the *smallest* number of digits beyond the decimal point, 9986.0 g. Note that this calculation is *not* limited by significant figures. In fact, the sum has more significant figures (six) than do any of the terms in the addition.

There are two situations when a quantity appearing in a calculation may be *exact*, that is, not subject to errors in measurement. This may occur

• by definition (such as 1 min = 60 s, or 1 in = 2.54 cm)

or as a result of

▶ Later in the text, we will need to apply ideas about significant figures to logarithms. This concept is discussed in Appendix A.

• counting (such as *six* faces on a cube, or *two* hydrogen atoms in a water molecule).

> *Exact* numbers can be considered to have an unlimited number of significant figures.

▶ As added practice in working with significant figures, review the calculations in Section 1-6. You will note that they conform to the significant figure rules presented here.

CONCEPT ASSESSMENT ✔

Which of the following is a more precise statement of the length 1 inch:
1 in = 2.54 cm or 1 m = 39.37 in? Explain.

ROUNDING OFF NUMERICAL RESULTS

To three significant figures, we should express 15.453 as 15.5 and 14,775 as 1.48×10^4. If we need to drop just one digit, that is, to round off a number, the rule that we will follow is to increase the final digit by one unit if the digit dropped is 5, 6, 7, 8, or 9 and to leave the final digit unchanged if the digit dropped is 0, 1, 2, 3, or 4.* To three significant figures, 15.44 rounds off to 15.4, and 15.45 rounds off to 15.5.

EXAMPLE 1-5

Applying Significant Figure Rules: Multiplication/Division. Express the result of the following calculation with the correct number of significant figures.

$$\frac{0.225 \times 0.0035}{2.16 \times 10^{-2}} = ?$$

Solution

By inspecting the three quantities, we see that the least precisely known is 0.0035, with *two* significant figures. Our result must also contain only *two* significant figures. The fact that two of the quantities are given in decimal form and one in exponential form is immaterial. Simply enter the numbers, as written, into an electronic calculator and read off the answer: 0.0364583. Express the result to *two* significant figures: 0.036. Alternatively, write the answer in exponential form: 3.6×10^{-2}. To check for any possible calculator error, we can estimate the correct answer through a quick mental calculation using exponential numbers. The answer should be $(2 \times 10^{-1})(4 \times 10^{-3})/2 \times 10^{-2} \approx 4 \times 10^{-2}$, and it is.

Practice Example A: Perform the following calculation, and express the result with the appropriate number of significant figures.

$$\frac{62.356}{0.000456 \times 6.422 \times 10^3} = ?$$

Practice Example B: Perform the following calculation, and express the result with the appropriate number of significant figures.

$$\frac{8.21 \times 10^4 \times 1.3 \times 10^{-3}}{0.00236 \times 4.071 \times 10^{-2}} = ?$$

EXAMPLE 1-6

Applying Significant Figure Rules: Addition/Subtraction. Express the result of the following calculation with the correct number of significant figures.

$$(2.06 \times 10^2) + (1.32 \times 10^4) - (1.26 \times 10^3) = ?$$

Solution

If the calculation is performed with an electronic calculator, the quantities can be entered just as they are written and the answer obtained adjusted to the correct number of significant figures. We can see that this correct number is *three* by writing the three factors with the same power of ten, that is, 10^4.

$$\begin{aligned}
(2.06 \times 10^2) &+ (1.32 \times 10^4) - (1.26 \times 10^3) \\
&= (0.0206 \times 10^4) + (1.32 \times 10^4) - (0.126 \times 10^4) \\
&= (0.0206 + 1.32 - 0.126) \times 10^4 \\
&= 1.2146 \times 10^4 \\
&= 1.21 \times 10^4
\end{aligned}$$

CHECK: The answer can have no more digits beyond the decimal point (*two*) than the factor with the smallest number of such digits (1.32×10^4).

*C. J. Guare, *J. Chem. Educ.*, **68**, 818 (1991)

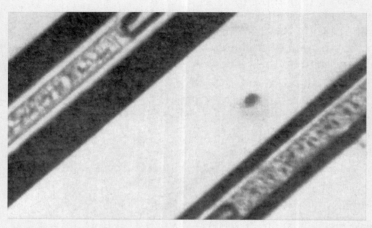

▲ The melting behavior of polywater–water mixtures. Two polywater–water mixtures at −10 °C. The sample at the left has just begun to melt. At −6 °C, both samples will have completely melted. Pure water, by contrast, does not melt until the temperature reaches 0 °C.

About 35 years ago, the scientific community was heatedly debating the reported discovery of a new form of water called polywater. The report stated that if a sample of water were confined in a quartz capillary tube (a very small-diameter tube of a special high-purity glass), some liquid water condensed in another part of the tube. The recondensed water had some peculiar properties, including a high boiling point (over 150 °C), a low freezing point (below −30 °C), and a density greater than that of ordinary water.

At first, this discovery was largely overlooked, probably because it was not published in any widely read journals. Only after the scientists who made the discovery described their experiments and presented an interpretation of their results at an international meeting did other scientists begin to take note. The experiments yielded similar results when repeated by many laboratories and thus met the first criterion of a valid scientific result: It must be reproducible. There was no dispute, then, about the facts—but their interpretation sparked active debate.

Practice Example A: Express the result of the following calculation with the appropriate number of significant figures.

$$0.236 + 128.55 - 102.1 = ?$$

Practice Example B: Perform the following calculation, and express the result with the appropriate number of significant figures.

$$\frac{(1.302 \times 10^3) + 952.7}{(1.57 \times 10^2) - 12.22} = ?$$

✓ *Intermediate calculator results* sometimes need to be written down in order to apply the rules for significant figures, but we do this without erasing and reentering values.

KEEP IN MIND ▶
that addition/subtraction is governed by one significant-figure rule, and multiplication/division is governed by a different rule.

Are You Wondering . . .

At what point(s) to round off numerical results during a calculation?

What's nice about using electronic calculators is that we don't have to record intermediate results. However, for clarity, we will often follow a stepwise approach for in-text examples. When we do, we will write down and round off intermediate results as well as the final result. In general, though, disregard occasional situations where intermediate rounding may be justified and store all intermediate results in your electronic calculator without regard to significant figures. Then, round off to the correct number of significant figures only in the final answer.

Summary

1-1 The Scientific Method—The **scientific method** is a set of procedures used to develop explanations of natural phenomena and possibly to predict additional phenomena. The four basic stages of the scientific method are (1) gathering data through observations and experiments; (2) reducing the data to simple verbal or mathematical expressions known as **natural laws**; (3) offering a plausible explanation of the data through a **hypothesis**;

The properties of the recondensed water could be explained in one of two ways, and each explanation was consistent with the observations. One explanation was that the water contained impurities that had dissolved during the preparation of the water sample. The other was that the water was of a form in which simple water molecules (each consisting of two hydrogen atoms and one oxygen atom) aggregate into large clusters. Such "super" molecules are known as *polymers*.

In one critical experiment, researchers subjected recondensed water to very careful examination by a method known as spectroscopy. The method is designed to reveal the structure of a substance at the molecular level. The spectroscopic data suggested that the recondensed water was a pure substance, not a solution. Further, the data suggested a polymer-like structure for the water. Hence the name polywater was coined. The publication of these results in 1969 created a sensation, both among scientists and in the popular press.

Those who firmly believed in polywater employed the reasoning of Sherlock Holmes, a fictional but ardent follower of the scientific method: "When you have eliminated the impossible, whatever remains, however im-

probable, must be the truth." The trouble was that the impossible had not been eliminated. Within a year or so, new reports pointed to dissolved impurities in polywater. At about the same time, new spectroscopic data indicated that the results interpreted as due to polywater could not be due to any form of water. They were now attributed to impurities in the water. Finally, in 1973, the scientists who had made the original observations reported that they could not produce polywater in capillary tubes that had been freed of all impurities. And so ended this brief but fascinating chapter in the history of science.

The polywater story may seem to reveal a failure of science, but actually it represents a great success of the scientific method. A novel idea was thoroughly examined by many scientists using a variety of techniques. Hypotheses were proposed, experiments were conducted, and the experimental results were discussed openly. After all of this, the scientific community reached a consensus: Polywater is an impure form of water. A crucial aspect of the scientific method was also revealed: the self-correcting nature of science. Science may veer off course at times, but eventually it gets back on the right track.

(4) testing the hypothesis through predictions and further experimentation, leading ultimately to a conceptual model called a **theory** that explains the hypothesis, often together with other related hypotheses.

1-2 Properties of Matter—**Matter** is defined as anything that occupies space, possesses mass, and displays inertia. **Composition** refers to the component parts of a sample of matter and their relative proportions. **Properties** are the qualities or attributes that distinguish one sample of matter from another. Properties of matter can be grouped into two broad categories: **physical** and **chemical**. Matter can undergo two types of changes: **chemical changes** or **reactions** are changes in composition; **physical changes** are changes in state or physical form and do not affect composition.

1-3 Classification of Matter—The basic building blocks of matter are called **atoms**. Matter that is composed of a collection of a single type of atom is known as an **element**. A sample of matter composed of two or more elements is known as a **compound**. A **molecule** is the smallest entity of a compound having the same proportions of the constituent atoms as does the compound as a whole. Collectively, elements and compounds comprise the types of matter called **substances**. **Mixtures** of substances can be classified as **homogeneous** or **heterogeneous** (Fig. 1-4). The three states of matter are **solid**, **liquid**, and **gas**.

1-4 Measurement of Matter: SI (Metric) Units—Chemistry is a quantitative science, meaning that chemical measurements are usually expressed in terms of a number and an accompanying unit. The scientific system of measurement, called the *Système Internationale d'Unités* (abbreviated **SI**), involves seven base quantities

(Table 1.1). **Mass** describes a quantity of matter. Weight measures the force of gravity on an object; weight is related to, but different from, mass. The temperature scales used by chemists are the **Celsius** and **Kelvin** scales. The Fahrenheit temperature scale, commonly used in daily life in the United States, is also used in some industrial settings. The three temperature scales can be related algebraically (Fig. 1-8).

1-5 Density and Percent Composition: Their Use in Problem Solving—Mass and volume are **extensive properties**; they *depend* on the amount of matter in a sample. **Density**, the ratio of the mass of a sample to its volume, is an **intensive property**, a property *independent* of the amount of matter sampled. Density is used as a conversion factor in a variety of calculations.

1-6 Uncertainties in Scientific Measurements—Measurements are subject to **systematic** and **random errors**. In making a series of measurements, the degree to which the measurements agree with one another is known as the **precision** of the measurement, while the degree to which the measurement agrees with the actual value is referred to as the **accuracy** of the measurement.

1-7 Significant Figures—The proper use of **significant figures** is important in that it prevents one from suggesting a higher degree of precision in a calculated quantity than is warranted by the precision of the measured quantities used in the calculation. The precision of an answer cannot be greater than the precision of the numbers used in the calculation. In addition to reporting the correct number of significant figures in a calculated quantity, it is important to know the rules for rounding off numerical results.

Integrative Example

Consider a 58.35-g hexagonal block of wood that is 5.00 cm on edge and 1.25 cm thick, with a 2.50-cm diameter hole drilled through its center. Also given are the densities of the liquids hexane ($d = 0.667$ g/mL) and decane ($d = 0.845$ g/mL). Assume that the density of a mixture of the two liquids is a linear function of the volume percent composition of the solution. Determine the volume percent of hexane required in the solution so that the hexagonal block of wood will just barely float on the solution.

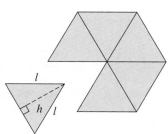

Strategy

The first task is to determine the density of the wood block, $d = m/V$. The mass is given, so the critical calculation is that of the volume. The key to the volume calculation is recognizing that the volume of the block is the *difference* between two volumes: The volume of the block if there were no hole *minus* the volume of the cylindrical hole. The second task is to write a simple equation relating density to the volume percent composition of the liquid solution, and then to solve that equation for the volume percent hexane that yields a solution density equal to the density calculated for the wood.

Solution

The solid hexagonal block can be divided into six smaller blocks, each an equilateral triangle of length, l, and height, h. The area of a triangle is given by the formula

$$A = \frac{1}{2}(\text{base} \times \text{height}) = \frac{1}{2} \times l \times h$$

Only the base, l, is given (5.00 cm). To express h in terms of l, we use the Pythagorean theorem for the right triangle pictured, that is, $a^2 + b^2 = c^2$, rearranged to the form $a^2 = c^2 - b^2$.

$$h^2 = l^2 - \left(\frac{l}{2}\right)^2 = l^2 - \frac{l^2}{4} = \frac{3l^2}{4} \text{ and}$$

$$h = \frac{\sqrt{3}}{2} \times l$$

Now, for the area of one of the six triangles we have

$$A = \frac{1}{2} \times l \times \frac{\sqrt{3}}{2} \times l = \frac{\sqrt{3}}{4} \times l^2$$

Substituting $l = 5.00$ cm and multiplying the cross-sectional area by the thickness, 1.25 cm, we obtain a volume of

$$V = \frac{\sqrt{3}}{4} \times (5.00 \text{ cm})^2 \times 1.25 \text{ cm} = 13.5 \text{ cm}^3$$

The volume of the hexagonal block of wood, without the cylindrical hole, is that of six triangular blocks.

$$V = 6 \times 13.5 \text{ cm}^3 = 81.0 \text{ cm}^3$$

The volume of the cylindrical hole with a radius of 1.25 cm (one-half the 2.50 cm diameter) and a height of 1.25 cm is

$$V = \pi r^2 h = 3.1416 \times (1.25 \text{ cm})^2 \times 1.25 \text{ cm}$$
$$= 6.14 \text{ cm}^3$$

The volume of the block of wood is the difference

$$V = 81.0 \text{ cm}^3 - 6.14 \text{ cm}^3 = 74.9 \text{ cm}^3$$

The density of the wood is

$$d = \frac{m}{V} = \frac{58.35 \text{ g}}{74.9 \text{ cm}^3} = 0.779 \text{ g/cm}^3 \text{ or } 0.779 \text{ g/mL}$$

The general formula for a linear (straight-line) relationship is

$$y = mx + b$$

In the present case, let y represent the density, d, of a solution (in g/mL) and x, the volume fraction of hexane (volume percent/100). By substituting the density of pure decane into the equation, we note that $x = 0$ and find that $b = 0.845$.

$$d = 0.845 = (m \times 0) + b$$

Now, using the density of pure hexane, $d = 0.667$, and the values $x = 1.00$ and $b = 0.845$, we obtain the value of m.

$$d = 0.667 = (m \times 1.00) + 0.845$$
$$m = 0.667 - 0.845 = -0.178$$

Our final step is to find the value of x for a solution having the same density as the wood: 0.779 g/mL.

$$d = 0.779 = -0.178x + 0.845$$
$$x = \frac{0.845 - 0.779}{0.178} = 0.37$$

The volume fraction of hexane is 0.37, and the volume percent composition of the solution is 37% hexane and 63% decane.

Assessment

There is an early point in this calculation where we can check the correctness of our work. We have two expectations for the density of the block of wood: (1) it should be less than 1 g/cm^3 (practically all wood floats on water), and (2) it must fall between 0.667 g/cm^3 and 0.845 g/cm^3. If the calculated density of the wood were outside this range, the block of wood would either float on both liquids or sink in both of them, making the rest of the calculation impossible.

Another point to notice in this calculation is that we are justified in carrying three significant figures throughout the calculation up to the last step. There, because we must take the difference between two numbers of similar magnitudes, the number of significant figures drops from three to two.

Exercises   *(see also Appendices A-1 and A-5)*

The Scientific Method

1. What are the principal reasons that one theory might be adopted over a conflicting one?
2. Can one predict how many experiments are required to verify a natural law? Explain.
3. A common belief among scientists is that there exists an underlying order to nature. Einstein described this belief in the words "God is subtle, but He is not malicious." What do you think Einstein meant by this remark?
4. Describe several ways in which a scientific law differs from a legislative law.
5. Describe the necessary characteristics of an experiment that is suitable to test a theory.
6. Describe the necessary characteristics of a scientific theory.

Properties and Classification of Matter

7. State whether the following properties of matter are physical or chemical.
   (a) An iron nail is attracted to a magnet.
   (b) A piece of paper spontaneously ignites when its temperature reaches 451 °F.
   (c) A bronze statue develops a green coating (patina) over time.
   (d) A block of wood floats on water.

8. State whether the following properties are physical or chemical.
   (a) A piece of sliced apple turns brown.
   (b) A slab of marble feels cool to the touch.
   (c) A sapphire is blue.
   (d) A clay pot fired in a kiln becomes hard and covered by a glaze.

9. Indicate whether each sample of matter listed is a substance or a mixture; if it is a mixture, indicate whether it is homogeneous or heterogeneous.
   (a) clean fresh air
   (b) a silver-plated spoon
   (c) garlic salt
   (d) ice
10. Indicate whether each sample of matter listed is a substance or a mixture; if it is a mixture, indicate whether it is homogeneous or heterogeneous.
    (a) a wooden beam
    (b) red ink
    (c) distilled water
    (d) freshly squeezed orange juice

11. Suggest physical changes by which the following mixtures can be separated.
    (a) iron filings and wood chips
    (b) ground glass and sucrose (cane sugar)
    (c) water and olive oil
    (d) gold flakes and water
12. What type of change—physical or chemical—is necessary to separate the following?
    [*Hint:* Refer to a listing of the elements.]
    (a) sugar from a sand/sugar mixture
    (b) iron from iron oxide (rust)
    (c) pure water from seawater
    (d) water from a slurry of sand in water

Exponential Arithmetic

13. Express each number in exponential notation.
    (a) 8950; (b) 10,700; (c) 0.0240; (d) 0.0047; (e) 938.3;
    (f) 275,482
14. Express each number in common decimal form.
    (a) 3.21×10^{-2}; (b) 5.08×10^{-4}; (c) 121.9×10^{-5};
    (d) 16.2×10^{-2}
15. Express each value in exponential form. Where appropriate, include units in your answer.
    (a) speed of sound (sea level): 34,000 centimeters per second
    (b) equatorial radius of Earth: 6378 kilometers
    (c) the distance between the two hydrogen atoms in the hydrogen molecule: 74 trillionths of a meter
    (d) $\dfrac{(2.2 \times 10^3) + (4.7 \times 10^2)}{5.8 \times 10^{-3}} =$

16. Express each value in exponential form. Where appropriate, include units in your answer.
    (a) solar radiation received by Earth: 173 thousand trillion watts
    (b) average human cell diameter: 1 ten-millionth of a meter
    (c) the distance between the centers of the atoms in silver metal: 142 trillionths of a meter
    (d) $\dfrac{(5.07 \times 10^4) \times (1.8 \times 10^{-3})^2}{0.065 + (3.3 \times 10^{-2})} =$

Significant Figures

17. Indicate whether each of the following is an exact number or a measured quantity subject to uncertainty.
    (a) the number of sheets of paper in a ream of paper
    (b) the volume of milk in a liter bottle
    (c) the distance between Earth and the sun
    (d) the distance between the centers of the two oxygen atoms in the oxygen molecule
18. Indicate whether each of the following is an exact number or a measured quantity subject to uncertainty.
    (a) the number of pages in this text
    (b) the number of days in the month of January
    (c) the area of a city lot
    (d) the distance between the centers of the atoms in a gold medal
19. Express each of the following to *four* significant figures. (a) 3984.6; (b) 422.04; (c) 186,000; (d) 33,900; (e) 6.321×10^4; (f) 5.0472×10^{-4}
20. How many significant figures are shown in each of the following? If this is indeterminate, explain why.
    (a) 450; (b) 98.6; (c) 0.0033; (d) 902.10; (e) 0.02173;
    (f) 7000; (g) 7.02; (h) 67,000,000

21. Perform the following calculations; express each answer in exponential form and with the appropriate number of significant figures.
    (a) $0.406 \times 0.0023 =$
    (b) $0.1357 \times 16.80 \times 0.096 =$
    (c) $0.458 + 0.12 - 0.037 =$
    (d) $32.18 + 0.055 - 1.652 =$
22. Perform the following calculations; express each number and the answer in exponential form and with the appropriate number of significant figures.
    (a) $\dfrac{320 \times 24.9}{0.080} =$
    (b) $\dfrac{432.7 \times 6.5 \times 0.002300}{62 \times 0.103} =$
    (c) $\dfrac{32.44 + 4.9 - 0.304}{82.94} =$
    (d) $\dfrac{8.002 + 0.3040}{13.4 - 0.066 + 1.02} =$

23. Perform the following calculations and retain the appropriate number of significant figures in each result.

(a) $(38.4 \times 10^{-3}) \times (6.36 \times 10^5) =$

(b) $\dfrac{(1.45 \times 10^2) \times (8.76 \times 10^{-4})}{(9.2 \times 10^{-3})^2} =$

(c) $24.6 + 18.35 - 2.98 =$

(d) $(1.646 \times 10^3) - (2.18 \times 10^2) + [(1.36 \times 10^4) \\ \times (5.17 \times 10^{-2})] =$

(e)

$$\dfrac{-7.29 \times 10^{-4} + \sqrt{(7.29 \times 10^{-4})^2 + 4(1.00)(2.7 \times 10^{-5})}}{2 \times (1.00)}$$

[*Hint:* The significant figure rule for the extraction of a root is the same as for multiplication.]

24. Express the result of each of the following calculations in exponential form and with the appropriate number of significant figures.

(a) $(4.65 \times 10^4) \times (2.95 \times 10^{-2}) \times (6.663 \times 10^{-3}) \\ \times 8.2 =$

(b) $\dfrac{1912 \times (0.0077 \times 10^4) \times (3.12 \times 10^{-3})}{(4.18 \times 10^{-4})^3} =$

(c) $(3.46 \times 10^3) \times 0.087 \times 15.26 \times 1.0023 =$

(d) $\dfrac{(4.505 \times 10^{-2})^2 \times 1.080 \times 1545.9}{0.03203 \times 10^3} =$

(e)

$$\dfrac{(-3.61 \times 10^{-4}) + \sqrt{(3.61 \times 10^{-4})^2 + 4(1.00)(1.9 \times 10^{-5})}}{2 \times (1.00)}$$

[*Hint:* The significant figure rule for the extraction of a root is the same as for multiplication.]

25. An American press release describing the 1986 non-stop, round-the-world trip by the ultra-lightweight aircraft *Voyager* included the following data:

> flight distance: 25,012 mi
> flight time: 9 days, 3 minutes, 44 seconds
> fuel capacity: nearly 9000 lb
> fuel remaining at end of flight: 14 gal

To the maximum number of significant figures permitted, calculate
(a) the average speed of the aircraft in kilometers per hour
(b) the fuel consumption in kilometers per kilogram of fuel (assume a density of 0.70 g/mL for the fuel)

26. Use the concept of significant figures to criticize the way in which the following information was presented. "The estimated proved reserve of natural gas as of January 1, 1982, was 2,911,346 trillion cubic feet."

Units of Measurement

27. Perform the following conversions.
(a) 0.127 L = ____ mL
(b) 15.8 mL = ____ L
(c) 981 cm^3 = ____ L
(d) 2.65 m^3 = ____ cm^3

28. Perform the following conversions.
(a) 1.55 kg = ____ g
(b) 642 g = ____ kg
(c) 2896 mm = ____ cm
(d) 0.086 cm = ____ mm

29. Perform the following conversions from non-SI to SI units. (Use information from Figure 1-10, as needed.)
(a) 68.4 in = ____ cm
(b) 94 ft = ____ m
(c) 1.42 lb = ____ g

(d) 248 lb = ____ kg
(e) 1.85 gal = ____ dm^3
(f) 3.72 qt = ____ mL

30. Determine the number of
(a) square meters (m^2) in 1 square kilometer (km^2);
(b) cubic centimeters (cm^3) in 1 cubic meter (m^3);
(c) square meters (m^2) in 1 square mile (mi^2) (1 mi = 5280 ft).

31. Which is the greater mass, 3245 μg or 0.00515 mg? Explain.

32. Which is the greater mass, 3257 mg or 0.000475 kg? Explain.

33. The non-SI unit, the hand (used by equestrians), is 4 inches. What is the height, in meters, of a horse that stands 15 hands high?

34. The unit *furlong* is used in horse racing. The units *chain* and *link* are used in surveying. There are exactly 8 furlongs in 1 mi, 10 chains in 1 furlong, and 100 links in 1 chain. To three significant figures, what is the length of 1 link in centimeters?

35. A sprinter runs the 100-yd dash in 9.3 s. At this same rate,
    (a) how long would it take the sprinter to run 100.0 m?
    (b) What is the sprinter's speed in meters per second?
    (c) How long would it take the sprinter to run a distance of 1.45 km?

36. A non-SI unit of mass used in pharmaceutical work is the grain (gr) (15 gr = 1.0 g). An aspirin tablet contains 5.0 gr of aspirin. A 155-lb arthritic individual takes two aspirin tablets per day.
    (a) What is the quantity of aspirin in two tablets, expressed in milligrams?
    (b) What is the dosage rate of aspirin, expressed in milligrams of aspirin per kilogram of body mass?

37. In SI units, land area is measured in *hectares* (1 hectare = 1 hm^2). The commonly used unit for land area in the United States is the *acre*. How many acres correspond to 1 hectare? (1 mi^2 = 640 acres, 1 mi = 5280 ft, 1 ft = 12 in).

38. In an engineering reference book, you find that the density of iron is 0.284 lb/in^3. What is the density in g/cm^3?

39. In a user's manual accompanying an American-made automobile, a typical gauge pressure for optimal performance of automobile tires is 32 lb/in^2. What is this pressure in grams per square centimeter and kilograms per square meter?

40. The volume of a red blood cell is about 90.0×10^{-12} cm^3. Assuming that red blood cells are spherical, what is the diameter of a red blood cell in millimeters?

(c) At the given rate of consumption of aspirin tablets, how many days would it take to consume 1.0 kg of aspirin?

Temperature Scales

41. We wish to mark off a thermometer in both Celsius and Fahrenheit temperatures. On the Celsius scale, the lowest temperature mark is at −10 °C, and the highest temperature mark is at 50 °C. What are the equivalent Fahrenheit temperatures?

42. The highest and lowest temperatures on record for San Bernardino, California, are 118 and 17 °F, respectively. What are these temperatures on the Celsius scale?

43. The absolute zero of temperature is −273.15 °C. Should it be possible to achieve a temperature of −465 °F? Explain.

44. A family/consumer science class is given an assignment in candy-making that requires a sugar mixture to be brought to a "soft-ball" stage (234–240 °F). A student borrows a thermometer having a range from −10 to 110 °C from the chemistry laboratory to do this assignment. Will this thermometer serve the purpose? Explain.

45. You decide to establish a new temperature scale on which the melting point of mercury (−38.9 °C) is 0 °M, and the boiling point of mercury (356.9 °C) is 100 °M. What would be **(a)** the boiling point of water in °M; and **(b)** the temperature of absolute zero in °M?

46. You decide to establish a new temperature scale on which the melting point of ammonia (−77.75 °C) is 0 °A and the boiling point of ammonia (−33.35 °C) is 100 °A. What would be **(a)** the boiling point of water in °A; and **(b)** the temperature of absolute zero in °A?

Density

47. A 2.18-L sample of butyric acid, a substance present in rancid butter, has a mass of 2088 g. What is the density of butyric acid in grams per milliliter?

48. A 15.2-L sample of chloroform at 20 °C has a mass of 22.54 kg. What is the density of chloroform at 20 °C, in grams per milliliter?

49. To determine the density of acetone, a 55.0-gal drum is weighed twice. The drum weighs 75.0 lb when empty and 437.5 lb when filled with acetone. What is the density of acetone expressed in grams per milliliter?

50. To determine the volume of an irregularly shaped glass vessel, the vessel is weighed empty (121.3 g) and when filled with carbon tetrachloride (283.2 g). What is the volume capacity of the vessel, in milliliters, given that the density of carbon tetrachloride is 1.59 g/mL?

51. A solution consisting of 8.50% acetone and 91.5% water by mass has a density of 0.9867 g/mL. What mass of acetone, in kilograms, is present in 7.50 L of the solution?

52. A solution contains 10.05% sucrose (cane sugar) by mass. What mass of the solution, in grams, is needed for an application that requires 1.00 kg sucrose?

53. A fertilizer contains 21% nitrogen by mass. What mass of this fertilizer, in kilograms, is required for an application requiring 225 g of nitrogen?

54. A vinegar sample is found to have a density of 1.006 g/mL and to contain 5.4% acetic acid by mass. How many grams of acetic acid are present in 1.00 L of this vinegar?

55. Calculate the mass of a block of iron ($d = 7.86$ g/cm^3) with dimensions of 52.8 cm × 6.74 cm × 3.73 cm.

56. Calculate the mass of a cylinder of stainless steel ($d = 7.75$ g/cm^3) with a height of 18.35 cm and a radius of 1.88 cm.

57. The following densities are given at 20 °C: water, 0.998 g/cm^3; iron, 7.86 g/cm^3; aluminum 2.70 g/cm^3. Arrange the following items in terms of *increasing* mass.
    (a) a rectangular bar of iron,
         81.5 cm × 2.1 cm × 1.6 cm
    (b) a sheet of aluminum foil,
         12.12 m × 3.62 m × 0.003 cm
    (c) 4.051 L of water

58. To determine the approximate mass of a small spherical shot of copper, the following experiment is performed. When 125 pieces of the shot are counted out and added to 8.4 mL of water in a graduated cylinder, the total volume becomes 8.9 mL. The density of copper is 8.92 g/cm^3. Determine the approximate mass of a single piece of shot, assuming that all of the pieces are of the same dimensions.

59. The density of aluminum is 2.70 g/cm^3. A square piece of aluminum foil, 22.86 cm on a side is found to weigh 2.568 g. What is the thickness of the foil, in millimeters?

60. The angle iron pictured here is made of steel with a density of 7.78 g/cm^3. What is the mass, in grams, of this object?

1.35 cm
12.78 cm
10.26 cm
1.35 cm
2.75 cm

61. In normal blood, there are about 5.4×10^9 red blood cells per milliliter. The volume of a red blood cell is about 90.0×10^{-12} cm^3, and its density is 1.096 g/mL. How many liters of whole blood would be needed to collect 0.5 kg of red blood cells?

62. A technique once used by geologists to measure the density of a mineral is to mix two dense liquids in such proportions that the mineral grains just float. When a sample of the mixture in which the mineral calcite just floats is put in a special density bottle, the weight is 15.4448 g. When empty, the bottle weighs 12.4631 g, and when filled with water, it weighs 13.5441 g. What is the density of the calcite sample? (All measurements were carried out at 25 °C, and the density of water at 25 °C is 0.9970 g/mL).

▲ At the left, grains of the mineral *calcite* float on the surface of the liquid bromoform (d = 2.890 g/mL). At the right, the grains sink to the bottom of liquid chloroform (d = 1.444 g/mL). By mixing bromoform and chloroform in just the proportions required so that the grains barely float, the density of the calcite can be determined (Exercise 62).

Percent Composition

63. In a class of 76 students, the results of a particular examination were 7 A's, 22 B's, 37 C's, 8 D's, 2 F's. What was the percent distribution of grades, that is, % A's, % B's, and so on?

64. A class of 84 students had a final grade distribution of 18% A's, 25% B's, 32% C's, 13% D's, 12% F's. How many students received each grade?

65. A solution of sucrose in water is 28.0% sucrose by mass and has a density of 1.118 g/mL. What mass of sucrose, in grams, is contained in 3.50 L of this solution?

66. A solution containing 12.0% sodium hydroxide by mass in water has a density of 1.131 g/mL. What volume of this solution, in liters, must be used in an application requiring 2.25 kg of sodium hydroxide?

Integrative and Advanced Exercises

67. According to the rules on significant figures, the product of the measured quantities 99.9 m and 1.008 m should be expressed to three significant figures—101 m^2. Yet, in this case, it would be more appropriate to express the result to *four* significant figures—100.7 m^2. Explain why.

68. For a solution containing 6.38% para-diclorobenzene by mass in benzene, the density of the solution as a function of temperature (t) in the temperature range 15 to 65 °C is given by the equation

$$d(\text{g/mL}) = 1.5794 - 1.836 \times 10^{-3}\,(t - 15)$$

At what temperature will the solution have a density of 1.543 g/mL?

69. A solution used to chlorinate a home swimming pool contains 7% chlorine by mass. An ideal chlorine level for the pool is one part per million (1 ppm). (Think of 1 ppm as being 1 g chlorine per million grams of water.) If you assume densities of 1.10 g/mL for the chlorine solution and 1.00 g/mL for the swimming pool water, what volume of the chlorine solution, in liters, is required to produce a chlorine level of 1 ppm in an 18,000-gallon swimming pool?

70. A standard 1.000-kg mass is to be cut from a bar of steel having an equilateral triangular cross section with sides equal to 2.50 in. The density of the steel is 7.70 g/cm^3. How many inches long must the section of bar be?

71. The volume of seawater on Earth is about 330,000,000 mi^3. If seawater is 3.5% sodium chloride by mass and has a density of 1.03 g/mL, what is the approximate mass of sodium chloride, in tons, dissolved in the seawater on Earth (1 ton = 2000 lb)?

72. The diameter of metal wire is often referred to by its American wire-gauge number. A 16-gauge wire has a diameter of 0.05082 in. What length of wire, in meters, is found in a 1.00-lb spool of 16-gauge copper wire? The density of copper is 8.92 g/cm^3.

73. Magnesium occurs in seawater to the extent of 1.4 g magnesium per kilogram of seawater. What volume of seawater, in cubic meters, would have to be processed to produce 1.00×10^5 tons of magnesium (1 ton = 2000 lb)? Assume a density of 1.025 g/mL for seawater.

74. A typical rate of deposit of dust ("dustfall") from unpolluted air was reported as 10 tons per square mile per month. **(a)** Express this dustfall in milligrams per square meter per hour. **(b)** If the dust has an average density of 2 g/cm^3, how long would it take to accumulate a layer of dust 1 mm thick?

75. In the United States volume of irrigation water is usually expressed in acre-feet. One acre-foot is a volume of water sufficient to cover 1 acre of land to a depth of 1 ft (640 acres = 1 mi^2; 1 mi = 5280 ft). The principal lake in the California Water Project is Lake Oroville, whose water storage capacity is listed as 3.54×10^6 acre-feet. Express the volume of Lake Oroville in **(a)** cubic feet; **(b)** cubic meters; **(c)** gallons.

76. A Fahrenheit and a Celsius thermometer are immersed in the same medium. At what Celsius temperature will the numerical reading on the Fahrenheit thermometer be
    (a) 49° less than that on the Celsius thermometer;
    (b) twice that on the Celsius thermometer;
    (c) one-eighth that on the Celsius thermometer;
    (d) 300° more than that on the Celsius thermometer?

77. The accompanying illustration shows a 100.0-mL graduated cylinder half-filled with 8.0 g of diatomaceous earth, a material consisting mostly of silica and used as a filtering medium in swimming pools. How many milliliters of water are required to fill the cylinder to the 100.0-mL mark? The diatomaceous earth is insoluble in water and has a density of 2.2 g/cm^3.

78. The simple device pictured here, a pycnometer, is used for precise density determinations. From the data presented, together with the fact that the density of water at 20 °C is 0.99821 g/mL, determine the density of methanol, in grams per milliliter.

| Empty | Filled with water | Filled with methanol |
| 25.601 g | at 20 °C: 35.552 g | at 20 °C: 33.490 g |

79. If the pycnometer of Exercise 78 is filled with ethanol at 20 °C instead of methanol, the observed mass is 33.470 g. What is the density of ethanol? How precisely could you determine the composition of an ethanol–methanol solution by measuring its density with a pycnometer? Assume that the density of the solution is a linear function of the volume percent composition.

80. A pycnometer (see Exercise 78) weighs 25.60 g empty and 35.55 g when filled with water at 20 °C. The density of water at 20 °C is 0.9982 g/mL. When 10.20 g lead is placed in the pycnometer and the pycnometer is again filled with water at 20 °C, the total mass is 44.83 g. What is the density of the lead in grams per cubic centimeter?

81. The Greater Vancouver Regional District (GVRD) chlorinates the water supply of the region at the rate of 1 ppm, that is, 1 kilogram of chlorine per million kilograms of water. The chlorine is introduced in the form of sodium hypochlorite, which is 47.62% chlorine. The population of the GVRD is 1.8 million persons. If each person uses 750 L of water per day, how many kilograms of sodium hypochlorite must be added to the water supply each week to produce the required chlorine level of 1 ppm?

82. A Boeing 767 due to fly from Montreal to Edmonton required refueling. Because the fuel gauge on the aircraft was not working, a mechanic used a dipstick to determine that 7682 L of fuel were left on the plane. The plane required 22,300 kg of fuel to make the trip. In order to determine the volume of fuel required, the pilot asked for the conversion factor needed to convert a volume of fuel to a mass of fuel. The mechanic gave the factor as 1.77. Assuming that this factor was in metric units (kg/L), the pilot calculated the volume to be added as 4916 L. This volume of fuel was added and the 767 subsequently ran out the fuel, but landed safely by gliding into Gimli Airport near Winnipeg. The error arose because the factor 1.77 was in units of pounds per liter. What volume of fuel should have been added?

83. The following equation can be used to relate the density of liquid water to Celsius temperature in the range from 0 °C to about 20 °C:

$$d(\text{g/cm}^3) = \frac{0.99984 + (1.6945 \times 10^{-2} t) - (7.987 \times 10^{-6} t^2)}{1 + (1.6880 \times 10^{-2} t)}$$

(a) To four significant figures, determine the density of water at 10 °C.

(b) At what temperature does water have a density of 0.99860 g/cm³?

(c) In the following ways, show that the density passes through a maximum somewhere in the temperature range to which the equation applies.
   (i) by estimation
   (ii) by a graphical method
   (iii) by a method based on differential calculus

Feature Problems

84. In an attempt to determine any possible relationship between the year in which a U.S. penny was minted and its current mass (in grams), students weighed an assortment of pennies and obtained the following data.

1968	1973	1977	1980	1982	1983	1985
3.11	3.14	3.13	3.12	3.12	2.51	2.54
3.08	3.06	3.10	3.11	2.53	2.49	2.53
3.09	3.07	3.06	3.08	2.54	2.47	2.53

What valid conclusion(s) might they have drawn about the relationship between the masses of the pennies within a given year and from year to year?

85. In the third century BC, the Greek mathematician Archimedes is said to have discovered an important principle that is useful in density determinations. The story told is that King Hiero of Syracuse (in Sicily) asked Archimedes to verify that an ornate crown made for him by a goldsmith consisted of pure gold and not a gold–silver alloy. Archimedes had to do this, of course, without damaging the crown in any way. Describe how Archimedes did this, or if you don't know the rest of the story, rediscover Archimedes's principle and explain how it can be used to settle the question.

86. The Galileo thermometer shown in the photograph is based on the dependence of density on temperature. The liquid in the outer cylinder and the liquid in the partially filled floating glass balls are the same except that a colored dye has been added to the liquid in the balls. Explain how the Galileo thermometer works.

87. The canoe gliding gracefully along the water in the photograph is made of concrete, which has a density of about 2.4 g/cm³. Explain why the canoe does not sink.

88. The accompanying sketches suggest four observations made on a small block of plastic material. Tell what conclusions can be drawn from each sketch, and conclude by giving your best estimate of the density of the plastic.

(a)   (b)   (c)   (d)

89. As mentioned on page 13, the MCO was lost because of a mix-up in the units used to calculate the force needed to correct its trajectory. Ground-based computers generated the force correction file. On September 29, 1999, it was discovered that the forces reported by the ground-based computer for use in MCO navigation software were low by a factor of 4.45. The erroneous trajectory brought the MCO 56 km above the surface of Mars; the correct trajectory would have brought the MCO approximately 250 km above the surface. At 250 km, the MCO would have successfully

entered the desired elliptic orbit. The data contained in the force correction file were delivered in lb-sec instead of the required SI units of newton-sec for the MCO navigation software. The newton is the SI unit of force and is described in Appendix B. The British Engineering (gravitational) system uses a pound (lb) as a unit of force and ft/s² as a unit of acceleration. In turn, the pound is defined as the pull of Earth on a unit of mass at a location where the acceleration due to gravity is 32.174 ft/s². The unit of mass in this case is the slug, which is 14.59 kg. Thus,

$$\text{BE unit of force} = 1 \text{ pound} = (\text{slug})(\text{ft/s}^2)$$

Use this information to confirm that

$$\text{BE unit of force} = 4.45 \times \text{SI unit of force}$$
$$1 \text{ pound} = 4.45 \text{ newton}$$

Self-Assessment Exercises

90. In your own words, define or explain the following terms or symbols: **(a)** mL; **(b)** % by mass; **(c)** °C; **(d)** density; **(e)** element.

91. Briefly describe each of the following ideas: **(a)** SI base units; **(b)** significant figures; **(c)** natural law; **(d)** exponential notation.

92. Explain the important distinctions between each pair of terms: **(a)** mass and weight; **(b)** intensive and extensive properties; **(c)** substance and mixture; **(d)** systematic and random errors; **(e)** hypothesis and theory.

93. The fact that the volume of a fixed amount of gas at a fixed temperature is inversely proportional to the gas pressure is an example of: **(a)** a hypothesis; **(b)** a theory; **(c)** a paradigm; **(d)** the absolute truth; **(e)** a natural law.

94. A good example of a homogeneous mixture is
(a) a cola drink in a tightly capped bottle
(b) distilled water leaving a distillation apparatus
(c) oxygen gas in a cylinder used in welding
(d) the material produced in a kitchen blender

95. Compared to its mass on Earth, the mass of the same object on the moon should be **(a)** less; **(b)** more; **(c)** the same; **(d)** nearly the same, but somewhat less.

96. Of the following masses, two are expressed to the nearest milligram. The two are **(a)** 32.7 g; **(b)** 0.03271 kg; **(c)** 32.7068 g; **(d)** 32.707 g; **(e)** 30.7 mg; **(f)** 3 × 10³ μg.

97. The highest temperature of the following group is **(a)** 217 K; **(b)** 273 K; **(c)** 217 °F; **(d)** 105 °C; **(e)** 373 K

98. Which of the following quantities has the greatest mass?
(a) 752 mL of water at 20 °C
(b) 1.05 L of ethanol at 20 °C (d = 0.789 g/mL)
(c) 750 g of chloroform at 20 °C (d = 1.483 g/mL)
(d) a cube of balsa wood (d = 0.11 g/cm³) that is 19.20 cm on edge

99. The reported value for the volume of a rectangular piece of cardboard with the dimensions 36 cm × 20.2 cm × 9 mm should be **(a)** 6.5 × 10³ cm³; **(b)** 7 × 10² cm³; **(c)** 655 cm³; **(d)** 6.5 × 10² cm³

100. List the following in the order of increasing precision, indicating any quantities about which the precision is uncertain. **(a)** 1400 km; **(b)** 1516 kg; **(c)** 0.00304 g; **(d)** 125.34 cm; **(e)** 2000 mg

101. *Without doing detailed calculations*, explain which of the following objects contains the greatest mass of the element iron.
(a) A 1.00-kg pile of pure iron filings.
(b) A cube of wrought iron, 5.0 cm on edge. Wrought iron contains 98.5% iron by mass and has a density of 7.7 g/cm³.
(c) A square sheet of stainless steel 0.30 m on edge and 1.0 mm thick. The stainless steel is an alloy (mixture) containing iron, together with 18% chromium. 8% nickel and 0.18% carbon by mass. Its density is 7.7 g/cm³.
(d) 10.0 L of a solution characterized as follows: d = 1.295 g/mL. This solution is 70.0% water and 30.0% of a compound of iron, by mass. The iron compound consists of 34.4% iron by mass.

102. A lump of pure copper weighs 25.305 g in air and 22.486 g when submerged in water (d = 0.9982 g/mL) at 20.0 °C. Suppose the copper is then rolled into a 248-cm² foil of uniform thickness. What will this thickness be, in millimeters?

103. Water, a compound, is a substance. Is there any circumstance under which a sample of pure water can exist as a heterogeneous mixture? Explain.

104. Appendix E describes a useful study aid known as concept mapping. Using the method presented in Appendix E, construct a concept map illustrating the different concepts presented in Sections 1-2, 1-3, and 1-4.

eMedia Exercises

105. Using the **Classification of Matter** activity (*Activebook 1-3*), classify the following as a compound, element, homogeneous mixture, or heterogeneous mixture. For mixtures, propose a method of separating the individual components.
     (a) tea sweetened with sugar ($C_{12}H_{22}O_{11}$)
     (b) magnesium oxide (MgO)
     (c) metallic brass (containing zinc and copper)
     (d) iron

106. **(a)** View the **Phases of Water** illustration (*Activebook 1-3*) and describe the different physical properties of the three states of water. **(b)** On some winter days, ice on the roads can "disappear" when the temperature remains below the melting temperature that would cause a change to the liquid phase. Based upon the representations of the states of matter shown in the diagram, propose a mechanism by which the ice disappears.

107. Using the **Density** activity to calculate densities (*Activebook 1-5*), determine the mass (in kg) required to produce a change in volume of 2.50 mL for each element available in the activity. From this information, formulate a mathematical statement that describes the relationship between density and the relative mass of objects or elements of the same volume.

eLaboratory Exercises

These exercises allow students to apply the concepts and skills for this chapter in the simulated laboratory of Virtual ChemLab. Worksheets for each of these exercises are found in the Virtual ChemLab Workbook in your MediaPak.

108. *(VCL 1-1) Measuring Mass*
     The ability to measure the mass of a sample is an important part of many laboratory experiments. In this assignment, you will learn the important fundamentals of using an analytical balance by measuring the mass of various types of samples.

109. *(VCL 1-2) Measuring Temperature*
     When measuring temperature, we often use different temperature scales depending on where we live and what we are doing, and it is often necessary to be able to convert between the different temperature scales. In this assignment, you will measure the temperature of an ice–water mixture and then measure the temperature of the water at several points as you heat it to its boiling point. You will then convert the temperatures you measured to the Fahrenheit and Kelvin temperature scales.

110. *(VCL 1-3) Calculating Density*
     The density of a material is an important physical property since it relates the mass of a sample to its volume. In this assignment, you will calculate the density of several metallic samples by using the volume given and measuring the mass of the sample.

2

ATOMS AND THE ATOMIC THEORY

CONTENTS

Image of silicon atoms that are only 78 pm apart; image produced using the latest scanning transmission electron microscope (STEM). The hypothesis that all matter is made up of atoms has existed for over 2000 years. It is only within the last few decades, however, that techniques have been developed that can render individual atoms visible.

We begin this chapter with a brief survey of early chemical discoveries, culminating in Dalton's atomic theory. This is followed by a description of the physical evidence leading to the modern picture of the *nuclear atom*, in which protons and neutrons are combined into a nucleus with electrons in space surrounding the nucleus. We will also introduce the periodic table as the primary means of organizing elements into groups with similar properties. Finally, we will introduce the concept of the mole and the Avogadro constant, which are the principal tools for counting atoms and molecules and measuring amounts of substances. We will use these tools throughout the text.

2-1   EARLY CHEMICAL DISCOVERIES AND THE ATOMIC THEORY

Chemistry has been practiced for a very long time, even if its practitioners were much more interested in its applications than in its underlying principles. The blast furnace for extracting iron from iron ore appeared as early as AD 1300, and such important chemicals as sulfuric acid (oil of vitriol), nitric acid (aqua fortis), and sodium sulfate (Glauber's salt) were all well known and used several hundred years ago. Before the end of the eighteenth century, the principal gases of the atmosphere—nitrogen and oxygen—had been isolated, and natural laws had been proposed describing the physical behavior of gases. Yet chemistry cannot be said to have entered the modern age until the process of combustion was explained. In this section, we explore the direct link between the explanation of combustion and Dalton's atomic theory.

LAW OF CONSERVATION OF MASS

The process of combustion—burning—is so familiar that it is hard to realize what a difficult riddle it posed for early scientists. Some of the difficult-to-explain observations are described in Figure 2-1.

In 1774, Antoine Lavoisier (1743–1794) performed an experiment in which he heated a sealed glass vessel containing a sample of tin and some air. He found that the mass before heating (glass vessel + tin + air) and after heating (glass vessel + "tin calx" + remaining air) were the same. Through further experiments, he showed that the product of the reaction, tin calx (tin oxide), consisted of the original tin together with a portion of the air. Experiments like this proved to Lavoisier that oxygen from air is essential to combustion, and it also led him to formulate the **law of conservation of mass**:

> The total mass of substances present after a chemical reaction is the same as the total mass of substances before the reaction.

This law is illustrated in Figure 2-2, where the reaction between silver nitrate and potassium chromate to give a red solid (silver chromate) is monitored by placing the reactants on a single-pan balance—the total mass does not change. Stated another way, the law of conservation of mass says that matter is neither created nor destroyed in a chemical reaction.

▲ **FIGURE 2-1**
Two combustion reactions
The apparent product of the combustion of the match—the ash—weighs *less* than the match. The product of the combustion of the magnesium ribbon (the "smoke") weighs *more* than the ribbon. Actually, in each case, the total mass remains unchanged. To understand this, you have to know that oxygen gas enters into both combustions and that water and carbon dioxide are also products of the combustion of the match.

Conservation of Mass. Glue a vial onto the bottom of a flask. Pipet into the vial some $Fe(NO_3)_3(aq)$. Pipet around this some NaOH(aq). Stopper the flask. Weigh the setup using the most accurate balance available. Tip the flask and allow the solutions to react. Weigh again.

(a)   (b)

▲ **FIGURE 2-2**
Mass is conserved during a chemical reaction
(a) Before the reaction, a beaker with a silver nitrate solution and a graduated cylinder with a potassium chromate solution are placed on a single-pan balance, which displays their combined mass—104.50 g. **(b)** When the solutions are mixed, a chemical reaction occurs that forms silver chromate (red precipitate) in a potassium nitrate solution. Note that the total mass—104.50 g—remains unchanged.

EXAMPLE 2-1

Applying the Law of Conservation of Mass. A 0.455-g sample of magnesium is allowed to burn in 2.315 g of oxygen gas. The sole product is magnesium oxide. After the reaction, no magnesium remains and the mass of unreacted oxygen is 2.015 g. What mass of magnesium oxide is produced?

Solution

To answer this question, we need to identify the substances present before and after the reaction. The total mass is unchanged.

First determine the total mass prior to the reaction. This is the sum of the masses of the substances present initially.

$$\text{mass before reaction} = 0.455 \text{ g magnesium} + 2.315 \text{ g oxygen}$$
$$= 2.770 \text{ g mass before reaction}$$

The law of conservation of mass states that the mass after the reaction is the same as before the reaction.

$$2.770 \text{ g mass after reaction} = ? \text{ g magnesium oxide after reaction}$$
$$+ 2.015 \text{ g oxygen after reaction}$$

The mass of magnesium oxide after the reaction will be the total mass minus the mass of the unreacted oxygen.

$$? \text{ g magnesium oxide after reaction} = 2.770 \text{ g mass after reaction}$$
$$- 2.015 \text{ g oxygen after reaction}$$
$$= 0.755 \text{ g magnesium oxide after reaction}$$

Practice Example A: A 0.382-g sample of magnesium reacts with 2.652 g of nitrogen gas. The sole product is magnesium nitride. After the reaction, the mass of unreacted nitrogen is 2.505 g. What mass of magnesium nitride is produced?

Practice Example B: A 7.12-g sample of magnesium is heated with 1.80 g of bromine. All the bromine is used up, and 2.07 g of magnesium bromide is the only product. What mass of magnesium remains *unreacted*?

(a)

(b)

▲ The mineral malachite **(a)** and the green patina on a copper roof **(b)** are both basic copper carbonate, just like the basic copper carbonate prepared by Proust in 1799.

CONCEPT ASSESSMENT ✓

Jan Baptista van Helmont (1579–1644) weighed a young willow tree and the soil in which the tree was planted. Five years later he found that the mass of soil had decreased by only 0.057 kg, while that of the tree had increased by 75 kg. During that period he had added only water to the bucket in which the tree was planted. Helmont concluded that essentially all the mass gained by the tree had come from the water. Was this a valid conclusion? Explain.

LAW OF CONSTANT COMPOSITION

In 1799, Joseph Proust (1754–1826) reported, "One hundred pounds of copper, dissolved in sulfuric or nitric acids and precipitated by the carbonates of soda or potash, invariably gives 180 pounds of green carbonate."* This and similar observations became the basis of the **law of constant composition**, or the **law of definite proportions**:

> All samples of a compound have the same composition—the same proportions by mass of the constituent elements.

To see how the law of constant composition works, consider the compound water. Water is made up of two atoms of hydrogen (H) for every atom of oxygen (O), a fact that can be represented symbolically by a *chemical formula*, the familiar H_2O. The two samples described below have the same proportions of the two elements, expressed as percentages by mass. To determine the percent

*The substance Proust worked with is actually a more complex substance called *basic* copper carbonate. Proust's results were valid because, like all compounds, basic copper carbonate has a constant composition.

by mass of hydrogen, for example, simply divide the mass of hydrogen by the sample mass and multiply by 100%. For each sample, you will obtain the same result: 11.19% H.

Sample A and Its Composition		Sample B and Its Composition	
10.000 g		**27.000 g**	
1.119 g H	% H = 11.19	3.021 g H	% H = 11.19
8.881 g O	% O = 88.81	23.979 g O	% O = 88.81

EXAMPLE 2-2

Using the Law of Constant Composition. Use data from Example 2-1 to determine the mass of magnesium contained in a 0.500-g sample of magnesium oxide.

Solution

In Example 2-1 we found that when 0.455 g of magnesium reacted with an excess of oxygen, 0.755 g of magnesium oxide was obtained. According to the law of constant composition, the mass ratio: 0.455 g magnesium/0.755 g magnesium oxide should exist in all samples of magnesium oxide. Thus, in 0.500 g of magnesium oxide, the mass of magnesium is

$$? \text{ g magnesium} = 0.500 \text{ g magnesium oxide} \times \frac{0.455 \text{ g magnesium}}{0.755 \text{ g magnesium oxide}}$$

$$= 0.301 \text{ g magnesium}$$

Practice Example A: What masses of magnesium and oxygen must be combined to make exactly 2.000 g of magnesium oxide?

Practice Example B: What substances are present, and what are their masses, after the reaction of 10.00 g of magnesium and 10.00 g of oxygen?

CONCEPT ASSESSMENT ✔

When 4.15 g magnesium and 82.6 g bromine react, (1) all the magnesium is used up, (2) some bromine remains unreacted, and (3) magnesium bromide is the only product. With this information alone, is it possible to deduce the mass of magnesium bromide produced? Explain.

DALTON'S ATOMIC THEORY

From 1803 to 1808, John Dalton, an English schoolteacher, used the two fundamental laws of chemical combination just described as the basis of an atomic theory. His theory involved three assumptions:

1. Each chemical element is composed of minute, indivisible particles called atoms. Atoms can be neither created nor destroyed during a chemical change.

2. All atoms of an element are alike in mass (weight) and other properties, but the atoms of one element are different from those of all other elements.

3. In each of their compounds, different elements combine in a simple numerical ratio: for example, one atom of A to one of B (AB), or one atom of A to two of B (AB$_2$).

   If atoms of an element are indestructible (assumption 1), then the *same* atoms must be present after a chemical reaction as before. The total mass remains unchanged. Dalton's theory explains the law of conservation of mass. If all atoms of an element are alike in mass (assumption 2) and if atoms unite in *fixed* numerical ratios (assumption 3), the percent composition of a compound must have a unique value, regardless of the origin of the sample analyzed. Dalton's theory also explains the law of constant composition.

Dalton's atomic theory is an excellent example of the use of the scientific method: the distinction between laws and assumptions and how these relate, and the importance of careful quantitative measurement.

A good topic for discussion, possibly at the end of this or the next chapter, is how each of Dalton's assumptions has had to be modified in light of modern observations.

The *law of multiple proportions* is probably the hardest concept in this chapter for students to grasp. Emphasize that we are dealing with mass ratios, and the ratio of these ratios. Give students some mass percentages and have them convert them into mass ratios.

Reactions with Oxygen movie

▲ John Dalton (1766–1844), developer of the atomic theory. Dalton has not been considered a particularly good experimenter, perhaps because of his color blindness (a condition sometimes called daltonism). However, he did skillfully use the data of others in formulating his atomic theory. (The Granger Collection)

Multiple Proportions animation

KEEP IN MIND ▶
that all we know is the second oxide is twice as rich in oxygen as the first. If the first is CO, the possibilities for the second are CO_2, C_2O_4, C_3O_6, and so on. (See also Exercise 18.)

▲ **FIGURE 2-3**
Molecules CO and CO_2 illustrating the law of multiple proportions
The mass of carbon is the same in the two molecules, but the mass of oxygen in CO_2 is twice the mass of oxygen in CO. Thus, in accordance with the law of multiple proportions, the masses of oxygen in the two compounds, relative to a fixed mass of carbon, are in a ratio of small whole numbers, 2:1.

Mention here that we will use *electrostatics* (charge attractions and repulsions) to explain and understand many chemical properties.

Coulomb's Law simulation

Like all good theories, Dalton's atomic theory led to a prediction—the **law of multiple proportions**.

> If two elements form more than a single compound, the masses of one element combined with a fixed mass of the second are in the ratio of small whole numbers.

To illustrate, consider two oxides of carbon (an oxide is a combination of an element with oxygen). In one oxide, 1.000 g of carbon is combined with 1.333 g of oxygen, and in the other, with 2.667 g of oxygen. We see that the second oxide is richer in oxygen; in fact, it contains twice as much oxygen as the first, 2.667 g/1.333 g = 2.00. We now know that the first oxide corresponds to the formula CO and the second, CO_2 (Fig. 2-3).

The characteristic relative masses of the atoms of the various elements became known as atomic weights, and throughout the nineteenth century, chemists worked at establishing reliable values of relative atomic weights. Mostly, however, chemists directed their attention to discovering new elements, synthesizing new compounds, developing techniques for analyzing materials, and in general, building up a vast body of chemical knowledge. Efforts to unravel the structure of the atom became the focus of physicists, as we see in the next several sections.

2-2   ELECTRONS AND OTHER DISCOVERIES IN ATOMIC PHYSICS

Fortunately, we can acquire a qualitative understanding of atomic structure without having to retrace all the discoveries that preceded atomic physics. We do, however, need a few key ideas about the interrelated phenomena of electricity and magnetism, which we briefly discuss here. Electricity and magnetism were used in the experiments that led to the current theory of atomic structure.

Certain objects display a property called electric charge, which can be either positive $(+)$ or negative $(-)$. Positive and negative charges attract each other, while two positive or two negative charges repel each other. As we learn in this section, all objects of matter are made up of charged particles. An object having equal numbers of positively and negatively charged particles carries no net charge and is electrically neutral. If the number of positive charges exceeds the number of negative charges, the object has a net positive charge. If negative charges exceed positive charges, the object has a net negative charge. Sometimes when one substance is rubbed against another, as in combing hair, net electric charges build up on the objects, implying that rubbing separates some positive and negative charges (Fig. 2-4). Moreover, when a stationary (static) positive charge builds up in one place, a negative charge of equal size appears somewhere else; charge is balanced.

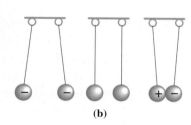

(a)   (b)

▲ **FIGURE 2-4**
Forces between electrically charged objects
(a) Electrostatically charged comb. If you comb your hair on a dry day, a static charge develops on the comb and causes bits of paper to be attracted to the comb.
(b) Both objects on the left carry a negative electric charge. Objects with like charge repel each other. The objects in the center lack any electric charge and exert no forces on each other. The objects on the right carry opposite charges—one positive and one negative—and attract each other.

◀ **FIGURE 2-5**
Effect of a magnetic field on charged particles
When charged particles travel through a magnetic field so that their path is perpendicular to the field, they are deflected by the field. Negatively charged particles are deflected in one direction, and positively charged particles in the opposite direction. Several phenomena described in this section depend on this behavior.

Figure 2-5 shows how charged particles behave when they move through the field of a magnet. They are deflected from their straight-line path into a curved path in a plane perpendicular to the field. Think of the field or region of influence of the magnet as represented by a series of invisible "lines of force" running from the north pole to the south pole of the magnet.

THE DISCOVERY OF ELECTRONS

CRT, the abbreviation for cathode-ray tube, has become a familiar acronym. The CRT is the heart of computer monitors and TV sets. The first cathode-ray tube was made by Michael Faraday (1791–1867) about 150 years ago. In passing electricity through glass tubes from which most of the air had been evacuated, Faraday discovered **cathode rays**, a type of radiation emitted by the negative terminal, or *cathode*. The radiation crossed the evacuated tube to the positive terminal, or *anode*. Later scientists found that cathode rays travel in straight lines and have properties that are independent of the cathode material (that is, whether it is iron, platinum, and so on). The construction of a CRT is shown in Figure 2-6. The cathode rays produced in the CRT are invisible, and they can be detected only by the light emitted by materials that they strike. These materials, called *phosphors*, are painted on the end of the CRT so that the path of the cathode rays can be revealed. (*Fluorescence* is the term used to describe the emission of light by a phosphor when it is struck by energetic radiation.) Another significant observation about cathode rays is that they are deflected by electric and magnetic fields in the manner expected for negatively charged particles (Fig. 2-7a, b).

Thomson Cathode-Ray Tube Experiment

▲ **FIGURE 2-6**
A cathode-ray tube
The high-voltage source of electricity creates a negative charge on the electrode at the left (cathode) and a positive charge on the electrode at the right (anode). Cathode rays pass from the cathode (C) to the anode (A), which is perforated to allow the passage of a narrow beam of cathode rays. The rays are visible only through the green fluorescence that they produce on the zinc sulfide–coated screen at the end of the tube. They are invisible in other parts of the tube.

Cathode-Ray Tube. If available, show a CRT as in Figure 2-6. Try reversing the leads and see the effect. Mention that this demonstrates "Ben Franklin guessed wrong." We now know that the flow of charge in wires and in a CRT is by negative electrons moving from − to +. We still talk today, however, of current flowing from + to −. Also demonstrate the effect of a magnetic field. Note that the electrons are not attracted or repelled but rather are deflected by a magnetic field.

Condenser plates (E)

Magnet (M)

(a)

(b)

(c)

▲ **FIGURE 2-7**
Cathode rays and their properties
(a) Deflection of cathode rays in an electric field. The beam of cathode rays is deflected as it travels from left to right in the field of the electrically charged condenser plates (E). The deflection corresponds to that expected of negatively charged particles. **(b)** Deflection of cathode rays in a magnetic field. The beam of cathode rays is deflected as it travels from left to right in the field of the magnet (M). The deflection corresponds to that expected of negatively charged particles. **(c)** Determining the mass-to-charge ratio, m/e, for cathode rays. The cathode-ray beam strikes the end screen undeflected if the forces exerted on it by the electric and magnetic fields are counterbalanced. By knowing the strengths of the electric and magnetic fields, together with other data, a value of m/e can be obtained. Precise measurements yield a value of -5.6857×10^{-9} g per coulomb. (Because cathode rays carry a negative charge, the sign of the mass-to-charge ratio is also negative.)

The *effect of a magnetic field* on a charge is somewhat of a surprise to many students. Emphasize that the effect only works when a charge is *moving*, and results in a *deflection* perpendicular to the direction of motion and perpendicular to the magnetic field.

The magnetic deflection effect can be used to identify the poles of a magnet. With a cathode ray traveling from left to right, the deflection will be "down" if the north pole is closer to the observer.

VCL *Millikan Oil-Drop Experiment*

▶ The coulomb (C) is the SI unit of electric charge (see also Appendix B).

In 1897, by the method outlined in Figure 2-7c, J. J. Thomson (1856–1940) established the ratio of mass (m) to electric charge (e) for cathode rays, that is, m/e. Also, Thomson concluded that cathode rays are negatively charged *fundamental* particles of matter found in all atoms. (The properties of cathode rays are *independent* of the composition of the cathode.) Cathode rays subsequently became known as **electrons**, a term first proposed by George Stoney in 1874.

Robert Millikan (1868–1953) determined the electronic charge e through a series of oil-drop experiments (1906–1914), described in Figure 2-8. The currently accepted value of the electronic charge e, expressed in coulombs to five significant figures, is -1.6022×10^{-19} C. By combining this value with an accurate value of the mass-to-charge ratio for an electron, we find that the mass of an electron is 9.1094×10^{-28} g.

Once the electron was seen to be a fundamental particle of matter found in all atoms, atomic physicists began to speculate on how these particles were incorporated into atoms. The commonly accepted model was that proposed by J. J. Thomson. Thomson thought that the positive charge necessary to counterbalance the negative charges of electrons in a neutral atom was in the form of a nebulous cloud. Electrons, he suggested, floated in a diffuse cloud of positive charge (rather like a lump of gelatin with electron "fruit" embedded in it). This model became known as the plum-pudding model because of its similarity to a popular English dessert. The plum-pudding model is illustrated in Figure 2-9 for a neutral atom and for atomic species, called *ions*, which carry a net charge.

▲ FIGURE 2-8
Millikan's oil-drop experiment
Ions (charged atoms or molecules) are produced by energetic radiation such as X-rays (X). Some of these ions become attached to oil droplets, giving them a net charge. The fall of a droplet in the electric field between the condenser plates is speeded up or slowed down, depending on the magnitude and sign of the charge on the droplet. By analyzing data from a large number of droplets, Millikan concluded that the magnitude of the charge, q, on a droplet is an *integral* multiple of the electric charge, e. That is, $q = ne$ (where $n = 1, 2, 3, \ldots$).

X-Rays and Radioactivity

Cathode-ray research had many important spin-offs. In particular, two natural phenomena of immense theoretical and practical significance were discovered in the course of other investigations.

In 1895, Wilhelm Roentgen (1845–1923) noticed that when cathode-ray tubes were operating, certain materials *outside* the tubes glowed or fluoresced. He showed that this fluorescence was caused by radiation emitted by the cathode-ray tubes. Because of the unknown nature of this radiation, Roentgen coined the term *X-ray*. We now recognize the X-ray as a form of high-energy electromagnetic radiation, which is discussed in Chapter 8.

Antoine Henri Becquerel (1852–1908) associated X-rays with fluorescence and wondered if naturally fluorescent materials produce X-rays. To test this idea, he wrapped a photographic plate with black paper, placed a coin on the paper, covered the coin with a uranium-containing fluorescent material, and exposed the entire assembly to sunlight. When he developed the film, a clear image of the coin could be seen. The fluorescent material had emitted radiation (presumably X-rays) that penetrated the paper and exposed the film. On one occasion, because the sky was overcast, Becquerel placed the experimental assembly inside a desk drawer for a few days while waiting for the weather to clear. On resuming the experiment, Becquerel decided to replace the original photographic film, expecting that it may have become slightly exposed. He developed the original film and found that instead of the expected feeble image, there was a very sharp one. The film had become strongly exposed because the uranium-containing material had emitted radiation continuously, even when it was not fluorescing. Becquerel had discovered **radioactivity**.

Ernest Rutherford (1871–1937) identified two types of radiation from radioactive materials, alpha (α) and beta (β). **Alpha particles** carry two fundamental units of positive charge and have essentially the same mass as helium atoms. In fact, alpha particles are identical to He^{2+} ions. **Beta particles** are negatively charged particles produced by changes occurring within the nuclei of radioactive atoms and have the same properties as electrons. A third form of radiation, which is not affected by electric or magnetic fields, was discovered in 1900 by Paul Villard. This radiation, called **gamma rays** (γ), is not made up of particles; it is electromagnetic radiation of extremely high penetrating power. These three forms of radioactivity are illustrated in Figure 2-10.

▲ FIGURE 2-9
The plum-pudding atomic model
According to this model, a helium atom would have a +2 cloud of positive charge and two electrons (−2). If a helium atom loses one electron, it becomes charged and is called an *ion*. This ion, referred to as He⁺, has a net charge of 1+. If the helium atom loses both electrons, the He²⁺ ion forms.

Investigating the Properties of Alpha and Beta Particles

Alpha, Beta, and Gamma Rays animation

Discuss, possibly at the end of the next section, that *beta particles* result from the decay of a neutron into a proton and a high kinetic-energy electron.

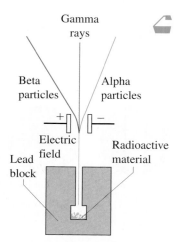

▲ FIGURE 2-10
Three types of radiation from radioactive materials
The radioactive material is enclosed in a lead block. All the radiation except that passing through the narrow opening is absorbed by the lead. When the escaping radiation is passed through an electric field, it splits into three beams. One beam is undeflected—these are gamma (γ) rays. A second beam is attracted to the negatively charged plate. These are the positively charged alpha (α) particles. The third beam, of negatively charged beta (β) particles, is deflected toward the positive plate.

▶ Perhaps because he found it tedious to sit in the dark and count spots of light on a zinc sulfide screen, Geiger was motivated to develop an automatic radiation detector. The result was the well-known Geiger counter.

Rutherford Experiment animation

Rutherford's Backscattering Experiment

 Rutherford's interpretation was quite remarkable. He proposed the nuclear atomic structure without observation of any direct form of imagery. Atomic level scattering experiments became important again in the latter half of the twentieth century.

By the early 1900s, additional radioactive elements were discovered, principally by Marie and Pierre Curie. Rutherford and Frederick Soddy made another profound finding: The chemical properties of a radioactive element *change* as it undergoes radioactive decay. This observation suggests that radioactivity involves fundamental changes at the *subatomic* level—in radioactive decay, one element is changed into another, a process known as *transmutation*.

2-3 THE NUCLEAR ATOM

In 1909, Rutherford, with his assistant Hans Geiger, began a line of research using α particles as probes to study the inner structure of atoms. Based on Thomson's plum-pudding model, Rutherford expected that most particles in a beam of α particles would pass through thin sections of matter largely undeflected, but that some α particles would be slightly scattered or deflected as they encountered electrons. By studying these scattering patterns, he hoped to deduce something about the distribution of electrons in atoms.

The apparatus used for these studies is pictured in Figure 2-11. Alpha particles were detected by the flashes of light they produced when they struck a zinc sulfide screen mounted on the end of a telescope. When Geiger and Ernst Marsden, a student, bombarded very thin foils of gold with α particles, they observed that

- The majority of α particles penetrated the foil undeflected.
- Some α particles experienced slight deflections.
- A few (about one in every 20,000) suffered rather serious deflections as they penetrated the foil.
- A similar number did not pass through the foil at all, but bounced back in the direction from which they had come.

The large-angle scattering greatly puzzled Rutherford. As he commented some years later, this observation was "about as credible as if you had fired a 15-inch shell at a piece of tissue paper and it came back and hit you." By 1911, though, Rutherford had an explanation. He based his explanation on a model of the atom known as the *nuclear atom* and having these features:

1. Most of the mass and all of the positive charge of an atom are centered in a very small region called the *nucleus.* The remainder of the atom is mostly *empty space.*

2. The magnitude of the positive charge is different for different atoms and is approximately one-half the atomic weight of the element.

3. There are as many electrons outside the nucleus as there are units of positive charge on the nucleus. The atom as a whole is electrically neutral.

Rutherford's initial expectation and his explanation of the α-particle experiments are described in Figure 2-12.

▶ **FIGURE 2-11**
The scattering of α particles by metal foil
The telescope travels in a circular track around an evacuated chamber containing the metal foil. Most α particles pass through the metal foil undeflected, but some are deflected through large angles.

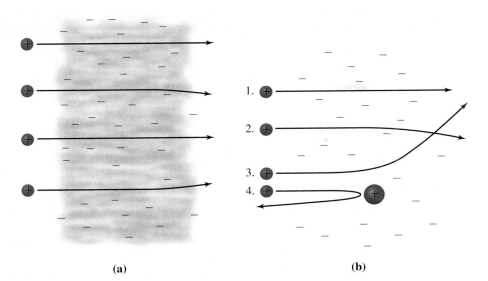

(a)   (b)

▲ FIGURE 2-12
Explaining the results of α-particle scattering experiments
(a) Rutherford's expectation was that small, positively charged α particles should pass through the nebulous, positively charged cloud of the Thomson plum-pudding model largely undeflected. Some would be slightly deflected by passing near electrons (present to neutralize the positive charge of the cloud). **(b)** Rutherford's explanation was based on a nuclear atom. With an atomic model having a small, dense, positively charged nucleus and extranuclear electrons, one would expect the four different types of paths actually observed.

1. undeflected straight-line paths exhibited by most of the α particles
2. slight deflections of α particles passing close to electrons
3. severe deflections of α particles passing close to a nucleus
4. reflections from the foil of α particles approaching a nucleus head-on

DISCOVERY OF PROTONS AND NEUTRONS

Rutherford's nuclear atom suggested the existence of positively charged fundamental particles of matter in the nuclei of atoms. Rutherford himself discovered these particles, called **protons**, in 1919 in studies involving the scattering of α particles by nitrogen atoms in air. The protons were freed as a result of collisions between α particles and the nuclei of nitrogen atoms. At about this same time, Rutherford predicted the existence in the nucleus of electrically neutral fundamental particles. In 1932, James Chadwick showed that a newly discovered penetrating radiation consisted of beams of *neutral* particles. These particles, called **neutrons**, originated from the nuclei of atoms. Thus, it has been only for about the past 75 years that we have had the atomic model suggested by Figure 2-13.

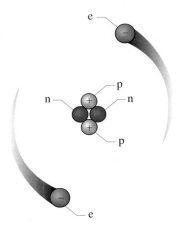

▲ FIGURE 2-13
The nuclear atom—illustrated by the helium atom
In this drawing, electrons are shown much closer to the nucleus than is the case. The actual situation is more like this: If the entire atom were represented by a room, 5 m $\times$ 5 m $\times$ 5 m, the nucleus would occupy only about as much space as the period at the end of this sentence.

CONCEPT ASSESSMENT ✓

In light of information presented to this point in the text, explain which of the three assumptions of Dalton's atomic theory (page 37) can still be considered correct and which can not.

PROPERTIES OF PROTONS, NEUTRONS, AND ELECTRONS

The number of protons in a given atom is called the **atomic number**, or the **proton number, Z**. The number of electrons in the atom is also equal to Z because the atom is electrically neutral. The total number of protons and neutrons in an atom is called the **mass number, A**. The number of neutrons, the **neutron number**, is $A - Z$. An electron carries an atomic unit of negative

TABLE 2.1 Properties of Three Fundamental Particles

	Electric Charge		Mass	
	SI (C)	Atomic	SI (g)	Atomic (u)[a]
Proton	$+1.6022 \times 10^{-19}$	$+1$	1.6726×10^{-24}	1.0073
Neutron	0	0	1.6749×10^{-24}	1.0087
Electron	-1.6022×10^{-19}	-1	9.1094×10^{-28}	0.00054858

[a]u is the SI symbol for atomic mass unit (abbreviated as amu).

charge, a proton carries an atomic unit of positive charge, and a neutron is electrically neutral. Table 2.1 presents the charges and masses of protons, neutrons, and electrons in two ways.

The **atomic mass unit** (described more fully on page 46) is defined as exactly 1/12 of the mass of the atom known as carbon-12 (read as carbon twelve). An atomic mass unit is abbreviated as amu and denoted by the symbol u. As we see from Table 2.1, the proton and neutron masses are just slightly greater than 1 u. By comparison, the mass of an electron is only about 1/2000th the mass of the proton or neutron.

The three subatomic particles considered in this section are the only ones involved in the phenomena of interest to us in this text. You should be aware, however, that a study of matter at its most fundamental level must consider many additional subatomic particles. This is the subject of elementary particle physics.

> ✓ The masses of the proton and neutron are different in the fourth significant figure. The charges of the proton and electron, however, are believed to be exactly equal in magnitude (but opposite in sign).

> ✓ The electron is believed to be truly fundamental. However, modern particle physics now considers the neutron and proton to be composed of other, more fundamental, particles.

2-4 CHEMICAL ELEMENTS

Now that we have acquired some fundamental ideas about atomic structure, we can more thoroughly discuss the concept of chemical elements.

All atoms of a particular element have the same atomic number, Z, and conversely, all atoms with the same number of protons are atoms of the same element. The elements shown on the inside front cover have atomic numbers from $Z = 1$ to 112, and $Z = 114$ and 116. Each element has a name and a distinctive symbol. **Chemical symbols** are one- or two-letter abbreviations of the name (usually the English name). The first (but never the second) letter of the symbol is capitalized; for example: carbon, C; oxygen, O; neon, Ne; and silicon, Si. Some elements known since ancient times have symbols based on their Latin names, such as Fe for iron (*ferrum*) and Pb for lead (*plumbum*). The element sodium has the symbol Na, based on the Latin *natrium* for sodium carbonate. Potassium has the symbol K, based on the Latin *kalium* for potassium carbonate. The symbol for tungsten, W, is based on the German *wolfram*.

Elements beyond uranium ($Z = 92$) do not occur naturally and must be synthesized in particle accelerators (described in Chapter 25). Elements of the very highest atomic numbers have been produced only on a limited number of occasions, a few atoms at a time. Inevitably, controversies have arisen about which research team discovered a new element and, in fact, whether a discovery was made at all. However, international agreement has been reached on the first 111 elements, each of which now has an official name and symbol.

> ✓ Other atomic symbols not based on English names include Cu, Ag, Sn, Sb, Au, and Hg.

ISOTOPES

To represent the composition of any particular atom, we need to specify its number of protons (p), neutrons (n), and electrons (e). We can do this with the symbolism

$$\text{number p + number n} \longrightarrow {}_Z^A E \longleftarrow \text{symbol of element}$$
$$\text{number p} \longrightarrow$$

(2.1)

This symbolism indicates that the atom is element E and that it has atomic number Z and mass number A. For example, an atom of aluminum represented as $^{27}_{13}\text{Al}$ has 13 protons and 14 neutrons in its nucleus and 13 electrons outside the nucleus. (Recall that an atom has the same number of electrons as protons.)

Contrary to what Dalton thought, we now know that atoms of an element do not necessarily all have the same mass. In 1912, J. J. Thomson measured the mass-to-charge ratios of positive ions formed from neon atoms. From these ratios he deduced that about 91% of the atoms had one mass and that the remaining atoms were about 10% heavier. All neon atoms have 10 protons in their nuclei, and most have 10 neutrons as well. A very few neon atoms, however, have 11 neutrons and some have 12. We can represent these three different types of neon atoms as

$$^{20}_{10}\text{Ne} \qquad ^{21}_{10}\text{Ne} \qquad ^{22}_{10}\text{Ne}$$

Atoms that have the *same* atomic number (Z) but *different* mass numbers (A) are called **isotopes**. Of all Ne atoms on Earth, 90.51% are $^{20}_{10}\text{Ne}$. The percentages of $^{21}_{10}\text{Ne}$ and $^{22}_{10}\text{Ne}$ are 0.27% and 9.22%, respectively. These percentages—90.51%, 0.27%, 9.22%—are the **percent natural abundances** of the three neon isotopes. Sometimes the mass numbers of isotopes are incorporated into the names of elements, such as neon-20 (neon twenty). Percent natural abundances are always based on *numbers*, not masses. Thus, 9051 of every 10,000 neon atoms are neon-20 atoms. Some elements, as they exist in nature, consist of just a single type of atom and therefore do not have naturally occurring isotopes.* Aluminum, for example, consists only of aluminum-27 atoms.

IONS

When atoms lose or gain electrons, for example, in the course of a chemical reaction, the species formed are called **ions** and carry net charges. Because an electron is negatively charged, adding electrons to an electrically neutral atom produces a negatively charged ion. Removing electrons results in a positively charged ion. The number of protons does not change when an atom becomes an ion. For example, $^{20}\text{Ne}^+$ and $^{22}\text{Ne}^{2+}$ are ions. The first one has 10 protons, 10 neutrons, and *9* electrons. The second one also has 10 protons, but 12 neutrons and *8* electrons. The charge on an ion is equal to the number of protons *minus* the number of electrons. That is

$$\begin{array}{c} \text{number p + number n} \\ \text{number p} \end{array} \longrightarrow {}^{A}_{Z}\text{E}^{\pm ?} \longleftarrow \text{number p} - \text{number e} \qquad (2.2)$$

Another example is the $^{16}\text{O}^{2-}$ ion. In this ion, there are 8 protons (atomic number 8), 8 neutrons (mass number − atomic number), and *10* electrons $(8 - 10 = -2)$.

> Some elements only have one naturally-occurring isotope. Common examples are beryllium-9, fluorine-19, sodium-23 and aluminum-27.

> *Isotopes of Hydrogen activity*

> ◀ Because neon is the only element with Z = 10, the symbols ^{20}Ne, ^{21}Ne, and ^{22}Ne convey the same meaning as $^{20}_{10}\text{Ne}$, $^{21}_{10}\text{Ne}$, and $^{22}_{10}\text{Ne}$.

> ◀ Odd-numbered elements tend to have fewer isotopes than do even-numbered elements. Section 25-7 will explain why.

> Usually all the isotopes of an element share the same name and atomic symbol. The exception is hydrogen. Isotope $^{2}_{1}\text{H}$ is called deuterium (symbol D), and $^{3}_{1}\text{H}$ is tritium (T).

> Heavy Water. Exhibit stoppered test tubes of H_2O and D_2O, cooled to 0 °C in an ice bath. D_2O melts at 3.8 °C and will be a solid. Hydrogen is unusual in that the different isotopes and their compounds have significantly different properties.

EXAMPLE 2-3

Relating the Numbers of Protons, Neutrons, and Electrons in Atoms and Ions. Through an appropriate symbol, indicate the number of protons, neutrons, and electrons in **(a)** an atom of barium-135 and **(b)** the double negatively charged ion of selenium-80.

*****Nuclide** is the general term used to describe an atom with a particular atomic number and mass number. Although there are several elements with only one naturally occurring nuclide, it is possible to produce additional nuclides of these elements—isotopes—by artificial means (Section 25-3). The artificial isotopes are radioactive, however. In all, the number of synthetic isotopes exceeds the number of naturally occurring ones by several fold.

Solution

(a) We are given the name (barium) and the mass number of the atom (135). From a list of the elements and a periodic table we obtain the symbol (Ba) and the atomic number ($Z = 56$), leading to the symbolic representation

$$^{135}_{56}\text{Ba}$$

From this symbol one can deduce that the neutral atom has 56 protons; a neutron number of $A - Z = 135 - 56 = 79$ neutrons; and a number of electrons equal to Z, that is, 56 electrons.

(b) We are given the name (selenium) and the mass number of the ion (80). From a list of the elements and a periodic table we obtain the symbol (Se) and the atomic number (34). Together with the fact that the ion carries a charge of 2−, we have the data required to write the symbol

$$^{80}_{34}\text{Se}^{2-}$$

From this symbol one can deduce that the ion has 34 protons; a neutron number of $A - Z = 80 - 34 = 46$ neutrons; and 36 electrons, leading to a net charge of $+34 - 36 = -2$.

Practice Example A: Use the notation $^A_Z E$ to represent the isotope of silver having a neutron number of 62.

Practice Example B: Use the notation $^A_Z E$ to represent a tin ion having the same number of electrons as an atom of the isotope cadmium-112. Explain why there can be more than answer.

CONCEPT ASSESSMENT ✓

What is the single exception to the statement that all atoms are comprised of protons, neutrons, and electrons?

Traces of naturally occurring radioactive isotopes appear in our ecosystem in carbon, hydrogen, and potassium.

▶ Ordinarily we expect like-charged objects (such as protons) to repel each other. The forces holding protons and neutrons together in the nucleus are very much stronger than ordinary electrical forces (Section 25-6).

▶ This definition also establishes that one atomic mass unit (1 u) is *exactly* 1/12 the mass of a carbon-12 atom.

Mass Spectrometer simulation

✓ The mass spectrometer depicted in Figure 2-14 uses magnetic deflection to separate a beam of ions. Other designs use an electrostatic deflection effect.

ISOTOPIC MASSES

We cannot determine the mass of an individual atom just by adding up the masses of its fundamental particles. When protons and neutrons combine to form a nucleus, a very small portion of their original mass is converted to energy and released. However, we cannot predict exactly how much this so-called nuclear binding energy will be. Determining the masses of individual atoms, then, is something that must be done by experiment, in the following way. By international agreement, one type of atom has been chosen and assigned a specific mass. This standard is an atom of the isotope carbon-12, which is assigned a mass of exactly 12 atomic mass units, that is, *12 u*. Next, the masses of other atoms relative to carbon-12 are determined with a **mass spectrometer**. In this device, a beam of gaseous ions passing through electric and magnetic fields separates into components of differing masses. The separated ions are focused on a measuring instrument, which records their presence and amounts. Figure 2-14 illustrates mass spectrometry and a typical mass spectrum.

Although mass numbers are whole numbers, the actual masses of individual atoms (in atomic mass units, u) are never whole numbers, except for carbon-12. However, they are very close in value to the corresponding mass numbers, as we can see for the isotope oxygen-16. From mass spectral data the ratio of the mass of ^{16}O to ^{12}C is found to be 1.33291. Thus, the mass of the oxygen-16 atom is

$$1.33291 \times 12\ \text{u} = 15.9949\ \text{u}$$

which is very nearly equal to the mass number of 16.

▲ **FIGURE 2-14**
A mass spectrometer and mass spectrum
In this mass spectrometer, a gaseous sample is ionized by bombardment with electrons in the lower part of the apparatus (not shown). The positive ions thus formed are subjected to an electrical force by the electrically charged velocity selector plates and a magnetic force by a magnetic field perpendicular to the page. Only ions with a particular velocity pass through and are deflected into circular paths by the magnetic field. Ions with different masses strike the detector (here a photographic plate) in different regions. The more ions of a given type, the greater the response of the detector (intensity of line on the photographic plate). In the mass spectrum shown for mercury, the response of the ion detector (intensity of lines on photographic plate) has been converted to a scale of relative numbers of atoms. The percent natural abundances of the mercury isotopes are ^{196}Hg, 0.146%; ^{198}Hg, 10.02%; ^{199}Hg, 16.84%; ^{200}Hg, 23.13%; ^{201}Hg, 13.22%; ^{202}Hg, 29.80%; ^{204}Hg, 6.85%.

The primary standard for atomic masses has evolved over time. Dalton used H = 1u as his original definition of atomic masses. Later, chemists took naturally occurring oxygen at 16 u to be the definition of the atomic-weight scale. Concurrently, physicists defined the oxygen-16 isotope as 16 u. This resulted in conflicting values. In 1971 the adoption of carbon-12 as the universal standard resolved this disparity.

Students frequently confuse the terms atomic number, mass number, isotopic mass and atomic mass.

EXAMPLE 2-4

Establishing Isotopic Masses by Mass Spectrometry. With mass spectral data, the mass of an oxygen-16 atom is found to be 1.06632 times that of a nitrogen-15 atom. What is the mass of an nitrogen-15 atom in amu?

Solution
We are given the mass ratio: ^{16}O/^{15}N, and we have previously compared the mass of oxygen-16 to that of carbon-12, obtaining 15.9949 u as the atomic mass of oxygen-16. Thus, we can write,

$$\frac{\text{mass of } ^{16}\text{O}}{\text{mass of } ^{15}\text{N}} = 1.06632$$

and

$$\text{mass of } ^{15}\text{N} = \frac{\text{mass of } ^{16}\text{O}}{1.06632} = \frac{15.9949 \text{ u}}{1.06632} = 15.0001 \text{ u}$$

The mass of ^{15}N is very nearly 15, as we should expect. If we had mistakenly multiplied instead of dividing by the ratio 1.06632, the result would have been slightly larger than 16, and clearly incorrect.

Practice Example A: What is the ratio of masses for ^{202}Hg/^{12}C, if the isotopic mass for ^{202}Hg is 201.97062 u?

Practice Example B: An isotope with atomic number 64 and mass number 158 is found to have a mass ratio relative to that of carbon-12 of 13.16034. What is the isotope, what is its atomic mass in amu, and what is its mass relative to oxygen-16?

2-5 ATOMIC MASS

▶ Carbon-14, used for radiocarbon dating, is formed in the upper atmosphere. The amount of carbon-14 on Earth is too small to affect the atomic mass of carbon.

In a table of atomic masses, the value listed for carbon is 12.011, yet the atomic mass standard is *exactly* 12. Why the difference? The atomic mass standard is based on a sample of carbon containing only atoms of carbon-12, whereas naturally occurring carbon contains some carbon-13 atoms as well. The existence of these two isotopes causes the observed atomic mass to be greater than 12. The **atomic mass (weight)*** of an element is the average of the isotopic masses, *weighted* according to the naturally occurring abundances of the isotopes of the element. In a weighted average, we must assign greater importance—give greater weight—to the quantity that occurs more frequently. Since carbon-12 atoms are much more abundant than carbon-13, the weighted average must lie much closer to 12 than to 13. This is the result that we get by applying the following general equation, where the right-hand side of the equation includes one term for each naturally occurring isotope.

KEEP IN MIND ▶

that the fractional abundance is the percent abundance divided by 100%. Thus, a 98.892% abundance is a 0.98892 fractional abundance.

$$\begin{pmatrix} \text{at. mass} \\ \text{of an} \\ \text{element} \end{pmatrix} = \begin{pmatrix} \text{fractional} \\ \text{abundance of} \times \text{isotope 1} \\ \text{isotope 1} \end{pmatrix} + \begin{pmatrix} \text{fractional} \\ \text{abundance of} \times \text{isotope 2} \\ \text{isotope 2} \end{pmatrix} + \dots \quad (2.3)$$

The mass spectrum of carbon shows that 98.892% of carbon atoms are carbon-12 with a mass of *exactly* 12 u and 1.108% are carbon-13 with a mass of 13.00335 u.

$$98{,}992 \text{ atoms of C} \, {}^{12}_{6} \, (12 \text{ u exactly})$$

$$+$$

$$1{,}108 \text{ atoms of C} \, {}^{13}_{6} \, (13.00335 \text{ u})$$

$$\downarrow$$

100,000 atoms of naturally occurring C (12.011 u)

In the setup below, we calculate the contribution of each isotope to the weighted average separately and then add these contributions together.

$$\begin{array}{l} \dfrac{\text{contribution to}}{\text{at. mass by } {}^{12}\text{C}} = \dfrac{\text{fraction of carbon}}{\text{atoms that are } {}^{12}\text{C}} \times \text{mass } {}^{12}\text{C atom} \\ \qquad = 0.98892 \qquad\qquad\quad \times 12 \text{ u} \qquad\qquad = 11.867 \text{ u} \\ \dfrac{\text{contribution to}}{\text{at. mass by } {}^{13}\text{C}} = \dfrac{\text{fraction of carbon}}{\text{atoms that are } {}^{13}\text{C}} \times \text{mass } {}^{13}\text{C atom} \\ \qquad = 0.01108 \qquad\qquad\quad \times 13.00335 \text{ u} \qquad = 0.1441 \text{ u} \\ \dfrac{\text{at. mass of naturally}}{\text{occurring carbon}} = (\text{contribution by } {}^{12}\text{C}) + (\text{contribution by } {}^{13}\text{C}) \\ \qquad = 11.867 \text{ u} \qquad\qquad\quad + 0.1441 \text{ u} \\ \qquad = 12.011 \text{ u} \end{array}$$

✓ Point out that *atomic mass* means average or weighted-average atomic mass unless the reference clearly applies to an isotope.

To determine the atomic mass of an element having three naturally occurring isotopes, such as potassium, we would have to combine three contributions to the weighted average, and so on.

The percent natural abundances of most of the elements remain very nearly constant from one sample of matter to another. For example, the proportions of ${}^{12}\text{C}$ and ${}^{13}\text{C}$ atoms are the same in samples of pure carbon (diamond), carbon dioxide gas, and a mineral form of calcium carbonate (calcite). We can treat all natural carbon-containing materials as if there were a single *hypothetical* type of carbon atom with a mass of 12.011 u. This means that once weighted-average atomic masses have been determined and tabulated,* we can simply use these values in calculations requiring atomic masses.

*Since Dalton's time, atomic masses have been called atomic weights. They still are by most chemists, yet what we are describing here is mass, not weight. Old habits die hard.

Sometimes a qualitative understanding of the relationship between isotopic masses, percent natural abundances, and weighted-average atomic mass is all that we need, and no calculation is necessary, as illustrated in Example 2-5. Example 2-6 and the accompanying Practice Examples provide additional applications of equation (2.3).

One can easily review a table of atomic masses to find elements that must contain two or more isotopes, each with appreciable (more than 1%) abundances. Based on "isotopic mass ≠ mass number," elements like lithium (6.941 u) and boron (10.81 u) must be mixtures. The other atomic masses on row 2, and many others, are nearly integral. This suggests that these elements have a single, predominant isotope. Chromium (52.00 u), however, consists of four "appreciable" isotopes: 50, 52, 53, and 54. The abundances of these just happen to average close to an integer!

EXAMPLE 2-5

Understanding the Meaning of a Weighted-Average Atomic Mass. The two naturally occurring isotopes of lithium, lithium-6 and lithium-7, have masses of 6.01513 u and 7.01601 u, respectively. Which of these two occurs in greater abundance?

Solution

From a table of atomic masses (inside the front cover) we see that the atomic mass of lithium is 6.941 u. Because this value—a weighted-average atomic mass—is much closer to 7.01601u than to 6.01513 u, lithium-7 must be the more abundant isotope.

Practice Example A: The two naturally occurring isotopes of boron, boron-10 and boron-11, have masses of 10.012937 u and 11.009305 u, respectively. Which of these two occurs in greater abundance?

Practice Example B: Indium has two naturally occurring isotopes and a weighted atomic mass of 114.82 u. One of the isotopes has a mass of 112.9043 u. Which of the following must be the second isotope: ^{111}In, ^{112}In, ^{114}In, or ^{115}In? Which of the two naturally occurring isotopes must be the more abundant?

EXAMPLE 2-6

Relating the Masses and Natural Abundances of Isotopes to the Atomic Mass of an Element. Bromine has two naturally occurring isotopes. One of them, bromine-79, has a mass of 78.9183 u and an abundance of 50.69%. What must be the mass and percent natural abundance of the other, bromine-81?

Solution

Because the sum of the percent natural abundances must total 100%, the percent natural abundance of ^{81}Br is 100.00% − 50.69% = 49.31% ^{81}Br, and as required by equation (2.3),

$$\text{atomic mass} = \begin{pmatrix} \text{fraction of atoms} \\ \text{that are } ^{79}\text{Br} \times \\ \text{mass of } ^{79}\text{Br} \end{pmatrix} + \begin{pmatrix} \text{fraction of atoms} \\ \text{that are } ^{81}\text{Br} \times \\ \text{mass of } ^{81}\text{Br} \end{pmatrix}$$

From the inside front cover, the weighted-average atomic mass of bromine is 79.904 u. Substituting this value and the fractional abundances of the two isotopes into equation (2.3), we obtain

$$79.904 \text{ u} = (0.5069 \times 78.9183 \text{ u}) + (0.4931 \times \text{mass of } ^{81}\text{Br})$$

$$= 40.00 \text{ u} + (0.4931 \times \text{mass of } ^{81}\text{Br})$$

$$\text{mass of } ^{81}\text{Br} = \frac{79.904 \text{ u} - 40.00 \text{ u}}{0.4931} = 80.92 \text{ u}$$

To four significant figures, the natural abundance of the bromine-81 isotope is 49.31% and its mass is 80.92 u.

Practice Example A: The masses and percent natural abundances of the three naturally occurring isotopes of silicon are ^{28}Si, 27.97693 u, 92.23%; ^{29}Si, 28.97649 u, 4.67%; ^{30}Si, 29.97376 u, 3.10%. Calculate the weighted-average atomic mass of silicon.

Practice Example B: Use data from Example 2-5 to determine the percent natural abundances of lithium-6 and lithium-7.

◀ **KEEP IN MIND**

that the sum of the fractional abundances must equal one.

Are You Wondering . . .

Why some atomic masses (for example, F = 18.9984032 u) are stated so much more precisely than others?

There is one naturally occurring type of fluorine atom: fluorine-19. Determining the atomic mass of fluorine means establishing the mass of this type of atom as precisely as possible. On the other hand, krypton, with an atomic mass of 83.80 u, has six naturally occurring isotopes. Because the percent distribution of the isotopes of krypton differs very slightly from one sample to another, the weighted-average atomic mass of krypton cannot be stated with high precision.

CONCEPT ASSESSMENT ✓

The value listed for chromium in the table of atomic masses inside the front cover is 51.9961 u. Should we conclude that naturally occurring chromium atoms are all of the type $^{52}_{24}$Cr? The same table lists a value of 65.39 u for zinc. Should we conclude that zinc occurs as a mixture of isotopes? Explain.

2-6   INTRODUCTION TO THE PERIODIC TABLE

Interactive Periodic Table activity

Sodium in Water. This can be performed safely in miniature. Use an evaporating dish with a watch-glass cover on an overhead projector. Cut a small corner off of a larger piece of sodium and blot to remove any oil. Use tweezers to drop the sodium onto the water and cover quickly. Note that the sodium melts due to the heat of reaction. Complete and balance a net ionic equation for the reaction. Repeat the experiment after adding phenolphthalein indicator to a fresh portion of water. The point here is that all group 1 metals do this, with varying rates of reaction.(Avoid using potassium. This forms explosive peroxides and is not recommended.)

Scientists spend a lot of time organizing information into useful patterns. Before they can organize information, however, they must possess it, and it must be correct. Botanists had enough information about plants to organize their field in the eighteenth century. Because of uncertainties in atomic masses and because many elements remained undiscovered, chemists were not able to organize the elements until a century later.

We can distinguish one element from all others by its particular set of observable physical properties. For example, sodium has a low density of 0.971 g/cm³ and a low melting point of 97.81 °C. No other element has this same combination of density and melting point. Potassium, though, also has a low density (0.862 g/cm³) and low melting point (63.65 °C), much like sodium. Sodium and potassium further resemble each other in that both are good conductors of heat and electricity, and both react vigorously with water to liberate hydrogen gas. Gold, on the other hand, has a density (19.32 g/cm³) and melting point (1064 °C) that are very much higher than those of sodium or potassium, and gold does not react with water or even with ordinary acids. It does resemble sodium and potassium in its ability to conduct heat and electricity, however. Chlorine is very different still from sodium, potassium, and gold. It is a gas under ordinary conditions, which means that the melting point of solid chlorine is far below room temperature (−101 °C). Also, chlorine is a nonconductor of heat and electricity.

Even from these very limited data, we get an inkling of a useful classification scheme of the elements. If the scheme is to group together elements with similar properties, then sodium and potassium should appear in the same group. And if the classification scheme is in some way to distinguish between elements that are good conductors of heat and electricity and those that are not, chlorine should be set apart from sodium, potassium, and gold. The classification system we seek is the one shown in Figure 2-15 (and inside the front cover), known as the **periodic table** of the elements. In Chapter 9, we will describe how the periodic table was formulated, and we will also learn its theoretical basis. For the present, we will consider only a few features of the table.

Features of the Periodic Table   In the periodic table, elements are listed according to increasing atomic number starting at the upper left and arranged in a series of horizontal rows. This arrangement places similar elements in *vertical*

Periodic table of the elements (Figure 2-15):

1 1A	2 2A	3 3B	4 4B	5 5B	6 6B	7 7B	8	9 8B	10	11 1B	12 2B	13 3A	14 4A	15 5A	16 6A	17 7A	18 8A
1 H 1.00794																	2 He 4.00260
3 Li 6.941	4 Be 9.01218											5 B 10.811	6 C 12.011	7 N 14.0067	8 O 15.9994	9 F 18.9984	10 Ne 20.1797
11 Na 22.9898	12 Mg 24.3050											13 Al 26.9815	14 Si 28.0855	15 P 30.9738	16 S 32.066	17 Cl 35.4527	18 Ar 39.948
19 K 39.0983	20 Ca 40.078	21 Sc 44.9559	22 Ti 47.88	23 V 50.9415	24 Cr 51.9961	25 Mn 54.9381	26 Fe 55.847	27 Co 58.9332	28 Ni 58.693	29 Cu 63.546	30 Zn 65.39	31 Ga 69.723	32 Ge 72.61	33 As 74.9216	34 Se 78.96	35 Br 79.904	36 Kr 83.80
37 Rb 85.4678	38 Sr 87.62	39 Y 88.9059	40 Zr 91.224	41 Nb 92.9064	42 Mo 95.94	43 Tc (98)	44 Ru 101.07	45 Rh 102.906	46 Pd 106.42	47 Ag 107.868	48 Cd 112.411	49 In 114.818	50 Sn 118.710	51 Sb 121.757	52 Te 127.60	53 I 126.904	54 Xe 131.29
55 Cs 132.905	56 Ba 137.327	57 *La 138.906	72 Hf 178.49	73 Ta 180.948	74 W 183.84	75 Re 186.207	76 Os 190.23	77 Ir 192.22	78 Pt 195.08	79 Au 196.967	80 Hg 200.59	81 Tl 204.383	82 Pb 207.2	83 Bi 208.980	84 Po (209)	85 At (210)	86 Rn (222)
87 Fr (223)	88 Ra 226.025	89 †Ac 227.028	104 Rf (261)	105 Db (262)	106 Sg (266)	107 Bh (264)	108 Hs (277)	109 Mt (268)	110 Ds (271)	111 Rg (272)	112 (273)		114 (287)		116 (289)		

*Lanthanide series	58 Ce 140.115	59 Pr 140.908	60 Nd 144.24	61 Pm (145)	62 Sm 150.36	63 Eu 151.965	64 Gd 157.25	65 Tb 158.925	66 Dy 162.50	67 Ho 164.930	68 Er 167.26	69 Tm 168.934	70 Yb 173.04	71 Lu 174.967
†Actinide series	90 Th 232.038	91 Pa 231.036	92 U 238.029	93 Np 237.048	94 Pu (244)	95 Am (243)	96 Cm (247)	97 Bk (247)	98 Cf (251)	99 Es (252)	100 Fm (257)	101 Md (258)	102 No (259)	103 Lr (262)

◀ **FIGURE 2-15**
Periodic table of the elements
Atomic masses are relative to carbon-12. For certain radioactive elements, the numbers listed in parentheses are the mass numbers of the most stable isotopes. Metals are shown in tan, nonmetals in blue, and metalloids in green. The noble gases (also nonmetals) are shown in pink.

groups, or **families**. For example, sodium and potassium are found together in a group labeled 1 (called the *alkali metals*). We should expect other members of the group, such as cesium and rubidium, to have properties similar to sodium and potassium. Chlorine is found at the other end of the table in a group labeled 17. Some of the groups are given distinctive names, mostly related to an important property of the elements in the group. For example, the group 17 elements are called the *halogens*, a term derived from Greek, meaning "salt former."

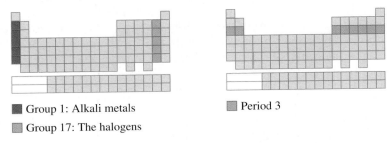

■ Group 1: Alkali metals
■ Group 17: The halogens
■ Period 3

Each element is listed in the periodic table by placing its symbol in the middle of a box in the table. The atomic number (Z) of the element is shown above the symbol, and the weighted-average atomic mass of the element is shown below its symbol. Some periodic tables provide other information, such as density and melting point, but the atomic number and atomic mass are generally sufficient for our needs. Elements with atomic masses in parentheses, such as plutonium, Pu (244), are produced synthetically, and the number shown is the mass number of the most stable isotope.

It is customary also to divide the elements into two broad categories—**metals** and **nonmetals**. In Figure 2-15, colored backgrounds are used to distinguish the metals (tan) from the nonmetals (blue and pink). Except for mercury, a liquid, metals are solids at room temperature. They are generally malleable (capable of being flattened into thin sheets), ductile (capable of being drawn into fine wires), good conductors of heat and electricity, and have a lustrous or shiny appearance. The properties of nonmetals are generally opposite those of metals; for example, nonmetals are poor conductors of heat and electricity. Several of the nonmetals, such as nitrogen, oxygen, and chlorine, are gases at room temperature. Some, such as silicon and sulfur, are brittle solids. One—bromine—is a liquid.

Two other highlighted categories in Figure 2-15 are a special group of nonmetals known as the **noble gases** (pink), and a small group of elements, often called **metalloids** (green), that have some metallic and some nonmetallic properties.

◀ There is lack of agreement on just which elements to label as metalloids. However, they are generally considered either to lie adjacent to the stair-step line or to be close by.

That elements in one group have similar properties is perhaps the most useful simplifying feature of atomic properties. Significant differences within a group do occur. The manner and reason for such differences is much of what we try to discover in studying chemistry.

Mendeleev's arrangement of the elements in the original periodic table was based on observed chemical and physical properties of the elements and their compounds. The arrangement of the elements in the modern periodic table is based on atomic properties–atomic number and electron configuration.

An advantage of the older American number and letter system is that a single rule "maximum charge = group number" applies to most main-group metals.

Perhaps the most constant property of the elements in each group is their *combining capacity*, as indicated by the formula of their compounds. Two compounds more dissimilar than CO_2 and SiO_2, in terms of their physical and chemical properties, probably cannot be found. They do have the same formula.

The *horizontal* rows of the table are called **periods**. (The periods are numbered at the extreme left in the periodic table inside the front cover.) The first period of the table consists of just two elements, hydrogen and helium. This is followed by two periods of eight elements each, lithium through neon and sodium through argon. The fourth and fifth periods contain 18 elements each, ranging from potassium through krypton and from rubidium through xenon. The sixth period is a long one of 32 members. To fit this period in a table that is held to a maximum width of 18 members, 14 members of the period are placed at the bottom of the periodic table. This series of 14 elements follows lanthanum ($Z = 57$), and these elements are called the **lanthanides**. The seventh and final period is incomplete (some members are yet to be discovered), but it is known to be a long one. A 14-member series is also extracted from the seventh period and placed at the bottom of the table. Because the elements in this series follow actinium ($Z = 89$), they are called the **actinides**.

The labeling of the groups of the periodic table has been a matter of some debate among chemists. The 1-18 numbering system used in Figure 2-15, is the one most recently adopted. Group labels previously used in the United States consisted of a letter and a number, closely following the method adopted by Mendeleev, the developer of the periodic table. As seen in Figure 2-15, the A groups 1 and 2 are separated from the remaining A groups (3 to 8) by B groups 1 through 8. The International Union of Pure and Applied Chemistry (IUPAC) recommended the simple 1 to 18 numbering scheme in order to avoid confusion between the American number and letter system and that used in Europe, where some of the A and B designations were switched! Currently, the IUPAC system is officially recommended by the American Chemical Society (ACS) and chemical societies in other nations. Because both numbering systems are in use, we show both in Figure 2-15 and in the periodic table inside the front cover. However, except for an occasional reminder of the earlier system, we will use the IUPAC numbering system in this text.

USEFUL RELATIONSHIPS FROM THE PERIODIC TABLE

The periodic table helps chemists describe and predict the properties of chemical compounds and the outcomes of chemical reactions. Throughout this text, we will use it as an aid to understanding chemical concepts. One application of the table worth mentioning here is how it can be used to predict likely charges on simple monatomic ions.

Main-group elements are those in groups 1, 2, and 13 to 18. When main-group metal atoms in groups 1 and 2 form ions, they lose the same number of electrons as the IUPAC group number. Thus, Na atoms (group 1) lose one electron to become Na^+, and Ca atoms (group 2) lose two electrons to become Ca^{2+}. Aluminum, in group 13, loses three electrons to form Al^{3+} (here the charge is "group number minus 10"). The few other metals in groups 13 and higher form more than one possible ion, a matter that we deal with in Chapter 9.

When nonmetal atoms form ions, they gain electrons. The number of electrons gained is normally 18 minus the IUPAC group number. Thus, an O atom gains $18 - 16 = 2$ electrons to become O^{2-}, and a Cl atom gains $18 - 17 = 1$ electron to become Cl^-. The "18 minus group number" rule suggests that an atom of Ne in group 18 gains no electrons: $18 - 18 = 0$. The very limited tendency of the noble gas atoms to form ions is one of several characteristics of this family of elements.

The elements in groups 3 to 12 are the **transition elements**, and because all of them are metals, they are also called the **transition metals**. Like the main-group metals, the transition metals form positive ions, but the number of electrons lost is not related in any simple way to the group number, mostly because transition metals can form two or more ions of differing charge.

EXAMPLE 2-7

Describing Relationships Based on the Periodic Table. Refer to the periodic table on the inside front cover, and indicate

    (a) the element that is in group 14 and the fourth period;

    (b) two elements with properties similar to those of molybdenum (Mo);

    (c) the ion most likely formed from a strontium atom.

Solution

    (a) The elements in the fourth period range from K ($Z = 19$) to Kr ($Z = 36$). Those in group 14 are C, Si, Ge, Sn, and Pb. The only element that is common to both of these groupings is Ge ($Z = 32$).

    (b) Molybdenum is in group 6. Two other members of this group that should resemble it are chromium (Cr) and tungsten (W).

    (c) Strontium (Sr) is in group 2. It should form the ion Sr^{2+}.

Practice Example A: Write a symbol for the ion most likely formed by an atom of each of the following: Li, S, Ra, F, I, and Al.

Practice Example B: Classify each of the following elements as a main-group or transition element. Also, specify whether they are metals, metalloids, or nonmetals: Na, Re, S, I, Kr, Mg, U, Si, B, Al, As, H.

2-7   THE CONCEPT OF THE MOLE AND THE AVOGADRO CONSTANT

Starting with Dalton, chemists have recognized the importance of relative numbers of atoms, as in the statement that *two* hydrogen atoms and *one* oxygen atom combine to form *one* molecule of water. Yet it is physically impossible to count every atom in a macroscopic sample of matter. Instead, some other measurement must be employed, which requires a relationship between the measured quantity, usually mass, and some known, but uncountable, number of atoms. Consider a practical example of mass substituting for a desired number of items. Suppose you want to nail down new floorboards on the deck of a mountain cabin, and you have calculated how many nails you will need. If you have an idea of how many nails there are in a pound, then you can buy the nails by the pound.

The SI quantity that describes an amount of substance by relating it to a number of particles of that substance is called the *mole* (abbreviated *mol*). A **mole** is the amount of a substance that contains the same number of elementary entities as there are atoms in exactly 12 g of pure carbon-12. The "number of elementary entities (atoms, molecules, and so on)" in a mole is the **Avogadro constant, N_A**.

$$N_A = 6.02214199 \times 10^{23} \text{ mol}^{-1}$$

Often the value of N_A is rounded off to $6.022 \times 10^{23} \text{ mol}^{-1}$, or even to $6.02 \times 10^{23} \text{ mol}^{-1}$. The unit mol^{-1} signifies that the entities being counted are those present in one mole.

If a substance contains atoms of a single isotope, then

$$1 \text{ mol } {}^{12}\text{C} = 6.02214 \times 10^{23} \ {}^{12}\text{C atoms} = 12.0000 \text{ g}$$

$$1 \text{ mol } {}^{16}\text{O} = 6.02214 \times 10^{23} \ {}^{16}\text{O atoms} = 15.9949 \text{ g (and so on)}$$

Most elements are composed of mixtures of two or more isotopes so that the atoms in a sample of the element are not all of the same mass but are present in their naturally occurring proportions. Thus, in one mole of carbon, most of the atoms are carbon-12, but some are carbon-13. In one mole of oxygen, most of the atoms are oxygen-16, but some are oxygen-17 and some are oxygen-18. As a result,

$$1 \text{ mol of C} = 6.02214 \times 10^{23} \text{ C atoms} = 12.011 \text{ g}$$

$$1 \text{ mol of O} = 6.02214 \times 10^{23} \text{ O atoms} = 15.9994 \text{ g and so on.}$$

The *value of Avogadro's number* is based on both a definition and a measurement. A mole of carbon-12 is defined to be 12 g. The mass of one carbon-12 atom is measured using a mass spectrometer and found to be 1.99927×10^{-23} g. The *ratio* of these two masses is Avogadro's number. In the mid-twentieth century the value first fluctuated and then stabilized, as mass spectra methods were revised and improved.

◀ The number $6.02214199 \times 10^{23}$ is known as Avogadro's *number*. The Avogadro *constant* is the number and unit (mol^{-1}) together.

When rounding Avogadro's number or any other accurately known value, keep one more significant figure than that of the least accurate number in the calculation to avoid rounding errors.

◀ We established the atomic mass of ${}^{16}\text{O}$ relative to that of ${}^{12}\text{C}$ on page 46.

(a) 6.02214×10^{23} F atoms
$= 18.9984$ g

(b) 6.02214×10^{23} Cl atoms
$= 35.4527$ g

(c) 6.02214×10^{23} Mg atoms
$= 24.3050$ g

(d) 6.02214×10^{23} Pb atoms
$= 207.2$ g

▲ **FIGURE 2-16**
Distribution of isotopes in four elements
(a) There is only one type of fluorine atom, ^{19}F (shown in red). **(b)** In chlorine, 75.77% of the atoms are ^{35}Cl (red) and the remainder are ^{37}Cl (blue). **(c)** Magnesium has one principal isotope, ^{24}Mg (red), and two minor ones, ^{25}Mg (gray) and ^{26}Mg (blue). **(d)** Lead has four naturally occurring isotopes: 1.4% ^{204}Pb (yellow), 24.1% ^{206}Pb (blue), 22.1% ^{207}Pb (gray), and 52.4% ^{208}Pb (red).

▶ The weighted-average atomic mass of carbon was calculated on page 48.

KEEP IN MIND ▶
that molar mass has the unit g/mol.

☑ The mole was purposely defined so that atomic masses (in u, per atom) and molar masses (in g/mol) would conveniently be the same number, with different units. Some students require some time to understand this.

☑ The mole concept and Avogadro's number are difficult for some students to understand. Using quantities like a *dozen* and a *gross* to help explain these topics is helpful.

The Avogadro constant was purposely chosen so that the mass of one mole of carbon-12 atoms—exactly 12 g—would have the same *numeric* value as the mass of a single carbon-12 atom—exactly 12 u. As a result, for all other elements the numeric value of the mass in grams of one mole of atoms and the weighted-average atomic mass in atomic mass units are equal. Thus, we can easily establish the mass of one mole of atoms, called the **molar mass, *M*,** from a table of atomic masses.* For example, the molar mass of lithium is 6.941 g Li/mol Li. Figure 2-16 attempts to portray the distribution of isotopes of an element, and Figure 2-17 pictures one mole each of four common elements.

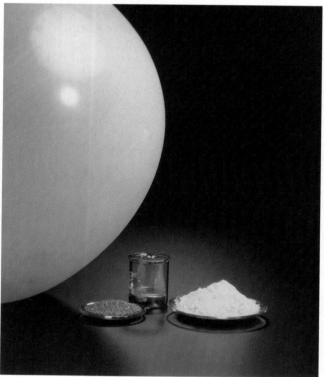

FIGURE 2-17 ▶
One mole of an element
The watch glasses contain one mole of copper atoms (left) and one mole of sulfur atoms (right). The beaker contains one mole of mercury atoms as liquid mercury, and the balloon contains one mole of helium atoms in the gaseous state.

*Atomic mass (atomic weight) values in tables are often written without units, especially if they are referred to as *relative* atomic masses. This simply means that the values listed are in relation to *exactly* 12 (rather than 12 u) for carbon-12. We will use the atomic mass unit (u) when referring to atomic masses (atomic weights). Most chemists do.

Dividing the molar mass of gold by the Avogadro constant yields the mass of any individual atom of naturally occurring gold. In contrast, no naturally occurring atom of silver has the mass obtained by dividing the molar mass of silver by the Avogadro constant. How can this be?

THINKING ABOUT AVOGADRO'S NUMBER

Avogadro's number (6.02214×10^{23}) is an enormously large number and practically inconceivable in terms of ordinary experience. Suppose we were counting garden peas instead of atoms. If the typical pea had a volume of about 0.1 cm^3, the required pile of peas would cover the United States to a depth of about 6 km (4 mi). Or imagine that grains of wheat could be counted at the rate of 100 per minute. A given individual might be able to count out about 4 billion grains in a lifetime. Even so, if all the people currently on Earth were to spend their lives counting grains of wheat, they could not reach Avogadro's number. In fact, if all the people who ever lived on Earth had spent their lifetimes counting grains of wheat, the total would still be far less than Avogadro's number. (And Avogadro's number of wheat grains is far more wheat than has been produced in human history.) Now consider a much more efficient counting device, a modern personal computer; it is capable of counting at a rate of about 1 billion units per second. The task of counting out Avogadro's number would still take about 20 million years!

Avogadro's number is clearly not a useful number for counting ordinary objects. On the other hand, when this inconceivably large number is used to count inconceivably small objects such as atoms and molecules, the result is a quantity of material that is easily within our grasp, essentially a "handful."

 Moles of Elements. Display samples of 1 mole of several elements such as C, S, Al, Cu, Zn, Pb, and Hg. Note that 1 mole is a convenient "handful-sized" quantity. While molar masses vary considerably, say from carbon to lead, the volume stays reasonably constant. We shall discuss important atomic radius differences later, but many atoms have roughly the same size.

◄ You will have an opportunity to calculate a value of N_A at several points in the text, starting with Exercise 101 in Chapter 3.

VCL *Counting Atoms*

2-8   USING THE MOLE CONCEPT IN CALCULATIONS

Throughout the text, the mole concept will provide conversion factors for problem-solving situations. With each new situation, we will explore how the mole concept applies. For now, we will deal with the relationship between numbers of atoms and the mole. Consider the statement: 1 mol S = 6.022×10^{23} S atoms = 32.07 g S. This allows us to write the conversion factors

$$\frac{1 \text{ mol S}}{6.022 \times 10^{23} \text{ S atoms}} \quad \text{and} \quad \frac{32.07 \text{ g S}}{1 \text{ mol S}}$$

In calculations requiring the Avogadro constant, students often ask when to multiply and when to divide by N_A. One answer is always to use the constant in a way that gives the proper cancellation of units. Another answer is to think in terms of the expected result. In calculating a number of atoms, we expect the answer to be a very large number, and certainly *never* smaller than one. The number of moles of atoms, on the other hand, is generally a number of more modest size, and will often be less than one.

▲ **FIGURE 2-18**
Measurement of 7.65×10^{22} S atoms (0.127 mol S)—Example 2-8 illustrated
The balance is set to zero (tared) when just the weighing boat is present. The sample of sulfur weighs 4.07 g.

◄ **KEEP IN MIND**
that you should always check for the proper cancellation of units when solving a problem. From this point on, we will not routinely show the cancellation of units.

EXAMPLE 2-8

Relating Number of Atoms, Amount in Moles, and Mass in Grams. In the sample of sulfur weighing 4.07 g pictured in Figure 2-18, **(a)** how many moles of sulfur are present, and **(b)** what is the total number of sulfur atoms in the sample?

Solution

(a) For the conversion g S → mol S, we must use the molar mass of sulfur in a conversion factor. Moreover, to achieve the proper cancellation of units the molar mass must be inverted.

$$? \text{ mol S} = 4.07 \text{ g S} \times \frac{1 \text{ mol S}}{32.07 \text{ g S}} = 0.127 \text{ mol S}$$

Iron is one of the most abundant elements in Earth's crust. Iron compounds give soils a characteristic red color, as in the Navajo Sandstone Paria Canyon Wilderness Area of Arizona.

What is the most abundant element? This seemingly simple question does not have a simple answer. If we consider the entire universe, hydrogen accounts for about 90% of all the atoms and 75% of the mass, and helium accounts for most of the rest. If we consider only the elements present on Earth, iron is probably the most abundant element. However, most of this iron is believed to be in Earth's core. The currently accessible elements are those present in Earth's atmosphere, oceans, and solid continental crust. The relative abundances of some elements and common materials containing these elements are listed in Table 2.2.

Not all the known elements exist in Earth's crust. Trace amounts of neptunium ($Z = 93$) and plutonium ($Z = 94$) are found in uranium minerals, but for practical purposes, elements with atomic numbers higher than 92 can be produced only artificially by nuclear processes. Moreover, most of the elements do not occur *free* in nature—that is, as the uncombined element—only about 20% of them do. The remaining elements occur only in chemical combination with other elements.

We cannot assume that the ease and cost of obtaining a pure element from its natural sources are necessarily related to the relative abundance of the element. Aluminum is the most abundant of the metals in Earth's crust, but it cannot be produced as cheaply as iron. This is partly because concentrated deposits of iron-containing compounds—iron ores—are more common than are ores of aluminum. Some elements whose percent abundances are quite low are nevertheless widely used because their ores are fairly common. This is the case with copper, for example, whose abundance in Earth's crust is only 0.005%. On the other hand, some elements have a fairly high abundance but no characteristic ores of their own. They are not easily obtainable, as in the case of rubidium, the twenty-third most abundant element.

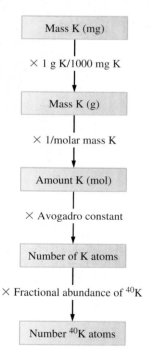

▲ FIGURE 2-19
Outlining a calculation—
Example 2-9 visualized

(b) We can begin with the result of part **(a)** and complete the conversion mol S → atoms S by using the Avogadro constant as a conversion factor.

$$? \text{ atoms S} = 0.127 \text{ mol S} \times \frac{6.022 \times 10^{23} \text{ atoms S}}{1 \text{ mol S}} = 7.65 \times 10^{22} \text{ atoms S}$$

But notice that if our concern is only to calculate the number of sulfur atoms in the sample, we can simply combine parts **(a)** and **(b)** into a single equation without recording an intermediate result.

$$? \text{ atoms S} = 4.07 \text{ g S} \times \frac{1 \text{ mol S}}{32.07 \text{ g S}} \times \frac{6.022 \times 10^{23} \text{ atoms S}}{1 \text{ mol S}} = 7.65 \times 10^{22} \text{ atoms S}$$

Practice Example A: What is the mass of 2.35×10^{24} atoms of Cu?

Practice Example B: How many lead-206 atoms are present in a 22.6-g sample of lead metal? [*Hint:* See Figure 2-17.]

Example 2-9 is perhaps the most representative use of the mole concept. Here it is part of a larger problem that requires other unrelated conversion factors as well. One approach is to outline a conversion pathway to get from the given to the desired information. The path in Example 2-9 is represented schematically in Figure 2-19.

TABLE 2.2 Abundances of the Elements in Earth's Crust[a]

Element	Abundance, Mass (%)	Principal Materials Containing the Element
Oxygen	49.3	Water; silica; silicates; metal oxides; the atmosphere
Silicon	25.8	Silica (sand, quartz, agate, flint); silicates (feldspar, clay, mica)
Aluminum	7.6	Silicates (clay, feldspar, mica); oxide (bauxite)
Iron	4.7	Oxide (hematite, magnetite)
Calcium	3.4	Carbonate (limestone, marble, chalk); sulfate (gypsum); fluoride (fluorite); silicates (feldspar, zeolites)
Sodium	2.7	Chloride (rock salt, ocean waters); silicates (feldspar, zeolites)
Potassium	2.4	Chloride; silicates (feldspar, mica)
Magnesium	1.9	Carbonate; chloride (seawater); sulfate (Epsom salts)
Hydrogen	0.7	Oxide (water); natural gas and petroleum; organic matter
Titanium	0.4	Oxide
Chlorine	0.2	Common salt (rock salt, ocean waters)
Phosphorus	0.1	Phosphate rock; organic matter
all others[b]	0.8	

[a] Earth's crust is taken to consist of the solid crust, terrestrial waters, and the atmosphere.
[b] This number includes C, N, and S—all essential to life—and less abundant, although commercially important, elements, such as B, Be, Cr, Cu, F, I, Pb, Sn, and Zn.

In later chapters, we will describe the ways in which elements are obtained from natural sources: oxygen, nitrogen, and argon from the atmosphere; hydrogen from natural gas; magnesium and bromine from seawater; sulfur from underground and underwater deposits and from hydrogen sulfide in natural gas; sodium and chlorine from ordinary rock salt; and several metals from their ores.

Are You Wondering . . .

How many significant figures to carry in atomic masses or the Avogadro constant when using them in calculations?

As a general rule, to ensure the maximum precision allowable, carry at least one more significant figure in well-known physical constants than in other measured quantities. For example, in calculating the mass of 0.600 mol of sulfur, the answers 0.600 mol S $\times$ 32.066 g S/mol S = 19.2 g S or 0.600 mol S $\times$ 32.07 mol S = 19.2 g S are more accurate responses than 0.600 mol S $\times$ 32.1 g S/mol S = 19.3 g S.

EXAMPLE 2-9

Combining Several Factors in a Calculation—Molar Mass, the Avogadro Constant, Percent Abundances. Potassium-40 is one of the few naturally occurring radioactive isotopes of elements of low atomic number. Its percent natural abundance among K isotopes is 0.012%. How many ^{40}K atoms are present in 225 mL of whole milk containing 1.65 mg K/mL?

Solution

First, use two conversion factors, one stated in the problem and one from your general knowledge, to determine the mass of potassium in the sample.

$$? \text{ g K} = 225 \text{ mL milk} \times \frac{1.65 \text{ mg K}}{1 \text{ mL milk}} \times \frac{1 \text{ g K}}{1000 \text{ mg K}} = 0.371 \text{ g K}$$

Next, use the reciprocal of the molar mass of K and the Avogadro constant to find the total number of K atoms.

$$? \text{ K atoms} = 0.371 \text{ g K} \times \frac{1 \text{ mol K}}{39.10 \text{ g K}} \times \frac{6.022 \times 10^{23} \text{ K atoms}}{1 \text{ mol K}} = 5.71 \times 10^{21} \text{ K atoms}$$

Finally, formulate a conversion factor based on the percent natural abundance of ^{40}K to establish the number of ^{40}K atoms in the milk.

$$? {}^{40}\text{K atoms} = 5.71 \times 10^{21} \text{ K atoms} \times \frac{0.012 \; {}^{40}\text{K atoms}}{100 \text{ K atoms}} = 6.9 \times 10^{17} \; {}^{40}\text{K atoms}$$

Alternatively, based on an outline such as Figure 2-19, write a single setup for the entire calculation.

$$? {}^{40}\text{K atoms} = 225 \text{ mL milk} \times \frac{1.65 \text{ mg K}}{1 \text{ mL milk}} \times \frac{1 \text{ g K}}{1000 \text{ mg K}} \times \frac{1 \text{ mol K}}{39.10 \text{ g K}}$$

$$\times \frac{6.022 \times 10^{23} \text{ K atoms}}{1 \text{ mol K}} \times \frac{0.012 \; {}^{40}\text{K atoms}}{100 \text{ K atoms}}$$

$$= 6.9 \times 10^{17} \; {}^{40}\text{K atoms}$$

Practice Example A: How many Pb atoms are present in a small piece of lead with a volume of 0.105 cm^3? The density of Pb = 11.34 g/cm^3.

Practice Example B: Rhenium-187 is a radioactive isotope that can be used to determine the age of meteorites. A 0.100-mg sample of Re contains 2.02×10^{17} atoms of ^{187}Re. What is the percent abundance of rhenium-187 in the sample?

Summary

2-1 Early Chemical Discoveries and the Atomic Theory— Modern chemistry began with eighteenth-century discoveries leading to the formulation of two basic laws of chemical combination, the **law of conservation of mass** and the **law of constant composition (definite proportions)**. These discoveries led to Dalton's atomic theory—that matter is composed of indestructible particles called atoms; that the atoms of an element are identical to one another but different from atoms of all other elements; and that chemical compounds are combinations of atoms of different elements. Based on this theory, Dalton proposed still another law of chemical combination, the **law of multiple proportions**.

2-2 Electrons and Other Discoveries in Atomic Physics— The first clues to the structures of atoms came through the discovery and characterization of **cathode rays (electrons)**. Key experiments were those that established the mass-to-charge ratio (Fig. 2-7) and then the charge on an electron (Fig. 2-8). Two important accidental discoveries made in the course of cathode-ray research were of X-rays and **radioactivity**. The principal types of radiation emitted by radioactive substances are **alpha (α) particles, beta (β) particles**, and **gamma (γ) rays** (Fig. 2-10).

2-3 The Nuclear Atom—Studies on the scattering of α particles by thin metal foils (Fig. 2-11) led to the concept of the nuclear atom—a tiny, but massive, positively charged nucleus surrounded by lightweight, negatively charged electrons (Fig. 2-12). A more complete description of the nucleus was made possible by the discovery of **protons** and **neutrons**. An individual atom is characterized in terms of its **atomic number (proton number)** Z and **mass number**, A. The difference, $A - Z$, is the **neutron number**. The masses of individual atoms and their component parts are expressed in **atomic mass units (u)**.

2-4 Chemical Elements—All elements from $Z = 1$ to $Z = 111$ have been characterized and given a name and **chemical symbol**. Knowledge of the several elements following $Z = 111$ is more tenuous. **Nuclide** is the term used to describe an atom with a particular atomic number and a particular mass number. Atoms of the same element that differ in mass number are called **isotopes**. The **percent natural abundance** of an isotope and the precise mass of its atoms can be established with a **mass spectrometer** (Fig. 2-14). A special symbolism (expression 2.2) is used to represent the composition of an atom or an **ion** derived from the atom.

2-5 Atomic Mass—The **atomic mass (weight)** of an element is a weighted average based on an assigned value of exactly 12 u for the isotope carbon-12. This weighted average is calculated from the experimentally determined atomic masses and percent abundances of the naturally occurring isotopes of the element through expression (2.3).

2-6 Introduction to the Periodic Table—The **periodic table** (Fig. 2-15) is an arrangement of the elements in horizontal rows called **periods** and vertical columns called **groups** or **families**. Each group consists of elements with similar physical and chemical properties. The elements can also be subdivided into broad categories. One categorization is that of **metals, nonmetals, metalloids**, and **noble gases**. Another is that of **main-group elements** and **transition elements (transition metals)**. Included among the transition elements are the two subcategories **lanthanides** and **actinides**. The table has many uses, as will be seen throughout the text. Emphasis in this chapter is on the periodic table as an aid in writing symbols for simple ions.

2-7 The Concept of the Mole and Avogadro Constant— The **Avogadro constant**, $N_A = 6.02214 \times 10^{23}$ mol^{-1}, represents the number of carbon-12 atoms in *exactly* 12 g of carbon-12. More generally, it is the number of elementary entities (for example, atoms or molecules) present in an amount known as one **mole** of substance. The mass of one mole of atoms of an element is called its **molar mass**, *M*.

2-8 Using the Mole Concept in Calculations—Molar mass and the Avogadro constant are used in a variety of calculations involving the mass, amount (in moles), and number of atoms in a sample of an element. Other conversion factors may also be involved in these calculations. The mole concept is encountered in ever broader contexts throughout the text.

Integrative Example

A stainless steel ball bearing has a radius of 6.35 mm and a density of 7.75 g/cm^3. Iron is the principal element in steel. Carbon is a key minor element. The ball bearing contains 0.25% carbon, by mass. Given that the percent natural abundance of ^{13}C is 1.108%, how many ^{13}C atoms are present in the ball bearing?

Strategy

The goal is to determine the number of carbon-13 atoms found in a ball bearing with a particular composition. The critical point in this problem is recognizing that we can relate number of atoms to mass by using molar mass and Avogadro's constant. The first step is to use the radius of the ball bearing to determine its volume. The second step is to determine the mass of carbon present by using the density of steel along with the percent composition. The third step uses the molar mass of carbon to convert grams of carbon to moles of carbon; Avogadro's constant is then used to convert moles of carbon to the number of carbon atoms. In the final step, the natural abundance of carbon-13 atoms is used to find the number of carbon-13 atoms in the total number of carbon atoms in the ball bearing.

Solution

The ball-bearing volume in cubic centimeters is found by applying the formula for the volume of a sphere, $V = 4/3\,\pi r^3$. Remember to convert the given radius from millimeters to centimeters, so that the volume will be in cubic centimeters.

$$V = \frac{4\pi}{3}\left[6.35 \text{ mm} \times \frac{1 \text{ cm}}{10 \text{ mm}}\right]^3 = 1.07 \text{ cm}^3$$

The product of the volume of the ball bearing and the density of steel equals the mass. The mass of the ball bearing multiplied by the percent carbon in the steel gives the mass of carbon present.

$$? \text{ g C} = 1.07 \text{ cm}^3 \times \frac{7.75 \text{ g steel}}{1 \text{ cm}^3 \text{ steel}} \times \frac{0.25 \text{ g C}}{100 \text{ g steel}} = 0.021 \text{ g C}$$

The mass of carbon is first converted to moles of carbon by using the inverse of the molar mass of carbon. Avogadro's constant is then used to convert moles of carbon to atoms of carbon.

$$? \text{ C atoms} = 0.021 \text{ g C} \times \frac{1 \text{ mol C}}{12.011 \text{ g C}} \times \frac{6.022 \times 10^{23} \text{ C atoms}}{1 \text{ mol C}}$$

$$= 1.1 \times 10^{21} \text{ C atoms}$$

The number of ^{13}C atoms is determined by using the percent natural abundance of carbon-13.

$$? \ ^{13}\text{C atoms} = 1.1 \times 10^{21} \text{ C atoms} \times \frac{1.108 \ ^{13}\text{C atoms}}{100 \text{ C atoms}}$$

$$= 1.2 \times 10^{19} \ ^{13}\text{C atoms}$$

Assessment

The number of carbon-13 atoms is smaller than the number of carbon atoms, which it should be, given that the natural abundance of carbon-13 is just 1.108%. To avoid mistakes, every quantity should be clearly labeled with its appropriate unit so that units cancel properly. Two points made by this problem are, first, that the relatively small ball bearing contains a large number of carbon-13 atoms even though carbon-13's abundance is only 1.108% of all carbon atoms. Second, the size of any atom must be very small.

Exercises

Law of Conservation of Mass

1. When an iron object rusts, its mass increases. When a match burns, its mass decreases. Do these observations violate the law of conservation of mass? Explain.

2. When a strip of magnesium metal is burned in air (recall Figure 2-1), it produces a white powder that weighs more than the original metal. When a strip of magnesium is burned in a flashbulb, the bulb weighs the same before and after it is flashed. Explain the difference in these observations.

3. A 0.406-g sample of magnesium reacts with oxygen, producing 0.674 g of magnesium oxide as the only product. What mass of oxygen was consumed in the reaction?

4. A 1.446-g sample of potassium reacts with 8.178 g of chlorine to produce potassium chloride as the only product. After the reaction, 3.960 g of chlorine remains unreacted. What mass of potassium chloride was formed?

5. When a solid mixture consisting of 10.500 g calcium hydroxide and 11.125 g ammonium chloride is strongly heated, gaseous products are evolved and 14.336 g of a solid residue remains. The gases are passed into 62.316 g water, and the mass of the resulting solution is 69.605 g. Within the limits of experimental error, show that these data conform to the law of conservation of mass.

6. Within the limits of experimental error, show that the law of conservation of mass was obeyed in the following experiment: 10.00 g calcium carbonate (found in limestone) was dissolved in 100.0 mL hydrochloric acid ($d = 1.148$ g/mL). The products were 120.40 g solution (a mixture of hydrochloric acid and calcium chloride) and 2.22 L carbon dioxide gas ($d = 1.9769$ g/L).

Law of Constant Composition

7. In Example 2-1, we established that the mass ratio of magnesium to magnesium oxide is 0.455 g magnesium/0.755 g magnesium oxide.
   (a) What is the ratio of oxygen to magnesium oxide, by mass?
   (b) What is the mass ratio of oxygen to magnesium in magnesium oxide?
   (c) What is the percent by mass of magnesium in magnesium oxide?

8. Samples of pure carbon weighing 3.62, 5.91, and 7.07 g were burned in an excess of air. The masses of carbon dioxide obtained (the sole product in each case) were 13.26, 21.66, and 25.91 g, respectively.
   (a) Do these data establish that carbon dioxide has a fixed composition?
   (b) What is the composition of carbon dioxide, expressed in % C and % O, by mass?

9. In one experiment, 2.18 g sodium was allowed to react with 16.12 g chlorine. All the sodium was used up, and 5.54 g sodium chloride (salt) was produced. In a second experiment, 2.10 g chlorine was allowed to react with 10.00 g sodium. All the chlorine was used up, and 3.46 g sodium chloride was produced.

Show that these results are consistent with the law of constant composition.

10. When 3.06 g hydrogen was allowed to react with an excess of oxygen, 27.35 g water was obtained. In a second experiment, a sample of water was decomposed by electrolysis, resulting in 1.45 g hydrogen and 11.51 g oxygen. Are these results consistent with the law of constant composition? Demonstrate why or why not.

11. In one experiment, the burning of 0.312 g sulfur produced 0.623 g sulfur dioxide as the sole product of the reaction. In a second experiment, 0.842 g sulfur dioxide was obtained. What mass of sulfur must have been burned in the second experiment?

12. In one experiment, the reaction of 1.00 g mercury and an excess of sulfur yielded 1.16 g of a sulfide of mercury as the sole product. In a second experiment, the same sulfide was produced in the reaction of 1.50 g mercury and 1.00 g sulfur.
    (a) What mass of the sulfide of mercury was produced in the second experiment?
    (b) What mass of which element (mercury or sulfur) remained *unreacted* in the second experiment?

Law of Multiple Proportions

13. Sulfur forms two compounds with oxygen. In the first compound, 1.000 g sulfur is combined with 0.998 g oxygen, and in the second, 1.000 g sulfur is combined with 1.497 g oxygen. Show that these results are consistent with Dalton's law of multiple proportions.

14. Phosphorus forms two compounds with chlorine. In the first compound, 1.000 g of phosphorus is combined with 3.433 g chlorine, and in the second, 2.500 g phosphorus is combined with 14.308 g chlorine. Show that these results are consistent with Dalton's law of multiple proportions.

15. The following data were obtained for compounds of nitrogen and hydrogen:

Compound	Mass of Nitrogen, g	Mass of Hydrogen, g
A	0.500	0.108
B	1.000	0.0720
C	0.750	0.108

   (a) Show that these data are consistent with the law of multiple proportions.
   (b) If the formula of compound B is N_2H_2, what are the formulas of compounds A and C?

16. The following data were obtained for compounds of iodine and fluorine:

Compound	Mass of Iodine, g	Mass of Fluorine, g
A	1.000	0.1497
B	0.500	0.2246
C	0.750	0.5614
D	1.000	1.0480

   (a) Show that these data are consistent with the law of multiple proportions.
   (b) If the formula for compound A is IF, what are the formulas for compounds B, C, and D?

17. There are two oxides of copper. One oxide has 20% oxygen, by mass. The second oxide has a *smaller* percent of oxygen than the first. What is the probable percent of oxygen in the second oxide?

18. The two oxides of carbon described on page 38 were CO and CO_2. Another oxide of carbon has 1.106 g of oxygen in a 2.350-g sample. In what ratio are carbon and oxygen atoms combined in molecules of this third oxide? Explain.

Fundamental Charges and Mass-to-Charge Ratios

19. The following observations were made for a series of five oil drops in an experiment similar to Millikan's (see Figure 2-8). Drop 1 carried a charge of 1.28×10^{-18} C; drops 2 and 3 each carried $\frac{1}{2}$ the charge of drop 1; drop 4 carried $\frac{1}{8}$ the charge of drop 1; drop 5 had a charge four times that of drop 1. Are these data consistent with the value of the electronic charge given in the text? Could Millikan have inferred the charge on the electron from this particular series of data? Explain.

20. In an experiment similar to that described in Exercise 19, drop 1 carried a charge of 6.41×10^{-19} C; drop 2 had $\frac{1}{2}$ the charge of drop 1; drop 3 had twice the charge of drop 1; drop 4 had a charge of 1.44×10^{-18} C; and drop 5 had $\frac{1}{3}$ the charge of drop 4. Are these data consistent with the value of the electronic charge given in the text? Could Millikan have inferred the charge on the electron from this particular series of data? Explain.

21. Use data from Table 2.1 to verify that
    (a) the mass of electrons is about 1/2000 that of H atoms;
    (b) the mass-to-charge ratio (m/e) for positive ions is considerably larger than that for electrons.

22. Determine the approximate value of m/e in coulombs per gram for the ions $^{127}_{53}I^-$ and $^{32}_{16}S^{2-}$. Why are these values only approximate?

Atomic Number, Mass Number, and Isotopes

23. The following radioactive isotopes have applications in medicine. Write their symbols in the form $^A_Z E$. (a) cobalt-60; (b) phosphorus-32; (c) iron-59; (d) radium-226.

24. For the isotope ^{202}Hg, express the percentage of the fundamental particles in the nucleus that are neutrons.

25. Complete the following table. What minimum amount of information is required to completely characterize an atom or ion?
    [*Hint:* Not all rows can be completed.]

Name	Symbol	Number Protons	Number Electrons	Number Neutrons	Mass Number
Sodium	$^{23}_{11}$Na	11	11	12	23
Silicon	—	—	—	14	—
—	—	37	—	—	85
—	^{40}K	—	—	—	—
—	—	—	33	42	—
—	^{20}Ne^{2+}	—	—	—	—
—	—	—	—	—	80
—	—	—	—	126	—

26. Arrange the following species in order of increasing (a) number of electrons; (b) number of neutrons; (c) mass.

    $^{112}_{50}$Sn $^{40}_{18}$Ar $^{122}_{52}$Te $^{59}_{29}$Cu $^{120}_{48}$Cd $^{58}_{27}$Co $^{39}_{19}$K

27. For the atom ^{108}Pd with mass 107.90389 u, determine
    (a) the numbers of protons, neutrons, and electrons in the atom;
    (b) the ratio of the mass of this atom to that of an atom of $^{12}_6$C.

28. For the ion ^{228}Ra^{2+} with a mass of 228.030 u, determine
    (a) the numbers of protons, neutrons, and electrons in the ion;
    (b) the ratio of the mass of this ion to that of an atom of ^{16}O (refer to page 46).

29. An isotope of silver has a mass that is 6.68374 times that of oxygen-16. What is the mass in u of this isotope? (Refer to page 46.)

30. The ratio of the masses of the two naturally occurring isotopes of indium is 1.0177:1. The heavier of the two isotopes has 7.1838 times the mass of ^{16}O. What are the masses in u of the two isotopes? (Refer to page 46.)

31. The following data on isotopic masses are from a chemical handbook. What is the ratio of each of these masses to that of $^{12}_6$C? (a) $^{35}_{17}$Cl, 34.96885 u; (b) $^{26}_{12}$Mg, 25.98259 u; (c) $^{222}_{86}$Rn, 222.0175 u.

32. The following ratios of masses were obtained with a mass spectrometer: $^{19}_9$F/$^{12}_6$C = 1.5832; $^{35}_{17}$Cl/$^{19}_9$F = 1.8406; $^{81}_{35}$Br/$^{35}_{17}$Cl = 2.3140. Determine the mass of a $^{81}_{35}$Br atom in amu.

33. Which of the following species has
    (a) equal numbers of neutrons and electrons;
    (b) protons, neutrons, and electrons in the ratio 9:11:8;
    (c) a number of neutrons equal to the number of protons plus one-half the number of electrons?

    ^{24}Mg^{2+}, ^{47}Cr, ^{60}Co^{3+}, ^{35}Cl$^-$, ^{124}Sn^{2+}, ^{226}Th, ^{90}Sr

34. Given the same species as listed in Exercise 33, which has
    (a) equal numbers of neutrons and protons;
    (b) protons contributing more than 50% of the mass;
    (c) about 50% more neutrons than protons?

35. An isotope with mass number 44 has four more neutrons than protons. This is an isotope of what element?

36. Identify the isotope X that has one more neutron than protons and a mass number equal to nine times the charge on the ion X^{3+}.

Atomic Mass Units, Atomic Masses

37. Which statement is probably true concerning the masses of *individual* chlorine atoms: *All, some,* or *none* has a mass of 35.4527 u? Explain.

38. The mass of a carbon-12 atom is taken to be exactly 12 u. Are there likely to be any other atoms with an *exact* integral (whole number) mass, expressed in u? Explain.

39. There are three naturally occurring isotopes of magnesium. Their masses and percent natural abundances are 23.985042 u, 78.99%; 24.985837 u, 10.00%; and 25.982593 u, 11.01%. Calculate the weighted-average atomic mass of magnesium.

40. There are four naturally occurring isotopes of chromium. Their masses and percent natural abundances are 49.9461 u, 4.35%; 51.9405 u, 83.79%; 52.9407 u, 9.50%; and 53.9389 u, 2.36%. Calculate the weighted-average atomic mass of chromium.

41. The two naturally occurring isotopes of silver have the following abundances: ^{107}Ag, 51.84%; ^{109}Ag, 48.16%. The mass of ^{107}Ag is 106.905092 u. What is the mass of ^{109}Ag?

42. Bromine has two naturally occurring isotopes. One of them, bromine-79, has a mass of 78.918336 u and a natural abundance of 50.69%. What must be the mass and percent natural abundance of the other isotope, bromine-81?

43. The three naturally occurring isotopes of potassium are ^{39}K, 38.963707 u; ^{40}K, 39.963999 u; and ^{41}K. The percent natural abundances of ^{39}K and ^{41}K are 93.2581% and 6.7302%, respectively. Determine the isotopic mass of ^{41}K.

44. What are the percent natural abundances of the two naturally occurring isotopes of boron, ^{10}B and ^{11}B? These isotopes have masses of 10.012937 u and 11.009305 u, respectively.

Mass Spectrometry

45. A mass spectrum of germanium displayed peaks at mass numbers 70, 72, 73, 74, and 76, with relative heights of 20.5, 27.4, 7.8, 36.5, and 7.8, respectively.
   (a) In the manner of Figure 2-14, sketch this mass spectrum.
   (b) Estimate the weighted-average atomic mass of germanium, and state why this result is only approximately correct.

46. Hydrogen and chlorine atoms react to form simple diatomic molecules in a 1:1 ratio, that is, HCl. The natural abundances of the chlorine isotopes are 75.77% ^{35}Cl and 24.23% ^{37}Cl. The natural abundances of ^2H and ^3H are 0.015% and less than 0.001%, respectively.
   (a) How many different HCl molecules are possible, and what are their mass numbers (that is, the sum of the mass numbers of the H and Cl atoms)?
   (b) Which is the most abundant of the possible HCl molecules? Which is the second most abundant?

The Periodic Table

47. Refer to the periodic table inside the front cover and identify
   (a) the element that is in group 14 and the fourth period
   (b) one element similar to and one unlike sulfur
   (c) the alkali metal in the fifth period
   (d) the halogen element in the sixth period

48. Refer to the periodic table inside the front cover and identify
   (a) the element that is in group 11 and the sixth period
   (b) an element with atomic number greater than 50 that has properties similar to the element with atomic number 18

   (c) the group number of an element E that forms an ion E^{2-}
   (d) an element M that you would expect to form the ion M^{3+}

49. Assuming that the seventh period of the periodic table has 32 members, what should be the atomic number of (a) the noble gas following radon (Rn); (b) the alkali metal following francium (Fr)?

50. Find the several pairs of elements that are "out of order" in terms of increasing atomic mass and explain why the reverse order is necessary.

The Avogadro Constant and the Mole

51. What is the total number of atoms in (a) 15.8 mol Fe; (b) 0.000467 mol Ag; (c) 8.5×10^{-11} mol Na?

52. *Without doing detailed calculations*, indicate which of the following quantities contains the greatest number of atoms: 6.022×10^{23} Ni atoms, 25.0 g nitrogen, 52.0 g Cr, 10.0 cm^3 Fe ($d = 7.86$ g/cm^3). Explain your reasoning.

53. Determine
   (a) the number of moles of Zn in a 415.0-g sample of zinc metal
   (b) the number of Cr atoms in 147.4 kg chromium
   (c) the mass of a one-trillion-atom (1.0×10^{12}) sample of metallic gold

   (d) the mass of one fluorine atom

54. Determine
   (a) the number of Kr atoms in a 5.25-mg sample of krypton
   (b) the molar mass, M, and identity of an element if the mass of a 2.80×10^{22}-atom sample of the element is 2.09 g
   (c) the mass of a sample of phosphorus that contains the same number of atoms as 44.75 g of magnesium

55. How many Cu atoms are present in a piece of sterling-silver jewelry weighing 33.24 g? (Sterling silver is a silver–copper alloy containing 92.5% Ag by mass.)

56. How many atoms are present in a 75.0-cm^3 sample of plumber's solder, a lead–tin alloy containing 67% Pb by mass and having a density of 9.4 g/cm^3?

57. How many ^{204}Pb atoms are present in a piece of lead weighing 215 mg? The percent natural abundance of ^{204}Pb is 1.4%.

58. A particular lead–cadmium alloy is 8.0% cadmium by mass. What mass of this alloy, in grams, must you weigh out to obtain a sample containing 6.50×10^{23} Cd atoms?

59. Medical experts generally believe a level of 30 μg Pb per deciliter of blood poses a significant health risk (1 dL = 0.1 L). Express this level **(a)** in the unit mol Pb/L blood; **(b)** as the number of Pb atoms per milliliter blood.

60. During a severe episode of air pollution, the concentration of lead in the air was observed to be 3.01 μg Pb/m^3.

How many Pb atoms would be present in a 0.500-L sample of this air (the approximate lung capacity of a human adult)?

61. *Without doing detailed calculations*, determine which of the following samples has the greatest number of atoms:
    (a) a cube of iron with a length of 10.0 cm (d = 7.86 g/cm^3)
    (b) 1.00 kg of hydrogen contained in a 10,000-L balloon
    (c) a mound of sulfur weighing 20.0 kg
    (d) a 76-lb sample of liquid mercury (d = 13.5 g/mL)

62. *Without doing detailed calculations*, determine which of the following samples occupies the largest volume:
    (a) 25.5 mol of sodium metal (d = 0.971 g/cm^3)
    (b) 0.725 L of liquid bromine (d = 3.12 g/mL)
    (c) 1.25×10^{25} atoms of chromium metal (d = 9.4 g/cm^3)
    (d) 2.15 kg of plumber's solder (d = 9.4 g/cm^3), a lead–tin alloy with a 2:1 atom ratio of lead to tin

Integrative and Advanced Exercises

63. A solution was prepared by dissolving 2.50 g potassium chlorate (a substance used in fireworks and flares) in 100.0 mL water at 40°C. When the solution was cooled to 20°C, its volume was still found to be 100.0 mL, but some of the potassium chlorate had crystallized (deposited from the solution as a solid). At 40°C, the density of water is 0.9922 g/mL, and at 20°C, the potassium chlorate solution had a density of 1.0085 g/mL.
    (a) Estimate, to two significant figures, the mass of potassium perchlorate that crystallized.
    (b) Why can't the answer in **(a)** be given more precisely?

64. William Prout (1815) proposed that all other atoms are built up of hydrogen atoms, suggesting that all elements should have integral atomic masses based on an atomic mass of one for hydrogen. This hypothesis appeared discredited by the discovery of atomic masses, such as 24.3 u for magnesium and 35.5 u for chlorine. In terms of modern knowledge, explain why Prout's hypothesis is actually quite reasonable.

65. Fluorine has a single atomic species, ^{19}F. Determine the atomic mass of ^{19}F by summing the masses of its protons, neutrons, and electrons, and compare your results with the value listed on the inside front cover. Explain why the agreement is poor.

66. Use 1×10^{-13} cm as the approximate diameter of the spherical nucleus of the hydrogen-1 atom, together with data from Table 2.1, to estimate the density of matter in a proton.

67. Use fundamental definitions and statements from Chapters 1 and 2 to establish the fact that 6.022×10^{23} u = 1.000 g.

68. In each case, identify the element in question.
    (a) The mass number of an atom is 234 and the atom has 60.0% more neutrons than protons.
    (b) An ion with a 2+ charge has 10.0% more protons than electrons.
    (c) An ion with a mass number of 110 and a 2+ charge has 25.0% more neutrons than electrons.

69. Determine the only possible 2+ ion for which the following two conditions are both satisfied:
    • The net ionic charge is *one-tenth* the nuclear charge.
    • The number of neutrons is *four* more than the number of electrons.

70. Determine the only possible isotope (E) for which the following conditions are met:
    • The mass number of E is 2.50 times its atomic number.
    • The atomic number of E is equal to the mass number of another isotope (Y). In turn, isotope Y has a neutron number that is 1.33 times the atomic number of Y and equal to the neutron number of selenium-82.

71. Suppose we redefined the atomic mass scale by arbitrarily assigning to the naturally occurring *mixture* of chlorine isotopes an atomic mass of 35.00000 u.
    (a) What would be the atomic masses of helium, sodium, and iodine on this new atomic mass scale?
    (b) Why do these three elements have nearly integral (whole-number) atomic masses based on carbon-12, but not based on naturally occurring chlorine?

72. The two naturally occurring isotopes of nitrogen have masses of 14.0031 and 15.0001 u, respectively. Determine the percentage of ^{15}N atoms in naturally occurring nitrogen.

73. The masses of the naturally occurring mercury isotopes are ^{196}Hg, 195.9658 u; ^{198}Hg, 197.9668 u; ^{199}Hg, 198.9683 u; ^{200}Hg, 199.9683 u; ^{201}Hg, 200.9703 u; ^{202}Hg, 201.9706 u; and ^{204}Hg, 203.9735 u. Use these data, together with data from Figure 2-14, to calculate the weighted-average atomic mass of mercury.

74. Germanium has three major naturally occurring isotopes: ^{70}Ge (69.92425 u, 20.85%), ^{72}Ge (71.92208 u, 27.54%), ^{74}Ge (73.92118 u, 36.29%). There are also two minor isotopes: ^{73}Ge (72.92346 u) and ^{76}Ge (75.92140 u). Calculate the percent natural abundances of the two minor isotopes. Comment on the precision of these calculations.

75. From the densities of the lines in the mass spectrum of krypton gas, the following observations were made:
    - Somewhat more than 50% of the atoms were krypton-84.
    - The numbers of krypton-82 and krypton-83 atoms were essentially equal.
    - The number of krypton-86 atoms was 1.50 times greater than the number of krypton-82 atoms.
    - The number of krypton-80 atoms was 19.6% of the number of krypton-82 atoms.
    - The number of krypton-78 atoms was 3.0% of the number of krypton-82 atoms.

    The masses of the isotopes are

    ^{78}Kr, 77.9204 u ^{80}Kr, 79.9164 u ^{82}Kr, 81.9135 u

    ^{83}Kr, 82.9141 u ^{84}Kr, 83.9115 u ^{86}Kr, 85.9106 u

    The weighted-average atomic mass of Kr is 83.80. Use these data to calculate the percent natural abundances of the krypton isotopes.

76. The two naturally occurring isotopes of chlorine are ^{35}Cl (34.9689 u, 75.77%) and ^{37}Cl (36.9658 u, 24.23%). The two naturally occurring isotopes of bromine are ^{79}Br (78.9183 u, 50.69%) and ^{81}Br (80.9163 u, 49.31%). Chlorine and bromine combine to form bromine monochloride, BrCl. Sketch a mass spectrum for BrCl with the relative number of molecules plotted against molecular mass (similar to Figure 2-14b).

77. How many atoms are present in a 1.00-m length of 20-gauge copper wire? A 20-gauge wire has a diameter of 0.03196 in, and the density of copper is 8.92 g/cm^3.

78. Monel metal is a corrosion-resistant copper–nickel alloy used in the electronics industry. A particular alloy with a density of 8.80 g/cm^3 and containing 0.022% Si by mass is used to make a rectangular plate 15.0 cm long, 12.5 cm wide, 3.00 mm thick, and has a 2.50-cm diameter hole drilled through its center. How many silicon-30 atoms are found in this plate? The mass of a silicon-30 atom is 29.97376 u, and the percent natural abundance of silicon-30 is 3.10%.

79. Deuterium, ^{2}H (2.0140 u), is sometimes used to replace the principal hydrogen isotope ^{1}H in chemical studies. The percent natural abundance of deuterium is 0.015%. If it can be done with 100% efficiency, what mass of naturally occurring hydrogen gas would have to be processed to obtain a sample containing 2.50×10^{21} ^{2}H atoms?

80. An alloy that melts at about the boiling point of water has Bi, Pb, and Sn atoms in the ratio 10:6:5, respectively. What mass of alloy contains a total of one mole of atoms?

81. A particular silver solder (used in the electronics industry to join electrical components) is to have the *atom* ratio of 5.00 Ag/4.00 Cu/1.00 Zn. What masses of the three metals must be melted together to prepare 1.00 kg of the solder?

82. A low-melting Sn–Pb–Cd alloy called *eutectic alloy* is analyzed. The *mole* ratio of tin to lead is 2.73:1.00, and the *mass* ratio of lead to cadmium is 1.78:1.00. What is the mass percent composition of this alloy?

Feature Problems

83. The data Lavoisier obtained in the experiment described on page 35 are as follows:

    Before heating: glass vessel + tin + air

    $$= 13 \text{ onces, 2 gros, 2.50 grains}$$

    After heating: glass vessel + tin calx + remaining air

    $$= 13 \text{ onces, 2 gros, 5.62 grains}$$

    How closely did Lavoisier's results conform to the law of conservation of mass? (1 livre = 16 onces; 1 once = 8 gros; 1 gros = 72 grains. In modern terms, 1 livre = 30.59 g.)

84. Some of Millikan's oil-drop data are shown here. The measured quantities were not actual charges on oil drops, but were proportional to these charges. Show that these data are consistent with the idea of a fundamental electronic charge.

Observation	Measured Quantity	Observation	Measured Quantity
1	19.66	8	53.91
2	24.60	9	59.12
3	29.62	10	63.68
4	34.47	11	68.65
5	39.38	12	78.34
6	44.42	13	83.22
7	49.41		

85. Prior to 1961, the standard for atomic masses was the isotope ^{16}O, to which physicists assigned a value of exactly 16. At the same time, chemists assigned a value of exactly 16 to the naturally occurring mixture of the isotopes ^{16}O, ^{17}O, and ^{18}O. Would you expect atomic masses listed in a 50-year-old text to be the same, generally higher, or generally lower than in this text? Explain.

86. The German chemist Fritz Haber proposed paying off the reparations imposed against Germany after World War I by extracting gold from seawater. Given that (1) the amount of the reparations was $28.8 billion dollars, (2) the value of gold at the time was about $21.25 per troy ounce (1 troy ounce = 31.103 g), and (3) gold occurs in seawater to the extent of 4.67×10^{17} atoms per ton of seawater (1 ton = 2000 lb), how many cubic kilometers of seawater would have had to be processed to obtain the required amount of gold? Assume that the density of seawater is 1.03 g/cm^3. (Haber's scheme proved to be commercially infeasible, and the reparations were never fully paid.)

87. Mass spectrometry is one of the most versatile and powerful tools in chemical analysis because of its capacity to discriminate between atoms of different masses. When a sample containing a mixture of isotopes is introduced into a mass spectrometer, the ratio of the peaks observed reflects the ratio of the percent natural abundances of the isotopes. This ratio provides an internal standard from which the amount of a certain isotope present in a sample can be determined.

This is accomplished by deliberately introducing a known quantity of a particular isotope into the sample to be analyzed. A comparison of the new isotope ratio to the first ratio allows the determination of the amount of the isotope present in the original sample.

An analysis was done on a rock sample to determine its rubidium content. The rubidium content of a portion of rock weighing 0.350 g was extracted, and to the extracted sample was added an additional 29.45 μg of ^{87}Rb. The mass spectrum of this spiked sample showed a ^{87}Rb peak that was 1.12 times as high as the peak for ^{85}Rb. Assuming that the two isotopes react identically, what is the Rb content of the rock (expressed in parts per million by mass)? The natural abundances and isotopic masses are shown in the table.

Isotope	% Natural Abundance	Atomic Mass, u
^{87}Rb	27.83	86.909
^{85}Rb	72.17	84.912

Self-Assessment Exercises

88. In your own words, define or explain these terms or symbols: **(a)** $^{A}_{Z}E$ **(b)** β particle **(c)** isotope **(d)** ^{16}O **(e)** molar mass
89. Briefly describe
    (a) law of conservation of mass
    (b) Rutherford's nuclear atom
    (c) weighted-average atomic mass
    (d) a mass spectrum
90. Explain the important distinctions between each pair of terms:
    (a) cathode rays and X-rays
    (b) protons and neutrons
    (c) nuclear charge and ionic charge
    (d) periods and groups of the periodic table
    (e) metal and nonmetal
    (f) the Avogadro constant and the mole
91. When 10.0 g zinc and 8.0 g sulfur are allowed to react, all the zinc is consumed, 15.0 g zinc sulfide is produced, and the mass of unreacted sulfur remaining is
    (a) 2.0 g;
    (b) 3.0 g;
    (c) 5.0 g;
    (d) impossible to predict from this information alone.
92. One oxide of rubidium has 0.187 g O per gram of Rb. A possible O:Rb mass ratio for a second oxide of rubidium is
    (a) 16:85.5; **(b)** 8:42.7; **(c)** 1:2.674; **(d)** any of these.
93. Cathode rays
    (a) may be positively or negatively charged
    (b) are a form of electromagnetic radiation similar to visible light
    (c) have properties identical to β particles
    (d) have masses that depend on the cathode that emits them
94. The scattering of α particles by thin metal foils established that
    (a) the mass of an atom is concentrated in a positively charged nucleus
    (b) electrons are fundamental particles of all matter
    (c) all electrons carry the same charge
    (d) atoms are electrically neutral
95. The two species that have the same number of electrons as ^{32}S are **(a)** ^{32}Cl **(b)** ^{34}S$^+$ **(c)** ^{33}P$^+$ **(d)** ^{28}Si^{2-} **(e)** ^{35}S^{2-} **(f)** ^{40}Ar^{2+} **(g)** ^{40}Ca^{2+}.
96. To four significant figures, all of the following masses are possible for an individual titanium atom except one. The exception is **(a)** 45.95 u; **(b)** 46.95 u; **(c)** 47.88 u; **(d)** 47.95 u **(e)** 48.95 u **(f)** 49.94 u.
97. The mass of the isotope $^{84}_{36}$Xe is 83.9115 u. If the atomic mass scale were redefined so that $^{84}_{36}$Xe = 84 u, *exactly*, the mass of the $^{12}_{6}$C isotope would be **(a)** 11.9115 u; **(b)** 11.9874 u; **(c)** 12 exactly; **(d)** 12.0127 u **(e)** 12.0885 u.
98. A 5.585-kg sample of iron (Fe) contains
    (a) 10.0 mol Fe;
    (b) twice as many atoms as does 600.6 g C;
    (c) 10 times as many atoms as does 52.00 g Cr;
    (d) 6.022×10^{24} atoms.
99. There are three common iron-oxygen compounds. The one with the greatest proportion of iron has one Fe atom for every O atom and the formula FeO. A second compound has 2.327 g Fe per 1.000 g O, and the third has 2.618 g Fe per 1.000 g O. What are the formulas of these other two iron-oxygen compounds?
100. The four naturally occurring isotopes of strontium have the atomic masses 83.9134 u; 85.9093 u; 86.9089 u; and 87.9056 u. The percent natural abundance of the lightest isotope is 0.56% and of the heaviest, 82.58%. Estimate the percent natural abundances of the other two. Why is this result only a rough approximation?
101. Gold is present in seawater to the extent of 0.15 mg/ton. Assume the density of the seawater is 1.03 g/mL and determine how many Au atoms could conceivably be extracted from 0.250 L of seawater (1 ton = 2.000×10^3 lb; 1 kg = 2.205 lb).
102. Appendix E describes a useful study aid known as concept mapping. Using the method presented in Appendix E, construct a concept map illustrating the different concepts in Sections 2-7 and 2-8.

 ## eMedia Exercises

103. After viewing the **Multiple Proportions** animation (*Activebook 2-1*), consider a similar process being carried out with solid phosphorus. In the reaction with phosphorus, two compounds containing only oxygen and phosphorus form. The ratio of the oxygen/ phosphorus mass ratios of the two compounds is 1.66. If both formula units contain four phosphorus atoms, determine the compositions of these two compounds. Why is the ratio of mass ratios not equal to a whole number in this case?

104. Review the animation of the **Millikan Oil-Drop Experiment** (*Activebook 2-2*), and provide an explanation for each of the following:
     (a) Oil droplets could be localized in the field of view of the microscope objective by controlling an external voltage.
     (b) The calculated charge of the electron did not depend directly upon the mass of the oil droplet.
     (c) Oil droplets that became doubly charged were observed to rise.

105. Referring to the **Rutherford Experiment** animation (*Activebook 2-3*), describe the conclusions about the nuclear atom reached from the following pieces of experimental data:
     (i) the majority of alpha particles passed through the gold foil
     (ii) a few alpha particles were reflected at large angles
     (iii) the angle of deflection of the alpha particles varied

106. Using information in the **Mass Spectrometer** simulation (*Activebook 2-4*), calculate the average atomic mass of fluorine and compare your answer to the value listed in the periodic table.

107. Explore the **Interactive Periodic Table** activity (*Activebook 2-6*) to provide the answer to the following questions.
     (a) Which group has the lowest average melting point?
     (b) Can the majority of known elements be categorized as metals or nonmetals?
     (c) Which is greater, the number of main-group elements or the number of transition elements?
     (d) Which element has the highest boiling point?

---

 eLaboratory Exercises

These exercises allow students to apply the concepts and skills for this chapter in the simulated laboratory of Virtual ChemLab. Worksheets for each of these exercises are found in the Virtual ChemLab Workbook in your MediaPak.

108. **(VCL 2-1) Thomson Cathode-Ray Tube Experiment**
     In 1897, Thomson showed that if you could measure how much a beam of electrons was bent in an electric field and measure the magnetic field required to move the beam of electrons back to center, you could determine the charge-to-mass ratio (q/m_e) for the electrons. In this problem, you will duplicate the Thomson cathode-ray tube experiment and calculate the charge-to-mass ratio of an electron.

109. **(VCL 2-2) Millikan Oil-Drop Experiment**
     In 1909, Robert Millikan and his graduate student Harvey Fletcher showed that they could measure the charge of an electron by making very small oil drops, depositing electrons on these drops, and then applying an electric field. You will get a chance to repeat their experiments and, using the results from the Thomson assignment, be able to experimentally calculate the mass of an electron.

110. **(VCL 2-3) Investigating the Properties of Alpha and Beta Particles**
     As scientists began investigating the properties of atoms, their first discovery was that they could extract negatively charged particles. They called these particles electrons, but they are also known as beta particles in the context of nuclear decay. Robert Millikan used beta particles in his famous oil-drop experiment. Another particle ejected during nuclear decay is the alpha particle. An alpha particle is a helium nucleus, or a helium atom without its two electrons. Consequently, an alpha particle is positively charged. Ernest Rutherford used alpha particles in his gold-foil experiment. In this assignment you will investigate the properties of alpha and beta particles using the virtual laboratory.

111. **(VCL 2-4) Rutherford's Backscattering Experiment**
     A key experiment in understanding the nature of atomic structure was completed by Ernest Rutherford in 1911. He set up an experiment that directed a beam of alpha particles (helium nuclei) through a gold foil and then onto a detector screen. According to the plum-pudding atomic model, electrons float around inside a cloud of positive charge. Based on this model, Rutherford expected that almost all the alpha particles should pass through the gold foil and not be deflected. A few of the alpha particles would experience a slight deflection because of the attraction to the negative electrons. Imagine his surprise when a few alpha particles deflected at all angles, even nearly straight backward. You will have a chance to repeat this experiment and observe the number of alpha particles that are deflected at different angles. You will also be able to experiment with other metals and understand why Rutherford selected gold.

112. **(VCL 2-5) Counting Atoms**
     It is a common problem for students to be asked to calculate the number of atoms in a pure elemental material or compound, given the mass of the sample. In this problem you will go into the virtual laboratory, retrieve a sample of gold (Au), use an analytical balance to measure its mass, and then calculate the number of atoms in the sample.

113. **(VCL 2-6) Counting Atoms**
     In this problem you will go into the virtual laboratory, retrieve a sample of lead (Pb) and of uranium (U), use an analytical balance to measure the mass of each sample, and then calculate the number of atoms in each sample.

114. **(VCL 2-7) Counting Atoms**
     In this problem you will go into the virtual laboratory; retrieve samples of erbium (Er), sodium (Na), tungsten (W), and a fourth sample of your choice; use an analytical balance to measure the mass of each sample; and then calculate the number of atoms in each sample.

115. **(VCL 2-8) Counting Protons, Neutrons, and Electrons**
     In this problem you will enter the virtual laboratory and weigh out an isotopically pure sample of scandium (^{45}Sc), calculate the number of moles in the sample, and then calculate the number of protons, neutrons, and electrons.

116. **(VCL 2-9) Counting Protons, Neutrons, and Electrons**
     In this problem you will enter the virtual laboratory and weigh out an isotopically pure sample of bismuth (^{209}Bi), calculate the number of moles in the sample, and then calculate the number of protons, neutrons, and electrons in ^{209}Bi^{5+}.

3

CHEMICAL COMPOUNDS

CONTENTS

Scanning electron microscope image of sodium chloride crystals. Chemical compounds, their formulas, and names are topics discussed in this chapter.

Water, ammonia, carbon monoxide, and carbon dioxide—all familiar substances—are rather simple chemical compounds. Only slightly less familiar are sucrose (cane sugar), acetylsalicylic acid (aspirin), and ascorbic acid (vitamin C). They too are chemical compounds. In fact, the study of chemistry is mostly about chemical compounds, and in this chapter, we will consider a number of ideas about compounds.

The common feature of all compounds is that they are composed of two or more elements. The full range of compounds can be divided into a few broad categories by applying ideas from the periodic table of the elements. Compounds are represented by chemical formulas, which in turn are derived from the symbols of their constituent elements. In this chapter, you will learn how to deduce and write chemical formulas and how to use the information incorporated into chemical formulas. The chapter ends with an overview of the relationship between names and formulas—chemical nomenclature.

3-1   TYPES OF CHEMICAL COMPOUNDS AND THEIR FORMULAS

▶ In our later study of chemical bonding, we will find that the distinction between covalent and ionic bonding is not as clear-cut as these statements imply, but we will consider this matter in Chapter 10.

Generally speaking, there are two fundamental kinds of chemical bonds that hold together the atoms in a compound. *Covalent* bonds, which involve a sharing of electrons between atoms, give rise to molecular compounds. *Ionic* bonds, which involve a transfer of electrons from one atom to another, give rise to ionic compounds. In this section we consider only the basic features of molecular and ionic compounds that we need as background for the early chapters of the text. Our in-depth discussion of chemical bonding will come in Chapters 10 and 11.

MOLECULAR COMPOUNDS

A **molecular compound** is made up of discrete units called **molecules**, which typically consist of a small number of *nonmetal* atoms held together by covalent bonds. Molecular compounds are represented by **chemical formulas**, symbolic representations that, at minimum, indicate

A useful example for clarifying the different types of formulas is H_2O_2. This has different molecular and empirical formulas and significant shape features (bond angles and a torsion angle).

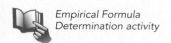
Empirical Formula Determination activity

- the elements present
- the relative number of atoms of each element

In the formula for water, the constituent elements are denoted by their symbols. The relative numbers of atoms are indicated by *subscripts*. Where no subscript is written, the number 1 is understood.

$$H_2O$$

The two elements present

Lack of subscript means one atom of O per molecule

Two H atoms per molecule

Another example of a chemical formula is CCl_4, which represents the compound carbon tetrachloride. The formulas H_2O and CCl_4 both represent distinct entities—*molecules*. Thus, we can refer to water and carbon tetrachloride as molecular compounds.

An **empirical formula** is the simplest formula for a compound; it shows the types of atoms present and their relative numbers. The subscripts in an empirical formula are reduced to their simplest whole-number ratio. For example, P_2O_5 is the empirical formula for a compound whose molecules have the formula P_4O_{10}. Generally, the empirical formula does not tell us a great deal about a compound. Acetic acid ($C_2H_4O_2$), formaldehyde (CH_2O, used to make certain plastics and resins), and glucose ($C_6H_{12}O_6$, blood sugar) all have the empirical formula CH_2O.

A **molecular formula** is based on an actual molecule of a compound. In some cases, the empirical and molecular formulas are identical, such as CH_2O for formaldehyde. In other cases, the molecular formula is a multiple of the empirical formula. A molecule of acetic acid, for example, consists of eight atoms—two C atoms, four H atoms, and two O atoms, so the molecular formula of acetic acid is $C_2H_4O_2$. This is twice the number of atoms in the formula unit (CH_2O). Empirical and molecular formulas tell us the combining ratio of the atoms in the compound, but they show nothing about how the atoms are attached to each other. Other types of formulas, however, do convey this information. Figure 3-1 shows several representations of acetic acid, the acid constituent that gives vinegar its sour taste.

A **structural formula** shows the order in which atoms are bonded together in a molecule and by what types of bonds. Thus, the structural formula of acetic acid tells us that three of the four H atoms are bonded to one of the C atoms, and the remaining H atom is bonded to an O atom. Both of the O atoms are bonded to one of the C atoms, and the two C atoms are bonded to each

Molecular model:
("ball-and-stick")

Empirical formula: CH_2O

Molecular formula: $C_2H_4O_2$

Structural formula:
$$\begin{array}{ccc} & H & O \\ & | & \| \\ H - & C - & C - O - H \\ & | & \\ & H & \end{array}$$

Molecular model:
("space-filling")

▲ **FIGURE 3-1**
Several representations of the compound acetic acid
In the molecular model, the black spheres are carbon, the red are oxygen, and
the white are hydrogen. To show that one H atom in the molecule is fundamentally
different from the other three, the formula of acetic acid is often written as $HC_2H_3O_2$
(see Section 5-3). To show that this H atom is bonded to an O atom, the formulas
CH_3COOH and CH_3CO_2H are also used. For a few chemical compounds you may
find different versions of chemical formulas in different sources.

Acetic Acid model

other. The covalent bonds in the structural formula are represented by lines or
dashes (—). One of the bonds is represented by a double dash (=) and is
called a *double* covalent bond. Differences between single and double bonds
are discussed later in the text. For now, just think of a double bond as being a
stronger or tighter bond than a single bond.

A **condensed structural formula**, which is written on a single line, is an
alternative, less cumbersome way of showing how the atoms of a molecule are
connected. Thus, the acetic acid molecule is represented as either CH_3COOH
or CH_3CO_2H. With this type of formula, the different ways in which the H
atoms are attached are still apparent.

Condensed structural formulas can also be used to show how a group of
atoms is attached to another atom. Consider methylpropane, C_4H_{10}, in Figure
3-2(b). The structural formula shows that there is a —CH_3 group of atoms attached to the central carbon atom. In the condensed structural formula, this is
indicated by enclosing the CH_3 in parentheses to the right of the atom to
which it is attached, thus $CH_3CH(CH_3)CH_3$. Alternatively, because the central
C atom is bonded to each of the other three C atoms, we can write the condensed structural formula $CH(CH_3)_3$.

Organic compounds are made up principally of carbon and hydrogen, with
oxygen and/or nitrogen as important constituents in many of them. Each carbon atom forms *four covalent bonds*. Organic compounds can be very complex,
and one way of simplifying their structural formulas is to write structures
without showing the C and H atoms explicitly. We do this by using a **line-
angle formula** (also referred to as a *line structure*), in which lines represent
chemical bonds. A carbon atom exists wherever a line ends or meets another
line, and the number of H atoms needed to complete each carbon atom's four
bonds are assumed to be present. The symbols of other atoms or groups
of atoms and the bond lines joining them to C atoms are written explicitly.
The formula of the complex male hormone molecule testosterone, seen in
Figure 3-2(c), is a line-angle formula.

Molecules occupy space and have a three-dimensional shape, but empirical
and molecular formulas do not convey any information about the spatial
arrangements of atoms. Structural formulas can sometimes show this, but
usually the only satisfactory way to represent the three-dimensional structure
of molecules is with models. In a *ball-and-stick model*, atoms are represented by
small balls, and the bonds between atoms by sticks (see Figure 3-1). Such models help us to visualize distances between the nuclei of atoms (bond lengths)
and the geometrical shapes of molecules. Ball-and-stick models are easy to

Most students will need
a fair amount of practice
to become proficient at
drawing condensed structural
formulas and line structures
of even simple organic molecules.

A common misconception
among students is that
the structural formula of
a molecule is a good description
of its shape. As discussed here,
use ball-and-stick molecular
models to show students the three-
dimensional shapes of molecules.

(a) Butane

(b) Methylpropane

(c) Testosterone

▲ **FIGURE 3-2**
Visualizations of (a) butane, (b) methylpropane, and (c) testosterone

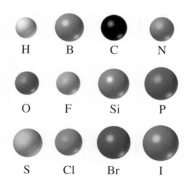

draw and interpret, but they can be somewhat misleading. Chemical bonds are forces that draw atoms in a molecule into direct contact. The atoms are not held apart as implied by a ball-and-stick model.

A *space-filling model* shows that the atoms in a molecule occupy space and that they are in actual contact with one another. Certain computer programs generate images of space-filling models such as those shown in Figures 3-1 and 3-2. A space-filling model is the most accurate representation of the size and shape of a molecule because it is constructed to scale (that is, a nanometer-size molecule is magnified to a millimeter or centimeter scale).

The acetic acid molecule is made up of three types of atoms (C, H, and O) and models of the molecule reflect this fact. Different colors are used to distinguish the various types of atoms in ball-and-stick and space-filling models. A common color scheme is shown in the margin. You will notice that the colored spheres are of different sizes, which correspond to the size differences between the various atoms in the periodic table.

The various depictions of molecules just discussed will be used throughout this book. In fact, visualization of the sizes and shapes of molecules and interpretation of the physical and chemical properties in terms of molecular sizes and shapes is one of the most important aspects of modern chemistry.

CONCEPT ASSESSMENT ✓

Represent the succinic acid molecule, $HOOCCH_2CH_2COOH$, through empirical, molecular, structural, and line-angle formulas.

IONIC COMPOUNDS

Chemical combination of a metal and a nonmetal usually results in an ionic compound. An **ionic compound** is made up of positive and negative ions joined together by electrostatic forces of attraction (recall the attraction of oppositely charged objects pictured in Figure 2-4). The atoms of metallic elements tend to lose one or more electrons when they combine with nonmetal atoms, and the nonmetal atoms tend to gain one or more electrons. As a result of this electron transfer, the metal atom becomes a positive ion, or **cation**, and the nonmetal atom becomes a negative ion, or **anion**. We can usually deduce the charge on a main-group cation or anion from the group of the periodic table to which the element belongs (recall Section 2-6). Thus the periodic table can help us to write the formulas of ionic compounds.

In the formation of sodium chloride—ordinary table salt—each sodium atom gives up one electron to become a sodium ion, Na^+, and each chlorine atom gains one electron to become a chloride ion, Cl^-. This fact conforms to the relationship between locations of the elements in the periodic table and the charges on their simple ions (see page 52). For sodium chloride to be electrically neutral, there must be one Na^+ ion for each Cl^- ion ($+1 - 1 = 0$). Thus, the formula of sodium chloride is NaCl, and its structure is shown in Figure 3-3.

We observe that each Na^+ ion in sodium chloride is surrounded by six Cl^- ions, and vice versa, and we cannot say that any one of these six Cl^- ions belongs exclusively to a given Na^+ ion. Yet, the ratio of Cl^- to Na^+ ions in sodium chloride is 1:1, and so we arbitrarily select a combination of one Na^+ ion and one Cl^- ion as a formula unit. The **formula unit** of an ionic compound is the smallest electrically neutral collection of ions. The ratio of atoms (ions) in the formula unit is the same as in the chemical formula. Because it is buried in a vast network of ions, called a crystal, a formula unit of an ionic compound does not exist as a distinct entity. Thus it is inappropriate to call a formula unit of solid sodium chloride a molecule.

The situation with magnesium chloride is similar. In magnesium chloride, found in trace quantities in table salt, magnesium atoms lose two electrons to become magnesium ions, Mg^{2+} (Mg is in group 2). To obtain an electrically neutral formula unit, there must be two Cl^- ions, each with a charge of -1, for every Mg^{2+} ion. The formula of magnesium chloride is $MgCl_2$.

The ions Na^+, Mg^{2+}, and Cl^- are *monatomic*, meaning that each consists of a single ionized atom. By contrast, a *polyatomic* ion is made up of two or more atoms. In the nitrate ion, NO_3^-, the subscripts signify that *three* O atoms and *one* N atom are joined by covalent bonds into the single ion NO_3^-. Magnesium nitrate is an ionic compound made up of magnesium and nitrate ions. An electrically neutral formula unit of this compound must consist of one Mg^{2+} ion and two NO_3^- ions. The formula based on this formula unit is denoted by enclosing NO_3 in parentheses, followed by the subscript 2; thus, $Mg(NO_3)_2$. Polyatomic ions are discussed further in Section 3-6.

Sodium Chloride model

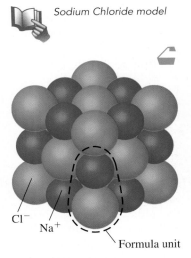

Cl⁻   Na⁺

Formula unit

▲ **FIGURE 3-3**
Portion of an ionic crystal and a formula unit of NaCl
Solid sodium chloride consists of enormous numbers of Na^+ and Cl^- ions in a network called a crystal. The combination of one Na^+ and one Cl^- ion is the smallest collection of ions from which we can deduce the formula NaCl. It is a formula unit.

Stress that the formula units of *all* ionic compounds must be electrically neutral. A consequence of this is that there is only *one* possible formula unit for any given cation and anion.

Emphasize that some ionic compounds contain covalent bonds. Many students find this confusing.

Are You Wondering . . .

If a compound can be formed between different metal atoms?

In a metal, electrons of the atoms interact to form *metallic* bonds. The bonded atoms are usually of the same element, but they may also be of different elements, giving rise to *intermetallic* compounds. The metallic bond gives metals and intermetallic compounds their characteristic properties of electrical and heat conductivity. These bonds are described in Chapter 11.

3-2 THE MOLE CONCEPT AND CHEMICAL COMPOUNDS

▶ The terms *formula weight* and *molecular weight* are often used in place of formula mass and molecular mass. This is similar to the situation described for atomic mass and atomic weight in the footnote on page 48.

Once we know the chemical formula of a compound, we can determine its formula mass. **Formula mass** is the mass of a *formula unit* in atomic mass units. It is always appropriate to use the term formula mass, but for a molecular compound, the formula unit is an actual molecule, so we can speak of molecular mass. **Molecular mass** is the mass of a *molecule* in atomic mass units.

Weighted-average formula and molecular masses can be obtained just by adding up weighted-average atomic masses (those on the inside front cover). Thus, for the molecular compound water, H_2O:

$$\text{molecular mass } H_2O = 2 \text{ (atomic mass H)} + \text{(atomic mass O)}$$
$$= 2 (1.008 \text{ u}) + 15.999 \text{ u}$$
$$= 18.015 \text{ u}$$

▶ The terms *formula mass* and *molecular mass* have essentially the same meaning, although when referring to ionic compounds, such as NaCl and $MgCl_2$, formula mass is the proper term.

For the ionic compound magnesium chloride, $MgCl_2$,

$$\text{formula mass } MgCl_2 = \text{atomic mass Mg} + 2 \text{ (atomic mass Cl)}$$
$$= 24.305 \text{ u} + 2 (35.453 \text{ u})$$
$$= 95.211 \text{ u}$$

and for the ionic compound magnesium nitrate, $Mg(NO_3)_2$,

$$\text{formula mass } Mg(NO_3)_2 = \text{atomic mass Mg} + 2 \text{ [atomic mass N} + 3 \text{ (atomic mass O)]}$$
$$= 24.305 \text{ u} + 2 [14.007 \text{ u} + 3 (15.999 \text{ u})]$$
$$= 148.313 \text{ u}$$

MOLE OF A COMPOUND

KEEP IN MIND ▶
that although *molecular mass* and *molar mass* sound similar and are related, they are not the same. Molecular mass is the weighted-average mass of one molecule expressed in atomic mass units, u. *Molar mass* is the mass of Avogadro's number of molecules expressed in grams per mole, g/mol. The two terms have the same numerical value but different units.

Recall that in Chapter 2 a mole was defined as an amount of substance having the same number of elementary entities as there are atoms in exactly 12 g of pure carbon-12. This definition carefully avoids saying that the entities to be counted are always atoms. As a result, we can apply the concept of a mole to any quantity that we can represent by a symbol or formula—atoms, ions, formula units, or molecules. Specifically, a *mole of compound* is an amount of compound containing Avogadro's number (6.02214×10^{23}) of formula units or molecules. The **molar mass** is the mass of one mole of compound—one mole of molecules of a molecular compound and one mole of formula units of an ionic compound.

The weighted-average molecular mass of H_2O is 18.015 u compared with a mass of exactly 12 u for a carbon-12 atom. If we compare samples of water molecules and carbon atoms using Avogadro's number of each, we get a mass of 18.015 g H_2O compared with exactly 12 g for carbon-12. The molar mass of H_2O is 18.015 g H_2O/mol H_2O. If we know the formula of a compound, we can equate the following terms, as illustrated for H_2O, $MgCl_2$, and $Mg(NO_3)_2$.

 Counting Molecules

$$1 \text{ mol } H_2O = 18.015 \text{ g } H_2O = 6.02214 \times 10^{23} H_2O \text{ molecules}$$
$$1 \text{ mol } MgCl_2 = 95.211 \text{ g } MgCl_2 = 6.02214 \times 10^{23} MgCl_2 \text{ formula units}$$
$$1 \text{ mol } Mg(NO_3)_2 = 148.313 \text{ g } Mg(NO_3)_2$$
$$= 6.02214 \times 10^{23} Mg(NO_3)_2 \text{ formula units}$$

☑ Emphasize that the mole concept and molar masses provide us with *unit equivalencies*. We can, as needed, convert the amount of a sample into grams, moles, or numbers of atoms and molecules.

Expressions such as these provide several different types of conversion factors that can be applied in a variety of problem-solving situations. The strategy that works best for a particular problem will depend, in part, on how the necessary conversions are visualized. As we learned in Section 2-7, the most direct link to an amount in moles is through a mass in grams, so generally the central focus of a problem is the conversion of a mass in grams to an amount in moles, or vice versa. This conversion must often be preceded or followed by other conversions involving volumes, densities, percentages, and so on. As we saw in Chapter 2, one helpful tool in problem solving is to establish a conversion pathway.

EXAMPLE 3-1

Relating Molar Mass, the Avogadro Constant, and Formula Units of an Ionic Compound. An analytical balance can detect a mass of 0.1 mg. What is the total number of ions present in this minimally detectable quantity of $MgCl_2$?

Solution

After making the mass conversion, mg $\longrightarrow$ g, we can use the molar mass to convert from mass to number of moles of $MgCl_2$. Then, with the Avogadro constant as a conversion factor, we can convert from moles to number of formula units. The final factor we need is based on the fact that there are *three* ions (*one* Mg^{2+} and *two* Cl^-) per formula unit (fu) of $MgCl_2$. As noted in Chapter 2, it is often helpful to map out a conversion pathway that starts with the information given and proceeds through a series of conversion factors to the information sought. For this problem, we can begin with milligrams of $MgCl_2$ and make the following conversions:

$$mg \longrightarrow g \longrightarrow mol \longrightarrow fu \longrightarrow \text{number of ions}$$

$$? \text{ ions} = 0.1 \text{ mg MgCl}_2 \times \frac{1 \text{ g MgCl}_2}{1000 \text{ mg MgCl}_2} \times \frac{1 \text{ mol MgCl}_2}{95 \text{ g MgCl}_2}$$

$$\times \frac{6.0 \times 10^{23} \text{ fu MgCl}_2}{1 \text{ mol MgCl}_2} \times \frac{3 \text{ ions}}{1 \text{ fu MgCl}_2}$$

$$= 2 \times 10^{18} \text{ ions}$$

Practice Example A: How many grams of $MgCl_2$ would you need to obtain 5.0×10^{23} Cl^- ions?

Practice Example B: How many nitrate ions, NO_3^-, and how many oxygen atoms are present in 1.00 μg of magnesium nitrate, $Mg(NO_3)_2$?

EXAMPLE 3-2

Combining Several Factors in a Calculation Involving Molar Mass. The volatile liquid ethyl mercaptan, C_2H_6S, is one of the most odoriferous substances known. It is sometimes added to natural gas to make gas leaks detectable. How many C_2H_6S molecules are contained in a 1.0-μL sample? ($d = 0.84$ g/mL.)

◄ Given that a normal drop of liquid is about 0.05 mL, a volume of 1.0 μL is only *0.02 of a drop.*

Solution

First, based on the meanings of the prefixes micro and milli, convert from microliters to liters, and then to milliliters. At this point, bring in density as a conversion factor to obtain the mass in grams. The remaining factors use molar mass to convert mass to the number of moles of substance and, finally, the Avogadro constant to convert number of moles to number of molecules. In summary, the conversion pathway is μL $\longrightarrow$ L $\longrightarrow$ mL $\longrightarrow$ g $\longrightarrow$ mol $\longrightarrow$ molecules.

$$? \text{ molecules C}_2\text{H}_6\text{S} = 1.0 \text{ }\mu\text{L} \times \frac{1 \times 10^{-6} \text{ L}}{1 \text{ }\mu\text{L}} \times \frac{1000 \text{ mL}}{1 \text{ L}} \times \frac{0.84 \text{ g C}_2\text{H}_6\text{S}}{1 \text{ mL}}$$

$$\times \frac{1 \text{ mol C}_2\text{H}_6\text{S}}{62.1 \text{ g C}_2\text{H}_6\text{S}} \times \frac{6.022 \times 10^{23} \text{ molecules C}_2\text{H}_6\text{S}}{1 \text{ mol C}_2\text{H}_6\text{S}}$$

$$= 8.1 \times 10^{18} \text{ molecules C}_2\text{H}_6\text{S}$$

Practice Example A: Gold has a density of 19.32 g/cm³. A piece of gold foil is 2.50 cm on each side and 0.100 mm thick. How many atoms of gold are in this piece of gold foil?

Practice Example B: If the 1.0-μL sample of liquid ethyl mercaptan from Example 3-2 is allowed to evaporate and distribute itself throughout a chemistry lecture room with dimensions 62 ft × 35 ft × 14 ft, will the odor of the vapor be detectable in the room? The limit of detectability is 9×10^{-4} μmol/m³.

Moles of Compounds. Display 1-mole samples of several compounds as a follow-up to a previous display of 1-mole samples of elements. Possibilities are H_2O, NaCl, HgO, sucrose, and 1 mole of carbon as a reference. Again, 1 mole is often a handful-size quantity. The exceptions include substances with large formulas, as 1 mol $C_{12}H_{22}O_{11}$ with 45 moles of atoms, and gases. A 25-L flask or a 36-cm diameter balloon can serve as samples of 1 mole of air molecules.

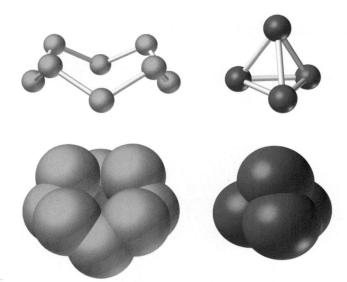

▶ **FIGURE 3-4**
Molecular forms of elemental sulfur and phosphorus
In a sample of solid sulfur, there are eight sulfur atoms in a sulfur molecule. In solid white phosphorus, there are four phosphorus atoms per molecule.

MOLE OF AN ELEMENT—A SECOND LOOK

> Students commonly associate atoms with elements and molecules or formula units with compounds. For this reason, they typically find it confusing that a bulk sample of an element, such as sulfur, contains molecules and is not a collection of unbonded atoms.

In Chapter 2, we took one mole of an element to be 6.02214×10^{23} *atoms* of the element. This is the only definition possible for elements such as iron, magnesium, sodium, and copper, in which enormous numbers of individual spherical atoms are clustered together, much like marbles in a can. But the atoms of some elements are joined together to form molecules. Bulk samples of these elements are composed of collections of molecules. The molecules of P_4 and S_8 are represented in Figure 3-4. The molecular formulas of elements that you should become familiar with are

$$H_2 \quad O_2 \quad N_2 \quad F_2 \quad Cl_2 \quad Br_2 \quad I_2 \quad P_4 \quad S_8$$

For these elements, we speak of an *atomic* mass or a *molecular* mass, and molar mass can be expressed in two ways. Hydrogen, for example, has an atomic mass of 1.008 u and a molecular mass of 2.016 u; its molar mass can be expressed as 1.008 g H/mol H or 2.016 g H_2/mol H_2.

Another phenomenon occasionally encountered is the existence of an element in more than one molecular form, a situation referred to as *allotropy*. Thus, oxygen exists in two allotropic forms, the predominantly abundant diatomic oxygen, O_2, and the much less abundant allotrope *ozone*, O_3. The molar mass of ordinary dioxygen is 32.00 g O_2/mol O_2, and that of ozone is 48.00 g O_3/mol O_3.

Are You Wondering . . .

What is meant by "a mole of hydrogen?"

We really don't know, because the phrase "a mole of hydrogen" is ambiguous. That is, do we mean a mole of hydrogen *atoms* or a mole of hydrogen *molecules*? We should write "a mole of H atoms" or "a mole of H_2 molecules," and we must express the molar mass as 1.008 g H/mol H when dealing with H atoms and 2.016 g H_2/mol H_2 when working with H_2 molecules. We must also distinguish between H atoms and H_2 molecules when using the Avogadro constant. An analogy to the distinction between hydrogen atoms and hydrogen molecules is that between one dozen socks and one dozen pairs of socks.

CONCEPT ASSESSMENT ✓

Without doing detailed calculations, determine which of the following quantities has the greatest mass and which, the smallest mass: **(a)** 0.50 mol O_2; **(b)** 2.0×10^{23} Cu atoms; **(c)** 1.0×10^{24} H_2O molecules; **(d)** a 20.000-g brass weight; **(e)** 1.0 mol Ne.

3-3 COMPOSITION OF CHEMICAL COMPOUNDS

A chemical formula conveys considerable quantitative information about a compound and its constituent elements. We have already learned how to determine the molar mass of a compound, and in this section, we consider some other types of calculations based on the chemical formula.

The colorless, volatile liquid halothane has been used as a fire extinguisher and also as an inhalation anesthetic. Both its empirical and molecular formulas are $C_2HBrClF_3$; its molecular mass is 197.38 u and its molar mass is 197.38 g/mol, as calculated below:

$$M_{C_2HBrClF_3} = 2M_C + M_H + M_{Br} + M_{Cl} + 3M_F$$
$$= [(2 \times 12.01) + 1.01 + 79.90 + 35.45 + (3 \times 19.00)]\,g$$
$$= 197.38\,g/mol$$

The molecular formula of $C_2HBrClF_3$ tells us that *per mole* of halothane there are two moles of C atoms, one mole each of H, Br, and Cl atoms, and three moles of F atoms. This factual statement can be turned into conversion factors to answer questions such as, "How many C atoms are present per mole of halothane?" In this case, the factor needed is 2 mol C/mol $C_2HBrClF_3$. That is,

$$? \text{ C atoms} = 1.000 \text{ mol } C_2HBrClF_3 \times \frac{2 \text{ mol C}}{1 \text{ mol } C_2HBrClF_3} \times \frac{6.022 \times 10^{23} \text{ C atoms}}{1 \text{ mol C}}$$

$$= 1.204 \times 10^{24} \text{ C atoms}$$

In Example 3-3, we use another conversion factor derived from the formula for halothane. This factor is shown in blue in the setup, which includes other familiar factors to make the conversion pathway:

$$mL \longrightarrow g \longrightarrow mol\ C_2HBrClF_3 \longrightarrow mol\ F$$

▼ Two representations of halothane.

Students who don't yet have a clear understanding of the mole concept may find it confusing that one mole of a compound can contain *eight* moles of atoms as is the case with halothane. Take time to discuss this concept with your students.

EXAMPLE 3-3

Using Relationships Derived from a Chemical Formula. How many moles of F atoms are in a 75.0-mL sample of halothane ($d = 1.871$ g/mL)?

Solution

First, convert the volume of the sample to mass; this requires density as a conversion factor. Next, convert the mass of halothane to its amount in moles; this requires the inverse of the molar mass as a conversion factor. The final conversion factor is based on the formula of halothane.

$$? \text{ mol F} = 75.0 \text{ mL } C_2HBrClF_3 \times \frac{1.871 \text{ g } C_2HBrClF_3}{1 \text{ mL } C_2HBrClF_3}$$

$$\times \frac{1 \text{ mol } C_2HBrClF_3}{197.4 \text{ g } C_2HBrClF_3} \times \frac{3 \text{ mol F}}{1 \text{ mol } C_2HBrClF_3}$$

$$= 2.13 \text{ mol F}$$

Practice Example A: How many grams of Br are contained in 25.00 mL of halothane ($d = 1.871$ g/mL)?

Practice Example B: How many milliliters of halothane would contain 1.00×10^{24} Br atoms?

CONCEPT ASSESSMENT ✔

In hexachlorophene, $C_{13}H_6Cl_6O_2$, a compound used in germicidal soaps, which element contributes the greatest number of atoms and which, the greatest mass?

CALCULATING PERCENT COMPOSITION FROM A CHEMICAL FORMULA

Stress that the percent composition of a compound is independent of the mass of the compound chosen.

When chemists believe that they have synthesized a new compound, a sample is generally sent to an analytical laboratory where its percent composition is determined. This experimentally determined percent composition is then compared with the percent composition calculated from the formula of the expected compound. In this way, one can see if the compound obtained could be the one expected.

Equation (3.1) establishes how the mass percent of an element in a compound is calculated. In applying the equation, as in Example 3-4, think in terms of the following steps.

1. Determine the molar mass of the compound. This is the *denominator* in equation (3.1).

2. Determine the contribution of the given element to the molar mass. This product of the formula subscript and the molar mass of the element appears in the *numerator* of equation (3.1).

3. Formulate the ratio of the mass of the given element to the mass of the compound as a whole. This is the ratio of the numerator from step 2 to the denominator from step 1.

4. Multiply this ratio by 100% to obtain the mass percent of the element.

$$\text{Mass \% element} = \frac{\left(\begin{array}{c}\text{number of}\\\text{atoms of element}\\\text{per formula unit}\end{array}\right) \times \left(\begin{array}{c}\text{molar mass}\\\text{of element}\end{array}\right)}{\text{molar mass of compound}} \times 100\% \qquad (3.1)$$

The mass composition of a compound is the collection of mass percentages of the individual elements in the compound.

 Molecular Mass and Mass Percent activity

EXAMPLE 3-4

Calculating the Mass Percent Composition of a Compound. What is the mass percent composition of halothane, $C_2HBrClF_3$?

Solution

First, determine the molar mass of $C_2HBrClF_3$. This was shown on page 75 to be 197.38 g/mol.

Then, for one mole of compound, formulate mass ratios and percents.

$$\% \text{ C} = \frac{\left(2 \text{ mol C} \times \dfrac{12.01 \text{ g C}}{1 \text{ mol C}}\right)}{197.38 \text{ g } C_2HBrClF_3} \times 100\% = 12.17\% \text{ C}$$

$$\% \text{ H} = \frac{\left(1 \text{ mol H} \times \dfrac{1.01 \text{ g H}}{1 \text{ mol H}}\right)}{197.38 \text{ g } C_2HBrClF_3} \times 100\% = 0.51\% \text{ H}$$

$$\% \text{ Br} = \frac{\left(1 \text{ mol Br} \times \dfrac{79.90 \text{ g Br}}{1 \text{ mol Br}}\right)}{197.38 \text{ } C_2HBrClF_3} \times 100\% = 40.48\% \text{ Br}$$

$$\% \text{ Cl} = \frac{\left(1 \text{ mol Cl} \times \dfrac{35.45 \text{ g Cl}}{1 \text{ mol Cl}}\right)}{197.38 \text{ g } C_2HBrClF_3} \times 100\% = 17.96\% \text{ Cl}$$

$$\% \text{ F} = \left(\frac{3 \text{ mol F} \times \dfrac{19.00 \text{ g F}}{1 \text{ mol F}}}{197.38 \text{ g } C_2HBrClF_3}\right) \times 100\% = 28.88\% \text{ F}$$

Thus, the percent composition of halothane is 12.17% C, 0.51% H, 40.48% Br, 17.96% Cl, and 28.88% F.

Practice Example A: Adenosine triphosphate (ATP) is the main energy-storage molecule in cells. Its chemical formula is $C_{10}H_{16}N_5P_3O_{13}$. What is its mass percent composition?

Practice Example B: *Without doing detailed calculations*, determine which two compounds from the following list have the same percent oxygen by mass: **(a)** CO; **(b)** CH_3COOH; **(c)** C_2O_3; **(d)** N_2O; **(e)** $C_6H_{12}O_6$; **(f)** $HOCH_2CH_2OH$.

The percentages of the elements in a compound should add up to 100.00%, and we can use this fact in two ways.

1. Check the accuracy of the computations by ensuring that the percentages total 100.00%. As applied to the results of Example 3-4:

$$12.17\% + 0.51\% + 40.48\% + 17.96\% + 28.88\% = 100.00\%$$

2. Determine the percentages of all the elements but one. Obtain that one by difference (subtraction). From Example 3-4:

$$\% \text{ H} = 100.00\% - \% \text{ C} - \% \text{ Br} - \% \text{ Cl} - \% \text{ F}$$
$$= 100.00\% - 12.17\% - 40.48\% - 17.96\% - 28.88\%$$
$$= 0.51\%$$

ESTABLISHING FORMULAS FROM THE EXPERIMENTALLY DETERMINED PERCENT COMPOSITION OF COMPOUNDS

At times, a chemist isolates a chemical compound—say, from an exotic tropical plant—and has no idea what it is. A report from an analytical laboratory on the percent composition of the compound yields data needed to determine its formula.

Percent composition establishes the relative proportions of the elements in a compound on a *mass* basis. A chemical formula requires these proportions to be on a *mole* basis, that is, in terms of *numbers* of atoms. Consider the following five-step approach to determining a formula from the experimentally determined percent composition of the compound 2-deoxyribose, a sugar that is a basic constituent of DNA (deoxyribonucleic acid). The mass percent composition of 2-deoxyribose is 44.77% C, 7.52% H, and 47.71% O.

> Remind students that the subscripts in the formula of a compound refer to a mole ratio not a mass ratio. So, as an example, explain that one mole of H_2O contains two moles of hydrogen atoms and one mole of oxygen atoms.

1. Although we could choose any sample size, if we take one of *exactly* 100 g, the masses of the elements are numerically equal to their percentages, that is, 44.77 g C, 7.52 g H, and 47.71 g O.

2. Convert the masses of the elements in the 100.0-g sample to amounts in moles.

$$? \text{ mol C} = 44.77 \text{ g C} \times \frac{1 \text{ mol C}}{12.011 \text{ g C}} = 3.727 \text{ mol C}$$

$$? \text{ mol H} = 7.52 \text{ g H} \times \frac{1 \text{ mol H}}{1.008 \text{ g H}} = 7.46 \text{ mol H}$$

$$? \text{ mol O} = 47.71 \text{ g O} \times \frac{1 \text{ mol O}}{15.999 \text{ g O}} = 2.982 \text{ mol O}$$

3. Write a tentative formula based on the numbers of moles just determined.

$$C_{3.727}H_{7.46}O_{2.982}$$

4. Attempt to convert the subscripts in the tentative formula to small whole numbers. This requires dividing each of the subscripts by the smallest one (2.982).

$$C_{\frac{3.727}{2.982}} H_{\frac{7.46}{2.982}} O_{\frac{2.982}{2.982}} = C_{1.25} H_{2.50} O$$

If all subscripts at this point differ only slightly from whole numbers—which is not the case here—round them off to whole numbers, concluding the calculation at this point.

5. If one or more subscripts is still not a whole number—which is the case here—multiply all subscripts by a small whole number that will make them all integral. Thus, multiply by 4 here.

$$C_{(4\times1.25)} H_{(4\times2.50)} O_{(4\times1)} = C_5H_{10}O_4$$

The formula that we get by the method just outlined, $C_5H_{10}O_4$, is the simplest possible formula—the *empirical formula*. The actual *molecular formula* may be equal to, or some multiple of, the empirical formula, such as $C_{10}H_{20}O_8$, $C_{15}H_{30}O_{12}$, $C_{20}H_{40}O_{16}$, and so on. To find the multiplying factor, we must compare the formula mass based on the empirical formula with the true molecular mass of the compound. We can establish the molecular mass from a separate experiment (by methods introduced in Chapters 6 and 13). The experimentally determined molecular mass of 2-deoxyribose is 134 u. The formula mass based on the empirical formula, $C_5H_{10}O_4$, is 134.1 u. The measured molecular mass is the same as the empirical formula mass. The molecular formula is also $C_5H_{10}O_4$.

We outline the five-step approach described above in the flow diagram below and then apply the approach to Example 3-5, where we will find that the empirical formula and the molecular formula are not the same.

(3.2)

EXAMPLE 3-5

Determining the Empirical and Molecular Formulas of a Compound from Its Mass Percent Composition. Dibutyl succinate is an insect repellent used against household ants and roaches. Its composition is 62.58% C, 9.63% H, and 27.79% O. Its experimentally determined molecular mass is 230 u. What are the empirical and molecular formulas of dibutyl succinate?

Solution

The first five steps are the same as those illustrated previously.

1. Determine the mass of each element in a 100.0-g sample.

62.58 g C, 9.63 g H, 27.79 g O

2. Convert each of these masses to an amount in moles.

$$? \text{ mol C} = 62.58 \text{ g C} \times \frac{1 \text{ mol C}}{12.011 \text{ g C}} = 5.210 \text{ mol C}$$

$$? \text{ mol H} = 9.63 \text{ g H} \times \frac{1 \text{ mol H}}{1.008 \text{ g H}} = 9.55 \text{ mol H}$$

$$? \text{ mol O} = 27.79 \text{ g O} \times \frac{1 \text{ mol O}}{15.999 \text{ g O}} = 1.737 \text{ mol O}$$

3. Write a tentative formula based on these numbers of moles.

$$C_{5.21} H_{9.55} O_{1.74}$$

4. Divide each of the subscripts of the tentative formula by the smallest subscript (1.74),

$$C_{\frac{5.21}{1.74}} H_{\frac{9.55}{1.74}} O_{\frac{1.74}{1.74}} = C_{2.99} H_{5.49} O$$

and round off any subscripts that differ only slightly from whole numbers; that is, round 2.99 to 3.

$$C_3H_{5.49}O$$

5. Multiply all subscripts by a small whole number to make them integral (here by the factor 2), and write the empirical formula.

$$C_{2\times3} H_{2\times5.49} O_{2\times1} = C_6 H_{10.98} O_2$$
$$2 \times 5.49 = 10.98 \approx 11$$

Empirical formula: $C_6H_{11}O_2$

To establish the molecular formula, first determine the empirical formula mass.

$$[(6 \times 12.0) + (11 \times 1.0) + (2 \times 16.0)]u = 115 \text{ u}$$

Since the experimentally determined formula mass (230 u) is twice the empirical formula mass, the molecular formula is twice the empirical formula.

Molecular formula: $C_{12}H_{22}O_4$

Practice Example A: Sorbitol, used as a sweetener in some "sugar-free" foods, has a molecular mass of 182 u and a mass percent composition of 39.56% C, 7.74% H, and 52.70% O. What are the empirical and molecular formulas of sorbitol?

Practice Example B: The chlorine-containing narcotic drug pentaerythritol chloral has 21.51% C, 2.22% H, and 17.64% O, by mass, as its other elements. Its molecular mass is 726 u. What are the empirical and molecular formulas of pentaerythritol chloral?

CONCEPT ASSESSMENT ✔

Explain why, if the percent composition *and* the molar mass of a compound are both known, the molecular formula can be determined much more readily by using the molar mass rather than a 100-g sample in the first step of the five-step procedure in Example 3-5. In this instance, how would you then obtain the empirical formula?

Are You Wondering . . .

How much rounding off to do to get integral subscripts in an empirical formula and what factors to use to convert fractional to whole numbers?

How much rounding off is justified depends on how precisely the elemental analysis is done. As a result, there is no ironclad rule on the matter. For the examples in this text, if you carry all the significant figures allowable in a calculation, you can generally round off a subscript that is within a few hundredths of a whole number (for example, 3.98 rounds off to 4). If the deviation is more than this, you will need to adjust subscripts to integral values by multiplying by the appropriate constant. If the appropriate constant is larger than a simple integer such as 2, 3, 4, or 5, you may sometimes find it easier to make the adjustment by multiplying twice, for example, by 2 and then by 4 if the necessary constant is 8.

> ✓ The rules for significant figures provide a useful clue as to whether to round the subscripts in an empirical formula. If the data are good to only three significant figures, then rounding 3.98 to 4 is justified. If the data are good to four or more significant figures, and the molecule is large, rounding may not be valid.

COMBUSTION ANALYSIS

Figure 3-5 on the next page illustrates an experimental method for establishing an empirical formula for compounds that are easily burned, such as compounds containing carbon and hydrogen with oxygen, nitrogen, and a few other elements. In *combustion analysis*, a weighed sample of a compound is burned in a stream of oxygen gas. The water vapor and carbon dioxide gas produced in the combustion are absorbed by appropriate substances. The increases in mass of these absorbers correspond to the masses of water and carbon dioxide. We can think of the matter as shown below. (The subscripts x, y, and z are integers whose values we do not know initially.)

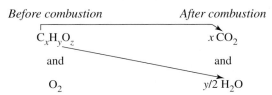

After combustion, all the carbon atoms in the sample are found in the CO_2. All the H atoms are in the H_2O. Moreover, the only source of the carbon and hydrogen atoms was the sample being analyzed. Oxygen atoms in the CO_2 and H_2O could have come partly from the sample and partly from the oxygen gas consumed in the combustion. Thus, the quantity of oxygen in the sample has to be determined indirectly. These ideas are applied in Example 3-6.

Furnace

Stream
of O_2 → | $H_2O + CO_2 + O_2$ → | $CO_2 + O_2$ → | → O_2

H_2O

CO_2

Absorbent
for H_2O

Absorbent
for CO_2

Sample ←
CH_3CH_2OH

Furnace

(a)

+ ⟶

(b)

▲ **FIGURE 3-5**
Apparatus for combustion analysis
(a) Oxygen gas passes through the combustion tube containing the sample being
analyzed. This portion of the apparatus is enclosed in a high-temperature furnace.
Products of the combustion are absorbed as they leave the furnace—water vapor
by magnesium perchlorate, and carbon dioxide gas by sodium hydroxide (producing
sodium carbonate). The differences in mass of the absorbers, after and before the
combustion, yield the masses of H_2O and CO_2 produced in the combustion reaction.
(b) A molecular picture of the combustion of ethanol. Each molecule of ethanol
produces two CO_2 molecules and three H_2O molecules. Combustion takes place in
an excess of oxygen, so that there are oxygen molecules present at the end of the
reaction. Note the conservation of mass.

EXAMPLE 3-6

Determining an Empirical Formula from Combustion Analysis Data. Vitamin C
is essential for the prevention of scurvy. Combustion of a 0.2000-g sample of this
carbon–hydrogen–oxygen compound yields 0.2998 g CO_2 and 0.0819 g H_2O. What
are the percent composition and the empirical formula of vitamin C?

Solution

Percent Composition
First, determine the mass of carbon in 0.2988 g CO_2, by converting to mol C,

$$? \text{ mol C} = 0.2998 \text{ g CO}_2 \times \frac{1 \text{ mol CO}_2}{44.010 \text{ g CO}_2} \times \frac{1 \text{ mol C}}{1 \text{ mol CO}_2} = 0.006812 \text{ mol C}$$

and then to g C.

$$? \text{ g C} = 0.006812 \text{ mol C} \times \frac{12.011 \text{ g C}}{1 \text{ mol C}} = 0.08182 \text{ g C}$$

Proceed in a similar fashion for 0.0819 g H_2O to obtain

$$? \text{ mol H} = 0.0819 \text{ g H}_2O \times \frac{1 \text{ mol H}_2O}{18.02 \text{ g H}_2O} \times \frac{2 \text{ mol H}}{1 \text{ mol H}_2O} = 0.00909 \text{ mol H}$$

and

$$? \text{ g H} = 0.00909 \text{ mol H} \times \frac{1.008 \text{ g H}}{1 \text{ mol H}} = 0.00916 \text{ g H}$$

Obtain the mass of O in the 0.2000-g sample as the difference

$$? \text{ g O} = 0.2000 \text{ g sample} - 0.08182 \text{ g C} - 0.00916 \text{ g H} = 0.1090 \text{ g O}$$

Finally, multiply the mass fractions of the three elements by 100% to obtain mass percentages.

$$\% \text{ C} = \frac{0.08182 \text{ g C}}{0.2000 \text{ g sample}} \times 100\% = 40.91\% \text{ C}$$

$$\% \text{ H} = \frac{0.00916 \text{ g H}}{0.2000 \text{ g sample}} \times 100\% = 4.58\% \text{ H}$$

$$\% \text{ O} = \frac{0.1090 \text{ g O}}{0.2000 \text{ g sample}} \times 100\% = 54.50\% \text{ O}$$

Empirical Formula

At this point we can choose either of two alternatives. The first is to obtain the empirical formula from the mass percent composition, in the same manner illustrated in Example 3-5. The second is to note that we have already determined the number of moles of C and H in the 0.2000-g sample. The number of moles of O is

$$? \text{ mol O} = 0.1090 \text{ g O} \times \frac{1 \text{ mol O}}{15.9994 \text{ g O}} = 0.006813 \text{ mol O}$$

From the numbers of moles of C, H, and O in the 0.2000-g sample, we obtain the tentative empirical formula

$$C_{0.006812}H_{0.00909}O_{0.006813}$$

Next, divide each subscript by the smallest (0.006812) to obtain

$$CH_{1.33}O$$

Finally, multiply all the subscripts by 3 to obtain

Empirical formula of vitamin C: $C_3H_4O_3$

Note that this second alternative does not require determining the mass percent composition as a preliminary calculation. The empirical formula can be based on a sample of any size, as long as the numbers of moles of the different atoms in that sample can be determined.

Practice Example A: Isobutyl propionate is the substance that flavors rum extract. Combustion of a 1.152-g sample of this carbon–hydrogen–oxygen compound yields 2.726 g CO_2 and 1.116 g H_2O. What is the empirical formula of isobutyl propionate?

Practice Example B: Complete combustion of a 1.505-g sample of thiophene, a carbon–hydrogen–sulfur compound, yields 3.149 g CO_2, 0.645 g H_2O, and 1.146 g SO_2 as the only products of the combustion. What is the empirical formula of thiophene?

CONCEPT ASSESSMENT ✓

When combustion is carried out in an excess of oxygen, the quantity producing the greatest mass of both CO_2 and H_2O is **(a)** 0.50 mol $C_{10}H_8$; **(b)** 1.25 mol CH_4; **(c)** 0.500 mol C_2H_5OH; **(d)** 1.00 mol C_6H_5OH.

We have just seen how combustion reactions can be used to analyze chemical substances, but not all samples can be easily burned. Fortunately, several other types of reactions can be used for chemical analyses. Also, modern methods in chemistry rely much more on physical measurements with instruments than on chemical reactions. We will cite some of these methods later in the text.

3-4 OXIDATION STATES: A USEFUL TOOL IN DESCRIBING CHEMICAL COMPOUNDS

Oxidation States activity

Most basic concepts in chemistry deal with measurable properties or phenomena. In a few instances, though, a concept has been devised more for convenience than because of any fundamental significance. This is the case with **oxidation state** (oxidation number),* which is related to the number of electrons that an atom loses, gains, or otherwise appears to use in joining with other atoms in compounds.

Consider NaCl. In this compound an Na atom, a metal, loses one electron to a Cl atom, a nonmetal. The compound consists of the ions Na^+ and Cl^- (see Figure 3-3). Na^+ is in a +1 oxidation state and Cl^- is in a −1 state.

In $MgCl_2$, an Mg atom loses two electrons to become Mg^{2+}, and each Cl atom gains one electron to become Cl^-. As in NaCl, the oxidation state of Cl is −1, but that of Mg is +2. If we take the *total* of the oxidation states of all the atoms (ions) in a formula unit of $MgCl_2$, we get $+2 - 1 - 1 = 0$.

In the molecule Cl_2, the two Cl atoms are identical and should have the same oxidation state. But if their total is to be zero, each oxidation state must itself be 0. Thus, the oxidation state of an element can vary, depending on the compounds in which it occurs. In the molecule H_2O, we arbitrarily assign H the oxidation state +1. Then, because the total of the oxidation states of the atoms must be zero, the oxidation state of oxygen must be −2.

From these examples you can see that we need some conventions or rules for assigning oxidation states. The following seven rules are sufficient to deal with most cases in this text, with this understanding: *The rules must be applied in the numerical order listed, and whenever two rules appear to contradict each other (which they sometimes will), follow the lower numbered rule.* Some examples are given for each rule, and the rules are applied in Example 3-7.

1. *The oxidation state (O.S.) of an individual atom in a free element (uncombined with other elements) is 0.*

   [*Examples:* The O.S. of an isolated Cl atom is 0; the two Cl atoms in the molecule Cl_2 both have an O.S. of 0.]

2. *The total of the O.S. of all the atoms in*

   (a) *neutral species, such as isolated atoms, molecules, and formula units, is 0;*

   [*Examples:* The sum of the O.S. of all the atoms in CH_3OH and of all the ions in $MgCl_2$ is 0.]

   (b) *an ion is equal to the charge on the ion.*

   [*Examples:* The O.S. of Fe in Fe^{3+} is +3. The sum of the O.S. of all atoms in MnO_4^- is −1.]

3. *In their compounds, the group 1 metals have an O.S. of +1 and the group 2 metals have an O.S. of +2.*

   [*Examples:* The O.S. of K is +1 in KCl and K_2CO_3; the O.S. of Mg is +2 in $MgBr_2$ and $Mg(NO_3)_2$.]

4. *In its compounds, the O.S. of fluorine is −1.*

   [*Examples:* The O.S. of F is −1 in HF, ClF_3, and SF_6.]

5. *In its compounds, hydrogen usually has an O.S. of +1.*

   [*Examples:* The O.S. of H is +1 in HI, H_2S, NH_3, and CH_4.]

6. *In its compounds, oxygen usually has an O.S. of −2.*

   [*Examples:* The O.S. of O is −2 in H_2O, CO_2 and $KMnO_4$.]

Oxidation state (O.S.) can be described as "a sometimes fictional charge." With monatomic ions, O.S. and charge are the same thing. For polyatomic ions and molecules, O.S. is fictional, but equal to what the charge would be if the compounds were entirely ionic. Point out that the O.S. of most elements follow the periodic table rules for ion charges, as maximum O.S. = group number (American system).

▶ The principal exceptions to rule 5 occur when H is bonded to metals, as in LiH, NaH, and CaH_2; exceptions to rule 6 occur in compounds with O—F bonds, such as OF_2, and in compounds where O atoms are bonded to one another, as in H_2O_2, and KO_2.

*Because oxidation state refers to a number, the term *oxidation number* is often used synonymously. We will use the two terms interchangeably.

7. *In binary (two-element) compounds with metals, group 17 elements have an O.S. of −1; group 16 elements, −2; and group 15 elements, −3.*

  [*Examples:* The O.S. of Br is −1 in $MgBr_2$; the O.S. of S is −2 in Li_2S; and the O.S. of N is −3 in Li_3N.]

Calculating Oxidation States activity

EXAMPLE 3-7

Assigning Oxidation States. What is the oxidation state of the underlined element in **(a)** $\underline{P}_4$; **(b)** $\underline{Al}_2O_3$; **(c)** $\underline{Mn}O_4^-$; **(d)** Na$\underline{H}$; **(e)** $H_2\underline{O}_2$; **(f)** $\underline{Fe}_3O_4$?

Solution

   (a) P_4: This formula represents a molecule of elemental phosphorus. For an atom of a free element, the O.S. = 0 (rule 1). The O.S. of P in P_4 is 0.

   (b) Al_2O_3: The total of the oxidation states of all the atoms in this formula unit is 0 (rule 2). The O.S. of oxygen is −2 (rule 6). The total for three O atoms is −6. The total for two Al atoms is +6. The O.S. of Al is +3.

   (c) MnO_4^-: This is the formula for permanganate ion. The total of the oxidation states of all the atoms in the ion is −1 (rule 2). The total for the four O atoms is −8. The O.S. of Mn is +7.

   (d) NaH: This is a formula unit of the ionic compound sodium hydride. Rule 3 states that the O.S. of Na is +1. Rule 5 indicates that H should also have O.S. +1. If both atoms had O.S. +1, the total for the formula unit would be +2. This violates rule 2. *Rules 2 and 3 take precedence over rule 5.* Na has O.S. +1; the total for the formula unit is 0; and the O.S. of H must be −1.

   (e) H_2O_2: This is hydrogen peroxide. Rule 5, stating that H has O.S. +1, takes precedence over rule 6 (which says that oxygen has O.S. −2). The sum of the oxidation states of the two H atoms is +2 and that of the two O atoms must be −2. The O.S. of O must be −1.

   (f) Fe_3O_4: The total of the oxidation states of four O atoms is −8. For three Fe atoms, the total must be +8. The O.S. per Fe atom is $\frac{8}{3}$ or $+2\frac{2}{3}$.

Practice Example A: What is the oxidation state of the underlined element in each of the following: $\underline{S}_8$; $\underline{Cr}_2O_7^{2-}$; $\underline{Cl}_2O$; $K\underline{O}_2$?

Practice Example B: What is the oxidation state of the underlined element in each of the following: $\underline{S}_2O_3^{2-}$; $Hg_2\underline{Cl}_2$; $K\underline{Mn}O_4$; $H_2\underline{C}O$?

Periodic Trends: Acid–Base Behavior of Oxides animation

  In part (f) of Example 3-7, we got the somewhat surprising answer of $+2\frac{2}{3}$ for the oxidation state of the iron atoms in Fe_3O_4. Prior to that, we saw only integral values for oxidation states. How does this fractional value come about? Generally, it comes from the assumption that all the atoms of an element have the same oxidation state in a given compound. Usually they do, but not always. Fe_3O_4, for example, is probably better represented as $FeO \cdot Fe_2O_3$, that is, through a combination of two simpler formula units. In FeO, the O.S. of the Fe atom is +2. In Fe_2O_3, the O.S. of each of *two* Fe atoms is +3. When we *average* the oxidation states over all three Fe atoms, we get a nonintegral value: $(2 + 3 + 3)/3 = \frac{8}{3} = 2\frac{2}{3}$.

  Also, we may at times need to "fragment" a formula into its constituent parts before assigning oxidation states. The ionic compound NH_4NO_3, for instance, consists of the ions NH_4^+ and NO_3^-. The oxidation state of N in NH_4^+ is −3, and in NO_3^-, +5, and we do *not* want to average them. It is far more useful to know the oxidation states of the individual N atoms than it is to deal with an average oxidation state of +1 for the two N atoms.

  Our first use of oxidation states comes in the naming of chemical compounds in the next section.

CONCEPT ASSESSMENT ✓

A nitrogen–hydrogen compound with molar mass 32 g/mol has N in a higher oxidation state than in NH_3. What is a plausible formula for that compound?

3-5   NAMING COMPOUNDS: ORGANIC AND INORGANIC COMPOUNDS

Throughout this chapter, we have referred to compounds mostly by their formulas, but we do need to give them names. When we know the name of a compound, we can look up its properties in a handbook, locate a chemical on a storeroom shelf, or discuss an experiment with a colleague. Later in the text we will see cases in which different compounds have the same formula. In these instances, we will find it essential to distinguish among compounds by name. We cannot give two substances the same name, yet we do want some similarities in the names of similar substances (Fig. 3-6). If all compounds were referred to by a common or trivial name, such as water (H_2O), ammonia (NH_3) or glucose ($C_6H_{12}O_6$), we would have to learn millions of unrelated names—an impossibility. What we need is a systematic method of assigning names—a system of *nomenclature*. Several systems are used, and we will introduce each at an appropriate point in the text. Compounds formed by carbon and hydrogen or carbon and hydrogen together with oxygen, nitrogen, and a few other elements are **organic compounds**. They are generally considered in a special branch of chemistry with its own set of nomenclature rules—*organic chemistry*. Compounds that do not fit this description are **inorganic compounds**. The branch of chemistry that concerns itself with the study of these compounds is called *inorganic chemistry*. In the next section, we will consider the naming of inorganic compounds, and in Section 3-7, we will introduce the naming of organic compounds.

> Nomenclature provides a good break from the highly mathematical tedium of stoichiometry. It can be helpful to *intersperse the topics* of mole calculations and nomenclature. Doing some of each over 2–3 days provides variety and reinforcement.

▲ **FIGURE 3-6**
Two oxides of lead
These two compounds contain the same elements—lead and oxygen—but in different proportions. Their names and formulas must convey this fact: lead(IV) oxide = PbO_2 (red-brown); lead(II) oxide = PbO (yellow).

3-6   NAMES AND FORMULAS OF INORGANIC COMPOUNDS

BINARY COMPOUNDS OF METALS AND NONMETALS

> **VCL** *Names and Formulas of Ionic Compounds*

Binary compounds are those formed between *two elements*. If one of the elements is a metal and the other a nonmetal, the binary compound is usually made up of ions; that is, it is a binary *ionic* compound. To name a binary compound of a metal and a nonmetal

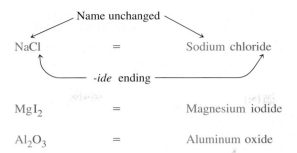

- write the *unmodified* name of the metal
- then write the name of the nonmetal, modified to end in -*ide*

Ionic compounds, though made up of positive and negative ions, must be *electrically neutral*. The net, or total, charge of the ions in a formula unit must be zero. This means one Na^+ to one Cl^- in NaCl; one Mg^{2+} to two I^- in MgI_2; two Al^{3+} to three O^{2-} in Al_2O_3; and so on. Table 3.1 lists the names and symbols of simple ions formed by metals and nonmetals. You will find this list useful when writing names and formulas of binary compounds of metals and nonmetals. Notice that the main-group metals and nonmetals form ions related to their group number, as discussed in Section 2-6. The transition metals, however, may form several ions, and it is important to distinguish between them in naming their compounds. The metal iron, for example, forms *two* common ions, Fe^{2+} and Fe^{3+}. The first is called the *iron(II)* ion, and the second is the *iron(III)* ion. The Roman numeral immediately following the name of the metal indicates its oxidation state or simply the charge on the ion. Thus, $FeCl_2$ is *iron(II)* chloride, while $FeCl_3$ is *iron(III)* chloride.

An earlier system of nomenclature that is still used to some extent uses two different word endings to distinguish between two binary compounds containing the same two elements but in different proportions, such as Cu_2O and CuO. In Cu_2O, the oxidation state of copper is +1, and in CuO it is +2.

The topic of nomenclature is used to introduce some *important chemical principles*: that metal plus nonmetal compounds tend to be ionic, and nonmetal plus nonmetal substances tend to be molecular. Also, ionic compounds must necessarily be electrically neutral. Some elements have only one common ion charge, while others are variable.

Inorganic Compounds activity

Table 3.1 simplifies considerably once one understands the pattern. All group 1 ions are 1+, group 2 ions are 2+, and Al^{3+}, Zn^{2+}, and Ag^+ have only the one common charge. Most other metal ions have variable charges. Monatomic halogen ions are −1 and oxygen is −2. Almost everything else can be worked out from these basics and the rule that the sum of all O.S. equals the total charge.

TABLE 3.1   Some Simple Ions

Name	Symbol	Name	Symbol
Positive ions (cations)			
Lithium ion	Li^+	Chromium(II) ion	Cr^{2+}
Sodium ion	Na^+	Chromium(III) ion	Cr^{3+}
Potassium ion	K^+	Iron(II) ion	Fe^{2+}
Rubidium ion	Rb^+	Iron(III) ion	Fe^{3+}
Cesium ion	Cs^+	Cobalt(II) ion	Co^{2+}
Magnesium ion	Mg^{2+}	Cobalt(III) ion	Co^{3+}
Calcium ion	Ca^{2+}	Copper(I) ion	Cu^+
Strontium ion	Sr^{2+}	Copper(II) ion	Cu^{2+}
Barium ion	Ba^{2+}	Mercury(I) ion	Hg_2^{2+}
Aluminum ion	Al^{3+}	Mercury(II) ion	Hg^{2+}
Zinc ion	Zn^{2+}	Tin(II) ion	Sn^{2+}
Silver ion	Ag^+	Lead(II) ion	Pb^{2+}
Negative ions (anions)			
Hydride ion	H^-	Iodide ion	I^-
Fluoride ion	F^-	Oxide ion	O^{2-}
Chloride ion	Cl^-	Sulfide ion	S^{2-}
Bromide ion	Br^-	Nitride ion	N^{3-}

Mention that the use of the *-ic* and *-ous* endings with metals is out of favor. Names based on these endings still appear, however, on many reagent bottles. The obvious advantage of using numerals is that one need not memorize all the possible O.S. of metals. The *-ic* and *-ous* endings are still used in the names of oxoacids.

Cu_2O is assigned the name cup*rous* oxide, and CuO is cup*ric* oxide. Similarly, $FeCl_2$ is fer*rous* chloride, and $FeCl_3$ is fer*ric* chloride. The idea is to use the *-ous* ending for the lower oxidation state of the metal and *-ic* for the higher oxidation state. The *ous/ic* system has several inadequacies though, and we will not use it in this text. For example, the *-ous* and *-ic* endings do not help in naming the four oxides of vanadium: VO, V_2O_3, VO_2, and V_2O_5.

EXAMPLE 3-8

Writing Formulas When Names of Compounds Are Given. Write formulas for the compounds barium oxide, calcium fluoride, and iron(III) sulfide.

Solution

In each case, identify the cations and their charges, based on periodic table group numbers or on oxidation states appearing as Roman numerals in names: Ba^{2+}, Ca^{2+}, and Fe^{3+}. Then identify the anions and their charges: O^{2-}, F^-, and S^{2-}. Combine the cations and anions in the relative numbers required to produce electrically *neutral* formula units.

barium oxide: *one* Ba^{2+} and *one* O^{2-} = BaO
calcium fluoride: *one* Ca^{2+} and   *two* F^- = CaF_2
iron(III) sulfide: *two* Fe^{3+} and *three* S^{2-} = Fe_2S_3

Note that in the first case, an electrically neutral formula unit results from the combination of the charges 2+ and 2−; in the second case, 2+ and 2 × (1−); and in the third case, 2 × (3+) and 3 × (2−).

Practice Example A: Write formulas for lithium oxide, tin(II) fluoride, and lithium nitride.

Practice Example B: Write formulas for the compounds aluminum sulfide, magnesium nitride, and vanadium(III) oxide.

EXAMPLE 3-9

Naming Compounds When Their Formulas Are Given. Write acceptable names for the compounds Na_2S, AlF_3, Cu_2O.

Solution

This task is generally easier than that of Example 3-8 because all you need to do is name the ions present. However, you must recognize that copper forms two different ions and that the cation in Cu_2O is Cu^+, copper(I).

Na_2S: sodium sulfide
AlF_3:   aluminum fluoride
Cu_2O: copper(I) oxide

Practice Example A: Write acceptable names for CsI, CaF_2, FeO, $CrCl_3$.
Practice Example B: Write acceptable names for CaH_2, CuCl, Ag_2S, Hg_2Cl_2.

Are You Wondering . . .

Why we don't use names such as sodium(I) chloride for NaCl and magnesium(II) chloride for MgCl$_2$?

Each proposed name clearly indicates the compound in question, but as a general rule, chemists always write the *simplest name possible*. The metals of periodic table group 1 (including Na) and group 2 (including Mg) have *only one ionic form*, one oxidation state. Roman numerals designating these oxidation states are superfluous. Later in the text, we will discuss which elements can exist in several oxidation states. For now, use the information in Table 3.1 as a guide.

One of the most common errors that students make when naming ionic compounds is not using Roman numerals when they should, as when naming $FeCl_3$, and using them when they shouldn't, as when naming NaCl.

BINARY COMPOUNDS OF TWO NONMETALS

If the two elements in a binary compound are both nonmetals instead of a metal and a nonmetal, the compound is a molecular compound. The method of naming these compounds is similar to that just discussed. For example,

HCl = hydrogen chloride

In both the formula and the name, we write the element with the positive oxidation state first: HCl and *not* ClH.

Some pairs of nonmetals form more than one binary molecular compound, and we need to distinguish among them. Generally, we indicate relative numbers of atoms through *prefixes: mono* = 1, *di* = 2, *tri* = 3, *tetra* = 4, *penta* = 5, *hexa* = 6, *hepta* = 7, *octa* = 8, *nona* = 9, *deca* = 10, and so on. Thus, for the two principal oxides of sulfur we write

SO_2 = sulfur *di*oxide

SO_3 = sulfur *tri*oxide

and for the following boron–bromine compound

B_2Br_4 = *di*boron *tetra*bromide

Additional examples are given in Table 3.2. Note that in these examples the prefix *mono-* is treated in a special way. We do not use it for the first named element. Thus, NO is called nitrogen monoxide, *not mono*nitrogen *mon*oxide. Finally, several substances have common or trivial names that are so well established that their systematic names are almost never used. For example,

H_2O = water (*di*hydrogen *mon*oxide)

NH_3 = ammonia (H_3N = *tri*hydrogen *mono*nitride)

The naming system used is determined by the types of elements (metal vs. nonmetal), not the type of compound (ionic vs. molecular). A number of metal–nonmetal compounds are molecular, but we name them without using prefixes. Historic usages do persist, however, such as "lead dioxide."

TABLE 3.2   Naming Binary Molecular Compounds

Formula	Name[a]
BCl_3	Boron trichloride
CCl_4	Carbon tetrachloride
CO	Carbon monoxide
CO_2	Carbon dioxide
NO	Nitrogen monoxide
NO_2	Nitrogen dioxide
N_2O	Dinitrogen monoxide
N_2O_3	Dinitrogen trioxide
N_2O_4	Dinitrogen tetroxide
N_2O_5	Dinitrogen pentoxide
PCl_3	Phosphorus trichloride
PCl_5	Phosphorus pentachloride
SF_6	Sulfur hexafluoride

[a]When the prefix ends in *a* or *o* and the element name begins with *a* or *o*, the final vowel of the prefix is dropped for ease of pronunciation. For example, carbon *mon*oxide, not carbon *mono*oxide, and dinitrogen *tetr*oxide, not dinitrogen *tetra*oxide. However, PI_3 is phosphorus *tri*iodide, not phosphorus *tr*iodide.

Are You Wondering . . .

Why isn't $MgCl_2$ called magnesium dichloride and $FeCl_3$, iron trichloride?

The names do give a clear indication of the compounds we mean, but they do *not* conform to the conventions that chemists use. Because the magnesium ion can be only Mg^{2+}, the name *magnesium chloride* can only mean $MgCl_2$. Similarly, *iron(III) chloride* can refer only to a compound of Fe^{3+} and Cl^-, that is, $FeCl_3$. On the other hand, to name the several oxides of nitrogen, we do need prefixes (*mono, di, tri*).

Acids are sometimes named as if hydrogen were a metal. Thus H_2S is called hydrogen sulfide (not dihydrogen monosulfide). Gaseous HCl is called hydrogen chloride, whereas its solutions are referred to as hydrochloric acid.

BINARY ACIDS

Even though we use names like hydrogen chloride for pure binary molecular compounds, we sometimes want to emphasize that their aqueous solutions are acids. Although acids will be discussed in detail later in the text, for now, so that we can recognize these substances and name them when we see their formulas, let us say that an *acid* is a substance that *ionizes* or breaks down in water to produce hydrogen ions (H^+)* and anions. A *binary acid* is a two-element compound of hydrogen and a nonmetal. For example, HCl ionizes into hydrogen ions (H^+) and chloride ions (Cl^-) in water; it is a binary acid. NH_3 in water is *not* an acid. It shows practically no tendency to produce H^+ under any conditions. NH_3 belongs to a complementary category of substances called *bases*. As we shall see in Chapter 5, bases yield hydroxide ions (OH^-) in aqueous solutions.

In naming acids we use the prefix *hydro-* followed by the name of the other nonmetal modified with an *-ic* ending. The most important binary acids are listed below.

▶ The symbol (aq) signifies a substance in aqueous (water) solution.

$$HF(aq) = hydrofluoric \text{ acid}$$
$$HBr(aq) = hydrobromic \text{ acid}$$
$$HCl(aq) = hydrochloric \text{ acid}$$
$$HI(aq) = hydroiodic$$
$$H_2S(aq) = hydrosulfuric \text{ acid}$$

POLYATOMIC IONS

With the exception of Hg_2^{2+}, the ions listed in Table 3.1 are *monatomic*—each consists of a single atom. In **polyatomic ions**, two or more atoms are joined together by covalent bonds. These ions are common, especially among the nonmetals. A number of polyatomic ions and compounds containing them are listed in Table 3.3. From this table, you can see that:

1. Polyatomic anions are more common than polyatomic cations. The most familiar polyatomic cation is the ammonium ion, NH_4^+.

2. Very few polyatomic anions carry the *-ide* ending in their names. Of those listed, only OH^- (hydroxide ion) and CN^- (cyanide ion) do. The common endings are *-ite* and *-ate*, and some names carry prefixes, *hypo-* or *per-*.

3. An element common to many polyatomic anions is *oxygen*, usually in combination with another nonmetal. Such anions are called **oxoanions**.

4. Certain nonmetals (such as Cl, N, P, and S) form a series of oxoanions containing different numbers of oxygen atoms. Their names are related to the oxidation state of the nonmetal atom to which the O atoms are bonded, ranging from *hypo-* (lowest) to *per-* (highest) according to the scheme

$$\text{Increasing oxidation state of nonmetal} \rightarrow$$
$$hypo\_\_\_ite \quad \_\_\_ite \quad \_\_\_ate \quad per\_\_\_ate \qquad (3.3)$$
$$\text{Increasing number of oxygen atoms} \rightarrow$$

5. All the common oxoanions of Cl, Br, and I carry a charge of $1-$.

6. Some series of oxoanions also contain varying numbers of H atoms and are named accordingly. For example, HPO_4^{2-} is the *hydrogen phosphate* ion and $H_2PO_4^-$, the *dihydrogen phosphate* ion.

7. The prefix *thio-* signifies that a sulfur atom has been substituted for an oxygen atom. (The sulfate ion has *one* S and *four* O atoms; thiosulfate ion has *two* S and *three* O atoms.)

*The species produced in aqueous solution is actually more complex than the simple ion H^+. The H^+ combines with an H_2O molecule to produce an ion known as the hydronium ion, H_3O^+. Chemists often use H^+ for H_3O^+, and that is what we will do until we discuss this matter more fully in Chapter 5.

TABLE 3.3   Some Common Polyatomic Ions

Name	Formula	Typical Compound
Cation		
Ammonium ion	NH_4^+	NH_4Cl
Anions		
Acetate ion	$C_2H_3O_2^-$	$NaC_2H_3O_2$
Carbonate ion	CO_3^{2-}	Na_2CO_3
Hydrogen carbonate ion[a] (or bicarbonate ion)	HCO_3^-	$NaHCO_3$
Hypochlorite ion	ClO^-	$NaClO$
Chlorite ion	ClO_2^-	$NaClO_2$
Chlorate ion	ClO_3^-	$NaClO_3$
Perchlorate ion	ClO_4^-	$NaClO_4$
Chromate ion	CrO_4^{2-}	Na_2CrO_4
Dichromate ion	$Cr_2O_7^{2-}$	$Na_2Cr_2O_7$
Cyanide ion	CN^-	$NaCN$
Hydroxide ion	OH^-	$NaOH$
Nitrite ion	NO_2^-	$NaNO_2$
Nitrate ion	NO_3^-	$NaNO_3$
Oxalate ion	$C_2O_4^{2-}$	$Na_2C_2O_4$
Permanganate ion	MnO_4^-	$NaMnO_4$
Phosphate ion	PO_4^{3-}	Na_3PO_4
Hydrogen phosphate ion[a]	HPO_4^{2-}	Na_2HPO_4
Dihydrogen phosphate ion[a]	$H_2PO_4^-$	NaH_2PO_4
Sulfite ion	SO_3^{2-}	Na_2SO_3
Hydrogen sulfite ion[a] (or bisulfite ion)	HSO_3^-	$NaHSO_3$
Sulfate ion	SO_4^{2-}	Na_2SO_4
Hydrogen sulfate ion[a] (or bisulfate ion)	HSO_4^-	$NaHSO_4$
Thiosulfate ion	$S_2O_3^{2-}$	$Na_2S_2O_3$

[a]These anion names are sometimes written as a single word—for example, hydrogencarbonate, hydrogenphosphate, and so forth.

Polyatomic Ions activity

Table 3.3 is somewhat formidable at first. Assign students a subset of the table to learn when ions are liable to show up on exams. Suggested are NH_4^+, CO_3^{2-}, OH^-, NO_3^-, PO_4^{3-}, and SO_4^{2-}. When the ending system that will be introduced in Table 3.4 is understood, several others will become obvious. The rest will become familiar as they are used.

OXOACIDS

The majority of acids are **ternary compounds**. They contain *three* different elements—hydrogen and two other nonmetals. If one of the nonmetals is oxygen, the acid is called an **oxoacid**. Or, think of oxoacids as combinations of hydrogen ions (H^+) and oxoanions. The scheme for naming oxoacids is similar to that outlined for oxoanions, except that the ending *-ous* is used instead of *-ite* and *-ic* instead of *-ate*. Several oxoacids are listed in Table 3.4. Also listed are the names and formulas of compounds in which the hydrogen of the oxoacid has been replaced by a metal such as sodium. These compounds are called *salts;* we will say much more about them in later chapters, beginning in Chapter 5. Acids are molecular compounds, and salts are ionic compounds.

Mention that "salt" and "ionic compound" are functionally the same thing.

TABLE 3.4   Nomenclature of Some Oxoacids and Their Salts

Oxidation State	Formula of Acid[a]	Name of Acid[b]	Formula of Salt[b]	Name of Salt
Cl: +1	HClO	*Hypo*chlor*ous* acid	NaClO	Sodium *hypo*chlor*ite*
Cl: +3	HClO$_2$	Chlor*ous* acid	NaClO$_2$	Sodium chlor*ite*
Cl: +5	HClO$_3$	Chlor*ic* acid	NaClO$_3$	Sodium chlor*ate*
Cl: +7	HClO$_4$	*Per*chlor*ic* acid	NaClO$_4$	Sodium *per*chlor*ate*
N: +3	HNO$_2$	Nitr*ous* acid	NaNO$_2$	Sodium nitr*ite*
N: +5	HNO$_3$	Nitr*ic* acid	NaNO$_3$	Sodium nitr*ate*
S: +4	H$_2$SO$_3$	Sulfur*ous* acid	Na$_2$SO$_3$	Sodium sulf*ite*
S: +6	H$_2$SO$_4$	Sulfur*ic* acid	Na$_2$SO$_4$	Sodium sulf*ate*

[a] In all these acids, H atoms are bonded to O atoms, not the central nonmetal atom. Often formulas are written to reflect this fact, for instance, HOCl instead of HClO and HOClO instead of HClO$_2$.

[b] In general, the *-ic* and *-ate* names are assigned to compounds in which the central nonmetal atom has an oxidation state equal to the periodic table group number minus 10. Halogen compounds are exceptional in that the *-ic* and *-ate* names are assigned to compounds in which the halogen has an oxidation state of +5 (even though the group number is 17).

KEEP IN MIND ▶

that ClO$_2$ is *not* a chlorite ion (it carries no net charge). Furthermore, there can be no compound called chlorite. A compound cannot consist of just a single type of ion.

EXAMPLE 3-10

Applying Various Rules for Naming Compounds. Name the compounds **(a)** CuCl$_2$; **(b)** ClO$_2$; **(c)** HIO$_4$; **(d)** Ca(H$_2$PO$_4$)$_2$.

Solution

(a) In this compound, the oxidation state of Cu is +2. Because Cu can also exist in the oxidation state +1, we must clearly distinguish between the two possible chlorides. CuCl$_2$ is copper(II) chloride.

(b) Both Cl and O are nonmetals. ClO$_2$ is a binary molecular compound called chlorine dioxide.

(c) The oxidation state of I is +7. By analogy to the chlorine-containing oxoacids in Table 3.4, we should name this compound periodic acid (pronounced "purr-eye-oh-dic" acid).

(d) The polyatomic anion H$_2$PO$_4^-$ is dihydrogen phosphate ion. Two of these ions are present for every Ca^{2+} ion in the compound calcium dihydrogen phosphate.

Practice Example A: Name the compounds SF$_6$, HNO$_2$, Ca(HCO$_3$)$_2$, FeSO$_4$.

Practice Example B: Name the compounds NH$_4$NO$_3$, PCl$_3$, HBrO, AgClO$_4$, Fe$_2$(SO$_4$)$_3$.

EXAMPLE 3-11

Applying Various Rules in Writing Formulas. Write the formula of the compound **(a)** tetranitrogen tetrasulfide; **(b)** ammonium chromate; **(c)** bromic acid; **(d)** calcium hypochlorite.

Solution

(a) Molecules of this compound consist of *four* N atoms and *four* S atoms. The formula is N$_4$S$_4$.

(b) Two ammonium ions (NH$_4^+$) must be present for every chromate ion (CrO$_4^{2-}$). Place parentheses around NH$_4^+$, followed by the subscript 2. The formula is (NH$_4$)$_2$CrO$_4$. (This formula is read as "N-H-4, taken twice, C-R-O-4.")

(c) The *-ic* acid for the oxoacids of the halogens (group 17) has the halogen in oxidation state +5. Bromic acid is $HBrO_3$ (analogous to $HClO_3$ in Table 3.4).

(d) Here there are one Ca^{2+} and two ClO^- ions in a formula unit. This leads to the formula $Ca(ClO)_2$.

Practice Example A: Write formulas for the compounds **(a)** boron trifluoride, **(b)** potassium dichromate, **(c)** sulfuric acid, **(d)** calcium chloride.

Practice Example B: Write formulas for the compounds **(a)** aluminum nitrate, **(b)** tetraphosphorous decoxide, **(c)** chromium(III) hydroxide, **(d)** iodic acid.

◄ **KEEP IN MIND**
the importance of the proper placement of parentheses in chemical formulas. Without parentheses, we would have $CaClO_2$, an *incorrect* formula for both calcium hypochlorite and calcium chlorite.

SOME COMPOUNDS OF GREATER COMPLEXITY

The copper compound that Joseph Proust used to establish the law of constant composition (page 36) is referred to in different ways. If you look up Proust's compound in a handbook of minerals, you will find it listed as *malachite*, with the formula $Cu_2(OH)_2CO_3$. In a handbook that specializes in pharmaceutical applications, this same compound is listed as *basic cupric carbonate*, with the formula $CH_2Cu_2O_5$. In a chemistry handbook, it is listed as *copper(II) carbonate dihydroxide*, with the formula $CuCO_3 \cdot Cu(OH)_2$. All you need to understand at this point is that regardless of the formula you use, you should obtain the same molar mass (221.12 g/mol), the same mass percent copper (57.48% Cu), the same $H:O$ mole ratio (2 mol H/5 mol O), and so on. In short, you should be able to interpret a formula, no matter how complex its appearance.

Some complex substances you are certain to encounter are known as hydrates. In a **hydrate**, each formula unit of the compound has associated with it a certain number of water molecules. This does not mean that the compounds are "wet," however. The water molecules are incorporated in the solid structure of the compound. The formula shown below signifies six H_2O molecules per formula unit of $CoCl_2$.

$$CoCl_2 \cdot 6\,H_2O$$

The prefix for six is *hexa-* and this compound is cobalt(II) chloride *hexa*hydrate. Its formula mass is that of $CoCl_2$ *plus* that associated with six H_2O: $129.8\,u + (6 \times 18.02\,u) = 237.9\,u$. We can speak of the mass percent water in a hydrate; for $CoCl_2 \cdot 6\,H_2O$ this is

$$\% \, H_2O = \frac{(6 \times 18.02)\,g\,H_2O}{237.9\,g\,CoCl_2 \cdot 6\,H_2O} \times 100\% = 45.45\%$$

The water present in compounds as water of hydration can generally be removed, in part or totally, by heating. When the water is totally removed, the resulting compound is said to be *anhydrous* (without water). Anhydrous compounds can be used as water absorbers, as in the use of anhydrous magnesium perchlorate in combustion analysis (recall Figure 3-5). $CoCl_2$ gains and loses water quite readily and indicates this through a color change. Anhydrous $CoCl_2$ is blue, whereas the hexahydrate is pink. This fact can be used to make a simple moisture detector (Fig. 3-7).

✓ Examples of common hydrates are chromium(III) chloride hexahydrate, nickel(II) sulfate heptahydrate and copper(II) sulfate pentahydrate.

◄ In general, centered dots ($\cdot$) show that a formula is a composite of two or more simpler formulas.

✓ The importance of understanding that solid hydrates exist is, for the present, that the water of hydration must be included in the molar mass when performing mole calculations.

3-7   NAMES AND FORMULAS OF ORGANIC COMPOUNDS

Organic compounds abound in nature. The foods we eat are made up almost exclusively of organic compounds, including not only energy-producing fats and carbohydrates and muscle-building proteins but also trace compounds that impart color, odor, and flavor to these foods. Almost all fuels, whether used to power automobiles, trucks, trains, or airplanes, are mixtures of organic compounds of a type called hydrocarbons. Most of the drugs produced by pharmaceutical companies are complex organic compounds, as are common plastics. The multiplicity of organic compounds is so vast that *organic chemistry* exists as a distinctive field of chemistry.

▲ **FIGURE 3-7**
Effect of moisture on $CoCl_2$
The piece of filter paper was soaked in a water solution of cobalt(II) chloride and then allowed to dry. When kept in dry air, the paper is blue in color (anhydrous $CoCl_2$). In humid air, the paper changes to pink ($CoCl_2 \cdot 6\,H_2O$).

The great diversity of organic compounds arises from the ability of carbon atoms to combine readily with other carbon atoms and with atoms of a number of other elements. Carbon atoms join together to form a framework of chains or rings to which other atoms are attached. All organic compounds contain carbon atoms; almost all contain hydrogen atoms; and many common ones also have oxygen, nitrogen, or sulfur atoms. These possibilities allow for an almost limitless number of different organic compounds. Organic compounds are mostly molecular; a few are ionic.

There are millions of organic compounds, many comprised of highly complex molecules. Their names are equally complicated. A systematic approach to naming these compounds is crucial, and the rules for naming inorganic compounds are of little use here. The usual name, often called the common or *trivial* name, for a familiar sweetener is sucrose (sugar). The systematic name is α-D-glucopyranosyl-β-D-fructofuranoside. At this point, however, we only need to recognize organic compounds and use their common names, together with an occasional systematic name. We will look at the systematic nomenclature of organic compounds in more detail in Chapter 26.

> The nomenclature of organic compounds can easily be postponed. The topic combines well with Chapters 10 and 11, or with Chapter 26.

> Many of the figures included in this section and the following problems can be useful when discussing the shapes of molecules (Section 10-7) and elsewhere with other topics.

HYDROCARBONS

Compounds containing only carbon and hydrogen are called **hydrocarbons**. The simplest hydrocarbon contains one carbon atom and four hydrogen atoms—methane, CH_4 (Fig. 3-8a). As the number of carbon atoms increases, the number of hydrogen atoms also increases in a systematic way, depending

Representations of Methane activity

(a) Methane

(b) Ethane

(c) Propane

(d) Ethene (ethylene)

(e) Benzene

▶ **FIGURE 3-8**
Visualizations of some hydrocarbons

on the type of hydrocarbon. The complexity of organic chemistry arises because carbon atoms can form chains and rings, and the nature of the chemical bonds between the carbon atoms can vary. Hydrocarbons containing only single bonds are called **alkanes**. The simplest alkane is methane, followed by ethane, C_2H_6 (Fig. 3-8b), and then propane, C_3H_8 (Fig. 3-8c). The fourth member of the series, butane, C_4H_{10}, was shown in Figure 3-2(a). Notice that each succeeding member of the alkane series is formed by the addition of one C atom and two H atoms to the preceding member.

The names of the alkanes are composed of two parts: a word stem and the ending (suffix) -*ane* indicating that the molecule is an alk*ane*. The first four word stems in Table 3.5 reflect common names, while the rest indicate the number of carbon atoms in the alkane. Thus C_3H_8 is propane and C_7H_{16} is heptane (hept = 7).

Hydrocarbon molecules with one or more double bonds between carbon atoms are called *alkenes*. The simplest of the alkenes is ethene (Fig. 3-8d); its name consists of the stem *eth*- and the ending -*ene*. Benzene, C_6H_6 (Fig. 3-8e), is a molecule with six carbon atoms arranged in a hexagonal ring. Molecules with structures related to benzene make up a large proportion of known organic compounds.

Refer to Figure 3-2 and you will notice that butane and methylpropane have the same molecular formula, C_4H_{10}, but different structural formulas. Butane is based on a four-carbon chain, whereas in methylpropane, a —CH_3 group, called a *methyl* group, is attached to the middle carbon atom of the three-carbon propane chain. Butane and methylpropane are *isomers*. **Isomers** are molecules that have the same molecular formula but different arrangements of atoms in space. As organic molecules become more complex, the possibilities for isomerism increase very rapidly.

TABLE 3.5 Word stem (or prefix) indicating the number of carbon atoms in simple organic molecules	
Stem (or prefix)	**Number of C Atoms**
Meth-	1
Eth-	2
Prop-	3
But-	4
Pent-	5
Hex-	6
Hept-	7
Oct-	8
Non-	9
Dec-	10

✓ If time permits, allow students to build molecular models of simple molecules that are isomers such as 2-methylpropane and butane.

EXAMPLE 3-12

Recognizing Isomers.   Are the following pairs of molecules isomers or not?

(a) $CH_3CH(CH_3)(CH_2)_3CH_3$ and $CH_3CH_2CH(CH_3)(CH_2)_3CH_3$

(b) $CH_3—CH—CH_2—CH_3$ and $CH_3—CH—CH_2—CH_2—CH_3$
$\qquad\quad |$ $\qquad\qquad\qquad\qquad\quad\ |$
$\qquad\ CH_2—CH_3$ $\qquad\qquad\qquad\quad CH_3$

Solution

Isomers have the same molecular formula but different structures. We first check to see if the molecular formulas are the same. If the formulas are not the same, they represent different compounds. If the formulas are the same, the compounds *may* be isomers, but only if their structures are different.

(a) The molecular formula of the first compound is C_7H_{16}, while that of the second compound is C_8H_{18}. The molecules are not isomers.

(b) These molecules have the same formula, C_6H_{14}, but they differ in structure. They are isomers. The difference in structure is that in the first structure, a methyl side chain is on the middle carbon atom of a five-carbon chain, and in the second structure it is on the second carbon atom from the end of the chain.

Practice Example A: Are the following pairs of molecules isomers?

(a) $CH_3C(CH_3)_2(CH_2)_3CH_3$ and $CH_3CH(CH_3)CH(CH_3)(CH_2)_3CH_3$

(b) $CH_3—CH—CH_2—CH_3$ and $CH_3—CH—CH_2—CH—CH_3$
$\qquad\quad |$ $\qquad\qquad\qquad\qquad\quad |\qquad\qquad |$
$\qquad\ CH_2—CH_2—CH_3$ $\qquad\qquad CH_3\qquad CH_3$

Practice Example B: Are the pairs of molecules represented by the following structural formulas isomers?

(a)

$$CH_2-CH_2$$
$$CH \qquad CH$$
$$CH_3 \quad CH_2 \quad CH_3$$

$$H_2C-CH_2$$
$$H_2C-C \qquad CH_3$$
$$\quad | \qquad CH$$
$$\quad H \qquad |$$
$$\qquad\qquad CH_3$$

(b)

$$CH_3 \qquad\qquad CH_3$$
$$\quad\ \ \ C=C$$
$$H \qquad\qquad\ \ H$$

$$CH_3 \qquad\qquad H$$
$$\quad\ \ \ C=C$$
$$CH_3 \qquad\qquad CH_3$$

CONCEPT ASSESSMENT ✓

In the complete combustion of a hydrocarbon, can the mass of H_2O produced ever exceed that of the CO_2? Explain.

FUNCTIONAL GROUPS

Carbon chains provide the framework of organic compounds; other atoms or groups of atoms replace one or more of the hydrogen atoms to form different compounds. We can illustrate this with the common alcohol molecule that occurs in beer, wine, and spirits. The molecule is *ethanol*, CH_3CH_2OH, in which one of the H atoms of ethane is replaced by an —OH group (Fig. 3-9a).

(a) Ethanol, or
Ethyl alcohol

(b) Methanol, or
Methyl alcohol

(c) 1-Propanol, or
Propyl alcohol

(d) 2-Propanol, or
Isopropyl alcohol

▶ **FIGURE 3-9**
Visualizations of some alcohols

The systematic name ethanol is derived from the name of the alkane, ethane, with the final *-e* replaced by the suffix *-ol*. The suffix *-ol* designates the presence of the OH group in a class of organic molecules called **alcohols**.

Ethyl alcohol, the common name of ethanol, also indicates attachment of the —OH group to the ethane hydrocarbon chain. To name the alkane chain as a group, replace the final *-e* by *-yl*, so that ethane becomes *ethyl*; thus *ethyl alcohol* for CH_3CH_2OH. It is often the case that the common name of one compound, alcohol in this case, will provide the generic name for a complete class of compounds; that is, all alcohols contain at least one —OH group.

Another common alcohol is *methanol*, or wood alcohol, which has the formula CH_3OH (Fig. 3-9b). The common name for methanol is methyl alcohol. It is interesting to note that wood alcohol is a dangerous poison, whereas the grain alcohol in beer and wine is safe to consume in moderate quantities.

The —OH group in alcohols is one of the many *functional groups* found in organic compounds. **Functional groups** are individual atoms or groupings of atoms that are attached to the carbon chains or rings of organic molecules and give the molecules their characteristic properties. Compounds with the same functional group generally have similar properties. The —OH group is called the *hydroxyl group*. At this point only a few functional groups will be introduced; functional groups are discussed in more detail in Chapter 26.

The presence of functional groups also increases the possibility of isomers. For example, there is only one propane molecule, C_3H_8. However, if one of the H atoms is replaced by a hydroxyl group, two possibilities exist for the point of attachment: at one of the end C atoms or at the middle C atom (Figs. 3-9c and d). This leads to two isomers. The alcohol with the —OH group attached to the end carbon atom is commonly called propyl alcohol or, systematically, 1-propanol; the prefix *1-* indicates that the —OH group is on the first or end C atom. The alcohol with the —OH group attached to the middle carbon atom is commonly called isopropyl alcohol or, systematically, 2-propanol; the prefix *2-* indicates that the —OH group is on the second C atom from the end.

Another important functional group is the *carboxyl* group, —COOH, which confers acidic properties on a molecule. The C atom in the carboxyl group is bound to the two O atoms in two ways. One bond is a single bond to an oxygen atom that is also attached to a H atom, and the other is a double bond to a lone O atom (Fig. 3-10a). The hydrogen attached to one of the O atoms in a carboxyl group is *ionizable* or *acidic*. Compounds containing the carboxyl group are called **carboxylic acids**. The first carboxylic acid based on alkanes is *methanoic* acid, HCOOH (Fig. 3-10b). In the systematic name, the *methan-*

Point out that carbon–hydrogen and carbon–carbon bonds are relatively unreactive, especially in saturated compounds. Because of this, functional groups are most important in determining the characteristic properties of organic compounds. These properties are explored in several later chapters.

Functional Group activity

Point out to students that isopropyl alcohol is the alcohol in rubbing alcohol.

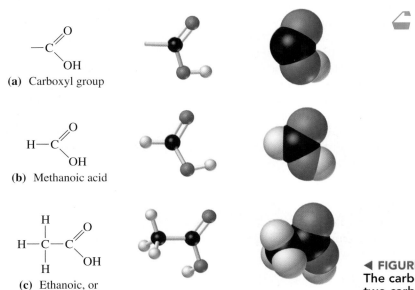

(a) Carboxyl group

(b) Methanoic acid

(c) Ethanoic, or Acetic acid

◄ **FIGURE 3-10**
The carboxyl group and visualizations of two carboxylic acids

▲ **Instrumentation for mass spectometry**

In Chapter 2, we learned how the masses and relative abundances of the isotopes of an element are determined by mass spectrometry (Fig. 2-14), thereby making it possible to establish weighted-average atomic masses.

If the ions analyzed by a mass spectrometer are *molecular* ions, the experimental data yield a *molecular* mass. For example, through mass spectrometry the molecular mass of vitamin C is found to be 176 u. Combining this fact with the empirical formula from Example 3-6 ($C_3H_4O_3$), we obtain the true molecular formula, $C_6H_8O_6$ (that is, 176 u = 2 × 88 u).

Actually, mass spectrometry is capable of providing much more than molecular masses. It can tell us about the *structures* of molecules. To see how this is possible, consider 2-methylpentane, which has a molecular mass of 86 u. Ionization occurs when an energetic electron in a cathode-ray beam strikes a molecule. The resulting molecular fragment, called a *radical*, is actually a cation, the *radical cation* $[CH_3CH_2CH_2CH(CH_3)_2]^+$. The released electron joins the electrons in the cathode-ray beam.

Ionization:
$$CH_3CH_2CH_2\overset{\overset{\displaystyle CH_3}{|}}{C}HCH_3 + e^- \longrightarrow$$

$$\left[CH_3CH_2CH_2\overset{\overset{\displaystyle CH_3}{|}}{C}HCH_3 \right]^+ + 2e^-$$

An impinging electron in the cathode-ray beam has more than enough energy to induce ionization and transfer some of its excess energy to the radical cation. When this energy is distributed throughout the ion, some of the bonds in the ion rupture, producing fragments. Some of these fragments carry a unit of positive charge and are detected in the mass spectrum. Others are neutral species and are not detected. The fragmentation pattern outlined below includes mass-to-charge ratios (*m/z*) of a few of the several ions produced.

Fragmentation:

$$\left[CH_3CH_2CH_2\overset{\overset{\displaystyle CH_3}{|}}{C}HCH_3 \right]^+ \\ m/z = 86$$

$$\longrightarrow \left[CH_3CH_2CH_2\overset{\overset{\displaystyle CH_3}{|}}{C}H \right]^+ + CH_3 \\ m/z = 71$$

$$\longrightarrow CH_3CH_2CH_2 + \left[\overset{\overset{\displaystyle CH_3}{|}}{C}HCH_3 \right]^+ \\ m/z = 43$$

$$\longrightarrow CH_3CH_2 + \left[\overset{\overset{\displaystyle CH_3}{|}}{C}H_2CHCH_3 \right]^+ \\ m/z = 57$$

indicates one carbon atom and the *-oic* acid indicates a carboxylic acid. The common name for methanoic acid is formic acid, deriving from the Latin word *formica*, meaning "ant." Formic acid is injected by an ant when it bites; this leads to the burning sensation that accompanies the bite.

The simplest carboxylic acid containing two carbon atoms is *ethanoic* acid, more commonly known as acetic acid. The molecular formula is CH_3COOH, and the structure is shown in Figure 3-10(c). Vinegar is a solution of acetic acid in water. An additional functional group is introduced in the examples that follow—a halogen atom (F, Cl, Br, I) substituting for one or more H atoms. When present as functional groups, the halogens carry the names, *fluoro-*, *chloro-*, *bromo-*, and *iodo-*.

EXAMPLE 3-13

Recognizing Types of Organic Compounds. What type of compound is each of the following?

(a) $CH_3CH_2CH_2CH_3$

(b) $CH_3CHClCH_2CH_3$

(c) $CH_3CH_2CO_2H$

(d) $CH_3CH_2CH(OH)CH_2CH_3$

In the mass spectrum in Figure 3-11, we arbitrarily assign a value of 100 to the radical cation present in the greatest abundance ($m/z = 43$) and relate the abundances of the other ions to this base peak. The mass spectrum of 3-methylpentane, shown in Figure 3-12, differs in significant ways from that of its isomer, 2-methylpentane. Notably, the base peak with value 100 now has $m/z = 57$. This is because there are two possible modes of fragmentation that produce the $[CH_2CH(CH_3)_2]^+$ radical cation.

▲ FIGURE 3-11
Partial mass spectrum of 2-methylpentane
Peaks are shown only for the four radical cations described in the text. Several additional ions are present in the complete spectrum.

$$\begin{bmatrix} & CH_3 \\ & | \\ CH_3CH_2CH & \end{bmatrix}^+ + CH_2CH_3$$
$m/z = 57$

$$\begin{bmatrix} & CH_3 \\ & | \\ CH_3CH_2CHCH_2CH_3 & \end{bmatrix}^+$$

$$CH_3CH_2 + \begin{bmatrix} & CH_3 \\ & | \\ CHCH_2CH_3 & \end{bmatrix}^+$$
$m/z = 57$

Altogether there are five isomers of the alkane hydrocarbon C_6H_{14}. Each has a unique mass spectrum, and the differences among them can be explained by applying a set of rules for analyzing fragmentation patterns. However, we need go no further to emphasize the main point of this discussion: Mass spectrometry enables us to establish both molecular and structural formulas.

▶ FIGURE 3-12
Partial spectrum of 3-methylpentane
The same four peaks are shown as in Figure 3-11.

Solution

(a) The carbon–carbon bonds are all single bonds in this hydrocarbon. This compound is an alkane.

(b) In its molecules, there are only single bonds, and one H atom has been replaced by a Cl atom. This compound is a chloroalkane.

(c) The presence of the carboxyl group, —CO_2H, in its molecules means that this compound is a carboxylic acid.

(d) The presence of the hydroxyl group, —OH, in its molecules means that this compound is an alcohol.

Practice Example A: What types of compounds correspond to each of the following formulas?

(a) $CH_3CH_2CH_3$　　　　**(b)** $ClCH_2CH_2CH_3$

(c) $CH_3CH_2CH_2CO_2H$　　**(d)** $CH_3CHCHCH_3$

Practice Example B: What types of compounds correspond to these formulas?

(a) $CH_3CH(OH)CH_3$　　　**(b)** $CH_3CH(OH)CH_2CO_2H$

(c) $CH_2ClCH_2CO_2H$　　　**(d)** $BrCHCHCH_3$

Organic nomenclature is traditionally a difficult subject for students. Some students may need a lot of practice before they are able to correctly name simple organic molecules.

EXAMPLE 3-14

Naming Organic Compounds. Name these compounds.

(a) $CH_3CH_2CH_2CH_2CH_3$ (b) $CH_3CHFCH_2CH_3$

(c) $CH_3CH_2CO_2H$ (d) $CH_3CH_2CH(OH)CH_2CH_3$

Solution

(a) The structure is that of an alkane molecule with a five-carbon chain, so the compound is pentane.

(b) The structure is that of a fluoroalkane molecule with the F atom on the *second* C atom of a four-carbon chain. The compound is called 2-fluorobutane.

(c) The carbon chain in this structure is three C atoms long with the end C atom in a carboxyl group. The compound is propanoic acid.

(d) This structure is that of an alcohol with the hydroxyl group on the *third* C atom of a five-carbon chain. The compound is called 3-pentanol.

Practice Example A: Name the following compounds: (a) $CH_3CH(OH)CH_3$; (b) $ICH_2CH_2CH_3$; (c) $CH_3CH(CH_3)CH_2CO_2H$; (d) CH_3CHCH_2.

Practice Example B: Give plausible names for the molecules that correspond to the following ball-and-stick models.

(a)   (b)   (c)

EXAMPLE 3-15

Writing Structural Formulas from the Names of Organic Compounds. Write the condensed structural formula for the organic compounds: (a) butane, (b) butanoic acid, (c) 1-chloropentane, (d) 1-hexanol.

Solution

(a) The word stem *but-* indicates a structure with a four-carbon chain, and the suffix *-ane* indicates an alkane. There are no functional groups indicated; hence the condensed structural formula is $CH_3(CH_2)_2CH_3$.

(b) The *-oic* ending indicates that the end carbon atom of the four-carbon chain is part of a carboxylic acid group. The condensed structural formula is $CH_3(CH_2)_2CO_2H$.

(c) The prefix *chloro-* indicates the substitution of a chlorine atom for a H atom, and the 1- designates that it is on the first C atom of the carbon chain. The carbon chain is five C atoms long, as signified by the word stem *pent*. The condensed structural formula is $CH_3(CH_2)_3CH_2Cl$.

(d) The suffix *-ol* indicates the presence of a hydroxyl group in place of a H atom, and the 1- designates that it is on the first C atom of the carbon chain. The word stem *hex* signifies that the carbon chain is six C atoms long. The condensed structural formula is $CH_3(CH_2)_4CH_2OH$.

Practice Example A: Write the condensed structural formula for the organic compounds (a) pentane, (b) ethanoic acid, (c) 1-iodooctane, (d) 1-pentanol.

Practice Example B: Write the line-angle formula for the organic compounds (a) propene, (b) 1-heptanol, (c) chloroacetic acid, (d) hexanoic acid.

Summary

3-1 Types of Chemical Compounds and Their Formulas— The two main classes of chemical compounds are **molecular compounds** and **ionic compounds**. The fundamental unit of a molecular compound is a **molecule** and that of an ionic compound is a **formula unit**. A formula unit is the smallest collection of positively charged ions—called **cations**—and negatively charged ions—called **anions**—that is electrically neutral overall. A **chemical formula** is a symbolic representation of a compound that can be written in several ways (Fig. 3-1). If the formula has the smallest integral subscripts possible, it is an **empirical formula**; if the formula represents an actual molecule, it is a **molecular formula**; and if the formula is written to show how individual atoms are joined together into molecules, it is a **structural formula**. Abbreviated structural formulas, called **condensed structural formulas**, are often used for organic molecules. Also used for organic molecules is the **line-angle formula**, in which all bond lines are shown except those between C and H atoms and in which the symbols C and H are mostly omitted. The relative sizes and positions of the atoms in molecules can be depicted by ball-and-stick and space-filling molecular models.

3-2 The Mole Concept and Chemical Compounds— In this section, the concept of atomic mass is extended to **molecular mass**, the mass in atomic mass units of a molecule of a molecular compound, and **formula mass**, the mass in atomic mass units of a formula unit of an ionic compound. Likewise, the concept of the Avogadro constant and the mole is now applied to compounds, with emphasis on quantitative applications involving the mass of a mole of compound—the **molar mass** M. For several elements, we can distinguish between a mole of molecules (for example, P_4) and a mole of atoms (that is, P).

3-3 Composition of Chemical Compounds— The mass percent composition of a compound can be established from its formula (equation 3.1). Conversely, a chemical formula can be deduced from the experimentally determined percent composition of the compound. For organic compounds, this often involves combustion analysis (Fig. 3-5). Formulas determined from experimental percent composition data are empirical formulas—the simplest formulas that can be written. Molecular formulas can be related to empirical formulas when experimentally determined molecular masses are available.

3-4 Oxidation States: A Useful Tool in Describing Chemical Compounds— The **oxidation state** of an atom is roughly related to the number of electrons involved in the formation of a bond between that atom and another atom. Oxidation states are expressed as numbers assigned according to a set of conventions. The oxidation state concept has several uses, one of which is to aid in naming chemical compounds and in writing chemical formulas.

3-5 Naming Compounds: Organic and Inorganic Compounds— Assigning names to the formulas of chemical compounds—nomenclature—is an important activity in chemistry. The topic is introduced in this section and applied to two broad categories: (1) **organic compounds**, which are compounds formed by the elements carbon and hydrogen, often together with a few other elements such as oxygen and nitrogen; and (2) **inorganic compounds**, a category that includes the remaining chemical compounds. The subject of nomenclature is extended to additional contexts throughout the text.

3-6 Names and Formulas of Inorganic Compounds— In this section on the nomenclature of inorganic compounds, the names and formulas of two-element or **binary compounds** are considered first. The names and symbols of some simple ions (Table 3.1) and the names of a few typical binary molecular compounds (Table 3.2) are listed. Also listed are some common ions comprised of two or more atoms, **polyatomic ions**, and typical ionic compounds containing them (Table 3.3). The naming of binary acids is related to the names of the corresponding binary hydrogen compounds. The majority of acids, however, are **ternary compounds**; they consist of three elements—hydrogen and two other nonmetals. Typically, one of the elements in ternary acids is oxygen, giving rise to the name **oxoacids**. The polyatomic anions derived from oxoacids are **oxoanions**. A scheme for relating the names and formulas of oxoanions is given (expression 3.3), and the nomenclature of oxoacids and their salts is summarized (Table 3.4). Also described in this section are **hydrates**, ionic compounds having fixed numbers of water molecules associated with their formula units.

3-7 Names and Formulas of Organic Compounds— Organic compounds are based on the element carbon. **Hydrocarbons** contain only carbon and hydrogen (Fig. 3-8). **Alkane** hydrocarbon molecules contain only single bonds, and alkenes contain at least one double bond. A common phenomenon found in organic compounds is isomerism— the existence of different compounds, called **isomers**, having identical molecular formulas but different structural formulas. **Functional groups** confer distinctive properties on organic molecules when they are substituted for H atoms on carbon chains or rings. The hydroxyl group —OH is present in **alcohols** (Fig. 3-9) and the carboxyl group —COOH, in **carboxylic acids** (Fig. 3-10).

Integrative Example

Molecules of a dicarboxylic acid have *two* carboxyl groups (—COOH). A 2.250-g sample of a dicarboxylic acid was burned in an excess of oxygen and yielded 4.548 g CO_2 and 1.629 g H_2O. In a separate experiment, the molecular mass of the acid was found to be 174 u. From these data, what can we deduce about the structural formula of this acid?

Strategy

Our approach will require several steps, which we can identify in this general way: (1) Use the combustion data to determine the percent composition of the compound (similar to Example 3-6). (2) Determine the empirical formula from the percent composition (similar to Example 3-5). (3) Obtain the molecular formula from the empirical formula and the molecular mass. (4) Determine how the C, H, and O atoms represented in the molecular formula might be assembled into a dicarboxylic acid.

Solution

1. *Determine the percent composition.* Calculate the mass of H in 1.629 g H_2O

$$? \text{ g H} = 1.629 \text{ g } H_2O \times \frac{1 \text{ mol } H_2O}{18.015 \text{ g } H_2O}$$

$$\times \frac{2 \text{ mol H}}{1 \text{ mol } H_2O} \times \frac{1.00794 \text{ g H}}{1 \text{ mol H}} = 0.1823 \text{ g H}$$

and then the mass percent H in the 2.250-g sample of the dicarboxylic acid.

$$\% \text{ H} = \frac{0.1823 \text{ g H}}{2.250 \text{ g compd.}} \times 100\% = 8.102\% \text{ H}$$

Also, calculate the mass of C in 4.548 g CO_2,

$$? \text{ g C} = 4.548 \text{ g } CO_2 \times \frac{1 \text{ mol } CO_2}{44.0098 \text{ g } CO_2}$$

$$\times \frac{1 \text{ mol C}}{1 \text{ mol } CO_2} \times \frac{12.011 \text{ g C}}{1 \text{ mol C}} = 1.241 \text{ g C}$$

followed by the mass percent C in the 2.250-g sample of dicarboxylic acid,

$$\% \text{ C} = \frac{1.241 \text{ g C}}{2.250 \text{ g compd.}} \times 100\% = 55.16\% \text{ C}$$

The % O in the compound is obtained as a difference, that is,

$$\% \text{ O} = 100.00\% - 55.16\% \text{ C} - 8.102\% \text{ H} = 36.74\% \text{ O}$$

2. *Obtain the empirical formula from the percent composition.* The masses of the elements in 100.0 g of the compound are

55.16 g C   8.102 g H   36.74 g O

The numbers of moles of the elements in 100.0 g of the compound are

$$55.16 \text{ g C} \times \frac{1 \text{ mol C}}{12.01 \text{ g C}} = 4.593 \text{ mol C}$$

$$8.102 \text{ g H} \times \frac{1 \text{ mol H}}{1.00794 \text{ g H}} = 8.038 \text{ mol H}$$

$$36.74 \text{ g O} \times \frac{1 \text{ mol O}}{15.999 \text{ g O}} = 2.296 \text{ mol O}$$

The tentative formula based on these numbers is

$$C_{4.593}H_{8.038}O_{2.296}$$

Divide all the subscripts by 2.296 to obtain

$$C_2H_{3.50}O$$

Multiply all subscripts by two to obtain the empirical formula,

$$C_4H_7O_2$$

and then determine the empirical formula mass.

$$(4 \times 12 \text{ u}) + (7 \times 1 \text{ u}) + (2 \times 16 \text{ u}) = 87 \text{ u}$$

3. *Obtain the molecular formula.* The experimentally determined molecular mass of 174 u is twice the empirical formula mass. The molecular formula is

$$C_8H_{14}O_4$$

4. *Assemble the atoms in $C_8H_{14}O_4$ into a plausible structural formula.* The dicarboxylic acid must contain two —COOH groups. This accounts for the two C atoms, two H atoms, and all four O atoms. The remainder of the structure is based on C_6H_{12}. For example, arrange the six —CH_2 segments into a six-carbon chain and attach the —COOH groups at the ends of the chain.

$$HOOC—CH_2(CH_2)_4CH_2—COOH$$

However, there are other possibilities based on shorter chains with branches, for example

$$HOOC-CH_2-\overset{\overset{\displaystyle CH_3}{|}}{\underset{\underset{\displaystyle CH_3}{|}}{C}}-CH_2-CH_2-COOH$$

Assessment

We have found a plausible structural formula, but there are many other possibilities. For example, the following three isomers have a seven-carbon chain with one methyl group ($-CH_3$) substituted for an H atom on the chain:

$$HOOCCHCH_3(CH_2)_4COOH; \quad HOOCCH_2CHCH_3(CH_2)_3COOH; \quad HOOC(CH_2)_2CHCH_3(CH_2)_2COOH$$

An isomer structure with two methyl groups on a six-carbon chain was written above, and there are even isomers with rings of carbon atoms. In conclusion, we cannot identify a specific isomer with only the data given.

Exercises

Representing Molecules

1. Refer to the color scheme on page 70, and give the molecular formulas for the molecules whose ball-and-stick models are given here.

(a)

(b)

(c)

(d)

(e)

2. Give the molecular formulas for the molecules whose ball-and-stick models are given here.

(a)

(b)

(c)

(d)

(e)

3. Give the structural formulas of the molecules shown in Exercise 1 **(b)**, **(d)**, and **(e)**.
4. Give the structural formulas of the molecules shown in Exercise 2 **(b)**, **(d)**, and **(e)**.

The Avogadro Constant and the Mole

5. Calculate the total number of **(a)** atoms in one molecule of trinitrotoluene (TNT), $CH_3C_6H_2(NO_2)_3$; **(b)** atoms in 0.00102 mol $CH_3(CH_2)_4CH_2OH$; **(c)** F atoms in 12.15 mol $C_2HBrClF_3$.

6. Determine the *mass*, in grams, of **(a)** 7.34 mol N_2O_4; **(b)** 3.16×10^{24} O_2 molecules; **(c)** 18.6 mol $CuSO_4 \cdot 5 H_2O$; **(d)** 4.18×10^{24} molecules of $C_2H_4(OH)_2$.

7. The amino acid methionine, which is essential in human diets, has the molecular formula $C_5H_{11}NO_2S$. Determine **(a)** its molecular mass; **(b)** the number of moles of H atoms per mole of methionine; **(c)** the number of grams of C per mole of methionine; **(d)** the number of C atoms in 9.07 mol methionine.

8. Determine the number of moles of Br_2 in a sample consisting of **(a)** 8.08×10^{22} Br_2 molecules; **(b)** 2.17×10^{24} Br atoms; **(c)** 11.3 kg bromine; **(d)** 2.65 L liquid bromine ($d = 3.10$ g/mL).

9. *Without doing detailed calculations,* explain which of the following has the greatest number of N atoms **(a)** 50.0 g N_2O; **(b)** 17.0 g NH_3; **(c)** 150 mL of liquid pyridine, C_5H_5N ($d = 0.983$ g/mL); **(d)** 1.0 mol N_2.

10. *Without doing detailed calculations,* determine which of the following has the greatest number of S atoms **(a)** 0.12 mol of solid sulfur, S_8; **(b)** 0.50 mol of gaseous S_2O; **(c)** 65 g of gaseous SO_2; **(d)** 75 mL of liquid thiophene, C_4H_4S ($d = 1.064$ g/mL).

11. Determine the number of *moles* of **(a)** N_2O_4 in a 115-g sample **(b)** N atoms in 43.5 g of $Mg(NO_3)_2$ **(c)** N atoms in a sample of $C_7H_5(NO_2)_3$ that has the same number of O atoms as 12.4 g $C_6H_{12}O_6$

12. Determine the *mass*, in grams, of **(a)** 6.25×10^{-2} mol P_4 **(b)** 4.03×10^{24} molecules of stearic acid, $C_{18}H_{36}O_2$ **(c)** a quantity of the amino acid lysine, $C_6H_{14}N_2O_2$, containing 3.03 mol N atoms.

13. The hemoglobin content of blood is about 15.5 g/100 mL blood. The molar mass of hemoglobin is about 64,500 g/mol, and there are four iron (Fe) atoms in a hemoglobin molecule. Approximately how many Fe atoms are present in the 6 L of blood in a typical adult?

14. In white phosphorus, P atoms are joined into P_4 molecules (see Figure 3-4). White phosphorus is commonly supplied in chalk-like cylindrical form. Its density is 1.823 g/cm^3. For a cylinder of white phosphorus 6.50 cm long and 1.22 cm in diameter, determine **(a)** the number of moles of P_4 present; **(b)** the total number of P atoms.

Chemical Formulas

15. Explain which of the following statement(s) is (are) correct concerning glucose (blood sugar), $C_6H_{12}O_6$.
   (a) The percentages, by mass, of C and O are the same as in CO.
   (b) The ratio of C:H:O atoms is the same as in dihydroxyacetone, $(CH_2OH)_2CO$.
   (c) The proportions, by mass, of C and O are equal.
   (d) The highest percentage, by mass, is that of H.

16. Explain which of the following statement(s) is (are) correct for sorbic acid, $C_6H_8O_2$, an inhibitor of mold and yeast.
   (a) It has a C:H:O mass ratio of 3:4:1.
   (b) It has the same mass percent composition as the aquatic herbicide, acrolein, C_3H_4O.
   (c) It has the same empirical formula as aspidinol, $C_{12}H_{16}O_4$, a drug used to kill parasitic worms.

   (d) It has four times as many H atoms as O atoms, but four times more O than H by mass.

17. For the mineral torbernite, $Cu(UO_2)_2(PO_4)_2 \cdot 8 H_2O$, determine:
   (a) the total number of atoms in one formula unit
   (b) the ratio, by number, of H atoms to O atoms
   (c) the ratio, by mass, of Cu to P
   (d) the element present in the greatest mass percent
   (e) the mass required to contain 1.00 g P

18. For the compound $Ge[S(CH_2)_4CH_3]_4$, determine:
   (a) the total number of atoms in one formula unit
   (b) the ratio, by number, of C atoms to H atoms
   (c) the ratio, by mass, of Ge to S
   (d) the number of g S in 1 mol of the compound
   (e) the number of C atoms in 33.10 g of the compound

Percent Composition of Compounds

19. Determine the mass percent H in the hydrocarbon decane, $C_{10}H_{22}$.

20. Determine the mass percent O in the mineral malachite, $Cu_2(OH)_2CO_3$.

21. Determine the mass percent H in the hydrocarbon isooctane, $C(CH_3)_3CH_2CH(CH_3)_2$.

22. Determine the mass percent H_2O in the hydrate $Cr(NO_3)_3 \cdot 9 H_2O$.

23. Determine the mass percent of each of the elements in the antimalarial drug quinine, $C_{20}H_{24}N_2O_2$.

24. Determine the mass percent of each of the elements in the fungicide copper(II) oleate, $Cu(C_{18}H_{33}O_2)_2$.

25. Determine the percent, by mass, of the indicated element:

   (a) Pb in tetraethyl lead, $Pb(C_2H_5)_4$, once extensively used as an additive to gasoline to prevent engine knocking
   (b) Fe in Prussian blue, $Fe_4[Fe(CN)_6]_3$, a pigment used in paints and printing inks
   (c) Mg in chlorophyll, $C_{55}H_{72}MgN_4O_5$, the green pigment in plant cells

26. All of the following minerals are semiprecious or precious stones. Determine the mass percent of the indicated element.
   (a) Zr in zircon, $ZrSiO_4$
   (b) Be in beryl (emerald), $Be_3Al_2Si_6O_{18}$
   (c) Fe in almandine (garnet), $Fe_3Al_2Si_3O_{12}$
   (d) S in lazurite (lapis lazuli), $Na_4SSi_3Al_3O_{12}$

27. *Without doing detailed calculations*, arrange the following in order of increasing % Cr, by mass, and explain your reasoning: CrO, Cr_2O_3, CrO_2, CrO_3.

28. *Without doing detailed calculations*, explain which of the following has the greatest mass percent of sulfur: SO_2, S_2Cl_2, Na_2S, $Na_2S_2O_3$, or CH_3CH_2SH.

Chemical Formulas from Percent Composition

29. Two oxides of sulfur have nearly identical molecular masses. One oxide consists of 40.05% S. What are the simplest possible formulas for the two oxides?

30. An oxide of chromium used in chrome plating has a formula mass of 100.0 u and contains *four* atoms per formula unit. Establish the formula of this compound, *with a minimum of calculation*.

31. Diethylene glycol, used to deice aircraft, is a carbon–hydrogen–oxygen compound with 45.27% C and 9.50% H by mass. What is its empirical formula?

32. The food flavor enhancer monosodium glutamate (MSG) has the composition 13.6% Na, 35.5% C, 4.8% H, 8.3% N, 37.8% O, by mass. What is the empirical formula of MSG?

33. Determine the empirical formula of **(a)** the rodenticide (rat killer) warfarin, which consists of 74.01% C, 5.23% H, and 20.76% O, by mass; **(b)** the antibacterial agent sulfamethizole, which consists of 39.98% C, 3.73% H, 20.73% N, 11.84% O, and 23.72% S, by mass.

34. Determine the empirical formula of **(a)** benzo-[*a*]pyrene, a suspected carcinogen found in cigarette smoke, consisting of 95.21% C and 4.79% H, by mass; **(b)** hexachlorophene, used in germicidal soaps, which consists of 38.37% C, 1.49% H, 52.28% Cl, and 7.86% O by mass.

35. A compound of carbon and hydrogen consists of 94.34% C and 5.66% H, by mass. The molecular mass

of the compound is found to be 178 u. What is its molecular formula?

36. Selenium, an element used in the manufacture of photoelectric cells and solar energy devices, forms two oxides. One has 28.8% O, by mass, and the other, 37.8% O. What are the formulas of these oxides? Propose acceptable names for them.

37. Indigo, the dye for blue jeans, has a percent composition, by mass, of 73.27% C, 3.84% H, 10.68% N, and the remainder is oxygen. The molecular mass of indigo is 262.3 u. What is the molecular formula of indigo?

38. Adenine, a component of nucleic acids, has the mass percent composition: 44.45% C, 3.73% H, 51.82% N. Its molecular mass is 135.14 u. What is its molecular formula?

39. The element X forms the chloride XCl_4 containing 75.0% Cl, by mass. What is element X?

40. The element X forms the compound $XOCl_2$ containing 59.6% Cl. What is element X?

41. Chlorophyll contains 2.72% Mg by mass. Assuming one Mg atom per chlorophyll molecule, what is the molecular mass of chlorophyll?

42. Two compounds of Cl and X are found to have molecular masses and % Cl, by mass, as follows: 137 u, 77.5% Cl; 208 u, 85.1% Cl. What is element X? What is the formula for each compound?

Combustion Analysis

43. A 0.1888-g sample of a hydrocarbon produces 0.6260 g CO_2 and 0.1602 g H_2O in combustion analysis. Its molecular mass is found to be 106 u. For this hydrocarbon, determine its **(a)** mass percent composition; **(b)** empirical formula; **(c)** molecular formula.

44. *Para*-cresol (*p*-cresol) is used as a disinfectant and in the manufacture of herbicides. A 0.4039-g sample of this carbon–hydrogen–oxygen compound yields 1.1518 g CO_2 and 0.2694 g H_2O in combustion analysis. Its molecular mass is 108.1 u. For *p*-cresol, determine its **(a)** mass percent composition; **(b)** empirical formula; **(c)** molecular formula.

45. Dimethylhydrazine is a carbon–hydrogen–nitrogen compound used in rocket fuels. When burned completely, a 0.312-g sample yields 0.458 g CO_2 and 0.374 g H_2O. The nitrogen content of a 0.486-g sample is converted to 0.226 g N_2. What is the empirical formula of dimethylhydrazine?

46. The organic solvent thiophene is a carbon–hydrogen–sulfur compound that yields CO_2, H_2O, and SO_2 on complete combustion. When subjected to combustion

analysis, a 1.3020-g sample of thiophene produces 2.7224 g CO_2, 0.5575 g H_2O, and 0.9915 g SO_2. What is the empirical formula of thiophene?

47. *Without doing detailed calculations*, explain which of these compounds produces the *greatest* mass of CO_2 when 1.00 mol of the compound undergoes complete combustion: CH_4, C_2H_5OH, $C_{10}H_8$, C_6H_5OH.

48. *Without doing detailed calculations*, explain which of these compounds produces the *greatest* mass of H_2O when 1.00 g of the compound undergoes complete combustion: CH_4, C_2H_5OH, $C_{10}H_8$, C_6H_5OH.

49. A 1.562-g sample of the alcohol $CH_3CHOHCH_2CH_3$ is burned in an excess of oxygen. What masses of CO_2 and H_2O should be obtained?

50. Refer to the compound ethyl mercaptan described in Example 3-2. Assuming that the complete combustion of this compound produces CO_2, H_2O, and SO_2, what masses of each of these three products would be produced in the complete combustion of 3.15 mL of ethyl mercaptan?

Oxidation States

51. Indicate the oxidation state of the underlined element in (a) $\underline{C}H_4$; (b) $\underline{S}F_4$; (c) $Na_2\underline{O}_2$; (d) $\underline{C}_2H_3O_2^-$; (e) $\underline{Fe}O_4^{2-}$.

52. Indicate the oxidation state of S in (a) $\underline{S}O_3^{2-}$; (b) $\underline{S}_2O_3^{2-}$; (c) $\underline{S}_2O_8^{2-}$; (d) $H\underline{S}O_4^-$; (e) $\underline{S}_4O_6^{2-}$.

53. Chromium forms three principal oxides. Write appropriate formulas for these compounds in which the oxidation states of Cr are +3, +4, and +6, respectively.

54. Nitrogen forms five oxides in which its oxidation states are +1, +2, +3, +4, and +5, respectively. Write appropriate formulas for these compounds.

Nomenclature

55. Name these compounds: (a) SrO; (b) ZnS; (c) K_2CrO_4; (d) Cs_2SO_4; (e) Cr_2O_3; (f) $Fe_2(SO_4)_3$; (g) $Mg(HCO_3)_2$; (h) $(NH_4)_2HPO_4$; (i) $Ca(HSO_3)_2$; (j) $Cu(OH)_2$; (k) HNO_3; (l) $KClO_4$; (m) $HBrO_3$; (n) H_3PO_3.

56. Name these compounds: (a) $Ba(NO_3)_2$; (b) HNO_2; (c) CrO_2; (d) KIO_3; (e) $LiCN$; (f) KIO; (g) $Fe(OH)_2$; (h) $Ca(H_2PO_4)_2$; (i) H_3PO_4; (j) $NaHSO_4$; (k) $Na_2Cr_2O_7$; (l) $NH_4C_2H_3O_2$; (m) MgC_2O_4; (n) $Na_2C_2O_4$.

57. Assign suitable names to the compounds (a) CS_2; (b) SiF_4; (c) ClF_5; (d) N_2O_5; (e) SF_6; (f) I_2Cl_6.

58. Assign suitable names to the compounds (a) ICl; (b) ClF_3; (c) SF_4; (d) BrF_5; (e) N_2O_4; (f) S_4N_4.

59. Write formulas for the compounds: (a) aluminum sulfate; (b) ammonium dichromate; (c) silicon tetrafluoride; (d) iron(III) oxide; (e) tricarbon disulfide; (f) cobalt(II) nitrate; (g) strontium nitrite; (h) hydrobromic acid; (i) iodic acid; (j) phosphorus dichloride trifluoride.

60. Write formulas for the compounds: (a) magnesium perchlorate; (b) lead(II) acetate; (c) tin(IV) oxide; (d) hydroiodic acid; (e) chlorous acid; (f) sodium hydrogen sulfite; (g) calcium dihydrogen phosphate; (h) aluminum phosphate; (i) dinitrogen tetroxide; (j) disulfur dichloride

61. Write a formula for (a) the chloride of titanium having Ti in the O.S. +4; (b) the sulfate of iron having Fe in the O.S. +3; (c) an oxide of chlorine with Cl in the O.S. +7; (d) an oxoanion of sulfur in which the apparent O.S. of S is +7 and the ionic charge is 2−.

62. Write a formula for (a) an oxide of nitrogen with N in the O.S. +5; (b) an oxoacid of nitrogen with N in the O.S. +3; (c) an oxide of carbon in which the apparent O.S. of C is +4/3; (d) a sulfur-containing oxoanion in which the apparent O.S. of S is +2.5 and the ionic charge is 2−.

63. Name the acids: (a) $HClO_2$; (b) H_2SO_3; (c) H_2Se; (d) HNO_2.

64. Supply the formula for the acids: (a) hydrofluoric acid; (b) nitric acid; (c) phosphorous acid; (d) sulfuric acid.

Hydrates

65. *Without performing detailed calculations,* indicate which of the following hydrates has the greatest % H_2O by mass: $CuSO_4 \cdot 5\,H_2O$, $Cr_2(SO_4)_3 \cdot 18\,H_2O$, $MgCl_2 \cdot 6\,H_2O$, and $LiC_2H_3O_2 \cdot 2\,H_2O$.

66. *Without performing detailed calculations,* determine the hydrate of Na_2SO_3 that contains almost exactly 50% H_2O, by mass.

67. Anhydrous $CuSO_4$ can be used to dry liquids in which it is insoluble. The $CuSO_4$ is converted to $CuSO_4 \cdot 5\,H_2O$, which can be filtered off from the liquid. What is the minimum mass of anhydrous $CuSO_4$ needed to remove 12.6 g H_2O from a tankful of gasoline?

68. Anhydrous sodium sulfate, Na_2SO_4, absorbs water vapor and is converted to the decahydrate, $Na_2SO_4 \cdot 10\,H_2O$. How much would the mass of 24.05 g of anhydrous Na_2SO_4 increase if converted completely to the decahydrate?

69. A certain hydrate is found to have the composition 20.3% Cu, 8.95% Si, 36.3% F, and 34.5% H_2O by mass. What is the empirical formula of this hydrate?

70. An 8.129-g sample of $MgSO_4 \cdot x\,H_2O$ is heated until all the water of hydration is driven off. The resulting anhydrous compound, $MgSO_4$, weighs 3.967 g. What is the formula of the hydrate?

Organic Compounds and Organic Nomenclature

71. Which of the following names is most appropriate for the molecule with the structure shown below? (a) butyl alcohol, (b) 2-butanol, (c) 1-butanol, (d) isopentyl alcohol.

$$
\begin{array}{cccc}
 & H & H & OH\ H \\
 & | & | & |\ \ | \\
H- & C- & C- & C-\ C-H \\
 & | & | & |\ \ | \\
 & H & H & H\ \ H
\end{array}
$$

72. Which of the following names is most appropriate for the molecule $CH_3(CH_2)_2COOH$? (a) dimethyleneacetic acid, (b) propanoic acid, (c) butanoic acid, (d) oxobutylalcohol.

73. Which of the following structures are isomers?

(a) $CH_3-CH-CH_2-OH$
$\qquad\quad |$
$\qquad\ CH_2-CH_3$

(b) $CH_3-\underset{\underset{CH_3}{|}}{CH}-CH_2-CH_2-OH$

(c) $CH_3-CH_2-\underset{\overset{|}{CH_3}}{\overset{CH_3}{\overset{|}{CH}}}-CH_2-OH$

(d) $CH_3-\underset{\underset{CH_3}{|}}{CH}-CH_2-O-CH_3$

(e) $CH_3-\underset{\underset{CH_3}{|}}{CH}-CH_2-\underset{\underset{OH}{|}}{CH}-CH_3$

74. Which of the following structures are isomers?

(a) $CH_3-\underset{\underset{CH_2-CH_3}{|}}{CH}-CH_2-Cl$

(b) $CH_3-\underset{\underset{CH_2Cl}{|}}{CH}-CH_2-CH_3$

(c) $CH_3-CH-\underset{\underset{CH_3}{|}}{CHClCH_3}$

(d) $CH_3-\underset{\underset{CH_3}{|}}{CH}-CH_2-\underset{\underset{Cl}{|}}{CH}-CH_3$

75. Write the condensed structural formulas for the organic compounds:
(a) heptane   (b) propanoic acid
(c) 2-methyl-1-pentanol   (d) fluoroethane

76. Write the condensed structural formulas for the organic compounds:
(a) octane   (b) heptanoic acid
(c) 3-hexanol   (d) 2-chlorobutane

77. Give the name, condensed structural formula, and molecular mass of the molecule whose ball-and-stick model is shown. Refer to the color scheme on page 70.

78. Give the name, condensed structural formula, and molecular mass of the molecule whose ball-and-stick model is shown. Refer to the color scheme on page 70.

Integrative and Advanced Exercises

79. The mineral spodumene has the empirical formula $LiAlSi_2O_6$. Given that the percentage of lithium-6 atoms in naturally occuring lithium is 7.40%, how many lithium-6 atoms are present in a 518-g sample of spodumene?

80. A particular type of brass contains Cu, Sn, Pb, and Zn. A 1.1713-g sample is treated in such a way as to convert the Sn to 0.245 g SnO_2, the Pb to 0.115 g $PbSO_4$, and the Zn to 0.246 g $Zn_2P_2O_7$. What is the mass percent of each element in the sample?

81. A brand of lunchmeat contains 0.10% by mass of sodium benzoate, C_6H_5COONa. How many mg of Na does a person ingest by eating 2.52 oz of this meat?

82. The important natural sources of boron compounds are the minerals kernite, $Na_2B_4O_7 \cdot 4 H_2O$, and borax, $Na_2B_4O_7 \cdot 10 H_2O$. How much *additional* mass of mineral must be processed per kilogram of boron obtained if the mineral is borax rather than kernite?

83. To deposit exactly one mole of Ag from an aqueous solution containing Ag^+ requires a quantity of electricity known as one faraday (F). The electrodeposition requires that each Ag^+ ion gain one electron to become an Ag atom. Use appropriate physical constants listed on the inside back cover to obtain a precise value of the Avogadro constant, N_A.

84. Can there be an alkane hydrocarbon that yields a greater mass of H_2O than CO_2 upon its complete combustion? Explain.

85. A hydrocarbon mixture consists of 60.0% by mass of C_3H_8 and 40.0% of C_xH_y. When 10.0 g of this mixture is burned, 29.0 g CO_2 and 18.8 g H_2O are the only products. What is the formula of the unknown hydrocarbon?

86. A 0.732-g mixture of methane, CH_4, and ethane, C_2H_6, is burned, yielding 2.064 g CO_2. What is the percent composition of this mixture (a) by mass; (b) on a mole basis?

87. A public water supply was found to contain 1 part per billion (ppb) by mass of chloroform, $CHCl_3$. (a) How many $CHCl_3$ molecules would be present in a 225-mL glassful of this water? (b) If the $CHCl_3$ in part (a) could be isolated, would this quantity be detectable on an ordinary analytical balance that measures mass with a precision of ± 0.0001 g?

88. A sample of the compound MSO_4 weighing 0.1131 g reacts with barium chloride and yields 0.2193 g $BaSO_4$. What must be the atomic mass of the metal M? [*Hint:* All the SO_4^{2-} from the MSO_4 appears in the $BaSO_4$.]

89. The metal M forms the sulfate $M_2(SO_4)_3$. A 0.738-g sample of this sulfate is converted to 1.511 g $BaSO_4$. What is the atomic mass of M? [*Hint:* Refer to Exercise 88.]

90. A 0.622-g sample of a metal oxide with the formula M_2O_3 is converted to 0.685 g of the sulfide, MS. What is the atomic mass of the metal M?

91. $MgCl_2$ often occurs in table salt (NaCl) and is responsible for caking of the salt. A 0.5200-g sample of table salt is found to contain 61.10% Cl, by mass. What is the % $MgCl_2$ in the sample? Why is the precision of this calculation so poor?

92. When 2.750 g of the oxide of lead Pb_3O_4 is strongly heated, it decomposes and produces 0.0640 g of oxygen gas and 2.686 g of a second oxide of lead. What is the empirical formula of this second oxide?

93. A 1.013-g sample of $ZnSO_4 \cdot x\,H_2O$ is dissolved in water and the sulfate ion precipitated as $BaSO_4$. The mass of pure, dry $BaSO_4$ obtained is 0.8223 g. What is the formula of the zinc sulfate hydrate?

94. The iodide ion in a 1.552-g sample of the ionic compound MI is removed through precipitation. The precipitate is found to contain 1.186 g I. What is the element M?

95. An oxoacid with the formula $H_xE_yO_z$ has a formula mass of 178 u, has 13 atoms in its formula unit, contains 34.80% by mass, and 15.38% by number of atoms, of the element E. What is the element E, and what is the formula of this oxoacid?

96. The insecticide dieldrin contains carbon, hydrogen, oxygen, and chlorine. Upon complete combustion, a 1.510-g sample yields 2.094 g CO_2 and 0.286 g H_2O. The compound has a molecular mass of 381 u and has half as many chlorine atoms as carbon atoms. What is the molecular formula of dieldrin?

97. A thoroughly dried 1.271-g sample of Na_2SO_4 is exposed to the atmosphere and found to gain 0.387 g in mass. What is the percent, by mass, of $Na_2SO_4 \cdot 10\,H_2O$ in the resulting mixture of anhydrous Na_2SO_4 and the decahydrate?

98. The atomic mass of Bi is to be determined by converting the compound $Bi(C_6H_5)_3$ to Bi_2O_3. If 5.610 g of $Bi(C_6H_5)_3$ yields 2.969 g Bi_2O_3, what is the atomic mass of Bi?

Feature Problems

99. All-purpose fertilizers contain the essential elements nitrogen, phosphorus, and potassium. A typical fertilizer carries numbers on its label, such as "5-10-5". These numbers represent the % N, % P_2O_5, and % K_2O, respectively. The N is contained in the form of a nitrogen compound such as $(NH_4)_2SO_4$, NH_4NO_3, or $CO(NH_2)_2$ (urea). The P is generally present as a phosphate, and the K as KCl. The expressions % P_2O_5 and % K_2O were devised in the nineteenth century, before the nature of chemical compounds was fully understood. To convert from % P_2O_5 to % P and from % K_2O to % K, the factors 2 mol P/mol P_2O_5 and 2 mol K/mol K_2O must be used, together with molar masses.
(a) Assuming three-significant-figure precision, what is the percent composition of the "5-10-5" fertilizer in % N, % P, and % K?
(b) What is the % P_2O_5 in the following compounds (both common fertilizers)? (i) $Ca(H_2PO_4)_2$; (ii) $(NH_4)_2HPO_4$
(c) In a similar manner to the "5-10-5" fertilizer described in this exercise, how would you describe a fertilizer in which the mass ratio of $(NH_4)_2HPO_4$ to KCl is 5.00:1.00?
(d) Can a "5-10-5" fertilizer be prepared in which $(NH_4)_2HPO_4$ and KCl are the sole fertilizer components, with or without inert nonfertilizer additives? If so, what should be the proportions of the constituents of the fertilizer mixture? If this "5-10-5" fertilizer cannot be prepared, why not?

100. A hydrate of copper(II) sulfate, when heated, goes through the succession of changes suggested by the photograph. In this photograph, (a) is the original fully hydrated copper(II) sulfate; (b) is the product obtained by heating the original hydrate to 140°C; (c) is the product obtained by further heating to 400°C; and (d) is the product obtained at 1000°C.

(a)   (b)   (c)   (d)

A 2.574-g sample of $CuSO_4 \cdot x\,H_2O$ was heated to 140°C, cooled, and reweighed. The resulting solid was reheated to 400°C, cooled, and reweighed. Finally, this solid was heated to 1000°C, cooled, and weighed for the last time.

Original sample	2.574 g
After heating to 140°C	1.833 g
After reheating to 400°C	1.647 g
After reheating to 1000°C	0.812 g

(a) Assuming that all the water of hydration is driven off at 400°C, what is the formula of the original hydrate?

(b) What is the formula of the hydrate obtained when the original hydrate is heated to only 140°C? **(c)** The black residue obtained at 1000°C is an oxide of copper. What is its percent composition and empirical formula?

101. Some substances that are only very slightly soluble in water will spread over the surface of water to produce a film that is called a *monolayer* because it is only one molecule thick. A practical use of this phenomenon is to cover ponds to reduce the loss of water by evaporation. Stearic acid forms a monolayer on water. The molecules are arranged upright and in contact with one another, rather like pencils tightly packed and standing upright in a coffee mug. The model at the right represents an individual stearic acid molecule in the monolayer.

(a) How many square meters of water surface would be covered by a monolayer made from 10.0 g of stearic acid?
[*Hint:* What is the formula of stearic acid?]
(b) If stearic acid has a density of 0.85 g/cm³, estimate the length (in nanometers) of a stearic acid molecule. [*Hint:* What is the thickness of the monolayer described in part a?]
(c) A very dilute solution of oleic acid in liquid pentane is prepared in the following way:

1.00 mL oleic acid + 9.00 mL pentane → solution (1);

1.00 mL solution (1) + 9.00 mL pentane → solution (2);

1.00 mL solution (2) + 9.00 mL pentane → solution (3);

1.00 mL solution (3) + 9.00 mL pentane → solution (4).

A 0.10-mL sample of solution (4) is spread in a monolayer on water. The area covered by the monolayer is 85 cm². Assume that oleic acid molecules are arranged in the same way as described for stearic acid, and that the cross-sectional area of the molecule is 4.6×10^{-15} cm². The density of oleic acid is 0.895 g/mL. Use these data to obtain an approximate value of Avogadro's number.

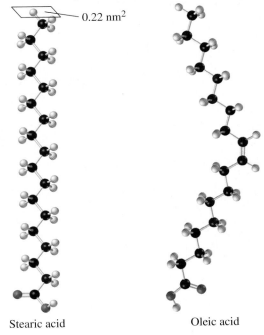

0.22 nm²

Stearic acid   Oleic acid

Self-Assessment Exercises

102. In your own words, define or explain the following terms or symbols: **(a)** formula unit; **(b)** P_4; **(c)** molecular compound; **(d)** binary compound; **(e)** hydrate.

103. Briefly describe each of the following ideas or methods: **(a)** mole of a compound; **(b)** structural formula; **(c)** oxidation state; **(d)** carbon–hydrogen–oxygen determination by combustion analysis.

104. Explain the important distinctions between each pair of terms: **(a)** molecular mass and molar mass; **(b)** empirical and molecular formulas; **(c)** systematic and trivial, or common, name; **(d)** hydroxyl and carboxyl functional group.

105. Explain each term as it applies to the element nitrogen. **(a)** atomic mass; **(b)** molecular mass; **(c)** molar mass.

106. One mole of liquid bromine, Br_2, **(a)** has a mass of 79.9 g; **(b)** contains 6.022×10^{23} Br atoms; **(c)** contains the same number of atoms as in 12.01 g H_2O; **(d)** has twice the mass of 0.500 mole of gaseous Cl_2.

107. Three of the following formulas might be either an empirical or a molecular formula. The formula that must be a molecular formula is **(a)** N_2O; **(b)** N_2H_4; **(c)** NaCl; **(d)** NH_3.

108. The compound $C_7H_7NO_2$ contains **(a)** 17 atoms per mole; **(b)** equal percentages by mass of C and H; **(c)** about twice the percent by mass of O as of N; **(d)** about twice the percent by mass of N as of H.

109. The greatest number of N atoms is found in **(a)** 50.0 g N_2O; **(b)** 17.0 g NH_3; **(c)** 150 mL of liquid pyridine, C_5H_5N ($d = 0.983$ g/mL); **(d)** 1.0 mol N_2.

110. XF_3 consists of 65% F by mass. The atomic mass of the element X must be **(a)** 8 u; **(b)** 11u; **(c)** 31 u; **(d)** 35 u.

111. The oxidation state of I in the ion $H_4IO_6^-$ is **(a)** -1; **(b)** $+1$; **(c)** $+7$; **(d)** $+8$.

112. The formula for calcium chlorite is **(a)** $CaClO_2$; **(b)** $Ca(ClO_2)_2$; **(c)** $CaClO_3$; **(d)** $Ca(ClO_4)_2$.

113. A formula unit of the compound $[Cu(NH_3)_4]SO_4$ has nearly equal masses of **(a)** S and O; **(b)** N and O; **(c)** H and N; **(d)** Cu and O.

114. An isomer of the compound $CH_3CH_2CHOHCH_3$ is **(a)** $C_4H_{10}O$; **(b)** $CH_3CHOHCH_2CH_3$; **(c)** $CH_3(CH_2)_2OH$; **(d)** $CH_3CH_2OCH_2CH_3$.

115. A hydrate of Na_2SO_3 contains almost exactly 50% H_2O by mass. What is the formula of this hydrate?

116. Malachite is a common copper-containing mineral with the formula $CuCO_3 \cdot Cu(OH)_2$. **(a)** What is the mass percent copper in malachite? **(b)** When malachite is strongly heated, carbon dioxide and water are driven off, yielding copper(II) oxide as the sole product. What mass of copper(II) oxide is produced per kg of malachite?

117. Acetaminophen, an analgesic and antipyretic drug, has a molecular mass of 151.2 u and a mass percent composition of 63.56% C, 6.00% H, 9.27% N, and 21.17% O. What is the molecular formula of acetaminophen?

118. Ibuprofen is a compound used in painkillers. When a 2.174-g sample is burned completely, it yields 6.029 g CO_2 and 1.709 g H_2O as the sole products. **(a)** What is the percent composition, by mass, of ibuprofen? **(b)** What is the empirical formula of ibuprofen?

119. Appendix E describes a useful study aid known as concept mapping. Using the method presented in Appendix E, construct a concept map illustrating the different concepts in Sections 3-2 and 3-3.

 eMedia Exercises

120. Observe the three-dimensional models of acetic acid and sodium chloride found in (*Activebook 3-1*). By using the pop-up menu (right-click for Windows, click and hold for Macintosh), change the representation of the models to both the ball-and-stick and space-filling representations. **(a)** Describe the general differences between a molecular compound and an ionic compound in terms of the number of atoms present in the compound. **(b)** What is different about the way the two types of compounds are represented in the animations?

121. **(a)** Use the **Oxidation States** activity (*Activebook 3-4*) to help estimate the different oxidation states of manganese in these oxides and anions of this transition metal: Mn_2O_3, MnO_2, $MnO_4{}^{2-}$, $MnO_4{}^-$. Adjust the number of metal and oxygen atoms and their

relative charges to obtain the desired net charge. **(b)** If the last two species were combined with sodium, what would be the expected compositions of the compounds?

122. Because of the need to exactly describe a structure, some molecular names become awkward to pronounce. Consider for example the eight-carbon alcohol that is known to attract mosquitoes, 1-octen-3-ol. **(a)** Use the **Functional Groups** activity (*Activebook 3-7*) to deduce the structure of this molecule by observing first the structure of the alkene and then the structure of the alcohol. **(b)** What would the name of the structure be if the carbon chain contained two double bonds (at 1 and 4) and a carboxyl group on carbon 8? **(c)** Draw the structures of both of these molecules.

 eLaboratory Exercises

These exercises allow students to apply the concepts and skills for this chapter in the simulated laboratory of Virtual ChemLab. Worksheets for each of these exercises are found in the Virtual ChemLab Workbook in your MediaPak.

123. *(VCL 3-1) Counting Molecules*
In this problem you will go into the virtual laboratory and retrieve a bottle of NaCl, weigh out approximately 1 g of the sample on an analytical balance, and then calculate the number of atoms of Na and Cl in the sample.

124. *(VCL 3-2) Counting Molecules*
In this problem you will go into the virtual laboratory

and retrieve a bottle of sugar, weigh out approximately 1 g of the sample on an analytical balance, and then calculate the number of atoms of C, H, and O in the sample. You will also repeat this with a bottle of NH_4Cl.

125. *(VCL 3-3) Names and Formulas of Ionic Compounds*
In this problem you will go into the virtual laboratory and make a series of ionic compounds containing the cations Ag^+, Pb^{2+}, Ca^{2+}, Fe^{3+}, and Cu^{2+}; observe the reactions and identify the color of the compounds formed; write the chemical formulas; and write the chemical names.

4

CHEMICAL REACTIONS

The space shuttle Discovery lifts off on mission STS-26. Combustion reactions in the solid-fuel rocket engines provide the thrust to lift the shuttle off the launch pad. In this chapter, we learn to write and use balanced chemical equations for a wide variety of chemical reactions, including combustion reactions.

We are all aware that iron rusts and natural gas burns. These processes are chemical reactions. Chemical reactions are the central concern—not just of this chapter but of the entire science of chemistry.

In this chapter we will first learn to represent chemical reactions by chemical equations, and then we will use chemical equations to establish quantitative (numerical) relationships among the reactants and products of a reaction, a topic known as reaction stoichiometry. Because many chemical reactions occur in solution, we will also introduce a method of describing the composition of a solution, called *solution molarity*. Throughout the chapter, we will discuss new aspects of problem solving and more uses for the mole concept.

▲ **FIGURE 4-1**
Precipitation of silver chromate
When aqueous solutions of silver nitrate and potassium chromate are mixed, the disappearance of the distinctive yellow color of chromate ion and the appearance of the red-brown solid, silver chromate, provide physical evidence of a reaction.

▶ Sometimes products react, partially or completely, to re-form the original reactants. Such reactions are called *reversible reactions* and are designated by a double arrow (⇌). In this chapter, we assume that any reverse reactions are negligible and that reactions go only in the forward direction. We consider reversible reactions in detail in Chapter 15.

Reactions with Oxygen movie

4-1   CHEMICAL REACTIONS AND CHEMICAL EQUATIONS

A **chemical reaction** is a process in which one set of substances, called **reactants**, is converted to a new set of substances, called **products**. In other words, a chemical reaction is the process by which a chemical change occurs. In many cases, though, nothing happens when substances are mixed; each retains its original composition and properties. We need evidence before we can say that a reaction has occurred. Some of the types of physical evidence to look for are shown here.

- a color change (Fig. 4-1)
- formation of a solid (precipitate) within a clear solution (Fig. 4-1)
- evolution of a gas (Fig. 4-2a)
- evolution or absorption of heat (Fig. 4-2b)

While observations such as these usually signify that a reaction has occurred, conclusive evidence still requires a detailed chemical analysis of the reaction mixture to identify all the substances present. Moreover, a chemical analysis may reveal that a chemical reaction has occurred even in the absence of obvious physical signs.

Just as there are symbols for elements and formulas for compounds, there is a symbolic, or shorthand, way of representing a chemical reaction—the **chemical equation**. In a chemical equation, formulas for the reactants are written on the left side of the equation and formulas for the products are written on the right. The two sides of the equation are joined by an arrow (⟶). We say that the reactants *yield* the products. Consider the reaction of colorless nitrogen monoxide and oxygen gases to form red-brown nitrogen dioxide gas, a reaction that occurs in the manufacture of nitric acid.

$$\text{nitrogen monoxide} + \text{oxygen} \longrightarrow \text{nitrogen dioxide}$$

To complete the shorthand representation of this reaction, we must do two things:

1. Substitute chemical formulas for names, to obtain the following expression.

$$NO + O_2 \longrightarrow NO_2$$

In this expression, there are three O atoms on the left side (one in the molecule NO and two in the molecule O_2), but only two O atoms (in the molecule NO_2) on the right. Because atoms are neither created nor destroyed in a chemical reaction, this expression needs to be *balanced*.

(a)   (b)

▲ **FIGURE 4-2**
Evidence of a chemical reaction
(a) Evolution of a gas: When a copper penny reacts with nitric acid, the red-brown gas NO_2 is evolved. **(b)** Evolution of heat: When iron gauze (steel wool) is ignited in an oxygen atmosphere, evolved heat and light provide physical evidence of a reaction.

2. Balance the numbers of atoms of each kind on either side of the expression to obtain a balanced chemical equation.* In this step, the coefficient two is placed in front of the formulas NO and NO_2. This means that two molecules of NO are consumed and two molecules of NO_2 are produced for every molecule of O_2 consumed. In the balanced equation there are two N atoms and four O atoms on each side. In a **balanced equation**, the total number of atoms of each element present is the same on both sides of the equation. We see this below, both in the symbolic equation and in the molecular representation of the reaction.

$$2\,NO + O_2 \longrightarrow 2\,NO_2$$

Chemical Reactions. Any of the reactions in the figures on page 110 can be performed in class. Chromate waste needs to be saved for proper disposal and another precipitation reaction may be substituted. When performing precipitation demonstrations generally, don't be too quick to stir the system. The billowing clouds of forming solids can be visually very pleasing. Another good reaction to perform is that of Ca and water.

The coefficients required to balance a chemical equation are called **stoichiometric coefficients**. These coefficients are essential in relating the amounts of reactants used and products formed in a chemical reaction, through a variety of calculations.

In balancing a chemical equation, keep the following points in mind.

(1) An equation can be balanced only by adjusting the coefficients of formulas.

(2) The equation must include only the reactants and products known to participate in the reaction.

$$\text{(incorrect)}\quad NO + O_2 \longrightarrow NO_2 + O$$

Although this equation is balanced, it is incorrect. From the description of the reaction we were given, no atomic oxygen (O) is produced; NO_2 is the only product.

(3) Never balance an equation by changing a formula.

$$\text{(incorrect)}\quad NO + O_2 \longrightarrow NO_3$$

Again, the equation is balanced, but it is incorrect. The formula for nitrogen dioxide, the sole product of the reaction, can only be NO_2. It must not be changed to NO_3 just to balance an equation.

The method of equation balancing described above is called *balancing by inspection*. Balancing by inspection means to adjust stoichiometric coefficients by trial and error until a balanced condition is found. Although the elements can generally be balanced in any order, equation balancing need not be a hit-or-miss affair. Here are some useful strategies for balancing equations.

- If an element occurs in only one compound on each side of the equation, try balancing this element first.
- When one of the reactants or products exists as the free element, balance this element last.

Oxides of Nitrogen. Drop pieces of copper into a large test tube filled about one-fifth full with 1 M HNO_3. Warm the system in a beaker of hot water. The gas bubbles formed are, while in the test tube, mostly colorless NO. Upon contact with air, NO reacts with O_2, forming brown NO_2. Perform this in a hood as the NO_2 fumes are corrosive.

The reaction of NO + O_2 is of considerable environmental interest. Automobile engines—and all other combustion devices—make NO. One purpose of a catalytic converter is to reduce the amount of NO emitted from a tailpipe. Once in the atmosphere, NO is converted into brown NO_2 by the reaction illustrated on this page. This is why many urban atmospheres have a brown tinge.

Balancing Equations activity

Stress to students that they must write the correct formulas for reactants and products before they can write a balanced chemical equation. If necessary, ask students to review the material in Chapter 3 dealing with naming and writing formulas of compounds.

*An equation—whether mathematical or chemical—must have the left and right sides equal. We should not call an expression an equation until it is balanced. The term *chemical equation* automatically signifies that this balance exists. Although unnecessary, the term *balanced* is commonly used when referring to a chemical equation.

▶ We will encounter a few situations in Chapters 7 and 19 where some fractional coefficients are actually required.

☑ Emphasize that carbon, hydrogen, and sulfur compounds can be counted on, in a plentiful supply of O_2, to burn to form CO_2, H_2O, and SO_2. Students should be able to both complete and balance an equation for the combustion of any carbon, hydrogen, oxygen, or sulfur compound. With nitrogen, however, the products obtained are variable and must be given in order to balance an equation.

- In some reactions, certain groups of atoms (for example, polyatomic ions) remain unchanged. In such cases, balance these groups as a unit.
- It is permissible to use fractional as well as integral numbers as coefficients. At times, an equation can be balanced most easily by using one or more fractional coefficients and then, if desired, clearing the fractions by multiplying *all* coefficients by a common multiplier.

In this chapter you should concentrate on learning to write formulas for the reactants and products of a reaction and balance the equation representing the reaction. A third task, which you will face in later chapters, is to predict the products formed when certain reactants are brought together under the appropriate conditions. Even now, however, based on concepts presented in the previous chapter, you should be able to predict the products of a *combustion reaction*. In a plentiful supply of oxygen gas, the combustion of hydrocarbons and of carbon–hydrogen–oxygen compounds produces carbon dioxide and water as the only products. If the compound contains sulfur as well, sulfur dioxide will also be a product. These ideas and an equation-balancing strategy are illustrated in Examples 4-1 and 4-2.

EXAMPLE 4-1

Balancing an Equation. Ammonia and oxygen can react in several different ways, including the following. Balance the equation for this reaction.

$$NH_3 + O_2 \longrightarrow N_2 + H_2O$$

Solution

Since there is *one* N atom in NH_3 on the left, and *two* N atoms in N_2 on the right, the coefficient 2 must be added in front of NH_3.

$$2\,NH_3 + O_2 \longrightarrow N_2 + H_2O$$

Since there are *six* H atoms (in $2\,NH_3$) on the left of the equation just written and only *two* on the right (in H_2O), the coefficient 3 must be added in front of H_2O.

$$2\,NH_3 + O_2 \longrightarrow N_2 + 3\,H_2O$$

There are now *two* O atoms on the left (in O_2) and *three* O atoms on the right (in $3\,H_2O$). Three O atoms can be shown on the left by placing the coefficient $\frac{3}{2}$ in front of O_2.

$$2\,NH_3 + \tfrac{3}{2}O_2 \longrightarrow N_2 + 3\,H_2O \quad \text{(balanced)}$$

Multiply all the coefficients by 2 to produce a balanced equation in which all the coefficients are integers.

$$4\,NH_3 + 3\,O_2 \longrightarrow 2\,N_2 + 6\,H_2O \quad \text{(balanced)}$$

CHECK: Note that the final equation above is balanced, with four N atoms, twelve H atoms, and six O atoms on each side.

Practice Example A: Balance the equations.

    (a) $H_3PO_4 + CaO \longrightarrow Ca_3(PO_4)_2 + H_2O$
    (b) $C_3H_8 + O_2 \longrightarrow CO_2 + H_2O$

Practice Example B: Balance the equations.

    (a) $NH_3 + O_2 \longrightarrow NO_2 + H_2O$
    (b) $NO_2 + NH_3 \longrightarrow N_2 + H_2O$

EXAMPLE 4-2

Writing and Balancing an Equation: The Combustion of a Carbon–Hydrogen–Oxygen Compound Liquid triethylene glycol is used as a solvent and plasticizer for vinyl and polyurethane plastics. Write a balanced chemical equation for its complete combustion.

Triethylene glycol

Solution

As seen in the molecular model, triethylene glycol is a carbon–hydrogen–oxygen compound, and like a hydrocarbon, it yields carbon dioxide and water when burned in an excess of oxygen gas. The formulas of the two products, CO_2 and H_2O, and one of the reactants, O_2, are easy to write; but the formula of triethylene glycol is not readily apparent from its name. We can, however, deduce its formula from the molecular model. We clearly see six C atoms (black) and four O atoms (red). The remaining 14 atoms are H atoms. The formula is $C_6H_{14}O_4$.

Starting expression:	$C_6H_{14}O_4 + O_2 \longrightarrow CO_2 + H_2O$
Balance C:	$C_6H_{14}O_4 + O_2 \longrightarrow 6\,CO_2 + H_2O$
Balance H:	$C_6H_{14}O_4 + O_2 \longrightarrow 6\,CO_2 + 7\,H_2O$

At this point, the right side of the expression has 19 O atoms (12 in six CO_2 molecules and 7 in seven H_2O molecules), and the left side, only 4 O atoms (in $C_6H_{14}O_4$). To obtain 15 more O atoms requires a fractional coefficient of $15/2$ for O_2.

Balance O: $\quad C_6H_{14}O_4 + \dfrac{15}{2}O_2 \longrightarrow 6\,CO_2 + 7\,H_2O \qquad$ (balanced)

To remove the fractional coefficient, multiply all coefficients by two, the denominator of the fractional coefficient, $15/2$.

$$2\,C_6H_{14}O_4 + 15\,O_2 \longrightarrow 12\,CO_2 + 14\,H_2O \qquad \text{(balanced)}$$

Check:

Left: $(2 \times 6) = 12\ C;\quad (2 \times 14) = 28\ H;\quad [(2 \times 4) + (15 \times 2)] = 38\ O$

Right: $(12 \times 1) = 12\ C;\quad (14 \times 2) = 28\ H;\quad [(12 \times 2) + (14 \times 1)] = 38\ O$

Practice Example A: Write a balanced equation to represent the reaction of mercury(II) sulfide and calcium oxide to produce calcium sulfide, calcium sulfate, and mercury metal.

Practice Example B: Write a balanced equation for the combustion of thiosalicylic acid, $C_7H_6O_2S$, used in the manufacture of indigo dyes.

Thiosalicylic acid

Counting Atoms activity

STATES OF MATTER

Ammonia (Example 4-1) is a gas, but triethylene glycol (Example 4-2) is a liquid. Facts such as these are inconsequential if our interest is only in balancing an equation. Still, we convey a more complete representation of the reaction by including this information, and sometimes it is essential to include such information in a chemical equation. The state of matter or physical form of reactants and products is shown by symbols in parentheses.

$$\text{(g) gas} \qquad \text{(l) liquid} \qquad \text{(s) solid}$$

Thus, the equation for combustion of triethylene glycol can be written as

$$2\,C_6H_{14}O_4(l) + 15\,O_2(g) \longrightarrow 12\,CO_2(g) + 14\,H_2O(l)$$

Another commonly used symbol for reactants or products dissolved in water is

$$\text{(aq) \emph{aqueous} solution}$$

REACTION CONDITIONS

The equation for a chemical reaction does not provide enough information to enable you to carry out the reaction in a laboratory or chemical plant. An important aspect of modern chemical research involves working out the conditions for a reaction. The reaction conditions are often written above or below the arrow in an equation. For example, the Greek capital letter delta, Δ, means that a high temperature is required—that is, the reaction mixture must be heated, as in the decomposition of silver oxide.

$$2\,Ag_2O(s) \xrightarrow{\ \Delta\ } 4\,Ag(s) + O_2(g)$$

◀ At the high combustion temperature, water is present as $H_2O(g)$. But when the reaction products are returned to the initial temperature, the water condenses to a liquid, $H_2O(l)$.

◀ In a *decomposition reaction*, a substance is broken down into simpler substances (for instance, into its elements).

▶ In a *synthesis reaction*, a new compound is formed from the reaction of two or more simpler substances, usually called the reactants or starting materials.

An even more explicit statement of reaction conditions is shown below for the BASF (Badische Anilin & Soda-Fabrik) process for the synthesis of methanol from CO and H_2. This reaction occurs at 350°C, under a total gas pressure that is 340 times greater than the normal pressure of the atmosphere, and on the surface of a mixture of ZnO and Cr_2O_3 acting as a *catalyst*. As we shall learn later in the text, a catalyst is a substance that enters into a reaction in such a way that it speeds up the reaction without itself being consumed or changed by the reaction.

$$CO(g) + 2\,H_2(g) \xrightarrow[\substack{340\ \text{atm} \\ \text{ZnO, Cr}_2\text{O}_3}]{350°C} CH_3OH(g)$$

It is important to be able to calculate how much of a particular product will be produced when certain quantities of the reactants are consumed. In the next section, we will see how to use chemical equations to set up conversion factors that we can use for these and related calculations.

✓ At this stage, consider introducing how to balance some equations that include ions. This might include precipitation reactions (such as $Fe^{3+} + 3\,OH^- \longrightarrow Fe(OH)_3$) and some simple metal displacements (such as $2\,Ag^+ + Cu \longrightarrow 2\,Ag + Cu^{2+}$). Omit discussion of the types of chemistry involved and of net ionic equations, but make the point that charge must balance.

CONCEPT ASSESSMENT ✓

For the elements K, Cl, and O in the following equations, the requirement that the number of atoms be equal on either side of the equation is met. Yet, why is none of them an acceptable balanced equation for the decomposition of solid potassium chlorate yielding solid potassium chloride and oxygen gas?

(a) $KClO_3(s) \longrightarrow KCl(s) + 3\,O(g)$

(b) $KClO_3(s) \longrightarrow KCl(s) + O_2(g) + O(g)$

(c) $KClO_3(s) \longrightarrow KClO(s) + O_2(g)$

✓ This section is part three of this text's three-part introduction to the mole concept. Emphasize that the importance of the chemical equation is in supplying conversion relationships relating the different reactants and products in a reaction. As done previously, we convert from grams to moles of reactant, using the molar mass. Then, using the chemical equation, we convert moles of reactant into moles of product. Finally, if needed, we convert moles of product into mass in grams.

4-2 CHEMICAL EQUATIONS AND STOICHIOMETRY

In Greek, the word *stoicheion* means element. The term **stoichiometry** (stoy-key-om'-eh-tree) means, literally, to measure the elements—but from a practical standpoint, it includes all the quantitative relationships involving atomic and formula masses, chemical formulas, and chemical equations. We considered the quantitative meaning of chemical formulas in Chapter 3, and now we will explore some additional quantitative aspects of chemical equations.

The coefficients in the chemical equation

$$2\,H_2(g) + O_2(g) \longrightarrow 2\,H_2O(l) \tag{4.1}$$

mean that

$$2x \text{ molecules } H_2 + x \text{ molecules } O_2 \longrightarrow 2x \text{ molecules } H_2O$$

Suppose we let $x = 6.02214 \times 10^{23}$ (Avogadro's number). Then x molecules represents *1 mole*. Thus the chemical equation also means that

$$2 \text{ mol } H_2 + 1 \text{ mol } O_2 \longrightarrow 2 \text{ mol } H_2O$$

The coefficients in the chemical equation allow us to make statements, such as

- *Two* moles of H_2O are *produced* for every *two* moles of H_2 *consumed*.
- *Two* moles of H_2O are *produced* for every *one* mole of O_2 *consumed*.
- *Two* moles of H_2 are *consumed* for every *one* mole of O_2 *consumed*.

 Formation of Water movie

Moreover, we can turn such statements into conversion factors, called stoichiometric factors. A **stoichiometric factor** relates the amounts, on a mole basis, of any two substances involved in a chemical reaction; thus a stoichiometric factor is a mole ratio. In the following examples, stoichiometric factors are printed in blue.

✓ Emphasize that chemical equations are applied at atomic and macroscopic levels. Although equations are usually balanced in terms of individual atoms and molecules, most of the actual use of the balanced equation is in terms of mole amounts of reactants and products.

EXAMPLE 4-3

Relating the Numbers of Moles of Reactant and Product. How many moles of CO_2 are produced in the combustion of 2.72 mol of triethylene glycol, $C_6H_{14}O_4$, in an excess of O_2?

Solution

"An excess of O_2" means that there is more than enough O_2 available to permit the complete conversion of the triethylene glycol to CO_2 and H_2O. To obtain the factor for converting from moles of $C_6H_{14}O_4$ to moles of CO_2, we need the balanced equation for the combustion reaction. The first step is to write this equation, as we did in Example 4-2.

$$2\,C_6H_{14}O_4 + 15\,O_2 \longrightarrow 12\,CO_2 + 14\,H_2O$$

Thus, 12 mol CO_2 are produced for every 2 mol $C_6H_{14}O_4$ burned. Think of this as 12 mol CO_2 = 2 mol $C_6H_{14}O_4$.

$$\text{? mol } CO_2 = 2.72 \text{ mol } C_6H_{14}O_4 \times \frac{12 \text{ mol } CO_2}{2 \text{ mol } C_6H_{14}O_4} = 16.3 \text{ mol } CO_2$$

Practice Example A: How many moles of O_2 are produced from the decomposition of 1.76 moles of potassium chlorate?

$$2\,KClO_3(s) \longrightarrow 2\,KCl(s) + 3\,O_2(g)$$

Practice Example B: How many moles of Ag are produced in the decomposition of 1.00 kg of silver(I) oxide?

$$2\,Ag_2O(s) \longrightarrow 4\,Ag(s) + O_2(g)$$

◀ **KEEP IN MIND**

that in using the equals sign we don't mean, literally, that 12 mol CO_2 and 2 mol $C_6H_{14}O_4$ are identical. We mean that in this reaction, the production of 12 mol CO_2 is *equivalent* to the consumption of 2 mol $C_6H_{14}O_4$. Sometimes this distinction is made by using the equivalent sign $\backsimeq$, that is, 12 mol $CO_2 \backsimeq$ 2 mol $C_6H_{14}O_4$.

Representation of a Chemical Equation activity

Reaction stoichiometry problems range from relatively simple to complex, yet all can be solved by the same general strategy. This strategy, outlined in Figure 4-3, yields information about one substance, B, from information given about a second substance, A. Thus, the conversion pathway is from the *known* A to the *unknown* B. The heart of the calculation, shown in blue in Figure 4-3, is conversion from the number of moles of A to the number of moles of B using a factor based on stoichiometric coefficients from the balanced chemical equation—that is, stoi. coeff. B/stoi. coeff. A. Example 4-3 was a single-step calculation requiring only the stoichiometric factor. Examples 4-4 through 4-7 require additional steps, both before and after the stoichiometric factor is employed.

Stoichiometric Conversions activity

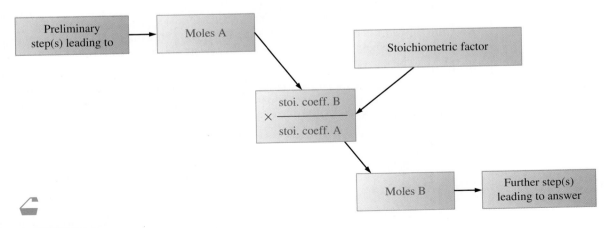

▲ **FIGURE 4-3**
A generalized stoichiometry diagram
A key step in working stoichiometric problems is applying the appropriate stoichiometric factor (mole ratio) that converts from moles A to moles B. The stoichiometric factor is the stoichiometric coefficient of B divided by the stoichiometric coefficient of A.

Grams of $C_6H_{14}O_4$
GIVEN.

Use inverse of molar mass as conversion factor:
1 mol $C_6H_{14}O_4$/150.2 g $C_6H_{14}O_4$

Moles of $C_6H_{14}O_4$

Use coefficients in balanced chemical equation to find mole ratio:
12 mol CO_2/2 mol $C_6H_{14}O_4$

Moles of $C_6H_{14}O_4$

Use molar mass as conversion factor:
44.01 g CO_2/1 mol CO_2

Grams of CO_2
FOUND

▲ FIGURE 4-4
Strategy for a stoichiometric calculation for the reaction

$$2\,C_6H_{14}O_4(l) + 15\,O_2(g) \longrightarrow 12\,CO_2(g) + 14\,H_2O(l)$$

Reduction of CuO movie

EXAMPLE 4-4

Relating the Mass of a Reactant and a Product. What mass of CO_2 is formed in the reaction of 4.16 g triethylene glycol, $C_6H_{14}O_4$, with an excess of O_2?

Solution

This problem concerns the same reaction as Example 4-3, but differs from it in requiring one step before and one step following the stoichiometric factor. The three steps are:

1. Convert the quantity of $C_6H_{14}O_4$ from grams to moles. This conversion requires using the molar mass of $C_6H_{14}O_4$.

$$M_{C_6H_{14}O_4} = (6 \times 12.01) + (14 \times 1.008) + (4 \times 16.00) = 150.17 \text{ g/mol}$$

2. From the number of moles of $C_6H_{14}O_4$, calculate the number of moles of CO_2. For this, use the same stoichiometric factor as in Example 4-3.

3. Convert the quantity of CO_2 from moles to grams, using the molar mass of CO_2.

The general strategy introduced in Figure 4-3 takes the form of Figure 4-4 for this specific problem.

Another simple method of outlining this strategy is through a conversion pathway written on a single line, where the individual steps are joined by arrows and noted by the small numbers above the arrows. Thus three steps can be combined into a single setup. The conversion pathway and setup are

$$(\text{g } C_6H_{14}O_4 \xrightarrow{1} \text{mol } C_6H_{14}O_4 \xrightarrow{2} \text{mol } CO_2 \xrightarrow{3} \text{g } CO_2)$$

$$? \text{ g } CO_2 = 4.16 \text{ g } C_6H_{14}O_4 \times \frac{1 \text{ mol } C_6H_{14}O_4}{150.2 \text{ g } C_6H_{14}O_4} \times \frac{12 \text{ mol } CO_2}{2 \text{ mol } C_6H_{14}O_4} \times \frac{44.01 \text{ g } CO_2}{1 \text{ mol } CO_2}$$

$$= 7.31 \text{ g } CO_2$$

CHECK: A quick scan of the numbers to the right of 4.16 g $C_6H_{14}O_4$ indicates that the stoichiometric factor has a value of 6; 6×44.01 is between 250 and 300 which, when divided by 150.2, yields a factor somewhat smaller than 2. The mass of CO_2 should be somewhat less than twice that of the $C_6H_{14}O_4$, and it is (compare 7.31 to 2×4.16). Also, note that all units cancel properly in the ultimate conversion from g $C_6H_{14}O_4$ to g CO_2.

Practice Example A: How many grams of magnesium nitride are produced by the reaction of 3.82 g Mg with an excess of N_2?

Practice Example B: How many grams of $H_2(g)$ are required to produce 1.00 kg methanol, CH_3OH, by the reaction $CO + 2\,H_2 \longrightarrow CH_3OH$?

EXAMPLE 4-5

Relating the Masses of Two Reactants to Each Other. What mass of O_2 is consumed in the complete combustion of 6.86 g of triethylene glycol, $C_6H_{14}O_4$?

Solution

As in Example 4-4, the molar masses and the appropriate stoichiometric factor from the balanced equation for the combustion of triethylene glycol are used as conversion factors in a three-step setup.

$$(\text{g } C_6H_{14}O_4 \longrightarrow \text{mol } C_6H_{14}O_4 \longrightarrow \text{mol } O_2 \longrightarrow \text{g } O_2)$$

$$? \text{ g } O_2 = 6.86 \text{ g } C_6H_{14}O_4 \times \frac{1 \text{ mol } C_6H_{14}O_4}{150.2 \text{ g } C_6H_{14}O_4} \times \frac{15 \text{ mol } O_2}{2 \text{ mol } C_6H_{14}O_6} \times \frac{32.00 \text{ g } O_2}{1 \text{ mol } O_2}$$

$$= 11.0 \text{ g } O_2$$

CHECK: A quick scan of the numbers to the right of 6.86 g $C_6H_{14}O_4$ indicates that the stoichiometric factor has a value of 7.5; the product, 7.5×32.00, is about 250 which, when divided by 150.2, yields a factor of about $250/150 = 5/3$. The mass of O_2 should be about $5/3$ that of the $C_6H_{14}O_4$, and it is—that is, compare 11.0 to $5/3$ of 6.86, which is about $35/3$ or somewhat less than 12. As in Example 4-4, note that the proper cancellation of units occurs.

Practice Example A: For the reaction in Example 4-1, how many grams of NH_3 are consumed per gram of O_2?

Practice Example B: In the combustion of octane, C_8H_{18}, how many grams of O_2 are consumed per gram of octane?

CONCEPT ASSESSMENT ✓

Which statements are correct for the reaction $2\,H_2S + SO_2 \longrightarrow 3\,S + 2\,H_2O$. Explain your reasoning.

(a) 3 mol S is produced per mole of H_2S.

(b) 3 g S is produced for every gram of SO_2 consumed.

(c) 1 mol H_2O is produced per mole of H_2S consumed.

(d) Two-thirds of the S produced comes from H_2S.

(e) The number of moles of products formed equals the number of moles of reactants consumed.

(f) The number of moles of atoms present after the reaction is the same as the number of moles of atoms before the reaction.

What lends great variety to stoichiometric calculations is that many other conversions may be required before and after the mol A $\longrightarrow$ mol B step at the center of the stoichiometric scheme shown in Figure 4-3. In Examples 4-4 and 4-5, the additional conversions involved molar mass. Other common conversions may require such factors as volume, density, and percent composition. In every case, however, we must always use the appropriate stoichiometric factor from the chemical equation as a key conversion factor.

The reaction pictured in Figure 4-5, a simple laboratory method for preparing small volumes of hydrogen gas, provides a range of possibilities for calculations.

Examples 4-6 and 4-7 are based on this reaction.

$$2\,Al(s) + 6\,HCl(aq) \longrightarrow 2\,AlCl_3(aq) + 3\,H_2(g) \qquad (4.2)$$

▲ **FIGURE 4-5**
The reaction $2\,Al(s) + 6\,HCl(aq) \longrightarrow 2\,AlCl_3(aq) + 3\,H_2(g)$
HCl(aq) is introduced to the flask on the left. The reaction occurs within the flask. The liberated $H_2(g)$ is conducted to a gas-collection apparatus, where it displaces water. Hydrogen is only very slightly soluble in water.

🜂 Reaction of an Al–Cu Alloy with HCl. The reaction shown in Figure 4-5 can be performed as a demonstration. Use a sidearm filter flask to avoid having to insert bent tubing into a stopper. Use pieces of Al and Cu in place of an actual alloy. Start with 1 M HCl and, if the reaction is too slow, add small amounts of 6 M HCl. Quantitative measurement of the H_2 produced need not be actually undertaken.

✓ Including use of additional conversion factors, as in Examples 4-6 and 4-7, provides valuable reinforcement of previous material.

EXAMPLE 4-6

Additional Conversion Factors in a Stoichiometric Calculation: Volume, Density, and Percent Composition. An alloy used in aircraft structures consists of 93.7% Al and 6.3% Cu by mass. The alloy has a density of 2.85 g/cm^3. A 0.691-cm^3 piece of the alloy reacts with an excess of HCl(aq). If we assume that *all* the Al but *none* of the Cu reacts with HCl(aq), what is the mass of H_2 obtained?

Solution

A simple approach to this calculation is outlined below. Each numbered arrow refers to a conversion factor that changes the unit on the left to the one on the right.

$$cm^3 \text{ alloy} \xrightarrow{1} \text{g alloy} \xrightarrow{2} \text{g Al} \xrightarrow{3} \text{mol Al} \xrightarrow{4} \text{mol } H_2 \xrightarrow{5} \text{g } H_2$$

The calculation can be done in five distinct steps, or with a single setup in which the five conversions are performed in sequence. This approach, shown below, avoids the need to write down intermediate results and reduces rounding errors.

$$(cm^3 \text{ alloy} \xrightarrow{1} \text{g alloy} \xrightarrow{2} \text{g Al} \xrightarrow{3} \text{mol Al}$$

$$? \text{ g } H_2 = 0.691 \text{ cm}^3 \text{ alloy} \times \frac{2.85 \text{ g alloy}}{1 \text{ cm}^3 \text{ alloy}} \times \frac{93.7 \text{ g Al}}{100.0 \text{ g alloy}} \times \frac{1 \text{ mol Al}}{26.98 \text{ g Al}}$$

$$\xrightarrow{4} \text{mol } H_2 \xrightarrow{5} \text{g } H_2)$$

$$\times \frac{3 \text{ mol } H_2}{2 \text{ mol Al}} \times \frac{2.016 \text{ g } H_2}{1 \text{ mol } H_2}$$

$$= 0.207 \text{ g } H_2$$

Practice Example A: What volume of the aluminum–copper alloy described in Example 4-6 must be dissolved in an excess of HCl(aq) to produce 1.00 g H_2?

[*Hint:* Think of this as the "inverse" of Example 4-6.]

Practice Example B: A fresh sample of the aluminum–copper alloy described in Example 4-6 yielded 1.31 g H_2. How many grams of copper were present in the sample?

EXAMPLE 4-7

Additional Conversion Factors in a Stoichiometric Calculation: Volume, Density, and Percent Composition of a Solution. A hydrochloric acid solution consists of 28.0% HCl by mass and has a density of 1.14 g/mL. What volume of this solution is required to react completely with 1.87 g Al in reaction (4.2)?

Solution

The first challenge here is to determine where to begin. Although the problem refers to 28.0% HCl and a density of 1.14 g/mL, the appropriate starting point is with the given information—1.87 g Al. The goal of our calculation is a solution volume—mL HCl solution.

$$\text{g Al} \xrightarrow{1} \text{mol Al} \xrightarrow{2} \text{mol HCl} \xrightarrow{3}$$

$$\text{g HCl} \xrightarrow{4} \text{g HCl solution} \xrightarrow{5} \text{mL HCl solution}$$

The conversion factors in the calculation involve (1) the molar mass of Al, (2) stoichiometric coefficients from equation (4.2), (3) the molar mass of HCl, (4) the percent composition of the HCl solution, and (5) the density of the HCl solution. The strategy is outlined below.

$$(\text{g Al} \xrightarrow{\;1\;} \text{mol Al} \xrightarrow{\;2\;} \text{mol HCl} \xrightarrow{\;3\;} \text{g HCl}$$

$$? \text{ mL HCl soln} = 1.87 \text{ g Al} \times \frac{1 \text{ mol Al}}{26.98 \text{ g Al}} \times \frac{6 \text{ mol HCl}}{2 \text{ mol Al}} \times \frac{36.46 \text{ g HCl}}{1 \text{ mol HCl}}$$

$$\xrightarrow{\;4\;} \text{g HCl soln} \xrightarrow{\;5\;} \text{mL HCl soln})$$

$$\times \frac{100.0 \text{ g HCl soln}}{28.0 \text{ g HCl}} \times \frac{1 \text{ mL HCl soln}}{1.14 \text{ g HCl soln}}$$

$$= 23.8 \text{ mL HCl soln}$$

Practice Example A: How many milligrams of H_2 are produced when one drop (0.05 mL) of the hydrochloric acid solution described in Example 4-7 reacts with an excess of aluminum in reaction (4.2)?

Practice Example B: A particular vinegar contains 4.0% $HC_2H_3O_2$, by mass. It reacts with sodium carbonate to produce sodium acetate, carbon dioxide, and water. How many grams of carbon dioxide are produced by the reaction of 5.00 mL of this vinegar with an excess of sodium carbonate? The density of the vinegar is 1.01 g/mL.

CONCEPT ASSESSMENT ✓

Without performing detailed calculations, determine which reaction produces the maximum quantity of $O_2(g)$ per gram of reactant.

(a) $2 NH_4NO_3(s) \xrightarrow{\;\Delta\;} 2 N_2(g) + 4 H_2O(l) + O_2(g)$

(b) $2 Ag_2O(s) \xrightarrow{\;\Delta\;} 4 Ag(s) + O_2(g)$

(c) $2 HgO(s) \xrightarrow{\;\Delta\;} 2 Hg(l) + O_2(g)$

(d) $2 Pb(NO_3)_2(s) \xrightarrow{\;\Delta\;} 2 PbO(s) + 4 NO_2(g) + O_2(g)$

4-3   CHEMICAL REACTIONS IN SOLUTION

Most reactions in the general chemistry laboratory are carried out in solutions. This is partly because mixing the reactants in solution helps to achieve the close contact between atoms, ions, or molecules necessary for a reaction to occur. The stoichiometry of reactions in solutions can be described in the same way as the stoichiometry of other reactions, as we saw in Example 4-7. A few new ideas that apply specifically to solution stoichiometry are also helpful.

One component of a solution, called the **solvent**, determines whether the solution exists as a solid, liquid, or gas. In this discussion we will limit ourselves to *aqueous solutions*—solutions in which liquid water is the solvent. The other components of a solution, called **solutes**, are dissolved in the solvent. NaCl(aq), for example, describes a solution in which liquid water is the solvent and NaCl is the solute. The term *aqueous* does not convey any information, however, about the relative proportions of NaCl and H_2O in the solution. For this purpose, the property called *molarity* is commonly used.

Dissolution of NaCl in Water animation

MOLARITY

Concentration, or **molarity**, is a solution property defined as the number of moles solute per liter of solution, or

$$\text{molarity } (M) = \frac{\text{amount of solute (in moles)}}{\text{volume of solution (in liters)}} \qquad (4.3)$$

If 0.440 mol urea, $CO(NH_2)_2$, is dissolved in enough water to make 1.000 L of solution, the solution concentration, or molarity, is

$$\frac{0.440 \text{ mol } CO(NH_2)_2}{1 \text{ L soln}} = 0.440 \text{ M } CO(NH_2)_2$$

Alternatively, if 0.110 mol urea is present in 250.0 mL of solution, the solution is also 0.440 M.

$$\frac{0.110 \text{ mol } CO(NH_2)_2}{0.2500 \text{ L soln}} = 0.440 \text{ M } CO(NH_2)_2$$

The symbol M stands for the term *molar*, or mol/L. Thus, a solution that has 0.440 mol $CO(NH_2)_2$/L is 0.440 M $CO(NH_2)_2$ or 0.440 molar $CO(NH_2)_2$.

When defining concentration, an amount in moles must be related to other quantities that can be readily measured. Also, we need not always work with exactly one liter of solution. Sometimes a much smaller volume is sufficient, and sometimes larger volumes are needed. In Example 4-8, the mass of a liquid solute is related to its volume by using density as a conversion factor. Then, molar mass is used to convert from the mass of solute to an amount of solute in moles. Also, the solution volume is converted from milliliters (mL) to liters (L).

Acetone

EXAMPLE 4-8

Calculating Molarity from Measured Quantities. A solution is prepared by dissolving 25.0 mL ethanol, C_2H_5OH ($d = 0.789$ g/mL), in enough water to produce 250.0 mL solution. What is the molarity of ethanol in the solution?

Solution

To determine the molarity, we must first calculate how many moles of ethanol are in the solution. To calculate the number of moles of ethanol in a 25.0-mL sample, we need conversion factors based on density and molar mass.

$$? \text{ mol } C_2H_5OH = 25.0 \text{ mL } C_2H_5OH \times \frac{0.789 \text{ g } C_2H_5OH}{1 \text{ mL } C_2H_5OH} \times \frac{1 \text{ mol } C_2H_5OH}{46.07 \text{ g } C_2H_5OH}$$
$$= 0.428 \text{ mol } C_2H_5OH$$

To apply the definition of molarity given in expression (4.3), note that 250.0 mL = 0.2500 L.

$$\text{Molarity} = \frac{0.428 \text{ mol } C_2H_5OH}{0.2500 \text{ L soln}} = 1.71 \text{ M } C_2H_5OH$$

Practice Example A: A 22.3-g sample of acetone (see margin) is dissolved in enough water to produce 1.25 L of solution. What is the molarity of acetone in this solution?

Practice Example B: 15.0 mL of acetic acid, CH_3COOH ($d = 1.048$ g/mL), is dissolved in enough water to produce 500.0 mL of solution. What is the molarity of acetic acid in the solution?

Figure 4-6 illustrates a method commonly used to prepare a solution. A solid sample is weighed out and dissolved in sufficient water to produce a solution of known volume—250.0 mL. To fill a beaker to a 250-mL mark is not nearly precise enough as a volume measurement. As discussed in Section 1-6, there would

(a)

(b)

(c)

◀ **FIGURE 4-6**
Preparation of 0.250 M K₂CrO₄—Example 4-9 illustrated

The solution cannot be prepared just by adding 12.1 g K_2CrO_4(s) to 250.0 mL water. Instead, **(a)** the weighed quantity of K_2CrO_4(s) is first added to a clean, dry volumetric flask; **(b)** the K_2CrO_4(s) is dissolved in less than 250 mL of water; and **(c)** the flask is filled to the 250.0-mL calibration mark by the careful addition (dropwise) of the remaining water.

be a systematic error because the beaker is not calibrated with sufficient precision. (The error in volume could be 10 to 20 mL or more.) To dissolve the solute in water and bring the solution level to the 250-mL mark in a graduated cylinder is also not sufficiently precise. Although the graduated cylinder is calibrated more precisely than the beaker, the error might still be 1 to 2 mL or more. On the other hand, when filled to the calibration mark, the volumetric flask pictured in Figure 4-6 contains 250.0 mL with only about 0.1 mL of error.

In Example 4-9, we calculate the mass of solute needed to produce the solution in Figure 4-6. The key to this calculation is to formulate a conversion factor based on molarity. Thus, when we write 0.250 M K_2CrO_4, we are in effect saying that 1 L of the solution is equivalent to 0.250 mol K_2CrO_4. The conversion pathway required in Example 4-9 is L soln ⟶ mol solute ⟶ g solute.

EXAMPLE 4-9

Calculating the Mass of Solute in a Solution of Known Molarity. What mass of K_2CrO_4 is needed to prepare exactly 0.2500 L (250.0 mL) of a 0.250 M K_2CrO_4 solution in water? (See Figure 4-6.)

Solution

As just stated, we can use solution molarity (printed in blue) to convert between volume of solution and amount of solute. The other conversion factor we need is the molar mass of K_2CrO_4.

$$(\text{L soln} \longrightarrow \text{mol } K_2CrO_4 \longrightarrow \text{g } K_2CrO_4)$$

$$? \text{ g } K_2CrO_4 = 0.2500 \text{ L soln} \times \frac{0.250 \text{ mol } K_2CrO_4}{1 \text{ L soln}} \times \frac{194.2 \text{ g } K_2CrO_4}{1 \text{ mol } K_2CrO_4}$$

$$= 12.1 \text{ g } K_2CrO_4$$

Practice Example A: An aqueous solution saturated with $NaNO_3$ at 25 °C is 10.8 M $NaNO_3$. How many grams of $NaNO_3$ are present in 125 mL of this solution at 25 °C?

Practice Example B: How many grams of $Na_2SO_4 \cdot 10 \, H_2O$ are needed to prepare 355 mL of 0.445 M Na_2SO_4?

SOLUTION DILUTION

▶ A *concentrated solution* has a relatively large amount of dissolved solute; a *dilute solution* has a relatively small amount.

A common sight in chemistry storerooms and laboratories is rows of bottles containing solutions for use in chemical reactions. It is not practical, however, to store solutions of every possible concentration. Instead, most labs store fairly concentrated solutions, so-called *stock solutions*, which can then be used to prepare more dilute solutions by adding water. The principle of dilution, which you have probably already inferred, is that the same solute that was present in a sample of stock solution is distributed throughout the larger volume of a diluted solution (see Figure 4-7).

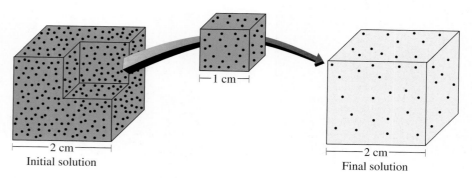

───2 cm───
Initial solution

├─1 cm─┤

───2 cm───
Final solution

▲ **FIGURE 4-7**
Visualizing the dilution of a solution
The final solution is prepared by extracting $\frac{1}{8}$ of the initial solution—1 cm³—and diluting it with water to a volume of 8 cm³. The number of dots in the 8 cm³ of final solution, representing the number of solute particles, is the same as in the 1 cm³ of initial solution.

 Solution Formation by Dilution. Again, the preparation depicted in Figure 4-8 and in the CD Demonstration referenced below can be performed in class. Use an empty washing bottle as a suction device to draw solutions into a pipet.

This statement and the definition of molarity are all that you need to work out dilution problems. You may, however, prefer a method based on expression (4.3). If solution concentration (molarity) is M, solution volume, in liters, is V, and the amount of solute, in moles, is n, then expression (4.3) becomes $M = n/V$, or

$$n = M \times V$$

When a solution is diluted, the amount of solute *remains constant* between the initial (i) solution taken and the final (f) solution produced. That is,

$$M_i V_i = n_i = n_f = M_f V_f$$

or

Solution Formation by Dilution animation

▶ An alternative expression uses subscripts "conc" and "dil" in place of "i" and "f."

$$M_i \times V_i = M_f \times V_f \qquad (4.4)$$

Figure 4-8 illustrates the laboratory procedure for preparing a solution by dilution. Example 4-10 explains the necessary calculation.

EXAMPLE 4-10

Preparing a Solution by Dilution. A particular analytical chemistry procedure requires 0.0100 M K_2CrO_4. What volume of 0.250 M K_2CrO_4 must be diluted with water to prepare 0.250 L of 0.0100 M K_2CrO_4?

Solution

To solve this problem, imagine reversing the arrow in Figure 4-7. Start with the final solution because we know the most about it, and then determine something about the initial solution.

(a)

(b)

(c)

▲ **FIGURE 4-8**
Preparing a solution by dilution—Example 4-10 illustrated
(a) A pipet is used to withdraw a 10.0-mL sample of 0.250 M K_2CrO_4(aq). **(b)** The pipetful of 0.250 M K_2CrO_4 is discharged into a 250.0-mL volumetric flask. **(c)** Water is then added to bring the level of the solution to the calibration mark on the neck of the flask. At this point, the solution is 0.0100 M K_2CrO_4.

First, calculate the amount of solute that must be present in the final solution.

$$? \text{ mol } K_2CrO_4 = 0.250 \text{ L soln} \times \frac{0.0100 \text{ mol } K_2CrO_4}{1 \text{ L soln}} = 0.00250 \text{ mol } K_2CrO_4$$

Second, calculate the volume of 0.250 M K_2CrO_4 that contains 0.00250 mol K_2CrO_4.

$$? \text{ L soln} = 0.00250 \text{ mol } K_2CrO_4 \times \frac{1 \text{ L soln}}{0.250 \text{ mol } K_2CrO_4} = 0.0100 \text{ L soln}$$

An alternative approach is to use equation (4.4). The known factors include the volume of solution to be prepared, ($V_f = 250.0$ mL), and the concentrations of the final (0.0100 M) and initial (0.250 M) solutions. We must solve for the initial volume, V_i. Note that although in deriving equation (4.4) volumes were expressed in liters, in applying the equation any volume unit can be used as long as we use the same unit for both V_i and V_f (milliliters in the present case). The term needed to convert volumes to liters would appear on both sides of the equation and cancel out.

$$V_i = V_f \times \frac{M_f}{M_i} = 250.0 \text{ mL} \times \frac{0.0100 \text{ M}}{0.250 \text{ M}} = 10.0 \text{ mL}$$

Practice Example A: A 15.00-mL sample of 0.450 M K_2CrO_4 is diluted to 100.00 mL. What is the concentration of the new solution?

Practice Example B: When left in an open beaker for a period of time, the volume of 275 mL of 0.105 M NaCl is found to decrease to 237 mL due to the evaporation of water. What is the new concentration of the solution?

Emphasize that when preparing and diluting solutions, the *actual final volume* must be used in calculating the concentration. Total volume can change when combining different materials (see demonstration below), or when diluting concentrated solutions. Usually the final volume is set experimentally, using a volumetric flask. Sometimes it can be calculated from the masses of the components and handbook tables of density vs. mass percent.

Change in Volume on Mixing. Fill a 250.0-mL volumetric flask with water to which a small amount of blue food coloring has been added. Fill another with ethanol with some yellow coloring. Pour the contents of these flasks simultaneously through a funnel into a 500.0-mL volumetric flask. Emphasize the 500.0-mL mark with a felt pen. Note the loss of about 20 mL, or 4% of the original total volume. See Shakhashiri, B. Z., *Chemical Demonstrations 3*, University of Wisconsin Press (1989), p. 225.

CONCEPT ASSESSMENT ✓

Remind students that they must start with a correctly balanced chemical equation before performing any stoichiometric calculation involving a chemical reaction.

Without doing detailed calculations, and assuming that the volumes of solutions and water are additive, indicate the molarity of the final solution obtained as a result of

(a) adding 200.0 mL of water to 100.0 mL of 0.150 M NaCl;

(b) evaporating 50.0 mL water from 250.0 mL of 0.800 M $C_{12}H_{22}O_{11}$;

(c) mixing 150.0 mL 0.270 M KCl and 300.0 mL 0.135 M KCl.

STOICHIOMETRY OF REACTIONS IN SOLUTION

The central conversion factor in Example 4-11 is the same as in previous stoichiometry problems—the appropriate stoichiometric factor. What differs from previous examples is that we use molarity as a conversion factor from solution volume to number of moles of reactant in a preliminary step preceding the stoichiometric factor.

EXAMPLE 4-11

Relating the Mass of a Product to the Volume and Molarity of a Reactant Solution. A 25.00-mL pipetful of 0.250 M K_2CrO_4(aq) is added to an excess of $AgNO_3$(aq). What mass of Ag_2CrO_4(s) will precipitate from the solution?

$$K_2CrO_4(aq) + 2\,AgNO_3(aq) \longrightarrow Ag_2CrO_4(s) + 2\,KNO_3(aq)$$

Solution

The fact that an excess of $AgNO_3$(aq) is used tells us that all of the K_2CrO_4 in the 25.00-mL of K_2CrO_4(aq) is consumed. The calculation begins with a volume of 25.00 mL and ends with a mass of Ag_2CrO_4(s) expressed in grams.

Convert the volume of K_2CrO_4(aq) from milliliters to liters, then use molarity as a conversion factor between volume of solution and moles of solute (as in Example 4-10).

$$? \text{ mol } K_2CrO_4 = 25.00 \text{ mL} \times \frac{1 \text{ L}}{1000 \text{ mL}} \times \frac{0.250 \text{ mol } K_2CrO_4}{1 \text{ L}}$$
$$= 6.25 \times 10^{-3} \text{ mol } K_2CrO_4$$

Use a stoichiometric factor from the equation to convert from moles of K_2CrO_4 to moles of Ag_2CrO_4.

$$? \text{ mol } Ag_2CrO_4 = 6.25 \times 10^{-3} \text{ mol } K_2CrO_4 \times \frac{1 \text{ mol } Ag_2CrO_4}{1 \text{ mol } K_2CrO_4}$$
$$= 6.25 \times 10^{-3} \text{ mol } Ag_2CrO_4$$

Use the molar mass to convert from moles to grams of Ag_2CrO_4.

$$? \text{ g } Ag_2CrO_4 = 6.25 \times 10^{-3} \text{ mol } Ag_2CrO_4 \times \frac{331.7 \text{ g } Ag_2CrO_4}{1 \text{ mol } Ag_2CrO_4}$$
$$= 2.07 \text{ g } Ag_2CrO_4$$

The same final answer can be obtained more directly by combining the three steps into a single setup.

$$? \text{ g } Ag_2CrO_4 = 25.00 \text{ mL} \times \frac{1 \text{ L}}{1000 \text{ mL}} \times \frac{0.250 \text{ mol } K_2CrO_4}{1 \text{ L}}$$
$$\times \frac{1 \text{ mol } Ag_2CrO_4}{1 \text{ mol } K_2CrO_4} \times \frac{331.7 \text{ g } Ag_2CrO_4}{1 \text{ mol } Ag_2CrO_4}$$
$$= 2.07 \text{ g } Ag_2CrO_4$$

Practice Example A: How many milliliters of 0.250 M K_2CrO_4 must be added to excess $AgNO_3$(aq) to produce 1.50 g Ag_2CrO_4?

[*Hint:* Think of this as the inverse of Example 4-11.]

Practice Example B: How many milliliters of 0.150 M $AgNO_3$(aq) are required to react completely with 175 mL of 0.0855 M K_2CrO_4(aq)? What mass of Ag_2CrO_4(s) is formed?

We will consider a number of additional examples of stoichiometric calculations involving solutions in Chapter 5.

4-4   DETERMINING THE LIMITING REACTANT

When all the reactants are completely and simultaneously consumed in a chemical reaction, the reactants are said to be in **stoichiometric proportions**; that is, they are present in the mole ratios dictated by the coefficients in the balanced equation. This condition is sometimes required, for example, in certain chemical analyses. At other times, as in a precipitation reaction, one of the reactants is completely converted into products by using an excess of all the other reactants. The reactant that is completely consumed—the **limiting reactant**—determines the quantities of products formed. In the reaction described in Example 4-11, K_2CrO_4 is the limiting reactant and $AgNO_3$ is present in excess. Up to this point, we have stated which reactant(s) is present in excess and, by implication, which is the limiting reactant. In some cases, however, the limiting reactant will not be indicated explicitly. If the quantities of two or more reactants are given, you must determine which is the limiting reactant, as suggested by the analogy in Figure 4-9.

◄ By an excess of a reactant we mean that more of the reactant is present than is consumed in the reaction. Some is left over.

◄ Chemicals are often referred to as *reagents*, and the limiting reactant in a reaction is sometimes called the *limiting reagent*.

Title page — 87 copies

Instructions — 83 copies

Data sheets — 168 copies

Graph paper — 328 copies

An assembled handout experiment

4 sheets of graph paper
2 data sheets
1 sheet of instructions
1 title page

▲ **FIGURE 4-9**
An analogy to determining the limiting reactant in a chemical reaction—assembling a handout experiment
From the numbers of copies available and the instructions on how to assemble the handout, can you see that only 82 complete handouts are possible and that the graph paper is the limiting reactant?

This article describes the use of cut-out molecular models on an overhead projector to illustrate limiting reactants in chemical reactions: Kashmar, Richard J. *J. Chem. Educ.* **1997:** *74, 791.*

EXAMPLE 4-12

Determining the Limiting Reactant in a Reaction. Phosphorus trichloride, PCl_3, is a commercially important compound used in the manufacture of pesticides, gasoline additives, and a number of other products. It is made by the direct combination of phosphorus and chlorine.

$$P_4(s) + 6\,Cl_2(g) \longrightarrow 4\,PCl_3(l)$$

What mass of $PCl_3(l)$ forms in the reaction of 125 g P_4 with 323 g Cl_2?

Solution

One approach to this problem, outlined in Figure 4-10, is to compare the initial mole ratio of the two reactants to the ratio in which the reactants combine—6 mol Cl_2 to 1 mol P_4. If more than 6 mol Cl_2 is available per mole of P_4, chlorine is in excess and P_4 is the limiting reactant. If less than 6 mol Cl_2 is available per mole of P_4, chlorine is the limiting reactant.

$$? \text{ mol } Cl_2 = 323 \text{ g } Cl_2 \times \frac{1 \text{ mol } Cl_2}{70.91 \text{ g } Cl_2} = 4.56 \text{ mol } Cl_2$$

$$? \text{ mol } P_4 = 125 \text{ g } P_4 \times \frac{1 \text{ mol } P_4}{123.9 \text{ g } P_4} = 1.01 \text{ mol } P_4$$

◄ **KEEP IN MIND**
that the first step in a stoichiometric calculation is to write a balanced equation for the reaction. If the equation is not given, you must supply your own.

Phosphorus trichloride

Since there are fewer than 6 mol Cl_2 per mole of P_4, chlorine is the limiting reactant. The remainder of the calculation is to determine the mass of PCl_3 formed in the reaction of 323 g Cl_2 with an excess of P_4.

$$? \text{ g } PCl_3 = 323 \text{ g } Cl_2 \times \frac{1 \text{ mol } Cl_2}{70.91 \text{ g } Cl_2} \times \frac{4 \text{ mol } PCl_3}{6 \text{ mol } Cl_2} \times \frac{137.3 \text{ g } PCl_3}{1 \text{ mol } PCl_3} = 417 \text{ g } PCl_3$$

A different approach that leads to the same result is to do two separate calculations: Calculate the mass of PCl_3 produced by the reaction of 323 g Cl_2 with an excess of P_4 (= 417 g PCl_3), and then calculate the mass of PCl_3 produced by the reaction of 125 g P_4 with an excess of Cl_2 (= 554 g PCl_3). Only one answer can be correct, and it must be the *smaller* of the two.

Practice Example A: If 215 g P_4 is allowed to react with 725 g Cl_2 in the reaction in Example 4-12, how many grams of PCl_3 are formed?

Practice Example B: If 1.00 kg each of PCl_3, Cl_2, and P_4O_{10} are allowed to react, how many kilograms of $POCl_3$ will be formed?

$$6 \text{ } PCl_3(l) + 6 \text{ } Cl_2(g) + P_4O_{10}(s) \longrightarrow 10 \text{ } POCl_3(l)$$

▲ **FIGURE 4-10**
Determining the limiting reactant for the reaction

$$P_4(s) + 6 \text{ } Cl_2(g) \longrightarrow 4 \text{ } PCl_3(l)$$

Sometimes our interest in a limiting reactant problem is in determining how much of an excess reactant remains, as well as how much product is formed. This additional calculation is illustrated in Example 4-13.

EXAMPLE 4-13

Determining the Quantity of Excess Reactant(s) Remaining After a Reaction. What mass of P_4 remains following the reaction in Example 4-12?

Solution

The key to this problem is to calculate the mass of P_4 that is consumed, and we can base this calculation either on the mass of Cl_2 consumed

$$? \text{ g } P_4 = 323 \text{ g } Cl_2 \times \frac{1 \text{ mol } Cl_2}{70.91 \text{ g } Cl_2} \times \frac{1 \text{ mol } P_4}{6 \text{ mol } Cl_2} \times \frac{123.9 \text{ g } P_4}{1 \text{ mol } P_4} = 94.1 \text{ g } P_4$$

or on the mass of PCl_3 produced

$$? \text{ g } P_4 = 417 \text{ g } PCl_3 \times \frac{1 \text{ mol } PCl_3}{137.3 \text{ g } PCl_3} \times \frac{1 \text{ mol } P_4}{4 \text{ mol } PCl_3} \times \frac{123.9 \text{ g } P_4}{1 \text{ mol } P_4} = 94.1 \text{ g } P_4$$

The mass of P_4 remaining after the reaction is simply the difference between what was originally present and what was consumed; that is,

$$125 \text{ g } P_4 \text{ initially} - 94.1 \text{ g } P_4 \text{ consumed} = 31 \text{ g } P_4 \text{ remaining}$$

Practice Example A: In Practice Example 4-12A, which reactant is in excess and what mass of that reactant remains after the reaction to produce PCl_3?

Practice Example B: If 12.2 g H_2 and 154 g O_2 are allowed to react, which gas and what mass of that gas remains after the reaction?

$$2 \text{ H}_2(g) + O_2(g) \longrightarrow 2 \text{ H}_2O(l)$$

◀ **KEEP IN MIND**
that in subtraction, the quantity with the smallest number of digits beyond the decimal point determines how the answer should be expressed. Because there is no digit beyond the decimal point in 125, there can be none after the decimal point in 31.

CONCEPT ASSESSMENT ✔

Suppose that the reaction of 1.00 mol $NH_3(g)$ and 1.00 mol $O_2(g)$ is carried to completion, producing $NO(g)$ and $H_2O(l)$ as the only products. Which, if any, of the following statements is correct about this reaction? **(a)** 1.0 mol $NO(g)$ is produced; **(b)** 4.0 mol $NO(g)$ is produced; **(c)** 1.5 mol $H_2O(l)$ is produced; **(d)** all the $O_2(g)$ is consumed; **(e)** $NH_3(g)$ is the limiting reactant.

4-5   OTHER PRACTICAL MATTERS IN REACTION STOICHIOMETRY

In this section we consider a few additional factors in reaction stoichiometry—both in the laboratory and in the manufacturing plant. First, the calculated outcome of a reaction may not be what is actually observed. Specifically, the amount of product may be, unavoidably, less than expected. Second, the route to producing a desired chemical may require several reactions carried out in sequence. And third, in some cases two or more reactions may occur simultaneously.

THEORETICAL YIELD, ACTUAL YIELD, AND PERCENT YIELD

The **theoretical yield** of a reaction is the calculated quantity of product expected from given quantities of reactants. The quantity of product that is actually produced is called the **actual yield**. The **percent yield** is defined as

$$\text{percent yield} = \frac{\text{actual yield}}{\text{theoretical yield}} \times 100\% \qquad (4.5)$$

Percent Yield activity

In many reactions the actual yield almost exactly equals the theoretical yield, and the reactions are said to be *quantitative*. Such reactions can be used in quantitative chemical analyses. On the other hand, in some reactions the actual yield is less than the theoretical yield, and the percent yield is less than 100%. The reduced yield may occur for a variety of reasons. (1) The product of a reaction rarely appears in a pure form, and some product may be lost during the necessary purification steps, which reduces the yield. (2) In many cases the reactants may participate in reactions other than the one of central interest. These are called **side reactions**, and the unintended products are called **by-products**. To the extent that side reactions occur, the yield of the main product is reduced. (3) If a reverse reaction occurs, some of the expected product may react to reform the reactants, and again the yield is less than expected.

At times, the apparent yield is greater than 100%. Because one cannot get something from nothing, this situation usually indicates an error in technique. Some products are formed as a precipitate from a solvent. If the product is weighed when it is wet with solvent, the result will be a larger-than-expected mass. More thorough drying of the product would give a more accurate yield determination. Another possibility is that the product is contaminated with an excess reactant or a by-product. This makes the mass of product appear larger than expected. In any case, a product must be purified before its yield is determined.

In Example 4-14, we establish the theoretical, actual, and percent yields of an important industrial process.

Urea

EXAMPLE 4-14

Determining Theoretical, Actual, and Percent Yields. Billions of pounds of urea, $CO(NH_2)_2$, are produced annually for use as a fertilizer. The reaction used is

$$2\,NH_3 + CO_2 \longrightarrow CO(NH_2)_2 + H_2O$$

The typical starting reaction mixture has a $3:1$ mole ratio of NH_3 to CO_2. If 47.7 g urea forms *per mole* of CO_2 that reacts, what is the **(a)** theoretical yield; **(b)** actual yield; and **(c)** percent yield in this reaction?

Solution

(a) The stoichiometric proportions are 2 mol NH_3:1 mol CO_2. Because the mole ratio of NH_3 to CO_2 used is 3:1, NH_3 is in excess and CO_2 is the limiting reactant. Because the quantity of urea is given per mole of CO_2, we should base the calculation on 1.00 mol CO_2.

$$\text{theoretical yield} = 1.00 \text{ mol } CO_2 \times \frac{1 \text{ mol } CO(NH_2)_2}{1 \text{ mol } CO_2} \times \frac{60.1 \text{ g } CO(NH_2)_2}{1 \text{ mol } CO(NH_2)_2}$$

$$= 60.1 \text{ g } CO(NH_2)_2$$

(b) actual yield $= 47.7$ g $CO(NH_2)_2$

(c) percent yield $= \dfrac{47.7 \text{ g } CO(NH_2)_2}{60.1 \text{ g } CO(NH_2)_2} \times 100\% = 79.4\%$

Practice Example A: Formaldehyde, CH_2O, can be made from methanol by the following reaction, using a copper catalyst.

$$CH_3OH(g) \longrightarrow CH_2O(g) + H_2(g)$$

If 25.7 g $CH_2O(g)$ is produced per mole of methanol that reacts, what are **(a)** the theoretical yield, **(b)** the actual yield, and **(c)** the percent yield in this reaction?

Practice Example B: What is the percent yield if the reaction of 25.0 g P_4 with 91.5 g Cl_2 produces 104 g PCl_3?

$$P_4 + 6\,Cl_2 \longrightarrow 4\,Cl_3$$

If we know that a yield will be less than 100%, we need to adjust the amounts of reactants used to produce the desired amount of product. We cannot simply use the theoretical amounts of reactants; we must use more. This point is illustrated in Example 4-15.

Cyclohexanol

Cyclohexene

▶ Think of this first step as an algebra problem. If 83% of a number is equal to 25, what is the number? $0.83x = 25$; $x = 25/0.83 = 30$.

EXAMPLE 4-15

Adjusting the Quantities of Reactants in Accordance with the Percent Yield of a Reaction. When heated with sulfuric or phosphoric acid, cyclohexanol, $C_6H_{11}OH$, is converted to cyclohexene, C_6H_{10}.

$$C_6H_{11}OH(l) \longrightarrow C_6H_{10}(l) + H_2O(l) \qquad (4.6)$$

If the percent yield of this reaction is 83%, what mass of cyclohexanol must we use to obtain 25 g cyclohexene?

Solution

First, calculate the theoretical yield if 25 g of C_6H_{10} represents only 83% of the theoretical yield. Then calculate the quantity of $C_6H_{11}OH$ required to produce this theoretical yield of C_6H_{10}.

Step 1. Rearrange equation (4.5), and calculate the theoretical yield.

$$\text{theoretical yield} = \frac{\text{actual yield} \times 100\%}{\text{percent yield}} = \frac{25 \text{ g} \times 100\%}{83\%} = 30 \text{ g}$$

Step 2. Calculate the quantity of $C_6H_{11}OH$ needed to produce 30 g C_6H_{10}.

$$? \text{ g } C_6H_{11}OH = 30 \text{ g } C_6H_{10} \times \frac{1 \text{ mol } C_6H_{10}}{82.1 \text{ g } C_6H_{10}} \times \frac{1 \text{ mol } C_6H_{11}OH}{1 \text{ mol } C_6H_{10}}$$

$$\times \frac{100.2 \text{ g } C_6H_{11}OH}{1 \text{ mol } C_6H_{11}OH}$$

$$= 37 \text{ g } C_6H_{11}OH$$

Practice Example A: If the percent yield for the formation of urea in Example 4-14 were 87.5%, what mass of CO_2, together with an excess of NH_3, would have to be used to obtain 50.0 g $CO(NH_2)_2$?

Practice Example B: Calculate the mass of cyclohexanol ($C_6H_{11}OH$) needed to produce 45.0 g cyclohexene (C_6H_{10}) by reaction (4.6) if the reaction has a 86.2% yield and the cyclohexanol is 92.3% pure.

CONSECUTIVE, SIMULTANEOUS, AND OVERALL REACTIONS

Both in laboratory work and in manufacturing, the preferred processes are those that yield a product through a single reaction. Often such processes give a higher yield because there is no need to remove products from one reaction mixture for further processing in subsequent reactions. However, in many cases a multistep process is unavoidable. **Consecutive reactions** are reactions carried out one after another in sequence to yield a final product. In **simultaneous reactions**, two or more substances react independently of one another in separate reactions occurring at the same time.

Example 4-16 presents an industrial process that is carried out in two consecutive reactions. The key to the calculation is to use a stoichiometric factor for each reaction. Example 4-16B deals with two reactions that occur simultaneously to produce a common product, hydrogen gas.

EXAMPLE 4-16

Calculating the Quantity of a Substance Produced by Reactions Occurring Consecutively. Titanium dioxide, TiO_2, is the most widely used white pigment for paints, having displaced most lead-based pigments, which are environmental hazards. Before it can be used, however, naturally occurring TiO_2 must be freed of colored impurities. One process for doing this converts impure $TiO_2(s)$ to $TiCl_4(g)$, which is then converted back to pure $TiO_2(s)$. What mass of carbon is consumed in producing 1.00 kg of pure $TiO_2(s)$ in this process?

$$2 \text{ TiO}_2 \text{ (impure)} + 3 \text{ C(s)} + 4 \text{ Cl}_2(g) \longrightarrow 2 \text{ TiCl}_4(g) + \text{CO}_2(g) + 2 \text{ CO}(g)$$

$$\text{TiCl}_4(g) + \text{O}_2(g) \longrightarrow \text{TiO}_2(s) + 2 \text{ Cl}_2(g)$$

Titanium tetrachloride

Solution

In this calculation we begin with the product, TiO_2, and work backward to one of the reactants, carbon. To do so, we convert from moles of TiO_2 to moles of $TiCl_4$ in the second reaction, using the stoichiometric factor labeled (a). We then convert from moles of $TiCl_4$ to moles of C in the *first* reaction, using the stoichiometric factor labeled (b). Together with other conversions between grams and moles of substances, the overall conversion pathway is

$$? \text{ g C} = 1.00 \text{ kg TiO}_2 \times \frac{1000 \text{ g TiO}_2}{1 \text{ kg TiO}_2} \times \frac{1 \text{ mol TiO}_2}{79.88 \text{ g TiO}_2} \times \overset{(a)}{\frac{1 \text{ mol TiCl}_4}{1 \text{ mol TiO}_2}} \times \overset{(b)}{\frac{3 \text{ mol C}}{2 \text{ mol TiCl}_4}}$$

$$\times \frac{12.01 \text{ g C}}{1 \text{ mol C}} = 226 \text{ g C}$$

STEPWISE REACTIONS, INTERMEDIATES, AND THE OVERALL CHEMICAL EQUATION

An industrial process is usually carried out in steps. The Raschig process involves three steps:

Step 1: $Cl_2(g)$ and $NaOH(aq)$ react to produce sodium hypochlorite, $NaOCl(aq)$.

$$2\,NaOH(aq) + Cl_2(g) \longrightarrow NaOCl(aq) + NaCl(aq) + H_2O(l)$$

Step 2: $NH_3(aq)$ reacts with $NaOCl(aq)$ to form chloramine, $NH_2Cl(aq)$.

$$NaOCl(aq) + NH_3(aq) \longrightarrow NH_2Cl(aq) + NaOH(aq)$$

Step 3: Additional $NH_3(l)$ reacts with $NH_2Cl(aq)$ to form hydrazine, $N_2H_4(aq)$.

$$NH_3(l) + NH_2Cl(aq) + NaOH(aq) \longrightarrow N_2H_4(aq) + NaCl(aq) + H_2O(l)$$

$NaOCl(aq)$ and $NH_2Cl(aq)$ are intermediates in the process. Their presence is crucial to the overall process, but they are consumed immediately after their formation. Hydrazine is the *end product* of the process, and the overall process can be represented through the overall chemical equation

$$2\,NaOH(aq) + Cl_2(g) + 2\,NH_3(aq) \longrightarrow N_2H_4(aq) + 2\,NaCl(aq) + 2\,H_2O \quad (4.7)$$

Notice that the intermediates do not show up as part of the overall chemical equation for this reaction.

Chemicals are manufactured on a large scale and sold for use in everything from food to pharmaceuticals. Every day, tons of chemicals are made to be used directly or to serve as reactants in the production of other materials. It is important that these chemicals be made in high yield and be of high purity, but this is not always easy. Industrial chemists and engineers must consider many factors when making decisions about building and operating a chemical plant.

Let us examine some of these factors using the production of hydrazine (N_2H_4) by the Raschig process as an example. Hydrazine is used as a rocket fuel, as a starting material in the production of pesticides, and in water treatment to remove dissolved oxygen from water in hot-water heating systems.

Practice Example A: Nitric acid, HNO_3, is produced from ammonia and oxygen by the consecutive reactions

$$4\,NH_3(g) + 5\,O_2(g) \longrightarrow 4\,NO(g) + 6\,H_2O(g)$$
$$2\,NO(g) + O_2(g) \longrightarrow 2\,NO_2(g)$$
$$3\,NO_2(g) + H_2O(l) \longrightarrow 2\,HNO_3(aq) + NO(g)$$

How many grams of nitric acid can be obtained from 1.00 kg $NH_3(g)$, if $NO(g)$ in the third reaction is *not* recycled?

Practice Example B: Magnalium alloys are widely used in aircraft construction. One magnalium alloy contains 70.0% Al and 30.0% Mg, by mass. How many grams of $H_2(g)$ are produced in the reaction of a 0.710-g sample of this alloy with excess $HCl(aq)$?

$$2\,Al(s) + 6\,HCl(aq) \longrightarrow 2\,AlCl_3(aq) + 3\,H_2(g)$$
$$Mg(s) + 2\,HCl(aq) \longrightarrow MgCl_2(aq) + H_2(g)$$

CONCEPT ASSESSMENT ✓

Suppose that each of these reactions has a 90% yield.

$$CH_4 + Cl_2 \longrightarrow CH_3Cl + HCl$$
$$CH_3Cl + Cl_2 \longrightarrow CH_2Cl_2 + HCl$$

BY-PRODUCTS AND SIDE REACTIONS

Equation (4.7) shows two products in addition to N_2H_4 (NaCl and H_2O). Substances formed along with the desired end product are called by-products. The by-products themselves may be commercially valuable, a feature that improves the economic success of a process.

By-products may also form as a result of side reactions, reactions that compete with the main reaction. For example, one intermediate, chloramine (NH_2Cl) reacts with hydrazine to produce NH_4Cl and N_2 as by-products

$$2\,NH_2Cl(aq) + N_2H_4(aq) \longrightarrow$$
$$2\,NH_4Cl(aq) + N_2(g) \quad (4.8)$$

Side reactions lower the yield of the desired product, so it is important for industrial chemists and chemical engineers to find conditions that minimize them.

REACTION CONDITIONS

Even if the conditions for a chemical reaction are shown in a chemical equation (placed above the arrow), the reasons for these conditions are probably not given. Temperature, pressure, and the presence of catalysts that help speed up the reaction are all important conditions that need to be controlled in order to get the best yield of the end product.

A modern modification of the reaction shown in equation (4.7) has the reaction being carried out in acetone, $(CH_3)_2CO$, rather than water. This change of solvent changes the mechanism of the reaction—that is, the path by which the reactant molecules become the product molecules. As a result, the side reaction (equation 4.8) is largely eliminated, and the yield of hydrazine increases from 60–80% to nearly 100%. Currently, most chemical plants in the United States use the modified process, but some still use the original process. This illustrates two points:

- Industrial methods of manufacturing chemicals undergo constant change.

- The changeover to a new process takes time, as new plants are built or old ones converted.

PURIFICATION

Purifying the product is an essential last step of any process. Rarely is the end product sufficiently pure for its intended uses. Hydrazine produced in reaction (4.7) is in a dilute aqueous solution, together with NH_3, NaCl, NH_4Cl, and traces of NaOH. Ammonia and water are removed by evaporating them from the solution (distillation). Substances such as NaCl, NH_4Cl, and NaOH deposit as solids (crystallization) when water is evaporated from solution. The solids are removed by filtration. Ultimately, a product that is more than 98% N_2H_4 is obtained. The NH_3 recovered in the purification process is reused in step 2 of the process. This illustrates another important principle of industrial chemistry. *Materials are recycled whenever possible.*

Starting with 50.0 g CH_4 in the first reaction and an excess of $Cl_2(g)$, the number of grams of CH_2Cl_2 formed in the second reaction is

(a) $50.0 \times 0.81 \times (85/16)$

(b) 50.0×0.90

(c) $50.0 \times 0.90 \times 0.90$

(d) $50.0 \times 0.90 \times 0.90 \times (16/50.5)(70.9/85)$

Usually, we can combine a series of chemical equations to obtain a single equation to represent the **overall reaction**. The equation for this overall reaction is the **overall equation**. At times we can use the overall equation for solving problems instead of working with the individual equations. This strategy does not work, however, if the substance of interest is not a starting material or final product but appears only in one of the intermediate reactions. Any substance that is produced in one step and consumed in another step of a multistep process is called an **intermediate**. In Example 4-16, $TiCl_4(g)$ is an intermediate.

To write an overall equation for Example 4-16, multiply the coefficients in the second equation by the factor 2, add the second equation to the first, and cancel any substances that appear on both sides of the overall equation.

$$2\,\cancel{TiO_2}\text{ (impure)} + 3\,C(s) + 4\,\cancel{Cl_2(g)} \longrightarrow 2\,\cancel{TiCl_4}(g) + CO_2(g) + 2\,CO(g)$$
$$2\,\cancel{TiCl_4}(g) + 2\,O_2(g) \longrightarrow 2\,\cancel{TiO_2}(s) + 4\,\cancel{Cl_2}(g)$$

Overall equation: $\quad 3\,C(s) + 2\,O_2(g) \longrightarrow CO_2(g) + 2\,CO(g)$

The result suggests that (1) we should obtain as much TiO_2 in the second reaction as we started with in the first, (2) the $Cl_2(g)$ produced in the second reaction can be recycled back into the first reaction, and (3) the only substances actually consumed in the overall reaction are C(s) and $O_2(g)$. You can also see that we could not have used this overall equation in the calculation of Example 4-16—$TiO_2(s)$ does not appear in it.

Summary

4-1 Chemical Reactions and Chemical Equations—
Chemical reactions are processes in which one or more starting substances, the **reactants**, form one or more new substances, the **products**. A chemical reaction can be represented symbolically in a **chemical equation**, with formulas of reactants on the left and formulas of products on the right; reactants and products are separated by an arrow. The equation must be balanced. A **balanced equation** reflects the true quantitative relationships between reactants and products. An equation is balanced by placing **stoichiometric coefficients** before formulas to signify that the total number of each kind of atom is the same on each side of the equation. The physical states of reactants and products can be indicated by symbols such as (s), (l), (g), and (aq), signifying solid, liquid, gas, and aqueous solution, respectively.

4-2 Chemical Equations and Stoichiometry—**Stoichiometry**
comprises quantitative relationships based on atomic and molecular masses, chemical formulas, balanced chemical equations, and related matters. The stoichiometry of chemical reactions makes use of conversion factors derived from balanced chemical equations and called **stoichiometric factors** (Fig. 4-3). Stoichiometric calculations usually require molar masses, densities, percent compositions, along with other factors (Fig. 4-4).

4-3 Chemical Reactions in Solution—The **molarity** of a
solution is the amount of **solute** (in moles) per liter of solution (expression 4.3). Molarity can be treated as a conversion factor between solution volume and amount of solute. Molarity as a conversion factor may be applied to individual solutions, to solutions that are mixed or diluted

by adding more **solvent** (Fig. 4-7; expression 4.4), and to reactions occurring in solution.

4-4 Determining the Limiting Reactant—In some reactions, one of the reactants is completely consumed, while the other reactants remain in excess. The reactant that is completely consumed determines that amount of product formed and is called the **limiting reactant**. In some reactions, the reactants are consumed simultaneously, with no reactant remaining in excess; such reactants are said to be in **stoichiometric proportions**. In some reactions, the limiting reactant must be determined before a stoichiometric calculation can be completed.

4-5 Other Practical Matters in Reaction Stoichiometry—
Stoichiometric calculations sometimes involve additional factors, including the reaction's **actual yield**, the presence of **by-products**, and how the reaction or reactions proceed. For example, some reactions yield exactly the quantity of product calculated—the **theoretical yield**. When the actual yield equals the theoretical yield, the **percent yield** is 100%. In some reactions, the actual yield is less than the theoretical, in which case the percent yield is less than 100%. Lower yields may result from the formation of by-products, substances that replace some of the desired product due to reactions other than the one of interest, called **side reactions**. Some stoichiometric calculations are complicated by the fact that two or more **simultaneous reactions** may occur. In other cases, a final product may be formed through a sequence of **consecutive reactions**. An **intermediate** is any substance that is a product of one reaction and a reactant in a subsequent reaction. The equations for a series of consecutive reactions are often replaced with a single **overall equation** for the **overall reaction**.

Integrative Example

Sodium nitrite is used in the production of dyes for coloring fabrics, as a preservative in meat processing (to prevent botulism), as a bleach for fibers, and in photography. It can be prepared by passing nitrogen monoxide and oxygen gases into an aqueous solution of sodium carbonate. Carbon dioxide gas is another product of the reaction.

In one reaction with a 95.0% yield, 225 mL of 1.50 M aqueous solution of sodium carbonate, 22.1 g of nitrogen monoxide, and a large excess of oxygen gas are allowed to react. What mass of sodium nitrite is obtained?

Strategy

Five tasks must be performed in this problem: (1) Represent the reaction by a chemical equation in which the names of reactants and products are replaced with formulas. (2) Balance the formula equation by inspection. (3) Determine the limiting reactant. (4) Calculate the theoretical yield of sodium nitrite based on the quantity of limiting reactant. (5) Use expression (4.5) to calculate the actual yield of sodium nitrite.

Solution

Obtain the unbalanced equation: Substitute formulas for names.

$$Na_2CO_3(aq) + NO(g) + O_2(g) \longrightarrow NaNO_2(aq) + CO(g)$$

Obtain the balanced equation: Begin by noting that there must be 2 $NaNO_2$ for every Na_2CO_3.

$$Na_2CO_3(aq) + NO(g) + O_2(g) \longrightarrow 2\,NaNO_2(aq) + CO_2(g)$$

To balance the N atoms requires 2 NO on the left side:

$$Na_2CO_3(aq) + 2\,NO(g) + O_2(g) \longrightarrow 2\,NaNO_2(aq) + CO_2(g)$$

To balance the O atoms requires $\frac{1}{2}O_2$ on the left, resulting in six O atoms on each side:

$$Na_2CO_3(aq) + 2\,NO(g) + \frac{1}{2}O_2(g) \longrightarrow 2\,NaNO_2(aq) + CO_2(g)$$

Multiply coefficients by 2 to make all of them integers in the final balanced equation.

$$2 \, Na_2CO_3(aq) + 4 \, NO(g) + O_2(g) \longrightarrow 4 \, NaNO_2(aq) + 2 \, CO_2(g)$$

Determine the limiting reactant: The problem states that oxygen is in excess. To determine the limiting reactant, the number of moles of Na_2CO_3, requiring molarity as a conversion factor, must be compared to the number of moles of NO, requiring a conversion factor based on the molar mass of NO.

$$? \text{ mol } Na_2CO_3 = 0.225 \text{ L soln} \times \frac{1.50 \text{ mol } Na_2CO_3}{1 \text{ L soln}}$$

$$= 0.338 \text{ mol } Na_2CO_3$$

$$? \text{ mol } NO = 22.1 \text{ g } NO \times \frac{1 \text{ mol } NO}{30.01 \text{ g } NO} = 0.736 \text{ mol } NO$$

From the balanced equation, the stoichiometric mole ratio is

$$4 \text{ mol } NO : 2 \text{ mol } Na_2CO_3 = 2:1$$

The available mole ratio is

$$0.736 \text{ mol } NO : 0.338 \text{ mol } Na_2CO_3 = 2.18:1$$

Because the available mole ratio exceeds $2:1$, NO is in excess and Na_2CO_3 is the limiting reactant.

Determine the theoretical yield of the reaction: This calculation is based on the amount of Na_2CO_3, the limiting reactant.

$$? \text{ g } NaNO_2 = 0.338 \text{ mol } Na_2CO_3 \times \frac{4 \text{ mol } NaNO_2}{2 \text{ mol } Na_2NCO_3}$$

$$\times \frac{69.00 \text{ g } NaNO_2}{1 \text{ mol } NaNO_2} = 46.6 \text{ g } NaNO_2$$

Determine the actual yield: Use expression (4.5), which relates percent yield (95.0%), theoretical yield (46.6 g $NaNO_2$), and the actual yield.

$$\text{actual yield} = \frac{\text{percent yield} \times \text{theoretical yield}}{100\%}$$

$$= \frac{95.0\% \times 46.6 \text{ g } NaNO_2}{100\%} = 44.3 \text{ g } NaNO_2$$

Exercises

Writing and Balancing Chemical Equations

1. Balance the following equations by inspection.
   (a) $SO_3 \longrightarrow SO_2 + O_2$
   (b) $Cl_2O_7 + H_2O \longrightarrow HClO_4$
   (c) $NO_2 + H_2O \longrightarrow HNO_3 + NO$
   (d) $PCl_3 + H_2O \longrightarrow H_3PO_3 + HCl$
2. Balance the following equations by inspection.
   (a) $P_2H_4 \longrightarrow PH_3 + P_4$
   (b) $P_4 + Cl_2 \longrightarrow PCl_3$
   (c) $FeCl_3 + H_2S \longrightarrow Fe_2S_3 + HCl$
   (d) $Mg_3N_2 + H_2O \longrightarrow Mg(OH)_2 + NH_3$
3. Balance the following equations by inspection.
   (a) $PbO + NH_3 \longrightarrow Pb + N_2 + H_2O$
   (b) $FeSO_4 \longrightarrow Fe_2O_3 + SO_2 + O_2$
   (c) $S_2Cl_2 + NH_3 \longrightarrow N_4S_4 + NH_4Cl + S_8$
   (d) $C_3H_7CHOHCH(C_2H_5)CH_2OH + O_2 \longrightarrow$
   $ CO_2 + H_2O$
4. Balance the following equations by inspection.
   (a) $SO_2Cl_2 + HI \longrightarrow H_2S + H_2O + HCl + I_2$
   (b) $FeTiO_3 + H_2SO_4 + H_2O \longrightarrow$
   $ FeSO_4 \cdot 7 \, H_2O + TiOSO_4$
   (c) $Fe_3O_4 + HCl + Cl_2 \longrightarrow FeCl_3 + H_2O + O_2$
   (d) $C_6H_5CH_2SSCH_2C_6H_5 + O_2 \longrightarrow$
   $ CO_2 + SO_2 + H_2O$
5. Write balanced equations based on the information given.
   (a) solid magnesium + oxygen gas $\longrightarrow$
    solid magnesium oxide
   (b) nitrogen monoxide gas + oxygen gas $\longrightarrow$
    nitrogen dioxide gas

(c) gaseous ethane(C_2H_6) + oxygen gas $\longrightarrow$
 carbon dioxide gas + liquid water
(d) aqueous silver sulfate +
 aqueous barium iodide $\longrightarrow$
 solid barium sulfate + solid silver iodide
6. Write balanced equations based on the information given.
   (a) solid magnesium + nitrogen gas $\longrightarrow$
    solid magnesium nitride
   (b) solid potassium chlorate $\longrightarrow$
    solid potassium chloride + oxygen gas
   (c) solid sodium hydroxide +
    solid ammonium chloride $\longrightarrow$
    solid sodium chloride + gaseous ammonia +
    water vapor
   (d) solid sodium + liquid water $\longrightarrow$
    aqueous sodium hydroxide + hydrogen gas
7. Write balanced equations to represent the complete combustion of (a) butane, C_4H_{10}; (b) isopropyl alcohol, $CH_3CH(OH)CH_3$; (c) lactic acid, $CH_3CH(OH)COOH$.
8. Write balanced equations to represent the complete combustion of (a) propylene, C_3H_6; (b) glycerol, $CH_2(OH)CH(OH)CH_2OH$; (c) thiobenzoic acid, C_6H_5COSH.
9. Write balanced equations to represent:
   (a) the decomposition, by heating, of solid ammonium nitrate to produce dinitrogen monoxide gas (laughing gas) and water vapor;

(b) the reaction of aqueous sodium carbonate with hydrochloric acid to produce water, carbon dioxide gas, and aqueous sodium chloride;

(c) the reaction of methane (CH_4), ammonia, and oxygen gases to form gaseous hydrogen cyanide and water vapor.

10. Write balanced equations to represent:
(a) the reaction of sulfur dioxide gas with oxygen gas to produce sulfur trioxide gas (one of the reactions involved in the industrial preparation of sulfuric acid);
(b) the dissolving of limestone (calcium carbonate) in water containing dissolved carbon dioxide to produce calcium hydrogen carbonate (a reaction producing temporary hardness in groundwater);
(c) the reaction of ammonia and nitrogen monoxide to form nitrogen gas and water vapor.

Stoichiometry of Chemical Reactions

13. Iron metal reacts with chlorine gas. How many moles of $FeCl_3$ are obtained when 7.26 mol Cl_2 reacts with excess Fe?

$$2\,Fe(s) + 3\,Cl_2(g) \longrightarrow 2\,FeCl_3(s)$$

14. If 0.337 mol PCl_3 is produced by the reaction

$$6\,Cl_2 + P_4 \longrightarrow 4\,PCl_3$$

how many grams each of Cl_2 and P_4 are consumed?

15. A laboratory method of preparing $O_2(g)$ involves the decomposition of $KClO_3(s)$.

$$2\,KClO_3(s) \xrightarrow{\Delta} 2\,KCl(s) + 3\,O_2(g)$$

(a) How many moles of $O_2(g)$ can be produced by the decomposition of 32.8 g $KClO_3$?
(b) How many grams of $KClO_3$ must be decomposed to produce 50.0 g O_2?
(c) How many grams of KCl are formed, together with 28.3 g O_2, in the decomposition of $KClO_3$?

16. A commercial method of manufacturing hydrogen involves the reaction of iron and steam.

$$3\,Fe(s) + 4\,H_2O(g) \xrightarrow{\Delta} Fe_3O_4(s) + 4\,H_2(g)$$

(a) How many moles of H_2 can be produced from 42.7 g Fe and an excess of $H_2O(g)$ (steam)?
(b) How many grams of H_2O are consumed in the conversion of 63.5 g Fe to Fe_3O_4?
(c) If 7.36 mol H_2 is produced, how many grams of Fe_3O_4 must also be produced?

17. How many grams of Ag_2CO_3 are decomposed to yield 75.1 g Ag in this reaction?

$$Ag_2CO_3(s) \xrightarrow{\Delta}$$
$$Ag(s) + CO_2(g) + O_2(g) \text{ (not balanced)}$$

18. How many kilograms of HNO_3 are consumed to produce 125 kg $Ca(H_2PO_4)_2$ in this reaction?

$$Ca_3(PO_4)_2 + HNO_3 \longrightarrow$$
$$Ca(H_2PO_4)_2 + Ca(NO_3)_2 \text{ (not balanced)}$$

19. The reaction of calcium hydride with water can be used to prepare small quantities of hydrogen gas, as is done to fill weather-observation balloons.

$$CaH_2(s) + H_2O(l) \longrightarrow$$
$$Ca(OH)_2(s) + H_2(g) \text{ (not balanced)}$$

11. Write a balanced chemical equation for the reaction depicted below.

12. Write a balanced chemical equation for the reaction depicted below.

(a) How many moles of $H_2(g)$ result from the reaction of 127 g CaH_2 with an excess of water?
(b) How many grams of water are consumed in the reaction of 56.2 g CaH_2?
(c) What mass of $CaH_2(s)$ must react with an excess of water to produce 8.12×10^{24} molecules of H_2?

20. The reaction of potassium superoxide, KO_2, is used in life-support systems to replace $CO_2(g)$ in expired air with $O_2(g)$.

$$4\,KO_2(s) + 2\,CO_2(g) \longrightarrow 2\,K_2CO_3(s) + 3\,O_2(g)$$

(a) How many moles of $O_2(g)$ are produced by the reaction of 156 g $CO_2(g)$ with excess $KO_2(s)$?
(b) How many grams of $KO_2(s)$ are consumed per 100.0 g $CO_2(g)$ removed from expired air?
(c) How many O_2 molecules are produced per milligram of KO_2 consumed?

21. Iron ore is impure Fe_2O_3. When Fe_2O_3 is heated with an excess of carbon (coke), metallic iron and carbon monoxide gas are produced. From a sample of ore weighing 938 kg, 523 kg of pure iron is obtained. What is the mass percent Fe_2O_3, by mass, in the ore sample, assuming that none of the impurities contain Fe?

22. Silver oxide decomposes at temperatures in excess of 300°C, yielding metallic silver and oxygen gas. A 3.13-g sample of impure silver oxide yields 0.187 g $O_2(g)$. What is the mass percent Ag_2O in the sample? Assume that $Ag_2O(s)$ is the only source of $O_2(g)$.
[*Hint:* Write a balanced equation for the reaction.]

23. A piece of aluminum foil measuring 10.25 cm × 5.50 cm × 0.601 mm is dissolved in excess HCl(aq). What mass of $H_2(g)$ is produced? Use equation (4.2) and $d = 2.70$ g/cm^3 for Al.

24. An excess of aluminum foil is allowed to react with 225 mL of an aqueous solution of HCl ($d = 1.088$ g/mL) that contains 18.0% HCl by mass. What mass of $H_2(g)$ is produced?
[*Hint:* Use equation (4.2).]

25. *Without performing detailed calculations*, which of the following metals yields the greatest amount of H_2 per gram of metal reacting with HCl(aq)? **(a)** Na, **(b)** Mg, **(c)** Al, **(d)** Zn.
[*Hint:* Write equations similar to (4.2).]

26. *Without performing detailed calculations*, which of the following yields the same mass of $CO_2(g)$ per gram of compound as does ethanol, CH_3CH_2OH, when combusted in excess oxygen? **(a)** H_2CO; **(b)** $HOCH_2CH_2OH$; **(c)** $HOCH_2CHOHCH_2OH$; **(d)** CH_3OCH_3; **(e)** C_6H_5OH.

Molarity

27. What are the molarities of the following solutes when dissolved in water?
    (a) 2.92 mol CH_3OH in 7.16 L of solution
    (b) 7.69 mmol C_2H_5OH in 50.00 mL of solution
    (c) 25.2 g $CO(NH_2)_2$ in 275 mL of solution

28. What are the molarities of the following solutes when dissolved in water?
    (a) 2.25×10^{-4} mol CH_3CH_2OH in 125 mL of solution
    (b) 57.5 g $(CH_3)_2CO$ in 525 mL of solution
    (c) 18.5 mL of $C_3H_5(OH)_3$ ($d = 1.26$ g/mL) in 375 mL of solution

29. What are the molarities of the following solutes?
    (a) sucrose ($C_{12}H_{22}O_{11}$) if 150.0 g is dissolved per 250.0 mL of water solution
    (b) urea, $CO(NH_2)_2$, if 98.3 mg of the 97.9% pure solid is dissolved in 5.00 mL of aqueous solution
    (c) methanol, CH_3OH, ($d = 0.792$ g/mL) if 125.0 mL is dissolved in enough water to make 15.0 L of solution

30. What are the molarities of the following solutes?
    (a) aspartic acid ($H_2C_4H_5NO_4$) if 0.405 g is dissolved in enough water to make 100.0 mL of solution
    (b) acetone, C_3H_6O, ($d = 0.790$ g/mL) if 35.0 mL is dissolved in enough water to make 425 mL of solution
    (c) diethyl ether, $(C_2H_5)_2O$, if 8.8 mg is dissolved in enough water to make 3.00 L of solution

31. How much
    (a) glucose, $C_6H_{12}O_6$, in grams, must be dissolved in water to produce 75.0 mL of 0.350 M $C_6H_{12}O_6$?
    (b) methanol, CH_3OH ($d = 0.792$ g/mL), in milliliters, must be dissolved in water to produce 2.25 L of 0.485 M CH_3OH?

32. How much
    (a) ethanol, C_2H_5OH ($d = 0.789$ g/mL), in liters, must be dissolved in water to produce 200.0 L of 1.65 M C_2H_5OH?
    (b) concentrated hydrochloric acid solution (36.0% HCl by mass; $d = 1.18$ g/mL), in milliliters, is required to produce 12.0 L of 0.234 M HCl?

33. Which of the following is a 0.500 M KCl solution? **(a)** 0.500 g KCl/mL solution; **(b)** 36.0 g KCl/L solution; **(c)** 7.46 mg KCl/mL solution; **(d)** 373 g KCl in 10.00 L solution

34. Which two solutions have the same concentration? **(a)** 55.45 g NaCl/L solution; **(b)** 5.545 g NaCl/100 g solution; **(c)** 55.45 g NaCl/kg water; **(d)** 55.45 mg NaCl/1.00 mL solution; **(e)** 5.00 mmol NaCl/5.00 mL solution

35. Which has the higher concentration of sucrose: a 46% sucrose solution by mass ($d = 1.21$ g/mL), or 1.50 M $C_{12}H_{22}O_{11}$? Explain your reasoning.

36. Which has the greater molarity of ethanol: a white wine ($d = 0.95$ g/mL) with 11% C_2H_5OH by mass, or the solution described in Example 4-8? Explain your reasoning.

37. A 10.00-mL sample of 2.05 M KNO_3 is diluted to a volume of 250.0 mL. What is the concentration of the diluted solution?

38. What volume of 0.750 M $AgNO_3$ must be diluted with water to prepare 250.0 mL of 0.425 M $AgNO_3$?

39. Water is evaporated from 125 mL of 0.198 M K_2SO_4 solution until the volume becomes 105 mL. What is the molarity of K_2SO_4 in the remaining solution?

40. A 25.0-mL sample of HCl(aq) is diluted to a volume of 500.0 mL. If the concentration of the diluted solution is found to be 0.085 M HCl, what was the concentration of the original solution?

41. Given a 0.250 M K_2CrO_4 stock solution, describe how you would prepare a solution that is 0.0125 M K_2CrO_4. That is, what combination(s) of pipet and volumetric flask would you use? Typical sizes of volumetric flasks found in a general chemistry laboratory are 100.0, 250.0, 500.0, and 1000.0 mL, and typical sizes of volumetric pipets are 1.00, 5.00, 10.00, 25.00, and 50.00 mL.

42. Given two liters of 0.496 M KCl, describe how you would use this solution to prepare 250.0 mL of 0.175 M KCl. Give sufficient details so that another student could follow your instructions.

Chemical Reactions in Solution

43. For the reaction

    $$2\,AgNO_3(aq) + Na_2S(aq) \longrightarrow$$
    $$Ag_2S(s) + 2\,NaNO_3(aq)$$

    (a) How many grams of $Na_2S(s)$ are required to react completely with 27.8 mL of 0.163 M $AgNO_3$?
    (b) How many grams of $Ag_2S(s)$ are obtained from the reaction in part **(a)**?

44. Excess $NaHCO_3(s)$ is added to 525 mL of 0.220 M $Cu(NO_3)_2(aq)$ for the reaction

    $$Cu(NO_3)_2(aq) + 2\,NaHCO_3(s) \longrightarrow$$
    $$CuCO_3(s) + 2\,NaNO_3(aq) + H_2O(l) + CO_2(g)$$

    (a) How many grams of the $NaHCO_3(s)$ will be consumed?
    (b) How many grams of $CuCO_3(s)$ will be produced?

45. How many milliliters of 0.650 M K_2CrO_4 are needed to precipitate all the silver in 415 mL of 0.186 M $AgNO_3$ as $Ag_2CrO_4(s)$?

$$2\ AgNO_3(aq) + K_2CrO_4(aq) \longrightarrow$$
$$Ag_2CrO_4(s) + 2\ KNO_3(aq)$$

46. For the reaction

$$Ca(OH)_2(s) + 2\ HCl(aq) \longrightarrow$$
$$CaCl_2(aq) + 2\ H_2O(l)$$

(a) How many grams of $Ca(OH)_2$ are required to react completely with 415 mL of 0.477 M HCl?
(b) How many kilograms of $Ca(OH)_2$ are required to react with 324 L of a HCl solution that is 24.28% HCl by mass, and has a density of 1.12 g/mL?

47. Refer to Example 4-7 and equation (4.2). For the conditions stated in Example 4-7, determine **(a)** the number of moles of $AlCl_3$ and **(b)** the molarity of the $AlCl_3(aq)$ if the solution volume is simply the 23.8 mL calculated in the example.

48. Refer to the Integrative Example on page 132.. If 138 g Na_2CO_3 in 1.42 L of aqueous solution is treated with an excess of NO(g) and $O_2(g)$, what is the molarity of the $NaNO_2(aq)$ solution that results? (Assume that the reaction goes to completion.)

49. How many grams of Ag_2CrO_4 will precipitate if excess $K_2CrO_4(aq)$ is added to the 415 mL of 0.186 M $AgNO_3$ in Exercise 45?

50. What volume of 0.0797 M $KMnO_4(aq)$ is necessary to convert 9.13 g KI to I_2 in the reaction

$$2\ KMnO_4 + 10\ KI + 8\ H_2SO_4 \longrightarrow$$
$$6\ K_2SO_4 + 2\ MnSO_4 + 5\ I_2 + 8\ H_2O$$

51. How many grams of sodium must react with 155 mL H_2O to produce a solution that is 0.175 M NaOH? (Assume a final solution volume of 155 mL.)

$$2\ Na(s) + 2\ H_2O(l) \longrightarrow 2\ NaOH(aq) + H_2(g)$$

52. A method of lowering the concentration of HCl(aq) is to allow the solution to react with a small quantity of Mg. How many milligrams of Mg must be added to 250.0 mL of 1.023 M HCl to reduce the solution concentration to exactly 1.000 M HCl?

$$Mg(s) + 2\ HCl(aq) \longrightarrow MgCl_2(aq) + H_2(g)$$

53. A 0.3126-g sample of oxalic acid, $H_2C_2O_4$, requires 26.21 mL of a particular concentration of NaOH(aq) to complete the following reaction. What is the molarity of the NaOH(aq)?

$$H_2C_2O_4(s) + 2\ NaOH(aq) \longrightarrow$$
$$Na_2C_2O_4(aq) + 2\ H_2O(l)$$

54. A 25.00-mL sample of HCl(aq) was added to a 0.1000-g sample of $CaCO_3$. All the $CaCO_3$ reacted, leaving some excess HCl(aq).

$$CaCO_3(s) + 2\ HCl(aq) \longrightarrow$$
$$CaCl_2(aq) + H_2O(l) + CO_2(g)$$

The excess HCl(aq) required 43.82 mL of 0.01185 M $Ba(OH)_2(aq)$ to complete the following reaction. What was the molarity of the original HCl(aq)?

$$2\ HCl(aq) + Ba(OH)_2(aq) \longrightarrow$$
$$BaCl_2(aq) + 2\ H_2O(l)$$

Determining the Limiting Reactant

55. How many moles of NO(g) can be produced in the reaction of 3.00 mol $NH_3(g)$ and 4.00 mol $O_2(g)$?

$$4\ NH_3(g) + 5\ O_2(g) \xrightarrow{\Delta} 4\ NO(g) + 6\ H_2O(l)$$

56. The reaction of calcium hydride and water produces calcium hydroxide and hydrogen as products. How many moles of $H_2(g)$ will be formed in the reaction between 0.82 mol $CaH_2(s)$ and 1.54 mol $H_2O(l)$?

57. A 0.696-mol sample of Cu is added to 136 mL of 6.0 M $HNO_3(aq)$. Assuming the following reaction is the only one that occurs, will the Cu react completely?

$$3\ Cu(s) + 8\ HNO_3(aq) \longrightarrow$$
$$3\ Cu(NO_3)_2(aq) + 4\ H_2O(l) + 2\ NO(g)$$

58. How many grams of $H_2(g)$ are produced by the reaction of 1.84 g Al with 75.0 mL of 2.95 M HCl? [*Hint:* Recall equation (4.2).]

59. A side reaction in the manufacture of rayon from wood pulp is

$$3\ CS_2 + 6\ NaOH \longrightarrow$$
$$2\ Na_2CS_3 + Na_2CO_3 + 3\ H_2O$$

How many grams of Na_2CS_3 are produced in the reaction of 92.5 mL of liquid CS_2 ($d = 1.26$ g/mL) and 2.78 mol NaOH?

60. Lithopone is a brilliant white pigment used in water-based interior paints. It is a mixture of $BaSO_4$ and ZnS produced by the reaction

$$BaS(aq) + ZnSO_4(aq) \longrightarrow ZnS(s) + BaSO_4(s)$$
$$\text{lithopone}$$

How many grams of lithopone are produced in the reaction of 315 mL of 0.275 M $ZnSO_4$ and 285 mL of 0.315 M BaS?

61. Ammonia can be generated by heating together the solids NH_4Cl and $Ca(OH)_2$. $CaCl_2$ and H_2O are also formed. **(a)** If a mixture containing 33.0 g each of NH_4Cl and $Ca(OH)_2$ is heated, how many grams of NH_3 will form? **(b)** Which reactant remains in excess, and in what mass?

62. Chlorine can be generated by heating together calcium hypochlorite and hydrochloric acid. Calcium chloride and water are also formed. **(a)** If 50.0 g $Ca(OCl)_2$ and 275 mL of 6.00 M HCl are allowed to react, how many grams of chlorine gas will form? **(b)** Which reactant, $Ca(OCl)_2$ or HCl, remains in excess, and in what mass?

Theoretical, Actual, and Percent Yields

63. In the reaction of 1.80 mol CCl_4 with an excess of HF, 1.55 mol CCl_2F_2 is obtained. What are the **(a)** theoretical, **(b)** actual, and **(c)** percent yields of this reaction?

$$CCl_4 + 2\,HF \longrightarrow CCl_2F_2 + 2\,HCl$$

64. In the reaction shown, 100.0 g $C_6H_{11}OH$ yielded 64.0 g C_6H_{10}. **(a)** What is the theoretical yield of the reaction? **(b)** What is the percent yield? **(c)** What mass of $C_6H_{11}OH$ would produce 100.0 g C_6H_{10} if the percent yield is that determined in part **(b)**?

$$C_6H_{11}OH \longrightarrow C_6H_{10} + H_2O$$

65. The reaction of 15.0 g C_4H_9OH, 22.4 g NaBr, and 32.7 g H_2SO_4 yields 17.1 g C_4H_9Br in the reaction shown. What are the **(a)** theoretical yield, **(b)** actual yield, and **(c)** percent yield of this reaction?

$$C_4H_9OH + NaBr + H_2SO_4 \longrightarrow$$
$$C_4H_9Br + NaHSO_4 + H_2O$$

66. Azobenzene, an intermediate in the manufacture of dyes, can be prepared from nitrobenzene by reaction with triethylene glycol in the presence of Zn and KOH. In one reaction, 0.10 L of nitrobenzene ($d = 1.20$ g/mL) and 0.30 L of triethylene glycol ($d = 1.12$ g/mL) yields 55 g azobenzene. What are the **(a)** theoretical yield, **(b)** actual yield, and **(c)** percent yield of this reaction?

$$2\,C_6H_5NO_2 + 4\,C_6H_{14}O_4 \xrightarrow[\text{KOH}]{\text{Zn}}$$

nitrobenzene   triethylene glycol

$$(C_6H_5N)_2 + 4\,C_6H_{12}O_4 + 4\,H_2O$$

azobenzene

67. How many grams of commercial acetic acid (97% $C_2H_4O_2$ by mass) must be allowed to react with an excess of PCl_3 to produce 75 g of acetyl chloride (C_2H_3OCl), if the reaction has a 78.2% yield?

$$C_2H_4O_2 + PCl_3 \longrightarrow$$
$$C_2H_3OCl + H_3PO_3 \text{ (not balanced)}$$

68. Suppose that reactions **(a)** and **(b)** have a 92% yield. Starting with 112 g CH_4 in reaction **(a)** and an excess of $Cl_2(g)$, how many grams of CH_2Cl_2 are formed in reaction **(b)**?
(a) $CH_4 + Cl_2 \longrightarrow CH_3Cl + HCl$
(b) $CH_3Cl + Cl_2 \longrightarrow CH_2Cl_2 + HCl$

69. An essentially 100% yield is necessary for a chemical reaction used to *analyze* a compound, but it is almost never expected for a reaction that is used to *synthesize* a compound. Explain this difference.

70. Suppose we carry out the precipitation of $Ag_2CrO_4(s)$ described in Example 4-11. If we obtain 2.058 g of precipitate, we might conclude that it is nearly pure $Ag_2CrO_4(s)$, but if we obtain 2.112 g, we can be quite sure that the precipitate is not pure. Explain this difference.

Consecutive Reactions, Simultaneous Reactions

71. How many grams of HCl are consumed in the reaction of 425 g of a mixture containing 35.2% $MgCO_3$ and 64.8% $Mg(OH)_2$, by mass?

$$Mg(OH)_2 + 2\,HCl \longrightarrow MgCl_2 + 2\,H_2O$$
$$MgCO_3 + 2\,HCl \longrightarrow MgCl_2 + H_2O + CO_2(g)$$

72. How many grams of CO_2 are produced in the complete combustion of 406 g of a bottled gas that consists of 72.7% propane (C_3H_8) and 27.3% butane (C_4H_{10}), by mass?

73. Dichlorodifluoromethane, once widely used as a refrigerant, can be prepared by the reactions shown. How many moles of Cl_2 must be consumed in the first reaction to produce 2.25 kg CCl_2F_2 in the second? Assume that all the CCl_4 produced in the first reaction is consumed in the second.

$$CH_4 + Cl_2 \longrightarrow CCl_4 + HCl \text{ (not balanced)}$$
$$CCl_4 + HF \longrightarrow CCl_2F_2 + HCl \text{ (not balanced)}$$

74. $CO_2(g)$ produced in the combustion of a sample of ethane is absorbed in $Ba(OH)_2(aq)$, producing 0.506 g $BaCO_3(s)$. How many grams of ethane (C_2H_6) must have been burned?

$$C_2H_6(g) + O_2(g) \longrightarrow$$
$$CO_2(g) + H_2O(l) \text{ (not balanced)}$$
$$CO_2(g) + Ba(OH)_2(aq) \longrightarrow BaCO_3(s) + H_2O(l)$$

75. The following process has been used to obtain iodine from oil-field brines in California. How many grams of silver nitrate are required in the first step for every kilogram of iodine produced in the third step?

sodium iodide + silver nitrate $\longrightarrow$
silver iodide + sodium nitrate

silver iodide + iron $\longrightarrow$ iron(II) iodide + silver

iron(II) iodide + chlorine gas $\longrightarrow$
iron(III) chloride + solid iodine

76. Sodium bromide, used to produce silver bromide for use in photography, can be prepared as shown. How many kilograms of iron are consumed to produce 2.50×10^3 kg NaBr?

$$Fe + Br_2 \longrightarrow FeBr_2$$
$$FeBr_2 + Br_2 \longrightarrow Fe_3Br_8 \text{ (not balanced)}$$
$$Fe_3Br_8 + Na_2CO_3 \longrightarrow$$
$$NaBr + CO_2 + Fe_3O_4 \text{ (not balanced)}$$

Integrative and Advanced Exercises

77. Write chemical equations to represent the following reactions.
(a) Limestone rock (calcium carbonate) is heated (calcined) and decomposes to calcium oxide and carbon dioxide gas.
(b) Zinc sulfide ore is heated in air (roasted) and is converted to zinc oxide and sulfur dioxide gas. (Note that oxygen gas in the air is also a reactant.)
(c) Propane gas reacts with gaseous water to produce a mixture of carbon monoxide and hydrogen gases. (This mixture, called *synthesis gas*, is used to produce a variety of organic chemicals.)
(d) Sulfur dioxide gas is passed into an aqueous solution containing sodium sulfide and sodium carbonate. The reaction products are carbon dioxide and an aqueous solution of sodium thiosulfate.

78. Write chemical equations to represent the following reactions.
(a) (Tri)calcium phosphate is heated with silicon dioxide and carbon, producing calcium silicate ($CaSiO_3$), phosphorus (P_4), and carbon monoxide. The phosphorus and chlorine react to form phosphorus trichloride, and the phosphorus trichloride and water react to form phosphorous acid.
(b) Copper metal reacts with gaseous oxygen, carbon dioxide, and water to form green basic copper carbonate, $Cu_2(OH)_2CO_3$ (a reaction responsible for the formation of the green patina, or coating, often seen on outdoor bronze statues).
(c) White phosphorus and oxygen gas react to form tetraphosphorus decoxide. The tetraphosphorus decoxide reacts with water to form an aqueous solution of phosphoric acid.
(d) Calcium dihydrogen phosphate reacts with sodium hydrogen carbonate (bicarbonate), producing (tri)calcium phosphate, (di)sodium hydrogen phosphate, carbon dioxide, and water (the principal reaction occurring when ordinary baking powder is added to cakes, bread, and biscuits).

79. Chalkboard chalk is made from calcium carbonate and calcium sulfate, with minor impurities such as SiO_2. Only the $CaCO_3$ reacts with dilute HCl(aq). What is the mass percent $CaCO_3$ in a piece of chalk if a 3.28-g sample yields 0.981 g $CO_2(g)$?

$$CaCO_3(s) + 2\ HCl(aq) \longrightarrow$$
$$CaCl_2(aq) + H_2O(l) + CO_2(g)$$

80. $H_2(g)$ is passed over $Fe_2O_3(s)$ at 400°C. Water vapor is formed together with a black residue—a compound consisting of 72.3% Fe and 27.7% O. Write a balanced equation for this reaction.

81. A sulfide of iron, containing 36.5% S by mass, is heated in $O_2(g)$, and the products are sulfur dioxide and an oxide of iron containing 27.6% O, by mass. Write a balanced chemical equation for this reaction.

82. What is the molarity of NaCl(aq) if a solution has 1.52 ppm Na? Assume that NaCl is the only source of Na and that the solution density is 1.00 g/mL. (The unit *ppm* is parts per million; here it can be taken to mean g Na per million grams of solution.)

83. How many milligrams $Ca(NO_3)_2$ must be present in 50.0 L of a solution containing 2.35 ppm Ca? [*Hint:* See also Exercise 82.]

84. A drop (0.05 mL) of 12.0 M HCl is spread over a sheet of thin aluminum foil. Assume that all the acid reacts with, and thus dissolves through, the foil. What will be the area, in cm^2, of the cylindrical hole produced? (density of Al = 2.70 g/cm^3; foil thickness = 0.10 mm.)

$$2\ Al(s) + 6\ HCl(aq) \longrightarrow 2\ AlCl_3(aq) + 3\ H_2(g)$$

85. A small piece of zinc is dissolved in 50.00 mL of 1.035 M HCl. At the conclusion of the reaction, the concentration of the 50.00-mL sample is redetermined and found to be 0.812 M HCl. What must have been the mass of the piece of zinc that dissolved?

$$Zn(s) + 2\ HCl(aq) \longrightarrow ZnCl_2(aq) + H_2(g)$$

86. How many milliliters of 0.715 M NH_4NO_3 solution must be diluted with water to produce 1.00 L of a solution with a concentration of 2.37 mg N/mL?

87. A seawater sample has a density of 1.03 g/mL and 2.8% NaCl by mass. A saturated solution of NaCl in water is 5.45 M NaCl. How many liters of water would have to be evaporated from 1.00×10^6 L of the seawater before NaCl would begin to crystallize? (A saturated solution contains the maximum amount of dissolved solute possible.)

88. A 99.8-mL sample of a solution that is 12.0% KI by mass ($d = 1.093$ g/mL) is added to 96.7 mL of another solution that is 14.0% $Pb(NO_3)_2$ by mass ($d = 1.134$ g/mL). How many grams of PbI_2 should form?

$$Pb(NO_3)_2(aq) + 2\ KI(aq) \longrightarrow PbI_2(s) + 2\ KNO_3(aq)$$

89. $CaCO_3(s)$ reacts with HCl(aq) to form H_2O, $CaCl_2(aq)$ and $CO_2(g)$. If a 45.0-g sample of $CaCO_3(s)$ is added to 1.25 L of HCl(aq) that is 25.7% HCl by mass ($d = 1.13$ g/mL), what will be the molarity of HCl in the solution after the reaction is completed? Assume that the solution volume remains constant.

90. A 2.05-g sample of an iron–aluminum alloy (ferroaluminum) is dissolved in excess HCl(aq) to produce 0.105 g $H_2(g)$. What is the percent composition, by mass, of the ferroaluminum?

$$Fe(s) + 2\ HCl(aq) \longrightarrow FeCl_2(aq) + H_2(g)$$
$$2\ Al(s) + 6\ HCl(aq) \longrightarrow 2\ AlCl_3(aq) + 3\ H_2(g)$$

91. A 0.155-g sample of an Al–Mg alloy reacts with an excess of HCl(aq) to produce 0.0163 g H_2. What is the percent Mg in the alloy? [*Hint:* Write equations similar to (4.2).]

92. An organic liquid is either methyl alcohol (CH_3OH), ethyl alcohol (C_2H_5OH), or a mixture of the two. A 0.220-g sample of the liquid is burned in an excess of $O_2(g)$ and yields 0.352 g $CO_2(g)$. Is the liquid a pure alcohol or a mixture of the two?

93. The manufacture of ethyl alcohol, C_2H_5OH, yields diethyl ether, $(C_2H_5)_2O$, as a by-product. The complete combustion of a 1.005-g sample of the product of this process yields 1.963 g CO_2. What must be the mass percents of C_2H_5OH and of $(C_2H_5)_2O$ in this sample?

94. Under appropriate conditions, copper sulfate, potassium chromate, and water react to form a product containing Cu^{2+}, CrO_4^{2-}, and OH^- ions. Analysis

of the compound yields 48.7% Cu^{2+}, 35.6% CrO_4^{2-}, and 15.7% OH^-.
(a) Determine the empirical formula of the compound.
(b) Write a plausible equation for the reaction.

95. Write a chemical equation to represent the complete combustion of malonic acid, a compound with 34.62% C, 3.88% H, and 61.50% O, by mass.

96. A mixture of 4.800 g H_2 and 36.40 g O_2 reacts.
(a) Write a balanced equation for this reaction.
(b) What substances are present after the reaction?
(c) Show that the total mass of substances present before and after the reaction is the same.

97. Silver nitrate is a very expensive chemical. For a particular experiment, you need 100.0 mL of 0.0750 M $AgNO_3(aq)$, but only 60 mL of 0.0500 M $AgNO_3$ is available. You decide to pipet exactly 50.00 mL of the solution into a 100.0-mL flask, add an appropriate mass of $AgNO_3$, and then dilute the resulting solution to exactly 100.0 mL. What mass of $AgNO_3$ must you use?

98. When sulfur (S_8) and chlorine are mixed in a reaction vessel, disulfur dichloride is the sole product. The starting mixture below is represented by yellow spheres for the S_8 molecules and green spheres for the chlorine molecules.

Which of the following is (are) a valid representation(s) of the contents of the reaction vessel after some disulfur dichloride (represented by red spheres) has formed?

(a)

(b)

(c)

(d)

99. Refer to Figure 1-6 on page 7 and explain why, if ammonium dichromate is the only reactant and chromium(III) oxide and water are two of the products, the only possible nitrogen-containing product is nitrogen gas. How many grams of nitrogen are produced per kilogram of ammonium dichromate decomposed?

100. It is desired to produce as large a volume of 1.25 M urea $[CO(NH_2)_2(aq)]$ as possible from these three sources: 345 mL of 1.29 M $CO(NH_2)_2$, 485 mL of 0.653 M $CO(NH_2)_2$, and 835 mL of 0.775 M $CO(NH_2)_2$. How can this be done? What is the maximum volume of this solution obtainable?

101. The mineral ilmenite, $FeTiO_3$, is an important source of titanium dioxide for use as a white pigment. In the first step in its conversion to titanium dioxide, ilmenite is treated with sulfuric acid and water to form $TiOSO_4$ and iron(II) sulfate heptahydrate. Titanium dioxide is obtained in two subsequent steps. How many kilograms of iron(II) sulfate heptahydrate are produced for every 1.00×10^3 kg of ilmenite processed?

102. Refer to Exercise 101. Iron(II) sulfate heptahydrate formed in the processing of ilmenite ore cannot be released into the environment. Its further treatment involves dehydration by heating to produce anhydrous iron(II) sulfate. Upon further heating, the iron(II) sulfate decomposes to iron(III) oxide, and sulfur dioxide and oxygen gases. The iron(III) oxide is used in the production of iron and steel. How many kilograms of iron(III) oxide are obtained for every 1.00×10^3 kg of iron(II) sulfate heptahydrate?

103. Refer to Exercises 101 and 102. How many kilograms of $H_2SO_4(l)$ can be produced from the sulfur dioxide by-product formed in the processing of 1.00×10^3 kg of ilmenite ore?

104. Melamine, $C_3N_3(NH_2)_3$, is used in adhesives and resins. It is manufactured in a two-step process in which urea, $CO(NH_2)_2$, is the sole starting material, isocyanic acid (HNCO) is an intermediate, and ammonia and carbon dioxide gases are by-products.
(a) Write a balanced equation for the overall reaction.
(b) What mass of melamine will be obtained from 100.0 kg of urea if the yield of the overall reaction is 84%?

105. Acrylonitrile is used in the production of synthetic fibers, plastics, and rubber goods. It can be prepared from propylene (propene), ammonia, and oxygen in the reaction illustrated below.
(a) Write a balanced chemical equation for this reaction.
(b) The actual yield of the reaction is 0.73 lb acrylonitrile per pound of propylene. What is the minimum mass of ammonia required to produce 1.00 ton (2000 lb) of acrylonitrile?

Feature Problems

106. It is often difficult to determine the concentration of a species in solution, particularly if it is a biological species that takes part in complex reaction pathways. One way to do this is through a dilution experiment with labeled molecules. Instead of molecules, however, we will use fish.

An angler wants to know the number of fish in a particular pond, and so puts an indelible mark on

100 fish and adds them to the pond's existing population. After waiting for the fish to spread throughout the pond, the angler starts fishing, eventually catching 18 fish. Of these, five are marked. What is the total number of fish in the pond?

107. Lead nitrate and potassium iodide react in aqueous solution to form a yellow precipitate of lead iodide. In one series of experiments, the masses of the two reactants were varied, but the *total* mass of the two was held constant at 5.000 g. The lead iodide formed was filtered from solution, washed, dried, and weighed. The table gives data for a series of reactions.

Experiment	Mass of Lead Nitrate, g	Mass of Lead Iodide, g
1	0.500	0.692
2	1.000	1.388
3	1.500	2.093
4	3.000	2.778
5	4.000	1.391

(a) Plot the data in a graph of mass of lead iodide versus mass of lead nitrate, and draw the appropriate curve(s) connecting the data points. What is the maximum mass of precipitate that can be obtained?
(b) Explain why the maximum mass of precipitate is obtained when the reactants are in their stoichiometric proportions. What are these stoichiometric proportions expressed as a mass ratio, and as a mole ratio?
(c) Show how the stoichiometric proportions determined in part (b) are related to the balanced equation for the reaction.

108. Some situations in the business world require balancing supplies (reactants) and products. For example, a business firm makes necklaces using beads of three colors: red, blue, and green. Each necklace contains 70 beads, as shown in the sketch. The firm has on hand 8 boxes of red beads, 11 boxes of blue beads, and 10 boxes of green beads. Each box contains 10.0 kg of beads, and the average masses of the beads are red: 1.98 g; blue: 3.05 g; green: 1.82 g.
(a) Write a "balanced equation" for forming a necklace from individual beads.
(b) How many necklaces can be made with the supplies on hand?
(c) Explain the limitations on the precision of your answer.

109. The emerging field of *green chemistry* comprises all the methods used to minimize the environmental impact of chemical activities. One of the dozen or so factors in green chemistry is *atom economy*—the efficiency in rearranging the atoms in a set of reactants into the desired product. Atom economy (AE) is expressed as a percentage by the equation

$$AE = \frac{\text{formula mass of desired product}}{\substack{\text{sum of formula masses} \\ \text{of all the reactants}}} \times 100\%$$

For example, when $H_2(g)$ burns in $O_2(g)$, the sole product is H_2O. All the atoms of the reactants appear in the product and the atom economy is 100%, as implied by the equation $2\,H_2(g) + O_2(g) \longrightarrow 2\,H_2O(l)$. For the Raschig process described on pages 130–131,
(a) what is the theoretical maximum AE for the synthesis of hydrazine (equation 4.7)?
(b) Why is the actual AE less than that calculated in part (a)?
(c) Explain why substituting acetone for water improves the AE.
(d) Propose a reaction for the synthesis of hydrazine that would have a theoretical AE of 100%.

110. Baking soda, $NaHCO_3$, is made from soda ash, a common name for sodium carbonate. The soda ash is obtained in two ways. It can be manufactured in a process in which carbon dioxide, ammonia, sodium chloride, and water are the starting materials. Alternatively, it is mined as a mineral called *trona* (left photo). Whether the soda ash is mined or manufactured, it is dissolved in water and carbon dioxide is bubbled through the solution. Sodium bicarbonate precipitates from the solution.

As a chemical analyst you are presented with two samples of sodium bicarbonate—one from the manufacturing process and the other derived from trona. You are asked to determine which is purer and are told that the impurity is sodium carbonate. You decide to treat the samples with just sufficient hydrochloric acid to convert all the sodium carbonate and bicarbonate to sodium chloride, carbon dioxide, and water. You then precipitate silver chloride in the reaction of sodium chloride with silver nitrate. A 6.93-g sample of baking soda derived from trona gave 11.89 g of silver chloride. A 6.78-g sample from manufactured sodium carbonate gave 11.77 g of silver chloride. Which sample is purer; that is, which has the greater mass percent $NaHCO_3$?

Trona	Baking soda
$Na_2CO_3 \cdot NaHCO_3 \cdot 2H_2O$	$NaHCO_3$

Self-Assessment Exercises

111. In your own words, define or explain these terms or symbols.

(a) $\xrightarrow{\Delta}$ (b) (aq)

(c) stoichiometric coefficient   (d) overall equation

112. Briefly describe **(a)** balancing a chemical equation; **(b)** preparing a solution by dilution; **(c)** determining the limiting reactant in a reaction.

113. Explain the important distinctions between **(a)** chemical formula and chemical equation; **(b)** stoichiometric coefficient and stoichiometric factor; **(c)** solute and solvent; **(d)** actual yield and percent yield.

114. When the equation below is balanced, the correct set of stoichiometric coefficients is **(a)** 1, 6 $\longrightarrow$ 1, 3, 4; **(b)** 1,4 $\longrightarrow$ 1, 2, 2; **(c)** 2, 6 $\longrightarrow$ 2, 3, 2; **(d)** 3, 8 $\longrightarrow$ 3, 4, 2.

$$? \, Cu(s) + ? \, HNO_3(aq) \longrightarrow$$
$$? \, Cu(NO_3)_2(aq) + ? \, H_2O(l) + ? \, NO(g)$$

115. 1.0 mol $CaCN_2$ (calcium cyanamide) and 1.0 mol H_2O are allowed to react. The number of moles of NH_3 produced is **(a)** 3.0; **(b)** 2.0; **(c)** between 1.0 and 2.0; **(d)** less than 1.0.

$$CaCN_2(s) + 3 \, H_2O(l) \longrightarrow CaCO_3 + 2 \, NH_3(g)$$

116. In the decomposition of silver(I) carbonate to form metallic silver, carbon dioxide gas, and oxygen gas, **(a)** one mol of oxygen gas is formed for every 2 mol of carbon dioxide gas; **(b)** 2 mol of silver metal is formed for every 1 mol of oxygen gas; **(c)** equal numbers of moles of carbon dioxide and oxygen gases are produced; or **(d)** the same number of moles of silver metal are formed as silver(I) carbonate decomposed.

117. To obtain a solution that is 1.00 M $NaNO_3$(aq), you should prepare **(a)** 1.00 L of aqueous solution containing 100 g $NaNO_3$; **(b)** one kg of aqueous solution containing 85.0 g $NaNO_3$; **(c)** 5.00 L of aqueous solution containing 425 g $NaNO_3$; or **(d)** an aqueous solution containing 8.5 mg $NaNO_3$/mL.

118. To prepare a solution that is 0.50 M KCl(aq) starting with 100.0 mL of 0.40 M KCl(aq), you should **(a)** add 20.0 mL of water; **(b)** add 0.075 g KCl; **(c)** add 0.10 mol KCl; **(d)** evaporate 20.0 mL of water.

119. In the reaction of 2.00 mol CCl_4 with an excess of HF, 1.70 mol CCl_2F_2 is obtained.

$$CCl_4 + 2 \, HF \longrightarrow CCl_2F_2 + 2 \, HCl$$

(a) The theoretical yield is 1.70 mol CCl_2F_2.

(b) The theoretical yield is 1.00 mol CCl_2F_2.

(c) The theoretical yield depends on how large an excess of HF is used.

(d) The percent yield is 85%.

120. The incomplete combustion of gasoline produces CO(g) as well as CO_2(g). Write an equation for **(a)** the complete combustion of the gasoline component octane, C_8H_{18}(l), and **(b)** incomplete combustion of octane with 25% of the carbon appearing as CO(g).

121. The minerals calcite, $CaCO_3$, magnesite, $MgCO_3$, and dolomite, $CaCO_3 \cdot MgCO_3$, decompose when strongly heated to form the corresponding metal oxide(s) and carbon dioxide gas. A 1.000-g sample known to be one of the three minerals was strongly heated and 0.477 g CO_2 was obtained. Which of the three minerals was it?

122. Appendix E describes a useful study aid known as concept mapping. Using the method presented in Appendix E, construct a concept map relating the topics found in Sections 4-3, 4-4, and 4-5.

 # eMedia Exercises

123. View the **Reactions with Oxygen** movie (*Activebook 4-1*). **(a)** Describe the physical evidence indicative of a chemical reaction in each case. **(b)** Why is a proportionately different amount of oxygen incorporated into the different products in the reactions presented in this movie?

124. The reaction of carbon and copper oxide is illustrated in the **Reduction of CuO** movie (*Activebook 4-2*). **(a)** If the reaction were carried out with 124.3 grams of CuO in the presence of excess carbon, how many grams of copper would be present at the end of the experiment? **(b)** Describe two reasons why the mass of the solid poured from the test tube may be greater than the amount you calculated.

125. The steps involved in preparing an aqueous solution of known concentration are discussed in the **Solution Formation from a Solid** animation (*Activebook 4-3*).

(a) What would be the effect on the actual concentration of the solution if the mass of the weighing paper were neglected?

(b) What would be the effect on the actual concentration of the solution if water were added past the line indicating a volume of 250 mL?

(c) Propose an additional source of error related to composition of the starting compound that would lead to a concentration less than 1 M.

126. After viewing the **Limiting Reactant** animation (*Activebook 4-4*), **(a)** determine the mass of H_2 gas produced in the three different experiments. **(b)** Where a limiting reagent is involved, calculate the mass of the excess species present at the completion of the experiment.

5

INTRODUCTION TO REACTIONS IN AQUEOUS SOLUTIONS

Chapter 5 provides an early exposure to descriptive chemistry and is useful to support concurrent laboratory work. Solubility, acid–base, and redox chemistry will be dealt with again in later chapters. If desired, some of these topics can be postponed and these sections can be used later as introductions to the relevant principles chapters. It is important, however, that early on students become familiar with the concept of electrolytes and with writing net ionic equations.

Electrolytes and Nonelectrolytes. Use a light bulb conductivity detector to test $H_2O(l)$, $NaCl(s)$, a mixture of salt in water, sugar, a mixture of sugar in water, and aqueous acetic acid. Start with 0.1 M $HC_2H_3O_2$ and adjust the concentration so that the bulb glows very dimly. See also Shakhashiri, *Chemical Demonstrations 3*, Univ. Wisconsin Press (1989), p. 326.

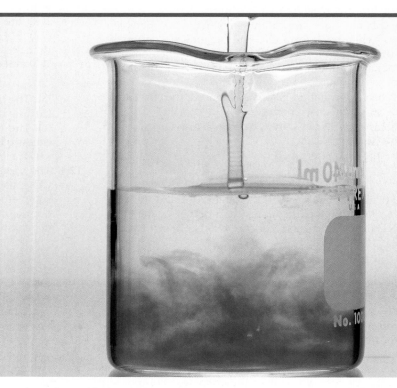

When clear, colorless aqueous solutions of cobalt(II) chloride and sodium hydroxide are mixed, a blue cloud of solid cobalt(II) hydroxide is formed. Such precipitation reactions are one of the three types of reactions considered in this chapter.

Precipitation, the formation of a solid when solutions are mixed, is probably the most common evidence of a chemical reaction that general chemistry students see. A practical application of precipitation is in determining the presence of certain ions in solution. If, for example, we are uncertain whether the clear, colorless liquid in an unlabeled bottle is a barium nitrate or a barium chloride solution, we can easily find out by adding a few drops of silver nitrate solution to a small sample of the liquid. If a white solid forms, the sample is a barium chloride solution; if nothing happens, it is barium nitrate. The Ag^+ from the silver nitrate and the Cl^- from the barium chloride combine to produce an insoluble precipitate of $AgCl(s)$. Precipitation reactions are the first reaction type we will study in this chapter. $Mg(OH)_2(s)$ is insoluble in water but soluble in hydrochloric acid, $HCl(aq)$, as a result of an acid–base reaction. This is the reaction by which milk of magnesia neutralizes excess stomach acid. Magnesium hydroxide is a base, and acid–base reactions are the second class of reactions presented in this chapter. The third class of reactions is oxidation–reduction reactions, which are found in all aspects of life, from reactions in organisms to processes for manufacturing chemicals, to such practical matters as bleaching fabrics, purifying water, and destroying toxic chemicals.

(a) (b)

▲ **FIGURE 5-1**
Molecular view of water and an aqueous solution of air
(a) Water molecules (red and white) are in close proximity in liquid water. **(b)** Dissolved oxygen (red) and nitrogen (blue) molecules are far apart, separated by water molecules.

5-1 THE NATURE OF AQUEOUS SOLUTIONS

Reactions in aqueous (water) solution are important because (1) water is inexpensive and able to dissolve a vast number of substances; (2) in aqueous solution, many substances are dissociated into ions, which can participate in chemical reactions; and (3) aqueous solutions are found everywhere, from seawater to living systems.

Let's try to form a mental image of a solution at the molecular level. The greatest number of molecules in a solution are generally solvent molecules, which are packed together rather tightly. Water is the solvent in an aqueous solution, and our mental image of water might look something like Figure 5-1(a). Solute particles—molecules or ions—are present in much smaller number and are randomly distributed among the solvent molecules. Our mental image of an aqueous solution of air might look something like Figure 5-1(b).

We have learned that ions are individual atoms or groupings of atoms that acquire a net electric charge by losing or gaining electrons. Thus, Mg^{2+} is a positively charged ion (a cation) formed when a Mg atom loses two electrons. Cl^- is a negatively charged ion (an anion) formed when a Cl atom gains one electron. When a group of three O atoms bonded to one N atom acquires an additional electron, it becomes the polyatomic nitrate anion, NO_3^-.

Unlike metallic conductors, where electrons carry the electric charge, in electrically conducting aqueous solutions it is ions that carry the electric charge. Pure water contains so few ions that it does not conduct electric current. However, some solutes dissociate into ions in water, thereby making the aqueous solution an electrical conductor; these solutes are called *electrolytes*. The manner in which the ions conduct electric current is suggested by Figure 5-2. With the apparatus pictured in Figure 5-3, we can detect the presence of ions in an aqueous solution by measuring how well the solution conducts electricity. Depending on which of the following observations we make, we can label a solute as a nonelectrolyte, strong electrolyte, or weak electrolyte.

- *The lamp fails to light up.* Conclusion: There are no ions present (or, if there are some present, their concentration is extremely low). A **nonelectrolyte** is a substance that is not ionized and does not conduct electric current (Fig. 5-3a).

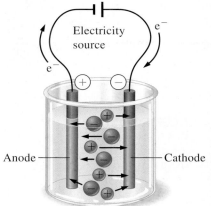

▲ **FIGURE 5-2**
Conduction of electricity through a solution
Two graphite rods called electrodes are placed in a solution. The external source of electricity pulls electrons from one rod and forces them onto the other, creating a positive charge on one electrode and a negative charge on the other (right). In the solution, positive ions (cations) are attracted to the negative electrode, the *cathode*; negative ions (anions) are attracted to the positive electrode, the *anode*. Thus, electric charge is carried through the solution by the migration of ions. Other important aspects of electrical conductivity are discussed in Chapter 20.

Electrolytes and Nonelectrolytes animation

(a)   (b)   (c)

▲ **FIGURE 5-3**
Three types of electrolytes
In **(a)**, there are no ions present to speak of—only molecules. Methanol (methyl alcohol), CH_3OH, is a *nonelectrolyte* in aqueous solutions. In **(b)**, the solute is present almost entirely as individual ions. $MgCl_2$ is a *strong electrolyte* in aqueous solutions. In **(c)**, although most of the solute is present as molecules, a small fraction of the molecules ionize. CH_3COOH is a *weak electrolyte* in aqueous solution. The CH_3COOH molecules that ionize produce acetate ions CH_3COO^- and H^+ ions, and the H^+ ions attach themselves to water molecules to form hydronium ions, H_3O^+.

KEEP IN MIND ▶
that the solvent molecules are densely packed. In diagrams such as Figure 5-3, we will often show the solvent as a uniformly colored background and depict only the solute particles.

 Strong and Weak Electrolytes

Conductivity of HCl. Shake some concentrated HCl(aq) with an equal volume of toluene in a separatory funnel. Allow to settle, and then collect the toluene layer. The layer will be cloudy, but this does not affect the results. Test the conductivity of HCl in toluene. In a nonaqueous solvent, HCl is nonconducting. Add some water to a depth sufficient to contact the electrodes. Stir the system to aid the reaction with water. The point is that HCl is a molecule that must react with water in order to form a solution of ions.

 Strong and Weak Electrolytes movie

Conductivity testers for aqueous solutions can be purchased from chemical supply companies or constructed from readily available materials as described in Zawacky, Susan K. S. *J. Chem. Educ.* **1995:** *72,* 728.

- *The lamp lights up brightly.* Conclusion: The concentration of ions in solution is high. A **strong electrolyte** is a substance that is essentially completely ionized in aqueous solution, and the solution is a good electrical conductor (Fig. 5-3b).
- *The lamp lights up only dimly.* Conclusion: The concentration of ions in solution is low. A **weak electrolyte** is partially ionized in aqueous solution, and the solution is only a fair conductor of electricity (Fig. 5-3c).

The following generalization is helpful when deciding whether a particular solute in an aqueous solution is most likely to be a nonelectrolyte, a strong electrolyte, or a weak electrolyte.

- Essentially all soluble ionic compounds and only a relatively few molecular compounds are strong electrolytes.
- Most molecular compounds are either nonelectrolytes or weak electrolytes.

Now let us consider how best to represent these three types of substances in chemical equations. For water-soluble $MgCl_2$, an ionic compound, we may write

$$MgCl_2(s) \xrightarrow{H_2O} Mg^{2+}(aq) + 2\,Cl^-(aq)$$

This equation means that, in the presence of water, formula units of $MgCl_2$ are dissociated into the separate ions. The best representation of $MgCl_2(aq)$, then, is $Mg^{2+}(aq) + 2\,Cl^-(aq)$.

The equation for a molecular compound that is a strong electrolyte can be written as

$$HCl(g) \xrightarrow{H_2O} H^+(aq) + Cl^-(aq)$$

which means that the best representation of hydrochloric acid, $HCl(aq)$, is $H^+(aq) + Cl^-(aq)$.

The hydrogen cation H^+ is an interesting and important species that has been the subject of intensive research. The ion H^+—a bare proton—is a small particle that interacts with the water molecules surrounding it. The simple hydrogen ion, H^+, does not exist in aqueous solutions. Its actual form is as *hydronium ion*, H_3O^+, in which an H^+ ion is attached to an H_2O molecule. The hydronium ion, in turn, interacts with the water molecules surrounding it to form additional species such as $H_5O_2^+$, $H_7O_3^+$, $H_9O_4^+$ (shown in the margin) and many others. These interactions are called *hydration*, and the hydrated proton is represented as $H^+(aq)$, a shorthand notation. The interaction of the proton with a single water molecule is emphasized by using $H_3O^+(aq)$. The basis for these interactions will be discussed in Chapter 12 and employed extensively in Chapter 16.

The situation in a solution characterized as a weak electrolyte is best described as a reaction that does not go to completion. In such solutions, only a fraction of the solute molecules in solution are ionized. Equations for solutions of this type are written with double arrows, as shown below.

$$HC_2H_3O_2(aq) \rightleftharpoons H^+(aq) + C_2H_3O_2^-(aq)$$

The double arrows indicate that the process is *reversible*—that is, while some $HC_2H_3O_2$ (acetic acid) molecules ionize, some H^+ and $C_2H_3O_2^-$ ions in solution recombine to form new $HC_2H_3O_2$ molecules. Although there is this constant change in any given acetic acid solution, the relative proportions of ionized and nonionized (molecular) acid remain fixed. The predominant species is the molecule $HC_2H_3O_2$, and the solution is best represented by $HC_2H_3O_2(aq)$, *not* $H^+(aq) + C_2H_3O_2^-(aq)$. If we could tag a particular $C_2H_3O_2$ group and watch it over time, we would sometimes see it as the ion $C_2H_3O_2^-$, but most of the time it would be in a molecule, $HC_2H_3O_2$.

For a nonelectrolyte, we simply write the molecular formula. Thus, for a solution of methanol in water we would write $CH_3OH(aq)$.

With this new information about the nature of aqueous solutions, we can introduce a useful notation for solution concentrations. In a solution that is 0.0050 M $MgCl_2$, we assume that the $MgCl_2$ is completely dissociated into ions. Because there are two Cl^- ions for every Mg^{2+} ion, the solution is 0.0050 M Mg^{2+} but 0.0100 M Cl^-. Better still, let us introduce a special symbol for the concentration of a species in solution—the bracket symbol [ ]. The statement $[Mg^{2+}] = 0.0050$ M means that the concentration of the species within the brackets—that is, Mg^{2+}—is 0.0050 mol/L. Thus,

in 0.0050 M MgCl$_2$: $[Mg^{2+}] = 0.0050$ M; $[Cl^-] = 0.0100$ M; $[MgCl_2] = 0$ M

Although we do not usually write expressions like $[MgCl_2] = 0$, it is done here to emphasize that there is essentially no undissociated $MgCl_2$ in the solution.*

Example 5-1 shows how to calculate the concentrations of ions in a strong electrolyte solution.

---

*To say that a strong electrolyte is completely dissociated into individual ions in aqueous solution is a good approximation, but somewhat of an oversimplification. Some of the cations and anions in solution may become associated into units called *ion pairs*. Generally, though, at the low solution concentrations we will be using, assuming complete dissociation will not seriously affect our results.

Hydronium ion
H_3O^+

A hydrated proton
$H_5O_2^+$

A hydrated proton
$H_9O_4^+$

▲ **The hydrated proton**
The hydronium ion, H_3O^+, interacts with other water molecules through electrostatic attractions.

◀ **KEEP IN MIND**
that there are different formulas for acetic acid. The molecular formula, $C_2H_4O_2$, makes no distinction between the types of H atoms; $HC_2H_3O_2$ indicates one ionizable H atom; and CH_3COOH and CH_3CO_2H show that the ionizable H atom is part of the carboxyl group.

Equilibrium of a Weak Acid animation

Introducing the square bracket notation at this point reinforces the concept of electrolytes. Emphasize that for electrolytes, the "as prepared" molarity and the actual species concentrations are not the same thing.

EXAMPLE 5-1

Calculating Ion Concentrations in a Solution of a Strong Electrolyte. What are the aluminum and sulfate ion concentrations in 0.0165 M $Al_2(SO_4)_3$(aq)?

Solution

First, identify the solute as a strong electrolyte—it is a soluble ionic compound—and write an equation to represent its dissociation. The solute consists of the ions Al^{3+} and SO_4^{2-}.

$$Al_2(SO_4)_3(s) \xrightarrow{H_2O} 2\,Al^{3+}(aq) + 3\,SO_4^{2-}(aq)$$

Now, with stoichiometric factors from this equation, relate $[Al^{3+}]$ and $[SO_4^{2-}]$ to the given molarity of $Al_2(SO_4)_3$. The stoichiometric factors shown in blue in the following equations are derived from the fact that 1 mol $Al_2(SO_4)_3$ consists of 2 mol Al^{3+} and 3 mol SO_4^{2-}.

$$[Al^{3+}] = \frac{0.0165\text{ mol }Al_2(SO_4)_3}{1\text{ L}} \times \frac{2\text{ mol }Al^{3+}}{1\text{ mol }Al_2(SO_4)_3} = \frac{0.0330\text{ mol }Al^{3+}}{1\text{ L}}$$

$$= 0.0330\text{ M}$$

$$[SO_4^{2-}] = \frac{0.0165\text{ mol }Al_2(SO_4)_3}{1\text{ L}} \times \frac{3\text{ mol }SO_4^{2-}}{1\text{ mol }Al_2(SO_4)_3} = \frac{0.0495\text{ mol }SO_4^{2-}}{1\text{ L}}$$

$$= 0.0495\text{ M}$$

Practice Example A: The chief ions in seawater are Na^+, Mg^{2+}, and Cl^-. Seawater is approximately 0.438 M NaCl and 0.0512 M $MgCl_2$. What is the molarity of Cl^-—that is, the total $[Cl^-]$—in seawater?

Practice Example B: A water treatment plant adds fluoride ion to the water to the extent of 1.5 mg F^-/L.

(a) What is the molarity of fluoride ion in this water?

(b) If the fluoride ion in the water is supplied by calcium fluoride, what mass of calcium fluoride is present in 1.00×10^6 L of this water?

CONCEPT ASSESSMENT ✓

(1) Which solution is the best electrical conductor? **(a)** 0.50 M CH_3COCH_3(aq); **(b)** 0.50 M CH_3CH_2OH(aq); **(c)** 1.00 M $CH_2OHCHOHCH_2OH$(aq); **(d)** 0.050 M $HC_2H_3O_2$(aq); **(e)** 0.025 M $RbNO_3$(aq).

(2) Which solution has the highest total molarity of ions? **(a)** 0.008 M $Ba(OH)_2$(aq); **(b)** 0.010 M KI(aq); **(c)** 0.011 M $HC_2H_3O_2$(aq); **(d)** 0.030 M $HOCH_2CH_2OH$(aq); **(e)** 0.004 M $Al_2(SO_4)_3$(aq)?

5-2 PRECIPITATION REACTIONS

▲ A qualitative test for Cl^- ion in tap water involves the addition of a few drops of $AgNO_3$(aq). The formation of a precipitate of AgCl(s) confirms the presence of Cl^-.

Some metal salts, such as NaCl, are quite soluble in water, while others, such as AgCl, are not very soluble at all. In fact, so little AgCl dissolves in water that this compound is generally considered to be *insoluble*. Precipitation reactions occur when certain cations and anions combine to produce an insoluble ionic solid called a **precipitate**. One laboratory use of precipitation reactions is in identifying the ions present in a solution (see Chapter 18). In industry, precipitation reactions are used to manufacture numerous chemicals. In the extraction of magnesium metal from seawater, for instance, the first step is to precipitate Mg^{2+} as $Mg(OH)_2$(s). In this section, the objective is to represent precipitation reactions by chemical equations and to apply some simple rules for predicting precipitation reactions.

(a)   (b)   (c)

◄ **FIGURE 5-4**
A precipitate of silver iodide
When an aqueous solution of $AgNO_3$ **(a)** is added to one of NaI **(b)**, insoluble pale yellow or cream-colored AgI(s) precipitates from solution **(c)**.

NET IONIC EQUATIONS

The reaction of silver nitrate and sodium iodide in an aqueous solution yields sodium nitrate in solution and a pale yellow or cream-colored precipitate of silver iodide (Fig. 5-4). Applying the principles of equation writing from Chapter 4, we can write

 Writing Balanced Precipitation Reactions

$$AgNO_3(aq) + NaI(aq) \longrightarrow AgI(s) + NaNO_3(aq) \qquad (5.1)$$

You might note a contradiction, however, between equation (5.1) and something we learned earlier in this chapter. In their aqueous solutions, the soluble ionic compounds $AgNO_3$, NaI, and $NaNO_3$—all *strong* electrolytes—should be represented by their separate ions.

$$Ag^+(aq) + NO_3^-(aq) + Na^+(aq) + I^-(aq) \longrightarrow AgI(s) + Na^+(aq) + NO_3^-(aq) \quad (5.2)$$

We might say that equation (5.1) is the "whole formula" form of the equation, whereas equation (5.2) is the "ionic" form. Notice also that in equation (5.2) $Na^+(aq)$ and $NO_3^-(aq)$ appear on both sides of the equation. These ions are not reactants; they go through the reaction unchanged. We might call them **spectator ions**. If we eliminate the spectator ions, all that remains is the net ionic equation.

$$Ag^+(aq) + I^-(aq) \longrightarrow AgI(s) \qquad (5.3)$$

A **net ionic equation** is an equation that includes only the actual participants in a reaction, with each participant denoted by the symbol or formula that best represents it. Symbols are written for individual ions, such as $Ag^+(aq)$, and whole formulas are written for insoluble solids such as AgI(s). Because net ionic equations include electrically charged species—ions—a net ionic equation must be balanced both for the numbers of atoms of all types and for electric charge. The same net electric charge must appear on both sides of the equation. Throughout the remainder of this chapter, we will represent most chemical reactions in aqueous solution by net ionic equations.

◄ **KEEP IN MIND**
that, although the insoluble solid consists of ions, we don't represent ionic charges in the whole formula. That is, we write AgI(s), not Ag^+I^-(s).

PREDICTING PRECIPITATION REACTIONS

Suppose we are asked whether precipitation occurs when the following aqueous solutions are mixed.

 Precipitation Reactions

$$AgNO_3(aq) + KBr(aq) \longrightarrow ? \qquad (5.4)$$

A simple guideline that predicts many of the solubility rules shown in Table 5.1 is "any salt involving a + 1 cation or a − 1 anion is *likely* to be soluble" (Blake, Bob. *J. Chem. Educ.* **2003**: *80*, 1348). An important exception to this guideline, which is noted in Table 5.1, is that AgCl, AgBr and AgI are insoluble.

A good way to begin is to rewrite expression (5.4) in the ionic form.

$$Ag^+(aq) + NO_3^-(aq) + K^+(aq) + Br^-(aq) \longrightarrow ?   \quad (5.5)$$

There are only two possibilities. Either some cation–anion combination leads to an insoluble solid—a precipitate—or no such combination is possible, and there is no reaction at all.

To predict what will happen without doing experiments, we need some information about which sorts of ionic compounds are water soluble and which are water insoluble. We expect the insoluble ones to form when the appropriate ions are mixed in solution. There are no all-encompassing rules for predicting solubilities, but there are a few guidelines that work for the majority of common ionic solutes. A concise form of these guidelines is presented in Table 5.1.

▶ In principle, all ionic compounds dissolve in water to some extent, though this may be very slight. For practical purposes, we consider a compound to be insoluble if the maximum amount that can dissolve is less than about 0.01 mol/L.

TABLE 5.1   Solubility Guidelines for Common Ionic Solids

Follow the lower-numbered guideline when two guidelines are in conflict. This leads to the correct prediction in most cases.
1. Salts of group 1 cations (with some exceptions for Li^+) and the NH_4^+ cation are soluble.
2. Nitrates, acetates, and perchlorates are soluble.
3. Salts of silver, lead, and mercury(I) are insoluble.
4. Chlorides, bromides, and iodides are soluble.
5. Carbonates, phosphates, sulfides, oxides, and hydroxides are insoluble (sulfides of group 2 cations and hydroxides of Ca^{2+}, Sr^{2+}, and Ba^{2+} are slightly soluble).
6. Sulfates are soluble except for those of calcium, strontium, and barium.

KEEP IN MIND ▶
that when two ionic compounds form a solid precipitate, they do so by exchanging ions. In the formation of AgBr from KBr and AgNO₃, the following exchange takes place.

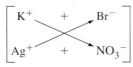

The guidelines from Table 5.1 are applied in the order listed, with the lower-numbered guideline taking precedence in inevitable cases of a conflict. According to these guidelines, AgBr(s) is insoluble in water (rule 3) and should precipitate, whereas KNO₃(s) is soluble (rule 1). Written as an ionic equation, expression (5.5) becomes

$$Ag^+(aq) + NO_3^-(aq) + K^+(aq) + Br^-(aq) \longrightarrow AgBr(s) + K^+(aq) + NO_3^-(aq)$$

For the net ionic equation, we have

$$Ag^+(aq) + Br^-(aq) \longrightarrow AgBr(s)   \quad (5.6)$$

The three predictions concerning precipitation reactions made in Example 5-2 are verified in Figure 5-5.

 Precipitation Reactions movie

▶ **FIGURE 5-5**
Verifying the predictions made in Example 5-2
(a) When NaOH(aq) is added to MgCl₂(aq), a white precipitate of Mg(OH)₂(s) forms. **(b)** When colorless BaS(aq) is added to blue CuSO₄(aq), a dark precipitate forms. The precipitate is a mixture of white BaSO₄(s) and black CuS(s); a slight excess of CuSO₄ remains in solution. **(c)** No reaction occurs when colorless (NH₄)₂SO₄(aq) is added to colorless ZnCl₂(aq).

Apply the solubility guidelines in Table 5.1 to predict whether each of the following solids is water soluble or insoluble. For which are the solubility guidelines inconclusive? **(a)** $Al_2(SO_4)_3$; **(b)** $Cr(OH)_3$; **(c)** K_3PO_4; **(d)** Li_2CO_3; **(e)** ZnS; **(f)** $Mg(MnO_4)_2$; **(g)** $AgClO_4$; **(h)** $CaSO_4$; **(i)** PbO.

EXAMPLE 5-2

Using Solubility Guidelines to Predict Precipitation Reactions. Predict whether a reaction will occur in each of the following cases. If so, write a net ionic equation for the reaction.

(a) $NaOH(aq) + MgCl_2(aq) \longrightarrow$?

(b) $BaS(aq) + CuSO_4(aq) \longrightarrow$?

(c) $(NH_4)_2SO_4(aq) + ZnCl_2(aq) \longrightarrow$?

Solution

(a) Because all common Na compounds are water soluble, Na^+ remains in solution. The combination of Mg^{2+} and OH^- produces insoluble $Mg(OH)_2$. With this information, we can write

$$2\,Na^+(aq) + 2\,OH^-(aq) + Mg^{2+}(aq) + 2\,Cl^-(aq) \longrightarrow$$
$$Mg(OH)_2(s) + 2\,Na^+(aq) + 2\,Cl^-(aq)$$

With the elimination of spectator ions, we obtain

$$2\,OH^-(aq) + Mg^{2+}(aq) \longrightarrow Mg(OH)_2(s)$$

(b) From the solubility guidelines, we conclude that the insoluble combinations formed when Ba^{2+}, S^{2-}, Cu^{2+}, and SO_4^{2-} are found together in solution are $BaSO_4(s)$ and $CuS(s)$. The net ionic equation is

$$Ba^{2+}(aq) + S^{2-}(aq) + Cu^{2+}(aq) + SO_4^{2-}(aq) \longrightarrow BaSO_4(s) + CuS(s)$$

(c) A careful review of the solubility guidelines shows that all the possible ion combinations lead to water-soluble compounds.

$$2\,NH_4^+(aq) + SO_4^{2-}(aq) + Zn^{2+}(aq) + 2\,Cl^-(aq) \longrightarrow \text{no reaction}$$

Practice Example A: Indicate whether a precipitate forms by completing each equation as a net ionic equation. If no reaction occurs, so state.

(a) $AlCl_3(aq) + KOH(aq) \longrightarrow$?

(b) $K_2SO_4(aq) + FeBr_3(aq) \longrightarrow$?

(c) $CaI_2(aq) + Pb(NO_3)_2(aq) \longrightarrow$?

Practice Example B: Indicate through a net ionic equation whether a precipitate forms when the following compounds in aqueous solution are mixed. If no reaction occurs, so state.

(a) sodium phosphate + aluminum chloride $\longrightarrow$?

(b) aluminum sulfate + barium chloride $\longrightarrow$?

(c) ammonium carbonate + lead nitrate $\longrightarrow$?

◀ Students should have Table 5.1 available when working problems such as in Example 5-2.

◀ As you gain experience, you should be able to go directly to a net ionic equation without first writing an ionic equation that includes spectator ions.

◀ **KEEP IN MIND**
that a solution made by combining $ZnSO_4(aq)$ and $NH_4Cl(aq)$ is indistinguishable from the combination of $ZnCl_2(aq)$ and $(NH_4)_2SO_4(aq)$.

◀ Point out that the net ionic equation for a precipitation reaction (ions $\longrightarrow$ solid) is the opposite of that for dissolving a soluble compound (solid $\longrightarrow$ ions).

Precipitation Reactions. Most of the reactions mentioned in this section make effective demonstrations and are easy to perform. Use very large glass containers. Hesitate before stirring to enjoy viewing the billowing clouds of precipitate.

5-3   ACID–BASE REACTIONS

Ideas about acids and bases (or alkalis) date back to ancient times. The word *acid* is derived from the Latin *acidus* (sour). *Alkali* (base) comes from the Arabic *al-qali*, referring to the ashes of certain plants from which alkaline substances can be extracted. The acid–base concept is a major theme in the history of chemistry. The view we describe in this section, proposed by Svante Arrhenius in 1884, is still used in many applications. Later in the text, we will explore more modern theories.

▶ **FIGURE 5-6**
An acid, a base, and an acid–base indicator
The acidic nature of lemon juice is shown by the red color of the acid–base indicator *methyl red*. The basic nature of soap is indicated by the change in color of the indicator from red to yellow.

> Some prefer to indicate $H^+(aq)$ as H_3O^+ and this will be done in Chapter 16. After Brønsted concepts have been introduced it is better to show acid–base reactions as a proton transfer process. A point to make here is that HCl doesn't just fall apart. Because H^+ bonds strongly to water molecules, the dissociation of many acids is highly exothermic.

KEEP IN MIND ▶

that $H^+(aq)$ actually represents a hydrated proton, that is, a proton attached to one H_2O molecule, as in H_3O^+, or to several H_2O molecules, as in $H_9O_4^+$.

ACIDS

From a practical standpoint, acids can be identified by their sour taste, their ability to react with a variety of metals and carbonate minerals, and their effect on the colors of substances called *acid–base indicators* (Fig. 5-6). From a chemist's point of view, however, an **acid** can be defined as a substance that provides hydrogen ions (H^+) in aqueous solution.

When hydrogen chloride dissolves in water, complete ionization into H^+ and Cl^- occurs (HCl is a strong electrolyte).

$$HCl(g) \xrightarrow{H_2O} H^+(aq) + Cl^-(aq)$$

An aqueous solution of nitric acid, also a strong electrolyte, can be represented as

$$H^+(aq) + NO_3^-(aq)$$

Strong acids are molecular compounds that are almost completely ionized into $H^+(aq)$ and accompanying anions when in aqueous solution. In dilute solution, we will consider the ionization to be complete. There are actually so few common strong acids that they make only a short list (Table 5.2).

As described on page 145, the ionization of acetic acid does not go to completion; it is a reversible reaction, and acetic acid is a weak electrolyte.

$$HC_2H_3O_2(aq) \rightleftharpoons H^+(aq) + C_2H_3O_2^-(aq)$$
acetic acid

Acids that are incompletely ionized in aqueous solution are called **weak acids**. Like acetic acid, the vast majority of acids are weak acids.

We can use the same method to calculate ion concentrations in a strong acid as we did in Example 5-1 for other strong electrolytes. Because the ionization of a weak acid does not go to completion, however, it is a more difficult matter to calculate ion concentrations in a weak acid solution. We will defer such calculations until Chapter 16.

BASES

From a practical standpoint, we can identify bases through their bitter taste, slippery feel, and effect on the colors of acid–base indicators (Fig. 5-6). The Arrhenius definition of a **base** is a substance that produces hydroxide ions (OH^-) in aqueous solution. Consider a soluble ionic hydroxide such as NaOH. In the solid state, this compound consists of Na^+ and OH^- ions. When the solid dissolves in water, the ions dissociate.

$$NaOH(s) \xrightarrow{H_2O} Na^+(aq) + OH^-(aq)$$

TABLE 5.2 Common Strong Acids and Strong Bases

Acids	Bases
HCl	LiOH
HBr	NaOH
HI	KOH
$HClO_4$	RbOH
HNO_3	CsOH
H_2SO_4[a]	$Ca(OH)_2$
	$Sr(OH)_2$
	$Ba(OH)_2$

[a] H_2SO_4 ionizes in two distinct steps. It is a strong acid only in its first ionization step (see Section 16-6).

A base that dissociates completely, or very nearly so, in aqueous solution is a **strong base**. As is true of strong acids, the number of common strong bases is small (see Table 5.2). They are primarily the hydroxides of group 1 and some group 2 metals.

Certain substances produce OH^- ions by reacting with water, not just by dissolving in it. Such substances, for example ammonia, are also bases.

$$NH_3(aq) + H_2O(l) \rightleftharpoons NH_4^+(aq) + OH^-(aq) \qquad (5.7)$$

NH_3 is a weak electrolyte; its reaction with water does not go to completion. A base that is incompletely ionized in aqueous solution is a **weak base**. Most basic substances are weak bases.

NEUTRALIZATION

Perhaps the most significant property of acids and bases is the ability of each to cancel or neutralize the properties of the other. In a **neutralization reaction**, an acid and a base react to form water and an aqueous solution of an ionic compound called a **salt**. Thus, in molecular form,

$$HCl(aq) + NaOH(aq) \longrightarrow NaCl(aq) + H_2O(l)$$
$$\text{(acid)} \ + \ \text{(base)} \ \longrightarrow \ \text{(salt)} \ + \text{(water)}$$

Switching to the ionic form we write,

$$\underbrace{H^+(aq) + Cl^-(aq)}_{\text{(acid)}} + \underbrace{Na^+(aq) + OH^-(aq)}_{\text{(base)}} \longrightarrow \underbrace{Na^+(aq) + Cl^-(aq)}_{\text{salt}} + \underbrace{H_2O(l)}_{\text{water}}$$

When the spectator ions are eliminated, the net ionic equation shows the essential nature of the neutralization of a strong acid by a strong base: H^+ ions from the acid and OH^- ions from the base combine to form water.

$$H^+(aq) + OH^-(aq) \longrightarrow H_2O(l)$$

In a neutralization involving the weak base $NH_3(aq)$, we can think of H^+ from an acid combining directly with NH_3 molecules to form NH_4^+. The neutralization can be represented by an ionic equation, for example,

$$\underbrace{H^+(aq) + Cl^-(aq)}_{\text{(acid)}} + \underbrace{NH_3(aq)}_{\text{(base)}} \longrightarrow \underbrace{NH_4^+(aq) + Cl^-(aq)}_{\text{(salt)}}$$

or by a net ionic equation

$$H^+(aq) + NH_3(aq) \longrightarrow NH_4^+(aq)$$

RECOGNIZING ACIDS AND BASES

Acids contain *ionizable* hydrogen atoms, which are generally identified by the way in which the formula of an acid is written. Ionizable H atoms are separated from other H atoms in the formula either by writing them first in the molecular formula or by indicating where they are found in the molecule. Thus, there are two ways that we can show that one H atom in the acetic acid molecule is ionizable and the other three H atoms are not.

$$\underbrace{HC_2H_3O_2 \text{ or } CH_3COOH}_{\text{acetic acid}}$$

In contrast to acetic acid, methane has four H atoms, but they are not ionizable. CH_4 is not an acid, nor is it a base.

A substance whose formula indicates a combination of OH^- ions with cations is generally a strong base (for example, NaOH). To identify a weak base, we usually need a chemical equation for the ionization reaction, as in equation (5.7). The main weak base we will work with at present is NH_3. Note that ethanol, C_2H_5OH, is not a base. The OH group is not present as OH^-, both in pure ethanol and in its aqueous solutions.

▶ **KEEP IN MIND**
that $NH_4^+(aq)$ is formed by the transfer of a proton from a H_2O to a NH_3 molecule, and NH_4^+ interacts with water in much the same way as the hydronium ion does.

Ammonium ion

◀ The formula of $NH_3(aq)$ is sometimes written as NH_4OH (ammonium hydroxide), and its ionization represented as

$$NH_4OH(aq) \rightleftharpoons$$
$$NH_4^+(aq) + OH^-(aq)$$

There is no hard evidence for the existence of NH_4OH, however, that is, in the sense of a discrete substance comprised of NH_4^+ and OH^- ions. We will use only the formula $NH_3(aq)$.

Introduction to Acids and Introduction to Bases animations

Reaction of $HC_2H_3O_2$ and NH_3. Use a light bulb conductivity detector to test 0.1 M $HC_2H_3O_2$ and then (separately) 0.1 M NH_3. Combination of these two solutions yields a highly conducting solution. Complete the net ionic equation.

▲ This marble statue has been eroded by acid rain. Marble consists primarily of $CaCO_3$. Acids react with and dissolve marble through the reaction described in equation (5.10).

MORE ACID–BASE REACTIONS

$Mg(OH)_2$ is a base because it contains OH^-, but this compound is quite insoluble in water. Its finely divided solid particles form a suspension in water that is the familiar milk of magnesia, used as an antacid. In this suspension, $Mg(OH)_2(s)$ does dissolve very slightly, producing some OH^- in solution. If an acid is added, H^+ from the acid combines with this OH^- to form water—neutralization occurs. More $Mg(OH)_2(s)$ dissolves to produce more OH^- in solution, which is neutralized by more H^+, and so on. In this way, the neutralization reaction results in the dissolving of otherwise insoluble $Mg(OH)_2(s)$. The net ionic equation for the reaction of $Mg(OH)_2(s)$ with a strong acid is

$$Mg(OH)_2(s) + 2\,H^+(aq) \longrightarrow Mg^{2+}(aq) + 2\,H_2O(l) \qquad (5.8)$$

$Mg(OH)_2(s)$ also reacts with a weak acid such as acetic acid. In the net ionic equation, acetic acid is written in its molecular form. But remember that some H^+ and $C_2H_3O_2^-$ ions are always present in an acetic acid solution. The H^+ ions react with OH^- ions, as in reaction (5.8), followed by further ionization of $HC_2H_3O_2$, more neutralization, and so on. If enough acetic acid is present, the $Mg(OH)_2$ will dissolve completely.

$$Mg(OH)_2(s) + 2\,HC_2H_3O_2(aq) \longrightarrow Mg^{2+}(aq) + 2\,C_2H_3O_2^-(aq) + 2\,H_2O(l) \quad (5.9)$$

Calcium carbonate (present in limestone and marble) is another water-insoluble solid that is soluble in strong and weak acids. Here the solid produces a low concentration of CO_3^{2-} ions, which combine with H^+ to form the weak acid H_2CO_3. This causes more of the solid to dissolve, and so on. H_2CO_3, carbonic acid, is a very unstable substance that decomposes into H_2O and $CO_2(g)$. Thus, a gas is given off when $CaCO_3(s)$ reacts with an acid and dissolves. Calcium carbonate, like magnesium hydroxide, is used as an antacid.

$$CaCO_3(s) + 2\,H^+(aq) \longrightarrow Ca^{2+}(aq) + H_2O(l) + CO_2(g) \qquad (5.10)$$

The Arrhenius definition recognizes only OH^- as a base, but when we reconsider acids and bases (Chapter 16), we will see that modern theories identify CO_3^{2-} and many other anions, including OH^-, as bases. Table 5.3 lists several common anions and one cation that produce gases in acid–base reactions.

TABLE 5.3	**Some Common Gas-Forming Reactions**
Ion	**Reaction**
HSO_3^-	$HSO_3^- + H^+ \longrightarrow SO_2(g) + H_2O(l)$
SO_3^{2-}	$SO_3^{2-} + 2\,H^+ \longrightarrow SO_2(g) + H_2O(l)$
HCO_3^-	$HCO_3^- + H^+ \longrightarrow CO_2(g) + H_2O(l)$
CO_3^{2-}	$CO_3^{2-} + 2\,H^+ \longrightarrow CO_2(g) + H_2O(l)$
S^{2-}	$S^{2-} + 2\,H^+ \longrightarrow H_2S(g)$
NH_4^+	$NH_4^+ + OH^- \longrightarrow NH_3(g) + H_2O(l)$

EXAMPLE 5-3

Writing Equation(s) for Acid–Base Reactions. Write a net ionic equation to represent the reaction of **(a)** aqueous strontium hydroxide with nitric acid; **(b)** solid aluminum hydroxide with hydrochloric acid.

Solution

These are neutralization reactions, which means they are of the general form: acid + base $\longrightarrow$ salt + water. We can start with the whole-formula equation, switch to the ionic equation, and then delete spectator ions to arrive at the net ionic equation.

In working Example 5-3 or related class examples, remind students again about the basics for writing net ionic equations. In particular, strong acids and ionic compounds are not represented as compounds in the pure (g, l, or s) state, but as ions in solution.

(a) $2 HNO_3(aq) + Sr(OH)_2(aq) \longrightarrow Sr(NO_3)_2(aq) + 2 H_2O(l)$

Ionic form:

$2 H^+(aq) + NO_3^-(aq) + Sr^{2+}(aq) + 2 OH^-(aq) \longrightarrow$
$$Sr^{2+}(aq) + NO_3^-(aq) + 2 H_2O(l)$$

Net ionic equation: Delete the spectator ions (Sr^{2+} and NO_3^-).

$$2 H^+(aq) + 2 OH^-(aq) \longrightarrow 2 H_2O(l)$$

or, more simply,

$$H^+(aq) + OH^-(aq) \longrightarrow H_2O(l)$$

(b) $Al(OH)_3(s) + 3 HCl(aq) \longrightarrow AlCl_3(aq) + 3 H_2O(l)$

Ionic form:

$$Al(OH)_3(s) + 3 H^+(aq) + 3 Cl^-(aq) \longrightarrow Al^{3+}(aq) + 3 Cl^-(aq) + 3 H_2O(l)$$

Net ionic equation: Delete the spectator ion (Cl^-).

$$Al(OH)_3(s) + 3 H^+(aq) \longrightarrow Al^{3+}(aq) + 3 H_2O(l)$$

Practice Example A: Write a net ionic equation to represent the reaction of aqueous ammonia with propionic acid, $HC_3H_5O_2$. What is the formula and name of the salt that results from this neutralization?

Practice Example B: Calcium carbonate is a major constituent of the hard water deposits found in teakettles and automatic coffeemakers. Vinegar, which is essentially a dilute aqueous solution of acetic acid, is commonly used to remove such deposits. Write a net ionic equation for the reaction that occurs.

CONCEPT ASSESSMENT ✓

You are given the four solids, K_2CO_3, CaO, $ZnSO_4$, and $BaCO_3$, and three solvents, $H_2O(l)$, HCl(aq), and $H_2SO_4(aq)$. You are asked to prepare four solutions, each containing one of the four cations, that is, one with $K^+(aq)$, one with $Ca^{2+}(aq)$, and so on. Using water as your *first* choice, what solvent would you use to prepare each solution? Explain your choices.

5-4   OXIDATION–REDUCTION: SOME GENERAL PRINCIPLES

Iron ores are minerals with a high iron content. One of them, hematite, Fe_2O_3, is chemically very similar to ordinary iron rust. In simplified fashion, the reaction in which iron metal is produced from hematite in a blast furnace is described as

$$Fe_2O_3(s) + 3 CO(g) \xrightarrow{\Delta} 2 Fe(l) + 3 CO_2(g) \qquad (5.11)$$

In this reaction, we can think of the CO(g) as taking O atoms away from Fe_2O_3 to produce $CO_2(g)$ and the free element iron. A commonly used term to describe a reaction in which a substance gains O atoms is *oxidation*, and a reaction in which a substance loses O atoms is *reduction*. In reaction (5.11), CO(g) is oxidized and $Fe_2O_3(s)$ is reduced. Oxidation and reduction must always occur together, and such a reaction is called an **oxidation–reduction**, or **redox, reaction**.

Definitions of oxidation and reduction based solely on the transfer of O atoms are too restrictive. By using broader definitions, many reactions in aqueous solution can be described as oxidation–reduction reactions, even when no oxygen is involved.

▲ In the thermite reaction, the iron atoms of iron(III) oxide give up O atoms to Al atoms, producing Al_2O_3.

$Fe_2O_3(s) + 2 Al(s) \longrightarrow$
$$Al_2O_3(s) + 2 Fe(l)$$

   Thermite movie

   Oxidation-Reduction Reactions I animation

◄ Because it is easier to say, the term *redox* is often used instead of oxidation–reduction.

OXIDATION STATE CHANGES

Suppose we rewrite equation (5.11) and indicate the oxidation states (O.S.) of the elements on both sides of the equation by using the rules listed on page 82.

$$\overset{+3 \ -2}{Fe_2O_3} + 3\overset{+2 \ -2}{CO} \longrightarrow 2\overset{0}{Fe} + 3\overset{+4 \ -2}{CO_2}$$

The O.S. of oxygen is -2 everywhere it appears in this equation. That of iron (shown in red) changes. It *decreases* from $+3$ in Fe_2O_3 to 0 in the free element, Fe. The O.S. of carbon (shown in blue) also changes. It *increases* from $+2$ in CO to $+4$ in CO_2. In terms of oxidation state changes, in an oxidation process, the O.S. of some element increases; in a reduction process, the O.S. of some element decreases.

> The reaction of sodium with chlorine is an example of oxidation without any oxygen being involved. Other examples of oxygen-free oxidations are the metal displacement reactions like (5.14).

> *Calculating Oxidation States II activity*

> Students should review the assignment of oxidation numbers in chapter 3 before attempting to write balanced chemical equations of redox reactions.

KEEP IN MIND ▶
that even though we assess oxidation state changes by element, oxidation and reduction involve the entire species in which the element is found. Thus, the compound MnO_2 is reduced, not just an Mn atom; and the ion Cl^- is oxidized, not just the Cl atom.

EXAMPLE 5-4

Identifying Oxidation–Reduction Reactions. Indicate whether each of the following is an oxidation–reduction reaction.

   (a) $MnO_2(s) + 4\,H^+(aq) + 2\,Cl^-(aq) \longrightarrow Mn^{2+}(aq) + 2\,H_2O(l) + Cl_2(g)$
   (b) $H_2PO_4^-(aq) + OH^-(aq) \longrightarrow HPO_4^{2-}(aq) + H_2O(l)$

Solution

In each case, indicate the oxidation states of the elements on both sides of the equation, and look for changes.

   (a) The O.S. of Mn decreases from $+4$ in MnO_2 to $+2$ in Mn^{2+}. MnO_2 is reduced to Mn^{2+}. The O.S. of O remains at -2 throughout the reaction, and that of H, at $+1$. The O.S. of Cl increases from -1 in Cl^- to 0 in Cl_2. Cl^- is oxidized to Cl_2. The reaction is an oxidation–reduction reaction.
   (b) The O.S. of H is $+1$ on both sides of the equation. Oxygen remains at O.S. -2 throughout. The O.S. of phosphorus is $+5$ in $H_2PO_4^-$ and also $+5$ in HPO_4^{2-}. There are no changes in O.S. This is not an oxidation–reduction reaction. (It is, in fact, an acid–base reaction.)

Practice Example A: Identify whether each of the following is an oxidation–reduction reaction.

   (a) $(NH_4)_2SO_4(aq) + Ba(NO_3)_2(aq) \longrightarrow BaSO_4(s) + 2\,NH_4NO_3(aq)$
   (b) $2\,Pb(NO_3)_2(s) \longrightarrow 2\,PbO(s) + 4\,NO_2(g) + O_2(g)$

Practice Example B: Identify the species that is oxidized and the species that is reduced in the reaction

   $$5\,VO^{2+}(aq) + MnO_4^-(aq) + H_2O \longrightarrow 5\,VO_2^+(aq) + Mn^{2+}(aq) + 2\,H^+(aq)$$

OXIDATION AND REDUCTION HALF-REACTIONS

The reaction illustrated in Figure 5-7 is an oxidation–reduction reaction.

$$Zn(s) + Cu^{2+}(aq) \longrightarrow Zn^{2+}(aq) + Cu(s)$$

We can show this by evaluating changes in oxidation state, but there is another especially useful way to establish that it is an oxidation–reduction reaction. Think of the reaction as involving two **half-reactions** occurring at the same time—an oxidation and a reduction. The overall reaction is the sum of the two half-reactions. We can represent the half-reactions by half-equations and the overall reaction by an overall equation.

> Silver Tree. The reaction of Cu with Ag^+ can be effectively (and inexpensively) performed in miniature on an overhead projector. Use a small glass dish. Bend some Cu wire into the shape of a tree and place into the dish. Cover with 0.01 M (or less) $AgNO_3$. The "tree" will slowly grow small needles of silver. Lower initial concentrations require more time to react but can produce better needles.

Oxidation:	$Zn(s) \longrightarrow Zn^{2+}(aq) + 2\,e^-$	(5.12)
Reduction:	$Cu^{2+}(aq) + 2\,e^- \longrightarrow Cu(s)$	(5.13)
Overall:	$Zn(s) + Cu^{2+}(aq) \longrightarrow Zn^{2+}(aq) + Cu(s)$	(5.14)

(a)

(b)

(c)

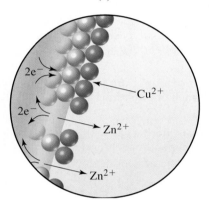

▲ **FIGURE 5-7**
An oxidation–reduction reaction
(a) A zinc rod above an aqueous solution of copper(II) sulfate.
(b) Following immersion of the Zn rod in the $CuSO_4$(aq) for several hours, the blue color of Cu^{2+}(aq) disappears and a deposit of copper forms on the rod. In the microscopic view of the reaction (left), Zn atoms lose electrons to the metal surface, entering the solution as Zn^{2+} ions. Cu^{2+} ions from solution pick up electrons and deposit on the metal surface as atoms of solid copper. **(c)** The pitted zinc rod (providing evidence that zinc entered into a chemical reaction) and the collected copper metal.

In half-reaction (5.12), Zn is oxidized—its oxidation state increases from 0 to +2. This change corresponds to a loss of two electrons by each zinc atom. In half-reaction (5.13), Cu^{2+} is reduced—its oxidation state decreases from +2 to 0. This change corresponds to the gain of two electrons by each Cu^{2+} ion. To summarize,

 Oxidation–Reduction Chemistry of Tin and Zinc movie

- **Oxidation** is a process in which the O.S. of some element *increases* as electrons are lost, appearing on the *right* side of a half-equation.
- **Reduction** is a process in which the O.S. of some element *decreases* as electrons are gained, appearing on the *left* side of a half-equation.
- Oxidation and reduction half-reactions must always occur together, and the total number of electrons associated with the oxidation must *equal* the total number associated with the reduction.

EXAMPLE 5-5

Representing an Oxidation–Reduction Reaction Through Half-Equations and an Overall Equation. Show the oxidation and reduction that occur, and write an overall ionic equation for the reaction of iron with hydrochloric acid solution to produce H_2(g) and Fe^{2+} (Fig. 5-8).

Solution

Oxidation: $Fe(s) \longrightarrow Fe^{2+}(aq) + 2\,e^-$

Reduction: $2\,H^+(aq) + 2\,e^- \longrightarrow H_2(g)$

Overall: $Fe(s) + 2\,H^+(aq) \longrightarrow Fe^{2+}(aq) + H_2(g)$

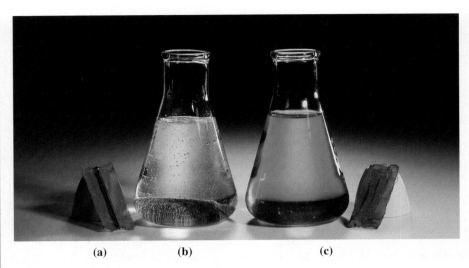

(a)   (b)   (c)

▲ **FIGURE 5-8**
Displacement of H^+(aq) by iron—Example 5-5 illustrated
(a) An iron nail is wrapped in a piece of copper screen. **(b)** The nail and screen are placed in HCl(aq). Hydrogen gas is evolved as the nail reacts. **(c)** The nail reacts completely and produces Fe^{2+}(aq), but the copper does not react.

Practice Example A: Represent the reaction of aluminum with hydrochloric acid (reaction 4.2) by oxidation and reduction half-equations and an overall equation.

Practice Example B: Represent the reaction of chlorine gas with aqueous sodium bromide to produce liquid bromine and aqueous sodium chloride by oxidation and reduction half-equations and an overall equation.

Figure 5-8 and Example 5-5 suggest some fundamental questions about oxidation–reduction. For example,

- Why does Fe react with HCl(aq), displacing H_2(g), whereas Cu does not?
- Why does Fe form Fe^{2+} and not Fe^{3+} in this reaction?

Even now, you can probably see that the answers to these questions lie in the relative abilities of Fe and Cu atoms to give up electrons—to become oxidized. Fe gives up electrons more easily than does Cu; also, Fe is more readily oxidized to Fe^{2+} than it is to Fe^{3+}. We can give more complete answers after we develop specific criteria describing electron loss and gain in Chapter 20. For now, the information in Table 5.4 should be helpful. The table lists some common metals that react with acids to displace H_2(g) and a few that do not. As noted in the table, most of the group 1 and 2 metals are so reactive that they will react with cold water to produce H_2(g) and a solution of the metal hydroxide.

Precipitation, Redox and Neutralization Reactions activity

TABLE 5.4 **Behavior of Some Common Metals with Nonoxidizing Acids[a]**	
React to Produce H_2(g)	**Do Not React**
Alkali metals (group 1)[b]	Cu, Ag, Au, Hg
Alkaline earth metals (group 2)[b]	
Al, Zn, Fe, Sn, Pb	

[a] A nonoxidizing acid (for example, HCl, HBr, HI) is one in which the only possible reduction half-reaction is the reduction of H^+ to H_2. Additional possibilities for metal–acid reactions are considered in Chapter 20.
[b] With the exception of Be and Mg, all group 1 and group 2 metals also react with cold water to produce H_2(g); the metal hydroxide is the other product.

CONCEPT ASSESSMENT ✔

Disregarding the fact that the equations below are not balanced, is it likely that either represents a reaction that could possibly occur? Explain.

(a) $MnO_4^-(aq) + Cr_2O_7^{2-}(aq) + H^+(aq) \longrightarrow MnO_2(s) + Cr^{3+}(aq) + H_2O(l)$

(b) $Cl_2(g) + OH^-(aq) \longrightarrow Cl^-(aq) + ClO_3^-(aq) + H_2O(l)$

5-5   BALANCING OXIDATION–REDUCTION EQUATIONS

The same principles of equation balancing apply to oxidation–reduction (redox) equations as to other equations—balance for numbers of atoms, and balance for electric charge. However, it is often a little more difficult to apply these principles in redox equations. In fact, only a small proportion of redox equations can be balanced by simple inspection. We need a systematic approach, and while several methods are available, we emphasize one that considers the overall reaction to occur as a combination of separate half-reactions for oxidation and reduction.

THE HALF-EQUATION METHOD

The basic steps in this method of balancing a redox equation are:

- Write and balance separate half-equations for oxidation and reduction.
- Adjust coefficients in the two half-equations so that the same number of electrons appear in each half-equation.
- Add together the two half-equations (canceling out electrons) to obtain the balanced overall equation.

This method is applied in Example 5-6.

> ✔ *Half-reaction* or *half-equation*, which is it? *Reaction* refers to the actual process. An *equation* is a notation we write out to indicate the formulas of the reactants and products, and their mole relationships. Many refer to what we balance here as half-reactions but half-equation is more proper.

> *Balancing Redox Equations activity*

EXAMPLE 5-6

Balancing the Equation for a Redox Reaction in Acidic Solution. The reaction described by expression (5.15) below is used to determine the sulfite ion concentration present in wastewater from a papermaking plant. Write the balanced equation for this reaction in acidic solution.

$$SO_3^{2-}(aq) + MnO_4^-(aq) \longrightarrow SO_4^{2-}(aq) + Mn^{2+}(aq) \tag{5.15}$$

Solution

Step 1. *Write skeleton half-equations based on the species undergoing oxidation and reduction.* The O.S. of sulfur increases from +4 in SO_3^{2-} to +6 in SO_4^{2-}. The O.S. of Mn decreases from +7 in MnO_4^- to +2 in Mn^{2+}. The half-equations are

$$SO_3^{2-}(aq) \longrightarrow SO_4^{2-}(aq)$$
$$MnO_4^+(aq) \longrightarrow Mn^{2+}(aq)$$

Step 2. *Balance each half-equation for numbers of atoms, in this order:*

- atoms other than H and O
- O atoms, by adding H_2O with the appropriate coefficient
- H atoms, by adding H^+ with the appropriate coefficient

The other atoms (S and Mn) are already balanced in the half-equations. To balance O atoms, we add one H_2O molecule to the left side of the first half-equation and four to the right side of the second.

$$SO_3^{2-}(aq) + H_2O(l) \longrightarrow SO_4^{2-}(aq)$$
$$MnO_4^-(aq) \longrightarrow Mn^{2+}(aq) + 4\,H_2O(l)$$

◀ Try balancing expression (5.15) by inspection just for numbers of atoms. You will see that the electric charge does not balance.

◀ In most cases, you should be able to identify the key species in half-equations without having to evaluate oxidation states.

Several methods for balancing half-equations are available and everyone has their favorite. It should be much less confusing to the student, however, if the method taught in class is the same as that presented in the text. If the instructor does have a "better" method, handout materials should be provided to the students to replace this section.

Students commonly miscalculate the charges, and sometimes they omit them altogether. (SO_3 and SO_3^{2-} are not the same thing!) Consequently, many will have trouble here at step 3. The number of electrons transferred in a half-equation should be the same as the oxidation state change. Some balancing methods use this to set the number of electrons. Here this can serve as a valuable check.

Reduction of MnO_4^- by Sulfite in Acidic Solution. Use a large beaker of water and first add sufficient $KMnO_4(aq)$ so as to obtain a fairly intense violet color. Add some $H_2SO_4(aq)$ to make the solution acidic. Add freshly prepared $NaHSO_3(aq)$, slowly with stirring. The Mn^{2+} formed is nearly colorless. Display a sample of saturated $MnSO_4$ to show that it is actually a pale pink.

Reduction of $Cr_2O_7^{2-}$ by Sulfite in Acidic Solution. Repeat as above, now using $K_2Cr_2O_7$. This goes from orange to midnight blue (Cr^{3+}). Use more $Cr_2O_7^{2-}$ to obtain a deeper colored product.

Students have difficulty balancing half-equations in which more than one atom per formula is oxidized or reduced, as with $Cr_2O_7^{2-}$. The above demonstration works well as a class example of how to handle this situation.

To balance H atoms, we add two H^+ ions to the right side of the first half-equation and eight to the left side of the second.

$$SO_3^{2-}(aq) + H_2O(l) \longrightarrow SO_4^{2-}(aq) + 2\,H^+(aq)$$

$$MnO_4^-(aq) + 8\,H^+(aq) \longrightarrow Mn^{2+}(aq) + 4\,H_2O(l)$$

Step 3. *Balance each half-equation for electric charge.* Add the number of electrons necessary to get the same electric charge on both sides of each half-equation. By doing this, you will see that the half-equation in which electrons appear on the right side is the *oxidation half-equation*. The other half-equation, with electrons on the left side, is the *reduction half-equation*.

Oxidation:
$$SO_3^{2-}(aq) + H_2O(l) \longrightarrow SO_4^{2-}(aq) + 2\,H^+(aq) + 2\,e^-$$
(net charge on each side, -2)

Reduction:
$$MnO_4^-(aq) + 8\,H^+(aq) + 5\,e^- \longrightarrow Mn^{2+}(aq) + 4\,H_2O(l)$$
(net charge on each side, $+2$)

Step 4. *Obtain the overall redox equation by combining the half-equations.* Multiply the oxidation half-equation by five and the reduction half-equation by two. This results in $10\,e^-$ on each side of the overall equation. These terms cancel out. *Electrons must not appear in the final equation.*

Overall:
$$5\,SO_3^{2-}(aq) + 5\,H_2O(l) \longrightarrow 5\,SO_4^{2-}(aq) + 10\,H^+(aq) + \cancel{10\,e^-}$$
$$\underline{2\,MnO_4^-(aq) + 16\,H^+(aq) + \cancel{10\,e^-} \longrightarrow 2\,Mn^{2+}(aq) + 8\,H_2O(l)}$$
$$5\,SO_3^{2-}(aq) + 2\,MnO_4^-(aq) + 5\,H_2O(l) + 16\,H^+(aq) \longrightarrow$$
$$5\,SO_4^{2-}(aq) + 2\,Mn^{2+}(aq) + 8\,H_2O(l) + 10\,H^+(aq)$$

Step 5. *Simplify.* The overall equation should not contain the same species on both sides. Subtract $5\,H_2O$ from each side of the equation in step 4. This leaves $3\,H_2O$ on the right. Also subtract $10\,H^+$ from each side, leaving $6\,H^+$ on the left.

$$5\,SO_3^{2-}(aq) + 2\,MnO_4^-(aq) + 6\,H^+(aq) \longrightarrow$$
$$5\,SO_4^{2-}(aq) + 2\,Mn^{2+}(aq) + 3\,H_2O(l)$$

Step 6. *Verify.* Check the overall equation to ensure that it is balanced both for numbers of atoms and electric charge. For example, show that in the balanced equation from step 5, the net charge on each side of the equation is -6:
$$(5 \times 2-) + (2 \times 1-) + (6 \times 1+) = (5 \times 2-) + (2 \times 2+) = -6$$

Practice Example A: Balance the equation for this reaction in acidic solution.
$$Fe^{2+}(aq) + MnO_4^-(aq) \longrightarrow Fe^{3+}(aq) + Mn^{2+}(aq)$$

Practice Example B: Balance the equation for this reaction in acidic solution.
$$UO^{2+}(aq) + Cr_2O_7^{2-}(aq) \longrightarrow UO_2^{2+}(aq) + Cr^{3+}(aq)$$

For ready reference, the procedure used in Example 5-6 is summarized in Table 5.5.

BALANCING REDOX EQUATIONS IN BASIC SOLUTION

To balance equations for redox reactions in basic solution, a step or two must be added to the procedure used in Example 5-6. The problem is that in basic solution, OH^-, not H^+, must appear in the final balanced equation. Because both OH^- and H_2O contain H and O atoms, at times it is hard to decide on which side of the half-equations to put each one. One simple approach is to treat the reaction as though it were occurring in an acidic solution, and balance it as in Example 5-6. Then, add to each side of the overall redox equation a number of OH^- ions equal to the number of H^+ ions. Where H^+ and OH^-

---

TABLE 5.5   Balancing Equations for Redox Reactions in Acidic Aqueous Solutions by the Half-Equation Method: A Summary

- Write the equations for the oxidation and reduction half-reactions.
- In each half-equation:
  (1) Balance atoms of all the elements except H and O.
  (2) Balance oxygen using H_2O.
  (3) Balance hydrogen using H^+.
  (4) Balance charge, using electrons.
- If necessary, equalize the number of electrons in the oxidation and reduction half-equations by multiplying one or both half-equations by appropriate integers.
- Add the half-equations, then cancel species common to both sides of the overall equation.
- Check that both numbers of atoms and charges balance.

---

appear on the same side of the equation, combine them to produce H_2O molecules. If H_2O now appears on both sides of the equation, subtract the same number of H_2O molecules from each side, leaving a remainder of H_2O on just one side. This method is illustrated in Example 5-7.

EXAMPLE 5-7

Balancing the Equation for a Redox Reaction in Basic Solution. Balance the equation for the reaction in which cyanide ion is oxidized to cyanate ion by permanganate ion in basic solution, and the permanganate is itself reduced to $MnO_2(s)$.

$$MnO_4^-(aq) + CN^-(aq) \longrightarrow MnO_2(s) + OCN^-(aq) \qquad (5.16)$$

Solution

The half-reactions and the overall reaction are initially treated as though they were occurring in an acidic solution and, finally, the overall equation is adjusted to a basic solution.

Step 1. *Write half-equations for the oxidation and reduction half-reactions, and balance them for Mn, C, and N atoms.*

$$MnO_4^-(aq) \longrightarrow MnO_2(s)$$
$$CN^-(aq) \longrightarrow OCN^-(aq)$$

Step 2. *Balance the half-equations for O and H atoms. Add H_2O and/or H^+ as required.* In the MnO_4^- half-equation, there are four O's on the left and two on the right. Adding $2\,H_2O$ balances the O's on the right. Since there are now four H's on the right, it is necessary to add $4\,H^+$ on the left side to balance them. In the CN^- half-equation, there is one O on the right but none on the left, so H_2O must be added to the left side and $2\,H^+$ to the right.

$$MnO_4^-(aq) + 4\,H^+(aq) \longrightarrow MnO_2(s) + 2\,H_2O(l)$$
$$CN^-(aq) + H_2O(l) \longrightarrow OCN^-(aq) + 2\,H^+(aq)$$

Step 3. *Balance the half-equations for electric charge by adding the appropriate numbers of electrons.*

Reduction: $MnO_4^-(aq) + 4\,H^+(aq) + 3\,e^- \longrightarrow MnO_2(s) + 2\,H_2O(l)$

Oxidation: $CN^-(aq) + H_2O(l) \longrightarrow OCN^-(aq) + 2\,H^+(aq) + 2\,e^-$

Step 4. *Combine the half-equations to obtain an overall redox equation.* Multiply the reduction half-equation by two and the oxidation half-equation by three to obtain the common multiple $6\,e^-$ in each half-equation. Make the appropriate cancellations of H^+ and H_2O.

$$2\,MnO_4^-(aq) + 8\,H^+(aq) + 6\,e^- \longrightarrow 2\,MnO_2(s) + 4\,H_2O(l)$$
$$\underline{\hspace{2cm} 3\,CN^-(aq) + 3\,H_2O(l) \longrightarrow 3\,OCN^-(aq) + 6\,H^+(aq) + 6\,e^-}$$

Overall: $2\,MnO_4^-(aq) + 3\,CN^-(aq) + 2\,H^+(aq) \longrightarrow$
$$2\,MnO_2(s) + 3\,OCN^-(aq) + H_2O(l)$$

Using H^+ (initially) to balance an equation in basic solution may look strange, but it works!

Reduction of MnO_4^- by Sulfite in Basic Solution. Proceed as previously (see page 158) but now using $NaOH(aq)$ instead of H_2SO_4. The reaction proceeds from MnO_4^- (violet) through MnO_4^{2-} (green) to MnO_2 (a brown-black solid). One can balance the equation stepwise or overall.

Reduction of MnO_4^- by Cellulose. Add about 5% by volume of 1 M NaOH to 0.1 M $KMnO_4$ in a beaker. Dip or dribble onto a piece of filter paper. Observe color changes as above. The reducing agent may be represented as $C(H_2O)_n$ reacting to form CO_3^{2-}.

Blue Sky and Sunset Reaction. Cut a 10-cm diameter hole in a piece of cardboard and place on an overhead projector. Place one 15-cm crystallizing dish upside down on the projector, and another dish on top of it right side up. Dissolve 5 g $Na_2S_2O_3 \cdot 5 H_2O$ in 700 mL water; pour into dish. Darken room. Add 5 mL concentrated HCl and stir. Ask students to look directly at the experiment, not "into the sun" on the screen. As colloidal sulfur slowly forms, this will preferentially scatter blue light. Explain that a similar effect, involving atmospheric nitrogen, causes our atmosphere to appear blue. After the colloid thickens, direct the class to look at the screen. What remains to be seen—after all of the blue has been lost—are the longer wavelengths, an artificial sunset.

Step 5. *Change from an acidic to a basic medium by adding 2 OH^- to both sides of the overall equation; combine 2 H^+ and 2 OH^- to form 2 H_2O; and simplify.*

$$2 MnO_4^-(aq) + 3 CN^-(aq) + 2 H^+(aq) + 2 OH^-(aq) \longrightarrow$$
$$2 MnO_2(s) + 3 OCN^-(aq) + H_2O(l) + 2 OH^-(aq)$$

$$2 MnO_4^-(aq) + 3 CN^-(aq) + 2 H_2O(l) \longrightarrow$$
$$2 MnO_2(s) + 3 OCN^-(aq) + H_2O(l) + 2 OH^-(aq)$$

Subtract one H_2O molecule from each side to obtain the overall balanced redox equation for reaction (5.16).

$$2 MnO_4^-(aq) + 3 CN^-(aq) + H_2O(l) \longrightarrow$$
$$2 MnO_2(s) + 3 OCN^-(aq) + 2 OH^-(aq)$$

Step 6. *Verify.* Check the final overall equation to ensure that it is balanced both for number of atoms and electric charge. For example, show that in the balanced equation from step 5, the net charge on each side of the equation is −5.

Practice Example A: Balance the equation for this reaction in basic solution.

$$S(s) + OCl^-(aq) \longrightarrow SO_3^{2-}(aq) + Cl^-(aq)$$

Practice Example B: Balance the equation for this reaction in basic solution.

$$MnO_4^-(aq) + SO_3^{2-}(aq) \longrightarrow MnO_2(s) + SO_4^{2-}(aq)$$

For ready reference, the procedure used in Example 5-7 is summarized in Table 5.6.

TABLE 5.6 Balancing Equations for Redox Reactions in Basic Aqueous Solutions by the Half-Equation Method: A Summary

- Balance the equation as if the reaction were occurring in acidic medium by using the method for acidic aqueous solutions summarized in Table 5.5.
- Add a number of OH^- ions equal to the number of H^+ ions to both sides of the overall equation.
- On the side of the overall equation containing both H^+ and OH^- ions, combine them to form H_2O molecules. If H_2O molecules now appear on both sides of the overall equation, cancel the same number from each side, leaving a remainder of H_2O on just one side.
- Check that both numbers of atoms and charges balance.

▶ As an alternate method for half-equations in basic solutions, add *two* OH^- for every O required to the O-deficient side, and add *one* H_2O to the other side (the net effect is adding one O to the O-deficient side). Then add *one* H_2O for every H required to the H-deficient side, and add *one* OH^- to the other side (the net effect is adding one H to the H-deficient side).

DISPROPORTIONATION REACTIONS

In some oxidation–reduction reactions, called **disproportionation reactions**, the same substance is both oxidized and reduced. Some of these reactions have practical significance. The decomposition of hydrogen peroxide, H_2O_2, produces $O_2(g)$. It is the $O_2(g)$ that has a germicidal effect when a dilute aqueous solution of hydrogen peroxide (usually 3%) is used as an antiseptic.

$$2 H_2O_2(aq) \longrightarrow 2 H_2O(l) + O_2(g) \tag{5.17}$$

In reaction (5.17), the oxidation state of oxygen changes from −1 in H_2O_2 to −2 in H_2O (a reduction) and to 0 in $O_2(g)$ (an oxidation). H_2O_2 is both oxidized and reduced.

Solutions of sodium thiosulfate ($Na_2S_2O_3$) are often used in the laboratory in redox reactions. The disproportionation of $S_2O_3^{2-}$ produces sulfur as one of its products, which is the reason that old stock solutions of $Na_2S_2O_3$ sometimes contain a pale yellow deposit.

$$S_2O_3^{2-}(aq) + 2 H^+(aq) \longrightarrow S(s) + SO_2(g) + H_2O(l) \tag{5.18}$$

The oxidation states of S are +2 in $S_2O_3^{2-}$, 0 in S(s), and +4 in $SO_2(g)$.

▲ Hydrogen peroxide "bubbles" when poured over a cut because of the production of gaseous oxygen.

The same substance appears on the left side in each half-equation for a disproportionation reaction. The balanced half-equations and overall equation for reaction (5.18) are

Oxidation: $S_2O_3^{2-}(aq) + H_2O(l) \longrightarrow 2\,SO_2(g) + 2\,H^+(aq) + 4\,e^-$

Reduction: $S_2O_3^{2-}(aq) + 6\,H^+(aq) + 4\,e^- \longrightarrow 2\,S(s) + 3\,H_2O(l)$

$\overline{2\,S_2O_3^{2-}(aq) + 4\,H^+(aq) \longrightarrow 2\,S(s) + 2\,SO_2(g) + 2\,H_2O(l)}$

Overall: $S_2O_3^{2-}(aq) + 2\,H^+(aq) \longrightarrow S(s) + SO_2(g) + H_2O(l)$

CONCEPT ASSESSMENT ✔

Is it possible for two different reactants in a redox reaction to yield a single product? Explain.

Are You Wondering . . .

How to balance the equation for a redox reaction that occurs in a medium other than an aqueous solution?

An example of such a reaction is the oxidation of $NH_3(g)$ to $NO(g)$, the first step in the commercial production of nitric acid.

$$NH_3(g) + O_2(g) \longrightarrow NO(g) + H_2O(g)$$

Some people prefer a method called the *oxidation-state change method** for reactions of this type, but the half-equation method works just as well. All that is needed is to treat the reaction as if it were occurring in an aqueous acidic solution; H^+ should appear as both a reactant and a product and cancel out in the overall equation, as seen below.

Oxidation: $4\{NH_3 + H_2O \longrightarrow NO + 5\,H^+ + 5\,e^-\}$

Reduction: $5\{O_2 + 4\,H^+ + 4\,e^- \longrightarrow 2\,H_2O\}$

Overall: $4\,NH_3 + 5\,O_2 \longrightarrow 4\,NO + 6\,H_2O$

*In this method, changes in oxidation states are identified. That of nitrogen increases from -3 in NH_3 to $+2$ in NO, corresponding to a "loss" of five electrons per N atom. That of oxygen decreases from 0 in O_2 to -2 in NO and H_2O, corresponding to a "gain" of two electrons per O atom. The proportion of N to O atoms must be 2 N (loss of $10\,e^-$) to 5 O (gain of $10\,e^-$).

$$2\,NH_3 + \frac{5}{2}\,O_2 \longrightarrow 2\,NO + 3\,H_2O \quad \text{or} \quad 4\,NH_3 + 5\,O_2 \longrightarrow 4\,NO + 6\,H_2O$$

5-6 OXIDIZING AND REDUCING AGENTS

Oxidation–Reduction Reactions II animation

Chemists frequently use the terms *oxidizing agent* and *reducing agent* to describe certain of the reactants in redox reactions, as in statements like "fluorine gas is a powerful oxidizing agent," or "calcium metal is a good reducing agent." Let us briefly consider the meaning of these terms.

In a redox reaction, the substance that makes it possible for some other substance to be oxidized is called the **oxidizing agent**, or **oxidant**. In doing so, the oxidizing agent is itself reduced. Similarly, the substance that causes some other substance to be reduced is called the **reducing agent**, or **reductant**. In the reaction, the reducing agent is itself oxidized. Or, stated in other ways,

An oxidizing agent (oxidant)

- contains an element whose oxidation state *decreases* in a redox reaction
- *gains* electrons (electrons are found on the left side of its half-equation)
- is reduced

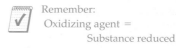

Remember:
Oxidizing agent =
Substance reduced
Reducing agent =
Substance oxidized
The point here is that whatever works as an oxidizing agent in one reaction is a good candidate for use as the same in another reaction.

Compound or ion	Oxidation state
NO_3^-	+5
N_2O_4	+4
NO_2^-	+3
NO	+2
N_2O	+1
N_2	0
NH_2OH	−1
N_2H_4	−2
NH_3	−3

This species cannot be oxidized further

This species cannot be reduced further

Oxidation half-reaction (reducing agent)

Reduction half-reaction (oxidizing agent)

▶ FIGURE 5-9
Oxidation states of nitrogen: Identifying oxidizing and reducing agents

A reducing agent (reductant)

- contains an element whose oxidation state *increases* in a redox reaction
- *loses* electrons (electrons are found on the right side of its half-equation)
- is oxidized

In general, a substance with an element in one of its highest possible oxidation states is an oxidizing agent. If the element is in one of its lowest possible oxidation states, the substance is a reducing agent.

Figure 5-9 shows the range of oxidation states of nitrogen and the species to which they correspond. The oxidation state of the nitrogen in dinitrogen tetroxide (N_2O_4) is nearly the maximum value attainable, and hence N_2O_4 is generally an oxidizing agent. On the other hand, the nitrogen atom in hydrazine (N_2H_4) is in nearly the lowest oxidation state, and hence hydrazine is generally a reducing agent. When these two liquid compounds are mixed, a vigorous reaction takes place.

$$N_2O_4(l) + 2 N_2H_4(l) \longrightarrow 3 N_2(g) + 4 H_2O(g)$$

In this reaction, one of the nitrogen-containing molecules is the oxidizing agent and the other the reducing agent. This reaction releases so much energy that it is used in some rocket propulsion systems.

Certain substances in which the oxidation state of an element is between its highest and lowest possible values may act as oxidizing agents in some instances and reducing agents in others. For example, in the reaction of hydrazine with hydrogen to produce ammonia, hydrazine acts as an oxidizing agent.

$$N_2H_4 + H_2 \longrightarrow 2 NH_3$$

EXAMPLE 5-8

Identifying Oxidizing and Reducing Agents. Hydrogen peroxide, H_2O_2, is a versatile chemical. Its uses include bleaching wood pulp and fabrics and substituting for chlorine in water purification. One reason for its versatility is that it can be either an oxidizing or a reducing agent. For the following reactions, identify whether hydrogen peroxide is an oxidizing or reducing agent.

(a) $H_2O_2(aq) + 2 Fe^{2+}(aq) + 2 H^+(aq) \longrightarrow 2 H_2O(l) + 2 Fe^{3+}(aq)$

(b) $5 H_2O_2(aq) + 2 MnO_4^-(aq) + 6 H^+(aq) \longrightarrow$

$$8 H_2O(l) + 2 Mn^{2+}(aq) + 5 O_2(g)$$

Solution

(a) Fe^{2+} is oxidized to Fe^{3+} and because H_2O_2 makes this possible, it is an oxidizing agent. Viewed another way, we see that the oxidation state of oxygen in H_2O_2 is -1. In H_2O, it is -2. Hydrogen peroxide is reduced and thereby acts as an oxidizing agent.

(b) MnO_4^- is reduced to Mn^{2+}, and H_2O_2 makes this possible. In this situation, hydrogen peroxide is a reducing agent. Or, the oxidation state of oxygen increases from -1 in H_2O_2 to 0 in O_2. Hydrogen peroxide is oxidized and thereby acts as a reducing agent.

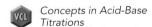
◀ When H_2O_2 acts as an oxidizing agent, it is reduced to H_2O in acidic solution or to OH^- in basic solution. When it acts as a reducing agent, it is oxidized to $O_2(g)$.

Practice Example A: Is $H_2(g)$ an oxidizing or reducing agent in this reaction? Explain.

$$2\,NO_2(g) + 7\,H_2(g) \longrightarrow 2\,NH_3(g) + 4\,H_2O(g)$$

Practice Example B: Identify the oxidizing agent and the reducing agent in the reaction.

$$4\,Au(s) + 8\,CN^-(aq) + O_2(g) + 2\,H_2O(l) \longrightarrow 4[Au(CN)_2]^-(aq) + 4\,OH^-(aq)$$

Permanganate ion, MnO_4^-, is a versatile oxidizing agent that has many uses in the chemical laboratory. In the next section, we describe its use in the quantitative analysis of iron—that is, the determination of the exact (quantitative) amount of iron in an iron-containing material. Ozone, $O_3(g)$, a triatomic form of oxygen, is an oxidizing agent used in water purification, as in the oxidation of the organic compound phenol, C_6H_5OH.

$$C_6H_5OH(aq) + 14\,O_3(g) \longrightarrow 6\,CO_2(g) + 3\,H_2O(l) + 14\,O_2(g)$$

Thiosulfate ion, $S_2O_3^{2-}$, is an important reducing agent. One of its industrial uses is as an antichlor to destroy residual chlorine from the bleaching of fibers.

$$S_2O_3^{2-}(aq) + 4\,Cl_2(aq) + 5\,H_2O(l) \longrightarrow 2\,HSO_4^-(aq) + 8\,H^+(aq) + 8\,Cl^-(aq)$$

Oxidizing and reducing agents also play important roles in biological systems—in photosynthesis (using solar energy to synthesize glucose), metabolism (oxidizing glucose), and the transport of oxygen.

▲ Colored material in the presence of bleach. A red colored cloth becomes white when immersed in liquid bleach, $NaOCl(aq)$. $NaOCl(aq)$, a powerful oxidizing agent, oxidizes the red pigment to colorless products.

CONCEPT ASSESSMENT ✔

A newspaper account of an accidental spill of hydrochloric acid in an area where sodium hydroxide solution was also stored spoke of the potential hazardous release of chlorine gas if the two solutions should come into contact. Was this an accurate accounting of the hazard involved? Explain.

5-7   STOICHIOMETRY OF REACTIONS IN AQUEOUS SOLUTIONS: TITRATIONS

VCL   *Concepts in Acid-Base Titrations*

If our objective is to obtain the maximum yield of a product at the lowest cost, we would generally choose the most expensive reactant as the limiting reactant and use excess amounts of the other reactants. This is the case in most precipitation reactions. In some instances, as in determining the concentration of a solution, we may not be interested in the products of a reaction but only in the relationship between two reactants. Then we have to carry out the reaction in such a way that neither reactant is in excess. A method that has long been used for doing this is known as *titration*.

A solution of one reactant is placed in a small beaker or flask. Another reactant, also in solution and commonly referred to as titrant, is in a *buret*, a long, graduated tube equipped with a stopcock valve. The second solution is slowly added to the first by manipulating the stopcock. **Titration** is a reaction carried out by the carefully controlled addition of one solution to another.

(a) (b) (c)

▲ **FIGURE 5-10**
An acid–base titration—Example 5-9 illustrated
(a) A 5.00-mL sample of vinegar, a small quantity of water, and a few drops of phenolphthalein indicator are added to a flask. **(b)** 0.1000 M NaOH from a previously filled buret is slowly added. **(c)** As long as the acid is in excess, the solution in the flask remains colorless. When the acid has been neutralized, an additional drop of NaOH(aq) causes the solution to become slightly basic. The phenolphthalein indicator turns a light pink. The first lasting appearance of the pink color is taken to be the equivalence point of the titration.

 Acid–Base Titration animation

▶ The key to a successful acid–base titration is in selecting the right indicator. We learn how to do this when we consider theoretical aspects of titration in Chapter 17.

The trick is to stop the titration at the point where both reactants have reacted completely, a condition called the **equivalence point** of the titration. Key to every titration is that at the equivalence point, the two reactants have combined in stoichiometric proportions; both have been consumed, and neither remains in excess.

In modern chemical laboratories appropriate measuring instruments are used to signal when the equivalence point is reached. Still widely used, though, is a technique in which a very small quantity of a substance added to the reaction mixture changes color at or very near the equivalence point. Such substances are called **indicators**. Figure 5-10 illustrates the neutralization of an acid by a base by the titration technique. Calculations that use titration data are much the same as those introduced in Section 4-3, and they are also illustrated in Example 5-9.

✓ These problems provide a comprehensive review of several techniques previously covered: mole, volume, molarity conversions, reaction stoichiometry, and mass percent. Proceed from the easy to the not-so-easy. Whether the titration reaction is acid–base or redox, the common point is that, at the equivalence point, the balanced equation can be used to convert moles of one reactant into moles of another reactant (or product).

EXAMPLE 5-9

Using Titration Data to Establish the Concentrations of Acids and Bases. Vinegar is a dilute aqueous solution of acetic acid produced by the bacterial fermentation of apple cider, wine or other carbohydrate material. The legal minimum acetic acid content of vinegar is 4% by mass. A 5.00-mL sample of a particular vinegar is titrated with 38.08 mL of 0.1000 M NaOH(aq). Does this sample exceed the minimum limit? (Vinegar has a density of about 1.01 g/mL.)

Solution

With ideas from Section 5-3, we can write a net ionic equation for the neutralization reaction.

$$HC_2H_3O_2(aq) + OH^-(aq) \longrightarrow C_2H_3O_2^-(aq) + H_2O(l)$$

From titration data, we calculate the amount of one reactant, and by using a stoichiometric factor, we then determine the amount of the other. In the present case, we know the volume and molarity of NaOH(aq), from which we determine the number of moles of OH^-. Then, using the factor $1\ mol\ HC_2H_3O_2/1\ mol\ OH^-$, we calculate the quantity of $HC_2H_3O_2$, first in moles and then in grams. Finally, as a separate calculation, we calculate the mass percent composition $HC_2H_3O_2$ in the 5.00-mL sample.

The conversions for the first part of the calculation are

$$mL\ NaOH \longrightarrow L\ NaOH \longrightarrow mol\ NaOH \longrightarrow mol\ OH^- \longrightarrow$$
$$mol\ HC_2H_3O_2 \longrightarrow g\ HC_2H_3O_2$$

$$?\ g\ HC_2H_3O_2 = 38.08\ mL \times \frac{1\ L}{1000\ mL} \times \frac{0.1000\ mol\ NaOH}{1\ L} \times \frac{1\ mol\ OH^-}{1\ mol\ NaOH}$$

$$\times \frac{1\ mol\ HC_2H_3O_2}{1\ mol\ OH^-} \times \frac{60.05\ g\ HC_2H_3O_2}{1\ mol\ HC_2H_3O_2}$$

$$= 0.2287\ g\ HC_2H_3O_2$$

This mass of $HC_2H_3O_2$ is found in 5.00 mL of vinegar of density 1.01 g/mL. The percent mass of $HC_2H_3O_2$ is

$$\%\ HC_2H_3O_2 = \frac{0.2287\ g\ HC_2H_3O_2}{5.00\ mL\ vinegar} \times \frac{1\ mL\ vinegar}{1.01\ g\ vinegar} \times 100\%$$

$$= 4.53\%\ HC_2H_3O_2$$

The vinegar sample exceeds the legal minimum limit, but only slightly. There is also a standard for the maximum amount of acetic acid allowed in vinegar. A vinegar producer might use this titration technique to ensure that the vinegar stays between these limits. The competitors' products might also be monitored in this way.

Practice Example A: A particular solution of NaOH is supposed to be approximately 0.100 M. To determine the exact molarity of the NaOH(aq), a 0.5000-g sample of $KHC_8H_4O_4$ is dissolved in water and titrated with 24.03 mL of the NaOH(aq). What is the actual molarity of the NaOH(aq)?

$$HC_8H_4O_4^-(aq) + OH^-(aq) \longrightarrow C_8H_4O_4^{2-}(aq) + H_2O(l)$$

Practice Example B: A 0.235-g sample of a solid that is 92.5% NaOH and 7.5% $Ca(OH)_2$, by mass, requires 45.6 mL of a HCl(aq) solution for its titration. What is the molarity of the HCl(aq)?

The use of "normality" and simplified equations as $N_1V_1 = N_2V_2$ is now discouraged. The normality of a solution can vary depending on the reaction in which it is used. It is safer to use molarity and the balanced chemical equation to convert moles of one substance to moles of another substance.

◀ Pure acetic acid is about 20 times more concentrated than is vinegar and must be handled with care (for example, it should not be inhaled). Whether a material is harmless or hazardous is sometimes simply a matter of its concentration.

CONCEPT ASSESSMENT ✓

A 10.00-mL sample of 0.311 M KOH is added to 31.10 mL of 0.100 M HCl. Is the resulting mixture acidic, basic, or exactly neutral? Explain.

Suppose we need a $KMnO_4$(aq) solution of exactly known molarity, close to 0.020 M. We cannot prepare this solution by weighing out the required amount of $KMnO_4$(s) and dissolving it in water. The solid is not pure, and its actual purity (that is, the mass percent $KMnO_4$) is *not known*. On the other hand, we can obtain iron wire in essentially pure form and allow the wire to react with an acid to yield Fe^{2+}(aq). Fe^{2+}(aq) is oxidized to Fe^{3+}(aq) by $KMnO_4$(aq) in an acidic solution. By determining the volume of $KMnO_4$(aq) required to oxidize a known quantity of Fe^{2+}(aq), we can calculate the exact molarity of the $KMnO_4$(aq). This procedure, which determines the exact molarity of a solution, is called **standardization of a solution**. It is illustrated in Example 5-10 and Figure 5-11.

Emphasize that *standardize* means "determine the concentration of" a solution, usually to three or four significant figures. It is not so important that the concentration be a round number (as 0.1000 vs. 0.1035 M), but rather that the concentration be accurately known.

◀ Aeration and chemicals are used to treat effluent wastewater from papermaking.

Water is not just water. Water often contains impurities that make it unsuitable for some purposes. For instance, a chemist would not use ordinary tap water to prepare an aqueous solution of silver nitrate. The solution would acquire a milky cast from the reaction of $Ag^+(aq)$ with traces of $Cl^-(aq)$ to form $AgCl(s)$. Yet this same tap water is probably perfectly safe to drink.

The way in which water is purified depends on how it is to be used or on how it has been used. Water for a certain industrial application may require a different prior treatment than does water for domestic use. Also, water that has been used in a chemical plant may require a different treatment after use than does domestic sewage. Still, these varying treatments of water share a common feature. They include reactions in aqueous solutions of the general types described in this chapter. Let us look at a few examples.

REMOVAL OF IRON FROM DRINKING WATER

Certain wells deliver water with up to 25 mg of iron per liter, but the federal recommended limit in drinking water in the United States is 0.3 mg/L. Methods of removing excess iron generally involve (1) making the chlorinated water slightly basic with slaked lime, $Ca(OH)_2$, (2) oxidizing Fe^{2+} to Fe^{3+} with hypochlorite ion, OCl^-, and (3) precipitating $Fe(OH)_3(s)$ from the basic solution. The reactions can be represented by these equations:

$$Cl_2(g) + 2\,OH^-(aq) \longrightarrow Cl^-(aq) + OCl^-(aq) + H_2O(l)$$

$$2\,Fe^{2+}(aq) + OCl^-(aq) + H_2O(l) \longrightarrow$$
$$2\,Fe^{3+}(aq) + Cl^-(aq) + 2\,OH^-(aq)$$

$$Fe^{3+}(aq) + 3\,OH^-(aq) \longrightarrow Fe(OH)_3(s)$$

(a)　　　　　　　　　　(b)　　　　　　　　　　(c)

▲ FIGURE 5-11

Standardizing a solution of an oxidizing agent through a redox titration—Example 5-10 illustrated

(a) The solution contains a known amount of Fe^{2+}, and the buret is filled with the intensely colored $KMnO_4(aq)$ to be standardized. **(b)** As it is added to the strongly acidic solution of $Fe^{2+}(aq)$, the $KMnO_4(aq)$ is immediately decolorized as a result of reaction (5.19). **(c)** When all the Fe^{2+} has been oxidized to Fe^{3+}, additional $KMnO_4(aq)$ has nothing left to oxidize and the solution turns a distinctive pink. Even a fraction of a drop of the $KMnO_4(aq)$ beyond the equivalence point is sufficient to cause this pink coloration.

While all of this is occurring, the OCl^- is also serving its primary function: destroying pathogenic microorganisms in the water.

REMOVAL OF OXYGEN FROM BOILER WATER

High-temperature boilers are used to convert water to steam in electric power plants. Dissolved oxygen in the water is highly objectionable because it promotes corrosion of the steel from which many of the boiler parts are made. Because $O_2(g)$ is a good oxidizing agent, a reducing agent such as hydrazine, N_2H_4, is needed to remove it.

$$O_2(aq) + N_2H_4(aq) \longrightarrow 2\,H_2O(l) + N_2(g)$$

REMOVAL OF PHOSPHATES FROM DOMESTIC SEWAGE

Eutrophication is a term that describes a series of events leading to the rapid growth of algae, killing of fish, and other deleterious effects in bodies of freshwater. These events are caused by an excess of nutrients, principally phosphates. The treatment of domestic sewage includes the removal of phosphates. A particularly simple method is to precipitate the phosphates with slaked lime, $Ca(OH)_2$. The phosphates may be present in a number of different forms, including hydrogen phosphate ion, HPO_4^{2-}.

$$5\,Ca^{2+}(aq) + 3\,HPO_4^{2-}(aq) + 4\,OH^-(aq) \longrightarrow$$
$$Ca_5OH(PO_4)_3(s) + 3\,H_2O(l)$$

The precipitate has the composition of the mineral hydroxyapatite.

DESTRUCTION OF CYANIDE ION IN INDUSTRIAL OPERATIONS

Cyanide compounds are used in metal-cleaning operations, in electroplating, and in extracting gold from gold-bearing rocks in mining operations. The cyanide ion must be destroyed in waste solutions from these operations. This can be done through an oxidation–reduction reaction, such as

$$2\,CN^-(aq) + 5\,OCl^-(aq) + 2\,OH^-(aq) \longrightarrow$$
$$N_2(g) + 2\,CO_3^{2-}(aq) + 5\,Cl^-(aq) + H_2O(l)$$

The poisonous $CN^-(aq)$ is converted to innocuous $N_2(g)$ and $CO_3^{2-}(aq)$.

Later in the text, we will consider additional examples of water treatment that have important domestic and industrial uses, such as reverse osmosis in Chapter 13 and water softening in Chapter 21. Also, we must not overlook the biological processes that play an important role in water treatment, particularly in the treatment of wastewater.

EXAMPLE 5-10

Standardizing a Solution for Use in Redox Titrations. A piece of iron wire weighing 0.1568 g is converted to $Fe^{2+}(aq)$ and requires 26.24 mL of a $KMnO_4(aq)$ solution for its titration. What is the molarity of the $KMnO_4(aq)$?

$$5\,Fe^{2+}(aq) + MnO_4^-(aq) + 8\,H^+(aq) \longrightarrow 5\,Fe^{3+}(aq) + Mn^{2+}(aq) + 4\,H_2O(l) \quad (5.19)$$

Solution

First, determine the amount (in moles) of $KMnO_4$ consumed in the titration.

$$? \text{ mol } KMnO_4 = 0.1568 \text{ g Fe} \times \frac{1 \text{ mol Fe}}{55.847 \text{ g Fe}} \times \frac{1 \text{ mol Fe}^{2+}}{1 \text{ mol Fe}}$$

$$\times \frac{1 \text{ mol MnO}_4^-}{5 \text{ mol Fe}^{2+}} \times \frac{1 \text{ mol KMnO}_4}{1 \text{ mol MnO}_4^-}$$

$$= 5.615 \times 10^{-4} \text{ mol KMnO}_4$$

The volume of solution containing the 5.615×10^{-4} mol $KMnO_4$ is 26.24 mL = 0.02624 L, which means that

$$\text{concn } KMnO_4(aq) = \frac{5.615 \times 10^{-4} \text{ mol KMnO}_4}{0.02624 \text{ L}} = 0.02140 \text{ M } KMnO_4(aq)$$

◄ **KEEP IN MIND**

that the key to a titration calculation is that the amounts of two reactants consumed in the titration are stoichiometrically equivalent—neither reactant is in excess. Here, 1 mol MnO_4^- is stoichiometrically equivalent to 5 mol Fe^{2+}.

Practice Example A: A 0.376-g sample of an iron ore is dissolved in acid, the iron reduced to $Fe^{2+}(aq)$ and then titrated with 41.25 mL of 0.02140 M $KMnO_4$. Determine the mass percent Fe in the iron ore.
[*Hint:* Use equation (5.19).]

Practice Example B: Another substance that may be used to standardize $KMnO_4(aq)$ is sodium oxalate. If 0.2482 g $Na_2C_2O_4$ is dissolved in water and titrated with 23.68 mL $KMnO_4$, what is the molarity of the $KMnO_4(aq)$?

$$MnO_4^-(aq) + C_2O_4^{2-}(aq) + H^+(aq) \longrightarrow$$
$$Mn^{2+}(aq) + H_2O(l) + CO_2(g) \quad \text{(not balanced)}$$

Summary

5-1 The Nature of Aqueous Solutions—Solutes in aqueous solution are characterized as **nonelectrolytes**, which are essentially undissociated; **weak electrolytes**, which dissociate to a limited extent, and **strong electrolytes**, which dissociate almost completely into ions. In addition to the molarity based on the solute as a whole, a solution's concentration can be stated in terms of the molarities of the individual solute species present—molecules and ions. Calculating ion concentrations in a strong electrolyte solution is easily done.

5-2 Precipitation Reactions—Some reactions in aqueous solution involve the combination of ions to yield a water-insoluble solid—a **precipitate**. Precipitation reactions are generally represented by **net ionic equations**, a form in which only the reacting ions and solid precipitates are shown, and **spectator ions** are deleted. Precipitation reactions usually can be predicted using a few simple solubility guidelines (Table 5.1).

5-3 Acid–Base Reactions—According to the Arrhenius theory, a substance that ionizes to produce H^+ ions in aqueous solution is an **acid**. It is a **strong acid** (Table 5.2) if the ionization goes essentially to completion and a **weak acid** if the ionization is limited. Similarly, a **base** produces OH^- ions in aqueous solution and is either a **strong base** (Table 5.2) or a **weak base**, depending on the extent of the ionization. In a typical acid–base, or **neutralization**, **reaction**, H^+ ions from the acid and OH^- ions from the base combine to form HOH (water). The other product of the reaction is an ionic compound, a **salt**. Some reactions in which gases are evolved can also be treated as acid–base reactions (Table 5.3).

5-4 Oxidation–Reduction: Some General Principles—In an **oxidation–reduction (redox) reaction** certain atoms undergo an increase in oxidation state, a process called **oxidation**. Other atoms undergo a decrease in oxidation state, or **reduction**. Another useful view of redox reactions is as the combination of separate **half-reactions** for the oxidation and the reduction.

5-5 Balancing Oxidation–Reduction Equations—An effective way to balance a redox equation is to break down the reaction into separate half-reactions, write and balance half-equations for these half-reactions, and recombine the balanced half-equations into an overall balanced equation (Table 5.5). A slight variation of this method is used for a reaction that occurs in a basic aqueous solution (Table 5.6). A redox reaction in which the same substance is both oxidized and reduced is called a **disproportionation reaction**.

5-6 Oxidizing and Reducing Agents—The **oxidizing agent (oxidant)** is the key reactant in an oxidation half-reaction and is *reduced* in the redox reaction. The **reducing agent (reductant)** is the key reactant in a reduction half-reaction and is *oxidized* in the redox reaction. Some substances act only as oxidizing agents; others, only as reducing agents. Many can act as either, depending on the reaction (Fig. 5-9).

5-7 Stoichiometry of Reactions in Aqueous Solutions: Titrations—A common laboratory technique applicable to precipitation, acid–base, and redox reactions is **titration**. The key point in a titration is the **equivalence point**, which is assessed with the aid of an **indicator**. Titration data can be used to establish a solution's molarity, called **standardization of a solution**, or to provide other information about the compositions of samples being analyzed.

Integrative Example

Sodium dithionite, $Na_2S_2O_4$, is an important reducing agent. One interesting use is the reduction of chromate ion to insoluble chromium(III) hydroxide by dithionite ion, $S_2O_4^{2-}$, in basic solution. Sulfite ion is another product. The chromate ion may be present in wastewater from a chromium-plating plant, for example. What mass of $Na_2S_2O_4$ is consumed in a reaction with 100.0 L of wastewater having $[CrO_4^{2-}] = 0.0148$ M?

Solution

◀ White solid sodium dithionite, $Na_2S_2O_4$, is added to a yellow solution of potassium chromate, $K_2CrO_4(aq)$ (left). A product of the reaction is gray-green chromium(III) hydroxide, $Cr(OH)_3(s)$ (right).

1. *Write an ionic expression representing the reaction.* $\quad CrO_4^{2-}(aq) + S_2O_4^{2-}(aq) + OH^-(aq) \longrightarrow Cr(OH)_3(s) + SO_3^{2-}(aq)$

2. *Balance the redox equation.* Begin by writing skeleton half-equations.

$$CrO_4^{2-} \longrightarrow Cr(OH)_3$$
$$S_2O_4^{2-} \longrightarrow SO_3^{2-}$$

Balance the half-equations for Cr, S, O, and H atoms as if the half-reactions occur in acidic solution.

$$CrO_4^{2-} + 5\,H^+ \longrightarrow Cr(OH)_3 + H_2O$$
$$S_2O_4^{2-} + 2\,H_2O \longrightarrow 2\,SO_3^{2-} + 4\,H^+$$

Balance the half-equations for charge, and label them as oxidation and reduction.

Oxidation: $\quad S_2O_4^{2-} + 2\,H_2O \longrightarrow 2\,SO_3^{2-} + 4\,H^+ + 2\,e^-$

Reduction: $\quad CrO_4^{2-} + 5\,H^+ + 3\,e^- \longrightarrow Cr(OH)_3 + H_2O$

Combine the half-equations into an overall equation.

$$3 \times [S_2O_4^{2-} + 2\,H_2O \longrightarrow 2\,SO_3^{2-} + 4\,H^+ + 2\,e^-]$$
$$\underline{2 \times [CrO_4^{2-} + 5\,H^+ + 3\,e^- \longrightarrow Cr(OH)_3 + H_2O]}$$
$$3\,S_2O_4^{2-} + 2\,CrO_4^{2-} + 4\,H_2O \longrightarrow$$
$$6\,SO_3^{2-} + 2\,Cr(OH)_3 + 2\,H^+$$

3. *Change the conditions to basic solution.* Add 2 OH$^-$ to each side of the equation for acidic solution, and combine 2 H$^+$ and 2 OH$^-$ to form 2 H$_2$O on the right.

$$3\,S_2O_4^{2-} + 2\,CrO_4^{2-} + 4\,H_2O + 2\,OH^- \longrightarrow$$
$$6\,SO_3^{2-} + 2\,Cr(OH)_3 + 2\,H_2O$$

Subtract 2 H$_2$O from each side of the equation to obtain the final balanced equation.

$$3\,S_2O_4^{2-}(aq) + 2\,CrO_4^{2-}(aq) + 2\,H_2O(l) + 2\,OH^-(aq) \longrightarrow$$
$$6\,SO_3^{2-}(aq) + 2\,Cr(OH)_3(s)$$

4. *Complete the stoichiometric calculation.* The conversion pathway is 100.0 L waste water $\longrightarrow$ mol CrO$_4^{2-}$ $\longrightarrow$ mol S$_2$O$_4^{2-}$ $\longrightarrow$ mol Na$_2$S$_2$O$_4$ $\longrightarrow$ g Na$_2$S$_2$O$_4$.

$$? \text{ g Na}_2\text{S}_2\text{O}_4 = 100.0 \text{ L} \times \frac{0.0148 \text{ mol CrO}_4^{2-}}{1 \text{ L}}$$
$$\times \frac{3 \text{ mol S}_2\text{O}_4^{2-}}{2 \text{ mol CrO}_4^{2-}} \times \frac{1 \text{ mol Na}_2\text{S}_2\text{O}_4}{1 \text{ mol S}_2\text{O}_4^{2-}}$$
$$\times \frac{174.1 \text{ g Na}_2\text{S}_2\text{O}_4}{1 \text{ mol Na}_2\text{S}_2\text{O}_4} = 387 \text{ g Na}_2\text{S}_2\text{O}_4$$

Assessment

In solving this problem the major effort was to balance a redox equation for a reaction under basic conditions. This allowed us to find the molar relationship between dithionite and chromate ions. The remainder of the problem was a stoichiometry calculation for a reaction in solution, much like Example 4-11 (page 124). A quick check of the final result involves (1) ensuring that the redox equation is balanced, and (2) noting that the number of moles of CrO$_4^{2-}$ is about 1.5 (i.e., 100 × 0.0148), that the number of moles of S$_2$O$_4^{2-}$ is about 2.25 (i.e., 1.5 × 3/2), and that the mass of Na$_2$S$_2$O$_4$ is somewhat more than 350 (i.e., 2.25 × 175).

Exercises

Strong Electrolytes, Weak Electrolytes, and Nonelectrolytes

1. Using information from this chapter, indicate whether each of the following substances in aqueous solution is a nonelectrolyte, weak electrolyte, or strong electrolyte. (a) HC$_6$H$_5$O; (b) Li$_2$SO$_4$; (c) MgI$_2$; (d) (CH$_3$CH$_2$)$_2$O; (e) Sr(OH)$_2$.

2. Select the (a) best and (b) poorest electrical conductors from the following solutions, and explain the reason for your choices: 0.10 M NH$_3$; 0.10 M NaCl; 0.10 M HC$_2$H$_3$O$_2$ (acetic acid); 0.10 M C$_2$H$_5$OH (ethanol).

3. What response would you expect in the apparatus of Figure 5-3 if the solution tested were 1.0 M HCl? What response would you expect if the solution were both 1.0 M HCl and 1.0 M HC$_2$H$_3$O$_2$?

4. NH$_3$(aq) conducts electric current only weakly. The same is true for HC$_2$H$_3$O$_2$(aq). When these solutions are mixed, however, the resulting solution is a good conductor. How do you explain this?

5. Sketches (a–c) are molecular views of the solute in an aqueous solution. For each of the sketches, indicate whether the solute is a strong, weak, or nonelectrolyte; and which of these substances it is: sodium chloride, propionic acid, hypochlorous acid, ammonia, barium bromide, ammonium chloride, methanol.

(a)   (b)   (c)

6. After identifying the three substances represented by the sketches in Exercise 5, sketch molecular views of aqueous solutions of the remaining four substances listed.

Ion Concentrations

7. Determine the concentration of the ion indicated in each solution. **(a)** $[K^+]$ in 0.238 M KNO_3; **(b)** $[NO_3^-]$ in 0.167 M $Ca(NO_3)_2$; **(c)** $[Al^{3+}]$ in 0.083 M $Al_2(SO_4)_3$; **(d)** $[Na^+]$ in 0.209 M Na_3PO_4.

8. Which solution has the greatest $[SO_4^{2-}]$: 0.075 M H_2SO_4; 0.22 M $MgSO_4$; 0.15 M Na_2SO_4; 0.080 M $Al_2(SO_4)_3$; 0.20 M $CuSO_4$?

9. A solution is prepared by dissolving 0.132 g $Ba(OH)_2 \cdot 8 H_2O$ in 275 mL of water solution. What is $[OH^-]$ in this solution?

10. A solution is 0.126 M KCl and 0.148 M $MgCl_2$. What are $[K^+]$, $[Mg^{2+}]$, and $[Cl^-]$ in this solution?

11. Express the following data for cations in solution as molarities. **(a)** 14.2 mg Ca^{2+}/L; **(b)** 32.8 mg K^+/100 mL; **(c)** 225 μg Zn^{2+}/mL.

12. What molarity of NaF(aq) corresponds to a fluoride ion content of 0.9 mg F^-/L, the federal government's recommended limit for fluoride ion in drinking water?

13. Which of the following aqueous solutions has the highest concentration of K^+? **(a)** 0.0850 M K_2SO_4; **(b)** a solution containing 1.25 g KBr/100 mL; **(c)** a solution having 8.1 mg K^+/mL.

14. Which aqueous solution has the greatest $[H^+]$: **(a)** 0.011 M $HC_2H_3O_2$; **(b)** 0.010 M HCl; **(c)** 0.010 M H_2SO_4; **(d)** 1.00 M NH_3? Explain your choice.

15. How many milligrams of MgI_2 must be added to 250.0 mL of 0.0876 M KI to produce a solution with $[I^-] = 0.1000$ M?

16. If 25.0 mL H_2O evaporates from a 1.00 L of a solution containing 12.0 mg K_2SO_4/mL, what is $[K^+]$ in the solution that remains?

17. Assuming the volumes are additive, what is the $[Cl^-]$ in a solution obtained by mixing 225 mL of 0.625 M KCl and 615 mL of 0.385 M $MgCl_2$?

18. Assuming the volumes are additive, what is the $[NO_3^-]$ in a solution obtained by mixing 275 mL of 0.283 M KNO_3, 328 mL of 0.421 M $Mg(NO_3)_2$, and 784 mL of H_2O?

Predicting Precipitation Reactions

19. Complete each of the following as a net ionic equation, indicating whether a precipitate forms. If no reaction occurs, so state.
    (a) $Na^+ + Br^- + Pb^{2+} + 2 NO_3^- \longrightarrow$
    (b) $Mg^{2+} + 2 Cl^- + Cu^{2+} + SO_4^{2-} \longrightarrow$
    (c) $Fe^{3+} + 3 NO_3^- + Na^+ + OH^- \longrightarrow$

20. Complete each of the following as a net ionic equation. If no reaction occurs, so state.
    (a) $Ca^{2+} + 2 I^- + 2 Na^+ + CO_3^{2-} \longrightarrow$
    (b) $Ba^{2+} + S^{2-} + 2 Na^+ + SO_4^{2-} \longrightarrow$
    (c) $2 K^+ + S^{2-} + Ca^{2+} + 2 Cl^- \longrightarrow$

21. Predict in each case whether a reaction is likely to occur. If so, write a net ionic equation.
    (a) $HI(aq) + Zn(NO_3)_2(aq) \longrightarrow$
    (b) $CuSO_4(aq) + Na_2CO_3(aq) \longrightarrow$
    (c) $Cu(NO_3)_2(aq) + Na_3PO_4(aq) \longrightarrow$

22. Predict in each case whether a reaction is likely to occur. If so, write a net ionic equation.
    (a) $AgNO_3(aq) + CuCl_2(aq) \longrightarrow$
    (b) $Na_2S(aq) + FeCl_2(aq) \longrightarrow$
    (c) $Na_2CO_3(aq) + AgNO_3(aq) \longrightarrow$

23. What reagent solution might you use to separate the cations in the following mixtures, that is, with one ion appearing in solution and the other in a precipitate? [*Hint:* Refer to Table 5.1, and consider water also to be a reagent.]
    (a) $BaCl_2(s)$ and $MgCl_2(s)$
    (b) $MgCO_3(s)$ and $Na_2CO_3(s)$
    (c) $AgNO_3(s)$ and $Cu(NO_3)_2(s)$

24. What reagent solution might you use to separate the cations in each of the following mixtures? [*Hint:* Refer to Exercise 23.]
    (a) $PbSO_4(s)$ and $Cu(NO_3)_2(s)$
    (b) $Mg(OH)_2(s)$ and $BaSO_4(s)$
    (c) $PbCO_3(s)$ and $CaCO_3(s)$

25. You are provided with NaOH(aq), $K_2SO_4(aq)$, $Mg(NO_3)_2(aq)$, $BaCl_2(aq)$, NaCl(aq), $Sr(NO_3)_2(aq)$, $AgNO_3(aq)$, and $BaSO_4(s)$. Write net ionic equations to show how you would use one or more of those reagents to obtain **(a)** $SrSO_4(s)$; **(b)** $Mg(OH)_2(s)$; **(c)** KCl(aq).

26. Write net ionic equations to show how you would use one or more of the reagents in Exercise 25 to obtain **(a)** $BaSO_4(s)$; **(b)** AgCl(s); **(c)** $KNO_3(aq)$.

Acid–Base Reactions

27. Complete each of the following as a *net ionic equation*. If no reaction occurs, so state.
    (a) $Ba^{2+} + 2 OH^- + HC_2H_3O_2 \longrightarrow$
    (b) $H^+ + Cl^- + HC_3H_5O_2 \longrightarrow$
    (c) $FeS(s) + H^+ + I^- \longrightarrow$
    (d) $K^+ + HCO_3^- + H^+ + NO_3^- \longrightarrow$
    (e) $Mg(s) + H^+ \longrightarrow$

28. Every antacid contains one or more ingredients capable of reacting with excess stomach acid (HCl). The es-

sential neutralization products are CO_2 and/or H_2O. Write net ionic equations to represent the neutralizing action of the following popular antacids.
    (a) Alka-Seltzer (sodium bicarbonate)
    (b) Tums (calcium carbonate)
    (c) milk of magnesia (magnesium hydroxide)
    (d) Maalox (magnesium hydroxide; aluminum hydroxide)
    (e) Rolaids [$NaAl(OH)_2CO_3$]

29. In this chapter, we described an acid as a substance capable of producing H^+ and a salt as the ionic compound formed by the neutralization of an acid by a base. Write ionic equations to show that sodium hydrogen sulfate has the characteristics of both a salt and an acid (sometimes called an *acid salt*).

30. A neutralization reaction between an acid and a base is a common method of preparing useful salts. Give net ionic equations showing how the following salts could be prepared in this way: $(NH_4)_2HPO_4$; NH_4NO_3; and $(NH_4)_2SO_4$.

31. Which solutions would you use to precipitate Mg^{2+} from an aqueous solution of $MgCl_2$? Explain your choice. **(a)** $KNO_3(aq)$; **(b)** $NH_3(aq)$; **(c)** $H_2SO_4(aq)$; **(d)** $HC_2H_3O_2(aq)$.

32. Determine which of the following react(s) with $HCl(aq)$ to produce a gas, and write a net ionic equation(s) for the reaction(s). Na_2SO_4; $KHSO_3$; $Zn(OH)_2$; $CaCl_2$.

Oxidation–Reduction (Redox) Equations

33. Assign oxidation states to the elements involved in the following reactions. Indicate which are redox reactions and which are not.
    (a) $MgCO_3(s) + 2\,H^+(aq) \longrightarrow$
    $$Mg^{2+}(aq) + H_2O(l) + CO_2(g)$$
    (b) $Cl_2(aq) + 2\,Br^-(aq) \longrightarrow 2\,Cl^-(aq) + Br_2(aq)$
    (c) $Ag(s) + 2\,H^+(aq) + NO_3^-(aq) \longrightarrow$
    $$Ag^+(aq) + H_2O(l) + NO_2(g)$$
    (d) $2\,Ag^+(aq) + CrO_4^{2-}(aq) \longrightarrow Ag_2CrO_4(s)$

34. Explain why these reactions cannot occur as written.
    (a) $Fe^{3+}(aq) + MnO_4^-(aq) + H^+(aq) \longrightarrow$
    $$Mn^{2+}(aq) + Fe^{2+}(aq) + H_2O(l)$$
    (b) $H_2O_2(aq) + Cl_2(aq) \longrightarrow$
    $$ClO^-(aq) + O_2(g) + H^+(aq)$$

35. Complete and balance these half-equations.
    (a) $SO_3^{2-} \longrightarrow S_2O_3^{2-}$ (acidic solution)
    (b) $HNO_3 \longrightarrow N_2O(g)$ (acidic solution)
    (c) $Al(s) \longrightarrow Al(OH)_4^-$ (basic solution)
    Indicate whether oxidation or reduction is involved.

36. Complete and balance these half-equations.
    (a) $C_2O_4^{2-} \longrightarrow CO_2$ (acidic solution)
    (b) $Cr_2O_7^{2-} \longrightarrow Cr^{3+}$ (acidic solution)
    (c) $MnO_4^- \longrightarrow MnO_2$ (basic solution)
    Indicate whether oxidation or reduction is involved.

37. Balance these equations for redox reactions occurring in acidic solution.
    (a) $MnO_4^- + I^- \longrightarrow Mn^{2+} + I_2(s)$
    (b) $BrO_3^- + N_2H_4 \longrightarrow Br^- + N_2$
    (c) $VO_4^{3-} + Fe^{2+} \longrightarrow VO^{2+} + Fe^{3+}$
    (d) $UO^{2+} + NO_3^- \longrightarrow UO_2^{2+} + NO(g)$

38. Balance these equations for redox reactions occurring in acidic solution.
    (a) $P_4(s) + NO_3^- \longrightarrow H_2PO_4^- + NO(g)$
    (b) $S_2O_3^{2-} + MnO_4^- \longrightarrow SO_4^{2-} + Mn^{2+}$
    (c) $HS^- + HSO_3^- \longrightarrow S_2O_3^{2-}$
    (d) $Fe^{3+} + NH_3OH^+ \longrightarrow Fe^{2+} + N_2O(g)$

39. Balance these equations for redox reactions in basic solution.
    (a) $MnO_2(s) + ClO_3^- \longrightarrow MnO_4^- + Cl^-$
    (b) $Fe(OH)_3(s) + OCl^- \longrightarrow FeO_4^{2-} + Cl^-$
    (c) $ClO_2 \longrightarrow ClO_3^- + Cl^-$

40. Balance these equations for redox reactions occurring in basic solution.
    (a) $CN^- + MnO_4^- \longrightarrow MnO_2(s) + CNO^-$
    (b) $[Fe(CN)_6]^{3-} + N_2H_4 \longrightarrow [Fe(CN)_6]^{4-} + N_2(g)$

    (c) $Fe(OH)_2(s) + O_2(g) \longrightarrow Fe(OH)_3(s)$
    (d) $C_2H_5OH(aq) + MnO_4^- \longrightarrow$
    $$C_2H_3O_2^- + MnO_2(s)$$

41. Balance these equations for disproportionation reactions.
    (a) $Cl_2(g) \longrightarrow Cl^- + ClO_3^-$ (basic solution)
    (b) $S_2O_4^{2-} \longrightarrow S_2O_3^{2-} + HSO_3^-$ (acidic solution)

42. Balance these equations for disproportionation reactions.
    (a) $MnO_4^{2-} \longrightarrow MnO_2(s) + MnO_4^-$ (basic solution)
    (b) $P_4(s) \longrightarrow H_2PO_2^- + PH_3(g)$ (basic solution)
    (c) $S_8(s) \longrightarrow S^{2-} + S_2O_3^{2-}$ (basic solution)
    (d) $As_2S_3 + H_2O_2 \longrightarrow AsO_4^{3-} + SO_4^{2-}$

43. Write a balanced equation for these redox reactions.
    (a) The oxidation of nitrite ion to nitrate ion by permanganate ion, MnO_4^-, in acidic solution (MnO_4^- ion is reduced to Mn^{2+}).
    (b) The reaction of manganese(II) ion and permanganate ion in basic solution to form solid manganese dioxide.
    (c) The oxidation of ethanol by dichromate ion in acidic solution, producing chromium(III) ion, acetaldehyde (CH_3CHO), and water as products.

44. Write a balanced equation for the redox reactions.
    (a) The reaction of sodium metal with hydroiodic acid.
    (b) The reduction of vanadyl ion (VO^{2+}) to vanadic ion (V^{3+}) in acidic solution with zinc metal as the reducing agent.
    (c) The oxidation of methanol by chlorate ion in acidic solution, producing carbon dioxide gas, water, and chlorine dioxide gas as products.

45. The following reactions do not occur in aqueous solutions. Balance their equations by the half-equation method, as suggested in the Are You Wondering feature on page 161.
    (a) $CH_4(g) + NO(g) \longrightarrow$
    $$CO_2(g) + N_2(g) + H_2O(g)$$
    (b) $H_2S(g) + SO_2(g) \longrightarrow S_8(s) + H_2O(g)$
    (c) $Cl_2O(g) + NH_3(g) \longrightarrow$
    $$N_2(g) + NH_4Cl(s) + H_2O(l)$$

46. The following reactions do not occur in aqueous solutions. Balance their equations by the half-equation method, as suggested in the Are You Wondering feature on page 161.
    (a) $CH_4(g) + NH_3(g) + O_2(g) \longrightarrow$
    $$HCN(g) + H_2O(g)$$
    (b) $NO(g) + H_2(g) \longrightarrow NH_3(g) + H_2O(g)$
    (c) $Fe(s) + H_2O(l) + O_2(g) \longrightarrow Fe(OH)_3(s)$

Oxidizing and Reducing Agents

47. What are the oxidizing and reducing agents in the following redox reactions?

(a) $5 SO_3^{2-} + 2 MnO_4^- + 6 H^+ \longrightarrow$
$$5 SO_4^{2-} + 2 Mn^{2+} + 3 H_2O$$

(b) $2 NO_2(g) + 7 H_2(g) \longrightarrow 2 NH_3(g) + 4 H_2O(g)$

(c) $2 [Fe(CN)_6]^{4-} + H_2O_2 + 2 H^+ \longrightarrow$
$$2 [Fe(CN)_6]^{3-} + 2 H_2O$$

48. Thiosulfate ion, $S_2O_3^{2-}$, is a reducing agent that can be oxidized to different products, depending on the strength of the oxidizing agent and other conditions. By adding H^+, H_2O, and/or OH^- as necessary, write redox equations to show the oxidation of $S_2O_3^{2-}$ to

(a) $S_4O_6^{2-}$ by I_2 (iodide ion is another product)

(b) HSO_4^- by Cl_2 (chloride ion is another product)

(c) SO_4^{2-} by OCl^- in basic solution (chloride ion is another product)

Neutralization and Acid–Base Titrations

49. What volume of 0.0962 M NaOH is required to exactly neutralize 10.00 mL of 0.128 M HCl?

50. The exact neutralization of 10.00 mL of 0.1012 M $H_2SO_4(aq)$ requires 23.31 mL of NaOH(aq). What must be the molarity of the NaOH(aq)?

$$H_2SO_4(aq) + 2 NaOH(aq) \longrightarrow$$
$$Na_2SO_4(aq) + 2 H_2O(l)$$

51. How many milliliters of 2.155 M KOH(aq) are required to titrate 25.00 mL of 0.3057 M $HC_3H_5O_2(aq)$ (propionic acid)?

52. How many milliliters of 0.0844 M $Ba(OH)_2(aq)$ are required to titrate 50.00 mL of 0.0526 M HNO_3?

53. An NaOH(aq) solution cannot be made up to an exact concentration simply by weighing out the required mass of NaOH, because the NaOH is not pure. Also, water vapor condenses on the solid as it is being weighed. The solution must be standardized by titration. For this purpose, a 25.00-mL sample of an NaOH(aq) solution requires 28.34 mL of 0.1085 M HCl. What is the molarity of the NaOH(aq)?

$$HCl(aq) + NaOH(aq) \longrightarrow NaCl(aq) + H_2O(l)$$

54. Household ammonia, used as a window cleaner and for other cleaning purposes, is $NH_3(aq)$. The NH_3 present in a 5.00-mL sample is neutralized by 28.72 mL of 1.021 M HCl(aq). The net ionic equation for the neutralization is

$$NH_3(aq) + H^+(aq) \longrightarrow NH_4^+(aq)$$

What is the molarity of NH_3 in the sample?

55. We want to determine the acetylsalicylic acid content of a series of aspirin tablets by titration with NaOH(aq). Each of the tablets is expected to contain about 0.32 g of $HC_9H_7O_4$. What molarity of NaOH(aq) should we use for titration volumes of about 23 mL? (This procedure ensures good precision and allows the titration of two samples with the contents of a 50-mL buret.)

$$HC_9H_7O_4(aq) + OH^-(aq) \longrightarrow$$
$$C_9H_7O_4^-(aq) + H_2O(l)$$

56. For use in titrations, we wish to prepare 20 L of HCl(aq) with a concentration known to four significant figures. This is a two-step procedure beginning with the preparation of a solution of about 0.10 M HCl. A sample of this dilute HCl(aq) is titrated with a NaOH(aq) solution of known concentration.

(a) How many milliliters of concentrated HCl(aq) ($d = 1.19$ g/mL; 38% HCl, by mass) must be diluted with water to 20.0 L to prepare 0.10 M HCl?

(b) A 25.00 mL sample of the approximately 0.10 M HCl prepared in part (a) requires 20.93 mL of 0.1186 M NaOH for its titration. What is the molarity of the HCl(aq)?

(c) Why is a titration necessary? That is, why not prepare a standard solution of 0.1000 M HCl simply by an appropriate dilution of the concentrated HCl(aq)?

57. A 25.00-mL sample of 0.132 M HNO_3 is mixed with 10.00 mL of 0.318 M KOH. Is the resulting solution acidic, basic, or exactly neutralized?

58. A 7.55-g sample of $Na_2CO_3(s)$ is added to 125 mL of a vinegar that is 0.762 M $HC_2H_3O_2$. Will the resulting solution still be acidic? Explain.

59. Refer to Example 5-9. Suppose the analysis of all vinegar samples uses 5.00 mL of the vinegar and 0.1000 M NaOH for the titration. What volume of the 0.1000 M NaOH would represent the legal minimum 4.0%, by mass, acetic acid content of the vinegar? That is, calculate the volume of 0.1000 M NaOH so that if a titration requires more than this volume, the legal minimum limit is met (less than this volume, and the limit is not met).

60. The electrolyte in a lead storage battery must have a concentration between 4.8 and 5.3 M H_2SO_4 if the battery is to be most effective. A 5.00-mL sample of a battery acid requires 49.74 mL of 0.935 M NaOH for its complete reaction (neutralization). Does the concentration of the battery acid fall within the desired range? [*Hint:* Keep in mind that the H_2SO_4 produces two H^+ ions per formula unit.]

61. Which of the following points in a titration is represented by the molecular view shown in the sketch?

(a) 20% of the necessary titrant added in the titration of $NH_4Cl(aq)$ with HCl(aq)

(b) 20% of the necessary titrant added in the titration of $NH_3(aq)$ with HCl(aq)

(c) the equivalence point in the titration of $NH_3(aq)$ with HCl(aq)

(d) 120% of the necessary titrant added in the titration of $NH_3(aq)$ with $HCl(aq)$

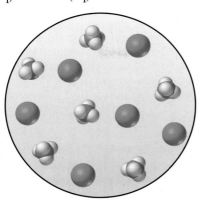

62. Using the sketch in Exercise 61 as a guide, sketch the molecular view of a solution in which
   (a) $HCl(aq)$ is titrated to the equivalence point with $KOH(aq)$
   (b) $CH_3COOH(aq)$ is titrated halfway to the equivalence point with $NaOH(aq)$.

Stoichiometry of Oxidation–Reduction Reactions

63. A $KMnO_4(aq)$ solution is to be standardized by titration against $As_2O_3(s)$. A 0.1078-g sample of As_2O_3 requires 22.15 mL of the $KMnO_4(aq)$ for its titration. What is the molarity of the $KMnO_4(aq)$?

$$5 \, As_2O_3 + 4 \, MnO_4^- + 9 \, H_2O + 12 \, H^+ \longrightarrow$$
$$10 \, H_3AsO_4 + 4 \, Mn^{2+}$$

64. Refer to Example 5–6. Assume that the only reducing agent present in a particular wastewater is SO_3^{2-}. If a 25.00-mL sample of this wastewater requires 31.46 mL of 0.02237 M $KMnO_4$ for its titration, what is the molarity of SO_3^{2-} in the wastewater?

65. An iron ore sample weighing 0.9132 g is dissolved in $HCl(aq)$, and the iron is obtained as $Fe^{2+}(aq)$. This solution is then titrated with 28.72 mL of 0.05051 M $K_2Cr_2O_7(aq)$. What is the mass percent Fe in the ore sample?

$$6 \, Fe^{2+} + 14 \, H^+ + Cr_2O_7^{2-} \longrightarrow$$
$$6 \, Fe^{3+} + 2 \, Cr^{3+} + 7 \, H_2O$$

66. The concentration of $Mn^{2+}(aq)$ can be determined by titration with $MnO_4^-(aq)$ in basic solution. A 25.00-mL sample of $Mn^{2+}(aq)$ requires 37.21 mL of 0.04162 M $KMnO_4(aq)$ for its titration. What is $[Mn^{2+}]$ in the sample?

$$Mn^{2+} + MnO_4^- \longrightarrow MnO_2(s) \quad \text{(not balanced)}$$

67. The titration of 5.00 mL of a saturated solution of sodium oxalate, $Na_2C_2O_4$, at 25°C requires 25.8 mL of 0.02140 M $KMnO_4$ in acidic solution. What mass of $Na_2C_2O_4$ in grams would be present in 1.00 L of this saturated solution?

$$C_2O_4^{2-} + MnO_4^- \longrightarrow$$
$$Mn^{2+} + CO_2(g) \quad \text{(not balanced)}$$

68. Refer to the Integrative Example. In the treatment of 1.00×10^2 L of a wastewater solution that is 0.0126 M CrO_4^{2-}, how many grams of **(a)** $Cr(OH)_3(s)$ would precipitate; **(b)** $Na_2S_2O_4$ would be consumed?

Integrative and Advanced Exercises

69. Write net ionic equations for the reactions depicted in photo (a) sodium metal reacts with water to produce hydrogen; photo (b) an excess of aqueous iron(III) chloride is added to the solution in (a); and photo (c) the precipitate from (b) is collected and treated with an excess of $HCl(aq)$.

(a)   **(b)**   **(c)**

70. Following are some laboratory methods occasionally used for the preparation of small quantities of chemicals. Write a balanced equation for each.
   (a) preparation of $H_2S(g)$: $HCl(aq)$ is heated with $FeS(s)$
   (b) preparation of $Cl_2(g)$: $HCl(aq)$ is heated with $MnO_2(s)$; $MnCl_2(aq)$ and $H_2O(l)$ are other products
   (c) preparation of N_2: Br_2 and NH_3 react in aqueous solution; NH_4Br is another product
   (d) preparation of chlorous acid: an aqueous suspension of solid barium chlorite is treated with dilute $H_2SO_4(aq)$

71. When concentrated $CaCl_2(aq)$ is added to $Na_2HPO_4(aq)$, a white precipitate forms that is 38.7% Ca by mass. Write a net ionic equation representing the probable reaction that occurs.

72. You have a solution that is 0.0250 M $Ba(OH)_2$ and the following pieces of equipment: 1.00-, 5.00-, 10.00-, 25.00-, and 50.00-mL pipets and 100.0-, 250.0-, 500.0-, and 1000.0-mL volumetric flasks. Describe how you would use this equipment to produce a solution in which $[OH^-]$ is 0.0100 M.

73. Sodium hydroxide used to make standard NaOH(aq) solutions for acid–base titrations is invariably contaminated with some sodium carbonate. **(a)** Explain why, except in the most precise work, the presence of this sodium carbonate generally does not seriously affect the results obtained, for example, when NaOH(aq) is used to titrate HCl(aq). **(b)** On the other hand, show that if Na_2CO_3 comprises more than 1 to 2% of the solute in NaOH(aq), the titration results are affected.

74. A 110.520-g sample of mineral water is analyzed for its magnesium content. The Mg^{2+} in the sample is first precipitated as $MgNH_4PO_4$, and this precipitate is then converted to $Mg_2P_2O_7$, which is found to weigh 0.0549 g. Express the quantity of magnesium in the sample in parts per million (that is, in grams of Mg per million grams of H_2O).

75. What volume of 0.248 M $CaCl_2$ must be added to 335 mL of 0.186 M KCl to produce a solution with a concentration of 0.250 M Cl^-? Assume that the solution volumes are additive.

76. An unknown white solid consists of two compounds, each containing a different cation. As suggested in the illustration, the unknown is partially soluble in water. The solution is treated with NaOH(aq) and yields a white precipitate. The part of the original solid that is insoluble in water dissolves in HCl(aq) with the evolution of a gas. The resulting solution is then treated with $(NH_4)_2SO_4$(aq) and yields a white precipitate. **(a)** Is it possible that any of the cations Mg^{2+}, Cu^{2+}, Ba^{2+}, Na^+, or NH_4^+ were present in the original unknown? Explain your reasoning. **(b)** What compounds could be in the unknown mixture (that is, what anions might be present)?

77. Balance these equations for reactions in acidic solution.
    (a) $IBr + BrO_3^- + H^+ \longrightarrow IO_3^- + Br^- + H_2O$
    (b) $C_2H_5NO_3 + Sn \longrightarrow$
    $$NH_2OH + C_2H_5OH + Sn^{2+}$$
    (c) $As_2S_3 + NO_3^- \longrightarrow H_3AsO_4 + S + NO$
    (d) $H_5IO_6 + I_2 \longrightarrow IO_3^- + H^+ + H_2O$
    (e) $S_2F_2 + H_2O \longrightarrow S_8 + H_2S_4O_6 + HF$

78. Balance these equations for reactions in basic solution.
    (a) $Fe_2S_3 + H_2O + O_2 \longrightarrow Fe(OH)_3 + S$
    (b) $O_2^- + H_2O \longrightarrow OH^- + O_2$
    (c) $CrI_3 + H_2O_2 \longrightarrow CrO_4^{2-} + IO_4^-$
    (d) $Ag + CN^- + O_2 + OH^- \longrightarrow$
    $$[Ag(CN)_2]^- + H_2O$$
    (e) $B_2Cl_4 + OH^- \longrightarrow BO_2^- + Cl^- + H_2O + H_2$
    (f) $C_2H_5OH + MnO_4^- \longrightarrow C_2H_3O_2^- + MnO_2$

79. A method of producing phosphine, PH_3, from elemental phosphorus, P_4, involves heating the P_4 with H_2O. An additional product is phosphoric acid, H_3PO_4. Write a balanced equation for this reaction.

80. When iron pyrites, waste products from coal mining, are exposed to the environment, their sulfur content is oxidized to sulfuric acid. This creates the environmental problem known as *acid mine drainage*. Balance the equations for two of the main reactions involved.
    (a) $FeS_2(s) + O_2 + H_2O \longrightarrow Fe^{2+} + SO_4^{2-} + H^+$
    (b) $FeS_2(s) + Fe^{3+} + H_2O \longrightarrow$
    $$Fe^{2+} + SO_4^{2-} + H^+$$

81. A sample of battery acid is to be analyzed for its sulfuric acid content. A 1.00-mL sample weighs 1.239 g. This 1.00-mL sample is diluted to 250.0 mL, and 10.00 mL of this diluted acid requires 32.44 mL of 0.00498 M $Ba(OH)_2$ for its titration. What is the mass percent of H_2SO_4 in the battery acid? (Assume that complete ionization and neutralization of the H_2SO_4 occurs.)

82. A piece of marble (assume it is pure $CaCO_3$) reacts with 2.00 L of 2.52 M HCl. After dissolution of the marble, a 10.00-mL sample of the resulting solution is withdrawn, added to some water, and titrated with 24.87 mL of 0.9987 M NaOH. What must have been the mass of the piece of marble? Comment on the precision of this method; that is, how many significant figures are justified in the result?

83. The reaction below can be used as a laboratory method of preparing small quantities of $Cl_2(g)$. If a 62.6-g sample that is 98.5% $K_2Cr_2O_7$ by mass is allowed to react with 325 mL of HCl(aq) with a density of 1.15 g/mL and 30.1% HCl by mass, how many grams of $Cl_2(g)$ are produced?
    $$Cr_2O_7^{2-} + H^+ + Cl^- \longrightarrow$$
    $$Cr^{3+} + H_2O + Cl_2(g) \quad \text{(not balanced)}$$

84. Refer to Example 5-10. Suppose that the $KMnO_4$(aq) were standardized by reaction with As_2O_3 instead of iron wire. If a 0.1304-g sample that is 99.96% As_2O_3 by mass had been used in the titration, how many milliliters of the $KMnO_4$(aq) would have been required?
    $$As_2O_3 + MnO_4^- + H^+ + H_2O \longrightarrow$$
    $$H_3AsO_4 + Mn^{2+} \quad \text{(not balanced)}$$

85. A new method under development for water treatment uses chlorine dioxide rather than chlorine. One method of producing ClO_2 involves passing $Cl_2(g)$ into a concentrated solution of sodium chlorite. $Cl_2(g)$ and sodium chlorite are the sole reactants, and NaCl(aq) and $ClO_2(g)$ are the sole products. If the reaction has a 97% yield, what mass of ClO_2 is produced per gallon of 2.0 M $NaClO_2$(aq) treated in this way?

86. The active component in one type of calcium dietary supplement is calcium carbonate. A 1.2450-g tablet of the supplement is added to 50.00 mL of 0.5000 M HCl(aq) and allowed to react. After completion of the reaction, the excess HCl(aq) requires 40.20 mL of 0.2184 M NaOH(aq) for its titration to the equivalence point. What is the calcium content of the tablet, expressed in milligrams of Ca^{2+}?

87. A 0.4324-g sample of a potassium hydroxide–lithium hydroxide mixture requires 28.28 mL of 0.3520 M HCl for its titration to the equivalence point. What is the mass percent lithium hydroxide in this mixture?

88. Chile saltpeter is a natural source of $NaNO_3$; it also contains $NaIO_3$. The $NaIO_3$ can be used as a source of iodine. Iodine is produced from sodium iodate in a two-step process occurring under acidic conditions:

$$IO_3^-(aq) + HSO_3^-(aq) \longrightarrow$$
$$I^-(aq) + SO_4^{2-}(aq) \quad \text{(not balanced)}$$

$$I^-(aq) + IO_3^-(aq) \longrightarrow$$
$$I_2(s) + H_2O(l) \quad \text{(not balanced)}$$

In the illustration, a 5.00-L sample of a $NaIO_3(aq)$ solution containing 5.80 g $NaIO_3/L$ is treated with the stoichiometric quantity of $NaHSO_3$ (no excess of either reactant). Then, a further quantity of the initial $NaIO_3(aq)$ is added to the reaction mixture to bring

about the second reaction. **(a)** How many grams of $NaHSO_3$ are required in the first step? **(b)** What additional volume of the starting solution must be added in the second step?

5.80 g $NaIO_3/L$

(a) ? g $NaHSO_3$

5.00 L

(b) ? L

Feature Problems

89. Sodium cyclopentadienide (NaCp), NaC_5H_5, is a common reducing agent in the chemical laboratory, but there is a problem in using it: NaCp is contaminated with tetrahydrofuran (THF), C_4H_8O, a solvent used in its preparation. The THF is present as $NaCp \cdot (THF)_x$, and it is generally necessary to know exactly how much of this $NaCp \cdot (THF)_x$ is present. This is accomplished by allowing a small amount of the $NaCp \cdot (THF)_x$ to react with water,

$$NaCp \cdot (C_4H_8O)_x + H_2O \longrightarrow$$
$$NaOH(aq) + Cp-H + x\, C_4H_8O$$

followed by titration of the $NaOH(aq)$ with a standard acid. From the sample data tabulated below, determine the value of x in the formula $NaCp \cdot (THF)_x$.

	Trial 1	Trial 2
Mass of $NaCp \cdot (THF)_x$	0.242 g	0.199 g
Volume of 0.1001 M HCl required to titrate $NaOH(aq)$	14.92 mL	11.99 mL

90. Manganese is derived from pyrolusite ore, an impure manganese dioxide. In the procedure used to analyze a pyrolusite ore for its MnO_2 content, a 0.533-g sample is treated with 1.651 g oxalic acid ($H_2C_2O_4 \cdot 2\, H_2O$) in an acidic medium. Following this reaction, the excess oxalic acid is titrated with 0.1000 M $KMnO_4$, 30.06 mL being required. What is the mass percent MnO_2 in the ore?

$$H_2C_2O_4 + MnO_2 + H^+ \longrightarrow$$
$$Mn^{2+} + H_2O + CO_2 \quad \text{(not balanced)}$$

$$H_2C_2O_4 + MnO_4^- + H^+ \longrightarrow$$
$$Mn^{2+} + H_2O + CO_2 \quad \text{(not balanced)}$$

91. The Kjeldahl method is used in agricultural chemistry to determine the percent protein in natural products. The method is based on converting all the protein nitrogen to ammonia and then determining the amount

of ammonia by titration. The percent nitrogen in the sample under analysis can be calculated from the quantity of ammonia produced. Interestingly, the majority of protein molecules in living matter contain just about 16% nitrogen.

A 1.250-g sample of meat is heated with concentrated sulfuric acid and a catalyst to convert all the nitrogen in the meat to $(NH_4)_2SO_4$. Then excess $NaOH(aq)$ is added to the mixture, which is heated to expel $NH_3(g)$. All the nitrogen from the sample is found in the $NH_3(g)$, which is then absorbed in and neutralized by 50.00 mL of dilute $H_2SO_4(aq)$. The excess $H_2SO_4(aq)$ requires 32.24 mL of 0.4498 M $NaOH(aq)$ for its titration. A separate 25.00-mL sample of the dilute $H_2SO_4(aq)$ requires 22.24 mL of 0.4498 M NaOH for its titration. What is the percent protein in the meat?

92. In describing titration reactions, we noted that the equivalence point is often detected by measuring a physical property of the solution. One possibility is to measure the electrical conductance. The graph shows how the total electrical conductance of a solution varies as $NaOH(aq)$ is added to $HCl(aq)$. The measured conductances are represented by the two straight red lines. The two black lines lying below the red lines divide the graph into four areas, each area representing the contribution of a particular ion to the total conductance of the solution. Thus, the conductance at the start of the titration is high, with H^+ contributing most to the solution conductance, Cl^- making a secondary contribution, and Na^+ not yet contributing anything. Until the equivalence point is reached, Na^+ replaces H^+ and the total conductance drops. At the equivalence point, where the two red lines meet, the contribution of the H^+ ion has fallen to zero and the total conductance is that of $NaCl(aq)$. Beyond the equivalence point, the conductance again rises as excess NaOH accumulates in the solution. An important requirement to obtain straight lines in the graph is that the titrant solution [$NaOH(aq)$] be much more concentrated than the solution being titrated [$HCl(aq)$]. In this way, the total volume of solution changes little and dilution effects can be ignored.

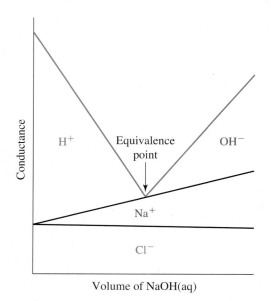

Volume of NaOH(aq)

The graph reveals that (1) ions differ in their intrinsic abilities to conduct electric current (H^+ and OH^- are much better conductors than Na^+ and Cl^-). (2) The greater the concentration of an ion, the greater is its contribution to the conductance of a solution. (3) The conductance of the solution as a whole can be expressed as the sum of the conductances of the ions present.

Assume that the contributions toward the total electrical conductance of a solution by several different ions are roughly: $H^+ = 350$; $NH_4^+ = 73$; $Ag^+ = 62$; $Na^+ = 50$; $OH^- = 198$; $Cl^- = 76$; $NO_3^- = 71$; $C_2H_3O_2^- = 41$, and sketch the graphs you would expect for these titrations:
(a) NaOH(aq) titrated with HNO_3(aq)
(b) $HC_2H_3O_2$(aq) titrated with NaOH(aq)
(c) HCl(aq) titrated with $AgNO_3$(aq)
(d) HCl(aq) titrated with NH_3(aq)

Self-Assessment Exercises

93. In your own words, define or explain the terms or symbols **(a)** $\rightleftharpoons$ **(b)** [ ]; **(c)** spectator ion; **(d)** weak acid.

94. Briefly describe **(a)** half-equation method of balancing redox equations; **(b)** disproportionation reaction; **(c)** titration; **(d)** standardization of a solution.

95. Explain the important distinctions between **(a)** a strong electrolyte and strong acid; **(b)** an oxidizing agent and reducing agent; **(c)** precipitation reactions and neutralization reactions; **(d)** half-reaction and overall reaction.

96. The number of moles of hydroxide ion in 0.300 L of 0.0050 M $Ba(OH)_2$ is **(a)** 0.0015; **(b)** 0.0030; **(c)** 0.0050; **(d)** 0.010.

97. The highest $[H^+]$ will be found in an aqueous solution that is **(a)** 0.10 M HCl; **(b)** 0.10 M NH_3; **(c)** 0.15 M $HC_2H_3O_2$; **(d)** 0.10 M H_2SO_4.

98. To precipitate Zn^{2+} from $Zn(NO_3)_2$(aq), add **(a)** NH_4Cl; **(b)** $MgBr_2$; **(c)** K_2CO_3; **(d)** $(NH_4)_2SO_4$.

99. When treated with dilute HCl(aq), the solid that reacts to produce a gas is **(a)** $BaSO_3$; **(b)** ZnO; **(c)** NaBr; **(d)** Na_2SO_4.

100. In the equation

$$? \, Fe^{2+}(aq) + O_2(g) + 4 \, H^+(aq) \longrightarrow$$
$$? \, Fe^{3+}(aq) + 2 \, H_2O(l)$$

the missing coefficients **(a)** are each 2; **(b)** are each 4; **(c)** can have any values as long as they are the same; **(d)** must be determined by experiment.

101. In the half-reaction in which NpO_2^+ is converted to Np^{4+}, the number of electrons appearing in the half-equation is **(a)** 1; **(b)** 2; **(c)** 3; **(d)** 4.

102. Similar to Figure 5-3(c), but using the formulas HAc, Ac^-, and H_3O^+, give a more accurate representation of $HC_2H_3O_2$(aq) in which ionization is 5% complete.

103. Appendix E describes a useful study aid known as concept mapping. Using the method presented in Appendix E, construct a concept map illustrating the different concepts introduced in Sections 5-4, 5-5, and 5-6.

eMedia Exercises

104. The **Equilibrium of a Weak Acid** animation (*Activebook 5-1*) illustrates both forward and reverse reactions taking place. It is important to keep a mental picture of this process in mind as you continue to view different reactions. Propose a method for quantitatively describing the relative concentrations of the species in solution when equilibrium is reached.

105. In the **Precipitation Reactions** movie (*Activebook 5-2*), what spectator ions are present following the formation of each of the precipitates? Why do these species remain in solution?

106. The **Introduction to Acids and Introduction to Bases** animations (*Activebook 5-3*) shows a relatively large number of species undergoing dissociation and recombination. **(a)** Using a density of water of 1.0 g/mL, calculate the number of protons produced in an aqueous solution of 0.10 M HNO_3. **(b)** According to your calculation, approximately how many ions would appear in the field of view of the animation?

107. From the **Oxidation–Reduction Chemistry of Tin and Zinc** movie (*Activebook 5-4*), **(a)** identify the species being oxidized and reduced in the reaction.

Notice that the reaction begins immediately but slows over time. **(b)** Considering the different steps to an oxidation–reduction reaction, what causes the reaction to slow down? **(c)** What could be changed about the reactants to speed up the reaction?

108. The measurement of a quantity called pH represents a convenient way of following relative concentrations of acid and base species in solution. **(a)** In the **Acid–Base Titration** animation (*Activebook 5-7*), what causes the rapid change in pH upon the addition of the single drop of base after the equivalence point has been reached? **(b)** If the concentration of the base being added were doubled, at what approximate volume would the equivalence point be reached?

---

eLaboratory Exercises

These exercises allow students to apply the concepts and skills for this chapter in the simulated laboratory of Virtual ChemLab. Worksheets for each of these exercises are found in the Virtual ChemLab Workbook in your MediaPak.

109. *(VCL 5-1) Strong and Weak Electrolytes*
As discussed in the chapter, strong electrolytes are compounds that fully dissociate in water and weak electrolytes are ones that do so only to a small extent. A method for measuring the degree of dissociation is to measure the electrical conductivity of the solution. In this assignment you will measure the conductivity of several solutions and make some important conclusions.

110. *(VCL 5-2) Writing Net Ionic Equations*
It is an important skill that students be able to write balanced net ionic reactions for reactions that are observed in the laboratory. In this problem you will go into the virtual laboratory and perform a series of precipitation reactions using Ag^+, Pb^{2+}, and Sb^{3+}. After observing the reactions, you will write the net ionic equations representing these reactions and then balance them.

111. *(VCL 5-3) Precipitation Reactions*
A precipitation reaction is defined as one in which a soluble cation and a soluble anion combine to form an insoluble combination product. In this assignment you will mix several different combinations of cations and anions and observe those that form precipitates and those that do not. You will also write full balanced equations and net ionic equations for these reactions.

112. *(VCL 5-4) Concepts in Acid–Base Titrations*
Titrations provide a method of quantitatively measuring the concentration of an unknown solution. In an acid-base titration this is done by delivering a titrant of known concentration into an analyte of known volume. The equivalence point of the titration, or the point where the analyte has been completely consumed by the titrant, is identified by the point where the pH changes rapidly over a small volume of titrant delivered. In this assignment you will titrate a strong acid, HCl, with a strong base, NaOH, and observe the pH of the solution as a function of the volume of titrant delivered.

113. *(VCL 5-5) Acid–Base Titration: Practice*
Titrations provide a method of quantitatively measuring the concentration of an unknown solution. In an acid-base titration this is done by delivering a titrant of known concentration into an analyte of known volume. In this assignment you will titrate a 0.3000 M solution of NaOH into 25.00 mL of 0.3000 M HCl. Although in this situation you know the concentration of both NaOH and HCl, this will give you practice in performing a titration and calculating the concentration of the analyte, which in this case is HCl.

114. *(VCL 5-6) Acid–Base Titration: Unknown HCl*
Titrations provide a method of quantitatively measuring the concentration of an unknown solution. In an acid-base titration this is done by delivering a titrant of known concentration into an analyte of known volume. In this assignment you will titrate a 0.2564 M solution of NaOH into 25.00 mL of an unknown concentration of HCl and calculate the concentration of the HCl solution.

6

<h1 style="text-align:right">GASES</h1>

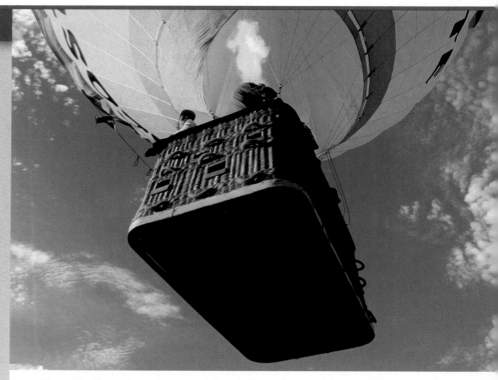

Hot-air balloons have intrigued people from the time the simple gas laws fundamental to their operation came to be understood over 200 years ago.

✓ Gases are discussed early because the topic can be understood well without any background of molecular structure and bonding, and because it can be the subject of several laboratory experiments. We expand here on a number of math/algebra skills, including the use of units, and develop a feeling for functional relationships. The topic demonstrates the working relationship of theory to observed laws.

You shouldn't overinflate a bicycle tire, or discard an aerosol can in an incinerator, or search for a gas leak with an open flame. In each case there is a danger of explosion. These and many other observations concerning gases can be explained by concepts considered in this chapter. The behavior of the bicycle tire and the aerosol can are based on relationships between pressure, temperature, volume, and amount of gas. Other examples of the behavior of gases can be seen in a balloon filled with helium or hot air rising in air, and carbon dioxide gas vaporizing from a block of dry ice and sinking to the floor. An understanding of the lifting power of lighter-than-air balloons comes in large part from knowledge of gas densities and their dependence on molar mass, temperature, and pressure. Predicting how far and how fast gas molecules migrate through air requires knowing something about the phenomenon of diffusion.

For a quantitative description of the behavior of gases we will employ some simple gas laws and a more general expression called the *ideal gas equation*. These laws will be explained by the kinetic-molecular theory of gases. The topics covered in this chapter extend the discussion of reaction stoichiometry from the previous two chapters and lay some groundwork for use in the following chapter on thermochemistry. The relationships between gases and the other states of matter—liquids and solids—are discussed in Chapter 12.

 An alternate sequencing of topics is to postpone this chapter and take it up later with Chapters 12 and 13 as a unit on the states of matter.

6-1   PROPERTIES OF GASES: GAS PRESSURE

Some characteristics of gases are familiar to everyone. Gases expand to fill their containers and assume the shapes of their containers. They diffuse into one another and mix in all proportions. We cannot see individual particles of a gas, although we can see the bulk gas if it is colored (Fig. 6-1). Some gases, such as hydrogen and methane, are combustible; whereas others, such as helium and neon, are chemically unreactive.

Motions of a Gas activity

Four properties determine the physical behavior of a gas: the amount of the gas (in moles) and the volume, temperature, and pressure of the gas. If we know any three of these, we can usually calculate the value of the remaining one using a mathematical equation called an *equation of state* (see page 190). To some extent we have already discussed the properties of amount, volume, and temperature, but we need to consider the idea of pressure.

▲ **FIGURE 6-1**
The gaseous states of three halogens (group 17)
The greenish yellow gas is $Cl_2(g)$; the brownish red gas is $Br_2(g)$ above a small pool of liquid bromine; the violet gas is $I_2(g)$ in contact with grayish black solid iodine. Most other common gases, such as H_2, O_2, N_2, CO, and CO_2, are colorless.

THE CONCEPT OF PRESSURE

A balloon expands when it is inflated with air, but what keeps the balloon in its distended shape? A plausible hypothesis is that molecules of a gas are in constant motion, frequently colliding with one another and with the walls of their container. In their collisions, the gas molecules exert a force on the container walls. This force keeps the balloon distended. It is not easy, however, to measure the total force exerted by a gas. Instead of focusing on this total force, we consider instead the gas pressure. **Pressure** is defined as a force per unit area, that is, a force divided by the area over which the force is distributed. Figure 6-2 illustrates the idea of pressure exerted by a solid.

▲ **FIGURE 6-2**
Illustrating the pressure exerted by a solid
The two cylinders have the same mass and exert the same force on the supporting surface ($F = g \times m$). The tall, thin one has a smaller area of contact, however, and exerts a greater pressure ($P = F/A$).

In SI, the unit of force is a *newton* (N), which is the force required to produce an acceleration of one meter per second per second (1 m s^{-2}) in a one-kilogram mass (1 kg), that is, 1 N = 1 kg m s^{-2}. The corresponding force per unit area—pressure—is expressed in the unit N/m^2. A pressure of one newton per square meter is defined as one **pascal** (**Pa**). Thus, a pressure in pascals is

$$P(\text{Pa}) = \frac{F(\text{N})}{A(\text{m}^2)} \qquad (6.1)$$

A pascal is a rather small pressure unit, so the **kilopascal** (**kPa**) is more commonly used. The pascal honors Blaise Pascal (1623–1662), who studied pressure and its transmission through fluids—the basis of modern hydraulics.

LIQUID PRESSURE

Because it is difficult to measure the total force exerted by gas molecules, it is also difficult to apply equation (6.1) to gases. The pressure of a gas is usually measured indirectly, by comparing it with a liquid pressure. Figure 6-3 illustrates the concept of liquid pressure and suggests that the pressure of a liquid depends only on the height of the liquid column and the density of the liquid. To confirm this statement, consider a liquid with density d, contained in a cylinder with cross-sectional area A, filled to a height h.

Now recall that (1) weight is a force, and weight and mass are proportional: $W = g \cdot m$. (2) The mass of a liquid is the product of its volume and density: $m = V \cdot d$. (3) The volume of a cylinder is the product of its height and cross-sectional area: $V = h \cdot A$. We use these facts to derive the equation:

$$P = \frac{F}{A} = \frac{W}{A} = \frac{g \times m}{A} = \frac{g \times V \times d}{A} = \frac{g \times h \times A \times d}{A} = g \times h \times d \qquad (6.2)$$

Thus, because g is a constant, *liquid pressure is directly proportional to the liquid density and the height of the liquid column.*

BAROMETRIC PRESSURE

In 1643, Evangelista Torricelli constructed the device pictured in Figure 6-4 to measure the pressure exerted by the atmosphere. This device is called a **barometer**.

If a glass tube that is open at both ends stands upright in a container of mercury (Fig. 6-4a), the mercury levels inside and outside the tube are the same. To create the situation in Figure 6-4(b), we seal one end of a long glass tube, completely fill the tube with Hg(l), cover the open end, and invert the tube into a container of Hg(l). Then we reopen the end that is submerged in the mercury. The mercury level in the tube falls to a certain height and stays there. Something keeps the mercury at a greater height inside the tube than outside. Some tried to ascribe this phenomenon to forces within the tube, but Torricelli understood that the forces involved originated outside the tube.

In the open-end tube (Fig. 6-4a), the atmosphere exerts the same pressure on the surface of the mercury both inside and outside the tube, and the liquid levels are equal. Inside the closed-end tube (Fig. 6-4b), there is no air above the mercury (only a trace of mercury vapor). The atmosphere exerts a force on the surface of the mercury in the outside container. This force is transmitted through the liquid, holding up the mercury column within the tube. The column exerts a downward pressure that depends on its height and the density of Hg(l). When the pressure at the bottom of the mercury column is equal to the pressure of the atmosphere, the column height is maintained.

The height of mercury in a barometer, a measure of **barometric pressure**, varies with atmospheric conditions and altitude. The **standard atmosphere** (**atm**) is defined as the pressure exerted by a mercury column of exactly 760 mm in height when the density of mercury = 13.5951 g/cm^3 (0 °C) and

▲ FIGURE 6-3
The concept of liquid pressure
All the interconnected vessels fill to the same height. As a result, the liquid pressures are the same despite the different shapes and volumes of the containers.

▲ **FIGURE 6-4**
Measurement of atmospheric pressure with a mercury barometer
Arrows represent the pressure exerted by the atmosphere. **(a)** The liquid mercury levels are equal inside and outside the open-end tube. **(b)** A column of mercury 760 mm high is maintained in the closed-end tube, regardless of the overall height of the tube **(c)** as long as it exceeds 760 mm. **(d)** A column of mercury fills a closed-end tube that is shorter than 760 mm. In the closed-end tubes in (b) and (c), the region above the mercury column is devoid of air and contains only a trace of mercury vapor.

the acceleration due to gravity $g = 9.80665 \ \text{m s}^{-2}$, exactly. This statement relates two useful units of pressure—the standard atmosphere (atm) and the **millimeter of mercury (mmHg)**.

$$1 \ \text{atm} = 760 \ \text{mmHg} \qquad (6.3)$$

The pressure unit called a **torr** and denoted by the symbol **Torr** honors Torricelli. It is defined as exactly 1/760 of a standard atmosphere. Or 1 atm = 760 Torr. Thus, we can use the pressure units Torr and mmHg interchangeably.

Mercury is a relatively rare, expensive, and poisonous liquid. Why use it rather than water in a barometer? As we will see in Example 6-1, the extreme height required for a water barometer is a distinct disadvantage.

EXAMPLE 6-1

Comparing Liquid Pressures. What is the height of a column of water that exerts the same pressure as a column of mercury 76.0 cm (760 mm) high?

Solution

Equation (6.2) can be used to describe the pressure of the mercury column of known height and the pressure of the water column of unknown height. Then we can set the two pressures equal to each other.

pressure of Hg column $= g \times h_{\text{Hg}} \times d_{\text{Hg}} = g \times 76.0 \ \text{cm} \times 13.6 \ \text{g/cm}^3$

pressure of H_2O column $= g \times h_{\text{H}_2\text{O}} \times d_{\text{H}_2\text{O}} = g \times h_{\text{H}_2\text{O}} \times 1.00 \ \text{g/cm}^3$

$\cancel{g} \times h_{\text{H}_2\text{O}} \times 1.00 \ \text{g/cm}^3 = \cancel{g} \times 76.0 \ \text{cm} \times 13.6 \ \text{g/cm}^3$

$$h_{\text{H}_2\text{O}} = 76.0 \ \text{cm} \times \frac{13.6 \ \text{g/cm}^3}{1.00 \ \text{g/cm}^3} = 1.03 \times 10^3 \ \text{cm} = 10.3 \ \text{m}$$

Thus, we see that the column height is inversely proportional to the liquid density: for a given liquid pressure, the lower the liquid density, the greater the height of the liquid column.

📖 The following article describes the construction and use of a water barometer: de Grys, Hans. *J. Chem. Educ.* **2003:** *80,* 1156.

◀ Whereas atmospheric pressure can be measured with a mercury barometer less than 1 m high, a water barometer would have to be as tall as a three-story building.

Practice Example A: A barometer is filled with diethylene glycol ($d = 1.118 \text{ g/cm}^3$). The liquid height is found to be 9.25 m. What is the barometric (atmospheric) pressure expressed in millimeters of mercury?

Practice Example B: A barometer is filled with triethylene glycol. The liquid height is found to be 9.14 m when the atmospheric pressure is 757 mmHg. What is the density of triethylene glycol?

When you use a drinking straw, you reduce the air pressure above the liquid inside the straw by inhaling. Atmospheric pressure outside the straw then pushes the liquid up the straw and into your mouth. An old-fashioned hand suction pump for pumping water (once common in rural areas) works by the same principle. The result of Example 6-1 indicates, however, that even if all the air could be removed from inside a pipe, atmospheric pressure outside the pipe could not raise water to a height of more than about 10 m. A suction pump works only for shallow wells. To pump water from a deep well, a mechanical pump is required. The force of the mechanical pump pushing the water upward is greater than the force of the atmosphere pushing the water downward.

CONCEPT ASSESSMENT ✓

Explain how the action of a water siphon is related to that of a suction pump.

The preparation of a low-cost manometer is described in these articles: Pollnow, Gilbert F. *J. Chem. Educ.* **1989:** *66,* 333 and Garrett, D. Dewayne, Banta, M. C. *J. Chem. Educ.* **1990:** *67,* 523.

Manometer activity

MANOMETERS

Although a mercury barometer is indispensable for measuring the pressure of the atmosphere, it is rarely used alone to measure other gas pressures. The difficulty with a barometer is in placing it inside the container of gas whose pressure is to be measured. However, the pressure of the gas to be measured can be compared with barometric pressure using a **manometer**. Figure 6-5 illustrates the principle of an open-end manometer. When the gas pressure being measured and the prevailing atmospheric (barometric) pressure are equal, the heights of the mercury columns in the two arms of the manometer are equal. A difference in height of the two arms signifies a difference between the gas pressure and barometric pressure.

(a) Gas pressure equal to barometric pressure
$$P_{\text{gas}} = P_{\text{bar.}}$$

(b) Gas pressure greater than barometric pressure
$$P_{\text{gas}} = P_{\text{bar.}} + \Delta P \quad (\Delta P > 0)$$

(c) Gas pressure less than barometric pressure
$$P_{\text{gas}} = P_{\text{bar.}} + \Delta P \quad (\Delta P < 0)$$

▲ **FIGURE 6-5**
Measurement of gas pressure with an open-end manometer
The possible relationships between barometric pressure and a gas pressure under measurement are pictured here and described in Example 6-2.

EXAMPLE 6-2

Using a Manometer to Measure Gas Pressure. When the manometer in Figure 6-5(c) is filled with liquid mercury ($d = 13.6$ g/cm^3), the barometric pressure is 748.2 mmHg, and the difference in mercury levels is 8.6 mmHg. What is the gas pressure P_{gas}?

Solution

Whether the situation corresponds to Figure 6-5(b) or (c), the pressure we seek is $P_{gas} = P_{bar.} + \Delta P$. The crucial difference between the two situations is that in Figure 6-5(b), the measured gas pressure is greater than barometric pressure, and ΔP is positive. In Figure 6-5(c), P_{gas} is less than barometric pressure, and ΔP is negative. In the question we have been asked, ΔP is *negative*. (Because all pressures are expressed in millimeters of mercury, the density of mercury does not enter into the calculation.)

$$P_{gas} = P_{bar.} + \Delta P = 748.2 \text{ mmHg} - 8.6 \text{ mmHg} = 739.6 \text{ mmHg}$$

Practice Example A: Suppose that the mercury level in Example 6-2 is 7.8 mm higher in the arm open to the atmosphere than in the closed arm. What would be the value of P_{gas}?

Practice Example B: Suppose $P_{bar.}$ and P_{gas} are those described in Example 6-2, but the manometer is filled with liquid glycerol ($d = 1.26$ g/cm^3) instead of mercury. What would be the difference in the two levels of the liquid?

Students have difficulty determining whether the ΔP should be added or subtracted in the calculations outlined in Example 6-2.

UNITS OF PRESSURE: A SUMMARY

Table 6.1 lists several different units used to express pressure. In this text, we will use primarily the first three units (shown in red). When we use the units millimeter of mercury and torr, we substitute the height of a liquid column for an actual pressure. The units shown in blue are those preferred in the SI system. To understand why their values are all based on the sequence of digits 101325, let us calculate the pressure exerted by a column of mercury that is exactly 0.76 m (760 mm) high. To do this, we use equation (6.2) as follows;

$$P = d \times g \times h = (1.35951 \times 10^4 \text{ kg m}^{-3})(9.80665 \text{ m s}^{-2})(0.760000 \text{ m})$$

$$= 1.01325 \times 10^5 \text{ kg m}^{-1}\text{ s}^{-2}$$

The unit that arises in this calculation, kg m^{-1} s^{-2}, is the SI unit for pressure and, as mentioned earlier, is called the pascal (Pa). One standard atmosphere (1 atm) is defined, in SI units, as exactly 1.01325×10^5 Pa or 101.325 kPa. The unit *bar* is one hundred times as large as a kilopascal (the unit *millibar* is commonly used by meteorologists). Although we can generally choose freely among the pressure units in Table 6.1 when doing calculations involving gases, occasionally a situation arises that requires SI units. This is the case in Example 6-3.

Collapsing Cans. See Shakhashiri, "Chemical Demonstrations 2," *Univ. Wisconsin Press* (1985), p. 6–8. Each of the three procedures mentioned makes a highly effective demonstration. Mention the equivalence 1 atm = 14.7 psi. Those pounds add up quickly over a significant surface area.

TABLE 6.1 Some Common Pressure Units		
Atmosphere	atm	
Millimeter of mercury	mmHg	1 atm = 760 mmHg
Torr	Torr	= 760 Torr
Pascal	Pa	= 101,325 Pa
Kilopascal	kPa	= 101.325 kPa
Bar	bar	= 1.01325 bar
Millibar	mb	= 1013.25 mb

EXAMPLE 6-3

Obtaining an SI Unit of Pressure. The 1.000-kg red cylinder in Figure 6-2 has a diameter of 4.10 cm. What pressure, expressed in torr, does this cylinder exert on the surface beneath it?

Solution

Expression (6.1) defines pressure as force divided by area.

$$P = \frac{F}{A}$$

The force exerted by the cylinder is its weight.

$$F = W = m \times g$$

The mass is 1.000 kg, and g (the acceleration due to gravity) is 9.81 m s^{-2}. The product of these two terms is the force in newtons.

$$F = m \times g = 1.000 \text{ kg} \times 9.81 \text{ m s}^{-2} = 9.81 \text{ N}$$

The force is exerted on the area of contact between the cylinder and the underlying surface. This circular area is calculated using the radius of the cylinder—one-half the 4.10-cm diameter, expressed in meters.

$$A = \pi r^2 = 3.1416 \times \left(2.05 \text{ cm} \times \frac{1 \text{ m}}{100 \text{ cm}} \right)^2 = 1.32 \times 10^{-3} \text{ m}^2$$

The force divided by the area (in square meters) gives the pressure in pascals.

$$P = \frac{F}{A} = \frac{9.81 \text{ N}}{1.32 \times 10^{-3} \text{ m}^2} = 7.43 \times 10^3 \text{ Pa}$$

The relationship between the units torr and pascal (Table 6.1) is used for the final conversion.

$$P = 7.43 \times 10^3 \text{ Pa} \times \frac{760 \text{ Torr}}{101,325 \text{ Pa}} = 55.7 \text{ Torr}$$

CHECK: It's difficult to tell at a glance whether this is a reasonable result. The best check is to compare the calculated pressure with another pressure that is easier to visualize, that of a 55.7-mm column of mercury. The volume of the mercury column is $V = \pi r^2 h = \pi (2.05 \text{ cm})^2 \times 5.57 \text{ cm} = 73.5 \text{ cm}^3$. The density of mercury is about 13.6 g/cm^3 (page 180). The mass of the mercury column is 73.5 cm^3 × 13.6 g/cm^3 = 1.00 × 10^3 g = 1.00 kg, and this is exactly the mass of the steel cylinder.

Practice Example A: The 1.000-kg green cylinder in Figure 6-2 has a diameter of 2.60 cm. What pressure, expressed in torr, does this cylinder exert on the surface beneath it?

Practice Example B: We want to increase the pressure exerted by the 1.000-kg red cylinder in Example 6-3 to 100.0 mb by placing a weight atop it. What must be the mass of this weight? Must the added weight have the same cross-sectional area as the cylinder? Explain.

6-2 THE SIMPLE GAS LAWS

In this section, we consider relationships involving the pressure, volume, temperature, and amount of a gas. Specifically, we will see how one variable depends on another, as the remaining two are held fixed. Collectively, these relationships are referred to as the simple gas laws. You can use these laws in problem solving, but you will probably prefer the equation developed in the next section—the ideal gas equation. You may find that the greatest use of the simple gas laws is in solidifying your qualitative understanding of the behavior of gases.

BOYLE'S LAW

Boyle's Law: Pressure and Volume

In 1662, working with air, Robert Boyle discovered the first of the simple gas laws, now known as **Boyle's law**.

> For a fixed amount of gas at a constant temperature, the gas volume is inversely proportional to the gas pressure.

(6.4)

◀ **FIGURE 6-6**
Relationship between gas volume and pressure—Boyle's law
When the temperature and amount of gas are held constant, gas volume is inversely proportional to the pressure: A doubling of the pressure causes the volume to decrease to one-half its original value.

Consider the gas in Figure 6-6. It is confined in a cylinder closed off by a freely moving "weightless" piston. The pressure of the gas depends on the total weight placed on top of the piston. This weight (a force) divided by the area of the piston yields the gas pressure. If the weight on the piston is doubled, the pressure doubles and the gas volume decreases to one-half its original value. If the pressure of the gas is tripled, the volume decreases to one-third. On the other hand, if the pressure is reduced by one-half, the gas volume doubles, and so on. Mathematically, the inverse relationship between gas pressure and volume is expressed as

$$P \propto \frac{1}{V} \quad \text{or} \quad PV = a \text{ (a constant)} \tag{6.5}$$

P–V Relationships animation

Point out to students that a straight line is obtained when the pressure of a gas is plotted versus the *inverse* volume $(1/V)$ of the gas.

When the proportionality sign ($\propto$) is replaced with an equal sign and a proportionality constant, the product of the pressure and volume of a fixed amount of gas at a given temperature is seen to be a constant (a). The value of a depends on the amount of gas and the temperature. The graph in Figure 6-6 is that of $PV = a$. It is called a hyperbola.

EXAMPLE 6-4

Relating Gas Volume and Pressure—Boyle's Law. The volume of the large, irregularly shaped, closed tank pictured in Figure 6-7 can be determined as follows. The tank is first evacuated and then connected to a 50.0-L cylinder of compressed nitrogen gas. The gas pressure in the cylinder, originally at 21.5 atm, falls to 1.55 atm after it is connected to the evacuated tank. What is the volume of the tank?

▲ **FIGURE 6-7**
An application of Boyle's law—Example 6-4 illustrated
The final volume is the volume of the cylinder plus the volume of the tank. The amount of gas and its temperature remain constant when the cylinder is connected to the tank, but the pressure drops from 21.5 atm (the initial pressure) to 1.55 atm.

✓ When solving the problem in Example 6-4 point out to students that the volume of the gas is increasing because the 50.0-liter nitrogen cylinder is being connected to the evacuated tank and that the *increase* in volume is equal to the volume of the tank. Many students will forget to subtract the volume of the cylinder (50.0 L) from the volume calculated using Boyle's Law to obtain the volume of the tank.

▲ Charles experimented with the first hydrogen-filled balloons, much like the one shown here, though smaller. He also invented most of the features of modern ballooning, including the suspended basket and the valve to release excess gas.

Charles's Law:
Temperature and Volume

▶ When converting from °C to K, apply the addition and subtraction significant figure rule: the two-significant-digit 25 °C, when added to 273.15, becomes the three-significant-digit 298 K. Similarly, 25.0 °C becomes 298.2 K (that is, 25.0 + 273.15 = 298.15, which rounds to 298.2).

▶ Charles's ideas about the effect of temperature on the volume of a gas were probably influenced by his passion for hot-air balloons, a popular craze of the late eighteenth century.

Solution

One way to solve this problem is by writing equation (6.5) twice: for the initial condition (i) and for the final condition (f).

$$P_i V_i = a = P_f V_f$$

Now solve for the final volume, V_f.

$$V_f = V_i \times \frac{P_i}{P_f} = 50.0 \text{ L} \times \frac{21.5 \text{ atm}}{1.55 \text{ atm}} = 694 \text{ L}$$

Of this volume, 50.0 L is that of the cylinder. The volume of the tank is 694 L − 50.0 L = 644 L.

CHECK: Reasoning qualitatively from Boyle's law, we expect a large increase in volume as the decrease in pressure allows the gas to expand into the tank. The final gas volume (694 L) should be larger than the initial volume (50.0 L).

Practice Example A: A cylinder like that pictured in Figure 6-6 contains a gas at 5.25 atm pressure. When the gas is allowed to expand to a final volume of 12.5 L, the pressure drops to 1.85 atm. What was the original volume of the gas?

Practice Example B: 1.50 L of gas at 2.25 atm pressure expands to a final volume of 8.10 L. What is the final gas pressure in millimeters of mercury?

CHARLES'S LAW

The relationship between the volume of a gas and temperature was discovered by the French physicists Jacques Charles in 1787 and, independently, by Joseph Louis Gay-Lussac, who published it in 1802.

Figure 6-8 pictures a fixed amount of gas confined in a cylinder. The pressure is held constant at 1 atm while the temperature is varied. The volume of gas increases as the temperature is raised and decreases as the temperature is lowered. The relationship is linear. Figure 6-8 shows the linear dependence of volume on temperature for three gases at three different initial conditions. One point in common to the three lines is their intersection with the temperature axis. Although they differ at every other temperature, the gas volumes all reach a value of zero at the same temperature. The temperature at which the volume of a hypothetical* gas becomes zero is the absolute zero of temperature: −273.15 °C on the Celsius scale or 0 K on the **absolute**, or **Kelvin**, scale.

$$T(\text{K}) = t(°\text{C}) + 273.15 \tag{6.6}$$

Thus, from a volume of zero at 0 K, the gas volume is directly proportional to the temperature. The statement of **Charles's law** then becomes

> The volume of a fixed amount of gas at constant pressure is directly proportional to the Kelvin (absolute) temperature. (6.7)

In mathematical terms

$$V \propto T \quad \text{or} \quad V = bT \text{ (where } b \text{ is a constant)} \tag{6.8}$$

The value of the constant b depends on the amount of gas and the pressure. It does *not* depend on the identity of the gas.

From either expression (6.7) or (6.8), we see that doubling the Kelvin temperature of a gas causes its volume to double. Reducing the Kelvin temperature by one-half (say, from 300 to 150 K) causes the volume to decrease to one-half, and so on.

---

*All gases condense to liquids or solids before the temperature approaches absolute zero. Also, when we speak of the volume of a gas, we mean the free volume among the gas molecules, not the volume of the molecules themselves. Thus, the gas we refer to here is *hypothetical*. It is a gas whose molecules have mass but no volume and that does not condense to a liquid or solid.

▲ FIGURE 6-8
Gas volume as a function of temperature
Volume is plotted against temperature on two different scales—Celsius and Kelvin. Gases A, B, and C are shown at three different initial conditions, all at 1 atm. Gas C, for example, starts at 500 K (227 °C) and 50 mL. As the temperature is lowered, the volume decreases as predicted by Charles's law. Thus, at 250 K (−23 °C), one-half the initial temperature of 500 K, the volume has become 25 mL—one-half of the original 50 mL. Although the relationship between volume and temperature is linear for both the Celsius and Kelvin temperature scales, the volume is directly proportional only to the absolute temperature. That is, the volume must be zero at a temperature of zero. Only the Kelvin scale meets this requirement.

EXAMPLE 6-5

Relating a Gas Volume and Temperature—Charles's Law. A balloon is inflated to a volume of 2.50 L in a warm living room (24 °C). Then it is taken outside on a very cold winter day (−25 °C). Assume that the quantity of air in the balloon and its pressure both remain constant. What will be the volume of the balloon when it is outdoors?

Solution

Similar to the method used in Example 6-4, write equation (6.8) twice: for the initial (i) and the final (f) conditions. In doing this, though, first rearrange the equation and solve for b. That is, $b = V/T$.

$$\frac{V_i}{T_i} = b = \frac{V_f}{T_f}$$

Now, solve the above equation for V_f, but do not forget to change temperatures to the Kelvin scale—that is, $T_i = 24\ °C + 273 = 297\ K$, and $T_f = -25\ °C + 273 = 248\ K$.

$$V_f = V_i \times \frac{T_f}{T_i} = 2.50\ L \times \frac{248\ K}{297\ K} = 2.09\ L$$

CHECK: Reasoning qualitatively from Charles's law, because the gas temperature is lowered, we expect the volume to decrease. We expect V_f to be less than V_i.

Practice Example A: A gas at 25 °C and 0.987 atm pressure is confined in a cylinder by a piston. When the cylinder is heated, the gas volume expands from 0.250 L to 1.65 L. What is the new temperature of the gas, assuming the pressure remains constant?

Practice Example B: To what temperature must 50.5 mL of N_2 gas at 33.4 °C and 1.00 atm pressure be heated to produce the same percentage change in volume as observed when 35.0 mL of O_2 gas at 1.00 atm pressure is heated from −13.5 °C to 25.0 °C?

The 2:1:2 ratio of the combining volumes for the reaction forming water demonstrates that oxygen must be O_2 (or possibly some multiple of O_2). It has been stated that the 2:1:2 ratio also confirms H_2O as the formula of water—this is incorrect. The 2:1:2 ratio is also consistent with

$$2 H(g) + O_2(g) \longrightarrow 2 HO(g).$$

Only if hydrogen is known to be H_2 from some other experiment must water then be H_2O. The 3:1:2 ratio for the reaction forming ammonia would confirm the formulas H_2, N_2, and NH_3.

▲ **Amedeo Avogadro (1776–1856)—a scientist ahead of his time**
Avogadro's hypothesis and its ramifications were not understood by his contemporaries, but were effectively communicated by Stanislao Cannizzaro (1826–1910) about fifty years later.

▶ Avogadro's hypothesis and statements derived from it apply only to gases. There is no similar relationship for liquids or solids.

 Avogadro's Law: Moles and Volume

CONCEPT ASSESSMENT ✓

The Kelvin and degree Celsius temperature units indicate the same temperature interval. Because doubling a gas temperature from 100 K to 200 K causes a gas volume to double, would you expect a similar doubling of the gas volume when a gas is heated from 100 °C to 200 °C? Explain.

STANDARD CONDITIONS OF TEMPERATURE AND PRESSURE

Because gas properties depend on temperature and pressure, it is useful to have a set of standard conditions of temperature and pressure that can be used for comparing different gases. The standard temperature for gases is taken to be 0 °C = 273.15 K and standard pressure, 1 atm = 760 mmHg, exactly. **Standard conditions of temperature and pressure** are usually abbreviated as **STP**.

AVOGADRO'S LAW

In 1808, Gay-Lussac reported that gases react by volumes in the ratio of small whole numbers. One proposed explanation was that equal volumes of gases at the same temperature and pressure contain equal numbers of atoms. Dalton did not agree with this proposition, however. If Gay-Lussac's proposition were true, then the reaction of hydrogen and oxygen to form water would be $H(g) + O(g) \longrightarrow HO(g)$, with combining volumes of 1:1:1, rather than the 2:1:2 that was observed.

In 1811, Amedeo Avogadro resolved this dilemma by proposing not only the "equal volumes–equal numbers" hypothesis, but also that molecules of a gas may break up into half–molecules when they react. Using modern terminology, we would say that O_2 molecules split into atoms, which then combine with molecules of H_2 to form H_2O molecules. In this way, the volume of oxygen needed is only one-half that of hydrogen. Avogadro's reasoning is outlined in Figure 6-9.

Avogadro's equal volumes–equal numbers hypothesis can be stated in either of two ways.

1. Equal volumes of different gases compared at the same temperature and pressure contain equal numbers of molecules.

2. Equal numbers of molecules of different gases compared at the same temperature and pressure occupy equal volumes.

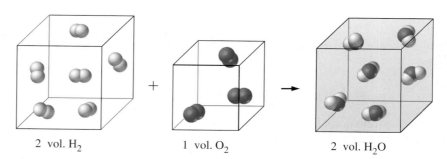

2 vol. H_2 1 vol. O_2 2 vol. H_2O

▲ **FIGURE 6-9**
Formation of water—actual observation and Avogadro's hypothesis
In the reaction $2 H_2(g) + 1 O_2(g) \longrightarrow 2 H_2O(g)$, only one-half as many O_2 molecules are required as are H_2 molecules. If equal volumes of gases contain equal numbers of molecules, this means the volume of $O_2(g)$ is one-half that of $H_2(g)$. The combining ratio by volume is 2:1:2.

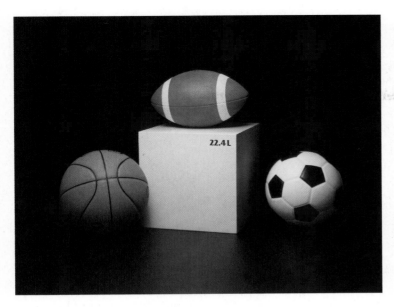

◄ **FIGURE 6-10**
Molar volume of a gas visualized
The wooden cube has the same volume as a mole of gas at STP: 22.4 L. By contrast, the volume of the basketball is 7.5 L; the soccer ball, 6.0 L; and the football, 4.4 L.

A relationship that follows from *Avogadro's hypothesis*, often called **Avogadro's law**, is as follows.

> At a fixed temperature and pressure, the volume of a gas is directly proportional to the amount of gas. (6.9)

If the number of moles of gas (n) is doubled, the volume doubles, and so on. A mathematical statement of this fact is

$$V \propto n \quad \text{and} \quad V = c \cdot n$$

At STP, the number of molecules contained in 22.4 L of a gas is 6.02×10^{23}, that is, *1 mol*.

> $$1 \text{ mol gas} = 22.4 \text{ L gas (at STP)} \qquad (6.10)$$

Figure 6-10 should help you to visualize 22.4 L of a gas.

🧪 Pop and Poop Bottles. Obtain 2 heavy-walled glass soda bottles, preferably the older returnable variety. Wrap about 50% of the surface with electrical tape. Mark, using typewriter correction fluid, the 1/3 full level. Fill, by displacement of water, 1/3 full with O_2 and then the remaining 2/3 with H_2. Stopper the bottle. Fill another with 1/3 H_2 and 2/3 O_2. Holding each bottle firmly, remove the stopper and pass over the flame of a burner. Compare the application and misapplication of Gay-Lussac's law of combining volume. Note that the poop bottle is the one with twice as much "O."

EXAMPLE 6-6

Using the Molar Volume of a Gas at STP as a Conversion Factor. What is the mass of 1.00 L of cyclopropane gas, C_3H_6 (used as an anesthetic), when measured at STP?

Solution

Expression (6.10) makes it possible to convert directly from volume at STP to number of moles of gas. The conversion from moles of gas to mass of gas requires the molar mass.

$$? \text{ g } C_3H_6 = 1.00 \text{ L} \times \frac{1 \text{ mol } C_3H_6}{22.4 \text{ L}} \times \frac{42.08 \text{ g } C_3H_6}{1 \text{ mol } C_3H_6} = 1.88 \text{ g } C_3H_6$$

Practice Example A: Propane, C_3H_8, is stored as a liquid under pressure for use in backyard barbecue units. The liquid vaporizes to a gas when the pressure is released. A small tank of propane is opened and releases 30.0 L of gas at STP. What mass of gas was released?

Practice Example B: A 128-g piece of solid carbon dioxide (dry ice) sublimes (evaporates without first melting) into $CO_2(g)$. How many liters of gas are formed at STP?

◄ If a gas is *not* at STP, relating the amount of gas and its volume is best done with the ideal gas equation (Section 6-3).

CONCEPT ASSESSMENT ✓

Without doing an actual calculation, determine which of the following expressions equals the final volume of gas if 20.0 g O_2 is added to 40.0 g O_2 at STP, the temperature is changed to 30 °C, and the pressure to 825 Torr.

(a) $\left(\dfrac{40.0}{20.0} \times \dfrac{1}{32.00} \times 22.4 \times \dfrac{760}{825} \times \dfrac{303}{273} \right) L$

(b) $\left(\dfrac{20.0}{40.0} \times \dfrac{1}{32.00} \times 22.4 \times \dfrac{825}{760} \times \dfrac{273}{303} \right) L$

(c) $\left(60.0 \times \dfrac{1}{32.00} \times 22.4 \times \dfrac{825}{760} \times \dfrac{303}{273} \right) L$

(d) $\left(\dfrac{3}{2} \times 40.0 \times \dfrac{1}{32.00} \times 22.4 \times \dfrac{760}{825} \times \dfrac{303}{273} \right) L$

(e) $\left(\dfrac{2}{3} \times 60.0 \times \dfrac{1}{32.00} \times 22.4 \times \dfrac{760}{825} \times \dfrac{303}{273} \right) L$

Ideal Gas Behavior activity

✓ Advise students that the ideal gas equation will not be supplied on exams and should be memorized. Values of *R* given here, however, will be available. Note that one can reconstruct the ideal gas equation from *R* using the units as given. Note also that there is really only one *R* but that, like many properties and constants, its value may be expressed in a variety of units.

Derivation of the Ideal Gas Law

6-3   COMBINING THE GAS LAWS: THE IDEAL GAS EQUATION AND THE GENERAL GAS EQUATION

Each of the three simple gas laws describes the effect that changes in one variable have on the gas volume when the other two variables are held constant.

1. Boyle's law describes the effect of pressure, $V \propto 1/P$.
2. Charles's law describes the effect of temperature, $V \propto T$.
3. Avogadro's law describes the effect of the amount of gas, $V \propto n$.

These three laws can be combined into a single equation—the **ideal gas equation**—that includes all four gas variables: volume, pressure, temperature, and amount of gas.

THE IDEAL GAS EQUATION

In accord with the three simple gas laws, the volume of a gas is *directly* proportional to the amount of gas, *directly* proportional to the Kelvin temperature, and *inversely* proportional to pressure. That is,

$$V \propto \frac{nT}{P} \qquad \text{and} \qquad V = \frac{RnT}{P}$$

$$PV = nRT \tag{6.11}$$

A gas whose behavior conforms to the ideal gas equation is called an **ideal**, or **perfect, gas**. Before we can apply equation (6.11), we need a value for the constant *R*, called the **gas constant**. The simplest way to obtain this is to substitute into equation (6.11) the molar volume of an ideal gas at STP. However, the value of *R* will then depend on which units are used to express pressure and volume. With a molar volume of 22.4140 L and pressure in atmospheres,

$$R = \frac{PV}{nT} = \frac{1 \text{ atm} \times 22.4140 \text{ L}}{1 \text{ mol} \times 273.15 \text{ K}} = 0.082057 \text{ L atm mol}^{-1} \text{ K}^{-1}$$

Using the SI units of m^3 for volume and Pa for pressure gives

$$R = \frac{PV}{nT} = \frac{101{,}325 \text{ Pa} \times 2.24140 \times 10^{-2} \text{ m}^3}{1 \text{ mol} \times 273.15 \text{ K}} = 8.3145 \text{ m}^3 \text{ Pa mol}^{-1} \text{ K}^{-1}$$

TABLE 6.2   Four Common Values of *R*

0.082057 L atm mol^{-1} K^{-1}
62.364 L Torr mol^{-1} K^{-1}
8.3145 m^3 Pa mol^{-1} K^{-1}
8.3145 J mol^{-1} K^{-1}

The units $m^3 \, Pa \, mol^{-1} \, K^{-1}$ also have another significance. The pascal has units $kg \, m^{-1} \, s^{-2}$, so the units $m^3 \, Pa$ become $kg \, m^2 \, s^{-2}$, which is the SI unit of energy—the joule. Thus R also has the value

$$R = 8.3145 \, J \, mol^{-1} \, K^{-1}$$

We will use this value of R when we consider the energy involved in gas expansion and compression.

Four common values of the gas constant are listed in Table 6.2, and you will have a chance to use all of them in the Practice Examples and end-of-chapter exercises in this chapter. In Example 6-7, to help organize the data, the known quantities are listed first followed by the unknown. As you become more familiar with the ideal gas equation, you may be able to bypass this step and substitute directly into the equation. A useful check of the calculated result is to make certain the units cancel properly. This general strategy is illustrated in the diagram in the margin.

▲ **Applying the ideal gas equation**

EXAMPLE 6-7

Calculating a Gas Volume with the Ideal Gas Equation. What is the volume occupied by 13.7 g $Cl_2(g)$ at 45 °C and 745 mmHg?

Solution

$$P = 745 \, mmHg \times \frac{1 \, atm}{760 \, mmHg} = \frac{745}{760} \, atm = 0.980 \, atm$$

$$V = ?$$

$$n = 13.7 \, g \, Cl_2 \times \frac{1 \, mol \, Cl_2}{70.91 \, g \, Cl_2} = 0.193 \, mol \, Cl_2$$

$$R = 0.08206 \, L \, atm \, mol^{-1} \, K^{-1}$$

$$T = 45 \, °C + 273 = 318 \, K$$

Divide both sides of the ideal gas equation by P to solve for V.

$$\frac{PV}{P} = \frac{nRT}{P} \quad \text{and} \quad V = \frac{nRT}{P}$$

$$V = \frac{nRT}{P} = \frac{0.193 \, mol \times 0.08206 \, L \, atm \, mol^{-1} \, K^{-1} \times 318 \, K}{0.980 \, atm} = 5.14 \, L$$

CHECK: Note that all units cancel in the setup above, except for L. This is a unit of volume.

Practice Example A: What is the volume occupied by 20.2 g $NH_3(g)$ at −25 °C and 752 mmHg?

Practice Example B: At what temperature will a 13.7-g Cl_2 sample exert a pressure of 745 mmHg when confined in a 7.50-L container?

◀ **KEEP IN MIND**

that when canceling units, a unit such as mol^{-1} is the same as $1/mol$. Thus, $mol \times mol^{-1} = 1$, and also $K \times K^{-1} = 1$.

EXAMPLE 6-8

Calculating a Gas Pressure with the Ideal Gas Equation. What is the pressure, in kilopascals, exerted by 1.00×10^{20} molecules of N_2 in a 305-mL flask at 175 °C?

Solution

Because we seek a pressure in kilopascals, let us use the form of the ideal gas equation having

$$R = 8.3145 \, m^3 \, Pa \, mol^{-1} \, K^{-1}$$

The first step is to convert from molecules to moles of a gas, n.

$$n = 1.00 \times 10^{20} \, \text{molecules } N_2 \times \frac{1 \, mol \, N_2}{6.022 \times 10^{23} \, \text{molecules } N_2}$$

$$= 0.000166 \, mol \, N_2$$

Convert from milliliters to liters and then to cubic meters (recall Figure 1-9).

$$V = 305 \text{ mL} \times \frac{1 \text{ L}}{1000 \text{ mL}} \times \frac{1 \text{ m}^3}{1000 \text{ L}} = 3.05 \times 10^{-4} \text{ m}^3$$

Express gas temperature on the Kelvin scale.

$$T = 175 \,°\text{C} + 273 = 448 \text{ K}$$

Rearrange the ideal gas equation to the form, $P = nRT/V$, and substitute the above data.

$$P = \frac{nRT}{V} = \frac{0.000166 \text{ mol} \times 8.3145 \text{ Pa m}^3 \text{ mol}^{-1} \text{ K}^{-1} \times 448 \text{ K}}{3.05 \times 10^{-4} \text{ m}^3} = 2.03 \times 10^3 \text{ Pa}$$

Finally, convert the pressure to the unit kilopascal.

$$P = 2.03 \times 10^3 \text{ Pa} \times \frac{1 \text{ kPa}}{1000 \text{ Pa}} = 2.03 \text{ kPa}$$

CHECK: Again, we see from the cancellation of units above that only the desired unit—a pressure unit—remains.

Practice Example A: How many moles of He(g) are in a 5.00-L storage tank filled with helium at 10.5 atm pressure at 30.0 °C?

Practice Example B: How many molecules of N_2(g) remain in an ultrahigh vacuum chamber of 3.45 m^3 volume when the pressure is reduced to 6.67×10^{-7} Pa at 25 °C?

To manometer

Thermometer

1.00 L O_2(g) at STP

(a) Ice bath

To manometer

Heater

Thermometer

1.00 L O_2(g) P = ?

(b) Boiling water

▲ **FIGURE 6-11**
Pressure of a gas as a function of temperature— Example 6-9 visualized
The amount of gas and volume are held constant.
(a) 1.00 L O_2(g) at STP;
(b) 1.00 L O_2(g) at 100 °C.

THE GENERAL GAS EQUATION

In Examples 6-7 and 6-8, the ideal gas equation was applied to a single set of conditions (P, V, n, and T). Sometimes a gas is described under two different sets of conditions. Here, the ideal gas equation must be applied twice—to an initial condition and a final condition. That is,

Initial condition (i)

$$P_i V_i = n_i R T_i$$

$$R = \frac{P_i V_i}{n_i T_i}$$

Final condition (f)

$$P_f V_f = n_f R T_f$$

$$R = \frac{P_f V_f}{n_f T_f}$$

The above expressions are equal to each other because each is equal to R.

$$\frac{P_i V_i}{n_i T_i} = \frac{P_f V_f}{n_f T_f} \qquad (6.12)$$

Expression (6.12) is called the **general gas equation**. It is often applied in cases in which one or two of the gas properties are held constant, and the equation can be simplified by eliminating these constants. For example, if a constant mass of gas is subject to changes in temperature, pressure, and volume, n_i and n_f cancel because they are equal (constant moles); thus we have

$$\frac{P_i V_i}{T_i} = \frac{P_f V_f}{T_f}$$

This equation is sometimes referred to as the *combined gas law*. In Example 6-9, both volume and mass are constant, and this establishes the simple relationship between gas pressure and temperature known as *Amontons's law*: The pressure of a fixed amount of gas confined to a fixed volume is directly proportional to the Kelvin temperature.

EXAMPLE 6-9

Applying the General Gas Equation. The situation pictured in Figure 6-11(a) is changed to that in Figure 6-11(b). What is the gas pressure in Figure 6-11(b)?

Solution

Identify the terms in the general gas equation that remain constant. Cancel out these terms and solve the remaining equation. In this case, the amount of O_2(g) is constant ($n_i = n_f$) and the volume is constant ($V_i = V_f$).

$$\frac{P_i \cancel{V_i}}{\cancel{n_i} T_i} = \frac{P_f \cancel{V_f}}{\cancel{n_f} T_f} \quad \text{and} \quad \frac{P_i}{T_i} = \frac{P_f}{T_f} \quad \text{and} \quad P_f = P_i \times \frac{T_f}{T_i}$$

Because P_i is standard pressure = 1.00 atm

$$P_f = 1.00 \text{ atm} \times \frac{(100 + 273) \text{ K}}{273 \text{ K}} = 1.00 \text{ atm} \times \frac{373 \text{ K}}{273 \text{ K}} = 1.37 \text{ atm}$$

CHECK: We can base our check on a qualitative, intuitive understanding of what happens when a gas is heated in a closed container. Its pressure increases (possibly to the extent that the container bursts). If, by error, we had used the ratio of temperatures 273 K/373 K, the final pressure would have been less than 1.00 atm—an impossible result.

Practice Example A: A 1.00-mL sample of $N_2(g)$ at 36.2 °C and 2.14 atm is heated to 37.8 °C, and the pressure changed to 1.02 atm. What volume does the gas occupy at this final temperature and pressure?

Practice Example B: Suppose that in Figure 6-11 we want the pressure to remain at 1.00 atm when the $O_2(g)$ is heated to 100 °C. What mass of $O_2(g)$ must we release from the flask?

USING THE GAS LAWS

When confronted with a problem involving gases, students sometimes wonder which gas equation to use. Gas law problems can often be thought of in more than one way. When a problem involves a comparison of two gases or two states (initial and final) of a single gas, use the general gas equation (6.12) after eliminating any term (n, P, T, V) that remains constant. Otherwise, use the ideal gas equation (6.11). If you prefer a diagrammatic approach to a problem-solving strategy, you should find Figure 6-12 helpful. The key step in this diagram is to determine whether the amount of gas (in mass or moles) is given in the problem or asked for in the answer to the problem.

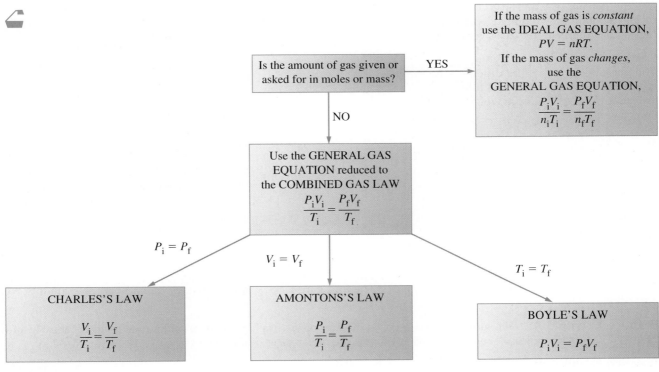

▲ **FIGURE 6-12**
Solving a gas law problem

6-4 APPLICATIONS OF THE IDEAL GAS EQUATION

Application of the Ideal Gas Equation activity

Although the ideal gas equation can always be used as it was presented in equation (6.11), it is useful to recast it into slightly different forms for some applications. We will consider two such applications in this section: determination of molar masses and gas densities.

MOLAR MASS DETERMINATION

Students should also be able to produce and use the ideal gas equation in the form given in equation (6.13). Point out that this or equation (6.11) can be used as the starting point for all ideal gas equation problems.

If we know the volume of a gas at a fixed temperature and pressure, we can solve the ideal gas equation for the amount of the gas in moles. Because the number of moles of gas (n) is equal to the mass of gas (m) divided by the molar mass (M), if we know the mass and number of moles of gas, we can solve the expression $n = m/M$ for the molar mass, M. An alternative is to make the substitution $n = m/M$ directly into the ideal gas equation.

$$PV = \frac{mRT}{M} \tag{6.13}$$

Equation (6.13) is used to determine a molar mass in Example 6-10, but note that the equation can also be used when the molar mass of a gas is known and the mass of a particular sample of the gas is sought.

EXAMPLE 6-10

Determining a Molar Mass with the Ideal Gas Equation. Propylene is an important commercial chemical (about ninth in the amount produced among manufactured chemicals) used in the synthesis of other organic chemicals and in production of plastics (polypropylene). A glass vessel weighs 40.1305 g when clean, dry, and evacuated; it weighs 138.2410 g when filled with water at 25.0 °C (density of water = 0.9970 g/mL) and 40.2959 g when filled with propylene gas at 740.3 mmHg and 24.0 °C. What is the molar mass of propylene?

Solution

First determine the mass of water required to fill the vessel.

$$\text{mass of water to fill vessel} = 138.2410 \text{ g} - 40.1305 \text{ g}$$
$$= 98.1105 \text{ g}$$

Use the density of water in a conversion factor to obtain the volume of water (and hence, the volume of the glass vessel).

$$\text{volume of water (volume of vessel)} = 98.1105 \text{ g H}_2\text{O} \times \frac{1 \text{ mL H}_2\text{O}}{0.9970 \text{ g H}_2\text{O}}$$
$$= 98.41 \text{ mL} = 0.09841 \text{ L}$$

The mass of the gas is the difference between the weight of the vessel filled with polypropylene gas and the weight of the empty vessel.

$$\text{mass of gas} = 40.2959 \text{ g} - 40.1305 \text{ g} = 0.1654 \text{ g}$$

The values of temperature and pressure are given.

$$T = 24.0 \text{ °C} + 273.15 = 297.2 \text{ K}$$

$$P = 740.3 \text{ mmHg} \times \frac{1 \text{ atm}}{760 \text{ mmHg}} = 0.9741 \text{ atm}$$

Substitute data into the rearranged version of equation (6.13).

$$M = \frac{mRT}{PV} = \frac{0.1654 \text{ g} \times 0.08206 \text{ L atm mol}^{-1} \text{ K}^{-1} \times 297.2 \text{ K}}{0.9741 \text{ atm} \times 0.09841 \text{ L}}$$
$$= 42.08 \text{ g/mol}$$

CHECK: Cancellations leave the units g and mol^{-1}. The unit g mol^{-1} or g/mol is that for molar mass, the quantity we are seeking.

Practice Example A: The same glass vessel used in Example 6-10 is filled with an unknown gas at 772 mmHg and 22.4 °C. The gas-filled vessel weighs 40.4868 g. What is the molar mass of the gas?

Practice Example B: A 1.27-g sample of an oxide of nitrogen, believed to be either NO or N_2O, occupies a volume of 1.07 L at 25 °C and 737 mmHg. Which oxide is it?

Suppose that we want to determine the formula of an unknown hydrocarbon. With combustion analysis we can establish the mass percent composition, and from this, we can determine the empirical formula. The method of Example 6-10 gives us a molar mass (g/mol), which is numerically equal to the molecular mass (u). This is all the information we need to establish the true molecular formula of the hydrocarbon (see Exercise 82).

GAS DENSITIES

To determine the density of a gas, we can start with the density equation, $d = m/V$. Then we can express the mass of gas as the product of the number of moles of gas and the molar mass: $m = n \times M$. This leads to

$$d = \frac{m}{V} = \frac{n \times M}{V} = \frac{n}{V} \times M$$

Now, with the ideal gas equation, we can replace n/V by its equivalent, P/RT, to obtain

$$d = \frac{m}{V} = \frac{MP}{RT} \qquad (6.14)$$

The density of a gas at STP can easily be calculated by dividing its molar mass by the molar volume (22.4 L/mol). For $O_2(g)$ at STP, for example, the density is 32.0 g/22.4 L = 1.43 g/L. Equation (6.14) can be used for other conditions of temperature and pressure.

> Molar Mass of Air. Attach a 250-mL bulb (a round-bottom flask) to a vacuum stopcock. Determine the volume of the bulb by weighing it empty and full of water. Evacuate the bulb using a pump and close the stopcock. Weigh the bulb on a cork ring using an analytical balance. Open the stopcock and weigh again. Calculate the average molar mass of air and compare the result to what is expected. See also Shakhashiri, p. 48–54.

> ◄ **KEEP IN MIND**
> that gas densities are typically much smaller than those of liquids and solids. Gas densities are usually expressed in grams per *liter* rather than grams per *milliliter*.

EXAMPLE 6-11

Using the Ideal Gas Equation to Calculate a Gas Density. What is the density of oxygen gas (O_2) at 298 K and 0.987 atm?

Solution

We can get the terms for the right side of equation (6.14) easily. Density (m/V) is the left side of the equation.

$$d = \frac{m}{V} = \frac{MP}{RT} = \frac{32.00 \text{ g mol}^{-1} \times 0.987 \text{ atm}}{0.08206 \text{ L atm mol}^{-1} \text{ K}^{-1} \times 298 \text{ K}} = 1.29 \text{ g/L}$$

CHECK: The calculated density (1.29 g/L) should be somewhat less than the density of $O_2(g)$ at STP (1.43 g/L). The gas pressure is somewhat less than 1.00 atm, and the temperature is somewhat greater than 273 K. From equation (6.14), note that decreasing pressure and increasing temperature both cause density to decrease.

Practice Example A: What is the density of helium gas at 298 K and 0.987 atm? Based on your answer, explain why we can say that helium is "lighter than air."

Practice Example B: At what temperature will the density of $O_2(g)$ be 1.00 g/L if the pressure is kept at 745 mmHg?

> Gas Densities. Fill a balloon with H_2 or He and weigh it, as in Figure 6-13. Also, fill a balloon with CO_2. To do this, put some water and dry ice into a filtering flask. Tape a balloon to the side arm. Set a large stopper firmly into the top of the flask. The water serves as a source of heat to accelerate the sublimation of CO_2. Remove the balloon and tie when full. Because the balloon does not rise, think of it as the proverbial "lead balloon." Now, tie this to the other end of the string holding the H_2 or He balloon.

The density of gases differs from that of solids and liquids in two important ways.

1. Gas densities depend strongly on pressure and temperature, increasing as the gas pressure increases and decreasing as the temperature increases. Densities of liquids and solids also depend somewhat on temperature, but they depend far less on pressure.

2. The density of a gas is directly proportional to its molar mass. No simple relationship exists between density and molar mass for liquids and solids.

An important application of gas densities is in establishing conditions for lighter-than-air balloons. A gas-filled balloon will rise in the atmosphere only if the density of the gas is less than that of the surrounding air. Because gas

▲ FIGURE 6-13
The helium-filled balloon exerts a lifting force on the 20.00-g weight, so that the balloon and the weight together weigh only 19.09 g.

Air Bags animation

densities are directly proportional to molar masses, the lower the molar mass of the gas, the greater its lifting power. The lowest molar mass is that of hydrogen, but hydrogen is flammable and forms explosive mixtures with air. The explosion of the dirigible *Hindenburg* in 1937 spelled the end to transoceanic travel by hydrogen-filled airships. Now, airships such as the Goodyear blimps use helium, which has a molar mass only twice that of hydrogen (Fig. 6-13), but is inert. Hydrogen is still used for weather and other observational balloons.

Another alternative is to fill a balloon with *hot* air. Equation (6.14) indicates that the density of a gas is *inversely* proportional to temperature. Hot air is less dense than cold air. However, because the density of air decreases rapidly with altitude, there is a limit to how high a hot-air balloon or any gas-filled balloon can rise.

6-5   GASES IN CHEMICAL REACTIONS

Reactions involving gases as reactants or products (or both) are no strangers to us. We now have a new tool to apply to reaction stoichiometry calculations: the ideal gas equation. Specifically, we can now handle information about gases in terms of volumes, temperatures, and pressures, as well as by mass and amount in moles. A practical application is the nitrogen-forming reaction in an automobile air-bag safety system, which utilizes the rapid decomposition of sodium azide.

$$2\,NaN_3(s) \xrightarrow{\Delta} 2\,Na(l) + 3\,N_2(g)$$

The essential components of the system are an ignition device and a pellet containing sodium azide and appropriate additives. When activated, the system inflates an air bag in 20 to 60 ms and converts Na(l) to a harmless solid residue.

In many cases, the best method is to (1) use stoichiometric factors to relate the amount of a gas to amounts of other reactants or products, and (2) use the ideal gas equation to relate the amount of gas to volume, temperature, and pressure. In Example 6-12, we use this approach to determine the volume of $N_2(g)$ produced in a typical air-bag system.

EXAMPLE 6-12

Using the Ideal Gas Equation in Reaction Stoichiometry Calculations. What volume of N_2, measured at 735 mmHg and 26 °C, is produced when 70.0 g NaN_3 is decomposed?

$$2\,NaN_3(s) \xrightarrow{\Delta} 2\,Na(l) + 3\,N_2(g)$$

Solution

$$? \text{ mol } N_2 = 70.0 \text{ g } NaN_3 \times \frac{1 \text{ mol } NaN_3}{65.01 \text{ g } NaN_3} \times \frac{3 \text{ mol } N_2}{2 \text{ mol } NaN_3} = 1.62 \text{ mol } N_2$$

$$P = 735 \text{ mmHg} \times \frac{1 \text{ atm}}{760 \text{ mmHg}} = 0.967 \text{ atm}$$

$$V = ?$$
$$n = 1.62 \text{ mol}$$
$$R = 0.08206 \text{ L atm mol}^{-1}\,K^{-1}$$
$$T = 26\,°C + 273 = 299 \text{ K}$$
$$V = \frac{nRT}{P} = \frac{1.62 \text{ mol} \times 0.08206 \text{ L atm mol}^{-1}\,K^{-1} \times 299 \text{ K}}{0.967 \text{ atm}} = 41.1 \text{ L}$$

CHECK: 70.0 g NaN_3 is slightly more than one mole ($M \approx 65$ g/mol). From this amount of NaN_3 we should expect about 1.5 mol $N_2(g)$. At STP, 1.5 mol $N_2(g)$ would occupy a volume of $1.5 \times 22.4 = 33.6$ L. The gas collected is at a lower pressure and a higher temperature than STP; it should have a volume somewhat greater than 33.6 L.

Practice Example A: How many grams of NaN_3 are needed to produce 20.0 L of $N_2(g)$ at 30.0 °C and 776 mmHg?

Practice Example B: How many grams of Na(l) are produced per liter of $N_2(g)$ formed in the decomposition of sodium azide if the gas is collected at 25 °C and 751 Torr?

LAW OF COMBINING VOLUMES

If the reactants and products involved in a stoichiometric calculation are gases, sometimes we can use a particularly simple approach. Consider this reaction.

$$2\ NO(g) + O_2(g) \longrightarrow 2\ NO_2(g)$$
$$2\ mol\ NO(g) + 1\ mol\ O_2(g) \longrightarrow 2\ mol\ NO_2(g)$$

Suppose the gases are compared at the same T and P. Under these conditions, one mole of gas occupies a particular volume, call it V liters; 2 mol gas, 2 V liters; and so on.

$$2\ V\ L\ NO\ (g) + V\ L\ O_2(g) \longrightarrow 2\ V\ L\ NO_2(g)$$

Now divide each coefficient by V, and get

$$2\ L\ NO(g) + 1\ L\ O_2(g) \longrightarrow 2\ L\ NO_2(g)$$

When we describe the chemical reaction in this way, we can write conversion factors based on the statements:

$$2\ L\ NO_2(g)\ is\ equivalent\ to\ (\Leftrightarrow)\ 2\ L\ NO(g)$$
$$2\ L\ NO_2(g) \Leftrightarrow 1\ L\ O_2(g);\ 2\ L\ NO(g) \Leftrightarrow 1\ L\ O_2(g)$$

What we have just done is to develop, in modern terms, Gay-Lussac's **law of combining volumes**. We previewed this law on page 188 by suggesting that the volumes of gases involved in a reaction are in the ratio of small whole numbers. Here, we see that the small whole numbers are simply the stoichiometric coefficients in the balanced equation. We apply this law in Example 6-13.

Show how to use combining volumes to obtain molecular formulas. For example, combustion of 1 L of an unknown hydrocarbon requires 4 L O_2 and forms 3 L of CO_2 plus an undetermined quantity of liquid water. What is the formula, C_xH_y?

Remind students that the volume of a gas is directly proportional to the moles of gas if temperature and pressure are kept constant.

EXAMPLE 6-13

Applying the Law of Combining Volumes. Zinc blende, ZnS, is the most important zinc ore. Roasting (strong heating) of ZnS is the first step in the commercial production of zinc.

$$2\ ZnS(s) + 3\ O_2(g) \xrightarrow{\Delta} 2\ ZnO(s) + 2\ SO_2(g)$$

What volume of $SO_2(g)$ forms per liter of $O_2(g)$ consumed? Both gases are measured at 25 °C and 745 mmHg.

Solution

The reactant and product being compared are both gases and both are at the same temperature and pressure, so we can derive a ratio of combining volumes (in blue) from the balanced equation and use it as follows.

$$?\ L\ SO_2(g) = 1.00\ L\ O_2(g) \times \frac{2\ L\ SO_2(g)}{3\ L\ O_2(g)} = 0.667\ L\ SO_2(g)$$

Practice Example A: The first step in making nitric acid is to convert ammonia to nitrogen monoxide. This is done under conditions of high temperature and in the presence of a platinum catalyst. What volume of $O_2(g)$ is consumed per liter of NO(g) formed?

$$4\ NH_3(g) + 5\ O_2(g) \xrightarrow[850\ °C]{Pt} 4\ NO(g) + 6\ H_2O(g)$$

Practice Example B: If all gases are measured at the same temperature and pressure, what volume of $NH_3(g)$ is produced when 225 L $H_2(g)$ are consumed in the reaction $N_2(g) + H_2(g) \longrightarrow NH_3(g)$ (not balanced)?

CONCEPT ASSESSMENT ✓

What would be the answer in Example 6-13 if **(a)** both gases were measured at STP; **(b)** if the O_2 were measured at STP and the SO_2 were measured at 25 °C and 745 mmHg?

6-6 MIXTURES OF GASES

The simple gas laws, such as Boyle's and Charles's laws, were based on the behavior of air—a mixture of gases. So, the simple gas laws and the ideal gas equation apply to a *mixture* of nonreactive gases as well as to individual gases. Where possible, the simplest approach to working with gaseous mixtures is just to use for the value of n the *total* number of moles of the gaseous mixture (n_{tot}).

EXAMPLE 6-14

Applying the Ideal Gas Equation to a Mixture of Gases. What is the pressure exerted by a mixture of 1.0 g H_2 and 5.00 g He when the mixture is confined to a volume of 5.0 L at 20 °C?

Solution

$$n_{tot} = \left(1.0 \text{ g } H_2 \times \frac{1 \text{ mol } H_2}{2.02 \text{ g } H_2}\right) + \left(5.00 \text{ g He} \times \frac{1 \text{ mol He}}{4.003 \text{ g He}}\right)$$

$$= 0.50 \text{ mol } H_2 + 1.25 \text{ mol He} = 1.75 \text{ mol gas}$$

$$P = \frac{n_{tot}RT}{V} \tag{6.15}$$

$$= \frac{1.75 \text{ mol} \times 0.0821 \text{ L atm mol}^{-1} \text{ K}^{-1} \times 293 \text{ K}}{5.0 \text{ L}} = 8.4 \text{ atm}$$

Practice Example A: What will be the total gas pressure if 12.5 g Ne is added to the mixture of gases described in Example 6-14 and the temperature is then raised to 55 °C?

[*Hint:* What is the new number of moles of gas? What effect does raising the temperature have on the pressure of a gas at constant volume?]

Practice Example B: 2.0 L of O_2(g) and 8.0 L of N_2(g), each at STP, are mixed together. The nonreactive gaseous mixture is compressed to occupy 2.0 L at 298 K. What is the pressure exerted by this mixture?

John Dalton made an important contribution to the study of gaseous mixtures. He proposed that in a mixture, each gas expands to fill the container and exerts the same pressure (called its **partial pressure**) that it would if it were alone in the container. **Dalton's law of partial pressures** states that the total pressure of a mixture of gases is the sum of the partial pressures of the components of the mixture (Fig. 6-14). For a mixture of gases, A, B, and so on,

$$P_{tot} = P_A + P_B + \cdots \tag{6.16}$$

In a gaseous mixture of n_A moles of A, n_B moles of B, and so on, the volume each gas would individually occupy at a pressure equal to P_{tot} is

$$V_A = n_ART/P_{tot}; V_B = n_BRT/P_{tot}; \cdots$$

The total volume of the gaseous mixture is

$$V_{tot} = V_A + V_B \cdots$$

and the commonly used expression *percent by volume* is

$$\text{volume \% A} = \frac{V_A}{V_{tot}} \times 100\%; \text{Volume \% B} = \frac{V_B}{V_{tot}} \times 100\%; \cdots$$

Emphasize that it is number of *moles* that matters in an ideal gas equation calculation.

 Dalton's Law of Partial Pressures

KEEP IN MIND ▶
that when this expression is used, $V_A = V_B = \cdots = V_{tot}$

KEEP IN MIND ▶
that when using this expression, $P_A = P_B = \cdots = P_{tot}$

$P_{H_2} = 2.4$ atm

0.50 mol H_2

(a) 5.0 L at 20 °C

$P_{He} = 6.0$ atm

1.25 mol He

(b) 5.0 L at 20 °C

$P_{tot} = 8.4$ atm

$\dfrac{\text{1.25 mol He}}{\text{0.50 mol } H_2}$
1.75 mol gas

(c) 5.0 L at 20 °C

We can derive a particularly useful expression from the following ratios,

$$\frac{P_A}{P_{tot}} = \frac{n_A(RT/V_{tot})}{n_{tot}(RT/V_{tot})} = \frac{n_A}{n_{tot}} \quad \text{and} \quad \frac{V_A}{V_{tot}} = \frac{n_A(RT/P_{tot})}{n_{tot}(RT/P_{tot})} = \frac{n_A}{n_{tot}}$$

which means that

$$\frac{n_A}{n_{tot}} = \frac{P_A}{P_{tot}} = \frac{V_A}{V_{tot}} = x_A \qquad (6.17)$$

The term n_A/n_{tot} is given a special name, the mole fraction of A, x_A. The **mole fraction** of a component in a mixture is the fraction of all the molecules in the mixture contributed by that component. The sum of all the mole fractions in a mixture is one.

As illustrated in Example 6-15, we can often think about mixtures of gases in more than one way.

▲ **FIGURE 6-14**
Dalton's law of partial pressures illustrated
The pressure of each gas is proportional to the number of moles of gas. The total pressure is the sum of the partial pressures of the individual gases.

◄ A complex gas mixture we encounter daily is Earth's atmosphere. Table 6.3 (page 212) summarizes the composition of the atmosphere.

✓ An important gas mixture is the Earth's atmosphere. It might be useful at this point to introduce the data in Table 6.3 on page 212. Use this to calculate the partial pressure of O_2 at 1 atm.

EXAMPLE 6-15

Calculating the Partial Pressures in a Gaseous Mixture. What are the partial pressures of H_2 and He in the gaseous mixture described in Example 6-14?

Solution

One approach involves a direct application of Dalton's law in which we calculate the pressure that each gas would exert if it were alone in the container.

$$P_{H_2} = \frac{n_{H_2} \times RT}{V} = \frac{0.50 \text{ mol} \times 0.0821 \text{ L atm mol}^{-1} \text{ K}^{-1} \times 293 \text{ K}}{5.0 \text{ L}} = 2.4 \text{ atm}$$

$$P_{He} = \frac{n_{He} \times RT}{V} = \frac{1.25 \text{ mol} \times 0.0821 \text{ L atm mol}^{-1} \text{ K}^{-1} \times 293 \text{ K}}{5.0 \text{ L}} = 6.0 \text{ atm}$$

Expression (6.17) gives us a simpler way to answer the question because we already know the number of moles of each gas and the total pressure from Example 6-14 ($P_{tot} = 8.4$ atm).

$$P_{H_2} = \frac{n_{H_2}}{n_{tot}} \times P_{tot} = \frac{0.50}{1.75} \times 8.4 \text{ atm} = 2.4 \text{ atm}$$

$$P_{He} = \frac{n_{He}}{n_{tot}} \times P_{tot} = \frac{1.25}{1.75} \times 8.4 \text{ atm} = 6.0 \text{ atm}$$

CHECK: An effective way of checking an answer is to obtain the same answer when the problem is done in different ways, as was the case here.

Practice Example A: A mixture of 0.197 mol $CO_2(g)$ and 0.00278 mol $H_2O(g)$ is held at 30.0 °C and 2.50 atm. What is the partial pressure of each gas?

Practice Example B: The percent composition of air by volume is 78.08% N_2, 20.95% O_2, 0.93% Ar, and 0.036% CO_2. What are the partial pressures of these four gases in a sample of air at a barometric pressure of 748 mmHg?

▲ FIGURE 6-15
Collecting a gas over water
The bottle is filled with water and its open end is held below the water level in the container. Gas from a gas-generating apparatus is directed into the bottle. As gas accumulates in the bottle, water is displaced from the bottle into the container. To make the total gas pressure in the bottle equal to barometric pressure, the position of the bottle must be adjusted so that the water levels inside and outside the bottle are the same.

CONCEPT ASSESSMENT ✓

Without doing a detailed calculation, state the outcome(s) you would expect in Figure 6-14(c) if an additional 0.50 mol H_2 were added to the cylinder in Figure 6-14(a): **(a)** the mole fraction of H_2 would double; **(b)** the partial pressure of He would remain the same; **(c)** the mole fraction of He would remain the same; **(d)** the total gas pressure would increase by 50%; **(e)** the total mass of gas would increase by 1.0 g.

The correction for water vapor pressure, when a gas is collected over water, is probably relevant to a laboratory experiment the students will shortly be performing. Prepare them for this experiment by conducting a sample calculation related to such an experiment.

▶ Some early experimenters used mercury in the pneumatic trough so as to be able to collect gases soluble in water.

Vapor Pressure of Water at Various Temperatures

Temperature, °C	Vapor Pressure, mmHg
15.0	12.79
17.0	14.53
19.0	16.48
21.0	18.65
23.0	21.07
25.0	23.76
30.0	31.82
50.0	92.51

The device pictured in Figure 6-15, a *pneumatic trough*, played a crucial role in isolating gases in the early days of chemistry. The method works, of course, only for gases that are insoluble in and do not react with the liquid being displaced. But many important gases meet these criteria. For example, H_2, O_2, and N_2 are all essentially insoluble in and unreactive with water.

A gas collected in a pneumatic trough filled with water is said to be *collected over water* and is "wet." It is a mixture of two gases—the desired gas and water vapor. The gas being collected expands to fill the container and exerts its partial pressure, P_{gas}. Water vapor, formed by the evaporation of liquid water, also fills the container and exerts a partial pressure, P_{H_2O}. The pressure of the water vapor depends only on the temperature of the water. Water vapor pressure data are readily available in tabulated form (see the table in the margin).

According to Dalton's law, the total pressure of the wet gas is the sum of the two partial pressures. The total pressure can be made equal to the prevailing pressure of the atmosphere (barometric pressure).

$$P_{tot} = P_{bar.} = P_{gas} + P_{H_2O} \quad \text{or} \quad P_{gas} = P_{bar.} - P_{H_2O}$$

Once P_{gas} has been established, it can be used in stoichiometric calculations as illustrated in Example 6-16.

Explain to students, using Figure 6-15, why the total pressure of the gas inside the container is equal to barometric pressure.

EXAMPLE 6-16

Collecting a Gas over a Liquid (Water). In the following reaction, 81.2 mL of $O_2(g)$ is collected over water at 23 °C and barometric pressure 751 mmHg. What must have been the mass of $Ag_2O(s)$ decomposed? (The vapor pressure of water at 23 °C is 21.1 mmHg.)

$$2\ Ag_2O(s) \longrightarrow 4\ Ag(s) + O_2(g)$$

Solution

We need to calculate the number of moles of $O_2(g)$ produced. We can do this with the ideal gas equation. The key to this calculation is to remember that the gas collected is wet, that is, a *mixture* of $O_2(g)$ and water vapor.

$$P_{O_2} = P_{bar.} - P_{H_2O} = 751 \text{ mmHg} - 21.1 \text{ mmHg} = 730 \text{ mmHg}$$

$$P_{O_2} = 730 \text{ mmHg} \times \frac{1 \text{ atm}}{760 \text{ mmHg}} = 0.961 \text{ atm}$$

$$V = 81.2 \text{ mL} = 0.0812 \text{ L}$$

$$n = ?$$

$$R = 0.08206 \text{ L atm mol}^{-1} \text{ K}^{-1}$$

$$T = 23 \,°C + 273 = 296 \text{ K}$$

$$n = \frac{PV}{RT} = \frac{0.961 \text{ atm} \times 0.0812 \text{ L}}{0.08206 \text{ L atm mol}^{-1} \text{ K}^{-1} \times 296 \text{ K}} = 0.00321 \text{ mol}$$

From the chemical equation we obtain a factor to convert from moles of O_2 to moles of Ag_2O. The molar mass of Ag_2O provides the final factor.

$$? \text{ g } Ag_2O = 0.00321 \text{ mol } O_2 \times \frac{2 \text{ mol } Ag_2O}{1 \text{ mol } O_2} \times \frac{231.7 \text{ g } Ag_2O}{1 \text{ mol } Ag_2O}$$

$$= 1.49 \text{ g } Ag_2O$$

Practice Example A: The reaction of aluminum with hydrochloric acid produces hydrogen gas.

$$2 \text{ Al(s)} + 6 \text{ HCl(aq)} \longrightarrow 2 \text{ AlCl}_3\text{(aq)} + 3 \text{ H}_2\text{(g)}$$

If 35.5 mL of $H_2(g)$ is collected over water at 26 °C and a barometric pressure of 755 mmHg, how many moles of HCl must have been consumed? (The vapor pressure of water at 26 °C is 25.2 mmHg.)

Practice Example B: An 8.07-g sample that is 88.3% Ag_2O by mass decomposes into solid silver and $O_2(g)$. The $O_2(g)$ is collected over water at 25 °C and 749.2 mmHg barometric pressure. The vapor pressure of water at 25 °C is 23.8 mmHg. What is the volume of gas collected?

The Hydrogen Candle/Bomb. See Shakhashiri, p. 131. Introduce the "hydrogen candle" as an example of gas densities. While this burns, discuss how the lower density of H_2 causes it to rise through the "wick" at the top. The candle burns up, not down. After the surprise explosion, confess that this is also a "hydrogen bomb." This is an example of the kinetic nature of gases. At the H_2–air interface, mixing of the two gases occurs due to the motion of molecules. When this mixture reaches the flame, the explosion results. Test the system in advance to see whether the size of the system is appropriate for the room and intended audience.

6-7   KINETIC-MOLECULAR THEORY OF GASES

Let us apply some terminology that we introduced in Section 1-1 on the scientific method: The simple gas laws and the ideal gas equation are used to predict gas behavior. They are *natural laws*. To explain the gas laws, we need a *theory*. One theory developed during the mid-nineteenth century is called the **kinetic-molecular theory of gases**. It is based on the *model* illustrated in Figure 6-16 and outlined as follows.

- A gas is composed of a very large number of extremely small particles (molecules or, in some cases, atoms) in constant, random, straight-line motion.

- Molecules of a gas are separated by great distances. The gas is mostly empty space. (The molecules are treated as so-called point masses, as though they have mass but no volume.)

- Molecules collide only fleetingly with one another and with the walls of their container, and most of the time molecules are not engaged in collisions.

- There are assumed to be no forces between molecules except very briefly during collisions. That is, each molecule acts independently of all the others and is unaffected by their presence, except during collisions.

- Individual molecules may gain or lose energy as a result of collisions. In a collection of molecules at constant temperature, however, *the total energy remains constant*.

▲ **FIGURE 6-16**
Visualizing molecular motion
Molecules of a gas are in constant motion and undergo collisions with one another and with the container wall.

Because pressure is a force per unit area, the key to deriving a kinetic-molecular theory equation for pressure is in assessing the forces associated with molecular collisions. These depend on several factors.

Kinetic-Molecular Theory Simulator. A number of simple and not-so-simple molecular motion simulators have been devised. See, for example, Shakhashiri, p. 96. Points to emphasize: The pressure is the result of the impact of many molecules striking a wall; more moles of molecules or a smaller volume result in more collisions on a given surface area; molecules exchange energy on the wall and in collisions with each other; and there is a wide distribution of molecular speeds.

1. The amount of *translational kinetic energy* of the molecules. Translational kinetic energy is energy possessed by objects moving through space. Like speeding bullets, gas molecules have this energy of motion. The translational kinetic energy of a molecule is represented as e_k and has the value $e_k = \frac{1}{2}mu^2$, where m is the mass of the molecule and u is its speed. The faster the molecules move, the greater their translational kinetic energies and the greater the forces exerted between molecules during collisions.

2. The *frequency* of molecular collisions—the number of collisions per second. The higher this frequency, the greater the total force of these collisions. Collision frequency increases with the number of molecules per unit volume and with molecular speeds.

$$\text{collision frequency} \propto (\text{molecular speed}) \times (\text{molecules per unit volume})$$

$$\text{collision frequency} \propto (u) \times (N/V)$$

3. When a molecule hits the wall of a vessel, momentum is transferred as the molecule reverses direction. This momentum transfer is called an *impulse*. The magnitude of the impulse is directly proportional to the mass of a molecule and its velocity.

$$\text{impulse (momentum transfer)} \propto (\text{molecular speed}) \times (\text{mass of particle})$$

$$\text{impulse} \propto (mu)$$

The pressure of a gas (P) is the product of impulse and collision frequency. Thus, the complete proportionality expression for factors that affect pressure is

$$P \propto (mu) \times (u) \times (N/V) \propto (N/V)mu^2$$

▶ The bar over a quantity means that the quantity can have a range of values and that the *average* value is intended.

At any instant, however, the molecules in a gas sample are traveling at different speeds. The pressure depends on the average of these different molecular speeds. Because P is proportional to u^2, we must use a particular average—the *average* of the *squares* of the molecular speeds. The average of the squares of a group of speeds is called the *mean-square speed*, $\overline{u^2}$ (the overbar means "average"). To better understand the concept of the average of the squares of speeds, consider five molecules with speeds 400, 450, 525, 585, and 600 m/s. We find the average of the squares of these speeds by squaring the speeds, adding the squares, and dividing by the number of particles, in this case five.

$$\overline{u^2} = \frac{(400 \text{ m/s})^2 + (450 \text{ m/s})^2 + (525 \text{ m/s})^2 + (585 \text{ m/s})^2 + (600 \text{ m/s})^2}{5}$$

$$= 2.68 \times 10^5 \text{ m}^2/\text{s}^2$$

KEEP IN MIND ▶

that *mean-square speed* is not the same as *square mean speed*. The mean, or average, speed is $(400 + 450 + 525 + 585 + 600)/5 = 512$ m/s. The square of this average, the square mean speed, is $(512 \text{ m/s})^2 = 2.62 \times 10^5 \text{ m}^2/\text{s}^2$. Mean square speed is the quantity that must be used in equation (6.18).

Thus the proportionality expression for pressure becomes

$$P \propto \frac{N'}{V}\overline{mu^2}$$

A final factor to consider is that the path of every molecule has a component in each of the three perpendicular dimensions (x, y, and z). Our calculation of pressure must be based on motion in just one of these dimensions, leading to a factor of 1/3, which in fact is the proportionality constant in the above expression. Thus, when all factors are properly considered, the result is the basic equation of the kinetic-molecular theory

$$P = \frac{1}{3}\frac{N}{V}\overline{mu^2} \tag{6.18}$$

Equation (6.18) leads to some interesting results, as we see next.

▲ FIGURE 6-17
Distribution of molecular speeds—hydrogen gas at 0 °C
The percentages of molecules with a certain speed are plotted as a function of the speed. Three different speeds are noted on the graph.

Boltzmann Distribution simulation

DISTRIBUTION OF MOLECULAR SPEEDS

The averaging of molecular speeds referred to in establishing equation (6.18) is required because molecules of a gas do not all have the same speed. There is a distribution of speeds, as shown in Figure 6-17, and three characteristic speeds are also identified. More molecules have the speed u_m, the most probable, or modal, speed, than any other single speed. The average speed, $\bar{u}$, is the simple average. The **root-mean-square speed**, u_{rms}, is the *square root* of the *average* of the *squares* of the speeds of all the molecules in a sample.

We can derive a useful equation for u_{rms} by combining equation (6.18) with the ideal gas equation. Consider 1 mol of an ideal gas. The number of molecules present is $N = N_A$ (Avogadro's number), and the ideal gas equation becomes $PV = RT$ (that is, $n = 1$ in the equation $PV = nRT$). First, replace N by N_A, and multiply both sides of equation (6.18) by V. This leads to

◀ If the postulates of the kinetic-molecular theory hold, a gas is automatically an ideal gas.

$$PV = \frac{1}{3} N_A m \overline{u^2} \qquad (6.19)$$

Next, replace PV by RT and multiply both sides of the equation by three.

$$3 RT = N_A m \overline{u^2}$$

Now, note that the product $N_A m$ represents the mass of 1 mol of molecules, the molar mass, M.

$$3 RT = M \overline{u^2}$$

Finally, solve for $\overline{u^2}$ and then, $\sqrt{\overline{u^2}}$ which is u_{rms}.

$$u_{rms} = \sqrt{\overline{u^2}} = \sqrt{\frac{3 RT}{M}} \qquad (6.20)$$

Equation (6.20) shows that u_{rms} of a gas is directly proportional to the square root of its Kelvin temperature and inversely proportional to the square root of its molar mass. This means that lighter gas molecules have greater speeds than heavier ones, but that all molecular speeds increase as the temperature rises (Fig. 6-18).

To use equation (6.20) in calculating a root-mean-square speed, we must express the gas constant as

$$R = 8.3145 \, J \, mol^{-1} \, K^{-1}$$

The joule has the units $kg \, m^2 \, s^{-2}$, and consequently we must express molar mass in *kilograms* per mole, as we show in Example 6-17.

Compare Figure 6-17 with the score distribution for an exam. For a good class, or an easy test, the distribution will not be a symmetric "bell" but rather is skewed toward higher scores. Typically for an easy test the most probable score (the peak of the distribution) is greater than the average score. A molecular speed distribution is similar to a "tough test" distribution. There are many low-speed molecules, $u_m < \bar{u}$, and only a small fraction of molecules have high speeds. There is no maximum speed, however, and the distribution approaches zero as a limit at infinity.

Emphasize that all of the curves in Figure 6-18 have the same shape. Also, that the area under each curve is the same. Each curve is for the same total number of molecules. Raising T (or lowering M) is like stretching a rubber graph. The same number of molecules are spread out over a wider range of speeds.

Kinetic Energies in a Gas animation

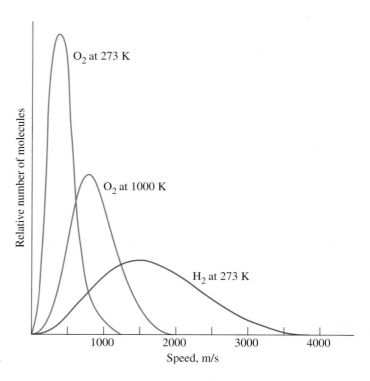

▶ **FIGURE 6-18**
Distribution of molecular speeds—the effect of mass and temperature
The relative numbers of molecules with a certain speed are plotted as a function of the speed. Note the effect of temperature on the distribution for oxygen molecules and the effect of mass—oxygen must be heated to a very high temperature to have the same distribution of speeds as does hydrogen at 273 K.

EXAMPLE 6-17

Calculating a Root-Mean-Square Speed. Which is the greater speed, that of a bullet fired from a high-powered M-16 rifle (2180 mi/h) or the root-mean-square speed of H_2 molecules at 25 °C?

Solution

Determine u_{rms} of H_2 with equation (6.20). In doing so, recall the points about R and M noted above.

$$u_{rms} = \sqrt{\frac{3 \times 8.3145 \text{ kg m}^2 \text{ s}^{-2} \text{ mol}^{-1} \text{ K}^{-1} \times 298 \text{ K}}{2.016 \times 10^{-3} \text{ kg mol}^{-1}}}$$

$$= \sqrt{3.69 \times 10^6 \text{ m}^2/\text{s}^2} = 1.92 \times 10^3 \text{ m/s}$$

The remainder of the problem requires us either to convert 1.92×10^3 m/s to a speed in miles per hour, or 2180 mi/h to meters per second. Then we can compare the two speeds. When we do this, we find that 1.92×10^3 m/s corresponds to 4.29×10^3 mi/h. The root-mean-square speed of H_2 molecules at 25 °C is greater than the speed of the high-powered rifle bullet.

Practice Example A: Which has the greater root-mean-square speed at 25 °C, $NH_3(g)$ or $HCl(g)$? Calculate u_{rms} for the one with the greater speed.

Practice Example B: At what temperature are u_{rms} of H_2 and the speed of the M-16 rifle bullet given in Example 6-17 the same?

CONCEPT ASSESSMENT ✓

Without performing an actual calculation, indicate which has the greater u_{rms}, He(g) at 1000 K or $H_2(g)$ at 250 K.

Are You Wondering . . .

How the distribution of molecular speeds can be demonstrated experimentally?

This can be done with the apparatus shown in Figure 6-19. An oven and attached evacuated chamber are separated by a wall with a small hole in it. Gas molecules are heated in the oven, emerge through the hole, and pass through a series of slits, called *collimators*, that herd the molecules into a beam. The number of molecules in the beam is kept low so that collisions between them will not disturb the beam.

The molecular beam passes through a series of rotating disks. Each disk has a slit cut in it. The slits on successive disks are offset from each other by a certain angle. A molecule passing through the first rotating disk will pass through the second disk only if its velocity is such that it arrives at the disk at the exact moment that the second slit appears. Thus, for a given rotation speed, only those molecules with the appropriate velocity can pass through the entire series of disks.

The number of molecules that pass through the disks and arrive at the detector is recorded for each chosen speed of rotation. The number of molecules for each speed of rotation is then plotted against the rotation speed. From the dimensions of the apparatus, the rotation speeds of the disks can be converted to molecular speeds, and a plot similar to that in Figure 6-19 can be obtained.

▲ **FIGURE 6-19**
Distribution of molecular speeds—an experimental determination
Only those molecules with the correct speed to pass through all rotating sectors will reach the detector, where they can be counted. By changing the rate of rotation of the sectors, the complete distribution of molecular speeds can be determined.

THE MEANING OF TEMPERATURE

We can gain an important insight into the meaning of temperature by starting with equation (6.19), the basic equation of the kinetic-molecular theory written for 1 mol of gas.

The kinetic-molecular theory also gives some insight into the meaning or significance of R. The gas constant relates temperature to the concentration of energy, in J per mole. R turns up again in several topics relevant to solids and liquids.

We modify it slightly by replacing the fraction $\frac{1}{3}$ by the equivalent product $\frac{2}{3} \times \frac{1}{2}$.

$$PV = \frac{1}{3}N_A\,\overline{mu^2} = \frac{2}{3}N_A\left(\frac{1}{2}\overline{mu^2}\right)$$

The terms in this equation that are gathered into $\left(\frac{1}{2}\overline{mu^2}\right)$ represent the average translational kinetic energy, $\overline{e_k}$, of a collection of molecules. When we make this substitution and replace PV by RT, we obtain

$$RT = \frac{2}{3}N_A\overline{e_k}$$

Then, we can solve this equation for e_k.

$$\overline{e_k} = \frac{3}{2}\frac{R}{N_A}(T) \tag{6.21}$$

Because R and N_A are constants, equation (6.21) simply states that $\overline{e_k}$ = constant $\times T$. This leads to an interesting new idea about temperature.

> The Kelvin temperature (T) of a gas is directly proportional to the average translational kinetic energy $(\overline{e_k})$ of its molecules. (6.22)

Also, we have a new concept of what changes in temperature mean—changes in the intensity of translational molecular motion. When heat flows from one object to another, molecules in the hotter object (higher temperature) give up some of their kinetic energy through collisions with molecules in the colder object (lower temperature). The flow of heat continues until the average translational kinetic energies of the molecules become equal, that is, until the temperatures become equalized. Finally, we have a new way of looking at the absolute zero of temperature: *It is the temperature at which translational molecular motion should cease.*

Are You Wondering . . .

What's the lowest temperature we can reach?

Charles's law suggests that there is an absolute zero of temperature, 0 K, but can we attain this temperature? The answer is no, but we can come mighty close. Current attempts have resulted in temperatures as low as just a few nanokelvins! However, it is not simply a matter of putting some hot atoms in a "refrigerator" operating at 0 K. We have seen that the temperature of a sample of gas is proportional to the kinetic energy of the gas molecules; therefore, to cool atoms down we have to remove their kinetic energy. Simple cooling will not do the trick, because the refrigerator would always have to be at a lower temperature than the atoms being cooled. The way that extremely cold atoms can be created is to remove their kinetic energy by stopping them in their tracks. This has been accomplished using a technique called laser cooling, in which a laser light is directed at a beam of atoms, hitting them head-on and dramatically slowing them down. Once the atoms are cooled, intersecting beams of six lasers are used to reduce their energies still further. The sample of cold atoms is then trapped by a magnetic field for about 1 s. In 1995, a team at the University of Colorado successfully cooled a beam of rubidium (Rb) atoms to 1.7×10^{-7} K using this procedure. The coldest man-made temperature, 450 picokelvins, was reported by scientists from the Massachusetts Institute of Technology in 2003.*

*A. E. Leanhardt, T. A. Pasquini, M. Saba, A. Schirotzek, Y. Shin, D. Kielpinski, D. E. Pritchard, and W. Ketterle, Cooling Bose-Einstein Condensates Below 500 Picokelvin, *Science* 2003 vol 301, p. 1513).

6-8 GAS PROPERTIES RELATING TO THE KINETIC-MOLECULAR THEORY

A molecular speed of 1500 m/s corresponds to about 1 mi/s, or 3600 mi/h. From this, it might seem that a given gas molecule could travel very long distances over a very short time, but this is not quite the case. Every gas molecule undergoes collisions with other gas molecules and, as a result, keeps changing direction. Gas molecules follow a tortuous path, which slows them down in getting from one point to another. Still, the net rate at which gas molecules move in a particular direction does depend on their average speeds.

Diffusion is the migration of molecules as a result of random molecular motion. Figure 6-20 pictures a common diffusion seen in a chemistry laboratory. The diffusion of two or more gases results in an intermingling of the molecules and, in a closed container, soon produces a homogeneous mixture (Fig. 6-21a). A related phenomenon, **effusion**, is the escape of gas molecules from their container through a tiny orifice or pinhole. The effusion of a hypothetical mixture of two gases is suggested by Figure 6-21(b).

▲ **FIGURE 6-20**
Diffusion of $NH_3(g)$ and $HCl(g)$

$NH_3(g)$ escapes from $NH_3(aq)$ (but labeled ammonium hydroxide in this photograph), and $HCl(g)$ escapes from $HCl(aq)$. The gases diffuse toward each other, and where they meet, a white cloud of ammonium chloride forms.

$$NH_3(g) + HCl(g) \longrightarrow NH_4Cl(s).$$

Because of their greater average speed, NH_3 molecules diffuse faster than HCl. As a result, the cloud forms close to the mouth of the $HCl(aq)$ container.

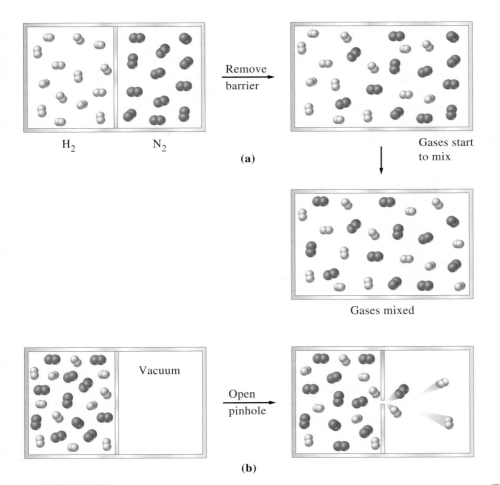

Gases start to mix

Gases mixed

Vacuum

(b)

Diffusion and Effusion activity

Diffusion of Bromine Vapor movie

▲ **FIGURE 6-21**
Diffusion and effusion
(a) Diffusion is the passage of one substance through another. In this case, the H_2 initially diffuses farther through the N_2 because it is lighter, although eventually a complete random mixing occurs. **(b)** Effusion is the passage of a substance through a pinhole or porous membrane into a vacuum. In this case, the lighter H_2 effuses faster across the empty space than does the N_2.

Effusion of Hydrogen Through a Porous Cup. Assemble a porous cup and pressure-sensing system as in Shakhashiri, p. 55–58 and Figure 2. Place the porous cup into an inverted beaker of H_2. Observe the pressure buildup as H_2 effuses rapidly into the cup. Allow the system to reach a dynamic equilibrium. Then remove the beaker of H_2. Observe the bubbling of air back into the flask as H_2 effuses out of the porous cup.

✓ Point out that the phenomenon of effusion provides one means of separating isotopes.

Diffusion of NO_2 into Air. Use an NO_2 generator to fill a glass cylinder with NO_2. Place a flat glass plate on top. The gas in the cylinder need not be pure NO_2, only enough in air to give a good brown coloration. Invert an empty cylinder and place this on top of the glass plate. Note that NO_2 is more dense than air and, based on this, when the plate is removed the NO_2 should stay at the bottom. Due to molecular motions, however, the NO_2 and air will indeed mix. Remind the class that u_{rms} is typically hundreds of m/s: Pay attention, if you blink your eyes you might miss something. Then remove the glass plate and observe the gases mixing. The rate is seen to be more a matter of cm/min. Diffusion is slow because of gas collisions that randomize the motions of molecules. The NO_2 is toxic and the system should be removed to and emptied in a hood. Replacing the divider plate and venting only the top cylinder usually leaves enough NO_2 in the lower cylinder for a repeat performance in the next class.

✓ Students have considerable difficulty handling effusion time with Graham's law. Emphasize that rate $= \Delta n/\Delta t$. Time is inversely related to rate. So is M. Thus $\Delta t \sim M^{1/2}$.

The rate at which effusion occurs is directly proportional to molecular speeds. That is, molecules with high speeds effuse faster than molecules with low speeds. Let us consider the effusion of two different gases at the same temperature and pressure. We can first compare effusion rates with root-mean-square speeds and then substitute expression (6.20) for these speeds.

$$\frac{\text{rate of effusion of A}}{\text{rate of effusion of B}} = \frac{(u_{rms})_A}{(u_{rms})_B} = \sqrt{\frac{3\,RT/M_A}{3\,RT/M_B}} = \sqrt{\frac{M_B}{M_A}} \qquad (6.23)$$

Any appropriate units (for example, g/s, mol/min) can be used to express a rate of effusion in equation (6.23) because in the ratio of two rates, the units cancel. Equation (6.23) is a kinetic-theory statement of a nineteenth-century law called **Graham's law**.

> The rates of effusion of two different gases are inversely proportional to the square roots of their molar masses. $\qquad (6.24)$

There are serious limitations to Graham's law that you should be aware of. It can be used to describe effusion only for gases at very low pressures, so that molecules escape through an orifice individually, not as a jet of gas. Also, the orifice must be tiny so that no collisions occur as molecules pass through. Graham proposed his law in 1831 to describe the diffusion of gases, but the law actually does not apply to diffusion. Molecules of a diffusing gas undergo collisions with each other and with the gas into which they are diffusing. Some even move in the opposite direction to the net flow. Nevertheless, diffusion does occur, and gases of low molar mass do diffuse faster than those of higher molar mass. We just cannot use Graham's law to make quantitative predictions about rates of diffusion.

When compared at the same temperature, two different gases have the same value of $\overline{e_k} = \frac{1}{2}mu^2$. This means that molecules with a smaller mass (m) have a higher speed (u_{rms}). When effusion takes place under the restrictions described above, equation (6.23) can be used to determine which of two gases effuses faster, which does so in a shorter period of time, which travels farther in a given period of time, and so on. An effective way to do this is to note that in every case, a ratio of effusion rates, times, distances, and so on is equal to the square root of a ratio of molar masses. That is, a ratio of

$$\left. \begin{array}{l} \text{molecular speeds} \\ \text{effusion rates} \\ \text{effusion times} \\ \text{distances traveled by molecules} \\ \text{amounts of gas effused} \end{array} \right\} = \sqrt{\text{ratio of two molar masses}} \qquad (6.25)$$

In using equation (6.25), first reason qualitatively and work out whether the ratio of properties should be greater or less than one. Then set up the ratio of molar masses accordingly. Examples 6-18 and 6-19 illustrate this line of reasoning.

EXAMPLE 6-18

Comparing Amounts of Gases Effusing Through an Orifice. 2.2×10^{-4} mol $N_2(g)$ effuses through a tiny hole in 105 s. How much $H_2(g)$ would effuse through the same orifice in 105 s?

Solution

Let us reason qualitatively: H_2 molecules have less mass than N_2 molecules, so they should have the greater speed when the gases are compared at the same temperature. Because $H_2(g)$ effuses faster, more H_2 than N_2 molecules should effuse in a given length of time. In the following setup, we need a ratio of molar masses *greater than one*.

$$\frac{? \text{ mol } H_2}{2.2 \times 10^{-4} \text{ mol } N_2} = \sqrt{\frac{M_{N_2}}{M_{H_2}}} = \sqrt{\frac{28.014}{2.016}} = 3.728$$

$$? \text{ mol } H_2 = 3.728 \times 2.2 \times 10^{-4} = 8.2 \times 10^{-4} \text{ mol } H_2$$

Practice Example A: In Example 6-18, how much $O_2(g)$ would effuse through the same orifice in 105 s?

Practice Example B: In Example 6-18, how long would it take for 2.2×10^{-4} mol H_2 to effuse through the same orifice as the 2.2×10^{-4} mol N_2?

> Graham's law works well with effusion but is only approximate when applied to diffusion. Diffusion rates depend on molecular sizes and intermolecular potentials as well as speeds. Diffusion is a mutual mixing process. The diffusion of B into A has the same rate as the diffusion of A into B. Otherwise a pressure differential would result!

EXAMPLE 6-19

Relating Effusion Times and Molar Masses.   A sample of $Kr(g)$ escapes through a tiny hole in 87.3 s. An unknown gas requires 42.9 s under identical conditions. What is the molar mass of the unknown gas?

Solution

Again, start with qualitative reasoning. Because the unknown gas effuses faster, it must have a smaller molar mass than Kr. The ratio of molar masses in the following setup must be *smaller than one*. M_{unk} goes in the numerator.

$$\frac{\text{effusion time for unknown}}{\text{effusion time for Kr}} = \frac{42.9 \text{ s}}{87.3 \text{ s}} = \sqrt{\frac{M_{unk}}{M_{Kr}}} = 0.491$$

$$M_{unk} = (0.491)^2 \times M_{Kr} = (0.491)^2 \times 83.80 = 20.2 \text{ g/mol}$$

Practice Example A: Under the same conditions as in Example 6-19, another unknown gas requires 131.3 s to escape. What is the molar mass of this unknown gas?

Practice Example B: Given all the same conditions as in Example 6-19, how long would it take for a sample of ethane gas, C_2H_6, to effuse?

> Rates of Diffusion of NH_3 and HCl into Air. See Shakhashiri, p. 59. This is a highly effective demonstration but one for which the results obtained are partly fortuitous. See the note above. The experiment performs well (and more quickly) on an overhead projector. Use a 1.0 cm ID $\times$ 24 cm glass tube and a transparent ruler. Insert a cotton swab into two one-hole stoppers. Soak the swabs with 1 to 2 drops of HCl or NH_3.

CONCEPT ASSESSMENT ✔

Which answer(s) is (are) true when comparing 1.0 mol $H_2(g)$ at STP and 0.50 mol $He(g)$ at STP? The two gases have equal **(a)** average molecular kinetic energies; **(b)** root-mean-square speeds; **(c)** masses; **(d)** volumes; **(e)** densities; **(f)** effusion rates through the same orifice.

APPLICATIONS OF DIFFUSION

The diffusion of gases into one another has many practical applications. Natural gas and liquefied petroleum gas (LPG) are odorless; for commercial use, a small quantity of a gaseous organic sulfur compound, methyl mercaptan, CH_3SH, is added to them. The mercaptan has an odor that can be detected in parts per billion (ppb) or less. When a leak occurs, which can lead to asphyxiation or an explosion, we rely on the diffusion of this odorous compound for a warning.

During World War II, the Manhattan Project (the secret, government-run program for developing the atomic bomb) used a method called gaseous diffusion to separate the desired isotope ^{235}U from the predominant ^{238}U. The method is based on the fact that uranium hexafluoride is one of the few compounds of uranium that can be obtained as a gas at moderate temperatures. When high-pressure $UF_6(g)$ is forced through a barrier having millions of submicroscopic holes per square centimeter, molecules containing the isotope ^{235}U pass through the barrier slightly faster than those containing ^{238}U, just as expected from expression (6.25), and therefore contains a slightly higher ratio of ^{235}U to ^{238}U than it did previously. The gas has become enriched in ^{235}U. Carrying this process through several thousand passes yields a product highly enriched in ^{235}U.

▲ **FIGURE 6-22**
The behavior of real gases—compressibility factor as a function of pressure at 0 °C
Values of the compressibility factor less than one signify that intermolecular forces of attraction are largely responsible for deviations from ideal gas behavior. Values greater than one are found when the volume of the gas molecules themselves is a significant fraction of the total gas volume.

 Ideal vs. Real Gases

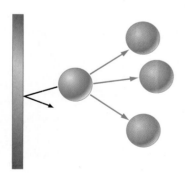

▲ **FIGURE 6-23**
Intermolecular forces of attraction
Attractive forces of the red molecules for the green molecule cause the green molecule to exert less force when it collides with the wall than if these attractions did not exist.

 Nonideal Gas Behavior simulation

6-9 NONIDEAL (REAL) GASES

The term *ideal gas law* suggests that real gases may not always be "ideal." We should comment briefly on the conditions under which a real gas is ideal or nearly so and what to do when the conditions lead to nonideal behavior. A useful measure of how much a gas deviates from ideal gas behavior is found in its compressibility factor. The *compressibility factor* of a gas is the ratio PV/nRT. From the ideal gas equation we see that for an ideal gas, $PV/nRT = 1$. For a real gas, the closeness of the experimentally determined ratio to 1 is a measure of how closely the behavior of the gas approaches that of an ideal gas. In Figure 6-22, the compressibility factor is plotted as a function of pressure for three different gases. The principal conclusion from this plot is that all gases behave ideally at sufficiently low pressures, say, below 1 atm, but that deviations set in at increased pressures. At very high pressures, the compressibility factor is always greater than one.

Nonideal gas behavior can be described as follows: Boyle's law predicts that at very high pressures a gas volume becomes extremely small and approaches zero. This cannot be, however, because the molecules themselves occupy space and are practically incompressible. The PV product is larger than predicted for an ideal gas, and the compressibility factor is greater than one. Another consideration is that intermolecular forces exist in gases. Figure 6-23 shows that because of attractive forces between the molecules, the force of the collisions of gas molecules with the container walls is less than expected for an ideal gas. Intermolecular forces of attraction account for compressibility factors of less than one. These forces become increasingly important at low temperatures, where translational molecular motion slows down. To summarize:

- Gases tend to behave *ideally* at *high temperatures* and *low pressures*.
- Gases tend to behave *nonideally* at *low temperatures* and *high pressures*.

THE VAN DER WAALS EQUATION

A number of equations can be used for real gases, equations that apply over a wider range of temperatures and pressures than the ideal gas equation. Such equations are not as general as the ideal gas equation. They contain terms that have specific, but different, values for different gases. Such equations must correct for the volume associated with the molecules themselves and for intermolecular forces of attraction. In the **van der Waals equation**,

$$\left(P + \frac{n^2a}{V^2} \right)(V - nb) = nRT \tag{6.26}$$

V is the volume of n moles of gas. The term n^2a/V^2 is related to intermolecular forces of attraction. It is added to P because the measured pressure is lower than expected (recall Figure 6-23). The value b, called the *excluded volume per mole*, is related to the volume of the gas molecules, and nb is subtracted from the measured volume to represent the *free volume* within the gas: $V - nb$. Both a and b have specific values for particular gases, values that vary somewhat with temperature and pressure. In Example 6-20 we calculate the pressure of a real gas using the van der Waals equation. Solving the equation for either n or V is more difficult, however (see Exercise 103).

EXAMPLE 6-20

Using the van der Waals Equation to Calculate the Pressure of a Gas. Use the van der Waals equation to calculate the pressure exerted by 1.00 mol $Cl_2(g)$ confined to a volume of 2.00 L at 273 K. The value of $a = 6.49\ L^2\ atm\ mol^{-2}$, and that of $b = 0.0562\ L\ mol^{-1}$.

Solution

Solve equation (6.26) for P.

$$P = \frac{nRT}{V - nb} - \frac{n^2a}{V^2}$$

Then substitute the following values into the equation.

$$n = 1.00 \text{ mol}; V = 2.00 \text{ L}; T = 273 \text{ K}; R = 0.08206 \text{ L atm mol}^{-1} \text{ K}^{-1}$$

$$n^2a = (1.00)^2 \text{ mol}^2 \times 6.49 \frac{\text{L}^2 \text{ atm}}{\text{mol}^2} = 6.49 \text{ L}^2 \text{ atm}$$

$$nb = 1.00 \text{ mol} \times 0.0562 \text{ L mol}^{-1} = 0.0562 \text{ L}$$

$$P = \frac{1.00 \text{ mol} \times 0.08206 \text{ L atm mol}^{-1} \text{ K}^{-1} \times 273 \text{ K}}{(2.00 - 0.0562)\text{L}} - \frac{6.49 \text{ L}^2 \text{ atm}}{(2.00)^2 \text{ L}^2}$$

$$P = 11.5 \text{ atm} - 1.62 \text{ atm} = 9.9 \text{ atm}$$

The pressure calculated with the ideal gas equation is 11.2 atm. By including only the b term in the van der Waals equation, we get a value of 11.5 atm. Including the a term reduces the calculated pressure by 1.62 atm. Under the conditions of this problem, intermolecular forces of attraction are the main cause of the departure from ideal behavior.

◀ Although the deviation from ideality here is rather large, in problem-solving situations, you can generally assume that the ideal gas equation will give satisfactory results.

✓ Point out to students that the Kinetic Molecular Theory (page 201) does not accurately describe or predict the behavior of nonideal gases.

Practice Example A: Substitute $CO_2(g)$ for $Cl_2(g)$ in Example 6-20, given the values $a = 3.59 \text{ L}^2 \text{ atm mol}^{-2}$ and $b = 0.0427 \text{ L mol}^{-1}$. Which gas, CO_2 or Cl_2, shows the greater departure from ideal gas behavior?

[*Hint:* For which gas do you find the greater difference in calculated pressures, first using the ideal gas equation and then the van der Waals equation?]

Practice Example B: Substitute $CO(g)$ for $Cl_2(g)$ in Example 6-20, given the values $a = 1.49 \text{ L}^2 \text{ atm mol}^{-2}$ and $b = 0.0399 \text{ L mol}^{-1}$. Including CO_2 from Practice Example 6-20A, which of the three gases—Cl_2, CO_2, or CO—shows the greatest departure from ideal gas behavior?

CONCEPT ASSESSMENT ✓

Following are the measured densities at 20.0 °C and 1 atm pressure of three gases: O_2, 1.331 g/L; OF_2, 2.26 g/L; NO, 1.249 g/L. Arrange them in the order of increasing adherence to the ideal gas equation. [*Hint:* What property can you calculate and compare with a known value?]

Summary

6-1 Properties of Gases: Gas Pressure—A gas is described in terms of its **pressure**, temperature, volume, and amount. Gas pressure is most readily measured by comparing it with the pressure exerted by a liquid column, usually mercury (equation 6.2). The pressure exerted by a column of mercury in a **barometer** and called the **barometric pressure** is equal to the prevailing pressure of the atmosphere (Fig. 6-4). Other gas pressures can be measured with a **manometer** (Fig. 6-5). Pressure can be expressed in a variety of units (Table 6.1), including the SI units **pascal (Pa)** and **kilopascal (kPa)**. Also commonly used are **millimeter of mercury (mmHg)**; **torr (Torr)**, where 1 Torr = 1 mmHg; and **standard atmosphere (atm)**, where 1 atm = 760 mmHg = 760 Torr.

6-2 The Simple Gas Laws—The most common simple gas laws are **Boyle's law** relating gas pressure and volume (equation 6.5, Fig. 6-6); **Charles's law** relating gas volume and temperature (equation 6.8, Fig. 6-8); and **Avogadro's law**, relating volume and amount of gas. Some important ideas that originate from the simple gas laws are the **Kelvin (absolute)** scale of temperature (equation 6.6), the **standard conditions of temperature and pressure (STP)**, and the molar volume of a gas at STP—22.4 L/mol (expression 6.10).

6-3 Combining the Gas Laws: The Ideal Gas Equation and the General Gas Equation—The simple gas laws can be combined into the **ideal gas equation**, $PV = nRT$ (equation 6.11), where R is called the **gas constant**. A gas whose behavior can be predicted with this equation is known as an **ideal**, or **perfect, gas**. The ideal gas equation can be solved for any one of the variables when all the others are known. The **general gas equation** (equation 6.12) is a useful variant of the ideal gas equation for describing the behavior of a gas when certain variables are held constant and others are allowed to change.

▲ The aurora borealis, or northern lights, observed at high northern latitudes produced by light emissions from atoms, ions, and molecules in the ionosphere.

When astronauts look at Earth from space, they see it surrounded by a thin blue shell—the atmosphere. Commonly, we use the word *air* to describe the substances that make up the atmosphere. Air is a mixture of nitrogen and oxygen, with smaller quantities of argon, carbon dioxide, and the other gases listed in Table 6.3. This blanket of air protects us from harmful radiation and its composition is crucial to the existence of life on Earth.

TABLE 6.3 Composition of Dry Air (near sea level)

Component	Volume Percent[a]
Nitrogen (N_2)	78.084
Oxygen (O_2)	20.946
Argon (Ar)	0.934
Carbon dioxide (CO_2)	0.0379
Neon (Ne)	0.001818
Helium (He)	0.000524
Methane (CH_4)	0.0002
Krypton (Kr)	0.000114
Hydrogen (H_2)	0.00005
Dinitrogen monoxide (N_2O)	0.00005
Xenon (Xe)	0.000009
Ozone (O_3)	
Sulfur dioxide (SO_2)	
Nitrogen dioxide (NO_2)	trace
Ammonia (NH_3)	
Carbon monoxide (CO)	
Iodine (I_2)	

[a]Recall the meaning of percent by volume of a gaseous mixture introduced in Section 6-6.

STRUCTURE OF THE ATMOSPHERE

About 90% of the mass of the atmosphere is in the first 12 km above Earth's surface. This familiar layer of air is called the *troposphere*, and it is the region in which weather phenomena occur. Temperatures in the troposphere fall continuously with increasing altitude to a minimum of about 220 K (Fig. 6-24).

The region from about 12 to 55 km above Earth's surface, the *stratosphere*, is less familiar to us, although supersonic aircraft fly in its lower reaches. The temperature–altitude profile of the stratosphere is much different from that of the troposphere. At altitudes from about 12 to 25 km, the temperature is fairly constant at about 220 K; it then rises to about 280 K at 50 km. In part, this is due to heat-producing reactions that occur between the atoms in the thinning atmosphere and ultraviolet radiation from the sun. These reactions produce the protective *ozone layer* that will be discussed in some detail in Chapter 22.

Beyond the stratosphere, the atmosphere is very thin, with densities rapidly falling to the range of micrograms and nanograms per liter. In the region from 55 to 80 km, the *mesophere*, the temperature falls continuously to about 180 K. Beyond this, in a region known as the *thermosphere*, or *ionosphere*, temperatures rise to about 1500 K. Here, the atmosphere consists of positive and negative ions, free electrons, neutral atoms, and molecules. The dissociation of molecules into atoms and the ionization of atoms into positive ions and free electrons require the absorption of energy. The source of that energy is electromagnetic radiation from the sun. An interesting natural phenomenon associated with the ionosphere is the *aurora borealis*, or northern lights.

Normally, at 1500 K an iron object glows a bright red, but a cold iron object brought to the thermosphere would not glow. From the kinetic-molecular theory of gases (Section 6-7), we know that at 1500 K gaseous atoms and molecules travel at high speeds. And these energetic atoms and molecules transfer energy as heat when they collide with a cold object. Because the concentration of gaseous particles in the thermosphere is so low, however, molecular collisions are infrequent and very little heat is transferred. An object does not "heat up" the way it would in the lower atmosphere. Thus, as meteors fall toward Earth, they do not begin to glow in the high-temperature thermosphere. They do so only at lower elevations where collisions with molecules of air cause surface atoms of the meteor to vaporize, ionize, and emit light.

WATER VAPOR IN THE ATMOSPHERE

Table 6.3 lists the components of dry air, but air is not ordinarily dry. It contains water vapor, $H_2O(g)$, in quantities ranging from traces to as much as 4% by volume. This water vapor plays an essential role in the hydrologic (water) cycle: Ocean water evaporates; air masses move from the oceans to the land; water vapor in the atmosphere, when cooled, forms clouds; and the clouds produce rain. Water falling on land returns to the oceans through systems of lakes, rivers, and groundwater.

The amount of water vapor (n_{H_2O}) in a sample of air and the partial pressure of the water vapor (P_{H_2O}) are proportional, as we see from the ideal gas equation: $P = nRT/V$. The maximum possible partial pressure of water vapor at a given temperature is a quantity that we have previously introduced: the vapor pressure of water (see page 200). For example, at 25 °C, the vapor pressure of water is 23.8 mmHg.

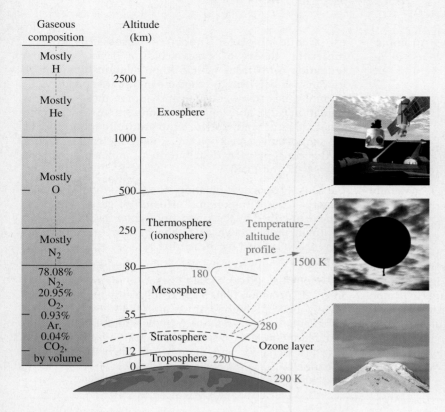

Gaseous composition

Mostly H

Mostly He

Mostly O

Mostly N_2

78.08% N_2,
20.95% O_2,
0.93% Ar,
0.04% CO_2,
by volume

Altitude (km)

2500

1000

500

250 — Thermosphere (ionosphere)

80

55

12

0

Exosphere

Mesosphere

Stratosphere

Troposphere 220

Temperature–altitude profile

1500 K

180

280

Ozone layer

290 K

◄ **FIGURE 6-24**
Regions of the atmosphere: composition and temperature–altitude profile
The left side of the figure shows the composition of the atmosphere at different altitudes. The temperature–altitude profile in the center gives approximate temperatures for the first 80 km and indicates that the temperature rises to 1500 K in the thermosphere. The small photographs at the right picture some familiar objects and indicate the regions of the atmosphere associated with them. The values given here are only approximate. For example, the height of the troposphere varies from about 8 km at the poles to 16 km at the equator. Also, temperatures in the thermosphere vary greatly between day and night.

This is the highest partial pressure of water vapor that can be maintained at 25 °C. If a sample of air at 25 °C has a water vapor pressure higher than 23.8 mmHg, we expect some of the vapor to condense to liquid water.

A common method of describing the water vapor content of air is through its relative humidity. *Relative humidity* is the ratio of the partial pressure of water vapor to the vapor pressure of water at the same temperature, expressed on a percent basis. Thus, if the partial pressure of water vapor in air at 25 °C is 12.2 mmHg, the relative humidity of the air is 51.3%.

$$\frac{\text{Relative}}{\text{humidity}} = \frac{\text{partial pressure of water vapor}}{\text{vapor pressure of water}} \times 100\%$$

$$= \frac{12.2 \text{ mmHg}}{23.8 \text{ mmHg}} \times 100\% = 51.3\% \qquad (6.27)$$

Because the vapor pressure of water increases with temperature, air having $P_{H_2O} = 12.2$ mmHg would have a relative humidity of only 38.4% at 30 °C, where the vapor pressure of water is 31.8 mmHg. Conversely, at 10 °C, where the vapor pressure of water is only 9.2 mmHg, some water vapor in the air sample would condense as liquid. This fluctuation of the relative humidity with temperature accounts for the formation of dew or frost that is sometimes observed in the early morning hours.

▶ **Dew and frost formation**
When the temperature drops below the value at which the relative humidity is 100%, water vapor condenses as *dew* (top), or if the ambient temperature is below the freezing point of water, *frost* (bottom).

6-4 Applications of the Ideal Gas Equation—An important application of the ideal gas equation is its use in determining molecular masses (equation 6.13) and gas densities (equation 6.14).

6-5 Gases in Chemical Reactions—Because it relates the volume of a gas at a given temperature and pressure to the amount of gas, the ideal gas equation often enters into stoichiometric calculations for reactions involving gases. In calculations based on the volumes of two gaseous reactants and/or products measured at the same temperature and pressure, the **law of combining volumes** is generally applicable.

6-6 Mixtures of Gases—The ideal gas equation applies to mixtures of ideal gases as well as to pure gases. The enabling principle, known as **Dalton's law of partial pressures**, is that each gas expands to fill the container, exerting the same pressure as if it were alone in the container (Fig. 6-14). The total pressure is the sum of these **partial pressures** (equation 6.16). A useful concept in dealing with mixtures of gases is that of **mole fraction**, the fraction of the molecules in a mixture contributed by each component (equation 6.17). In the common procedure of collecting a gas over water (Fig. 6-15), the particular gas being isolated is mixed with water vapor.

6-7 Kinetic-Molecular Theory of Gases—The **kinetic-molecular theory of gases** yields a basic expression (equation 6.18) from which other relationships can be established between the **root-mean-square speed** (u_{rms}) of molecules, temperature, and molar mass of a gas (equation 6.20), and the average molecular translational kinetic energy and Kelvin temperature (equation 6.21). An important aspect of the kinetic-molecular theory is the concept of a distribution of molecular speeds (Figs. 6-17 and 6-18).

6-8 Gas Properties Relating to the Kinetic-Molecular Theory—The **diffusion** and **effusion** of gases (Fig. 6-21) can be described by the kinetic-molecular theory. Using an approximation known as **Graham's law**, molar masses can be determined by measuring rates of effusion (equation 6.23).

6-9 Nonideal (Real) Gases—Because of intermolecular forces of attraction (Fig. 6-23), real gases generally behave ideally only at high temperatures and low pressures. Other equations of state, such as the **van der Waals equation** (equation 6.26), take into account the factors causing nonideal behavior and often work when the ideal gas equation fails.

Integrative Example

Complete combustion of 1.110 g of a gaseous hydrocarbon yields 3.613 g CO_2 and 1.109 g H_2O. A 0.288-g sample of the hydrocarbon occupies a volume of 131 mL at 24.8 °C and 753 mmHg. Write a plausible structural formula for a hydrocarbon corresponding to these data.

Strategy

Use the combustion data for the 1.110-g sample of hydrocarbon and the method of Example 3-6 on page 80 to determine the empirical formula. Use the P–V–T data in equation (6.13) for the 0.288-g sample to determine the molar mass and molecular mass of the hydrocarbon. By comparing the empirical formula mass and the molecular mass, establish the molecular formula. Now write a structural formula consistent with the molecular formula.

Solution

Calculate the number of moles of C and H in the 1.110-g sample of hydrocarbon based on the masses of CO_2 and H_2O obtained in its combustion.

$$? \text{ mol C} = 3.613 \text{ g CO}_2 \times \frac{1 \text{ mol CO}_2}{44.01 \text{ g CO}_2} \times \frac{1 \text{ mol C}}{1 \text{ mol CO}_2} = 0.08209 \text{ mol C}$$

$$? \text{ mol H} = 1.109 \text{ g H}_2\text{O} \times \frac{1 \text{ mol H}_2\text{O}}{18.02 \text{ g H}_2\text{O}} \times \frac{2 \text{ mol H}}{1 \text{ mol H}_2\text{O}} = 0.1231 \text{ mol H}$$

Use these numbers of moles as the provisional subscripts in the formula.

$C_{0.08209}H_{0.1231}$

Divide each provisional subscript by the smaller of the two to obtain the empirical formula.

$C_{\frac{0.08209}{0.08209}}H_{\frac{0.1231}{0.08209}}$

$CH_{1.500} = C_2H_3$

To determine the molar mass, use a modified form of equation (6.13).

$$M = \frac{mRT}{PV} = \frac{0.288 \text{ g} \times 0.08206 \text{ L atm} \times (24.8 + 273.2) \text{ K}}{\text{mol K} \times (753 \text{ mmHg} \times 1 \text{ atm}/760 \text{ mmHg}) \times 0.131 \text{ L}}$$

$$= 54.3 \text{ g/mol}$$

The empirical formula mass is

$$\left(2 \text{ C atoms} \times \frac{12.0 \text{ u}}{1 \text{ C atom}}\right) + \left(3 \text{ H atoms} \times \frac{1.01 \text{ u}}{1 \text{ H atom}}\right) = 27.0 \text{ u}$$

The molar mass based on the empirical formula, 27.0 g/mol, is almost exactly one-half the observed molar mass of 54.3 g/mol. The molecular formula of the hydrocarbon is

$C_{2\times2}H_{2\times3} = C_4H_6$

The four-carbon alkane is butane, C_4H_{10}. Removal of 4 H atoms to obtain the formula C_4H_6 is achieved by inserting two C-to-C double bonds.

$$H_2C\!=\!CH\!-\!CH\!=\!CH_2 \quad \text{or} \quad H_2C\!=\!C\!=\!CH\!-\!CH_3$$

Two other possibilities involve the presence of a C-to-C triple bond.

$$H_3C\!-\!C\!\equiv\!C\!-\!CH_3 \quad \text{or} \quad H_3C\!-\!CH_2\!-\!C\!\equiv\!CH$$

Assessment

The combination of combustion data and gas-law data yields a molecular formula with certainty. However, because of isomerism the exact structural formula cannot be pinpointed. All that we can say is that the hydrocarbon might have any one of the four structures shown, but it might be still another structure, for example, based on a ring of C atoms rather than a straight chain.

Exercises

Pressure and Its Measurement

1. Convert each pressure to an equivalent pressure in standard atmospheres. **(a)** 736 mmHg; **(b)** 58.2 cm Hg; **(c)** 892 Torr; **(d)** 225 kPa.
2. Calculate the height of a mercury column required to produce a pressure **(a)** of 0.984 atm; **(b)** of 928 Torr; **(c)** equal to that of a column of water 142 ft high.
3. Calculate the height of a column of liquid benzene ($d = 0.879$ g/cm^3), in meters, required to exert a pressure of 0.970 atm.
4. Calculate the height of a column of liquid glycerol ($d = 1.26$ g/cm^3), in meters, required to exert the same pressure as 3.02 m of CCl_4(l) ($d = 1.59$ g/cm^3).
5. What is P_{gas} for the manometer reading (millimeters of mercury) in the figure below when barometric pressure is 744 mmHg?

6. The mercury level in the open arm of an open-end manometer is 276 mm above a reference point. In the arm connected to a container of gas, the level is 49 mm above the same reference point. If barometric pressure is 749 mmHg, what is the pressure of the gas in the container?
   [*Hint:* Refer to the figure for Exercise 5.]
7. At times, a pressure is stated in units of *mass* per unit area rather than *force* per unit area. What is the standard atmosphere of pressure expressed in the unit kg/cm^2? [*Hint:* How is a mass in kilograms related to a force?]
8. What is the standard atmosphere of pressure expressed in pounds per square inch (psi)? [*Hint:* Refer to Exercise 7.]

The Simple Gas Laws

9. A sample of O_2(g) has a volume of 26.7 L at 762 Torr. What is the new volume if, with the temperature and amount of gas held constant, the pressure is **(a)** lowered to 385 Torr; **(b)** increased to 3.68 atm?
10. An 886-mL sample of Ne(g) is at 752 mmHg and 26 °C. What will be the new volume if, with the pressure and amount of gas held constant, the temperature is **(a)** increased to 98 °C; **(b)** lowered to −20 °C?
11. We want to increase the volume of a fixed amount of gas from 57.3 to 165 mL while holding the pressure constant. To what value must we change the temperature if the initial temperature is 22 °C?
12. We want to change the volume of a fixed amount of gas from 725 mL to 2.25 L while holding the temperature constant. To what value must we change the pressure if the initial pressure is 105 kPa?
13. A 35.8-L cylinder of Ar(g) is connected to an evacuated 1875-L tank. If the temperature is held constant and the final pressure is 721 mmHg, what must have been the original gas pressure in the cylinder, in atmospheres?
14. A sample of N_2(g) occupies a volume of 42.0 mL under the existing barometric pressure. Increasing the pressure by 85 mmHg reduces the volume to 37.7 mL. What is the prevailing barometric pressure, in millimeters of mercury?
15. What is the percent change in volume of a fixed amount of gas at a fixed pressure if the temperature is changed from 1.00 °C to 2.00 °C? Is this the same percent increase as produced by a temperature change from 10.00 °C to 20.00 °C? Explain.

16. The photographs show the contraction of an argon-filled balloon when it is cooled by liquid nitrogen. To what approximate fraction of its original volume will the balloon shrink when it is cooled from a room temperature of 71 °F to a final temperature of about −120 °C?

17. What is the mass of argon gas in a 75.0-mL volume at STP?

18. What volume of gaseous chlorine at STP would you need to obtain a 250.0-g sample of gas?

19. A 27.6-mL sample of $PH_3(g)$ (used in the manufacture of flame-retardant chemicals) is obtained at STP.
    (a) What is the mass of this gas, in milligrams?
    (b) How many molecules of PH_3 are present?

20. A 5.0×10^{17}-atom sample of radon gas is obtained.
    (a) What is the mass of this sample, in micrograms?
    (b) What is the volume of this sample at STP, in microliters?

21. You purchase a bag of potato chips at an ocean beach to take on a picnic in the mountains. At the picnic, you notice that the bag has become inflated, almost to the point of bursting. Use your knowledge of gas behavior to explain this phenomenon.

22. Scuba divers know that they must not ascend quickly from deep underwater because of a condition known as the *bends*, discussed in Chapter 13. Another concern is that they must constantly exhale during their ascent to prevent damage to the lungs and blood vessels. Describe what would happen to the lungs of a diver who inhaled compressed air at a depth of 30 m and held her breath while rising to the surface.

General Gas Equation

23. A sample of gas has a volume of 4.25 L at 25.6 °C and 748 mmHg. What will be the volume of this gas at 26.8 °C and 742 mmHg?

24. A 10.0-g sample of a gas has a volume of 5.25 L at 25 °C and 762 mmHg. If 2.5 g of the same gas is added to this *constant* 5.25-L volume and the temperature raised to 62 °C, what is the new gas pressure?

25. A constant-volume vessel contains 12.5 g of a gas at 21 °C. If the pressure of the gas is to remain constant as the temperature is raised to 210 °C, how many grams of gas must be released?

26. A 34.0-L cylinder contains 305 g $O_2(g)$ at 22 °C. How many grams of $O_2(g)$ must be released to reduce the pressure in the cylinder to 1.15 atm if the temperature remains constant?

Ideal Gas Equation

27. What is the volume, in milliliters, occupied by 89.2 g $CO_2(g)$ at 37 °C and 737 mmHg?

28. A 12.8-L cylinder contains 35.8 g O_2 at 46 °C. What is the pressure of this gas, in atmospheres?

29. $Kr(g)$ in a 18.5-L cylinder exerts a pressure of 11.2 atm at 28.2 °C. How many grams of gas are present?

30. A 72.8-L constant-volume cylinder containing 1.85 mol He is heated until the pressure reaches 3.50 atm. What is the final temperature in degrees Celsius?

31. A laboratory high vacuum system is capable of evacuating a vessel to the point that the amount of gas remaining is 5.0×10^9 molecules per cubic meter. What is the residual pressure in pascals?

32. What is the pressure, in pascals, exerted by 1242 g $CO(g)$ when confined at −25 °C to a cylindrical tank 25.0 cm in diameter and 1.75 m high?

Determining Molar Mass

33. A 0.418-g sample of gas has a volume of 115 mL at 66.3 °C and 743 mmHg. What is the molar mass of this gas?

34. What is the molar mass of a gas found to have a density of 0.841 g/L at 415 K and 725 Torr.

35. What is the molecular formula of a gaseous fluoride of sulfur containing 70.4% F and having a density of approximately 4.5 g/L at 20 °C and 1 atm?

36. A 2.650-g sample of a gaseous compound occupies 428 mL at 24.3 °C and 742 mmHg. The compound consists of 15.5% C, 23.0% Cl, and 61.5% F, by mass. What is its molecular formula?

37. A gaseous hydrocarbon weighing 0.231 g occupies a volume of 102 mL at 23 °C and 749 mmHg. What is the molar mass of this compound? What conclusion can you draw about its molecular formula?

38. A 132.10-mL glass vessel weighs 56.1035 g when evacuated and 56.2445 g when filled with the gaseous hydrocarbon acetylene at 749.3 mmHg and 20.02 °C. What is the molar mass of acetylene? What conclusion can you draw about its molecular formula?

Gas Densities

39. A particular application calls for $N_2(g)$ with a density of 1.80 g/L at 32 °C. What must be the pressure of the $N_2(g)$ in millimeters of mercury?

40. Monochloroethylene is used to make polyvinyl-chloride (PVC). It has a density of 2.56 g/L at 22.8 °C and 756 mmHg. What is the molar mass of mono-chloroethylene?

41. In order for a gas-filled balloon to rise in air, the density of the gas in the balloon must be less than that of air.
(a) Consider air to have a molar mass of 28.96 g/mol; determine the density of air at 25 °C and 1 atm, in g/L.
(b) Show by calculation that a balloon filled with car-bon dioxide at 25 °C and 1 atm could not be expected to rise in air at 25 °C.

42. Refer to Exercise 41, and determine the minimum temperature to which the balloon described in part (b) would have to be heated before it could begin to rise in air. (Ignore the mass of the balloon itself.)

43. The density of phosphorus vapor at 310 °C and 775 mmHg is 2.64 g/L. What is the molecular formula of the phosphorus under these conditions?

44. A particular gaseous hydrocarbon that is 82.7% C and 17.3% H by mass has a density of 2.33 g/L at 23 °C and 746 mmHg. What is the molecular formula of this hydrocarbon?

Gases in Chemical Reactions

45. What volume of $O_2(g)$ is consumed in the combustion of 75.6 L $C_3H_8(g)$ if both gases are measured at STP?

46. How many liters of $H_2(g)$ at STP are produced per gram of Al(s) consumed in the following reaction?

$$2\,Al(s) + 6\,HCl(aq) \longrightarrow 2\,AlCl_3(aq) + 3\,H_2(g)$$

47. A particular coal sample contains 3.28% S by mass. When the coal is burned, the sulfur is converted to $SO_2(g)$. What volume of $SO_2(g)$, measured at 23 °C and 738 mmHg, is produced by burning 2.7×10^6 lb of this coal?

48. One method of removing $CO_2(g)$ from a spacecraft is to allow the CO_2 to react with LiOH. How many liters of $CO_2(g)$ at 25.9 °C and 751 Torr can be removed per kilogram of LiOH consumed?

$$2\,LiOH(s) + CO_2(g) \longrightarrow Li_2CO_3(s) + H_2O(l)$$

49. A 3.57-g sample of a KCl–KClO₃ mixture is decom-posed by heating and produces 119 mL $O_2(g)$, mea-sured at 22.4 °C and 738 mmHg. What is the mass percent of $KClO_3$ in the mixture?

$$2\,KClO_3(s) \longrightarrow 2\,KCl(s) + 3\,O_2(g)$$

50. Hydrogen peroxide, H_2O_2, is used to disinfect contact lenses. How many milliliters of $O_2(g)$ at 22 °C and 752 mmHg can be liberated from 10.0 mL of an aqueous solution containing 3.00% H_2O_2 by mass? The density of the aqueous solution of H_2O_2 is 1.01 g/mL.

$$2\,H_2O_2(aq) \longrightarrow 2\,H_2O(l) + O_2(g)$$

51. Calculate the volume of $H_2(g)$, measured at 26 °C and 751 Torr required to react with 28.5 L CO(g), mea-sured at 0 °C and 760 Torr, in this reaction.

$$3\,CO(g) + 7\,H_2(g) \longrightarrow C_3H_8(g) + 3\,H_2O(l)$$

52. The Haber process is the principal method for fixing nitrogen (converting N_2 to nitrogen compounds).

$$N_2(g) + 3\,H_2(g) \longrightarrow 2\,NH_3(g)$$

Assume that the reactant gases are completely con-verted to $NH_3(g)$ and that the gases behave ideally.
(a) What volume of $NH_3(g)$ can be produced from 313 L of $H_2(g)$ if the gases are measured at 315 °C and 5.25 atm?
(b) What volume of $NH_3(g)$, measured at 25 °C and 727 mmHg, can be produced from 313 L $H_2(g)$, mea-sured at 315 °C and 5.25 atm?

Mixtures of Gases

53. What is the volume, in liters, occupied by a mixture of 15.2 g Ne(g) and 34.8 g Ar(g) at 7.15 atm pressure and 26.7 °C?

54. A balloon filled with $H_2(g)$ at STP has a volume of 2.24 L. What is the final gas volume if 0.10 mol He(g) is added to the balloon and the temperature is then raised to 100 °C while the pressure and amount of gas are held constant?

55. A gas cylinder of 53.7 L volume contains $N_2(g)$ at a pressure of 28.2 atm and 26 °C. How many grams of Ne(g) must we add to this same cylinder to raise the total pressure to 75.0 atm?

56. A 2.35-L container of $H_2(g)$ at 762 mmHg and 24 °C is connected to a 3.17-L container of He(g) at 728 mmHg and 24 °C. After mixing, what is the total gas pressure, in millimeters of mercury, with the temperature re-maining at 24 °C?

57. Which actions would you take to establish a pressure of 2.00 atm in a 2.24-L cylinder containing 1.60 g $O_2(g)$ at 32 °F? (a) add 1.60 g O_2; (b) release 0.80 g O_2; (c) add 2.00 g He; (d) add 0.60 g He.

58. A mixture of 4.0 g $H_2(g)$ and 10.0 g He(g) in a 4.3-L flask is maintained at 0 °C.
(a) What is the total pressure in the container?
(b) What is the partial pressure of each gas?

59. A 2.00-L container is filled with Ar(g) at 752 mmHg and 35 °C. A 0.728-g sample of C_6H_6 vapor is then added.
(a) What is the total pressure in the container?
(b) What is the partial pressure of Ar and of C_6H_6?

60. The chemical composition of air that is exhaled (expired) is different from ordinary air. A typical analysis of expired air at 37 °C and 1.00 atm, expressed as percent by volume, is 74.2% N_2, 15.2% O_2, 3.8% CO_2, 5.9% H_2O, and 0.9% Ar. The composition of ordinary air is given in Practice Example 6-15B.
    (a) What is the ratio of the partial pressure of $CO_2(g)$ in expired air to that in ordinary air?
    (b) Would you expect the density of expired air to be greater or less than that of ordinary air at the same temperature and pressure? Explain.
    (c) Confirm your expectation by calculating the densities of ordinary air and expired air at 37 °C and 1.00 atm.
61. In the drawing on the right, 1.00 g $H_2(g)$ is maintained at 1 atm pressure in a cylinder closed off by a freely moving piston. Which sketch, (a), (b), or (c), best represents the mixture obtained when 1.00 g He(g) is added? Explain.

1.00 g H_2 **(a)**   **(b)**   **(c)**

62. Sketch H_2 molecules and He atoms in the drawings shown in Exercise 61. Specifically, choose some small number of symbols to represent 1.00 g H_2. Then, sketch in the appropriate number of symbols of He atoms to account for the conditions indicated for (a), (b), and (c). Make your sketches reflect the mixtures at the molecular level to the best of your ability.

Collecting Gases over Liquids

63. A 1.65-g sample of Al reacts with excess HCl, and the liberated H_2 is collected over water at 25 °C at a barometric pressure of 744 mmHg. What volume of gaseous mixture, in liters, is collected?

$$2\,Al(s) + 6\,HCl(aq) \longrightarrow 2\,AlCl_3(aq) + 3\,H_2(g)$$

64. An 89.3-mL sample of "wet" $O_2(g)$ is collected over water at 21.3 °C at a barometric pressure of 756 mmHg (vapor pressure of water at 21.3 °C = 19 mmHg).
    (a) What is the partial pressure of $O_2(g)$ in the sample collected, in millimeters of mercury? (b) What is the volume percent O_2 in the gas collected? (c) How many grams of O_2 are present in the sample?

65. A sample of $O_2(g)$ is collected over water at 24 °C. The volume of gas is 1.16 L. In a subsequent experiment, it is determined that the mass of O_2 present is 1.46 g. What must have been the barometric pressure at the time the gas was collected? (Vapor pressure of water = 22.4 Torr.)
66. A 1.072-g sample of He(g) is found to occupy a volume of 8.446 L when collected over hexane at 25.0 °C and 738.6 mmHg barometric pressure. Use these data to determine the vapor pressure of hexane at 25 °C.

Kinetic-Molecular Theory

67. Calculate u_{rms}, in meters per second, for $Cl_2(g)$ molecules at 30 °C.
68. The u_{rms} of H_2 molecules at 273 K is 1.84×10^3 m/s. At what temperature is u_{rms} for H_2 twice this value?
69. Refer to Example 6-17. What must be the molecular mass of a gas if its molecules are to have a root-mean-square speed at 25 °C equal to that of the M-16 rifle bullet?

70. Refer to Example 6-17. Noble gases (group 18) exist as atoms, not molecules (they are monatomic). Cite one noble gas whose u_{rms} at 25 °C is higher than the rifle bullet's and one whose u_{rms} is lower.
71. At what temperature will u_{rms} for Ne(g) be the same as u_{rms} for He at 300 K?
72. Determine u_m, $\bar{u}$, and u_{rms} for a group of ten automobiles clocked by radar at speeds of 38, 44, 45, 48, 50, 55, 55, 57, 58, and 60 mi/h, respectively.

Diffusion and Effusion of Gases

73. If 0.00484 mol $N_2O(g)$ effuses through an orifice in a certain period of time, how much $NO_2(g)$ would effuse in the same time under the same conditions?
74. A sample of $N_2(g)$ effuses through a tiny hole in 38 s. What must be the molar mass of a gas that requires 64 s to effuse under identical conditions?
75. What are the ratios of the diffusion rates for the pairs of gases (a) N_2 and O_2; (b) H_2O and D_2O (D = deuterium, i.e., ^2_1H); (c) $^{14}CO_2$ and $^{12}CO_2$; (d) $^{235}UF_6$ and $^{238}UF_6$?
76. Which of the following visualizations best represents the distribution of O_2 and SO_2 molecules near an orifice some time after effusion occurs in the direction indicated by the arrows? The initial condition was one of equal numbers of O_2 molecules (•) and SO_2 molecules (•). Explain.

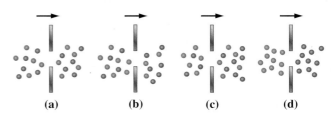

   (a)   **(b)**   **(c)**   **(d)**

Nonideal Gases

77. Refer to Example 6-20. Recalculate the pressure of $Cl_2(g)$ using both the ideal gas equation and van der Waals equation at the temperatures **(a)** 100 °C; **(b)** 200 °C; **(c)** 400 °C. From the results, confirm the statement that a gas tends to be more ideal at high temperatures than at low temperatures.

78. Use both the ideal gas equation and the van der Waals equation to calculate the pressure exerted by 1.50 mol of $SO_2(g)$ when it is confined at 298 K to a volume of **(a)** 100.0 L, **(b)** 50.0 L, **(c)** 20.0 L, **(d)** 10.0 L. Under which of these conditions is the pressure calculated with the ideal gas equation within a few percent of that calculated with the van der Waals equation? For SO_2, the value of $a = 6.71$ L^2 atm mol^{-2} and $b = 0.0564$ L mol^{-1}.

Integrative and Advanced Exercises

79. Explain why it is necessary to include the density of $Hg(l)$ and the value of the acceleration due to gravity, g, in a precise definition of a standard atmosphere of pressure (pages 180-181).

80. Assume the following initial conditions for the graphs labeled A, B, and C in Figure 6-8. (A) 10.0 mL at 400 K; (B) 20.0 mL at 400 K; (C) 40.0 mL at 400 K. Use Charles's law to calculate the volume of each gas at 0, -100, -200, -250, and -270 °C; show that the volume of each gas becomes zero at -273.15 °C.

81. The "initial" sketch illustrates, both at the macroscopic and molecular levels, an initial condition: 1 mol of a gas at STP. With as much detail as possible, represent the final condition after each of the following changes.
    (a) The pressure is changed to 250 mmHg while standard temperature is maintained.
    (b) The temperature is changed to 140 K while standard pressure is maintained.
    (c) The pressure is changed to 0.5 atm while the temperature is changed to 550 K.
    (d) An additional 0.5 mol of gas is introduced into the cylinder, the temperature is changed to 135 °C, and the pressure is changed to 2.25 atm.

Initial   Final

82. Complete combustion of 1.110 g of a gaseous hydrocarbon yields 3.613 g CO_2 and 1.109 g H_2O. A 0.288-g sample of the hydrocarbon occupies a volume of 131 mL at 24.8 °C and 753 mmHg. What is the molecular formula of the hydrocarbon?

83. A balloon is inflated with 2.15 ft^3 of He(g) at STP and released. What is the gas pressure in the balloon when it has expanded to a volume of 155 L? Assume a temperature of -20 °C at this altitude.

84. In the drawings below, the diver toy floats at the top of the liquid (left); but when the bottle is squeezed, the diver descends (right). Explain the phenomena illustrated here.

85. In the photographs below, we see two balloons connected by a stopcock. At the top, one balloon is inflated to a greater volume than the other. At the bottom, we see what happens when the stopcock is opened. Explain this observation, which seems contrary to what we would expect intuitively.

86. A 3.05-g sample of $NH_4NO_3(s)$ is introduced into an evacuated 2.18-L flask and then heated to 250 °C. What is the total gas pressure, in atmospheres, in the flask at 250 °C when the NH_4NO_3 has completely decomposed?

$$NH_4NO_3(s) \longrightarrow N_2O(g) + 2 H_2O(g)$$

87. A mixture of 1.00 g H_2 and 8.60 g O_2 is introduced into a 1.500-L flask at 25 °C. **(a)** What is the total gas pressure in the flask? **(b)** When the mixture is ignited, an explosive reaction occurs in which water is the only product. What is the total gas pressure when the flask is returned to 25 °C? (The vapor pressure of water at 25 °C is 23.8 mmHg.)

88. In the reaction of $CO_2(g)$ and sodium peroxide (Na_2O_2), sodium carbonate and oxygen gas are formed.

$$2\,Na_2O_2(s) + 2\,CO_2(g) \longrightarrow 2\,Na_2CO_3(s) + O_2(g)$$

This reaction is used in submarines and space vehicles to remove expired $CO_2(g)$ and to generate some of the $O_2(g)$ required for breathing. Assume that the volume of gases exchanged in the lungs equals 4.0 L/min, the CO_2 content of expired air is 3.8% CO_2 by volume, and the gases are at 25 °C and 735 mmHg. If the $CO_2(g)$ and $O_2(g)$ in the above reaction are measured at the same temperature and pressure, **(a)** how many milliliters of $O_2(g)$ are produced per minute; **(b)** at what rate is the $Na_2O_2(s)$ consumed, in grams per hour?

89. What is the partial pressure of $Cl_2(g)$, in millimeters of mercury, at STP in a gaseous mixture that consists of 46.5% N_2, 12.7% Ne, and 40.8% Cl_2, by mass?

90. A gaseous mixture of He and O_2 has a density of 0.518 g/L at 25 °C and 721 mmHg. What is the mass percent He in the mixture?

91. When working with a mixture of gases, it is sometimes convenient to use an *apparent molar mass* (a weighted-average molar mass). Think in terms of replacing the mixture with a hypothetical single gas. What is the apparent molar mass of air, given that air is 78.08% N_2, 20.95% O_2, 0.93% Ar, and 0.036% CO_2, by volume?

92. Gas cylinder A has a volume of 48.2 L and contains $N_2(g)$ at 8.35 atm at 25 °C. Gas cylinder B, of unknown volume, contains He(g) at 9.50 atm and 25 °C. When the two cylinders are connected and the gases mixed, the pressure in each cylinder becomes 8.71 atm. What is the volume of cylinder B?

93. The accompanying sketch is that of a closed-end manometer. Describe how it is constructed and how the gas pressure is measured. Why is a measurement of $P_{bar.}$ not necessary when using this manometer? Explain why the closed-end manometer is more suitable for measuring low pressures and the open-end manometer more suitable for measuring pressures nearer atmospheric pressure.

Gas

94. Producer gas is a type of fuel gas made by passing air or steam through a bed of hot coal or coke. A typical producer gas has the following composition in percent by volume: 8.0% CO_2, 23.2% CO, 17.7% H_2, 1.1% CH_4, and 50.0% N_2.
    (a) What is the density of this gas at 23 °C and 763 mmHg, in grams per liter?
    (b) What is the partial pressure of CO in this mixture at STP?
    (c) What volume of air, measured at 23 °C and 741 Torr, is required for the complete combustion of 1.00×10^3 L of this producer gas, also measured at 23 °C and 741 Torr?
    [*Hint:* Which three of the constituent gases are combustible?]

95. A mixture of $H_2(g)$ and $O_2(g)$ is prepared by electrolyzing 1.32 g water, and the mixture of gases is collected over water at 30 °C and 748 mmHg. The volume of "wet" gas obtained is 2.90 L. What must be the vapor pressure of water at 30 °C?

$$2\,H_2O(l) \xrightarrow{\text{electrolysis}} 2\,H_2(g) + O_2(g)$$

96. A 0.168-L sample of $O_2(g)$ is collected over water at 26 °C and a barometric pressure of 737 mmHg. In the gas that is collected, what is the percent water vapor **(a)** by volume; **(b)** by number of molecules; **(c)** by mass? (Vapor pressure of water at 26 °C = 25.2 mmHg.)

97. What volume of air, measured at 22 °C and 745 mmHg, is required for the complete combustion of 1.00 L of $CH_4(g)$ at 22 °C and 3.55 atm? [Air contains 20.95% $O_2(g)$, by volume.]

98. A breathing mixture is prepared in which He is substituted for N_2. The gas is 79% He and 21% O_2, by volume. **(a)** What is the density of this mixture in grams per liter at 25 °C and 1.00 atm? **(b)** At what pressure would the He–O_2 mixture have the same density as that of air at 25 °C and 1.00 atm? See Table 6.3 for the composition of air.

99. Explain why the mass percent N_2 in air is less than the 78.084% listed in Table 6.3, whereas the mass percent O_2 is greater than the 20.946%. Recompute the data in Table 6.3 to express the percentages of atmospheric gases on a mass basis.

100. With reference to the discussion on page 213, a 0.1052-g sample of $H_2O(l)$ in an 8.050-L sample of dry air at 30.1 °C evaporates completely. To what temperature must the air be cooled to give a relative humidity of 80.0%? Vapor pressures of water: 20 °C, 17.54 mmHg; 19 °C, 16.48 mmHg; 18 °C, 15.48 mmHg; 17 °C, 14.53 mmHg; 16 °C, 13.63 mmHg; 15 °C, 12.79 mmHg.

101. An alternative to Figure 6-6 is to plot P against $1/V$. The resulting graph is a straight line passing through the origin. Use Boyle's data from Feature Problem 106 to draw such a straight-line graph. What factors would affect the *slope* of this straight line? Explain.

102. We have noted that atmospheric pressure depends on altitude. Atmospheric pressure as a function of altitude can be calculated with an equation known as the barometric formula:

$$P = P_0 \times 10^{-Mgh/2.303RT}$$

In this equation, P and P_0 can be in any pressure units, for example, Torr. P_0 is the pressure at sea level, generally taken to be 1.00 atm or its equivalent. The units in the exponential term must be SI units, however. Use the barometric formula to
(a) estimate the barometric pressure at the top of Mt. Whitney in California (altitude: 14,494 ft; assume a temperature of 10 °C)
(b) show that barometric pressure decreases by one-thirtieth in value for every 900-ft increase in altitude

103. If the van der Waals equation is solved for volume, a cubic equation is obtained.
(a) Derive this equation by rearranging equation (6.26).

$$V^3 - n\left(\frac{RT + bP}{P}\right)V^2 + \left(\frac{n^2a}{P}\right)V - \frac{n^3ab}{P} = 0$$

(b) What is the volume, in liters, occupied by 185 g $CO_2(g)$ at a pressure of 12.5 atm and 286 K? For $CO_2(g)$, $a = 3.59\ L^2\ atm\ mol^{-2}$ and $b = 0.0427\ L\ mol^{-1}$.

104. A particular equation of state for $O_2(g)$ has the form

$$P\overline{V} = RT\left(1 + \frac{B}{\overline{V}} + \frac{C}{\overline{V}^2}\right)$$

where $\overline{V}$ is the molar volume, $B = -21.89\ cm^3/mol$ and $C = 1230\ cm^6/mol$.
(a) Use the equation to calculate the pressure exerted by 1 mol $O_2(g)$ confined to a volume of 500 cm³ at 273 K.
(b) Is the result calculated in part (a) consistent with that suggested for $O_2(g)$ by Figure 6-22? Explain.

105. A 0.156-g sample of a magnesium–aluminum alloy dissolves completely in an excess of HCl(aq). The liberated $H_2(g)$ is collected over water at 5 °C when the barometric pressure is 752 Torr. After the gas is collected, the water and gas gradually warm to the prevailing room temperature of 23 °C. The pressure of the collected gas is again equalized against the barometric pressure of 752 Torr, and its volume is found to be 202 mL. What is the percent composition of the magnesium–aluminum alloy? (Vapor pressure of water: 6.54 mmHg at 5 °C and 21.07 mmHg at 23 °C)

Feature Problems

106. Shown below is a diagram of Boyle's original apparatus. At the start of the experiment, the length of the air column (A) on the left was 30.5 cm and the heights of mercury in the arms of the tube were equal. When mercury was added to the right arm of the tube, a difference in mercury levels (B) was produced, and the entrapped air on the left was compressed into a shorter length of the tube (smaller volume) as shown in the illustration for A = 27.9 cm and B = 7.1 cm. Boyle's values of A and B, in centimeters, are listed as follows:

A:	30.5	27.9	25.4	22.9	20.3
B:	0.0	7.1	15.7	25.7	38.3
A:	17.8	15.2	12.7	10.2	7.6
B:	53.8	75.4	105.6	147.6	224.6

Barometric pressure at the time of the experiment was 739.8 mmHg. Assuming that the length of the air column (A) is proportional to the volume of air, show that these data conform reasonably well to Boyle's law.

$P_{bar.} = 739.8$ mmHg

A = 27.9 cm

B = 7.1 cm

107. In 1860, Stanislao Cannizzaro showed how Avogadro's hypothesis could be used to establish the atomic masses of elements in gaseous compounds. Cannizzaro took the atomic mass of hydrogen to be exactly one and assumed that hydrogen exists as H_2 molecules (molecular mass = 2). Next, he determined the volume of $H_2(g)$ at STP that has a mass of exactly 2 g. This volume is 22.4 L. Then he assumed that 22.4 L of any other gas would have the same number of molecules as in 22.4 L of $H_2(g)$. (Here is where Avogadro's hypothesis entered in.) Finally, he reasoned that the ratio of the mass of 22.4 L of any other gas to the mass of 22.4 L of $H_2(g)$ should be the same as the ratio of their molecular masses. The sketch on page 222 illustrates Cannizzaro's reasoning in establishing the atomic weight of oxygen as 16. The gases in the table all contain the element X. Their molecular masses were determined by Cannizzaro's method. Use the percent composition data to deduce the atomic mass of X, the number of atoms of X in each of the gas molecules, and the identity of X.

Compound	Molecular Mass, u	Mass Percent X, %
Nitryl fluoride	65.01	49.4
Nitrosyl fluoride	49.01	32.7
Thionyl fluoride	86.07	18.6
Sulfuryl fluoride	102.07	31.4

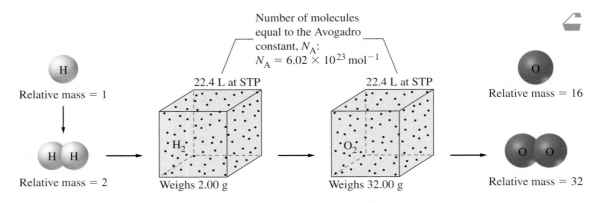

108. In research that required the careful measurement of gas densities, John Rayleigh, a physicist, found that the density of $O_2(g)$ had the same value whether the gas was obtained from air or derived from one of its compounds. The situation with $N_2(g)$ was different, however. The density of $N_2(g)$ had the same value when the $N_2(g)$ was derived from any of various compounds, but a *different* value if the $N_2(g)$ was extracted from air. In 1894, Rayleigh enlisted the aid of William Ramsay, a chemist, to solve this apparent mystery; in the course of their work they discovered the noble gases.
(a) Why do you suppose that the $N_2(g)$ extracted from liquid air did *not* have the same density as $N_2(g)$ obtained from its compounds?
(b) Which gas do you suppose had the greater density, $N_2(g)$ extracted from air or $N_2(g)$ prepared from nitrogen compounds? Explain.
(c) The way in which Ramsay proved that nitrogen gas extracted from air was itself a mixture of gases involved allowing this nitrogen to react with magnesium metal to form magnesium nitride. Explain the significance of this experiment.
(d) Use data on the composition of air from Table 6.3 to calculate the *percent difference* in the densities at STP of Rayleigh's $N_2(g)$ extracted from air and $N_2(g)$ derived from nitrogen compounds.

109. The equation $d/P = M/RT$, which can be derived from equation (6.14), suggests that the ratio of the density (d) to pressure (P) of a gas at constant temperature should be a constant. The gas density data below were obtained for $O_2(g)$ at various pressures at 273.15 K.

(a) Calculate values of d/P, and with a graph or by other means determine the ideal value of the term d/P for $O_2(g)$ at 273.15 K.
[*Hint:* The ideal value is that associated with a perfect (ideal) gas.]
(b) Use the value of d/P from part (a) to calculate a precise value for the atomic mass of oxygen, and compare this value with that listed on the inside front cover.

P, mmHg:	760.00	570.00	380.00	190.00
d, g/L:	1.428962	1.071485	0.714154	0.356985

110. A sounding balloon is a rubber bag filled with $H_2(g)$ and carrying a set of instruments (the payload). Because this combination of bag, gas, and payload has a smaller mass than a corresponding volume of air, the balloon rises. As the balloon rises, it expands. From the table below, estimate the maximum height to which a spherical balloon can rise given the mass of balloon, 1200 g; payload, 1700 g: quantity of $H_2(g)$ in balloon, 120 ft^3 at STP; diameter of balloon at maximum height, 25 ft. Air pressure and temperature as function of altitude are:

Altitude, km	Pressure, mb	Temperature, K
0	1.0×10^3	288
5	5.4×10^2	256
10	2.7×10^2	223
20	5.5×10^1	217
30	1.2×10^1	230
40	2.9×10^0	250
50	8.1×10^{-1}	250
60	2.3×10^{-1}	256

Self-Assessment Exercises

111. In your own words, define or explain each term or symbol. (a) atm; (b) STP; (c) R; (d) partial pressure; (e) u_{rms}.
112. Briefly describe each concept or process: (a) absolute zero of temperature; (b) collection of a gas over water; (c) effusion of a gas; (d) law of combining volumes.
113. Explain the important distinctions between (a) barometer and manometer; (b) Celsius and Kelvin temperature; (c) ideal gas equation and general gas equation; (d) ideal gas and real gas.
114. Which exerts the greatest pressure, (a) a 75.0-cm column of Hg(l) ($d = 13.6$ g/mL); (b) a column of air 10 mi high; (c) a 5.0-m column of $CCl_4(l)$ ($d = 1.59$ g/mL); (d) 10.0 g $H_2(g)$ at STP?
115. For a fixed amount of gas at a fixed pressure, changing the temperature from 100.0 °C to 200 K causes the gas volume to (a) double; (b) increase, but not to twice its original value; (c) decrease; (d) stay the same.
116. The gas with the greatest density at STP is (a) N_2O; (b) Kr; (c) SO_3; (d) Cl_2.

117. A sample of $O_2(g)$ is collected over water at 23 °C and a barometric pressure of 751 Torr. The vapor pressure of water at 23 °C is 21 mmHg. The partial pressure of $O_2(g)$ in the sample collected is **(a)** 21 mmHg; **(b)** 751 Torr; **(c)** 0.96 atm; **(d)** 1.02 atm.

118. At 0 °C and 0.500 atm, 4.48 L of gaseous NH_3 **(a)** contains 6.02×10^{22} molecules; **(b)** has a mass of 17.0 g; **(c)** contains 0.200 mol NH_3; **(d)** has a mass of 3.40 g.

119. To establish a pressure of 2.00 atm in a 2.24-L cylinder containing 1.60 g $O_2(g)$ at 0 °C, **(a)** add 1.60 g O_2; **(b)** add 0.60 g $He(g)$; **(c)** add 2.00 g He; **(d)** release 0.80 g $O_2(g)$.

120. A mixture of 5.0×10^{-5} mol $H_2(g)$ and 5.0×10^{-5} mol $SO_2(g)$ is placed in a 10.0-L container at 25 °C. The container has a "pinhole" leak. After a period of time, the partial pressure of $H_2(g)$ in the container **(a)** is less than that of the $SO_2(g)$; **(b)** is equal to that of the $SO_2(g)$; **(c)** exceeds that of the $SO_2(g)$; **(d)** is the same as in the original mixture.

121. Under which conditions is Cl_2 most likely to behave like an ideal gas? Explain. **(a)** 100 °C and 10.0 atm; **(b)** 0 °C and 0.50 atm; **(c)** 200 °C and 0.50 atm; **(d)** 400 °C and 10.0 atm.

122. Explain why the height of the mercury column in a barometer is independent of the diameter of the barometer tube.

123. A gaseous hydrocarbon that is 82.7% C and 17.3% H by mass has a density of 2.35 g/L at 25 °C and 752 Torr. What is the molecular formula of this hydrocarbon?

124. Draw a box to represent a sample of air containing N_2 molecules (represented as squares) and O_2 molecules (represented as circles) in their correct proportions. How many squares and circles would you need to draw to also represent the $CO_2(g)$ in air through a single mark? What else should you add to the box for this more complete representation of air? [*Hint:* See Table 6.3.]

125. Appendix E describes a useful study aid known as concept mapping. Using the method presented in Appendix E, construct a concept map illustrating the different concepts to show the relationships among all the gas laws described in this chapter.

 ## eMedia Exercises

126. **(a)** View the **Motions of a Gas** activity (*Activebook 6-1*) and list the different forces experienced by the molecules. **(b)** Would any of the forces be potentially attractive in nature? **(c)** Under what conditions would attractive forces affect the pressure of the system predicted by the ideal gas law?

127. Use the **Ideal Gas Behavior** activity (*Activebook 6-3*) to simulate the relationships between the different variables found in the ideal gas law. Which variable pairs, when plotted against one another, give rise to data that fit a straight line? Propose a means to extract the value of the ideal gas constant from this activity.

128. Consider the reaction of solid sodium azide as seen in the **Air Bags** animation (*Activebook 6-5*). **(a)** Calculate the volume of gas produced from the reaction of 30 g sodium azide at a pressure of 1.1 atm and a temperature of 25 °C. **(b)** If the exothermic nature of the reaction raised the temperature of the same volume of gas to 100 °C, what would be the resulting pressure within the same volume of the air bag?

129. **(a)** Use the **Boltzman Distribution** simulation (*Activebook 6-7*) to confirm the relationship given in equation (6.20). Do this by determining the u_{rms} of each gas at a fixed temperature and plotting this value against the square root of the molecular masses of the different gases. **(b)** What is the slope of this plot and how does this relationship confirm the relationship described in equation (6.20)? **(c)** Does the relationship hold at more than one temperature?

130. In the **Diffusion of Bromine Vapor** movie (*Activebook 6-8*) the gas phase molecules experience a resistance to their upward propagation. **(a)** What is the primary source of resistance to the upward propagation of bromine in the test tube? **(b)** Describe the difference between this resistance to propagation with that found in a situation where a gas undergoes effusion. What physical properties of a gas influence both the rates of diffusion and effusion?

 ## eLaboratory Exercises

These exercises allow students to apply the concepts and skills for this chapter in the simulated laboratory of Virtual ChemLab. Worksheets for each of these exercises are found in the Virtual ChemLab Workbook in your MediaPak.

131. *(VCL 6-1) Boyle's Law: Pressure and Volume*
Robert Boyle, a philosopher and theologian, studied the properties of gases in the seventeenth century. He noticed that gases behave similarly to springs; when compressed or expanded, they tend to spring back to their original volume. He published his findings in 1662 in a monograph entitled *The Spring of the Air and Its Effects*. You will make observations similar to those of Robert Boyle and learn about the relationship between the pressure and volume of an ideal gas.

132. *(VCL 6-2) Charles's Law: Temperature and Volume*
Charles's law was discovered by Joseph Louis Gay-Lussac in 1802, based on unpublished work done by Jacques Charles in about 1787. Charles had found that a number of gases expand to the same extent over the same 80° temperature interval. You will be observing the relationship between the temperature and volume of a gas similar to that studied by Charles.

133. *(VCL 6-3) Avogadro's Law: Moles and Volume*
In 1808, Joseph Gay-Lussac observed the *law of combining values*, which states that the volumes of gases that react with one another react in the ratio of small whole numbers. Three years later, Amedeo Avogadro built upon this observation by proposing what is now known as *Avogadro's hypothesis*: Equal volumes of gases at the same temperature and pressure contain equal numbers of molecules. Avogadro's law, which states the relationship between moles and volume, followed from his hypothesis. You will be observing the same principle that Avogadro stated 200 years ago.

134. *(VCL 6-4) Derivation of the Ideal Gas Law*
An ideal gas is a hypothetical gas whose pressure, volume, and temperature follow the relationship $PV = nRT$. Ideal gases do not actually exist, although all real gases can behave like an ideal gas at certain temperatures and pressures. All gases can be described to some extent using the ideal gas law, and it is important in our understanding of how all gases behave. In this assignment you will derive the ideal gas law from experimental observations.

135. *(VCL 6-5) Dalton's Law of Partial Pressure*
Dalton's law of partial pressure, named after its discoverer John Dalton, describes the behavior of gas mixtures. It states that the total pressure of the gas, P_{tot}, is the sum of the partial pressures of each gas, or the sum of the pressures that each gas would exert if it were alone in the container. In this assignment you will become more familiar with Dalton's law.

136. *(VCL 6-6) Ideal vs. Real Gases*
At room temperature and normal atmospheric pressures, real gases behave similarly to ideal gases, but real gases can deviate significantly from ideal gas behavior at extreme conditions such as high temperatures and high pressures. It is not always easy to find an effective means to show the deviation from ideal gas behavior for real gases. An effective but simple method to see these deviations is to calculate the value of R, the ideal gas constant, for real gases, *assuming* they follow the ideal gas law, and then compare the value for R against the actual value of 0.08205 L-atm/mol-K. In this assignment you will measure P, V, T, and n for various real gases under different conditions and then calculate the value for R and compare it to its actual value.

137. *(VCL 6-7) The Effect of Mass on Pressure*
An understanding of pressure is an integral part of our understanding of the behavior of gases. Pressure is defined as the force per unit area exerted by a gas or other medium. The pressure of a gas is affected by many variables, such as temperature, external pressure, volume, moles of a gas, and other factors. This assignment will help you become more familiar with pressure and the effect of adding mass to a frictionless, massless piston.

7 THERMOCHEMISTRY

CONTENTS

Brouwer, Henry. "Small-scale thermochemistry experiment (ML)." *J. Chem. Educ.* **1991**: *68*, A178.

▶ Thermochemistry is a subfield of a larger discipline called *thermodynamics*. The broader aspects of thermodynamics are considered in Chapters 19 and 20.

Potassium reacts with water liberating sufficient heat to ignite the hydrogen evolved. The transfer of heat between substances in chemical reactions is an important aspect of thermochemistry.

Natural gas consists mostly of methane, CH_4. As we learned in Chapter 4, the complete combustion of a hydrocarbon such as methane yields carbon dioxide and water as products. More important, however, is another "product" of this reaction, which we have not previously mentioned: heat. This heat can be used to produce hot water in a water heater, to heat a house, or to cook food.

Thermochemistry is the branch of chemistry concerned with the heat effects that accompany chemical reactions. Much of this chapter deals with determining quantities of heat both by measurement and by calculation. Some of these calculations make it possible to establish, indirectly, a quantity of heat that would be difficult or impossible to measure directly. This type of calculation, which relies on compilations of tabulated data, will come up again in later chapters. Finally, concepts introduced in this chapter answer a host of practical questions, such as why natural gas is a better fuel than coal and why the energy value of fats is greater than that of carbohydrates and proteins.

7-1   GETTING STARTED: SOME TERMINOLOGY

In this section, we introduce and define some very basic terms. Most are discussed in greater detail in later sections, and your understanding of these terms should grow as you proceed through the chapter.

A **system** is the part of the universe chosen for study, and it can be as large as all the oceans on Earth or as small as the contents of a beaker. Most of the systems we will examine will be small and we will look, particularly, at the transfer of *energy* (as heat and work) and *matter* between the system and its surroundings. The **surroundings** are that part of the universe outside the system with which the system interacts. Figure 7-1 pictures three common systems: first, as we see them and, then, in an abstract form that chemists commonly use. An **open system** freely exchanges energy and matter with its surroundings (Fig. 7-1a). A **closed system** can exchange energy with its surroundings, but not matter (Fig. 7-1b). An **isolated system** does not interact with its surroundings (approximated in Figure 7-1c).

The remainder of this section says more, in a general way, about energy and its relationship to work. Like many other scientific terms, *energy* is derived from Greek. It means "work within." **Energy** is the capacity to do work. **Work** is done when a force acts through a distance. Moving objects do work when they slow down or are stopped. Thus, when one billiard ball strikes another and sets it in motion, work is done. The energy of a moving object is called **kinetic energy** (the word *kinetic* means "motion" in Greek). We can see the relationship between work and energy by comparing the units for these two quantities. The kinetic energy of an object is based on its mass (m) and velocity (u) through the first equation below; work (w) is related to force [mass (m) × acceleration (a)] and distance (d) by the second equation.

$$\text{kinetic energy} = \tfrac{1}{2} \times m(\text{kg}) \times [u(\text{m/s})]^2 \tag{7.1}$$

$$\text{work} = \text{force} \times \text{distance} = [m(\text{kg}) \times a(\text{m s}^{-2})] \times d(\text{m})$$

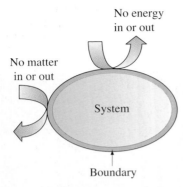

No matter in or out

No energy in or out

System

Boundary

▲ **Isolated system**
No interactions occur across the system boundary with the surroundings.

Types of Energy activity

Give examples:

– Isolated system: a stick of dynamite explodes deep within a mountain cavity. Discuss what goes on.
– Closed system: a cylinder of a steam engine when all the valves are closed.
– Open system: titration of a sample.

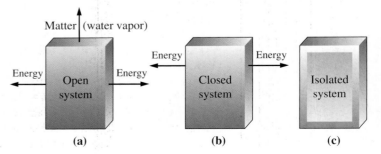

Matter (water vapor)

Energy   Open system   Energy

Energy   Closed system   Energy

Energy   Isolated system

(a)   (b)   (c)

▶ **FIGURE 7-1**
Systems and their surroundings
(a) *Open system.* The beaker of hot coffee transfers energy to the surroundings—it loses heat as it cools. Matter is also transferred in the form of water vapor. **(b)** *Closed system.* The flask of hot coffee transfers energy (heat) to the surroundings as it cools. Because the flask is stoppered, no water vapor escapes and no matter is transferred. **(c)** *Isolated system.* Hot coffee in an insulated container approximates an isolated system. No water vapor escapes, and for a time at least, little heat is transferred to the surroundings. (Eventually, though, the coffee in the container cools to room temperature.)

◀ **FIGURE 7-2**
Potential energy (P.E.) and kinetic energy (K.E.)
The energy of the bouncing tennis ball changes continuously from potential to kinetic energy and back again. The maximum potential energy is at the top of each bounce, and the maximum kinetic energy occurs at the moment of impact. The sum of P.E. and K.E. decreases with each bounce as the thermal energies of the ball and the surroundings increase. The ball soon comes to rest.

When the units for the expressions for work and energy are collected together, in both cases, the resultant unit is $kg\,m^2\,s^{-2}$. This corresponds to the SI unit of energy called the joule (J). That is, 1 *joule* (J) $= 1\,kg\,m^2\,s^{-2}$.

The bouncing ball in Figure 7-2 suggests something about the nature of energy and work. First, to lift the ball to the starting position, we have to apply a force through a distance (to overcome the force of gravity). The work we do is "stored" in the ball as energy. This stored energy has the potential to do work when released and is therefore called potential energy. **Potential energy** is energy due to condition, position, or composition; it is an energy associated with forces of attraction or repulsion between objects.

When we release the ball, it is pulled toward Earth's center by the force of gravity—it falls. Potential energy is converted to kinetic energy during this fall. The kinetic energy reaches its maximum just as the ball strikes the surface. On its rebound, the kinetic energy of the ball decreases (the ball slows down) and its potential energy increases (the ball rises). If the collision of the ball with the surface were perfectly *elastic*, like collisions between molecules in the kinetic-molecular theory, the sum of the potential and kinetic energies of the ball would remain constant. The ball would reach the same maximum height on each rebound, and it would bounce forever. But we know this doesn't happen—the bouncing ball soon comes to rest. All the energy originally invested in the ball as potential energy (by raising it to its initial position) eventually appears as additional kinetic energy of the atoms and molecules that make up the ball, the surface, and the surrounding air. This kinetic energy associated with random molecular motion is called **thermal energy**.

In general, thermal energy is proportional to the temperature of a system, as suggested by the kinetic theory of gases. The more vigorous the motion of the molecules in the system, the hotter the sample and the greater is its thermal energy. However, the thermal energy of a system also depends on the number of particles present, so that a small sample at a high temperature (for example, a cup of coffee at 75 °C) may have less thermal energy than a larger sample at a lower temperature (for example, a swimming pool at 30 °C). Thus, temperature and thermal energy must be carefully distinguished. Equally important, we need to distinguish between energy changes produced by the action of forces through distances—*work*—and those involving the transfer of thermal energy—*heat*.

Barrow, Gordon M. "Thermodynamics should be built on energy-not on heat and work." *J. Chem. Educ.* **1988:** *65*, 122.

Point out that a unit of work, heat and energy is the joule but that work and heat are not forms of energy but *processes* by which the energy of a system is changed. An article that discusses this point and recommends good analogies for explaining the concepts of work, heat and energy is Peckham, Gavin D., McNaught, Ian J. *J. Chem. Educ.* **1993:** *70*, 103.

Fry an egg with an exothermic reaction. On a piece of glass put a layer of lime (CaO) and add water. Cover the mixture with a sheet of aluminum foil and crack an egg on the foil. The heat of reaction cooks the egg.

Students commonly misunderstand the concepts of heat and temperature and the relationship between them.

 Work and Heat simulation

CONCEPT ASSESSMENT ✓

Consider the following situations, a stick of dynamite exploding deep within a mountain cavern, the titration of an acid with base in a laboratory, and a cylinder of a steam engine with all of its valves closed. To what type of thermodynamic systems do these situations correspond?

▲ **James Joule (1818–1889)— an amateur scientist**
Joule's primary occupation was running a brewery, but he also conducted scientific research in a home laboratory. His precise measurements of quantities of heat formed the basis of the law of conservation of energy.

✓ By the first law, both heat and work are energy and are related. Heat is the disordered flow of energy and work is the ordered flow of energy.

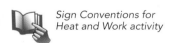

Sign Conventions for Heat and Work activity

Kimbrough, Doris R. "Heat Capacity, Body Temperature, and Hypothermia." *J. Chem. Educ.* **1998**: *75*, 48 (January 1998).

7-2   HEAT

Heat is energy transferred between a system and its surroundings as a result of a temperature difference. Energy, as heat, passes from a warmer body (with a higher temperature) to a colder body (with a lower temperature). At the molecular level, molecules of the warmer body, through collisions, lose kinetic energy to those of the colder body. Thermal energy is transferred— "heat flows"—until the average molecular kinetic energies of the two bodies become the same, until the temperatures become equal. Heat, like work, describes energy in transit between a system and its surroundings.

Not only can heat transfer cause a change in temperature but in some instances, it can change a state of matter. For example, when a solid is heated, the molecules, atoms, or ions of the solid move with greater vigor and eventually break free from their neighbors by overcoming the attractive forces between them. Energy is required to overcome these attractive forces. During the process of melting, the temperature remains constant as a thermal energy transfer (heat) is used to overcome the forces holding the solid together. A process occurring at a constant temperature is said to be *isothermal*. Once a solid has melted completely, any further heat flow will raise the temperature of the resulting liquid.

Although we commonly use expressions like "heat is lost," "heat is gained," "heat flows," and "the system loses heat to the surroundings," you should not take these statements to mean that a system contains heat. It does not. The energy content of a system, as we shall see in Section 7-5, is a quantity called the *internal energy*. Heat is simply a form in which a quantity of energy may be *transferred* across a boundary between a system and its surroundings.

It is reasonable to expect that the quantity of heat, q, required to change the temperature of a substance depends on

* how much the temperature is to be changed
* the quantity of substance
* the nature of the substance (type of atoms or molecules)

Historically, the quantity of heat required to change the temperature of one gram of water by one degree Celsius has been called the **calorie (cal)**. The calorie is a small unit of energy, and the unit *kilocalorie* (kcal) has also been widely used. The SI unit for heat is simply the basic SI energy unit, the joule (J).

$$1 \text{ cal} = 4.184 \text{ J} \tag{7.2}$$

Although the joule is used almost exclusively in this text, the calorie is widely encountered in older scientific literature. In the United States, the kilocalorie is commonly used for measuring the energy content of foods (see page 263).

The quantity of heat required to change the temperature of a system by one degree is called the **heat capacity** of the system. If the system is a mole of substance, the term *molar heat capacity* is applicable. If the system is one gram of substance, the applicable term is *specific heat capacity*, or more commonly, **specific heat** (sp ht).* The specific heats of substances are somewhat temperature dependent. Over the range from 0 to 100 °C, the specific heat of water averages about

$$\frac{4.18 \text{ J}}{\text{g °C}} = 4.18 \text{ J g}^{-1} \text{ °C}^{-1} \tag{7.3}$$

---

*The original meaning of specific heat was that of a *ratio*: the quantity of heat required to change the temperature of a mass of substance divided by the quantity of heat required to produce the same temperature change in the same mass of water—this definition would make specific heat dimensionless. The meaning given here is more commonly used.

In Example 7-1, the objective is to calculate a quantity of heat based on the amount of a substance, the specific heat of that substance, and its temperature change.

EXAMPLE 7-1

Calculating a Quantity of Heat. How much heat is required to raise the temperature of 7.35 g of water from 21.0 to 98.0 °C? (Assume the specific heat of water is 4.18 J g^{-1} °C^{-1} throughout this temperature range.)

Solution

The specific heat is the heat capacity of 1.00 g water:

$$\frac{4.18 \text{ J}}{\text{g water °C}}$$

The heat capacity of the system (7.35 g water) is

$$7.35 \text{ g water} \times \frac{4.18 \text{ J}}{\text{g water °C}} = 30.7 \frac{\text{J}}{\text{°C}}$$

The required temperature change in the system is

$$(98.0 - 21.0) \text{ °C} = 77.0 \text{ °C}$$

The heat required to produce this temperature change is

$$30.7 \frac{\text{J}}{\text{°C}} \times 77.0 \text{ °C} = 2.36 \times 10^3 \text{ J}$$

Practice Example A: How much heat, in kilojoules (kJ), is required to raise the temperature of 237 g of ice water from 4.0 to 37.0 °C (body temperature)?

Practice Example B: How much heat, in kilojoules (kJ), is required to raise the temperature of 2.50 kg Hg(l) from −20.0 to −6.0 °C? Assume a density of 13.6 g/mL and a molar heat capacity of 28.0 J mol^{-1} °C^{-1} for Hg(l).

The line of reasoning used in Example 7-1 can be summarized in equation (7.5), which relates a quantity of heat to the mass of a substance, its specific heat, and the temperature change.

$$\text{quantity of heat} = \underbrace{\text{mass of substance} \times \text{specific heat}}_{\text{heat capacity} = C} \times \text{temperature change} \quad (7.4)$$

$$q = m \times \text{specific heat} \times \Delta T = C \times \Delta T \quad (7.5)$$

◀ The Greek letter delta, Δ, indicates a *change* in some quantity.

In equation (7.5), the temperature change is expressed as $\Delta T = T_f - T_i$, where T_f is the final temperature and T_i is the initial temperature. When the temperature of a system increases ($T_f > T_i$), ΔT is *positive*. A positive q signifies that heat is absorbed or *gained* by the system. When the temperature of a system decreases ($T_f < T_i$), ΔT is *negative*. A negative q signifies that heat is evolved or *lost* by the system.

◀ The symbol $>$ means "greater than," and $<$ means "less than."

Another idea that enters into calculations of quantities of heat is the **law of conservation of energy**: In interactions between a system and its surroundings, the total energy remains *constant*—energy is neither created nor destroyed. Applied to the exchange of heat, this means that

Students frequently have trouble understanding when a quantity of heat (q) should be positive (+) or negative (−).

$$q_{\text{system}} + q_{\text{surroundings}} = 0 \quad (7.6)$$

Thus, heat *gained* by a system is *lost* by its surroundings, and vice versa.

$$q_{\text{system}} = -q_{\text{surroundings}} \quad (7.7)$$

▲ **FIGURE 7-3**
Determining the specific heat of lead—Example 7-2 illustrated
(a) A 150.0-g sample of lead is heated to the temperature of boiling water (100.0 °C).
(b) A 50.0-g sample of water is added to a thermally insulated beaker, and its
temperature is found to be 22.0 °C. **(c)** The hot lead is dumped into the cold water,
and the temperature of the final lead–water mixture is 28.8 °C.

Bindel, T. H. , Fochi,
J. C. "Guided Discovery:
Law of Specific Heats." *J. Chem.
Educ.* **1997:** *74*, 955 (August 1997).

EXPERIMENTAL DETERMINATION OF SPECIFIC HEATS

Let us consider how the law of conservation of energy is used in the experiment outlined in Figure 7-3. The object is to determine the specific heat of lead.
The transfer of energy, as heat, from the lead to the cooler water causes the
temperature of the lead to decrease and that of the water to increase, until
the lead and water are at the same temperature. Either the lead or the water
can be considered the system. If we consider lead to be the system, we can
write $q_{lead} = q_{system}$. Furthermore, if the lead and water are maintained in a
thermally insulated enclosure, we can assume that $q_{water} = q_{surroundings}$. Then,
applying equation (7.7), we have

VCL *Specific Heat of Pb*

$$q_{lead} = -q_{water} \tag{7.8}$$

We complete the calculation in Example 7-2.

EXAMPLE 7-2

Determining a Specific Heat from Experimental Data. Use data presented in
Figure 7-3 to calculate the specific heat of lead.

Solution

First, use equation (7.5) to calculate q_{water}.

$$q_{water} = 50.0 \text{ g water} \times \frac{4.18 \text{ J}}{\text{g water °C}} \times (28.8 - 22.0) \text{ °C} = 1.4 \times 10^3 \text{ J}$$

From equation (7.8) we can write

$$q_{lead} = -q_{water} = -1.4 \times 10^3 \text{ J}$$

Now, from equation (7.5) again, we obtain

$$q_{lead} = 150.0 \text{ g lead} \times \text{specific heat of lead} \times (28.8 - 100.0) \text{ °C}$$
$$= -1.4 \times 10^3 \text{ J}$$

$$\text{specific heat of lead} = \frac{-1.4 \times 10^3 \text{ J}}{150.0 \text{ g lead} \times (28.8 - 100.0) \text{ °C}}$$

$$= \frac{-1.4 \times 10^3 \text{ J}}{150.0 \text{ g lead} \times -71.2 \text{ °C}} = 0.13 \text{ J g}^{-1} \text{ °C}^{-1}$$

Practice Example A: When 1.00 kg lead (specific heat = 0.13 J g^{-1} °C^{-1}) at 100.0 °C is added to a quantity of water at 28.5 °C, the final temperature of the lead–water mixture is 35.2 °C. What is the mass of water present?

Practice Example B: A 100.0-g copper sample (specific heat = 0.385 J g^{-1} °C^{-1}) at 100.0 °C is added to 50.0 g water at 26.5 °C. What is the final temperature of the copper–water mixture?

◀ **KEEP IN MIND**

that if you know any four of the five quantities—q, m, specific heat, T_f, T_i—you can solve equation (7.5) for the remaining one.

CONCEPT ASSESSMENT ✔

With a minimum of calculation, estimate the final temperature reached when 100.0 mL of water at 10.00 °C is added to 200.0 mL of water at 70.00 °C. What basic principle did you use and what assumptions did you make in arriving at this estimate?

SIGNIFICANCE OF SPECIFIC-HEAT VALUES

Table 7.1 lists the specific heats of several solid elements. The relatively high specific heat of aluminum compared with other metals helps to account for its use in "miracle thaw" products designed to thaw frozen foods rapidly. The aluminum cools only slowly as it transfers heat to the frozen food, and the food thaws more quickly than when simply exposed to air.

Because of their greater complexity at the molecular level, compounds generally have more ways of storing internal energy than do the elements; they tend to have higher specific heats. Water, for example, has a specific heat that is more than 30 times greater than that of lead. We need a much larger quantity of heat to change the temperature of a sample of water than of an equal mass of a metal. To return to the food-thawing example, we expect frozen food placed in room-temperature water to thaw much faster than if just exposed to room-temperature air.

An environmental consequence of the high specific heat of water is found in the effect of large lakes on local climates. Because a lake takes much longer to heat up in summer and cool down in winter than other types of terrain, lakeside communities tend to be cooler in summer and warmer in winter than communities more distant from the lake.

TABLE 7.1   Specific Heats of Several Solid Elements, J g^{-1} °C^{-1}

Metals	
Lead	0.128
Copper	0.385
Iron	0.449
Aluminum	0.903
Magnesium	1.024
Nonmetals	
Selenium	0.321
Sulfur	0.706
Phosphorus	0.777
Metalloids	
Tellurium	0.202
Arsenic	0.329

▲ An ice cube thawing on a block of aluminum alloy (miracle thaw).

CONCEPT ASSESSMENT ✔

Two objects of the same mass absorb the same amount of heat when heated in a flame, but the temperature of one object increases more than the temperature of the other. Which object has the greater specific heat?

7-3   HEATS OF REACTION AND CALORIMETRY

In Section 7-1, we introduced the notion of *thermal energy*—kinetic energy associated with random molecular motion. Another type of energy that contributes to the internal energy of a system is **chemical energy**. This is energy associated with chemical bonds and intermolecular attractions. If we think of a chemical reaction as a process in which some chemical bonds are broken and others are formed, then, in general, we expect the chemical energy of a system to change as a result of a reaction. Furthermore, we might expect some of this energy change to appear as heat. A **heat of reaction**, q_{rxn}, is the quantity of heat exchanged between a system and its surroundings when a chemical reaction occurs within the system at *constant temperature*. One of the most common reactions studied is the combustion reaction. This is such a common reaction that we often refer to the *heat of combustion* when describing the heat released by a combustion reaction.

  Point out to students that physical changes can also be classified as endothermic or exothermic.

VCL *Endothermic vs. Exothermic*

✔ Although no perfectly reversible process exists, the melting and freezing of a substance at its transition temperature is an example of a process that is nearly reversible: pump in heat (melts), take out heat (freezes).

(a)

(b)

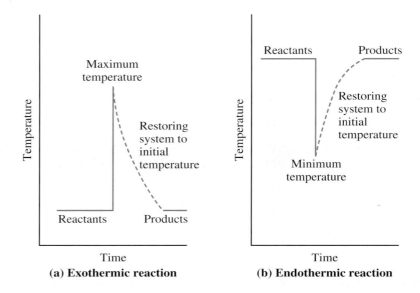

(a) Exothermic reaction   **(b) Endothermic reaction**

▲ **Exothermic and
endothermic reactions
(a)** An exothermic reaction.
Slaked lime, $Ca(OH)_2$, is
produced by the action of
water on quicklime, (CaO).
The reactants are mixed at
room temperature, but the
temperature of the mixture
rises to 40.5 °C.

$$CaO(s) + H_2O(l) \longrightarrow$$
$$Ca(OH)_2(s)$$

(b) An endothermic reaction.
$Ba(OH)_2 \cdot 8\,H_2O(s)$ and
$NH_4Cl(s)$ are mixed at
room temperature, and the
temperature falls to 5.8 °C
in the reaction.

$$Ba(OH)_2 \cdot 8\,H_2O(s) +$$
$$2\,NH_4Cl(s) \longrightarrow$$
$$BaCl_2 \cdot 2H_2O(s) +$$
$$2\,NH_3(aq) + 8\,H_2O(l)$$

▲ **FIGURE 7-4**
Conceptualizing a heat of reaction at constant temperature
The solid lines indicate the initial temperature and the **(a)** maximum and
(b) minimum temperature reached in an isolated system, in an exothermic and an
endothermic reaction, respectively. The broken lines represent pathways to restoring
the system to the initial temperature. The heat of reaction is the heat lost or gained
by the system in this restoration.

If a reaction occurs in an *isolated* system, that is, one that exchanges no
matter or energy with its surroundings, the reaction produces a change in
the thermal energy of the system—the temperature either increases or decreases. Imagine that the previously isolated system is allowed to interact
with its surroundings. The heat of reaction is the quantity of heat exchanged between the system and its surroundings as the system is restored
to its initial temperature (Fig. 7-4). In actual practice, we do not physically
restore the system to its initial temperature. Instead, we calculate the quantity of heat that *would be* exchanged in this restoration. To do this, a probe
(thermometer) is placed within the system to record the temperature
change produced by the reaction. Then, we use the temperature change and
other system data to calculate the heat of reaction that would have occurred
at constant temperature.

Two widely used terms related to heats of reaction are exothermic and
endothermic reactions. An **exothermic reaction** is one that produces a temperature increase in an isolated system or, in a nonisolated system, gives off
heat to the surroundings. For an exothermic reaction, the heat of reaction is a
negative quantity ($q_{rxn} < 0$). In an **endothermic reaction**, the corresponding
situation is a temperature decrease in an isolated system or a gain of heat
from the surroundings by a nonisolated system. In this case, the heat of reaction is a positive quantity ($q_{rxn} > 0$). Heats of reaction are experimentally
determined in a **calorimeter**, a device for measuring quantities of heat. We
will consider two types of calorimeters in this section, and we will treat both
of them as *isolated* systems.

BOMB CALORIMETRY

Figure 7-5 shows a **bomb calorimeter**, which is ideally suited for measuring the
heat evolved in a combustion reaction. The system is everything within the
double-walled outer jacket of the calorimeter. This includes the bomb and its
contents, the water in which the bomb is immersed, the thermometer, the stirrer,
and so on. The system is *isolated* from its surroundings. When the combustion

Thermometer
Wire for ignition
Stirrer
Water
Reactants
Steel bomb

◀ **FIGURE 7-5**
A bomb calorimeter assembly
An iron wire is embedded in the sample in the lower half of the bomb. The bomb is assembled and filled with $O_2(g)$ at high pressure. The assembled bomb is immersed in water in the calorimeter, and the initial temperature is measured. A short pulse of electric current heats the sample, causing it to ignite. The final temperature of the calorimeter assembly is determined after the combustion. Because the bomb confines the reaction mixture to a fixed volume, the reaction is said to occur at *constant volume*. The significance of this fact is discussed on page 242.

Bomb Calorimetry simulation

reaction occurs, chemical energy is converted to thermal energy, and the temperature of the system rises. The heat of reaction, as described earlier, is the quantity of heat that the system would have to *lose* to its surroundings to be restored to its initial temperature. This quantity of heat, in turn, is just the *negative* of the thermal energy gained by the calorimeter and its contents ($q_{calorim}$).

$$q_{rxn} = -q_{calorim} \text{ (where } q_{calorim} = q_{bomb} + q_{water} \cdots \text{)} \qquad (7.9)$$

If the calorimeter is assembled in exactly the same way each time we use it—that is, use the same bomb, the same quantity of water, and so on—we can define a *heat capacity of the calorimeter*. This is the quantity of heat required to raise the temperature of the calorimeter assembly by one degree Celsius. When this heat capacity is multiplied by the observed temperature change, we get $q_{calorim}$.

$$q_{calorim} = \text{heat capacity of calorim} \times \Delta T \qquad (7.10)$$

And from $q_{calorim}$, we then establish q_{rxn}, as in Example 7-3, where we determine the heat of combustion of sucrose (table sugar).

Vollmer, John J. 'Out of "Thin Air": Exploring Phase Changes.' *J. Chem. Educ.* **2000:** *77,* 488A (April 2000).

◀ **KEEP IN MIND**
that the temperature of a reaction mixture usually changes during a reaction, so the mixture must be returned to the initial temperature (actually or hypothetically) before we assess how much heat is exchanged with the surroundings.

EXAMPLE 7-3

Using Bomb Calorimetry Data to Determine a Heat of Reaction. The combustion of 1.010 g sucrose, $C_{12}H_{22}O_{11}$, in a bomb calorimeter causes the temperature to rise from 24.92 to 28.33 °C. The heat capacity of the calorimeter assembly is 4.90 kJ/°C. **(a)** What is the heat of combustion of sucrose expressed in kilojoules per mole of $C_{12}H_{22}O_{11}$? **(b)** Verify the claim of sugar producers that one teaspoon of sugar (about 4.8 g) contains only 19 Calories.

Solution

(a) Calculate $q_{calorim}$ with equation (7.10).

$$q_{calorim} = 4.90 \text{ kJ/°C} \times (28.33 - 24.92) \text{ °C} = (4.90 \times 3.41) \text{ kJ} = 16.7 \text{ kJ}$$

Now, using equation (7.9), we get

$$q_{rxn} = -q_{calorim} = -16.7 \text{ kJ}$$

This is the heat of combustion of the 1.010-g sample.
Per gram $C_{12}H_{22}O_{11}$:

$$q_{rxn} = \frac{-16.7 \text{ kJ}}{1.010 \text{ g } C_{12}H_{22}O_{11}} = -16.5 \text{ kJ/g } C_{12}H_{22}O_{11}$$

Per mole $C_{12}H_{22}O_{11}$:

$$q_{rxn} = \frac{-16.5 \text{ kJ}}{\text{g } C_{12}H_{22}O_{11}} \times \frac{342.3 \text{ g } C_{12}H_{22}O_{11}}{1 \text{ mol } C_{12}H_{22}O_{11}}$$

$$= -5.65 \times 10^3 \text{ kJ/mol } C_{12}H_{22}O_{11}$$

 Heat of Combustion: Sugar

Scott, Earle S. "A spontaneous exothermic reaction between two solids: A safe demonstration (TD)." *J. Chem. Educ.* **1992:** *69,* 1028.

Kauffman, G. B., Ferguson, C. A. "The endothermic dissolution of ammonium nitrate (TD)." *J. Chem. Educ.* **1988:** *65,* 267.

Marzzacco, Charles J. "The Enthalpy of Decomposition of Hydrogen Peroxide: A General Chemistry Calorimetry Experiment." *J. Chem. Educ.* **1999:** *76,* 1517 (November 1999).

(b) To determine the caloric content of sucrose, we can use the heat of combustion per gram of sucrose determined in part **(a)**, together with a factor to convert from kilojoules to kilocalories. (Because 1 cal = 4.184 J, 1 kcal = 4.184 kJ.)

$$? \text{ kcal} = \frac{4.8 \text{ g C}_{12}\text{H}_{22}\text{O}_{11}}{\text{tsp}} \times \frac{-16.5 \text{ kJ}}{\text{g C}_{12}\text{H}_{22}\text{O}_{11}} \times \frac{1 \text{ kcal}}{4.184 \text{ kJ}} = \frac{-19 \text{ kcal}}{\text{tsp}}$$

1 food Calorie (1 Calorie with a capital C) is actually 1000 cal, or 1 kcal. Therefore, 19 kcal = 19 Calories. The claim is justified.

Practice Example A: Vanillin is a natural constituent of vanilla. It is also manufactured for use in artificial vanilla flavoring. The combustion of 1.013 g of vanillin, $C_8H_8O_3$, in the same bomb calorimeter as in Example 7-3 causes the temperature to rise from 24.89 to 30.09 °C. What is the heat of combustion of vanillin, expressed in kilojoules per mole?

Practice Example B: The heat of combustion of benzoic acid is -26.42 kJ/g. The combustion of a 1.176-g sample of benzoic acid causes a temperature *increase* of 4.96 °C in a bomb calorimeter assembly. What is the heat capacity of the assembly?

▶ The heat capacity of a bomb calorimeter must be determined by experiment.

▲ FIGURE 7-6
A Styrofoam "coffee-cup" calorimeter
The reaction mixture is in the inner cup. The outer cup provides additional thermal insulation from the surrounding air. The cup is closed off with a cork stopper through which a thermometer and a stirrer are inserted and immersed into the reaction mixture. The reaction in the calorimeter occurs under the *constant pressure* of the atmosphere. We consider the difference between constant-volume and constant-pressure reactions in Section 7-6.

VCL *Heat of Reaction: NaOH(aq) + HCl(aq)*

THE "COFFEE-CUP" CALORIMETER

In the general chemistry laboratory you are much more likely to run into the simple calorimeter pictured in Figure 7-6 than a bomb calorimeter. We mix the reactants (generally in aqueous solution) in a Styrofoam cup and measure the temperature change. Styrofoam is a good heat insulator, so there is very little heat transfer between the cup and the surrounding air. We treat the system—the cup and its contents—as an *isolated* system.

As with the bomb calorimeter, the heat of reaction is defined as the quantity of heat that would be exchanged with the surroundings in restoring the calorimeter to its initial temperature. But, again, the calorimeter is not physically restored to its initial conditions. We simply take the heat of reaction to be the *negative* of the quantity of heat producing the temperature change in the calorimeter. That is, we use equation (7.9): $q_{\text{rxn}} = -q_{\text{calorim}}$.

In Example 7-4, we make certain assumptions to simplify the calculation, but for more precise measurements, these assumptions would not be made (see Exercise 23).

EXAMPLE 7-4

Determining a Heat of Reaction from Calorimetric Data. In the neutralization of a strong acid with a strong base, the essential reaction is the combination of $H^+(aq)$ and $OH^-(aq)$ to form water (recall page 153).

$$H^+(aq) + OH^-(aq) \longrightarrow H_2O(l)$$

Two solutions, 25.00 mL of 2.50 M HCl(aq) and 25.00 mL of 2.50 M NaOH(aq), both initially at 21.1 °C, are added to a Styrofoam-cup calorimeter and allowed to react. The temperature rises to 37.8 °C. Determine the heat of the neutralization reaction, expressed per mole of H_2O formed. Is the reaction endothermic or exothermic?

In addition to assuming that the calorimeter is an isolated system, assume that all there is in the system to absorb heat is 50.00 mL of water. This assumption ignores the fact that 0.0625 mol each of NaCl and H_2O are formed in the reaction, that the density of the resulting NaCl(aq) is not exactly 1.00 g/mL, and that its specific heat is not exactly $4.18 \text{ J g}^{-1} \text{ °C}^{-1}$. Also, ignore the small heat capacity of the Styrofoam cup itself.

Solution

Because the reaction is a neutralization reaction, let us call the heat of reaction q_{neutr}. Now, according to equation (7.9), $q_{\text{neutr}} = -q_{\text{calorim}}$, and if we make the assumptions described above,

$$q_{\text{calorim}} = 50.00 \text{ mL} \times \frac{1.00 \text{ g}}{\text{mL}} \times \frac{4.18 \text{ J}}{\text{g °C}} \times (37.8 - 21.1) \text{ °C} = 3.5 \times 10^3 \text{ J}$$

$$q_{\text{neutr}} = -q_{\text{calorim}} = -3.5 \times 10^3 \text{ J} = -3.5 \text{ kJ}$$

In 25.00 mL of 2.50 M HCl, the amount of H^+ is

$$? \text{ mol } H^+ = 25.00 \text{ mL} \times \frac{1 \text{ L}}{1000 \text{ mL}} \times \frac{2.50 \text{ mol}}{1 \text{ L}} \times \frac{1 \text{ mol } H^+}{1 \text{ mol HCl}} = 0.0625 \text{ mol } H^+$$

Similarly, in 25.00 mL of 2.50 M NaOH there is 0.0625 mol OH^-. Thus, the H^+ and the OH^- combine to form 0.0625 mol H_2O. (The two are in *stoichiometric* proportions; neither is in excess.)

The amount of heat produced per mole of H_2O is

$$q_{neutr} = \frac{-3.5 \text{ kJ}}{0.0625 \text{ mol } H_2O} = -56 \text{ kJ/mol } H_2O$$

Because q_{neutr} is a *negative* quantity, the neutralization reaction is *exothermic*.

Practice Example A: Two solutions, 100.0 mL of 1.00 M $AgNO_3$(aq) and 100.0 mL of 1.00 M NaCl(aq), both initially at 22.4 °C, are added to a Styrofoam-cup calorimeter and allowed to react. The temperature rises to 30.2 °C. Determine q_{rxn} per mole of AgCl(s) in the reaction.

$$Ag^+(aq) + Cl^-(aq) \longrightarrow AgCl(s)$$

Practice Example B: Two solutions, 100.0 mL of 1.020 M HCl and 50.0 mL of 1.988 M NaOH, both initially at 24.52 °C, are mixed in a Styrofoam-cup calorimeter. What will be the final temperature of the mixture? Make the same assumptions, and use the heat of neutralization established in Example 7-4.

[*Hint:* Which is the limiting reactant?]

7-4   WORK

We have just learned that heat effects generally accompany chemical reactions. In some reactions, work is also involved—that is, the system may do work on its surroundings or vice versa. Consider the decomposition of potassium chlorate to potassium chloride and oxygen. Suppose that this decomposition is carried out in the strange vessel pictured in Figure 7-7. The walls of the container resist moving under the pressure of the expanding O_2(g) except for the piston that closes off the cylindrical top of the vessel. The pressure of the O_2(g) exceeds the atmospheric pressure and the piston is lifted—the system does work on the surroundings. Can you see that even if the piston were removed, work still would be done as the expanding O_2(g) pushed aside other atmospheric gases? Work involved in the expansion or compression of gases is called **pressure–volume work**. Pressure–volume, or *P–V*, work is the type of work performed by explosives and by the gases formed in the combustion of gasoline in an automobile engine.

Koubek, E. "PV work demonstration (TD)."
J. Chem. Educ. **1980:** *57*, 374.

Figure 7-7 shows chemical energy being converted to work. It is a small step to relate this to the work performed by burning gasoline in cylinders.

P_{atm}

P_{atm}

O_2

KClO₃   KCl

◄ **FIGURE 7-7**
Illustrating work (expansion) during the chemical reaction
2 KClO₃(s) ⟶ 2 KCl(s) + 3 O₂(g)
The oxygen gas that is formed pushes back the weight and, in doing so, does work on the surroundings.

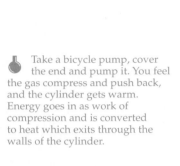

Take a bicycle pump, cover the end and pump it. You feel the gas compress and push back, and the cylinder gets warm. Energy goes in as work of compression and is converted to heat which exits through the walls of the cylinder.

Gasparro, Francis P. "Remembering the sign conventions for q and w in $\Delta U = q - p$." *J. Chem. Educ.* **1976**: 53, 389.

Levine, Ira N. "Thermodynamic internal energy of an ideal gas of rigid rotors." *J. Chem. Educ.* **1985**: 62, 53.

▲ **FIGURE 7-8**
Pressure–volume work
(a) In this hypothetical apparatus, a gas is confined by a massless piston of area A. A massless wire is attached to the piston and the gas is held back by two weights with a combined mass of $2M$ resting on the massless pan. The cylinder is immersed in a large water bath in order to keep the gas temperature constant. The initial state of the gas is $P_i = 2\,Mg/A$ with a volume V_i at temperature, T. **(b)** When the external pressure on the confined gas is suddenly lowered by removing one of the weights the gas expands, pushing the piston up by the distance, Δh. The increase in volume of the gas (ΔV) is the product of the cross-sectional area of the cylinder (A) and the distance (Δh). The final state of the gas is $P_f = Mg/A$, V_f, and T.

Now let us switch to a somewhat simpler situation to see how to calculate a quantity of P–V work.

In the hypothetical apparatus pictured in Figure 7-8(a), attached to a weightless piston is a weightless wire support, to which is attached a weightless pan. On the pan are two identical weights just sufficient to restrain the gas from expanding. The gas is confined by the cylinder walls and piston, and the space above the piston is a vacuum. The cylinder is contained in a constant-temperature water bath, which keeps the temperature of the gas constant. Now imagine that one of the two weights is removed, leaving half the original mass on the pan. Let us call this remaining mass M. The gas will expand and the remaining weight will move against gravity, the situation represented by Figure 7-8(b). After the expansion, we find that the piston has risen through a vertical distance, Δh; that the volume of gas has doubled; and that the pressure of the gas has decreased.

Now let us see how pressure and volume enter into calculating how much *pressure–volume* work the expanding gas does. First we can calculate the work done by the gas in moving the weight of mass M through a displacement Δh. Recall from equation (7.1) that the work can be calculated by

$$\text{work } (w) = \text{force } (M \times g) \times \text{distance } (\Delta h) = -M \times g \times \Delta h$$

The magnitude of the force exerted by the weight is $M \times g$, where g is the acceleration due to gravity. The negative sign appears because the force is acting in a direction opposite to the piston's direction of motion.

Now recall equation (6.1)—pressure = force ($M \times g$)/area (A)—so that if the expression for work is multiplied by A/A we get

$$w = -\frac{M \times g}{A} \times \Delta h \times A = -P_{ext}\Delta V \qquad (7.11)$$

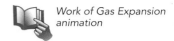

Work of Gas Expansion animation

The "pressure" part of the pressure–volume work is seen to be the external pressure (P_{ext}) on the gas, which in our thought experiment is due to the weight pulling down on the piston and is given by (Mg/A). Note that the product of the area (A) and height (Δh) is equal to a volume—the volume change, ΔV, produced by the expansion.

Two significant features to note in equation (7.11) are the *negative* sign and the term P_{ext}. The negative sign is necessary to conform to sign conventions that we will introduce in the next section. When a gas expands, ΔV is positive and w is negative, signifying that energy leaves the system as work. When a gas is compressed, ΔV is negative and w is positive, signifying that energy (as work) enters the system. The term P_{ext} is the *external* pressure—the pressure against which a system expands or the applied pressure that compresses a system. In many instances the internal pressure in a system will be essentially equal to the external pressure, in which case the pressure in equation (7.11) is expressed simply as P.

If pressure is stated in atmospheres and volume in liters, the unit of work is the liter-atmosphere, L atm; while the SI unit of work is the joule. The conversion factor between these two units of work can be obtained from the gas constant, R.

$8.3145 \text{ m}^3 \text{ Pa mol}^{-1} \text{ K}^{-1} = 8.3145 \text{ m}^3 \text{ N m}^{-2} \text{ mol}^{-1} \text{ K}^{-1} = 8.3145 \text{ kg m}^2 \text{ s}^{-2} \text{ mol}^{-1} \text{ K}^{-1}$

$8.3145 \text{ J mol}^{-1} \text{ K}^{-1} = 0.082057 \text{ L atm mol}^{-1} \text{ K}^{-1}$

and

$$\frac{8.3145 \text{ J}}{0.082057 \text{ L atm}} = 101.33 \frac{\text{J}}{\text{L atm}}$$

Work is negative when energy is transferred out of the system and is positive when energy is transferred into the system. Remind students that this is consistent with the signs associated with the heat of a reaction (q) during endothermic and exothermic processes.

EXAMPLE 7-5

Calculating Pressure–Volume Work. Suppose the gas in Figure 7-8 is 0.100 mol He at 298 K and that the two weights correspond to an external pressure of 2.40 atm in Figure 7-8(a) and the single weight in Figure 7-8(b) corresponds to an external pressure of 1.20 atm. How much work, in joules, is associated with the gas expansion at constant temperature?

Solution
We are given enough data to calculate the initial and final gas volumes (note that the identity of the gas does not enter into the calculations because we are assuming ideal gas behavior). With these volumes, we can obtain ΔV. The external pressure term in the pressure–volume work is the *final* pressure—1.20 atm. The product $-P_{ext} \times \Delta V$ must be multiplied by a factor to convert work in liter-atmospheres to work in joules.

$$V_{initial} = \frac{nRT}{P_i} = \frac{0.100 \text{ mol} \times 0.0821 \text{ L atm mol}^{-1} \text{ K}^{-1} \times 298 \text{ K}}{2.40 \text{ atm}} = 1.02 \text{ L}$$

$$V_{final} = \frac{nRT}{P_f} = \frac{0.100 \text{ mol} \times 0.0821 \text{ L atm mol}^{-1} \text{ K}^{-1} \times 298 \text{ K}}{1.20 \text{ atm}} = 2.04 \text{ L}$$

$$\Delta V = V_f - V_i = 2.04 \text{ L} - 1.02 \text{ L} = 1.02 \text{ L}$$

$$w = -P_{ext} \times \Delta V = -1.20 \text{ atm} \times 1.02 \text{ L} \times \frac{101 \text{ J}}{1 \text{ L atm}} = -1.24 \times 10^2 \text{ J}$$

The negative value signifies that the expanding gas does work on its surroundings.

◄ **KEEP IN MIND**
that the ideal gas equation embodies Boyle's law: The volume of a fixed amount of gas at a fixed temperature is inversely proportional to the pressure. Thus, in Example 7-5 we could simply write that

$$V_f = 1.02 \text{ L} \times \frac{2.40 \text{ atm}}{1.20 \text{ atm}}$$

$$V_f = 2.04 \text{ L}$$

Practice Example A: How much work, in joules, is involved when 0.225 mol N_2 at a constant temperature of 23 °C is allowed to expand by 1.50 L in volume against an external pressure of 0.750 atm?

[*Hint:* How much of this information is required?]

Practice Example B: How much work is done, in joules, when an external pressure of 2.50 atm is applied, at a constant temperature of 20.0 °C, to 50.0 g $N_2(g)$ in a 75.0-L cylinder? The cylinder is like that shown in Figure 7-8.

7-5 THE FIRST LAW OF THERMODYNAMICS

The absorption or evolution of heat and the performance of work require changes in the energy of a system and its surroundings. When considering the energy of a system, we use the concept of internal energy and how heat and work are related to it.

Internal energy, U, is the total energy (both kinetic and potential) in a system, including *translational kinetic energy* of molecules, the energy associated with molecular rotations and vibrations, the energy stored in chemical bonds and intermolecular attractions, and the energy associated with electrons in atoms. Some of these forms of internal energy are illustrated in Figure 7-9. Internal energy also includes energy associated with the interactions of protons and neutrons in atomic nuclei, although this component is unchanged in chemical reactions. A system contains *only* internal energy. A system does not contain energy in the form of heat or work. Heat and work are the means by which a system exchanges energy with its surroundings. *Heat and work exist only during a change in the system.* The relationship between heat (q), work (w), and changes in internal energy (ΔU) is dictated by the law of conservation of energy, expressed in the form known as the **first law of thermodynamics**.

$$\Delta U = q + w \qquad (7.12)$$

An isolated system is unable to exchange either heat or work with its surroundings, so that $\Delta U_{\text{isolated system}} = 0$, and we can say

> The energy of an isolated system is constant.

In using equation (7.12) we must keep these important points in mind.

- Any energy *entering* the system carries a *positive* sign. Thus, if heat is *absorbed* by the system, $q > 0$. If work is done *on* the system, $w > 0$.
- Any energy *leaving* the system carries a *negative* sign. Thus, if heat is *given off* by the system, $q < 0$. If work is done *by* the system, $w < 0$.
- In general, the internal energy of a system changes as a result of energy entering or leaving the system as heat and/or work. If, on balance, more energy enters the system than leaves, ΔU is *positive*. If more energy leaves than enters, ΔU is *negative*.
- A consequence of $\Delta U_{\text{isolated system}} = 0$ is that $\Delta U_{\text{system}} = -\Delta U_{\text{surroundings}}$; that is, energy is conserved.

These ideas are summarized in Figure 7-10 and illustrated in Example 7-6.

Translational

Rotational

Vibrational

$\delta-$
$\delta+$ $\delta+$
$\delta-$ $\delta-$

Electrostatic
(Intermolecular attractions)

▲ **FIGURE 7-9**
Some contributions to the internal energy of a system
The models represent water molecules, and the arrows represent the types of motion they can undergo. In the intermolecular attractions between water molecules, the symbols $\delta+$ and $\delta-$ signify a separation of charge, producing centers of positive and negative charge that are smaller than ionic charges. These intermolecular attractions are discussed in Chapter 12.

Hamby, Marcy.
"Understanding the language: Problem solving and the first law of thermodynamics."
J. Chem. Educ. **1990**: 67, 923.

▶ **FIGURE 7-10**
Illustration of sign conventions used in thermodynamics
Arrows represent the direction of heat flow (⟶) and work (⟶). In the left diagram, the minus (−) signs signify energy leaving the system and entering the surroundings. In the right diagram the plus (+) signs refer to energy entering the system from the surroundings These sign conventions are consistent with the expression $\Delta U = q + w$.

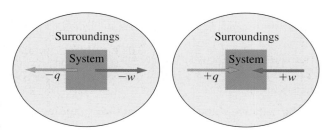

EXAMPLE 7-6

Relating ΔU, q, and w Through the First Law of Thermodynamics. A gas, while expanding (recall Figure 7-8), absorbs 25 J of heat and does 243 J of work. What is ΔU for the gas?

Solution

The key to problems of this type lies in assigning the correct signs to the quantities of heat and work. Because heat is absorbed by (enters) the system, q is *positive*. Because work done *by* the system represents energy *leaving* the system, w is *negative*. You may find it useful to represent the values of q and w, with their correct signs, within parentheses. Then complete the algebra.

$$\Delta U = q + w = (+25\text{ J}) + (-243\text{ J}) = 25\text{ J} - 243\text{ J} = -218\text{ J}$$

Practice Example A: In compressing a gas, 355 J of work is done on the system. At the same time, 185 J of heat escapes from the system. What is ΔU for the system?

Practice Example B: If the internal energy of a system *decreases* by 125 J at the same time that the system *absorbs* 54 J of heat, does the system do work or have work done on it? How much?

> This article describes the use of a handmade device to illustrate the concepts of heat, work and energy transfer: Mills, P., Sweeney, W. V., Waldemar, C. *J. Chem. Educ.* **2001:** *78,* 1360.

CONCEPT ASSESSMENT ✓

When water is injected into a balloon filled with ammonia gas, the balloon shrinks and feels warm. What are the sources of heat and work, and what are the signs of q and w in this process?

FUNCTIONS OF STATE

To describe a system completely, we must indicate its temperature, pressure, and the kinds and amounts of substances present. When we have done this, we have specified the *state* of the system. Any property that has a unique value for a specified state of a system is said to be a **function of state**, or a **state function**. For example, a sample of pure water at 20 °C (293.15 K) and under one standard atmosphere of pressure is in a specified state. The density of water in this state is 0.99820 g/mL. We can establish that this density is a unique value—a function of state—in the following way: Obtain three different samples of water—one purified by extensive distillation of groundwater; one synthesized by burning pure $H_2(g)$ in pure $O_2(g)$; and one prepared by driving off the water of hydration from $CuSO_4 \cdot 5\,H_2O$ and condensing the gaseous water to a liquid. The densities of the three different samples for the state that we specified will all be the same—0.99820 g/mL. Thus, the value of a function of state depends on the state of the system, and not on how that state was established.

The internal energy of a system is a function of state, although there is no simple measurement or calculation that we can use to establish its value. That is, we cannot write down a value of U for a system in the same way that we can write $d = 0.99820$ g/mL for the density of water at 20 °C. Fortunately, we don't need to know actual values of U. Consider, for example, heating 10.0 g of ice at 0 °C to a final temperature of 50 °C. The internal energy of the ice at 0 °C has one unique value, U_1, while that of the liquid water at 50 °C has another, U_2. The *difference* in internal energy between these two states also has a unique value, $\Delta U = U_2 - U_1$, and this difference *is* something that we can precisely measure. It is the quantity of energy (as heat) that must be transferred from the surroundings to the system during the change from state 1 to state 2. As a further illustration, consider the scheme outlined here and illustrated by the diagram on page 240. Imagine that a system changes from state 1 to state 2 and then back to state 1.

State and Path Function activity

> Yi, L., Sheng-Lu, K., Song-Sheng, Qu. "Some Views in the Internal Energy and Enthalpy of Gases." *J. Chem. Educ.* **1995:** *72,* 408.

$$\text{State 1 }(U_1) \xrightarrow{\ \Delta U\ } \text{State 2 }(U_2) \xrightarrow{\ -\Delta U\ } \text{State 1 }(U_1)$$

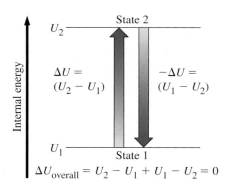

$$\Delta U_{overall} = U_2 - U_1 + U_1 - U_2 = 0$$

Because U has a unique value in each state, ΔU also has a unique value; it is $U_2 - U_1$. The change in internal energy when the system is returned from state 2 to state 1 is $-\Delta U = U_1 - U_2$. Thus, the *overall* change in internal energy is

$$\Delta U + (-\Delta U) = (U_2 - U_1) + (U_1 - U_2) = 0$$

This means that the internal energy returns to its initial value of U_1, which it must do, since it is a function of state. It is important to note here that when we reverse the direction of change, we change the sign of ΔU.

PATH-DEPENDENT FUNCTIONS

Unlike internal energy and changes in internal energy, heat (q) and work (w) are *not* functions of state. Their values depend on the path followed when a system undergoes a change. We can see why this is so by considering again the process described by Figure 7-8 and Example 7-5. Think of the 0.100 mol of He at 298 K and under a pressure of 2.40 atm as *state 1*, and under a pressure of 1.20 atm as *state 2*. The change from state 1 to state 2 occurred in a single step. Suppose that in another instance, we allowed the expansion to occur through an intermediate stage pictured in Figure 7-11. That is, suppose the external pressure on the gas was first reduced from 2.40 atm to 1.80 atm (at which point, the gas volume would be 1.36 L). Then, in a second stage, reduced from 1.80 atm to 1.20 atm, thereby arriving at state 2.

▶ **FIGURE 7-11**
A two-step expansion for the gas shown in Figure 7-8
In the initial state there are four weights of mass $M/2$ holding the gas back. In the intermediate state one of these weights has been removed and in the final state a second weight of mass $M/2$ has been removed. The initial and final states in this figure are the same as in Figure 7-8. This two-step expansion helps us to establish that the work of expansion depends on the path taken.

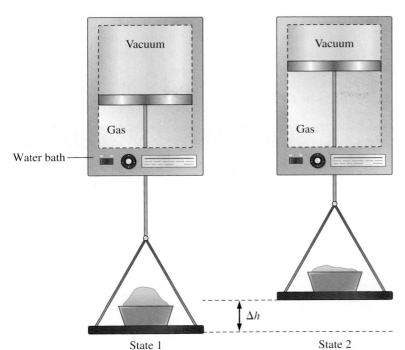

◀ **FIGURE 7-12**
A different method of achieving the expansion of a gas
In this expansion process, the weights in Figures 7-8 and 7-11 have been replaced by a pan containing sand, which has a mass of $2M$, equivalent to that of the weights in the initial state. In the final state the mass of the sand has been reduced to M.

We calculated the amount of work done by the gas in a single-stage expansion in Example 7-5; it was $w = -1.24 \times 10^2$ J. The amount of work done in the two-stage process is the sum of two terms: the pressure–volume work for each stage of the expansion.

$$w = -1.80 \text{ atm} \times (1.36 \text{ L} - 1.02 \text{ L}) - 1.20 \text{ atm} \times (2.04 \text{ L} - 1.36 \text{ L})$$

$$= -0.61 \text{ L atm} - 0.82 \text{ L atm}$$

$$= -1.43 \text{ L atm} \times \frac{101 \text{ J}}{1 \text{ L atm}} = -1.44 \times 10^2 \text{ J}$$

The value of ΔU is the same for the single- and two-stage expansion processes because internal energy is a function of state. However, we see that slightly more work is done in the two-stage expansion. Work is not a function of state; it is path dependent. In the next section, we will stress that heat is also path dependent.

Now consider a different way to carry out the expansion from state 1 to state 2 (see Figure 7-12). The weights in Figures 7-8 and 7-11 have now been replaced by an equivalent amount of sand so that the gas is in state 1. Imagine sand is removed very slowly from this pile—say, one grain at a time. When exactly half the sand has been removed, the gas will have reached state 2. This very slow expansion proceeds in a nearly reversible fashion. A **reversible process** is one that can be made to reverse its direction when an infinitesimal change is made in a system variable. For example, adding a grain of sand rather than removing one would reverse the expansion we are describing. However, the process is not quite reversible because grains of sand have more than an infinitesimal mass. In this approximately reversible process we have made a very large number of intermediate expansions. This process provides more work than when the gas expands directly from state 1 to state 2.

The important difference between the expansion in a finite number of steps and the reversible expansion is that the gas in the reversible process is always in equilibrium with its surroundings whereas in a stepwise process this is never the case. The stepwise processes are said to be **irreversible** because the system is not in equilibrium with the surroundings, and the process cannot be reversed by an infinitesimal change in a system variable.

◀ **KEEP IN MIND**
that if w differs in the two expansion processes, q must also differ, and in such a way that $q + w = \Delta U$ has a unique value, as required by the first law of thermodynamics.

In comparing the quantity of work done in the two different expansions (Figs. 7-8 and 7-11), we found them to be different, thereby proving that work is not a state function. Additionally, the quantity of work performed is greater in the two-step expansion (Fig. 7-11) than in the single-step expansion (Fig. 7-8). We leave it to the interested student to demonstrate, through Problem 108, that the maximum possible work is that done in a reversible expansion (Fig. 7-12).

CONCEPT ASSESSMENT ✓

A sample can be heated very slowly or very rapidly. The darker shading in the illustration indicates a higher temperature. Which of the two sets of diagrams do you think corresponds to reversible heating and which to spontaneous, or irreversible, heating?

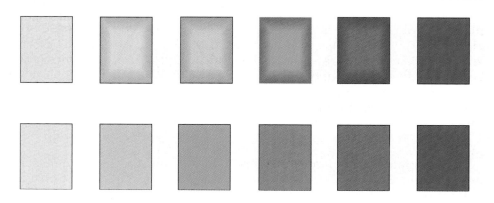

7-6 HEATS OF REACTION: ΔU AND ΔH

Think of the reactants in a chemical reaction as the initial state of a system and the products as the final state.

$$\text{reactants} \longrightarrow \text{products}$$
$$\text{(initial state)} \qquad \text{(final state)}$$
$$U_i \qquad\qquad U_f$$
$$\Delta U = U_f - U_i$$

According to the first law of thermodynamics, we can also say that $\Delta U = q + w$. We have previously identified a heat of reaction as q_{rxn}, and so we can write

$$\Delta U = q_{rxn} + w$$

Now consider again a combustion reaction carried out in a bomb calorimeter (see Figure 7-5). The original reactants and products are confined within the bomb, and we say that the reaction occurs at *constant volume*. Because the volume is constant, $\Delta V = 0$, and no work is done. That is, $w = -P\Delta V = 0$. Denoting the heat of reaction for a constant-volume reaction as q_V, we see that $\Delta U = q_V$.

$$\Delta U = q_{rxn} + w = q_{rxn} + 0 = q_{rxn} = q_V \qquad (7.13)$$

The heat of reaction measured in a bomb calorimeter is equal to ΔU.

Chemical reactions are not ordinarily carried out in bomb calorimeters. The metabolism of sucrose occurs under the conditions present in the human body. The combustion of methane (natural gas) in a water heater occurs in an open flame. This question then arises: How does the heat of a reaction measured in a bomb calorimeter compare with the heat of reaction if the reaction is carried out in some other way? The usual other way is in beakers, flasks, and other containers open to the atmosphere and under the *constant pressure* of the atmosphere. We live in a world of constant pressure! The neutralization reaction of Example 7-4 is typical of this more common method of conducting chemical reactions.

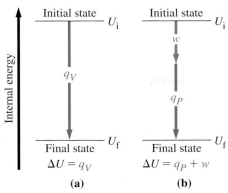

◀ **FIGURE 7-13**
Two different paths leading to the same internal energy change in a system
In path **(a)**, the volume of the system remains constant and no internal energy is converted into work—think of burning gasoline in a bomb calorimeter. In path **(b)**, the system does work, so some of the internal energy change is used to do work—think of burning gasoline in an automobile engine to produce heat and work.

In many reactions carried out at constant pressure, a small amount of pressure–volume work is done as the system expands or contracts (recall Figure 7-7). In these cases, the heat of reaction, q_P, is different from q_V. We know that the change in internal energy (ΔU) for a reaction carried out between a given initial and a given final state has a unique value. Furthermore, for a reaction at constant volume, $\Delta U = q_V$. From Figure 7-13 and the first law of thermodynamics, we see that for the same reaction at constant pressure $\Delta U = q_P + w$, which means $\Delta U = q_V = q_P + w$. Thus, unless $w = 0$, q_V and q_P must be different. The fact that q_V and q_P for a reaction may differ, even though ΔU has the same value, underscores that U is a function of state and q and w are not.

The relationship between q_V and q_P can be used to devise another state function that represents the heat flow for a process at constant pressure. To do this, we begin by writing

$$q_V = q_P + w$$

Now, using $\Delta U = q_V$, $w = -P\Delta V$ and rearranging terms, we obtain

$$\Delta U = q_P - P\Delta V$$
$$q_P = \Delta U + P\Delta V$$

The quantities U, P, and V are all state functions, so it should be possible to derive the expression $\Delta U + P\Delta V$ from yet another state function. This state function, called **enthalpy**, H, is the sum of the internal energy and the pressure–volume product of a system: $H = U + PV$. The **enthalpy change**, ΔH, for a process between initial and final states is

$$\Delta H = H_f - H_i = (U_f + P_f V_f) - (U_i + P_i V_i)$$
$$\Delta H = (U_f - U_i) + (P_f V_f - P_i V_i)$$
$$\Delta H = \Delta U + \Delta PV$$

If the process is carried out at a constant temperature and pressure ($P_i = P_f$) and with work limited to pressure–volume work, the enthalpy change is

$$\Delta H = \Delta U + P\Delta V$$

and the heat flow for the process under these conditions is

$$\Delta H = q_P \tag{7.14}$$

> Whenever you say that enthalpy is the heat of reaction, remember to say "at constant pressure." Likewise whenever you say that the internal energy U is the heat of reaction (bomb calorimeter) remember to say "at constant volume."

CONCEPT ASSESSMENT ✔

Suppose a system is subjected to the following changes: a 40-kJ quantity of heat is added and the system does 15 kJ of work; then the system is returned to its original state by cooling and compression. What is the value of ΔH?

ENTHALPY (ΔH) AND INTERNAL ENERGY (ΔU) CHANGES IN A CHEMICAL REACTION

We have noted that the heat of reaction at constant pressure, ΔH, and the heat of reaction at constant volume, ΔU, are related by the expression

$$\Delta U = \Delta H - P\Delta V \qquad (7.15)$$

The last term in this expression is the energy associated with the change in volume of the system under a constant external pressure. To assess just how significant pressure–volume work is, consider the following reaction, which is also illustrated in Figure 7-14.

$$2\,CO(g) + O_2(g) \longrightarrow 2\,CO_2(g)$$

If the heat of this reaction is measured under constant-pressure conditions at a constant temperature of 298 K, we get −566.0 kJ, indicating that 566.0 kJ of energy has left the system as heat: $\Delta H = -566.0$ kJ. To evaluate the pressure–volume work, we begin by writing

$$P\Delta V = P(V_f - V_i)$$

Then we can use the ideal gas equation to write this alternate expression.

$$P\Delta V = RT(n_f - n_i)$$

Here, n_f is the number of moles of gas in the products (2 mol CO_2) and n_i is the number of moles of gas in the reactants (2 mol CO + 1 mol O_2). Thus,

$$P\Delta V = 0.0083145 \text{ kJ mol}^{-1}\,\text{K}^{-1} \times 298 \text{ K} \times [2 - (2 + 1)]\,\text{mol} = -2.5 \text{ kJ}$$

The change in internal energy is

$$\begin{aligned}\Delta U &= \Delta H - P\Delta V \\ &= -566.0 \text{ kJ} - (-2.5 \text{ kJ}) \\ &= -563.5 \text{ kJ}\end{aligned}$$

 Kennedy, Sr., Alvin P. "Determination of Enthalpy of Vaporization Using a Microwave Oven." *J. Chem. Educ.* **1997**: 74, 1231 (October 1997).

☑ Point out that in Figure 7-14 (b) work is done on the system which results in a larger amount of energy released from the system as compared to the situation described in Figure 7-14 (a) where work is not done on the system. In both cases, energy leaves the system to maintain a constant temperature.

▶ **FIGURE 7-14**
Comparing heats of reaction at constant volume and constant pressure for the reaction 2 CO(g) + O₂(g) ⟶ 2 CO₂(g)
(a) *No* work is performed at constant volume because the piston cannot move due to the stops placed through the cylinder walls; $q_V = \Delta U = -563.5$ kJ. **(b)** When the reaction is carried out at constant pressure, the stops are removed. This allows the piston to move and the surroundings do work on the system, causing it to shrink into a smaller volume. More heat is evolved than in the constant-volume reaction; $q_P = \Delta H = -566.0$ kJ.

This calculation shows that the $P\Delta V$ term is quite small compared to ΔH and that ΔU and ΔH are almost the same. An additional interesting fact here is that the volume of the system decreases as a consequence of the work done by the surroundings of the system.

In the combustion of sucrose at a fixed temperature, the heat of combustion turns out to be the same, whether at constant volume (q_V) or constant pressure (q_P). Only heat is transferred between the reaction mixture and the surroundings; no pressure–volume work is done. This is because the volume of a system is almost entirely determined by the volume of gas and because 12 mol $CO_2(g)$ occupies the same volume as 12 mol $O_2(g)$. There is no change in volume in the combustion of sucrose: $q_P = q_V$. Thus, the result of Example 7-3 can be represented as

$$C_{12}H_{22}O_{11}(s) + 12\,O_2(g) \longrightarrow 12\,CO_2(g) + 11\,H_2O(l)\quad \Delta H = -5.65 \times 10^3\,kJ\quad (7.16)$$

Heats of Reaction simulation

That is, 1 mol $C_{12}H_{22}O_{11}(s)$ reacts with 12 mol $O_2(g)$ to produce 12 mol $CO_2(g)$, 11 mol $H_2O(l)$, and 5.65×10^3 kJ of evolved heat.*

In summary, in most reactions, the heat of reaction we measure is ΔH. In some reactions, notably combustion reactions, we measure ΔU (that is, q_V). In reaction (7.16), $\Delta U = \Delta H$, but this is not always the case. Where it is not, a value of ΔH can be obtained from ΔU by the method illustrated in the discussion of expression (7.15), but even in those cases, ΔH and ΔU will be nearly equal. In this text, all heats of reactions are treated as ΔH values unless there is an indication to the contrary.

Example 7-7 shows how enthalpy changes can provide conversion factors for problem solving.

Point out to students that q_p for a reaction is equal to q_v when there is no change in the volume of the reaction. This is essentially true for reactions that don't involve gases, like the neutralization reaction described in Example 7-4.

EXAMPLE 7-7

Stoichiometric Calculations Involving Quantities of Heat. How much heat is associated with the complete combustion of 1.00 kg of sucrose, $C_{12}H_{22}O_{11}$?

Solution

Express the quantity of sucrose in moles.

$$? \text{ mol} = 1.00 \text{ kg } C_{12}H_{22}O_{11} \times \frac{1000 \text{ g } C_{12}H_{22}O_{11}}{1 \text{ kg } C_{12}H_{22}O_{11}} \times \frac{1 \text{ mol } C_{12}H_{22}O_{11}}{342.3 \text{ g } C_{12}H_{22}O_{11}}$$

$$= 2.92 \text{ mol } C_{12}H_{22}O_{11}$$

Formulate a conversion factor (shown in blue) based on the information in equation (7.16)—that is, -5.65×10^3 kJ of heat is associated with the combustion of 1 mol $C_{12}H_{22}O_{11}$.

$$? \text{ kJ} = 2.92 \text{ mol } C_{12}H_{22}O_{11} \times \frac{-5.65 \times 10^3 \text{ kJ}}{1 \text{ mol } C_{12}H_{22}O_{11}} = -1.65 \times 10^4 \text{ kJ}$$

The negative sign denotes that heat is given off in the combustion.

Practice Example A: What mass of sucrose must be burned to produce 1.00×10^3 kJ of heat?

Practice Example B: A 25.0-mL sample of 0.1045 M HCl(aq) was neutralized by NaOH(aq). Use the result of Example 7-4 to determine the heat evolved in this neutralization.

Variations of calculations shown in Example 7-7 will make intuitive sense to most students. For example, most students would agree that doubling the amount of sucrose in the combustion reaction should double the amount of heat.

---

*Strictly speaking, the unit for ΔH should be kilojoules per mole, meaning per mole of reaction. "One mole of reaction" relates to the amounts of reactants and products in the equation as written. Thus, reaction (7.16) involves mol $C_{12}H_{22}O_{11}(s)$, 12 mol $O_2(g)$, 12 mol $CO_2(g)$, 11 mol $H_2O(l)$, and -5.65×10^3 kJ of enthalpy change *per mol reaction*. The mol^{-1} part of the unit of ΔH is often dropped, but there are times we need to carry it to achieve the proper cancellation of units. We will find this to be the case in Chapters 19 and 20.

Are You Wondering . . .

Why introduce the term ΔH anyway? Why not work just with ΔU, q, and w?

It's mainly a matter of convenience. Think of an analogous situation from daily life—buying gasoline at a filling station. The gasoline price posted on the pump is actually the sum of a base price and various federal, state, and perhaps local taxes. This breakdown is important to the accountants who must determine how much tax is to be paid to which agencies. To the consumer, however, it's easier to be given just the total cost per gallon. After all, this determines what he or she must pay. In thermochemistry, our chief interest is generally in heats of reaction, not pressure–volume work. And because most reactions are carried out under atmospheric pressure, it's helpful to have a function of state, enthalpy, H, whose change is exactly equal to something we can measure: q_P.

Canagaratna, Sebastian G. "A Visual Aid in Enthalpy Calculations." *J. Chem. Educ.* **2000:** 77, 1178 (September 2000).

States of Matter animation

ENTHALPY CHANGE (ΔH) ACCOMPANYING A CHANGE IN STATE OF MATTER

When a liquid is in contact with the atmosphere, energetic molecules at the surface of the liquid can overcome forces of attraction to their neighbors and pass into the gaseous, or vapor, state. We say that the liquid *vaporizes*. If the temperature of the liquid is to remain constant, the liquid must absorb heat from its surroundings to replace the energy carried off by the vaporizing molecules. The heat required to vaporize a fixed quantity of liquid is called the enthalpy (or heat) of vaporization. Usually the fixed quantity of liquid chosen is one mole, and we can call this quantity the *molar enthalpy of vaporization*. For example,

$$H_2O(l) \longrightarrow H_2O(g) \qquad \Delta H = 44.0 \text{ kJ at 298 K}$$

✓ Point out to students that the phase changes described here (the conversion of liquid water to gaseous water and the conversion of solid water to liquid water) occur at constant temperature.

We described the melting of a solid in a similar fashion (page 228). The energy requirement in this case is called the enthalpy (or heat) of fusion. For the melting of one mole of ice, we can write

$$H_2O(s) \longrightarrow H_2O(l) \qquad \Delta H = 6.01 \text{ kJ at 273.15 K}$$

We can use the data represented in these equations, together with other appropriate data, to answer questions like those posed in Example 7-8 and its accompanying Practice Examples.

Heating–Cooling Curves activity

EXAMPLE 7-8

Enthalpy Changes Accompanying Changes in States of Matter. Calculate ΔH for the process in which 50.0 g of water is converted from liquid at 10.0 °C to vapor at 25.0 °C.

Solution

The key to this calculation is to view the process as proceeding in two steps: first raising the temperature of liquid water from 10.0 to 25.0 °C, and then completely vaporizing the liquid at 25.0 °C. The total enthalpy change is the sum of the changes in the two steps. For a process at constant pressure, $\Delta H = q_P$, so we need to calculate the heat absorbed in each step.

HEATING WATER FROM 10.0 TO 25.0 °C
This heat requirement can be determined by the method shown in Example 7-1; that is, we apply equation (7.5).

$$? \text{ kJ} = 50.0 \text{ g } H_2O \times \frac{4.18 \text{ J}}{\text{g } H_2O \text{ °C}} \times (25.0 - 10.0) \text{ °C} \times \frac{1 \text{ kJ}}{1000 \text{ J}} = 3.14 \text{ kJ}$$

VAPORIZING WATER AT 25.0 °C

For this part of the calculation, the quantity of water must be expressed in moles so that we can then use the molar enthalpy of vaporization at 25 °C: 44.0 kJ/mol.

$$? \text{ kJ} = 50.0 \text{ g H}_2\text{O} \times \frac{1 \text{ mol H}_2\text{O}}{18.02 \text{ g H}_2\text{O}} \times \frac{44.0 \text{ kJ}}{1 \text{ mol H}_2\text{O}} = 122 \text{ kJ}$$

TOTAL ENTHALPY CHANGE

$$\Delta H = 3.14 \text{ kJ} + 122 \text{ kJ} = 125 \text{ kJ}$$

Practice Example A: What is the enthalpy change when a cube of ice 2.00 cm on edge is brought from -10.0 °C to a final temperature of 23.2 °C? For ice, use a density of 0.917 g/cm^3, a specific heat of 2.01 J g^{-1} °C^{-1}, and an enthalpy of fusion of 6.01 kJ/mol.

Practice Example B: What is the maximum mass of ice at -15.0 °C that can be completely converted to water vapor at 25.0 °C if the available heat for this transition is 5.00×10^3 kJ?

STANDARD STATES AND STANDARD ENTHALPY CHANGES

The measured enthalpy change for a reaction has a unique value *only* if the initial state (reactants) and final state (products) are precisely described. If we define a particular state as *standard* for the reactants and products, we can then say that the standard enthalpy change is the enthalpy change in a reaction in which the reactants and products are in their standard states. This so-called **standard enthalpy of reaction** is denoted with a degree symbol, $\Delta H°$.

The **standard state** of a solid or liquid substance is the pure element or compound at a pressure of *1 bar* $(10^5$ Pa)* and at the temperature of interest. For a gas, the standard state is the pure gas behaving as an (hypothetical) ideal gas at a pressure of 1 bar and the temperature of interest. While temperature is not part of the definition of a standard state, it still must be specified in tabulated values of $\Delta H°$, because $\Delta H°$ depends on temperature. The values given in this text are all for 298.15 K (25 °C) unless otherwise stated.

In the rest of this chapter, we will mostly use standard enthalpy changes. We will explore the details of nonstandard conditions in Chapter 19.

ENTHALPY DIAGRAMS

The negative sign of ΔH in equation (7.16) means that the enthalpy of the products is lower than that of the reactants. This *decrease* in enthalpy appears as heat evolved to the surroundings. The combustion of sucrose is an exothermic reaction. In the reaction

$$N_2(g) + O_2(g) \longrightarrow 2 \text{ NO}(g) \qquad \Delta H° = 180.50 \text{ kJ} \qquad (7.17)$$

the products have a *higher* enthalpy than the reactants; ΔH is positive. To produce this increase in enthalpy, heat is absorbed from the surroundings. The reaction is endothermic. An **enthalpy diagram** is a diagrammatic representation of enthalpy changes in a process. Figure 7-15 shows how exothermic and endothermic reactions can be represented through such diagrams.

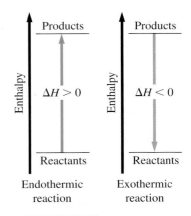

▲ **FIGURE 7-15**
Enthalpy diagrams
Horizontal lines represent absolute values of enthalpy. The higher a horizontal line, the greater the value of H that it represents. Vertical lines or arrows represent changes in enthalpy (ΔH). Arrows pointing up signify increases in enthalpy—endothermic reactions. Arrows pointing down signify decreases in enthalpy—exothermic reactions.

---

*The International Union of Pure and Applied Chemistry (IUPAC) recommended that the standard-state pressure be changed from 1 atm to 1 bar about 20 years ago, but some data tables are still based on the 1-atm standard. Fortunately, the differences in values resulting from this change in standard-state pressure are very small—almost always small enough to be ignored.

Are You Wondering . . .

Why ΔH depends on temperature?

The difference in ΔH for a reaction at two different temperatures is determined by the amount of heat involved in changing the reactants and products from one temperature to the other under constant pressure. These quantities of heat can be calculated with the help of equation (7.5): q_P = heat capacity $\times$ temperature change = $C_P \times \Delta T$. We write an expression of this type for each reactant and product and combine these expressions with the measured ΔH value at one temperature to obtain the value of ΔH at another. This method is illustrated in Figure 7-16 and applied in Exercise 101.

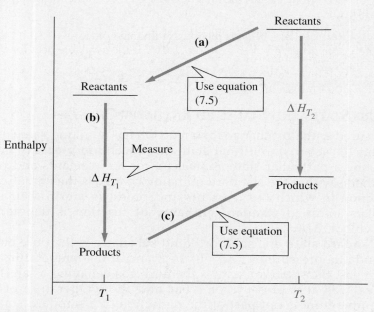

▲ FIGURE 7-16
Conceptualizing ΔH as a function of temperature
In the three-step process outlined here, **(a)** the reactants are cooled from the temperature T_2 to T_1. **(b)** The reaction is carried out at T_1, and **(c)** the products are warmed from T_1 to T_2. When the quantities of heat associated with each step are combined, the result is the same as if the reaction had been carried out at T_2, that is, ΔH_{T_2}.

Canagaratna, Sebastian G. "Intensive and extensive: Underused concepts." *J. Chem. Educ.* **1992**: *69*, 957.

 Hess's Law

7-7 INDIRECT DETERMINATION OF ΔH: HESS'S LAW

One of the reasons that the enthalpy concept is so useful is that a large number of heats of reaction can be calculated from a small number of measurements. The following features of enthalpy change (ΔH) make this possible.

- **ΔH Is an Extensive Property.** Consider the standard enthalpy change in the formation of NO(g) from its elements at 25 °C.

$$N_2(g) + O_2(g) \longrightarrow 2\,NO(g) \qquad \Delta H° = 180.50 \text{ kJ}$$

To express the enthalpy change in terms of *one mole* of NO(g), we divide all coefficients *and the* ΔH value by *two*.

▶ Although we have avoided fractional coefficients previously, we need them here. The coefficient of NO(g) must be one.

$$\frac{1}{2}N_2(g) + \frac{1}{2}O_2(g) \longrightarrow NO(g) \qquad \Delta H° = \frac{1}{2} \times 180.50 = 90.25 \text{ kJ}$$

Enthalpy change is directly proportional to the amounts of substances in a system.

• **ΔH Changes Sign When a Process Is Reversed.** As we learned on page 240, if a process is reversed, the change in a function of state reverses sign. Thus, ΔH for the *decomposition* of one mole of NO(g) is $-\Delta H$ for the *formation* of one mole of NO(g).

$$NO(g) \longrightarrow \frac{1}{2}N_2(g) + \frac{1}{2}O_2(g) \quad \Delta H^\circ = -90.25 \text{ kJ}$$

• **Hess's Law of Constant Heat Summation.** To describe the standard enthalpy change for the formation of $NO_2(g)$ from $N_2(g)$ and $O_2(g)$,

$$\frac{1}{2}N_2(g) + O_2(g) \longrightarrow NO_2(g) \quad \Delta H^\circ = ?$$

we can think of the reaction as proceeding in two steps: First we form NO(g) from $NO_2(g)$ and $O_2(g)$, and then $NO_2(g)$ from NO(g) and $O_2(g)$. When the equations for these two steps are added together with their individual and distinctive ΔH° values, we get the overall equation and ΔH° value that we are seeking.

$$\frac{1}{2}N_2(g) + \frac{1}{2}O_2(g) \longrightarrow \cancel{NO(g)} \quad \Delta H^\circ = +90.25 \text{ kJ}$$

$$\cancel{NO(g)} + \frac{1}{2}O_2(g) \longrightarrow NO_2(g) \quad \Delta H^\circ = -57.07 \text{ kJ}$$

$$\overline{\frac{1}{2}N_2(g) + O_2(g) \longrightarrow NO_2(g) \quad \Delta H^\circ = +33.18 \text{ kJ}}$$

Note that in summing the two equations NO(g), a species that would have appeared on both sides of the overall equation, canceled out. Figure 7-17 uses an enthalpy diagram to illustrate what we just did. **Hess's law** states the principle we used:

> If a process occurs in stages or steps (even if only hypothetically), the enthalpy change for the overall process is the sum of the enthalpy changes for the individual steps.

Hess's law is simply a consequence of the state function property of enthalpy. Regardless of the path taken in going from the initial state to the final state, ΔH (or ΔH° if the process is carried out under standard conditions) has the same value.

Suppose we want the standard enthalpy change for the reaction

$$3\,C(\text{graphite}) + 4\,H_2(g) \longrightarrow C_3H_8(g) \qquad \Delta H^\circ = ? \qquad (7.18)$$

How should we proceed? If we try to get graphite and hydrogen to react, a slight reaction will occur, but it will not go to completion. Furthermore, the product will not be limited to propane (C_3H_8); several other hydrocarbons will form as well. The fact is that we cannot directly measure ΔH° for reaction (7.18). Instead, we must resort to an *indirect calculation* from ΔH° values that can be established by experiment. Here is where Hess's law is of greatest value. It permits us to calculate ΔH values that we cannot measure directly. In Example 7-9, we use the following standard heats of combustion to calculate ΔH° for reaction (7.18).

$$\Delta H^\circ \text{ Combustion:} \quad C_3H_8(g) = -2219.9 \text{ kJ/mol } C_3H_8(g)$$

$$C(\text{graphite}) = -393.5 \text{ kJ/mol } C(\text{graphite})$$

$$H_2(g) = -285.8 \text{ kJ/mol } H_2(g)$$

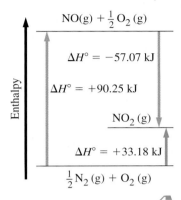

▲ **FIGURE 7-17**
An enthalpy diagram illustrating Hess's law
Whether the reaction occurs through a single step (blue arrow) or in two steps (red arrows), the enthalpy change is $\Delta H^\circ = 33.18$ kJ for the overall reaction

$$\frac{1}{2}N_2(g) + O_2(g) \longrightarrow NO_2(g).$$

Hess's Law activity

◀ **KEEP IN MIND**
that ΔH° is an extensive property. In a chemical equation, the stoichiometric coefficients specify the amounts involved, and the unit kJ suffices for ΔH°. When ΔH° is not accompanied by an equation, the amount involved must somehow be specified, such as per mole of $C_3H_8(g)$ in the expression $\Delta H^\circ_{\text{comb}} = -2219.9$ kJ/mol $C_3H_8(g)$.

EXAMPLE 7-9

Applying Hess's Law. Use the heat of combustion data from page 249 to determine $\Delta H°$ for reaction (7.18): $3 \text{ C(graphite)} + 4 \text{ H}_2(g) \longrightarrow \text{C}_3\text{H}_8(g)$ $\Delta H° = ?$

Solution

To determine an enthalpy change with Hess's law, we need to combine the appropriate chemical equations. A good starting point is to write chemical equations for the given combustion reactions based on *one mole* of the indicated reactant. Recall from Section 3-4 that the products of the combustion of carbon–hydrogen–oxygen compounds are $\text{CO}_2(g)$ and $\text{H}_2\text{O(l)}$.

(a) $\text{C}_3\text{H}_8(g) + 5 \text{ O}_2(g) \longrightarrow 3 \text{ CO}_2(g) + 4 \text{ H}_2\text{O(l)}$ $\Delta H° = -2219.9 \text{ kJ}$

(b) $\text{C(graphite)} + \text{O}_2(g) \longrightarrow \text{CO}_2(g)$ $\Delta H° = -393.5 \text{ kJ}$

(c) $\text{H}_2(g) + \dfrac{1}{2}\text{O}_2(g) \longrightarrow \text{H}_2\text{O(l)}$ $\Delta H° = -285.8 \text{ kJ}$

Because our objective in reaction (7.18) is to *produce* $\text{C}_3\text{H}_8(g)$, the next step is to find a reaction in which $\text{C}_3\text{H}_8(g)$ is formed—the *reverse* of reaction **(a)**.

$- \textbf{(a)}$: $3 \text{ CO}_2(g) + 4 \text{ H}_2\text{O(l)} \longrightarrow \text{C}_3\text{H}_8(g) + 5 \text{ O}_2(g)$ $\Delta H° = -(-2219.9) \text{ kJ}$
$= +2219.9 \text{ kJ}$

Now, we turn our attention to the reactants, C(graphite) and $\text{H}_2(g)$. To get the proper number of moles of each, we must multiply equation **(b)** by three and equation **(c)** by four.

$3 \times \textbf{(b)}$: $3 \text{ C(graphite)} + 3 \text{ O}_2(g) \longrightarrow 3 \text{ CO}_2(g)$ $\Delta H° = 3(-393.5 \text{ kJ})$
$= -1181 \text{ kJ}$

$4 \times \textbf{(c)}$: $4 \text{ H}_2(g) + 2 \text{ O}_2(g) \longrightarrow 4 \text{ H}_2\text{O(l)}$ $\Delta H° = 4(-285.8 \text{ kJ})$
$= -1143 \text{ kJ}$

Here is the overall change we have described: 3 mol C(graphite) and 4 mol $\text{H}_2(g)$ have been consumed, and 1 mol $\text{C}_3\text{H}_8(g)$ has been produced. This is exactly what is required in equation (7.18). We can now combine the three modified equations.

$- \textbf{(a)}$: $3 \text{ CO}_2(g) + 4 \text{ H}_2\text{O(l)} \longrightarrow \text{C}_3\text{H}_8(g) + 5 \text{ O}_2(g)$ $\Delta H° = +2219.9 \text{ kJ}$
$3 \times \textbf{(b)}$: $3 \text{ C(graphite)} + 3 \text{ O}_2(g) \longrightarrow 3 \text{ CO}_2(g)$ $\Delta H° = -1181 \text{ kJ}$
$4 \times \textbf{(c)}$: $4 \text{ H}_2(g) + 2 \text{ O}_2(g) \longrightarrow 4 \text{ H}_2\text{O(l)}$ $\Delta H° = -1143 \text{ kJ}$
_____
$3 \text{ C(graphite)} + 4 \text{ H}_2(g) \longrightarrow \text{C}_3\text{H}_8(g)$ $\Delta H° = -104 \text{ kJ}$

Practice Example A: The standard heat of combustion of propene, $\text{C}_3\text{H}_6(g)$, is -2058 kJ/mol $\text{C}_3\text{H}_6(g)$. Use this value and other data from this example to determine $\Delta H°$ for the hydrogenation of propene to propane.

$\text{CH}_3\text{CH}{=}\text{CH}_2(g) + \text{H}_2(g) \longrightarrow \text{CH}_3\text{CH}_2\text{CH}_3(g)$ $\Delta H° = ?$

Practice Example B: From the data in Practice Example 7-9A and the following equation, determine the standard enthalpy of combustion of one mole of 2-propanol, $\text{CH}_3\text{CHOHCH}_3(l)$.

$\text{CH}_3\text{CH}{=}\text{CH}_2(g) + \text{H}_2\text{O(l)} \longrightarrow \text{CH}_3\text{CH(OH)CH}_3(l)$ $\Delta H° = -52.3 \text{ kJ}$

CONCEPT ASSESSMENT ✔

The heat of reaction between carbon (graphite) and the corresponding stoichiometric amounts of hydrogen gas to form $\text{C}_2\text{H}_2(g)$, $\text{C}_2\text{H}_4(g)$, and $\text{C}_2\text{H}_6(g)$ are 226.7, 52.3, and -84.7 kJmol^{-1}, respectively. Relate these values to the enthalpy diagram shown in the margin. Indicate on the diagram the standard enthalpy change for the reaction $\text{C}_2\text{H}_2(g) + 2 \text{ H}_2(g) \longrightarrow \text{C}_2\text{H}_6(g)$.

Enthalpy change

0

7-8   STANDARD ENTHALPIES OF FORMATION

In the enthalpy diagrams we have drawn, we have not written any numerical values on the enthalpy axis. This is because we cannot determine *absolute* values of enthalpy, H. However, enthalpy *is* a function of state, so *changes* in enthalpy, ΔH, have unique values. We can deal just with these changes. Nevertheless, as with many other properties, it is still useful to have a starting point, a zero value.

Consider a map-making analogy: What do we list as the height of a mountain? Do we mean by this the vertical distance between the mountaintop and the center of Earth? Between the mountaintop and the deepest trench in the ocean? No. By agreement, we mean the vertical distance between the mountaintop and mean sea level. We *arbitrarily* assign to mean sea level an elevation of zero, and all other points on Earth are relative to this zero elevation. The elevation of Mt. Everest is +8848 m; that of Badwater, Death Valley, California, is −86 m. We do something similar with enthalpies. We relate our zero to the enthalpies of certain forms of the elements and determine the enthalpies of other substances relative to this zero.

The **standard enthalpy of formation** (ΔH_f°) of a substance is the enthalpy *change* that occurs in the formation of one mole of the substance in the standard state from the *reference* forms of the elements in their standard states. The reference forms of the elements in all but a few cases are the most stable forms of the elements at one bar and the given temperature. The degree symbol denotes that the enthalpy change is a standard enthalpy change, and the subscript "f" signifies that the reaction is one in which a substance is formed from its elements. Because the formation of the most stable form of an element from itself is no change at all,

> the standard enthalpy of formation of a pure element in its reference form is 0.

Listed here are the most stable forms of several elements at 298.15 K, the temperature at which thermochemical data are commonly tabulated.

$$Na(s) \quad H_2(g) \quad N_2(g) \quad O_2(g) \quad C(graphite) \quad Br_2(l)$$

The situation with carbon is an interesting one. In addition to graphite, carbon also exists naturally in the form of diamond. However, because there is a measurable enthalpy difference between them, they cannot both be assigned $\Delta H_f^\circ = 0$.

$$C(graphite) \longrightarrow C(diamond) \qquad \Delta H^\circ = 1.9 \text{ kJ}$$

We choose as the reference form the more stable form, the one with the lower enthalpy. Thus, we assign $\Delta H_f^\circ(\text{graphite}) = 0$, and $\Delta H_f^\circ(\text{diamond}) = 1.9$ kJ/mol. Although we can obtain bromine in either the gaseous or liquid state at 298.15 K, $Br_2(l)$ is the most stable form. $Br_2(g)$, if obtained at 298.15 K and 1 bar pressure, immediately condenses to $Br_2(l)$.

$$Br_2(l) \longrightarrow Br_2(g) \qquad \Delta H_f^\circ = 30.91 \text{ kJ}$$

The enthalpies of formation are $\Delta H_f^\circ[Br_2(l)] = 0$ and $\Delta H_f^\circ[Br_2(g)] = 30.91$ kJ/mol.

A rare case in which the reference form is not the most stable form is the element phosphorus. Although over time it converts to solid red phosphorus, solid white phosphorus has been chosen as the reference form.

$$P(s, \text{white}) \longrightarrow P(s, \text{red}) \qquad \Delta H^\circ = -17.6 \text{ kJ}$$

Treptow, Richard S. "How Thermodynamic Data and Equilibrium Constants Changed When the Standard-State Pressure Became 1 Bar." *J. Chem. Educ.* **1999**: *76*, 212 (February 1999).

Formation of Aluminum Bromide movie

VCL *Heat of Formation: Aspirin*

◀ **KEEP IN MIND**
that we use the expression "standard enthalpy of formation" even though what we are describing is actually a standard enthalpy *change*.

▲ Diamond and graphite.

▲ Liquid bromine vaporizing.

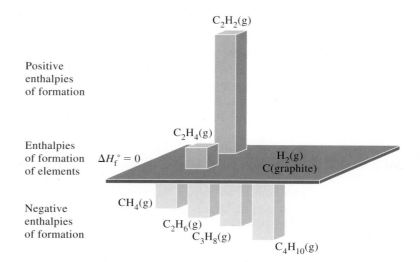

► **FIGURE 7-18**
Some standard enthalpies of formation at 298.15 K
Standard enthalpies of formation of elements are shown in the central plane, with $\Delta H_f^\circ = 0$. Substances with positive enthalpies of formation are above the plane, while those with negative enthalpies of formation are below the plane.

The standard enthalpies of formation are $\Delta H_f^\circ[\text{P(s, white)}] = 0$ and $\Delta H_f^\circ[\text{P(s, red)}] = -17.6$ kJ/mol.

Standard enthalpies of formation of some common substances are presented in Table 7.2. Figure 7-18 emphasizes that both positive and negative standard enthalpies of formation are possible. It also suggests that standard enthalpies of formation are related to molecular structure.

We will use standard enthalpies of formation in a variety of calculations. Often, the first thing we must do is write the chemical equation to which a ΔH_f° value applies, as in Example 7-10.

TABLE 7.2	Some Standard Molar Enthalpies of Formation at 298.15 K, ΔH_f°		
Substance	**kJ/mol[a]**	**Substance**	**kJ/mol[a]**
$CO(g)$	−110.5	$HBr(g)$	−36.40
$CO_2(g)$	−393.5	$HI(g)$	26.48
$CH_4(g)$	−74.81	$H_2O(g)$	−241.8
$C_2H_2(g)$	226.7	$H_2O(l)$	−285.8
$C_2H_4(g)$	52.26	$H_2S(g)$	−20.63
$C_2H_6(g)$	−84.68	$NH_3(g)$	−46.11
$C_3H_8(g)$	−103.8	$NO(g)$	90.25
$C_4H_{10}(g)$	−125.6	$N_2O(g)$	82.05
$CH_3OH(l)$	−238.7	$NO_2(g)$	33.18
$C_2H_5OH(l)$	−277.7	$N_2O_4(g)$	9.16
$HF(g)$	−271.1	$SO_2(g)$	−296.8
$HCl(g)$	−92.31	$SO_3(g)$	−395.7

[a]Values are for reactions in which one mole of substance is formed. Most of the data have been rounded off to four significant figures.

▲ **FIGURE 7-19**
Standard enthalpy of formation of formaldehyde, HCHO(g)
The formation of HCHO(g) from its elements in their standard states is an exothermic reaction. The heat evolved per mole of HCHO(g) formed is the standard enthalpy (heat) of formation.

EXAMPLE 7-10

Relating a Standard Enthalpy of Formation to a Chemical Equation. The enthalpy of formation of formaldehyde at 298 K is $\Delta H_f^\circ = -108.6$ kJ/mol HCHO(g). Write the chemical equation to which this value applies.

Solution

The equation must be written for the formation of one mole of gaseous HCHO. The most stable forms of the elements at 298.15 K and 1 bar are gaseous H_2 and O_2 and solid carbon in the form of graphite (Fig. 7-19). Note that we need one fractional coefficient in this equation.

$$H_2(g) + \frac{1}{2}O_2(g) + C(\text{graphite}) \longrightarrow HCHO(g) \qquad \Delta H_f^\circ = -108.6 \text{ kJ}$$

Practice Example A: The standard enthalpy of formation for the amino acid leucine is -637.3 kJ/mol $C_6H_{13}O_2N(s)$. Write the chemical equation to which this value applies.

Practice Example B: How is $\Delta H°$ for the following reaction related to the standard enthalpy of formation of $NH_3(g)$ listed in Table 7.2? What is the value of $\Delta H° = ?$

$$2\,NH_3(g) \longrightarrow N_2(g) + 3\,H_2(g) \qquad \Delta H° = ?$$

Are You Wondering . . .

What is the significance of the sign of a $\Delta H_f°$ value?

A compound having a positive value of $\Delta H_f°$ is formed from its elements by an endothermic reaction. If the reaction is reversed, the compound decomposes into its elements in an exothermic reaction. We say that the compound is unstable with respect to its elements. This does not mean that the compound cannot be made, but it does suggest a tendency for the compound to enter into chemical reactions yielding products with lower enthalpies of formation.

When no other criteria are available, chemists sometimes use enthalpy change as a rough indicator of the likelihood of a chemical reaction occurring—exothermic reactions generally being more likely to occur unassisted than endothermic ones. We'll present much better criteria later in the text.

STANDARD ENTHALPIES OF REACTION

We have learned that if the reactants and products of a reaction are in their standard states, the enthalpy change is a *standard* enthalpy change, which we can denote as $\Delta H°$ or $\Delta H_{rxn}°$. One of the primary uses of standard enthalpies of formation is in calculating standard enthalpies of reaction.

Let us use Hess's law to calculate the standard enthalpy of reaction for the decomposition of sodium bicarbonate, a minor reaction that occurs when baking soda is used in baking.

> Remind students that enthalpy changes are extensive and that they will often need to multiply stoichiometric coefficients and enthalpy changes by the proper factors when using Hess's Law.

$$2\,NaHCO_3(s) \longrightarrow Na_2CO_3(s) + H_2O(l) + CO_2(g) \qquad \Delta H° = ? \qquad (7.19)$$

From Hess's law, we see that the following four equations yield equation (7.19) when added together.

(a) $2\,NaHCO_3(s) \longrightarrow 2\,Na(s) + H_2(g) + 2\,C\,(graphite) + 3\,O_2(g)$

$$\Delta H° = -2 \times \Delta H_f°[NaHCO_3(s)]$$

(b) $2\,Na(s) + C(graphite) + \dfrac{3}{2}O_2(g) \longrightarrow Na_2CO_3(s)$

$$\Delta H° = \Delta H_f°[Na_2CO_3(s)]$$

(c) $H_2(g) + \dfrac{1}{2}O_2(g) \longrightarrow H_2O(l) \qquad\qquad \Delta H° = \Delta H_f°[H_2O(l)]$

(d) $C(graphite) + O_2(g) \longrightarrow CO_2(g) \qquad\quad \Delta H° = \Delta H_f°[CO_2(g)]$

$$2\,NaHCO_3(s) \longrightarrow Na_2CO_3(s) + H_2O(l) + CO_2(g) \qquad\quad \Delta H° = ?$$

Equation (a) is the *reverse* of the equation representing the formation of two moles of $[NaHCO_3(s)]$ from its elements. This means that $\Delta H°$ for reaction (a) is the *negative* of twice $\Delta H_f°[NaHCO_3(s)]$. Equations (b), (c) and (d) represent the formation of *one* mole each of $Na_2CO_3(s)$, $CO_2(g)$ and $H_2O(l)$. Thus, we can express the value of $\Delta H°$ for the decomposition reaction as

$$\Delta H° = \Delta H_f°[Na_2CO_3(s)] + \Delta H_f°[H_2O(l)] +$$
$$\Delta H_f°[CO_2(g)] - 2 \times \Delta H_f°[NaHCO_3(s)] \qquad (7.20)$$

▲ **FIGURE 7-20**
Computing heats of reaction from standard enthalpies of formation
Enthalpy is a state function, hence $\Delta H°$ for the overall reaction $2 NaHCO_3(s) \longrightarrow$ $Na_2CO_3(s) + CO_2(g) +$ $H_2O(l)$ is the sum of the enthalpy changes for the two steps shown.

We can use the enthalpy diagram in Figure 7-20 to visualize the Hess's law procedure and to show how the state function property of enthalpy enables us to arrive at equation (7.20). Imagine the decomposition of sodium bicarbonate taking place in two steps. In the first step, suppose a vessel contains 2 mol $NaHCO_3$, which is allowed to decompose into 2 mol $Na(s)$, 2 mol $C(graphite)$, 1 mol $H_2(g)$, and 3 mol $O_2(g)$, as in equation (a) on page 253. In the second step, recombine the 2 mol $Na(s)$, 2 mol $C(graphite)$, 1 mol $H_2(g)$, and 3 mol $O_2(g)$ to form the products according to equations (b), (c) and (d) on page 253.

The pathway shown in Figure 7-20 *is not* how the reaction actually occurs. This does not matter, though, because enthalpy is a state function and the change of any state function is independent of the path chosen. The enthalpy change for the overall reaction is the sum of the standard enthalpy changes of the individual steps.

$$\Delta H° = \Delta H°_{decomposition} + \Delta H_{recombination}$$

$$\Delta H°_{decomposition} = -2 \times \Delta H°_f[NaHCO_3(s)]$$

$$\Delta H°_{recombination} = \Delta H°_f[Na_2CO_3(s)] + \Delta H°_f[H_2O(l)] + \Delta H°_f[CO_2(g)]$$

so that

$$\Delta H° = \Delta H°_f[Na_2CO_3(s)] + \Delta H°_f[H_2O(l)] + \Delta H°_f[CO_2(g)] - 2 \times \Delta H°_f[NaHCO_3(s)]$$

Equation (7.20) is a specific application of the following more general relationship for a standard enthalpy of reaction.

$$\Delta H° = \sum v_p \Delta H°_f(\text{products}) - \sum v_r \Delta H°_f(\text{reactants}) \qquad (7.21)$$

The symbol Σ (Greek, sigma) means "the sum of." The terms that are added together are the products of the standard enthalpies of formation ($\Delta H°_f$) and their stoichiometric coefficients, v. One sum is required for the reaction products (subscript p), and another for the initial reactants (subscript r). The enthalpy change of the reaction is the sum of terms for the products *minus* the sum of terms for the reactants. Equation (7.21) avoids the manipulation of a number of chemical equations. The state function basis for equation (7.21) is shown in Figure 7-21 and is applied in Example 7-11.

▶ **FIGURE 7-21**
Diagrammatic representation of equation (7.21)

Endothermic reaction

Exothermic reaction

EXAMPLE 7-11

Calculating $\Delta H°$ from Tabulated Values of $\Delta H°_f$. Let us apply equation (7.21) to calculate the standard enthalpy of combustion of ethane, $C_2H_6(g)$, a component of natural gas.

Solution
The reaction is

$$C_2H_6(g) + \frac{7}{2}O_2(g) \longrightarrow 2 CO_2(g) + 3 H_2O(l)$$

The relationship we need is equation (7.21). The data we substitute into the relationship are from Table 7.2.

$$\Delta H° = \{2 \text{ mol } CO_2 \times \Delta H_f°[CO_2(g)] + 3 \text{ mol } H_2O \times \Delta H_f°[H_2O(l)]\}$$

$$- \{1 \text{ mol } C_2H_6 \times \Delta H_f°[C_2H_6(g)] + \frac{7}{2} \text{mol } O_2 \times \Delta H_f°[O_2(g)]\}$$

$$= 2 \text{ mol } CO_2 \times (-393.5 \text{ kJ/mol } CO_2) + 3 \text{ mol } H_2O \times (-285.8 \text{ kJ/mol } H_2O)$$

$$- 1 \text{ mol } C_2H_6 \times (-84.7 \text{ kJ/mol } C_2H_6) - \frac{7}{2} \text{mol } O_2 \times 0 \text{ kJ/mol } O_2$$

$$= -787.0 \text{ kJ} - 857.4 \text{ kJ} + 84.7 \text{ kJ} = -1559.7 \text{ kJ}$$

◀ **KEEP IN MIND**
that the standard enthalpy
of formation of an element in
its reference form is zero.
Thus, we can drop the term
involving $\Delta H_f°[O_2(g)]$ at any
time in the calculation.

Practice Example A: Use data from Table 7.2 to calculate the standard enthalpy of combustion of ethanol, $CH_3CH_2OH(l)$, at 298.15 K.

Practice Example B: Calculate the standard enthalpy of combustion at 298.15 K *per mole* of a gaseous fuel that contains C_3H_8 and C_4H_{10} in the mole fractions 0.62 and 0.38, respectively.

A type of calculation as important as the one illustrated in Example 7-11 is the determination of an unknown $\Delta H_f°$ value from a set of known $\Delta H_f°$ values and a known standard enthalpy of reaction, $\Delta H°$. As shown in Example 7-12, the essential step is to rearrange expression (7.21) to isolate the unknown $\Delta H_f°$ on one side of the equation. Also shown is a way of organizing the data that you may find helpful.

Point out to students that combustion reactions are exothermic and standard enthalpy changes for these reactions should be negative.

EXAMPLE 7-12

Calculating an Unknown $\Delta H_f°$ Value.   Use the data here and in Table 7.2 to calculate $\Delta H_f°$ of benzene, $C_6H_6(l)$.

$$2 C_6H_6(l) + 15 O_2(g) \longrightarrow 12 CO_2(g) + 6 H_2O(l) \qquad \Delta H° = -6535 \text{ kJ}$$

Solution

To organize the data needed in the calculation, begin by writing the chemical equation for the reaction with $\Delta H_f°$ data listed under the chemical formulas.

$$2 C_6H_6(l) + 15 O_2(g) \longrightarrow 12 CO_2(g) + 6 H_2O(l) \qquad \Delta H° = -6535 \text{ kJ}$$

$\Delta H_f°$, kJ/mol   ?   0   −393.5   −285.8

Now, we can substitute known data into expression (7.21) and rearrange the equation to obtain a lone term on the left: $\Delta H_f°[C_6H_6(l)]$. The remainder of the problem simply involves numerical calculations.

$$\Delta H° = \{12 \text{ mol } CO_2 \times -(393.5 \text{ kJ/mol } CO_2 + 6 \text{ mol } H_2O \times$$

$$(-285.8 \text{ kJ/mol } H_2O)\} - 2 \text{ mol } C_2H_6 \times \Delta H_f°[C_6H_6(l)] = -6535 \text{ kJ}$$

$$\Delta H_f°[C_6H_6(l)] = \frac{\{-4722 \text{ kJ} - 1715 \text{ kJ}\} + 6535 \text{ kJ}}{2 \text{ mol } C_6H_6} = 49 \text{ kJ/mol } C_6H_6(l)$$

Practice Example A: The overall reaction that occurs in photosynthesis in plants is

$$6 CO_2(g) + 6 H_2O(l) \longrightarrow C_6H_{12}O_6(s) + 6 O_2(g) \qquad \Delta H° = 2803 \text{ kJ}$$

Determine the standard enthalpy of formation of glucose, $C_6H_{12}O_6(s)$, at 298 K.

Practice Example B: A handbook lists the standard enthalpy of combustion of gaseous dimethyl ether at 298 K as -31.70 kJ/g$(CH_3)_2O(g)$. What is the standard molar enthalpy of formation of dimethyl ether at 298 K?

Ionic Reactions in Solutions

Many chemical reactions in aqueous solution are best thought of as reactions between ions and best represented by net ionic equations. Consider the neutralization of a strong acid by a strong base. Using a somewhat more accurate enthalpy of neutralization than we obtained in Example 7-4, we can write

$$H^+(aq) + OH^-(aq) \longrightarrow H_2O(l) \qquad \Delta H° = -55.8 \text{ kJ} \qquad (7.22)$$

We should also be able to calculate this enthalpy of neutralization by using enthalpy of formation data in expression (7.21), but this requires us to have enthalpy of formation data for individual ions. And there is a slight problem in getting these. We cannot create ions of a single type in a chemical reaction. We always produce cations and anions simultaneously, as in the reaction of sodium and chlorine to produce Na^+ and Cl^- in NaCl. We must choose a particular ion to which we assign an enthalpy of formation of *zero* in its aqueous solutions. We then compare the enthalpies of formation of other ions to this reference ion. The ion we arbitrarily choose for our zero is $H^+(aq)$. Now let us see how we can use expression (7.21) and data from equation (7.22) to determine the enthalpy of formation of $OH^-(aq)$.

$$\Delta H° = \{1 \text{ mol } H_2O \times \Delta H_f°[H_2O(l)] - 1 \text{ mol } H^+ \times \Delta H_f°[H^+(aq)]\}$$
$$- 1 \text{ mol } OH^- \times \Delta H_f°[OH^-(aq)] = -55.8 \text{ kJ}$$

$$\Delta H_f°[OH^-(aq)] =$$

$$\frac{55.8 \text{ kJ} + (1 \text{ mol } H_2O \times \Delta H_f°[H_2O(l)]) - (1 \text{ mol } H^+ \times \Delta H_f°[H^+(aq)])}{1 \text{ mol } OH^-}$$

$$\Delta H_f°[OH^-(aq)] = \frac{55.8 \text{ kJ} - 285.8 \text{ kJ} - 0 \text{ kJ}}{1 \text{ mol } OH^-} = -230.0 \text{ kJ/mol } OH^-$$

Table 7.3 lists data for several common ions in aqueous solution. Enthalpies of formation in solution depend on the solute concentration. These data are representative for *dilute* aqueous solutions (about 1 M), the type of solution that we normally deal with. Some of these data are used in Example 7-13.

TABLE 7.3 Some Standard Molar Enthalpies of Formation of Ions in Aqueous Solution at 298.15 K, $\Delta H_f°$

Ion	kJ/mol	Ion	kJ/mol
H^+	0	OH^-	−230.0
Li^+	−278.5	Cl^-	−167.2
Na^+	−240.1	Br^-	−121.6
K^+	−252.4	I^-	−55.19
NH_4^+	−132.5	NO_3^-	−205.0
Ag^+	105.6	CO_3^{2-}	−677.1
Mg^{2+}	−466.9	S^{2-}	33.05
Ca^{2+}	−542.8	SO_4^{2-}	−909.3
Ba^{2+}	−537.6	$S_2O_3^{2-}$	−648.5
Cu^{2+}	64.77	PO_4^{3-}	−1277
Al^{3+}	−531		

EXAMPLE 7-13

Calculating the Enthalpy Change in an Ionic Reaction. Given that $\Delta H_f^\circ[\text{BaSO}_4(s)] = -1473$ kJ/mol, what is the standard enthalpy change for the precipitation of barium sulfate?

Solution

First, write the net ionic equation for the reaction and introduce the relevant data.

$$\text{Ba}^{2+}(aq) + \text{SO}_4{}^{2-}(aq) \longrightarrow \text{BaSO}_4(s) \qquad \Delta H^\circ = ?$$

ΔH_f°, kJ/mol -537.6 -909.3 -1473

Then substitute data into equation (7.21).

$$\Delta H^\circ = 1 \text{ mol BaSO}_4 \times \Delta H_f^\circ[\text{BaSO}_4(s)] - 1 \text{ mol Ba}^{2+} \times \Delta H_f^\circ[\text{Ba}^{2+}(aq)]$$
$$- 1 \text{ mol SO}_4{}^{2-} \times \Delta H_f^\circ[\text{SO}_4{}^{2-}(aq)]$$
$$= 1 \text{ mol BaSO}_4 \times (-1473 \text{ kJ/mol BaSO}_4) - 1 \text{ mol Ba}^{2+}$$
$$\times (-537.6 \text{ kJ/mol Ba}^{2+}) - 1 \text{ mol SO}_4{}^{2-} \times (-909.3 \text{ kJ/mol SO}_4{}^{2-})$$
$$= -1473 \text{ kJ} + 537.6 \text{ kJ} + 909.3 \text{ kJ} = -26 \text{ kJ}$$

Practice Example A: Given that $\Delta H_f^\circ[\text{AgI}(s)] = -61.84$ kJ/mol, what is the standard enthalpy change for the precipitation of silver iodide?

Practice Example B: The standard enthalpy change for the precipitation of $\text{Ag}_2\text{CO}_3(s)$ is -39.9 kJ per mole of $\text{Ag}_2\text{CO}_3(s)$ formed. What is $\Delta H_f^\circ[\text{Ag}_2\text{CO}_3(s)]$?

> Precipitate BaSO_4. Dissolve $\text{Ba(NO}_3)_2$ in water and add Na_2SO_4 to produce BaSO_4. Barium sulfate can be ingested and used as a tracer in X-ray examinations because it is opaque to X rays.

CONCEPT ASSESSMENT ✓

Is it possible to calculate a heat of reaction at 373.15 K using standard enthalpies of formation at 298.15 K? If so, explain how you would do this, and indicate any additional data you might need.

7-9   FUELS AS SOURCES OF ENERGY

One of the most important uses of thermochemical measurements and calculations is in assessing materials as energy sources. For the most part, these materials, called fuels, liberate heat through the process of combustion. We will briefly survey some common fuels, emphasizing matters that a thermochemical background helps us to understand.

FOSSIL FUELS

The bulk of current energy needs are met by petroleum, natural gas, and coal—so-called fossil fuels. These fuels are derived from plant and animal life of millions of years ago. The original source of the energy locked into these fuels is solar energy. In the process of *photosynthesis*, CO_2 and H_2O, in the presence of enzymes, the pigment chlorophyll, and sunlight, are converted to *carbohydrates*. These are compounds with formulas $C_m(H_2O)_n$, where m and n are integers. For example, in the sugar glucose $m = n = 6$, that is, $C_6(H_2O)_6 = C_6H_{12}O_6$. Its formation through photosynthesis is an *endothermic* process, represented as

$$6\,CO_2(g) + 6\,H_2O(l) \xrightarrow[\text{sunlight}]{\text{chlorophyll}} C_6H_{12}O_6(s) + 6\,O_2(g) \qquad \Delta H^\circ = +2.8 \times 10^3 \text{ kJ} \quad (7.23)$$

> Heinhorst, S., Cannon, G. "Nature: Cleaner Fuels for the Future." *J. Chem. Educ.* **2000**: 77, 810 (July 2000).

◄ Although the formula $C_m(H_2O)_n$ suggests a "hydrate" of carbon, in carbohydrates, there are no H_2O units as there are in hydrates such as $CuSO_4 \cdot 5\,H_2O$. H and O atoms are simply found in the same numerical ratio as in H_2O.

When reaction (7.23) is reversed, as in the combustion of glucose, heat is evolved. The combustion reaction is *exothermic*.

The complex carbohydrate cellulose, with molecular masses ranging up to 500,000 u, is the principal structural material of plants. When plant life decomposes in the presence of bacteria and out of contact with air, O and H atoms are removed and the approximate carbon content of the residue increases in the progression

Peat $\longrightarrow$ lignite (32% C) $\longrightarrow$ sub-bituminous coal (40% C) $\longrightarrow$

bituminous coal (60% C) $\longrightarrow$ anthracite coal (80% C)

For this process to progress all the way to anthracite coal may take about 300 million years. Coal, then, is a combustible organic rock consisting of carbon, hydrogen, and oxygen, together with small quantities of nitrogen, sulfur, and mineral matter (ash). (One proposed formula for a "molecule" of bituminous coal is $C_{153}H_{115}N_3O_{13}S_2$).

Petroleum and natural gas formed in a different way. The remains of plants and animals living in ancient seas fell to the ocean floor, where they were decomposed by bacteria and covered with sand and mud. Over time, the sand and mud were converted to sandstone by the weight of overlying layers of sand and mud. The high pressures and temperatures resulting from this overlying sandstone rock formation transformed the original organic matter into petroleum and natural gas. The ages of these deposits range from about 250 million to 500 million years.

A typical natural gas consists of about 85% methane (CH_4), 10% ethane (C_2H_6), 3% propane (C_3H_8), and small quantities of other combustible and noncombustible gases. A typical petroleum consists of several hundred different hydrocarbons that range in complexity from C_1 molecules (CH_4) to C_{40} or higher (such as $C_{40}H_{82}$).

One way to compare different fuels is through their heats of combustion: In general, *the higher the heat of combustion, the better the fuel*. Table 7.4 lists approximate heats of combustion for the fossil fuels. These data show that *biomass* (living matter or materials derived from it—wood, alcohols, municipal waste) is a viable fuel, but that fossil fuels yield more energy per unit mass.

TABLE 7.4 Approximate Heats of Combustion of Some Fuels

Heat of Combustion

Fuel	kJ/g
Municipal waste	−12.7
Cellulose	−17.5
Pinewood	−21.2
Methanol	−22.7
Peat	−20.8
Bituminous coal	−28.3
Isooctane (a component of gasoline)	−47.8
Natural gas	−49.5

Problems Posed by Fossil Fuel Use. There are two fundamental problems with the use of fossil fuels. First, fossil fuels are essentially *nonrenewable* energy sources. The world consumption of fossil fuels is expected to increase for the foreseeable future (Fig. 7-22), but when will Earth's supply of these fuels run out? There is currently a debate about whether oil production has peaked now and is about to decline, or whether it will peak more toward the middle of the 21st century. The second problem with fossil fuels is their environmental effect. Sulfur impurities in fuels produce oxides of sulfur. The high temperatures associated with combustion cause the reaction of N_2 and O_2 in air to form oxides of nitrogen. Oxides of sulfur and nitrogen are implicated in air pollution and are important contributors to the environmental problem known as acid rain. Another inevitable product of the combustion of fossil fuels is carbon dioxide, one of the "greenhouse" gases leading to *global warming* and potential changes in Earth's climate.

▶ Environmental issues associated with oxides of sulfur and nitrogen are discussed more fully in later chapters.

Global Warming—An Environmental Issue Involving Carbon Dioxide. We do not normally think of CO_2 as an air pollutant because it is essentially nontoxic and is a natural and necessary component of air. Its ultimate effect on the environment, however, could be very significant. A buildup of $CO_2(g)$ in the atmosphere may disturb the energy balance on Earth.

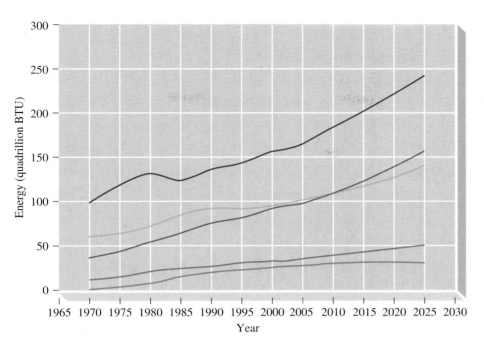

◀ **FIGURE 7-22**
World primary energy consumption by energy source
These graphs show the history of energy consumption since 1970, with predictions to 2025. Petroleum (dark blue line) is seen to be the major source of energy for the foreseeable future, followed by coal (yellow) and natural gas (pink), which are about the same. Other sources of energy included are wind power (purple) and nuclear power (light blue). [Source *http://www.eia.doe.gov/oiaf/*]

Earth's atmosphere, discussed in Chapter 6 (page 212) is largely transparent to visible and UV radiation from the sun. This radiation is absorbed at Earth's surface, which is warmed by it. Some of this absorbed energy is reradiated as infrared radiation. Certain atmospheric gases, primarily CO_2, methane, and water vapor, absorb some of this infrared radiation, and the energy thus retained in the atmosphere produces a warming effect. This process, outlined in Figure 7-23, is often compared to the retention of thermal energy in a greenhouse and is called the "greenhouse effect."* The natural greenhouse effect is essential in maintaining the proper temperature for life on Earth. Without it, Earth would be permanently covered with ice.

Over the past 400,000 years, the atmospheric carbon dioxide concentration has varied from 180 to 300 parts per million with the preindustrial-age concentration at about 285 ppm. By 2005, the level had increased to about 376 ppm and is still rising (Fig. 7-24). Increasing atmospheric carbon dioxide concentrations result from the burning of carbon-containing fuels such as wood, coal, natural gas, and gasoline (Fig. 7-24) and from the deforestation of tropical regions (plants, through photosynthesis, consume CO_2 from the atmosphere). The expected effect of a CO_2 buildup is an increase in Earth's average temperature, a **global warming**. Some estimates are that a doubling of the CO_2 content over that of preindustrial times could occur before the end of the present century and that this doubling could produce an average global temperature increase of from 1.5 to 4.5 °C.

Predicting the probable effects of a CO_2 buildup in the atmosphere is done largely through computer models, and it is very difficult to know all the factors that should be included in these models and the relative importance of these factors. For example, global warming could lead to the increased evaporation of water and increased cloud formation. In turn, an increased cloud cover could reduce the amount of solar radiation reaching Earth's surface and, to some extent, offset global warming.

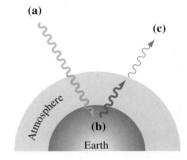

(a)
(c)
Atmosphere
(b)
Earth

▲ **FIGURE 7-23**
The "greenhouse" effect
(a) Some incoming radiation from sunlight is reflected back into space by the atmosphere, and some, such as certain UV light, is absorbed by stratospheric ozone. Much of the radiation from sunlight, however, reaches Earth's surface.
(b) Earth's surface re-emits some of this energy as infrared radiation.
(c) Infrared radiation leaving Earth's atmosphere is less intense than that emitted by Earth's surface because some of this radiation is absorbed by CO_2 and other greenhouse gases and warms the atmosphere.

---

*Glass, like CO_2, is transparent to visible and some UV light but absorbs infrared radiation. The glass in a greenhouse, though, acts primarily to prevent the bulk flow of warm air out of the greenhouse.

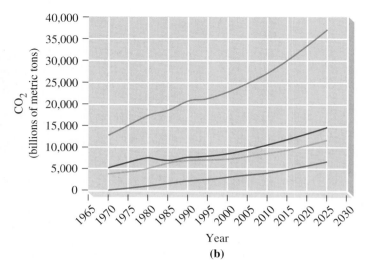

▲ **FIGURE 7-24**

Increasing carbon dioxide content of the atmosphere

(a) The global average atmospheric carbon dioxide level over a 50-year span, expressed in parts per million by volume, as measured by a worldwide cooperative sampling network. **(b)** The actual and predicted CO_2 emissions for a 55-year span due to the combustion of natural gas (pink line), coal (yellow), and petroleum (dark blue), together with the total of all CO_2 emissions (light blue).

Materials developed by the Intergovernmental Panel on Climate Change (IPCC) regarding the risks of human-induced climate change, its potential impacts and options for mitigation can be found at http://www.ipcc.ch/pub/reports.htm.

Some of the significant possible effects of global warming are

- local temperature changes. The average number of days of daily maximum temperatures in excess of 90 °F in New York City might increase from 15 days per year at the close of the 20th century to 48 days per year before the close of the 21st century.

- a rise in sea level caused by the thermal expansion of seawater and increased melting of continental ice caps. A potential increase in sea level of up to 1 m by 2100 would displace tens of millions of inhabitants in Bangladesh alone.

- the migration of plant and animal species. Vegetation now characteristic of certain areas of the globe could migrate into regions several hundred kilometers closer to the poles. The areas in which diseases such as malaria are endemic could also expand.

Although some of the current thinking involves speculation, a growing body of evidence supports the likelihood of global warming. For example, analyses of tiny air bubbles trapped in the Antarctic ice cap show a strong correlation between the atmospheric CO_2 content and temperature for the past 160,000 years—low temperatures during periods of low CO_2 levels and higher temperatures with higher levels of CO_2.

CO_2 is not the only greenhouse gas. Several gases are even stronger infrared absorbers—specifically, methane (CH_4), ozone (O_3), nitrous oxide (N_2O), and chlorofluorocarbons (CFCs). Furthermore, atmospheric concentrations of some of these gases have been growing at a faster rate than that of CO_2. No strategies beyond curtailing the use of chlorofluorocarbons and fossil fuels have emerged for countering a possible global warming. Like several other major environmental issues, some aspects of global warming are not well understood, and research, debate, and action are all likely to occur simultaneously for a long time to come.

▲ An ice core from the ice sheet in Antarctica is cut into sections in a refrigerated clean room. The ice core is then analyzed to determine the amount and type of trapped gases and trace elements it contains. These data provide information regarding past changes in climate and current trends in the pollution of the atmosphere.

COAL AND OTHER ENERGY SOURCES

In the United States, reserves of coal far exceed those of petroleum and natural gas. Despite this relative abundance, however, the use of coal has not increased significantly in recent years. In addition to the environmental effects cited above, the expense and hazards involved in the deep mining of coal are considerable. Surface mining, which is less hazardous and expensive than deep mining, is also more damaging to the environment. One promising possibility for using coal reserves is to convert coal to gaseous or liquid fuels, either in surface installations or while the coal is still underground.

Gasification of Coal.   Before cheap natural gas became available in the 1940s, gas produced from coal (variously called producer gas, town gas, or city gas) was widely used in the United States. This gas was manufactured by passing steam and air through heated coal and involved reactions such as

Mueller, M. R., McCorkle, K. L. "Simultaneous Determinations of Sulfur and Heat Content of Coal: Revitalization of a Traditional Physical Chemistry Experiment." *J. Chem. Educ.* **1994:** *71,* 169.

$$C(graphite) + H_2O(g) \longrightarrow CO(g) + H_2(g) \qquad \Delta H° = +131.3 \text{ kJ} \qquad (7.24)$$

$$CO(g) + H_2O(g) \longrightarrow CO_2(g) + H_2(g) \qquad \Delta H° = -41.2 \text{ kJ} \qquad (7.25)$$

$$2C(graphite) + O_2(g) \longrightarrow 2 CO(g) \qquad \Delta H° = -221.0 \text{ kJ} \qquad (7.26)$$

$$C(graphite) + 2 H_2(g) \longrightarrow CH_4(g) \qquad \Delta H° = -74.8 \text{ kJ} \qquad (7.27)$$

The principal gasification reaction (7.24) is highly endothermic. The heat requirements for this reaction are met by the carefully controlled partial burning of coal (reaction 7.26).

A typical producer gas consists of about 23% CO, 18% H_2, 8% CO_2, and 1% CH_4 by volume. It also contains about 50% N_2 because air is used in its production. Because the N_2 and CO_2 are noncombustible, producer gas has only about 10 to 15% of the heat value of natural gas. Modern gasification processes include several features:

1. They use $O_2(g)$ instead of air, thereby eliminating $N_2(g)$ in the product.

2. They provide for the removal of noncombustible $CO_2(g)$ and sulfur impurities. For example,

$$CaO(s) + CO_2(g) \longrightarrow CaCO_3(s)$$

$$2 H_2S(g) + SO_2(g) \longrightarrow 3 S(s) + 2 H_2O(g)$$

3. They include a step (called *methanation*) to convert CO and H_2, in the presence of a catalyst, to CH_4.

$$CO(g) + 3 H_2(g) \longrightarrow CH_4(g) + H_2O(l)$$

The product is called *substitute natural gas* (SNG), a gaseous mixture with composition and heat value similar to that of natural gas.

Liquefaction of Coal.   The first step in obtaining liquid fuels from coal generally involves gasification of coal, as in reaction (7.24). This step is followed by catalytic reactions in which liquid hydrocarbons are formed.

$$n \text{ CO} + (2n + 1)H_2 \longrightarrow C_nH_{2n+2} + n \text{ H}_2O$$

In still another process, liquid methanol is formed.

$$CO(g) + 2 H_2(g) \longrightarrow CH_3OH(l) \qquad (7.28)$$

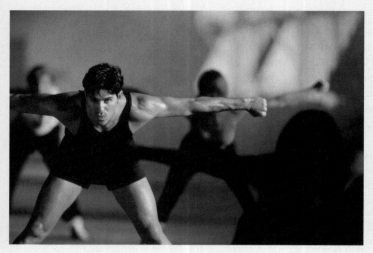

◄ Aerobic exercise is an excellent way to burn fat and build muscle.

Aerobics, tennis, weight lifting, and jogging are popular forms of exercise, which is important to maintaining a healthy body. Where do we get the energy to do these things? Surprisingly, mostly from fat, the body's chief energy storage system.

During exercise, fat molecules react with water (hydrolyze) to form a group of compounds called fatty acids.

Through a complex series of reactions, these fatty acids are converted to carbon dioxide and water. Energy released in these reactions is used to power muscles. A typical human fatty acid is palmitic acid, $CH_3(CH_2)_{14}COOH$.

The direct combustion of $CH_3(CH_2)_{14}COOH$ in a bomb calorimeter yields the same products as its metabolism in the body, together with a large quantity of heat.

$$CH_3(CH_2)_{14}COOH + 23\,O_2(g) \longrightarrow$$
$$16\,CO_2(g) + 16\,H_2O(l) \qquad \Delta H° = -9977\ \text{kJ}$$

A hydrocarbon with a similar carbon and hydrogen content, $C_{16}H_{34}$, yields a similar quantity of heat on complete combustion, −10,700 kJ—the fat stored in our bodies (our fuel) is comparable to the jet fuel in an airplane. In both cases, the fuel adds weight but can be burned to produce the large amount of energy needed for movement and life support.

Simple carbohydrates are broken down and their energy released more rapidly than fats, and this is why we consume sugars (fruit juice, candy bars, and so on) for a quick burst of energy. The combustion of 1 mol $C_{12}H_{22}O_{11}$

In 1942, some 32 million gallons of aviation fuel were made from coal in Germany. In South Africa, the Sasol process for coal liquefaction has been a major source of gasoline and a variety of other petroleum products and chemicals for over 50 years.

METHANOL

The octane rating of fuels is presented in Section 26-2.

Methanol, CH_3OH, can be obtained from coal by reaction (7.28). It can also be produced by thermal decomposition (pyrolysis) of wood, manure, sewage, or municipal waste. The heat of combustion of methanol is only about one-half that of a typical gasoline on a mass basis, but methanol has a high octane number—106—compared with 100 for the gasoline hydrocarbon isooctane and about 92 for premium gasoline. Methanol has been tested and used as a fuel in internal combustion engines and is cleaner burning than gasoline. Methanol can also be used for space heating, electric power generation, fuel cells, and as a reactant to make a variety of other organic compounds.

ETHANOL

Ethanol, C_2H_5OH, is produced mostly from ethylene, C_2H_4, which in turn is derived from petroleum. Current interest centers on the production of ethanol by the fermentation of organic matter, a process known throughout recorded history. Ethanol production by fermentation is probably most advanced in Brazil, where sugarcane and cassava (manioc) are the plant matter (biomass) used. In the United States, corn-based ethanol is used chiefly as an additive to gasoline to improve its octane rating and reduce air pollution. Also, a 90% gasoline–10% ethanol mixture is used as an automotive fuel under the name *gasohol*.

(sucrose or cane sugar), however, yields much less energy (-5640 kJ/mol) than does a fatty acid of similar carbon and hydrogen content. In the enthalpy diagram of Figure 7-25, we can think of the sucrose molecule as in a condition somewhere between a hydrocarbon and the ultimate oxidation products: CO_2 and H_2O. A fatty acid, on the other hand, is in a condition closer to that of the hydrocarbon.

▲ FIGURE 7-25
Energy values of a fatty acid, a carbohydrate, and a hydrocarbon
Each of these three comparable 12-carbon compounds produces 12 mol $CO_2(g)$ and some $H_2O(l)$ as combustion products. The hydrocarbon, $C_{12}H_{24}$, releases the most energy on combustion. The fatty acid lauric acid, $CH_3(CH_2)_{10}COOH$, yields nearly as much, but the carbohydrate sucrose, $C_{12}H_{22}O_{11}$, yields considerably less.

As discussed in Section 7-2, the common energy unit for expressing the energy values of food is the Calorie (Cal), which is actually a kilocalorie.

$$1 \text{ Cal} = 1 \text{ kcal} = 4.184 \text{ kJ}$$

As energy sources, fats yield about 9 Cal/g (38 kJ/g), whereas carbohydrates and proteins both yield about 4 Cal/g (17 kJ/g).

Consider a 65-kg (143-lb) person of average height and build. Typically this person would have about 11 kg (24 lb) of stored fats—a fuel reserve of about 4.2×10^5 kJ. On the other hand, if the body stored only carbohydrates, the stored reservoir would have to be about 25 kg. The 65-kg person would have to weigh about 80 kg (176 lb). A more dramatic picture might be that of a bird carrying its energy reserves as carbohydrates instead of fat. The excess "baggage" might make it impossible for the bird to fly.

It is important to understand some other matters about fat. First, the quantity of stored fat that an individual typically carries is greater than what is needed to meet energy requirements. Excess body fat leads to an increased risk of heart disease, diabetes, and other medical problems. Second, one does not have to consume fats in order to store body fats. All food types are broken down into small molecules during digestion, and these small molecules are reassembled into the more complex structures that the body needs. In the body, fat molecules can be synthesized from the small molecules produced from carbohydrates, for example.

HYDROGEN

Another fuel with great potential is hydrogen. Its most attractive features are that

- on a per gram basis, its heat of combustion is more than twice that of methane and about three times that of gasoline;
- the product of its combustion is H_2O, not CO and CO_2 as with gasoline.

Currently, the bulk of hydrogen used commercially is made from petroleum and natural gas, but for hydrogen to be a significant fuel of the future, efficient methods must be perfected for obtaining hydrogen from other sources, especially water. Alternative methods of producing hydrogen and the prospects of developing an economy based on hydrogen are discussed later in the text (page 951).

Piezo popper: Take a plastic film canister and add a few drops of methanol. Put a hole in the top and attach wires to a BBQ (piezoelectric igniter). Push the wires into the canister top so that when the igniter is pressed a spark ignites the methanol and the canister pops off from the top. Before ignition, warm the canister with your hands to vaporize the methanol. Use ethanol or acetone as a substitute. With practice, you can pop the canister, shoot it in the air and catch it on the way down.

ALTERNATIVE ENERGY SOURCES

Combustion reactions are only one means of extracting useful energy from materials. An alternative, for example, is to carry out reactions that yield the same products as combustion reactions in electrochemical cells called *fuel cells*. The energy is released as electricity rather than as heat (see Section 20-5). Solar energy can be used directly, without recourse to photosynthesis. Nuclear processes can be used in place of chemical reactions (Chapter 25). Other alternative sources in various stages of development and use include hydroelectric energy, geothermal energy, and tidal and wind power.

A large amount of information about alternative energy sources can be found at http://eia.doe.gov/fuelrenewable_njava.html.

Summary

7-1 Getting Started: Some Terminology—The subject of a thermochemical study is broken down into the **system** of interest and the portions of the universe with which the system may interact, the **surroundings**. An **open system** can exchange both energy and matter with its surroundings. A **closed system** can exchange only energy, and not matter. An **isolated system** can exchange neither energy nor matter with its surroundings (Fig. 7-1). **Energy** is the capacity to do work, and **work** is performed when a force acts through a distance. Energy can be further characterized (Fig. 7-2) as **kinetic energy** (energy associated with matter in motion) or **potential energy** (energy resulting from the position or composition of matter). Kinetic energy associated with random molecular motion is sometimes called **thermal energy**.

7-2 Heat—**Heat** is energy transferred between a system and its surroundings as a result of a temperature difference between the two. In some cases, heat can be transferred at constant temperature, as in a change in state of matter in the system. A quantity of heat is the product of the heat capacity of the system and the temperature change (equation 7.5). In turn, **heat capacity** is the product of mass and **specific heat**, the amount of heat required to change the temperature of one gram of substance by one degree Celsius. Historically, the unit for measuring heat has been the **calorie** (**cal**), but the SI unit of heat is the joule, the same as for other forms of energy (equation 7.2). Energy transfers between a system and its surroundings must conform to the **law of conservation of energy**, meaning that all heat lost by a system is gained by its surroundings (equation 7.6).

7-3 Heats of Reaction and Calorimetry—In a chemical reaction, a change in the **chemical energy** associated with the reactants and products may appear as heat. The **heat of reaction** is the quantity of heat exchanged between a system and its surroundings when the reaction occurs at a constant temperature. In an **exothermic reaction**, heat is given off by the system; in an **endothermic reaction** the system absorbs heat. Heats of reaction are determined in a **calorimeter**, a device for measuring quantities of heat (equation 7.10). Exothermic combustion reactions are usually studied in a **bomb calorimeter** (Fig. 7-5). A common type of calorimeter used in the general chemistry laboratory is constructed from ordinary Styrofoam cups (Fig. 7-6).

7-4 Work—In some reactions an energy transfer between a system and its surroundings occurs as work. This is commonly the work involved in the expansion or compression of gases (Fig. 7-8) and is called **pressure–volume work** (equation 7.11).

7-5 The First Law of Thermodynamics—**Internal energy** (U) is the total energy (both kinetic and potential) in a

system. The **first law of thermodynamics** relates changes in the internal energy of a system (ΔU) to the quantities of heat (q) and work (w) exchanged between the system and its surroundings. The relationship is $\Delta U = q + w$ (equation 7.12) and requires that a set of sign conventions be consistently followed. A **function of state** (**state function**) has a value that depends only on the exact condition or state in which a system is found and not on how that state was reached. Internal energy is a state function. A path-dependent function, such as heat or work, depends on how a change in a system is achieved. A change that is accomplished through an infinite number of infinitesimal steps is a **reversible process** (Fig. 7-12), whereas a change accomplished in one step or a series of finite steps is **irreversible**.

7-6 Heats of Reaction: ΔU and ΔH—In a chemical reaction with work limited to pressure–volume work and conducted at constant volume, the heat of reaction is equal to the change in internal energy (equation 7.13). For reactions at constant pressure a more useful function is **enthalpy** (H), defined as the internal energy (U) of a system plus the pressure–volume product (P–V). The **enthalpy change** (ΔH) in a reaction proves to be the heat of reaction at constant pressure (equation 7.14). Most heats of reaction are reported as ΔH values. A substance under a pressure of 1 bar (10^5 Pa) and at the temperature of interest is said to be in its **standard state.** If the reactants and products of a reaction are in their standard states, the enthalpy change in a reaction is called the **standard enthalpy of reaction** and designated as $\Delta H°$. Enthalpy changes can be represented schematically through **enthalpy diagrams** (Fig. 7-15).

7-7 Indirect Determination of ΔH: Hess's Law—Often an unknown ΔH value can be established indirectly through **Hess's law**, which states that an overall enthalpy change is the sum of the enthalpy changes of the individual steps leading to the overall process (Fig. 7-17).

7-8 Standard Enthalpies of Formation—By arbitrarily assigning an enthalpy of zero to the reference forms of the elements in their standard states, the enthalpy change in the formation of a compound from its elements becomes a **standard enthalpy of formation** (ΔH_f°). Using tabulated standard enthalpies of formation (Table 7.2), it is possible to calculate standard enthalpies of reactions without having to perform additional experiments (equation 7.21).

7-9 Fuels as Sources of Energy—One of the chief applications of thermochemistry is in the study of the combustion of fuels as energy sources. Currently, the principal fuels are the fossil fuels, but potential alternative fuels are also mentioned in this chapter and discussed in more depth later in the text. One of the problems with the use of fossil fuels is the potential for **global warming**.

Integrative Example

The partial burning of coal in the presence of O_2 and H_2O produces a mixture of $CO(g)$ and $H_2(g)$ called *synthesis gas*. This gas can be used to synthesize organic compounds, or it can be burned as a fuel. A typical synthesis gas consists of 55.0% $CO(g)$, 33.0% $H_2(g)$, and 12.0% noncombustible gases (mostly CO_2), *by volume*. To what temperature can 25.0 kg water at 25.0 °C be heated with the heat liberated by the combustion of 0.205 m^3 of this typical synthesis gas, measured at 25.0 °C and 102.6 kPa pressure?

Strategy

First, use the ideal gas equation to calculate the total number of moles of gas, and then use equation (6.17) to establish the number of moles of each combustible gas. Next, write an equation for the combustion of each gas. Use these equations and enthalpy of formation data to calculate the total amount of heat released by the combustion. Finally, use equation (7.5) to calculate the temperature increase when this quantity of heat is absorbed by the 25.0 kg of water. The final water temperature is then easily established.

Solution

Substitute the applicable data into the ideal gas equation written for SI units, that is, with $R = 8.3145 \text{ m}^3 \text{ Pa mol}^{-1} \text{ K}^{-1}$. Solve for n.

$$n = \frac{PV}{RT} = \frac{102.6 \text{ kPa} \times 1000 \text{ Pa}/1 \text{ kPa} \times 0.205 \text{ m}^3}{8.3145 \text{ m}^3 \text{ Pa mol}^{-1} \text{ K}^{-1} \times 298.2 \text{ K}}$$
$$= 8.48 \text{ mol gas}$$

Now, apportion the 8.48 moles among the three gases present, converting the volume percents to mole fractions and using equation (6.17).

$n_{CO} = n_{tot} \times x_{CO} = 8.48 \text{ mol} \times 0.550 = 4.66 \text{ mol CO}$

$n_{H_2} = n_{tot} \times x_{H_2} = 8.48 \text{ mol} \times 0.330 = 2.80 \text{ mol H}_2$

(remaining gas noncombustible)

Write an equation for the combustion of $CO(g)$, list ΔH_f° data beneath the equation, and determine ΔH_{comb}° per mole of $CO(g)$.

$$CO(g) + \frac{1}{2}O_2(g) \longrightarrow CO_2(g)$$

ΔH_f°: -110.5 kJ/mol $\qquad\qquad -393.5 \text{ kJ/mol}$

$\Delta H_{comb}^\circ = 1 \text{ mol CO}_2 \times (-393.5 \text{ kJ/mol CO}_2) - 1 \text{ mol CO} \times (-110.5 \text{ kJ/mol CO})$
$\qquad = -283.0 \text{ kJ}$

Write another equation for the combustion of $H_2(g)$, again listing ΔH_f° data beneath the equation, and determining ΔH_{comb}° per mole of $H_2(g)$.

$$H_2(g) + \frac{1}{2}O_2(g) \longrightarrow H_2O(l)$$

ΔH_f°: $\quad 0 \text{ kJ/mol}$ $\qquad\qquad -285.8 \text{ kJ/mol}$

$\Delta H_{comb}^\circ = 1 \text{ mol H}_2O \times (-285.8 \text{ kJ/mol H}_2O) = -285.8 \text{ kJ}$

Determine the total heat released in the combustion of the amounts of CO and H_2 in the 0.205 m³ of gas.

$4.66 \text{ mol CO} \times (-283.0 \text{ kJ/mol CO}) + 2.80 \text{ mol H}_2 \times (-285.8 \text{ kJ/mol H}_2)$
$= -2.12 \times 10^3 \text{ kJ}$

The quantity of heat absorbed by the 25.0 kg of water is

$q_{water} = -q_{comb}$

$$= -\left(-2.12 \times 10^3 \text{ kJ} \times \frac{1000 \text{ J}}{1 \text{ kJ}}\right) = 2.12 \times 10^6 \text{ J}$$

Rearrange equation (7.6) to solve for the temperature change in the 2.50×10^4 g (25.0 kg) of water.

$$\Delta T = \frac{q_{water}}{\text{mass water} \times \text{sp.ht.water}}$$

$$\Delta T = \frac{2.12 \times 10^6 \text{ J}}{\left(2.50 \times 10^4 \text{ g H}_2O \times \dfrac{4.18 \text{ J}}{\text{g H}_2O \text{ °C}}\right)} = 20.3 \text{ °C}$$

From the initial temperature and the temperature change, determine the final temperature.

$T_f = T_i + \Delta T = 25.0 \text{ °C} + 20.3 \text{ °C} = 45.3 \text{ °C}$

Assessment

The assumption that the gas sample obeys the ideal gas law is probably valid since the temperature of the gas (25.0 °C) is not particularly low and the gas pressure, about 1 atm, is not particularly high. However, the implicit assumption that all the heat of combustion could be transferred to the water was probably not valid. If the transfer were to occur in an ordinary gas-fired water heater, some of the heat would undoubtedly be lost through the exhaust vent. Thus, our calculation was of the highest temperature that could possibly be attained. Note that in using the ideal gas equation the simplest approach was to work with SI units because those were the units of the data that were given.

Exercises

Heat Capacity (Specific Heat)

1. Calculate the quantity of heat, in kilojoules **(a)** required to raise the temperature of 9.25 L of water from 22.0 to 29.4 °C; **(b)** associated with a 33.5 °C decrease in temperature in a 5.85-kg aluminum bar (specific heat of aluminum = 0.903 J g^{-1} °C^{-1}).

2. Calculate the final temperature that results when **(a)** a 12.6-g sample of water at 22.9 °C absorbs 875 J of heat; **(b)** a 1.59-kg sample of platinum at 78.2 °C gives off 1.05 kcal of heat (specific heat of Pt = 0.032 cal g^{-1} °C^{-1}).

3. Refer to Example 7-2. The experiment is repeated with several different metals substituting for the lead. The masses of metal and water and the initial temperatures of the metal and water are the same as in Figure 7-3. The final temperatures are **(a)** Zn, 38.9 °C; **(b)** Pt, 28.8 °C; **(c)** Al, 52.7 °C. What is the specific heat of each metal, expressed in J g^{-1} °C^{-1}?

4. A 75.0-g piece of Ag metal is heated to 80.0 °C and dropped into 50.0 g of water at 23.2 °C. The final temperature of the Ag–H$_2$O mixture is 27.6 °C. What is the specific heat of silver?

5. A 465-g chunk of iron is removed from an oven and plunged into 375 g water in an insulated container. The temperature of the water increases from 26 to 87 °C. If the specific heat of iron is 0.449 J g^{-1} °C^{-1}, what must have been the original temperature of the iron?

6. A piece of stainless steel (specific heat = 0.50 J g^{-1} °C^{-1}) is transferred from an oven at 83 °C into 125 mL of water at 23.2 °C. The water temperature rises to 51.5 °C. What is the mass of the steel? How precise is this method of mass determination? Explain.

7. A 1.00-kg sample of magnesium at 40.0 °C is added to 1.00 L of water maintained at 20.0 °C in an insulated container. What will be the final temperature of the Mg–H$_2$O mixture (specific heat of Mg = 1.024 J g^{-1} °C^{-1})?

8. Brass has a density of 8.40 g/cm^3 and a specific heat of 0.385 J g^{-1} °C^{-1}. A 15.2-cm^3 piece of brass at an initial temperature of 163 °C is dropped into an insulated container with 150.0 g water initially at 22.4 °C. What will be the final temperature of the brass–water mixture?

9. A 74.8-g sample of copper at 143.2 °C is added to an insulated vessel containing 165 mL of glycerol, C$_3$H$_8$O$_3$(l) (d = 1.26 g/mL), at 24.8 °C. The final temperature is 31.1 °C. The specific heat of copper is 0.385 J g^{-1} °C^{-1}. What is the heat capacity of glycerol in J mol^{-1} °C^{-1}?

10. What volume of 18.5 °C water must be added, together with a 1.23-kg piece of iron at 68.5 °C, so that the temperature of the water in the insulated container shown in the figure remains constant at 25.6 °C?

1.23 kg iron
Temp. 68.5 °C
0.449 J g^{-1} °C^{-1}

? mL water
Temp. 18.5 °C

25.6 °C

25.6 °C

25.6 °C

Water

Water

Heats of Reaction

11. How much heat, in kilojoules, is associated with the production of 283 kg of slaked lime, Ca(OH)$_2$?

$$\text{CaO(s)} + \text{H}_2\text{O(l)} \longrightarrow$$
$$\text{Ca(OH)}_2\text{(s)} \qquad \Delta H° = -65.2 \text{ kJ}$$

12. The standard enthalpy change in the combustion of the hydrocarbon octane is $\Delta H° = -5.48 \times 10^3$ kJ/mol C$_8$H$_{18}$(l). How much heat, in kilojoules, is liberated *per gallon* of octane burned? (Density of octane = 0.703 g/mL; 1 gal = 3.785 L.)

13. How much heat, in kilojoules, is evolved in the complete combustion of **(a)** 1.325 g C$_4$H$_{10}$(g); **(b)** 28.4 L C$_4$H$_{10}$(g) at STP; **(c)** 2.6 L C$_4$H$_{10}$(g) at 23.6 °C and 738 mmHg? The complete combustion of butane, C$_4$H$_{10}$(g), is represented by the equation

$$\text{C}_4\text{H}_{10}\text{(g)} + \frac{13}{2}\text{O}_2\text{(g)} \longrightarrow 4 \text{ CO}_2\text{(g)} + 5 \text{ H}_2\text{O(l)}$$
$$\Delta H° = -2877 \text{ kJ}$$

14. Upon complete combustion, the indicated substances evolve the given quantities of heat. Write a balanced equation for the combustion of 1.00 mol of each substance, including the enthalpy change, ΔH, for the reaction.
   (a) 0.584 g of propane, C$_3$H$_8$(g), yields 29.4 kJ
   (b) 0.136 g of camphor, C$_{10}$H$_{16}$O(s), yields 5.27 kJ
   (c) 2.35 mL of acetone, (CH$_3$)$_2$CO(l) (d = 0.791 g/mL), yields 58.3 kJ

15. The combustion of methane gas, the principal constituent of natural gas, is represented by the equation

$$\text{CH}_4\text{(g)} + 2 \text{ O}_2\text{(g)} \longrightarrow \text{CO}_2\text{(g)} + 2 \text{ H}_2\text{O(l)}$$
$$\Delta H° = -890.3 \text{ kJ}$$

   (a) What mass of methane, in kilograms, must be burned to liberate 2.80×10^7 kJ of heat?
   (b) What quantity of heat, in kilojoules, is liberated in the complete combustion of 1.65×10^4 L of CH$_4$(g), measured at 18.6 °C and 768 mmHg?

(c) If the quantity of heat calculated in part **(b)** could be transferred with 100% efficiency to water, what volume of water, in liters, could be heated from 8.8 to 60.0 °C as a result?

16. Refer to the Integrative Example. What volume of the synthesis gas, measured at STP and burned in an open flame (constant-pressure process), is required to heat 40.0 gal of water from 15.2 to 65.0 °C? (1 gal = 3.785 L.)

17. The combustion of hydrogen–oxygen mixtures is used to produce very high temperatures (approximately 2500 °C) needed for certain types of welding operations. Consider the reaction to be

$$H_2(g) + \frac{1}{2}O_2(g) \longrightarrow H_2O(g) \quad \Delta H° = -241.8 \text{ kJ}$$

What is the quantity of heat evolved, in kilojoules, when a 180-g mixture containing equal parts of H_2 and O_2 by mass is burned?

18. Thermite mixtures are used for certain types of welding, and the thermite reaction is highly exothermic.

$$Fe_2O_3(s) + 2 \text{ Al}(s) \longrightarrow Al_2O_3(s) + 2 \text{ Fe}(s)$$
$$\Delta H° = -852 \text{ kJ}$$

1.00 mol of granular Fe_2O_3 and 2.00 mol of granular Al are mixed at room temperature (25 °C), and a reaction is initiated. The liberated heat is retained within the products, whose combined specific heat over a broad temperature range is about 0.8 J g^{-1} °C^{-1}. (The melting point of iron is 1530 °C.) Show that the quantity of heat liberated is more than sufficient to raise the temperature of the products to the melting point of iron.

19. A 0.205-g pellet of potassium hydroxide, KOH, is added to 55.9 g water in a Styrofoam coffee cup. The water temperature rises from 23.5 to 24.4 °C. [Assume that the specific heat of dilute KOH(aq) is the same as that of water.]

(a) What is the approximate heat of solution of KOH, expressed as kilojoules per mole of KOH?
(b) How could the precision of this measurement be improved *without* modifying the apparatus?

20. The heat of solution of KI(s) in water is +20.3 kJ/mol KI. If a quantity of KI is added to sufficient water at 23.5 °C in a Styrofoam cup to produce 150.0 mL of 2.50 M KI, what will be the final temperature? (Assume a density of 1.30 g/mL and a specific heat of 2.7 J g^{-1} °C^{-1} for 2.50 M KI.)

21. You are planning a lecture demonstration to illustrate an endothermic process. You desire to lower the temperature of 1400 mL water in an insulated container from 25 to 10 °C. Approximately what mass of $NH_4Cl(s)$ should you dissolve in the water to achieve this result? The heat of solution of NH_4Cl is +14.7 kJ/mol NH_4Cl.

22. Care must be taken in preparing solutions of solutes that liberate heat on dissolving. The heat of solution of NaOH is −44.5 kJ/mol NaOH. To what maximum temperature may a sample of water, originally at 21 °C, be raised in the preparation of 500 mL of 7.0 M NaOH? Assume the solution has a density of 1.08 g/mL and specific heat of 4.00 J g^{-1} °C^{-1}.

23. Refer to Example 7-4. The product of the neutralization is 0.500 M NaCl. For this solution, assume a density of 1.02 g/mL and a specific heat of 4.02 J g^{-1} °C^{-1}. Also, assume a heat capacity for the Styrofoam cup of 10 J/°C, and recalculate the heat of neutralization.

24. The heat of neutralization of HCl(aq) by NaOH(aq) is −55.84 kJ/mol H_2O produced. If 50.00 mL of 1.05 M NaOH is added to 25.00 mL of 1.86 M HCl, with both solutions originally at 24.72 °C, what will be the final solution temperature? (Assume that no heat is lost to the surrounding air and that the solution produced in the neutralization reaction has a density of 1.02 g/mL and a specific heat of 3.98 J g^{-1} °C^{-1}.)

Enthalpy Changes and States of Matter

25. What mass of ice can be melted with the same quantity of heat as required to raise the temperature of 3.50 mol $H_2O(l)$ by 50.0 °C? [$\Delta H°_{fusion} = 6.01$ kJ/mol $H_2O(s)$]

26. What will be the final temperature of the water in an insulated container as the result of passing 5.00 g of steam [$H_2O(g)$] at 100.0 °C into 100.0 g of water at 25.0 °C? ($\Delta H°_{vap} = 40.6$ kJ/mol H_2O)

27. A 125-g stainless steel ball bearing (sp. ht. = 0.50 J g^{-1} °C^{-1}) at 525 °C is dropped into 75.0 mL of water at 28.5 °C in an open Styrofoam cup. As a result, the water is brought to a boil when the temperature reaches 100.0 °C. What mass of water vaporizes while the boiling continues? ($\Delta H°_{vap} = 40.6$ kJ/mol H_2O)

28. If the ball bearing described in Exercise 27 is dropped onto a large block of ice at 0 °C, what mass of liquid water will form? ($\Delta H°_{fusion} = 6.01$ kJ/mol $H_2O(s)$)

Calorimetry

29. A sample gives off 5228 cal when burned in a bomb calorimeter. The temperature of the calorimeter assembly increases by 4.39 °C. Calculate the heat capacity of the calorimeter, in kilojoules per degree Celsius.

30. The following substances undergo complete combustion in a bomb calorimeter. The calorimeter assembly has a heat capacity of 5.136 kJ/°C. In each case, what is the final temperature if the initial water temperature is 22.43 °C?
    (a) 0.3268 g caffeine, $C_8H_{10}O_2N_4$ (heat of combustion = −1014.2 kcal/mol caffeine);

(b) 1.35 ml of methyl ethyl ketone, $C_4H_8O(l)$, $d = 0.805$ g/mL (heat of combustion = −2444 kJ/mol methyl ethyl ketone).

31. A bomb calorimetry experiment is performed with xylose, $C_5H_{10}O_5(s)$, as the combustible substance. The data obtained are

mass of xylose burned:	1.183 g
heat capacity of calorimeter:	4.728 kJ/°C
initial calorimeter temperature:	23.29 °C
final calorimeter temperature:	27.19 °C

(a) What is the heat of combustion of xylose, in kilojoules per mole? **(b)** Write the chemical equation for the complete combustion of xylose, and represent the value of ΔH in this equation. (Assume for this reaction that $\Delta U \approx \Delta H$.)

32. A coffee-cup calorimeter contains 100.0 mL of 0.300 M HCl at 20.3 °C. When 1.82 g Zn(s) is added, the temperature rises to 30.5 °C. What is the heat of reaction per mol Zn? Make the same assumptions as in Example 7-4, and also assume that there is no heat lost with the $H_2(g)$ that escapes.

$$Zn(s) + 2 H^+(aq) \longrightarrow Zn^{2+}(aq) + H_2(g)$$

33. A 0.75-g sample of KCl is added to 35.0 g H_2O in a Styrofoam cup and stirred until it dissolves. The temperature of the solution drops from 24.8 to 23.6 °C. **(a)** Is the process endothermic or exothermic? **(b)** What is the heat of solution of KCl expressed in kilojoules per mole of KCl?

34. The heat of solution of potassium acetate in water is -15.3 kJ/mol $KC_2H_3O_2$. What will be the final temperature when 0.136 mol $KC_2H_3O_2$ is dissolved in 525 mL water that is initially at 25.1 °C?

35. A 1.620-g sample of naphthalene, $C_{10}H_8(s)$, is completely burned in a bomb calorimeter assembly and a temperature increase of 8.44 °C is noted. If the heat of combustion of naphthalene is -5156 kJ/mol $C_{10}H_8$, what is the heat capacity of the bomb calorimeter?

36. Salicylic acid, $C_7H_6O_3$, has been suggested as a calorimetric standard. Its heat of combustion is -3.023×10^3 kJ/mol $C_7H_6O_3$. From the following data determine the heat capacity of a bomb calorimeter assembly (that is, the bomb, water, stirrer, thermometer, wires, and so forth).

mass of salicylic acid burned:	1.201 g
initial calorimeter temperature:	23.68 °C
final calorimeter temperature:	29.82 °C

37. Refer to Example 7-3. Based on the heat of combustion of sucrose established in the example, what should be the temperature change (ΔT) produced by the combustion of 1.227 g $C_{12}H_{22}O_{11}$ in a bomb calorimeter assembly with a heat capacity of 3.87 kJ/°C?

38. A 1.397-g sample of thymol, $C_{10}H_{14}O(s)$ (a preservative and a mold and mildew preventative), is burned in a bomb calorimeter assembly. The temperature increase is 11.23 °C, and the heat capacity of the bomb calorimeter is 4.68 kJ/°C. What is the heat of combustion of thymol, expressed in kilojoules per mole of $C_{10}H_{14}O$?

Pressure–Volume Work

39. Calculate the quantity of work associated with a 3.5-L expansion of a gas (ΔV) against a pressure of 748 mmHg in the units **(a)** liter atmospheres (L atm); **(b)** joules (J); **(c)** calories (cal).

40. Calculate the quantity of work, in joules, associated with the compression of a gas from 5.62 L to 3.37 L by a constant pressure of 1.23 atm.

41. A 1.00-g sample of Ne(g) at 1 atm pressure and 27 °C is allowed to expand into an *evacuated* vessel of 2.50-L volume. Does the gas do work? Explain.

42. Compressed air in aerosol cans is used to free electronic equipment of dust. Does the air do any work as it escapes from the can?

43. In each of the following processes, is any work done when the reaction is carried out at constant pressure in a vessel open to the atmosphere? If so, is work done by the reacting system or on it? **(a)** Neutralization of $Ba(OH)_2(aq)$ by HCl(aq); **(b)** conversion of gaseous nitrogen dioxide to gaseous dinitrogen tetroxide; **(c)** decomposition of calcium carbonate to calcium oxide and carbon dioxide gas.

44. In each of the following processes, is any work done when the reaction is carried out at constant pressure in a vessel open to the atmosphere? If so, is work done by the reacting system or on it? **(a)** Reaction of nitrogen monoxide and oxygen gases to form gaseous nitrogen dioxide; **(b)** precipitation of magnesium hydroxide by the reaction of aqueous solutions of NaOH and $MgCl_2$; **(c)** reaction of copper(II) sulfate and water vapor to form copper(II) sulfate pentahydrate.

First Law of Thermodynamics

45. What is the change in internal energy of a system if the system **(a)** absorbs 58 J of heat and does 58 J of work; **(b)** absorbs 125 J of heat and does 687 J of work; **(c)** evolves 280 cal of heat and has 1.25 kJ of work done on it?

46. What is the change in internal energy of a system if the *surroundings* **(a)** transfer 235 J of heat and 128 J of work to the system; **(b)** absorb 145 J of heat from the system while doing 98 J of work on the system; **(c)** exchange no heat, but receive 1.07 kJ of work from the system?

47. The internal energy of a fixed quantity of an ideal gas depends only on its temperature. A sample of an ideal gas is allowed to expand at a constant temperature (isothermal expansion). **(a)** Does the gas do work? **(b)** Does the gas exchange heat with its surroundings? **(c)** What happens to the temperature of the gas? **(d)** What is ΔU for the gas?

48. In an *adiabatic* process, a system is thermally insulated—there is no exchange of heat between system and surroundings. For the adiabatic expansion of an ideal gas **(a)** does the gas do work? **(b)** Does the internal energy of the gas increase, decrease, or remain constant? **(c)** What happens to the temperature of the gas?
[*Hint*: Refer to Exercise 47.]

49. Do you think the following observation is in any way possible? An ideal gas is expanded isothermally and is observed to do twice as much work as the heat absorbed from its surroundings. Explain your answer.
[*Hint*: Refer to Exercises 47 and 48.]

50. Do you think the following observation is any way possible? A gas absorbs heat from its surroundings while being compressed. Explain your answer.
[*Hint*: Refer to Exercises 45 and 46.]

Relating ΔH and ΔU

51. Only one of the following expressions holds true for the heat of a chemical reaction, *regardless of how the reaction is carried out.* Which is the correct expression and why? **(a)** q_V; **(b)** q_P; **(c)** $\Delta U - w$; **(d)** ΔU; **(e)** ΔH.

52. Determine whether ΔH is equal to, greater than, or less than ΔU for the following reactions. Keep in mind that "greater than" means more positive or less negative, and "less than" means less positive or more negative. Assume that the only significant change in volume during a reaction at constant pressure is that associated with changes in the amounts of gases.

(a) The complete combustion of one mole of 1-butanol (l).

(b) The complete combustion of one mole of glucose, $C_6H_{12}O_6(s)$.

(c) The decomposition of solid ammonium nitrate to produce liquid water and gaseous dinitrogen monoxide.

53. The heat of combustion of 2-propanol at 298.15 K, determined in a bomb calorimeter, is -33.41 kJ/g. For the combustion of one mole of 2-propanol, determine **(a)** ΔU, and **(b)** ΔH.

54. Write an equation to represent the combustion of thymol referred to in Exercise 38. Include in this equation the values for ΔU and ΔH.

Hess's Law

55. The standard enthalpy of formation of $NH_3(g)$ is -46.11 kJ/mol NH_3. What is ΔH° for the following reaction?

$$\frac{2}{3}NH_3(g) \longrightarrow \frac{1}{3}N_2(g) + H_2(g) \qquad \Delta H^\circ =$$

56. Use Hess's law to determine ΔH° for the reaction $CO(g) + \frac{1}{2}O_2(g) \longrightarrow CO_2(g)$, given that

(a) $C(graphite) + \frac{1}{2}O_2(g) \longrightarrow CO(g)$
$$\Delta H^\circ = -110.54 \text{ kJ}$$

(b) $C(graphite) + O_2(g) \longrightarrow CO_2(g)$
$$\Delta H^\circ = -393.51 \text{ kJ}$$

57. Use Hess's law to determine ΔH° for the reaction $C_3H_4(g) + 2H_2(g) \longrightarrow C_3H_8(g)$, given that

(a) $H_2(g) + \frac{1}{2}O_2(g) \longrightarrow H_2O(l) \quad \Delta H^\circ = -285.8 \text{ kJ}$

(b) $C_3H_4(g) + 4O_2(g) \longrightarrow 3CO_2(g) + 2H_2O(l)$
$$\Delta H^\circ = -1937 \text{ kJ}$$

(c) $C_3H_8(g) + 5O_2(g) \longrightarrow 3CO_2(g) + 4H_2O(l)$
$$\Delta H^\circ = -2219.1 \text{ kJ}$$

58. Given the following information:

$$\frac{1}{2}N_2(g) + \frac{3}{2}H_2(g) \longrightarrow NH_3(g) \qquad \Delta H_1^\circ$$

$$NH_3(g) + \frac{5}{4}O_2(g) \longrightarrow NO(g) + \frac{3}{2}H_2O(l) \quad \Delta H_2^\circ$$

$$H_2(g) + \frac{1}{2}O_2(g) \longrightarrow H_2O(l) \qquad \Delta H_3^\circ$$

Determine ΔH° for the following reaction, expressed in terms of ΔH_1°, ΔH_2°, and ΔH_3°.

$$N_2(g) + O_2(g) \longrightarrow 2NO(g) \qquad \Delta H^\circ = ?$$

59. For the reaction $C_2H_4(g) + Cl_2(g) \longrightarrow C_2H_4Cl_2(l)$, determine ΔH°, given that

$4HCl(g) + O_2(g) \longrightarrow 2Cl_2(g) + 2H_2O(l)$
$$\Delta H^\circ = -202.4 \text{ kJ}$$

$2HCl(g) + C_2H_4(g) + \frac{1}{2}O_2(g) \longrightarrow$
$$C_2H_4Cl_2(l) + H_2O(l) \qquad \Delta H^\circ = -318.7 \text{ kJ}$$

60. Determine ΔH° for the reaction
$N_2H_4(l) + 2H_2O_2(l) \longrightarrow N_2(g) + 4H_2O(l)$
from these data.

$N_2H_4(l) + O_2(g) \longrightarrow N_2(g) + 2H_2O(l)$
$$\Delta H^\circ = -622.2 \text{ kJ}$$

$H_2(g) + \frac{1}{2}O_2(g) \longrightarrow H_2O(l) \qquad \Delta H^\circ = -285.8 \text{ kJ}$

$H_2(g) + O_2(g) \longrightarrow H_2O_2(l) \qquad \Delta H^\circ = -187.8 \text{ kJ}$

61. Substitute natural gas (SNG) is a gaseous mixture containing $CH_4(g)$ that can be used as a fuel. One reaction for the production of SNG is

$4CO(g) + 8H_2(g) \longrightarrow$
$$3CH_4(g) + CO_2(g) + 2H_2O(l) \qquad \Delta H^\circ = ?$$

Use appropriate data from the following list to determine ΔH° for this SNG reaction.

$C(graphite) + \frac{1}{2}O_2(g) \longrightarrow CO(g)$
$$\Delta H^\circ = -110.5 \text{ kJ}$$

$CO(g) + \frac{1}{2}O_2(g) \longrightarrow CO_2(g) \quad \Delta H^\circ = -283.0 \text{ kJ}$

$H_2(g) + \frac{1}{2}O_2(g) \longrightarrow H_2O(l) \qquad \Delta H^\circ = -285.8 \text{ kJ}$

$C(graphite) + 2H_2(g) \longrightarrow CH_4(g)$
$$\Delta H^\circ = -74.81 \text{ kJ}$$

$CH_4(g) + 2O_2(g) \longrightarrow CO_2(g) + 2H_2O(l)$
$$\Delta H^\circ = -890.3 \text{ kJ}$$

62. CCl_4, an important commercial solvent, is prepared by the reaction of $Cl_2(g)$ with a carbon compound. Determine ΔH° for the reaction

$$CS_2(l) + 3Cl_2(g) \longrightarrow CCl_4(l) + S_2Cl_2(l).$$

Use appropriate data from the following listing.

$CS_2(l) + 3O_2(g) \longrightarrow CO_2(g) + 2SO_2(g)$
$$\Delta H^\circ = -1077 \text{ kJ}$$

$2S(s) + Cl_2(g) \longrightarrow S_2Cl_2(l) \qquad \Delta H^\circ = -58.2 \text{ kJ}$

$C(s) + 2Cl_2(g) \longrightarrow CCl_4(l) \qquad \Delta H^\circ = -135.4 \text{ kJ}$

$S(s) + O_2(g) \longrightarrow SO_2(g) \qquad \Delta H^\circ = -296.8 \text{ kJ}$

$SO_2(g) + Cl_2(g) \longrightarrow SO_2Cl_2(l) \qquad \Delta H^\circ = +97.3 \text{ kJ}$

$$C(s) + O_2(g) \longrightarrow CO_2(g) \qquad \Delta H° = -393.5 \text{ kJ}$$
$$CCl_4(l) + O_2(g) \longrightarrow COCl_2(g) + Cl_2O(g)$$
$$\Delta H° = -5.2 \text{ kJ}$$

63. Use Hess's law and the following data
$$CH_4(g) + 2 O_2(g) \longrightarrow CO_2(g) + 2 H_2O(g)$$
$$\Delta H° = -802 \text{ kJ}$$
$$CH_4(g) + CO_2(g) \longrightarrow 2 CO(g) + 2 H_2(g)$$
$$\Delta H° = +247 \text{ kJ}$$
$$CH_4(g) + H_2O(g) \longrightarrow CO(g) + 3 H_2(g)$$
$$\Delta H° = +206 \text{ kJ}$$

to determine $\Delta H°$ for the following reaction, an important source of hydrogen gas

$$CH_4(g) + \frac{1}{2}O_2(g) \longrightarrow CO(g) + 2 H_2(g)$$

64. The standard heats of combustion ($\Delta H°$) per mole of 1,3-butadiene $C_4H_6(g)$, butane [$C_4H_{10}(g)$], and $H_2(g)$ are -2540.2, -2877.6, and -285.8 kJ, respectively. Use these data to calculate the heat of hydrogenation of 1,3-butadiene to butane.

$$C_4H_6(g) + 2 H_2(g) \longrightarrow C_4H_{10}(g) \qquad \Delta H° = ?$$

[*Hint:* Write equations for the combustion reactions. In each combustion, the products are $CO_2(g)$ and $H_2O(l)$.]

Standard Enthalpies of Formation

65. Use standard enthalpies of formation from Table 7.2 and equation (7.21) to determine the standard enthalpy changes in the following reactions.
    (a) $C_3H_8(g) + H_2(g) \longrightarrow C_2H_6(g) + CH_4(g)$;
    (b) $2 H_2S(g) + 3 O_2(g) \longrightarrow 2 SO_2(g) + 2 H_2O(l)$.

66. Use standard enthalpies of formation from Tables 7.2 and 7.3 and equation (7.21) to determine the standard enthalpy change in the following reaction.
$$NH_4{}^+(aq) + OH^-(aq) \longrightarrow H_2O(l) + NH_3(g).$$

67. Use the information given here, data from Appendix D, and equation (7.21) to calculate the standard enthalpy of formation per mole of ZnS(s).
$$2 ZnS(s) + 3 O_2(g) \longrightarrow 2 ZnO(s) + 2 SO_2(g)$$
$$\Delta H° = -878.2 \text{ kJ}$$

68. Use the data in Figure 7-18 and information from Section 3-7 to establish possible relationships between the molecular structure of the hydrocarbons and their standard enthalpies of formation.

69. Use standard enthalpies of formation from Table 7.2 to determine the enthalpy change at 25 °C for the following reaction.
$$2 Cl_2(g) + 2 H_2O(l) \longrightarrow 4 HCl(g) + O_2(g)$$
$$\Delta H° = ?$$

70. Use data from Appendix D to calculate the standard enthalpy change for the following reaction at 25 °C.
$$Fe_2O_3(s) + 3 CO(g) \longrightarrow 2 Fe(s) + 3 CO_2(g)$$
$$\Delta H° = ?$$

71. Use data from Table 7.2 to determine the standard heat of combustion of $C_2H_5OH(l)$, if reactants and products are maintained at 25 °C and 1 atm.

72. Use data from Table 7.2, together with the fact that $\Delta H° = -3509$ kJ for the complete combustion of one

mole of pentane, $C_5H_{12}(l)$, to calculate $\Delta H°$ for the synthesis of 1 mol $C_5H_{12}(l)$ from CO(g) and $H_2(g)$.
$$5 CO(g) + 11 H_2(g) \longrightarrow C_5H_{12}(l) + 5 H_2O(l)$$
$$\Delta H° = ?$$

73. Use data from Table 7.2 and $\Delta H°$ for the following reaction to determine the standard enthalpy of formation of $CCl_4(g)$ at 25 °C and 1 atm.
$$CH_4(g) + 4 Cl_2(g) \longrightarrow CCl_4(g) + 4 HCl(g)$$
$$\Delta H° = -397.3 \text{ kJ}$$

74. Use data from Table 7.2 and $\Delta H°$ for the following reaction to determine the standard enthalpy of formation of hexane, $C_6H_{14}(l)$, at 25 °C and 1 atm.
$$2 C_6H_{14}(l) + 19 O_2(g) \longrightarrow 12 CO_2(g) + 14 H_2O(l)$$
$$\Delta H° = -8326 \text{ kJ}$$

75. Use data from Table 7.3 and Appendix D to determine the standard enthalpy change in the following reaction.
$$Al^{3+}(aq) + 3 OH^-(aq) \longrightarrow Al(OH)_3(s)$$
$$\Delta H° = ?$$

76. Use data from Table 7.3 and Appendix D to determine the standard enthalpy change in the following reaction.
$$Mg(OH)_2(s) + 2 NH_4{}^+(aq) \longrightarrow$$
$$Mg^{2+}(aq) + 2 H_2O(l) + 2 NH_3(g) \qquad \Delta H° = ?$$

77. The decomposition of limestone, $CaCO_3(s)$, into quicklime, CaO(s), and $CO_2(g)$ is carried out in a gas-fired kiln. Use data from Appendix D to determine how much heat is required to decompose 1.35×10^3 kg $CaCO_3(s)$. (Assume that heats of reaction are the same as at 25 °C and 1 atm.)

78. Use data from Table 7.2 to calculate the volume of butane, $C_4H_{10}(g)$, measured at 24.6 °C and 756 mmHg, that must be burned to liberate 5.00×10^4 kJ of heat.

Integrative and Advanced Exercises

79. A British thermal unit (Btu) is defined as the quantity of heat required to change the temperature of 1 lb of water by 1 °F. Assume the specific heat of water to be independent of temperature. How much heat is required to raise the temperature of the water in a 40-gal water heater from 48 to 145 °F in (a) Btu; (b) kcal; (c) kJ?

80. A 7.26-kg shot (as used in the sporting event, the shot put) is dropped from the top of a building 168 m high. What is the maximum temperature increase that could occur in the shot? Assume a specific heat of 0.47 J g^{-1} °C^{-1} for the shot. Why would the actual measured temperature increase likely be less than the calculated value?

81. An alternative approach to bomb calorimetry is to establish the heat capacity of the calorimeter, *exclusive* of the water it contains. The heat absorbed by the water and by the rest of the calorimeter must be calculated separately and then added together. A bomb calorimeter assembly containing 983.5 g water is calibrated by the combustion of 1.354 g anthracene. The temperature of the calorimeter rises from 24.87 to 35.63 °C. When 1.053 g citric acid is burned in the same assembly, but with 968.6 g water, the temperature increases from 25.01 to 27.19 °C. The heat of combustion of anthracene, $C_{14}H_{10}(s)$, is -7067 kJ/mol $C_{14}H_{10}$. What is the heat of combustion of citric acid, $C_6H_8O_7$, expressed in kJ/mol?

82. The method of Exercise 81 is used in some bomb calorimetry experiments. A 1.148-g sample of benzoic acid is burned in excess $O_2(g)$ in a bomb immersed in 1181 g of water. The temperature of the water rises from 24.96 to 30.25 °C. The heat of combustion of benzoic acid is -26.42 kJ/g. In a second experiment, a 0.895-g powdered coal sample is burned in the same calorimeter assembly. The temperature of 1162 g of water rises from 24.98 to 29.81 °C. How many metric tons (1 metric ton = 1000 kg) of this coal would have to be burned to release 2.15×10^9 kJ of heat?

83. A handbook lists two different values for the heat of combustion of hydrogen: 33.88 kcal/g H_2 if $H_2O(l)$ is formed, and 28.67 kcal/g H_2 if $H_2O(g)$ is formed. Explain why these two values are different, and indicate what property this difference represents. Devise a means of verifying your conclusions.

84. Determine the missing values of $\Delta H°$ in the diagram shown below.

85. A particular natural gas consists, in mole percents, of 83.0% CH_4, 11.2% C_2H_6, and 5.8% C_3H_8. A 385-L sample of this gas, measured at 22.6 °C and 739 mmHg, is burned at constant pressure in an excess of oxygen gas. How much heat, in kilojoules, is evolved in the combustion reaction?

86. An overall reaction for a coal gasification process is

$$2\,C(graphite) + 2\,H_2O(g) \longrightarrow CH_4(g) + CO_2(g)$$

Show that this overall equation can be established by an appropriate combination of equations from Section 7-9.

87. Which of the following gases has the greater fuel value on a per liter (STP) basis? That is, which has the greater heat of combustion?
[*Hint:* The only combustible gases are CH_4, C_3H_8, CO, and H_2.]

(a) coal gas: 49.7% H_2, 29.9% CH_4, 8.2% N_2, 6.9% CO, 3.1% C_3H_8, 1.7% CO_2, and 0.5% O_2, by volume.
(b) sewage gas: 66.0% CH_4, 30.0% CO_2, and 4.0% N_2, by volume.

88. A calorimeter that measures an exothermic heat of reaction by the quantity of ice that can be melted is called an ice calorimeter. Now consider that 0.100 L of methane gas, $CH_4(g)$, at 25.0 °C and 744 mmHg is burned at constant pressure in air. The heat liberated is captured and used to melt 9.53 g ice at 0 °C (ΔH_{fusion} of ice = 6.01 kJ/mol).
(a) Write an equation for the complete combustion of CH_4, and show that combustion is incomplete in this case.
(b) Assume that $CO(g)$ is produced in the incomplete combustion of CH_4, and represent the combustion as best you can through a single equation with small whole numbers as coefficients. ($H_2O(l)$ is another product of the combustion.)

89. For the reaction
$$C_2H_4(g) + 3\,O_2(g) \longrightarrow 2\,CO_2(g) + 2\,H_2O(l)$$
$$\Delta H° = -1410.9 \text{ kJ}$$
if the H_2O were obtained as a gas rather than a liquid, **(a)** would the heat of reaction be greater (more negative) or smaller (less negative) than that indicated in the equation? **(b)** Explain your answer. **(c)** Calculate the value of $\Delta H°$ in this case.

90. Some of the butane, $C_4H_{10}(g)$, in a 200.0-L cylinder at 26.0 °C is withdrawn and burned at a constant pressure in an excess of air. As a result, the pressure of the gas in the cylinder falls from 2.35 atm to 1.10 atm. The liberated heat is used to raise the temperature of 132.5 L of water from 26.0 to 62.2 °C. Assume that the combustion products are $CO_2(g)$ and $H_2O(l)$ exclusively, and determine the efficiency of the water heater. (That is, what percent of the heat of combustion was absorbed by the water?)

91. The metabolism of glucose, $C_6H_{12}O_6$, yields $CO_2(g)$ and $H_2O(l)$ as products. Heat released in the process is converted to useful work with about 70% efficiency. Calculate the mass of glucose metabolized by a 58.0-kg person in climbing a mountain with an elevation gain of 1450 m. Assume that the work performed in the climb is about four times that required to simply lift 58.0 kg by 1450 m. ($\Delta H_f°$ of $C_6H_{12}O_6(s)$ is -1273.3 kJ/mol.)

92. An alkane hydrocarbon has the formula C_nH_{2n+2}. The enthalpies of formation of the alkanes decrease (become more negative) as the number of C atoms increases. Starting with butane, $C_4H_{10}(g)$, for each additional CH_2 group in the formula, the enthalpy of formation, $\Delta H_f°$, changes by about -21 kJ/mol. Use this fact and data from Table 7.2 to estimate the heat of combustion of heptane, $C_7H_{16}(l)$.

93. Upon complete combustion, a 1.00-L sample (at STP) of a natural gas gives off 43.6 kJ of heat. If the gas is a mixture of $CH_4(g)$ and $C_2H_6(g)$, what is its percent composition, *by volume*?

94. Under the entry H_2SO_4, a reference source lists many values for the standard enthalpy of formation. For example, for pure $H_2SO_4(l)$, $\Delta H_f° = -814.0$ kJ/mol; for a solution with 1 mol H_2O per mole of H_2SO_4, -841.8; with 10 mol H_2O, -880.5; with 50 mol H_2O; -886.8;

with 100 mol H_2O, -887.7; with 500 mol H_2O, -890.5; with 1000 mol H_2O, -892.3, with 10,000 mol H_2O, -900.8, and with 100,000 mol H_2O, -907.3.

(a) Explain why these values are not all the same.

(b) The value of $\Delta H_f^\circ[H_2SO_4(aq)]$ in an infinitely dilute solution is -909.3 kJ/mol. What data from this chapter can you cite to confirm this value? Explain.

(c) If 500.0 mL of 1.00 M $H_2SO_4(aq)$ is prepared from pure $H_2SO_4(l)$, what is the approximate change in temperature that should be observed? Assume that the $H_2SO_4(l)$ and $H_2O(l)$ are at the same temperature initially and that the specific heat of the $H_2SO_4(aq)$ is about 4.2 J g^{-1} $°C^{-1}$.

95. Refer to the discussion of the gasification of coal (page 261), and show that some of the heat required in the gasification reaction (equation 7.24) can be supplied by the *methanation* reaction. This fact contributes to the success of modern processes that produce *synthetic natural gas* (SNG).

96. A 1.103-g sample of a gaseous carbon–hydrogen–oxygen compound that occupies a volume of 582 mL at 765.5 Torr and 25.00 °C is burned in an excess of $O_2(g)$ in a bomb calorimeter. The products of the combustion are 2.108 g $CO_2(g)$, 1.294 g $H_2O(l)$, and enough heat to raise the temperature of the calorimeter assembly from 25.00 to 31.94 °C. The heat capacity of the calorimeter is 5.015 kJ/°C. Write an equation for the combustion reaction, and indicate $\Delta H°$ for this reaction at 25.00 °C.

97. Several factors are involved in determining the cooking times required for foods in a microwave oven. One of these factors is specific heat. Determine the approximate time required to warm 250 mL of chicken broth from 4 °C (a typical refrigerator temperature) to 50 °C in a 700-W microwave oven. Assume that the density of chicken broth is about 1 g/mL and that its specific heat is approximately 4.2 J g^{-1} $°C^{-1}$.

98. Suppose you have a setup similar to the one depicted in Figure 7-8 except that there are two different weights rather than two equal weights. One weight is a steel cylinder 10.00 cm in diameter and 25 cm long, the other weight produces a pressure of 745 Torr. The temperature of the gas in the cylinder in which the expansion takes place is 25.0 °C. The piston restraining the gas has a diameter of 12.00 cm, and the height of the piston above the base of the gas expansion cylinder is 8.10 cm. The density of the steel is 7.75 g/cm^3. How much work is done when the steel cylinder is suddenly removed from the piston?

99. When one mole of sodium carbonate decahydrate (washing soda) is gentle warmed, 155.3 kJ of heat is absorbed, water vapor is formed, and sodium carbonate heptahydrate remains. On more vigorous heating, the heptahydrate absorbs 320.1 kJ of heat and loses more water vapor to give the monohydrate. Continued heating gives the anhydrous salt (soda ash) while 57.3 kJ of heat is absorbed. Calculate ΔH for the conversion of one mole of washing soda into soda ash. Estimate ΔU for this process. Why is the value of ΔU only an estimate?

100. The oxidation of $NH_3(g)$ to $NO(g)$ in the Ostwald process must be very carefully controlled in terms of temperature, pressure, and contact time with the catalyst. This is because the oxidation of $NH_3(g)$ can yield any one of the products $N_2(g)$, $N_2O(g)$, $NO(g)$, and $NO_2(g)$, depending on conditions. Show that oxidation of $NH_3(g)$ to $N_2(g)$ is the most exothermic of the four possible reactions.

101. In the Are You Wondering box on page 248, the temperature variation of enthalpy is discussed, and the equation q_P = heat capacity × temperature change = $C_P \times \Delta T$ was introduced to show how enthalpy changes with temperature for a constant-pressure process. Strictly speaking, the heat capacity of a substance at constant pressure is the slope of the line representing the variation of enthalpy (H) with temperature, that is

$$C_P = \frac{dH}{dT} \qquad \text{(at constant pressure)}$$

where C_P is the heat capacity of the substance in question. Heat capacity is an extensive quantity and heat capacities are usually quoted as molar heat capacities $C_{P,m}$, the heat capacity of one mole of substance; an intensive property. The heat capacity at constant pressure is used to estimate the change in enthalpy due to a change in temperature. For infinitesimal changes in temperature,

$$dH = C_P dT \qquad \text{(at constant pressure)}$$

To evaluate the change in enthalpy for a particular temperature change, from T_1 to T_2 we write

$$\int_{H(T_1)}^{H(T_2)} dH = H(T_2) - H(T_1) = \int_{T_1}^{T_2} C_P dT$$

If we assume that C_P is independent of temperature, then we recover equation (7.5)

$$\Delta H = C_P \times \Delta T$$

On the other hand, we often find that the heat capacity is a function of temperature; a convenient empirical expression is

$$C_{P,m} = a + bT + \frac{c}{T^2}$$

What is the change in molar enthalpy of N_2 when it is heated from 25.0 °C to 100.0 °C? The molar heat capacity of nitrogen is given by

$$C_{P,m} = 28.58 + 3.77 \times 10^{-3} T - \frac{0.5 \times 10^5}{T^2} \text{J K}^{-1} \text{mol}^{-1}$$

102. The standard enthalpy of formation of gaseous H_2O at 298.15 K is -241.82 kJ mol^{-1}. Using the ideas contained in Figure 7-16, estimate its value at 100.0 °C given the following values of the molar heat capacities at constant pressure: $H_2O(g)$: 33.58 J K^{-1} mol^{-1}; $H_2(g)$: 28.84 J K^{-1} mol^{-1}; $O_2(g)$: 29.37 J K^{-1} mol^{-1}. Assume the heat capacities are independent of temperature.

Feature Problems

103. James Joule published his definitive work related to the first law of thermodynamics in 1850. He stated that "the quantity of heat capable of increasing the temperature of one pound of water by 1 °F requires for its evolution the expenditure of a mechanical force represented by the fall of 772 lb through the space of one foot." Validate this statement by relating it to information given in this text.

104. Based on specific heat measurements, Pierre Dulong and Alexis Petit proposed in 1818 that the specific heat of an element is inversely related to its atomic weight (atomic mass). Thus, by measuring the specific heat of a new element, its atomic weight could be readily established.

    (a) Use data from Table 7.1 and inside the front cover to plot a *straight-line* graph relating atomic mass and specific heat. Write the equation for this straight line.

    (b) Use the measured specific heat of 0.23 J g^{-1} °C^{-1} and the equation derived in part **(a)** to obtain an approximate value of the atomic mass of cadmium, an element discovered in 1817.

    (c) To raise the temperature of 75.0 g of a particular metal by 15 °C requires 450 J of heat. What might this metal be?

105. We can use the heat liberated by a neutralization reaction as a means of establishing the stoichiometry of the reaction. The data in the table are for the reaction of 1.00 M NaOH with 1.00 M citric acid, $C_6H_8O_7$, in a total solution volume of 60.0 mL.

mL 1.00 M NaOH Used	mL 1.00 M Citric Acid Used	ΔT, °C
20.0	40.0	4.7
30.0	30.0	6.3
40.0	20.0	8.2
50.0	10.0	6.7
55.0	5.0	2.7

    (a) Plot ΔT versus mL 1.00 M NaOH, and identify the exact stoichiometric proportions of NaOH and citric acid at the equivalence point of the neutralization reaction.

    (b) Why is the temperature change in the neutralization greatest when the reactants are in their exact stoichiometric proportions? That is, why not use an excess of one of the reactants to ensure that the neutralization has gone to completion to achieve the maximum temperature increase?

    (c) Rewrite the formula of citric acid to reflect more precisely its acidic properties. Then write a balanced net ionic equation for the neutralization reaction.

106. In a student experiment to confirm Hess's law, the reaction

    $$NH_3(\text{concd aq}) + HCl(aq) \longrightarrow NH_4Cl(aq)$$

was carried out in two different ways. First, 8.00 mL of concentrated $NH_3(aq)$ was added to 100.0 mL of 1.00 M HCl in a calorimeter. [The $NH_3(aq)$ was slightly in excess.] The reactants were initially at 23.8 °C, and the final temperature after neutralization was 35.8 °C. In the second experiment, air was bubbled through 100.0 mL of concentrated $NH_3(aq)$, sweeping out $NH_3(g)$ (see sketch). The $NH_3(g)$ was neutralized in 100.0 mL of 1.00 M HCl. The temperature of the concentrated $NH_3(aq)$ fell from 19.3 to 13.2 °C. At the same time, the temperature of the 1.00 M HCl rose from 23.8 to 42.9 °C as it was neutralized by $NH_3(g)$. Assume that all solutions have densities of 1.00 g/mL and specific heats of 4.18 J g^{-1} °C^{-1}.

    (a) Write the two equations and ΔH values for the processes occurring in the second experiment. Show that the sum of these two equations is the same as the equation for the reaction in the first experiment.

    (b) Show that, within the limits of experimental error, ΔH for the overall reaction is the same in the two experiments, thereby confirming Hess's law.

107. When an ideal gas is heated, the change in internal energy is limited to increasing the average translational kinetic energy of the gas molecules. Thus, there is a simple relationship between ΔU of the gas and the change in temperature that occurs. Derive this relationship with the help of ideas about the kinetic-molecular theory of gases developed in Chapter 6. After doing so, obtain numerical values (in J mol^{-1} K^{-1}) for the following molar heat capacities.

    (a) The heat capacity, C_V, for one mole of gas under constant-volume conditions;

    (b) The heat capacity, C_P, for one mole of gas under constant-pressure conditions.

108. Refer to Example 7-5 dealing with the work done by 0.100 mol He at 298 K in expanding in a single step from 2.40 to 1.20 atm. Review also the two-step expansion (2.40 atm $\longrightarrow$ 1.80 atm $\longrightarrow$ 1.20 atm) described on page 240 (see Figure 7-11).

    (a) Determine the total work that would be done if the He expanded in a series of steps, at 0.10 atm intervals, from 2.40 to 1.20 atm.

(b) Represent this total work on the accompanying graph, in which the quantity of work done in the two-step expansion is represented by the sum of the colored rectangles.

(c) Show that the maximum amount of work would occur if the expansion occurred in an infinite number of steps. To do this, express each infinitesimal quantity of work as $dw = P\,dV$ and use the methods of integral calculus (integration) to sum these quantities. Assume ideal behavior for the gas.

(d) Imagine reversing the process, that is, compressing the He from 1.20 to 2.40 atm. What are the maximum and minimum amounts of work required to produce this compression? Explain.

(e) In the isothermal compression described in part **(d)**, what is the change in internal energy assuming ideal gas behavior? What is the value of q?

(f) Using the formula for the work derived in part **(c)**, obtain an expression for q/T. Is this new function a state function? Explain.

Self-Assessment Exercises

109. In your own words, define or explain the following terms or symbols: **(a)** ΔH; **(b)** $P\Delta V$; **(c)** ΔH_f°; **(d)** standard state; **(e)** fossil fuel.

110. Briefly describe each of the following ideas or methods: **(a)** law of conservation of energy; **(b)** bomb calorimetry; **(c)** function of state; **(d)** enthalpy diagram; **(e)** Hess's law.

111. Explain the important distinctions between each pair of terms: **(a)** system and surroundings; **(b)** heat and work; **(c)** specific heat and heat capacity; **(d)** endothermic and exothermic; **(e)** constant-volume process and constant-pressure process.

112. The temperature increase of 225 mL of water at 25 °C contained in a Styrofoam cup is noted when a 125-g sample of a metal at 75 °C is added. With reference to Table 7.1, the greatest temperature increase will be noted if the metal is **(a)** lead; **(b)** aluminum; **(c)** iron; **(d)** copper.

113. A plausible final temperature when 75.0 mL of water at 80.0 °C is added to 100.0 mL of water at 20 °C is **(a)** 28 °C; **(b)** 40 °C; **(c)** 46 °C; **(d)** 50 °C.

114. $\Delta U = 100$ J for a system that gives off 100 J of heat and **(a)** does no work; **(b)** does 200 J of work; **(c)** has 100 J of work done on it; **(d)** has 200 J of work done on it.

115. The heat of solution of NaOH(s) in water is -41.6 kJ/mol NaOH. When NaOH(s) is dissolved in water the solution temperature **(a)** increases; **(b)** decreases; **(c)** remains constant; **(d)** either increases or decreases, depending on how much NaOH is dissolved.

116. The standard molar enthalpy of formation of $CO_2(g)$ is equal to **(a)** 0; **(b)** the standard molar heat of combustion of graphite; **(c)** the sum of the standard molar enthalpies of formation of CO(g) and $O_2(g)$; **(d)** the standard molar heat of combustion of CO(g).

117. Which two of the following statements are false? **(a)** $q_V = q_P$ for the reaction $N_2(g) + O_2(g) \longrightarrow 2\,NO(g)$; **(b)** $\Delta H > 0$ for an endothermic reaction; **(c)** By convention, the most stable form of an element must always be chosen as the reference form and assigned the value $\Delta H_f^\circ = 0$; **(d)** ΔU and ΔH for a reaction can never have the same value; **(e)** $\Delta H < 0$ for the neutralization of a strong acid by a strong base.

118. A 1.22-kg piece of iron at 126.5 °C is dropped into 981 g water at 22.1 °C. The temperature rises to 34.4 °C. What will be the final temperature if this same piece of iron at 99.8 °C is dropped into 325 mL of glycerol, $CH_2OHCHOHCH_2OH(l)$ at 26.2 °C? For glycerol, $d = 1.26$ g/mL; $C_p = 219$ J K^{-1} mol^{-1}.

119. Write the balanced chemical equations for reactions that have the following as their standard enthalpy changes.
    (a) $\Delta H_f^\circ = +82.05$ kJ/mol $N_2O(g)$
    (b) $\Delta H_f^\circ = -394.1$ kJ/mol $SO_2Cl_2(l)$
    (c) $\Delta H_{combustion}^\circ = -1527$ kJ/mol $CH_3CH_2COOH(l)$

120. The standard molar heats of combustion of C(graphite) and CO(g) are −393.5 and −283 kJ/mol, respectively. Use those data and that for the following reaction

    $$CO(g) + Cl_2(g) \longrightarrow COCl_2(g) \qquad \Delta H^\circ = -108 \text{ kJ}$$

    to calculate the standard molar enthalpy of formation of $COCl_2(g)$.

121. Can a chemical compound have a standard enthalpy of formation of zero? If so, how likely is this to occur? Explain.

122. Is it possible for a chemical reaction to have $\Delta U < 0$ and $\Delta H > 0$? Explain.

123. Use principles from this chapter to explain the observation that professional chefs prefer to cook with a gas stove rather than an electric stove.

124. Construct a concept map encompassing the ideas behind the first law of thermodynamics.

125. Construct a concept map to show the use of enthalpy for chemical reactions

126. Construct a concept map to show the interrelationships between path-dependent and path-independent quantities in thermodynamics.

 ## eMedia Exercises

127. From the **Types of Energy** activity (*Activebook 7-1*), describe the differences in the motions of particles possessing predominantly high kinetic energy, predominantly high thermal energy, and predominantly high potential energy.

128. From the **Bomb Calorimetry** simulation (*Activebook 7-3*), estimate which of the compounds, benzoic acid or sucrose, has a higher heat of combustion. [*Hint:* Consider the reaction of equal masses of material.]

129. Consider the gas contained in the cylinder shown in the **Work of Gas Expansion** animation (*Activebook 7-4*). Calculate the amount of work done by the system through the expansion of the gas if the cylinder has a radius of 10 cm and the piston is displaced upward by 20 cm against an opposing pressure of 1.2 atm.

130. Using only the graphs generated through the **Heating-Cooling Curves** activity (*Activebook 7-6*), (a) estimate whether ethanol or ethane has a higher heat capacity. (b) Which one has a higher molar enthalpy of vaporization? (c) Which part of the graphs is used to derive this information?

131. For the reaction described in the **Formation of Aluminum Bromide** movie (*Activebook 7-8*), (a) calculate the amount of heat released from the complete reaction of 27.2 g of Al in the presence of excess bromine, given that the heat of formation of $AlBr_3(s)$ is −527 kJ/mol. (b) What aspects of this reaction make it difficult to quantify the reaction yield of both products, heat and aluminum bromide?

 ## eLaboratory Exercises

These exercises allow students to apply the concepts and skills for this chapter in the simulated laboratory of Virtual ChemLab. Worksheets for each of these exercises are found in the Virtual ChemLab Workbook in your MediaPak.

132. **(VCL 7-1) Specific Heat of Pb**
    On a sunny day the water in a swimming pool may warm up a degree or two while the concrete around the pool may become too hot to walk on with bare feet. This may seem strange since the water and concrete are being heated by the same source—the Sun. This evidence suggests it takes more heat to raise the temperature of some substances than others, which is true. The amount of heat required to raise the temperature of 1 g of a substance by 1 °C is called the specific heat capacity or specific heat of that substance. Water, for instance, has a specific heat of 4.18 J K^{-1} g^{-1}. This value is high in comparison with the specific heats for other materials, such as concrete or metals. In this experiment you will use a simple calorimeter and your knowledge of the specific heat of water to measure the specific heat of lead (Pb).

133. **(VCL 7-2) Specific Heat of Al**
    In this problem you will repeat the previous specific heat experiment except measure the specific heat of Al.

134. **(VCL 7-3) Endothermic Versus Exothermic**
    In various chemical processes, such as reactions and the dissolving of salts, heat is either absorbed or given off. We call these events either an endothermic (heat in) or exothermic (heat out) process. It is usual to detect these heat events by measuring the temperature change associated with the process. In this problem you will dissolve several salts in water and measure the resulting temperature change and then make deductions about the nature of the process.

135. **(VCL 7-4) Heat of Combustion: Sugar**
    The heat of combustion (ΔH_{comb}) is the heat of reaction for the complete burning (reacting with O_2) of one mole of a substance to form CO_2 and H_2O. Calorimetry experiments that measure the heat of combustion can be performed at constant volume using a device called a bomb calorimeter. In a bomb calorimeter a sample is burned in a constant-volume chamber in the presence of oxygen at high pressure. The heat that is released warms the water surrounding the chamber. By measuring the temperature increase of the water, it is possible to calculate the quantity of heat released during the combustion

reaction. In this assignment you will calculate the heat of combustion of sugar.

136. **(VCL 7-5) Heat of Combustion: Chicken Fat**
In this assignment you will measure the heat of combustion of chicken fat as outlined in the heat of combustion problem on sugar.

137. **(VCL 7-6) Heat of Combustion: TNT**
In this assignment you will measure the heat of combustion of 2,4,6-trinitrotoluene (TNT) as outlined in the heat of combustion problem on sugar.

138. **(VCL 7-7) Heat of Reaction: NaOH(aq) + HCl(aq)**
Energy that is either absorbed or released in a chemical reaction is known as the enthalpy of reaction (ΔH_{rxn}). An endothermic reaction absorbs energy, and the enthalpy of reaction is positive. An exothermic reaction gives off energy, and the enthalpy of reaction is negative. Most chemical reactions are exothermic. In this problem you will measure the amount of heat released when aqueous solutions of NaOH and HCl are mixed in a neutralization reaction to form water and a salt, and calculate the heat of reaction.

139. **(VCL 7-8) Heat of Reaction: MgO(s) + HCl(aq)**
In this assignment you will measure the heat of reaction for MgO(s) + HCl(aq) as outlined in the heat of reaction problem for NaOH(aq) and HCl(aq).

140. **(VCL 7-9) Hess's Law**
In this experiment you will measure the amount of heat released in these three related exothermic reactions:

$$NaOH(s) \longrightarrow Na^+(aq) + OH^-(aq) \quad \Delta H_1$$

$$NaOH(s) + H^+(aq) + Cl^-(aq) \longrightarrow$$
$$H_2O(l) + Na^+(aq) + Cl^-(aq) \quad \Delta H_2$$
$$Na^+(aq) + OH^-(aq) + H^+(aq) + Cl^-(aq) \longrightarrow$$
$$H_2O(l) + Na^+(aq) + Cl^-(aq) \quad \Delta H_3$$

After determining the heats of reaction (ΔH_1, ΔH_2 and ΔH_3), you will then analyze your data and verify Hess's law, or $\Delta H_1 + \Delta H_3 = \Delta H_2$.

141. **(VCL 7-10) Heat of Formation: Aspirin**
The heat of formation is the heat of reaction for the formation of a compound from the elements. The heat of formation can be determined by measuring the heat of combustion for the compound and then using Hess's law to convert the heat of combustion to a heat of formation. Calorimetry experiments that measure the heat of combustion can be performed at constant volume, using a device called a bomb calorimeter. In a bomb calorimeter a sample is burned in a constant-volume chamber in the presence of oxygen at high pressure. The heat that is released warms the water surrounding the chamber. By measuring the temperature increase of the water, it is possible to calculate the quantity of heat released during the combustion reaction. In this assignment you will first measure the heat of combustion of aspirin and convert the heat of combustion to a heat of formation.

142. **(VCL 7-11) Heat of Formation: Ethanol**
In this assignment you will measure the heat of combustion of ethanol (ethyl alcohol, C_2H_5OH) and then calculate the heat of formation as outlined in the heat of formation problem for aspirin.

8

ELECTRONS IN ATOMS

CONTENTS

This image of two neurons (gray objects) is produced by an electron microscope that relies on the wave properties of electrons discussed in this chapter.

At the end of the nineteenth century, some observers of the scientific scene believed that it was nearly time to close the books on the field of physics. They thought that with the accumulated knowledge of the previous two or three centuries, the main work left to be done was to apply this body of physics—classical physics—to fields such as chemistry and biology.

Only a few fundamental problems remained, including an explanation of certain details of light emission and a phenomenon known as the photoelectric effect. But the solution to these problems, rather than marking an end in the study of physics, spelled the beginning of a new golden age of physics. These problems were solved through a bold new proposal—the quantum theory—a scientific breakthrough of epic proportions. In this chapter, we will see that to explain phenomena at the atomic and molecular level, classical physics is inadequate—only the quantum theory will do.

The aspect of quantum mechanics emphasized in this chapter is how electrons are described through features known as quantum numbers and electron orbitals. The model of atomic structure developed here will explain many of the topics discussed in the next several chapters: periodic trends in the physical and chemical properties of the elements, chemical bonding, and intermolecular forces.

8-1   ELECTROMAGNETIC RADIATION

Our understanding of the electronic structures of atoms will be gained by studying the interactions of electromagnetic radiation and matter. The chapter begins with background information about electromagnetic radiation and then turns to connections between electromagnetic radiation and atomic structure. The best approach to learning material in this chapter is to concentrate on the basic ideas relating to atomic structure, many of which are illustrated through the in-text examples. At the same time, pursue further details of interest in some of the Are You Wondering features and portions of Sections 8-6, 8-8, and 8-10.

Electromagnetic radiation is a form of energy transmission in which electric and magnetic fields are propagated as waves through empty space (a vacuum) or through a medium such as glass. A **wave** is a disturbance that transmits energy through space or a material medium. Anyone who has sat in a small boat on a large body of water has experienced wave motion. The wave moves across the surface of the water, and the disturbance alternately lifts the boat and allows it to drop. Although water waves may be more familiar, let us use a simpler example to illustrate some important ideas and terminology about waves—a traveling wave in a rope.

Imagine tying one end of a long rope to a post and holding the other end in your hand (Fig. 8-1). Imagine also that you have marked one small segment of the rope with red ink. As you move your hand up and down, you set up a wave motion in the rope. The wave travels along the rope toward the distant post, but the colored segment simply moves up and down. In relation to the center line (the broken line in Figure 8-1), the wave consists of *crests*, or high points, where the rope is at its greatest height above the center line, and *troughs*, or low points, where the rope is at its greatest depth below the center line. The maximum height of the wave above the center line or the maximum depth below is called the **amplitude**. The distance between the tops of two successive crests (or the bottoms of two troughs) is called the **wavelength**, designated by the Greek letter lambda, λ.

Wavelength is one important characteristic of a wave. Another feature, **frequency**, designated by the Greek letter nu, ν, is the number of crests or troughs that pass through a given point per unit of time. Frequency has the unit, time^{-1}, usually s^{-1} (per second), meaning the number of events or cycles per second. The product of the length of a wave (λ) and the frequency (ν) shows how far the wave front travels in a unit of time. This is the speed of the wave. Thus, if the wavelength in Figure 8-1 were 0.5 m and the frequency, 3 s^{-1} (meaning three complete up-and-down hand motions per second), the speed of the wave would be 0.5 m $\times$ 3 s^{-1} = 1.5 m/s.

We cannot actually see an electromagnetic wave as we do the traveling wave in a rope, but we can try to represent it as in Figure 8-2. As the figure shows, the magnetic field component lies in a plane perpendicular to the electric field component. An electric field is the region around an electrically charged particle. The presence of an electric field can be detected by measuring the force on an electrically charged object when it is brought into the field. A magnetic field is found in the region surrounding a magnet. According to a theory proposed by James Clerk Maxwell (1831–1879) in 1865, electromagnetic radiation—a propagation of electric and magnetic fields—is produced by an

▶ Water waves, sound waves, and seismic waves (which produce earthquakes) are unlike electromagnetic radiation. They require a material medium for their transmission.

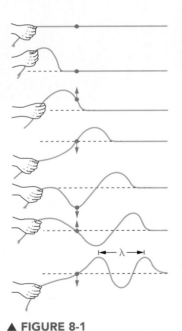

▲ **FIGURE 8-1**
The simplest wave motion— traveling wave in a rope
As a result of the up-and-down hand motion (top to bottom), waves pass along the long rope from left to right. This one-dimensional moving wave is called a traveling wave. The wavelength of the wave, λ—the distance between two successive crests—is identified.

▲ FIGURE 8-2
Electromagnetic waves
This sketch of two different electromagnetic waves shows the propagation of mutually perpendicular oscillating electric and magnetic fields. For a given wave, the wavelengths, frequencies, and amplitudes of the electric and magnetic field components are identical. If these views are of the same instant of time, we would say that **(a)** has the longer wavelength and lower frequency, and **(b)** has the shorter wavelength and higher frequency.

accelerating electrically charged particle (a charged particle whose velocity changes). Radio waves, for example, are a form of electromagnetic radiation produced by causing oscillations (fluctuations) of the electric current in a specially designed electrical circuit. With visible light, another form of electromagnetic radiation, the accelerating charged particles are the electrons in atoms or molecules.

FREQUENCY, WAVELENGTH, AND SPEED
OF ELECTROMAGNETIC RADIATION

The SI unit for frequency, s^{-1}, is the **hertz (Hz)**, and the basic SI wavelength unit is the meter (m). Because many types of electromagnetic radiation have very short wavelengths, however, smaller units, including those listed below, are also used. The angstrom, named for the Swedish physicist Anders Ångström (1814–1874), is not an SI unit.

1 centimeter (cm) $= 1 \times 10^{-2}$ m

1 micrometer (μm) $= 1 \times 10^{-6}$ m

1 nanometer (nm) $= 1 \times 10^{-9}$ m $= 1 \times 10^{-7}$ cm $= 10$ Å

1 picometer (pm) $= 1 \times 10^{-12}$ m $= 1 \times 10^{-10}$ cm $= 10^{-2}$ Å

1 angstrom (Å) $= 1 \times 10^{-10}$ m $= 1 \times 10^{-8}$ cm $= 100$ pm

A distinctive feature of electromagnetic radiation is its *constant* speed of 2.997925×10^8 m s^{-1} in a vacuum, often referred to as the **speed of light**. The speed of light is represented by the symbol c, and the relationship between this speed and the frequency and wavelength of electromagnetic radiation is

$$c = \nu \cdot \lambda \qquad (8.1)$$

The instructor will need to carefully select what topics in this chapter to cover. Some of the material is essential for a basic understanding of modern chemistry. Some is appropriate for honors level courses. In between are topics that can be mentioned as a matter of background but students need not be expected to fully master them. The irreducible minimum includes the wave–particle duality of light, the quantum nature of electron orbitals, orbital and subshell energy diagrams, and electron configurations.

Electromagnetic Spectrum activity

Electromagnetic waves are *transverse* waves—the electric and magnetic fields are *perpendicular* to the perceived direction of motion. So also, to a first approximation, are water waves. Sound waves, by contrast, are *longitudinal*. This effect is the result of small pulses of pressure that move in the *same* direction as the sound travels.

◄ The speed of light is commonly rounded off to 3.00×10^8 m s^{-1}.

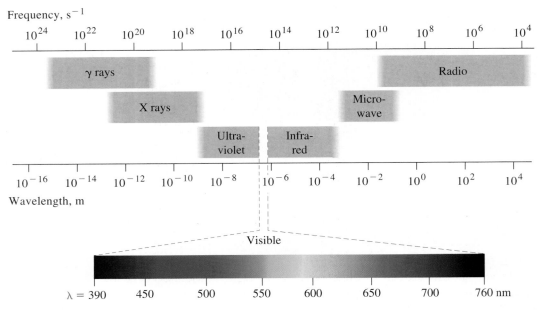

▲ **FIGURE 8-3**
The electromagnetic spectrum
The visible region, which extends from violet at the shortest wavelength to red at the longest wavelength, is only a small portion of the entire spectrum. The approximate wavelength and frequency ranges of some other forms of electromagnetic radiation are also indicated.

Figure 8-3 indicates the wide range of possible wavelengths and frequencies for some common types of electromagnetic radiation and illustrates this important fact: The wavelength of electromagnetic radiation is shorter for high frequencies and longer for low frequencies. Example 8-1 illustrates the use of equation (8.1).

EXAMPLE 8-1

Relating Frequency and Wavelength of Electromagnetic Radiation. Most of the light from a sodium vapor lamp has a wavelength of 589 nm. What is the frequency of this radiation?

Solution
We can first convert the wavelength of the light from nanometers to meters and then apply equation (8.1).

$$\lambda = 589 \text{ nm} \times \frac{1 \times 10^{-9} \text{ m}}{1 \text{ nm}} = 5.89 \times 10^{-7} \text{ m}$$
$$c = 2.998 \times 10^{8} \text{ m s}^{-1}$$
$$\nu = ?$$

Rearrange equation (8.1) to the form $\nu = c/\lambda$, and solve for ν.

$$\nu = \frac{c}{\lambda} = \frac{2.998 \times 10^{8} \text{ m s}^{-1}}{5.89 \times 10^{-7} \text{ m}} = 5.09 \times 10^{14} \text{ s}^{-1} = 5.09 \times 10^{14} \text{ Hz}$$

Practice Example A: The light from red LEDs (light-emitting diodes) is commonly seen in many electronic devices. A typical LED produces 690-nm light. What is the frequency of this light?

Practice Example B: An FM radio station broadcasts on a frequency of 91.5 megahertz (MHz). What is the wavelength of these radio waves in meters?

(a) (b)

◀ **FIGURE 8-4**
Examples of interference
(a) Stones and ripples.
(b) CD reflection.

AN IMPORTANT CHARACTERISTIC OF ELECTROMAGNETIC WAVES

The properties of electromagnetic radiation that we will use most extensively are those just introduced—amplitude, wavelength, frequency, and speed. Another essential characteristic of electromagnetic radiation, which will underpin our discussion of atomic structure later in the chapter, is described next.

If two pebbles are dropped close together into a pond, ripples (waves) emerge from the points of impact of the two stones. The two sets of waves intersect, and there are places where the waves disappear and places where the waves persist, creating a crisscross pattern (Fig. 8-4a). Where the waves are "in step" upon meeting, their crests coincide, as do their troughs. The waves combine to produce the highest crests and deepest troughs in the water. The waves are said to be *in phase,* and the addition of the waves is called *constructive interference* (Fig. 8-5a). Where the waves meet in such a way that the peak of one wave occurs at the trough of another, the waves cancel and the water is flat (Fig. 8-5b). These out-of-step waves are said to be *out of phase,* and the cancellation of the waves is called *destructive interference.*

An everyday illustration of interference involving electromagnetic waves is seen in the rainbow of colors that shine from the surface of a compact disc (Fig. 8-4b). White light, such as sunlight, contains all the colors of the rainbow. The colors differ in wavelength (and frequency), and when these different wavelength components are reflected off the tightly spaced grooves of the CD,

Emphasize that the *wave nature of light* is demonstrated by its ability to be dispersed by diffraction and refraction.

◀ **KEEP IN MIND**
that destructive interference occurs when waves are out of phase by one-half wavelength. If waves are out of phase by more or less than this, but also not completely in phase, then only partial destructive interference occurs.

Diffraction of Light. Cut a 2 mm × 5 cm slit in a sheet of card stock or sheet metal. Place on an overhead projector and darken the room. Hold a grating in front of the projector lens and observe a visible spectrum on the screen.

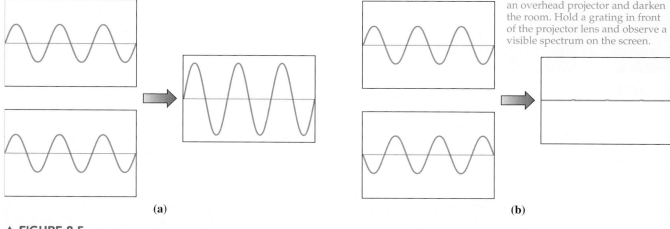

(a) (b)

▲ **FIGURE 8-5**
Interference in two overlapping light waves
(a) In constructive interference, the troughs and crests are in step (in phase), leading to addition of the two waves. **(b)** In destructive interference, the troughs and crests are out of step (out of phase), leading to cancellation of the two waves.

Are You Wondering . . .

What happens to the energy of an electromagnetic wave when interference takes place?

As noted in Figure 8-2, an electromagnetic wave is made up of oscillating electric (E) and magnetic (B) fields. The magnitudes of E and B continuously oscillate, or switch, from positive to negative. These oscillating fields create an oscillating electromagnetic force. A charged particle will interact with the electromagnetic force and will oscillate back and forth with a constantly changing velocity. The changing velocity gives the particle a changing kinetic energy that is proportional to the square of the velocity (that is, $e_k = \frac{1}{2}mu^2$). Consequently the energy of a wave depends not on the values of E and B alone, but on the sum of their squares, that is, on $E^2 + B^2$. The energy is also related to the *intensity* (I) of a wave, a quantity which, in turn, is related to the *square* of the wave amplitude. Suppose we let the amplitude of the waves = 1. Then for each wave, whether a pair of waves is in phase or out of phase, the energy is proportional to $1^2 + 1^2 = 2$. The average energy of the pair of waves is also proportional to two [that is, $(2 + 2)/2$]. In constructive interference, the amplitudes become two, so that the energy is proportional to four. In destructive interference, the amplitude is zero and the energy is zero. Note, however, that the *average* between the two situations is still two [that is, $(4 + 0)/2$] so that energy is conserved, as it must be.

they travel slightly different distances. This creates phase differences that depend on the angle at which we hold the CD to the light source. The light waves in the beam interfere with each other, and for a given angle between the incoming and reflected light, all colors cancel except one. Light waves of that color interfere constructively and reinforce one another. Thus, as we change the angle of the CD to the light source, we see different colors. The dispersion of different wavelength components of a light beam through the interference produced by reflection from a grooved surface is called **diffraction**.

Diffraction is a phenomenon that can be explained only as a property of waves. Both the physical picture and mathematics of interference and diffraction are the same for water waves and electromagnetic waves.

THE VISIBLE SPECTRUM

The speed of light is lower in any medium than it is in a vacuum. Also, the speed is different in different media. As a consequence, light is refracted, or bent, when it passes from one medium to another (Fig. 8-6). Moreover, although electromagnetic waves all have the same speed in a vacuum, waves of differing wavelengths have slightly differing speeds in air and other media. Thus, when a beam of white light is passed through a transparent medium, the wavelength components are refracted differently. The light is dispersed into a band of colors, a *spectrum*. In Figure 8-7(a), a beam of white light (for example, sunlight) is dispersed by a glass prism into a continuous band of colors corresponding to all the wavelength components from red to violet. This is the visible spectrum shown in Figure 8-3 and also seen in a rainbow, where the medium that disperses the sunlight is droplets of water (Fig. 8-7b).

▲ **FIGURE 8-6**
Refraction of light
Light is refracted (bent) as it passes from air into the glass prism, and again as it emerges from the prism into air. This photograph shows that red light is refracted the least and blue light the most. The blue light strikes the prism at such an angle that the beam undergoes an internal reflection before it emerges from the prism.

CONCEPT ASSESSMENT ✓

Red laser light is passed through a device called a frequency doubler. What is the approximate color of the light that exits the frequency doubler? How are the wavelengths of the original light and the frequency-doubled light related?

(a)   (b)

▲ **FIGURE 8-7**
The spectrum of "white" light
(a) Dispersion of light through a prism. Red light is refracted the least and violet light the most when "white" light is passed through a glass prism. The other colors of the visible spectrum are found between red and violet. **(b)** Rainbow near a waterfall. Here, water droplets are the dispersion medium.

The *importance of light* to chemistry is that light is a form of energy and that by studying light–matter interactions we can detect energy changes in atoms and molecules. Another means of monitoring the energy of a system is through observations of heat transfer. Light can be more closely controlled and thus gives us more detailed information than can be obtained with heat measurements.

8-2   ATOMIC SPECTRA

The visible spectrum in Figure 8-7 is said to be a *continuous spectrum* because the light being diffracted consists of many wavelength components. If the source of a spectrum produces light having only a relatively small number of wavelength components, then a *discontinuous spectrum* is observed. For example, if the light source is an electric discharge passing through a gas, only certain colors are seen in the spectrum (Fig. 8-8a and b). Or, if the light source is a gas flame into which an ionic compound has been introduced, the flame may acquire a distinctive color indicative of the metal ion present (Fig. 8-8c–e). In each of these cases, the emitted light produces a spectrum consisting of only a limited number of discrete wavelength components, observed as colored lines with dark spaces between them. These discontinuous spectra are called **atomic**, or **line**, **spectra**.

The production of the line spectrum of helium is illustrated in Figure 8-9. The light source is a lamp containing helium gas at a low pressure. When an electric discharge is passed through the lamp, helium atoms absorb energy, which they then emit as light. The light is passed through a narrow slit and

The colors seen in fireworks result from certain wavelengths of light given off from compounds as they are heated.

 Flame Tests for Metals

 Flame Tests for Metals movie

Atomic Spectra. Atomic light sources are commercially available and can be displayed unresolved and compared as to their color differences. Mention the everyday application: neon signs, many of which contain elements other than neon.

(a)   (b)   (c)   (d)   (e)

▲ **FIGURE 8-8**
Sources for light emission
Light emitted by an electric discharge through **(a)** hydrogen gas and **(b)** helium gas. Light emitted when compounds of the alkali metals are excited in the gas flames: **(c)** lithium, **(d)** sodium, and **(e)** potassium.

► **FIGURE 8-9**
The atomic, or line, spectrum of helium
The apparatus pictured here, in which the spectral lines are photographed, is called a *spectrograph*. If the observations are made by visual sighting alone, the device is called a *spectroscope*. If the positions and brightness of the lines are measured and recorded by other than visual or photographic means, the term generally used is *spectrometer*.

Slit   Prism

Photographic film

Helium
lamp

► Bunsen designed a special gas burner for his spectroscopic studies. This burner, the common laboratory Bunsen burner, produces very little background radiation to interfere with spectral observations.

 Atomic Emission Spectra

Atomic Spectra Resolved. Mount an atomic light source in front of a projector screen with a backing so the class will not be looking directly at the source. Clamp a magnifying glass or other large lens so as to focus the light onto the screen. Hold a grating between the light source and the lens. Observe the atomic spectrum produced on the screen.

then dispersed by a prism. The colored components of the light are detected and recorded on photographic film. Each wavelength component appears as an image of the slit—a thin line. In all, there are five lines in the spectrum of helium that can be seen with the unaided eye.

Each element has its own distinctive line spectrum—a kind of atomic fingerprint. Robert Bunsen (1811–1899) and Gustav Kirchhoff (1824–1887) developed the first spectroscope and used it to identify elements. In 1860, they discovered a new element and named it cesium (Latin, *caesius*, sky blue) because of the distinctive blue lines in its spectrum. They discovered rubidium in 1861 in a similar way (Latin, *rubidius*, deepest red). Still another element characterized by its unique spectrum is helium (Greek, *helios*, the sun). Its spectrum was observed during the solar eclipse of 1868, but helium was not isolated on Earth for another 27 years.

Among the most extensively studied atomic spectra has been the hydrogen spectrum. Light from a hydrogen lamp appears to the eye as a reddish purple color (Fig. 8-8a). The principal wavelength component of this light is red light of wavelength 656.3 nm. Three other lines appear in the visible spectrum of atomic hydrogen, however: a greenish blue line at 486.1 nm, a violet line at 434.0 nm, and another violet line at 410.1 nm. The visible atomic spectrum of hydrogen is shown in Figure 8-10. In 1885, Johann Balmer, apparently through trial and error, deduced a formula for the wavelengths of these spectral lines. Balmer's equation, rearranged to a form based on frequency, is

$$\nu = 3.2881 \times 10^{15} \, \text{s}^{-1}\left(\frac{1}{2^2} - \frac{1}{n^2}\right) \tag{8.2}$$

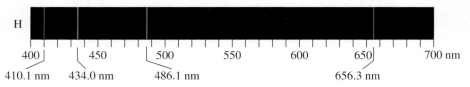

H

400   450   500   550   600   650   700 nm

410.1 nm   434.0 nm   486.1 nm   656.3 nm

 ▲ **FIGURE 8-10**
The Balmer series for hydrogen atoms—a line spectrum
The four lines shown are the only ones visible to the unaided eye. Additional, closely spaced lines lie in the ultraviolet (UV) region.

In this equation, ν is the frequency of the spectral line, and n must be an *integer* (whole number) *greater than two*. If $n = 3$ is substituted into the equation, the frequency of the red line is obtained. If $n = 4$ is used in equation 8.2, the frequency of the greenish blue line is obtained, and so on.

The fact that atomic spectra consist of only limited numbers of well-defined wavelength lines provides a great opportunity to learn about the structures of atoms. For example, it suggests that only a limited number of energy values are available to excited gaseous atoms. Classical (nineteenth-century) physics, however, was not able to provide an explanation of atomic spectra. The key to this puzzle lay in a great breakthrough of modern science—the quantum theory.

CONCEPT ASSESSMENT ✓

When comet Schumacher-Levy crashed into Jupiter's surface, scientists viewed the event with spectrographs. What did they hope to discover?

▲ Light emission by molten iron.

8-3   QUANTUM THEORY

We are aware that hot objects emit light of different colors, from the dull red of an electric-stove heating element to the bright white of a light bulb filament. Light emitted by a hot radiating object can be dispersed by a prism to produce a continuous color spectrum. As seen in Figure 8-11, the light intensity varies smoothly with wavelength, peaking at a wavelength fixed by the source temperature. As with atomic spectra, classical physics could not provide a complete explanation of light emission by heated solids, a process known as *blackbody radiation*. Classical theory predicts that the intensity of the radiation emitted would increase indefinitely, as indicated by the dashed lines in Figure 8-11. In 1900, to explain the fact that the intensity does not increase indefinitely, Max Planck (1858–1947) made a revolutionary proposal: *Energy, like matter, is discontinuous.* Here, then, is the essential difference between the classical physics of Planck's time and the new quantum theory that he proposed: Classical physics places no limitations on the amount of energy a system may possess, whereas quantum theory limits this energy to a discrete set of specific values. The *difference* between any two allowed energies of a system also has a specific value, called a **quantum** of energy. This means that when the energy increases from one allowed value to another, it increases by a tiny jump, or quantum. Here is a way of thinking about a quantum of energy: It bears a similar relationship to the total energy of a system as a single atom does to an entire sample of matter.

The model Planck used for the emission of electromagnetic radiation was that of a group of atoms on the surface of the heated object oscillating together with the same frequency. Planck's assumption was that the group of atoms, the oscillator, must have an energy corresponding to the equation

$$\epsilon = nh\nu$$

where ϵ is the energy, n is a positive integer, ν is the oscillator frequency, and h is a constant that had to be determined by experiment. Using his theory and experimental data for the distribution of frequencies with temperature, Planck established the following value for the constant h. We now call it **Planck's constant**, and it has the value

$$h = 6.62607 \times 10^{-34}\,\text{J s}$$

Planck's postulate can be rephrased in this more general way: The energy of a quantum of electromagnetic radiation is proportional to the frequency of the radiation—the higher the frequency, the greater the energy. This is summarized by what we now call Planck's equation.

$$E = h\nu \tag{8.3}$$

▲ **FIGURE 8-11**
Spectrum of radiation given off by a heated body
A red-hot object has a spectrum that peaks around 675 nm, whereas a white-hot object has a spectrum that has comparable intensities for all wavelengths in the visible region. The sun has a blackbody temperature of about 5750 K. Objects emit radiation at *all* temperatures, not just at high temperatures. For example, night-vision goggles makes infrared radiation emitted by objects visible in the dark.

 Blackbody Radiation

Planck's equation can be used to develop relationships between frequency, wavelength and energy. Using this information, the relative energies of radiation on the electromagnetic spectrum can be compared.

▲ **Max Planck (1858–1947)**

The depth of coverage of the topic of quantum theory is a matter of instructor choice. Points to include are that light energy is transferred as "particles" or photons of energy $h\nu$, and that electrons in atoms are restricted to certain energy orbitals.

Studies of the photoelectric effect led to our modern understanding of the particle (photon) nature of light. Emphasize that light–matter interactions usually involve *one photon per atom or electron*. An increased light intensity usually results in more photons being absorbed, and thus more electrons being produced, but all with the same energy. Only by changing frequency are the energies of the electrons changed.

VCL *Photoelectric Effect*

▶ To escape from a photoelectric surface, an electron must do so with the energy from a single photon collision. The electron cannot accumulate the energy from several hits by photons.

Are You Wondering . . .

How Planck's ideas account for the fact that the intensity of blackbody radiation drops off at higher frequencies?

Planck was aware of the work of Ludwig Boltzmann, who, with James Maxwell, had derived an equation to account for the distribution of molecular speeds. Boltzmann had shown that the relative chance of finding a molecule with a particular speed was related to its energy by the following expression.

$$\text{relative chance} \propto e^{-\frac{\text{kinetic energy}}{k_{B}T}}$$

where k_{B} is the Boltzmann constant, and T is the Kelvin temperature. You will also notice that the curve of intensity versus wavelength in Figure 8-11 bears a strong resemblance to the distribution of molecular speeds in Figure 6-17. Planck assumed that the energies of the substance oscillating to emit blackbody radiation were distributed according to the Boltzmann distribution law. That is, the relative chance of an oscillator having the energy $nh\nu$ is proportional to $e^{-\frac{nh\nu}{k_{B}T}}$, where n is an integer, 1, 2, 3, and so on. So this expression shows that the chance of an oscillator having a high frequency is lower than for oscillators having lower frequencies because as n increases, $e^{-\frac{nh\nu}{k_{B}T}}$ decreases. The assumption that the energy of the oscillators in the light-emitting source cannot have continuous values leads to excellent agreement between theory and experiment.

At the time Planck made his quantum hypothesis scientists had had no previous experience with macroscopic physical systems that required the existence of separate energy levels and that energy may only be emitted or absorbed in specific quanta. Their experience was that there were no theoretical limits on the energy of a system and that the transfer of energy was continuous. Thus it is not surprising that scientists, including Planck himself, were initially skeptical of the quantum hypothesis. It had been designed to explain radiation from heated bodies and certainly could not be accepted as a general principle until it had been tested on other applications.

Only after the quantum hypothesis was successfully applied to phenomena other than blackbody radiation did it acquire status as a great new scientific theory. The first of these successes came in 1905 with Albert Einstein's quantum explanation of the photoelectric effect.

THE PHOTOELECTRIC EFFECT

In 1888, Heinrich Hertz discovered that when light strikes the surface of certain metals, electrons are ejected. This phenomenon is called the **photoelectric effect** and its salient features are that

- electron emission only occurs when the frequency of the incident light exceeds a particular threshold value (ν_0).

When this condition is met,

- the number of electrons emitted depends on the intensity of the incident light, but
- the kinetic energies of the emitted electrons depend on the frequency of the light.

These observations, especially the dependency on frequency, could not be explained by classical wave theory. However, Albert Einstein showed that they are exactly what would be expected with a particle interpretation of radiation. In 1905, Einstein proposed that electromagnetic radiation has particle-like qualities and that "particles" of light, subsequently called **photons** by G. N. Lewis, have a characteristic energy given by Planck's equation, $E = h\nu$.

In the particle model, a photon of energy $h\nu$ strikes a bound electron, which absorbs the photon energy. If the photon energy, $h\nu$, is greater than the energy

Frequency, ν

(a)   **(b)**

◀ **FIGURE 8-12**
The photoelectric effect
(a) Schematic diagram of the apparatus for photoelectric effect measurements. **(b)** Stopping voltage of photoelectrons as a function of frequency of incident radiation. The stopping voltage (V_s) is plotted against the frequency of the incident radiation. The threshold frequency (ν_0) of the metal is found by extrapolation.

binding the electron to the surface (a quantity known as the *work function*) a photoelectron is liberated. Thus, the lowest frequency light producing the photoelectric effect is the threshold frequency, and any energy in excess of the work function appears as kinetic energy in the emitted photoelectrons.

In the discussion that follows, based on the experimental setup shown in Figure 8-12, we will see how the threshold frequency and work function are evaluated. Also, we will see that the photoelectric effect provides an independent evaluation of Planck's constant, h.

In Figure 8-12, light (designated $h\nu$) is allowed to shine on a piece of metal in an evacuated chamber. The electrons emitted by the metal (photoelectrons) travel to the upper plate and complete an electric circuit set up to measure the photoelectric current through an ammeter. From the magnitude of the current we can determine the rate at which photoelectrons are emitted. A second circuit is set up to measure the velocity of the photoelectrons, and hence their kinetic energy. In this circuit, a potential difference (voltage) is maintained between the photoelectric metal and an open-grid electrode placed below the upper plate. For electric current to flow, electrons must pass through the openings in the grid and onto the upper plate. The negative potential on the grid acts to slow down the approaching electrons. As the potential difference between the grid and the emitting metal is increased, a point is reached at which the photoelectrons are stopped at the grid and the current ceases to flow through the ammeter. The potential difference at this point is called the *stopping voltage*, V_s. At the stopping voltage, the kinetic energy of the photoelectrons has been converted to potential energy, expressed through the following equation (in which m, u, and e are the mass, speed, and charge of an electron, respectively).

$$\frac{1}{2}mu^2 = eV_s$$

As a result of experiments of the type just described, we find that V_s is proportional to the frequency of the incident light but independent of the light intensity. Also, as shown in Figure 8-12, if the frequency, ν, is below the *threshold frequency*, ν_0, no photoelectric current is produced. At frequencies greater than ν_0, the empirical equation for the stopping voltage is

$$V_s = k(\nu - \nu_0)$$

The constant k is independent of the metal used, but ν_0 varies from one metal to another. Although there is no relation between V_s and the light intensity, the photoelectric current is proportional to the intensity (I) of the light.

The work function is a quantity of work and, hence, of energy. One way to express this quantity is as the product of Planck's constant and the threshold frequency: $E = h\nu_0$. Another way is as the product of the charge on the electron, e, and the potential, V_0, that has to be overcome in the metal: $E = eV_0$.

With the advent of lasers we have observed the simultaneous absorption of two photons by one electron. Instances of two adjacent molecules cooperatively absorbing one photon are also known. Such occurrences are exceptions to the more normal one photon/one electron phenomena.

Photoelectric Effect animation

Albert Einstein received a Nobel Prize for his work on the photoelectric effect. He is better known for his development of the theory of relativity, and $E = mc^2$. Selection for a Nobel Prize for theory is rare.

▲ **Albert Einstein (1879–1955)**

Are You Wondering . . .

How the energy of a photon is manifested?

We begin with an important relationship between the mass and velocity of a particle given by Einstein. Let the mass of a particle when the particle and the measuring device are at rest be denoted as m_0. If we remeasure the mass when the particle moves with a velocity u, we find that its mass increases according to the equation

$$m = \frac{m_0}{\sqrt{1 - u^2/c^2}}$$

where m is the particle mass, referred to as the *relativistic mass*, and c is the speed of light. For particles moving at speeds less than 90% of the speed of light, the relativistic mass (m) is essentially the same as the rest mass (m_0).

We have seen that the kinetic energy of a particle is given by

$$E_K = \frac{1}{2}mu^2$$

However, because photons travel at the speed of light they must have zero rest mass (otherwise their relativistic mass m would become infinite). So where is their energy?

Although photons have zero rest mass, they do possess momentum, which is defined as the relativistic mass times the velocity of the particle, because they are in motion. Einstein's theory of special relativity states that a particle's energy and momentum ($p = mu$, recall page 202) are related by the expression

$$E^2 = (pc)^2 + (m_0c^2)^2$$

where m_0 is the rest mass of the particle. For photons traveling at the speed of light c, the rest mass is zero. Hence

$$E = pc = h\nu$$

$$p = \frac{h\nu}{c} = \frac{h}{\lambda}$$

Photons possess momentum, and it is this momentum that is transferred to an electron in a collision. In all collisions between photons and electrons, momentum is conserved. Thus, we see that the wave and the photon models are intimately connected. The energy of a photon is related to the frequency of the wave by Planck's equation, and the momentum of the photon is related to the wavelength of the wave by the equation just derived! When a photon collides with an electron, it transfers momentum to the electron, which accelerates to a new velocity. The energy of the photon decreases, and, as a consequence, its wavelength increases. This phenomenon, called the Compton effect, was discovered in 1923 and confirmed the particulate nature of light.

Thus, the threshold frequency for the photoelectric effect is given by the expression

$$\nu_0 = \frac{eV_0}{h}$$

Since the work function (eV_0) is a characteristic of the metal used in the experiment, then ν_0 is also a characteristic of the metal, as confirmed by experiment.

When a photon of energy $h\nu$ strikes an electron, the electron overcomes the work function eV_0 and is liberated with kinetic energy $\left(\frac{1}{2}\right)mu^2$. Thus, by the law of conservation of energy, we have

$$\frac{1}{2}mu^2 + eV_0 = h\nu$$

which gives

$$eV_s = \frac{1}{2}mu^2 = h\nu - eV_0$$

which is identical to the empirically determined equation for V_s with $k = h/e$ when $h\nu_0 = eV_0$. Careful experiments showed that the constant h had the same value as determined by Planck for blackbody radiation. The additional fact that the number of photoelectrons increases with the intensity of light indicates that we should associate light intensity with the number of photons arriving at a point per unit time.

> A common misconception about the photoelectric effect is that the kinetic energy of emitted electrons should increase as the intensity of the light increases. Stress that the intensity of the light is proportional to the number of photons and not photon energy.

CONCEPT ASSESSMENT ✔

The wavelength of light needed to eject electrons from hydrogen atoms is 91.2 nm. When light of 80.0 nm is shone on a sample of hydrogen atoms, electrons are emitted from the hydrogen gas. If, in a different experiment, the wavelength of the light is changed to 70.0 nm, what is the effect compared to the use of 80.0 nm light? Are more electrons emitted? If not, what happens?

PHOTONS OF LIGHT AND CHEMICAL REACTIONS

Chemical reactions that are induced by light are called *photochemical reactions*. Because they are essential to these reactions, we can think of photons as "reactants" and we can designate them in chemical equations by the symbol $h\nu$. The reactions by which ozone molecules, O_3, are produced from oxygen molecules, O_2, are represented below.

$$O_2 + h\nu \longrightarrow O + O$$
$$O_2 + O + M \longrightarrow O_3 + M$$

The radiation required in the first reaction is UV radiation with wavelength less than 242.4 nm. O atoms from the first reaction then combine with O_2 to form O_3. In the second reaction, a "third body," M, such as $N_2(g)$, is needed to carry away excess energy to prevent immediate dissociation of O_3 molecules.

Photochemical reactions involving ozone are the subject of Example 8-2. There we see that the product of Planck's constant (h) and frequency (ν) yields the energy of a single photon of electromagnetic radiation in the unit joule. Invariably, this energy is only a tiny fraction of a joule. Often it is useful to deal with the much larger energy of a mole of photons (6.02214×10^{23} photons).

Stratospheric Ozone animation

> The reactions shown here describing the formation ozone from oxygen gas are the reactions which occur in the atmosphere to produce ozone.

EXAMPLE 8-2

Using Planck's Equation to Calculate the Energy of Photons of Light. For radiation of wavelength 242.4 nm, the longest wavelength that will bring about the photodissociation of O_2, what is the energy of **(a)** one photon, and **(b)** a mole of photons of this light?

Solution

(a) To use Planck's equation, we need the frequency of the radiation. This we can get from equation (8.1) after first expressing the wavelength in meters.

$$\nu = \frac{c}{\lambda} = \frac{2.998 \times 10^8 \text{ m s}^{-1}}{242.4 \times 10^{-9} \text{ m}} = 1.237 \times 10^{15} \text{ s}^{-1}$$

Planck's equation is written for *one* photon of light. We emphasize this by including the unit, photon^{-1}, in the value of h.

$$E = h\nu = 6.626 \times 10^{-34} \times \frac{\text{J s}}{\text{photon}} \times 1.237 \times 10^{15} \text{ s}^{-1}$$

$$= 8.196 \times 10^{-19} \text{ J/photon}$$

(b) Once we have the energy per photon, we can multiply it by the Avogadro constant to convert to a per-mole basis.

$$E = 8.196 \times 10^{-19} \text{ J/photon} \times 6.022 \times 10^{23} \text{ photons/mol}$$

$$= 4.936 \times 10^5 \text{ J/mol}$$

(This quantity of energy is sufficient to raise the temperature of 10.0 L of water by 11.8 °C.)

Practice Example A: The protective action of ozone in the atmosphere comes through ozone's absorption of UV radiation in the 230 to 290-nm wavelength range. What is the energy, in kilojoules per mole, associated with radiation in this wavelength range?

Practice Example B: Chlorophyll absorbs light at energies of 3.056×10^{-19} J/photon and 4.414×10^{-19} J/photon. To what color and frequency do these absorptions correspond?

8-4   THE BOHR ATOM

The Rutherford model of a nuclear atom (Section 2-3) does not indicate how electrons are arranged outside the nucleus of an atom. According to classical physics, stationary, negatively charged electrons would be pulled into the positively charged nucleus. This suggests that the electrons in an atom must be in motion, like the planets orbiting the sun. However, again according to classical physics, orbiting electrons should be constantly accelerating and should radiate energy. By losing energy, the electrons would be drawn ever closer to the nucleus and soon spiral into it. In 1913, Niels Bohr (1885–1962) resolved this problem by using Planck's quantum hypothesis. In an interesting blend of classical and quantum theory, Bohr postulated that for a hydrogen atom:

1. The electron moves in circular orbits about the nucleus with the motion described by classical physics.

2. The electron has only a fixed set of allowed orbits, called *stationary states*. The allowed orbits are those in which certain properties of the electron have unique values. Even though classical theory would predict otherwise, *as long as an electron remains in a given orbit, its energy is constant and no energy is emitted*. The particular property of the electron having only certain allowed values, leading to only a discrete set of allowed orbits, is called the *angular momentum*. Its possible values are $nh/2\pi$, where n must be an integer. Thus the quantum numbers progress: $n = 1$ for the first orbit; $n = 2$ for the second orbit; and so on.

3. An electron can pass only from one allowed orbit to another. In such transitions, fixed discrete quantities of energy (quanta) are involved—either absorbed or emitted.

The atomic model of hydrogen based on these ideas is pictured in Figure 8-13. The allowed states for the electron are numbered, $n = 1$, $n = 2$, $n = 3$, and so on. These *integral* numbers, which arise from Bohr's assumption that only certain values are allowed for the angular momentum of the electron, are called **quantum numbers**.

The Bohr theory predicts the radii of the allowed orbits in a hydrogen atom.

$$r_n = n^2 a_0, \text{ where } n = 1, 2, 3, \ldots \quad \text{and} \quad a_0 = 53 \text{ pm } (0.53 \text{ Å}) \qquad (8.4)$$

▲ Niels Bohr (1885–1962)
In addition to his work on the hydrogen atom, Bohr headed the Institute of Theoretical Physics in Copenhagen, which became a mecca for theoretical physicists in the 1920s and 1930s.

KEEP IN MIND ▶
that momentum (p) is the product of the mass and the velocity of a particle. If the particle undergoes a circular motion, then the particle possesses angular momentum.

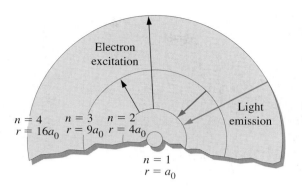

◀ **FIGURE 8-13**
Bohr model of the hydrogen atom
A portion of the hydrogen atom is pictured. The nucleus is at the center, and the electron is found in one of the discrete orbits, $n = 1, 2$, and so on. Excitation of the atom raises the electron to higher-numbered orbits, as shown with black arrows. Light is emitted when the electron falls to a lower-numbered orbit. Two transitions that produce lines in the Balmer series of the hydrogen spectrum are shown in the approximate colors of the spectral lines.

The theory also allows us to calculate the electron velocities in these orbits and, most important, the energy. When the electron is free of the nucleus, by convention, it is said to be at a *zero* of energy. When a free electron is attracted to the nucleus and confined to the orbit n, the electron energy becomes negative, with its value lowered to

$$E_n = \frac{-R_H}{n^2} \qquad (8.5)$$

Bohr Model activity

According to the Bohr model lower energy orbits are closer to the nucleus and electrons associated with low energy orbits must absorb more energy to be removed from the atom.

R_H is a numerical constant with a value of 2.179×10^{-18} J.

With expression (8.5), we can calculate the energies of the allowed energy states, or *energy levels*, of the hydrogen atom. These levels can be represented schematically as in Figure 8-14. This representation is called an **energy-level diagram**. Example 8-3 shows how Bohr's model can be used to predict whether certain energy levels are possible (allowed) or impossible (not allowed).

◀ **FIGURE 8-14**
Energy-level diagram for the hydrogen atom
If the electron acquires 2.179×10^{-18} J of energy, it moves to the orbit $n = \infty$; ionization of the H atom occurs (black arrow). Energy emitted when the electron falls from higher-numbered orbits to the orbit $n = 1$ is in the form of ultraviolet light, which produces a spectral series called the Lyman series (gray lines). Electron transitions to the orbit $n = 2$ yield lines in the Balmer series (recall Figure 8-10); three of the lines are shown here (in color). Transitions to $n = 3$ yield spectral lines in the infrared.

EXAMPLE 8-3

Understanding the Meaning of Quantization of Energy. Is it likely that there is an energy level for the hydrogen atom, $E_n = -1.00 \times 10^{-20}$ J?

Solution

We really do not need to do a detailed calculation to conclude that the answer is very likely *no*. We cannot expect some random value to correspond to one of the unique set of allowed energy levels. Let us rearrange equation (8.5), solve for n^2, and then for n.

$$n^2 = \frac{-R_H}{E_n}$$

$$= \frac{-2.179 \times 10^{-18} \text{ J}}{-1.00 \times 10^{-20} \text{ J}} = 2.179 \times 10^2 = 217.9$$

$$n = \sqrt{217.9} = 14.76$$

Because the value of n is not an integer, this is not an allowed energy level for the hydrogen atom.

Practice Example A: Is there an energy level for the hydrogen atom, $E_n = 2.69 \times 10^{-20}$ J?

Practice Example B: Is it likely that one of the electron orbits in the Bohr atom has a radius of 1.00 nm?

▶ Think of a person on a stairway going up steps (excitation) or down steps (emission). The person must stop on a step—in-between levels are not available.

Normally, the electron in a hydrogen atom is found in the orbit closest to the nucleus ($n = 1$). This is the lowest allowed energy, or the **ground state**. When the electron gains a quantum of energy, it moves to a higher level ($n = 2, 3$, and so on) and the atom is in an **excited state**. When the electron drops from a higher to a lower numbered orbit, a unique quantity of energy is emitted—the difference in energy between the two levels. Equation (8.5) can be used to derive an expression for the difference in energy between two levels, where n_f is the final level and n_i is the initial one.

 The Rydberg Equation

$$\Delta E = E_f - E_i = \frac{-R_H}{n_f^2} - \frac{-R_H}{n_i^2} = R_H\left(\frac{1}{n_i^2} - \frac{1}{n_f^2}\right) = 2.179 \times 10^{-18} \text{ J}\left(\frac{1}{n_i^2} - \frac{1}{n_f^2}\right) \quad (8.6)$$

▶ Notice the resemblance of this equation to the Balmer equation (8.2). In addition to developing a theory of atomic structure to account for Rutherford's atomic model, Bohr sought a theoretical explanation of the Balmer equation.

The energy of the photon, either absorbed or emitted, is calculated in accordance with Planck's equation, expressed in the form

$$\Delta E = h\nu$$

where ΔE represents the energy difference between the energy levels involved in the electronic transition.

Example 8-4 uses equation (8.6) as a basis for calculating the lines in the hydrogen emission spectrum. Because the differences between energy levels are limited in number, so too are the energies of the emitted photons. Therefore, only certain wavelengths (or frequencies) are observed for the spectral lines.

✓ Students at this point will be asking "What do we really need to know?" Reasonable expectations include being able to calculate the energy, frequency, and wavelength for any hydrogen atom transition, as in Example 8-4, and characterizing the light involved as UV, VIS, or IR. Also, being able to interrelate E, l, and n for any photon process, as in Example 8-2.

EXAMPLE 8-4

Calculating the Wavelength of a Line in the Hydrogen Spectrum. Determine the wavelength of the line in the Balmer series of hydrogen corresponding to the transition from $n = 5$ to $n = 2$.

Solution

The specific data for equation (8.6) are $n_i = 5$ and $n_f = 2$.

$$\Delta E = 2.179 \times 10^{-18} \text{ J}\left(\frac{1}{5^2} - \frac{1}{2^2}\right)$$

$$= 2.179 \times 10^{-18} \times (0.04000 - 0.25000)$$

$$= -4.576 \times 10^{-19} \text{ J}$$

The negative sign of ΔE signifies that, as expected, energy is *emitted*. This quantity of energy is emitted as a photon, hence the magnitude of ΔE, the difference between two energy levels, is equal to the energy of the photon emitted. The photon frequency can be obtained from the Planck equation: $\Delta E = E_{\text{photon}} = h\nu$, which can be rearranged to the form

$$\nu = \frac{E_{\text{photon}}}{h} = \frac{4.576 \times 10^{-19}\,\text{J photon}^{-1}}{6.626 \times 10^{-34}\,\text{J s photon}^{-1}} = 6.906 \times 10^{14}\,\text{s}^{-1}$$

Finally, equation (8.1) is used to calculate the wavelength of this line.

$$\lambda = \frac{c}{\nu} = \frac{2.998 \times 10^{8}\,\text{m s}^{-1}}{6.906 \times 10^{14}\,\text{s}^{-1}} = 4.341 \times 10^{-7}\,\text{m} = 434.1\,\text{nm}$$

Note the good agreement between this result and data in Figure 8-10.

Practice Example A: Determine the wavelength of light absorbed in an electron transition from $n = 2$ to $n = 4$ in a hydrogen atom.

Practice Example B: Refer to Figure 8-14 and determine which transition produces the longest wavelength line in the Lyman series of the hydrogen spectrum. What is the wavelength of this line in nanometers and in angstroms?

One photon is emitted for each electron that undergoes a transition as described in Example 8-4. More electrons undergoing the same transition will result in more emitted photons (increased intensity) but will not result in higher energy photons.

THE BOHR THEORY AND SPECTROSCOPY

As shown in Example 8-4, the Bohr theory provides a model for understanding the emission spectra of atoms. Emission spectra are obtained when the individual atoms in a collection of atoms (roughly 10^{20} of them) are excited to the various possible excited states of the atom. The atoms then relax to states of lower energy by emitting photons of frequency given by

$$\nu_{\text{photon}} = \frac{E_i - E_f}{h} \tag{8.7}$$

Thus, the quantization of the energy states of atoms leads to line spectra.

Earlier in this chapter, we learned how the emission spectrum of a sample can be measured by dispersing emitted light through a prism and determining the wavelengths of the individual components of that light. We can conceive of an alternate technique in which we pass electromagnetic radiation, such as white light, through a sample of atoms in their ground states and then pass the emerging light through a prism. Now we observe which frequencies of light the atoms *absorb*. This form of spectroscopy is called *absorption spectroscopy*. The two types of spectroscopy—emission and absorption—are illustrated in Figure 8-15.

For absorption of a photon to take place, the energy of the photon must exactly match the energy difference between the final and initial states, that is,

$$\nu = \frac{E_f - E_i}{h} \tag{8.8}$$

Note that the farther apart the energy levels, the shorter the wavelength of the photon needed to induce a transition.

You may have also noticed that in equation (8.7) the energy difference is expressed as $E_i - E_f$, whereas in equation (8.8) it is $E_f - E_i$. This is done to signify that energy is conserved during photon absorption and emission. That is, during emission $E_f = E_i - h\nu$, so that $\nu = (E_i - E_f)/h$. During photon absorption, $E_f = E_i + h\nu$, so that $\nu = (E_f - E_i)/h$.

Spectroscopic techniques have been used extensively in the study of molecular structures. Other forms of spectroscopy available to chemists are described elsewhere in the text.

Flame Tests. Obtain a supply of spray bottles from a hardware store. Prepare solutions of chloride salts (Na^+, K^+, Li^+, Ca^{2+}, Sr^{2+}, Ba^{2+}) in methanol. Spray a fine mist of each of these over a burner.

The following article describes how vibrational, electronic and nuclear magnetic resonance spectroscopy are used to help explain absorption spectroscopy to students: Macomber, Roger S. *J. Chem. Educ.* **1997**: *74*, 65.

(a)

(b)

 Emission spectra are generally more complicated than *absorption spectra*. An excited sample will contain atoms with a variety of states, each being able to drop down to any of several lower states. An absorbing sample generally is cool and transitions are possible only from the ground state. The hydrogen Balmer lines are not seen, for example, in absorption from cold hydrogen atoms.

▶ **FIGURE 8-15**
Emission and absorption spectroscopy
(a) Emission spectroscopy. Bright lines are observed on a dark background of the photographic plate. **(b)** Absorption spectroscopy. Dark lines are observed on a bright background on the photographic plate.

The Bohr Theory and the Ionization Energy of Hydrogen

The Bohr model of the atom helps to clarify the mechanism of formation of cations. In the special case where the energy of a photon interacting with a hydrogen atom is just enough to remove an electron from the ground state ($n = 1$), the electron is freed, the atom is ionized, and the energy of the free electron is zero.

$$h\nu_{\text{photon}} = E_i = -E_1$$

The quantity E_i is called the *ionization energy* of the hydrogen atom. If $n_i = 1$ and $n_f = \infty$ are substituted in the Bohr expression for an electron initially in the ground state of an H atom, then

$$h\nu_{\text{photon}} = E_i = -E_1 = \frac{R_H}{1^2} = R_H$$

The ideas just developed about the ionization of atoms are applied in Example 8-5, where they are coupled with another aspect of the Bohr model: The model also works for hydrogen-like species, such as the ions He^+ and Li^{2+}, which have only one electron. For these species, the nuclear charge (atomic number) appears in the energy-level expression. That is,

 Emphasize that equation 8.9 applies to hydrogen and hydrogen-like ions only and that no simple formula exists for other atoms. The concept of fixed (quantum) energy states is what is common to all atoms and ions.

$$E_n = \frac{-Z^2 R_H}{n^2} \tag{8.9}$$

Are You Wondering . . .

Why a photon of light is not immediately re-emitted after having been absorbed?

This should certainly be possible, since for any given pair of energy levels, the exact same quantity of energy is involved, whether the photon is absorbed or emitted. It does not happen very often, however, because the excited state of an atom has a limited lifetime, and during this lifetime the atom can undergo collisions with other atoms in the sample. (Remember, even a gas at low pressures contains a lot of atoms.) During all these collisions, the energy imparted to the atom by the absorbed photon can be lost as kinetic energy, so that through a succession of such losses the atom eventually reverts to the ground state. Thus, there is a net absorption of photons. If photons were immediately re-emitted following absorption, there would be no net absorption of photons.

EXAMPLE 8-5

Using the Bohr Model. Determine the kinetic energy of the electron ionized from a Li^{2+} ion in its ground state, using a photon of frequency $5.000 \times 10^{16} \, s^{-1}$.

Solution

The energy of the electron in the Li^{2+} ion is calculated using equation (8.9).

$$E_1 = \frac{-3^2 \times 2.179 \times 10^{-18} \, J}{1^2} = -1.961 \times 10^{-17} \, J$$

The energy of a photon of frequency $5.000 \times 10^{16} \, s^{-1}$ is

$$E = h\nu = 6.626 \times 10^{-34} \times \frac{J \, s}{photon} \times 5.000 \times 10^{16} \, s^{-1} = 3.313 \times 10^{-17} \, J \, photon^{-1}$$

The ionization energy, the energy required to remove the electron, is $E_i = E_1 = 1.961 \times 10^{-17} \, J$. The extra energy from the photon is transferred as kinetic energy to the electron. Thus, the kinetic energy of the electron is

$$\text{kinetic energy} = 3.313 \times 10^{-17} \, J - 1.961 \times 10^{-17} \, J = 1.352 \times 10^{-17} \, J$$

Practice Example A: Determine the wavelength of light emitted in an electron transition from $n = 5$ to $n = 3$ in a Be^{3+} ion.

Practice Example B: The frequency of the $n = 3$ to $n = 2$ transition for an unknown hydrogen-like ion occurs at a frequency 16 times that of the hydrogen atom. What is the identity of the ion?

INADEQUACIES OF THE BOHR MODEL

Despite the accomplishments of the Bohr model for the hydrogen atom and hydrogen-like ions, the Bohr theory has a number of weaknesses. From an experimental point of view, the theory cannot explain the emission spectra of atoms and ions with more than one electron, despite numerous attempts to do so. In addition, the theory cannot explain the effect of magnetic fields on emission spectra. From a fundamental standpoint, the Bohr theory is an uneasy mixture of classical and nonclassical physics. Bohr understood at the time that there is no fundamental basis for the postulate of quantized angular momentum forcing an electron into a circular orbit. He made the postulate only so that his theory would agree with experiment.

Much of the material in Sections 8-5 and 8-6 is optional. Students should be exposed to the wave nature of electron orbitals and the uncertainty principle. These ideas can be postponed, however, until after the types and shapes of orbitals have been discussed.

Modern quantum mechanics replaced the Bohr theory in 1926. The quantization of energy and angular momentum arose out of the postulates of this new quantum theory and required no extra assumptions. However, the circular orbits of the Bohr theory do not occur in quantum mechanics. In summary, the Bohr theory gave the paradigm shift—the quantum leap—from classical physics to the new quantum physics, and we must not underestimate its importance as a scientific development.

CONCEPT ASSESSMENT ✔

Which of the following electronic transitions in a hydrogen atom will lead to the emission of a photon with the shortest wavelength, $n = 1$ to $n = 4$, $n = 4$ to $n = 2$, $n = 3$ to $n = 2$?

8-5 TWO IDEAS LEADING TO A NEW QUANTUM MECHANICS

In the previous section, we examined some successes of the Bohr theory and pointed out its inability to deal with multielectron atoms. A decade or so after Bohr's work on hydrogen, two landmark ideas stimulated a new approach to quantum mechanics. Those ideas are considered in this section and the new quantum mechanics—wave mechanics—in the next.

WAVE–PARTICLE DUALITY

To explain the photoelectric effect, Einstein suggested that light has particle-like properties, which are displayed through photons. Other phenomena, however, such as the dispersion of light into a spectrum by a prism, are best understood in terms of the wave theory of light. Light, then, appears to have a *dual* nature.

In 1924, Louis de Broglie, considering the nature of light and matter, offered a startling proposition: *Small particles of matter may at times display wave-like properties.* How did de Broglie come up with such a suggestion? He was aware of Einstein's famous equation

$$E = mc^2$$

where m is the relativistic mass of the photon and c is the speed of light. He combined this equation with the Planck relationship for the energy of a photon $E = h\nu$ as follows

$$h\nu = mc^2$$

$$\frac{h\nu}{c} = mc = p$$

where p is the momentum of the photon. Using $\nu\lambda = c$, we have

$$p = \frac{h}{\lambda}$$

In order to use this equation for a material particle, such as an electron, de Broglie substituted for the momentum, p, its equivalent—the product of the mass of the particle, m, and its velocity, u. When this is done, we arrive at de Broglie's famous relationship.

$$\lambda = \frac{h}{p} = \frac{h}{mu} \tag{8.10}$$

De Broglie called the waves associated with material particles "matter waves." If matter waves exist for small particles, then beams of particles such as electrons should exhibit the characteristic properties of waves, namely diffraction (recall page 281). If the distance between the objects that the waves

▲ **Louis de Broglie (1892–1987)**
De Broglie conceived of the wave–particle duality of small particles while working on his doctorate degree. He was awarded the Nobel Prize in physics 1929 for this work.

KEEP IN MIND ▶
that in equation (8.10), wavelength is in meters, mass is in kilograms, and velocity is in meters per second. Planck's constant must also be expressed in units of mass, length, and time. This requires replacing the joule by the equivalent units $kg\ m^2\ s^{-2}$.

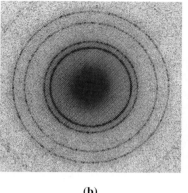

(a)   (b)

◄ **FIGURE 8-16**
Wave properties of electrons demonstrated.
(a) Diffraction of X-rays by metal foil. **(b)** Diffraction of electrons by metal foil, confirming the wave-like properties of electrons.

scatter from is about the same as the wavelength of the radiation, diffraction occurs and an interference pattern is observed. For example, X-rays are highly energetic photons with an associated wavelength of about 1 Å (100 pm). X-rays are scattered by the regular array of atoms in the metal aluminum, where the atoms are about 2 Å (200 pm) apart, producing the diffraction pattern shown in Figure 8-16.

In 1927, C. J. Davisson and L. H. Germer of the United States showed that a beam of slow electrons is diffracted by a crystal of nickel. In a similar experiment in that same year, G. P. Thomson of Scotland directed a beam of electrons at a thin metal foil. He obtained the same pattern for the diffraction of electrons by aluminum foil as with X-rays of the same wavelength (Fig. 8-16).

Thomson and Davisson shared the 1937 Nobel Prize in physics for their electron diffraction experiments. George P. Thomson was the son of J. J. Thomson, who had won the Nobel Prize in physics in 1906 for his discovery of the electron. It is interesting to note that Thomson the father showed that the electron is a particle, and Thomson the son showed that the electron is a wave. Father and son together demonstrated the **wave–particle duality** of electrons.

The following article describes the use of an overhead projector to simulate X-ray diffraction: Dragojlovic, Veljko. *J. Chem. Educ.* **1999**: *76*, 1240.

EXAMPLE 8-6

Calculating the Wavelength Associated with a Beam of Particles. What is the wavelength associated with electrons traveling at one-tenth the speed of light?

Solution

The electron mass, expressed in kilograms, is 9.109×10^{-31} kg (recall Table 2.1). The electron velocity is $u = 0.100 \times c = 0.100 \times 3.00 \times 10^8$ m s^{-1} = 3.00×10^7 m s^{-1}. Planck's constant $h = 6.626 \times 10^{-34}$ J s = 6.626×10^{-34} kg m^2 s^{-2} s = 6.626×10^{-34} kg m^2 s^{-1}. Substituting these data into equation (8.10), we obtain

$$\lambda = \frac{6.626 \times 10^{-34} \text{ kg m}^2 \text{ s}^{-1}}{(9.109 \times 10^{-31} \text{ kg})(3.00 \times 10^7 \text{ m s}^{-1})}$$

$$= 2.42 \times 10^{-11} \text{ m} = 24.2 \text{ pm}$$

Practice Example A: Assuming Superman has a mass of 91 kg, what is the wavelength associated with him if he is traveling at one-fifth the speed of light?

Practice Example B: To what velocity (speed) must a beam of protons be accelerated to display a de Broglie wavelength of 10.0 pm? Obtain the proton mass from Table 2.1.

The wavelength calculated in Example 8-6, 24.2 pm, is about one-half the radius of the first Bohr orbit of a hydrogen atom. It is only when wavelengths are comparable to atomic or nuclear dimensions that wave–particle duality is important. The concept has little meaning when applied to large (macroscopic) objects, such as baseballs and automobiles, because their wavelengths are too small to measure. For these macroscopic objects, the laws of classical physics are quite adequate.

▲ **Werner Heisenberg (1901–1976)**
In addition to his enunciation of the uncertainty principle, for which he won the Nobel Prize in physics in 1932, Heisenberg also developed a mathematical description of the hydrogen atom that gave the same results as Schrödinger's equation (page 302). Heisenberg (left) is shown here dining with Niels Bohr.

▶ The uncertainty principle is not easy for most people to accept. Einstein spent a good deal of time from the middle 1920s until his death in 1955 attempting, unsuccessfully, to disprove it.

 Heisenberg Uncertainty Principle

THE UNCERTAINTY PRINCIPLE

The laws of classical physics permit us to make precise predictions. For example, we can calculate the exact point at which a rocket will land after it is fired. The more precisely we measure the variables that affect the rocket's trajectory (path), the more accurate our calculation (prediction) will be. In effect, there is no limit to the accuracy we can achieve. In classical physics, nothing is left to chance—physical behavior can be predicted with certainty.

During the 1920s, Niels Bohr and Werner Heisenberg considered hypothetical experiments to establish just how precisely the behavior of subatomic particles can be determined. The two variables that must be measured are the position of the particle (x) and its momentum ($p = mu$). The conclusion they reached is that there must *always* be uncertainties in measurement such that the product of the uncertainty in position, Δx, and the uncertainty in momentum, Δp, is

$$\Delta x \Delta p \geq \frac{h}{4\pi} \tag{8.11}$$

The significance of this expression, called the **Heisenberg uncertainty principle**, is that we cannot measure position and momentum with great precision simultaneously. An experiment designed to locate the position of a particle with great precision cannot also measure the momentum of the particle precisely, and vice versa. In simpler terms, if we know precisely where a particle is, we cannot also know precisely where it has come from or where it is going. If we know precisely how a particle is moving, we cannot also know precisely where it is. In the subatomic world, things must always be "fuzzy." Why should this be so?

The de Broglie relationship (equation 8.10) implies that for a wavelength λ, the momentum of the associated particle is precisely known. However, since the wave itself is spread out over all space, we do not know exactly where the particle is! To get around this inability to locate the particle we can combine several waves of different wavelengths into a "wave packet" to produce an interference pattern that tends to localize the wave, as suggested in Figure 8-17.

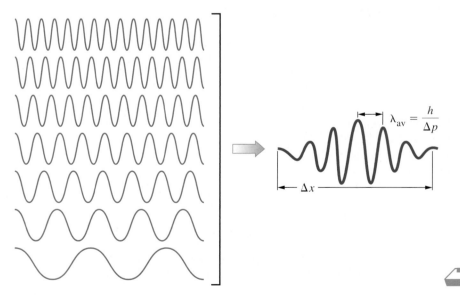

▲ **FIGURE 8-17**
The uncertainty principle interpreted graphically
A collection of waves with varying wavelengths (left) can combine into a "wave packet" (right). The superposition of the different wavelengths yields an average wavelength (λ_{av}) and causes the wave packet to be more localized (Δx) than the individual waves. The greater the number of wavelengths that combine, the more precisely an associated particle can be located, that is, the smaller Δx. However, because each of the wavelengths corresponds to a different value of momentum according to the de Broglie relationship, the greater is the uncertainty in the resultant momentum.

However, because each wavelength in the wave packet corresponds to a specific, but different, momentum, the momentum of the particle corresponding to the collection of waves has become uncertain. So as we combine more and more waves to localize the particle, the momentum becomes more and more uncertain. And, conversely, the more precisely we wish to know the momentum of a particle the fewer and fewer wavelengths we should combine, meaning that the position becomes more spread out. Thus as we proceed downward in size to atomic dimensions, it is no longer valid to consider a particle to be like a hard sphere. Instead, it becomes more and more wavelike, and it is no longer possible to determine with precision both its position and momentum.

Once we understand that the consequence of wave–particle duality is the uncertainty principle, we realize that a fundamental error of the Bohr model was to constrain an electron to a one-dimensional orbit (1-D in the sense that the electron cannot move off a circular path of a fixed radius). We are now ready to turn our attention to a modern description of electrons in atoms.

EXAMPLE 8-7

Calculating the Uncertainty of the Position of an Electron. A 12-eV electron can be shown to have a speed of 2.05×10^6 m/s. Assuming that the precision (uncertainty) of this value is 1.5%, with what precision can we simultaneously measure the position of the electron?

Solution

The uncertainty in the electron speed is

$$\Delta u = 0.015 \times 2.05 \times 10^6 \text{ m s}^{-1} = 3.1 \times 10^4 \text{ m s}^{-1}$$

The electron mass, 9.109×10^{-31} kg (recall Table 2.1), is known much more precisely than the electron speed, which means that

$$\Delta p = m\Delta u = 9.109 \times 10^{-31} \text{ kg} \times 3.1 \times 10^4 \text{ m s}^{-1}$$
$$= 2.8 \times 10^{-26} \text{ kg m s}^{-1}$$

From equation (8.11), the uncertainty in the electron's position is

$$\Delta x = \frac{h}{4\pi\Delta p} = \frac{6.63 \times 10^{-34} \text{ kg m}^2 \text{ s}^{-1}}{4 \times 3.14 \times 2.8 \times 10^{-26} \text{ kg m s}^{-1}} = 1.9 \times 10^{-9} \text{ m} = 1.9 \times 10^3 \text{ pm}$$

which is about 10 atomic diameters. Given the uncertainty in its speed, there is simply no way to pin down the electron's position with any greater precision than that.

Practice Example A: Superman has a mass of 91 kg and is traveling at one-fifth the speed of light. If the speed at which Superman travels is known with a precision of 1.5%, what is the uncertainty in his position?

Practice Example B: What is the uncertainty in the speed of a beam of protons whose position is known with the uncertainty of 24 nm?

These two references describe the use of an overhead projector to help explain the concept of the Heisenburg Uncertainty Principle: Cosser, Ronald C. *J. Chem. Educ.* **1982:** *59*, 300 and Peckham, Gavin D. *J. Chem. Educ.* **1984:** *61*, 868.

CONCEPT ASSESSMENT ✔

An electron has a mass approximately 1/2000th of the mass of a proton. Assuming that a proton and an electron have similar wavelengths, how would their speeds compare?

8-6   WAVE MECHANICS

De Broglie's relationship suggests that electrons are matter waves and thus should display wavelike properties. A consequence of this wave–particle duality is the limited precision in determining an electron's position and momentum imposed by the Heisenberg uncertainty principle. How then are we to view electrons in atoms? To answer this question, we must begin by identifying two types of waves.

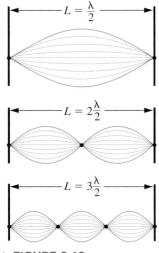

▲ FIGURE 8-18
Standing waves in a string
The string can be set into motion by plucking it. The blue boundaries outline the range of displacements at each point for each standing wave. The relationships between the wavelength, string length, and the number of nodes—points that are not displaced—are given by equation (8.12). The nodes are marked by bold dots.

KEEP IN MIND ▶

that a circle is one dimensional in the sense that all points on the circumference are at the same distance from the center. Thus, only one value needs to be given to define a circle—its radius.

STANDING WAVES

On an ocean, the wind produces waves on the surface whose crests and troughs travel great distances. These are called *traveling waves*. In the traveling wave shown in Figure 8-1, every portion of a very long rope goes through an identical up-and-down motion. The wave transmits energy along the entire length of the rope. An alternative form of a wave is seen in the vibrations in a plucked guitar string, suggested by Figure 8-18.

Segments of the string experience up-and-down displacements with time, and they oscillate or vibrate between the limits set by the blue curves. The important aspect of these waves is that the crests and troughs of the wave occur at fixed positions and the amplitude of the wave at the fixed ends is zero. Of special interest is the fact that the magnitudes of the oscillations differ from point to point along the wave, including certain points, called *nodes*, that undergo no displacement at all. A wave with these characteristics is called a **standing wave**.

We might say that the permitted wavelengths of standing waves are quantized. They are equal to twice the path length (L) divided by a whole number (n), that is,

$$\lambda = \frac{2L}{n} \text{ where } n = 1, 2, 3, \ldots \text{ and the total number of nodes } = n + 1 \quad (8.12)$$

The plucked guitar string represents a one-dimensional standing wave, and so does an electron in a Bohr orbit. We now understand why only an integral number of electron orbits are permitted in the Bohr theory (Fig. 8-19). Also, the fact that Bohr orbits are one-dimensional (they are defined by a single dimension, the radius) also points up a serious deficiency in the Bohr model: The matter waves of electrons in the hydrogen atom must be three-dimensional.

STANDING WAVES, QUANTUM PARTICLES, AND WAVE FUNCTIONS

In 1927, Erwin Schrödinger, an expert on the theory of vibrations and standing waves, suggested that an electron (or any other particle) exhibiting wavelike properties should be describable by a mathematical equation called a **wave function**. The wave function, denoted by the Greek letter psi, ψ, should correspond to a standing wave within the boundary of the system being described. The simplest system for which we can write a wave function is another one-dimensional system, that of a particle confined to move in a one-dimensional

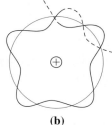

(a)   (b)

▶ Beating a drum produces a two-dimensional standing wave, and ringing a spherical bell, produces a three-dimensional standing wave.

▲ FIGURE 8-19
The electron as a matter wave
These patterns are two-dimensional cross sections of a much more complicated three-dimensional wave. The wave pattern in **(a)**, a *standing wave*, is an acceptable representation. It has an integral number of wavelengths (five) about the nucleus; successive waves reinforce one another. The pattern in **(b)** is unacceptable. The number of wavelengths is nonintegral, and successive waves tend to cancel each other; that is, the crest in one part of the wave overlaps a trough in another part of the wave, and there is no resultant wave at all.

box, a line. The wave function for this so-called "particle in a box" looks like those of a guitar string (Fig. 8-18), but now it represents the matter waves of a particle. Since the particle is constrained to be in the box, the waves also must be in the box, as illustrated in Figure 8-20.

If the length of the box is L and the particle moves along the x direction, then the equation for the standing wave is

$$\psi_n(x) = \sqrt{\frac{2}{L}} \sin\left(\frac{n\pi x}{L}\right) \quad n = 1, 2, 3, \ldots$$

where the quantum number, n, labels the wave function.

This wave function is a sine function. (A sine function undergoes the same up-and-down motion that is characteristic of waves.) To illustrate, consider the case where $n = 2$.

When

$x = 0,$	$\sin 2\pi x/L = \sin 0 = 0,$	and $\psi_n(x) = 0$
$x = L/4,$	$\sin 2\pi(L/4)/L = \sin \pi/2 = 1,$	and $\psi_n(x) = (2/L)^{1/2}$
$x = L/2,$	$\sin 2\pi(L/2)/L = \sin \pi = 0,$	and $\psi_n(x) = 0$
$x = 3L/4,$	$\sin 2\pi(3L/4)/L = \sin 3\pi/2 = -1$	and $\psi_n(x) = -(2/L)^{1/2}$
$x = L,$	$\sin 2\pi(L)/L = \sin 2\pi = 0,$	and $\psi_n(x) = 0$

At one end of the box ($x = 0$), both the sine function and the wave function are zero. At one-fourth the length of the box ($x = L/4$), the sine function and the wave function both reach their maximum values. At the midpoint of the box, both are again zero; the wave function has a node. At three-fourths the box length, both functions reach their minimum values (negative quantities), and at the farther end of the box, both functions are again zero.

What sense can we make of the wave function and the quantum number? First consider the quantum number, n. What can we relate it to? The particle that we are considering is freely moving (not acted upon by any outside forces) with a kinetic energy given by the expression

$$E_k = \frac{1}{2}mu^2 = \frac{m^2u^2}{2m} = \frac{p^2}{2m} \tag{8.13}$$

Now, to associate this kinetic energy with a wave, we can use de Broglie's relationship ($\lambda = h/p$) to get

$$E_k = \frac{p^2}{2m} = \frac{h^2}{2m\lambda^2}$$

The wavelengths of the matter wave have to fit the standing wave conditions described earlier for the standing waves of a guitar string (equation 8.12). Substituting the wavelength of the matter wave from equation (8.12) into the equation for the energy of the wave yields

$$E_k = \frac{h^2}{2m\lambda^2} = \frac{h^2}{2m(2L/n)^2} = \frac{n^2h^2}{8mL^2}$$

So we see that the standing wave condition naturally gives rise to quantization of the wave's energy, with the allowable values determined by the value of n. Note also that as we decrease the size of the box, the kinetic energy of the particle increases, and according to the uncertainty principle, our knowledge of the momentum must decrease. A final noteworthy point is that the energy of the particle *cannot be zero*. The lowest possible energy, corresponding to $n = 1$, is called the **zero-point energy**. Because the zero-point energy is not zero, the particle cannot be at rest. This observation is consistent with the uncertainty principle because the position and momentum both must be uncertain, and there is nothing uncertain about a particle at rest.

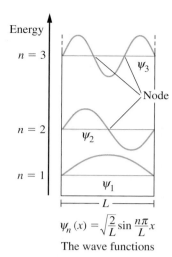

$$\psi_n(x) = \sqrt{\frac{2}{L}} \sin \frac{n\pi}{L}x$$

The wave functions

▲ **FIGURE 8-20**
The standing waves of a particle in a one-dimensional box
The first three wave functions and their energies are shown in relation to the position of the particle within the box. The wave function changes sign at the nodes.

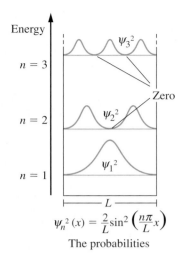

$$\psi_n^2(x) = \frac{2}{L}\sin^2\left(\frac{n\pi}{L}x\right)$$

The probabilities

▲ **FIGURE 8-21**
The probabilities of a particle in a one-dimensional box
The squares of the first three wave functions and their energies are shown in relation to the position of the particle within the box. There is no chance of finding the particle at the points where $\psi^2 = 0$.

The particle-in-a-box model helps us see the origin of the quantization of energy, but how are we to interpret the wave function, ψ? What does it mean that the value of the wave function can be positive or negative? Actually, unlike the trajectory of a classical particle, the wave function of a particle has no physical significance. We need to take a different approach, one suggested by the German physicist Max Born in 1926. From the electron-as-particle standpoint, we have a special interest in the *probability* that the electron is at some particular point; from the electron-as-wave standpoint, our interest is in *electron charge density*. In a classical wave (such as visible light), the amplitude of the wave corresponds to ψ, and the intensity of the wave to ψ^2. The intensity relates to the photon density—the number of photons present in a region. For an electron wave, then, ψ^2 relates to electron charge density. Electron probability is proportional to electron charge density, and both these quantities are associated with ψ^2. Thus, in Born's interpretation of the wave function, the total probability of finding an electron in a small volume of space is the product of the square of the wave function, ψ^2, and the volume of interest. The factor ψ^2 is called the electron probability density.

Now let us return to a particle constrained to a one-dimensional path in a box and look at the probabilities for the wave functions. These are shown in Figure 8-21. First, notice that even where the wave function is negative, the probability density is positive, as it should be in all cases. Next, look at the probability density for the wave function corresponding to $n = 1$. The highest value of ψ^2 is at the center of the box; that is, the particle is most likely to be found there. The probability density for the state with $n = 2$ indicates that the particle is most likely to be found between the center of the box and the walls.

A final consideration of the particle-in-a-box model concerns its extension to a three-dimensional box. In this case, the particle can move in all three directions—x, y, and z—and the quantization of energy is described by the following expression.

$$E_{n_x n_y n_z} = \frac{h^2}{8m}\left[\frac{n_x^2}{L_x^2} + \frac{n_y^2}{L_y^2} + \frac{n_z^2}{L_z^2}\right]$$

where there is one quantum number for each dimension. Thus, a three-dimensional system needs three quantum numbers. With these particle-in-a-box ideas, we can now discuss solving the quantum mechanical problem of the hydrogen atom.

KEEP IN MIND ▶
that the particle in Figure 8-21 exhibits wave–particle duality, rendering inappropriate a question about how it gets from one side of the node to the other (but an appropriate question for a *classical* particle). All we know is that in the state $n = 2$, for example, the particle is in the box somewhere. When we make a measurement, we'll find the particle on one side of the node or the other!

Emphasize that the *orbitals* of modern atomic theory are different from the *orbits* of the Bohr theory and that the Bohr model is not the current model of an atom.

CONCEPT ASSESSMENT ✓

For a particle in a one-dimensional box, in which state (value of n) is the greatest probability of finding the particle at one-quarter the length of the box from either end?

WAVE FUNCTIONS OF THE HYDROGEN ATOM

In 1927, Schrödinger showed that the wave functions of a quantum mechanical system can be obtained by solving a wave equation that has since become known as the **Schrödinger equation**. We shall not go into the details of its solution but just describe and interpret the solution using ideas introduced in the previous discussion.

Solutions of the Schrödinger equation for the hydrogen atom give the wave functions for the electron in the hydrogen atom. These wave functions are called **orbitals** to distinguish them from the orbits of the Bohr theory. The mathematical form of these orbitals is more complex than for the particle in a box, but nonetheless they can be interpreted in a straightforward way.

Wave functions are most easily analyzed in terms of the three variables required to define a point with respect to the nucleus. In the usual Cartesian coordinate system, these three variables are the x, y, and z dimensions. In the spherical polar coordinate system, they are r, the distance of the point from the nucleus, and the angles θ (theta) and ϕ (phi), which describe the orientation of the distance line, r, with respect to the x, y, and z axes (Fig. 8-22).

Are You Wondering . . .

What the Schrödinger equation looks like?

If you are familiar with differential calculus, you will recognize the equation written below as a differential equation. Specifically, it describes a one-dimensional standing wave for the simple system of a particle in a box. The solution of this equation is the wave function for the system.

$$\frac{d^2\psi}{dx^2} = -\left(\frac{2\pi}{\lambda}\right)^2 \psi$$

Notice the form of the wave equation: By differentiating the wave function twice, we obtain the wave function times a constant. To obtain the Schrödinger equation, we substitute de Broglie's relationship for the wavelength of a matter wave.

$$\frac{d^2\psi}{dx^2} = -\left(\frac{2\pi}{h}p\right)^2 \psi$$

Finally, we use the relationship between momentum and kinetic energy, equation 8.13, to obtain

$$-\frac{h^2}{8\pi^2 m}\frac{d^2\psi}{dx^2} = E_k\psi$$

This is the Schrödinger equation of a free particle moving in one dimension. If the particle is subjected to a force, $V(x)$, then we have

$$-\frac{h^2}{8\pi^2 m}\frac{d^2\psi}{dx^2} + V(x)\psi = E_{\text{total}}\psi$$

Extending this treatment to three dimensions, we obtain the Schrödinger equation for the hydrogen atom or hydrogen-like ion, where we understand the force $V(r)$ to be $-Ze^2/r$, the attractive force between the electron and the charge on the nucleus, Ze, where Z is the atomic number of the one electron ion.

$$-\frac{h^2}{8\pi^2 m_e}\left(\frac{\partial^2\psi}{\partial x^2} + \frac{\partial^2\psi}{\partial y^2} + \frac{\partial^2\psi}{\partial z^2}\right) - \frac{Ze^2}{r}\psi = E\psi$$

This is the equation that Schrödinger obtained, and following a suggestion by Eugene Wigner, he used spherical polar coordinates to solve it rather than the Cartesian coordinates shown here. That is, Schrödinger substituted the values of x, y, and z in terms of spherical polar coordinates given in the caption for Figure 8-22 and performed the necessary lengthy algebra to collect the variables r, θ, and ϕ. The equation he obtained is

$$-\frac{h^2}{8\pi^2 \mu r^2}\left[\frac{\partial}{\partial r}\left(r^2\frac{\partial\psi}{\partial r}\right) + \frac{1}{\sin\theta}\frac{\partial}{\partial\theta}\left(\sin\theta\frac{\partial\psi}{\partial\theta}\right) + \frac{1}{\sin^2\theta}\frac{\partial^2\psi}{\partial\phi^2}\right] - \frac{Ze^2}{r}\psi = E\psi$$

where the mass of the electron has been replaced by the more correct reduced mass of the atom, μ, given by

$$\frac{1}{\mu} = \frac{1}{m_e} + \frac{1}{m_{\text{nucleus}}}$$

This is the Schrödinger equation in spherical polar coordinates for a hydrogen-like ion of atomic number Z or the hydrogen atom if $Z = 1$. The solutions are shown in Table 8.1 on page 307.

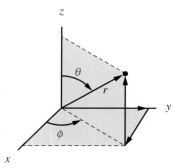

Spherical polar coordinates
$x^2 + y^2 + z^2 = r^2$
$x = r\sin\theta\cos\phi$
$y = r\sin\theta\sin\phi$
$z = r\cos\theta$

▲ **FIGURE 8-22**
The relationship between spherical polar coordinates and Cartesian coordinates
The coordinates x, y, and z are expressed in terms of the distance r and the angles θ and ϕ.

Either coordinate system could be used in solving the Schrödinger equation. However, whereas in the Cartesian coordinate system the orbitals would involve all three variables, x, y, and z, in the spherical polar system the orbitals can be expressed in terms of one function R that depends only on r, and a second function Y that depends on θ and ϕ. That is,

$$\psi(r, \theta, \phi) = R(r)Y(\theta, \phi)$$

The function $R(r)$ is called the **radial wave function**, and the function $Y(\theta, \phi)$ is called the **angular wave function**. Each orbital has three quantum numbers to define it since the hydrogen atom is a three-dimensional system. The particular set of quantum numbers confers a particular functional form to $R(r)$ and $Y(\theta, \phi)$.

Probability densities and the spatial distribution of these densities can be derived from these functional forms. We will first discuss quantum numbers and the orbitals they define, and then the distribution of probability densities associated with the orbitals.

8-7   QUANTUM NUMBERS AND ELECTRON ORBITALS

In the preceding section we stated that by specifying three quantum numbers in a wave function ψ, we obtain an orbital. Here, we explore the combinations of quantum numbers that produce different orbitals. First, though, we need to learn more about the nature of these three quantum numbers.

ASSIGNING QUANTUM NUMBERS

The following relationships involving the three quantum numbers arise from the solution of the Schrödinger wave equation for the hydrogen atom. In this solution the values of the quantum numbers are fixed *in the order listed*.

The first number to be fixed is the *principal quantum number*, n, which may have only a positive, nonzero integral value.

$$n = 1, 2, 3, 4, \ldots \tag{8.14}$$

Second is the *orbital angular momentum quantum number*, ℓ, which may be zero or a positive integer, but not larger than $n - 1$ (where n is the principal quantum number).

$$\ell = 0, 1, 2, 3, \ldots, n - 1 \tag{8.15}$$

Third is the *magnetic quantum number*, m_ℓ, which may be a negative or positive integer, including zero, and ranging from $-\ell$ to $+\ell$ (where ℓ is the orbital angular momentum quantum number).

$$m_\ell = -\ell, -\ell + 1, \ldots, -2, -1, 0, 1, 2 \ldots, (\ell - 1), +\ell \tag{8.16}$$

EXAMPLE 8-8

Applying Relationships Among Quantum Numbers. Can an orbital have the quantum numbers $n = 2$, $\ell = 2$, and $m_\ell = 2$?

Solution

No. The ℓ quantum number cannot be greater than $n - 1$. Thus, if $n = 2$, ℓ can be only 0 or 1. And if ℓ can be only 0 or 1, m_ℓ cannot be 2; m_ℓ must be 0 if $\ell = 0$ and may be -1, 0, or $+1$ if $\ell = 1$.

Practice Example A: Can an orbital have the quantum numbers $n = 3$, $\ell = 0$, and $m_\ell = 0$?

Practice Example B: For an orbital with $n = 3$ and $m_\ell = 1$, what is (are) the possible value(s) of ℓ?

PRINCIPAL SHELLS AND SUBSHELLS

All orbitals with the same value of n are in the same **principal electronic shell** or **principal level**, and all orbitals with the same n and ℓ values are in the same **subshell**, or **sublevel**.

Principal electronic shells are numbered according to the value of n. The first principal shell consists of orbitals with $n = 1$; the second principal shell of orbitals with $n = 2$; and so on. The value of n relates to the energy and most probable distance of an electron from the nucleus. The higher the value of n,

---

Students need to be aware of the *quantum number rules* for electrons and how these lead to the possible set of orbitals, shells, and subshells, as shown in Figure 8-23 (page 305). The quantum number rules can be presented as results of the quantum theory, as outlined in the two preceding sections, regardless of how much of that theory was actually covered by the class.

Each quantum number has a *physical significance*. Quantum number n determines the radial distribution and the average *distance* of the electron from the nucleus and, thus, is most important in determining the *energy* of an electron. Quantum number ℓ determines the angular distribution or *shape* of an orbital. Finally, m_ℓ determines the *orientation* of the orbital.

▶ Chemists often refer to the three quantum numbers simply as the "n," "ℓ" and "m_ℓ" quantum numbers rather than designating them by name.

the greater the electron energy and the farther, on average, the electron is from the nucleus. The principal quantum number, therefore, has a physical significance, as do the other quantum numbers. The quantum number ℓ determines the angular distribution, or *shape*, of an orbital and m_ℓ determines the *orientation* of the orbital.

The number of subshells in a principal electronic shell is the same as the number of allowed values of the orbital angular momentum quantum number, ℓ. In the first principal shell, with $n = 1$, the only allowed value of ℓ is 0, and there is a single subshell. The second principal shell ($n = 2$), with the allowed ℓ values of 0 and 1, consists of two subshells; the third principal shell ($n = 3$) has three subshells ($\ell = 0, 1,$ and 2); and so on. Or, to put the matter in another way, because there are n possible values of the ℓ quantum number, that is, $0, 1, 2, \ldots (n - 1)$, the number of subshells in a principal shell is equal to the principal quantum number. As a result, there is one subshell in the principal shell with $n = 1$, two subshells in the principal shell with $n = 2$, and so on. The name given to a subshell, regardless of the principal shell in which it is found, depends on the value of the ℓ quantum number. The first four subshells are

s subshell	p subshell	d subshell	f subshell
$\ell = 0$	$\ell = 1$	$\ell = 2$	$\ell = 3$

The number of orbitals in a subshell is the same as the number of allowed values of m_ℓ for the particular value of ℓ. Recall that the allowed values of m_ℓ are $0, \pm1, \pm2, \ldots \pm \ell$, and thus the total number of orbitals in a subshell is $2\ell + 1$. The names of the orbitals are the same as the names of the subshells in which they appear.

s orbitals	p orbitals	d orbitals	f orbitals
$\ell = 0$	$\ell = 1$	$\ell = 2$	$\ell = 3$
$m_\ell = 0$	$m_\ell = 0, \pm1$	$m_\ell = 0, \pm1, \pm2$	$m_\ell = 0, \pm1, \pm2, \pm3$
one s orbital in an s subshell	three p orbitals in a p subshell	five d orbitals in a d subshell	seven f orbitals in an f subshell

To designate the particular principal shell in which a given subshell or orbital is found, we use a combination of a number and a letter. For example, the symbol 2p is used to designate both the p subshell of the second principal shell and any of the three p orbitals in that subshell.

The energies of the orbitals for a hydrogen atom, in joules, are given by an equation with a familiar appearance.

$$E_n = -2.178 \times 10^{-18}\left(\frac{1}{n^2}\right)\text{J}$$

It is the same as equation (8.5), the formula derived by Bohr. Orbital energies for a hydrogen atom depend only on the principal quantum number n. This means that all the subshells within a principal electronic shell have the same energy, as do all the orbitals within a subshell. Orbitals at the same energy level are said to be **degenerate**. Figure 8-23 shows an energy-level diagram and the arrangement of shells and subshells for a hydrogen atom.

Emphasize that "s" and "$\ell = 0$" are equivalent designations, and "2p" specifies "$n = 2, \ell = 1$."

Quantum Number activity

The energy-level diagram shown in Figure 8-23 is for a hydrogen atom (or other hydrogen-like particles). Students should understand that the diagrams for atoms with more electrons are more complicated.

◀ In Section 8-10 and in Chapter 24, we will see that orbital energies of multielectron atoms also depend on the quantum numbers ℓ and m_ℓ.

The quantum numbers, and the rules for the possible values of these, determine the *number of orbitals* in each shell and subshell. Note that there are n^2 orbitals in shell n. What simple formula specifies how many orbitals there are in a subshell?

Shell $n = 3$ $3s$ — $3p$ — — — $3d$ — — — — —

$n = 2$ E $2s$ — $2p$ — — —

$n = 1$ $1s$ —

Subshell $\ell = 0$ $\ell = 1$ $\ell = 2$
Each subshell is made up of ($2\ell + 1$) orbitals.

◀ **FIGURE 8-23**
Shells and subshells of a hydrogen atom
The hydrogen atom orbitals are organized into shells and subshells.

Some of the points discussed in the preceding paragraphs are illustrated in Example 8-9.

EXAMPLE 8-9

Relating Orbital Designations and Quantum Numbers. Write an orbital designation corresponding to the quantum numbers $n = 4$, $\ell = 2$, $m_\ell = 0$.

Solution

The magnetic quantum number, m_ℓ, is not reflected in the orbital designation. The type of orbital is determined by the ℓ quantum number. Because $\ell = 2$, the orbital is of the d type. Because $n = 4$, the orbital designation is $4d$.

Practice Example A: Write an orbital designation corresponding to the quantum numbers $n = 3$, $\ell = 1$, and $m_\ell = 1$.

Practice Example B: Write all the combinations of quantum numbers that define hydrogen-atom orbitals with the same energy as the $3s$ orbital.

8-8 INTERPRETING AND REPRESENTING THE ORBITALS OF THE HYDROGEN ATOM

An alternative approach is to skip from Section 8-7 to Section 8-9 and then to 8-11 and 8-12. It is important that students have time to develop proficiency in working electron configurations. Return here later to discuss the shapes of orbitals.

Our major undertaking in this section will be to describe the three-dimensional probability density distributions obtained for the various orbitals in the hydrogen atom. Through the Born interpretation of wave functions (page 302), we will represent the probability densities of the orbitals of the hydrogen atom as surfaces that encompass most of the electron probability. We shall see that the probability density for each type of orbital has its own distinctive shape, and like all waves, probability densities exhibit nodes and differing phase behavior. In studying this section, it is important for you to remember that, even though we will offer some additional quantitative information about orbitals, your primary concern should be to acquire a broad qualitative understanding. It is this qualitative understanding that you can apply in our later discussion of how orbitals enter into a description of chemical bonding.

Throughout this discussion, recall that orbitals are wave functions, mathematical solutions of the Schrödinger wave equation. The wave function itself has no physical significance. However, the square of the wave function, ψ^2, is a quantity that is related to probabilities. Probability density distributions based on ψ^2 are three-dimensional, and it is these three-dimensional regions that we mean when we refer to the shape of an orbital.

▶ In Chapter 11, we will discover important uses of the wave function, ψ, itself as a basis for discussing bonding between atoms.

The forms of the radial wave function $R(r)$ and the angular wave function $Y(\theta, \phi)$ for a one-electron, hydrogen-like atom are shown in Table 8.1. The first thing to note is that the angular part of the wave function for an s orbital, $\left(\dfrac{1}{4\pi}\right)^{1/2}$, is always the same, regardless of the principal quantum number. Next, note that the angular parts of the p and d orbitals are also independent of the quantum number n. Therefore all orbitals of a given type (s, p, d, f) have the same angular behavior. Also note that the equations in Table 8.1 are in a general form where the atomic number Z is included. This means that the equations apply to any one-electron atom, that is, to a hydrogen atom or a hydrogen-like ion. Finally, note that the term σ appearing throughout the table is equal to $2Zr/na_0$.

To obtain the wave function for a particular state, we simply multiply the radial part by the angular part. We will now illustrate this by looking at the three major types of orbitals.

TABLE 8.1   The Angular and Radial Wave Functions of a Hydrogen-like Atom

Angular Part $Y(\theta, \phi)$	Radial Part $R_{n,\ell}(r)$
$Y(s) = \left(\dfrac{1}{4\pi}\right)^{1/2}$	$R(1s) = 2\left(\dfrac{Z}{a_0}\right)^{3/2} e^{-\sigma/2}$
	$R(2s) = \dfrac{1}{2\sqrt{2}}\left(\dfrac{Z}{a_0}\right)^{3/2}(2-\sigma)e^{-\sigma/2}$
	$R(3s) = \dfrac{1}{9\sqrt{3}}\left(\dfrac{Z}{a_0}\right)^{3/2}(6-6\sigma+\sigma^2)e^{-\sigma/2}$
$Y(p_x) = \left(\dfrac{3}{4\pi}\right)^{1/2}\sin\theta\cos\phi$	$R(2p) = \dfrac{1}{2\sqrt{6}}\left(\dfrac{Z}{a_0}\right)^{3/2}\sigma e^{-\sigma/2}$
$Y(p_y) = \left(\dfrac{3}{4\pi}\right)^{1/2}\sin\theta\sin\phi$	$R(3p) = \dfrac{1}{9\sqrt{6}}\left(\dfrac{Z}{a_0}\right)^{3/2}(4-\sigma)\sigma e^{-\sigma/2}$
$Y(p_z) = \left(\dfrac{3}{4\pi}\right)^{1/2}\cos\theta$	
$Y(d_{z^2}) = \left(\dfrac{5}{16\pi}\right)^{1/2}(3\cos^2\theta - 1)$	$R(3d) = \dfrac{1}{9\sqrt{30}}\left(\dfrac{Z}{a_0}\right)^{3/2}\sigma^2 e^{-\sigma/2}$
$Y(d_{x^2-y^2}) = \left(\dfrac{15}{16\pi}\right)^{1/2}\sin^2\theta\cos 2\phi$	
$Y(d_{xy}) = \left(\dfrac{15}{16\pi}\right)^{1/2}\sin^2\theta\sin 2\phi$	
$Y(d_{xz}) = \left(\dfrac{15}{4\pi}\right)^{1/2}\sin\theta\cos\theta\cos\phi$	$\sigma = \dfrac{2Zr}{na_0}$
$Y(d_{yz}) = \left(\dfrac{15}{4\pi}\right)^{1/2}\sin\theta\cos\theta\sin\phi$	

The *wave functions* in Table 8.1 will seem a little formidable to many students. For most, it is only necessary to be aware that these functions are known. Some advanced and honors students might be asked to use these to prepare computer plots, as in some of the following figures.

s Orbitals

To obtain a complete wave function for the hydrogen 1s orbital, we use $Z = 1$ and $n = 1$, and combine the angular and radial wave functions where the red (radial) and blue (angular) colors indicate the origin of the two parts of the wave function.

$$\psi(1s) = R(r) \times Y(\theta,\phi) = \frac{2e^{-r/a_0}}{a_0^{3/2}} \times \frac{1}{\sqrt{4\pi}} = \frac{e^{-r/a_0}}{\sqrt{(\pi a_0^3)}}$$

The term a_0 has the same significance as in the Bohr theory; it is the first Bohr radius—53 pm. By squaring $\psi(1s)$ we obtain an expression for the probability density of finding a 1s electron at a distance r from the nucleus in a hydrogen atom.

$$\psi^2(1s) = \frac{1}{\pi}\left(\frac{1}{a_0}\right)^3 e^{-2r/a_0} \tag{8.17}$$

How can we represent ψ^2 in expression (8.17)? One way is to pass a plane through the nucleus (for example, the xy plane) and plot a graph of electron probability densities (ψ^2) as perpendicular heights above the many points in the plane at which the electron might be found. The resultant graph, seen in

◄ $\psi^2(1s)$ is the probability density for a 1s electron at *one* point a distance r from the nucleus. Equally important is the probability density distribution, which gives the total probability for *all* points at a distance r from the nucleus. In Section 8-10 we will see that this distribution is given by $4\pi r^2\psi^2$.

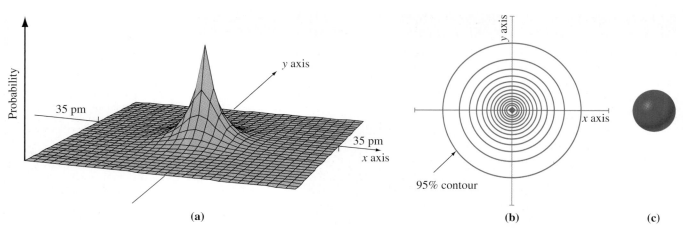

▲ **FIGURE 8-24**
Three representations of the electron probability density for the 1s orbital
(a) In this diagram the probability density is represented by the height above the xy plane (the xy plane is an arbitrary choice, any plane could have been chosen). **(b)** A contour map of the 1s orbital probability density in the xy plane, pointing out the 95% contour. **(c)** A reduced scale 3D representation of the 95% contour of a 1s orbital.

Figure 8-24(a), looks like a symmetrical, cone-shaped "hill" (think of a volcano) of electron probability densities with its peak directly above the nucleus. As in topographical maps of Earth's surface, we can project the three-dimensional surface onto a two-dimensional contour map. The contour map of the "hill" of electron probability densities is shown in Figure 8-24(b). The circular contour lines join points of equal electron probability density. The contours close to the nucleus join points of high probability of finding the electron, those farther away correspond to a lower probability. A simpler way to display the electron probability is to select just one large contour which, together with all the contours within it, encompasses an area of high probability of finding the electron. The contour usually chosen is the one outlining an area in which the chance of finding the electron is 95%. The 95% contour just described is for a plane passing through the nucleus, but an electron in a 1s orbital moves in three-dimensional space. The complete 95% probability surface is a sphere, as seen in Figure 8-24(c).

Now let's look at the wave function of the 2s orbital.

$$\psi(2s) = R(r) \times Y(\theta,\phi) = \frac{1}{2\sqrt{2}}\frac{1}{a_0^{3/2}}\left(2 - \frac{r}{a_0}\right)e^{-r/2a_0} \times \frac{1}{\sqrt{4\pi}} = \frac{1}{4}\left(\frac{1}{2\pi a_0^3}\right)^{1/2}\left(2 - \frac{r}{a_0}\right)e^{-r/2a_0}$$

The electron probability density for the 2s orbital is given by

$$\psi^2(2s) = \frac{1}{8\pi}\left(\frac{1}{a_0}\right)^3\left(2 - \frac{r}{a_0}\right)^2 e^{-r/a_0} \tag{8.18}$$

which, when compared to expression (8.17) for the 1s orbital, shows that the 2s electron tends to stay farther from the nucleus than the 1s electron, because the exponential has changed from $-2r/a_0$ for the 1s (equation 8.17) to $-r/a_0$ for the 2s orbital (equation 8.18). The exponential of the 2s orbital decays more slowly than that of the 1s.

The factor $\left(2 - \frac{r}{a_0}\right)$ in the 2s wave function controls the sign of the function. For small values of r, r/a_0 is smaller than two and the wave function is positive, but for large values of r, r/a_0 is larger than two and the wave function is negative. At $r = 2a_0$, the pre-exponential factor is zero and the wave function is said to have a *radial node*. The wave function changes phase (sign) at this radial node.

The fact that the electron probability density of the 2s orbital extends farther from the nucleus than that of the 1s orbital, together with the presence of the node, means that the 95% electron probability density sphere of a 2s orbital is bigger than that of a 1s orbital and contains a sphere of zero probability due to the radial node. These features are illustrated in Figure 8-25, which compares the 1s, 2s, and 3s orbitals. Note that the 3s orbital exhibits two radial nodes and is larger than both the 1s and 2s orbitals. The number of nodes increases as the energy is increased—a characteristic of high-energy standing waves. To highlight the change in phase of an orbital in progressing outward from the nucleus, we have adopted the modern usage of different colors to represent a change in phase. Thus in Figure 8-25 the 1s orbital is a single red color throughout, whereas the 2s orbital starts out red and then switches to blue; and finally, the 3s starts out red, changes to blue and then back to red, reflecting the presence of two radial nodes. We now turn our attention to the p orbitals.

p ORBITALS

The radial part of $\psi(2p)$ for a hydrogen atom is

$$R(2p) = \frac{1}{2\sqrt{6}}\left(\frac{1}{a_0}\right)^{3/2}\frac{r}{a_0}e^{-r/2a_0}$$

Thus, the 2p orbital has no radial nodes at finite values of r. In contrast to the s orbitals, which are nonzero at $r = 0$, the p orbitals vanish at $r = 0$. This difference will have an important consequence when we consider multielectron atoms.

In contrast to the angular function of the 2s orbital, the angular part of the 2p orbital is not a constant, but a function of θ and ϕ. This means that the electron probability density distribution of a p orbital is not spherically symmetric; that is, it does not have a spherical shape. We see this most easily in Table 8.1 in the functional form of the angular part of the $2p_z$ wave function; it is proportional to $\cos\theta$. Thus the $2p_z$ wave function has an angular maximum along the positive z axis, for there $\theta = 0$ and $\cos 0 = +1$. Along the negative z axis, the p_z wave function has its most negative value, for there $\theta = \pi$ and $\cos\pi = -1$. That the angular part has its maximum magnitude along the z axis is the reason for the designation p_z. Everywhere in the xy plane $\theta = \pi/2$ and $\cos\theta = 0$, so the xy plane is a node. Because this node arises in the angular function, it is called an *angular node*. A similar analysis of the p_x and p_y orbitals shows that they are similar to the p_z orbital, but with angular nodes in the yz and xz planes, respectively.

Figure 8-26 shows the two ways of representing the angular part of the p_z wave function. In Figure 8-26(a), the function $\cos\theta$ is plotted as a function of θ and results in two tangential circles. In Figure 8-26(b), the function $\cos^2\theta$,

3s

2s

1s

▲ **FIGURE 8-25**
Three-dimensional representations of the 95% electron probability density for the 1s, 2s, and 3s orbitals
The first three s orbitals of the hydrogen atom. Note the increasing size of the 95% probability density contour in proceeding from 1s to 2s and on to 3s.

◀ The points at which a wave function changes sign are nodes. However, even though the 2p wave function becomes zero at $r = 0$ and $r = \infty$, these points are not true nodes because the function does not change sign at these points. These points are sometimes called *trivial nodes*.

◀ **FIGURE 8-26**
Two representations of the p orbital angular function
(a) A plot of $\cos\theta$ in the zx plane, representing the angular part of the $2p_z$ wave function. Note the difference in the color of the function in the two lobes representing the phase of the angular wave function. **(b)** A plot of $\cos^2\theta$ in the zx plane, representing the square of the wave function and proportional to the angular probability density of finding the electron.

(a)

(b)

(a)

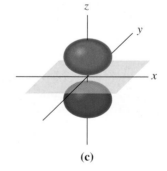

(b)

(c)

▶ **FIGURE 8-27**
Three representations of electron probability for a 2p orbital
(a) The value of ψ^2 is plotted as a height above a plane passing through the nucleus, such as the xy plane. The value of ψ^2 is zero at the nucleus, rises to a maximum on either side, and then falls off with distance (r) along a line through the nucleus (that is, along the x, y, or z axis). (b) A contour plot of the electron probability in a plane passing through the nucleus, for example, the xz plane. (c) Electron probabilities and charge densities represented in three dimensions. The greatest probability of finding an electron is within the two lobes of the dumbbell-shaped region. Note that this region is *not* spherically symmetric. Note also that the probability drops to zero in the shaded plane—the nodal plane (the xy plane). As with the 2s and 3s orbitals, we have indicated changes of phase through different colors.

which is related to the angular electron probability density, is plotted as a function of θ, resulting in a double teardrop shape. Both these representations are used. What is important to note in part (a) of the figure is the phase of the plot of $\cos\theta$ and in (b), the lack of phase of $\cos^2\theta$, which is always positive. We shall see later in the text that the phase of the orbital is important in understanding chemical bonding.

The simultaneous display of both the radial and angular parts of $\psi^2(2p)$ is more difficult to achieve, but Figure 8-27 attempts to do this for the 95% probability surface of the p_z orbital. All three of the p orbitals are shown in Figure 8-28 and are seen to be directed along the three perpendicular axes of the Cartesian system. Again we have used different colors to represent the phase alternation in these orbitals. However, we must remember that these refer only to the phases of the original wave function, *not* to ψ^2.

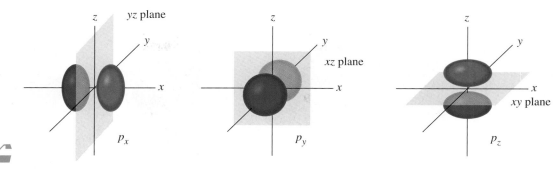

▲ FIGURE 8-28
The three 2p orbitals
The p orbitals are usually represented as directed along the perpendicular x, y, and z axes, and the symbols p_x, p_y, and p_z are often used. The p_z orbital has $m_\ell = 0$. The situation with p_x and p_y is more complex, however. Each of these orbitals has contributions from both $m_\ell = 1$ and $m_\ell = -1$. Our main concern is just to recognize that p orbitals occur in sets of three and can be represented in the orientation shown here. In higher-numbered shells, p orbitals have a somewhat different appearance, but we will use these general shapes for all p orbitals. The colors of the lobes signify the different phases of the original wave function.

d ORBITALS

The d orbitals occur for the first time when $n = 3$. The angular function in these cases possesses two angular (or planar) nodes. Let's illustrate this with the orbital that has an angular function proportional to

$$\sin^2 \theta \cos 2\phi$$

How should we visualize this function? We can proceed by setting $\theta = \pi/2$ and plotting the function $\cos 2\phi$. Study Figure 8-22 and you will see that the angle $\theta = \pi/2$ corresponds to the xy plane, yielding the cross section in the upper left of Figure 8-29. The wave function exhibits positive and negative lobes, indicated by the red and blue lobes, respectively, along the x and y axes. This orbital, in common with all the other d orbitals, is a function of two of the three variables (x, y, and z). It is designated $d_{x^2-y^2}$. The other d orbitals, d_{xy}, d_{xz}, d_{yz}, and d_{z^2}, are also displayed in Figure 8-29. We observe that four of them have the same basic shape except for orientation with respect to the axes and that d_{z^2} has quite a different shape.

Standing Waves.
Tie one end of a long rubber hose or rope to some fixed object. Holding the other end, spin it like a jump rope. This forms an s-like wave with one lobe. Ask at what point on the hose does the wave exist. It exists simultaneously at all points along the hose with varying intensity. Next, spin the hose so as to form a p-like wave with two lobes and a node at the center. Ask how does the wave get from one lobe to the other, across the node. Again, the wave exists simultaneously everywhere along the hose with zero amplitude at, but connected across, the node. How does a $2p_x$ electron get from $-x$ to $+x$? The fallacy again is in thinking of the electron as a point particle. It exists simultaneously at $-x$ and $+x$. Electrons exist as matter waves. The shape of an orbital is the shape of the electron that occupies that orbital.

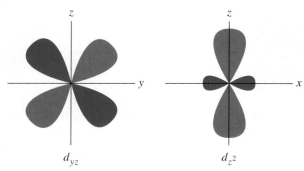

◄ FIGURE 8-29
Cross sections of the five d orbitals
The two-dimensional cross sections of the angular functions of the five d orbitals in the planes indicated.

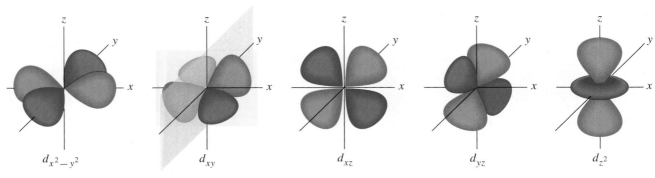

▲ **FIGURE 8-30**
Representations of the five *d* orbitals
The designations xy, xz, yz, and so on are related to the values of the quantum number m_ℓ, but this is a detail that we will not pursue in the text. The number of nodal surfaces for an orbital is equal to the ℓ quantum number. For d orbitals, there are two such surfaces. The nodal planes for the d_{xy} orbital are shown here. (The nodal surfaces for the d_{z^2} orbital are actually cone-shaped.)

The 95% probability surfaces of the five d orbitals are shown in Figure 8-30. Two of the d orbitals ($d_{x^2-y^2}$ and d_{z^2}) are seen to be directed along the three perpendicular axes of the Cartesian system, and the remaining three (d_{xy}, d_{xz}, d_{yz}) are seen to point between these Cartesian axes. Again, the relative phases of the lobes of the original wave function are indicated by the different colors. The d orbitals are important in understanding the chemistry of the transition elements, as we shall see in Chapter 23.

Are You Wondering . . .

What a 3p_z and a 4d_{xy} orbital looks like?

When considering the shapes of the atomic orbitals with higher principal quantum number, we can draw on what we have discussed already and include the extra radial nodes that occur. For example, the 3p_z orbital has a total of two nodes (number of nodes = $n - 1$); one of these nodes is taken up with the angular node of the angular part of the 3p_z wave function, so that the radial part of the wave function will also have a node. Figure 8-31 shows a contour plot of the value of the 3p_z wave function in the xz plane in the manner of Figure 8-27(b). We notice that the 3p_z orbital has the same general shape as a 2p_z orbital due to the angular node, but the radial node has appeared as a circle (dashed in Figure 8-31). The appearance of the 3p_z orbital is that of a smaller p orbital inside a larger one. Similarly the 4d_{xy} orbital appears as a smaller d_{xy} inside a larger one. In Figure 8-31 the radial node is indicated by the dashed circle and the presence of the node is indicated by the alternation in color. This idea can be extended to enable us to sketch orbitals of increasing principal quantum number.

▶ **FIGURE 8-31**
Contour plots for 3p_z and the 4d_{xy} orbital
The relative phases in these orbitals are shown by the colors red and blue. The radial nodes are represented by the dashed circles.

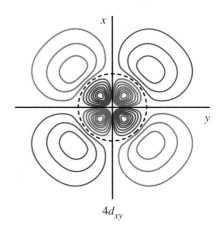

CONCEPT ASSESSMENT ✓

What type of orbital has three angular nodes and one radial node?

8-9   ELECTRON SPIN: A FOURTH QUANTUM NUMBER

Wave mechanics provides three quantum numbers with which we can develop a description of electron orbitals. However, in 1925, George Uhlenbeck and Samuel Goudsmit proposed that some unexplained features of the hydrogen spectrum could be understood by assuming that an electron acts as if it spins, much as Earth spins on its axis. As suggested by Figure 8-32, there are two possibilities for **electron spin**. Thus, these two possibilities require a fourth quantum number, the electron spin quantum number m_s. The electron spin quantum number may have a value of $+\frac{1}{2}$ (also denoted by the arrow ↑) or $-\frac{1}{2}$ (denoted by the arrow ↓); the value of m_s does not depend on any of the other three quantum numbers.

What is the evidence that the phenomenon of electron spin exists? An experiment by Otto Stern and Walter Gerlach in 1920, though designed for another purpose, seems to yield this proof (Fig. 8-33). Silver was vaporized in an oven, and a beam of silver atoms was passed through a nonuniform magnetic field, where the beam split in two. Here is a simplified explanation.

1. An electron, because of its spin, generates a magnetic field.
2. A pair of electrons with opposing spins has no net magnetic field.
3. In a silver atom, 23 electrons have a spin of one type and 24 of the opposite type. The direction of the net magnetic field produced depends only on the spin of the unpaired electron.
4. In a beam of a large number of silver atoms there is an equal chance that the unpaired electron will have a spin of $+\frac{1}{2}$ or $-\frac{1}{2}$. The magnetic field induced by the silver atoms interacts with the nonuniform field, and the beam of silver atoms splits into two beams.

> The direction of the magnetic field produced by a negative spinning charge, like an electron, is predicted using the left-hand rule. Alternatively, the direction of the magnetic field produced by a positive spinning charge, like a proton, is predicted using the right-hand rule. For more information see Vincent, John B. *J. Chem. Educ.* **1999**: 76, 1460.

$m_s = +\frac{1}{2}$ $m_s = -\frac{1}{2}$

◄ **FIGURE 8-32**
Electron spin visualized
Two possibilities for electron spin are shown with their associated magnetic fields. Two electrons with opposing spins have opposing magnetic fields that cancel, leaving no net magnetic field for the pair.

Ag atoms

Oven   Slit   Magnet   Detector

▲ **FIGURE 8-33**
The Stern–Gerlach experiment
Ag atoms vaporized in the oven are collimated into a beam by the slit, and the beam is passed through a nonuniform magnetic field. The beam splits in two. The beam of atoms would not experience a force if the magnetic field were uniform. The field strength must be stronger in certain directions than in others.

ELECTRONIC STRUCTURE OF THE H ATOM: REPRESENTING THE FOUR QUANTUM NUMBERS

Now that we have described the four quantum numbers, we are in a position to bring them together into a description of the electronic structure of the hydrogen atom. The electron in a ground-state hydrogen atom is found at the lowest energy level. This corresponds to the principal quantum number $n = 1$, and because the first principal shell consists only of an s orbital, the orbital quantum number $\ell = 0$. The only possible value of the magnetic quantum number is $m_\ell = 0$. Either spin state is possible for the electron, and we do not know which it is unless we do an experiment like that of Uhlenbeck and Goudsmit. Thus,

$$n = 1 \qquad \ell = 0 \qquad m_\ell = 0 \qquad m_s = +\frac{1}{2} \text{ or } -\frac{1}{2}$$

KEEP IN MIND ▶
that orbitals are mathematical functions and not themselves physical regions in space. However, it is customary to refer to an electron that is described by a particular orbital as being "in the orbital."

Chemists often say that the electron in the ground-state hydrogen atom is in the 1s orbital, or that it is a 1s electron, and they represent this by the notation

$$1s^1$$

where the superscript 1 indicates one electron in the 1s orbital. Either spin state is allowed, but we do not designate the spin state in this notation.

In the excited states of the hydrogen atom, the electron occupies orbitals with higher values of n. Thus, when excited to the level with $n = 2$, the electron can occupy either the 2s or one of the 2p orbitals; all have the same energy. Because the probability density extends farther from the nucleus in the 2s and 2p orbitals than in the 1s orbital, the excited-state atom is larger than is the ground-state atom. The excited states just described can be represented as

$$2s^1 \text{ or } 2p^1$$

In the remaining sections of the chapter this discussion will be extended to the electronic structures of atoms having more than one electron—*multielectron* atoms.

8-10 MULTIELECTRON ATOMS

Section 8-10 is largely optional. That orbitals with different values of ℓ are not degenerate is covered more fully in Section 8-11. The concept of a radial distribution is a difficult one for many to grasp.

Schrödinger developed his wave equation for the hydrogen atom—an atom containing just one electron. For multielectron atoms, a new factor arises: mutual repulsion between electrons. The repulsion between the electrons means that the electrons in a multielectron atom tend to stay away from each other, and their motions become inextricably entangled. The approximate approach taken to solve this many-particle problem is to consider the electrons, one by one, in the environment established by the nucleus and the other electrons. When this is done, the electron orbitals obtained are of the same types as those obtained for the hydrogen atom; they are called *hydrogen-like* orbitals. Compared to the hydrogen atom, the angular parts of the orbitals of a multielectron atom are unchanged, but the radial parts are different.

We have seen that the solution of the Schrödinger equation for a hydrogen atom gives the energies of the orbitals and that all orbitals with the same principal quantum number n are degenerate—they have the same energy. In a hydrogen atom, the orbitals 2s and 2p are degenerate, as are 3s, 3p, and 3d.

In multielectron atoms, the attractive force of the nucleus for a given electron increases as the nuclear charge increases. As a result, we find that orbital energies become lower (more negative) with increasing atomic number of the atom. Also, orbital energies in multielectron atoms depend on the type of orbital; the orbitals with different values of ℓ within a principal shell are not degenerate.

KEEP IN MIND ▶
that orbital-wave functions extend farther out from the nucleus as n increases. Thus, an electron in a 3s or 3p orbital has a higher probability of being farther from the nucleus than does an electron in a 1s orbital.

PENETRATION AND SHIELDING

Think about the attractive force of the atomic nucleus for one particular electron some distance from the nucleus. Electrons in orbitals closer to the nucleus *screen* or *shield* the nucleus from electrons farther away. In effect, the screening electrons reduce the effectiveness of the nucleus in attracting the particular more-distant electron. They effectively reduce the nuclear charge.

The magnitude of the reduction of the nuclear charge depends on the types of orbitals the inner electrons are in and the type of orbital that the screened electron is in. We have seen that electrons in *s* orbitals have a high probability density at the nucleus, whereas *p* and *d* orbitals have zero probability densities at the nucleus. Thus electrons in *s* orbitals are more effective at screening the nucleus from outer electrons than are electrons in *p* or *d* orbitals. This ability of electrons in *s* orbitals that allows them to get close to the nucleus is called *penetration*. An electron in an orbital with good penetration is better at screening than one with low penetration.

We must consider a different kind of probability distribution to describe the penetration to the nucleus by orbital electrons. Rather than considering the probability at a point, which we did to ascribe three-dimensional shapes to orbitals, we need to consider the probability of finding the electron anywhere in a spherical shell of radius *r* and an infinitesimal thickness. This type of probability is called a *radial probability distribution* and is found by multiplying the radial probability density, $R^2(r)$, by the factor $4\pi r^2$, the area of a sphere of radius *r*. Figure 8-34 offers a dartboard analogy that might help clarify the distinction between probability at a point and probability in a region of space.

The quantity $4\pi r^2 \times R^2(r)$ provides a different insight into the behavior of the electron. The radial probability distributions for some hydrogenic (hydrogen-like) orbitals are plotted in Figure 8-35. The radial probability density, $R^2(r)$, for a 1*s* orbital predicts that the maximum probability for a 1*s* electron is *at* the nucleus. However, because the volume of this region is vanishingly small ($r = 0$), the radial probability distribution $[4\pi r^2 \times R^2(r)]$ is zero at the nucleus. The electron in a hydrogen atom is most likely to be found 53 pm from the nucleus; this is where the radial probability distribution reaches a maximum. This is the same radius as the first Bohr orbit. The boundary surface within which there is a 95% probability of finding an electron (see Figure 8-25) is a much larger sphere, one with a radius of about 141 pm.

In comparing the radial probability curves for the 1*s*, 2*s*, and 3*s* orbitals, we find that a 1*s* electron has a greater probability of being close to the nucleus than a 2*s* electron, which in turn has a greater probability than a 3*s* electron.

▲ **FIGURE 8-34**
Dartboard analogy to a 1s orbital
Imagine that a single dart (electron) is thrown at a dartboard 1500 times. The board contains 95% of all the holes; it is analogous to the 1*s* orbital. Where is a thrown dart most likely to hit? The number of holes per unit area is greatest in the "50" region—that is, the 50 region has the greatest probability density. The most likely score is "30," however, because the most probable area hit is in the 30 ring and not the 50 ring, which is smaller than the 30 ring. The 30 *ring* on the dartboard is analogous to a spherical *shell* of 53 pm radius within the larger sphere representing the 1*s* orbital.

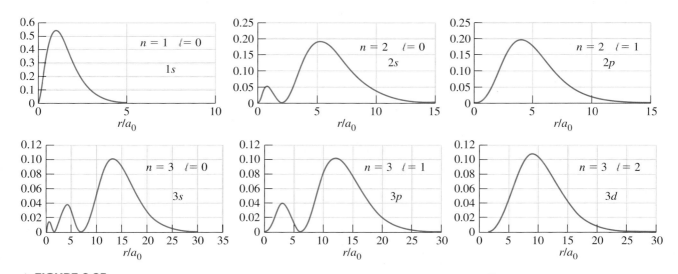

▲ **FIGURE 8-35**
Radial probability distributions
Graphs of the value of $4\pi r^2 R^2(r)$ as a function of *r* for the orbitals in the first three principal shells. Note that the smaller the orbital angular momentum quantum number, the more closely an electron approaches the nucleus. Thus, *s* orbital electrons penetrate more, and are less shielded from the nucleus, than electrons in other orbitals with the same value of *n*.

Radial Electron Distribution animation

KEEP IN MIND ▶

that, similar to the situation in equation (8.9), the energy of an orbital (E_n) is given by the proportionality

$$E_n \propto - \frac{Z_{eff}^2}{n^2}.$$

In comparing $2s$ and $2p$ orbitals, a $2s$ electron has a greater chance of being close to the nucleus than a $2p$ electron. The $2s$ electron exhibits greater penetration than the $2p$ electron. Electrons having a high degree of penetration effectively "block the view" of an electron in an outer orbital "looking" for the nucleus.

The nuclear charge that an electron would experience if there were no intervening electrons is Z, the atomic number. The nuclear charge that an electron actually experiences is reduced by intervening electrons to a value of Z_{eff}, called the **effective nuclear charge**. The less of the nuclear charge that an outer electron "sees" (that is, the smaller the value of Z_{eff}), the smaller is the attraction of the electron to the nucleus, and hence the *higher* is the energy of the orbital in which the electron is found.

To summarize, compared to a p electron in the same principal shell, an s electron is more penetrating and not as well screened. The s electron experiences a higher Z_{eff}, is held more tightly, and is at a lower energy than a p electron. Similarly, the p electron is at a lower energy than a d electron in the same principal shell. Thus, the energy level of a principal shell is split into separate levels for its subshells. There is no further splitting of energies within a subshell, however, because all the orbitals in the subshell have the same radial characteristics, and thereby experience the same effective nuclear charge, Z_{eff}. As a result, all three p orbitals of a principal shell have the same energy; all five d orbitals have the same energy; and so on.

In a few instances, the combined effect of the decreased spacing between successive energy levels at higher quantum numbers (due to the energy dependence on $1/n^2$) and the splitting of subshell energy levels (due to shielding and penetration) causes some energy levels to overlap. For example, because of the extra penetration of a $4s$ electron over that of a $3d$ electron, the $4s$ energy level is below the $3d$ level despite its higher principal quantum number n (Fig. 8-36). We will see some of the consequences of this energy-level splitting in the next two sections, where we consider the relationship between the electronic structures of atoms and their positions in the periodic table.

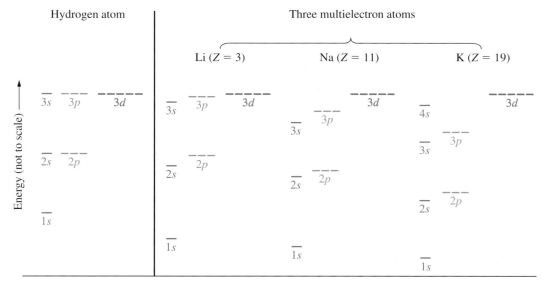

▲ **FIGURE 8-36**
Orbital energy-level diagram for the first three electronic shells
Energy levels are shown for a hydrogen atom (left) and three typical multielectron atoms (right). Each multielectron atom has its own energy-level diagram. Note that for the hydrogen atom, orbital energies within a principal shell—for example, $3s$, $3p$, $3d$—are alike (degenerate), but in a multielectron atom they become rather widely separated. Another feature of the diagram is the steady decrease in all orbital energies with increasing atomic number. Finally, note that the $4s$ orbital is at a lower energy than $3d$.

8-11   ELECTRON CONFIGURATIONS

The **electron configuration** of an atom is a designation of how electrons are distributed among various orbitals in principal shells and subshells. In later chapters, we will find that many of the physical and chemical properties of elements can be correlated with electron configurations. In this section, we will see how the results of wave mechanics, expressed as a set of rules, can help us to write probable electron configurations for the elements.

RULES FOR ASSIGNING ELECTRONS TO ORBITALS

1. **Electrons occupy orbitals in a way that minimizes the energy of the atom.**
   Figure 8-36 suggests the order in which electrons occupy the subshells in the principal electronic shells; first the $1s$, then $2s$, $2p$, and so on. The exact order of filling of orbitals has been established by experiment, principally through spectroscopy and magnetic studies, and it is this order based on experiment that we must follow in assigning electron configurations to the elements. With only a few exceptions, the order in which orbitals fill is

$$1s, 2s, 2p, 3s, 3p, 4s, 3d, 4p, 5s, 4d, 5p, 6s, 4f, 5d, 6p, 7s, 5f, 6d, 7p \qquad (8.19)$$

   Some students find the diagram pictured in Figure 8-37 a useful way to remember this order, but the best method of establishing the order of filling of orbitals is based on the periodic table, as we will see in Section 8-12.

2. **No two electrons in an atom may have all four quantum numbers alike—the Pauli exclusion principle.** In 1926, Wolfgang Pauli explained complex features of emission spectra associated with atoms in magnetic fields by proposing that no two electrons in an atom can have all four quantum numbers alike. The first three quantum numbers, n, ℓ, and m_ℓ, determine a specific orbital. Two electrons may have these three quantum numbers alike; but if they do, they must have different values of m_s, the spin quantum number. Another way to state this result is that *only two electrons may occupy the same orbital, and these electrons must have opposing spins.*

   Because of this limit of two electrons per orbital, the capacity of a subshell for electrons can be obtained by doubling the number of orbitals in the subshell. Thus, the s subshell consists of *one* orbital with a capacity of *two* electrons; the p subshell consists of *three* orbitals with a total capacity of *six* electrons; and so on.

3. **When orbitals of identical energy (degenerate orbitals) are available, electrons initially occupy these orbitals singly.** In line with this rule, known as **Hund's rule**, an atom tends to have as many unpaired electrons as possible. This behavior can be rationalized by saying that electrons, because they all carry the same electric charge, try to get as far apart as possible. They do this by seeking out empty orbitals of similar energy in preference to pairing up with an electron in a half-filled orbital.

REPRESENTING ELECTRON CONFIGURATIONS

Before we assign electron configurations to atoms of the different elements, we need to introduce methods of representing these configurations. The electron configuration of a carbon atom is shown in three different ways:

spdf notation (condensed):	C	$1s^2 2s^2 2p^2$
spdf notation (expanded):	C	$1s^2 2s^2 2p_x^1 2p_y^1$
orbital diagram:	C	

$$\begin{array}{ccc} \boxed{\uparrow\downarrow} & \boxed{\uparrow\downarrow} & \boxed{\uparrow\ \uparrow\ \ } \\ 1s & 2s & 2p \end{array}$$

In each of these methods we assign six electrons because the atomic number of carbon is 6. Two of these electrons are in the $1s$ subshell, two in the $2s$, and two in the $2p$. The condensed *spdf* notation denotes only the total number of

Discuss *degeneracy* and how multielectron atoms are different from hydrogen. *Electron–electron repulsions* are what cause the several subshells in one shell to be at different energy levels. Orbitals with different shape "feel" the repulsions of the other electrons differently. Orbitals within one subshell, having the same shape but different orientations, feel these repulsions equally.

Students sometimes mistakenly believe that when adding electrons to orbitals they have to totally fill a shell before placing electrons in the next shell. Examination of Figure 8-37 proves otherwise.

◀ This order of filling corresponds roughly to the order of increasing orbital energy, but the overriding principle governing the order of filling of orbitals is that the energy of the atom as a whole be kept at a minimum.

▲ **FIGURE 8-37**
The order of filling of electronic subshells
Beginning with the top line, follow the arrows, and the order obtained is the same as in expression (8.19).

Students should at first learn to work out *electron configurations* using Figure 8-36 and the rules for assigning electrons to orbitals. Also learn how to calculate the number of unpaired electrons. The filling diagram, Figure 8-37, can be useful but is not essential. Once proficiency with the principles has been mastered, students can learn to use the periodic table to obtain electron configurations more quickly.

◀ When listed in tables, as in Appendix D, electron configurations are usually written in the condensed *spdf* notation.

electrons in each subshell; it does not show how electrons are distributed among orbitals of equal energy. In the expanded *spdf* notation, Hund's rule is reflected in the assignment of electrons to the 2*p* subshell—two 2*p* orbitals are singly occupied and one remains empty. The **orbital diagram** breaks down each subshell into individual orbitals (drawn as boxes). This notation is similar to an energy-level diagram except that the direction of increasing energy is from left to right instead of vertically.

Electrons in orbitals are shown as arrows. An arrow pointing up corresponds to one type of spin $\left(+\dfrac{1}{2} \right)$, and an arrow pointing down to the other $\left(-\dfrac{1}{2} \right)$. Electrons in the same orbital with opposing (opposite) spins are said to be *paired* (↑↓). The electrons in the 1*s* and 2*s* orbitals of the carbon atom are paired. Electrons in different, singly occupied orbitals of the same subshell have the same, or *parallel*, spins (arrows pointing in the same direction). This is conveyed in the orbital diagram for carbon, where we write [↑][↑][ ] rather than [↑][↓][ ] for the 2*p* subshell. Both experiment and theory confirm that an electron configuration in which electrons in singly occupied orbitals have parallel spins is a better representation of the lowest energy state of an atom than any other electron configuration that we can write.

The most stable or the most energetically favorable configurations for isolated atoms, those discussed here, are called *ground-state electron configurations*. Later in the text we will briefly mention some electron configurations that are not the most stable. Atoms with such configurations are said to be in an *excited state*.

Electron Configurations animation

THE AUFBAU PROCESS

To write electron configurations we will use the **aufbau process**. *Aufbau* is a German word that means "building up," and what we do is assign electron configurations to the elements in order of increasing atomic number. To proceed from one atom to the next, we add a proton and some neutrons to the nucleus and then describe the orbital into which the added electron goes.

Z = 1, H. The lowest energy state for the electron is the 1*s* orbital. The electron configuration is $1s^1$.

Z = 2, He. A second electron goes into the 1*s* orbital, and the two electrons have opposing spins, $1s^2$.

Z = 3, Li. The third electron cannot be accommodated in the 1*s* orbital (Pauli exclusion principle). It goes into the lowest energy orbital available, 2*s*. The electron configuration is $1s^2 2s^1$.

Z = 4, Be. The configuration is $1s^2 2s^2$.

Z = 5, B. Now the 2*p* subshell begins to fill: $1s^2 2s^2 2p^1$.

Z = 6, C. A second electron also goes into the 2*p* subshell, but into one of the remaining empty *p* orbitals (Hund's rule) with a spin parallel to the first 2*p* electron.

$$\boxed{\uparrow\downarrow}\ \boxed{\uparrow\downarrow}\ \boxed{\uparrow}\ \boxed{\uparrow}\ \boxed{}$$
$$\ \ 1s\quad\ 2s\qquad\quad 2p$$

Z = 7–10, N through Ne. In this series of four elements, the filling of the 2*p* subshell is completed. The number of unpaired electrons reaches a maximum (three) with nitrogen and then decreases to zero with neon.

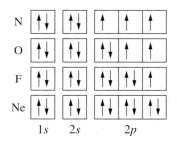

Z = 11–18, Na through Ar. The filling of orbitals for this series of eight elements closely parallels the eight elements from Li through Ne, except that electrons go into $3s$ and $3p$ subshells. Each element has the $1s$, $2s$, and $2p$ subshells filled. Because the configuration $1s^22s^22p^6$ is that of neon, we will call this the neon core, represent it as [Ne], and concentrate on the electrons beyond the core. Electrons that are added to the electronic shell of highest principal quantum number (the outermost, or *valence shell*) are called **valence electrons**. The electron configuration of Na is written below in a form called a *noble-gas-core-abbreviated electron configuration*, consisting of [Ne] as the noble gas core and $3s^1$ as the configuration of the valence electron. For the other third-period elements, only the valence-shell electron configurations are shown.

Na	Mg	Al	Si	P	S	Cl	Ar
$[Ne]3s^1$	$3s^2$	$3s^23p^1$	$3s^23p^2$	$3s^23p^3$	$3s^23p^4$	$3s^23p^5$	$3s^23p^6$

Z = 19 and 20, K and Ca. After argon, instead of $3d$, the next subshell to fill is $4s$. Using the symbol [Ar] to represent the noble gas core, $1s^22s^22p^63s^23p^6$, we get the electron configurations shown below for K and Ca.

$$K: [Ar]4s^1 \quad \text{and} \quad Ca: [Ar]4s^2$$

Z = 21–30, Sc through Zn. In this next series of elements, electrons fill the d orbitals of the third shell. The d subshell has a total capacity of ten electrons—ten elements are involved. There are two possible ways to write the electron configuration of scandium.

$$\text{(a) Sc: } [Ar]3d^14s^2 \quad \text{or} \quad \text{(b) Sc: } [Ar]4s^23d^1$$

Both methods are commonly used. Method (a) groups together all the sub-shells of a principal shell and places subshells of the highest principal quantum level last. Method (b) lists orbitals in the apparent order in which they fill. In this text, we will use method (a).

The electron configurations of this series of ten elements are listed below in both the orbital diagram and the *spdf* notation.

Both methods (a) and (b) are correct. Recommend the use of method (a) as a good habit to develop. It leads one more easily, in the next chapter, to the electron configuration of ions.

◀ Although method (b) conforms better to the order in which orbitals fill, method (a) better represents the order in which electrons are lost on ionization, as we will see in the next chapter.

The d orbitals fill in a fairly regular fashion in this series, but there are two exceptions: chromium (Cr) and copper (Cu). These exceptions are usually explained in terms of a special stability for configurations in which a $3d$ subshell is half-filled with electrons, as with Cr ($3d^5$), or completely filled, as with Cu ($3d^{10}$).

Z = 31–36, Ga through Kr. In this series of six elements, the $4p$ subshell is filled, ending with krypton.

$$Kr: [Ar]3d^{10}4s^24p^6$$

Are You Wondering . . .

Why chromium and copper have "anomalous" electron configurations?

First we need to recognize that the balance between electron–electron repulsions, electron–nuclear attractions, and other electron–electron interactions, due to the fact that electron motions in a multielectron atom are correlated, determines the most stable electron configuration. Next, recall Hund's rule that the subshell electron configuration with the greatest number of unpaired electrons is the most stable. On page 318, this led us to the conclusion that the ground-state electron configuration of carbon is $1s^2 2s^2 2p^2$, with two unpaired electrons in the $2p$ subshell. Calculations on simple atoms and ions have shown that, although there is a larger electron–electron repulsion in the state with the unpaired electrons, this repulsion is more than offset by a larger electron–nucleus attraction because the electrons are closer to the nucleus in the configuration with unpaired electrons. Thus, configurations with unpaired electrons are favored.

In determining the ground-state electron configuration of Cr, we have to choose between $[Ar]3d^4 4s^2$ and $[Ar]3d^5 4s^1$, because the energies of the $3d$ and $4s$ orbitals are very similar. In this case, we can use Hund's rule to decide that the most stable electron configuration is that with the most unpaired electrons, that is, $[Ar]3d^5 4s^1$.

For Cu we have to choose between $[Ar]3d^9 4s^2$ and $[Ar]3d^{10} 4s^1$, and there is no difference between the number of unpaired electrons—Hund's rule is no help here. So where does the extra stability for the configuration $[Ar]3d^{10} 4s^1$ come from? A filled (or half-filled) subshell has a spherically symmetrical charge density that leads to a more stable electron configuration; and the greater the number of electrons in that subshell, the greater the stabilization. The $[Ar]3d^{10} 4s^1$ electron configuration is more stable than $[Ar]3d^9 4s^2$ because of its filled $3d$ subshell. Thus nearly all the anomalous configurations contain either filled or half-filled subshells.

Electron Configuration activity

Many mnemonic devices for writing electron configurations have appeared in the *J. Chem. Educ.* One of the more recent articles is Mabrouk, Suzanne T. *J. Chem. Educ.* 2003: 80, 894 which describes a method of writing electron configurations using a periodic table and lists several references describing other methods.

$Z = 37$–54, Rb to Xe. In this series of 18 elements, the subshells fill in the order $5s$, $4d$, and $5p$, ending with the configuration of xenon.

$$\text{Xe: } [Kr]4d^{10}5s^2 5p^6$$

$Z = 55$–86, Cs to Rn. In this series of 32 elements, with a few exceptions, the subshells fill in the order $6s$, $4f$, $5d$, $6p$. The configuration of radon is

$$\text{Rn: } [Xe]4f^{14}5d^{10}6s^2 6p^6$$

$Z = 87$–?, Fr to ? Francium starts a series of elements in which the subshells that fill are $7s$, $5f$, $6d$, and presumably $7p$, although atoms in which filling of the $7p$ subshell is expected have only recently been discovered and are not yet characterized.

Appendix D gives a complete listing of probable electron configurations.

8-12 ELECTRON CONFIGURATIONS AND THE PERIODIC TABLE

We have just described the aufbau process of making probable assignments of electrons to the orbitals in atoms. Although electron configurations may seem rather abstract, they actually lead us to a better understanding of the periodic table. Around 1920, Niels Bohr began to promote the connection between the periodic table and quantum theory. The chief link, he pointed out, is in electron configurations. *Elements in the same group of the table have similar electron configurations.*

To construct Table 8.2, we have taken three groups of elements from the periodic table and written their electron configurations. The similarity in electron configuration within each group is readily apparent. If the shell of the highest principal quantum number—the outermost, or valence, shell—is labeled n, then

▶ Hydrogen is found in group 1 because of its electron configuration, $1s^1$. However, it is not an alkali metal.

- The group 1 atoms (alkali metals) have *one* outer-shell (valence) electron in an s orbital, that is, ns^1.

TABLE 8.2   Electron Configurations of Some Groups of Elements

Group	Element	Configuration
1	H	$1s^1$
	Li	$[He]2s^1$
	Na	$[Ne]3s^1$
	K	$[Ar]4s^1$
	Rb	$[Kr]5s^1$
	Cs	$[Xe]6s^1$
	Fr	$[Rn]7s^1$
17	F	$[He]2s^2 2p^5$
	Cl	$[Ne]3s^2 3p^5$
	Br	$[Ar]3d^{10}4s^2 4p^5$
	I	$[Kr]4d^{10}5s^2 5p^5$
	At	$[Xe]4f^{14}5d^{10}6s^2 6p^5$
18	He	$1s^2$
	Ne	$[He]2s^2 2p^6$
	Ar	$[Ne]3s^2 3p^6$
	Kr	$[Ar]3d^{10}4s^2 4p^6$
	Xe	$[Kr]4d^{10}5s^2 5p^6$
	Rn	$[Xe]4f^{14}5d^{10}6s^2 6p^6$

- The group 17 atoms (halogens) have *seven* outer-shell (valence) electrons, in the configuration $ns^2 np^5$.
- The group 18 atoms (noble gases)—with the exception of helium, which has only two electrons—have outermost shells with *eight* electrons, in the configuration $ns^2 np^6$.

Although it is not correct in all details, Figure 8-38 relates the aufbau process to the periodic table by dividing the table into the following four blocks of elements according to the subshells being filled:

- *s block.* The *s* orbital of highest principal quantum number (*n*) fills. The *s* block consists of groups 1 and 2 (plus He in group 18).
- *p block.* The *p* orbitals of highest quantum number (*n*) fill. The *p* block consists of groups 13, 14, 15, 16, 17, and 18 (except He).
- *d block.* The *d* orbitals of the electronic shell $n - 1$ (the next to outermost) fill. The *d* block includes groups 3, 4, 5, 6, 7, 8, 9, 10, 11, and 12.
- *f block.* The *f* orbitals of the electronic shell $n - 2$ fill. The *f* block elements are the lanthanides and the actinides.

Another point to notice from Table 8.2 is that the electron configuration consists of a noble-gas core corresponding to the noble gas from the previous period plus the additional electrons required to satisfy the atomic number. Recognizing this and dividing the periodic table into blocks can simplify the task of assigning electron configurations. For example, strontium is in group 2, the second *s* block group, so that its valence-shell configuration is $5s^2$ since it is in the fifth period. The remaining electrons are in the krypton core configuration (the noble gas in the previous period); thus the electron configuration of Sr is

$$\text{Sr: } [Kr]5s^2$$

▲ **FIGURE 8-38**
Electron configurations and the periodic table
To use this figure as a guide to the aufbau process, locate the position of an element in the table. Subshells listed ahead of this position are filled. For example, germanium ($Z = 32$) is located in group 14 of the blue $4p$ row. The filled subshells are $1s^2$, $2s^2$, $2p^6$, $3s^2$, $3p^6$, $4s^2$, and $3d^{10}$. At ($Z = 32$), a second electron has entered the $4p$ subshell. The electron configuration of Ge is $[Ar]3d^{10}4s^24p^2$. Exceptions to the orderly filling of subshells suggested here are found among a few of the d-block and some of the f-block elements.

Emphasize the method of *reading the periodic table* to quickly obtain electron configurations. It is fair to say that the modern periodic table is arranged to facilitate this process.

For the p block elements in groups 13 to 18, the number of valence electrons is from 1 to 6. For example, aluminum is in period 3 and group 13, its valence-shell electron configuration is $3s^23p^1$. We use $n = 3$ since Al is in the third period and we have to accommodate three electrons after the neon core, which contains 10 electrons. Thus the electron configuration of Al is

Al: $[Ne]3s^23p^1$

Gallium is also in group 13, but in period 4. Its valence-shell electron configuration is $4s^24p^1$. To write the electron configuration of Ga, we can start with the electron configuration of the noble gas that closes the third period, argon, and we add to it the subshells that fill in the fourth period: $4s$, $3d$, and $4p$. The $3d$ subshell must fill with 10 electrons before the $4p$ subshell begins to fill. Consequently, the electron configuration of gallium must be

Ga: $[Ar]3d^{10}4s^24p^1$

Thallium is in group 13 and period 6. Its valence-shell electron configuration is $6s^26p^1$. Again, we indicate the electron configuration of the noble gas that closes the fifth period as a core, and add the subshells that fill in the sixth period: $6s$, $4f$, $5d$, and $6p$.

Tl: $[Xe]4f^{14}5d^{10}6s^26p^1$

Students should be able to write out electron configurations and calculate the number of unpaired electrons for *all s and p block and 3d subblock* elements, using only a standard periodic table. The exceptions for Cr and Cu should be remembered. These can be rationalized based on the extra stability of half and completely filled subshells.

The elements in group 13 have the common valence configuration ns^2np^1, again illustrating the repeating pattern of valence electron configurations down a group, which is the basis of the similar chemical properties of the elements within a group of the periodic table.

The transition elements correspond to the d block, and their electron configurations are established in a similar manner. To write the electron configuration of a transition element, start with the electron configuration of the noble gas that closes the prior period and add the subshells that fill in the period of the transition element being considered. The s subshell fills immediately after the preceding noble gas; most transition metal atoms have two electrons in the s subshell of the valence shell, but some have only one. Thus, vanadium ($Z = 23$), which has two valence electrons in the $4s$ subshell and core electrons in the configuration of the noble gas argon, must have *three* $3d$ electrons ($2 + 18 + 3 = 23$).

$$\text{V: } [Ar]3d^34s^2$$

Chromium ($Z = 24$), as we have seen before, has only one valence electron in the $4s$ subshell and core electrons in the argon configuration. Consequently it must have *five* $3d$ electrons ($1 + 18 + 5 = 24$).

$$\text{Cr: } [Ar]3d^54s^1$$

Copper ($Z = 29$) also has only one valence electron in the $4s$ subshell in addition to its argon core, so the copper atom must have *ten* $3d$ electrons ($1 + 18 + 10 = 29$).

$$\text{Cu: } [Ar]3d^{10}4s^1$$

Chromium and copper are two exceptions to the straightforward filling of atomic subshells in the first d-block row. An examination of the electron configurations of the heavier elements (Appendix D) will reveal that there are other special cases that are not easily explained—for example, gadolinium has the configuration $[Xe]4f^76d^16s^2$. Examples 8-10 through 8-12 provide several more illustrations of the assignment of electron configurations using the ideas presented here.

> ✓ The electron configurations for the *lower d and f block* - elements contain many exceptions that need not be remembered. Few people know all of them. One needing any of these configurations may look them up when needed in tables such as in Appendix D.

CONCEPT ASSESSMENT ✓

The accompanying diagrams help to summarize some ideas about the electron configurations of the elements. The diagrams contain some features marked with a question mark (?) and others by leaders (straight-line pointers). Replace each (?) by the symbol of the appropriate element or noble-gas core. Use terms from the following list to attach a label to each leader. You may use a label only once and some labels are inappropriate.

(a) an unpaired electron	**(b)** a filled subshell
(c) a valence shell	**(d)** a valence electron
(e) an f subshell	**(f)** a principal shell
(g) a half-filled subshell	**(h)** a d orbital
(i) a p subshell	**(j)** a d subshell
(k) an electron pair	**(l)** an s subshell

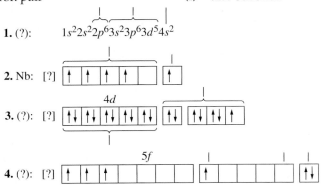

1. (?): $1s^22s^22p^63s^23p^63d^54s^2$

2. Nb: [?]

4d

3. (?): [?]

5f

4. (?): [?]

◀ Helium–neon laser device for use as a bar-code scanner.

Laser devices are in use everywhere—from reading bar codes at supermarket checkout counters to maintaining quality control in factory assembly lines, in compact disc players, laboratory instruments, and, increasingly, as tools in surgery. The word *laser* is an acronym for *light amplification by stimulated emission of radiation.*

Consider a neon sign. An electric discharge produces high-energy electrons that strike Ne atoms and excite certain Ne electrons to a higher energy state. When an excited electron in the neon atom returns to a lower-energy orbital, a photon of light is emitted. Although we know how long Ne atoms remain in an excited state *on average*, we do not know precisely when an atom will emit a photon, nor do we know in which direction the photon will travel. Light emission in a neon sign is a spontaneous, or random, event. *Spontaneous* light emission is pictured in Figure 8-39(a).

Like a neon sign, a helium–neon laser also produces red light (633 nm), but the similarity ends here. The He–Ne laser works on this principle: If a 633-nm photon interacts with an excited Ne atom *before* the atom spontaneously emits a photon, the atom will be induced, or *stimulated*, to emit its photon at the precise time of the interaction. Moreover, this second photon will be *coherent*, or *in phase*, with the first; that is, the crests and troughs of the two waves will match exactly. *Stimulated* light emission is pictured in Figure 8-39(b).

A He–Ne laser consists of a tube containing a helium–neon mixture at a pressure of about 1 mmHg. One end of the tube is a totally reflecting mirror, and the other end is a mirror that allows about 1% of the light to leave. An electric discharge is used to produce excited He atoms. These atoms transfer their excitation energy to Ne atoms through collisions. The Ne atoms enter a *metastable* state, an excited state that is stable for a relatively long time before the spontaneous emission of a photon occurs. Most of the Ne atoms must remain "pumped up" to this metastable state during the operation of the laser.

Following the first spontaneous release of a photon, other excited atoms release photons of the same frequency and in phase with the stimulating photon. This is rather like lining up a row of dominoes and knocking over the first one. This is the beginning of the laser beam. As shown in Figure 8-40, the beam is *amplified* as it bounces back and forth between the two mirrors. The output is the portion of the laser beam that escapes through the partially reflecting mirror. Because the photons of light travel in phase and in the same direction, laser light can be produced at a much higher intensity than would normally be achieved with spontaneous light emission.

Shown below are the transitions that produce (1) excited He atoms, (2) Ne atoms in the metastable state, and (3) laser light. After the laser light emission, (4) Ne atoms return to the ground state by way of two additional transitions. Ground-state Ne atoms are then pumped back up to the metastable state by collisions with excited He atoms. (The symbols * and $^\#$ represent electronically excited species.)

(1) $\text{He} \xrightarrow{e^-} \text{He}^*$

$\quad 1s^2 \qquad 1s^1 2s^1$

(2) $\text{He}^* + \text{Ne} \longrightarrow \text{He} + \text{Ne}^*$ (metastable)

$\quad [\text{He}]2s^2 2p^6 \qquad [\text{He}]2s^2 2p^5 5s^1$

(3) $\text{Ne}^* \longrightarrow \text{Ne}^\# + \longrightarrow h\nu$

$\quad [\text{He}]2s^2 2p^5 3p^1 \qquad (633 \text{ nm})$

(4) $\text{Ne}^\# \longrightarrow \longrightarrow \text{Ne}$ (return to step 2)

EXAMPLE 8-10

Using *spdf* Notation for an Electron Configuration.

(a) Identify the element having the electron configuration
$$1s^2 2s^2 2p^6 3s^2 3p^5$$

(b) Write the electron configuration of arsenic.

Solution

(a) All electrons must be accounted for in an electron configuration. Add the superscript numerals $(2 + 2 + 6 + 2 + 5)$ to obtain the atomic number 17. The element with this atomic number is chlorine.

(a) Spontaneous emission

1

2

3

4

5

(b) Stimulated emission

◀ **FIGURE 8-39**

Spontaneous and stimulated light emission by Ne atoms

(a) The waves *a*, *b*, *c*, and *d*, although having the same frequency and wavelength, are emitted in different directions. Waves *a* and *b* are out of phase. The crests of one wave line up with the troughs of the other. The two waves cancel, and they transmit no energy at all. **(b)** Photon (1) interacts with a Ne atom in a metastable energy state and stimulates it to emit photon (2). Photon (2) stimulates another Ne atom to emit photon (3), and so on. The waves are coherent, or in phase. The crests and troughs of the waves match perfectly.

Laser beam

Totally
reflecting
mirror

Partially
reflecting
mirror

 ▲ **FIGURE 8-40**

Operation of a He–Ne laser

Pictured here is a hypothetical laser tube arbitrarily divided into three sections representing the same portion of the tube at different times. At the top left, a 633-nm photon (⟶) stimulates light emission from an excited Ne atom. Now there are two photons, and one of them in turn stimulates emission of a third photon. The photons are reflected by the mirror on the right, and their transit of the tube in the opposite direction is shown in the center. Three photons are amplified to five. At the bottom, the five photons are amplified to seven, and so on. A small portion of the photons is drawn off as the laser beam.

(b) Arsenic ($Z = 33$) is in period 4 and group 15. Its valence-shell electron configuration is $4s^2 4p^3$. The noble gas that closes the third period is Ar ($Z = 18$), and the subshells that fill in the fourth period are $4s$, $3d$, and $4p$, in that order. Note that we account for 33 electrons in the configuration

$$\text{As: } [\text{Ar}]3d^{10}4s^2 4p^3$$

Practice Example A: Identify the element having the electron configuration $1s^2 2s^2 2p^6 3s^2 3p^6 3d^2 4s^2$.

Practice Example B: Use *spdf* notation to show the electron configuration of iodine. How many electrons does the I atom have in its $3d$ subshell? How many unpaired electrons are there in an I atom?

Students should be able to calculate the *number of unpaired electrons* for any electron configuration, once given, regardless of any "exceptions." Simply complete an outer subshell diagram.

EXAMPLE 8-11

Representing Electron Configurations. Write **(a)** the electron configuration of mercury, and **(b)** an orbital diagram for the electron configuration of tin.

Solution

(a) Mercury, in period 6 and group 12, is the transition element at the end of the third transition series, in which the $5d$ subshell fills ($5d^{10}$). The noble gas that closes period 5 is xenon, and the lanthanide series intervenes between xenon and mercury, in which the $4f$ subshell fills ($4f^{14}$). When we put all these facts together, we conclude that the electron configuration of mercury is

$$[\text{Xe}]4f^{14}5d^{10}6s^2$$

(b) Tin is in period 5 and group 14. Its valence-shell electron configuration is $5s^25p^2$. The noble gas that closes the fourth period is Kr ($Z = 36$), and the subshells that fill in the fifth period are $5s$, $4d$, and $5p$. Note that all subshells are filled in the orbital diagram except for $5p$. Two of the $5p$ orbitals are occupied by single electrons with parallel spins; one $5p$ orbital remains empty.

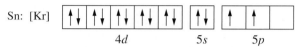

Sn: [Kr]

$4d$ $5s$ $5p$

Practice Example A: Represent the electron configuration of iron with an orbital diagram.

Practice Example B: Represent the electron configuration of bismuth with an orbital diagram.

EXAMPLE 8-12

Relating Electron Configurations to the Periodic Table. Indicate the number of **(a)** valence electrons in an atom of bromine; **(b)** $5p$ electrons in an atom of tellurium; **(c)** unpaired electrons in an atom of indium; **(d)** $3d$ and $4d$ electrons in a silver atom.

Solution

Determine the atomic number and the periodic table location of each element. Then establish the significance of the location.

(a) Bromine ($Z = 35$) is in group 17. There are seven outer-shell, or valence, electrons in all atoms in this group.

(b) Tellurium ($Z = 52$) is in period 5 and group 16. There are six outer-shell electrons, two of them are s, and the other four are p. The valence-shell electron configuration of tellurium is $5s^25p^4$; the tellurium atom has four $5p$ electrons.

(c) Indium ($Z = 49$) is in period 5 and group 13. The electron configuration of its inner shells is [Kr]$4d^{10}$. All the electrons in this inner-shell configuration are paired. The valence-shell electron configuration is $5s^25p^1$. The two $5s$ electrons are paired, and the $5p$ electron is unpaired. The In atom has one unpaired electron.

(d) Ag ($Z = 47$) is in period 5 and group 11. The noble gas that closes period 4 is krypton, and the $4d$ subshell fills $4(d^{10})$. There is one electron in the $5s$ orbital; thus the electron configuration of silver is

$$\text{Ag: [Kr]}4d^{10}5s^1$$

There are ten $3d$ electrons and ten $4d$ electrons in a silver atom.

Practice Example A: For an atom of Sn, indicate the number of **(a)** electronic shells that are either filled or partially filled; **(b)** $3p$ electrons; **(c)** $5d$ electrons; and **(d)** unpaired electrons.

Practice Example B: Indicate the number of **(a)** $3d$ electrons in Y atoms; **(b)** $4p$ electrons in Ge atoms; and **(c)** unpaired electrons in Au atoms.

Summary

8-1 Electromagnetic Radiation—Electromagnetic radiation is a type of energy transmission in the form of a **wave**. The waves of electromagnetic radiation are characterized by an **amplitude**, the maximum height of wave crests and maximum depth of wave troughs, a **wavelength**, λ, the distance between wave crests and **frequency**, ν, which signifies how often the fluctuations occur. Frequency is measured in **hertz**, **Hz** (cycles per second). Wavelength and frequency are related by the equation (8.1): $c = \lambda\nu$, where c is the **speed of light**. The wave character of electromagnetic radiation means that the waves can be dispersed into individual components of differing wavelength, a **diffraction** pattern, by striking a closely grooved surface (Fig. 8-4).

8-2 Atomic Spectra—A rainbow results from the dispersion of all the wavelength components of visible light by a prism or raindrops; it is an example of a continuous spectrum (Fig. 8-7). The spectra produced by light emitted from excited atoms and ions are called **atomic spectra** or **line spectra**, because only certain frequencies are observed.

8-3 Quantum Theory—The study of electromagnetic radiation emitted from hot objects led to Planck's theory, which postulates that quantities of energy can have only certain discrete values, with the smallest unit of energy being that of a **quantum**. The energy of a quantum is given by equation (8.3): $E = h\nu$, where h is **Planck's constant**. Einstein's interpretation of the **photoelectric effect**—the ability of light to eject electrons when striking certain surfaces (Fig. 8-12)—led to a new interpretation of electromagnetic radiation: Light has a particle-like nature in addition to its wave-like properties. Light particles are called **photons**. The energy of a photon is related to the frequency of the radiation by $E_{\text{photon}} = h\nu$.

8-4 The Bohr Atom—The first attempt to explain atomic (line) spectra was made by Niels Bohr who postulated that an electron in a hydrogen atom exists in a circular orbit designated by a **quantum number**, n, that describes the energy of the electron in the orbit. The state of the electron with the lowest quantum number, $n = 1$, is called the **ground state**. An **excited state** of a hydrogen atom corresponds to those states with $n > 1$. The Bohr theory also provided a means for constructing an **energy-level diagram** (Fig. 8-14) so that emission spectra could be understood.

8-5 Two Ideas Leading to a New Quantum Mechanics—Louis de Broglie postulated a **wave–particle duality** in which particles of matter such as protons and electrons would at times display wave-like properties (equation 8.10). Because of an inherent uncertainty of the position and momentum of a wave-like particle, Heisenberg postulated that we cannot simultaneously know a subatomic particle's precise momentum and its position, a proposition referred to as the **Heisenberg uncertainty principle** (equation 8.11).

8-6 Wave Mechanics—The application of the concept of wave–particle duality requires that we view the electron in a system through a **wave function** that corresponds to a **standing wave** within the boundary of the system (Figs. 8-18 and 8-19). Application of these ideas to a particle in a one-dimensional box shows that at the lowest energy level the energy of the particle is nonzero that is, the system has a **zero-point energy**. The solution of the **Schrödinger equation** for the hydrogen atom provides wave functions called **orbitals**, which are the product of an **angular wave function**, $Y(\theta, \phi)$, and a **radial wave function**, $R(r)$.

8-7 Quantum Numbers and Electron Orbitals—The three quantum numbers arising from the Schrödinger wave equation are the *principal quantum number*, n, the *orbital angular momentum quantum number*, ℓ, and the *magnetic quantum number*, m_ℓ. All orbitals with the same value of n are in the same **principal electronic shell** (**principal level**), and all orbitals with the same values of n and ℓ are in the same **subshell** (**sublevel**). The orbitals with different values of ℓ (0, 1, 2, 3, and so on) are designated s, p, d, f (Fig. 8-23). Orbitals in the same subshell of a hydrogen-like species have the same energy and are said to be **degenerate**.

8-8 Interpreting and Representing the Orbitals of the Hydrogen Atom—Interpreting the solutions to the Schrödinger equation for the hydrogen atom leads to a description of the shapes of the electron probability distributions for electrons in the s, p, and d orbitals. The number of nodes $(n - 1)$ in an orbital increases as n increases. Nodes are where the wave function changes sign.

8-9 Electron Spin: A Fourth Quantum Number—Stern and Gerlach demonstrated that electrons possess a quality called **electron spin** (Figs. 8-32 and 8-33). The electron spin quantum number, m_s, takes the value $+\frac{1}{2}$ or $-\frac{1}{2}$.

8-10 Multielectron Atoms—In multielectron atoms, orbitals with different values of ℓ are not degenerate. The loss of degeneracy within a principal shell is a result of the different **effective nuclear charge**, Z_{eff}, experienced by electrons in different subshells.

8-11 Electron Configurations—**Electron configuration** describes how the electrons are distributed among the various orbitals in principal shells and subshells of an atom. Electrons fill orbitals from the lowest energy to the highest, ensuring that the energy of the atom is at a minimum (Fig. 8-36). The **Pauli exclusion principle** states that a maximum of two electrons may occupy an orbital. **Hund's rule** says that when degenerate orbitals are available, electrons initially occupy these orbitals singly. Electron configurations are represented by either expanded or condensed *spdf* notation or an **orbital diagram** (page 317). The **aufbau process** is used to assign electron configurations to the elements of the periodic table. Electrons added to the shell of highest quantum number in the aufbau process are called **valence electrons**.

8-12 Electron Configurations and the Periodic Table—Elements in the same group of the periodic table have similar electron configurations. Groups 1 and 2 correspond to the *s* **block** with filled or partially filled valence-shell s orbitals. Groups 13 through 18 correspond to the *p* **block** with filled or partially filled valence-shell p orbitals. The *d* **block** corresponds to groups 3 through 12 as the $n - 1$ energy level is being filled—that is, having filled or partially filled d orbitals. In the *f* **block** elements, also called the lanthanides and actinides, the $n - 2$ shell fills with electrons; that is, they have filled or partially filled f orbitals.

Integrative Example

Microwave ovens have become increasingly popular in kitchens around the world. They are also useful in the chemical laboratory, particularly in drying samples for chemical analysis. A typical microwave oven uses microwave radiation with a wavelength of 12.2 cm.

Are there any electronic transitions in the hydrogen atom that could *conceivably* produce microwave radiation of wavelength 12.2 cm? Estimate the principal quantum levels between which the transition occurs.

Strategy

Use the wavelength of microwaves to calculate the frequency of the radiation. Calculate the energy of the photon that has this frequency. Estimate where in the emission spectrum for a hydrogen atom such a photon emission might be found, by using equation (8.6).

Solution

1. Calculate the frequency of the microwave radiation. Microwaves are a form of electromagnetic radiation and thus travel at the speed of light, 2.998×10^8 m s^{-1}. Convert the wavelength to meters, and then use the equation

$$\nu = c/\lambda$$

$$\nu = \frac{2.998 \times 10^8 \text{ m s}^{-1}}{12.2 \text{ cm} \times 1 \text{ m}/100 \text{ cm}} = 2.46 \times 10^9 \text{ Hz}$$

2. Calculate the energy associated with one photon of the microwave radiation. This is a direct application of Planck's equation.

$$E = h\nu = 6.626 \times 10^{-34} \text{ J s} \times 2.46 \times 10^9 \text{ s}^{-1}$$
$$= 1.63 \times 10^{-24} \text{ J}$$

3. Determine whether there are any electronic transitions in the hydrogen atom with an energy per photon of 1.63×10^{-24} J. Let the principal quantum number of the final state (n_f) be n. And that of the initial state (n_i) is then $n + 1$. Substitute these two values into equation (8.9).

$$E_{\text{photon}} = \Delta E = 2.179 \times 10^{-18} \text{ J}\left(\frac{1}{(n + 1)^2} - \frac{1}{n^2}\right)$$

Solving for n

$$E_{\text{photon}} = \Delta E = 2.179 \times 10^{-18} \text{ J}\left(\frac{n^2 - (n + 1)^2}{n^2(n + 1)^2}\right)$$

$$= -2.179 \times 10^{-18} \text{ J}\left(\frac{2n + 1}{n^2(n + 1)^2}\right)$$

4. The negative sign indicates that a photon is emitted and now can be ignored. Substitute the value for the energy of the photon and rearrange the equation

$$E_{\text{photon}} = 1.63 \times 10^{-24} \text{ J} = 2.179 \times 10^{-18} \text{ J}\left(\frac{2n + 1}{n^2(n + 1)^2}\right)$$

$$\frac{1.63 \times 10^{-24} \text{ J}}{2.179 \times 10^{-18} \text{ J}} = 7.48 \times 10^{-7} = \left(\frac{2n + 1}{n^2(n + 1)^2}\right)$$

5. Look at Figure 8-14, the *energy*-level diagram for the Bohr hydrogen atom. Energy differences between the low-lying levels are of the order 10^{-19} to 10^{-20} J. These are orders of magnitude (10^4 to 10^5 times) greater than the energy per photon of 1.63×10^{-24} J from part 2. Note, however, that the energy differences become progressively smaller for high-numbered orbits. As n approaches ∞, the energy differences approach zero, and some transitions between high-numbered orbits should correspond to microwave radiation. Thus we expect n to be large, so that to a good approximation we can neglect one with respect to n and write

$$7.48 \times 10^{-7} = \left(\frac{2n + 1}{n^2(n + 1)^2}\right) \simeq \left(\frac{2n}{n^2 n^2}\right) \simeq \left(\frac{2}{n^3}\right)$$

Solving for n

$$n \simeq \left(\frac{2}{7.48 \times 10^{-7}}\right)^{1/3} \simeq 138.8$$

6. We can check this result by substituting this value of $n = 139$ into the exact expression

$$7.48 \times 10^{-7} = \frac{2n + 1}{n^2(n + 1)^2} = \frac{2(139) + 1}{139^2(139 + 1)^2} = 7.37 \times 10^{-7}$$

The agreement is not very good, so let's try $n = 138$

$$7.48 \times 10^{-7} = \frac{2n + 1}{n^2(n + 1)^2} = \frac{2(138) + 1}{138^2(138 + 1)^2} = 7.53 \times 10^{-7}$$

This provides closer agreement. The value of the principal quantum number is $n = 138$.

Assessment

Using equation (8.6) we have shown that the emission of a photon for the deexcitation of an electron from $n = 139$ to $n = 138$ produces a wavelength for that photon in the microwave region. However, we might question whether the $n = 139$ state is still a bound state or whether the energy required to create this state causes ionization (see Exercise 106).

Exercises

Electromagnetic Radiation

1. A hypothetical electromagnetic wave is pictured here. What is the wavelength of this radiation?

1.17 nm

2. For the electromagnetic wave described in Exercise 1, what are **(a)** the frequency, in hertz, and **(b)** the energy, in joules per photon?

3. The magnesium spectrum has a line at 266.8 nm. Which of these statements about this radiation is (are) correct? Explain.
(a) It has a higher frequency than radiation with wavelength 402 nm.
(b) It is visible to the eye.
(c) It has a greater speed in a vacuum than does red light of wavelength 652 nm.
(d) Its wavelength is longer than that of X-rays.

4. The most intense line in the cerium spectrum is at 418.7 nm.
(a) Determine the frequency of the radiation producing this line.
(b) In what part of the electromagnetic spectrum does this line occur?
(c) Is it visible to the eye? If so, what color is it? If not, is this line at higher or lower energy than visible light?

5. *Without doing detailed calculations,* determine which of the following wavelengths represents light of the highest frequency: **(a)** 5.9×10^{-4} cm; **(b)** 1.13 mm; **(c)** 860 Å; **(d)** 6.92 μm.

6. *Without doing detailed calculations,* arrange the following electromagnetic radiation sources in order of increasing frequency: **(a)** a red traffic light, **(b)** a 91.9 MHz radio transmitter, **(c)** light with a frequency of 3.0×10^{14} s^{-1}, **(d)** light with a wavelength of 485 Å.

7. How long does it take light from the sun, 93 million miles away, to reach Earth?

8. In astronomy, distances are measured in *light-years,* the distance that light travels in one year. What is the distance of one light-year expressed in kilometers?

Atomic Spectra

9. Use the Balmer equation (8.2) to determine
(a) the frequency, in s^{-1}, of the radiation corresponding to $n = 5$;
(b) the wavelength, in nanometers, of the line in the Balmer series corresponding to $n = 7$;
(c) the value of n corresponding to the Balmer series line at 380 nm.

10. How would the Balmer equation (8.2) have to be modified to predict lines in the infrared spectrum of hydrogen?
[*Hint:* Compare equations (8.2) and (8.6).]

11. Use Planck's equation (8.3) to determine
(a) the energy, in joules per photon, of radiation of frequency 8.62×10^{15} s^{-1};
(b) the energy, in kilojoules per mole, of radiation of frequency 1.53×10^{14} s^{-1}.

12. Use Planck's equation (8.3) to determine
(a) the frequency, in hertz, of radiation having an energy of 4.18×10^{-21} J/photon;
(b) the wavelength, in nanometers, of radiation with 215 kJ/mol of energy.

13. What is ΔE for the transition of an electron from $n = 5$ to $n = 3$ in a Bohr hydrogen atom? What is the frequency of the spectral line produced?

14. What is ΔE for the transition of an electron from $n = 6$ to $n = 2$ in a Bohr hydrogen atom? What is the frequency of the spectral line produced?

15. Calculate the wavelengths, in nanometers, of the first four lines of the Balmer series of the hydrogen spectrum, starting with the *longest* wavelength component.

16. A line is detected in the hydrogen spectrum at 1880 nm. Is this line in the Balmer series? Explain.

17. To what value of n in equation (8.2) does the line in the Balmer series at 389 nm correspond?

18. The Lyman series of the hydrogen spectrum can be represented by the equation

$$\nu = 3.2881 \times 10^{15}\ \text{s}^{-1}\left(\frac{1}{1^2} - \frac{1}{n^2}\right) \text{(where } n = 2, 3, \ldots)$$

(a) Calculate the maximum and minimum wavelength lines, in nanometers, in this series.
(b) What value of n corresponds to a spectral line at 95.0 nm?
(c) Is there a line at 108.5 nm? Explain.

Quantum Theory

19. A certain radiation has a wavelength of 474 nm. What is the energy, in joules, of (a) one photon; (b) a mole of photons of this radiation?

20. What is the wavelength, in nanometers, of light with an energy content of 1799 kJ/mol? In what portion of the electromagnetic spectrum is this light?

21. *Without doing detailed calculations*, indicate which of the following electromagnetic radiations has the greatest energy per photon and which has the least: (a) 662 nm; (b) 2.1×10^{-5} cm; (c) 3.58 μm; (d) 4.1×10^{-6} m.

22. *Without doing detailed calculations*, arrange the following forms of electromagnetic radiation in *increasing* order of energy per mole of photons: (a) radiation with $\nu = 3.0 \times 10^{15}$ s^{-1}, (b) an infrared heat lamp, (c) radiation having $\lambda = 7000$ Å, (d) dental X-rays.

23. In what region of the electromagnetic spectrum would you expect to find radiation having an energy per photon 100 times that associated with 988-nm radiation?

24. High-pressure sodium vapor lamps are used in street lighting. The two brightest lines in the sodium spectrum are at 589.00 and 589.59 nm. What is the difference in energy per photon of the radiations corresponding to these two lines?

The Photoelectric Effect

25. The lowest-frequency light that will produce the photoelectric effect is called the *threshold frequency*.
(a) The threshold frequency for indium is 9.96×10^{14} s^{-1}. What is the energy, in joules, of a photon of this radiation?
(b) Will indium display the photoelectric effect with UV light? With infrared light? Explain.

26. Sir James Jeans described the photoelectric effect in this way: "It not only prohibits killing two birds with one stone, but also the killing of one bird with two stones." Comment on the appropriateness of this analogy in reference to the marginal note on page 286.

The Bohr Atom

27. Use the description of the Bohr atom given in the text to determine (a) the radius, in nanometers, of the sixth Bohr orbit for hydrogen; (b) the energy, in joules, of the electron when it is in this orbit.

28. Calculate the increase in (a) distance from the nucleus and (b) energy when an electron is excited from the first to the third Bohr orbit.

29. What are the (a) frequency, in s^{-1}, and (b) wavelength, in nanometers, of the light emitted when the electron in a hydrogen atom drops from the energy level $n = 7$ to $n = 4$? (c) In what portion of the electromagnetic spectrum is this light?

30. *Without doing detailed calculations*, indicate which of the following electron transitions requires the greatest amount of energy to be *absorbed* by a hydrogen atom: from (a) $n = 1$ to $n = 2$; (b) $n = 2$ to $n = 4$; (c) $n = 3$ to $n = 9$; (d) $n = 10$ to $n = 1$.

31. For the Bohr hydrogen atom determine
(a) the radius of the orbit $n = 4$
(b) whether there is an orbit having a radius of 4.00 Å
(c) the energy level corresponding to $n = 8$
(d) whether there is an energy level at 25.00×10^{-18} J

32. *Without doing detailed calculations*, indicate which of the following electron transitions in the hydrogen atom results in the emission of light of the longest wavelength. (a) $n = 4$ to $n = 3$; (b) $n = 1$ to $n = 2$; (c) $n = 1$ to $n = 6$; (d) $n = 3$ to $n = 2$.

33. What electron transition in a hydrogen atom, starting from the orbit $n = 7$, will produce infrared light of wavelength 2170 nm?

34. What electron transition in a hydrogen atom, ending in the orbit $n = 5$, will produce light of wavelength 3740 nm?

35. The emission spectrum below for a one-electron (hydrogen-like) species in the gas phase shows all the lines, before they merge together, resulting from transitions to the ground state from higher energy states. Line A has a wavelength of 103 nm.

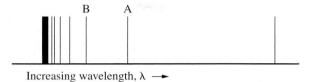

Increasing wavelength, λ ⟶

(a) What are the upper and lower principal quantum numbers corresponding to the lines labeled A and B?
(b) Identify the one-electron species that exhibits the spectrum.

36. The emission spectrum below for a one-electron (hydrogen-like) species in the gas phase shows all the lines, before they merge together, resulting from transitions to the first excited state from higher energy states. Line A has a wavelength of 434 nm.

Increasing wavelength, λ ⟶

(a) What are the upper and lower principal quantum numbers corresponding to the lines labeled A and B?
(b) Identify the one-electron species that exhibits the spectrum.

37. The emission spectrum below for a one-electron (hydrogen-like) species in the gas phase shows all the lines, before they merge together, resulting from transitions to the first excited state from higher energy states. Line A has a wavelength of 27.1 nm.

Increasing wavelength, λ ⟶

(a) What are the upper and lower principal quantum numbers corresponding to the lines labeled A and B?
(b) Identify the one-electron species that exhibits the spectrum.

38. The emission spectrum below for a one-electron (hydrogen-like) species in the gas phase shows all the lines, before they merge together, resulting from transitions to the ground state from higher energy states. Line A has a wavelength of 10.8 nm.

Increasing wavelength, λ ⟶

(a) What are the upper and lower principal quantum numbers corresponding to the lines labeled A and B?
(b) Identify the one-electron species that exhibits the spectrum.

Wave–Particle Duality

39. Which must possess a greater velocity to produce matter waves of the same wavelength (such as 1 nm), protons or electrons? Explain your reasoning.
40. What must be the velocity, in meters per second, of a beam of electrons if they are to display a de Broglie wavelength of 1 μm?
41. Calculate the de Broglie wavelength, in nanometers, associated with a 145-g baseball traveling at a speed of 168 km/h. How does this wavelength compare with typical nuclear or atomic dimensions?
42. What is the wavelength, in nanometers, associated with a 1000-kg automobile traveling at a speed of 25 m s^{-1}, that is, considering the automobile to be a matter wave? Comment on the feasibility of an experimental measurement of this wavelength.

The Heisenberg Uncertainty Principle

43. Describe how the Bohr model of the hydrogen atom appears to violate the Heisenberg uncertainty principle.
44. Although Einstein made some early contributions to quantum theory, he was never able to accept the Heisenberg uncertainty principle. He stated, "God does not play dice with the Universe." What do you suppose Einstein meant by this remark? In reply to Einstein's remark, Niels Bohr is supposed to have said, "Albert, stop telling God what to do." What do you suppose Bohr meant by this remark?
45. A proton is accelerated to one-tenth the velocity of light, and this velocity can be measured with a precision of 1%. What is the uncertainty in the position of this proton?
46. Show that the uncertainty principle is not significant when applied to large objects such as automobiles. Assume that m is precisely known; assign a reasonable value to either the uncertainty in position or the uncertainty in velocity, and estimate a value of the other.
47. What must be the velocity of electrons if their associated wavelength is to equal the radius of the first Bohr orbit of the hydrogen atom?
48. What must be the velocity of electrons if their associated wavelength is to equal the *longest* wavelength line in the Lyman series?
[*Hint:* Refer to Figure 8-14.]

Wave Mechanics

49. A standing wave in a string 42 cm long has a total of six nodes (including those at the ends). What is the wavelength, in centimeters, of this standing wave?

50. What is the length of a string that has a standing wave with four nodes (including those at the ends) and $\lambda = 17$ cm?

51. In a plucked guitar string, the frequency of the longest wavelength standing wave is called the *fundamental frequency*. The standing wave with one interior node is called the first *overtone*, and so on. What is the wavelength of the second overtone of a 24-in guitar string?

52. In the particle-in-a-box model, what is the wavelength of the third overtone of a box with a length of 100 pm? [*Hint:* Refer to Exercise 51.]

53. Describe some of the differences between the orbits of the Bohr atom and the orbitals of the wave mechanical atom. Are there any similarities?

54. The greatest probability of finding the electron in a small-volume element of the 1s orbital of the hydrogen atom is at the nucleus. Yet the most probable distance of the electron from the nucleus is 53 pm. How can you reconcile these two statements?

Quantum Numbers and Electron Orbitals

55. Select the correct answer and explain your reasoning. An electron having $n = 3$ and $m_\ell = 0$ **(a)** must have $m_s = +\frac{1}{2}$; **(b)** must have $\ell = 1$; **(c)** may have $\ell = 0, 1,$ or 2; **(d)** must have $\ell = 2$.

56. Write an acceptable value for each of the missing quantum numbers.
 (a) $n = 3, \ell = ?, m_\ell = 2, m_s = +\frac{1}{2}$
 (b) $n = ?, \ell = 2, m_\ell = 1, m_s = -\frac{1}{2}$
 (c) $n = 4, \ell = 2, m_\ell = 0, m_s = ?$
 (d) $n = ?, \ell = 0, m_\ell = ?, m_s = ?$

57. What type of orbital (i.e., 3s, 4p, . . .) is designated by these quantum numbers?
 (a) $n = 5, \ell = 1, m_\ell = 0$
 (b) $n = 4, \ell = 2, m_\ell = -2$
 (c) $n = 2, \ell = 0, m_\ell = 0$

58. Which of the following statements is (are) correct for an electron with $n = 4$ and $m_\ell = 2$? Explain.
 (a) The electron is in the fourth principal shell.
 (b) The electron may be in a d orbital.
 (c) The electron may be in a p orbital.
 (d) The electron must have $m_s = +\frac{1}{2}$.

59. Concerning the electrons in the shells, subshells, and orbitals of an atom, how many can have
 (a) $n = 3, \ell = 2, m_\ell = 0,$ and $m_s = +\frac{1}{2}$?
 (b) $n = 3, \ell = 2,$ and $m_\ell = 0$?
 (c) $n = 3$ and $\ell = 2$?
 (d) $n = 3$?
 (e) $n = 3, \ell = 2,$ and $m_s = +\frac{1}{2}$?

60. Concerning the concept of subshells and orbitals,
 (a) How many subshells are found in the $n = 4$ level?
 (b) What are the names of the subshells in the $n = 3$ level?
 (c) How many orbitals have the values $n = 4$ and $\ell = 3$?
 (d) How many orbitals have the values $n = 4, \ell = 3,$ and $m_\ell = -2$?
 (e) What is the total number of orbitals in the $n = 4$ level?

The Shapes of Orbitals and Radial Probabilities

61. Calculate the finite value of r, in terms of a_0, at which the node occurs in the wave function of the 2s orbital of a hydrogen atom.

62. Calculate the finite value of r, in terms of a_0, at which the node occurs in the wave function of the 2s orbital of a Li^{2+} ion.

63. Show that the probability of finding a $2p_y$ electron in the xz plane is zero.

64. Show that the probability of finding a $3d_{xz}$ electron in the xy plane is zero.

65. Prepare a two-dimensional plot of $Y(\theta, \phi)$ for the p_x orbital in the xy plane.

66. Prepare a two-dimensional plot of $Y(\theta, \phi)$ for the p_y orbital in the xy plane.

67. Prepare a two-dimensional plot of $Y^2(\theta, \phi)$ for the p_x orbital in the xy plane.

68. Prepare a two-dimensional plot of $Y^2(\theta, \phi)$ for the p_y orbital in the xy plane.

69. Using a graphical method, show that in a hydrogen atom the radius at which there is a maximum probability of finding an electron is a_0 (53 pm).

70. Use a graphical method or some other means to show that in a Li^{2+} ion, the radius at which there is a maximum probability of finding an electron is $\frac{a_0}{3}$ (18 pm).

71. Identify the orbital that has **(a)** one radial node and one angular node; **(b)** no radial nodes and two angular nodes; **(c)** two radial nodes and three angular nodes.

72. Identify the orbital that has **(a)** two radial nodes and one angular node; **(b)** five radial nodes and zero angular nodes; **(c)** one radial node and four angular nodes.

73. A contour map for an atomic orbital of hydrogen is shown at the top of page 333 for the xy and xz planes. Identify the orbital.

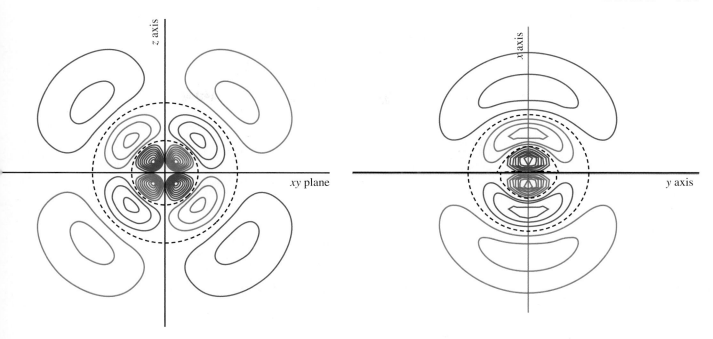

74. A contour map for an atomic orbital of hydrogen is shown below for the xy and xz planes. Identify the type ($s, p, d, f, g \ldots$) of orbital.

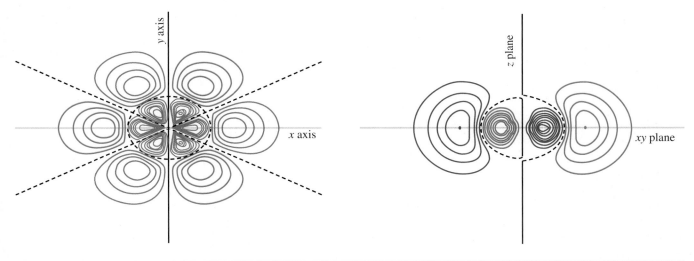

Electron Configurations

75. Which of the following is the correct orbital diagram for the ground-state electron configuration of phosphorus? Explain what is wrong with each of the others.

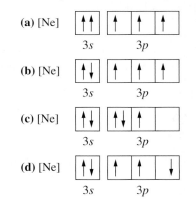

76. Which of the following is the correct orbital diagram for the ground-state electron configuration of molybdenum? Explain what is wrong with each of the others.

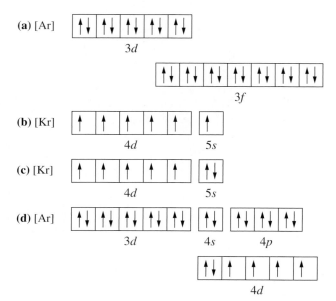

(a) [Ar]
3d

3f

(b) [Kr]
4d   5s

(c) [Kr]
4d   5s

(d) [Ar]
3d   4s   4p

4d

77. Use the basic rules for electron configurations to indicate the number of **(a)** unpaired electrons in an atom of P; **(b)** 3d electrons in an atom of Br; **(c)** 4p electrons in an atom of Ge; **(d)** 6s electrons in an atom of Ba; **(e)** 4f electrons in an atom of Au.

78. Use orbital diagrams to show the distribution of electrons among the orbitals in **(a)** the 4p subshell of Br; **(b)** the 3d subshell of Co^{2+}, given that the two electrons lost are 4s; **(c)** the 5d subshell of Pb.

79. On the basis of the periodic table and rules for electron configurations, indicate the number of **(a)** 2p electrons in N; **(b)** 4s electrons in Rb; **(c)** 4d electrons in As; **(d)** 4f electrons in Au; **(e)** unpaired electrons in Pb; **(f)** elements in group 14 of the periodic table; **(g)** elements in the sixth period of the periodic table.

80. Based on the relationship between electron configurations and the periodic table, give the number of **(a)** outer-shell electrons in an atom of Sb; **(b)** electrons in the fourth principal electronic shell of Pt; **(c)** elements whose atoms have six outer-shell electrons; **(d)** unpaired electrons in an atom of Te; **(e)** transition elements in the sixth period.

81. The recently discovered element 114 should most closely resemble Pb.
(a) Write the electron configuration of Pb.
(b) Propose a plausible electron configuration for element 114.

82. Without referring to any tables or listings in the text, mark an appropriate location in the blank periodic table provided for each of the following: **(a)** the fifth-period noble gas; **(b)** a sixth-period element whose atoms have three unpaired p electrons; **(c)** a d-block element having one 4s electron; **(d)** a p-block element that is a metal.

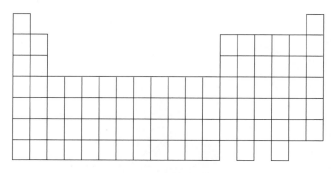

83. Which of the following electron configurations corresponds to the ground state and which to an excited state?

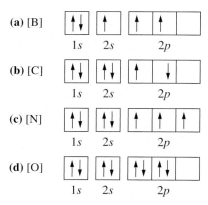

(a) [B]
1s   2s   2p

(b) [C]
1s   2s   2p

(c) [N]
1s   2s   2p

(d) [O]
1s   2s   2p

84. To what neutral atom do the following valence-shell configurations correspond? Indicate whether the configuration corresponds to the ground state or an excited state.

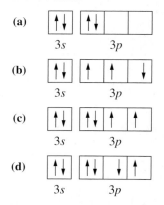

(a)
3s   3p

(b)
3s   3p

(c)
3s   3p

(d)
3s   3p

85. What is the expected ground-state electron configuration for each of the following elements: **(a)** gold; **(b)** magnesium; **(c)** bismuth; **(d)** indium; **(e)** molybdenum; **(f)** bromine?

86. What is the expected ground-state electron configuration for each of the following elements: **(a)** selenium; **(b)** rubidium; **(c)** tellurium; **(d)** palladium; **(e)** rhodium; **(f)** manganese?

87. The following electron configurations correspond to the ground states of certain elements. Name each element. **(a)** $[Rn]7s^26d^1$; **(b)** $[He]2s^22p^3$; **(c)** $[Ar]3d^24s^2$; **(d)** $[Kr]4d^{10}5s^25p^5$; **(e)** $[Xe]4f^26s^2$.

88. The following electron configurations correspond to the ground states of certain elements. Name each element. **(a)** $[Ar]3d^{10}4s^24p^4$; **(b)** $[Ne]3s^23p^3$; **(c)** $[Ar]3d^24s^2$; **(d)** $[Kr]4d^15s^2$; **(e)** $[Xe]4f^{13}6s^2$.

Integrative and Advanced Exercises

89. Derive the Balmer equation from equation (8.6).

90. Electromagnetic radiation can be transmitted through a vacuum or empty space. Can heat be similarly transferred? Explain.

91. The *work function* is the energy that must be supplied to cause the release of an electron from a photoelectric material. The corresponding photon frequency is the threshold frequency. The higher the energy of the incident light, the more kinetic energy the electrons have in moving away from the surface. The work function for mercury is equivalent to 435 kJ/mol photons.
(a) Can the photoelectric effect be obtained with mercury by using visible light? Explain.
(b) What is the kinetic energy, in joules, of the ejected electrons when light of 215 nm strikes a mercury surface?
(c) What is the velocity, in meters per second, of the ejected electrons in part (b)?

92. Infrared lamps are used in cafeterias to keep food warm. How many photons per second are produced by an infrared lamp that consumes energy at the rate of 95 W and is 14% efficient in converting this energy to infrared radiation? Assume that the radiation has a wavelength of 1525 nm.

93. In 5.0 s, a 75-watt light source emits 9.91×10^{20} photons of a monochromatic (single wavelength) radiation. What is the color of the emitted light?

94. In everyday usage, the term "quantum jump" describes a change of a very significant magnitude compared to more gradual, incremental changes; it is similar in meaning to the term "a sea change." Does quantum jump have the same meaning when applied to events at the atomic or molecular level? Explain.

95. The Pfund series of the hydrogen spectrum has as its *longest* wavelength component a line at 7400 nm. Describe the electron transitions that produce this series. That is, give a Bohr quantum number that is common to this series.

96. Between which two orbits of the Bohr hydrogen atom must an electron fall to produce light of wavelength 1876 nm?

97. Use appropriate relationships from the chapter to determine the wavelength of the line in the emission spectrum of He^+ produced by an electron transition from $n = 5$ to $n = 2$.

98. Draw an energy-level diagram that represents all the possible lines in the emission spectrum of hydrogen atoms produced by electron transitions, in one or more steps, from $n = 5$ to $n = 1$.

99. An atom in which just one of the outer-shell electrons is excited to a very high quantum level (n) is called a "high Rydberg" atom. In some ways, all these atoms resemble a Bohr hydrogen atom with its electron in a high-numbered orbit. Explain why you might expect this to be the case.

100. If all other rules governing electron configurations were valid, what would be the electron configuration of cesium if **(a)** there were *three* possibilities for electron spin; **(b)** the quantum number ℓ could have the value n?

101. Ozone, O_3, absorbs ultraviolet radiation and dissociates into O_2 molecules and O atoms: $O_3 + h\nu \longrightarrow$ $O_2 + O$. A 1.00-L sample of air at 22 °C and 748 mmHg contains 0.25 ppm of O_3. How much energy, in joules, must be absorbed if all the O_3 molecules in the sample of air are to dissociate? Assume that each photon absorbed causes one O_3 molecule to dissociate, and that the wavelength of the radiation is 254 nm.

102. Radio signals from *Voyager 1* in the 1970s were broadcast at a frequency of 8.4 GHz. On Earth, this radiation was received by an antenna able to detect signals as weak as 4×10^{-21} W. How many photons per second does this detection limit represent?

103. Certain metal compounds impart colors to flames— sodium compounds, yellow; lithium, red; barium, green—and flame tests can be used to detect these elements.
(a) At a flame temperature of 800 °C, can collisions between gaseous atoms with average kinetic energies supply the energies required for the emission of visible light?
(b) If not, how do you account for the excitation energy?

104. The angular momentum of an electron in the Bohr hydrogen atom is *mur*, where m is the mass of the electron, u, its velocity, and r, the radius of the Bohr orbit. The angular momentum can have only the values $nh/2\pi$, where n is an integer (the number of the Bohr orbit). Show that the *circumferences* of the various Bohr orbits are integral multiples of the de Broglie wavelengths of the electron treated as a matter wave.

105. Combine ideas from Exercise 104 and other data given in the text to obtain, for an electron in the third orbit ($n = 3$) of a hydrogen atom, **(a)** its velocity; **(b)** the number of revolutions it makes about the nucleus per second.

106. Refer to the Integrative Example. Determine whether or not $n = 138$ is a bound state. If it is, what sort of state is it? What is the radius of the orbit and how many revolutions per second does the electron make about the nucleus?

107. Using the relationships given in Table 8.1, find the finite values of r, in terms of a_0, of the nodes for a 3s orbital.

108. Use a graphical method or some other means to determine the radius at which the probability of finding a 2s orbital is maximum.

109. Using the relationships in Table 8.1 to prepare a sketch of the 95% probability surface of a 4px orbital.

110. Show that the volume of a spherical shell of radius r and thickness dr is $4\pi r^2 dr$.
[*Hint*: This exercise requires calculus.]

111. In the ground state of a hydrogen atom, what is the probability of finding an electron anywhere in a sphere of radius **(a)** a_0, or **(b)** $2a_0$?
[*Hint*: This exercise requires calculus.]

112. When atoms in excited states collide with unexcited atoms they can transfer their excitation energy to those atoms. The most efficient energy transfer occurs when the excitation energy matches the energy of an excited state in the unexcited atom. Assuming that we have a collection of excited hydrogen atoms in the $2s^1$ excited state, are there any transitions of He^+ that could be most efficiently excited by the hydrogen atoms?

Feature Problems

113. We have noted that an emission spectrum is a kind of "atomic fingerprint." The various steels are alloys of iron and carbon, usually containing one or more other metals. Based on the principal lines of their atomic spectra, which of the metals in the table below are likely to be present in a steel sample whose hypothetical emission spectrum is pictured? Is it likely that still other metals are present in the sample? Explain.

Principal Spectral Lines of Some Period 4 Transition Metals (nm)							
V	306.64	309.31	318.40	318.54	327.11	437.92	438.47	439.00
Cr	357.87	359.35	360.53	361.56	425.44	427.48	428.97	520.45
Mn	257.61	259.37	279.48	279.83	403.08	403.31	403.45	
Fe	344.06	358.12	372.00	373.49	385.99			
Ni	341.48	344.63	345.85	346.17	349.30	351.51	352.45	361.94

300   325   350   375   400   425   450 nm

▲ **Hypothetical emission spectrum**

In a real spectrum, the photographic images of the spectral lines would differ in depth and thickness depending on the strengths of the emissions producing them. Some of the spectral lines would not be seen because of their faintness.

114. Balmer seems to have deduced his formula for the visible spectrum of hydrogen just by manipulating numbers. A more common scientific procedure is to graph experimental data and then find a mathematical equation to describe the graph. Show that equation (8.2) describes a straight line. Indicate which variables must be plotted, and determine the numerical values of the slope and intercept of this line. Use data from Figure 8-10 to confirm that the four lines in the visible spectrum of hydrogen fall on the straight-line graph.

115. Follow up on the dartboard analogy of Figure 8-34 by plotting a graph of the scoring summary tabulated below. That is, plot the number of hits as a function of the scoring ring: 50, 40, ... What illustration in the text does this plot most resemble? Explain similarities and differences between the two.

Summary of Scoring (1500 darts)	
Darts	Score
200	"50"
300	"40"
400	"30"
250	"20"
200	"10"
150	off the board

116. Emission and absorption spectra of the hydrogen atom exhibit line spectra characteristic of quantized systems. In an absorption experiment, a sample of hydrogen atoms is irradiated with light with wavelengths ranging from 100 to 1000 nm. In an emission spectrum experiment, the hydrogen atoms are excited through an energy source that provides a range of energies from 1230 to 1240 kJ mol^{-1} to the atoms. Assume that the absorption spectrum is obtained at room temperature, when all atoms are in the ground state.
(a) Calculate the position of the lines in the absorption spectrum.
(b) Calculate the position of the lines in the emission spectrum.
(c) Compare the line spectra observed in the two experiments. In particular, will the number of lines observed be the same?

117. Diffraction of radiation takes place when the distance between the scattering centers is comparable to the wavelength of the radiation.
(a) What velocity must helium atoms possess to be diffracted by a film of silver atoms in which the spacing is 100 pm?
(b) Electrons accelerated through a certain potential are diffracted by a thin film of gold. Would you expect a beam of protons accelerated through the same potential to be diffracted when it strikes the film of gold? If not, what would you expect to see instead?

118. The emission spectrum below is for hydrogen atoms in the gas phase. The spectrum is of the first few emission lines from principal quantum number 6 down to all possible lower levels.

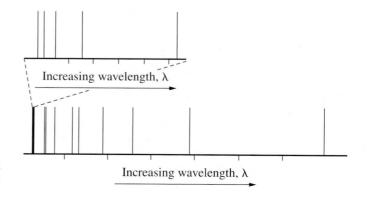

Increasing wavelength, λ

Increasing wavelength, λ

Not all possible de-excitations are possible; the transitions are governed by what is known as a *selection rule*. The selection rule states that the allowed transitions correspond to Δn is arbitrary, $\Delta \ell = \pm 1$. This selection rule can be understood in terms of conservation of momentum, since a photon has an angular momentum of unity. Using this selection rule, identify the transitions, in terms of the types of orbital (s, p, d, f), involved, that are observed in the spectrum shown on page 336.

In the presence of a magnetic field, the lines split into more lines according to the magnetic quantum number. The selection rule for transitions between different magnetic quantum numbers is $\Delta m_\ell = 0$ and ± 1. Identify the line(s) in the spectrum that splits into the greatest number of lines.

Self-Assessment Exercises

119. In your own words, define the following terms or symbols: **(a)** λ; **(b)** ν; **(c)** h; **(d)** ψ; **(e)** principal quantum number, n.

120. Briefly describe each of the following ideas or phenomena: **(a)** atomic (line) spectrum; **(b)** photoelectric effect; **(c)** matter wave; **(d)** Heisenberg uncertainty principle; **(e)** electron spin; **(f)** Pauli exclusion principle; **(g)** Hund's rule; **(h)** orbital diagram; **(i)** electron charge density; **(j)** radial electron density.

121. Explain the important distinctions between each pair of terms: **(a)** frequency and wavelength; **(b)** ultraviolet and infrared light; **(c)** continuous and discontinuous spectra; **(d)** traveling and standing waves; **(e)** quantum number and orbital; **(f)** *spdf* notation and orbital diagram; **(g)** s block and p block; **(h)** main group and transition element; **(i)** the ground state and excited state of a hydrogen atom.

122. Describe two ways in which the orbitals of multielectron atoms resemble hydrogen orbitals and two ways in which they differ from hydrogen orbitals.

123. Explain the phrase *effective nuclear charge*. How is this related to the shielding effect?

124. With the help of sketches, explain the difference between a p_x, p_y, and p_z orbital.

125. With the help of sketches, explain the difference between a $2p_z$ and $3p_z$ orbital.

126. If traveling at equal speeds, which of the following matter waves has the longest wavelength? Explain. **(a)** electron; **(b)** proton; **(c)** neutron; **(d)** α particle (He^{2+}).

127. For electromagnetic radiation transmitted through a vacuum, state whether each of the following properties is directly proportional to, inversely proportional to, or independent of the frequency: **(a)** velocity; **(b)** wavelength; **(c)** energy per mole. Explain.

128. Construct a concept map representing the ideas of modern quantum mechanics.

129. Construct a concept map representing the atomic orbitals of hydrogen and their properties.

130. Construct a concept map for the configurations of multielectron atoms.

eMedia Exercises

131. Using the **Electromagnetic Spectrum** activity (*Activebook 8-1*), establish the mathematical relationship between the *energy* of radiation and the *wavelength* of radiation.
[*Hint:* You should have three to five data points to determine a relationship between two variables. Consider whether there is a linear or inversely linear relationship.]

132. After viewing the movie **Flame Tests for Metals** (*Activebook 8-2*), **(a)** suggest approximately where dominant lines should appear (in terms of wavelength) in the emission spectrum of each metal shown. **(b)** Why are these lines not accurately described by equation (8.2)?

133. View the **Quantum Number** activity (*Activebook 8-7*). This illustration demonstrates that the total number of populated orbitals in an energy level is equal to n^2, where n is the principal quantum number. At what value of n does this calculation no longer provide physically applicable information?
[*Hint:* See the periodic table and refer to the number of known elements.]

134. From the **Radial Electron Distribution** animation (*Activebook 8-10*), predict the number of nodes that would be expected for krypton. From the electronic configurations of the noble gases argon and krypton, suggest what might cause a significant difference in the radial distribution curve for krypton.

eLaboratory Exercises

These exercises allow students to apply the concepts and skills for this chapter in the simulated laboratory of Virtual ChemLab. Worksheets for each of these exercises are found in the Virtual ChemLab Workbook in your MediaPak.

135. *(VCL 8-1) Flame Tests for Metals*
Have you ever wondered why a candle flame is yellow? The characteristic yellow of the flame comes from the glow of burning carbon fragments. The carbon fragments are produced by the incomplete combustion reaction of the wick and candle wax. When elements, such as carbon, are heated to high temperatures, some of their electrons are excited to higher energy levels. When these excited electrons fall back to lower energy levels, they release excess energy in

packages of light called photons. The color of the emitted light depends on the individual energy level spacing in the atom. When heated, each element emits a characteristic pattern of photons, which is useful for identifying the element. The characteristic colors of light produced when substances are heated in the flame of a gas burner are the basis for flame tests of several elements. In this assignment you will perform flame tests that are used to identify several metallic elements.

136. **(VCL 8-2) Atomic Emission Spectra**
When a sample of gas is excited by applying a large alternating electric field, the gas emits light at certain discrete wavelengths. The intensity and wavelength of the light that is emitted is called the atomic emission spectrum and is unique for each gas. In this assignment you will measure the emission spectra for several gases and make some observations about the differences in their spectra.

137. **(VCL 8-3) Emission Spectra of Sodium and Mercury**
In the 1800s scientists found that when a sample of gas is excited by an alternating electric field, light with only certain discrete wavelengths is emitted. This property allowed for the development of spectroscopic techniques that can be used in the identification and analysis of elements and compounds. Even though scientists found spectroscopy very useful, they could not explain why the spectrum was not continuous. The explanation of this was left to Niels Bohr, a Danish physicist, who first proposed that energy levels of electrons are quantized and excited electrons can fall only to discrete energy levels. This assignment illustrates the measurements that helped Bohr develop his original quantum model and also illustrates some practical uses for this science by measuring the emission spectra for mercury and sodium. Mercury vapor is used in fluorescent lights, and sodium vapor in street lighting.

138. **(VCL 8-4) Blackbody Radiation**
In the early 1900s several experimental results appeared to be in conflict with classical physics. One of these experiments was the study of blackbody radiation. A blackbody is a solid (such as a piece of iron) that does not emit light at low temperatures, but when heated, the "blackbody" begins to emit first red and then orange light and at higher temperatures eventually becomes white-hot. The intensity of the emitted light is also a function of temperature. In this problem you will make observations similar to

those of Max Planck (1858–1947), who, through his study of blackbody radiation, found an explanation that revolutionized how scientists think about radiated energy.

139. **(VCL 8-5) Photoelectric Effect**
Though Albert Einstein is most famous for $E = mc^2$ and his work in describing relativity in mechanics, his Nobel Prize was for understanding a very simple experiment. It was long understood that if you directed light of a certain wavelength at a piece of metal, it would emit electrons. In classical theory the energy of the light was thought to be based on its intensity and not its frequency. However, the results of the photoelectric effect contradicted classical theory. These inconsistencies led Einstein to suggest that we need to think of light as being composed of particles (photons) and not just as waves. In this experiment you will reproduce a photoelectric experiment and show that the energy (E) of a photon of light is related to its frequency and not its intensity.

140. **(VCL 8-6) The Rydberg Equation**
When a sample of gas is excited by applying a large alternating electric field, the gas emits light at certain discrete wavelengths, but the classical picture of atoms would allow electrons to be at any energy level and thus the energy would be continuous over all wavelengths. In the late 1800s two scientists, Johann Balmer and Johannes Rydberg, developed a mathematical equation that correlated the wavelength of the emitted light for certain gases such as H_2. Later, Niels Bohr's concept of quantized "jumps" by electrons between orbits was shown to be consistent with the Rydberg equation. In this assignment you will measure the wavelengths of the lines in the hydrogen emission spectra and graphically determine the value of the Rydberg constant, R_H.

141. **(VCL 8-7) Heisenberg Uncertainty Principle**
It has long been known that if you shine light through narrow slits that are spaced at small intervals, the light will form a diffraction pattern. A diffraction pattern is a series of light and dark patterns caused by wave interference. The wave interference can be either constructive (light) or destructive (dark). In this experiment you will shine a laser through a device with two slits where the spacing can be adjusted, and you will investigate the patterns that will be made at a distance from the slits. From this you will be able to study the effect of the Heisenberg uncertainty principle on the diffraction of light.

9

THE PERIODIC TABLE AND SOME ATOMIC PROPERTIES

CONTENTS

A scanning tunneling microscope image of 48 iron atoms adsorbed onto a surface of copper atoms. The iron atoms were moved into position with the tip of the scanning tunneling microscope in order to create a barrier that forced some electrons of the copper atoms into a quantum state seen here as circular rings of electron density. The colors are from the computer rendering of the image. In this chapter we discuss the periodic table and the properties of atoms and ions.

By the middle of the nineteenth century, a large number of elements had been discovered and their relative atomic masses and a host of other properties determined. Chemists had assembled what amounted to the "white pages" of a chemistry directory, but they still needed a set of "yellow pages"—an arrangement that would group similar elements together. This tabulation would help them focus on similarities and differences among the known elements and predict properties of as yet undiscovered elements. In this chapter, we will continue to study the first successful tabulation—the periodic table of the elements. Chemists value the periodic table as a means of organizing their field, and they would continue to use it even if they had never figured out why it works. But the underlying rationale of the periodic table was discovered about 50 years after the table was proposed.

The basis of the periodic table is the electron configurations of the elements, a topic we studied in Chapter 8. In this chapter, we will use the table as a backdrop for a discussion of some properties of elements, including atomic radii, ionization energies, and electron affinities. These atomic properties also arise in the discussion of chemical bonding in the following two chapters, and the periodic table itself will be our indispensable guide throughout much of the remainder of the text.

9-1   CLASSIFYING THE ELEMENTS: THE PERIODIC LAW AND THE PERIODIC TABLE

In 1869, Dmitri Mendeleev and Lothar Meyer independently proposed the **periodic law**:

> When the elements are arranged in order of increasing atomic mass, certain sets of properties recur periodically.

Meyer based his periodic law on the property called atomic volume—the atomic mass of an element divided by the density of its solid form. We now just call this property *molar volume*.

$$\text{atomic (molar) volume (cm}^3/\text{mol)} = \text{molar mass (g/mol)} \times 1/d \text{ (cm}^3/\text{g)} \quad (9.1)$$

Meyer presented his results as a graph of atomic volume against atomic mass. Now it is customary to plot his results as molar volume against atomic number, as seen in Figure 9-1. Notice how high atomic volumes recur periodically for the alkali metals Li, Na, K, Rb, and Cs. Later, Meyer examined other physical properties of the elements and their compounds, such as hardness, compressibility, and boiling points, and found that these also vary periodically.

MENDELEEV'S PERIODIC TABLE

As previously described, the periodic table is a tabular arrangement of the elements that groups similar elements together. Mendeleev's work attracted more attention than Meyer's for two reasons: He left blank spaces in his table for undiscovered elements, and he corrected some atomic mass values. The blanks in his table came at atomic masses 44, 68, 72, and 100 for the elements we now know as scandium, gallium, germanium, and technetium. Two of the atomic mass values he corrected were those of indium and uranium.

 Gorin, George. "Mendeleev and Moseley: The Principal Discoverers of the Periodic Law." *J. Chem. Educ.* **1996**: 73, 490 (June 1996).

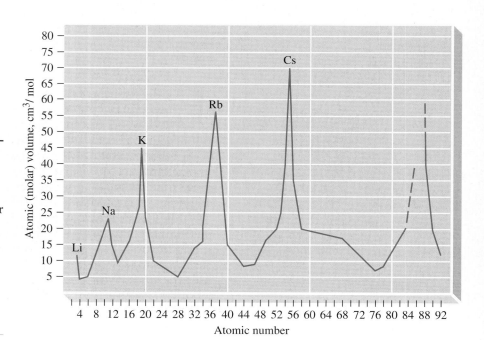

▶ **FIGURE 9-1**
An illustration of the periodic law—variation of atomic volume with atomic number
This adaptation of Meyer's 1870 graph plots atomic volumes against atomic numbers. Of course, a number of elements, such as the noble gases, were undiscovered in Meyer's time. The graph shows peaks at the alkali metals (Li, Na, K, and so on). Nonmetals fall on the ascending portions of the curve and metals at the peaks, on the descending portions, and in the valleys.

Reihen	Gruppe I. — R^2O	Gruppe II. — RO	Gruppe III. — R^2O^3	Gruppe IV. RH^4 RO^2	Gruppe V. RH^3 R^2O^5	Gruppe VI. RH^2 RO^3	Gruppe VII. RH R^2O^7	Gruppe VIII. — RO^4
1	H = 1							
2	Li = 7	Be = 9,4	B = 11	C = 12	N = 14	O = 16	F = 19	
3	Na = 23	Mg = 24	Al = 27,3	Si = 28	P = 31	S = 32	Cl = 35,5	
4	K = 39	Ca = 40	– = 44	Ti = 48	V = 51	Cr = 52	Mn = 55	Fe = 56, Co = 59, Ni = 59, Cu = 63.
5	(Cu = 63)	Zn = 65	– = 68	– = 72	As = 75	Se = 78	Br = 80	
6	Rb = 85	Sr = 87	?Yt = 88	Zr = 90	Nb = 94	Mo = 96	– = 100	Ru = 104, Rh = 104, Pd = 106, Ag = 108
7	(Ag = 108)	Cd = 112	In = 113	Sn = 118	Sb = 122	Te = 125	J = 127	
8	Cs = 133	Ba = 137	?Di = 138	?Ce = 140	–	–	–	– – – –
9	(–)	–	–	–	–	–		
10	–	–	?Er = 178	?La = 180	Ta = 182	W = 184	–	Os = 195, Ir = 197, Pt = 198, Au = 199
11	(Au = 199)	Hg = 200	Tl = 204	Pb = 207	Bi = 208			
12	–	–	–	Th = 231	–	U = 240		

▲ **Dmitri Mendeleev (1834–1907)**
Mendeleev's discovery of the periodic table came from his attempts to systematize properties of the elements for presentation in a chemistry textbook. His highly influential book went through eight editions in his lifetime and five more after his death.

In his periodic table Mendeleev arranged the elements into eight groups (Gruppe) and twelve rows (Reihen). The formulas are written as Mendeleev wrote them. R^2O, RO, and so on, are formulas of the element oxides (such as Li_2O, MgO, ...); RH^4, RH^3, and so forth, are formulas of the element hydrides (such as CH_4, NH_3, ...).

In Mendeleev's table, similar elements fall in vertical groups, and the properties of the elements change gradually from top to bottom in the group. As an example, we have seen that the alkali metals (Mendeleev's group I) have high molar volumes (Fig. 9-1). They also have low melting points, which decrease in the order

◀ Other properties of the alkali metals are discussed in Section 9-7.

$$\text{Li } (174\,°C) > \text{Na } (97.8\,°C) > \text{K } (63.7\,°C) > \text{Rb } (38.9\,°C) > \text{Cs } (28.5\,°C)$$

In their compounds, the alkali metals exhibit the oxidation state +1, forming ionic compounds such as NaCl, KBr, CsI, Li_2O, and so on.

DISCOVERY OF NEW ELEMENTS

Two of the elements predicted by Mendeleev were discovered shortly after the appearance of his 1871 periodic table (gallium, 1875; scandium, 1879). Table 9.1 illustrates how closely Mendeleev's predictions for eka-silicon agree with the observed properties of the element germanium, discovered in 1886. Often, new ideas in science take hold slowly, but the success of Mendeleev's predictions stimulated chemists to adopt his table fairly quickly.

One group of elements that Mendeleev did not anticipate was the noble gases. He left no blanks for them. William Ramsay, their discoverer, proposed placing them in a separate group of the table. Because argon, the first noble gas discovered (1894), had an atomic mass greater than that of chlorine and comparable to that of potassium, Ramsay placed the new group, which he called group 0, between the halogen elements (group VII) and the alkali metals (group I).

▶ The term *eka* is derived from Sanskrit and means "first." That is, eka-silicon means, literally, "first comes silicon" (and then comes the unknown element).

TABLE 9.1   Properties of Germanium: Predicted and Observed

Property	Predicted Eka-silicon (1871)	Observed Germanium (1886)
Atomic mass	72	72.6
Density, g/cm^3	5.5	5.47
Color	dirty gray	grayish white
Density of oxide, g/cm^3	EsO_2: 4.7	GeO_2: 4.703
Boiling point of chloride	$EsCl_4$: below 100 °C	$GeCl_4$: 86 °C
Density of chloride, g/cm^3	$EsCl_4$: 1.9	$GeCl_4$: 1.887

▲ **Henry G. J. Moseley (1887–1915)**
Moseley was one of a group of brilliant scientists whose careers were launched under Ernest Rutherford. He was tragically killed at Gallipoli, in Turkey, during World War I.

Haigh, C. W. "Moseley's Work on X-Rays and Atomic Number." *J. Chem. Educ.* **1995**: *72*, 1012 (November 1995).

Trimble, R. F. "Mendeleev's Discovery of the Periodic Law. (SBS)." *J. Chem. Educ.* **1981**: *58*, 28.

ATOMIC NUMBER AS THE BASIS FOR THE PERIODIC LAW

Mendeleev had to place certain elements out of the order of increasing atomic mass to get them into the proper groups of his periodic table. He assumed this was because of errors in atomic masses. With improved methods of determining atomic masses and with the discovery of argon (group 0, atomic mass 39.9), which was placed ahead of potassium (group I, atomic mass 39.1), it became clear that a few elements might always remain "out of order." At the time, these out-of-order placements were justified by chemical evidence. Elements were placed in the groups that their chemical behavior dictated. There was no theoretical explanation for this reordering. Matters changed in 1913 as a result of some research by H. G. J. Moseley on the X-ray spectra of the elements.

As we learned in Chapter 2, X-rays are a high-frequency form of electromagnetic radiation produced when a cathode-ray (electron) beam strikes the anode of a cathode-ray tube (see Figure 9-2a). The anode is called the *target*. Moseley was familiar with Bohr's atomic model, and explained X-ray emission in the following way. If the bombarding electrons have sufficient energy, they can eject electrons from the inner orbitals of target metal atoms. Electrons from higher orbitals then drop down to fill the vacancies, emitting X-ray photons with energies corresponding to the difference in energy between the originating level and the vacancy level (see Figure 8-13). Moseley reasoned that because the energies of electron orbitals depend on the nuclear charge, the frequencies of emitted X-rays should depend on the nuclear charges of atoms in the target. Using techniques newly developed by the father–son team of W. Henry Bragg and W. Lawrence Bragg, Moseley obtained photographic images of X-ray spectra and assigned frequencies to the spectral lines. His spectra for the elements from Ca to Zn are reproduced in Figure 9-2(b).

Moseley was able to correlate X-ray frequencies to numbers equal to the nuclear charges and corresponding to the positions of elements in Mendeleev's periodic table. For example, aluminum, the thirteenth element in the table, was assigned an *atomic number* of 13. Moseley's equation is $\nu = A(Z - b)^2$, where ν is the X-ray frequency, Z is the atomic number, and A and b are constants. Moseley used this relationship to predict three new elements ($Z = 43, 61,$ and 75), which were discovered in 1937, 1945, and 1925, respectively. Also, he proved that in the portion of the periodic table with which he worked (from $Z = 13$ to $Z = 79$), there could be no additional new elements beyond those three. All available atomic numbers had been assigned. From the standpoint of Moseley's work, then, we should restate the periodic law.

Similar properties recur periodically when elements are arranged according to increasing atomic number.

▲ **FIGURE 9-2**
Schematic of an X-ray tube and Moseley's X-ray spectra of several elements
(a) A heated filament emits electrons by a process called thermionic emission. The electrons are accelerated by a high voltage, and collide with the metal target. The highly energetic electrons ionize electrons from the inner shells of the metal atoms of the target. Subsequently, electrons from higher orbitals drop down to occupy the vacancies and in doing so, emit X-ray photons that correspond to the energy difference between the two orbitals. **(b)** In this photograph from Moseley's 1913 paper, you can see two lines for each element, beginning with Ca at the top. With each successive element, the lines are displaced to the left, the direction of increasing X-ray frequency in these experiments. Where more than two lines appear, the sample contained one or more other elements, or impurities. Notice, for example, that one line in the Co spectrum matches a line in the Fe spectrum, and another matches a line in the Ni spectrum. Brass, which is an alloy of copper and zinc, shows two lines for Cu and two for Zn.

DESCRIPTION OF A MODERN PERIODIC TABLE: THE LONG FORM

Mendeleev's periodic table consisted of 8 groups, but most modern periodic tables are arranged in 18 groups of elements. Let us briefly review the description of the periodic table given in Section 2-6.

In the periodic table (see inside front cover), the vertical groups bring together elements with similar properties. The horizontal periods of the table are arranged in order of increasing atomic number from left to right. The groups are numbered at the top, and the periods at the extreme left in the periodic table on the inside front cover. The first two groups—the *s* block—and the last six groups—the *p* block—together constitute the *main-group elements*. Because they come between the *s* block and the *p* block, the *d*-block elements are known as the *transition elements*. The *f*-block elements, sometimes called the *inner transition elements*, would extend the table to a width of 32 members if incorporated in the main body of the table. The table would generally be too wide to fit on a printed page, and so the *f*-block elements are extracted from the table and placed at the bottom. The 14 elements following lanthanum ($Z = 57$) are called the *lanthanides*, and the 14 following actinium ($Z = 89$) are called the *actinides*.

Orna, Mary Virginia, O.S.U. "On Naming the Elements with Atomic *Number* Greater than 100 (TS)." *J. Chem. Educ.* **1982:** *59*, 123.

 Interactive Periodic Table activity

 Mention that hydrogen is classified as a nonmetal even though it is placed on the far left on most periodic tables.

✓ The metalloids are important in semiconductor (microcomputer) technology.

 Poskozim, Paul S. "Multiply Bonded Main Group Metals and Metalloids (edited by Robert West and F. Gordon A. Stone)." *J. Chem. Educ.* **1998:** *75*, 698 (June 1998).

✓ Compounds containing radon, xenon and krypton have been prepared. Recently, compounds containing argon have also been prepared. See Khriachtchev, L. et al. *Nature* **2000:** *406*, 874 and Arik, C. *J. Chem. Phys.* **2003:** *119*, 3.

9-2 METALS AND NONMETALS AND THEIR IONS

In Section 2-6, we established two categories of elements, *metals* and *nonmetals*, and described them in terms of physical properties. Most metals are good conductors of heat and electricity, are malleable and ductile, and have moderate to high melting points. In general, nonmetals are nonconductors of heat and electricity and are nonmalleable (brittle) solids, though a number of nonmetals are gases at room temperature.

Through the color scheme of the periodic table on the inside front cover, we see that the majority of the elements are metals (orange) and that nonmetals (blue) are confined to the right side of the table. The noble gases (purple) are treated as a special group of nonmetals. Metals and nonmetals are often separated by a stairstep diagonal line, and several elements near this line are often called metalloids (green). **Metalloids** are elements that look like metals and in some ways behave like metals but also have some nonmetallic properties.

In the original periodic table, the positions of the elements were based on readily observable physical and chemical properties. In Chapter 8, we learned of the close correlation between electron configurations and the positions of the elements in the table. Thus, it appears that the physical and chemical properties of an element are determined largely by its electron configuration, particularly that of the *valence* (outermost) electronic shell. Adjacent members of a series of main-group elements in the same period (such as P, S, and Cl) have significantly different properties because they differ in their valence-electron configurations. Within a transition series, differences in electron configurations are mostly in inner shells, and so a transition element has some similarities to neighboring transition elements in the same period. In particular we find many similar properties for adjacent members of the same period within the *f* block. In fact, the strong similarities among the lanthanide elements presented a particular challenge to the nineteenth-century chemists who tried to separate and identify them.

Let's now briefly explore a few of the links between electron configurations and some other observations about the elements, starting with the noble gases.

NOBLE GASES

Atoms of the noble gases have the maximum number of electrons permitted in the valence shell of an atom, two in helium ($1s^2$) and eight in the other noble gas atoms (ns^2np^6). These electron configurations are very difficult to alter and seem to confer a high degree of chemical inertness to the noble gases. It is interesting to note, then, that the *s*-block metals, together with Al in group 13, tend to lose enough electrons to acquire the electron configurations of the noble gases. On the other hand, nonmetals tend to gain enough electrons to achieve the same configurations.

MAIN-GROUP METAL IONS

The atoms of elements of groups 1 and 2—the most active metals—have electron configurations that differ from those of the noble gas of the preceding period by only one and two electrons in the *s* orbital of a new electron shell. If a K atom is stripped of its outer-shell electron, it becomes the *positive ion* K^+ with the electron configuration [Ar]. A Ca atom acquires the [Ar] configuration following the removal of two electrons.

▲ Metals tend to lose electrons to attain noble gas electron configurations.

$$K\ ([Ar]4s^1) \longrightarrow K^+\ ([Ar]) + e^-$$
$$Ca\ ([Ar]4s^2) \longrightarrow Ca^{2+}\ ([Ar]) + 2\,e^-$$

Although metal atoms do not lose electrons spontaneously, the energy required to bring about ionization is often provided by other processes occurring at the same time (such as an attraction between positive and negative ions). Aluminum is the only *p*-block metal that forms an ion with a noble gas electron configuration—Al^{3+}. The electron configurations of the other *p*-block metal ions are summarized in Table 9.2.

TABLE 9.2   Electron Configurations of Some Metal Ions[a]

"Noble Gas"		"Pseudo-Noble Gas"[b]	"18 + 2"[c]	Other
Li^+	Be^{2+}	Ga^{3+}	In^+	Cr^{2+}, Cr^{3+}
Na^+	Mg^{2+}	Tl^{3+}	Tl^+	Mn^{2+}, Fe^{2+}
K^+	Ca^{2+}	Cu^+	Sn^{2+}	Fe^{3+}, Co^{2+}
Rb^+	Sr^{2+}	Ag^+, Au^+	Pb^{2+}	Ni^{2+}, Cu^{2+}
Cs^+	Ba^{2+}	Zn^{2+}	Sb^{3+}	
Fr^+	Ra^{2+}		Bi^{3+}	
Al^{3+}				

[a]Main-group metal ions are printed in black and transition metal ions in blue.
[b]In the configuration labeled "pseudo-noble gas," all electrons of the outermost shell have been lost. The next-to-outermost electron shell of the atom becomes the outermost shell of the ion and contains 18 electrons, for example, Ga^{3+}: $[Ne]3s^23p^63d^{10}$.
[c]In the configuration labeled "18 + 2" all outer-shell electrons except the two s electrons are lost, producing an ion with 18 electrons in the next-to-outermost shell and 2 electrons in the outermost, for example, Sn^{2+}: $[Ar]3d^{10}4s^24p^64d^{10}5s^2$.

Anderson, Wayne P. "Uncommon Oxidation Numbers of Nonmetals." *J. Chem. Educ.* **1998**: *75*, 187 (February 1998).

MAIN-GROUP NONMETAL IONS

The atoms of groups 17 and 16—the most active nonmetals—have one and two electrons fewer than the noble gas at the end of the period. Groups 17 and 16 atoms can acquire the electron configurations of noble gas atoms by *gaining* the appropriate numbers of electrons.

$$Cl\ ([Ne]3s^23p^5) + e^- \longrightarrow Cl^-\ ([Ar])$$

$$S\ ([Ne]3s^23p^4) + 2\ e^- \longrightarrow S^{2-}\ ([Ar])$$

In most cases, a nonmetal atom will gain a single electron spontaneously, but energy is required to force it to accept more than one. The necessary energy is often supplied by other processes that occur simultaneously (such as an attraction between positive and negative ions). Nonmetal ions with a charge of 3− are rare, but some metal nitrides are described as containing the nitride ion, N^{3-}.

1	2		13	14	15	16	17	18
H								He
Li	Be		B	C	N	O	F	Ne
Na	Mg		Al	Si	P	S	Cl	Ar
K	Ca		Ga	Ge	As	Se	Br	Kr
Rb	Sr		In	Sn	Sb	Te	I	Xe

▲ Nonmetals tend to gain electrons to attain noble-gas electron configurations.

TRANSITION METAL IONS

In the aufbau process, the *ns* subshell fills before electrons enter the $(n - 1)d$ subshell (page 318), but the energy levels of these two subshells are nearly the same (Fig. 8-36). Thus, it is not surprising that when transition metal atoms ionize, the *ns* subshell is emptied. For example, the electron configuration of Ti is $[Ar]3d^24s^2$, and that of Ti^{2+} is $[Ar]3d^2$. Moreover, in some cases one or more $(n - 1)d$ electrons might be lost together with the *ns* electrons. This happens in the formation of Ti^{4+}, which has the electron configuration $[Ar]$.

A few transition metal atoms acquire noble-gas electron configurations when forming cations, as do Sc in Sc^{3+} and Ti in Ti^{4+}, but most transition metal atoms do not (see Table 9.2). An iron atom does not acquire a noble-gas electron configuration when it loses its $4s^2$ electrons to form the ion Fe^{2+},

$$Fe\ ([Ar]3d^64s^2) \longrightarrow Fe^{2+}\ ([Ar]3d^6) + 2\ e^-$$

nor does it with the loss of an additional $3d$ electron to form the ion Fe^{3+}.

$$Fe\ ([Ar]3d^64s^2) \longrightarrow Fe^{3+}\ ([Ar]3d^5) + 3\ e^-$$

The $3d$ subshell in Fe^{3+} is half-filled, a fact that helps to account for the observed ease of oxidation of iron(II) to iron(III) compounds. Electron configurations with half-filled or filled d or f subshells have a special stability, and a number of transition metal ions have such configurations.

◄ A useful mnemonic is that the electron configuration of a cation can be obtained from the electron configuration of the parent atom by removing those electrons in orbitals with the *highest* quantum number first.

Are You Wondering . . .

Why hydrogen, a nonmetal, is included with the group 1 metals in the periodic table?

Although all the other elements have a definite place in the periodic table, hydrogen does not. Its uniqueness stems from the fact that its atoms have only one electron, in the configuration $1s^1$. This is what causes us to put hydrogen in group 1, even though we classify it as a nonmental.* Because hydrogen, like the halogens, is one electron short of having a noble-gas electron configuration, it is sometimes placed in group 17. Hydrogen, however, doesn't resemble the halogens very much. For example, F_2 and Cl_2 are excellent oxidizing agents, but H_2 isn't. Still another alternative places hydrogen by itself at the top of the periodic table and near the center.

*Hydrogen appears to become metallic when subjected to pressures of about 2 million atm, but these are hardly ordinary laboratory conditions.

CONCEPT ASSESSMENT ✓

On the blank periodic table in the margin indicate where elements that satisfy the following descriptions occur.

(a) A noble gas having the same electron configuration as the Na^+ cation.

(b) An anion of a nonmetal with a charge of 3− that has a noble-gas electron configuration.

(c) A transition metal ion with a charge of 2+ and no valence shell s and p electrons.

9-3   SIZES OF ATOMS AND IONS

In earlier chapters we discovered the importance of atomic masses in matters relating to stoichiometry. To understand certain physical and chemical properties, we need to know something about atomic sizes. In this section we describe atomic radius, the first of a group of atomic properties that we will examine in this chapter.

ATOMIC RADIUS

Unfortunately, atomic radius is hard to define. The probability of finding an electron decreases with increasing distance from the nucleus, but nowhere does the probability fall to zero, so there is no precise outer boundary to an atom. We might describe an *effective* atomic radius as, say, the distance from the nucleus within which 95% of all the electron charge density is found, but in fact, all that we can measure is the distance between the nuclei of adjacent atoms (internuclear distance). Even though it varies, depending on whether atoms are chemically bonded or merely in contact without forming a bond, we define atomic radius in terms of internuclear distance.

Because we are primarily interested in bonded atoms, we will emphasize an atomic radius based on the distance between the nuclei of two atoms joined by a chemical bond. The **covalent radius** is one-half the distance between the nuclei of two identical atoms joined by a single covalent bond. The **ionic radius** is based on the distance between the nuclei of ions joined by an ionic bond. Because the ions are not identical in size, this distance must be properly apportioned between

The major properties of the elements: atomic radii, ionization energy, and electron affinity can be rationalized on the basis of atomic number and electron shielding of the nuclear charge.

Pinto, Gabriel. "Using Balls of Different Sports to Model the Variation of Atomic Sizes." *J. Chem. Educ.* **1998**: *75*, 725 (June 1998).

the cation and anion. For example, starting with a radius of 140 pm for O^{2-}, the radius of Mg^{2+} can be obtained from the internuclear distance in MgO, the radius of Cl^- from the internuclear distance in $MgCl_2$, and the radius of Na^+ from the internuclear distance in NaCl. For metals, we define a **metallic radius** as one-half the distance between the nuclei of two atoms in contact in the crystalline solid metal. Similarly in a solid sample of a noble gas the distance between the centers of neighboring atoms is called the **van der Waals radius**. There is much debate about the values of the atomic radii of noble gases because the experimental determination of the van der Waals radii is difficult; consequently, the atomic radii of noble gases are left out of the discussion of trends in atomic radii.

The angstrom unit, Å, has long been used for atomic dimensions (1 Å = 10^{-10} m). The angstrom, however, is not a recognized SI unit. The SI units are the nanometer (nm) and picometer (pm).

$$1 \text{ nm} = 1 \times 10^{-9} \text{ m}; 1 \text{ pm} = 1 \times 10^{-12} \text{ m}; 1 \text{ nm} = 1000 \text{ pm} \qquad (9.2)$$

Figure 9-3 illustrates the definitions of covalent, ionic, and metallic radii by comparing these three radii for sodium. Figure 9-4 is a plot of atomic radius against atomic number for a large number of elements. In this plot metallic radii are used for metals and covalent radii for nonmetals. Figure 9-4 suggests certain trends in atomic radii, for example, large radii for group 1, decreasing across the periods to smaller radii for group 17. In order to interpret these trends, let us first return to a topic introduced in Chapter 8.

◄ Despite the SI convention, the angstrom unit, Å, is still widely used by X-ray crystallographers and others who work with atomic and molecular dimensions.

Covalent radius:

Metallic radius:

Ionic radius:

▲ **FIGURE 9-3**
Covalent, metallic, and ionic radii compared
Atomic radii are represented by the solid arrows. The covalent radius is based on the diatomic molecule $Na_2(g)$, found only in gaseous sodium. The metallic radius is based on adjacent atoms in solid sodium, Na(s). The value of the ionic radius of Na^+ is obtained by the comparative method described in the text.

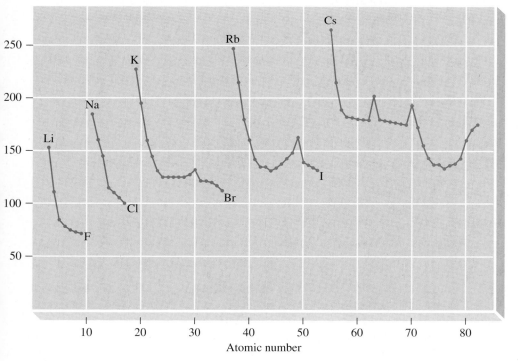

▲ **FIGURE 9-4**
Atomic radii
The values plotted are metallic radii for metals and covalent radii for nonmetals. Data for the noble gases are not included because of the difficulty of measuring covalent radii for these elements (only Kr and Xe compounds are known). The explanations usually given for the several small peaks in the middle of some periods are beyond the scope of this discussion.

Periodic Trends: Atomic Radii animation

SCREENING AND PENETRATION

In Section 8-10, penetration was described as a gauge of how close an electron gets to the nucleus. When interpreting the radial probability distributions, we saw that s electrons, by virtue of their extra humps of probability close to the nucleus (Fig. 8-35), penetrate better than p electrons, which in turn penetrate better than d electrons. Screening, or shielding, reflects how an outer electron is blocked from the nuclear charge by inner electrons.

Consider the hypothetical process of building up each atom in the third period from the atom preceding it, beginning with sodium. In this process, the number of inner-shell, or core, electrons is fixed at ten in the configuration $1s^2 2s^2 2p^6$. As a first approximation, let us *assume* that the core electrons completely cancel an equivalent charge on the nucleus. In this way, the core electrons shield, or screen, the outer-shell electrons from the full attractive force of the nucleus. Let us also assume that the outer-shell electrons do not screen one another. Finally, let us redefine an **effective nuclear charge**, Z_{eff}, first introduced in Section 8-10, as the true nuclear charge minus the charge that is screened out by electrons.

$$Z_{eff} = Z - S \tag{9.3}$$

Think of S as representing the number of inner electrons that appear to screen or shield an outer electron. Based on the two assumptions just stated, in sodium ($Z = 11$) the ten core electrons would screen out 10 units of nuclear charge (that is, $S = 10$), leaving an effective nuclear charge of $11 - 10 = +1$. In magnesium ($Z = 12$), Z_{eff} would be $+2$. In aluminum, Z_{eff} would be $+3$, and so on across the period.

Actually, neither assumption we made above—full screening by inner-shell electrons and no screening by outer-shell electrons—is correct. These assumptions ignore the fact that the electrons, both inner and outer, occupy orbitals with different radial probability distributions and, consequently, different degrees of penetration. Thus, an s electron, with its greater penetration, will be screened by inner electrons less than will a p electron. Similarly a p electron is shielded less than a d electron, which has a much lower penetration. In sodium, the 10 core electrons cancel only about 9 units of nuclear charge. Z_{eff} is more nearly $+2$ than $+1$. Also, outer-shell electrons do screen one another somewhat because of penetration effects. Each outer-shell electron is about one-third effective in screening the other outer-shell electrons. Thus, the Z_{eff} experienced by each of the two outer-shell electrons in magnesium is about $12 - 9 - \frac{1}{3} = 2\frac{2}{3}$ (Fig. 9-5).

The Effects of Penetration and Screening. The wave function of a multielectron atom provides a qualitative understanding of the effects of penetration and screening. In this simplified picture, the nuclear charge is replaced by Z_{eff}, so that the orbital energy is approximated by

$$E_n = -R_H \frac{Z_{eff}^2}{n^2} \tag{9.4}$$

where Z_{eff} is the effective nuclear charge in the shell corresponding to the value of n. All other symbols have their usual meaning (see Chapter 8). Equation (9.4) has the same form as the energy of the hydrogen atom obtained as a solution to the Schrödinger equation. The multielectron atom has been reduced to a one-electron approximation, a great, but useful, oversimplification nevertheless. The average size of an orbital is taken to be the average value of the distance, $\bar{r}_{nl}$, of the electron in that orbital from the nucleus.

$$\bar{r}_{nl} = \frac{n^2 a_0}{Z_{eff}} \left\{ 1 + \frac{1}{2}\left[1 - \frac{\ell(\ell + 1)}{n^2} \right] \right\} \tag{9.5}$$

Effective Nuclear Charge animation

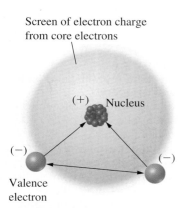

Screen of electron charge from core electrons

$(+)$ Nucleus

$(-)$ $(-)$

Valence electron

▲ **FIGURE 9-5**
The shielding effect and effective nuclear charge, Z_{eff}
Two valence electrons (blue) are attracted to the nucleus of a Mg atom. The atom's 12+ nuclear charge is screened by the 10 core electrons (gray), but not perfectly. The valence electrons also screen each other somewhat. The result is an *effective* nuclear charge, Z_{eff}, closer to 3+ than to 2+.

▶ The leading term of equation (9.5) is the Bohr radius of the nth Bohr orbit. The corresponding formula for the orbitals of the H atom can be obtained by setting $Z_{eff} = 1$.

Are You Wondering . . .

Where estimates of the screening by electrons come from?

These estimates come from an analysis of the wave functions of multielectron atoms. An exact solution of the Schrödinger equation can be obtained for the H atom, but for multielectron atoms, only approximate solutions are possible. The principle of the calculation is to assume each electron in the atom occupies an orbital much like those of the hydrogen atom. However, the functional form of the orbital is based on another assumption: that the electron moves in an effective or average field dictated by all the other electrons. With this assumption, the complicated multielectron Schrödinger equation is converted into a set of simultaneous equations—one for each electron. Each equation contains the unknown effective field and the unknown functional form of the orbital for the electron. The approach to solving such a set of equations is to guess at the functional forms of the orbitals, calculate an average potential for each electron to move in, and then solve for a new set of orbitals—one for each electron. The expectation is that the new orbitals are better than the initial guess. The new orbitals are then used to calculate a new effective field for the electrons, and the whole process is repeated until the calculated orbitals do not change much.

This iterative procedure, called the *self-consistent field* (SCF) *method*, was devised by Douglas Hartree in 1936, before the advent of computers. Currently, the wave functions of atoms and molecules are obtained by implementing the SCF procedures on computers. This has allowed the field of molecular modeling to become an important tool in modern chemical research.

The atomic orbitals obtained from SCF calculations closely resemble the atomic orbitals of the hydrogen atom in many ways. The angular dependence of the orbitals is identical, so that we can identify s, p, d, f orbitals by their characteristic shapes. The radial functions of the orbitals are different because the effective field is different from the one in the hydrogen atom, but the principal quantum number can still be defined. Thus, each electron in a multielectron atom has associated with it the four quantum numbers n, ℓ, m_ℓ, and m_s. Estimates of screening constants are based on an analysis of the radial functions obtained from SCF calculations.

This article discusses the calculation of "screening potentials" for atoms which provide indicators of shielding and distance from the nucleus for valence electrons. The trends that are found are presented in a "shaded" periodic table: Waldron, Kimberley A. et al. *J. Chem. Educ.* **2001:** *78*, 635.

In equation (9.5), all the symbols have their usual meaning. Again, equation (9.5) is the equation for the hydrogen atom or hydrogen-like ions with the nuclear charge replaced by Z_{eff} to approximate multielectron effects. Equations (9.4) and (9.5) are approximate but provide for a very useful semiquantitative interpretation of atomic properties. We consider next the three most important trends among atomic radii in relation to the periodic table.

1. **Variation of Atomic Radii Within a Group of the Periodic Table.** Radial probability densities extend farther out from the nucleus as n increases, a fact seen both in Figure 8-35 and in equation (9.5). Thus, we should expect that the more electron shells occupied by electrons, the larger the atom. This idea works for the group members of lower atomic numbers, where the increase in radius from one period to the next is large (as from Li to Na to K in group 1). At higher atomic numbers, the increase in radius is smaller (as from K to Rb to Cs in group 1). In these elements of higher atomic number, outer-shell electrons are held somewhat more tightly than expected because inner-shell electrons in d and f subshells are less effective than s and p electrons in screening outer-shell electrons from the nucleus; that is, Z_{eff} is larger than expected. Nevertheless, in general, the following is true.

◀ **KEEP IN MIND**
that s- and p-valence electrons have some probability of being near the nucleus (Fig. 8-35). These electrons penetrate the inner core of electrons and experience a greater attraction to the nucleus than otherwise expected.

◀ Group trends in the periodic table are largely governed by the principal quantum number, n.

The more electronic shells in an atom, the larger is the atom. Atomic radius increases from top to bottom through a group of elements.

▶ Values of Z_{eff} can be estimated using the rules set out in Problem 69.

▶ Period trends in the periodic table are largely governed by the effective nuclear charge, Z_{eff}.

2. **Variation of Atomic Radii Within a Period of the Periodic Table.** From Figure 9-4, we see that, in general, atomic radius decreases from left to right across a period. A careful look at the figure suggests that this trend does not apply to the transition elements. Let us look first at the general trend of decreasing radii and then at what is special about the transition elements.

Across a period, the atomic number increases by one for each succeeding element. For the main-group elements, each increase in atomic number is accompanied by the addition of one electron to the valence shell. The valence-shell electrons, being in the same shell, shield each other poorly from the increasing nuclear charge. The Z_{eff} for the 2s electron of Li is 1.3, and that for Be is 1.9; thus, Z_{eff} increases as Z increases across the main-group portions of a period. Across a period, the principal quantum number stays constant, so that whether we use Z_{eff} or just the nuclear charge Z in equation (9.5), the result is as follows.

> The atomic radius decreases from left to right through a period of elements.

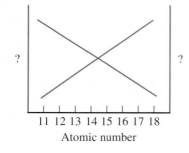

Draw electron configurations of some transition metals within a given period to help explain the variation of atomic radius within that period.

3. **Variation in Atomic Radius Within a Transition Series.** With the transition elements, the situation is a little different from that described above. In Figure 9-4, it is apparent that the atomic radii of transition elements tend to be about the same across a period but with a few unusual peaks. It is beyond the scope of this text to explain the exceptions; however, the general trend is not difficult to understand. In a series of transition elements, additional electrons go into an *inner* electron shell, where they participate in shielding outer-shell electrons from the nucleus. At the same time, the number of electrons in the *outer* shell tends to remain constant. Thus, the outer-shell electrons experience a roughly comparable force of attraction to the nucleus throughout a transition series. Consider Fe, Co, and Ni. Fe has 26 protons in the nucleus and 24 inner-shell electrons. In Co (Z = 27), there are 25 inner-shell electrons, and in Ni (Z = 28), there are 26. In each case, the two outer-shell electrons are under the influence of about the same net charge (about +2). That is, Z_{eff} for the 4s electrons of the first transition series is approximately constant. Thus, atomic radii do not change very much for this series of three elements, namely, 124 pm for Fe and 125 pm for Co and Ni.

CONCEPT ASSESSMENT ✓

The graph in the margin represents the variation of Z_{eff} and atomic radius with atomic number. Which axis and correspondingly colored line corresponds to Z_{eff} and which to atomic radius?

EXAMPLE 9-1

Relating Atomic Size to Position in the Periodic Table. Refer only to the periodic table on the inside front cover, and determine which is the largest atom: Sc, Ba, or Se.

Solution

Sc and Se are both in the fourth period, and we would expect Sc to be larger than Se because atomic sizes decrease from left to right in a period. Ba is in the sixth period and so has more electronic shells than either Sc or Se. Furthermore, it lies even closer to the left side of the table (group 2) than does Sc (group 3). We can say with confidence that the Ba atom should be the largest of the three. [The actual atomic radii are Se (117 pm), Sc (161 pm), and Ba (217 pm).]

Practice Example A: Use the periodic table on the inside front cover to predict which is the smallest atom: As, I, or S.

Practice Example B: Which of the following atoms do you think is closest in size to the Na atom: Br, Ca, K, or Al? Explain your reasoning, and do not use any tabulated data from the chapter in reaching your conclusion.

IONIC RADIUS

When a metal atom loses one or more electrons to form a positive ion, the positive nuclear charge exceeds the negative charge of the electrons in the resulting cation. The nucleus draws the electrons in closer, and as a consequence, the following holds true.

> Cations are smaller than the atoms from which they are formed.

Figure 9-6 compares four species: the atoms Na and Mg and the ions Na^+ and Mg^{2+}. As expected, the Mg atom is smaller than the Na atom, and the cations are smaller than the corresponding atoms. Na^+ and Mg^{2+} are **isoelectronic**—they have equal numbers of electrons (10) in identical configurations, $1s^2 2s^2 2p^6$. Mg^{2+} is smaller than Na^+ because its nuclear charge is larger (+12, compared with +11 for Na).

> For isoelectronic cations, the more positive the ionic charge, the smaller the ionic radius.

When a nonmetal atom gains one or more electrons to form a negative ion (anion), the nuclear charge remains constant, but Z_{eff} is reduced because of the additional electron(s). The electrons are not held as tightly. Repulsions among the electrons increase. The electrons spread out more, and the size of the atom increases, as suggested in Figure 9-7.

> Anions are larger than the atoms from which they are formed. For isoelectronic anions, the more negative the charge, the larger the ionic radius.

▲ **FIGURE 9-6**
A comparison of atomic and ionic sizes
Metallic radii are shown for Na and Mg and ionic radii for Na^+ and Mg^{2+}.

Gain and Loss of Electrons animation

EXAMPLE 9-2

Comparing the Sizes of Cations and Anions. Refer only to the periodic table on the inside front cover, and arrange the following species in order of increasing size, K^+, Cl^-, S^{2-}, and Ca^{2+}.

Solution

The key lies in recognizing that the four species are *isoelectronic*, having the electron configuration of argon: $1s^2 2s^2 2p^6 3s^2 3p^6$. For isoelectronic cations, the higher the charge on the ion, the smaller the ion. This means that Ca^{2+} is smaller than K^+. Because K^+ has a higher nuclear charge than Cl^- ($Z = 19$ compared with $Z = 17$), it is smaller than Cl^-. For isoelectronic anions, the higher the charge, the larger the ion. S^{2-} is larger than Cl^-. The order of increasing size is

$$Ca^{2+} < K^+ < Cl^- < S^{2-}$$

Practice Example A: Refer only to the periodic table on the inside front cover, and arrange the following species in order of increasing size: Ti^{2+}, V^{3+}, Ca^{2+}, Br^-, and Sr^{2+}.

Practice Example B: Refer only to the periodic table on the inside front cover, and determine which species is in the *middle* position when the following five are ranked according to size: the atoms N, Cs, and As and the ions Mg^{2+} and Br^-.

Covalent radius	Ionic radius
99 pm	181 pm

▲ **FIGURE 9-7**
Covalent and anionic radii compared
The two Cl atoms in a Cl_2 molecule gain one electron each to form two Cl^- ions.

◄ We can summarize the generalizations about isoelectronic atoms and ions into a single statement: Among isoelectronic species, the greater the atomic number, the smaller the size.

Knowledge of atomic and ionic radii can be used to vary certain physical properties. One example concerns strengthening glass. Normal window glass contains Na^+ and Ca^{2+} ions. The glass is brittle and shatters easily when struck a hard blow. One way to strengthen the glass is to replace the Na^+ ions at the surface with K^+ ions. The K^+ ions are larger and fill up the surface sites, leaving less opportunity for cracking than with the smaller Na^+ ions. The result is a shatter-resistant glass.

 Qureshi, Pushkin M., Kamoonpuri, S., Iqbal, M. "Ion Solvation: The Ionic Radii Problem." *J. Chem. Educ.* **1991:** *68*, 109.

▲ FIGURE 9-8
A comparison of some atomic and ionic radii
The values given, in picometers (pm), are metallic radii for metals, single covalent radii for nonmetals, and ionic radii for the ions indicated.

Ion Electron Configurations activity

Another example is the striking result when Cr^{3+} ions replace about 1% of the Al^{3+} ions in aluminum oxide, Al_2O_3. This substitution is possible because Cr^{3+} ions are only slightly larger (by 9 pm) than Al^{3+} ions. Pure aluminum oxide is colorless, but with this small amount of chromium(III) ion, it is a beautiful red color. This impure Al_2O_3 is the gem known as a ruby. Rubies and other gemstones can be made artificially and are used as jewelry and in devices such as lasers. The color of the ruby is further discussed in Chapter 24.

Figure 9-8, arranged in the format of the periodic table, shows relative sizes of typical atoms and ions, and summarizes the generalizations described in this section.

CONCEPT ASSESSMENT ✔

On the blank periodic table in the margin, locate

(a) The smallest group 13 atom

(b) The smallest period 3 atom

(c) The largest anion of a nonmetal in period 3

(d) The largest group 13 cation

9-4   IONIZATION ENERGY

In discussing metals, we talked about metal atoms losing electrons and thereby altering their electron configurations. But atoms do not eject electrons spontaneously. Electrons are attracted to the positive charge on the nucleus of an atom, and energy is needed to overcome that attraction. The more easily its electrons are lost, the more metallic an atom is considered to be. The **ionization energy**, *I*, is the quantity of energy a *gaseous* atom must absorb to be able to expel an electron. The electron that is lost is the one that is most loosely held.

Ionization energies are usually measured through experiments based on the photoelectric effect in which gaseous atoms at low pressures are bombarded with photons of sufficient energy to eject an electron from the atom. Here are two typical values.

$$Mg(g) \longrightarrow Mg^+(g) + e^- \qquad I_1 = 738 \text{ kJ/mol}$$
$$Mg^+(g) \longrightarrow Mg^{2+}(g) + e^- \qquad I_2 = 1451 \text{ kJ/mol}$$

The symbol I_1 stands for the *first* ionization energy—the energy required to strip one electron from a neutral gaseous atom.* I_2 is the *second* ionization energy—the energy to strip an electron from a gaseous ion with a charge of 1+. Further ionization energies are I_3, I_4, and so on. Each succeeding ionization energy is invariably larger than the preceding one. In the case of magnesium, for example, in the second ionization, the electron, once freed, has to move away from an ion with a charge of 2+ (Mg^{2+}). More energy must be invested than for a freed electron to move away from an ion with a charge of 1+ (Mg^+). This is a direct consequence of Coulomb's law, which states, in part, that the force of attraction between oppositely charged particles is directly proportional to the magnitudes of the charges.

First ionization energies (I_1) for many of the elements are plotted in Figure 9-9. In general, the farther an electron is from the nucleus, the more easily it can be extracted.

> Ionization energies decrease as atomic radii increase.

This observation reflects the effect of *n* and Z_{eff} on the ionization energy (*I*). Equation (9.4) suggests that the ionization energy is given by

$$I = R_H \times \frac{Z_{eff}^2}{n^2} \tag{9.6}$$

so that across a period, as Z_{eff} increases and the valence-shell principal quantum number *n* remains constant, the ionization energy should increase. And down a group, as *n* increases and Z_{eff} increases only slightly, the ionization energy should decrease. Thus, atoms lose electrons more easily (become more metallic) as we move from top to bottom in a group of the periodic table. The decreases in ionization energy and the parallel increases in atomic radii are outlined in Table 9.3 for group 1.

Table 9.4 lists ionization energies for the third-period elements. With minor exceptions, the trend in moving across a period (follow the colored stripe) is that atomic radii decrease, ionization energies increase, and the elements become less metallic, or more nonmetallic, in character. Table 9.4 lists stepwise ionization energies (I_1, I_2, and so forth.). Note particularly the large breaks that occur

This article discusses how information obtained for the visible emission spectrum of helium can be used to calculate the ionization energy of helium: Kaufman, Myron J., Trowbridge, C. G. *J. Chem. Educ.* **1999**: 76, 88.

Ionization Energy animation

A distinction between valence electrons and core electrons can be made based on the ionization energies for removing electrons one by one. The ionization energies of valence electrons are much smaller and show a big jump when the first core electron is removed.

Rioux, Frank, DeKock, Roger L. "The Crucial Role of Kinetic Energy in Interpreting Ionization Energies." *J. Chem. Educ.* **1998**: 75, 537 (May 1998).

◀ This generalization works well for main-group elements but less so for transition elements, where there are several exceptions.

TABLE 9.3 Atomic Radii and First Ionization Energies of the Alkali Metal (Group 1) Elements		
	Atomic Radius, pm	Ionization Energy (I_1), kJ/mol
Li	152	520.2
Na	186	495.8
K	227	418.8
Rb	248	403.0
Cs	265	375.7

---

*Ionization energies are sometimes expressed in the unit electron-volt (eV). One electron-volt is the energy acquired by an electron as it falls through an electric potential difference of 1 volt. It is a very small energy unit, especially suited to describing processes involving individual atoms. When ionization is based on a *mole* of atoms, kJ/mol is the preferred unit (1 eV/atom = 96.49 kJ/mol). Sometimes the term *ionization potential* is used instead of ionization energy. Further, the quantities I_1, I_2, . . . , may be replaced by enthalpy changes, ΔH_1, ΔH_2, and so on.

▲ **FIGURE 9-9**

First ionization energies as a function of atomic number

Because their electron configurations are so stable, more energy is required to
ionize noble gas atoms than to ionize atoms of the elements immediately preceding
or following them. The maxima on the graph come at the atomic numbers of the
noble gases. The alkali metals are the most easily ionized of all groups. The minima
in the graph come at their atomic numbers.

	Na	Mg	Al	Si	P	S	Cl	Ar
	TABLE 9.4		**Ionization Energies of the Third-Period Elements (in kJ/mol)**					
I_1	495.8	737.7	577.6	786.5	1012	999.6	1251.1	1520.5
I_2	4562	1451	1817	1577	1903	2251	2297	2666
I_3		7733	2745	3232	2912	3361	3822	3931
I_4			11,580	4356	4957	4564	5158	5771
I_5				16,090	6274	7013	6542	7238
I_6					21,270	8496	9362	8781
I_7						27,110	11,020	12,000

along the zigzag diagonal line. Consider magnesium as an example. To remove
a third electron, as measured by I_3, requires breaking into the especially stable
noble-gas inner-shell electron configuration $2s^2 2p^6$. I_3 is *much* larger than I_2—so
much larger that Mg^{3+} cannot be produced in ordinary chemical processes. Similarly, we do not encounter the ions Na^{2+} or Al^{4+} in chemical processes.

Now let us turn to the obvious exceptions to the regular trend in I_1 values
for the third-period elements and ask, Why is I_1 of Al smaller than that of Mg
and I_1 of S smaller than that of P?

Are You Wondering . . .

If ionization energies can be used to estimate the effective nuclear charge?

One of the earliest estimates of effective nuclear charge was obtained by analyzing ionization energies in terms of equation (9.6). Thus, for example, the ionization energy of Li in its ground state is 519 kJ mol^{-1} and from equation (9.6), we have

$$I_1 = 1312.1 \frac{Z_{eff}^2}{n^2} \text{ kJ mol}^{-1}$$

so that

$$519 \text{ kJ mol}^{-1} = 1312.1 \frac{Z_{eff}^2}{2^2} \text{ kJ mol}^{-1}$$

and we get

$$Z_{eff} = 1.26$$

The Z_{eff} obtained from the ionization energy of the first excited state of Li ($1s^2 2p$), 339 kJ mol^{-1}, is 1.02. The value of Z_{eff} is very close to one because the inner $1s^2$ core almost perfectly screens the $2p$ electron. By contrast, the penetration of the $2s$ electron leads to the somewhat larger $Z_{eff} = 1.26$ for the ground state.

This article gives a detailed discussion of the ionization energies of atoms and atomic ions from s, p, d, and f blocks and gives explanations for some of the exceptions in the periodic trends: Lang, Peter F., Smith, Barry C. *J. Chem. Educ.* **2003:** *80,* 938.

We expect I_1 of Al to be larger than for Mg. The reversal occurs because of the particular electrons lost. Mg loses a $3s$ electron, while Al loses a $3p$ electron. We expect that *more* energy is required to strip an electron from the lower energy $3s$ orbital in Mg ([↑↓]$_{3s}$[ ][ ][ ]$_{3p}$) than from a half-filled $3p$ orbital in Al ([↑↓]$_{3s}$[↑][ ][ ]$_{3p}$). I_1 for S is slightly lower than for P for a different reason. Although the orbitals in the $3p$ subshell are degenerate, we can think of repulsion between electrons in the filled $3p$ orbital of a S atom ([↑↓][↑][↑]$_{3p}$) as making it easier to remove one of those electrons than an electron from the half-filled $3p$ subshell of a P atom ([↑][↑][↑]$_{3p}$).

◄ **KEEP IN MIND**
the orbital energy diagram in Figure 8-36 and the order in which electrons occupy orbitals.

EXAMPLE 9-3

Relating Ionization Energies. Refer to the periodic table on the inside front cover, and arrange the following in the expected order of increasing first ionization energy, I_1: As, Sn, Br, Sr.

Solution

If we arrange these four atoms according to decreasing radius, we will likely have arranged them according to increasing ionization energy. The largest atoms are to the left and the bottom of the periodic table. Of the four atoms, the one that best fits the large-atom category is *Sr*. The smallest atoms are to the right and toward the top of the periodic table. Although none of the four atoms is particularly close to the top of the table, *Br* is the best fit for this category because it is farthest to the right. This fixes the two extremes: Sr with the lowest ionization energy and Br with the highest. A tin atom should be larger than an arsenic atom, and thus Sn should have a lower ionization energy than As. The expected order of *increasing* ionization energies is Sr < Sn < As < Br.

Practice Example A: Refer to the periodic table on the inside front cover, and arrange the following in the expected order of increasing first ionization energy, I_1: Cl, K, Mg, S.

Practice Example B: Refer to the periodic table on the inside front cover, and determine which element is most likely in the *middle* position when the following five elements are arranged according to first ionization energy, I_1. Rb, As, Sb, Br, Sr.

Electron Affinity animation

Students have difficulty with the sign of the electron affinity. "Which has the largest electron affinity?" should be clearly explained. The "largest" usually means the most negative, which, correctly speaking, is the smallest electron affinity.

Wheeler, John C. "Electron Affinities of the Alkaline Earth Metals and the Sign Convention for Electron Affinity." *J. Chem. Educ.* **1997:** *74*, 123 (January 1997).

Myers, R. Thomas. "The Periodicity of Electron Affinity." *J. Chem. Educ.* **1990:** *67*, 307.

CONCEPT ASSESSMENT ✓

On the blank periodic table in the margin locate the following:

(a) The group 14 element with the highest first ionization energy;

(b) The element with the greatest first ionization energy in period 4;

(c) A *p*-block element in period 4 that has a lower first ionization energy than the element immediately preceding it and the element directly following it.

9-5   ELECTRON AFFINITY

Ionization energy concerns the loss of electrons. **Electron affinity**, *EA*, is a measure of the energy change that occurs when a *gaseous* atom gains an electron. For example,

$$F(g) + e^- \longrightarrow F^-(g) \qquad EA = -328 \text{ kJ/mol}$$

When a F atom gains an electron, energy is given off. The process is *exothermic*, and following the thermochemical conventions established in Chapter 7, the electron affinity is a negative quantity.*

Why should a neutral fluorine atom so readily gain an electron? A plausible explanation is that when a free electron approaches a F atom from an "infinite" distance away, the electron "sees" a center of positive charge—the atomic nucleus—to which it is attracted. This attraction is offset to some extent by the repulsive effect of other electrons in the atom. But, so long as the attractive force on the additional electron exceeds the repulsive force, the electron is gained and energy is given off. In becoming F^-, a fluorine atom acquires the very stable electron configuration of the noble gas neon (Ne). That is,

$$F\ (1s^2 2s^2 2p^5) + e^- \longrightarrow F^-\ (1s^2 2s^2 2p^6)$$

Even metal atoms can form negative ions *in the gaseous state*, where they will only rarely contact one another. This is the situation for gaseous Li atoms, for example, where the added electron enters the half-filled 2*s* orbital.

$$Li(g) + e^- \longrightarrow Li^-(g) \qquad EA = -59.6 \text{ kJ/mol}$$
$$(1s^2 2s^1) \qquad\qquad (1s^2 2s^2)$$

Some atoms have no tendency to gain an electron. This is the case with the noble gases, where an added electron would have to enter the empty *s* orbital of the next electronic shell. Other cases include the groups 2 and 12 elements, where the electron would have to enter the *p* subshell of the valence shell and a few other elements, such as Mn, where the electron would have to enter either the *p* subshell of the valence shell or a half-filled 3*d* subshell.

In considering the gain of a second electron by a nonmetal atom, we encounter positive electron affinities. Here the electron to be added is approaching not a neutral atom, but a negative ion. There is a strong repulsive force between the electron and the ion, and the energy of the system increases. Thus, for an element like oxygen, the first electron affinity is negative and the second is positive.

$$O(g) + e^- \longrightarrow O^-(g) \qquad EA_1 = -141.0 \text{ kJ/mol}$$
$$O^-(g) + e^- \longrightarrow O^{2-}(g) \qquad EA_2 = +744 \text{ kJ/mol}$$

---

*We have defined electron affinity to reflect the tendency for a neutral atom to gain an electron. An alternative definition refers to the energy change in the process: $X^-(g) \longrightarrow X(g) + e^-$; that is, reflecting the tendency of an anion to lose an electron. This alternative definition leads to the opposite signs for *EA* values from those written in this text. You should be prepared to see electron affinities expressed in both ways in the chemical literature.

1	2	13	14	15	16	17	18
H −72.8							**He** >0
Li −59.6	**Be** >0	**B** −26.7	**C** −121.8	**N** +7	**O** −141.0	**F** −328.0	**Ne** >0
Na −52.9	**Mg** >0	**Al** −42.5	**Si** −133.6	**P** −72	**S** −200.4	**Cl** −349.0	**Ar** >0
K −48.4	**Ca** −2.37	**Ga** −28.9	**Ge** −119.0	**As** −78	**Se** −195.0	**Br** −324.6	**Kr** >0
Rb −46.9	**Sr** −5.03	**In** −28.9	**Sn** −107.3	**Sb** −103.2	**Te** −190.2	**I** −295.2	**Xe** >0
Cs −45.5	**Ba** −13.95	**Tl** −19.2	**Pb** −35.1	**Bi** −91.2	**Po** −186	**At** −270	**Rn** >0

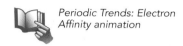
Periodic Trends: Electron Affinity animation

◀ **FIGURE 9-10**
Electron affinities of main-group elements
Values are in kilojoules per mole for the process
$X(g) + e^- \longrightarrow X^-(g)$.

The high positive value of EA_2 makes the formation of *gaseous* O^{2-} seem very unlikely. The ion O^{2-} can exist, however, in ionic compounds such as MgO(s), where formation of the ion is accompanied by other energetically favorable processes.

Some representative electron affinities are listed in Figure 9-10. It is more difficult to make generalizations about electron affinities than about ionization energies. The smaller atoms to the right of the periodic table (for example, group 17) tend to have large, negative electron affinities.* Electron affinities tend to become less negative in progressing toward the bottom of a group, with the notable exception of the second-period members of groups 15, 16, and 17. (namely, N, O, and F). It is likely that for these small atoms, an incoming electron encounters strong repulsive forces from other electrons in the atom and is thereby not as tightly bound as we might otherwise expect.

Matsuyama, Y., Yasuoka, T., Mitsuzawa, S., Sasaki, T. "Observation of Magnetic Repulsion Acting on Nitrogen Bubble on Water Surface—a Simple Experiment of Studying Diamagnetic Property of Nitrogen." *J. Chem. Educ.* **1997:** 74, 943 (August 1997).

CONCEPT ASSESSMENT ✓

On the blank periodic table in the margin locate the following:

(a) The group expected to have the most negative electron affinities in each period;
(b) The group expected to have the least negative electron affinities in each period;
(c) The group expected to have all positive electron affinities in each period.

9-6   MAGNETIC PROPERTIES

An important property related to the electron configurations of atoms and ions is their behavior in a magnetic field. A spinning electron is an electric charge in motion. It induces a magnetic field (recall the discussion on page 313). In a **diamagnetic** atom or ion, all electrons are paired and the individual magnetic effects cancel out. A diamagnetic species is weakly repelled by a magnetic field. A **paramagnetic** atom or ion has unpaired electrons, and the individual magnetic effects do not cancel out. The unpaired electrons possess a magnetic moment that causes the atom or ion to be attracted to an external magnetic field. The more unpaired electrons present, the stronger is this attraction.

◀ **KEEP IN MIND**
that it was the effect of the magnetic moments associated with the two different possibilities for an electron spin quantum number (equal in magnitude and opposite in sign) that allowed Stern and Gerlach to detect the presence of electron spin using a magnetic field.

---

*It is somewhat awkward to speak of larger and smaller with the term *electron affinity*. A strong tendency to gain an electron, which implies a high "affinity" for an electron, as with F and Cl, is reflected through a *low* value of *EA*—a large *negative* value.

Manganese has a paramagnetism corresponding to five unpaired electrons, which is consistent with the electron configuration

When a manganese atom loses two electrons, it becomes the ion Mn^{2+}, which is paramagnetic, and the strength of its paramagnetism corresponds to five unpaired electrons.

When a third electron is lost to produce Mn^{3+}, the ion has a paramagnetism corresponding to four unpaired electrons. The third electron lost is one of the unpaired $3d$ electrons.

Mn^{3+}:   [Ar] ↑ ↑ ↑ ↑ □   □
                    $3d$ $4s$

📖 Cortel, Adolf. "Demonstrations on Paramagnetism with an Electronic Balance." *J. Chem. Educ.* **1998**: *75*, 61 (January 1998).

📖 Geselbracht, M. J., Cappellari, A. M., Ellis, A. B., Rzeznik, M. A., Johnson, B. J. "Rare Earth Iron Garnets: Their Synthesis and Magnetic Properties." *J. Chem. Educ.* **1994**: *71*, 696.

📖 Shimada, H., Yasuoka, T., Mitsuzawa, S. "Observation of Paramagnetic Property of Oxygen by Simple Method: A Simple Experiment for College Chemistry and Physics Courses (TD)." *J. Chem. Educ.* **1990**: *67*, 63.

EXAMPLE 9-4

Determining the Magnetic Properties of an Atom or Ion. Which of the following would you expect to be diamagnetic and which paramagnetic?
    (a) Na atom,   **(b)** Mg atom,   **(c)** Cl^- ion,   **(d)** Ag atom.

Solution

(a) Paramagnetic. The Na atom has a single $3s$ electron outside the Ne core. This electron is unpaired.

(b) Diamagnetic. The Mg atom has *two* $3s$ electrons outside the Ne core. They must be paired, as are all the other electrons in the Ne core.

(c) Diamagnetic. Cl^- is isoelectronic with Ar, and Ar has all electrons paired ($1s^2 2s^2 2p^6 3s^2 3p^6$).

(d) Paramagnetic. We do not need to work out the exact electron configuration of Ag. Because the atom has 47 electrons—an odd number—at least one of the electrons must be unpaired (recall the Stern–Gerlach experiment, page 313).

Practice Example A: Which of the following are paramagnetic and which are diamagnetic: Zn, Cl, K^+, O^{2-}, and Al?

Practice Example B: Which has the greater number of unpaired electrons, Cr^{2+} or Cr^{3+}? Explain.

CONCEPT ASSESSMENT ✓

On the blank periodic table in the margin locate the following:

(a) The period 4 transition element having a cation in the +3 oxidation state that is diamagnetic;

(b) The period 5 element existing in the −2 oxidation state as an anion that is diamagnetic;

(c) The period 4 transition element having a 2+ cation that is paramagnetic and has a half-filled d subshell.

9-7   PERIODIC PROPERTIES OF THE ELEMENTS

As we noted at the beginning of the chapter, we can use the periodic law and the periodic table to predict some of the atomic, physical, and chemical properties of elements and compounds.

ATOMIC PROPERTIES

In this chapter we have learned how some atomic properties—atomic radius, ionization energy, electron affinity—vary within groups and periods of elements. We summarize these trends in relation to the periodic table in Figure 9-11. Trends are generally easy to apply within a group: The atomic radius of Sr is greater than that of Mg; both elements are in group 2. Usually, there is no difficulty in applying trends within a period either: The first ionization energy of P is greater than that of Mg; both elements are in the third period. However, comparing elements that are not within the same group or period can be difficult. The atomic radius of Sr is greater than that of P. Sr is farther down in its group of the periodic table and much farther to the left in its period than is P. Each of these directions is that of increasing atomic radius. On the other hand, we cannot easily predict whether Mg or I has the larger atomic radius. The position of Mg to the left in its period suggests that Mg should have the larger radius, but the position of I toward the bottom of its group argues for I. Despite this limitation, you should find Figure 9-11 helpful in most cases.

Smith, Derek W. "Atomization Enthalpies of Metallic Elemental Substances Using the Semi-Quantitative Theory of Ionic Solids: A Simple Model for Rationalizing Periodic Trends." *J. Chem. Educ.* **1993**: *70*, 368.

◀ **FIGURE 9-11**
Atomic properties and the periodic table—a summary
Atomic radius refers to metallic radius for metals and covalent radius for nonmetals. Ionization energies refer to first ionization energy. For electron affinity, the direction of increasing *EA* is that in which values become *more negative*. Metallic character relates generally to the ability to lose electrons, and nonmetallic character to the ability to gain electrons.

Variation of Physical Properties Within a Group.   Table 9.5 lists some properties of three of the halogens (group 17). The table has two blank spaces for bromine. We fill in these blanks in Example 9-5 by making an assumption that works often enough to make it useful:

> The value of a property often changes uniformly from the top to the bottom of a group of elements in the periodic table.

TABLE 9.5	Some Properties of Three Halogen (Group 17) Elements				
	Atomic Number	Atomic Mass, u	Molecular Form	Melting Point, K	Boiling Point, K
Cl	17	35.45	Cl_2	172	239
Br	35	79.90	Br_2	?	?
I	53	126.90	I_2	387	458

Physical Properties of the Halogens movie

▲ FIGURE 9-12
Three halogen elements
Chlorine is a yellow-green gas. Bromine is a dark red liquid. Iodine is a grayish black solid.

First, let us make some predictions about fluorine, the halogen not listed in Table 9.5. Its closest neighbor in group 17 is chlorine, which has a boiling point of 239 K (−34 °C); chlorine is a *gas* at room temperature (about 298 K). The other halogens are *liquid* bromine and *solid* iodine (Fig. 9-12). We would expect fluorine to have a lower melting point (mp) and lower boiling point (bp) than chlorine and also to be a gas at room temperature. (Observed values for F_2: mp = 53 K; bp = 85 K.)

EXAMPLE 9-5

Using the Periodic Table to Estimate Physical Properties. Use data from Table 9.5 to estimate the boiling point of bromine.

Solution

The atomic number of bromine (35) is intermediate to the atomic numbers of chlorine (17) and iodine (53). Its atomic mass (79.90 u) is also intermediate to those of chlorine and iodine. (The average of the atomic masses of Cl and I is 81.18 u.) It is reasonable to expect that the boiling point of liquid bromine might also be intermediate to the boiling points of chlorine and iodine.

$$\text{bp } Br_2 \approx \frac{239 \text{ K} + 458 \text{ K}}{2} = 349 \text{ K}$$

The observed boiling point is 332 K.

Practice Example A: Estimate the melting point of bromine.

Practice Example B: Estimate the boiling point of astatine, At.

TABLE 9.6 Melting Points of Two Series of Compounds		
	Molecular Mass, u	Melting Point, °C
CF_4	88.0	−183.7
CCl_4	153.8	−22.9
CBr_4	331.6	90.1
CI_4	519.6	171
HF	20.0	−83.6
HCl	36.5	−114.2
HBr	80.9	−86.8
HI	127.9	−50.8

▶ When evaluating trends, it is often useful to sketch a graph showing the variation of the property.

▶ Metallic bonds are described in Section 11-7; covalent bonding in substances like silicon is discussed in Section 12-7; and the topic of intermolecular forces is examined throughout Chapter 12.

The generalization that a property varies uniformly within a group of the periodic table can work for compounds as well as for elements. Table 9.6 lists the melting points of two sets of compounds, binary carbon–halogen compounds and the *hydrogen halides*, HX (where X = F, Cl, Br, or I). We see that the melting points increase fairly uniformly with increasing molecular mass for the carbon–halogen compounds. This trend between melting point (and boiling point) and molecular mass can be explained in terms of intermolecular forces, as we shall see in Chapter 12. Based on the melting points of HCl, HBr, and HI, the melting point of HF should be about −145 °C, but the observed value is −83.6 °C. Some factor other than molecular mass must be involved here. In Chapter 12, we will find that in HF there is a special intermolecular force of attraction that is missing or unimportant in the other compounds in Table 9.6.

Variation of Physical Properties Across a Period.   A few properties vary regularly across a period. The ability to conduct heat and electricity are two that do. Thus, among the third-period elements, the metals Na, Mg, and Al have good thermal and electrical conductivities. The metalloid Si is only a fair conductor of heat and electricity, while the nonmetals P, S, Cl, and Ar are poor conductors.

In some cases, the trend in a property reverses direction in the period (similar to the trend in melting points of the hydrogen halides reversing direction within a group). Consider, for example, the melting points of the third-period elements shown in a bar graph in Figure 9-13. Melting involves destruction of the orderly arrangement of the atoms or molecules in a crystalline solid. The amount of thermal energy needed for melting to occur, and hence the melting-point temperature, depends on the strength of the attractive forces between the atoms or molecules in the solid. For the metals Na, Mg, and Al, these forces are *metallic bonds*, which, roughly speaking, become stronger as the number of electrons available to participate in the bonding increases. Sodium, therefore, has the lowest melting point (371 K) of the third-period metals. With silicon, the forces between atoms are strong *covalent bonds* extending throughout the

▲ **FIGURE 9-13**
Melting points of the third-period elements
Sometimes the trend in a property reverses direction within a group as illustrated by this bar graph.

(a)

crystalline solid. Silicon has the highest melting point (1683 K) of the third-period elements. Phosphorus, sulfur, and chlorine exist as discrete molecules (P_4, S_8, and Cl_2). The bonds between atoms within molecules are strong, but *intermolecular forces*, the attractive forces between molecules, become progressively weaker across the period, and the melting points decrease. Argon atoms do not form molecules, and the forces between Ar atoms in solid argon are especially weak. Argon's melting point is the lowest for the entire period (84 K). The property of hardness also depends on forces between atoms and molecules in a solid. So the hardness of the solid third-period elements varies in much the same way as their melting points. Thus, on a 10-point scale in which solids are rated according to their abilities to scratch or abrade one another, sodium has a hardness of about 0.5; magnesium, 2; aluminum, 3; silicon, 7; and phosphorus and sulfur 1 to 2. Silicon has the greatest hardness.

Reducing Abilities of Group 1 and 2 Metals. We learned in Chapter 5 that a reducing agent makes possible a reduction half-reaction. The reducing agent itself, by losing electrons, is oxidized. In the following reactions, M, a group 1 or 2 metal, is the reducing agent and H_2O is the substance that is reduced.

$$2\,M(s) + 2\,H_2O(l) \longrightarrow 2\,M^+(aq) + 2\,OH^-(aq) + H_2(g) \qquad (M = \text{group 1 metal})$$

$$M(s) + 2\,H_2O(l) \longrightarrow M^{2+}(aq) + 2\,OH^-(aq) + H_2(g) \qquad (M = \text{Ca, Sr, Ba, or Ra})$$

At a first guess, we might think that the lower the energy requirement for extracting electrons—the lower the ionization energy—the better the metal is as a reducing agent and the more vigorous its reaction with water. Potassium, for instance, has a lower ionization energy ($I_1 = 419$ kJ/mol) than does the next member of the fourth period, calcium ($I_1 = 590$; $I_2 = 1145$ kJ/mol). Our expectation is that potassium should react more vigorously with water than calcium. This, indeed, is the case (Fig. 9-14). Mg and Be do not react with cold water as do the other alkaline earth metals. This might be explained in terms of the higher ionization energies for those two metals (Mg: $I_1 = 738$, $I_2 = 1451$ kJ/mol; Be: $I_1 = 900$, $I_2 = 1757$ kJ/mol).

Attributing the reactivity of these group 1 and 2 metals just to their ionization energies is an oversimplification, however. As long as the differences in ionization energies are very large it is possible to make comparisons by considering only this factor. Where differences in ionization energies are smaller, though, other factors must also be considered, as we shall see elsewhere in the text.

(b)

▲ **FIGURE 9-14**
A comparison of the reactions of potassium and calcium with water
(a) Potassium, a group 1 metal, reacts so rapidly that the hydrogen evolved bursts into flame. Notice that the metal is less dense than water. **(b)** Calcium, a group 2 metal, reacts more slowly than does potassium. Also, calcium is denser than water. The pink color of the acid–base indicator phenolphthalein signals the buildup of OH^- ions.

Sodium and Potassium in Water movie

▲ **FIGURE 9-15**
Reaction of sodium metal and chlorine gas
The contents of the flask glow in this exothermic reaction between Na(s) and Cl_2(g). The product is the ionic solid NaCl(s).

Oxidizing Abilities of the Halogen Elements (Group 17). An oxidizing agent gains the electrons that are lost in an oxidation half-reaction. The oxidizing agent, by gaining electrons, is itself reduced. Electron affinity is the atomic property introduced in this chapter that is related to the gain of electrons. We might expect an atom with a strong tendency to gain electrons (a large *negative* electron affinity) to take electrons away from atoms with low ionization energies—metals. In these terms, it is understandable that active metals form ionic compounds with active nonmetals. If M is a group 1 metal and X a group 17 nonmetal (halogen), this exchange of an electron leads to the formation of M^+ and X^- ions. In some cases, the reaction is especially vigorous (Fig. 9-15).

$$2 M + X_2 \longrightarrow 2 MX \qquad [\text{e.g., } 2 Na(s) + Cl_2 (g) \longrightarrow 2 NaCl(s)]$$

Another interesting oxidation–reduction reaction involving the halogens is a *displacement reaction*. Two halogens, one in molecular form and the other in ionic form, exchange places, as in this reaction (Fig. 9-16).

$$Cl_2(g) + 2 I^-(aq) \longrightarrow I_2(aq) + 2 Cl^-(aq)$$

We might think of this reaction as involving a competition between Cl and I atoms for an extra electron that only the I atoms (as I^-) have initially. The Cl atoms win out because they have a more negative electron affinity. (This is an oversimplified explanation, however, because strictly speaking electron affinities apply only to the behavior of isolated gaseous atoms and not to atoms in molecules or ions in solution.) By similar reasoning, can you see why no reaction occurs for this combination?

$$Br_2(l) + Cl^-(aq) \longrightarrow \text{no reaction}$$

Predictions such as those in the preceding paragraph work well for the halogens Cl_2, Br_2, and I_2, but not for F_2. We cannot account for the observed fact that F_2 is the strongest oxidizing agent among all chemical substances, just by considering electron affinities.

Acid–Base Nature of Element Oxides. Some metal oxides, such as Li_2O, react with water to produce the metal hydroxide.

$$\underset{\text{a basic oxide}}{Li_2O(s)} + H_2O(l) \longrightarrow \underset{\text{lithium hydroxide}}{2 Li^+(aq) + 2 OH^-(aq)}$$

These metal oxides are called *basic oxides* or *base anhydrides*. The term **anhydride** means "without water." A "base without water" becomes a base when the water is added. Thus, the base anhydride Li_2O becomes the base LiOH, and BaO becomes $Ba(OH)_2$ after reaction with water. Moving from top to bottom down a group, the elements become more metallic, and their oxides become more basic.

(a)   (b)

▲ **FIGURE 9-16**
Displacement of I^-(aq) by Cl_2(g)
(a) Cl_2(g) is bubbled through colorless, dilute I^-(aq). **(b)** The I_2 produced is extracted into CCl_4(l), in which it is much more soluble (purple layer).

Some nonmetal oxides react with water to produce an acidic solution. These are *acidic oxides* or *acid anhydrides*. SO_2(g) reacts with water to produce H_2SO_3, a weak acid.

$$\underset{\text{an acidic oxide}}{SO_2(g)} + H_2O(l) \longrightarrow \underset{\text{sulfurous acid}}{H_2SO_3(aq)}$$

Now let us examine the acid–base properties of the oxides of the third-period elements. We expect the metal oxides at the left of the period to be basic and the nonmetal oxides at the right to be acidic, but where and how does the changeover occur? Na_2O and MgO yield basic solutions in water. Cl_2O, SO_2, and P_4O_{10} produce acidic solutions. SiO_2 (quartz) does not dissolve in water. However, it does dissolve slightly in strongly basic solutions to produce silicates (similar to the carbonates formed by CO_2 in basic solutions). For this reason, we consider SiO_2 to be an acidic oxide.

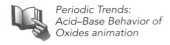

Periodic Trends: Acid–Base Behavior of Oxides animation

Aluminum, a good conductor of heat and electricity, is clearly metallic in its physical properties. Al_2O_3, however, can act as either an acidic or basic oxide. Oxides with this ability are called **amphoteric** (from the Greek word *amphos*, meaning "both"). Al_2O_3 is insoluble in water but exhibits its amphoterism by reacting with both acidic and basic solutions.

$$Al_2O_3(s) + 6\ HCl(aq) \longrightarrow 2\ AlCl_3(aq) + 3\ H_2O(l)$$

     base   acid

$$Al_2O_3(s) + 2\ NaOH(aq) + 3\ H_2O(l) \longrightarrow 2\ Na[Al(OH)_4](aq)$$

   acid   base   sodium aluminate

The amphoterism of Al_2O_3 signifies the point at which a changeover from basic to acidic oxides occurs in the third period of elements. Figure 9-17 summarizes the acid–base properties of the oxides of the main-group elements.

▲ FIGURE 9-17
Acidic, basic, and amphoteric oxides of the *s*- and *p*-block elements
The acidic oxides are pink, the basic oxides are blue, and the amphoteric oxides are tan.

CONCEPT ASSESSMENT ✔

On the blank periodic table in the margin locate the following:

(a) The group 13 element that is expected to form the most basic oxide;

(b) The group 15 element that is expected to form the most acidic oxide;

(c) The period 5 element that is expected to form the most basic oxide;

(d) The period 5 element that is expected to form the most acidic oxide;

(e) The period 3 element that exhibits amphoteric behavior.

Summary

9-1 Classifying the Elements: The Periodic Law and the Periodic Table—The experimental basis of the periodic table of the elements is the **periodic law**: Certain properties recur periodically when the elements are arranged by increasing atomic number. The theoretical basis is that the properties of an element are related to the electron configuration of its atoms, and elements in the same group of the periodic table have similar electron configurations.

9-2 Metals and Nonmetals and Their Ions—The three classes of elements of the periodic table are the *nonmetals, metals,* and *metalloids*. **Metalloids** have some properties characteristic of metals and some characteristics of nonmetals. The nonmetals are further divided into the noble gases and the remainder of the main-group nonmetals, while the metals include the main-group metals and transition elements.

9-3 Sizes of Atoms and Ions—Types of atomic radii include **covalent radii**, **metallic radii**, and **van der Waals radii** (Fig. 9-3). In general, atomic radii decrease across a period and increase down a group of the periodic table (Figs. 9-4 and 9-8), mirroring the variation in **effective nuclear charge**, Z_{eff}, (equation 9.3) across a period and down a group. The **ionic radii** of positive ions are smaller than the neutral atom, whereas negative ions are larger than the parent atom (Figs. 9-6 and 9-7). Ionic radii exhibit adherence to the periodic law similar to that of atomic radii. When atoms or ions have the same number of electrons, they are said to be *isoelectronic*. When the radii of isoelectronic species are compared, the more negative the charge, the larger the radius of the ion or atom.

9-4 Ionization Energy—A study of **ionization energies**, *I*, shows that the periodic relationship observed is governed by the variation of Z_{eff}—that is, the ionization energy decreases down a group and increases across a period (Fig. 9-9, Tables 9.3 and 9.4).

9-5 Electron Affinity—**Electron affinity**, *EA*, does not exhibit a clear-cut trend, but in general it becomes less negative down a group (Fig. 9-10).

9-6 Magnetic Properties—The magnetic properties of an atom or ion stem from the presence or absence of unpaired electrons. **Paramagnetic** atoms and ions have one or more unpaired electrons. In **diamagnetic** atoms and ions all electrons are paired.

9-7 Periodic Properties of the Elements—The metallic, nonmetallic, and metalloid characteristics of atoms can be related to a set of atomic properties. In general, large atomic radii and low ionization energies are associated with metals; small atomic radii, high ionization energies, and large negative electron affinities are associated with nonmetals. Metalloids occur first in the third row (at Si) where the break between acid–base properties becomes less defined. Metals usually form oxides that give basic solutions, whereas nonmetal oxides form acidic solutions. The nonmetal oxide is called an **anhydride** since the addition of water gives an acid. At the break between clearly basic and acidic properties, some metals and metalloids exhibit **amphoteric** behavior because they react with both acids and bases (Fig. 9-17).

Mercury is a liquid at room temperature. You are probably aware of this fact, but to chemists, it is surprising. Our expectation from the periodic law is that mercury should be a solid. Zinc and cadmium, the elements above mercury in group 12, are both solids. Their melting points are 419.6 and 320.9 °C, respectively. Based on these values and applying the predictive methods of Section 9-7, we should expect mercury to be a soft solid metal with a melting point of about 200 °C.

Suppose we base our prediction on mercury's sixth-period neighbors. To the immediate left of mercury, we find the metals Pt (Z = 78, mp = 1172 °C) and Au (Z = 79, mp = 1064 °C). To the immediate right are two more metals: T1 (Z = 81, mp = 303 °C) and Pb (Z = 82, mp = 328 °C). From these data, we might expect a melting point for Hg (Z = 80) of well over 300 °C. Instead, we observe a melting point of −38.86 °C.

Integrative Example

When the ionization energies of a series of isoelectronic atoms and ions are compared, an interesting relationship is observed for some of them. In particular, if the square root of the ionization energy (in kJ mol^{-1}) for the series Li, Be$^+$, B^{2+}, C^{3+}, N^{4+}, O^{5+}, and F^{6+} is plotted against the atomic number (Z) of the species, a linear relationship is obtained. The corresponding graph for the series Na, Mg$^+$, Al^{3+}, Si^{3+}, P^{4+}, S^{5+}, and Cl^{6+}, is also linear. The graph is shown below.

The equations for the two lines joining the points are

$$\text{Second-row elements:} \qquad \sqrt{I} = 18.4Z - 32.0 \qquad\qquad (9.7)$$
$$\text{Third-row elements:} \qquad \sqrt{I} = 13.5Z - 124 \qquad\qquad (9.8)$$

Explain the origin of these relationships and the differences in the numerical coefficients.

Strategy

We first notice that the electron configuration of the second-row atoms and ions is $1s^2 2s^1$, that is, a single electron $(2s^1)$ beyond the helium core $(1s^2)$. Similarly, for the third-row atoms and ions the electron configuration is $1s^2 2s^2 2p^6 3s^1$, that is, a single electron $(3s^1)$ beyond the neon core $(1s^2 2s^2 2p^6)$.

▶ Variation of $\sqrt{I}$ with atomic number for the second-row elements (black line) and the third-row elements (red line).

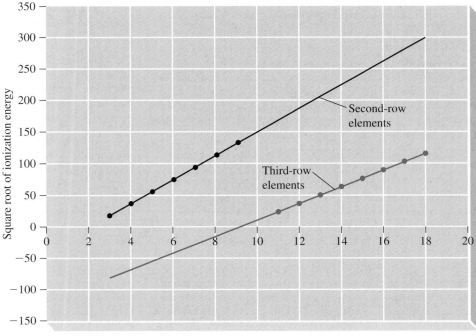

The reason that mercury is a liquid at room temperature is something of a mystery and not completely understood. In this limited discussion, the most likely explanation comes from an unlikely source—Einstein's theory of relativity. According to this theory, the mass of a particle *increases* if the particle travels at speeds approaching the speed of light. The value listed in Table 2.1 for the mass of an electron is its *rest mass*. We are justified in using the rest mass as long as an electron travels at low to moderate speeds. In atoms of high atomic number, though, because of the high nuclear charge, electrons that come close to the nucleus are accelerated to high speeds, and their masses increase.

In the wave–mechanical model, the relativity effect is especially pronounced for s electrons because these are the electrons that have a rather high probability of being found near the nucleus. As the electron increases in speed and in mass, there is a corresponding *decrease* in the size of the electron orbital and a lowering of the orbital energy. In Hg, because of the lowering of the energy of the $6s$ orbital and the stability of the $5s^2 5p^6 5d^{10} 6s^2$ electron configuration, the bonds between Hg atoms are too weak to maintain a solid structure at room temperature. Mercury becomes almost as stable as a noble gas—sort of a noble liquid.

The relativistic shrinking of s orbitals affects all the heavy metal atoms, but it is at a maximum with mercury. As new heavy elements are characterized, such as the recently discovered elements with $Z = 112$ and $Z = 114$, chemists may find other significant deviations from the periodic law.

Please point out that mercury is toxic and should never be touched. Mercury vapor is also toxic.

Everett, T. Stephen. "Eliminating Mercury Thermometers from the Lab." *J. Chem. Educ.* 1997: *74*, 1204 (October 1997).

Rapp, Bernard, FSC. "An Efficient and Inexpensive Device for Recovering Spilled Mercury." *J. Chem. Educ.* 1990: *67*, 338.

Norrby, Lars J. "Why is Mercury Liquid? Or, Why Do Relativistic Effects not get into Chemistry Textbooks?" *J. Chem. Educ.* 1991: *68*, 110.

Brown, R. F. C. "Melting Point and Molecular Symmetry." *J. Chem. Educ.* 2000: *77*, 724 (June 2000).

In both series of atoms and ions, the inner-core electrons screen the single valence-shell electron from the nucleus. These species are all reminiscent of the Bohr atom so that as an approximation we can use the expression for the energy levels for hydrogen-like atoms or hydrogen-like ions (equation 8.9). Specifically, we should be able to use equation (8.9) to derive equations for the energy required to remove the electron from the valence shells of a hydrogen-like species, that is, the ionization energy (I). Once we have these equations, we can compare them to the equations for the two straight-line graphs.

Solution

Equation (8.9), with the substitution $Z = Z_{\text{eff}}$, produces equation (9.4); and with the further substitution $R_H = 2.178 \times 10^{-18}$ J, we have

$$E_n = -2.178 \times 10^{-18} \left(\frac{Z_{\text{eff}}^2}{n^2} \right) \text{J}$$

E_n in equations (8.9) and (9.4) has the unit J atom^{-1}, which must be converted to kJ mol^{-1}—the unit of I in the two straight-line equations given to us.

$$E_n = -2.178 \times 10^{-18} \frac{\text{J}}{\text{atom}} \times 6.022 \times 10^{23} \frac{\text{atom}}{\text{mol}} \times \frac{Z_{\text{eff}}^2}{n^2}$$

$$= -1.3116 \times 10^{-6} \frac{Z_{\text{eff}}^2}{n^2} \text{J mol}^{-1} \times \frac{1 \text{ kJ}}{1000 \text{ J}}$$

The energy required to remove an electron from an orbital with principal quantum number n in a hydrogen-like species—the ionization energy—is the *negative* of that shown above, that is,

$$I = -E_n = 1311.6 \times \frac{Z_{\text{eff}}^2}{n^2} \text{ kJ mol}^{-1} \tag{9.9}$$

Equation (9.9) shows that the ionization energy (I) is a linear function of $(Z_{\text{eff}})^2$ and the straight-line graphs (equations 9.7 and 9.8) show that $\sqrt{I}$ is a linear function of Z. We are on the right track. However, we must now take into account that we are considering one-electron systems with a nucleus shielded by a closed shell.

First consider the second-row series (Li, Be$^+$, B^{2+}, C^{3+}, N^{4+}, O^{5+}, and F^{6+}), all members of which have the electron configuration $1s^2 2s^1$. If we assume that the closed shell $1s^2$ perfectly screens the outer electron $2s^1$, the value of Z_{eff} for this series will be $Z - 2$. Thus we should substitute $Z_{\text{eff}} = Z - 2$ into equation (9.9), and also $n = 2$ since ionization occurs from the $2s$ orbital, to obtain

$$I = 1311.6 \times \frac{(Z - 2)^2}{n^2} = 1311.6 \times \frac{(Z - 2)^2}{2^2}$$

Taking the square root of both sides and clearing the fraction gives

$$\sqrt{I} = 36.22 \times \left(\frac{Z - 2}{2} \right) = 18.11Z - 36.22 \tag{9.10}$$

Let us now look at the third-row series. In this case the configuration of the isoelectronic series is $1s^2 2s^2 2p^6 3s^1$ so that if we assume perfect screening of the $3s^1$ electron by the ten inner-core electrons we have

$$Z_{\text{eff}} = Z - 10$$

365

Proceeding as before and remembering that ionization occurs from the $n = 3$ level, we obtain

$$I = 1311.6 \times \frac{(Z - 10)^2}{n^2} = 1311.6 \times \frac{(Z - 10)^2}{3^2}$$

and

$$\sqrt{I} = 36.22 \times \left(\frac{Z - 10}{3}\right) = 12.07Z - 120.7 \tag{9.11}$$

Assessment

In comparing equations (9.10) and (9.11), we find that the difference in the slope (coefficient for Z) is due to the difference in the principal quantum number of the orbital from which the ionization occurs. The difference in the intercepts is due both to the principal quantum number from which the ionization occurs and to the number of electrons screening the valence-shell electron.

Equation (9.10) for the second-row elements is in remarkable agreement with the empirically observed equation (9.7) at the beginning of this example, especially considering our use of the modified Bohr model.

While the general form of equation (9.11) is correct for the third-row series, the agreement between the numerical constants is not so good. This is to be expected because we have assumed perfect screening by the core electrons, which completely ignores the differing characteristics of the electrons comprising the inner core. The intricate, correlated motions of the electrons in the core leads to a complicated combination of screening and penetration that cannot be accounted for with our simple model.

Exercises

The Periodic Law

1. Use data from Figure 9-1 and equation (9.1) to estimate the density of the recently discovered element 114. Assume a mass number of 298.
2. Suppose that lanthanum ($Z = 57$) were a newly discovered element having a density of 6.145 g/cm^3. Estimate its molar mass.
3. The following densities, in grams per cubic centimeter, are for the listed elements in their standard states at 298 K. Show that density is a periodic property of

these elements: Al, 2.699; Ar, 0.0018; As, 5.778; Br, 3.100; Ca, 1.550; Cl, 0.0032; Ga, 5.904; Ge, 5.323; Kr, 0.0037; Mg, 1.738; P, 1.823; K, 0.856; Se, 4.285; Si, 2.336; Na, 0.968; S, 2.069.
4. The following melting points are in degrees Celsius. Show that melting point is a periodic property of these elements: Al, 660; Ar, −189; Be, 1278; B, 2300; C, 3350; Cl, −101; F, −220; Li, 179; Mg, 651; Ne, −249; N, −210; O, −218; P, 590; Si, 1410; Na, 98; S, 119.

The Periodic Table

5. Mendeleev's periodic table did not preclude the possibility of a new group of elements that would fit within the existing table, as was the case with the noble gases. Moseley's work did preclude this possibility. Explain this difference.
6. Explain why the several periods in the periodic table do not all have the same number of members.
7. Assuming that the seventh period is 32 members long, what should be the atomic number of the noble gas following radon (Rn)? Of the alkali metal following francium (Fr)? What would you expect their approximate atomic masses to be?
8. Concerning the incomplete seventh period of the periodic table, what should be the atomic number of the element (a) for which the filling of the $6d$ subshell is completed; (b) that should most closely resemble bismuth; (c) that should be a noble gas?

Atomic Radii and Ionic Radii

9. For each of the following pairs, indicate the atom that has the *larger* size: (a) Te or Br; (b) K or Ca; (c) Ca or Cs; (d) N or O; (e) O or P; (f) Al or Au.
10. Indicate the *smallest* and the *largest* species (atom or ion) in the following group: Al atom, F atom, As atom, Cs$^+$ ion, I$^-$ ion, N atom.
11. Explain why the radii of atoms do not simply increase uniformly with increasing atomic number.
12. The masses of individual atoms can be determined with great precision, yet there is considerable uncertainty about the exact size of an atom. Explain why this is the case.
13. Which is (a) the smallest atom in group 13; (b) the smallest of the following atoms: Te, In, Sr, Po, Sb? Why?

14. How would you expect the sizes of the hydrogen ion, H$^+$, and the hydride ion, H$^-$, to compare with that of the H atom and the He atom? Explain.
15. Arrange the following in expected order of increasing radius: Br, Li$^+$, Se, I$^-$. Explain your answer.
16. Explain why the generalizations presented in Figure 9-11 cannot be used to answer the question, Which is larger, an Al atom or an I atom?
17. Among the following ions, several pairs are *isoelectronic*. Identify these pairs. Fe^{2+}, Sc^{3+}, Ca^{2+}, F$^-$, Co^{2+}, Co^{3+}, Sr^{2+}, Cu$^+$, Zn^{2+}, Al^{3+}.
18. The following species are isoelectronic with the noble gas krypton. Arrange them in order of increasing radius and comment on the principles involved in doing so: Rb$^+$, Y^{3+}, Br$^-$, Sr^{2+}, Se^{2-}.

19. All the isoelectronic species illustrated in the text had the electron configurations of noble gases. Can two ions be isoelectronic *without* having noble-gas electron configurations? Explain.

20. Is it possible for two different atoms to be isoelectronic? two different cations? two different anions? a cation and an anion? Explain.

Ionization Energies; Electron Affinities

21. Use principles established in this chapter to arrange the following atoms in order of *increasing* value of the first ionization energy: Sr, Cs, S, F, As.

22. Are there any atoms for which the second ionization energy (I_2) is smaller than the first (I_1)? Explain.

23. Some electron affinities are negative quantities, and some are zero or positive. Why is this not also the case with ionization energies?

24. How much energy, in joules, must be absorbed to convert to Na^+ all the atoms present in 1.00 mg of *gaseous* Na? The first ionization energy of Na is 495.8 kJ/mol.

25. How much energy, in kilojoules, is required to remove all the third-shell electrons in a mole of gaseous silicon atoms?

26. What is the maximum number of Cs^+ ions that can be produced per joule of energy absorbed by a sample of gaseous Cs atoms?

27. The production of gaseous bromide ions from bromine molecules can be considered a two-step process in which the first step is

$$Br_2(g) \longrightarrow 2\,Br(g) \qquad \Delta H = +193\ kJ$$

Is the formation of $Br^-(g)$ from $Br_2(g)$ an endothermic or exothermic process?

28. Use ionization energies and electron affinities listed in the text to determine whether the following reaction is endothermic or exothermic.

$$Mg(g) + 2\,F(g) \longrightarrow Mg^{2+}(g) + 2\,F^-(g)$$

29. The Na^+ ion and the Ne atom are isoelectronic. The ease of loss of an electron by a gaseous Ne atom, I_1, has a value of 2081 kJ/mol. The ease of loss of an electron from a gaseous Na^+ ion, I_2, has a value of 4562 kJ/mol. Why are these values not the same?

30. From the data in Figure 9-10, the formation of a gaseous anion Li^- appears energetically favorable. That is, energy is given off when gaseous Li atoms accept electrons. Comment on the likelihood of forming a stable compound containing the Li^- ion, such as $Li^+\,Li^-$ or $Na^+\,Li^-$.

Magnetic Properties

31. Unpaired electrons are found in only one of the following species. Indicate which one, and explain why: F^-, Ca^{2+}, Fe^{2+}, S^{2-}.

32. Which of the following species has the greatest number of unpaired electrons **(a)** Ge; **(b)** Cl; **(c)** Cr^{3+}; **(d)** Br^-?

33. Which of the following species would you expect to be diamagnetic and which paramagnetic? **(a)** K^+; **(b)** Cr^{3+}; **(c)** Zn^{2+}; **(d)** Cd; **(e)** Co^{3+}; **(f)** Sn^{2+}; **(g)** Br.

34. Write electron configurations consistent with the following data on numbers of unpaired electrons. Ni^{2+}, 2; Cu^{2+}, 1; Cr^{3+}, 3.

35. Must all atoms with an odd atomic number be paramagnetic? Must all atoms with an even atomic number be diamagnetic? Explain.

36. Neither Fe^{2+} nor Fe^{3+} has 4s electrons in its electron configuration. How many unpaired electrons would you expect to find in each of these ions? Explain.

Predictions Based on the Periodic Table

37. Use ideas presented in this chapter to indicate **(a)** three metals that you would expect to exhibit the photoelectric effect with visible light and three that you would not; **(b)** the noble gas element that should have the highest density in the liquid state; **(c)** the approximate I_1 of fermium $(Z = 100)$; **(d)** the approximate density of solid radium $(Z = 88)$.

38. The heat of atomization for an element is the amount of energy required to convert an appropriate amount of an element in its standard state to a mole of atoms in the gaseous state. The heats of atomization, in kilojoules per mole, for three of the group 14 elements are: carbon, 717; silicon, 452; and tin, 302 kJ/mol. Predict the heat of atomization of germanium.

39. Gallium is a commercially important element (used to make gallium arsenide for the semiconductor industry). Although gallium was unknown in Mendeleev's time, he predicted properties of this element. Predict the following for gallium: **(a)** density; **(b)** the formula and percent composition of its oxide.
[*Hint:* Use Figure 9-1, equation (9.1), and Mendeleev's periodic table (page 341).]

40. For the following groups of elements, select the one that has the property noted.

(a) the largest atom: Mg, Mn, Mo, Ba, Bi, Br

(b) the lowest first ionization energy: B, Sr, Al, Br, Mg, Pb

(c) the most negative electron affinity: As, B, Cl, K, Mg, S

(d) the largest number of unpaired electrons: F, N, S^{2-}, Mg^{2+}, Sc^{3+}, Ti^{3+}

41. The boiling points of the noble gases increase down the group as follows: He, 4.2; Ne, 27.1; Ar, 87.3; Kr, 119.7; and Xe, 165 K. What would you predict to be the boiling point of radon?

42. Estimate the missing boiling point in the following series of compounds.
 (a) CH_4, -164 °C; SiH_4, -112 °C; GeH_4, -90 °C; SnH_4, ? °C.
 (b) H_2O, ? °C; H_2S, -61 °C; H_2Se, -41 °C; H_2Te, -2 °C.
 Does your estimate in part (b) agree with the known value?

43. Match each of the lettered items on the left with an appropriate numbered item on the right. All the numbered items should be used, and some more than once.
 (a) $Z = 32$ 1. two unpaired p electrons
 (b) $Z = 8$ 2. diamagnetic
 (c) $Z = 53$ 3. more negative electron affinity than elements on either side of it in the same period
 (d) $Z = 38$
 (e) $Z = 48$
 (f) $Z = 20$ 4. first ionization energy lower than that of Ca but greater than that of Cs

44. Match each of the lettered items in the column on the left with the most appropriate numbered item(s) in the column on the right. Some of the numbered items may be used more than once and some not at all.
 (a) Tl   1. an alkaline earth metal
 (b) $Z = 70$ 2. element in period 5 and group 15
 (c) Ni   3. largest atomic radius of all the elements
 (d) $[Ar]4s^2$
 (e) a metalloid   4. an element in period 4 and group 16
 (f) a nonmetal   5. $3d^8$
           6. one p electron in the shell of highest n
           7. lowest ionization energy of all the elements
           8. an f-block element

Integrative and Advanced Exercises

45. Complete and balance the following equations. If no reaction occurs, so state.
 (a) $Rb(s) + H_2O(l) \longrightarrow$
 (b) $I_2(s) + Na^+(aq) + Br^-(aq) \longrightarrow$
 (c) $SrO(s) + H_2O(l) \longrightarrow$
 (d) $SO_3(g) + H_2O(l) \longrightarrow$

46. Write balanced equations to represent
 (a) the displacement of a halide anion from aqueous solution by liquid bromine;
 (b) the reaction with water of an alkali metal with $Z > 50$;
 (c) the reaction of tetraphosphorus decoxide with water;
 (d) the reaction of aluminum oxide with aqueous sulfuric acid.

47. Four atoms and/or ions are sketched below in accordance with their relative atomic and/or ionic radii.

 Which of the following sets of species are compatible with the sketch? Explain. (a) C, Ca^{2+}, Cl^-, Br^-; (b) Sr, Cl, Br^-, Na^+; (c) Y, K, Ca, Na^+; (d) Al, Ra^{2+}, Zr^{2+}, Mg^{2+}; (e) Fe, Rb, Co, Cs.

48. Discuss the likelihood that element 168, should it ever be synthesized in sufficient quantity, would be a "noble liquid" at 298 K and 1 atm. Some data that may be of use are tabulated here. Might element 168 be a "noble solid" at 298 K and 1 atm? Use $spdf$ notation to show the electron configuration you would expect for element 168.

Element	Atomic Mass, u	mp, K	bp, K
Argon	39.948	83.95	87.45
Helium	4.0026	—	4.25
Krypton	83.80	116.5	120.9
Neon	20.179	24.48	27.3
Radon	222	202	211.4
Xenon	131.29	161.3	166.1

49. Sketch a periodic table that would include *all* the elements in the main body of the table. How many "numbers" wide would the table be?

50. In Mendeleev's time, indium oxide, which is 82.5% In by mass, was thought to be InO. If this were the case, in which group of Mendeleev's table (page 341) should indium be placed?

51. Instead of accepting the atomic mass of indium implied by the data in Exercise 50, Mendeleev proposed that the formula of indium oxide is In_2O_3. Show that this assumption places indium in the proper group of Mendeleev's periodic table on page 341.

52. Listed below are two atomic properties of the element germanium. Refer only to the periodic table on the inside front cover and indicate probable values for each of the following elements, expressed as greater than, about equal to, or less than the value for Ge.

Element	Atomic Radius	First Ionization Energy
Ge	122 pm	762 kJ/mol
Al	?	?
In	?	?
Se	?	?

53. In estimating the boiling point and melting point of bromine in Example 9-5, could we have used Celsius or Fahrenheit instead of Kelvin temperature? Explain.

54. In the formula X_2, if the two X atoms are the same halogen, the substance is a halogen element (for example, Cl_2, Br_2). If the two X atoms are different (such as Cl and Br), the substance is an *interhalogen compound*. Use data from Table 9.5 to estimate the melting points and boiling points of the interhalogen compounds BrCl and ICl.

55. Refer to Figure 9-8 and explain why the difference between the ionic radii of the 1- and 2- anions does not remain constant from top to bottom of the periodic table.

56. Explain why the third ionization energy of Li(g) is an easier quantity to calculate than either the first or second ionization energies. Calculate I_3 for Li, and express the result in kJ/mol.

57. Studies done in 1880 showed that a chloride of uranium had 37.34% Cl by mass and an approximate formula mass of 382 u. Other data indicated the specific heat of uranium to be 0.0276 cal g^{-1} °C^{-1}. Are these data in agreement with the atomic mass of uranium assigned by Mendeleev, 240 u?
[*Hint:* Refer to Problem 104 of Chapter 7.]

58. Assume that atoms are hard spheres, and use the metallic radius of 186 pm for Na to estimate the volumes of one Na atom and of one mole of Na atoms. How does your result compare with the atomic volume found in Figure 9-1? Why is there so much disagreement between the two values?

59. When sodium chloride is strongly heated in a flame, the flame takes on the yellow color associated with the emission spectrum of sodium atoms. The reaction that occurs in the *gaseous* state is

$$Na^+(g) + Cl^-(g) \longrightarrow Na(g) + Cl(g).$$

Calculate ΔH for this reaction.

60. Use information from Chapters 8 and 9 to calculate the *second* ionization energy for the He atom. Compare your result with the tabulated value of 5251 kJ/mol.

61. Refer only to the periodic table on the inside front cover, and arrange the following ionization energies in order of increasing value: I_1 for F; I_2 for Ba; I_3 for Sc; I_2 for Na; I_3 for Mg. Explain the basis of any uncertainties.

62. Refer to the footnote on page 353. Then use values of basic physical constants and other data from the appendices to show that 1 eV/atom = 96.49 kJ/mol.

63. Plot a graph of the square roots of the ionization energies versus the nuclear charge for the two series Li, Be$^+$, B^{2+}, C^{3+}, and Na, Mg$^+$, Al^{2+}, Si^{3+}. Explain the observed relationship with the aid of Bohr's expression for the binding energy of an electron in a one-electron atom.

64. Francium is an extremely rare, radioactive element occurring in uranium minerals, but estimates are that no more than 15 g of francium occur in the top 1 km of Earth's crust. Few of francium's properties have been measured, but some can be inferred from its position in the periodic table. Estimate the melting point, density, and atomic (metallic) radius of francium.

Feature Problems

65. The work functions for a number of metals are given in the following table. How do the work functions vary
(a) down a group;
(b) across a period?
(c) Estimate the work function for potassium and compare it with a published value.
(d) What periodic property is the work function most like?

Metal	Work Function, J $\times 10^{19}$
Al	6.86
Cs	3.45
Li	4.6
Mg	5.86
Na	4.40
Rb	3.46

66. The following are a few elements and their characteristic X-ray wavelengths:

Element	X-ray Wavelength, pm
Mg	987
S	536
Ca	333
Cr	229
Zn	143
Rb	93

Use these data to determine the constants A and b in Moseley's relationship (page 342). Compare your value of A with the value obtained from Bohr's theory for the frequencies emitted by one-electron atoms. Suggest a reasonable interpretation of the quantity b.

67. Gaseous sodium atoms absorb quanta with the energies shown

Energy of Quanta, kJ mol^{-1}	Electron Configuration
0	[Ne]$3s^1$
203	[Ne]$3p^1$
308	[Ne]$4s^1$
349	[Ne]$3d^1$
362	[Ne]$4p^1$

(a) The ionization energy of the ground state is 496 kJ mol^{-1}. Calculate the ionization energies for each of the states given in the table.
(b) Calculate Z_{eff} for each state.
(c) Calculate $\bar{r}_{nl}$ for each state.
(d) Interpret the results obtained from parts (b) and (c) in terms of penetration and screening.

68. A method for estimating electron affinities is to extrapolate Z_{eff} values for atoms and ions that contain the same number of electrons as the negative ion of interest. Using the following data.

Atom or Ion: I (kJ mol^{-1})	Atom or Ion: I (kJ mol^{-1})	Atom or Ion: I (kJ mol^{-1})
Ne: 2080	F: 1681	O: 1314
Na$^+$: 4565	Ne$^+$: 3963	F$^+$: 3375
Mg^{2+}: 7732	Na^{2+}: 6912	Ne^{2+}: 6276
Al^{3+}: 11,577	Mg^{3+}: 10,548	Na^{3+}: 9540

(a) Estimate the electron affinity of F, and compare it with the experimental value;
(b) Estimate the electron affinities of O and N;
(c) Examine your results in terms of penetration and screening.

69. We have seen that the wave functions of hydrogen-like atoms contain the nuclear charge Z for hydrogen-like atoms and ions, but modified through equation (9.3) to account for the phenomenon of shielding or screening. In 1930, John C. Slater devised the following set of empirical rules to calculate a shielding constant for a designated electron in the orbital ns or np:

(i) Write the electron configuration of the element, and group the subshells as follows: $(1s)$, $(2s, 2p)$, $(3s, 3p)$, $(3d)$, $(4s, 4p)$, $(4d)$, $(4f)$, $(5s, 5p)$, and so on.

(ii) Electrons in groups to the right of the (ns, np) group contribute nothing to the shielding constant for the designated electron.

(iii) All the other electrons in the (ns, np) group shield the designated electron to the extent of 0.35 each.

(iv) All electrons in the $n - 1$ shell shield to the extent of 0.85 each.

(v) All electrons in the $n - 2$ shell, or lower, shield completely—their contributions to the shielding constant are 1.00 each.

When the designated electron being shielded is in an nd or nf group, rules (ii) and (iii) remain the same but rules (iv) and (v) are replaced by

(vi) Each electron in a group lying to the left of the nd or nf group contributes 1.00 to the shielding constant.

These rules are a simplified generalization based on the average behavior of different types of electrons. Use these rules to do the following:

(a) Calculate Z_{eff} for a valence electron of oxygen;

(b) Calculate Z_{eff} for the $4s$ electron in Cu;

(c) Calculate Z_{eff} for a $3d$ electron in Cu;

(d) Evaluate the Z_{eff} for the valence electrons in the group 1 elements (including H), and show that the ionization energies observed for this group are accounted for by using the Slater rules. [*Hint:* Do not overlook the effect of n on the orbital energy.]

(e) Evaluate Z_{eff} for a valence electron in the elements Li through Ne, and use the results to explain the observed trend in first ionization energies for these elements.

(f) Using the radial functions given in Table 8.1 and Z_{eff} estimated with the Slater rules, compare plots of the radial probability for the $3s$, $3p$, and $3d$ orbitals for the H atom and the Na atom. What do you observe from these plots regarding the effect of shielding on radial probability distributions?

Self-Assessment Exercises

70. In your own words, define the following terms: **(a)** isoelectronic; **(b)** valence-shell electrons; **(c)** metal; **(d)** nonmetal; **(e)** metalloid.

71. Briefly describe each of the following ideas or phenomena: **(a)** the periodic law; **(b)** ionization energy; **(c)** electron affinity; **(d)** paramagnetism.

72. Explain the important distinctions between each pair of terms: **(a)** actinide and lanthanide element; **(b)** covalent and metallic radius; **(c)** atomic number and effective nuclear charge; **(d)** ionization energy and electron affinity; **(e)** paramagnetic and diamagnetic.

73. The element whose atoms have the electron configuration $[Kr]4d^{10}5s^25p^3$ **(a)** is in group 13 of the periodic table; **(b)** bears a similarity to the element Bi; **(c)** is similar to the element Te; **(d)** is a transition element.

74. The fourth-period element with the largest atom is **(a)** K; **(b)** Br; **(c)** Pb; **(d)** Kr.

75. The largest of the following is **(a)** an Ar atom; **(b)** a K^+ ion; **(c)** a Ca^{2+} ion; **(d)** a Cl^- ion.

76. The highest first ionization energy of the following is that of **(a)** Cs; **(b)** Cl; **(c)** I; **(d)** Li.

77. The most negative electron affinity of the following elements is that of **(a)** Br; **(b)** Sn; **(c)** Ba; **(d)** Li.

78. An ion that is isoelectronic with Se^{2-} is **(a)** S^{2-}; **(b)** I^-; **(c)** Xe; **(d)** Sr^{2+}.

79. Find three pairs of elements that are out of order in the periodic table in terms of their atomic masses. Why is it necessary to invert their order in the table?

80. For the atom $^{119}_{50}Sn$, indicate the number of **(a)** protons in the nucleus; **(b)** neutrons in the nucleus; **(c)** $4d$ electrons; **(d)** $3s$ electrons; **(e)** $5p$ electrons; **(f)** electrons in the valence shell.

81. Refer to the periodic table on the inside front cover and indicate **(a)** the most nonmetallic element; **(b)** the transition metal with lowest atomic number; **(c)** a metalloid whose atomic number is exactly midway between those of two noble gas elements.

82. Give the symbol of the element **(a)** in group 14 that has the smallest atoms; **(b)** in period 5 that has the largest atoms; **(c)** in group 17 that has the lowest first ionization energy.

83. Refer only to the periodic table on the inside front cover and indicate which of the atoms, Bi, S, Ba, As, and Ca, **(a)** is most metallic; **(b)** is most nonmetallic; **(c)** has the intermediate value when the five are arranged in order of increasing first ionization energy.

84. Arrange the following elements in order of decreasing metallic character: Sc, Fe, Rb, Br, O, Ca, F, Te.

85. In multielectron atoms many of the periodic trends can be explained in terms of Z_{eff}. Consider the following statements and discuss whether or not the statement is true or false.

(a) Electrons in a p orbital are more effective than electrons in the s orbitals in shielding other electrons from the nuclear charge.

(b) Z_{eff} for an electron in an s orbital is lower than that for an electron in a p orbital in the same shell.

(c) Z_{eff} is usually less than Z.

(d) Electrons in orbitals having $\ell = 1$ penetrate better than those with $\ell = 2$.

(e) Z_{eff} for the orbitals of the elements Na($3s$), Mg($3s$), Al($3p$), P($3p$) and S($3p$) are in the order $Z_{eff}(Na) < Z_{eff}(Mg) > Z_{eff}(Al) < Z_{eff}(P) > Z_{eff}(S)$.

86. Consider a nitrogen atom in the ground state and comment on whether the following statements are true or false.
    (a) Z_{eff} for an electron in a 2s orbital is greater than that for the 1s orbital.
    (b) The Z_{eff} for the 2p and 2s orbitals is the same.
    (c) More energy is required to remove an electron from a 2s orbital than from the 2p orbital.
    (d) The 2s electron is less shielded than the 2p electron.

87. Describe how the ionization energies of the ions He^-, Li^-, Be^-, B^-, C^-, N^-, O^-, F^- vary with atomic number.

88. Describe how the ionization energies of the ions Be^+, B^+, C^+, N^+, O^+, F^+, Ne^+, Na^+ vary with atomic number.

89. Construct a concept map connecting the ideas that govern the periodic law and the periodic variation of atomic properties.

 eMedia Exercises

90. For each of the classes of elements illustrated in the **Interactive Periodic Table** activity (*Activebook 9-2*), describe the type of ions formed by the elements and the driving force behind the formation.

91. After watching the **Ionization Energy** animation (*Activebook 9-4*), **(a)** write balanced chemical equations describing the processes associated with the first four ionization energies of aluminum. **(b)** Write the electron configuration of each atom and ion found in these equations. **(c)** What is the percent increase in ionization energy for each of these steps? **(d)** Why is I_4 of aluminum so much larger than the third ionization energy?

92. The magnitudes of the electron affinities of argon and chlorine are explained by their respective electron configurations in the **Periodic Trends: Electron Affinity** animation (*Activebook 9-5*). Using a similar treat-ment, account for the irregular pattern in electron affinities of the other elements in the third row of the periodic table. For example, why would phosphorus have a less exothermic electron affinity than silicon?

93. The **Physical Properties of the Halogens** movie (*Activebook 9-7*) depicts the periodic variation of melting and boiling points with the atomic size of the elements. Referring to the **Interactive Periodic Table**, describe the trend in these physical properties for the period 2 elements and account for the variations observed across this row of the periodic table.

94. Of the properties described in this chapter (see animations in *Activebook 9-4* through *9-8*), which of the chemical properties exhibit trends that are dictated by common atomic factors? What are the underlying physical factors dictating each of these trends?

CHEMICAL BONDING I: BASIC CONCEPTS

10

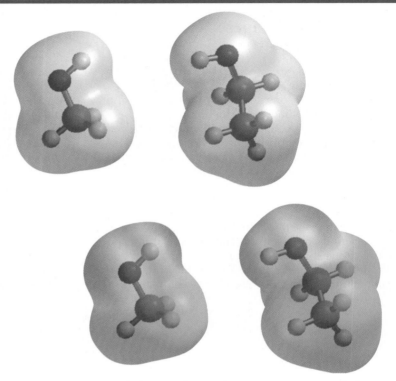

Computer-generated electron charge-density maps (gray) and electrostatic potential maps (colored) of methanol (CH_3OH) and ethanol (CH_3CH_2OH). The gray figures show the extent of electron charge density while the colored figures show the distribution of charge in the molecule. In this chapter, we study ideas that enable us to predict the geometric shapes and polarity of molecules.

Consider all that we already know about chemical compounds. We can determine their compositions and write their formulas. We can represent the reactions of compounds by chemical equations and perform stoichiometric and thermochemical calculations based on these equations. And we can do all this without really having to consider the ultimate structure of matter—the structure of atoms and molecules. Yet the shape of a molecule—that is, the arrangement of its atoms in space—often defines its chemistry. If water had a different shape, its properties would be significantly different, and life as we know it would not be possible.

In this chapter, we will describe the interactions between atoms called *chemical bonds*. Most of the discussion centers on the Lewis theory, one of the simplest methods of representing chemical bonding. We will also explore another relatively simple theory, one for predicting probable molecular shapes. Throughout the chapter, we will try to relate these theories to what is known about molecular structures from experimental measurements. In Chapter 11 we will examine the subject of chemical bonding in greater depth, and in Chapter 12 we will describe intermolecular forces—forces between molecules—and explore further the relationship between molecular shape and the properties of substances.

10-1   LEWIS THEORY: AN OVERVIEW

In the period from 1916–1919, two Americans, G. N. Lewis and Irving Langmuir, and a German, Walther Kossel, advanced an important proposal about chemical bonding: Something unique in the electron configurations of noble gas atoms accounts for their inertness, and atoms of other elements combine with one another to acquire electron configurations like noble gas atoms. The theory that grew out of this model has been most closely associated with G. N. Lewis and is called the **Lewis theory**. Some fundamental ideas associated with Lewis's theory are

1. Electrons, especially those of the outermost (valence) electronic shell, play a fundamental role in chemical bonding.

2. In some cases, electrons are *transferred* from one atom to another. Positive and negative ions are formed and attract each other through electrostatic forces called **ionic bonds**.

3. In other cases, one or more pairs of electrons are *shared* between atoms. A bond formed by the sharing of electrons between atoms is called a **covalent bond**.

4. Electrons are transferred or shared in such a way that each atom acquires an especially stable electron configuration. Usually this is a noble gas configuration, one with eight outer-shell electrons, or an **octet**.

LEWIS SYMBOLS AND LEWIS STRUCTURES

Lewis developed a special set of symbols for his theory. A **Lewis symbol** consists of a chemical symbol to represent the nucleus and *core* (inner-shell) *electrons* of an atom, together with dots placed around the symbol to represent the *valence* (outer-shell) *electrons*. Thus, the Lewis symbol for silicon, which has the electron configuration $[Ne]3s^2 3p^2$, is

$$\cdot \overset{\cdot}{\underset{\cdot}{Si}} \cdot$$

Electron spin had not yet been proposed when Lewis framed his theory, and so he did not show that two of the valence electrons ($3s^2$) are paired and two ($3p^2$) are unpaired. We will write Lewis symbols in the way Lewis did. We will place single dots on the sides of the symbol, up to a maximum of four. Then we will pair up dots until we reach an octet. Lewis symbols are commonly written for main-group elements but much less often for transition elements. Lewis symbols for several main-group elements are written in Example 10-1.

EXAMPLE 10-1

Writing Lewis Symbols. Write Lewis symbols for the following elements: **(a)** N, P, As, Sb, Bi; **(b)** Al, I, Se, Ar.

Solution

(a) These are group 15 elements, and their atoms all have five valence electrons ($ns^2 np^3$). The Lewis symbols all have five dots.

(b) Al is in group 13; I, in group 17 ; Se, in group 16; Ar, in group 18.

$$\cdot \dot{Al} \cdot \qquad :\overset{\cdot\cdot}{I}\cdot \qquad :\overset{\cdot\cdot}{Se}\cdot \qquad :\overset{\cdot\cdot}{\underset{\cdot\cdot}{Ar}}:$$

Note that for main-group elements, the number of valence electrons, and hence the number of dots appearing in a Lewis symbol, is equal to the group number for the *s*-block elements and to the "group number minus 10" for the *p*-block elements.

◀ Since 1962, a number of compounds of Xe and Kr have been synthesized. As we will see in this chapter, a focus on noble-gas electron configurations can still be useful, even if the idea that they confer complete inertness is invalid.

◀ The term *covalent* was introduced by Irving Langmuir.

▲ **Gilbert Newton Lewis (1875–1946)**
Lewis's contribution to the study of chemical bonding is evident throughout this text. Equally important, however, was his pioneering introduction of thermodynamics into chemistry.

 Stress to the student the importance of counting valence electrons for many aspects of bonding.

 Periodic Trends: Lewis Structures activity

Practice Example A: Write Lewis symbols for Mg, Ge, K, and Ne.

Practice Example B: Write the Lewis symbols expected for Sn, Br^-, Tl^+, and S^{2-}.

A **Lewis structure** is a combination of Lewis symbols that represents either the transfer or the sharing of electrons in a chemical bond.

Ionic bonding
(transfer of electrons):

$$Na\times \ + \ \cdot\overset{\cdot\cdot}{\underset{\cdot\cdot}{Cl}}: \ \longrightarrow \ [Na]^+[\overset{\cdot\cdot}{\underset{\cdot\cdot}{\times Cl}}:]^-$$ (10.1)

Lewis symbols   Lewis structure

Covalent bonding
(sharing of electrons):

$$H\times \ + \ \cdot\overset{\cdot\cdot}{\underset{\cdot\cdot}{Cl}}: \ \longrightarrow \ H\overset{\cdot\cdot}{\underset{\cdot\cdot}{\times Cl}}:$$ (10.2)

Lewis symbols   Lewis structure

In these two examples, we designated the electrons involved in bond formation differently—($\times$) from one atom and ($\cdot$) from the other. This helps to emphasize that an electron is transferred in ionic bonding and that a pair of electrons is shared in covalent bonding. Of course, it is impossible to distinguish between electrons, and henceforth we will use only dots ($\cdot$) to represent electrons in Lewis structures.

Lewis's work dealt mostly with covalent bonding, which we will emphasize throughout this chapter. However, Lewis's ideas also apply to ionic bonding, and we briefly describe this application next.

LEWIS STRUCTURES FOR IONIC COMPOUNDS

In Section 3-2, we learned that the formula unit of an ionic compound is the simplest electrically neutral collection of cations and anions from which the chemical formula of the compound can be established. The Lewis structure of sodium chloride (structure 10.1) represents its formula unit. For an ionic compound of a main-group element, (1) the Lewis symbol of the metal ion has no dots if all the valence electrons are lost, and (2) the ionic charges of both cations and anions are shown. These ideas are further illustrated through Example 10-2.

EXAMPLE 10-2

Writing Lewis Structures of Ionic Compounds. Write Lewis structures for the following compounds: **(a)** BaO; **(b)** $MgCl_2$; **(c)** aluminum oxide.

Solution

(a) Write the Lewis symbol, and determine how many electrons each atom must gain or lose to acquire a noble-gas electron configuration. Ba loses two electrons, and O gains two.

$$Ba\cdot \ + \ :\overset{\cdot\cdot}{O}: \ \longrightarrow \ [Ba]^{2+}[:\overset{\cdot\cdot}{\underset{\cdot\cdot}{O}}:]^{2-}$$

Lewis structure

(b) A Cl atom can accept only one electron because it already has seven valence electrons. One more will give it a complete octet. On the other hand, a Mg atom must lose two electrons to have the electron configuration of the noble gas neon. So two Cl atoms are required for each Mg atom.

$$Mg\cdot \ + \ \begin{array}{c} \cdot\overset{\cdot\cdot}{Cl}: \\ \\ \cdot\overset{\cdot\cdot}{Cl}: \end{array} \ \longrightarrow \ [Mg]^{2+}2[:\overset{\cdot\cdot}{\underset{\cdot\cdot}{Cl}}:]^-$$

Lewis structure

Bacskay, G. G., Reimers, J. R., Nordholm, S. "The Mechanism of Covalent Bonding." *J. Chem. Educ.* **1997:** *74,* 1494 (December 1997).

Reimers, J. R., Bacskay, G. G., Nordholm, S. "The Basics of Covalent Bonding." *J. Chem. Educ.* **1997:** *74,* 1503 (December 1997).

No bond is 100% ionic. All ionic bonds have some covalent character.

(c) The formula of aluminum oxide follows directly from the Lewis structure. The combination of one Al atom, which loses three electrons, and one O atom, which gains two, leaves an excess of one lost electron. To match the numbers of electrons lost and gained, the formula unit must be based on *two* Al atoms and *three* O atoms.

Lewis structure

Practice Example A: Write plausible Lewis structures for **(a)** Na_2S and **(b)** Mg_3N_2.

Practice Example B: Write plausible Lewis structures for **(a)** calcium iodide; **(b)** barium sulfide; **(c)** lithium oxide.

The compounds described in Example 10-2 are *binary ionic compounds* consisting of monatomic cations and monatomic anions. Commonly encountered *ternary ionic compounds* consist of monatomic and polyatomic ions. Bonding between atoms within the polyatomic ions is covalent. Some ternary ionic compounds are considered later in the chapter.

With the exception of ion pairs such as (Na^+Cl^-) that may be found in the *gaseous* state, formula units of solid ionic compounds do not exist as separate entities. Instead, each cation is surrounded by anions and each anion by cations. These very large numbers of ions are arranged in an orderly network called an *ionic crystal* (Fig. 10-1). Ionic crystal structures and the energy changes accompanying the formation of ionic crystals are described in Chapter 12.

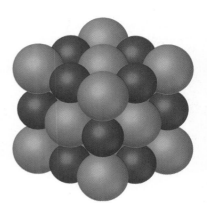

▲ **FIGURE 10-1**
Portion of an ionic crystal
This structure of alternating Na^+ and Cl^- ions extends in all directions and involves countless numbers of ions.

CONCEPT ASSESSMENT ✔

How many valence electrons do the Lewis symbols for the elements in group 16 have? Which of the following are correct Lewis symbols for sulfur?

$$:\ddot{\underset{\cdot\cdot}{S}}: \qquad :\ddot{\underset{\cdot}{S}}: \qquad \cdot\ddot{\underset{\cdot\cdot}{S}}\cdot \qquad \cdot\ddot{\underset{\cdot}{S}}:$$

10-2   COVALENT BONDING: AN INTRODUCTION

A chlorine atom shows a tendency to gain an electron, as indicated by its electron affinity (-349 kJ/mol). From which atom, sodium or hydrogen, can the electron most readily be extracted? Neither atom gives up an electron freely, but the energy required to extract an electron from Na ($I_1 = 496$ kJ/mol) is much smaller than that for H ($I_1 = 1312$ kJ/mol). In Chapter 9 we learned that the lower its ionization energy, the more metallic an element is; sodium is much more metallic than hydrogen (recall Figure 9-11). In fact, hydrogen is considered to be a nonmetal. A hydrogen atom in the gaseous state does not give up an electron to another nonmetal atom. Bonding between a hydrogen atom and a chlorine atom involves the sharing of electrons, which leads to a *covalent bond*.

To emphasize the sharing of electrons, let us think of the Lewis structure of HCl in this manner.

 The Lewis structure of HCl shows that the H atom does not obey the octet rule.

Purser, Gordon H. "Lewis Structures Are Models for Predicting Molecular Structure, Not Electronic Structure." *J. Chem. Educ.* **1999:** *76,* 1013 (July 1999).

▶ The Lewis structures for H_2O and Cl_2O suggest that these molecules have a linear shape. They do not. Lewis theory by itself does not address the question of molecular shape (see Section 10-7).

The broken circles represent the outermost electron shells of the bonded atoms. The number of dots lying on or within each circle represents the effective number of electrons in each valence shell. The H atom has two dots, as in the electron configuration of He. The Cl atom has eight dots, corresponding to the outer-shell configuration of Ar. Note that we counted the two electrons between H and Cl (:) *twice*. These two electrons are shared by the H and Cl atoms. This shared pair of electrons constitutes the covalent bond. Written below are two additional Lewis structures of simple molecules.

$$H\cdot \; + \; \cdot \overset{\displaystyle ..}{\underset{\displaystyle ..}{O}} \cdot \; + \; \cdot H \longrightarrow H \overset{\displaystyle ..}{\underset{\displaystyle ..}{O}} H \quad \text{and} \quad :\overset{\displaystyle ..}{\underset{\displaystyle ..}{Cl}} \cdot \; + \; \cdot \overset{\displaystyle ..}{\underset{\displaystyle ..}{O}} \cdot \; + \; \cdot \overset{\displaystyle ..}{\underset{\displaystyle ..}{Cl}} : \longrightarrow :\overset{\displaystyle ..}{\underset{\displaystyle ..}{Cl}} : \overset{\displaystyle ..}{\underset{\displaystyle ..}{O}} : \overset{\displaystyle ..}{\underset{\displaystyle ..}{Cl}} :$$

water   dichlorine oxide

As was the case for Cl in HCl, the O atom in the Lewis structure of H_2O and in Cl_2O is surrounded by eight electrons (when the bond-pair electrons are double counted). In attaining these eight electrons, the O atom conforms to the **octet rule**—a requirement of eight valence-shell electrons for the atoms in a Lewis structure. Note, however, that the H atom is an exception to this rule. The H atom can accommodate only two valence-shell electrons.

Lewis theory helps us to understand why elemental hydrogen and chlorine exist as diatomic molecules, H_2 and Cl_2. In each case, a pair of electrons is shared between the two atoms. The sharing of a single pair of electrons between bonded atoms produces a **single covalent bond**. To underscore the importance of electron pairs in the Lewis theory the term **bond pair** applies to a pair of electrons in a covalent bond, while **lone pair** applies to electron pairs that are not involved in bonding. Also, in writing Lewis structures it is customary to replace some electron pairs with dashes (—), especially for bond pairs. These features are shown in the following Lewis structures.

H_2 Bond Formation animation

$$H\cdot \; + \; \cdot H \longrightarrow H : H \quad \text{or} \quad H\!-\!H \tag{10.3}$$

Bond pair

$$\overset{\displaystyle ..}{Cl}\cdot \; + \; \cdot \overset{\displaystyle ..}{\underset{\displaystyle ..}{Cl}} : \longrightarrow :\overset{\displaystyle ..}{\underset{\displaystyle ..}{Cl}} : \overset{\displaystyle ..}{\underset{\displaystyle ..}{Cl}} : \quad \text{or} \quad :\overset{\displaystyle ..}{\underset{\displaystyle ..}{Cl}}\!-\!\overset{\displaystyle ..}{\underset{\displaystyle ..}{Cl}} : \quad \text{Lone pairs} \tag{10.4}$$

Bond pair

The use of the term "lone pair" can become confusing when discussing the Lewis structures of molecules that contain odd numbers of electrons as in the structure of nitrogen monoxide.

EXAMPLE 10-3

Writing Simple Lewis Structures. Write a Lewis structure for the ammonia molecule.

Solution

To write a Lewis structure you must know the formula of the molecule to be represented. The formula of ammonia, NH_3, shows how many and what types of atoms are in the structure. Another requirement for writing a Lewis structure is knowledge of the number of valence electrons associated with each of the atoms present. The valence electrons can then be represented in the Lewis symbols, as shown here.

$$H\cdot \quad H\cdot \quad H\cdot \quad \cdot \overset{\displaystyle \cdot}{N} :$$

Now we can assemble one N and three H atoms into a structure that gives the N atom a valence-shell octet and each of the H atoms two valence electrons (producing the electron configuration of He).

$$\begin{matrix} & H & \\ & \overset{\displaystyle ..}{..} & \\ H & : N : \\ & \overset{\displaystyle ..}{} & \\ & H & \end{matrix}$$

Octet Rule activity

Practice Example A: Write Lewis structures for Br_2, CH_4, and $HOCl$.

Practice Example B: Write Lewis structures for NI_3, N_2H_4, and C_2H_6.

COORDINATE COVALENT BONDS

The Lewis theory of bonding describes a covalent bond as the sharing of a pair of electrons, but this does not necessarily mean that each atom contributes an electron to the bond. A covalent bond in which a single atom contributes both of the electrons to a shared pair is called a **coordinate covalent bond**.

If we attempt to attach a fourth H atom to the Lewis structure of NH_3 shown in Example 10-3, we encounter a difficulty. The electron brought by the fourth H atom would raise the total number of valence electrons around the N atom to *nine*, so there would no longer be an octet. The *molecule* NH_4 does not form, but the *ammonium ion*, NH_4^+, does, as suggested in Figure 10-2. That is, the lone pair of electrons on a NH_3 molecule extracts an H atom from a HCl molecule, and the electrons in the H—Cl bond remain on the Cl atom. The result is equivalent to a H^+ ion joining with the NH_3 molecule to form the NH_4^+ ion,

$$\left[\begin{array}{c} H \\ H \!:\! \overset{\displaystyle ..}{\underset{\displaystyle ..}{N}} \!:\! H \\ H \end{array} \right]^+ \tag{10.5}$$

while the abandoned electron pair remaining on the Cl atom converts it to a Cl^- ion.

The bond formed between the N atom of NH_3 and the H^+ ion in structure (10.5) is a *coordinate covalent bond*. It is important to note, however, that once the bond has formed it is impossible to say which of the four N—H bonds is the coordinate covalent bond. Thus, a coordinate covalent bond is indistinguishable from a regular covalent bond.

Another example of coordinate covalent bonding is found in the familiar hydronium ion.

$$\left[\begin{array}{c} H \!:\! \overset{\displaystyle ..}{\underset{\displaystyle ..}{O}} \!:\! H \\ H \end{array} \right]^+ \tag{10.6}$$

◀ **FIGURE 10-2**
Formation of the ammonium ion, NH_4^+
The H atom of HCl leaves its electron with the Cl atom and, as H^+, attaches itself to the NH_3 molecule through the lone-pair electrons on the N atom. The ions NH_4^+ and Cl^- are formed.

MULTIPLE COVALENT BONDS

In the preceding description of the Lewis model for covalent chemical bonding, we have used a single pair of electrons between two atoms to describe a single covalent bond. Often, however, more than one pair of electrons must be shared if an atom is to attain an octet (noble gas electron configuration). CO_2 and N_2 are two molecules in which atoms share more than one pair of electrons.

First, let's apply the ideas about Lewis structures to CO_2. From the Lewis symbols, we see that the C atom can share a valence electron with each O atom, thus forming two carbon-to-oxygen single bonds.

$$:\!\overset{\displaystyle ..}{\underset{\displaystyle ..}{O}}\!\cdot \quad \cdot\overset{\displaystyle ..}{C}\cdot \quad \cdot\overset{\displaystyle ..}{\underset{\displaystyle ..}{O}}\!: \longrightarrow :\!\overset{\displaystyle ..}{\underset{\displaystyle ..}{O}}\!:\!C\!:\!\overset{\displaystyle ..}{\underset{\displaystyle ..}{O}}\!:$$

But this leaves the C atom and both O atoms still shy of an octet. The problem is solved by shifting the unpaired electrons into the region of the bond, as indicated by the red arrows.

$$:\!\overset{\displaystyle ..}{\underset{\displaystyle ..}{O}}\!:\!C\!:\!\overset{\displaystyle ..}{\underset{\displaystyle ..}{O}}\!: \longrightarrow :\!\overset{\displaystyle ..}{O}\!:\!:\!C\!:\!:\!\overset{\displaystyle ..}{O}\!: \longrightarrow :\!\overset{\displaystyle ..}{O}\!=\!C\!=\!\overset{\displaystyle ..}{O}\!: \tag{10.7}$$

In Lewis structure (10.7), the bonded atoms are seen to share *two* pairs of electrons (a total of four electrons) between them—a **double covalent bond** ($=$).

It is easy to show the formation of coordinate complexes. Dissolve white anhydrous $CuCl_2$ in water; it turns light blue due to the complex $[Cu(H_2O)_6]^{2+}$. Add ammonia to this and it turns deep blue as some of the water is replaced by ammonia to form complexes such as $[Cu(NH_3)_4(H_2O)_2]^{2+}$.

✓ Coordinate covalent bonds occur in the formation of transition metal complexes, discussed in Chapter 25.

✓ Formation of coordinate covalent bonds is an example of Lewis acid–base reactions.

✓ Point out that the additional bonds are always bonds formed from the *p* orbitals.

✓ A common misconception, which is perpetuated by the way Lewis structures are drawn, is that a double bond is composed of two single bonds and a triple bond is composed to three single bonds.

Paramagnetism here is a result of the presence of unpaired electrons. Recall that there are four types of magnetism: ferro (and anti) magnetism, diamagnetism, electron paramagnetism (treated here), and nuclear paramagnetism (responsible for NMR and MRI).

Now let's try our hand at writing a Lewis structure for the N_2 molecule. Our first attempt might again involve a single covalent bond and the incorrect structure shown below.

$$:\ddot{N}\cdot \ + \ \cdot\ddot{N}: \ \longrightarrow \ :\ddot{N}:\ddot{N}: \quad \textit{(Incorrect)}$$

Each N atom appears to have only six outer-shell electrons, not the expected eight. The situation can be corrected by bringing the four unpaired electrons into the region between the N atoms and using them for additional bond pairs. In all, we now show the sharing of *three* pairs of electrons between the N atoms. The bond between the N atoms in N_2 is a **triple covalent bond** ($\equiv$). Double and triple covalent bonds are known as **multiple covalent bonds**.

$$:\ddot{N}:\ddot{N}: \ \longrightarrow \ (N::N) \quad \text{or} \quad :N\equiv N: \qquad (10.8)$$

The triple covalent bond in N_2 is a very strong bond that is difficult to break in a chemical reaction. The unusual strength of this bond makes $N_2(g)$ quite inert. As a result, $N_2(g)$ coexists with $O_2(g)$ in the atmosphere and forms oxides of nitrogen only in trace amounts at high temperatures. The lack of reactivity of N_2 with O_2 is an essential condition for life on Earth. The inertness of $N_2(g)$ also makes it difficult to synthesize nitrogen compounds.

Another molecule whose Lewis structure features a multiple bond is O_2, which has a double bond.

$$:\ddot{O}\cdot \ + \ \cdot\ddot{O}: \ \longrightarrow \ :\ddot{O}:\ddot{O}: \ \longrightarrow \ (O::O) \ \longrightarrow \ :\ddot{O}=\ddot{O}: \ ? \qquad (10.9)$$

The blue question mark suggests that there is some doubt about the validity of structure (10.9), and the source of the doubt is illustrated in Figure 10-3. The structure fails to account for the *paramagnetism* of oxygen—the O_2 molecule must have *unpaired* electrons. Unfortunately, no completely satisfactory Lewis structure is possible for O_2, but in Chapter 11, bonding in the O_2 molecule is described in a way that accounts for both the double bond and the observed paramagnetism.

We could continue applying ideas introduced in this section, but our ability to write plausible Lewis structures will be greatly aided by a couple of new ideas that we introduce in Section 10-3.

▲ **FIGURE 10-3**
Paramagnetism of oxygen
Liquid oxygen is attracted into the magnetic field of a large magnet.

KEEP IN MIND ▶

that merely being able to write a plausible Lewis structure does not prove that it is the correct electronic structure. Proof can come only through confirming experimental evidence.

CONCEPT ASSESSMENT ✔

What types of bonds can be used to describe the chemical bonds in BF_4^-?

CONCEPT ASSESSMENT ✔

In which groups of the periodic table are the elements most likely to use multiple bonds?

10-3 POLAR COVALENT BONDS AND ELECTROSTATIC POTENTIAL MAPS

We have introduced ionic and covalent bonds as though they are of two distinctly different types: ionic bonds involving a *complete transfer* of electrons and covalent bonds involving an *equal sharing* of electron pairs. Such is not the case, however, and most chemical bonds fall between the two extremes of 100% ionic and 100% covalent. A covalent bond in which electrons are not shared equally between two atoms is called a **polar covalent bond**. In such a bond, electrons are displaced toward the more nonmetallic element. The unequal sharing of the electrons leads to a partial negative charge on the more non-metallic element, signified by $\delta-$, and a corresponding partial positive charge on the more metallic element, designated by $\delta+$. Thus we can represent the polar bond in HCl by a Lewis structure in which the partial charges $\delta+$ and $\delta-$ indicate that the bond pair of electrons lies closer to the Cl than to the H.

$$\delta^+ H : \overset{\displaystyle ..}{\underset{\displaystyle ..}{Cl}} : \delta^-$$

The advent of inexpensive fast computers has allowed chemists to develop methods for displaying the electron distribution within molecules. This distribution is obtained, in principle, by solving the Schrödinger equation for a molecule. Although the solution can only be obtained by using approximate methods, these methods provide an **electrostatic potential map**, a way to visualize the charge distribution within a molecule.

Before discussing these maps let us first review the notion of electron density, or charge density, introduced in Chapter 8. There we saw that the behavior of electrons in atoms can be described by mathematical functions called orbitals. The probability of finding an electron at some point in the three-dimensional region associated with an orbital is related to the square of an atomic orbital function. Typically, we refer to the region encompassing 95% of the probability of finding the electron as the shape of the orbital. In a similar way we can map the total electron density throughout a molecule, that is, not just the density of a single orbital. The electron density surface that encompasses 95% of the charge density in ammonia is depicted in Figure 10-4.

The *electrostatic potential* is the work done in moving a unit of positive charge at a constant speed from one region of a molecule to another. The electrostatic potential map is obtained by hypothetically probing an electron density surface with a positive point charge. The positive point charge will be attracted to an electron-rich region—a region of excess negative charge when all the charges of the nuclei and electrons have been taken into account—and the electrostatic potential will be *negative*. On the other hand, if the point charge is placed in an electron-poor region, a region of excess positive charge, the positive point charge will be repelled, and the electrostatic potential will be *positive*.

A permanent dipole moment exists if there is a separation of positive and negative charge.

The following article discusses using electron density to describe the bonding in a molecule: Gillespie, Ronald J. *J. Chem. Educ.* **2001:** *78,* 1688.

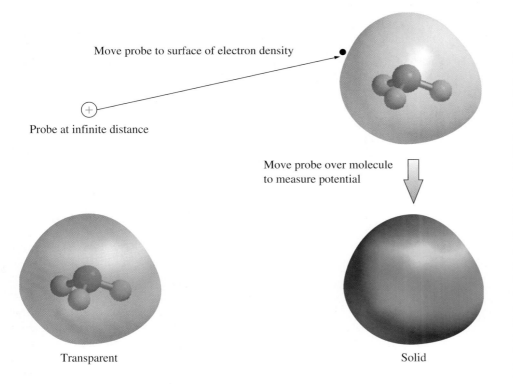

Move probe to surface of electron density

Probe at infinite distance

Move probe over molecule to measure potential

Transparent

Solid

◀ **FIGURE 10-4**
Determination of the electrostatic potential map for ammonia
The electrostatic potential at any point on the charge density surface of a molecule is defined as the change in energy that occurs when a unit positive charge is brought to this point, starting from another point that is infinitely far removed from the molecule. The surface encompassing the ammonia molecule is analogous to the 95% surface of electron charge density for atomic orbitals discussed in Chapter 8. The electrostatic potential map gives information about the distribution of electron charge within this surface.

The procedure for making an electrostatic potential map is illustrated in Figure 10-4, which shows the distribution of electron density in ammonia.

An electrostatic potential map gives information about the distribution of electron charge in a molecule. For example, in a neutral molecule, if the potential at a point is positive, it is likely that an atom at this point carries a net positive charge. An arbitrary "rainbow" color scheme is adopted in the display of an electrostatic potential map. Red, the low-energy end of the spectrum, is used for regions of the most negative electrostatic potential, and blue is used to color regions of the most positive electrostatic potential. Intermediate colors represent intermediate values of the electrostatic potential. Thus, the potential increases from red through yellow to blue, as seen in the scale in Figure 10-5. For example, the blue-green color surrounding the hydrogen atoms in Figure 10-4 suggests that they carry a slight positive charge. The nitrogen atom, being closest to the red region, carries a net negative charge.

Let us now look at the computed electrostatic potential maps for NaCl, Cl_2, and HCl (Fig. 10-5). We see that Cl_2 has a uniform distribution of electron charge density as depicted by the uniform color distribution in the electrostatic potential map. This is typical for a nonpolar covalent bond and occurs in all diatomic molecules containing identical atoms. The sodium chloride molecule, on the other hand, exhibits a highly nonuniform distribution of electron charge density. The sodium atom is almost exclusively in the blue extreme of positive charge and the chlorine in the red extreme of negative charge. This electrostatic potential map is typical of an ionic bond. Yet, it is clear from the map that the transfer of electron density from the sodium atom to the chlorine atom is not complete. That is, the NaCl bond is not completely ionic. Experiments show that the bond is only about 80% ionic. The molecule HCl also has an unsymmetrical distribution of electron charge density, as indicated by the gradation of color in the electrostatic potential map. Note, however, that in this case the chlorine atom is not completely in the extreme dark red corresponding to a large negative charge. Instead, it is in the orange-red region indicating a partial negative charge. Correspondingly, the hydrogen atom has a partial positive charge, as indicated by the pale blue. The electrostatic potential map clearly depicts the polar nature of the bond in HCl.

▶ Electrostatic potential is the work done in moving a unit of positive charge at a constant speed from one region of a molecule to another.

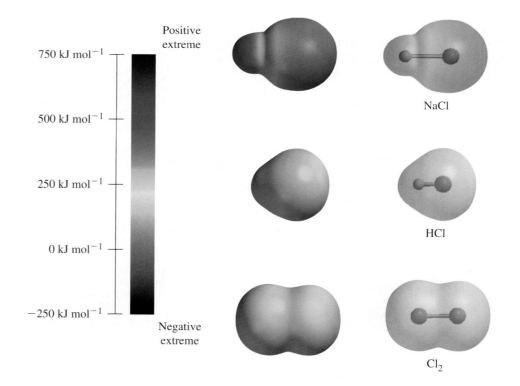

▶ **FIGURE 10-5**
The electrostatic potential maps for sodium chloride, hydrogen chloride, and chlorine
The dark red and dark blue on the electrostatic potential map correspond to the extremes of the electrostatic potential, negative to positive, for the particular molecule for which the map is calculated. To get a reliable comparison of different molecules, the values of the extremes in electrostatic potential (in kJ mol^{-1}) must be the same for all of the molecules compared. In the maps shown here the range is −250 to 750 kJ mol^{-1}.

Positive extreme

750 kJ mol^{-1}

500 kJ mol^{-1}

250 kJ mol^{-1}

0 kJ mol^{-1}

−250 kJ mol^{-1}

Negative extreme

NaCl

HCl

Cl_2

ELECTRONEGATIVITY

We expect the H—Cl bond to be polar because the Cl atom has a greater affinity for electrons than does the H atom. Electron affinity is an atomic property, however, and more meaningful predictions about bond polarities are those based on a molecular property, one that relates to the ability of atoms to lose or gain electrons when they are part of a molecule rather than isolated from other atoms.

Periodic Trends: Electronegativity animation

Electronegativity (EN) describes an atom's ability to compete for electrons with other atoms to which it is bonded. As such, electronegativity is related to ionization energy (I) and electron affinity (EA). To see how they are related consider the reaction between two hypothetical elements A and B, which could give the products A^+B^- or A^-B^+. We represent these two reactions by the expressions

$$A + B \longrightarrow A^+B^- \qquad \Delta E_1 = (I_A + EA_B) \qquad (10.10)$$

$$A + B \longrightarrow A^-B^+ \qquad \Delta E_2 = (I_B + EA_A) \qquad (10.11)$$

If the bonding electrons are shared approximately equally in these hypothetic structures, we would expect that $\Delta E_1 = \Delta E_2$ because neither extreme (A^+B^- or A^-B^+) is favored. If we make the assumption that the resultant bond is nonpolar, then

$$(I_A + EA_B) = (I_B + EA_A)$$

which gives, after collecting terms for each atom,

$$(I_A - EA_A) = (I_B - EA_B) \qquad (10.12)$$

Equation (10.12) tells us that a nonpolar bond will result when the difference between the ionization energy and the electron affinity is the same for both atoms involved in the bond. The quantity $(I - EA)$ provides a measure of the ability of an atom to attract electrons (or electron charge density) to itself relative to some other atom. Thus it is related to the electronegativity of the atom.

$$EN_A \propto (I_A - EA_A)$$

An element with a high ionization energy and an electron affinity that is large and negative, such as fluorine, will have a large electronegativity relative to an atom with a low ionization energy and a small electron affinity, such as sodium.

There are several methods for converting qualitative comparisons to actual numerical values of the electronegativities of the elements. One widely used electronegativity scale, with values given in Figure 10-6, is that devised by Linus Pauling (1901–1994). Pauling's EN values range from about 0.7 to 4.0. In general, the lower its EN, the more metallic the element is, and the higher the EN, the more nonmetallic it is. From Figure 10-6 we also see that electronegativity decreases from top to bottom in a group and increases from left to right in a period of the periodic table. These are the expected trends when we interpret electronegativity in terms of the quantity $(I - EA)$. That is, as the ionization energy (I) increases across the period we expect the electronegativity to increase. The distinction between electron affinity and electronegativity is clearly seen when we consider the electron affinities of F (-328 kJ mol^{-1}) and chlorine (-349 kJ mol^{-1}): Although the electron affinity of Cl (-349 kJ/mol) is somewhat more negative than that of F (-328 kJ/mol), the EN of Cl (3.0) is significantly lower than that of F (4.0) because of the decreased ionization energy of chlorine (1251 kJ/mol) relative to fluorine (1681 kJ/mol).

Students are frequently mixed up about electronegativity and electron affinity. The former refers to bonded atoms in molecules only, while the latter refers to the ability of an atom to attract an electron to itself.

CONCEPT ASSESSMENT ✓

With the aid of only a periodic table, decide which is the most electronegative atom of the following sets of elements **(a)** As, Se, Br, I; **(b)** Li, Be, Rb, Sr; **(c)** Ge, As, P, Sn.

1																	
H 2.1	**2**			below 1.0			2.0–2.4						**13**	**14**	**15**	**16**	**17**
Li 1.0	**Be** 1.5			1.0–1.4			2.5–2.9						**B** 2.0	**C** 2.5	**N** 3.0	**O** 3.5	**F** 4.0
Na 0.9	**Mg** 1.2	**3**	**4**	1.5–1.9	**6**	**7**	3.0–4.0	**9**	**10**	**11**	**12**		**Al** 1.5	**Si** 1.8	**P** 2.1	**S** 2.5	**Cl** 3.0
K 0.8	**Ca** 1.0	**Sc** 1.3	**Ti** 1.5	**V** 1.6	**Cr** 1.6	**Mn** 1.5	**Fe** 1.8	**Co** 1.8	**Ni** 1.8	**Cu** 1.9	**Zn** 1.6		**Ga** 1.6	**Ge** 1.8	**As** 2.0	**Se** 2.4	**Br** 2.8
Rb 0.8	**Sr** 1.0	**Y** 1.2	**Zr** 1.4	**Nb** 1.6	**Mo** 1.8	**Tc** 1.9	**Ru** 2.2	**Rh** 2.2	**Pd** 2.2	**Ag** 1.9	**Cd** 1.7		**In** 1.7	**Sn** 1.8	**Sb** 1.9	**Te** 2.1	**I** 2.5
Cs 0.8	**Ba** 0.9	**La*** 1.1	**Hf** 1.3	**Ta** 1.5	**W** 2.4	**Re** 1.9	**Os** 2.2	**Ir** 2.2	**Pt** 2.2	**Au** 2.4	**Hg** 1.9		**Tl** 1.8	**Pb** 1.8	**Bi** 1.9	**Po** 2.0	**At** 2.2
Fr 0.7	**Ra** 0.9	**Ac†** 1.1															

*Lanthanides: 1.1–1.3
†Actinides: 1.3–1.5

▲ **FIGURE 10-6**
Electronegativities of the elements
As a general rule, electronegativities *decrease* from *top to bottom* in a group and *increase* from *left to right* in a period of elements. The values are from L. Pauling, *The Nature of the Chemical Bond*, 3rd ed, Cornell University, Ithaca, NY, 1960, page 93. Values may be somewhat different when based on other electronegativity scales.

✓ Many periodic properties can be rationalized by using the variations in the magnitude of the atomic number, Z.

Electronegativity values allow an insight into the amount of polar character in a covalent bond based on **electronegativity difference**, **ΔEN**— the absolute value of the difference in EN values of the bonded atoms. If ΔEN for two atoms is very small, the bond between them is essentially covalent. If ΔEN is large, the bond is essentially ionic. For intermediate values of ΔEN, the bond is described as polar covalent. A useful rough relationship between ΔEN and percent ionic character of a bond is presented in Figure 10-7.

▶ Although Figure 10-7 suggests that the bond between two identical metal atoms should be covalent [as it is in Li₂(g), for example], in *solid* metals, where bonding extends throughout a network of many, many atoms, the bonding is of a type called *metallic* (explored in the next chapter).

Large EN differences are found between the more metallic and the more nonmetallic elements. Combinations of these elements are expected to produce bonds that are essentially ionic. Small EN differences are expected for two nonmetal atoms, and the bond between them should be essentially covalent. Thus, even without a compilation of EN values at hand, you should be able to predict the essential character of a bond between two atoms. Simply assess the metallic/nonmetallic characters of the bonded elements from the periodic table (recall Figure 9-11).

✓ An alternative way to explore the bonding character and electronegativity relationship is to use a method described in "Electronegativity and the Bond Triangle." Terry L. Meek and Leah D. Graner *J. Chem. Educ.* **2005:** *82*, 325.

▲ **FIGURE 10-7**
Percent ionic character of a chemical bond as a function of electronegativity difference

EXAMPLE 10-4

Assessing Electronegativity Differences and the Polarity of Bonds. (a) Which bond is more polar, H—Cl or H—O? **(b)** What is the percent ionic character of each of these bonds?

The following article discusses using electronegativity values to predict bond type: Sproul, Gordon *J. Chem. Educ.* **2001**: *78*, 387.

Solution

(a) Look up EN values of H, Cl, and O in Figure 10-6, and compute ΔEN. $EN_H = 2.1$; $EN_{Cl} = 3.0$; $EN_O = 3.5$. For the H—Cl bond, $\Delta EN = 3.0 - 2.1 = 0.9$. For the H—O bond, $\Delta EN = 3.5 - 2.1 = 1.4$. Because its ΔEN is somewhat greater, we expect the H—O bond to be the more polar bond.

(b) Determine the percent ionic character from Figure 10-7.

H—Cl bond: $\Delta EN = 0.9$;   ≈20% ionic

H—O bond: $\Delta EN = 1.4$;   ≈35% ionic

Practice Example A: Which of the following bonds are the most polar, that is, have the greatest ionic character: H—Br, N—H, N—O, P—Cl?

Practice Example B: Which is the most polar bond: C—S, C—P, P—O, or O—F?

To illustrate the variation of bond polarity with electronegativity using electrostatic potential maps, consider the electrostatic potential maps for HCl, HBr and HI displayed below.

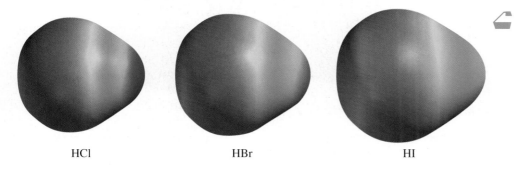

HCl   HBr   HI

The gradation of the charge on the H atom ranges from quite positive in HCl to less positive in HBr and HI, as is seen in the gradation of color on the H atom from dark blue to pale blue. This trend of decreasing charge separation in these three molecules corresponds to the decrease in electronegativity of the halogen atoms from Cl to Br to I. Correspondingly, the halogen atom becomes less red—signifying a decreasing negative charge in going from chlorine to iodine. Electrostatic potential maps are a powerful way of displaying the variation of polarity within a group of related molecules. We will use computed electrostatic potential maps later in this chapter and in subsequent chapters, whenever charge separation within a molecule contributes significantly to understanding the topic at hand.

EXAMPLE 10-5

Identifying a Molecular Structure Using Electronegativity and Electrostatic Potential Maps. Two electrostatic potential maps are shown below. One corresponds to NaF and the other to NaH. Which map corresponds to which molecule?

Solution

First look up the EN values of H, Na, and F in Figure 10-6, and compute ΔEN. $EN_H = 2.1$; $EN_{Na} = 0.9$; $EN_F = 4.0$. For the H—Na bond, $\Delta EN = 2.1 - 0.9 = 1.2$. For the F—Na bond, $\Delta EN = 4.0 - 0.9 = 3.1$. Because ΔEN for NaF is greater, we expect the F—Na bond to be the more polar bond. Consequently, we expect its electrostatic potential map to show the greater range of colors when the electrostatic potential maps are based on the same scale. We conclude that the electrostatic potential map on the left represents NaF.

Practice Example A: Which of the following electrostatic potential maps corresponds to IF, and which to IBr?

Practice Example B: Which of the following electrostatic potential maps corresponds to CH_3OH, and which to CH_3SH?

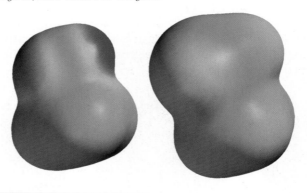

10-4   WRITING LEWIS STRUCTURES

In this section we combine the ideas introduced in the preceding three sections with a few new concepts to write a variety of Lewis structures.

FUNDAMENTAL REQUIREMENTS

Let us begin with a reminder of some of the essential features of Lewis structures that we have already encountered.

- *All* the valence electrons of the atoms in a Lewis structure must appear in the structure.
- *Usually*, all the electrons in a Lewis structure are paired.
- *Usually*, each atom acquires an outer-shell octet of electrons. Hydrogen, however, is limited to two outer-shell electrons.
- *Sometimes*, multiple covalent bonds (double or triple bonds) are needed. Multiple covalent bonds are formed most readily by C, N, O, P, and S atoms.

SKELETAL STRUCTURES

The usual starting point in writing a Lewis structure is to designate the **skeletal structure**—all the atoms in the structure arranged in the order in which they are bonded to one another. In a skeletal structure with more than two atoms, we generally need to distinguish between central and terminal atoms. A **central atom** is bonded to two or more atoms, and a **terminal atom** is bonded to just one other atom. As an example, consider ethanol, CH_3CH_2OH.

The teacher should point out that, although Lewis structures are useful, they have a number of shortcomings: electron-deficient species and those with expanded valence shells violate the octet rule. Lewis theory only works well for the first- and second-row elements; it fails to properly account for resonance; it does not predict structure; it does not account for molecules with an odd number of electrons; it does not predict the color of compounds; it does not account for paramagnetism; and it does not account for bond length and bond energy.

Skeletal structures are sigma bonds.
Additional multiple bonds and resonance are described by pi bonds.

Its skeletal structure is the same as the following structural formula. In this structure, the *central atoms*—both C atoms and the O atom—are printed in red. The *terminal atoms*—all six H atoms—are printed in blue.

$$
\begin{array}{ccc}
& H & H \\
& | & | \\
H- & C-C & -O-H \\
& | & | \\
& H & H
\end{array}
\qquad (10.13)
$$

Here are a few additional facts about central atoms, terminal atoms, and skeletal structures.

- *Hydrogen atoms are always terminal atoms.* This is because a H atom can accommodate only two electrons in its valence shell, so it can form only one bond to another atom. (An interesting and rare exception occurs in some unusual boron–hydrogen compounds.)

- *Central atoms are generally those with the lowest electronegativity.* In the skeletal structure (10.13), the atoms of lowest electronegativity (EN = 2.1) happen to be H atoms, but as noted above, H atoms can only be terminal atoms. Next lowest in electronegativity (EN = 2.5) are the C atoms, and these are central atoms. The O atom has the highest electronegativity (3.5) but nevertheless is also a central atom. For O to be a terminal atom in structure (10.13) would require it to exchange places with a H atom, but this would make the H atom a central atom and that is not possible. The chief cases where O atoms are central atoms are in structures with a *peroxo* linkage (—O—O—) or a *hydroxy* group (—O—H). Otherwise, expect an O atom to be a *terminal* atom.

- *Carbon atoms are always central atoms.* This is a useful fact to keep in mind when writing Lewis structures of organic molecules.

- Except for the very large number of chain-like organic molecules, *molecules and polyatomic ions generally have compact, symmetrical structures.* Thus, of the two skeletal structures below, the more compact structure on the right is the one actually observed for phosphoric acid, H_3PO_4.

$$
\begin{array}{cc}
\begin{array}{c}
H \\
| \\
H-O-O-P-O-O-H
\end{array}
&
\begin{array}{c}
O-H \\
| \\
H-O-P-O-H \\
| \\
O
\end{array}
\\
(Incorrect) & (Correct)
\end{array}
$$

A STRATEGY FOR WRITING LEWIS STRUCTURES

At this point, let us incorporate a number of the ideas that we have considered so far into a specific approach to writing Lewis structures. This strategy is designed to give you a place to begin as well as consecutive steps to follow to achieve a plausible Lewis structure.

1. Determine the total number of valence electrons that must appear in the structure.

   Examples: In the *molecule* CH_3CH_2OH, there are *4* valence electrons for each C atom, or *8* for the two C atoms; *1* for each H atom, or *6* for the six H atoms; and *6* for the lone O atom. The total number of valence electrons in the Lewis structure of CH_3CH_2OH is

   $$8 + 6 + 6 = 20$$

   In the *polyatomic ion* PO_4^{3-}, there are *5* valence electrons for the P atom and 6 for each O atom, or *24* for all four O atoms. To produce the charge of 3−, an additional *3* valence electrons must be brought into the structure. The total number of valence electrons in the Lewis structure of PO_4^{3-} is

   $$5 + 24 + 3 = 32$$

Stress to students that they will need to memorize the rules and steps, and practice a lot, to become proficient at writing Lewis structures. In addition, students should begin by writing structures of molecules that have only one central atom before trying to write the structures of more complicated molecules.

It is a good idea to tell students that before writing Lewis structures for more complicated molecules, the arrangement of the atoms (skeletal structure) needs to be known beforehand.

Point out to students that the charges associated with polyatomic ions give the structures the electrons they need to obey the octet rule. So for example, show students what happens when you try to draw the Lewis structures of NH_4 or PO_4 *without* their ionic charges.

In the *polyatomic ion* NH_4^+, there are *5* valence electrons for the N atom and *1* for each H atom, or *4* for all four H atoms. To account for the charge of 1+, one of the electrons must be *lost*. The total number of valence electrons in NH_4^+ is

$$5 + 4 - 1 = 8$$

2. Identify the central atoms(s) and terminal atoms.

3. Write a plausible skeletal structure. Join the atoms in the skeletal structure by *single* covalent bonds (single dashes, representing two electrons each).

4. For each bond in the skeletal structure, subtract *two* from the total number of valence electrons.

5. With the valence electrons remaining, *first* complete the octets of the terminal atoms. *Then*, to the extent possible, complete the octets of the central atom(s). If there are just enough valence electrons to complete octets for all the atoms, the structure at this point is a satisfactory Lewis structure.

6. If one or more central atoms is left with an incomplete octet after step 5, move lone-pair electrons from one or more terminal atoms to form *multiple* covalent bonds to central atoms. Do this to the extent necessary to give all atoms complete octets, thereby producing a satisfactory Lewis structure.

Figure 10-8 summarizes this procedure for writing Lewis structures.

Writing Lewis Structures activity

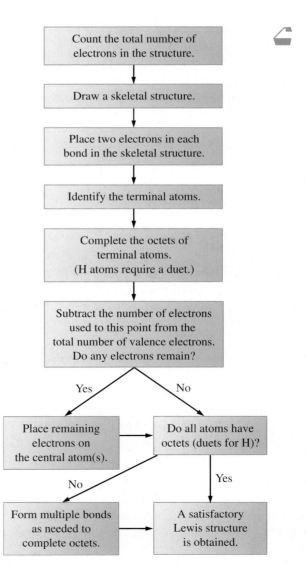

▶ **FIGURE 10-8**
Summary scheme for drawing Lewis structures

EXAMPLE 10-6

Applying the General Strategy for Writing Lewis Structures. Write a plausible Lewis structure for *cyanogen*, C_2N_2, a poisonous gas used as a fumigant and rocket propellant.

Solution

Step 1. Determine the total number of valence electrons. Each of the two C atoms (group 14) has *four* valence electrons, and each of the two N atoms (group 15) has *five*. The total number of valence electrons is $4 + 4 + 5 + 5 = 18$.

Step 2. Identify the central atom(s) and terminal atoms. The C atoms have a lower electronegativity (2.5) than do the N atoms (3.0). C atoms are central atoms, and N atoms are terminal atoms.

Step 3. Write a plausible skeletal structure by joining atoms through *single* covalent bonds.

$$N—C—C—N$$

Step 4. Subtract *two* electrons for each bond in the skeletal structure. The three bonds in this structure account for *6* of the 18 valence electrons. This leaves *12* valence electrons to be assigned.

Step 5. Complete octets for the terminal N atoms, and to the extent possible, the central C atoms. The remaining *12* valence electrons are sufficient only to complete the octets of the N atoms.

$$:\ddot{N}—C—C—\ddot{N}:$$

Writing Lewis Structures II activity

Step 6. Move lone pairs of electrons from the terminal N atoms to form multiple bonds to the central C atoms. Each C atom has only four electrons in its valence shell and needs four more to complete an octet. Thus, each C atom requires two additional pairs of electrons, which it acquires if we move two lone pairs from each N atom into its bond with a C atom, as shown below.

$$:\ddot{N}—C—C—\ddot{N}: \longrightarrow :N≡C—C≡N:$$

Practice Example A: Write plausible Lewis structures for **(a)** CS_2, **(b)** HCN, and **(c)** $COCl_2$.

Practice Example B: Write plausible Lewis structures for **(a)** formic acid, HCOOH, and **(b)** acetaldehyde, CH_3CHO.

EXAMPLE 10-7

Writing a Lewis Structure for a Polyatomic Ion. Write the Lewis structure for the *nitronium* ion, NO_2^+.

Solution

Step 1. Determine the total number of valence electrons. The N atom (group 15) has *five* valence electrons, and each of the two O atoms (group 16) has *six*. However, *one* valence electron must be removed to produce the charge of 1+.
The total number of valence electrons is $5 + 6 + 6 - 1 = 16$

Step 2. Identify the central atom(s) and terminal atoms. The N atom has a lower electronegativity (3.0) than the O atoms (3.5). N is the central atom, and the O atoms are the terminal atoms.

Step 3. Write a plausible skeletal structure by joining atoms through *single* covalent bonds.

$$O—N—O$$

Step 4. Subtract *two* electrons for each bond in the skeletal structure. The two bonds in this structure account for *4* of the 16 valence electrons. This leaves *12* valence electrons to be assigned.

Step 5. Complete octets for the terminal O atoms, and to the extent possible, the central N atom. The remaining *12* valence electrons are sufficient only to complete the octets of the O atoms.

$$\left[:\ddot{O}-N-\ddot{O}:\right]^{+}$$

Step 6. Move lone pairs of electrons from the terminal O atoms to form multiple bonds to the central N atom. The N atom has only four electrons in its valence shell and needs four more to complete an octet. Thus, the N atom requires two additional pairs of electrons, which it acquires if we move one lone pair from each O atom into its bond with the N atom, as shown below.

$$\left[:\ddot{O}-N-\ddot{O}:\right]^{+} \longrightarrow \left[:\ddot{O}=N=\ddot{O}:\right]^{+} \qquad (10.14)$$

Practice Example A: Write plausible Lewis structures for the following ions: **(a)** NO^{+}; **(b)** $N_2H_5^{+}$; **(c)** O^{2-}.

Practice Example B: Write plausible Lewis structures for the following ions: **(a)** BF_4^{-}; **(b)** NH_3OH^{+}; **(c)** NCO^{-}.

FORMAL CHARGE

Instead of writing Lewis structure (10.14) for the nitronium ion in Example 10-6, we might have written the following structure.

$$\left[:O\equiv N-\ddot{O}:\right]^{+} \qquad \qquad \textit{(improbable)} \quad (10.15)$$

Formal Charges animation

Despite the fact that this structure satisfies the usual requirements—the correct number of valence electrons and an octet for each atom—we have marked it improbable because it fails in one additional requirement. Have you noticed that in our strategy for writing Lewis structures, once the total number of valence electrons has been determined, there is no need to keep track of which electrons came from which atoms? Nevertheless, after we have a plausible Lewis structure, we can go back and assess where each electron apparently came from, and in this way we can evaluate formal charges. **Formal charges (FC)** are apparent charges on certain atoms in a Lewis structure that arise when atoms have not contributed equal numbers of electrons to the covalent bonds joining them. In cases where more than one Lewis structure seems possible, formal charges are used to ascertain which sequence of atoms and arrangement of bonds is most satisfactory.

The formal charge on an atom in a Lewis structure is the number of valence electrons in the free (uncombined) atom minus the number of electrons assigned to that atom in the Lewis structure, with the electrons assigned in the following way.

Students frequently confuse the rules for counting electrons on atoms when determining formal charge and when determining whether an atom is obeying the octet rule. When counting electrons for formal charge the bond-pair electrons are divided equally between the bonded atoms, whereas all the bond-pair electrons are assigned to an atom in a bond when counting electrons for the octet rule.

- Count *lone-pair electrons* as belonging entirely to the atom on which they are found.

- Divide *bond-pair electrons* equally between the bonded atoms.

Assigning electrons (e^{-}) in this way is equivalent to writing that

e^{-} assigned to a bonded atom in a Lewis structure

$$= \text{number lone-pair } e^{-} + \frac{1}{2} \text{ number bond-pair } e^{-}$$

Because formal charge is the difference between the assignment of valence electrons to a free (uncombined) atom and to the atom in a Lewis structure, it can be expressed as

$$\text{FC} = \text{number valence e}^- \text{ in free atom} - \text{number lone-pair e}^- \\ - \frac{1}{2} \text{ number bond-pair e}^-$$

(10.16)

Now, let us assign formal charges to the atoms in structure (10.15), proceeding from left to right.

:O≡   FC = 6 valence e⁻ in O − 2 lone-pair e⁻ − ½ (6 bond-pair e⁻) = 6 − 2 − 3 = +1

≡N—   FC = 5 valence e⁻ in N − 0 lone-pair e⁻ − ½ (8 bond-pair e⁻) = 5 − 0 − 4 = +1

—Ö: FC = 6 valence e⁻ in O − 6 lone-pair e⁻ − ½ (2 bond-pair e⁻) = 6 − 6 − 1 = −1

Formal charges in a Lewis structure can be shown using small, encircled numbers.

$$\left[\overset{⊕}{:O} {\equiv} \overset{⊕}{N} - \overset{⊖}{\ddot{\underset{..}{O}}:} \right]^+$$

(10.17)

The following are general rules that can help to determine the plausibility of a Lewis structure based on its formal charges.

- The sum of the formal charges in a Lewis structure must equal *zero* for a neutral molecule and must equal the magnitude of the charge for a polyatomic ion. [Thus for structure (10.17), this sum is +1 + 1 − 1 = +1.]

- Where formal charges are required, they should be as small as possible.

- Negative formal charges usually appear on the most electronegative atoms; positive formal charges, on the least electronegative atoms.

- Structures having formal charges of the same sign on adjacent atoms are unlikely.

◄ We will see some exceptions to the idea that formal charges should be kept to a minimum in Section 10-6.

Lewis structure (10.17) conforms to the first two rules, but is not in good accordance with the third rule. Despite the fact that O is the most electronegative element in the structure, one of the O atoms has a positive formal charge. The greatest failing, though, is in the fourth rule. Both the O atom on the left and the N atom adjacent to it have positive formal charges. Structure (10.17) is not a satisfactory Lewis structure. By contrast, the Lewis structure of NO_2^+ derived in Example 10-7 has only one formal charge, +1, on the central N atom. It conforms to the rules completely and is the accepted Lewis structure.

◄ **KEEP IN MIND**
that formal charges are not actual charges but simply "balances" in a form of "electron bookkeeping" that help us choose a probable Lewis structure.

EXAMPLE 10-8

Using Formal Charges in Writing Lewis Structures. Write the most plausible Lewis structure of nitrosyl chloride, NOCl, one of the oxidizing agents present in *aqua regia*, a mixture of concentrated nitric and hydrochloric acids capable of dissolving gold.

Solution

Although the formula is written as NOCl, we can pretty much reject the skeletal structure N—O—Cl. It places the most electronegative atom as the central atom (see also Practice Example A). This then leaves the following as possible skeletal structures.

O—Cl—N and O—N—Cl

Regardless of the skeletal structure chosen, the number of valence electrons (dots) that must appear in the final Lewis structure is

$$5 \text{ from N} + 6 \text{ from O} + 7 \text{ from Cl} = 18$$

When we apply the four steps listed below to the two possible skeletal structures, we obtain a total of four Lewis structures—two for each skeletal structure. This doubling occurs because in step 4, there are two ways to complete the octets of the central atoms. The final Lewis structures obtained are labeled (a₁), (a₂), (b₁), and (b₂).

(a)		(b)
O—Cl—N	1. Assign four electrons	O—N—Cl
:Ö—Cl—N̈:	2. Assign twelve more electrons	:Ö—N—C̈l:
:Ö—C̈l—N̈:	3. Assign the last two electrons	:Ö—N—C̈l:

4. Complete the octet on the central atom

(a₁)	(a₂)	(b₁)	(b₂)
:Ö=C̈l—N̈:	:Ö—C̈l=N̈:	:Ö=N—C̈l:	:Ö—N=C̈l:

Evaluate formal charges using equation (10.16). In structure (a₁), for the N atom,

$$FC = 5 - 6 - \frac{1}{2}(2) = -2$$

for the O atom,

$$FC = 6 - 4 - \frac{1}{2}(4) = 0$$

for the Cl atom,

$$FC = 7 - 2 - \frac{1}{2}(6) = +2$$

Proceed in a similar manner for the other three structures. Summarize the formal charges for the four structures.

	(a₁)	**(a₂)**	**(b₁)**	**(b₂)**
N:	−2	−1	0	0
O:	0	−1	0	−1
Cl:	+2	+2	0	+1

▶ Based on structure (b₁) ONCl is a better way to write the formula of nitrosyl chloride than NOCl.

Select the best Lewis structure in terms of the formal-charge rules. First, note that all four structures obey the requirement that formal charges of a neutral molecule add up to zero. In structure (a₁), the formal charges are large (+2 on Cl and −2 on N) and the negative formal charge is not on the most electronegative atom. Structure (a₂) has formal charges on all atoms, one of them large (+2 on Cl). Structure (b₁) is the ideal we seek—no formal charges. In structure (b₂), we again have formal charges. The best Lewis structure of nitrosyl chloride is

$$:Ö\!=\!N—C̈l:$$

Practice Example A: Write a Lewis structure for nitrosyl chloride based on the skeletal structure N—O—Cl, and show that this structure is not as plausible as the one obtained in Example 10-8.

Practice Example B: Write two Lewis structures for cyanamide, NH₂CN, an important chemical of the fertilizer and plastics industries. Use the formal charge concept to choose the more plausible structure.

CONCEPT ASSESSMENT ✓

For molecules, the most satisfactory Lewis structure may have no formal charges (FC = 0) in some cases and formal charges in others. For polyatomic ions, minimally the most satisfactory Lewis structure has a formal charge on at least one atom. Explain the basis of these observations.

10-5   RESONANCE

The ideas presented in the previous section allow us to write many Lewis structures, but some structures still present problems. We describe these problems in the next two sections.

Although we usually think of the formula of oxygen as O_2, there are actually two different oxygen molecules. Familiar oxygen is *dioxygen*, O_2; the other molecule is *trioxygen*—ozone, O_3. The term used to describe the existence of two or more forms of an element that differ in their bonding and molecular structure is *allotropy*—O_2 and O_3 are allotropes of oxygen. Ozone is found naturally in the stratosphere and is also produced in the lower atmosphere as a constituent of smog.

When we apply the usual rules for Lewis structures for ozone, we come up with these *two* possibilities.

$$:\ddot{O}=\ddot{O}-\ddot{\underset{..}{O}}: \qquad :\ddot{\underset{..}{O}}-\ddot{O}=\ddot{O}:$$

But there is something wrong with both structures. Each suggests that one oxygen-to-oxygen bond is single and the other is double. Yet, experimental evidence indicates that the two oxygen-to-oxygen bonds are the same; each has a length of 127.8 pm. This bond length is shorter than the O—O single-bond length of 147.5 pm in hydrogen peroxide, $H-\ddot{\underset{..}{O}}-\ddot{\underset{..}{O}}-H$, but it is longer than the double-bond length of 120.74 pm in diatomic oxygen, $:\ddot{O}=\ddot{O}:$. The bonds in ozone are intermediate between a single and a double bond. The difficulty is resolved if we say that the true Lewis structure of O_3 is *neither* of the previously proposed structures, but a composite, or *hybrid*, of the two, a fact that we can represent as

$$:\ddot{O}=\ddot{O}-\ddot{\underset{..}{O}}: \longleftrightarrow :\ddot{\underset{..}{O}}-\ddot{O}=\ddot{O}: \qquad (10.18)$$

The situation in which two or more plausible Lewis structures can be written but the "correct" structure cannot be written at all is called **resonance**. The true structure is a *resonance hybrid* of plausible contributing structures. Acceptable contributing structures to a resonance hybrid must all have the same skeletal structure (the atomic positions cannot change); they can differ only in how electrons are distributed within the structure. In expression (10.18), the two contributing structures are joined by a double-headed arrow. The arrow does *not* mean that the molecule has one structure part of the time and the other structure the rest of the time. *It has the same structure all the time.* By averaging the single bond in one structure with the double bond in the other, we might say that the oxygen-to-oxygen bonds in ozone are halfway between a single and double bond, that is, 1.5 bonds. The fact that the electrons in ozone are distributed over the whole molecule so as to produce two equivalent bonds is readily seen in the electrostatic potential map of ozone.

The two resonance structures in expression (10.18) are equivalent; that is, they contribute equally to the structure of the resonance hybrid. In many cases, there are several contributing resonance structures that do not contribute equally. For example, consider the azide anion, $N_3{}^-$, for which three resonance structures are given below.

$$\left[:\ddot{\underset{..}{N}}-N\equiv N:\right]^- \longleftrightarrow \left[\ddot{\underset{..}{N}}=N=\ddot{\underset{..}{N}}\right]^- \longleftrightarrow \left[:N\equiv N-\ddot{\underset{..}{N}}:\right]^-$$
$$\;\;\ominus{2}\;\;\oplus{1}\;\;\underset{0}{} \qquad\qquad \ominus{1}\;\;\oplus{1}\;\;\ominus{1} \qquad\qquad \underset{0}{}\;\;\oplus{1}\;\;\ominus{2}$$

We can decide which resonance structure likely contributes most to the hybrid by applying the general rules for formal charges (page 389). The central resonance structure avoids the unlikely large formal charge of -2 found on an N atom in the other two structures. Consequently, we expect that structure to contribute most to the resonance hybrid of the azide anion.

These two articles discuss useful analogies to help explain the concept of resonance: Silverstein, Todd P. *J. Chem. Educ.* **1999:** *76*, 206 and Starkey, Ronald. *J. Chem. Educ.* **1995:** *72*, 542.

◀ Bond lengths are discussed more fully in Section 10-8.

▲ Electrostatic potential map of ozone

▲ Electrostatic potential map of the azide anion

EXAMPLE 10-9

Representing the Lewis Structure of a Resonance Hybrid. Write the Lewis structure of the acetate ion, CH_3COO^-.

Solution

The skeletal structure has the three H atoms as terminal atoms bonded to a C atom as a central atom. The second C atom is also a central atom bonded to the first. The two O atoms are terminal atoms bonded to the second C atom.

$$\begin{array}{c} \overset{\displaystyle H}{\mid}\overset{\displaystyle O}{\mid} \\ H-C-C-O \\ \underset{\displaystyle H}{\mid} \end{array}$$

The number of valence electrons (dots) that must appear in the Lewis structure is

$$(3 \times 1) + (2 \times 4) + (2 \times 6) + 1 = 3 + 8 + 12 + 1 = 24$$

from H · · · · · from C · · · · · from O · · · · · to establish charge of 1−

Twelve of the valence electrons are used in the bonds in the skeletal structure, and the remaining twelve are distributed as lone-pair electrons on the two O atoms.

$$\left[\begin{array}{c} \overset{\displaystyle H}{\mid}\overset{\displaystyle :\ddot{O}:}{\mid} \\ H-C-C-\ddot{\underset{\displaystyle \cdot\cdot}{O}}: \\ \underset{\displaystyle H}{\mid} \end{array}\right]^{-}$$

In completing the octet of the C atom on the right, we discover that we can write two completely equivalent Lewis structures, depending on which of the two O atoms furnishes the lone pair of electrons to form a carbon-to-oxygen double bond. The true Lewis structure is a resonance hybrid of the following two contributing structures.

$$\left[\begin{array}{c} \overset{H}{\mid}\overset{:O:}{\parallel} \\ H-C-C-\ddot{O}: \\ \underset{H}{\mid} \end{array}\right]^{-} \longleftrightarrow \left[\begin{array}{c} \overset{H}{\mid}\overset{:\ddot{O}:}{\mid} \\ H-C-C=\ddot{O} \\ \underset{H}{\mid} \end{array}\right]^{-} \qquad (10.19)$$

Practice Example A: Draw Lewis structures to represent the resonance hybrid for the SO_2 molecule.

Practice Example B: Draw Lewis structures to represent the resonance hybrid for the nitrate ion.

▲ Acetate anion

10-6   EXCEPTIONS TO THE OCTET RULE

The octet rule has been our mainstay in writing Lewis structures, and it will continue to be one. Yet at times, we must depart from the octet rule, as we will see in this section.

ODD-ELECTRON SPECIES

The molecule NO has 11 valence electrons, an odd number. If the number of valence electrons in a Lewis structure is odd, there must be an unpaired electron somewhere in the structure. Lewis theory deals with electron pairs and does not tell us where to put the unpaired electron; it could be on either the N or the O atom. To obtain a structure free of formal charges, however, we will put the unpaired electron on the N atom.

$$\cdot\ddot{N}=\ddot{O}:$$

The presence of unpaired electrons causes odd-electron species to be paramagnetic. NO is paramagnetic. Molecules with an even number of electrons are expected to have all electrons paired and to be diamagnetic. An important exception is seen in the case of O_2, which is paramagnetic despite having 12 valence electrons. Lewis theory does not provide a good electronic structure for O_2, but the molecular orbital theory that we will consider in the next chapter is much more successful.

The number of stable odd-electron molecules is quite limited. More common are **free radicals**, or simply *radicals*, highly reactive molecular fragments with one or more unpaired electrons. The formulas of free radicals are usually written with a dot to emphasize the presence of an unpaired electron, such as in the *methyl* radical, ·CH_3, and the *hydroxyl* radical, ·OH. The Lewis structures of these two free radicals are

$$H—\underset{·}{\overset{H}{|}}—H \qquad ·\ddot{O}—H$$

◀ Experimental evidence for the paramagnetism of O_2 is shown in Figure 10-3.

Both of these free radicals are commonly encountered as transitory species in flames. In addition, ·OH is formed in the atmosphere in trace amounts as a result of photochemical reactions. Many important atmospheric reactions involve free radicals as reactants, such as in the oxidation of CO to CO_2. Free radicals, because of their unpaired electron, are highly reactive species. The hydroxyl radical, for example, is implicated in DNA damage that can lead to cancer.

$$·OH + CO \longrightarrow CO_2 + ·H$$

INCOMPLETE OCTETS

Our initial attempt to write the Lewis structure of boron trifluoride leads to a structure in which the B atom has only *six* electrons in its valence shell—an *incomplete octet*.

$$:\ddot{F}—B—\ddot{F}: \qquad (10.20)$$

We have learned to complete the octets of central atoms by shifting lone-pair electrons from terminal atoms to form multiple bonds. One of three equivalent structures with a boron-to-fluorine double bond is shown below.

$$:\ddot{F}—\overset{-1}{B}=\overset{+1}{\ddot{F}}: \qquad (10.21)$$

An observation in support of structure (10.21) is that the B—F bond length in BF_3 (130 pm) is less than expected for a single bond. A shorter bond suggests that more than two electrons are present, that is, that there is multiple-bond character in the bond. On the other hand, the placement of formal charges in structure (10.18) breaks an important rule—negative formal charge should be found on the more electronegative atom in the bond. In this structure, the positive formal charge is on the most electronegative of all atoms—F.

The high electronegativity of fluorine (4.0) and the much lower one of boron (2.0) suggest an appreciable ionic character to the boron-to-fluorine bond (see Figure 10-7). This suggests the possibility of ionic structures such as the following.

$$:\ddot{F}—B^+ \ ^-:\ddot{F}: \qquad (10.22)$$

◀ The primary industrial uses of BF_3 are not to produce chemicals containing the elements boron or fluorine. Rather, BF_3 is used because of properties stemming from its electronic structure. In most cases the BF_3 is recovered and recycled.

In view of its molecular properties and chemical behavior, the best representation of BF_3 appears to be a resonance hybrid of structures (10.20, 10.21, and 10.22), with perhaps the most important contribution made by the structure with an incomplete octet (10.20). Whichever BF_3 structure we choose to emphasize, an important characteristic of BF_3 is its strong tendency to form a coordinate covalent bond with a species capable of donating an electron pair to the B atom. This can be seen in the formation of the BF_4^- ion.

In BF_4^-, the bonds are single bonds and the bond length is 145 pm.

The number of species with incomplete octets is limited to some beryllium, boron, and aluminum compounds. Perhaps the best examples are the boron hydrides. Bonding in the boron hydrides will be discussed in Chapter 22.

EXPANDED VALENCE SHELLS

We have consistently tried to write Lewis structures in which all atoms except H have a complete octet, that is, in which each atom has eight valence electrons. There are a few Lewis structures that break this rule by having 10 or even 12 valence electrons around the central atom, creating what is called an **expanded valence shell**. Describing bonding in these structures is an area of active interest among chemists.

Molecules with expanded valence shells typically involve nonmetal atoms of the third period and beyond that are bonded to highly electronegative atoms. For example, phosphorus forms two chlorides, PCl_3 and PCl_5. We can write a Lewis structure for PCl_3 with the octet rule. In PCl_5, with five Cl atoms bonded directly to the central P atom, the outer shell of the P atom appears to have *ten* electrons. We might say that the valence shell has expanded to 10 electrons. In the SF_6 molecule, the valence shell appears to expand to 12.

Octet   Expanded valence shell   Expanded valence shell

Expanded valence shells have also been used in cases where they appear to give a better Lewis structure than strict adherence to the octet rule, as suggested by the two Lewis structures for the sulfate ion that follow.

Normal octet   Expanded valence shell

The argument for including the expanded valence-shell structure is that it reduces formal charges. Also, the experimentally determined sulfur-to-oxygen bond lengths in SO_4^{2-} and H_2SO_4 are in agreement with this idea. The experimental results for H_2SO_4, summarized in structure (10.23), indicate that the S—O bond with O as a central atom and with an attached H atom is longer than the S—O bond with O as a terminal atom.

$$
\begin{array}{c}
:\!O\!: \\
\|\|\\
H\!-\!\overset{\displaystyle ..}{\underset{\displaystyle ..}{O}}\!\rightharpoonup\!S\!\overset{\leftharpoondown}{=}\!\overset{\displaystyle ..}{O}\\
\end{array}
$$

(10.23)

154 pm ⟋   :Ö: ⟍ 143 pm
|
H

Experimental evidence appears to support using an expanded valence shell in the Lewis structure of sulfuric acid. The experimentally determined S—O bond length in the sulfate anion—149 pm—lies between the two S—O bond lengths found in sulfuric acid, suggesting a partial double-bond character. The expanded valence-shell structure is suggestive of this partial double-bond character, whereas the octet structure is not. For the sulfate anion, best agreement with the observed S—O bond lengths is found in a resonance hybrid having strong contributions from a series of resonance structures (10.24) based on expanded valence shells.

$$
\begin{bmatrix}
:O: \\
\| \\
:\ddot{O}-S=\ddot{O}: \\
| \\
:\ddot{O}:
\end{bmatrix}^{2-}
\longleftrightarrow
\begin{bmatrix}
:O: \\
| \\
:\ddot{O}-S-\ddot{O}: \\
\| \\
:\ddot{O}:
\end{bmatrix}^{2-}
\longleftrightarrow
\begin{bmatrix}
:\ddot{O}: \\
| \\
\ddot{O}=S=\ddot{O} \\
| \\
:\ddot{O}:
\end{bmatrix}^{2-}
$$

(10.24)

The problem with expanded valence-shell structures is, of course, to explain where the "extra" electrons go. This expansion has been rationalized by assuming that after the $3s$ and $3p$ subshells of the central atom fill to capacity (eight electrons), extra electrons go into the empty $3d$ subshell. If we assume that the energy difference between the $3p$ and $3d$ levels is not very large, the valence-shell expansion scheme seems reasonable. But is this a valid assumption? The use of the $3d$ orbitals for valence-shell expansion is a matter of scientific dispute.*† Although unresolved questions about the expanded valence-shell concept may be unsettling, the point to keep in mind is that the unmodified octet rule works perfectly well for most uses of Lewis structures. We will return to this topic, together with several other unsettled issues, in the concluding section of Chapter 11.

10-7   SHAPES OF MOLECULES

The Lewis structure for water gives the impression that the constituent atoms are arranged in a straight line.

$$H:\ddot{O}:H$$

However, the experimentally determined shape of the molecule is not linear. The molecule is *bent*, as shown in Figure 10-9. Does it really matter that the H_2O molecule is bent rather than linear? The answer is, decidedly yes. As we will learn in Chapter 12, the bent shape of water molecules helps to account for the fact that water is a liquid rather than a gas at room temperature. In Chapter 13, we will find that it also accounts for the ability of liquid water to dissolve so many different substances.

What we seek in this section is a simple model for predicting the approximate shape of a molecule. Unfortunately, Lewis theory tells us nothing about the shapes of molecules. On the other hand, it is an excellent place to begin. The next step is to use an idea based on repulsions between valence-shell electron pairs. We will discuss this idea after defining a few terms.

▲ FIGURE 10-9
Geometric shape of a molecule
To establish the shape of the triatomic H_2O molecule shown here, we need to determine the distances between the nuclei of the bonded atoms and the angle between adjacent bonds. In H_2O, the bond lengths $d_1 = d_2 = 95.8$ pm and the bond angle $\alpha = 104.45°$.

*L. Suidan et al., *J. Chem. Educ.*: 72, 583 (1995).
†G. H. Purser, *J. Chem. Educ.*: 78, 981 (2001).

Pfennig, B. W., Frock, R. L. "The Use of Molecular Modeling and VSEPR Theory in the Undergraduate Curriculum to Predict the Three-Dimensional Structure of Molecules." *J. Chem. Educ.* **1999:** *76,* 1018 (July 1999).

VSEPR can only rationalize molecular structure; it cannot predict it. Counting of electrons is important here. The VSEPR model does not account for odd number of electrons, bond length, bond strength, color, and paramagnetism.

By molecular shape, we mean the geometric figure we get when joining the nuclei of bonded atoms by straight lines. Figure 10-9 depicts the *triatomic* (three-atom) water molecule using a ball-and-stick model. The balls represent the three atoms in the molecule, and the straight lines (sticks), the bonds between atoms. In reality, the atoms in the molecule are in close contact, but for clarity we show only the centers of the atoms. To have a complete description of the shape of a molecule, we need to know two quantities.

- **bond lengths**, the distances between the nuclei of bonded atoms
- **bond angles**, the angles between adjacent lines representing bonds

We will concentrate on bond angles in this section and bond lengths in Section 10-8.

A diatomic molecule has only one bond and no bond angle. Because the geometric shape determined by two points is a straight line, *all diatomic molecules are linear*. A triatomic molecule has two bonds and one bond angle. If the bond angle is 180°, the three atoms lie on a straight line, and the molecule is *linear*. For any other bond angle, a triatomic molecule is said to be *angular, bent*, or *V-shaped*. Some polyatomic molecules with more than three atoms have planar or even linear shapes. More commonly, however, the centers of the atoms in these molecules define a three-dimensional geometric figure.

VSEPR animation

VALENCE-SHELL ELECTRON-PAIR REPULSION (VSEPR) THEORY

The shape of a molecule is established by experiment or by a quantum mechanical calculation confirmed by experiment. The results of these experiments and calculations are generally in good agreement with the **valence-shell electron-pair repulsion theory** (**VSEPR**). In VSEPR theory, we focus on *pairs* of electrons in the *valence* electron shell of a central atom in a structure.

> Electron pairs repel each other, whether they are in chemical bonds (bond pairs) or unshared (lone pairs). Electron pairs assume orientations about an atom to minimize repulsions.

This, in turn, results in particular geometric shapes for molecules.

Another aspect of VSEPR theory is a focus not just on electron pairs but on electron *groups*. A group of electrons can be a pair, either a lone pair or a bond pair, or it can be a single unpaired electron on an atom with an incomplete octet, as in NO. A group can also be a double or triple bond between two atoms. Thus in the $\ddot{O}{=}C{=}\ddot{O}$ molecule, the central C atom has *two* electron groups in its valence shell. Each of the double bonds with its two electron pairs is treated as *one* electron group.

Consider the methane molecule, CH_4, in which the central C atom has acquired the electron configuration of Ne by forming covalent bonds with four H atoms.

What orientation will the four electron groups (bond pairs) assume? The balloon analogy of Figure 10-10 suggests that electron-group repulsions will force the groups as far apart as possible—to the corners of a tetrahedron having the C atom at its center. The VSEPR method predicts, correctly, that CH_4 is a *tetrahedral* molecule.

▲ **FIGURE 10-10**
Balloon analogy to valence-shell electron-pair repulsion
When two elongated balloons are twisted together, they separate into four lobes. To minimize interferences, the lobes spread out into a tetrahedral pattern. (A regular tetrahedron has four faces, each an equilateral triangle.) The lobes are analogous to valence-shell electron pairs.

In NH_3 and H_2O, the central atom is also surrounded by four groups of electrons, but these molecules *do not* have a tetrahedral shape.

$$\overset{\overset{\text{H}}{\cdot\cdot}}{\text{H}\!:\!\text{N}\!:\!\text{H}} \quad \text{and} \quad \overset{\overset{\text{H}}{}}{:\!\overset{\cdot\cdot}{\underset{\cdot\cdot}{\text{O}}}\!:\!\text{H}}$$

Here is the situation: VSEPR theory predicts the distribution of electron groups, and in these molecules, electron groups are arranged tetrahedrally about the central atom. The shape of a molecule, however, is determined by the location of the atomic nuclei. To avoid confusion, we will call the geometric distribution of electron groups the **electron-group geometry** and the geometric arrangement of the atomic nuclei—the actual determinant of the molecular shape—the **molecular geometry**.

In the NH_3 molecule, only three of the electron groups are bond pairs; the fourth is a lone pair. Joining the N nucleus to the H nuclei by straight lines outlines a pyramid with the N atom at the apex and the three H atoms at the base; it is called a *trigonal pyramid*. We say that the electron-group geometry is tetrahedral and the molecular geometry is trigonal-pyramidal.

In the H_2O molecule, two of the four electron groups are bond pairs and two are lone pairs. The molecular shape is obtained by joining the two H nuclei to the O nucleus with straight lines. For H_2O, the electron-group geometry is tetrahedral and the molecular geometry is V-shaped, or bent. The geometric shapes of CH_4, NH_3, and H_2O are shown in Figure 10-11, together with computer generated space-filling molecular models, electron charge density maps, and electrostatic potential maps.

This article discusses the two main methods that have been used to determine the tetrahedral bond angle: ten Hoor, Marten. *J. Chem. Educ.* **2002:** *79, 956.*

The use of computer-generated models. Rasmol (PC Mac) or Chime (Web) can greatly enhance student understanding. On the Internet, thousands of molecular structures exist with the extension .pdb (Protein Data Bank). For example, http://www.eou.edu/chemweb/molmodel/mmp1.html and many others. Check CW for updates.

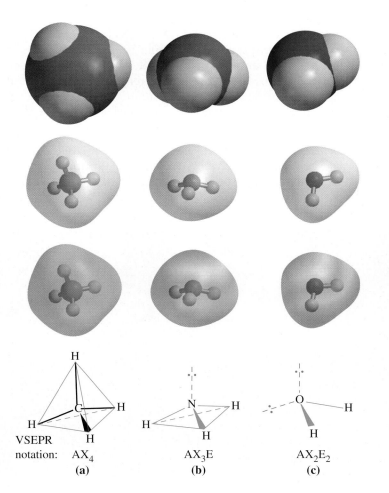

◀ **FIGURE 10-11**
Molecular shapes based on tetrahedral electron-group geometry of CH_4, NH_3, and H_2O
Molecular shapes are established by the blue lines. Lone-pair electrons are shown as red dots along broken lines originating at the central atom. **(a)** All electron groups around the central atom are bond pairs. The blue lines that outline the molecule are different from the black lines representing the carbon-to-hydrogen bonds. **(b)** The lone pair of electrons is directed to the "missing" corner of the tetrahedron. The nitrogen-to-hydrogen bonds form three of the edges of a trigonal pyramid. **(c)** The H_2O molecule is a bent molecule outlined by the two oxygen-to-hydrogen bonds.

▶ VSEPR theory works best for second-period elements. The predicted bond angle of 109.5° for H_2O is close to the measured angle of 104.5°. For H_2S, however, the predicted value of 109.5° is not in good agreement with the observed 92°.

In the VSEPR notation used in Figure 10-11, A is the central atom, X is a terminal atom or group of atoms bonded to the central atom, and E is a lone pair of electrons. Thus, the symbol AX_2E_2 signifies that *two* atoms or groups (X) are bonded to the central atom (A). The central atom also has *two* lone pairs of electrons (E). H_2O is an example of a molecule of the AX_2E_2 type.

For tetrahedral electron-group geometry, we expect bond angles of 109.5°, known as the *tetrahedral* bond angle. In the CH_4 molecule, the measured bond angles are, in fact, 109.5°. The bond angles in NH_3 and H_2O are slightly smaller: 107° for the H—N—H bond angle and 104.5° for the H—O—H bond angle. We can explain these less-than-tetrahedral bond angles by the fact that the charge cloud of the lone-pair electrons spreads out. This forces the bond-pair electrons closer together and reduces the bond angles.

POSSIBILITIES FOR ELECTRON-GROUP DISTRIBUTIONS

The most common situations are those in which central atoms have two, three, four, five, or six electron groups distributed around them.

Electron-group geometries

- two electron groups: linear
- three electron groups: trigonal-planar
- four electron groups: tetrahedral
- five electron groups: trigonal-bipyramidal
- six electron groups: octahedral

Figure 10-12 extends the balloon analogy to these cases. The cases for five- and six-electron groups are typified by PCl_5 and SF_6, molecules with expanded valence shells.

The molecular geometry is the same as the electron-group geometry *only* when all electron groups are bond pairs. These are for the VSEPR notation AX_n (that is, AX_2, AX_3, AX_4, and so on). In Table 10.1, the AX_n cases are illustrated by photographs of ball-and-stick models. If one or more electron groups are lone pairs, the molecular geometry is different from the electron-group geometry, although still derived from it. The relationship between electron-group geometry and molecular geometry is summarized in Table 10.1. To understand all the cases in Table 10.1, we need two more ideas.

- *The closer together two groups of electrons are forced, the stronger the repulsion between them.* The repulsion between two electron groups is much stronger at an angle of 90° than at 120° or 180°.

▶ **FIGURE 10-12**
Several electron-group geometries illustrated
The electron-group geometries pictured are trigonal-planar (orange), tetrahedral (gray), trigonal-bipyramidal (pink), and octahedral (yellow). The atoms at the ends of the balloons are not shown and are not important in this model.

TABLE 10.1 Molecular Geometry as a Function of Electron-Group Geometry

Number of Electron Groups	Electron-Group Geometry	Number of Lone Pairs	VSEPR Notation	Molecular Geometry	Ideal Bond Angles	Example
2	linear	0	AX_2	$X-A-X$ (linear)	180°	$BeCl_2$
3	trigonal-planar	0	AX_3	(trigonal planar)	120°	BF_3
	trigonal-planar	1	AX_2E	(bent)	120°	SO_2[a]
4	tetrahedral	0	AX_4	(tetrahedral)	109.5°	CH_4
	tetrahedral	1	AX_3E	(trigonal-pyramidal)	109.5°	NH_3
	tetrahedral	2	AX_2E_2	(bent)	109.5°	OH_2
5	trigonal-bipyramidal	0	AX_5	(trigonal-bipyramidal)	90°, 120°	PCl_5

VSEPR: Basic Molecular Configurations models

(continues)

TABLE 10.1 (Continued)

Number of Electron Groups	Electron-Group Geometry	Number of Lone Pairs	VSEPR Notation	Molecular Geometry	Ideal Bond Angles	Example
	trigonal-bipyramidal	1	AX_4E^b	(seesaw)	90°, 120°	SF_4
	trigonal-bipyramidal	2	AX_3E_2	(T-shaped)	90°	ClF_3
	trigonal-bipyramidal	3	AX_2E_3	(linear)	180°	XeF_2
6	octahedral	0	AX_6	(octahedral)	90°	SF_6
	octahedral	1	AX_5E	(square-pyramidal))	90°	BrF_5
	octahedral	2	AX_4E_2	(square-planar)	90°	XeF_4

[a] For a discussion of the structure of SO_2, see page 402.

[b] For a discussion of the placement of the lone-pair electrons in this structure, see page 401.

- *Lone-pair electrons spread out more than do bond-pair electrons.* As a result, the repulsion of one lone pair of electrons for another lone pair is greater than, say, between two bond pairs. The order of repulsive forces, from strongest to weakest, is:

lone pair–lone pair > lone pair–bond pair > bond pair–bond pair

Consider SF_4, with the VSEPR notation AX_4E. Two possibilities for its structure are presented in the margin, but only one is correct. The correct structure (top) places a lone pair of electrons in the central plane of the bipyramid. As a result, *two* lone pair–bond pair interactions are 90°. In the incorrect structure (bottom), the lone pair of electrons is at the bottom of the bipyramid and results in *three* lone pair–bond pair interactions of 90°. This is a less favorable arrangement.

APPLYING VSEPR THEORY

The following four-step strategy can be used for predicting the shapes of molecules.

1. Draw a plausible Lewis structure of the species (molecule or polyatomic ion).
2. Determine the number of electron groups around the central atom, and identify them as being either *bond-pair* electron groups or *lone pairs* of electrons.
3. Establish the electron-group geometry around the central atom—linear, trigonal-planar, tetrahedral, trigonal-bipyramidal, or octahedral.
4. Determine the molecular geometry from the positions around the central atom occupied by the other atomic nuclei—that is, from data in Table 10.1.

EXAMPLE 10-10

Using VSEPR Theory to Predict a Geometric Shape. Predict the molecular geometry of the polyatomic anion ICl_4^-:

Solution

Apply the four steps outlined above.

Step 1. Write the Lewis structure. The number of valence electrons is

From I	From Cl	To establish ionic charge of −1	
(1×7)	(4×7) +	1	= 36

To join 4 Cl atoms to the central I atom and to provide octets for all the atoms, we need 32 electrons. In order to account for all 36 valence electrons, we need to place an *additional* four electrons around the I atom as lone pairs. That is, we are forced to expand the valence shell of the I atom to accommodate all the electrons required in the Lewis structure.

$$\left[\begin{array}{cc} :\ddot{C}l: & :\ddot{C}l: \\ & :\ddot{I}: \\ :\ddot{C}l: & :\ddot{C}l: \end{array} \right]^-$$

Step 2. There are six electron groups around the I atom, four *bond pairs* and two *lone pairs*.

Step 3. The electron-group geometry (the orientation of six electron groups) is *octahedral*.

Step 4. The ICl_4^- anion is of the type AX_4E_2, which according to Table 10.1, leads to a molecular geometry that is square-planar.

Figure 10-13 suggests two possibilities for distributing bond pairs and lone pairs in ICl_4^-. The square-planar structure is correct because the lone pair–lone pair interaction is kept at 180°. In the incorrect structure, this interaction is at 90°, which results in a strong repulsion.

(Incorrect)

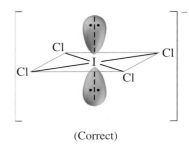

(Correct)

▲ **FIGURE 10-13**
Example 10-10 illustrated
The observed structure of ICl_4^- is square-planar.

◄ **KEEP IN MIND**
that we need to expand a valence shell only if more than eight electrons must be accommodated by the central atom in a Lewis structure. This leads to structures based on five or six electron groups. Otherwise, octet-based Lewis structures are perfectly satisfactory when applying the VSEPR theory.

Practice Example A: Predict the molecular geometry of nitrogen trichloride.

Practice Example B: Predict the molecular geometry of phosphoryl chloride, $POCl_3$, an important chemical in the manufacture of gasoline additives, hydraulic fluids, and fire retardants.

CONCEPT ASSESSMENT ✓

The ions ICl_2^- and ICl_2^+ differ by only two electrons. Would you expect them to have the same geometric shape? Explain.

STRUCTURES WITH MULTIPLE COVALENT BONDS

In a multiple covalent bond, all electrons in the bond are confined to the region between the bonded atoms, and together constitute one group of electrons. Let us test this idea by predicting the molecular geometry of sulfur dioxide. S is the central atom, and the total number of valence electrons is $3 \times 6 = 18$. The Lewis structure is the resonance hybrid of the two contributing structures in the margin.

It is immaterial which structure we use. In either case, we count the electrons in the double covalent bond as one group. This bond and the sulfur-to-oxygen single bond account for two electron groups. The third electron group around the central S atom is a lone pair of electrons. The electron-group geometry around the central S atom is that of *three* electron groups—*trigonal-planar*. Of the three electron groups, two are bonding groups and one is a lone pair. This is the case of AX_2E (see Table 10.1). The molecular shape is *angular,* or *bent*, with an expected bond angle of 120°. (The measured bond angle in SO_2 is 119°.)

 The need for resonance structures is an obvious failing of the Lewis structures. Note that the more valid resonance structures that exist, the more stable the actual structure is.

EXAMPLE 10-11

Using VSEPR Theory to Predict the Shape of a Molecule with a Multiple Covalent Bond. Predict the molecular geometry of formaldehyde, H_2CO, used to make a number of polymers, such as melamine resins.

Solution

The Lewis structure in the margin has a total of 12 valence electrons and C as the central atom. If all the bonds to the carbon atom were single bonds, C would lack an octet. This deficiency is corrected by moving a lone pair of electrons from the O atom into the carbon-to-oxygen bond, making it a double bond.

There are three electron groups around the C atom, two groups in the carbon-to-hydrogen single bonds and the third group in the carbon-to-oxygen double bond. The electron-group geometry for three electron groups is *trigonal-planar*. Because all the electron groups are involved in bonding, the VSEPR notation for this molecule is AX_3. The molecular geometry is also trigonal-planar.

Practice Example A: Predict the shape of the COS molecule.

Practice Example B: Nitrous oxide, N_2O, is the familiar laughing gas used as an anesthetic in dentistry. Predict the shape of the N_2O molecule.

MOLECULES WITH MORE THAN ONE CENTRAL ATOM

Although many of the structures of interest to us have only one central atom, VSEPR theory can also be applied to molecules or polyatomic anions with more than one central atom. In such cases, the geometric distribution of terminal atoms around *each* central atom must be determined and the results then combined into a single description of the molecular shape. We use this idea in Example 10-12.

EXAMPLE 10-12

Applying VSEPR Theory to a Molecule with More Than One Central Atom. Methyl isocyanate, CH_3NCO, is used in the manufacture of insecticides, such as carbaryl (Sevin). In the CH_3NCO molecule, the three H atoms and the O atom are terminal atoms and the two C and one N atom are central atoms. Sketch this molecule.

Solution

To apply the VSEPR method, let us begin with a plausible Lewis structure. The number of valence electrons in the structure is

From C	From N	From O	From H
(2×4)	(1×5)	(1×6)	$(3 \times 1) = 22$

In drawing the skeletal structure and assigning valence electrons, we first obtain a structure with incomplete octets. By shifting the indicated electrons, we can give each atom an octet.

$$H-\overset{\overset{\displaystyle H}{|}}{\underset{\underset{\displaystyle H}{|}}{C}}-\ddot{N}-\ddot{C}-\ddot{O}\colon \longrightarrow H-\overset{\overset{\displaystyle H}{|}}{\underset{\underset{\displaystyle H}{|}}{C}}-\ddot{N}=C=\ddot{O}\colon$$

The C atom on the left has four electron groups around it—all bond pairs. The shape of this end of the molecule is *tetrahedral*. The C atom to the right, by forming two double bonds, is treated as having two groups of electrons around it. This distribution is *linear*. For the N atom, three groups of electrons are distributed in a *trigonal-planar* manner. The $C-N-C$ bond angle should be about 120°.

$$\begin{array}{c}
180°\quad\ddot{O}\colon \\
\diagup\!\!\diagup C \\
\vdots N \\
|\,\diagdown 120° \\
C \\
H\,\diagup\diagdown H \\
H\quad 109°
\end{array}$$

Practice Example A: Sketch the methanol molecule, CH_3OH. Indicate the bond angles in this molecule.

Practice Example B: Glycine, an amino acid, has the formula H_2NCH_2COOH. Sketch the glycine molecule, and indicate the various bond angles.

MOLECULAR SHAPES AND DIPOLE MOMENTS

Let us recall some facts that we learned about polar covalent bonds in Section 10-3. In the HCl molecule, the Cl atom is more electronegative than the H atom. Electrons are displaced toward the Cl atom, as clearly shown in the electrostatic potential map in the margin. The HCl molecule is a **polar molecule**. In the representation below, we use a cross-base arrow ($\longleftrightarrow$) that points to the atom that attracts electrons more strongly.

$$^{\delta+}H \longleftrightarrow Cl^{\delta-}$$

The extent of the charge displacement in a polar covalent bond is given by the **dipole moment**, μ. The dipole moment is the product of a partial charge (δ) and distance (d).

$$\mu = \delta \times d \tag{10.25}$$

If the product, $\delta \times d$, has a value of 3.34×10^{-30} coulomb·meter (C·m), the dipole moment, μ, has a value called 1 *debye*, D. One experimental method of determining dipole moments is based on the behavior of polar molecules in an electric field, suggested in Figure 10-14.

Molecular Polarity activity

The students may have studied vectors. Use of vectors is a good way to show that a molecule has or does not have a dipole moment.

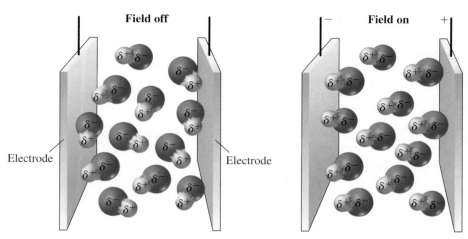

▲ **FIGURE 10-14**
Polar molecules in an electric field
The device pictured is called an electrical condenser (or capacitor). It consists of a pair of electrodes separated by a medium that does not conduct electricity but consists of polar molecules. **(a)** When the field is off, the molecules orient randomly. **(b)** When the electric field is turned on, the polar molecules orient in the field between the charged plates so that the negative ends of the molecules are toward the positive plate and vice versa.

The following article discusses the common difficulties and misconceptions students have about determining the geometries and polarities of molecules and poses some strategies for alleviating these problems: Furio, Carlos and Calatayud, Ma Luisa. *J. Chem. Educ.* **1996**: 73, 36.

The polarity of the H—Cl bond, as demonstrated on page 379, involves a shift of the electron charge density toward the Cl atom, and this produces a separation of the centers of positive and negative charge. Suppose, instead of a shift in electron charge density, we think of an equivalent situation—the transfer of a *fraction* of the charge of an electron from the H atom to the Cl atom through the entire internuclear distance. Let us determine the magnitude of this partial charge, δ. To do this, we need the measured dipole moment, 1.03 D; the H—Cl bond length, 127.4 pm; and equation (10.25) rearranged to

$$\delta = \frac{\mu}{d} = \frac{1.03 \text{ D} \times 3.34 \times 10^{-30} \text{ C} \cdot \text{m/D}}{127.4 \times 10^{-12} \text{ m}} = 2.70 \times 10^{-20} \text{ C}$$

This charge is about 17% of the charge on an electron (1.602×10^{-19} C) and suggests that HCl is about 17% ionic. This assessment of the percent ionic character of the H—Cl bond agrees well with the 20% we made based on electronegativity differences (recall Example 10-4).

CO₂. Carbon dioxide molecules are *nonpolar*. To understand this observation, we need to distinguish between the displacement of electron charge density in a particular bond and in the molecule as a whole. The electronegativity difference between C and O causes a displacement of electron charge density toward the O atom in each carbon-to-oxygen bond and gives rise to a *bond dipole*. However, because the two bond dipoles are equal in magnitude and point in opposite directions, they cancel each other and lead to a *resultant* dipole moment of zero for the molecule. The symmetrical nature of the electron charge density is clear in the electrostatic potential map for CO_2 in the margin.

▲ Electrostatic potential map of carbon dioxide

$$\overset{\longleftarrow \: + \: \longrightarrow}{\text{O}-\text{C}-\text{O}} \qquad \mu = 0$$

The fact that CO_2 is nonpolar is experimental proof that the three atoms in the molecule lie along a straight line in the order O—C—O. Of course, we can also predict that CO_2 is a linear molecule with the VSEPR theory, based on the Lewis structure

$$:\ddot{O}=C=\ddot{O}:$$

H₂O. Water molecules are *polar*. They have bond dipoles because of the electronegativity difference between H and O, and the bond dipoles combine to produce a resultant dipole moment of 1.84 D. The electrostatic potential map for water provides visual evidence of a net dipole moment on the water molecule. The molecule cannot be linear, for this would lead to a cancellation of bond dipoles, just as with CO_2. We have predicted with the VSEPR theory that the H_2O molecule is bent, and the observation that it is a polar molecule simply confirms the prediction.

▲ Electrostatic potential map of water

CCl₄. Carbon tetrachloride molecules are *nonpolar*. Based on the electronegativity difference between Cl and C, we expect a bond dipole for the C—Cl bond. The fact that the resultant dipole moment is *zero* means that the bond dipoles must be oriented in such a way that they cancel. The tetrahedral molecular geometry of CCl_4 provides the symmetrical distribution of bond dipoles that leads to this cancellation, as shown in Figure 10-15(a). Can you see that the molecule will be polar if one of the Cl atoms is replaced by an atom with a different electronegativity, say H? In the molecule, $CHCl_3$, there is a resultant dipole moment (Fig. 10-15b).

◀ **KEEP IN MIND**

that the lack of a molecular dipole moment cannot distinguish between the two possible molecular geometries: tetrahedral and square-planar. To do this, other experimental evidence, such as X-ray diffraction, is required.

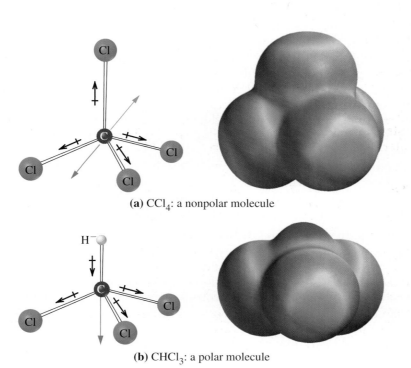

(a) CCl_4: a nonpolar molecule

(b) $CHCl_3$: a polar molecule

◀ **FIGURE 10-15**
Molecular shapes and dipole moments
(a) The resultant of two of the C—Cl bond dipoles is shown as a red arrow, and that of the other two, as a blue arrow. The red and blue arrows point in opposite directions and cancel. The CCl_4 molecule is nonpolar. The balance of the charge distribution in CCl_4 is clearly seen in the electrostatic potential map. **(b)** The individual bond dipoles do combine to yield a resultant dipole moment (red arrow) of 1.04 D. The electrostatic potential map indicates that the hydrogen atom has a partial positive charge.

EXAMPLE 10-13

Determining the Relationship Between Geometric Shapes and the Resultant Dipole Moments of Molecules. Which of these molecules would you expect to be polar: Cl_2, ICl, BF_3, NO, SO_2?

Solution

Polar: ICl, NO, SO_2. ICl and NO are diatomic molecules with an electronegativity difference between the bonded atoms. SO_2 is a bent molecule with an electronegativity difference between the S and O atoms.

Nonpolar: Cl_2 and BF_3. Cl_2 is a diatomic molecule of identical atoms; hence no electronegativity difference. For BF_3, refer to Table 10.1. BF_3 is a symmetrical planar molecule (120° bond angles). The B—F bond dipoles cancel each other.

Practice Example A: Only one of the following molecules is polar. Which is it, and why? SF_6, H_2O_2, C_2H_4.

Practice Example B: Only one of the following molecules is *nonpolar*. Which is it, and why? Cl_3CCH_3, PCl_5, CH_2Cl_2, NH_3.

CONCEPT ASSESSMENT ✓

The molecule NH_3 has the dipole moment $\mu = 1.47$ D, whereas for the similar molecule NF_3, $\mu = 0.24$ D. Why do you suppose there is such a large difference in these two values?

[*Hint:* What is the effect of the lone-pair electrons on the N atom?]

10-8 BOND ORDER AND BOND LENGTHS

The term **bond order** describes whether a covalent bond is *single* (bond order = 1), *double* (bond order = 2), or *triple* (bond order = 3). Think of electrons as the "glue" that binds atoms together in covalent bonds. The higher the bond order—that is, the more electrons present—the more glue and the more tightly the atoms are held together.

Bond length is the distance between the centers of two atoms joined by a covalent bond. A double bond between atoms is shorter than a single bond, and a triple bond is shorter still. You can see this relationship clearly in Table 10.2 by comparing the three different bond lengths for the nitrogen-to-nitrogen bond. For example, the measured length of the nitrogen-to-nitrogen triple bond in N_2 is 109.8 pm, whereas the nitrogen-to-nitrogen single bond in hydrazine, H_2N—NH_2, is 147 pm.

Perhaps you can now also better understand the meaning of covalent radius that we introduced in Section 9-3. The single covalent radius is one-half the distance between the centers of identical atoms joined by a *single* covalent bond. Thus, the single covalent radius of chlorine in Figure 9-8 (99 pm) is one-half the bond length given in Table 10.2, that is, $\frac{1}{2} \times 199$ pm. Furthermore, as a rough generalization,

> the length of the covalent bond between two atoms can be approximated as the sum of the covalent radii of the two atoms.

Some of these ideas about bond length are applied in Example 10-14.

It is a good idea to relate bond order and bond energies to thermodynamics. It is also important to remember that these bond orders depend upon the localized bond model and resonance cannot be accounted for with the energies in Table 10.3.

TABLE 10.2   Some Average Bond Lengths[a]

Bond	Bond Length, pm	Bond	Bond Length, pm	Bond	Bond Length, pm
H—H	74.14	C—C	154	N—N	145
H—C	110	C=C	134	N=N	123
H—N	100	C≡C	120	N≡N	109.8
H—O	97	C—N	147	N—O	136
H—S	132	C=N	128	N=O	120
H—F	91.7	C≡N	116	O—O	145
H—Cl	127.4	C—O	143	O=O	121
H—Br	141.4	C=O	120	F—F	143
H—I	160.9	C—Cl	178	Cl—Cl	199
				Br—Br	228
				I—I	266

[a]Most values (C—H, N—H, C—H, and so on) are averaged over a number of species containing the indicated bond and may vary by a few picometers. Where a diatomic molecule exists, the value given is the actual bond length in that molecule (H_2, N_2, HF, and so on) and is known more precisely.

EXAMPLE 10-14

Estimating Bond Lengths. Provide the best estimate you can of these bond lengths for the **(a)** the nitrogen-to-hydrogen bonds in NH_3; **(b)** the bromine-to-chlorine bond in BrCl.

Solution

(a) The Lewis structure of ammonia (page 376) shows the nitrogen-to-hydrogen bonds as single bonds. The value listed in Table 10.2 for the N—H bond is 100 pm, so this is the value we would predict. (The measured N—H bond length in NH_3 is 101.7 pm.)

(b) There is no bromine-to-chlorine bond length in Table 10.2 , so we need to calculate an approximate bond length using the relationship between bond length and covalent radii. BrCl contains a Br—Cl *single* bond [imagine substituting one Br atom for one Cl atom in structure (10.4)]. The length of the Br—Cl bond is one-half the Cl—Cl bond length *plus* one-half the Br—Br bond length: $\left(\frac{1}{2} \times 199 \text{ pm}\right) + \left(\frac{1}{2} \times 288 \text{ pm}\right) =$ 214 pm. (The measured bond length is 213.8 pm.)

Practice Example A: Estimate the bond lengths of the carbon-to-hydrogen bonds and the carbon-to-bromine bond in CH_3Br.

Practice Example B: In the thiocyanate ion, SCN^-, the length of the carbon-to-nitrogen bond is 115 pm. Write a plausible Lewis structure for this ion and describe its geometric shape.

CONCEPT ASSESSMENT ✓

NO_2^- and NO_2^+ are made up of the same atoms. How would you expect the nitrogen-to-oxygen bond lengths in these two ions to compare?

10-9 BOND ENERGIES

435.93 kJ/mol

H⁀H

498.7 kJ/mol

H⁀O—H

428.0 kJ/mol

O⁀H

▲ **FIGURE 10-16**
Some bond energies compared
The same quantity of energy, 435.93 kJ/mol, is required to break all H—H bonds. In H_2O, more energy is required to break the first bond (498.7 kJ/mol) than to break the second (428.0 kJ/mol). The second bond broken is that in the OH radical. The O—H bond energy in H_2O is the average of the two values: 463.4 kJ/mol.

KEEP IN MIND ▶
that tabulated bond energies are for isolated molecules in the gaseous state. They do not apply to molecules in close contact in liquids and solids.

Together with bond lengths, bond energies can be used to assess the suitability of a proposed Lewis structure. Bond energy, bond length, and bond order are interrelated properties in this sense: the higher the bond order, the shorter the bond between two atoms and the greater the bond energy.

Energy is *released* when isolated atoms join to form a covalent bond, and energy must be *absorbed* to break apart covalently bonded atoms. **Bond-dissociation energy**, D, is the quantity of energy required to break one mole of covalent bonds in a *gaseous* species. The SI units are kilojoules per mole of bonds (kJ/mol).

In the manner of Chapter 7, we can think of bond-dissociation energy as an enthalpy change or a heat of reaction. For example,

Bond breakage: $\quad H_2(g) \longrightarrow 2\,H(g) \qquad \Delta H = D(H—H) = +435.93$ kJ/mol

Bond formation: $\quad 2\,H(g) \longrightarrow H_2(g) \qquad \Delta H = -D(H—H) = -435.93$ kJ/mol

It is not hard to picture the meaning of bond energy for a diatomic molecule, because there is only one bond in the molecule. It is also not difficult to see that the bond-dissociation energy of a diatomic molecule can be expressed rather precisely, as is that of $H_2(g)$. With a polyatomic molecule such as H_2O, the situation is different (Fig. 10-16). The energy needed to dissociate one mole of H atoms by breaking one O—H bond per H_2O molecule

$$H—OH(g) \longrightarrow H(g) + OH(g) \qquad \Delta H = D(H—OH) = +498.7 \text{ kJ/mol}$$

is different from the energy required to dissociate one mole of H atoms by breaking the bonds in OH(g).

$$O—H(g) \longrightarrow H(g) + O(g) \qquad \Delta H = D(O—H) = +428.0 \text{ kJ/mol}$$

The two O—H bonds in H_2O are identical; therefore, they should have identical energies. This energy, which we can call the O—H bond energy in H_2O, is the *average* of the two values listed above: 463.4 kJ/mol. The O—H bond energy in other molecules containing the OH group will be somewhat different from that in H—O—H. For example, in methanol, CH_3OH, the O—H bond-dissociation energy, which we can represent as $D(H—OCH_3)$, is 436.8 kJ/mol. The usual method of tabulating bond energies (Table 10.3) is as *averages*. An **average bond energy** is the average of bond-dissociation energies for a number of different species containing the particular bond. Understandably, average bond energies cannot be stated as precisely as specific bond-dissociation energies.

As you can see from Table 10.3, double bonds have higher bond energies than do single bonds between the same atoms, but they are *not* twice as large. Triple bonds are stronger still, but their bond energies are *not* three times as large as single bonds between the same atoms. This observation about bond order and bond energy will seem quite reasonable after multiple bonds are more fully described in the next chapter.

Bond energies also have some interesting uses in thermochemistry. For a reaction involving *gases*, visualize the process

$$\text{gaseous reactants} \longrightarrow \text{gaseous atoms} \longrightarrow \text{gaseous products}$$

In this hypothetical process, we first break all the bonds in reactant molecules and form gaseous atoms. For this step, the enthalpy change is ΔH (bond breakage) = ΣBE (reactants), where BE stands for bond energy. Next, we allow the gaseous atoms to recombine into product molecules. In this step, bonds are formed and ΔH (bond formation) = $-\Sigma$BE (products). The enthalpy change of the reaction, then, is

$$\Delta H_{rxn} = \Delta H \text{ (bond breakage)} + \Delta H \text{ (bond formation)}$$

$$\approx \Sigma\text{BE (reactants)} - \Sigma\text{BE (products)}$$

(10.26)

TABLE 10.3   Some Average Bond Energies[a]

Bond	Bond Energy, kJ/mol	Bond	Bond Energy kJ/mol	Bond	Bond Energy kJ/mol
H—H	436	C—C	347	N—N	163
H—C	414	C=C	611	N=N	418
H—N	389	C≡C	837	N≡N	946
H—O	464	C—N	305	N—O	222
H—S	368	C=N	615	N=O	590
H—F	565	C≡N	891	O—O	142
H—Cl	431	C—O	360	O=O	498
H—Br	364	C=O	736[b]	F—F	159
H—I	297	C—Cl	339	Cl—Cl	243
				Br—Br	193
				I—I	151

[a] Although all data are listed with about the same precision (three significant figures), some values are actually known more precisely. Specifically, the values for the diatomic molecules H_2, HF, HCl, HBr, HI, N_2 (N≡N), O_2 (O=O), F_2, Cl_2, Br_2, and I_2 are actually bond-dissociation energies, rather than average bond energies.
[b] The value for the C=O bonds in CO_2 is 799 kJ/mol.

The approximately equal sign ($\approx$) in expression (10.26) signifies that some of the bond energies used are likely to be *average* bond energies rather than true bond-dissociation energies. Also, a number of terms often cancel out because some of the same types of bonds appear in the products as in the reactants. We can base the calculation of ΔH_{rxn} just on the *net* number and types of bonds broken and formed, as illustrated in Example 10-15.

> Calculate the bond energy of benzene based upon a localized bond model of six H—C bonds, three C—C bonds, and three C=C bonds. Compare the value with the experimental heat of formation and find that the localized bond model calculation, using Table 10.3, gives a value that is about 150 kJ mol^{-1} less than the experimental value. The difference is due to resonance stability.

EXAMPLE 10-15

Calculating an Enthalpy of Reaction from Bond Energies. The reaction of methane (CH_4) and chlorine produces a mixture of products called chloromethanes. One of these is monochloromethane, CH_3Cl, used in the preparation of silicones. Calculate ΔH for the reaction

$$CH_4(g) + Cl_2(g) \longrightarrow CH_3Cl(g) + HCl(g)$$

Solution

To assess which bonds are broken and formed, it helps to draw structural formulas (or Lewis structures), as in Figure 10-17. To apply expression (10.26) literally, we would break *four* C—H bonds and *one* Cl—Cl bond and form *three* C—H bonds, *one* C—Cl bond, and *one* H—Cl bond. The *net* change, however, is the breaking of *one* C—H bond and *one* Cl—Cl bond, followed by the formation of *one* C—Cl bond and *one* H—Cl bond.

> Point out this only works for the localized bond model, and predicting if a reaction is exothermic or endothermic for resonance structures cannot be done using bond energies.

ΔH *for net bond breakage:*

1 mol C—H bonds	+414 kJ
1 mol Cl—Cl bonds	+243 kJ
sum:	+657 kJ

ΔH *for net bond formation:*

1 mol C—Cl bonds	−339 kJ
1 mol H—Cl bonds	−431 kJ
sum:	−770 kJ

Enthalpy of reaction: $\Delta H_{rxn} = 657 - 770 = -113$ kJ

Enthalpy of Reaction activity

Practice Example A: Use bond energies to estimate the enthalpy change for the reaction

$$2 H_2(g) + O_2(g) \longrightarrow 2 H_2O(g)$$

Practice Example B: Use bond energies to estimate the enthalpy of formation of $NH_3(g)$.

▲ Radiotelescopes detect the emission spectra of rotationally excited molecules in clouds in interstellar space.

We have described how bond lengths contribute to our knowledge of molecular structure (Section 10-8), but how can bond lengths be measured? One method makes use of the interaction of electromagnetic radiation with the oscillating electric field produced by a rotating polar molecule in the gas phase.

Consider polar diatomic molecules such as HF. In the gas phase the molecules rotate about (1) an axis coinciding with the internuclear axis and (2) an axis perpendicular to the internuclear axis. It is this second rotation that creates the oscillating electric field that interacts with incoming radiation; some energy is absorbed from the radiation and this energy increases the rotational energy of the molecules. The rotational motion of a diatomic molecule is quantized, and the quantum mechanical rotational energy levels for the molecule are given by

$$E_{rot} = \frac{1}{2I}\left\{\frac{(J(J+1))h^2}{4\pi^2}\right\} \qquad (10.27)$$

where E_{rot} is the rotational energy; J is the rotational quantum number, which can have the values $J = 0, 1, 2, 3$, and so on; and I is the moment of inertia for rotation about the axis interacting with the electromagnetic radiation. The role of the moment of inertia in rotational motion is equivalent to that of simple mass in translational motion; its value is given by

$$I = \left(\frac{m_1 m_2}{m_1 + m_2}\right)r_0^2 \qquad (10.28)$$

where m_1 and m_2 are the masses of the atoms in the diatomic molecule and r_0 is the internuclear separation between the atoms, that is, the bond length.

The rotational energy given by equation (10.27) has the unit joule. However, rotational spectra are usually displayed in the unit favored by spectroscopists—cm^{-1}. At first glance, it is not obvious that the unit cm^{-1} is related to an energy unit. Let us briefly show that it is. Consider Planck's equation, $E = h\nu$. The unit of Planck's constant, h, is J s; that of radiation frequency, ν, is s^{-1}. Thus the unit of E is J s s^{-1} = J. Now suppose we replace the value of ν by its equivalent, c/λ. Then we have $E = hc/\lambda$, and $E/hc = 1/\lambda$. So, we see that the reciprocal of the wavelength is proportional to the energy in joules, with the proportionality constant being $1/hc$. If we express $1/\lambda$ in m^{-1}, we use $c = 2.998 \times 10^8$ m s^{-1}; but if $1/\lambda$ is in cm^{-1}, then $c = 2.998 \times 10^{10}$ cm s^{-1}. Thus, to convert equation (10.27) in the unit joule to an equation in the unit cm^{-1}, we must divide both sides of the equation by hc, as shown below.

$$E_{rot} = \frac{1}{2I}\left\{\frac{(J(J+1))h^2}{4\pi^2}\right\} \quad \text{(in J)}$$

$$\frac{E_{rot}}{hc} = \varepsilon_J = \frac{h}{8\pi^2 cI}\left(J(J+1)\right) \quad \text{(in cm}^{-1}) \qquad (10.29)$$

The various constants and the moment of inertia are combined into a single constant, the rotational constant B. We can therefore write

$$\varepsilon_J = B\left(J(J+1)\right) \quad \text{(in cm}^{-1}),$$

$$\text{where } B = \frac{h}{8\pi^2 cI} \quad \text{(in cm}^{-1}) \qquad (10.30)$$

414 kJ/mol   243 kJ/mol   −339 kJ/mol   −431 kJ/mol

$$\underset{\overset{|}{H}}{\overset{\overset{H}{|}}{H-C-H}} + Cl-Cl \longrightarrow \underset{\overset{|}{H}}{\overset{\overset{H}{|}}{H-C-Cl}} + H-Cl$$

▲ **FIGURE 10-17**
Net bond breakage and formation in a chemical reaction—Example 10-15 illustrated
Bonds that are broken are shown in red and bonds that are formed, in blue. Bonds that remain unchanged are black. The net change is that *one* C—H and *one* Cl—Cl bond break and *one* C—Cl and *one* H—Cl bond form.

With equation (10.30) we can calculate an energy level diagram (Fig. 10-18), in which is also displayed the expected rotational spectrum for a molecule in the gas phase. A molecule can increase its rotational energy if the incident radiation exactly fits the change in rotational energy that accompanies a change of rotational quantum number of one, that is $\Delta J = 1$. This gives

$$\Delta\varepsilon = B \times 2(J_i + 1) \qquad J_i = 0, 1, 2, 3, \ldots$$

where J_i is the initial rotational energy level. This relationship means that transitions from successive energy levels to the levels above them are associated with energy changes that have steadily increasing values with an increment of $2B$. Thus, the spacing between lines in the rotational spectrum can be measured and the internuclear separation calculated, yielding an experimental determination of the bond length r_0 from equation (10.31).

$$I = \left(\frac{m_1 m_2}{m_1 + m_2}\right)r_0^2 = \frac{h}{8\pi^2 cB} \quad \text{(in J s}^2 = \text{kg m}^2\text{)} \quad (10.31)$$

with the masses of atoms expressed in kilograms.

We have just shown how rotational spectra can be used to determine bond lengths. However, rotational spectra also play an important role in molecular astrophysics and radio astronomy. The wavelength of the electromagnetic radiation absorbed in rotational spectroscopy is in the 3 mm to 30 cm range, which is the microwave region of the electromagnetic spectrum. In radio astronomy the observed emission lines are from the de-excitation of excited molecules in interstellar clouds. Molecules such as HCl, NaCl, PN, and CS have been detected by combining an analysis of the observed emission lines with a knowledge of pure rotational spectra observed in the laboratory on Earth.

◀ **FIGURE 10-18**
Rotational energy levels of a diatomic molecule

There is no advantage to using bond energies over enthalpy-of-formation data. Enthalpies of formation are generally known rather precisely, whereas bond energies are only average values. But when enthalpy-of-formation data are lacking, bond energies can prove particularly useful.

Another way to use bond energies is in predicting whether a reaction will be *endothermic* or *exothermic*. In general, if

weak bonds ⟶ strong bonds $\Delta H < 0$ (exothermic)
(reactants)   (products)

and

strong bonds ⟶ weak bonds $\Delta H > 0$ (endothermic)
(reactants)   (products)

Example 10-16 applies this idea to a reaction involving highly reactive, unstable species for which enthalpies of formation are not normally listed.

EXAMPLE 10-16

Using Bond Energies to Predict Exothermic and Endothermic Reactions. One of the steps in the formation of monochloromethane (Example 10-15) is the reaction of a gaseous chlorine *atom* (a chlorine radical) with a molecule of methane. The products are an unstable methyl radical and HCl(g). Is this reaction endothermic or exothermic?

$$CH_4(g) + \cdot Cl(g) \longrightarrow \cdot CH_3(g) + HCl(g)$$

Solution

For every molecule of CH_4 that reacts, *one* C—H bond *breaks*, requiring 414 kJ per mole of bonds; and *one* H—Cl bond *forms*, releasing 431 kJ per mole of bonds. Because more energy is released in forming new bonds than is absorbed in breaking old ones, we predict that the reaction is exothermic.

Practice Example A: One naturally occurring reaction involved in the sequence of reactions leading to the destruction of ozone is $NO_2(g) + O(g) \longrightarrow NO(g) + O_2(g)$. Is this reaction endothermic or exothermic?

Practice Example B: Predict whether the following reaction should be exothermic or endothermic: $H_2O(g) + Cl_2(g) \longrightarrow \frac{1}{2}O_2(g) + 2 HCl(g)$.

Summary

10-1 Lewis Theory: An Overview—A **Lewis symbol** represents the valence electrons of an atom using dots placed around the chemical symbol. A **Lewis structure** is a combination of Lewis symbols used to represent chemical bonding. Normally, all the electrons in a Lewis structure are paired, and each atom in the structure acquires an **octet**—that is, there are eight electrons in the valence shell. The presence of eight electrons in the valence shell is known as the **octet rule**. In **Lewis theory**, chemical bonds are classified as **ionic bonds**, which are formed by electron transfer between atoms, or **covalent bonds**, which are formed by electrons shared between atoms. Most bonds, however, have partial ionic and partial covalent characteristics.

10-2 Covalent Bonding: An Introduction—In covalent bonds, pairs of electrons shared between two atoms to form the bonds are called **bond pairs**, while pairs of electrons not shared in a chemical bond are called **lone pairs**. A single pair of electrons shared between two atoms constitutes a **single covalent bond**. When both electrons in a covalent bond between two atoms are provided by only one of the atoms, the bond is called a **coordinate covalent bond**. To construct a Lewis structure for a molecule in which all atoms obey the octet rule it is often necessary for atoms to share more than one pair of electrons, thus forming **multiple covalent bonds**. Two shared electron pairs constitute a **double covalent bond** and three shared pairs a **triple covalent bond**.

10-3 Polar Covalent Bonds and Electrostatic Potential Maps—A covalent bond in which the electron pair is not shared equally by the bonded atoms is called a **polar covalent bond**. Whether a bond is polar or not can be predicted by comparing the **electronegativity (EN)** of the atoms involved (Fig. 10-6). The greater the **electronegativity**

difference (ΔEN) between two atoms in a chemical bond, the more polar the bond and the more ionic its character. The electron charge distribution in a molecule can be visualized by computing an **electrostatic potential map** (Figs. 10-4 and 10-5). The variation of charge in the molecule is represented by a color spectrum in which red is the most negative and blue the most positive. Electrostatic potential maps are a powerful way of representing electron charge distribution in both polar and nonpolar molecules.

10-4 Writing Lewis Structures—To draw the Lewis structure of a covalent molecule, one needs to know the **skeletal structure**—that is, which is the **central atom** and what atoms are bonded to it. Atoms that are bonded to just one other atom are called **terminal atoms** (structure 10.13). Typically, the atom with the lowest electronegativity is a central atom. At times, the concept of **formal charge** (expression 10.16) is useful in selecting a skeletal structure and assessing the plausibility of a Lewis structure.

10-5 Resonance—Often, more than one plausible Lewis structure can be written for a species; this situation is called **resonance**. In these cases the true structure is a resonance hybrid of two or more contributing structures.

10-6 Exceptions to the Octet Rule—There are often exceptions to the octet rule. (1) Odd-electron species, such as NO, have an unpaired electron and are paramagnetic. Many of these species are reactive molecular fragments, such as OH, called **free radicals**. (2) A few molecules have incomplete octets in their Lewis structures, that is, not enough electrons to provide an octet for every atom. (3) **Expanded valence shells** occur in some compounds of nonmetals of the third period and beyond. In these, the valence shell of the central atom must be expanded to 10 or 12 electrons in order to write a Lewis structure.

10-7 Shapes of Molecules—A powerful method for predicting the **molecular geometry**, or molecular shape, of a species is the **valence-shell electron-pair repulsion theory (VSEPR)**. The shape of a molecule or polyatomic ion depends on the geometric distribution of valence-shell electron groups—the **electron-group geometry**—and whether these groups contain bonding electrons or lone pairs (Fig. 10-11, Table 10.1). The angles between the electron groups provide a method for predicting **bond angles** in a molecule. An important use of information about the shapes of molecules is in establishing whether bonds in a molecule combine to produce a resultant **dipole moment** (Fig. 10-15). Molecules with a resultant dipole moment are **polar molecules**; those with no resultant dipole moment are nonpolar.

10-8 Bond Order and Bond Lengths—Single, double, and triple covalent bonds are said to have a **bond order** of 1, 2 and 3 respectively. **Bond length** is the distance between the centers of two atoms joined by a covalent bond. The greater the bond order, the shorter the bond length (Table 10.2).

10-9 Bond Energies—**Bond-dissociation energy**, D, is the quantity of energy required to break one mole of covalent bonds in a gaseous molecule. **Average bond energies** (Table 10.3) can be used to estimate enthalpy changes for reactions involving gases.

Integrative Example

Nitryl fluoride is a reactive gas useful in rocket propellants. Its mass percent composition is 21.55% N, 49.23% O, and 29.23% F. Its density is 2.7 g/L at 20 °C and 1.00 atm pressure. Describe the nitryl fluoride molecule as completely as possible—that is, its formula, Lewis structure, molecular shape, and polarity.

Strategy
First, determine the empirical formula of nitryl fluoride from the composition data and the molar mass based on that formula. Next, determine the true molar mass from the vapor density data. Now the two results can be compared to establish the molecular formula. Then, write a plausible Lewis structure based on the molecular formula, and apply VSEPR theory to the Lewis structure to predict the molecular shape. Finally, assess the polarity of the molecule from the molecular shape and electronegativity values.

Solution

To determine the empirical formula, use the method of Example 3-5 (page 78). In 100.0 g of the compound,

$$\text{mol N} = 21.55 \text{ g N} \times \frac{1 \text{ mol N}}{14.007 \text{ g N}} = 1.539 \text{ mol N}$$

$$\text{mol O} = 49.23 \text{ g O} \times \frac{1 \text{ mol O}}{15.999 \text{ g O}} = 3.077 \text{ mol O}$$

$$\text{mol F} = 29.23 \text{ g F} \times \frac{1 \text{ mol F}}{18.998 \text{ g F}} = 1.539 \text{ mol F}$$

The empirical formula is

$$N_{1.539}O_{3.077}F_{1.539} = NO_2F$$

The molar mass based on this formula is

$$14 + 32 + 19 = 65 \text{ g/mol}$$

Use the method of Example 6-10 (page 194) to determine the molar mass of the gas.

$$\text{molar mass} = \frac{mRT}{PV} = \frac{dRT}{P}$$

$$= \frac{2.7 \text{ g/L} \times 0.0821 \text{ L atm mol}^{-1} \text{ K}^{-1} \times 293 \text{ K}}{1.00 \text{ atm}}$$

$$= 65 \text{ g/mol}$$

Because the two molar mass results are the same, the molecular and empirical formulas are the same: NO_2F

Because N has the lowest electronegativity, it should be the lone central atom in the Lewis structure. There are two equivalent contributing structures to a resonance hybrid.

Three electron groups around the N atom produce a trigonal-planar electron-group geometry. All the electron groups participate in bonding, so the molecular geometry is also trigonal-planar. The predicted bond angles are 120°. (The experimentally determined F—N—O bond angle is 118°.)

The molecule has a symmetrical shape, but because the electronegativity of F is different from that of O, we should expect the electron charge distribution in the molecule to be nonsymmetrical, leading to a small resultant dipole moment. NO_2F is a polar molecule.

Assessment

In the contributing structures to the resonance hybrid Lewis structure, the F atom has a formal charge of zero and the two O atoms have an average formal charge of $-1/2$. As a result, we might expect the oxygen-atom region of the molecule to be the most negative in electron charge density and the fluorine region to be more neutral. This conclusion is confirmed by the electrostatic potential map for NO_2F. Notice also the positive charge density around the nitrogen nucleus, which is in accord with the fact that the nitrogen is the least electronegative of the three elements.

Exercises

Lewis Theory

1. Write Lewis symbols for the following atoms. **(a)** Kr; **(b)** Ge; **(c)** N; **(d)** Ga; **(e)** As; **(f)** Rb.
2. Write Lewis symbols for the following ions. **(a)** H^-; **(b)** Sn^{2+}; **(c)** K^+; **(d)** Br^-; **(e)** Se^{2-}; **(f)** Sc^{3+}.
3. Write plausible Lewis structures for the following molecules that contain only single covalent bonds. **(a)** ICl; **(b)** Br_2; **(c)** OF_2; **(d)** NI_3; **(e)** H_2Se.
4. Each of the following molecules contains at least one multiple (double or triple) covalent bond. Give a plausible Lewis structure for **(a)** CS_2; **(b)** $(CH_3)_2CO$; **(c)** Cl_2CO; **(d)** FNO.
5. By means of Lewis structures, represent bonding between the following pairs of elements. **(a)** Cs and Br; **(b)** H and Sb; **(c)** B and Cl; **(d)** Cs and Cl; **(e)** Li and O; **(f)** Cl and I. Your structures should show whether the bonding is essentially ionic or covalent.
6. Which of the following have Lewis structures that *do not* obey the octet rule: NH_3, BF_3, SF_6, SO_3, NH_4^+, SO_4^{2-}, NO_2? Explain.
7. Give several examples for which the following statement proves to be incorrect. "All atoms in a Lewis structure have an octet of electrons in their valence shells."
8. Suggest reasons why the following do not exist as stable molecules: **(a)** H_3; **(b)** HHe; **(c)** He_2; **(d)** H_3O.
9. Describe what is wrong with each of the following Lewis structures.

    (a) H—H—N̈—Ö—H

    (b) Ca—Ö:

10. Describe what is wrong with each of the following Lewis structures.

    (a) :Ö—C̈l—Ö:

    (b) [·C̈=N̈:]⁻

11. Only one of the following Lewis structures is correct. Select that one and indicate the errors in the others.

    (a) cyanate ion   [:Ö—C=N̈:]⁻

    (b) carbide ion   [C≡C:]²⁻

    (c) hypochlorite ion   [:C̈l—Ö:]⁻

    (d) nitrogen(II) oxide   :N̈=Ö:

12. Indicate what is wrong with each of the following Lewis structures. Replace each one with a more acceptable structure.

    (a) Mg :Ö:

    (b) [:Ö—N̈=Ö:]⁺

    (c) [:C̈l]⁺[:Ö:]²⁻[C̈l:]⁺

    (d) [:S̈ —C=N̈:]⁻

Ionic Bonding

13. Write Lewis structures for the following ionic compounds: **(a)** calcium chloride; **(b)** barium sulfide; **(c)** lithium oxide; **(d)** sodium fluoride.

14. Under appropriate conditions, both hydrogen and nitrogen can form monatomic anions. What are the Lewis symbols for these ions? What are the Lewis structures of the compounds **(a)** lithium hydride; **(b)** calcium hydride; **(c)** magnesium nitride?

15. Derive the correct formulas for the following ionic compounds by writing Lewis structures. **(a)** lithium sulfide; **(b)** sodium fluoride; **(c)** calcium iodide; **(d)** scandium chloride.

16. Each of the following ionic compounds consists of a combination of monatomic and polyatomic ions. Represent these compounds with Lewis structures. **(a)** $Ca(OH)_2$; **(b)** NH_4Br; **(c)** $Ca(OCl)_2$.

Formal Charge

17. Assign formal charges to each of the atoms in the following structures.

    (a) $[H-C\equiv C\colon]^-$

    (b)

    $$\left[\begin{array}{c} :\ddot{O}: \\ | \\ C \\ \diagup\ \diagdown \\ :\ddot{O}:\quad \ddot{O}: \end{array} \right]^{2-}$$

    (c) $[CH_3-CH-CH_3]^+$

18. Assign formal charges to each of the atoms in the following structures.

    (a) $:\ddot{I}-\ddot{I}:$

    (b)

    $$\ddot{S}$$
    $$\diagup\ \diagdown$$
    $$\cdot\ddot{O}\quad\quad \ddot{O}:$$

    (c)

    $$\dot{N}$$
    $$\diagup\ \diagdown$$
    $$\cdot\ddot{O}\quad\quad \ddot{O}:$$

19. Both oxidation state and formal charge involve conventions for assigning valence electrons to bonded atoms in compounds, but clearly they are not the same. Describe several ways in which these concepts differ.

20. Although the notion that a Lewis structure in which formal charges are zero or held to a minimum seems to apply in most instances, describe several significant situations in which this appears not to be the case.

21. What is the formal charge of the indicated atom in each of the following structures?
    (a) the central O atom in O_3
    (b) B in BF_4^-
    (c) N in NO_3^-
    (d) P in PCl_5
    (e) I in ICl_4^-

22. Assign formal charges to the atoms in the following species, and then select the more likely skeletal structure.
    (a) H_2NOH or H_2ONH
    (b) SCS or CSS
    (c) NFO or FNO
    (d) $SOCl_2$ or $OSCl_2$ or OCl_2S

23. The concept of formal charge helped us to choose the more plausible of the Lewis structures for NO_2^+ given in expressions (10.14) and (10.15). Can it similarly help us to choose a single Lewis structure as most plausible for CO_2H^+? Explain.

24. Show that the idea of minimizing the formal charges in a structure is at times in conflict with the observation that compact, symmetrical structures are more commonly observed than elongated ones with many central atoms. Use ClO_4^- as an illustrative example.

Lewis Structures

25. Write acceptable Lewis structures for the following molecules: **(a)** H_2NOH; **(b)** $HOClO_2$; **(c)** HONO; **(d)** O_2SCl_2.

26. Two molecules that have the same formulas but different structures are said to be isomers. (In isomers, the same atoms are present but linked together in different ways.) Draw acceptable Lewis structures for *two* isomers of S_2F_2.

27. The following polyatomic anions involve covalent bonds between O atoms and the central nonmetal atom. Propose an acceptable Lewis structure for each.
    (a) SO_3^{2-}; **(b)** NO_2^-; **(c)** CO_3^{2-}; **(d)** HO_2^-.

28. Represent the following ionic compounds by Lewis structures. **(a)** barium hydroxide; **(b)** sodium nitrite; **(c)** magnesium iodate; **(d)** aluminum sulfate.

29. Write a plausible Lewis structure for crotonaldehyde, $CH_3CHCHCHO$, a substance used in tear gas and insecticides.

30. Write a plausible Lewis structure for C_3O_2, a substance known as carbon suboxide.

31. Write Lewis structures for the molecules represented by the following molecular models.

(a)

(b)

32. Write Lewis structures for the molecules represented by the following molecular models.

(a)

(b)

33. Write Lewis structures for the molecules represented by the following line-angle formulas. [*Hint:* Recall page 69 and Figure 3-2.]

(a)

(b) HO

34. Write Lewis structures for the molecules represented by the following line-angle formulas. [*Hint:* Recall page 69 and Figure 3-2.]

(a)

(b) Cl   —NH$_2$

Polar Covalent Bonds and Electrostatic Potential Maps

35. Use your knowledge of electronegativities, but *do not* refer to tables or figures in the text, to arrange the following bonds in terms of *increasing* ionic character: C—H, F—H, Na—Cl, Br—H, K—F.

36. Which of the following molecules would you expect to have a resultant dipole moment (μ); (a) F$_2$, (b) NO$_2$, (c) BF$_3$, (d) HBr, (e) H$_2$CCl$_2$, (f) SiF$_4$, (g) OCS? Explain.

37. What is the percent ionic character of each of the following bonds: (a) S—H; (b) O—Cl; (c) Al—O; (d) As—O?

38. Plot the data of Figure 10-6 as a function of atomic number. Does the property of electronegativity conform to the periodic law? Do you think it should?

39. Which electrostatic potential map corresponds to F$_2$C=O, and which to H$_2$C=O?

40. Match the correct electrostatic potential map corresponding to HOCl, FOCl, and HOF.

41. Two electrostatic potential maps are shown, one corresponding to a molecule containing only S and F, the other Si and F. Match them. What are the molecular formulas of the compounds?

42. Two electrostatic potential maps are shown, one corresponding to a molecule containing only Cl and F, the other P and F. Match them. What are the molecular formulas of the compounds?

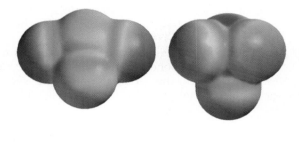

Resonance

43. Through appropriate Lewis structures, show that the phenomenon of resonance is involved in the nitrite ion.

44. Which of the following species requires a resonance hybrid for its Lewis structure, **(a)** CO_2, **(b)** OCl^-, **(c)** CO_3^{2-}, or **(d)** OH^-? Explain.

45. Dinitrogen oxide (nitrous oxide, or "laughing gas") is sometimes used as an anesthetic. Here are some data about the N_2O molecule: N—N bond length = 113 pm; N—O bond length = 119 pm. Use these data and other information from the chapter to comment on the plausibility of each of the following Lewis structures shown. Are they all valid? Which ones do you think contribute most to the resonance hybrid?

$$:N{\equiv}N-\ddot{\underset{\cdot\cdot}{O}}: \qquad :\ddot{N}=N=\ddot{\underset{\cdot\cdot}{O}}:$$
$$\text{(a)} \qquad\qquad\qquad \text{(b)}$$

$$:\ddot{\underset{\cdot\cdot}{N}}-N{\equiv}O: \qquad :\ddot{N}=O=\ddot{N}:$$
$$\text{(c)} \qquad\qquad\qquad \text{(d)}$$

46. The Lewis structure of nitric acid, $HONO_2$, is a resonance hybrid. How important do you think the contribution of the following structure is to the resonance hybrid? Explain.

$$H-\ddot{O}=N\overset{\textstyle :\ddot{\underset{\cdot\cdot}{O}}:}{\underset{\textstyle :\ddot{\underset{\cdot\cdot}{O}}:}{}}$$

Odd-Electron Species

47. Write plausible Lewis structures for the following odd-electron species. **(a)** CH_3; **(b)** ClO_2; **(c)** NO_3.

48. Write plausible Lewis structures for the following free radicals. **(a)** $\cdot C_2H_5$; **(b)** $HO_2\cdot$; **(c)** $ClO\cdot$.

49. Which of the following species would you expect to be diamagnetic and which paramagnetic: **(a)** OH^-; **(b)** OH; **(c)** NO_3; **(d)** SO_3; **(e)** SO_3^{2-}; **(f)** HO_2?

50. Write a plausible Lewis structure for NO_2, and indicate whether the molecule is diamagnetic or paramagnetic. Two NO_2 molecules can join together (*dimerize*) to form N_2O_4. Write a plausible Lewis structure for N_2O_4, and comment on the magnetic properties of the molecule.

Expanded Valence Shells

51. In which of the following species is it *necessary* to employ an expanded valence shell to represent the Lewis structure; PO_4^{3-}, PI_3, ICl_3, $OSCl_2$, SF_4, ClO_4^-? Explain your choices.

52. Describe the carbon-to-sulfur bond in H_2CSF_4. That is, is it most likely a single, double, or triple bond?

Molecular Shapes

53. Use VSEPR theory to predict the geometric shapes of the following molecules and ions. **(a)** N_2; **(b)** HCN; **(c)** NH_4^+; **(d)** NO_3^-; **(e)** NSF.

54. Use VSEPR theory to predict the geometric shapes of the following molecules and ions. **(a)** PCl_3; **(b)** SO_4^{2-}; **(c)** $SOCl_2$; **(d)** SO_3; **(e)** BrF_4^+.

55. Each of the following is either linear, angular (bent), planar, tetrahedral, or octahedral. Indicate the correct shape of **(a)** H_2S; **(b)** N_2O_4; **(c)** HCN; **(d)** $SbCl_6^-$; **(e)** BF_4^-.

56. Predict the geometric shapes of **(a)** CO; **(b)** $SiCl_4$; **(c)** PH_3; **(d)** ICl_3; **(e)** $SbCl_5$; **(f)** SO_2; **(g)** AlF_6^{3-}.

57. One of the following ions has a *trigonal-planar* shape: SO_3^{2-}; PO_4^{3-}; PF_6^-; CO_3^{2-}. Which ion is it? Explain.

58. Two of the following have the same shape. Which two, and what is their shape? What are the shapes of the other two? NI_3, HCN, SO_3^{2-}, NO_3^-.

59. Each of the following molecules contains one or more multiple covalent bonds. Draw plausible Lewis structures to represent this fact, and predict the shape of each molecule. **(a)** CO_2; **(b)** Cl_2CO; **(c)** $ClNO_2$.

60. Sketch the probable geometric shape of a molecule of **(a)** N_2O_4 (O_2NNO_2); **(b)** C_2N_2 (NCCN); **(c)** C_2H_6 (H_3CCH_3); **(d)** C_2H_6O (H_3COCH_3).

61. Use the VSEPR theory to predict the shapes of the anions **(a)** ClO_4^-; **(b)** $S_2O_3^{2-}$ (that is, SSO_3^{2-}); **(c)** PF_6^-; **(d)** I_3^-.

62. Use the VSEPR theory to predict the shape of **(a)** the molecule OSF_2; **(b)** the molecule O_2SF_2; **(c)** the ion SF_5^-; **(d)** the ion ClO_4^-; **(e)** the ion ClO_3^-.

63. The molecular shape of BF_3 is planar (see Table 10.1). If a fluoride ion is attached to the B atom of BF_3 through a coordinate covalent bond, the ion BF_4^- results. What is the shape of this ion?

64. Explain why it is not necessary to find the Lewis structure with the smallest formal charges to make a successful prediction of molecular geometry in the VSEPR theory. For example, write Lewis structures for SO_2 having different formal charges, and predict the molecular geometry based on these structures.

Shapes of Molecules with More Than One Central Atom

65. Sketch the propyne molecule, $CH_3C{\equiv}CH$. Indicate the bond angles in this molecule. What is the maximum number of atoms that can be in the same plane?

66. Sketch the propene molecule, $CH_3CH{=}CH_2$. Indicate the bond angles in this molecule. What is the maximum number of atoms that can be in the same plane?

67. Lactic acid has the formula $CH_3CH(OH)COOH$. Sketch the lactic acid molecule, and indicate the various bond angles.

68. Levulinic acid has the formula $CH_3(CO)CH_2CH_2COOH$. Sketch the levulinic acid molecule, and indicate the various bond angles.

Polar Molecules

69. Predict the shapes of the following molecules, and then predict which would have resultant dipole moments. **(a)** SO_2; **(b)** NH_3; **(c)** H_2S; **(d)** C_2H_4; **(e)** SF_6; **(f)** CH_2Cl_2.

70. Which of the following molecules would you expect to be polar: **(a)** HCN; **(b)** SO_3; **(c)** CS_2; **(d)** OCS; **(e)** $SOCl_2$; **(f)** SiF_4; **(g)** POF_3? Give reasons for your conclusions.

71. The molecule H_2O_2 has a resultant dipole moment of 2.2 D. Can this molecule be linear? If not, describe a shape that might account for this dipole moment.

72. Refer to the Integrative Example. A compound related to nitryl fluoride is nitrosyl fluoride, FNO. For this molecule, indicate **(a)** a plausible Lewis structure and **(b)** the geometric shape. **(c)** Explain why the measured resultant dipole moment for FNO is larger than the value for FNO_2.

Bond Lengths

73. *Without* referring to tables in the text, indicate which of the following bonds you would expect to have the greatest bond length, and give your reasons. **(a)** O_2; **(b)** N_2; **(c)** Br_2; **(d)** BrCl.

74. Estimate the lengths of the following bonds and indicate whether your estimate is likely to be too high or too low: **(a)** $I{-}Cl$; **(b)** $C{-}F$.

75. A relationship between bond lengths and single covalent radii of atoms is given on page 406. Use this relationship together with appropriate data from Table 10.2 to estimate these single-bond lengths. **(a)** $I{-}Cl$; **(b)** $O{-}Cl$; **(c)** $C{-}F$; **(d)** $C{-}Br$.

76. In which of the following molecules would you expect the oxygen-to-oxygen bond to be the *shortest*: **(a)** H_2O_2, **(b)** O_2, **(c)** O_3? Explain.

77. Refer to the Integrative Example. Use data from the chapter to estimate the length of the $N{-}F$ bond in FNO_2.

78. Write a Lewis structure of the hydroxylamine molecule, H_2NOH. Then, with data from Table 10.2, determine all the bond lengths.

Bond Energies

79. A reaction involved in the formation of ozone in the upper atmosphere is $O_2 \longrightarrow 2\,O$. *Without* referring to Table 10.3, indicate whether this reaction is endothermic or exothermic. Explain.

80. Use data from Table 10.3, but *without performing detailed calculations*, determine whether each of the following reactions is exothermic or endothermic.
   (a) $CH_4(g) + I(g) \longrightarrow \cdot CH_3(g) + HI(g)$
   (b) $H_2(g) + I_2(g) \longrightarrow 2\,HI(g)$

81. Use data from Table 10.3 to estimate the enthalpy change (ΔH) for the following reaction.
$$C_2H_6(g) + Cl_2(g) \longrightarrow C_2H_5Cl(g) + HCl(g)$$
$$\Delta H = ?$$

82. One of the chemical reactions that occurs in the formation of photochemical smog is $O_3 + NO \longrightarrow NO_2 + O_2$. Estimate the enthalpy change of this reaction by using appropriate Lewis structures and data from Table 10.3.

83. Estimate the standard enthalpies of formation at 25 °C and 1 atm of **(a)** OH(g); **(b)** $N_2H_4(g)$. Write Lewis structures and use data from Table 10.3, as necessary.

84. Use ΔH for the reaction in Example 10-15 and other data from Appendix D to estimate $\Delta H_f^\circ[CH_3Cl(g)]$.

85. Use bond energies from Table 10.3 to estimate the enthalpy change (ΔH) for the following reaction.
$$C_2H_2(g) + H_2(g) \longrightarrow C_2H_4(g) \qquad \Delta H = ?$$

86. Equations (1) and (2) can be combined to yield the equation for the formation of $CH_4(g)$ from its elements.

(1) $C(s) \longrightarrow C(g) \qquad \Delta H = 717\ kJ$
(2) $C(g) + 2\,H_2(g) \longrightarrow CH_4(g) \quad \Delta H = ?$

Overall: $C(s) + 2\,H_2(g) \longrightarrow CH_4(g) \quad \Delta H_f^\circ = -75\ kJ/mol$

Use the preceding data and a bond energy of 436 kJ/mol for H_2 to estimate the C—H bond energy. Compare your result with the value listed in Table 10.3.

Integrative and Advanced Exercises

87. Given the bond-dissociation energies: nitrogen-to-oxygen bond in NO, 631 kJ/mol; H—H in H_2, 436 kJ/mol; N—H in NH_3, 389 kJ/mol; O—H in H_2O, 463 kJ/mol; calculate ΔH for the reaction.
$$2\,NO(g) + 5\,H_2(g) \longrightarrow 2\,NH_3(g) + 2\,H_2O(g)$$

88. The following statements are not made as carefully as they might be. Criticize each one.
   (a) Lewis structures with formal charges are incorrect.
   (b) Triatomic molecules have a planar shape.
   (c) Molecules in which there is an electronegativity difference between the bonded atoms are polar.

89. A compound consists of 47.5% S and 52.5% Cl, by mass. Write a Lewis structure based on the empirical formula of this compound, and comment on its deficiencies. Write a more plausible structure with the *same* ratio of S to Cl.

90. A 0.325-g sample of a gaseous hydrocarbon occupies a volume of 193 mL at 749 mmHg and 26.1 °C. Determine the molecular mass, and write a plausible condensed structural formula for this hydrocarbon.

91. A 1.24-g sample of a hydrocarbon, when completely burned in an excess of $O_2(g)$, yields 4.04 g CO_2 and 1.24 g H_2O. Draw a plausible structural formula for the hydrocarbon molecule.
   [*Hint:* There is more than one possible arrangement of the C and H atoms.]

92. Draw Lewis structures for two different molecules with the formula C_3H_4. Is either of these molecules linear? Explain.

93. Sodium azide, NaN_3, is the nitrogen gas-forming substance used in automobile air-bag systems. It is an ionic compound containing the azide ion, N_3^-. In this ion, the two nitrogen-to-nitrogen bond lengths are 116 pm. Describe the resonance hybrid Lewis structure of this ion.

94. Use the bond-dissociation energies of $N_2(g)$ and $O_2(g)$ in Table 10.3, together with data from Appendix D, to estimate the bond-dissociation energy of NO(g).

95. Hydrogen azide, HN_3, is a liquid that explodes violently when subjected to physical shock. In the HN_3 molecule, one nitrogen-to-nitrogen bond length is 113 pm, and the other is 124 pm. The H—N—N bond angle is 112°. Draw Lewis structures and a sketch of the molecule consistent with these facts.

96. A few years ago the synthesis of a salt containing the N_5^+ ion was reported. What is the likely shape of this ion—linear, bent, zigzag, tetrahedral, seesaw, or square-planar? Explain your choice.

97. Carbon suboxide has the formula C_3O_2. The carbon-to-carbon bond lengths are 130 pm and carbon-to-oxygen, 120 pm. Propose a plausible Lewis structure to account for these bond lengths, and predict the shape of the molecule.

98. In certain polar solvents, PCl_5 undergoes an ionization reaction in which a Cl^- ion leaves one PCl_5 molecule and attaches itself to another. The products of the ionization are PCl_4^+ and PCl_6^-. Draw a sketch showing the changes in geometric shapes that occur in this ionization (that is, give the shapes of PCl_5, PCl_4^+, and PCl_6^-).
$$2\,PCl_5 \rightleftharpoons PCl_4^+ + PCl_6^-$$

99. Estimate the enthalpy of formation of HCN using bond energies from Table 10.3, data from elsewhere in the text, and the reaction scheme outlined as follows.

(1) $C(s) \longrightarrow C(g) \qquad \Delta H^\circ = ?$

(2) $C(g) + \dfrac{1}{2}N_2(g) + \dfrac{1}{2}H_2(g) \longrightarrow HCN(g) \quad \Delta H^\circ = ?$

Overall: $C(s) + \dfrac{1}{2}N_2(g) + \dfrac{1}{2}H_2(g) \longrightarrow HCN(g) \quad \Delta H_f^\circ = ?$

100. The enthalpy of formation of $H_2O_2(g)$ is -136 kJ/mol. Use this value, with other appropriate data from the text, to estimate the oxygen-to-oxygen single-bond energy. Compare your result with the value listed in Table 10.3.

101. Use the VSEPR theory to predict a probable shape of the molecule F_4SCH_2, and explain the source of any ambiguities in your prediction.

102. The enthalpy of formation of methanethiol, $CH_3SH(g)$, is -22.9 kJ/mol. Methanethiol can be synthesized by the reaction of gaseous methanol and $H_2S(g)$. Water vapor is another product. Use this information and data from elsewhere in the text to estimate the carbon-to-sulfur bond energy in methanethiol.

103. For LiBr, the dipole moment (measured in the gas phase) and the bond length (measured in the solid state) are 7.268 D and 217 pm, respectively. For NaCl, the corresponding values are 9.001 D and 236.1 pm. **(a)** Calculate the percent ionic character for each bond. **(b)** Compare these values with the expected ionic character based on differences in electronegativity (see Figure 10-7). **(c)** Account for any differences in the values obtained in these two different ways.

104. One possibility for the electron-group geometry for *seven* electron groups is pentagonal-bipyramidal, as found in the ion $[ZrF_7]^{3-}$ Write the VSEPR notation for this ion. Sketch the structure of the ion, labeling all the bond angles.

105. The extent to which an acid (HA) dissociates in water depends upon the stability of the anion (A^-); the more stable the anion, the more extensive is the dissociation of the acid. The anion is most stable when the negative charge is distributed over the whole anion rather than localized at one particular atom. Consider the following acids: acetic acid, fluoroacetic acid, cyanoacetic acid, and nitroacetic acid. Draw Lewis structures for their anions, including contributing resonance structures. Rank the acids in order of increasing extent of dissociation. Electrostatic potential maps for the four anions are provided below. Identify which map corresponds to which anion, and discuss whether the maps confirm conclusions based on Lewis structures.

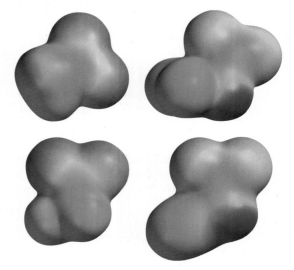

106. R. S. Mulliken proposed that the electronegativity (χ) of an atom is given by

$$\chi = k \times (I - EA)$$

where I and EA are the ionization energy and electron affinity of the atom, respectively. Using the electron affinities and ionization energy values for the halogen atoms up to iodine, estimate the value of k by employing the electronegativity values in Figure 10-6. Estimate the electron affinity of At.

107. When molten sulfur reacts with chlorine gas, a vile-smelling orange liquid forms. When analyzed, the liquid compound has the empirical formula SCl. Several possible Lewis structures are shown below. Criticize these structures and choose the best one.

(a) $:\ddot{C}l-\ddot{S}=\ddot{S}-\ddot{C}l:$

(b) $:\ddot{C}l=S-\ddot{S}=\ddot{C}l:$

(c) $:\ddot{S}=Cl-Cl=\ddot{S}:$

(d) $:\ddot{C}l-\ddot{S}\equiv S-\ddot{C}l:$

(e) $:\ddot{C}l-\ddot{S}-\ddot{S}-\ddot{C}l:$

108. Hydrogen azide, HN_3, can exist in two forms. One form has the three nitrogen atoms connected in a line; and the nitrogen atoms form a triangle in the other. Construct Lewis structures for these isomers and describe their shapes. Other interesting derivatives are nitrosyl azide (N_4O) and trifluoromethyl azide (CF_3N_3). Describe the shapes of these molecules based on a line of nitrogen atoms.

109. A pair of isoelectronic species for C and N exist with the formula X_2O_4 in which there is an $X-X$ bond. A corresponding fluoride of boron also exists. Draw Lewis structures for these species and describe their shapes.

110. Acetone $(CH_3)C=O$, a ketone, will react with a strong base (A^-) to produce the enolate anion, $CH_3(C=O)CH_2^-$. Draw the Lewis structure of the enolate anion, and describe the relative contributions of any resonance structures.

111. The species PBr_4^- has been synthesized and has been described as a tetrahedral anion. Comment on this description.

Feature Problems

112. Pauling's reasoning in establishing his original electronegativity scale went something like this: If we assume that the bond A—B is nonpolar, its bond energy is the average of the bond energies of A—A and B—B. The *difference* between the calculated and measured bond energies of the bond A—B is attributable to the partial ionic character of the bond and is called the *ionic resonance energy* (IRE). If the IRE is expressed in kilojoules per mole, the relationship between IRE and the electronegativity difference is $(\Delta EN)^2 = IRE/96$. To test this basis for an electronegativity scale,
(a) Use data from Table 10.3 to determine IRE for the H—Cl bond.
(b) Determine ΔEN for the H—Cl bond.
(c) Establish the approximate percent ionic character in the H—Cl bond by using the result of part (b) and Figure 10-7. Compare this result with that obtained in Example 10-4.

113. On page 405, the bond angle in the H_2O molecule is given as 104° and the resultant dipole moment as $\mu = 1.84$ D.
(a) By an appropriate geometric calculation, determine the value of the H—O bond dipole in H_2O.
(b) Use the same method as in part (a) to estimate the bond angle in H_2S, given that the H—S bond dipole is 0.67 D and that the resultant dipole moment is $\mu = 0.93$ D.

(c) Refer to Figure 10-15. Given the bond dipoles 1.87 D for the C—Cl bond and 0.30 D for the C—H bond, together with $\mu = 1.04$ D, estimate the H—C—Cl bond angle in $CHCl_3$.

114. Alternative strategies to the one used in this chapter have been proposed for applying the VSEPR theory to molecules or ions with a single central atom. In general, these strategies do not require writing Lewis structures. In one strategy, we write

(1) the total number of electron pairs = [(number of valence electrons) ± (electrons required for ionic charge)]/2
(2) the number of bonding electron pairs = (number of atoms) − 1
(3) the number of electron pairs around central atom = total number of electron pairs − 3 × [number of terminal atoms (excluding H)]
(4) the number of lone-pair electrons = number of central atom pairs − number of bonding pairs

After evaluating items 2, 3, and 4, establish the VSEPR notation and determine the molecular shape. Use this method to predict the geometrical shapes of the following: **(a)** PCl_5; **(b)** NH_3; **(c)** ClF_3; **(d)** SO_2; **(e)** ClF_4^-; **(f)** PCl_4^+. Justify each of the steps in the strategy, and explain why it yields the same results as the VSEPR method based on Lewis structures. How does the strategy deal with multiple bonds?

Self-Assessment Exercises

115. In your own words, define the following terms: **(a)** valence electrons; **(b)** electronegativity; **(c)** bond-dissociation energy; **(d)** double covalent bond; **(e)** coordinate covalent bond.

116. Briefly describe each of the following ideas: **(a)** formal charge; **(b)** resonance; **(c)** expanded valence shell; **(d)** bond energy.

117. Explain the important distinctions between **(a)** ionic and covalent bonds; **(b)** lone-pair and bond-pair electrons; **(c)** molecular geometry and electron-group geometry; **(d)** bond dipole and resultant dipole moment; **(e)** polar molecule and nonpolar molecule.

118. Of the following species, the one with a triple covalent bond is **(a)** NO_3^-; **(b)** CN^-; **(c)** CO_2; **(d)** $AlCl_3$.

119. The formal charges on the O atoms in the ion $[ONO]^+$ is **(a)** −2; **(b)** −1; **(c)** 0; **(d)** +1.

120. Which molecule is nonlinear? **(a)** SO_2; **(b)** CO_2; **(c)** HCN; **(d)** NO.

121. Which molecule is nonpolar? **(a)** SO_3; **(b)** CH_2Cl_2; **(c)** NH_3; **(d)** FNO.

122. The highest bond-dissociation energy is found in **(a)** O_2; **(b)** N_2; **(c)** Cl_2; **(d)** I_2.

123. The greatest bond length is found in **(a)** O_2; **(b)** N_2; **(c)** Br_2; **(d)** BrCl.

124. Draw plausible Lewis structures for the following species; use expanded valence shells where necessary. **(a)** Cl_2O; **(b)** PF_3; **(c)** CO_3^{2-}; **(d)** BrF_5.

125. Predict the shapes of the following sulfur-containing species. **(a)** SO_2; **(b)** SO_3^{2-}; **(c)** SO_4^{2-}.

126. Without referring to tables or figures in the text other than the periodic table, indicate which of the following atoms, Bi, S, Ba, As, or Mg, has the intermediate value when they are arranged in order of increasing electronegativity.

127. Use data from Tables 10.2 and 10.3 to determine for each bond in this following structure **(a)** the bond length and **(b)** the bond energy.

$$\begin{array}{ccc} O & & H \\ \| & & | \\ H-C-&C-&Cl \\ & & | \\ & & H \end{array}$$

128. Construct a concept map illustrating the connections between Lewis dot structures, the shapes of molecules, and polarity.

eMedia Exercises

129. In the **Periodic Trends: Lewis Structures** activity (*Activebook 10-1*), the similarity between the Lewis structures of elements found within the same group is illustrated. Use this concept to describe the similarity of the Lewis structures of ionic compounds involving atoms of a similar group (that is, NaCl, NaBr, and NaI).

130. After viewing the **H₂ Bond Formation** animation (*Activebook 10-2*), describe the forces involved in covalent bond formation in the simplest covalent compound. Which of the forces are attractive and which are repulsive?

131. Using the principles described in the **Writing Lewis Structures** activity and the **Formal Charges** animation (*Activebook 10-4*), generate the possible Lewis dot structures of the molecules O_3 and SO_2. What are the similarities and differences between the predicted structures of the two molecules?

132. In the **VSEPR** animation (*Activebook 10-7*), a sequential pattern in electron-group geometry is observed with the addition of each pair of electrons. Although the sequential addition of electron pairs (bonding or nonbonding) is *not* a realistic mechanism by which molecules are formed, it does illustrate the key principle behind the valence-shell electron-pair repulsion theory. **(a)** Use this principle to predict the structure if the central atom of a molecule were bonded to eight identical neighboring atoms. **(b)** Can you predict an approximate bond angle?

133. Use the **Molecular Polarity** activity (*Activebook 10-7*) to predict which of the following molecules possess (i) polar covalent bonds, and (ii) a net molecular dipole moment. **(a)** CF_4; **(b)** CF_2Cl_2; **(c)** CH_4; **(d)** NH_3; **(e)** H_2S.

11

CHEMICAL BONDING II: ADDITIONAL ASPECTS

CONTENTS

Impress on the students how important hybrid orbitals are for organic and inorganic chemistry.

Electrostatic potential maps of benzene (one solid and one transparent) showing the negative charge density due to the π molecular orbitals of benzene.

A lthough the Lewis theory has been useful in our discussion of chemical bonding, it does have shortcomings. For example, it does not help explain why metals conduct electricity or how a semiconductor works. While we will continue to use the Lewis theory for most purposes, there are cases that require more sophisticated approaches. One such approach involves the familiar *s*, *p*, and *d* atomic orbitals, or mixed-orbital types called *hybrid orbitals*. A second approach involves the creation of a set of orbitals that belongs to a molecule as a whole. Electrons are then assigned to these *molecular orbitals*.

Our purpose in this chapter is not to try to master theories of covalent bonding in all their details. We want simply to discover how these theories provide models that yield deeper insights into the nature of chemical bonding than do Lewis structures alone.

423

11-1 WHAT A BONDING THEORY SHOULD DO

Imagine bringing together two atoms that are initially very far apart. Three types of interactions occur: (1) the electrons are attracted to the two nuclei; (2) the electrons repel each other; and (3) the two nuclei repel each other. We can plot potential energy—the net energy of interaction of the atoms—as a function of the distance between the atomic nuclei. In this plot, negative energies correspond to a net attractive force between the atoms; positive energies, to a net repulsion.

Figure 11-1 shows the energy of interaction of two H atoms. This starts at zero when the atoms are very far apart. At very small internuclear distances, repulsive forces exceed attractive forces and the potential energy is positive. At intermediate distances, attractive forces predominate and the potential energy is negative. In fact, at one particular internuclear distance (74 pm) the potential energy reaches its lowest value (−436 kJ/mol). This is the condition in which the two H atoms combine into a H_2 molecule through a covalent bond. The nuclei continuously move back and forth; that is, the molecule vibrates, but the average internuclear distance remains constant. This internuclear distance corresponds to the *bond length*. The potential energy corresponds to the negative of the *bond-dissociation energy*. A theory of covalent bonding should help us understand why a given molecule has its particular set of observed properties—bond-dissociation energies, bond lengths, bond angles, and so on.

There are several approaches to understanding bonding. The approach used depends on the situation because different methods have different strengths and weaknesses. The strength of the Lewis theory is in the ease with which it can

 It is a common misconception that bonds store energy. Bonds do NOT store energy. The separate atoms that compose a molecule are of higher energy than they are in a bonding situation. When bonds are broken and made again in a chemical reaction, the process is exothermic if stronger bonds result, and endothermic if weaker bonds result.

 Frequently students have trouble with Figure 11-1. Note the energy is negative for attraction, but to the left of the minimum, the repulsive forces take over. Think of one atom fixed at the origin, and the distance from the origin to the potential energy curve is the distance between the two atoms in the diatomic molecule.

H_2 Bond Formation animation

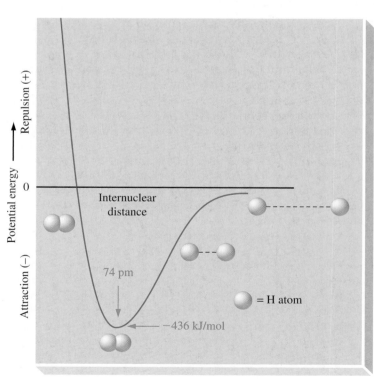

▲ FIGURE 11-1
Energy of interaction of two hydrogen atoms
This graph shows
- a zero of energy when two H atoms are separated by great distances
- a drop in potential energy (net attraction) as the two atoms approach each other
- a minimum in potential energy (−436 kJ/mol) at a particular internuclear distance (74 pm) corresponding to the stable molecule H_2
- an increase in potential energy as the atoms approach more closely; the electrons can no longer effectively screen the nuclei from each other, and repulsion occurs

be applied; a Lewis structure can be written rather quickly. VSEPR theory makes it possible to propose molecular shapes that are generally in good agreement with experimental results. However, neither of these methods yield quantitative information about bond energies and bond lengths, and the Lewis theory has problems with odd-electron species and situations in which it is not possible to represent a molecule through a single structure (resonance).

11-2   INTRODUCTION TO THE VALENCE-BOND METHOD

Recall the region of high electron probability in a H atom that we described in Chapter 8 through the mathematical function called a $1s$ orbital (page 307). As the two H atoms pictured in Figure 11-1 approach each other, these regions begin to interpenetrate. We say that the two orbitals overlap. Furthermore, we can say that a bond is produced between the two atoms because of the high electron probability found in the region between the atomic nuclei where the $1s$ orbitals overlap. In this way, a covalent bond is formed between the two H atoms in the H_2 molecule.

A description of covalent bond formation in terms of atomic orbital overlap is called the **valence-bond method**. The creation of a covalent bond in the valence-bond method is normally based on the overlap of half-filled orbitals, but sometimes such an overlap involves a filled orbital on one atom and an empty orbital on another. The valence-bond method gives a *localized* electron model of bonding: Core electrons and lone-pair valence electrons retain the same orbital locations as in the separated atoms, and the charge density of the bonding electrons is concentrated in the region of orbital overlap.

Figure 11-2 shows the imagined overlap of atomic orbitals in the formation of hydrogen-to-sulfur bonds in hydrogen sulfide. Note especially that maximum overlap between the $1s$ orbital of a H atom and a $3p$ orbital of a S atom occurs along a line joining the centers of the H and S atoms. The two half-filled sulfur $3p$ orbitals that overlap in H_2S are perpendicular to each other, and the valence-bond method suggests a H—S—H bond angle of 90°. This is in good agreement with the observed angle of 92°.

> ✓ The valence bond method actually underestimates the contributions from ionic bond character. Later we find that MO theory overestimates the contribution from ionic character.

> ◀ What we are calling "overlap" is actually an interpenetration of two orbitals.

> 📖 Haaland, A., Helgaker, T., Ruud, K., Shorokhov, D. J. "Should Gaseous BF₃ and SiF₄ Be Described as Ionic Compounds?" *J. Chem. Educ.* **2000**: *77*, 1076 (August 2000).

> 📖 Smith, Derek W. "The Antibonding Effect." *J. Chem. Educ.* **2000**: *77*, 780 (June 2000).

Isolated atoms   Covalent bonds

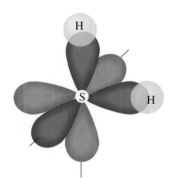

H | ↑ |
$1s$

S [Ne] | ↑↓ | | ↑↓ | ↑ | ↑ |
          $3s$ $3p$

▲ **FIGURE 11-2**
Bonding in H₂S represented by atomic orbital overlap
For S, only $3p$ orbitals are shown. Here, and in most other places in this chapter, even when the phase of the wave function is shown through the colors red and blue for opposite signs of phase (namely, minus and plus), p orbitals are depicted by their probability-density plots (recall Figure 8-27c), rather than by the p orbital functions themselves (recall Figure 8-26a). Bond formation occurs between orbitals that are in phase (same color), although the hydrogen $1s$ orbital is colored yellow for clarity.

> ✓ It might be helpful to show the formation of the bonds in H₂S using three-dimensional models so the students can see the 90° bond angle.

Are You Wondering . . .

Why the overlap of orbitals leads to a chemical bond?

The origin of this extra stability comes from the overlap of the two orbitals in which the two atomic wave functions are *in phase*, leading to constructive interference of the wave functions between the two nuclei and hence increased electron density between the two nuclei. The increased electron density, with its negative charge, attracts the two positively charged nuclei, leading an energy that is lower than that of the two separated atoms. Thus, the increased electron charge density between the nuclei produces the chemical bond. We will say more about the interaction between orbitals later in this chapter.

Because the energies of atomic orbitals differ from one type to another (see Figure 8-36), the valence-bond method implies different bond energies for different bonds. A quantitative application of the valence-bond method would show that the $1s–1s$ overlap in H_2 produces a greater bond energy than the $1s–3p$ overlap in a H—S bond in H_2S. The Lewis structures H—O—H and H—S—H provide no information about bond energies.

EXAMPLE 11-1

Using the Valence-Bond Method to Describe a Molecular Structure. Describe the phosphine molecule, PH_3, by the valence-bond method.

Solution

Here is a four-step approach to applying the valence-bond method.

Step 1. Draw valence-shell orbital diagrams for the separate atoms.

Step 2. Sketch the orbitals of the central atom (P) that are involved in the overlap. These are the half-filled $3p$ orbitals (Fig. 11-3).

Step 3. Complete the structure by bringing together the bonded atoms and representing the orbital overlap.

Step 4. Describe the structure. PH_3 is a *trigonal-pyramidal* molecule. The three H atoms lie in the same plane. The P atom is situated at the top of the pyramid above the plane of the H atoms, and the three H—P—H bond angles are 90°. (The experimentally measured H—P—H bond angles are 93° to 94°.)

Practice Example A: Use the valence-bond method to describe bonding and the expected molecular geometry in nitrogen triiodide, NI_3.

Practice Example B: Describe the molecular geometry of NH_3, first using the VSEPR method and then using the valence-bond method described above. How do your answers differ? Which method seems to be more appropriate in this case? Explain.

Bonding orbitals of P atom

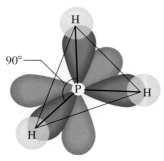

Covalent bonds formed

▲ **FIGURE 11-3**
Bonding and structure of the PH_3 molecule—Example 11-1 illustrated
Only bonding orbitals are shown. The $1s$ orbitals (yellow) of three H atoms overlap with the three $3p$ orbitals of the P atom.

Hybridization occurs only when the bonds are being formed. The orbitals rearrange themselves to minimize their energy. A hybrid orbital sp^3 has 25% s character and 75% p character.

11-3 HYBRIDIZATION OF ATOMIC ORBITALS

If we try to extend the unmodified valence-bond method of Section 11-2 to a greater number of molecules, we are quickly disappointed. In most cases, our descriptions of molecular geometry based on the simple overlap of unmodified atomic orbitals do not conform to observed measurements. For example, based on the *ground-state* electron configuration of the valence shell of carbon and employing only half-filled orbitals, we expect the existence of a molecule with the formula CH_2 and a bond angle of 90°. The CH_2 molecule is stable, but is not normally observed in the laboratory. It is a highly reactive molecule observed only under specially designed circumstances.

The simplest hydrocarbon observed under normal laboratory conditions is methane, CH_4. This is a stable, unreactive molecule with a molecular formula consistent with the octet rule of the Lewis theory. To obtain this molecular formula by the valence-bond method, we need an orbital diagram for carbon in which there are four unpaired electrons so that orbital overlap leads to four C—H bonds. To get such a diagram, imagine that one of the $2s$ electrons in a ground-state C atom absorbs energy and is promoted to the empty $2p$ orbital. The resulting electron configuration is that of an *excited state*.

$$\text{Excited state}\quad \text{C}\ \boxed{\uparrow}\ \boxed{\uparrow}\ \boxed{\uparrow}\ \boxed{\uparrow}$$
$$\phantom{\text{Excited state}\quad}\ 2s\qquad\quad 2p$$

The electron configuration of this excited state suggests a molecule with three mutually perpendicular C—H bonds based on the $2p$ orbitals of the C atom (90° bond angles). The fourth bond would be directed to whatever position in the molecule could accommodate the fourth H atom. This description, however, does not agree with the experimentally determined H—C—H bond angles, all four of which are found to be 109.5°, the same as predicted by VSEPR theory (Fig. 11-4). A bonding scheme based on the excited-state electron configuration does a poor job of explaining the bond angles in CH_4.

The problem is not with the theory but with the way the situation has been defined. We have been describing *bonded* atoms as though they have the same kinds of orbitals (that is, s, p, and so on) as isolated, *nonbonded* atoms. This assumption worked rather well for H_2S and PH_3, but there is no reason to expect these unmodified pure atomic orbitals to work equally well in all cases.

One way to deal with this problem is to modify the atomic orbitals of the bonded atoms. Recall that atomic orbitals are mathematical expressions of the electron waves in an atom. An algebraic combination of the wave equations of the $2s$ and three $2p$ orbitals of the carbon atom produces a new set of four identical orbitals. These new orbitals, which are directed in a tetrahedral fashion, have energies that are intermediate between those of the $2s$ and $2p$ orbitals. This mathematical process of replacing pure atomic orbitals with reformulated atomic orbitals for bonded atoms is called **hybridization**, and the new orbitals are called **hybrid orbitals**. Figure 11-5 pictures the hybridization of one s and three p orbitals into a new set of four sp^3 **hybrid orbitals**.

In a hybridization scheme, *the number of hybrid orbitals equals the total number of atomic orbitals that are combined*. The symbols identify the numbers and kinds of orbitals involved. Thus, sp^3 signifies that *one s* and *three p* orbitals are combined. A useful representation of sp^3 hybridization of the valence-shell orbitals of carbon is

Note that the three p orbitals move down by 1/4 of the energy difference between the s orbitals and the p orbitals and that the s orbital moves up by 3/4 of that energy difference; that is, energy is conserved. Figure 11-6 shows sp^3 hybrid orbitals and bond formation in methane.

◄ The word "stable" must be used carefully in chemistry. When we say the molecule is stable, we mean that the molecule is stable with respect to the separated atoms. The word "stable" should not be used without a qualifying statement if we are describing reactivity. Thus the metal sodium is stable (unreactive) in mineral oil but is unstable (highly reactive) in water.

▲ **FIGURE 11-4**
Ball-and-stick model of methane, CH_4
The molecule has a tetrahedral structure, and the H—C—H bond angles are 109.5°.

◄ The algebraic combination of wave functions is in fact a linear combination of atomic orbitals; that is, they are simply added or subtracted. The resultant linear combinations are solutions to the Schrödinger equation of the molecule.

Note that energy is conserved. The three p orbital energies move down by $\frac{1}{4}$ each and the single s orbital increases in energy by 75%.

This articles discusses a demonstration of sp^3, sp^2 and sp hybridization using an overhead projector: Emerson, David W. *J. Chem. Educ.* **1988**: 65, 454.

Hybridization animation

Combine to generate
four sp^3 orbitals

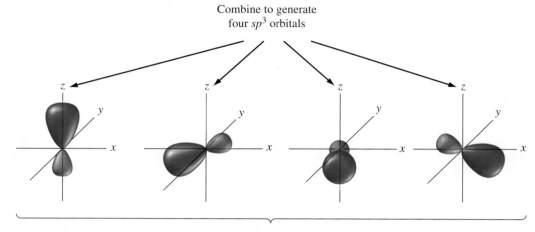

Which are represented
as the set

▲ **FIGURE 11-5**
The sp^3 hybridization scheme

▲ **FIGURE 11-6**
Bonding and structure of CH₄
The four carbon orbitals are sp^3 hybrid orbitals (blue). Those of the hydrogen atoms (yellow) are $1s$. The structure is tetrahedral, with H—C—H bond angles of 109.5° (more precisely, 109°28'). Remember that the hydrogen orbitals and the carbon hybrid orbitals have the same phase, but we have colored the hydrogen orbitals yellow for clarity.

The objective of a hybridization scheme is an after-the-fact rationalization of the experimentally observed shape of a molecule. Hybridization is not an actual physical phenomenon. We cannot observe electron charge distributions changing from those of pure orbitals to those of hybrid orbitals. Moreover, for some covalent bonds no single hybridization scheme works well. Nevertheless, the concept of hybridization works very well for carbon-containing molecules and is therefore used a great deal in organic chemistry.

Are You Wondering . . .

How real are hybrid orbitals?

Are they a good description of how electrons behave, or are they just a contrivance invented to fix up a bad theory? The fact is, they are just as real as the hydrogen-like orbitals we have used to describe multielectron atoms. The hydrogen-like orbitals are appropriate for describing the behavior of electrons in atoms. The hybrid orbitals are an appropriate way of describing the relative motions of electrons in molecules, and they are very useful in discussions of chemical bonding in polyatomic molecules.

Bonding in H_2O and NH_3

Applied to H_2O and NH_3, VSEPR theory describes a tetrahedral electron-group geometry for *four* electron groups. This, in turn, requires an sp^3 hybridization scheme for the central atoms in H_2O and NH_3. This scheme suggests angles of 109.5° for the H—O—H bond in water and the H—N—H bonds in NH_3. These angles are in reasonably good agreement with the experimentally observed bond angles of 104.5° in water and 107° in NH_3. Bonding in NH_3, for example, can be described in terms of the following valence-shell orbital diagram for nitrogen.

◀ Notice in this orbital diagram how hybrid orbitals can accommodate lone-pair electrons as well as bonding electrons.

Because one of the sp^3 orbitals is occupied by a lone pair of electrons, only the three half-filled sp^3 orbitals are involved in bond formation. This suggests the trigonal-pyramidal molecular geometry depicted in Figure 11-7, just as does VSEPR theory.

Even though the sp^3 hybridization scheme seems to work quite well for H_2O and NH_3, there is both theoretical and experimental (spectroscopic) evidence that favors a description based on *unhybridized p orbitals* of the central atoms. The H—O—H and H—N—H bond angle expected for $1s$ and $2p$ atomic orbital overlaps is 90°, which does not conform to the observed bond angles. One possible explanation is that because O—H and N—H bonds have considerable ionic character, repulsions between the positive partial charges associated with the H atoms force the H—O—H and H—N—H bonds to "open up" to values greater than 90°. The issue of how best to describe the bonding orbitals in H_2O and NH_3 is still unsettled and underscores the occasional difficulty of finding a single theory that is consistent with all the available evidence.

sp^2 Hybrid Orbitals

Carbon's group 13 neighbor, boron, has *four* orbitals but only *three* electrons in its valence shell. For most boron compounds, the appropriate hybridization scheme combines the $2s$ and two $2p$ orbitals into *three sp^2 hybrid orbitals* and leaves one p orbital unhybridized. Valence-shell orbital diagrams for this hybridization scheme for boron are shown here, and the scheme is further outlined in Figure 11-8.

The sp^2 hybridization scheme corresponds to trigonal-planar electron-group geometry and 120° bond angles, as in BF_3. Note again that in the hybridization schemes of valence-bond theory, the number of orbitals is conserved; that is, in an sp^2 hybridized atom there are still four orbitals, three sp^2 hybrids and an unhybridized p orbital.

sp Hybrid Orbitals

Boron's group 2 neighbor, beryllium, has *four* orbitals and only *two* electrons in its valence shell. In the hybridization scheme that best describes certain *gaseous* beryllium compounds, the $2s$ and one $2p$ orbital of Be are hybridized

There exists a beautiful program called atom in a box. http://dauger.com/orbitals/ which creates beautiful 3-D plots of hybrid orbitals up to $n = 7$. Check CW for updates.

▲ FIGURE 11-7
sp^3 hybrid orbitals and bonding in NH_3
An sp^3 hybridization scheme conforms to a molecular geometry in close agreement with experimental observations. Excluding the orbital occupied by a lone pair of electrons, the centers of the atoms form a trigonal pyramid. The hydrogen orbitals are colored yellow for clarity, but they have the same phase as the nitrogen hybrid orbitals.

Point out that the number of electron groups on the central atom of a species dictates the number of atomic orbitals that must be hybridized. In H_2O, with four electron groups around the O atom (two bond pairs and two lone pairs), four sp^3 orbitals are formed. In BF_3, with three electron groups (all bond pairs), the hybridization is sp^2; and so on.

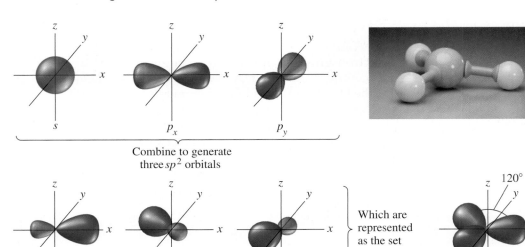

Combine to generate
three sp^2 orbitals

Which are
represented
as the set

120°

▲ FIGURE 11-8
The sp^2 hybridization scheme

In hybridization, molecular orbital, and valence-bond theory, not only is energy conserved, but also the number of orbitals is conserved. sp^2 hybrid orbitals still have one p orbital left over and this is particularly important for carbon. Carbon readily uses the leftover p orbitals to form π bonds. In contrast, silicon, the element one below carbon, does not use the p orbitals as readily because silicon is larger and the p orbitals do not project out far enough to form double and triple bonds.

into *two* **sp hybrid orbitals**, and the remaining two $2p$ orbitals are left unhybridized. Valence-shell orbital diagrams of beryllium in this hybridization scheme are shown here, and the scheme is further outlined in Figure 11-9.

The sp hybridization scheme corresponds to a linear electron-group geometry and a 180° bond angle, as in $BeCl_2(g)$.

CONCEPT ASSESSMENT ✔

Criticize the following statement: The hybridization of the C atom in CH_3^+ and CH_3^- are both expected to be the same as in CH_4.

Beautiful 3-D animations of hybrid orbitals are available on demos at:
http://www.mchmultimedia.com.
Check CW for updates.

Again point out that sp hybrid orbitals have two p orbitals left unhybridized that can form π bonds.

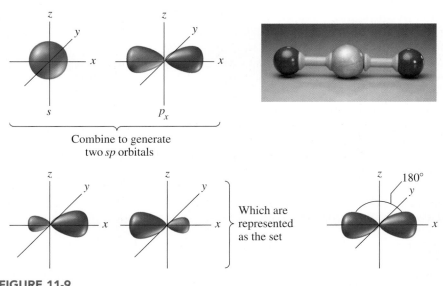

Combine to generate
two sp orbitals

Which are
represented
as the set

180°

▲ FIGURE 11-9
The sp hybridization scheme

Are You Wondering . . .

How the atomic orbitals mix to form a hybrid orbital?

A hybrid atomic orbital is the result of a mathematical combination (algebraic addition and subtraction) of the wave functions describing two or more atomic orbitals. When the algebraic functions that represent s and p orbitals are added, a new function is produced; this is an sp hybrid. When the same algebraic functions are subtracted, another new function is produced; this is a second sp hybrid. The hybridization process is shown in Figure 11-10, where we see the consequence of the phase of the p orbital when we add the s and p orbitals: The negative phase of the p orbital cancels part of the positive s orbital. This leads to the teardrop-shaped orbital pointing in the direction of the positive lobe of the p orbital. As shown in Figure 11-10, subtraction of the two orbitals reverses this situation. The two ways of combining an s and a p orbital generate the two equivalent sp hybrid orbitals, each having its greatest amplitude (or electron density if we square the amplitude) in a direction 180° from the other. A similar procedure is used to construct the three sp^2 and the four sp^3 hybrid orbitals, although the combinations of orbitals are slightly more complicated.

(a) $\psi_{2s} + \psi_{2p}$

(b) $\psi_{2s} - \psi_{2p}$

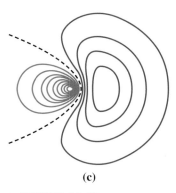

(c)

▲ **FIGURE 11-10**
The formation of an *sp* hybrid orbital
In **(a)** and **(b)**, the p, s, and sp hybrid orbitals themselves are depicted rather than their probability-density plots. **(c)** Contour map for one of the sp hybrids.

sp^3d AND sp^3d^2 HYBRID ORBITALS

To describe hybridization schemes that correspond to the 5- and 6-electron-group geometries of VSEPR theory, we need to go beyond the s and p subshells of the valence shell, and traditionally this has meant including d-orbital contributions. We can achieve the *five* half-filled orbitals of phosphorus to account for the five P—Cl bonds in PCl_5 and its trigonal-bipyramidal molecular geometry through the hybridization of the s, three p, and one d orbital of the valence shell into *five* **sp^3d hybrid orbitals**.

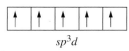

sp^3d

We can achieve the *six* half-filled orbitals of sulfur to account for the six S—F bonds in SF_6 and its octahedral molecular geometry through the hybridization of the s, three p, and two d orbitals of the valence shell into *six* **sp^3d^2 hybrid orbitals**.

sp^3d^2

The sp^3d and sp^3d^2 hybrid orbitals and two of the molecular geometries in which they can occur are featured in Figure 11-11.

We have previously stated that hybridization is not a real phenomenon, but an after-the-fact rationalization of an experimentally determined result. Perhaps there is no better illustration of this point than the issue of the sp^3d and sp^3d^2 hybrid orbitals. In discussing the concept of the expanded valence shell in Chapter 10, we noted that valence-shell expansion would seem to require d electrons in bonding schemes, but recent theoretical considerations cast serious doubt on d-electron participation. The same doubt, of course, extends to the use of d orbitals in hybridization schemes.

Despite the difficulty posed by hybridization schemes involving d orbitals, the sp, sp^2, and sp^3 hybridization schemes are well established and very commonly encountered, particularly among the second-period elements.

CONCEPT ASSESSMENT ✓

Give the formula of a compound or ion comprised of arsenic and fluorine in which the arsenic atom has a sp^3d^2 hybridization state.

Point out that an sp^3d^2 hybrid orbital has $\frac{1}{6}$ s character, $\frac{1}{2}$ p character, and $\frac{1}{3}$ d character.

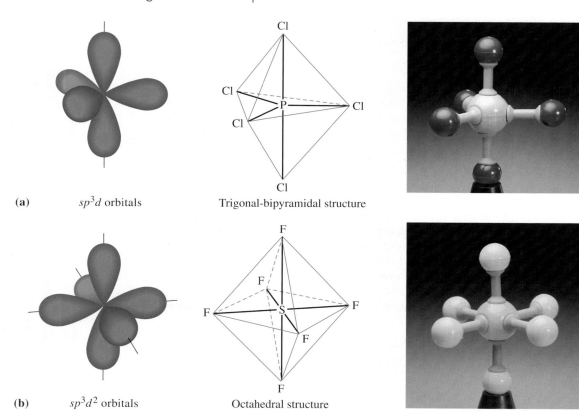

(a) sp^3d orbitals | Trigonal-bipyramidal structure

(b) sp^3d^2 orbitals | Octahedral structure

▲ **FIGURE 11-11**
sp^3d **and** sp^3d^2 **hybrid orbitals**

✓ A common error of students is to mix up the electron-pair geometry (including bonded and nonbonded electrons) with the structure of the molecule. Of course, the molecular structure ignores the lone pairs of electrons.

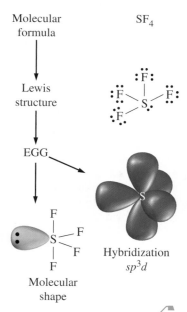

▲ **FIGURE 11-12**
Using electron-group geometry (EGG) to determine hybrid orbitals

HYBRID ORBITALS AND THE VALENCE-SHELL ELECTRON-PAIR REPULSION (VSEPR) THEORY

In the previous section, we used either the experimental geometry or the geometry predicted by VSEPR theory to help us decide on the appropriate hybridization scheme for the central atom. The concept of hybridization arose before the formulation of the VSEPR theory as we used it in Chapter 10. In 1931, Linus Pauling introduced the concept of hybridization of orbitals to account for the known geometries of CH_4, H_2O, and NH_3. It was first suggested by N. V. Sidgwick and H. E. Powell in 1940 that molecular geometry was determined by the arrangement of electron pairs in the valence shell, and this suggestion was subsequently developed into the set of rules known as VSEPR by Ronald Gillespie and Ronald Nyholm in 1957. The advantage of VSEPR is that it has a predictive capability based on Lewis structures, whereas hybridization schemes, as described here, require a prior knowledge of the molecular geometry. So how should we proceed to describe the bonding in molecules? We can choose the likely hybridization scheme for a central atom in a structure in the valence-bond method by

- writing a plausible Lewis structure for the species of interest;
- using VSEPR theory to predict the probable electron-group geometry of the central atom;
- selecting the hybridization scheme corresponding to the electron-group geometry.

The procedure outlined above is illustrated in Figure 11-12 using the molecule SF_4 as an example.

TABLE 11.1 Some Hybrid Orbitals and Their Geometric Orientations		
Hybrid Orbitals	Geometric Orientation	Example
sp	Linear	$BeCl_2$
sp^2	Trigonal-planar	BF_3
sp^3	Tetrahedral	CH_4
sp^3d	Trigonal-bipyramidal	PCl_5
sp^3d^2	Octahedral	SF_6

As suggested by Table 11.1, the hybridization scheme adopted for a central atom should be the one producing the same number of hybrid orbitals as there are valence-shell electron groups, and in the same geometric orientation. Thus, an sp^3 hybridization scheme for the central atom predicts that four hybrid orbitals are distributed in a tetrahedral fashion. This results in molecular structures that are tetrahedral, trigonal-pyramidal, or angular, depending on how many hybrid orbitals are involved in orbital overlap and how many contain lone-pair electrons, corresponding to the VSEPR notations AX_4, AX_3E, and AX_2E_2, respectively.

The s and p orbital hybridization schemes are especially important in organic compounds, whose principal elements are C, O, and N, in addition to H. We will consider some important applications to organic chemistry in the next section.

EXAMPLE 11-2

Proposing a Hybridization Scheme to Account for the Shape of a Molecule. Predict the shape of the XeF_4 molecule and a hybridization scheme consistent with this prediction.

Solution

Let's use the four-part strategy outlined here.

1. **Write a plausible Lewis structure.** The Lewis structure we write must account for 36 valence electrons—*eight* from the Xe atom and *seven* each from the *four* F atoms. To place this many electrons in the Lewis structure, we must expand the valence shell of the Xe atom to accommodate 12 electrons. The Lewis structure is

$$:\ddot{F}:$$
$$|$$
$$:\ddot{F}-\overset{\cdot\cdot}{Xe}-\ddot{F}:$$
$$|$$
$$:\ddot{F}:$$

2. **Use the VSEPR theory to establish the electron-group geometry of the central atom.** From the Lewis structure, we see that there are *six* electron groups around the Xe atom. Four electron groups are bond pairs and two are lone pairs. The electron-group geometry for *six* electron groups is *octahedral*.

3. **Describe the molecular geometry.** The VSEPR notation for XeF_4 is AX_4E_2, and the molecular geometry is *square-planar* (see Table 10.1). The four pairs of bond electrons are directed to the corners of a square, and the lone pairs of electrons are found above and below the plane of the Xe and F atoms, as shown here.

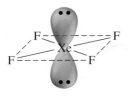

4. **Select a hybridization scheme that corresponds to the VSEPR prediction.** The only hybridization scheme consistent with an octahedral distribution of *six* electron groups is sp^3d^2. The orbital diagram for this scheme shows clearly that *four* of the eight valence electrons of the central Xe atom singly occupy four of the sp^3d^2 orbitals. The remaining *four* valence electrons of the atom occupy the remaining two sp^3d^2 orbitals as lone pairs. These are the lone pairs of electrons situated above and below the plane of the Xe and F atoms in the above sketch.

Valence shell of Xe atom | ↑↓ | ↑↓ | ↑ | ↑ | ↑ | ↑ |

sp^3d^2

Practice Example A: Describe the molecular geometry and propose a plausible hybridization scheme for the central atom in the ion Cl_2F^+.

Practice Example B: Describe the molecular geometry and propose a plausible hybridization scheme for the central atom in the ion BrF_4^+.

CONCEPT ASSESSMENT ✓

What hybridization do you expect for the central atom in a molecule that has a square-pyramidal geometry?

This article discusses using VSEPR and valence-bond theory to teach bonding and molecular geometry: Gillespie, Ronald J. J. Chem. Educ. 2004: 81, 298.

Are You Wondering . . .

Whether to use the VSEPR method (Section 10-7) or the valence-bond method in rationalizing the geometric shape of a molecule?

There is no "correct" method for describing molecular structures. The only correct information is the experimental evidence from which the structure is established. Once this experimental evidence is in hand, you may find it easier to rationalize this evidence by one method or another. For H_2S, the valence-bond method, which suggests a bond angle of 90°, seems to do a better job of explaining the observed 92° bond angle than does the VSEPR theory. For the Lewis structure, $H—\ddot{\underset{..}{S}}—H$ VSEPR theory predicts a tetrahedral electron-group geometry, which in turn suggests a tetrahedral bond angle—that is, 109.5°. However, by modifying this initial VSEPR prediction to accommodate lone-pair–lone-pair and lone-pair-bond-pair repulsions (see page 401), the predicted bond angle is less than 109.5°.

VSEPR theory gives reasonably good results in the majority of cases. Unless you have specific information to suggest otherwise, describing a molecular shape with the VSEPR theory is a good bet. It is important to remember that both the VSEPR and valence-bond methods are simply models we use to rationalize the shapes and bonding of polyatomic molecules and as such, should be viewed with a critical eye, always keeping experimental results in sight.

KEEP IN MIND ▶

that the VSEPR method uses empirical data to give an approximate molecular geometry, whereas the valence-bond method relates to the orbitals used in bonding based on a given geometry.

It might be useful to point out the difference between saturated and unsaturated hydrocarbons here.

11-4   MULTIPLE COVALENT BONDS

Two different types of orbital overlap occur when multiple bonds are described by the valence-bond method. In our discussion we will use as specific examples the carbon-to-carbon double bond in ethylene, C_2H_4, and the carbon-to-carbon triple bond in acetylene, C_2H_2.

BONDING IN C_2H_4

Ethylene has a carbon-to-carbon double bond in its Lewis structure.

The set of orbitals $sp^2 + p$

Sigma (σ) bonds

Overlap of p orbitals leading to pi (π) bond

Computed π orbitals of ethylene

◀ **FIGURE 11-13**
Sigma (σ) and pi (π) bonding in C_2H_4
The purple orbitals are sp^2 hybrid orbitals; the red and blue orbitals are $2p$, with the colors indicating their phase. The sp^2 hybrid orbitals overlap along the line joining the bonded atoms—a σ bond. The $2p$ orbitals overlap in a side-to-side fashion and form a π bond. Notice that the phase of the p orbitals is retained.

Ethylene is a planar molecule with 120° H—C—H and H—C—C bond angles. VSEPR theory treats each C atom as being surrounded by *three* electron groups in a trigonal-planar arrangement. VSEPR theory does *not* dictate that the two —CH$_2$ groups be coplanar, but as we shall see, valence-bond theory does.

The hybridization scheme that produces a set of hybrid orbitals with a trigonal-planar orientation is sp^2. The valence-shell orbital diagrams of carbon for this scheme are

The $sp^2 + p$ orbital set is pictured in Figure 11-13. One of the bonds between the carbon atoms results from the overlap of sp^2 hybrid orbitals from each atom. This overlap occurs along the line joining the nuclei of the two atoms. Orbitals that overlap in this end-to-end fashion produce a **sigma bond**, designated **σ bond**. Figure 11-13 shows that a second bond between the C atoms results from the overlap of the unhybridized p orbitals. In this bond, there is a region of high electron charge density above and below the plane of the carbon and hydrogen atoms. The bond produced by this side-to-side overlap of two parallel orbitals is called a **pi bond**, designated **π bond**.

The ball-and-stick model in Figure 11-14 illustrates bonding in ethylene. It helps to show that

*   the shape of a molecule is determined only by the orbitals forming σ bonds (the σ-bond framework).
*   rotation about the double bond is severely restricted. In the ball-and-stick model, we could easily twist or rotate the terminal H atoms about the s bonds that join them to a C atom. To twist one —CH$_2$ group out of the plane of the other, however, would reduce the amount of overlap of the p orbitals and weaken the π bond. The double bond is rigid, and the C$_2$H$_4$ molecule is planar.

Additionally, in carbon-to-carbon multiple bonds, the σ bond involves more extensive overlap than does the π bond. As a result, a carbon-to-carbon double bond ($\sigma + \pi$) is stronger than a single bond (σ), but not twice as strong (from Table 10.3, C—C, 347 kJ/mol; C=C, 611 kJ/mol; C≡C, 837 kJ/mol).

Multiple Bond Formation II activity

▲ **FIGURE 11-14**
Ball-and-stick model of ethylene, C_2H_4
The H—C—H and C—C—H bond angles are 120°. The model also distinguishes between the σ bond between the C atoms (the straight plastic tube) and the π bond extending above and below the plane of the molecule. The picture of the π bond suggested by the white plastic "arches" is somewhat distorted, but the model does convey the idea that the π bond places a high electron charge density above and below the plane of the molecule.

Formation of σ bonds

Formation of π bonds

Computed π orbitals of acetylene

▲ **FIGURE 11-15**
σ and π bonding in C₂H₂

The σ-bond framework joins the atoms H—C—C—H through 1s orbitals of the H atoms and *sp* orbitals of the C atoms. There are two π bonds. Each π bond consists of two parallel cigar-shaped segments. The four segments shown actually merge into a hollow cylindrical shell with the carbon-to-carbon σ bond as its axis. The computed model is shown on the right.

 Multiple Bond Formation activity

BONDING IN C₂H₂

Bonding in acetylene, C_2H_2, is similar to that in C_2H_4, but with these differences: The Lewis structure of C_2H_2 features a triple covalent bond, $H-C{\equiv}C-H$. The molecule is *linear*, as found by experiment and as expected from VSEPR theory. A hybridization scheme to produce hybrid orbitals in a linear orientation is *sp*. The valence-shell orbital diagrams representing *sp* hybridization are

KEEP IN MIND ▶

that only one of the bonds in a multiple bond is a σ bond; the others are π bonds—one π bond in a double bond and two in a triple bond.

In the triple bond in C_2H_2, one of the carbon-to-carbon bonds is a σ bond and *two* are π bonds, as suggested in Figure 11-15.

As discussed in the bonding of ethylene and acetylene, the number of electron groups around the central atoms(s) dictates the number of atomic orbitals that undergo hybridization. The carbon atom in formaldehyde (Example 11-3) contains three electron groups which means that three atomic orbitals are hybridized to form three sp^2 orbitals.

EXAMPLE 11-3

Proposing Hybridization Schemes Involving σ and π Bonds. Formaldehyde gas, H_2CO, is used in the manufacture of plastics; in aqueous solution, it is the familiar biological preservative called formalin. Describe the molecular geometry and a bonding scheme for the H_2CO molecule.

Solution

1. **Write the Lewis structure.** C is the central atom, and H and O are terminal atoms. The total number of valence electrons is 12. Note that this structure requires a carbon-to-oxygen double bond.

$$
\begin{array}{c}
\text{H} \\
| \\
\text{H}-\text{C}=\overset{\displaystyle ..}{\underset{\displaystyle ..}{\text{O}}}:
\end{array}
$$

2. **Determine the electron-group geometry of the central C atom.** The σ-bond framework is based on three electron groups around the central C atom. VSEPR theory, based on the distribution of three electron groups, suggests a trigonal-planar molecule with 120° bond angles.

▶ Now we see the VSEPR theory rationale of treating a multiple bond as a single group of electrons. The number of electron groups around the central atom is equal to the number of σ bonds in the σ-bond framework.

3. **Identify the hybridization scheme that conforms to the electron-group geometry.** A trigonal-planar orientation of orbitals is associated with sp^2 hybrid orbitals.

4. **Identify the orbitals of the central atom that are involved in orbital overlap.** The C atom is hybridized to produce the orbital set $sp^2 + p$, as in C_2H_4. Two of the sp^2 hybrid orbitals are used to form σ bonds with the H atoms. The remaining sp^2 hybrid orbital is used to form a σ bond with oxygen. The unhybridized *p* orbital of the C atom is used to form a π bond with O.

Valence shell of the C atom: ↑ ↑ ↑   ↑

sp^2 $2p$

5. **Sketch the bonding orbitals of the central and terminal atoms.** The bonding orbitals of the central C atom described above are pictured in Figure 11-16(a). The sp^2 hybrid orbitals are shown in lavender, and the pure p orbitals, in blue and red. The H atoms have only $1s$ orbitals available for bonding. For oxygen, the half-filled $2p$ orbital can be used for end-to-end overlap in the σ bond to carbon, and a half-filled $2p$ orbital can participate in the side-to-side overlap leading to a π bond. Thus the valence-shell orbital diagram we can use for oxygen is

$$2s \qquad 2p$$

The bonding and structure of the formaldehyde molecule are suggested by the three-dimensional sketch in Figure 11-16(b).

Practice Example A: Describe a plausible bonding scheme and the molecular geometry of dimethyl ether, CH_3OCH_3.

Practice Example B: Acetic acid, the acidic component of vinegar, has the formula CH_3COOH. Describe the molecular geometry and a bonding scheme for this molecule.

Drawing three-dimensional sketches to show orbital overlaps, as in Figure 11-16(b), is not easy. A simpler, two-dimensional representation of the bonding scheme for formaldehyde is shown in Figure 11-17. Bonds between atoms are drawn as straight lines. They are labeled σ or π, and the orbitals that overlap are indicated.

We have stressed a Lewis structure as the first step in describing a bonding scheme. Sometimes the starting point is a description of the species obtained by experiment. Example 11-4 illustrates such a case.

$$\pi: C(2p)\!-\!O(2p)$$

$$\sigma: H(1s)\!-\!C(sp^2) \overset{H}{\underset{H}{}} \!\!120°\, C\!=\!O$$
$$120°$$
$$\sigma: C(sp^2)\!-\!O(2p)$$

▲ **FIGURE 11-17**
Bonding in H₂CO—a schematic representation

EXAMPLE 11-4

Using Experimental Data to Assist in Selecting a Hybridization and Bonding Scheme. Formic acid, HCOOH, is an irritating substance released by ants when they bite (*formica* is Latin, meaning "ant"). A structural formula with bond angles is given here. Propose a hybridization and bonding scheme consistent with this structure.

$$\begin{array}{c} 124° \\ O \quad 108° \\ 118° \,\| \,\nearrow \\ C H \\ H O \end{array}$$

Solution

The 118° H—C—O bond angle on the left is very nearly the 120° angle for a trigonal-planar distribution of three groups of electrons. This requires an sp^2 hybridization scheme for the C atom. The 124° O—C—O bond angle is also close to the 120° expected for sp^2 hybridization. The C—O—H bond angle of 108° is close to the tetrahedral angle—109.5°. The O atom on the right employs an sp^3 hybridization scheme. The four σ and one π bonds and the orbital overlaps producing them are indicated in Figure 11-18.

◀ Because one of the main purposes of hybridizing orbitals is to describe molecular geometry (for example, bond angles), we generally apply hybridization schemes only to central atoms, although hybridization of terminal atoms (except H) may also be invoked.

(a)

(b)

▲ **FIGURE 11-16**
Bonding and structure of the H₂CO molecule— Example 11-3 illustrated **(a)** The orbital set $sp^2 + p$ is used for the C atom, $1s$ orbitals for H, and two half-filled $2p$ orbitals for O. For simplicity, only bonding orbitals of the valence shells are shown. **(b)** Computed π orbital for the CO group.

$$\sigma: C(sp^2)\!-\!O(2p)$$
$$\pi: C(2p)\!-\!O(2p)$$
$$\sigma: C(sp^2)\!-\!H(1s)\,\overset{O}{\underset{}{\|}}$$
$$ C H$$
$$H O$$
$$\sigma: C(sp^2)\!-\!O(sp^3)$$
$$\sigma: O(sp^3)\!-\!H(1s)$$

▲ **FIGURE 11-18**
Bonding and structure of HCOOH—Example 11-4 illustrated

Practice Example A: Acetonitrile is an industrial solvent. Propose a hybridization and bonding scheme consistent with its structure.

$$\begin{array}{c} H \\ | \\ H-C-C\equiv N \\ | \\ H \end{array}$$

Practice Example B: A reference source on molecular structures lists the following data for dinitrogen monoxide (nitrous oxide), N_2O: Bond lengths: $N-N = 113$ pm; $N-O = 119$ pm; bond angle = 180°. Show that the Lewis structure of N_2O is a resonance hybrid of two contributing structures, and describe a plausible hybridization and bonding scheme for each.

CONCEPT ASSESSMENT ✓

The molecule diazine has the molecular formula N_2H_2. What is the hybridization of the nitrogen and does the molecule contain a double or triple bond?

11-5 MOLECULAR ORBITAL THEORY

Molecular orbital theory improves several aspects of the previous approaches: It quantitatively accounts for bond energies, bond order, bond length, colors, and paramagnetism. Molecular orbital theory allows us to predict structures whereas the previous theories, as we presented them, can only rationalize structures. Molecular orbital theory allows us to predict if a bond will actually form.

Lewis structures, VSEPR theory, and the valence-bond method make a potent combination for describing covalent bonding and molecular structures. They are satisfactory for most of our purposes. Sometimes, however, chemists need a greater understanding of molecular structures and properties than these methods provide. None of these methods, for instance, provides an explanation of the electronic spectra of molecules, why oxygen is paramagnetic, or why H_2^+ is a stable species. To address these questions, we need a different method of describing chemical bonding.

This method, called **molecular orbital theory**, starts with a simple picture of molecules, but it quickly becomes complex in its details. We can provide only an overview here. The theory assigns the electrons in a molecule to a series of orbitals that belong to the molecule as a whole. These are called molecular orbitals. Like atomic orbitals, molecular orbitals are mathematical functions, but we can relate them to the probability of finding electrons in certain regions of a molecule. Also like an atomic orbital, a molecular orbital can accommodate just two electrons, and the electrons must have opposing spins.

Earlier in this chapter, we described the approach of two H atoms toward one another to form a chemical bond (see Figure 11-1). What happens to the atomic orbitals as the two H atoms merge to form a chemical bond? As the atoms approach, the two $1s$ wave functions combine; they do this by interfering constructively or destructively. Constructive interference corresponds to adding the two mathematical functions (the positive sign puts the waves in phase), while destructive interference corresponds to subtracting the two mathematical functions (the minus sign puts the waves out of phase). These two types of combination are illustrated in Figure 11-19.

▶ **FIGURE 11-19**
Formation of bonding and antibonding orbitals
(a) The addition of two $1s$ orbitals in phase to form a σ_{1s} molecular orbital. This orbital produces electron density between the nuclei, leading to a chemical bond. **(b)** The addition of two $1s$ orbitals out of phase to produce a σ_{1s}^* antibonding orbital. This orbital has a nodal plane perpendicular to the internuclear axis, as do all antibonding orbitals.

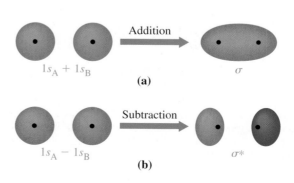

How do we interpret these two different combinations of wave functions? The constructive interference (addition) of the two wave functions leads to a greater probability of finding the electron between the nuclei. The increased electron charge density between the nuclei causes them to draw closer together, forming a chemical bond. The electron probability or electron charge density in the σ_{1s} orbital is $(1s_A + 1s_B)^2$, the square of the new function $(1s_A + 1s_B)$, where $1s_A$ and $1s_B$ are the two $1s$ orbitals on the two H atoms. The square is $1s_A^2 + 1s_B^2$ *plus* the extra term $2 \times 1s_A 1s_B$, which is the extra charge density between the nuclei.

The result of this constructive interference is a **bonding molecular orbital** because it places a high electron charge density between the two nuclei. A high electron charge density between atomic nuclei reduces repulsions between the positively charged nuclei and promotes a strong bond. This bonding molecular orbital, designated σ_{1s}, is at a *lower* energy than the $1s$ atomic orbitals.

The molecular orbital formed by the destructive interference (subtraction) of the two $1s$ orbitals leads to reduced electron probability between the nuclei. This produces an **antibonding molecular orbital**, designated by a superscript asterisk (*), because it places a very low electron charge density between the two nuclei. The electron probability or electron charge density in the σ_{1s}^* orbital is $(1s_A - 1s_B)^2$, the square of the new function $(1s_A - 1s_B)$, where $1s_A$ and $1s_B$ are the $1s$ orbitals on the two H atoms. The square is $1s_A^2 + 1s_B^2$ *minus* the extra term $2 \times 1s_A 1s_B$ which is the loss of charge density between the nuclei. Notice that $-2 \times 1s_A 1s_B$ here exactly balances the extra density $(+2 \times 1s_A 1s_B)$ in the molecular orbital formed by addition of the atomic functions.

With a low electron charge density between atomic nuclei, the nuclei are not screened from each other, strong repulsions occur, and the bond is weakened (hence the term "antibonding"). This antibonding molecular orbital, designated σ_{1s}^*, is at a *higher* energy than the $1s$ atomic orbitals.

The combination of two $1s$ orbitals of H atoms into two molecular orbitals in a H_2 molecule is summarized in Figure 11-20.

Molecular Orbital Theory animation

◀ **FIGURE 11-20**
The interaction of two hydrogen atoms according to molecular theory
The energy of the bonding σ_{1s} molecular orbital is lower and that of the antibonding σ_{1s}^* molecular orbital is higher than the energies of the $1s$ atomic orbitals. Electron charge density in a bonding molecular orbital is high in the internuclear region. In an antibonding orbital, it is high in parts of the molecule away from the internuclear region.

BASIC IDEAS CONCERNING MOLECULAR ORBITALS

Here are some useful ideas about molecular orbitals and how electrons are assigned to them.

1. The number of molecular orbitals (MOs) formed is equal to the number of atomic orbitals combined.
2. Of the two MOs formed when two atomic orbitals are combined, one is a *bonding* MO at a *lower* energy than the original atomic orbitals. The other is an *antibonding* MO at a *higher* energy.
3. In ground-state configurations, electrons enter the lowest energy MOs available.
4. The maximum number of electrons in a given MO is two (Pauli exclusion principle, page 317).
5. In ground-state configurations, electrons enter MOs of identical energies *singly* before they pair up (Hund's rule, page 317).

A stable molecular species has more electrons in bonding orbitals than in antibonding orbitals. For example, if the excess of bonding over antibonding electrons is *two*, this corresponds to a *single* covalent bond in Lewis theory. In molecular orbital theory, we say that the bond order is 1. **Bond order** is one-half the difference between the number (no.) of bonding and antibonding electrons (e^-), that is,

$$\text{bond order} = \frac{\text{no. of } e^- \text{ in bonding MOs} - \text{no. of } e^- \text{ in antibonding MOs}}{2} \quad (11.1)$$

DIATOMIC MOLECULES OF THE FIRST-PERIOD ELEMENTS

Let's use the ideas just outlined to describe some molecular species of the first-period elements, H and He (Fig. 11-21).

H_2^+ This species has a single electron. It enters the σ_{1s} orbital, a bonding molecular orbital. Using equation (11.1), we see that the bond order is $(1 - 0)/2 = \frac{1}{2}$. This is equivalent to a one-electron, or *half*, bond, a bond type that is not easily described by the Lewis theory.

H_2 This molecule has two electrons, both in the σ_{1s} orbital. The bond order is $(2 - 0)/2 = 1$. With Lewis theory and the valence-bond method, we describe the bond in H_2 as single covalent.

He_2^+ This ion has three electrons. Two electrons are in the σ_{1s} orbital, and one is in the σ_{1s}^* orbital. This species exists as a stable ion with a bond order of $(2 - 1)/2 = \frac{1}{2}$.

He_2 Two electrons are in the σ_{1s} orbital, and two are in the σ_{1s}^*. The bond order is $(2 - 2)/2 = 0$. No bond is produced—He_2 is not a stable species.

▶ **FIGURE 11-21**
Molecular orbital diagrams for the diatomic molecules and ions of the first-period elements
The 1s energy levels of the isolated atoms are shown to the left and right of each diagram. The line segments in the middle represent the molecular orbital energy levels—lower than the 1s levels for σ_{1s} and higher than the 1s levels for σ_{1s}^*.

EXAMPLE 11-5

Relating Bond Energy and Bond Order. The bond energy of H_2 is 436 kJ/mol. Estimate the bond energies of H_2^+ and He_2^+.

Solution

The bond order in H_2 is 1, equivalent to a single bond. In both H_2^+ and He_2^+, the bond order is $\frac{1}{2}$. We should expect the bonds in these two species to be only about half as strong as in H_2—about 220 kJ/mol. (Actual values: H_2^+, 255 kJ/mol; He_2^+, 251 kJ/mol.)

Practice Example A: The bond energy of Li_2 is 106 kJ/mol. Estimate the bond energy of Li_2^+.

Practice Example B: Do you think the ion H_2^- is stable? Explain.

CONCEPT ASSESSMENT ✔

A ground state H_2 molecule can absorb electromagnetic radiation to form the ion H_2^+ or an excited state with an electron promoted to the σ_{1s}^* orbital. Which process requires the greater amount of energy? Which species is most stable?

MOLECULAR ORBITALS OF THE SECOND-PERIOD ELEMENTS

For diatomic molecules and ions of H and He, we had to combine only 1s orbitals. In the second period, the situation is more interesting because we must work with both 2s and 2p orbitals. This results in *eight* molecular orbitals. Let's see how this comes about.

The molecular orbitals formed by combining 2s atomic orbitals are similar to those from 1s atomic orbitals, except they are at a higher energy. The situation for combining 2p atomic orbitals, however, is different. Two possible ways for 2p atomic orbitals to combine into molecular orbitals are shown in Figure 11-22: end-to-end and side-to-side. The best overlap for p orbitals is along a straight line (that is, end-to-end). This combination produces σ-type molecular orbitals: σ_{2p} and σ_{2p}^*. In forming the bonding and antibonding combinations along the

Students frequently have trouble with the phases of the lobes of some of the orbitals. This can be explained easily by a 1-D wave, like a sine wave, that is positive above the center line and negative below. The orbitals are just 3-D waves and the negative parts have the same interpretation as the negative parts of 1-D waves. Hence, adding wave functions in such a way as to make the lobes overlap will cause a buildup of electron density, if both are the same phase, and a canceling of electron density if the lobes are of opposite phase.

◀ In Figure 11-22, the actual p orbitals are used rather than their probability-density plots because our emphasis is on the phases of the orbitals that are being combined.

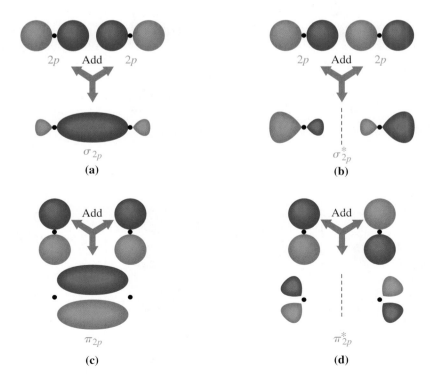

◀ **FIGURE 11-22**
Formation of bonding and antibonding orbitals from 2p orbitals
(a) The addition of two 2p orbitals in phase along the internuclear axis to form a σ_{2p} molecular orbital. This orbital produces electron density between the nuclei, leading to a chemical bond. **(b)** The addition of two 2p orbitals out of phase to produce an antibonding σ_{2p}^* orbital. This orbital has a nodal plane perpendicular to the internuclear axis, as do all antibonding orbitals. **(c)** The addition of two 2p orbitals in phase perpendicular to the internuclear axis to form a π_{2p} molecular orbital. This orbital produces electron density between the nuclei, contributing to a multiple chemical bond. **(d)** The addition of two 2p orbitals out of phase to produce a π_{2p}^* antibonding orbital with a nodal plane.

KEEP IN MIND ▶
that the different colors of
the orbitals depicted in these
various figures represent
the phases of the orbitals.

KEEP IN MIND ▶
that subtracting two wave
functions that are in phase is
equivalent to *adding* the same
functions when they are out
of phase.

▶ Note that assigning blue
to the positive lobe is
quite arbitrary. The
important aspect is that the
orbitals are in phase to create
a bonding orbital

internuclear axis, we must take into account the phase of the $2p$ orbitals. We set up the atomic orbitals as shown in Figure 11-22(a), with the positive (blue) lobe of each function pointing to the internuclear region. Then, since the wave functions are in phase, the addition of the two wave functions leads to an increase of electron density in the internuclear region and produces a σ_{2p} orbital. When the two atomic orbitals are set up as shown in Figure 11-22(b), with lobes of opposite phase pointing into the internuclear region, a nodal plane midway between the nuclei is formed, leading to an antibonding σ_{2p}^* orbital.

Only one pair of p orbitals can combine in an end-to-end fashion. The other two pairs must combine in a parallel or side-to-side fashion to produce π-type molecular orbitals: π_{2p} and π_{2p}^*. The two possible ways for the side-to-side combination of a pair of $2p$ orbitals are shown in Figure 11-22(c and d). The π_{2p} bonding orbital (Fig. 11-22c) is formed by adding the p orbital on one nucleus to a p orbital on the other nucleus, in such a way that the positive and negative lobes of one orbital are in phase with the positive and negative lobes of the other p orbital on the other nucleus. This produces additional electron density between the nuclei, but in a much less direct way than in the σ orbital because the additional electron density is not found along the internuclear axis. Typically, the π bond is weaker than the σ bond. The π_{2p}^* antibonding orbital is formed by subtracting the two p orbitals perpendicular to the internuclear axes, as shown in Figure 11-22(d). Now, in addition to the nodal plane that contains the nuclei, a node is formed between the nuclei, and this is a characteristic of antibonding character. There are actually *four* π-type molecular orbitals (two bonding and two antibonding) because there are *two* pairs of $2p$ atomic orbitals arranged in a parallel fashion. Figure 11-23 depicts the approximate probability distributions based on the orbital interactions described in Figure 11-22. Again, we see that bonding molecular orbitals place a high electron charge density between the atomic nuclei. In antibonding molecular orbitals, there are nodal planes between the nuclei, where the electron charge density falls to zero.

The shapes of these molecular orbitals comes from doing quantum mechanics. We can visualize the adding and canceling of electron density when doing a LCAO, but the actual shapes of these bonding and antibonding orbitals come from quantum calculations.

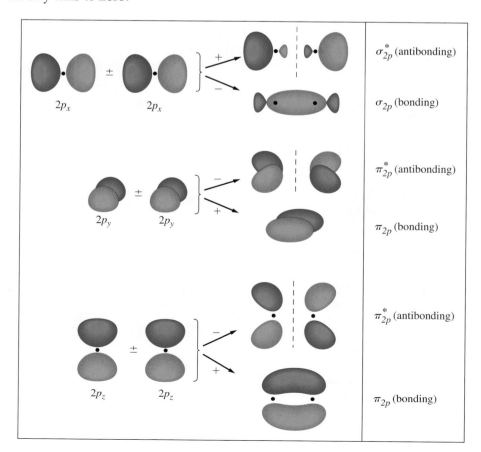

▶ FIGURE 11-23
Combining 2p atomic orbitals
These diagrams suggest the electron charge distributions for several orbitals. They are not exact in all details. Nodal planes for antibonding orbitals are represented by broken lines.

The energy-level diagram for the molecular orbitals formed from atomic orbitals of the second principal electronic shell is related to the atomic orbital energy levels. For example, molecular orbitals formed from $2s$ orbitals are at a lower energy than those formed from $2p$ orbitals—the same relationship as between the $2s$ and $2p$ atomic orbitals. Another expectation is that σ-type bonding orbitals should have lower energies than π-type because end-to-end overlap of $2p$ orbitals should be more extensive than side-to-side overlap, resulting in a lower energy. This ordering is shown in Figure 11-24(a). In constructing this energy-level diagram, we have made the assumption that s orbitals mix only with s orbitals and p orbitals mix only with p orbitals. However, if we use this assumption for some diatomic molecules, we will make predictions that do not match experimental results.

We need to take into account the fact that both the $2s$ and $2p$ orbitals form molecular orbitals (σ_{2s} and σ_{2p}) that produce electron density in the same region between the nuclei. These two σ orbitals are of such similar energy and shape that they themselves mix to form modified σ orbitals. The modified σ orbitals each contain a fraction of the original σ_{2s} and σ_{2p}. The modified σ_{2s} (with some σ_{2p} mixed in) goes down in energy, and the modified σ_{2p} (with some σ_{2s} mixed in) goes up in energy, producing a different ordering of energy levels. The important aspect of this mixing is that the modified σ_{2p} is pushed up in energy above the π_{2p} orbitals (Fig. 11-24b).

For the molecular orbitals in O_2 and F_2, the situation is as expected because the energy difference between the $2s$ and $2p$ orbitals is large, and little s and p mixing takes place; that is, the σ_{2s} and σ_{2p} orbitals are *not* modified as described above. For other diatomic molecules of the second-period elements (for example, C_2 and N_2), the π_{2p} orbitals are at a lower energy than σ_{2p} because the energy difference between the $2s$ and $2p$ orbitals is smaller, and $2s$–$2p$ orbital interactions affect the way in which atomic orbitals combine. This leads to the modified σ_{2s} and σ_{2p} orbitals described above.

Some computed molecular orbitals of F_2

✓ Point out that in the atomic orbitals of this diagram there is no mixing between atomic orbitals on the SAME atom that form the molecular orbitals with those of the OTHER atom.

📖 *Linear Combination of Atomic Orbitals activity*

(a) $Z \geq 8$

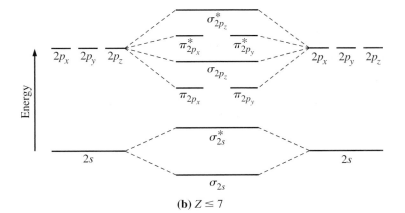

(b) $Z \leq 7$

◄ **FIGURE 11-24**
The two possible molecular orbital energy-level schemes for diatomic molecules of the second-period elements
(a) The expected ordering when σ_{2p} lies below the π_{2p}. This is the ordering for elements with $Z \geq 8$.
(b) The modified ordering due to s and p orbital mixing when σ_{2p} lies above the π_{2p}. This is the ordering for elements with $Z \leq 7$.

Stress that the atomic orbitals are mixed, between the 2s and 2p so that the σ_{2p} and π_{2p} orbitals are reversed in order. Physically electrons try to get as far away from each other as possible and putting electrons into the σ_{2p} orbitals first does not do this. Hence, the π_{2p} orbitals are more favorable than the σ_{2p} molecular orbital.

Point out to students that paramagnetic materials, like O_2, are slightly attracted by a magnet. This is different from ferromagnetic materials, like iron, which are strongly attracted by a magnet.

	Li$_2$	Be$_2$	B$_2$	C$_2$	N$_2$
σ_{2p}^*					
π_{2p}^*, π_{2p}^*					
σ_{2p}					↑↓
π_{2p}, π_{2p}			↑ ↑	↑↓ ↑↓	↑↓ ↑↓
σ_{2s}^*		↑↓	↑↓	↑↓	↑↓
σ_{2s}	↑↓	↑↓	↑↓	↑↓	↑↓
Bond order	1	0	1	2	3
Magnetism	Dia-magnetic	–	Para-magnetic	Dia-magnetic	Dia-magnetic

	O$_2$	F$_2$	Ne$_2$
σ_{2p}^*			↑↓
π_{2p}^*, π_{2p}^*	↑ ↑	↑↓ ↑↓	↑↓ ↑↓
π_{2p}, π_{2p}	↑↓ ↑↓	↑↓ ↑↓	↑↓ ↑↓
σ_{2p}	↑↓	↑↓	↑↓
σ_{2s}^*	↑↓	↑↓	↑↓
σ_{2s}	↑↓	↑↓	↑↓
Bond order	2	1	0
Magnetism	Para-magnetic	Dia-magnetic	–

▲ **FIGURE 11-25**
Molecular orbital diagrams for the homonuclear diatomic molecules of the second-period elements
In all cases, the σ_{1s} and σ_{1s}^* molecular orbitals are filled but not shown.

Here is how we assign electrons to the molecular orbitals of the diatomic molecules of the second-period elements: We start with the σ_{1s} and σ_{1s}^* orbitals filled. Then we add electrons, in order of increasing energy, to the available molecular orbitals of the second principal shell. Figure 11-25 shows the electron assignments for the homonuclear diatomic molecules of the second-period elements. Some molecular properties are also listed in the figure.

Just as we might arrange the valence-shell atomic orbitals of an atom, we can arrange the second-shell molecular orbitals of a diatomic molecule in the order of increasing energy. Then we can assign electrons to these orbitals, thereby obtaining a *molecular orbital diagram*. If we assign the eight valence electrons of the molecule C_2 to the diagram in Figure 11-24(a), we obtain

▶ A *homonuclear* diatomic molecule (X_2) is one in which both atoms are of the same kind. A *heteronuclear* diatomic molecule (XY) is one in which the two atoms are different.

KEEP IN MIND ▶
that Hund's rule applies to molecules as well as atoms.

σ_{2s} σ_{2s}^* σ_{2p} π_{2p} π_{2p}^* σ_{2p}^*

Experiment shows that the C_2 molecule is diamagnetic, not paramagnetic, and the configuration just described is *incorrect*. So here we see the importance of the modified energy-level diagram in Figure 11-24(b). Assignment of eight electrons to the following molecular orbital diagram is consistent with the observation that C_2 is diamagnetic.

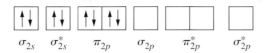

$$\sigma_{2s} \quad \sigma_{2s}^* \quad \pi_{2p} \quad \sigma_{2p} \quad \pi_{2p}^* \quad \sigma_{2p}^*$$

This modified energy-level diagram is used for homonuclear diatomic molecules involving elements with atomic numbers from three through seven.

A Special Look at O_2

Molecular orbital theory helps us understand some of the previously unexplained features of the O_2 molecule. Each O atom brings six valence electrons to the diatomic molecule, O_2. In Figure 11-25 we see that when 12 valence electrons are assigned to molecular orbitals, the molecule has *two unpaired electrons*. This explains the paramagnetism of O_2. There are eight valence electrons in bonding orbitals and four in antibonding orbitals so the bond order is two. This corresponds to a double covalent bond in O_2. This is summarized in the following molecular orbital diagram.

$$O_2 \quad \boxed{\uparrow\downarrow} \quad \boxed{\uparrow\downarrow} \quad \boxed{\uparrow\downarrow} \quad \boxed{\uparrow\downarrow \ \uparrow\downarrow} \quad \boxed{\uparrow \ \uparrow} \quad \boxed{} \quad (11.2)$$
$$\sigma_{2s} \quad \sigma_{2s}^* \quad \sigma_{2p} \quad \pi_{2p} \quad \pi_{2p}^* \quad \sigma_{2p}^*$$

▲ **Paramagnetism of oxygen**
Liquid oxygen is attracted into the magnetic field of a large magnet.

EXAMPLE 11-6

Writing a Molecular Orbital Diagram and Determining Bond Order. Represent bonding in O_2^+ with a molecular orbital diagram, and determine the bond order in this ion.

Solution

The ion O_2^+ has 11 valence electrons. Assign these to the available molecular orbitals in accordance with the ideas stated on page 440 (or simply remove one of the electrons from a π_{2p}^* orbital in expression 11.2). In the following diagram, there is an excess of *five* bonding electrons over antibonding ones. The bond order is 2.5.

$$O_2^+ \quad \boxed{\uparrow\downarrow} \quad \boxed{\uparrow\downarrow} \quad \boxed{\uparrow\downarrow} \quad \boxed{\uparrow\downarrow \ \uparrow\downarrow} \quad \boxed{\uparrow} \quad \boxed{}$$
$$\sigma_{2s} \quad \sigma_{2s}^* \quad \sigma_{2p} \quad \pi_{2p} \quad \pi_{2p}^* \quad \sigma_{2p}^*$$

Practice Example A: Refer to Figure 11-25. Write a molecular orbital diagram and determine the bond order of **(a)** N_2^+; **(b)** Ne_2^+; **(c)** C_2^{2-}.

Practice Example B: The bond lengths for O_2^+, O_2, O_2^-, and O_2^{2-} are 112, 121, 128, and 149 pm, respectively. Are these bond lengths consistent with the bond order determined from the molecular orbital diagram? Explain.

CONCEPT ASSESSMENT ✓

In valence bond theory, π bonds are always accompanied by a σ bond. Can the same also be said of the molecular orbital theory for diatomic molecules?

π^*_{2p}

π_{2p}

▲ **The π molecular orbitals of CO**

The carbon atom is on the left side of the diagram.

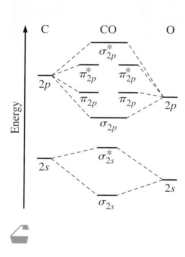

▶ See Focus on Photoelectron Spectroscopy on page 463 for a further discussion of this.

A LOOK AT HETERONUCLEAR DIATOMIC MOLECULES

The ideas that we have developed for homonuclear diatomic species can be extended, with some care, to give us an idea of the bonding in heteronuclear diatomic species. When we drew a diagram to illustrate the mixing of two $1s$ orbitals to form the σ bond in H_2, we understood that the two $1s$ orbitals have the same energy and mix fifty-fifty. This is not the case with heteronuclear diatomic species because, as we know from ionization energies, the orbitals of different atoms have different energies. To illustrate the differences, let us consider the construction of the π bonding and antibonding orbitals from the $2p$ orbitals of C and O atoms in the bonding for CO. The bonding combination is

$$\pi = c_O\,2p_O + c_C\,2p_C$$

and the antibonding combination is

$$\pi^* = c_O^*\,2p_O - c_C^*\,2p_C$$

where the coefficients c_O and c_C reflect the percentage mixing of the orbitals. In the homonuclear case, the two atoms are the same and the coefficients are equal because there is an equal probability of finding the electrons in the orbital associated with either nucleus. If the nuclei are different, we expect a greater probability of finding the electrons in the orbital associated with the more electronegative element. As a result, in our example we expect c_O to be greater than c_C in the bonding orbital. Thus, the bonding π_{2p} molecular orbital has a greater contribution from the oxygen $2p$ orbital than from the carbon $2p$ orbital. This can be seen in the computed molecular orbitals displayed in the margin. We can also see that in the antibonding orbital, the situation is reversed, with c_O^* less than c_C^*. In this case the antibonding orbital has a greater contribution from the carbon $2p$ orbital, on the left.

The energy of the bonding orbital is closer to that of the more electronegative element, whereas the energy of the antibonding orbital is closer to the energy of the less electronegative element, as clearly seen in the diagram in the margin. Thus the molecular orbital diagram shown in Figure 11-24 has to be modified to take this factor into account. Nevertheless, we can still use the molecular orbital diagrams in Figure 11-25 to discuss bonding in heteronuclear diatomic species with this restriction: The two atoms must not be too far apart in atomic number, so that the order of energy levels is not too different from that found for homonuclear diatomic species. The question arises as to which order of orbitals to use, the expected one or the modified one in which the σ_{2p} is above the π_{2p} in energy. If one of the elements is oxygen or fluorine, the appropriate energy-level diagram is that shown in Figure 11-24(a), that is, the unmodified one. The reason for this is that the energy difference between the $2s$ and $2p$ orbitals of oxygen and the $2s$ and $2p$ orbitals of any other element preceding oxygen in the periodic table is too great for significant mixing to take place.

Let's apply these ideas to carbon monoxide, which has 10 valence electrons. Applying the aufbau process to the molecular orbital diagram for O_2 in Figure 11-25, we obtain this configuration:

CO $\boxed{\uparrow\downarrow}$ $\boxed{\uparrow\downarrow}$ $\boxed{\uparrow\downarrow}$ $\boxed{\uparrow\downarrow\,\uparrow\downarrow}$ $\boxed{\,}$ $\boxed{}$

$\quad\;\;\sigma_{2s}\quad\;\;\sigma^*_{2s}\quad\;\;\sigma_{2p}\quad\;\;\;\pi_{2p}\quad\;\;\;\;\pi^*_{2p}\quad\;\;\sigma^*_{2p}$

Thus CO has a bond order of 3, in accord with experimental data. Notice that CO has a greater bond energy than NO, which has a bond order of 2.5, as predicted by the molecular orbital diagram

NO $\boxed{\uparrow\downarrow}$ $\boxed{\uparrow\downarrow}$ $\boxed{\uparrow\downarrow}$ $\boxed{\uparrow\downarrow\,\uparrow\downarrow}$ $\boxed{\uparrow}$ $\boxed{}$

$\quad\;\;\sigma_{2s}\quad\;\;\sigma^*_{2s}\quad\;\;\sigma_{2p}\quad\;\;\;\pi_{2p}\quad\;\;\;\;\pi^*_{2p}\quad\;\;\sigma^*_{2p}$

We see that NO is also predicted to be paramagnetic, which we know to be the case from experimental data.

It is useful to point out here that molecular orbital theory is dealing with an odd number of electrons.

EXAMPLE 11-7

Writing Molecular Orbital Diagrams for Heteronuclear Diatomic Species. Write the molecular orbital diagram for the cyanide ion, CN^-, and determine the bond order for this ion. Compare your results with the predicted bond order from a Lewis structure.

Solution

The number of valence electrons to be assigned in the molecular orbital diagram is $10\ (4 + 5 + 1)$. Notice that here we have to use the modified molecular orbital energy-level diagram, as both elements precede oxygen in the periodic table. That is, use the MO diagram for either C_2 or N_2, and introduce 10 electrons.

$$CN^- \quad \boxed{\uparrow\downarrow} \quad \boxed{\uparrow\downarrow} \quad \boxed{\uparrow\downarrow}\,\boxed{\uparrow\downarrow} \quad \boxed{\uparrow\downarrow} \quad \boxed{}\,\boxed{} \quad \boxed{}$$
$$\quad\ \ \sigma_{2s} \qquad \sigma_{2s}^* \qquad\ \pi_{2p} \qquad\quad \sigma_{2p} \qquad \pi_{2p}^* \qquad\quad \sigma_{2p}^*$$

The bond order is the difference between the number of bonding electrons and the number of antibonding electrons, divided by two, which is $(2 + 4 + 2 - 2)/2 = 3$, a triple bond. The Lewis structure also predicts a triple bond, that is, $[:C{\equiv}N:]^-$.

Practice Example A: Write a molecular orbital diagram for CN^+, and determine the bond order.

Practice Example B: Write a molecular orbital diagram for BN, and determine the bond order.

CONCEPT ASSESSMENT ✔

Would you expect NeO to be a stable molecule?

11-6   DELOCALIZED ELECTRONS: BONDING IN THE BENZENE MOLECULE

◀ The term "aromatic" relates to the fragrant aromas associated with some (but by no means all) of these compounds.

In Section 11-4 we discussed localized π bonds, such as those in ethylene, C_2H_4. Some molecules, such as benzene (C_6H_6) and substances related to it—aromatic compounds—have a network of π bonds. In this section we will use the bonding theories we have studied thus far to consider bonding in benzene; the conclusions we reach will help us understand other cases of bonding as well.

BONDING IN BENZENE

In 1865, Friedrich Kekulé advanced the first good proposal for the structure of benzene. He suggested that the C_6H_6 molecule consists of a flat, hexagonal ring of six carbon atoms joined by alternating single and double covalent bonds. Each C atom is joined to two other C atoms and to one H atom. To explain the fact that the carbon-to-carbon bonds are all alike, Kekulé suggested that the single and double bonds continually oscillate from one position to the other. Today, we say that the two possible Kekulé structures are actually contributing structures to a resonance hybrid. This view is suggested by Figure 11-26.

We can gain a more thorough understanding of bonding in the benzene molecule by combining the valence-bond and molecular orbital methods. A σ-bond framework for the observed planar structure can be constructed with 120° bond angles by using sp^2 hybridization at each carbon atom. End-to-end overlap of the sp^2 orbitals produces σ bonds. The six remaining $2p$ orbitals are used to construct the delocalized π bonds. Figure 11-27 gives a valence-bond theory representation of bonding in C_6H_6.

▲ Dame Kathleen Londsdale first determined the X-ray crystal structure of benzene. Her experiment demonstrated that the benzene molecule is flat, as predicted by theorists.

Point out to students that the resonance stability is about 150 kJ mol^{-1} over that of either one of the Kekulé structures.

Remind students that any given resonance structure does not accurately represent the structure of a molecule. Only the resonance hybrid is an accurate representation of a molecule. Also tell students that the resonance structures of a molecule are not in equilibrium with each other. Electrons do not move around the molecule to form the different resonance structures.

▲ FIGURE 11-26
Resonance in the benzene molecule and the Kekulé structures
(a) Lewis structure for C_6H_6 showing alternate carbon-to-carbon single and double bonds. **(b)** Two equivalent Kekulé structures for benzene. A carbon atom is at each corner of the hexagonal structure, and a hydrogen atom is bonded to each carbon atom. (The symbols for carbon and hydrogen, as well as the C—H bonds, are customarily omitted in these structures.) **(c)** A space-filling model.

(a) σ bond framework

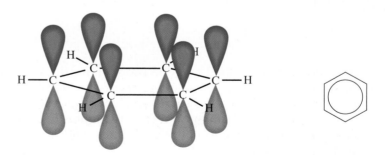

(b) Carbon $2p$ orbitals to be used in π bonding   **(c)** Symbolic representation

▲ FIGURE 11-27
Bonding in benzene, C_6H_6, by the valence-bond method
(a) Carbon atoms use sp^2 and p orbitals. Each carbon atom forms three σ bonds, two with neighboring C atoms in the hexagonal ring and a third with a H atom. **(b)** The unhybridized $2p$ orbitals on the carbon atoms of benzene, which produce the delocalized π bonds in benzene. **(c)** Because the π bonding is delocalized around the benzene ring, the molecule is often represented by a hexagon with an inscribed circle.

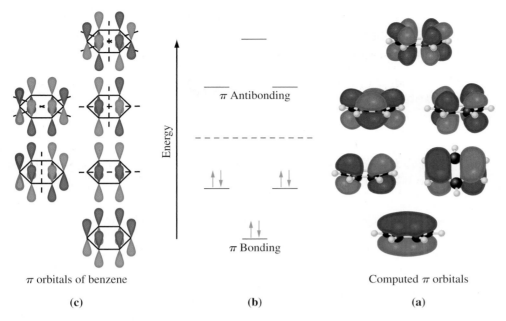

π Antibonding

Energy

π Bonding

π orbitals of benzene

(c)

(b)

Computed π orbitals

(a)

◀ **FIGURE 11-28**
π molecular orbital diagram for C₆H₆
Of the six π molecular orbitals, three are bonding orbitals and each of these is filled with an electron pair. The three antibonding molecular orbitals at a higher energy remain empty.

We do not need to think in terms of an oscillation between two structures (Kekulé) or of a resonance hybrid for benzene. The π bonds are not localized between specific carbon atoms but are spread out around the six-membered ring. To represent this *delocalized* π bonding, the symbol for benzene is often written as a hexagon with a circle inscribed within (Fig. 11-27c).

We can best understand delocalized π bonds through molecular orbital theory. Six $2p$ atomic orbitals (see Figure 11-27b) of the C atoms combine to form six molecular orbitals of the π type. Three of these π-type molecular orbitals are bonding, and three are antibonding. What do these π molecular orbitals look like? Recall that as the energy of orbitals increases, the number of nodes increases, so we expect that the lowest π molecular orbital will not possess a node, and this is the case (Fig. 11-28a). All six $2p$ orbitals are in phase as indicated by the fact that all the blue lobes are on one side of the σ framework. The next two π-bonding molecular orbitals each have one node (dashed line in Figure 11-28a) and consequently have the same energy; that is, they are degenerate (Fig. 11-28b). The next pair of orbitals, which are antibonding π orbitals, have two nodes, and the final orbital has three nodes (Fig. 11-28a). The computed π molecular orbitals of benzene are also included in Figure 11-28(c).

The three bonding orbitals fill with six electrons (one $2p$ electron from each C atom), and the three antibonding orbitals remain empty. The bond order associated with the six electrons in π-bonding molecular orbitals is $(6 - 0)/2 = 3$. The three bonds are distributed among the six C atoms, which amounts to 3/6, or a half-bond, between each pair of C atoms. Add to this the σ bonds in the σ-bond framework, and we have a bond order of 1.5 for each carbon-to-carbon bond. This is exactly what we also get by averaging the two Kekulé structures of Figure 11-26.

The three bonding π molecular orbitals in C₆H₆ describe the distribution of π electron charge in the molecule. We can think of this in terms of two doughnut-shaped regions: one above and one below the plane of the C and H atoms. Because they are spread out among all six C atoms instead of being concentrated between pairs of C atoms, these molecular orbitals are called **delocalized molecular orbitals**. Figure 11-29 pictures these delocalized molecular orbitals in the benzene molecule. The electrostatic potential maps of benzene displayed at the opening of this chapter also show the buildup of negative charge density above and below the plane of the benzene molecule.

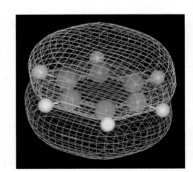

▲ **FIGURE 11-29**
Molecular orbital representation of π bonding in benzene
The computed π molecular orbitals of benzene.

(a) σ bond framework

(b) Delocalized π molecular orbital

▲ **FIGURE 11-30**
Structure of the ozone molecule, O_3
(a) The σ-bond framework and the assignment of bond-pair (:) and lone-pair (·) electrons to sp^2 hybrid orbitals are discussed in points 1 and 2. **(b)** The π molecular orbitals and assignments of electrons to them are discussed in points 3 and 4.

OTHER STRUCTURES WITH DELOCALIZED MOLECULAR ORBITALS

By using delocalized bonding schemes, we can avoid writing two or more contributing structures to a resonance hybrid, as is so often required in the Lewis theory. Consider the ozone molecule, O_3, that we used to introduce the concept of resonance in Section 10-5. In place of the resonance hybrid based on these contributing structures,

we can write the single structure shown in Figure 11-30. Here are the ideas that lead to Figure 11-30.

1. With VSEPR theory, we predict a trigonal-planar electron-group geometry (the measured bond angle is 117°). The hybridization scheme chosen for the central O atom is sp^2, and although we normally do not need to invoke hybridization for terminal atoms, this case is simplified if we assume sp^2 hybridization for the terminal O atoms as well. Thus, each O atom uses the orbital set $sp^2 + p$.

2. Of the 18 valence electrons in O_3, assign 14 to the sp^2 hybrid orbitals of the σ-bond framework. Four of these are bonding electrons (red) and ten are lone-pair electrons (blue).

3. The three unhybridized $2p$ orbitals combine to form *three* molecular orbitals of the π type (Fig. 11-31). One of these orbitals is a bonding molecular orbital, and the second is antibonding. The third is a type we have not described before—a *nonbonding molecular orbital*. A nonbonding molecular orbital has the same energy as the atomic orbitals from which it is formed, and it neither adds to nor detracts from bond formation.

4. The remaining four valence electrons are assigned to the π molecular orbitals. Two go into the bonding orbital and two into the nonbonding orbital. The antibonding orbital remains empty.

▶ **FIGURE 11-31**
π bonding orbitals of the ozone molecule O_3
The π-bonding molecular orbital has all the $2p$ orbitals in phase. The π-antibonding molecular orbital has all the three $2p$ orbitals out of phase. The π-nonbonding molecular orbital has a single node and makes zero contribution to the wave function from the central atom. This orbital is called nonbonding because there is no region of increased electron density between the central atom and its neighbors. The nonbonding orbital is at the same energy as the original $2p$ orbitals on the oxygen atoms, whereas the π-bonding molecular orbital is stabilized with respect to the original orbitals and the π-antibonding molecular orbital is destabilized by an equal amount with respect to the original $2p$ orbitals. The energy level diagram is shown in the middle of this figure, with the computed π molecular orbitals shown on the right.

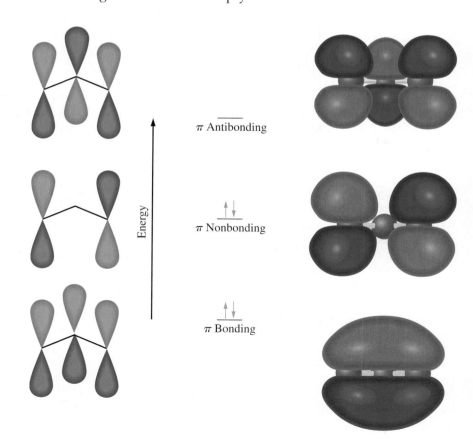

5. The bond order associated with the π molecular orbitals is $(2 - 0)/2 = 1$. This π bond is distributed between the two O—O bonds and amounts to one-half of a π bond for each.

The points listed here lead to a total bond order of 1.5 for the O—O bonds in O_3. This is equivalent to averaging the two Lewis structures. The O—O bond length suggested by this method was described in Section 10-5.

EXAMPLE 11-8

Representing Delocalized Molecular Orbitals with Atomic Orbital Diagrams. Represent π molecular orbital formation, bonding, and orbital occupancy in the nitrate ion, NO_3^-.

Solution

First, we should recognize that for this type of exercise, we need not concern ourselves with resonance; we can use any one of the following resonance structures.

Delocalized π molecular orbitals of NO_3^-

Let us use the first structure shown, in which the oxygen atoms are labeled (a), (b), and (c). Each atom in the structure has an electron-group geometry corresponding to three electron groups (an electron pair in each N-to-O single bond and two electron pairs in the N-to-O double bond). We must use sp^2 hybrid orbitals to form σ bonds and $2p$ orbitals to form π bonds. In assigning valence-shell electrons to the atoms, place one unpaired electron in an sp^2 for every σ bond that the atom forms and one unpaired electron for every π bond the atom forms. Then place lone-pair electrons in the orbitals that remain available. Because of the existence of formal charges in the structure, the number of valence electrons for each atom must be adjusted for the formal charge [for example, O atom (b) has a formal charge of −1 and must show seven electrons in its valence-shell orbitals, not the customary six].

Once you have assigned all the valence electrons to orbitals, show that all the unpaired electrons in sp^2 hybrid orbitals participate in σ-bond formation. Now combine the p orbitals to form the appropriate number of π molecular orbitals (four). Assign the p electrons to these molecular orbitals in the usual fashion.

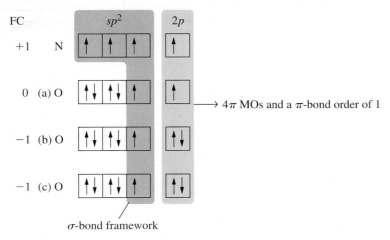

Practice Example A: Represent chemical bonding in the molecule SO_3 by using a combination of localized and delocalized orbitals.

Practice Example B: Represent chemical bonding in the ion NO_2^- by using a combination of localized and delocalized orbitals.

Are You Wondering . . .

What the π molecular orbitals of NO_3^- look like?

The construction of these orbitals is shown in Figure 11-32. The π-bonding molecular orbital has the four $2p$ orbitals (one on the N atom and one each on the three oxygen atoms) all in phase. The corresponding antibonding π orbital has two nodes and is at the highest energy. Since we are combining four $2p$ orbitals we expect to get four molecular orbitals. The remaining two molecular orbitals will each have one node. The only way to create a molecular orbital with one node in NO_3^- is for the molecular orbital to have a node at the nitrogen atom. Such a molecular orbital must be nonbonding with respect to nitrogen. That the nitrogen does not contribute to the degenerate nonbonding orbitals can be clearly seen in the computed molecular orbitals depicted in Figure 11-32.

▲ **FIGURE 11-32**
π **bonding orbitals of the nitrate anion, NO_3^-**
The π-bonding molecular orbital has all the p orbitals in phase, whereas the π-antibonding orbital has all the p orbitals out of phase. Each of the nonbonding orbitals has a node at the nitrogen atom.

CONCEPT ASSESSMENT ✔

Would you expect the delocalized π-bonding framework in HCO_2^- to be similar to that in ozone or to that in the nitrate anion?

11-7 BONDING IN METALS

In nonmetal atoms, the valence shells generally have more electrons than they do orbitals. To illustrate, a F atom has *four* valence-shell orbitals ($2s$, $2p_x$, $2p_y$, $2p_z$) and *seven* valence-shell electrons. Whether fluorine exists as a solid, liquid, or gas, F atoms join in pairs to form F_2 molecules. One pair of electrons is shared in the F—F bond, and the other electron pairs are lone pairs, as seen in the Lewis structure $:\!\ddot{F}\!-\!\ddot{F}\!:$. By contrast, the metal atom Li has the same four valence-shell orbitals as F but only *one* valence-shell electron ($2s^1$). This may account for the formation of the *gaseous* molecule Li:Li, but in the solid metal, each Li atom is somehow bonded to *eight* neighbors. The challenge to a bonding theory for metals is to explain how so much bonding can occur with so few electrons. Also, the theory should account for certain properties that metals display to a far greater extent than nonmetals—such as a lustrous appearance, an ability to conduct electricity, and ease of deformation (metals are easily flattened into sheets and drawn into wires).

THE ELECTRON SEA MODEL

An oversimplified theory, which can explain some of the properties of metals just cited, pictures a solid metal as a network of positive ions immersed in a "sea of electrons." In lithium, for instance, the ions are Li^+ and one electron per atom is contributed to the sea of electrons. Electrons in the sea are *free* (not attached to any particular ion), and they are mobile. Thus, if electrons from an external source enter a metal wire at one end, free electrons pass through the wire and leave the other end at the same rate. In this way, electrical conductivity is explained.

Free electrons (those in the electron sea) are not limited in their ability to absorb photons of visible light as are electrons bound to an atom. Thus, metals absorb visible light; they are opaque. Electrons at the surface of a metal are able to reradiate—at the same frequency—light that strikes the surface, which explains the lustrous appearance of metals. The ease of deformation of metals can be explained as follows: If one layer of metal ions is forced across another, perhaps by hammering, no bonds are broken, the internal structure of the metal remains essentially unchanged, and the sea of electrons rapidly adjusts to the new situation (Fig. 11-33).

◀ A dull metal surface usually signifies that the surface is coated with a compound of the metal (for example, an oxide, sulfide, or carbonate).

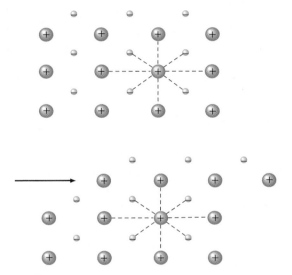

▲ **FIGURE 11-33**
The electron sea model of metals
A network of positive ions is immersed in a "sea of electrons," derived from the valence shells of the metal atoms and belonging to the crystal as a whole. One particular ion (red), its nearest neighboring ions (brown), and nearby electrons in the electron sea (blue) are emphasized. At the bottom of the figure, a force is applied (from left to right). The highlighted cation is unaffected; its immediate environment is unchanged. The electron sea model explains the ease of deformation of metals.

BAND THEORY

The electron-sea model is a simple qualitative description of the metallic state, but for most purposes, the theory of metallic bonding used is a form of molecular orbital theory called **band theory**.

Recall the formation of molecular orbitals and the bonding between two Li atoms (see Figure 11-25). Each Li atom contributes one $2s$ orbital to the production of two molecular orbitals: σ_{2s} and σ_{2s}^*. The electrons originally described as the $2s^1$ electrons of the Li atoms enter and half-fill these molecular orbitals. That is, they fill the σ_{2s} orbital and leave the σ_{2s}^* empty. If we extend this combination of Li atoms to a third Li atom, three molecular orbitals are formed, containing a total of three electrons. Again, the set of

Even though bands are formed in metals, the electrons still have to fill according to Pauli's exclusion principle. Although it is beyond the level of the course, you might want to tell them that at absolute zero, the electrons fill up the levels and the highest level filled is called the Fermi level.

▲ **FIGURE 11-34**
Formation of an energy band in lithium metal
As more and more Li atoms are added to the growing "molecule," Li_2, Li_3, and so on, additional energy levels are added and the spacing between levels becomes increasingly smaller. In an entire crystal of N atoms, the energy levels merge into a band of N closely spaced levels. The lowest $N/2$ levels are filled with electrons, and the upper $N/2$ levels are empty.

molecular orbitals is half-filled. We can extend this process to an enormously large number (N) of atoms—the total number of atoms in a crystal of Li. Here is the result we get: a set of N molecular orbitals with an extremely small energy separation between each pair of successive levels. This collection of very closely spaced molecular orbital energy levels is called an *energy band* (Fig. 11-34).

In the band just described, there are N electrons (a $2s$ electron from each Li atom) occupying, in pairs, $N/2$ molecular orbitals of lowest energy. These are the electrons responsible for bonding the Li atoms together. They are valence electrons, and the band in which they are found is called a *valence band*. Because the energy differences between the occupied and unoccupied levels in the valence band are so small, however, electrons can be easily excited from the highest filled levels to the unfilled levels that lie immediately above them in energy. This excitation, which has the effect of producing mobile electrons, can be accomplished by applying a small electric potential difference across the crystal. This is how the band theory explains the ability of metals to conduct electricity. The essential feature for electrical conductivity, then, is *an energy band that is only partly filled with electrons*. Such an energy band is called a *conduction band*. In lithium, the $2s$ band is both a valence band and a conduction band (Fig. 11-35a).

Let's extend our discussion to N atoms of beryllium, which has the electron configuration $1s^2 2s^2$. We expect the band formed from $2s$ atomic orbitals to be filled—N molecular orbitals and $2N$ electrons. But how can we reconcile this with the fact that Be is a good electric conductor? At the same time that $2s$ orbitals are being combined into a $2s$ band, $2p$ orbitals combine to form an *empty* $2p$ band. The lowest levels of the $2p$ band are at a *lower* energy than the highest levels of the $2s$ band. The bands overlap (Fig. 11-35b). As a consequence, empty molecular orbitals are available to the valence electrons in beryllium.

In an *electrical insulator*, like diamond or silica (SiO_2), not only is the valence band filled but there is a large energy gap between the valence band and the conduction band (Fig. 11-35d). Very few electrons are able to make the transition between the two.

Development of Band Structure activity

▲ **FIGURE 11-35**
Metals, semiconductors, and insulators as viewed by band theory
(a) In some metals, the valence band (blue) is only partially filled (for example, the half-filled $3s$ band in Na). The valence band also serves as a conduction band (outlined in black). **(b)** In other metals, the valence band is full, but a conduction band overlaps it (for example, the empty $2p$ band of Be overlaps the full $2s$ valence band). **(c)** In a semiconductor, the valence band is full and the conduction band is empty. The energy gap (ΔE) between the two is small enough, however, that some electrons make the transition between them just by acquiring thermal energy.
(d) In an insulator, the valence band is filled with electrons and a large energy gap (ΔE) separates the valence band from the conduction band. Few electrons can make the transition between bands, and the insulator does not conduct electricity.

SEMICONDUCTORS

Much of modern electronics depends on the use of semiconductor materials. Light-emitting diodes (LEDs), transistors, and solar cells are among the familiar electronic components using semiconductors. Semiconductors such as cadmium yellow (CdS) and vermilion (HgS) are brilliantly colored, and artists use them in paints.

What determines the electronic properties of a semiconductor is the energy gap (band gap) between the valence band and the conduction band (Fig. 11-35c). In some materials, such as CdS, this gap is of a fixed size. These materials are called *intrinsic semiconductors*. When white light interacts with the semiconductor, electrons are excited (promoted) to the conduction band. CdS absorbs violet light and some blue light, but other frequencies contain less energy than is needed to excite an electron above the energy gap. The frequencies that are not absorbed are reflected, and the color we is see yellow. Some semiconductors, such as GaAs and PbS, have a sufficiently small band gap that all frequencies of visible light are absorbed. There is no reflected visible light, and the materials have a black color.

In a semiconductor such as silicon or germanium, the filled valence band and empty conduction band are separated by only a small energy gap. Electrons in the valence band may acquire enough thermal energy to jump to a level in the conduction band. The greater the thermal energy, the more electrons can make the transition. In this way, band theory explains the observation that the electrical conductivity of semiconductors increases with temperature.

In many semiconductors, called *extrinsic semiconductors*, the size of the band gap is controlled by carefully adding impurities—a process called *doping*. Let's consider what doping does to one of the most common semiconductors, silicon.

When silicon is doped with phosphorus, the energy level of the P atoms lies just below the conduction band of the silicon, as shown in Figure 11-36. Each P atom uses *four* of its five valence electrons to form bonds to four neighboring Si atoms, and thermal energy alone is enough to cause the "extra" valence electron

Point out that the electrical conductivity of metals decreases with increasing temperature, but for semiconductors, the conductivity increases exponentially with increasing temperature because at higher temperatures more electrons can jump the small gap.

A natural semiconductor is called an intrinsic semiconductor. Semimetals that become semiconductors due to doping are called extrinsic semiconductors.

▲ **FIGURE 11-36**
p- and n-type semiconductors
In a semiconductor with donor atoms (for example, P in Si), the donor level lies just beneath the conduction band. Electrons (⬤) are easily promoted into the conduction band. The semiconductor is of the *n*-type. In a semiconductor with acceptor atoms (for example, Al in Si), the acceptor level lies just above the valence band. Electrons (⬤) are easily promoted to the acceptor level, leaving positive holes (◯) in the valence band. The semiconductor is of the *p*-type.

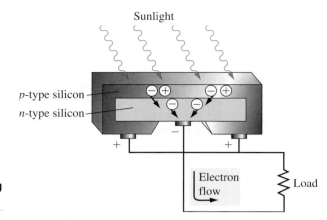

Sunlight

p-type silicon

n-type silicon

Electron flow

Load

▶ **FIGURE 11-37**
A photovoltaic (solar) cell using silicon-based semiconductors

to be promoted to the conduction band, leaving behind an immobile positive P^+ ion. The P atoms are called *donor* atoms, and electrical conductivity in this type of semiconductor involves primarily the movement of electrons from donor atoms through the conduction band. This type of semiconductor is called an *n-type*, where *n* refers to negative—the type of electric charge carried by electrons.

When silicon is doped with aluminum, the energy level of the Al atoms, called *acceptor* atoms, lies just above the valence band of the silicon (Fig. 11-36). Because an Al atom has only *three* valence electrons, it forms regular electron-pair bonds with three neighboring Si atoms but only a one-electron bond with a fourth Si atom. An electron is easily promoted from the valence band to an Al atom in the acceptor level, however, forming an immobile negative Al^- ion. When this occurs, a *positive hole* is created in the valence band. Because electrical conductivity in this type of semiconductor consists primarily of the migration of positive holes, it is called a *p-type* semiconductor.

Figure 11-37 suggests how semiconductors are used in photovoltaic (solar) cells. A thin layer of a *p-type* semiconductor is in contact with an *n-type* semiconductor in a region called the *junction*. Normally, migration of electrons and positive holes across the junction is very limited because such a migration would lead to a separation of charge: Positive holes crossing the junction from the *p-type* semiconductor would have to move away from immobile Al^- ions, and electrons crossing from the *n-type* semiconductor would have to move away from immobile P^+ ions.

Now imagine that the *p-type* semiconductor is struck by a beam of light. Electrons in the valence band can absorb energy and be promoted to the conduction band, creating positive holes in the valence band. Conduction electrons, unlike positive holes, can easily cross the junction into the *n-type* semiconductor. This sets up a flow of electrons, an electric current. Electrons can be carried by wires through an external load (lights, electric motors, and so forth) and eventually returned to the *p-type* semiconductor, where they fill positive holes. Further light absorption creates more conduction electrons and positive holes, and the process continues as long as light shines on the solar cell.

 A *p*-type semiconductor results when silicon is doped with an element that has one less electron in its valence shell, like aluminum or gallium. An *n*-type semiconductor results when silicon is doped with an element that has one more electron in its valence shell, like phosphorus or arsenic.

We have been experiencing leaps in computer speed with CPU time doubling about every 18 months. Using present techniques, this will soon stop as the ability to make ever smaller micro-components will eventually reach a limit of ultimate smallness.

Information about photovoltaic (solar cells) can be obtained at http://www.nrel.gov/clean_energy/photovoltaic.html and at http://www.fsec.ucf.edu/pvt/pvbasics/.

CONCEPT ASSESSMENT ✓

Do you think GaN is a semiconductor?

11-8 SOME UNRESOLVED ISSUES: CAN ELECTRON CHARGE-DENSITY PLOTS HELP?

In Chapters 10 and 11 we have presented a wide range of views of chemical bonding, from simple Lewis theory to the more advanced valence-bond and molecular orbital approaches. We must emphasize, however, that each of these models has its deficiencies, and their uncritical use can lead to incorrect conclusions.

Here are some of the unresolved issues we have encountered: Employing expanded valence shells in Lewis structures created the quandary of where to accommodate the extra valence electrons in molecules such as SF_6 and SF_4 (page 394), specifically, are d-orbitals used in the bonding description? A related issue is whether to use expanded valence shells to minimize formal charges in anions such as SO_4^{2-} (page 395). Still another issue is whether VSEPR theory or hybridization schemes of the valence-bond method gives the more fundamental view of molecular shapes. Finally, we might wonder how the valence-bond and molecular orbital theories are related. In this section, we shall attempt to provide answers to these questions—stressing the significance of electron charge density calculations.

BONDING IN THE MOLECULE SF_6

First let's see if it is possible to describe the bonding in SF_6 while maintaining the octet rule. One proposal has been to introduce resonance structures of the form

with the actual electronic structure being a combination of these resonance structures. The resonance structures illustrate the concept of *hyperconjugation*, a situation in which the number of electron pairs used to bond other atoms to a central atom is less than the number of bonds formed. In the case of SF_6, four electron pairs bond six F atoms to a central S atom and the octet rule is preserved. When resonance structures are written in this way, the assumption is that the bond lines represent nonpolar covalent bonds, whereas the other bonds are fully ionic. The molecule SF_6 has equivalent bonds and consequently would require a total of 15 structures of the type shown. This description implies a charge of 2+ on the sulfur and a charge of 1/3− on each F atom, corresponding to a collective charge of 2− on the six F atoms. This description of bonding, then, has the appeal of describing the polarity of the bonds while getting around the problem that arises when the Lewis structure is written as shown below, namely, where do the "extra" electrons go on the S atom?

Should we use hyperconjugation to describe the bonding in SF_6? One answer is to compare the suggested charges on the S and F atoms with those obtained from a quantum-mechanical calculation. The calculation gives a charge of 3.17+ on sulfur and 0.53− on each fluorine. To describe bonding through hyperconjugation that is in better agreement with the quantum-mechanical calculation, we would have to use additional resonance structures with higher charges and fewer covalent bonds. Such an approach is clearly cumbersome, and adoption of this large number of structures is not justified just to satisfy the octet rule.

The problem in describing molecules with expanded valence shells, so-called *hypervalent* molecules, is that there is no generally accepted way of denoting polar bonds in a structure. Furthermore, we must remember that Lewis devised his "rule of eight" in an era when only a few molecules such as PCl_5 and SF_6 were known, and he did not consider these exceptions to be of any great significance. Why was that? Lewis viewed the "rule of two" to be of greater fundamental importance than the rule of eight; that is, the electron charge density due to the electron pair is paramount in understanding bonding. Bonding in molecules with expanded valence shells is not a consequence of a special type of bonding. Bonds in these molecules are similar to those in other molecules and can vary from predominantly covalent to predominantly ionic.

If we do not use hyperconjugation, how are we to describe where the "extra" electrons go? This question arises because we seem implicitly to think about bonding in terms of hybridization of atomic orbitals. Thus, in order to describe bonding in the methane molecule consistent with its tetrahedral geometry we introduced the concept of sp^3 hybrid orbitals. That is, the hybridization was introduced *because* of the geometry. The geometry of a molecule can be determined only experimentally or estimated using VSEPR theory.

We extended the concept of hybridization of orbitals to molecules with expanded valence shells to include d orbitals, that is, sp^3d and sp^3d^2 hybrid orbitals to accommodate five- and six-electron pairs, respectively. While this is an appealing idea, it has come into question because of the relatively high energy of the d orbitals, and quantum-mechanical calculations have shown that the wave functions contain very little contribution from d orbitals. Thus, it appears that to describe bonding in SF_6 we should avoid using d orbitals in hybridization schemes.

How are we to proceed? Where are the electrons in the SF_6 molecule? Recall that we have already employed the results of quantum-mechanical calculations in constructing electrostatic potential maps (page 379). Let's turn again to the results of such calculations to improve our understanding of the bonding in SF_6 and similar molecules.

BONDING IN THE MOLECULE SCl_2

To continue our discussion consider first a simpler molecule—SCl_2. Figure 11-38 shows how the electron charge density (ρ) varies in the plane that contains the sulfur atom and the two chlorine atoms. The most striking feature of this diagram is that the electron density is very high at each nucleus; in fact, we have truncated the very large maxima in order to show other features in the diagram. An especially significant feature is the small ridge of increased electron density between the sulfur and each of the chlorine atoms. Despite its modest height, this ridge of electron density is responsible for an attractive force between the nuclei.

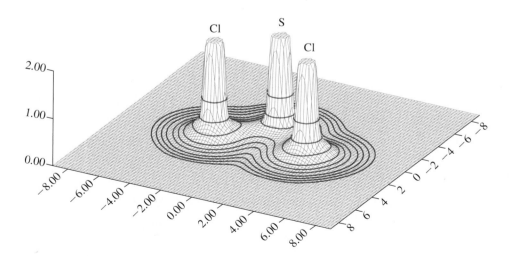

▲ FIGURE 11-38
Isodensity contour map of the electron density of SCl_2 in the plane of the nuclei
The isodensity contour lines, in atomic units (au), are shown in color, in the order 0.001, 0.002, 0.004, 0.008 (four outermost contours in blue); 0.2, 0.4, 0.8 (next three). Densities are truncated at 2.00 au (innermost green contour). The atomic unit of electron charge density = $e/a_0{}^3 = 1.081 \times 10^{12}$ C m^3, where a_0 is the Bohr radius, (adapted from Matta and Gillespie, *J. Chem. Ed.*: 79, 1141, 2002).

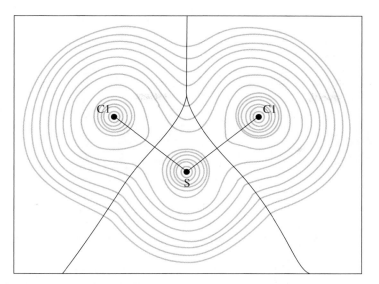

▲ **FIGURE 11-39**
Contour map of the electron density in SCl$_2$
The electron charge density increases from the outermost isodensity contour at 0.001 au in incremental steps of 2×10^{-3} au, 4×10^{-2} au, 8×10^{-1} au, 16×10^{0} au, and so on. The lines connecting the nuclei are the bond paths. The bond critical points are depicted by heavy black dots, (adapted from Matta and Gillespie, *J. Chem. Ed.*: 79, 1141, 2002).

An alternative representation of the electron density distribution is a contour map. Such a contour map for SCl$_2$ is shown in Figure 11-39. The lines drawn between the S atom and each Cl atom in Figure 11-39 represent the lines along the top of the small ridge of electron charge density between these atoms that we saw in Figure 11-38. The lines between the chlorine atoms and the sulfur atom are called the *bond paths* and represent the chemical bond between the S and one Cl atom as we would normally draw it in a Lewis structure. In Figure 11-39, notice the vertical line above the S atom that splits in two just before the sulfur atom is reached, with each segment intersecting the bond paths for the two sulfur-chlorine bonds between the S and a Cl atom. This bifurcated line represents a path tracing the minimum in the electron density, analogous to a path along the valley floor between the "mountains" of electron density. The point where this line intersects each bond line is called the *bond critical point*. The electron density at the bond critical point can be used to describe the type of bond connecting a pair of atoms in a molecule. The greater the electron density, the higher the bond order is.

◀ **KEEP IN MIND**
that a contour map represents changes in topology of a surface; similar maps are used by mountaineers to plan their ascent of a mountain.

BONDING IN THE MOLECULE H$_2$SO$_4$ AND THE ANION SO$_4^{2-}$

To decide whether or not to use expanded valence shells to minimize formal charges, we will consider the sulfuric acid molecule and the sulfate anion. Figure 11-40 is a three-dimensional representation of the electron charge distribution surfaces at a value of 0.001 atomic units (au); they correspond to the surface encompassing about 98% of the electron charge density in H$_2$SO$_4$ and SO$_4^{2-}$. If we choose a surface with a higher charge density value, then we include less of the electron charge distribution. Below the 98% surfaces are two electron charge density plots at increasing densities for the surfaces being calculated, also shown in Figure 11-40. What do these tell us? When we reach a density for the calculated surface just greater than the density at the bond critical point, the electron density in that bond disappears and we have established the amount of electron charge density in that bond. If there are bonds in the molecule that have more electron density at their bond critical

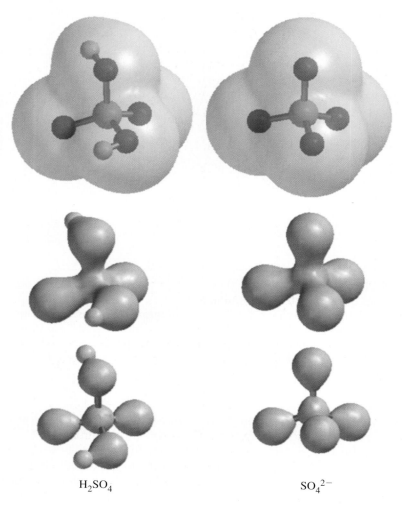

▲ **FIGURE 11-40**

Three-dimensional plots of the electron density in H_2SO_4 and SO_4^{2-}

The values for the outer isodensity envelope are set at 0.002 au, 0.22 au, and 0.28 au in the three figures for both species.

points, then electron density will still appear in the three-dimensional representation. To illustrate this point, observe that at 0.22 au of electron charge density, the electron density between the sulfur atom and the two oxygen atoms attached to hydrogen atoms has disappeared (the stick from the ball-and-stick model is apparent), but between the sulfur and the two oxygen atoms that do not have a hydrogen atom it is still visible. The electron density between the sulfur atom and the nonprotonated oxygen (the oxygen atom that does not have a hydrogen attached) atoms does not disappear until the density of the calculated surface is increased to 0.33 au. We conclude that there is more electron density in the bonds between the sulfur atom and the nonprotonated oxygen atoms than in the bonds between sulfur and oxygen attached to a proton. This extra electron density can be represented in a Lewis structure that places a double bond between the central S atom and the two terminal O atoms, thereby reducing the formal charges seen in the octet Lewis structure of H_2SO_4.

In considering the electron density surface for the sulfate anion, we see that the bond critical density is 0.28 au for the four bonds between the sulfur atom and the oxygen atoms. This is similar to that for the bond between sulfur and the nonprotonated oxygen atoms and greater than that for the sulfur–oxygen bonds attached to protonated oxygen atoms. The presence of this higher bond critical point in the sulfate anion suggests that maybe the Lewis structure that minimizes formal charges is the best. All four sulfur–oxygen bonds have the same bond critical point, which corresponds to the possible resonance structures that can be written.

We have reached a point at which minimizing the formal charges by using expanded valence shells seems best. However, one detailed analysis of the wavefunction of the sulfate anion suggests that the dominant form is the simple octet structure that does not minimize the formal charge.*

How Should We Proceed? What is the Correct Formulation?

Perhaps the answer to the several questions posed in this section lies in the work of R. J. Gillespie, a coauthor of the VSEPR method. He proposes that Lewis structures be written as Lewis would have written them—that is, with no expanded valence shells. In cases of highly polar bonds, there can be, simultaneously, considerable electron density between the atoms (a significantly covalent bond) *and* a large charge separation between the atoms (a significantly ionic bond). These two factors provide a better understanding of the strength of polar covalent bonds in molecules such as BF_3 (with a B—F bond dissociation enthalpy of 613 kJ/mol) or SiF_4 (with a Si—F bond dissociation enthalpy of 567 kJ/mol). By contrast, the nonpolar covalent C—C bond dissociation enthalpy is only 345 kJ/mol. An analysis of the electron densities in BF_3 and SiF_4 shows that they do have a combination of highly covalent and ionic bond characteristics, leading to very strong bonds.

The controversy as to how best to write Lewis structures will no doubt continue in the chemical literature, but you should not be too dismayed by this situation. Our mainstay for depicting the electronic structure of a molecule remains the simplest Lewis structure and its concomitant use in determining the shape of a molecule through VSEPR theory. In order to probe more deeply into the nature of a chemical bond—for example, to understand experimental results such as bond enthalpy values—we must analyze a computed electron density map for that molecule rather than rely just on the Lewis structure.

*L. Suidan, J. K. Badenhoop, E. D. Glendenning, and F. Weinhold, *J. Chem. Ed.* 72, 583 (1995).

Summary

11-1 What a Bonding Theory Should Do—A basic requirement of a bonding theory is that it provide a better description of the electronic structure of molecules than the simple ideas of the Lewis model.

11-2 Introduction to the Valence-Bond Method—**Valence-bond method** considers a covalent bond in terms of the overlap of atomic orbitals of the bonded atoms.

11-3 Hybridization of Atomic Orbitals—Some molecules can be described in terms of the overlap of simple orbitals, but often orbitals that are a composite of simple orbitals—**hybrid orbitals**—are needed. The hybridization scheme chosen is the one that produces an orientation of hybrid orbitals to match the electron-group geometry predicted by the VSEPR theory (Fig. 11-12). Consequently, an *sp* hybrid **orbital** corresponds to two electron pairs (Fig. 11-9), an *sp²*

◄ Photoelectron or XPS spectrometer

A typical experimental setup is shown in Figure 11-41. The ejected electrons are passed through an electrostatic analyzer whose field strength can be changed so that electrons are directed to a detector and give a signal. The strength of the field needed to obtain a signal can be used to calculate the speed of the ejected electrons. Then the kinetic energy of the ejected electrons can be calculated, and following that, the energy of the orbital from which the electrons were ejected.

$$E_{orbital} = h\upsilon - E_{kinetic}$$

Typically, the photons used are emitted by excited He^+ ions; they have an energy of 2104 kJ mol^{-1}. Higher energies are obtained from photons emitted from excited states of other atoms, or from X-rays. To understand why we need photons of differing energies, consider the photoelectron spectrum of neon atoms obtained with 11,900 kJ mol^{-1} radiation (from excited Mg), shown in Figure 11-42. The photoelectron spectrum consists of two peaks, one at 2080 kJ mol^{-1} and the other at 4680 kJ mol^{-1}, corresponding to the $2p$ and $2s$ orbitals, respectively. The 1s orbital energy is 75,000 kJ mol^{-1}, and consequently, electrons cannot be ejected from this orbital by the radiation employed. X-rays are needed to eject 1s electrons. The photoelectron spectrum shown in Figure 11-42 confirms the orbital structure of neon.

In a similar way, we can use photoelectron spectroscopy to provide confirmation of the orbital structure of molecules. The photoelectron spectra of N_2 and CO obtained using 2104 kJ mol^{-1} radiation are shown schematically in Figure 11-43. The first thing that we notice is that there are many more lines than in the neon spectrum. This is because the molecules undergo vibrations. The vibrations of a molecule are quantized, just like its electronic motions. The excitation of quantized molecular vibrations leads to a further loss of energy by the ionizing photons, and this in turn, leads to a range of kinetic energies corresponding to a given ionization. The spacing between these additional peaks corresponds to the energy needed to excite vibrations. The presence of these vibrational peaks is strongly indicative of whether the orbitals from which the electrons are ejected are strong σ-bonding orbitals, or moderate-strength π-bonding orbitals, or lone

The photoelectric effect was described in Chapter 8 when considering the particle-like nature of photons. Suppose, instead of shining light on the surface of a metal, we pass photons through a gaseous sample of molecules such as CO or N_2. What is likely to happen? If the energy of the photons is greater than the energy of occupied orbitals in the molecules, electrons will be ejected from these orbitals with a kinetic energy that we can measure. We can make this measurement in a manner similar to that described in Chapter 8 (page 287).

▲ **FIGURE 11-41**
Schematic of a photoelectron spectrometer

---

hybrid orbital corresponds to three electron pairs (Fig. 11-8), an sp^3 **hybrid orbital** corresponds to four electron pairs (Fig. 11-5), an sp^3d **hybrid orbital** corresponds to five electron pairs, and an sp^3d^2 **hybrid orbital** corresponds to six electron pairs (Fig. 11-11).

11-4 Multiple Covalent Bonds—End-to-end overlap of orbitals produces **σ (sigma) bonds**. Side-to-side overlap of two p orbitals produces a **π (pi) bond**. Single covalent bonds are σ bonds. A double bond consists of one σ bond and one π bond (Fig. 11-13). A triple bond consists of one σ

bond and two π bonds (Fig. 11-15). The geometric shape of a species determines the σ-bond framework, and π bonds are added as required to complete the bonding description.

11-5 Molecular Orbital Theory—In **molecular orbital theory**, electrons are assigned to molecular orbitals. The numbers and kinds of molecular orbitals are related to the atomic orbitals used to generate them. Electron charge density between atoms is high in **bonding molecular orbitals** and very low in **antibonding orbitals** (Fig. 11-20). **Bond order** is one-half the difference between the numbers of

▲ FIGURE 11-42
The photoelectron spectrum of Ne
The valence electron orbital structure of Ne. The inner $1s$ electrons, that is, the core electrons, exhibit a peak to the right of the $2s$ peak if radiation of sufficient energy is employed. The binding energy of the $1s$ electrons in Ne is at 75,000 kJ mol^{-1}.

(a)

(b)

▲ FIGURE 11-43
The photoelectron spectrum of N$_2$ and CO
The valence electron orbital structure of **(a)** N$_2$ and **(b)** CO. The extra peaks compared to the photoelectron spectrum of Ne correspond to quantized vibrational excitations in the molecules.

pairs of electrons (nonbonding) in σ-type orbitals. As an approximation, the more vibrational peaks observed, the stronger the bonding orbital.

In the photoelectron spectrum of N$_2$, the first ionization produces very few vibrational lines, corresponding to ionization from a lone pair in a σ-type orbital. The second ionization has a much richer structure, suggesting that ionization is from a π-bonding orbital, as expected. The third ionization exhibits some structure and corresponds to ionization from the σ-bonding orbital.

Thus, photoelectron spectroscopy confirms the orbital structure of molecules, but it also points out inadequacies in the simple analysis of photoelectron spectra based on an orbital picture. For example, the similarity of the photoelectron spectra of N$_2$ and CO suggests that ionization from the σ and π orbitals occurs in the same order in the two molecules. Reference to their orbital diagrams suggests that the *reverse* order should be observed. This is the nature of science, however—better theories are often needed to explain all aspects of our experiments.

electrons in bonding molecular orbitals and in antibonding molecular orbitals (equation 11.1). Molecular orbital energy-level diagrams and an aufbau process can be used to describe the electronic structure of a molecule; this is similar to what was done for atomic electron configurations in Chapter 8.

11-6 Delocalized Electrons: Bonding in the Benzene Molecule—Bonding in the benzene molecule, C$_6$H$_6$, is partly based on the concept of **delocalized molecular orbitals**. These are regions of high electron charge density

that extend over several atoms in a molecule (Fig. 11-29). Delocalized molecular orbitals also provide an alternative to the concept of resonance in other molecules and ions.

11-7 Bonding in Metals—Molecular orbital theory, in the form called **band theory**, can be applied to metals, semiconductors, and insulators (Fig. 11-35). Band theory explains thermal and electric conductivity, the ease of deformation, and the characteristic luster of metals. It also explains the colors of semiconductors and the fact that their electric conductivities increase with temperature.

Integrative Example

Hydrogen azide, HN_3, and its salts (metal azides) are unstable substances used in detonators for high explosives. Sodium azide, NaN_3, is used in air-bag safety systems in automobiles (see page 196). A reference source lists the following data for HN_3. (The subscripts a, b, and c distinguish the three N atoms from one another.) Bond lengths: N_a—N_b = 124 pm; N_b—N_c = 113 pm. Bond angles: H—N_a—N_b = 112.7°; N_a—N_b—N_c = 180°.

Write two contributing structures to the resonance hybrid for HN_3, and describe a plausible hybridization and bonding scheme for each structure.

Strategy

We can use data from Table 10.2 to estimate the bond order for the two nitrogen-to-nitrogen bonds. From this information we can write plausible Lewis structures, and by applying VSEPR theory to the Lewis structures, we can predict a likely geometric shape of the molecule. Finally, with this information we can propose hybridization schemes for the central atoms and an overall bonding scheme for the molecule.

Solution

From Table 10.2, the average bond lengths for N-to-N bonds are 145 pm for a single bond, 123 pm for a double bond, and 110 pm for a triple bond. Thus it is likely that the N_a—N_b bond (124 pm) has a considerable double-bond character, and the N_b—N_c bond (113 pm) has a considerable triple-bond character.

The HN_3 molecule has a total of 16 valence electrons in 8 electron pairs. The plausible Lewis structures have N_a and N_b atoms as central atoms, the N_c and H atoms as terminal atoms, and bonds reflecting the observed bond lengths.

(I) $H—\ddot{N}_a{=}N_b{=}\ddot{N}_c$ (II) $H—\dot{\ddot{N}}_a—N_b{\equiv}\ddot{N}_c$

According to VSEPR theory, both in structures (I) and (II) the electron-group geometry around N_b is linear. This corresponds to sp hybridization. In structure (I), the electron-group geometry around N_a is trigonal-planar, corresponding to sp^2 hybridization; in structure (II), the electron-group geometry around N_a is tetrahedral, corresponding to sp^3 hybridization. These hybridization schemes, the orbital overlaps, and the geometric structures of the two resonance structures are indicated on the right.

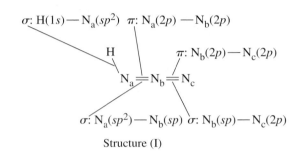

σ: $H(1s)$ — $N_a(sp^2)$ π: $N_a(2p)$ — $N_b(2p)$

π: $N_b(2p)$ — $N_c(2p)$

σ: $N_a(sp^2)$ — $N_b(sp)$ σ: $N_b(sp)$ — $N_c(2p)$

Structure (I)

σ: $H(1s)$ — $N_a(sp^3)$ σ: $N_a(sp^3)$ — $N_b(sp)$

π: $N_b(2p)$ — $N_c(2p)$

π: $N_b(2p)$ — $N_c(2p)$

σ: $N_b(sp)$ — $N_c(2p)$

Structure (II)

Assessment

Having arrived at these two resonance structures, which is the most favorable? We could try to use formal charges, but we find that in structure (I), the formal charges on N_a, N_b, and N_c are 0, +1 and −1, respectively; correspondingly in structure (II), the formal charges are −1, +1 and 0, respectively. Because the formal charges are so similar, we cannot make any definitive conclusion as to which structure is favored. The surest way to decide is to compare the observed molecular structure with that suggested by the two hybridization schemes given above. In structure (I), N_a is sp^2 hybridized so that a H—N_a—N_b angle is expected to be close to 120°; whereas in structure (II), the hybridization on N_a is sp^3 so that the H—N_a—N_b angle is expected to be close to 109°. Experimentally it is found that the H—N_a—N_b angle is 109°, so that the hybridization scheme in structure (II) is to be preferred. The electrostatic potential map for HN_3 is shown on the right, and we observe that N_a is relatively negatively charged as compared to N_b and N_c—in accord with our preferred structure (II).

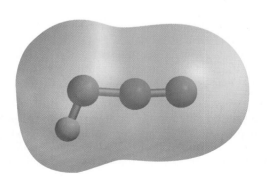

Exercises

Valence-Bond Method

1. Indicate several ways in which the valence-bond method is superior to Lewis structures in describing covalent bonds.

2. Explain why it is necessary to hybridize atomic orbitals when applying the valence-bond method—that is, why are there so few molecules that can be described by the overlap of pure atomic orbitals only?

3. Describe the molecular geometry of H_2O suggested by each of the following methods: **(a)** Lewis theory; **(b)** valence-bond method using simple atomic orbitals; **(c)** VSEPR theory; **(d)** valence-bond method using hybridized atomic orbitals.

4. Describe the molecular geometry of CCl_4 suggested by each of the following methods: **(a)** Lewis theory; **(b)** valence-bond method using simple atomic orbitals; **(c)** VSEPR theory; **(d)** valence-bond method using hybridized atomic orbitals.

5. In which of the following, CO_3^{2-}, SO_2, CCl_4, CO, NO_2^-, would you expect to find sp^2 hybridization of the central atom? Explain.

6. In the manner of Example 11-1, describe the probable structure and bonding in **(a)** HI; **(b)** BrCl; **(c)** H_2Se; **(d)** OCl_2.

7. For each of the following species, identify the central atom(s) and propose a hybridization scheme for those atom(s): **(a)** CO_2; **(b)** $HONO_2$; **(c)** ClO_3^-; **(d)** BF_4^-.

8. Propose a plausible Lewis structure, geometric structure, and hybridization scheme for the NSF molecule.

9. Describe a hybridization scheme for the central Cl atom in the molecule ClF_3 that is consistent with the geometric shape pictured in Table 11.1. Which orbitals of the Cl atom are involved in overlaps, and which are occupied by lone-pair electrons?

10. Describe a hybridization scheme for the central S atom in the molecule SF_4 that is consistent with the geometric shape pictured in Table 11.1. Which orbitals of the S atom are involved in overlaps, and which are occupied by lone-pair electrons?

11. Match each of the following species with one of these hybridization schemes: sp, sp^2, sp^3, sp^3d, sp^3d^2. **(a)** PF_6^-; **(b)** COS; **(c)** $SiCl_4$; **(d)** NO_3^-; **(e)** AsF_5.

12. Propose a hybridization scheme to account for bonds formed by the central carbon atom in each of the following molecules: **(a)** hydrogen cyanide, HCN; **(b)** methyl alcohol, CH_3OH; **(c)** acetone, $(CH_3)_2CO$; **(d)** carbamic acid,

$$\overset{\textstyle O}{\underset{\textstyle H_2NCOH}{\|}}$$

13. Indicate which of the following molecules and ions are linear, which are planar, and which are neither. Then propose hybridization schemes for the central atoms. **(a)** $Cl_2C{=}CCl_2$; **(b)** $N{\equiv}C{-}C{\equiv}N$; **(c)** $F_3C{-}C{\equiv}N$; **(d)** $[S{-}C{\equiv}N]^-$.

14. In the manner of Figure 11-16, indicate the structures of the following molecules in terms of the overlap of simple atomic orbitals and hybrid orbitals: **(a)** CH_2Cl_2; **(b)** OCN^-; **(c)** BF_3.

15. Write Lewis structures for the following molecules, and then label each σ and π bond. **(a)** HCN; **(b)** C_2N_2; **(c)** $CH_3CHCHCCl_3$; **(d)** HONO.

16. Represent bonding in the carbon dioxide molecule, CO_2, by **(a)** a Lewis structure and **(b)** the valence-bond method. Identify σ and π bonds, the necessary hybridization scheme, and orbital overlap.

17. Use the method of Figure 11-17 to represent bonding in each of the following molecules: **(a)** CCl_4; **(b)** ONCl; **(c)** HONO; **(d)** $COCl_2$.

18. Use the method of Figure 11-17 to represent bonding in each of the following ions: **(a)** NO_2^-; **(b)** I_3^-; **(c)** $C_2O_4^{2-}$; **(d)** HCO_3^-.

19. The molecular model below represents citric acid, an acidic component of citrus juices. Represent bonding in the citric acid molecule using the method of Figure 11-17 to indicate hybridization schemes and orbital overlaps.

20. Malic acid is a common organic acid found in unripe apples and other fruit. With the help of the molecular model shown below, represent bonding in the malic acid molecule, using the method of Figure 11-17 to indicate hybridization schemes and orbital overlaps.

21. Shown below are ball-and-stick models. Describe hybridization and orbital-overlap schemes consistent with these structures.

(a) S_2O **(b)** BrF_3

22. Shown below are ball-and-stick models. Describe hybridization and orbital-overlap schemes consistent with these structures.

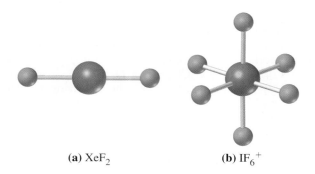

(a) XeF_2 **(b)** IF_6^+

23. Propose a bonding scheme that is consistent with the structure for propynal.
[*Hint:* Consult Table 10.2 to assess the multiple-bond character in some of the bonds.]

24. The structure of the molecule allene, CH_2CCH_2, is shown here. Propose hybridization schemes for the C atoms in this molecule.

Molecular Orbital Theory

25. Explain the essential difference in how the valence-bond method and molecular orbital theory describe a covalent bond.
26. Describe the bond order of diatomic carbon, C_2, with Lewis theory and molecular orbital theory, and explain why the results are different.
27. $N_2(g)$ has an exceptionally high bond energy. Would you expect either N_2^- or N_2^{2-} to be a stable diatomic species in the gaseous state? Explain.
28. The paramagnetism of gaseous B_2 has been established. Explain how this observation confirms that the π_{2p} orbitals are at a lower energy than the σ_{2p} orbital for B_2.
29. In our discussion of bonding, we have not encountered a bond order higher than triple. Use the energy-level diagrams of Figure 11-25 to show why this is to be expected.
30. Is it correct to say that when a diatomic molecule loses an electron, the bond energy always decreases (that is, that the bond is always weakened)? Explain.
31. For the following pairs of molecular orbitals, indicate the one you expect to have the lower energy, and state the reason for your choice. **(a)** σ_{1s} or σ_{1s}^* **(b)** σ_{2s} or σ_{2p}; **(c)** σ_{1s}^* or σ_{2s}; **(d)** σ_{2p} or σ_{2p}^*.
32. For each of the species C_2^+, O_2^-, F_2^+, and NO^+,
   (a) Write the molecular orbital diagram (as in Example 11-6).
   (b) Determine the bond order, and state whether you expect the species to be stable or unstable.

(c) Determine if the species is diamagnetic or paramagnetic; and if paramagnetic, indicate the number of unpaired electrons.

33. Assume that the energy-level diagrams of Figure 11-25 are applicable, and write plausible molecular orbital diagrams for the following *heteronuclear* diatomic species: **(a)** NO; **(b)** NO^+; **(c)** CO; **(d)** CN; **(e)** CN^-; **(f)** CN^+; **(g)** BN.
34. We have used the term "isoelectronic" to refer to atoms with identical electron configurations. In molecular orbital theory, this term can be applied to molecular species as well. Which of the species in Exercise 33 are isoelectronic?
35. Assume that the energy-level diagrams of Figure 11-25 apply to the diatomic ions NO^+ and N_2^+.
   (a) Predict the bond order of each.
   (b) Which of these ions is paramagnetic? Which is diamagnetic?
   (c) Which of these ions do you think has the greater bond length? Explain.
36. Assume that the energy-level diagrams of Figure 11-25 apply to the diatomic ions CO^+ and CN^-.
   (a) Predict the bond order of each.
   (b) Which of these ions is paramagnetic? Which is diamagnetic?
   (c) Which of these ions do you think has the greater bond length? Explain.

Delocalized Molecular Orbitals

37. Explain why the concept of delocalized molecular orbitals is essential to an understanding of bonding in the benzene molecule, C_6H_6.
38. Explain how it is possible to avoid the concept of resonance by using molecular orbital theory.

39. In which of the following molecules would you expect to find delocalized molecular orbitals: **(a)** C_2H_4; **(b)** SO_2; **(c)** H_2CO? Explain.
40. In which of the following ions would you expect to find delocalized molecular orbitals: **(a)** HCO_2^-; **(b)** CO_3^{2-}; **(c)** CH_3^+? Explain.

Metallic Bonding

41. Which of the following factors are especially important in determining whether a substance has metallic properties: (a) atomic number; (b) atomic mass; (c) number of valence electrons; (d) number of vacant atomic orbitals; (e) total number of electronic shells in the atom? Explain.

42. Based on the ground-state electron configurations of the atoms, how would you expect the melting points and hardnesses of sodium, iron, and zinc to compare? Explain.

43. How many energy levels are present in the $3s$ conduction band of a single crystal of sodium weighing 26.8 mg? How many electrons are present in this band?

44. Magnesium is an excellent electrical conductor even though it has a full $3s$ subshell with the electron configuration: $[Ne]3s^2$. Use band theory to explain why magnesium conducts electricity.

Semiconductors

45. From this list of terms—electrical conductor, insulator, semiconductor—choose the one that best characterizes each of the following materials: (a) stainless steel; (b) solid sodium chloride; (c) sulfur; (d) germanium; (e) seawater; (f) solid iodine.

46. In what type of material is the energy gap between the valence band and the conduction band greatest: metal, semiconductor, or insulator? Explain.

47. Which of the following substances, when added in trace amounts to silicon, would produce a p-type semiconductor: (a) sulfur, (b) arsenic, (c) lead, (d) boron, (e) gallium arsenide, (f) gallium? Explain.

48. Which of the following substances, when added in trace amounts to germanium, would produce an n-type semiconductor: (a) sulfur, (b) aluminum, (c) tin, (d) cadmium sulfide, (e) arsenic, (f) gallium arsenide? Explain.

49. The effect of temperature change on the electrical conductivity of ultrapure silicon is quite different from that on silicon containing a minute trace of arsenic. Why is this so?

50. Explain why the electrical conductivity of a semiconductor is significantly increased if trace amounts of either donor or acceptor atoms are present, but is unchanged if both are present in equal number.

51. The energy gap, ΔE, for silicon is 110 kJ/mol. What is the minimum wavelength of light that can promote an electron from the valence band to the conduction band in silicon? In what region of the electromagnetic spectrum is this light?

52. Explain why the solar cell in Figure 11-37 operates over a broad range of wavelengths rather than at a single wavelength (often the case when quantum effects are involved)?

Integrative and Advanced Exercises

53. The Lewis structure of N_2 indicates that the nitrogen-to-nitrogen bond is a triple covalent bond. Other evidence suggests that the σ bond in this molecule involves the overlap of sp hybrid orbitals.
    (a) Draw orbital diagrams for the N atoms to describe bonding in N_2.
    (b) Can this bonding be described by either sp^2 or sp^3 hybridization of the N atoms? Can bonding in N_2 be described in terms of unhybridized orbitals? Explain.

54. Show that both the valence-bond method and molecular orbital theory provide an explanation for the existence of the covalent molecule Na_2 in the gaseous state. Would you predict Na_2 by the Lewis theory?

55. A group of spectroscopists believe that they have detected one of the following species: NeF, NeF^+, or NeF^-. Assume that the energy-level diagrams of Figure 11-25 apply, and describe bonding in these species. Which of these species would you expect the spectroscopists to have observed?

56. Lewis theory is satisfactory to explain bonding in the ionic compound K_2O, but it does not readily explain formation of the ionic compounds potassium superoxide, KO_2, and potassium peroxide, K_2O_2.
    (a) Show that molecular orbital theory can provide this explanation.
    (b) Write Lewis structures consistent with the molecular orbital explanation.

57. The compound potassium sesquoxide has the empirical formula K_2O_3. Show that this compound can be described by an appropriate combination of potassium, peroxide, and superoxide ions. Write a Lewis structure for a formula unit of the compound.

58. Draw a Lewis structure for the urea molecule, $CO(NH_2)_2$, and predict its geometric shape with the VSEPR theory. Then revise your assessment of this molecule, given the fact that all the atoms lie in the same plane, and all the bond angles are 120°. Propose a hybridization and bonding scheme consistent with these experimental observations.

59. Methyl nitrate, CH_3NO_3, is used as a rocket propellant. The skeletal structure of the molecule is CH_3ONO_2. The N and three O atoms all lie in the same plane, but the CH_3 group is not in the same plane as the NO_3 group. The bond angle C—O—N is 105°, and the bond angle O—N—O is 125°. One nitrogen-to-oxygen bond length is 136 pm, and the other two are 126 pm.
    (a) Draw a sketch of the molecule showing its geometric shape.
    (b) Label all the bonds in the molecule as σ or π, and indicate the probable orbital overlaps involved.
    (c) Explain why all three nitrogen-to-oxygen bond lengths are not the same.

60. Fluorine nitrate, $FONO_2$, is an oxidizing agent used as a rocket propellant. A reference source lists the following data for FO_aNO_2. (The subscript "a" shows that this O atom is different from the other two.)

Bond lengths: $N—O = 129$ pm;
$N—O_a = 139$ pm; $O_a—F = 142$ pm

Bond angles: $O—N—O = 125°$;
$F—O_a—N = 105°$
NO_aF plane is perpendicular to the O_2NO_a plane

Use these data to construct a Lewis structure(s), a three-dimensional sketch of the molecule, and a plausible bonding scheme showing hybridization and orbital overlaps.

61. Draw a Lewis structure(s) for the nitrite ion, NO_2^-. Then propose a bonding scheme to describe the σ and π bonding in this ion. What conclusion can you reach about the number and types of π molecular orbitals in this ion? Explain.

62. Think of the reaction shown here as involving the transfer of a fluoride ion from ClF_3 to AsF_5 to form the ions ClF_2^+ and AsF_6^-. As a result, the hybridization scheme of each central atom must change. For each reactant molecule and product ion, indicate **(a)** its geometric structure and **(b)** the hybridization scheme for its central atom.

$$ClF_3 + AsF_5 \longrightarrow (ClF_2^+)(AsF_6^-)$$

63. In the gaseous state, HNO_3 molecules have two nitrogen-to-oxygen bond distances of 121 pm and one of 140 pm. Draw a plausible Lewis structure(s) to represent this fact, and propose a bonding scheme in the manner of Figure 11-17.

64. He_2 does not exist as a stable molecule, but there is evidence that such a molecule can be formed between electronically excited He atoms. Write a molecular orbital diagram to account for this.

65. The molecule formamide, $HCONH_2$, has the approximate bond angles $H—C—O$, 123°; $H—C—N$, 113°; $N—C—O$, 124°; $C—N—H$, 119°; $H—N—H$, 119°. The $C—N$ bond length is 138 pm. Two Lewis structures can be written for this molecule, with the true structure being a resonance hybrid of the two. Propose a hybridization and bonding scheme for each structure.

66. Pyridine, C_5H_5N, is used in the synthesis of vitamins and drugs. The molecule can be thought of in terms of replacing one CH unit in benzene with a N atom. Draw orbital diagrams to show the orbitals of the C and N atoms involved in the σ and π bonding in pyridine. How many bonding and antibonding π-type molecular orbitals are present? How many delocalized electrons are present?

67. One of the characteristics of antibonding molecular orbitals is the presence of a nodal plane. Which of the bonding molecular orbitals considered in this chapter have nodal planes? Explain how a molecular orbital can have a nodal plane and still be a bonding molecular orbital.

68. The ion F_2Cl^- is linear, but the ion F_2Cl^+ is bent. Describe hybridization schemes for the central Cl atom consistent with this difference in structure.

69. Melamine is a carbon–hydrogen–nitrogen compound used in the manufacture of adhesives, protective coatings, and textile finishing (such as in wrinkle-free, wash-and-wear fabrics). Its mass percent composition is 28.57% C, 4.80% H, and 66.64% N. The melamine molecule features a six-member ring with alternating carbon and nitrogen atoms. Half the nitrogen atoms and all the H atoms are outside the ring. For melamine, **(a)** write a plausible Lewis structure, **(b)** describe bonding in the molecule by the valence-bond method, and **(c)** describe bonding in the ring system through molecular orbital theory.

70. Ethyl cyanoacetate, a chemical used in the synthesis of dyes and pharmaceuticals, has the mass percent composition: 53.09% C, 6.24% H, 12.39% N, and 28.29% O. In the manner of Figure 11-17, show a bonding scheme for this substance. The scheme should designate orbital overlaps, σ and π bonds, and expected bond angles.

71. A certain monomer used in the production of polymers has one nitrogen atom and the mass composition 67.90% C, 5.70% H, and 26.40% N. Sketch the probable geometric structure of this molecule, labeling all the expected bond lengths and bond angles.

72. Dimethylglyoxime (DMG) is a carbon–hydrogen–nitrogen–oxygen compound with a molecular mass of 116.12 u. In a combustion analysis, a 2.464-g sample of DMG yields 3.735 g CO_2 and 1.530 g H_2O. In a separate experiment, the nitrogen in a 1.868-g sample of DMG is converted to $NH_3(g)$, and the NH_3 is neutralized by passing it into 50.00 mL of 0.3600 M $H_2SO_4(aq)$. After neutralization of the NH_3, the excess $H_2SO_4(aq)$ requires 18.63 mL of 0.2050 M NaOH(aq) for its neutralization. Using these data, determine for dimethylglyoxime **(a)** the most plausible Lewis structure, and **(b)** in the manner of Figure 11-17, a plausible bonding scheme.

73. A solar cell that is 15% efficient in converting solar to electric energy produces an energy flow of 1.00 kW/m^2 when exposed to full sunlight. If the cell has an area of 40.0 cm^2,
(a) what is the power output of the cell, in watts?
(b) If the power calculated in part (a) is produced at 0.45 V, how much current does the cell deliver?

74. Toluene-2,4-diisocyanate is used in the manufacture of polyurethane foam. Its structural formula is shown below. Describe the hybridization scheme for the atoms marked with an asterisk, and indicate the values of the bond angles marked α and β.

75. The anion I_4^{2-} is linear, and the anion I_5^- is V-shaped, with a 95° angle between the two arms of the V. For the central atoms in these ions, propose hybridization schemes that are consistent with these observations.

Feature Problems

76. Resonance energy is the difference in energy between a real molecule—a resonance hybrid—and its most important contributing structure. To determine the resonance energy for benzene, we can determine an energy change for benzene and the corresponding change for one of the Kekulé structures. The resonance energy is the difference between these two quantities.
(a) Use data from Appendix D to determine the enthalpy of hydrogenation of liquid benzene to liquid cyclohexane.
(b) Use data from Appendix D to determine the enthalpy of hydrogenation of liquid cyclohexene to liquid cyclohexane.

For the enthalpy of formation of liquid cyclohexene, use $\Delta H_f^\circ = -38.5$ kJ/mol.
(c) Assume that the enthalpy of hydrogenation of 1,3,5-cyclohexatriene is three times as great as that of cyclohexene, and calculate the resonance energy of benzene.
(d) Another way to assess resonance energy is through bond energies. Use bond energies from Table 10.3 (page 409) to determine the total enthalpy change required to break all the bonds in a Kekulé structure of benzene. Next, determine the enthalpy change for the dissociation of $C_6H_6(g)$ into its gaseous atoms by using data from Table 10.3 and Appendix D. Then calculate the resonance energy of benzene.

77. The 60-cycle alternating electric current (AC) commonly used in households changes direction 120 times per second. That is, in a one-second time period a terminal at an electric outlet is positive 60 times and negative 60 times. In direct electric current (DC), the flow between terminals is in one direction only. A *rectifier* is a device that converts alternating to direct current. One type of rectifier is the *p–n* junction rectifier. It is commonly incorporated in adapters required to operate electronic devices from ordinary house current. In the operation of this rectifier, a *p*-type semiconductor and an *n*-type semiconductor are in contact along a boundary, or junction. Each semiconductor is connected to one of the terminals in an AC electrical outlet. Describe how this rectifier works. That is, show that when the semiconductors are connected to the terminals in an AC outlet, half the time a large flow of charge occurs and half the time essentially no charge flows across the *p–n* junction.

78. Furan, C_4H_4O, is a substance derivable from oat hulls, corn cobs, and other cellulosic waste. It is a starting material for the synthesis of other chemicals used as pharmaceuticals and herbicides. The furan molecule is planar and the C and O atoms are bonded into a five-membered pentagonal ring. The H atoms are attached to the C atoms. The chemical behavior of the molecule suggests that it is a resonance hybrid of several

contributing structures. These structures show that the double bond character is associated with the entire ring in the form of a π electron cloud.
(a) Draw Lewis structures for the several contributing structures to the resonance hybrid mentioned above.
(b) Draw orbital diagrams to show the orbitals that are involved in the σ and π bonding in furan.
[*Hint:* You need use only one of the contributing structures, such as the one with no formal charges.]
(c) How many π electrons are there in the furan molecule? Show that this number of π electrons is the same, regardless of the contributing structure you use for this assessment.

79. As discussed in the Are You Wondering feature on page 431, the *sp* hybrid orbitals are algebraic combinations of the *s* and *p* orbitals. The required combinations of 2s and 2p orbitals are

$$\psi_1(sp) = \frac{1}{\sqrt{2}}[\psi(2s) + \psi(2p_z)]$$

$$\psi_2(sp) = \frac{1}{\sqrt{2}}[\psi(2s) - \psi(2p_z)]$$

(a) By combining the appropriate functions given in Table 8.1, construct a polar plot in the manner of Figure 8-26 for each of the above functions in the *xz* plane. In a polar plot, the value of r/a_0 is set at a fixed value (for example, 1). Describe the shapes and phases of the different portions of the hybrid orbitals, and compare them with those shown in Figure 11-10.
(b) Convince yourself that the combinations employing the $2p_x$ or $2p_y$ orbital also give similar hybrid orbitals but pointing in different directions.
(c) The combinations for the sp^2 hybrids in the *xy* plane are

$$\psi_1(sp^2) = \frac{1}{\sqrt{3}}\psi(2s) + \frac{\sqrt{2}}{\sqrt{3}}\psi(2p_x)$$

$$\psi_2(sp^2) = \frac{1}{\sqrt{3}}\psi(2s) - \frac{1}{\sqrt{6}}\psi(2p_x) + \frac{1}{\sqrt{2}}\psi(2p_y)$$

$$\psi_3(sp^2) = \frac{1}{\sqrt{3}}\psi(2s) - \frac{1}{\sqrt{6}}\psi(2p_x) - \frac{1}{\sqrt{2}}\psi(2p_y)$$

By constructing polar plots (in the *xy* plane), show that these functions correspond to the sp^2 hybrids depicted in Figure 11-8.

80. In Chapter 10, we saw that electronegativity differences determine whether bond dipoles exist in a molecule and that molecular shape determines whether bond dipoles cancel (nonpolar molecules) or combine to produce a resultant dipole moment (polar molecules). Thus, the ozone molecule, O_3, has no bond dipoles because all the atoms are alike. Yet, O_3 *does* have a resultant dipole moment: $\mu = 0.534$ D. The electrostatic potential map for ozone is shown below. Use the electrostatic potential map to decide the direction of the dipole. Using the ideas of delocalized bonding in molecules, can you rationalize this electrostatic potential map?

81. Borazine, $B_3N_3H_6$ is often referred to as inorganic benzene because of its similar structure. Like benzene, borazine has a delocalized π system. Describe the molecular orbitals of the π system. Identify the highest occupied molecular orbital (HOMO) and the lowest unoccupied molecular orbital (LUMO). How many nodes does the LUMO possess?

82. Compare the π bonding in 1,3-pentadiene and 1,4-pentadiene. Which has a delocalized π system and which does not?

Self-Assessment Exercises

83. In your own words, define the following terms or symbols: **(a)** sp^2; **(b)** σ^*_{2p}; **(c)** bond order; **(d)** π bond.

84. Briefly describe each of the following ideas: **(a)** hybridization of atomic orbitals; **(b)** σ-bond framework; **(c)** Kekulé structures of benzene, C_6H_6; **(d)** band theory of metallic bonding.

85. Explain the important distinctions between the terms in each of the following pairs: **(a)** σ and π bonds; **(b)** localized and delocalized electrons; **(c)** bonding and antibonding molecular orbitals; **(d)** metal and semiconductor.

86. A molecule in which sp^2 hybrid orbitals are used by the central atom in forming covalent bonds is **(a)** PCl_5; **(b)** N_2; **(c)** SO_2; **(d)** He_2.

87. The bond angle in H_2Se is best described as **(a)** between 109° and 120°; **(b)** less than in H_2S; **(c)** less than in H_2S, but not less than 90°; **(d)** less than 90°.

88. The hybridization scheme for the central atom includes a d orbital contribution in **(a)** I_3^-; **(b)** PCl_3; **(c)** NO_3^-; **(d)** H_2Se.

89. Of the following, the species with a bond order of 1 is **(a)** H_2^+; **(b)** Li_2; **(c)** He_2; **(d)** H_2^-.

90. The hybridization scheme for Xe in XeF_2 is **(a)** sp; **(b)** sp^3; **(c)** sp^3d; **(d)** sp^3d^2.

91. Delocalized molecular orbitals are found in **(a)** H_2; **(b)** HS^-; **(c)** CH_4; **(d)** CO_3^{2-}.

92. The best electrical conductor of the following materials is **(a)** Li(s); **(b)** Br_2(l); **(c)** Ge(s); **(d)** Si(s).

93. A substance in which the valence and conduction bands overlap is **(a)** a semiconductor; **(b)** a metalloid; **(c)** a metal; **(d)** an insulator.

94. Explain why the molecular structure of BF_3 cannot be adequately described through overlaps involving pure s and p orbitals.

95. Why does the hybridization sp^3d not account for bonding in the molecule BrF_5? What hybridization scheme does work? Explain.

96. What is the total number of **(a)** σ bonds and **(b)** π bonds in the molecule CH_3NCO?

97. Which of these diatomic molecules do you think has the greater bond energy, Li_2 or C_2? Explain.

98. Construct a concept map that embodies the ideas of valence bond theory.

99. Construct a concept map that connects the ideas of molecular orbital theory

100. Construct a concept map that describes the interconnection between valence-bond theory and molecular orbital theory in the description of resonance structures.

eMedia Exercises

101. The **H_2 Bond Formation** animation (*Activebook 11-1*) illustrates the formation of the simplest covalent bond in terms of bond energy and bond length. Describe the same bond formation in the language of the valence-bond method (atomic orbitals, orbital overlap, and electron density).

102. In the **Hybridization** animation (*Activebook 11-3*), the hybrid orbitals involved in bonding of NH_3 are identified as sp^3 orbitals. **(a)** Identify different molecules that would involve sp and sp^2 hybrid orbitals. **(b)** How many total electron pairs are associated with the central atom in each case?

103. Construct an energy level diagram for each of the geometries shown in the **Hybridization** animation (*Activebook 11-3*). **(a)** In each case, indicate the energy level and occupation of the atomic orbitals on the central atom before and after hybridization. **(b)** What is the general relationship between the energy of hybridized orbitals and the energy of the atomic orbitals from which they originated?

104. In the **Multiple Bond Formation** activity of acetylene (*Activebook 11-4*), we see that bonding occurs between both hybridized and unhybridized orbitals. Using acetylene as a model, predict the orbital that is occupied by the lone pairs of the diatomic molecule, nitrogen.

105. For each of the atomic and molecular orbitals represented in the **Molecular Orbital Theory** animation (*Activebook 11-5*), **(a)** construct electron charge density diagrams (a plot of density versus internuclear distance). **(b)** What is the primary difference between the diagrams describing the σ_{1s} and σ^*_{1s} molecular orbitals?

12

LIQUIDS, SOLIDS, AND INTER-MOLECULAR FORCES

In this scene from Antarctica, water exists in all three states of matter—solid in the ice, liquid in the sea, and gas in the atmosphere.

▶ Two of the many natural phenomena described in this chapter include the more ordered structure of the solid compared to the liquid state and the variation of density with the state of matter.

When we make ice cubes by placing water in a tray in a freezer, energy is removed from the water molecules, which gradually slow down. Attractive (intermolecular) forces between the molecules take over, and the water solidifies into ice. When an ice cube melts, energy from the surroundings is absorbed by the water molecules, which overcome the intermolecular forces within the ice cube and enter the liquid state. In our study of gases, we intentionally sought conditions in which the intermolecular forces were negligible. This approach allowed us to describe gases with the ideal gas equation and to explain their behavior with the kinetic–molecular theory of gases. To describe the other states of matter—liquids and solids—we must seek situations in which the intermolecular forces are significant. We then consider some interesting properties of liquids and solids related to the strengths of these forces.

471

12-1 INTERMOLECULAR FORCES AND SOME PROPERTIES OF LIQUIDS

▶ Solids, liquids, and gases were compared at the macroscopic and microscopic levels in Figure 1-7.

▲ **FIGURE 12-1**
An effect of surface tension illustrated
Despite being denser than water, the needle is supported on the surface of the water. The property of surface tension accounts for this unexpected behavior.

🍶 Pour water into a glass beaker and it fills the volume. Pour liquid nitrogen into the beaker, which shows the effects of a superfluid with no resistance to flow.

In our study of gases, we noted that at high pressures and low temperatures intermolecular forces cause gas behavior to depart from ideality. When these forces are sufficiently strong, a gas condenses to a liquid. That is, the intermolecular forces keep the molecules in such close proximity that they are confined to a definite volume, as expected for the liquid state.

Intermolecular forces are important in establishing the surface tension and viscosity of a liquid, two properties described in this section. Other properties of liquids closely associated with intermolecular forces will be described in Section 12-2.

SURFACE TENSION

The observation of a needle floating on water, as pictured in Figure 12-1, is puzzling. Steel is much denser than water and should not float. Something must overcome the force of gravity on the needle, allowing it to remain suspended on the surface of the water. What is this special quality associated with the surface of liquid water?

Figure 12-2 suggests an important difference in the forces between molecules within the bulk of a liquid and those at the surface: Interior molecules have more neighbors to which they are attracted by intermolecular forces than do surface molecules. This increased attraction by its neighboring molecules places an interior molecule in a lower energy state than a surface molecule. Consequently, as many molecules as possible tend to enter the bulk of a liquid, while as few as possible remain at the surface. Thus, there is a tendency for liquids to maintain a minimum surface area. This is most clearly seen in the formation of spherical drops in a rain shower. A sphere has a smaller ratio of surface area to volume than does any other geometric structure. To increase the surface area of a liquid requires that molecules be moved from the interior to the surface of a liquid, and this requires that work be done. The steel needle of Figure 12-1 remains suspended on the surface of the water because energy is required to spread the surface of the water over the top of the needle. This gain in potential energy is greater than can be offset by the loss of potential energy by the needle falling under the force of gravity.

▲ **FIGURE 12-2**
Intermolecular forces in a liquid
Molecules at the surface are attracted only by other surface molecules and by molecules below the surface. Molecules in the interior experience forces from neighboring molecules in all directions.

▲ **FIGURE 12-3**
Wetting of a surface
Water spreads into a thin film on a clean glass surface (left). If the glass is coated with oil or grease, the adhesive forces between the water and oil are not strong enough to spread the water, and drops of water stand on the surface (right).

▲ **FIGURE 12-4**
Meniscus formation
Water wets glass (left). The meniscus is concave—the bottom of the meniscus is below the level of the water–glass contact line. Mercury does not wet glass. The meniscus is convex— the top of the meniscus is above the mercury–glass contact line.

Surface tension is the energy, or work, required to increase the surface area of a liquid. Surface tension is often represented by the Greek letter gamma (γ) and has the units of energy per unit area, typically joules per square meter ($J\ m^{-2}$). As the temperature—and hence the intensity of molecular motion—increases, intermolecular forces become less effective. Less work is required to extend the surface of a liquid, meaning that surface tension *decreases* with *increased* temperature.

When a drop of liquid spreads into a film across a surface, we say that the liquid *wets* the surface. Whether a drop of liquid wets a surface or retains its spherical shape and stands on the surface depends on the strengths of two types of intermolecular forces. The forces exerted between molecules holding them together in the drop are **cohesive forces**, and the forces between liquid molecules and the surface are **adhesive forces**. If cohesive forces are strong compared with adhesive forces, a drop maintains its shape. If adhesive forces are strong enough, on the other hand, the energy requirement for spreading the drop into a film is met through the work done by the collapsing drop.

Water wets many surfaces, such as glass and certain fabrics. This characteristic is essential to its use as a cleaning agent. If glass is coated with a film of oil or grease, water no longer wets the surface and water droplets stand on the glass, as shown in Figure 12-3. When we clean glassware in the laboratory, we have done a good job if water forms a uniform thin film on the glass. When we wax a car, we have done a good job if water uniformly beads up all along the surface.

Adding a detergent to water has two effects: The detergent solution dissolves grease to expose a clean surface, and the detergent lowers the surface tension of water. Lowering the surface tension means lowering the energy required to spread drops into a film. Substances that reduce the surface tension of water and allow it to spread more easily are known as *wetting agents.* They are used in applications ranging from dish washing to industrial processes.

Figure 12-4 illustrates another familiar observation. If the liquid in the glass tube is water, the water is drawn slightly up the walls of the tube by adhesive forces between water and glass. The interface between the water and the air above it, called a *meniscus,* is concave, or curved in. With liquid mercury, the meniscus is convex, or curved out. Cohesive forces in mercury, consisting of metallic bonds between Hg atoms, are strong; mercury does not wet glass. The effect of meniscus formation is greatly magnified in tubes of small diameter, called *capillary tubes.* In the *capillary action* shown in Figure 12-5, the water level inside the capillary tube is noticeably higher than outside. The soaking action of a sponge depends on the rise of water into capillaries of a fibrous material such as cellulose. The penetration of water into soils also depends in part on capillary action. On the other hand, mercury—with its strong cohesive forces and weaker adhesive forces—does not show a capillary rise. Rather, mercury in a glass capillary tube will have a lower level than the mercury outside the capillary.

◀ The surface tension of water at 20 °C, for example, is $7.28 \times 10^{-2}\ J\ m^{-2}$, and that of mercury is over six times larger, at $47.2 \times 10^{-2}\ J\ m^{-2}$.

▲ **FIGURE 12-5**
Capillary action
A thin film of water spreads up the inside walls of the capillary because of strong adhesive forces between water and glass (water wets glass). The pressure below the meniscus falls slightly. Atmospheric pressure then pushes a column of water up the tube to eliminate the pressure difference. The *smaller* the diameter of the capillary, the *higher* the liquid rises. Because its magnitude is also directly proportional to surface tension, capillary rise provides a simple experimental method of determining surface tension, described in Exercise 108.

▲ FIGURE 12-6
Measuring viscosity
By measuring the velocity of a ball dropping through a liquid, a measure of the liquid viscosity can be obtained.

VISCOSITY

Another property at least partly related to intermolecular forces is **viscosity**—a liquid's resistance to flow. The stronger the intermolecular forces of attraction, the greater the viscosity. When a liquid flows, one portion of the liquid moves with respect to neighboring portions. Cohesive forces within the liquid create an "internal friction," which reduces the rate of flow. In liquids of low viscosity, such as ethyl alcohol and water, the effect is weak, and they flow easily. Liquids like honey and heavy motor oil flow much more sluggishly. We say that they are *viscous*. One method of measuring viscosity is to time the fall of a steel ball through a certain depth of liquid (Fig. 12-6). The greater the viscosity of the liquid, the longer it takes for the ball to fall. Because intermolecular forces of attraction can be offset by higher molecular kinetic energies, viscosity generally *decreases* with *increased* temperature.

CONCEPT ASSESSMENT ✓

The viscosity of automotive motor oil is designated by its SAE number, such as 40 W. When compared in a ball viscometer (Fig. 12-6), the ball drops much faster through 10 W oil than through 40 W oil. Which of these two oils provides better winter service in the Arctic region of Canada? Which is best suited for summer use in the American Southwest? Which oil has the stronger intermolecular forces of attraction?

12-2   VAPORIZATION OF LIQUIDS: VAPOR PRESSURE

In our study of the kinetic–molecular theory (Section 6-7), we saw that the speeds and kinetic energies of molecules vary over a wide range at any given temperature (Fig. 6-17). Then in Chapter 7, we learned that molecules having kinetic energies sufficiently above the average value are able to overcome intermolecular forces of attraction and escape from the surface of the liquid into the gaseous state. This passage of molecules from the surface of a liquid into the gaseous, or vapor, state is called **vaporization** or **evaporation**. Vaporization occurs more readily with

▲ Honey is a viscous liquid.

 Heat of Vaporization of Water

 Note that for liquids, the viscosity decreases with increasing temperature, but for gases, the viscosity increases with increasing temperature.

KEEP IN MIND ▶

that absolute enthalpies such as H_{vapor} and H_{liquid} cannot be measured (page 251). However, because enthalpy is a function of state, the difference between the absolute enthalpies has a unique value, and it *can* be measured.

- *increased temperature*—more molecules have sufficient kinetic energy to overcome intermolecular forces of attraction in the liquid
- *increased surface area* of the liquid—a greater proportion of the liquid molecules are at the surface
- *decreased strength of intermolecular forces*—the kinetic energy needed to overcome intermolecular forces of attraction is less, and more molecules have enough energy to escape

ENTHALPY OF VAPORIZATION

Because the molecules lost through evaporation are much more energetic than average, the average kinetic energy of the remaining molecules decreases. The temperature of the evaporating liquid falls. This accounts for the cooling sensation you feel when a volatile liquid such as ethyl alcohol evaporates on your skin.

To vaporize a liquid at constant temperature, we must replace the excess kinetic energy carried away by the vaporizing molecules by adding heat to the liquid. The *enthalpy of vaporization* is the quantity of heat that must be absorbed if a certain quantity of liquid is vaporized at a constant temperature. Stated in another way,

$$\Delta H_{vaporization} = H_{vapor} - H_{liquid}$$

Because vaporization is an *endothermic* process, $\Delta H_{vaporization}$—or ΔH_{vap} as it is more commonly denoted—is always positive. We will generally express enthalpies of vaporization in terms of one mole of liquid vaporized, as seen in Table 12.1.

TABLE 12.1 Some Enthalpies of Vaporization at 298 K[a]	
Liquid	ΔH_{vap}, kJ mol^{-1}
Diethyl ether, $(C_2H_5)_2O$	29.1
Methyl alcohol, CH_3OH	38.0
Ethyl alcohol, CH_3CH_2OH	42.6
Water, H_2O	44.0

[a] ΔH_{vap} values are somewhat temperature-dependent (see Exercise 82).

The conversion of a gas or vapor to a liquid is called **condensation**. From a thermochemical standpoint, condensation is the reverse of vaporization.

$$\Delta H_{condensation} = H_{liquid} - H_{vapor} = -\Delta H_{vap}$$

Because it is opposite in sign but equal in magnitude to ΔH_{vap}, $\Delta H_{condensation}$ (ΔH_{cond}) is always negative. Condensation is an *exothermic* process. This explains why burns produced by a given mass of steam (vaporized water) are very much more severe than burns produced by the same mass of hot water. Hot water burns only by releasing heat as it cools. Steam releases a large quantity of heat when it condenses to liquid water, followed by the further release of heat as the hot water cools.

EXAMPLE 12-1

Estimating the Heat Evolved in the Condensation of Steam. A 0.750-L sample of steam obtained at the normal boiling point of water was allowed to condense on a slightly cooler surface. Estimate the quantity of heat evolved. Why is the result only an estimate?

Solution

First, let us describe the steam sample a bit more precisely. Steam is water vapor, $H_2O(g)$; and when in equilibrium with liquid water at its normal boiling point, the steam is at 1.000 atm pressure. Thus, we are given a volume of gas (0.750 L) at a fixed temperature (100.00 °C) and pressure (1.000 atm), so we use the ideal gas equation to calculate the number of moles of $H_2O(g)$. That is,

$$n_{H_2O} = \frac{PV}{RT} = \frac{1.000 \text{ atm} \times 0.750 \text{ L}}{0.08206 \text{ L atm mol}^{-1} \text{ K}^{-1} \times (273.15 + 100.00)\text{K}}$$
$$= 0.0245 \text{ mol}$$

On a molar basis, estimate the enthalpy of condensation of the $H_2O(g)$ to be the *negative* of the value of ΔH_{vap} of H_2O given in Table 12.1, that is, -44.0 kJ mol^{-1}. For the 0.0245-mol sample of steam,

$$\Delta H_{cond} = 0.0245 \text{ mol} \times (-44.0 \text{ kJ mol}^{-1}) = -1.08 \text{ kJ}$$

This result is only an estimate for two reasons: (1) ΔH_{cond}, like ΔH_{vap}, is temperature dependent. The value used was for 298 K, whereas it should have been for 373 K, a value that was not given. (2) The condensed liquid water was at a temperature below 373 K ("slightly cooler surface"). An additional small quantity of heat was liberated as the condensed steam cooled to that lower temperature.

Practice Example A: How much heat is required to vaporize a 2.35-g sample of diethyl ether at 298 K?

Practice Example B: Calculate a more accurate answer to Example 12-1 by using $\Delta H_{vap} = 40.7$ kJ mol^{-1} for water at 100 °C, 85.0 °C as the temperature of the surface on which the steam condenses, and 4.21 J g^{-1} °C^{-1} as the average specific heat of $H_2O(l)$ in the temperature range 85 to 100 °C.

A relatively fast laboratory demonstration that can be performed to determine the heat of vaporization of nitrogen is described in the follow article: Hamlet, Peter. *J. Chem. Educ.* **1987**: 64, 1060.

▶ **FIGURE 12-7**
Establishing liquid–vapor equilibrium
(a) A liquid is allowed to evaporate into a closed container. Initially, only vaporization occurs.
(b) Condensation begins. The rate at which molecules evaporate is greater than the rate at which they condense, and the number of molecules in the vapor state continues to increase.
(c) The rate of condensation is equal to the rate of vaporization. The number of vapor molecules remains constant over time, as does the pressure exerted by this vapor.

- Molecules in vapor state
- Molecules undergoing vaporization
- Molecules undergoing condensation

(a)   (b)   (c)

VAPOR PRESSURE

Equilibrium Vapor Pressure simulation

Water left in an open beaker evaporates completely. A different condition results if the beaker containing water is placed in a closed container. As shown in Figure 12-7, in a container with both liquid and vapor present, vaporization and condensation occur simultaneously. If sufficient liquid is present, eventually a condition is reached in which the amount of vapor remains constant. This condition is one of *dynamic equilibrium*. Dynamic equilibrium always implies that two opposing processes are occurring simultaneously and at equal rates. As a result, there is no net change with time once equilibrium has been established. A symbolic representation of the liquid–vapor equilibrium is shown below.

$$\text{liquid} \underset{\text{condensation}}{\overset{\text{vaporization}}{\rightleftharpoons}} \text{vapor}$$

▶ Gasoline is a mixture of volatile hydrocarbons and is an important precursor of smog, whether it is vaporized from oil refineries, filling-station operations, automobile gas tanks, or power lawn mowers.

The pressure exerted by a vapor in dynamic equilibrium with its liquid is called the **vapor pressure**. Liquids with high vapor pressures at room temperature are said to be *volatile*, and those with very low vapor pressures are *nonvolatile*. Whether a liquid is volatile or not is determined primarily by the strengths of intermolecular forces—the weaker these forces, the more volatile the liquid (the higher its vapor pressure). Diethyl ether and acetone are volatile liquids; at 25 °C their vapor pressures are 534 and 231 mmHg, respectively. Water at ordinary temperatures is a moderately volatile liquid; at 25 °C, its vapor pressure is 23.8 mmHg. Mercury is essentially a nonvolatile liquid; at 25 °C, its vapor pressure is 0.0018 mmHg.

As an excellent first approximation, the vapor pressure of a liquid depends only on the particular liquid and its temperature. Vapor pressure depends neither on the amount of liquid or vapor, as long as some of each is present at equilibrium. These statements are illustrated in Figure 12-8. A graph of vapor pressure as a function of temperature is known as a **vapor pressure curve**.

(a)   (b)   (c)   (d)   (e)

▲ **FIGURE 12-8**
Vapor pressure illustrated
(a) A mercury barometer. **(b)** The pressure exerted by the vapor in equilibrium with a liquid injected to the top of the mercury column depresses the mercury level. **(c)** Compared to (b), the vapor pressure is independent of the volume of liquid injected. **(d)** Compared to (c), the vapor pressure is independent of the volume of vapor present. **(e)** Vapor pressure increases with an increase in temperature.

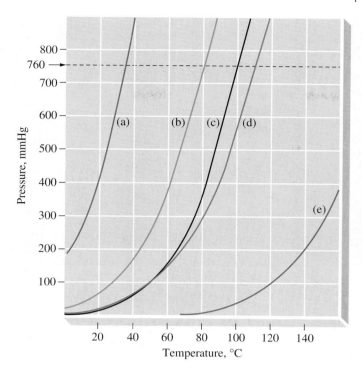

◀ **FIGURE 12-9**
Vapor pressure curves of several liquids
(a) Diethyl ether, $C_4H_{10}O$; (b) benzene, C_6H_6; (c) water, H_2O; (d) toluene, C_7H_8; (e) aniline, C_6H_7N. The normal boiling points are the temperatures at the intersection of the dashed line at $P = 760$ mmHg with the vapor pressure curves.

Vapor pressure curves always have the appearance of those in Figure 12-9: *Vapor pressure increases with temperature.* Vapor pressures of water at different temperatures are presented in Table 12.2.

TABLE 12.2   Vapor Pressure of Water at Various Temperatures

Temperature, °C	Pressure, mmHg	Temperature, °C	Pressure, mmHg	Temperature, °C	Pressure, mmHg
0.0	4.6	29.0	30.0	93.0	588.6
10.0	9.2	30.0	31.8	94.0	610.9
20.0	17.5	40.0	55.3	95.0	633.9
21.0	18.7	50.0	92.5	96.0	657.6
22.0	19.8	60.0	149.4	97.0	682.1
23.0	21.1	70.0	233.7	98.0	707.3
24.0	22.4	80.0	355.1	99.0	733.2
25.0	23.8	90.0	525.8	100.0	760.0
26.0	25.2	91.0	546.0	110.0	1074.6
27.0	26.7	92.0	567.0	120.0	1489.1
28.0	28.3				

This article describes a laboratory experiment which deals with the temperature dependence of vapor pressure using gas chromatography: Kildahl, Nicholas and Berka, Ladislav H. *J. Chem. Educ.* **1995:** *72,* 258.

BOILING AND THE BOILING POINT

When a liquid is heated in a container *open to the atmosphere,* there is a particular temperature at which vaporization occurs throughout the liquid rather than simply at the surface. Vapor bubbles form within the bulk of the liquid, rise to the surface, and escape. The pressure exerted by escaping molecules equals that exerted by molecules of the atmosphere, and **boiling** is said to occur. During boiling, energy absorbed as heat is used only to convert molecules of liquid to vapor. The temperature remains constant until all the liquid has boiled away, as is dramatically illustrated in Figure 12-10. The temperature at which the vapor pressure of a liquid is equal to standard atmospheric pressure (1 atm = 760 mmHg) is the **normal boiling point**. In other words, the normal boiling point is the boiling point of a liquid at 1 atm pressure. The normal boiling points of several liquids can be determined from the intersection of the dashed line in Figure 12-9 with the vapor pressure curves for the liquids.

 The Boiling Point of Water at High Altitude

◀ When a pan of water is put on the stove to boil, small bubbles are usually observed as the water begins to warm. These are bubbles of dissolved air being expelled. Once the water boils, however, all the dissolved air is expelled and the bubbles consist only of water vapor.

This article describes the derivation of a direct relationship between altitude and the boiling point of water: Earl, Boyd L. *J. Chem. Educ.* **1990:** *67,* 45.

Show a pressure cooker and how it has a valve to release pressure and why it cooks at a higher temperature than when not pressurized.

▲ **FIGURE 12-10**
Boiling water in a paper cup
An empty paper cup heated over a Bunsen burner quickly bursts into flame. If a paper cup is filled with water, it can be heated for an extended time as the water boils. This is possible for three reasons: (1) Because of the high heat capacity of water, heat from the burner goes primarily into heating the water, not the cup. (2) As the water boils, large quantities of heat (ΔH_{vap}) are required to convert the liquid to its vapor. (3) The temperature of the cup does not rise above the boiling point of water as long as liquid water remains. The boiling point of 99.9 °C instead of 100.0 °C suggests that the prevailing barometric pressure was slightly below 1 atm.

▶ A more extreme case is that on the summit of Mt. Everest, where a climber would barely be able to heat a cup of tea to 70 °C.

▲ **A liquid boils at low pressure**
Water boils when its vapor pressure equals the pressure on its surface. Bubbles form throughout the liquid.

Figure 12-9 also helps us see that the boiling point of a liquid varies significantly with barometric pressure. Shift the dashed line shown at $P = 760$ mmHg to higher or lower pressures, and the new points of intersection with the vapor pressure curves come at different temperatures. Barometric pressures below 1 atm are commonly encountered at high altitudes. At an altitude of 1609 m (that of Denver, Colorado), barometric pressure is about 630 mmHg. The boiling point of water at this pressure is 95 °C (203 °F). It takes longer to cook foods under conditions of lower boiling-point temperatures. A three-minute boiled egg takes longer than three minutes to cook. We can counteract the effect of high altitudes by using a pressure cooker. In a pressure cooker, the cooking water is maintained under higher-than-atmospheric pressure and its boiling temperature increases, for example, to about 120 °C at 2 atm pressure.

CONCEPT ASSESSMENT ✔

Why does a three-minute boiled egg take longer than three minutes to cook in Switzerland and not on Manhattan Island in New York City?

THE CRITICAL POINT

In describing boiling, we made an important qualification: Boiling occurs "in a container open to the atmosphere." If a liquid is heated in a *sealed* container, boiling does not occur. Instead, the temperature and vapor pressure rise continuously. Pressures many times atmospheric pressure may be attained. If just the right quantity of liquid is sealed in a glass tube and the tube is heated, as in Figure 12-11, the following phenomena can be observed:

• The density of the liquid decreases, that of the vapor increases, and eventually the two densities become equal.

• The surface tension of the liquid approaches zero. The interface between the liquid and vapor becomes less distinct and eventually disappears.

About 10 °C
below T_c

About 1 °C
below T_c

Critical
temp. T_c

◀ **FIGURE 12-11**
Attainment of the critical point
The meniscus separating a liquid from its vapor disappears at the critical point—the liquid and vapor become indistinguishable.

The **critical point** is the point at which these conditions are reached and the liquid and vapor become indistinguishable. The temperature at the critical point is the critical temperature, T_c, and the pressure is the critical pressure, P_c. The critical point is the highest point on a vapor pressure curve and represents the highest temperature at which the liquid can exist. Several critical temperatures and pressures are listed in Table 12.3.

A gas can be liquefied only at temperatures *below* its critical temperature, T_c. If room temperature is *below* T_c, this liquefaction can be accomplished just by applying sufficient pressure. If room temperature is *above* T_c, however, added pressure *and* a lowering of temperature to a value below T_c are required. We will comment further on the liquefaction of gases on page 486.

◀ Although the term "gas" can be used exclusively, sometimes the term "vapor" is used for the gaseous state at temperatures *below* T_c and gas at temperatures *above* T_c.

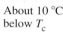 This article describes the construction and use of a cell that can be used to view the critical point of carbon dioxide: Botch, Beatrice and Battino, Rubin. *J. Chem. Educ.* **1987:** *64, 347.*

TABLE 12.3 Some Critical Temperatures, T_c, and Critical Pressures, P_c

Substance	T_c, K	P_c, atm
"Permanent" gases[a]		
H_2	33.3	12.8
N_2	126.2	33.5
O_2	154.8	50.1
CH_4	191.1	45.8
"Nonpermanent" gases[b]		
CO_2	304.2	72.9
HCl	324.6	82.1
NH_3	405.7	112.5
SO_2	431.0	77.7
H_2O	647.3	218.3

[a]Permanent gases cannot be liquefied at 25 °C (298 K).
[b]Nonpermanent gases can be liquefied at 25 °C.

CONCEPT ASSESSMENT ✓

Compare the critical temperatures of NH_3 and N_2 (Table 12.3). Which gas has the stronger intermolecular forces?

MEASURING VAPOR PRESSURE

Figure 12-8 suggests one method of determining vapor pressure—inject a small sample of the target liquid at the top of a mercury barometer, and measure the depression of the mercury level. The method does not give very precise results, however, and it is not useful for measuring vapor pressures that are either very low or quite high. Better results are obtained with methods in which the pressure above a liquid is continuously varied and measured, and the liquid–vapor equilibrium temperature is recorded. In short, the boiling point of the liquid changes in accordance with the change in the pressure above the liquid, and the vapor pressure curve of the liquid can be traced. The pressure measurements are made with either a closed-end or open-end manometer (page 182). A method that is useful for determining very low vapor pressures is based on the rate of effusion of a gas through a tiny orifice. In this method, equations from the kinetic–molecular theory (Section 6-7) are applied. Example 12-2 illustrates a method (called the transpiration method) in which an inert gas is saturated with the vapor under study. Then the ideal gas equation is used to calculate the vapor pressure.

This articles describes an inexpensive microscale method for measuring vapor pressures: DeMuro, Jason C. et al. *J. Chem. Educ.* **1999:** *76,* 1113.

EXAMPLE 12-2

Using the Ideal Gas Equation to Calculate a Vapor Pressure. A sample of 113 L of helium gas at 1360 °C and prevailing barometric pressure is passed through molten silver at the same temperature. The gas becomes saturated with silver vapor, and the liquid silver loses 0.120 g in mass. What is the vapor pressure of liquid silver at 1360 °C?

Solution

Let's assume that after the gas has become saturated with silver vapor, its volume remains at 113 L. This assumption will be valid if the vapor pressure of the silver is quite low compared to the barometric pressure. According to Dalton's law of partial pressures (page 198), we can deal with the silver vapor as if it were a single gas occupying a volume of 113 L. The data required in the ideal gas equation are listed below.

$$P = ? \qquad\qquad\qquad\qquad V = 113 \text{ L}$$

$$R = 0.08206 \text{ L atm mol}^{-1}\text{K}^{-1} \qquad T = 1360 + 273.15 = 1633 \text{ K}$$

$$n = 0.120 \text{ g Ag} \times \frac{1 \text{ mol Ag}}{107.9 \text{ g Ag}} = 0.00111 \text{ mol Ag}$$

$$P = \frac{nRT}{V}$$

$$P = \frac{0.00111 \text{ mol} \times 0.08206 \text{ L atm mol}^{-1}\text{K}^{-1} \times 1633 \text{ K}}{113 \text{ L}}$$

$$= 1.32 \times 10^{-3} \text{ atm (1.00 Torr)}$$

Practice Example A: Equilibrium is established between liquid hexane, C_6H_{14}, and its vapor at 25.0 °C. A sample of the vapor is found to have a density of 0.701 g/L. Calculate the vapor pressure of hexane at 25.0 °C, expressed in Torr.

Practice Example B: With the help of Figure 12-9, estimate the density of the vapor in equilibrium with liquid diethyl ether at 20.0 °C.

USING VAPOR PRESSURE DATA

One use of vapor pressure data is in calculations dealing with the collection of gases over liquids, particularly water (Section 6-6). Another use, illustrated in Example 12-3, is in predicting whether a substance exists solely as a gas (vapor) or as a liquid and vapor in equilibrium.

EXAMPLE 12-3

Making Predictions with Vapor Pressure Data. As a result of a chemical reaction, 0.132 g H_2O is produced and maintained at a temperature of 50.0 °C in a closed flask of 525-mL volume. Will the water be present as liquid only, vapor only, or liquid and vapor in equilibrium (Fig. 12-12)?

Solution

Let's consider each of the three possibilities in the order that they are given.

LIQUID ONLY

With a density of about 1 g/mL, a 0.132-g sample of H_2O has a volume of only about 0.13 mL. There is no way that the sample could completely fill a 525-mL flask. The condition of liquid only is *impossible*.

VAPOR ONLY

The portion of the flask that is not occupied by liquid water must be filled with something (it cannot remain a vacuum). That something is water vapor. The question is, will the sample vaporize completely, leaving no liquid? Let's use the ideal gas equation to calculate the pressure that would be exerted if the entire 0.132 g H_2O were present in the gaseous state.

$$P = \frac{nRT}{V}$$

$$= \frac{0.132 \text{ g } H_2O \times \dfrac{1 \text{ mol } H_2O}{18.02 \text{ g } H_2O} \times 0.08206 \text{ L atm mol}^{-1} \text{ K}^{-1} \times 323.2 \text{ K}}{0.525 \text{ L}}$$

$$= 0.370 \text{ atm} \times \frac{760 \text{ mmHg}}{1 \text{ atm}} = 281 \text{ mmHg}$$

Now compare this calculated pressure with the vapor pressure of water at 50 °C (Table 12.2). The calculated pressure—281 mmHg—greatly exceeds the vapor pressure—92.5 mmHg. Water formed in the reaction as $H_2O(g)$ condenses to $H_2O(l)$ when the gas pressure reaches 92.5 mmHg, for this is the pressure at which the liquid and vapor are in equilibrium at 50.0 °C. The condition of vapor only is *impossible*.

LIQUID AND VAPOR

This is the only possibility for the final condition in the flask. Liquid water and water vapor coexist in equilibrium at 50.0 °C and 92.5 mmHg.

Practice Example A: If the reaction described in this example resulted in H_2O produced and maintained at 80.0 °C, would the water be present as vapor only or as liquid and vapor in equilibrium? Explain.

Practice Example B: For the situation described in Example 12-3, what mass of water is present as liquid and what mass as vapor?

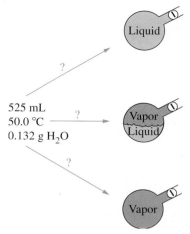

▲ FIGURE 12-12
Predicting states of matter—Example 12-3 illustrated
For the conditions given on the left, which of the final conditions pictured on the right will result?

AN EQUATION FOR EXPRESSING VAPOR PRESSURE DATA

If you seek vapor pressure data on a liquid in a handbook or in data tables, you are unlikely to find graphs like Figure 12-9. Also, with the exception of a few liquids, such as water and mercury, you are unlikely to find data tables like Table 12.2. What you will find, instead, are mathematical equations relating vapor pressures and temperatures. Such equations can summarize in one line data that might otherwise take a full page. Equation (12.1) is a particularly common form of vapor pressure equation. It expresses the natural logarithm (ln) of vapor pressure as a function of the reciprocal of the Kelvin temperature ($1/T$). The relationship is that of a straight line, and the straight-line plots for the liquids featured in Figure 12-9 are drawn in Figure 12-13.

$$\ln P = -A\left(\frac{1}{T}\right) + B$$

Equation of straight line: $y = m \times x + b$

(12.1)

To use equation (12.1), we need values for the two constants, A and B. The constant A is related to the enthalpy of vaporization of the liquid: $A = \Delta H_{vap}/R$, where ΔH_{vap} is expressed in the unit $J \text{ mol}^{-1}$ and the value used for R is 8.3145 $J \text{ mol}^{-1} \text{ K}^{-1}$. It is customary to eliminate B by rewriting (12.1) in a form called the Clausius–Clapeyron equation.

$$\ln\frac{P_2}{P_1} = \frac{\Delta H_{vap}}{R}\left(\frac{1}{T_1} - \frac{1}{T_2}\right)$$

(12.2)

We apply equation (12.2) in Example 12-4.

Vapor Pressure vs. Temperature animation

◄ Refer to Appendix A-4 to see how the constant B is eliminated to give equation (12.2).

◄ KEEP IN MIND
that the heat of vaporization in this equation cannot be ΔH_{vap}°, since in general the pressure is not 1 bar.

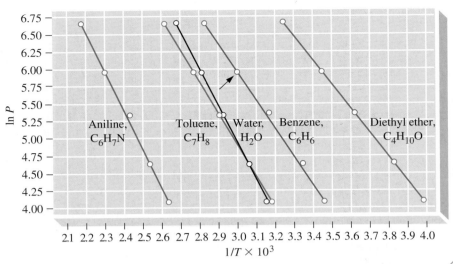

▲ **FIGURE 12-13**
Vapor pressure data plotted as ln P versus $1/T$
Pressures are in millimeters of mercury, and temperatures are in kelvins. Data from
Figure 12-9 have been recalculated and replotted as in the following example:
For benzene at 60 °C, the vapor pressure is 400 mmHg; ln P = ln 400 = 5.99.
T = 60 + 273 = 333 K; $1/T$ = 1/333 = 0.00300 = 3.00×10^{-3}; $1/T \times 10^3$ =
$3.00 \times 10^{-3} \times 10^3$ = 3.00. The point corresponding to (3.00, 5.99) is marked by the
black arrow.

EXAMPLE 12-4

Applying the Clausius–Clapeyron Equation. Calculate the vapor pressure of water
at 35.0 °C with data from Tables 12.1 and 12.2.

Solution

Designate the unknown vapor pressure as P_1 at the temperature T_1. That is,

$$P_1 = ? \qquad\qquad T_1 = (35.0 + 273.15)\ \text{K} = 308.2\ \text{K}$$

For P_2 and T_2 choose known data for a temperature close to 35.0 °C, for example, 40.0 °C.

$$P_2 = 55.3\ \text{mmHg} \qquad\qquad T_2 = (40.0 + 273.15)\ \text{K} = 313.2\ \text{K}$$

For ΔH_{vap}, let's assume that the value given in Table 12.1 applies throughout the
temperature range from 30.0 °C to 40.0 °C.

$$\Delta H_{\text{vap}} = 44.0\ \text{kJ/mol} \times \frac{1000\ \text{J}}{1\ \text{kJ}} = 44.0 \times 10^3\ \text{J mol}^{-1}$$

Now substitute these values into equation (12.2) to obtain

$$\ln \frac{55.3\ \text{mmHg}}{P_1} = \frac{44.0 \times 10^3\ \text{J mol}^{-1}}{8.3145\ \text{J mol}^{-1}\ \text{K}^{-1}} \left(\frac{1}{308.2} - \frac{1}{313.2} \right) \text{K}^{-1}$$

$$= 5.29 \times 10^3\ (0.003245 - 0.003193) = 0.28$$

Next, determine that $e^{0.28}$ = 1.32 (see Appendix A). Thus,

$$\frac{55.3\ \text{mmHg}}{P_1} = e^{0.28} = 1.32$$

$$P_1 = 55.3\ \text{mmHg}/1.32 = 41.9\ \text{mmHg}$$

(The experimentally determined vapor pressure of water at 35.0 °C is 42.175 mmHg.)

Practice Example A: A handbook lists the vapor pressure of methyl alcohol as
100 mmHg at 21.2 °C. What is its vapor pressure at 25.0 °C?

Practice Example B: A handbook lists the normal boiling point of isooctane,
a gasoline component, as 99.2 °C and its enthalpy of vaporization (ΔH_{vap}) as
35.76 kJ mol^{-1} C_8H_{18}. Calculate the vapor pressure of isooctane at 25 °C.

KEEP IN MIND ▶

that here P_1 must be *smaller
than* P_2 because $T_1 < T_2$.
Thus, regardless of how we
write equation (12.2)—
different formulations are
possible—or choose (T_1, P_1)
and (T_2, P_2), we are guided
by the fact that vapor
pressure always increases
with temperature.

12-3   SOME PROPERTIES OF SOLIDS

We mentioned some properties of solids (for example, malleability, ductility) at the beginning of this text, and we will continue to consider additional properties. For now, we will comment on some properties that allow us to think of solids in relation to the other states of matter—liquids and gases.

MELTING, MELTING POINT, AND HEAT OF FUSION

As a crystalline solid is heated, its atoms, ions, or molecules vibrate more vigorously. Eventually a temperature is reached at which these vibrations disrupt the ordered crystalline structure. The atoms, ions, or molecules can slip past one another, and the solid loses its definite shape and is converted to a liquid. This process is called **melting**, or fusion, and the temperature at which it occurs is the **melting point**. The reverse process, the conversion of a liquid to a solid, is called **freezing**, or solidification, and the temperature at which it occurs is the **freezing point**. The melting point of a solid and the freezing point of its liquid are identical. At this temperature, solid and liquid coexist in equilibrium.

If we add heat uniformly to a solid–liquid mixture at equilibrium, the temperature remains constant while the solid melts. Only when all the solid has melted does the temperature begin to rise. Conversely, if we remove heat uniformly from a solid–liquid mixture at equilibrium, the liquid freezes at a constant temperature. The quantity of heat required to melt a solid is the *enthalpy of fusion*, ΔH_{fus}. Some typical enthalpies of fusion, expressed in kilojoules per mole, are listed in Table 12.4. Perhaps the most familiar example of a melting (and freezing) point is that of water, 0 °C. This is the temperature at which liquid and solid water, in contact with air and under standard atmospheric pressure, are in equilibrium. The enthalpy of fusion of water is 6.01 kJ mol^{-1}, which we can express as

$$H_2O(s) \longrightarrow H_2O(l) \qquad \Delta H_{fus} = +6.01 \text{ kJ mol}^{-1} \qquad (12.3)$$

Here is an easy way to determine the freezing point of a liquid. Allow the liquid to cool, and measure the liquid temperature as it falls with time. When freezing begins, the temperature *remains constant* until all the liquid has frozen. Then the temperature is again free to fall as the solid cools. If we plot temperatures against time, we get a graph known as a *cooling curve*. Figure 12-14 is a cooling curve for water. We can also run this process backwards, that is, by starting with the solid and adding heat. Now the temperature remains constant while melting occurs. This temperature–time plot is called a *heating curve*. Generally speaking, the appearance of the heating curve is that of a cooling curve that has been flipped from left to right. A heating curve for water is sketched in Figure 12-15.

Often, an experimentally determined cooling curve does not look quite like the solid-line plot in Figure 12-14. The temperature may drop below the freezing point without any solid appearing. This condition is known as *supercooling*.

TABLE 12.4 Some Enthalpies of Fusion		
Substance	Melting Point, °C	ΔH_{fus}, kJ mol^{-1}
Mercury, Hg	−38.9	2.30
Sodium, Na	97.8	2.60
Methyl alcohol, CH$_3$OH	−97.7	3.21
Ethyl alcohol, CH$_3$CH$_2$OH	−114	5.01
Water, H$_2$O	0.0	6.01
Benzoic acid, C$_6$H$_5$COOH	122.4	18.08
Naphthalene, C$_{10}$H$_8$	80.2	18.98

 Examples of a supercooled substance are water droplets in the sky. They are still liquid at temperatures well below the freezing point. When they find a bit of dust on which they can nucleate, the droplets spontaneously turn to ice.

 Heat of Fusion of Water

Heating Curves activity

▲ **FIGURE 12-14**
Cooling curve for water
The broken-line portion represents the condition of supercooling that occasionally occurs.
(l) = liquid; (s) = solid.

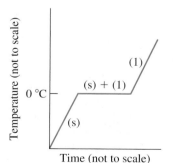

▲ **FIGURE 12-15**
Heating curve for water
This curve traces the changes that occur as ice is heated from below the melting point to produce liquid water somewhat above the melting point.

Point out that iodine vapor, like that of all the halogens, is highly toxic.

For a crystalline solid to start forming from a liquid at the freezing point, the liquid must contain some small particles (for example, suspended dust particles) on which crystals can form. If a liquid contains a very limited number of particles on which crystals can grow, it may supercool for a time before freezing. When a supercooled liquid does begin to freeze, however, the temperature rises back to the normal freezing point while freezing is completed. We can always recognize supercooling through a slight dip in a cooling curve just before the straight-line portion.

SUBLIMATION

Like liquids, solids can also give off vapors, although because of the stronger intermolecular forces present, solids are generally not as volatile as liquids at a given temperature. The direct passage of molecules from the solid to the vapor state is called **sublimation**. The reverse process, the passage of molecules from the vapor to the solid state, is called **deposition**. When sublimation and deposition occur at equal rates, a dynamic equilibrium exists between a solid and its vapor. The vapor exerts a characteristic pressure called the *sublimation pressure*. A plot of sublimation pressure as a function of temperature is called a *sublimation curve*. The *enthalpy of sublimation* (ΔH_{sub}) is the quantity of heat needed to convert a solid to vapor. At the melting point, sublimation (solid $\longrightarrow$ vapor) is equivalent to melting (solid $\longrightarrow$ liquid) followed by vaporization (liquid $\longrightarrow$ vapor). This suggests the following relationship between ΔH_{fus}, ΔH_{vap}, and ΔH_{sub} at the melting point.

$$\Delta H_{sub} = \Delta H_{fus} + \Delta H_{vap} \tag{12.4}$$

The value of ΔH_{sub} obtained with equation (12.4) can replace the enthalpy of vaporization in the Clausius–Clapeyron equation (12.2), so that sublimation pressures can be calculated as a function of temperature.

Two familiar solids with significant sublimation pressures are ice and dry ice (solid carbon dioxide). If you live in a cold climate, you are aware that snow may disappear from the ground even though the temperature may fail to rise above 0 °C. Under these conditions, the snow does not melt; it sublimes. The sublimation pressure of ice at 0 °C is 4.58 mmHg. That is, the solid ice has a vapor pressure of 4.58 mmHg at 0 °C. If the air is not already saturated with water vapor, the ice will sublime. The sublimation and deposition of iodine are pictured in Figure 12-16.

▲ **FIGURE 12-16**
Sublimation of iodine
Even at temperatures well below its melting point of 114 °C, solid iodine exhibits an appreciable sublimation pressure. Here, purple iodine vapor is produced at about 70 °C. Deposition of the vapor to solid iodine occurs on the colder walls of the flask.

CONCEPT ASSESSMENT ✓

Recall the discussion of dew and frost formation (page 213). Do the surroundings absorb or lose heat when water vapor condenses to dew or frost? Is the quantity of heat per gram of $H_2O(g)$ condensed the same whether the condensate is dew or frost? Explain.

12-4 PHASE DIAGRAMS

Imagine constructing a pressure–temperature graph in which each point on the graph represents a condition under which a substance might be found. At low temperatures and high pressures, such as the red points in Figure 12-17, we expect the atoms, ions, or molecules of a substance to be in a close orderly arrangement—a solid. At high temperatures and low pressures—the brown points in Figure 12-17—we expect the gaseous state; and at intermediate temperatures and pressures, we expect a liquid (blue points in Figure 12-17).

Figure 12-17 is a **phase diagram**, a graphical representation of the conditions of temperature and pressure at which solids, liquids, and gases (vapors) exist, either as single phases, or states, of matter or as two or more phases in equilibrium with one another. The different regions of the diagram correspond to single phases, or states, of matter. Straight or curved lines where single-phase regions adjoin represent two phases in equilibrium.

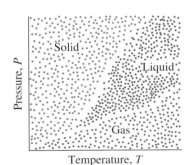

▲ **FIGURE 12-17**
Temperature, pressure, and states of matter
The outline of a phase diagram is suggested by the distribution of dots. (See also Figures 12-18 and 12-19.)

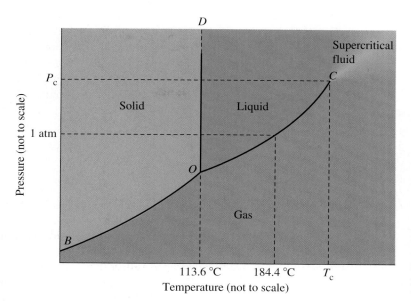

◀ **FIGURE 12-18**
Phase diagram for iodine
Note that the melting point and triple point temperatures for iodine are essentially the same. Generally, large pressure increases are required to produce even small changes in solid–liquid equilibrium temperatures. The pressure and temperature axes on a phase diagram are generally not drawn to scale so that the significant features of the diagram can be more readily emphasized.

IODINE

One of the simplest phase diagrams is that of iodine shown in Figure 12-18. The curve OC is the vapor pressure curve of liquid iodine, and C is the critical point. OB is the sublimation curve of solid iodine. The nearly vertical line OD represents the effect of pressure on the melting point of iodine; it is called the *fusion curve*. The point O has a special significance. It defines the *unique* temperature and pressure at which the *three* states of matter, solid, liquid, and gas, coexist in equilibrium. It is called a **triple point**. For iodine, the triple point is at 113.6 °C and 91.6 mmHg. The normal melting point (113.6 °C) and the boiling point (184.4 °C) are the temperatures at which a line at P = 1 atm intersects the fusion and vapor pressure curves, respectively. Melting is essentially unaffected by pressure in the limited range from 91.6 mmHg to 1 atm, and the normal melting point and the triple point are at almost the same temperature.

The extreme range of temperatures and pressures required for the entire phase diagram precludes plotting it to scale. This is why the axes are labeled "not to scale."

CARBON DIOXIDE

The case of carbon dioxide, shown in Figure 12-19, differs from that of iodine in one important respect—the pressure at the triple point O is greater than 1 atm. A line at P = 1 atm intersects the *sublimation curve*, not the vapor pressure curve.

Are You Wondering . . .

If the sublimation curve can ever be just an extension of the vapor pressure curve?

Although the sublimation curve for iodine in Figure 12-18 would look almost like a continuation of the vapor pressure curve if the data were plotted to scale, there is a discontinuity at the triple point O. Moreover, this must *always* be the case. If these two curves were continuous, then the lines representing the variation of ln P with $1/T$ (Fig. 12-13) would have the same slope—but this is not possible. The value of ΔH_{vap} determines the slope of the vapor pressure line (recall equation 12.1), whereas ΔH_{sub} determines the slope of the sublimation line. However, these two enthalpy changes can never be the same, because $\Delta H_{sub} = \Delta H_{vap} + \Delta H_{fus}$.

Put a block of dry ice on the bench top to show the effect of sublimation.

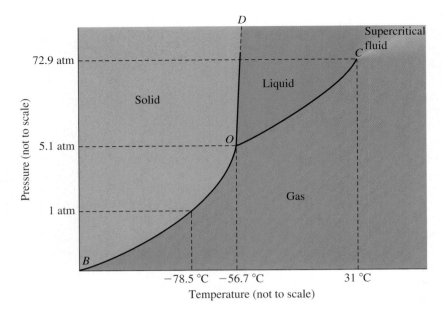

▶ **FIGURE 12-19**
Phase diagram for carbon dioxide
Several aspects of this diagram are described in the text. An additional feature not shown here is the curvature of the fusion curve *OD* to the right at very high pressures, ultimately reaching temperatures above the critical temperature.

This article describes a simple experiment which demonstrates the phase diagram of carbon dioxide: Lieu, Van T. *J. Chem. Educ.* **1996**: *73, 837.*

If solid CO_2 is heated in an open container, it sublimes away at a constant temperature of $-78.5\ ^\circ$C. It *does not melt* at atmospheric pressure (and so is called "Dry Ice"). Because it maintains a low temperature and does not produce a liquid by melting, Dry Ice is widely used in freezing and preserving foods.

Liquid CO_2 can be obtained at pressures above 5.1 atm and it is most frequently encountered in CO_2 fire extinguishers. All three states of matter are involved in the action of these fire extinguishers. When the liquid CO_2 is released, most of it quickly vaporizes. The heat required for this vaporization is extracted from the remaining $CO_2(l)$, which has its temperature lowered to the point that it freezes and falls as a $CO_2(s)$ "snow." In turn, the $CO_2(s)$ quickly sublimes to $CO_2(g)$. All of this helps to quench a fire by displacing the air around the fire with a "blanket" of $CO_2(g)$ and by cooling the area somewhat.

SUPERCRITICAL FLUIDS

Because the liquid and gaseous states become identical and indistinguishable at the critical point, it is difficult to know what to call the state of matter at temperatures and pressures above the critical point. For example, this state of matter has the high density of a liquid and the low viscosity of a gas. The term that is now commonly used is *supercritical fluid* (SCF). Above the critical temperature, no amount of pressure can liquefy a supercritical fluid. Consider the generic phase diagram in Figure 12-20. The path of dots starting with a vapor below the critical isotherm takes us to a low-density gas above the isotherm.

▶ **FIGURE 12-20**
Critical point and critical isotherm
Applying pressure to a gas at temperatures below the critical isotherm, T_c, causes a liquid to form with the appearance of a meniscus, a discontinuous phase change. Applying pressure above the critical isotherm simply increases the density of the supercritical fluid. In a path traced by the small arrows, gas changes to liquid without exhibiting a discontinuous phase transition.

When the pressure is greatly increased, we produce a supercritical fluid of much greater density. If, while the pressure exceeds the critical pressure, P_c, the temperature is reduced below the critical temperature, we obtain a liquid. Even with further reduction of pressure, the sample remains in the liquid phase. In following the path described, we have gone from a gas to a liquid without observing a liquid–gas interface. The only way to observe the liquid–vapor interface is to cross the phase boundary below the critical temperature. Note that in the present case we could observe the liquid–vapor interface by lowering the pressure on the liquid to a point on the vapor pressure curve.

Although we do not ordinarily think of liquids or solids as being soluble in gases, *volatile* liquids and solids are. The mole fraction solubility is simply the ratio of the vapor pressure (or the sublimation pressure) to the total gas pressure. And liquids and solids become much more soluble in a gas that is above its critical pressure and temperature, mostly because the density of the SCF is high and approaches that of a liquid. Molecules in supercritical fluids, being in much closer proximity than in ordinary gases, can exert strong attractive forces on the molecules of a liquid or solid solute. SCFs display solvent properties similar to ordinary liquid solvents. To vary the pressure of an SCF means to vary its density and also its solvent properties. Thus, a given SCF, such as carbon dioxide, can be made to behave like many different solvents.

Until recently, the principal method of decaffeinating coffee was to extract the caffeine with a solvent such as methylene chloride (CH_2Cl_2). This solvent is objectionable because it is hazardous in the workplace and difficult to completely remove from the coffee. Now, supercritical fluid CO_2 is used. In one process, green coffee beans are brought into contact with CO_2 at about 90 °C and 160 to 220 atm. The caffeine content of the coffee is reduced from its normal 1 to 3% to about 0.02%. When the temperature and pressure of the CO_2 are reduced, the caffeine precipitates and the CO_2 is recycled.

WATER

The phase diagram of water (Fig. 12-21) presents several new features. One is that the fusion curve *OD* has a *negative* slope; that is, it slopes toward the pressure axis. The melting point of ice *decreases* with an increase in pressure, and this is rather unusual behavior for a solid (bismuth and antimony also behave in this way). However, because large changes in pressure are required to produce even small decreases in the melting point, we do not commonly observe this melting behavior of ice. One example that has been given comes from ice-skating. Presumably, the pressure of the skate blades

▲ **Decaffeinated coffee**
"Naturally" decaffeinated coffee is made through a process that uses supercritical fluid CO_2 as a solvent to dissolve the caffeine in green coffee beans. Afterward, the beans are roasted and sold to consumers.

http://www.scrub.lanl.gov/ html/scf/default_nn.htm to get more information about supercritical fluids.

Since the L-S line in the phase diagram of water is negative, that means that ice floats. If ice did not float, then the polar seas would fill with ice that would never melt. Most solids are more dense than their liquid state. Water is, for us, a happy exception.

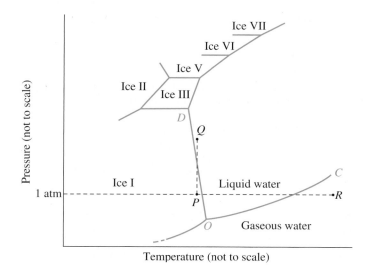

◀ **FIGURE 12-21**
Phase diagram for water
Point *O*, the triple point, is at 0.0098 °C and 4.58 mmHg. (The normal melting point is at exactly 0 °C and 760 mmHg.) The critical point, *C*, is at 374.1 °C and 218.2 atm. At point *D* the temperature is −22.0 °C and the pressure is 2045 atm. The negative slope of the fusion curve, *OD* (greatly exaggerated here), and the significance of the broken straight lines are discussed in the text.

▶ An increase in pressure to 125 atm lowers the freezing point of water by only about 1 °C.

melts the ice, and the skater skims along on a thin lubricating film of liquid water. This explanation is unlikely, however, because the pressure of the blades doesn't produce a significant lowering of the melting point and certainly cannot explain the ability to skate on ice at temperatures much below the freezing point. (Recent experimental evidence suggests that molecules in a very thin surface layer on ice are mobile in the same way as in liquid water, and this mobility persists even at very low temperatures.)

Another feature illustrated in the phase diagram of water is **polymorphism**, the existence of a solid substance in more than one form. Ordinary ice, called ice I, exists under ordinary pressures. The other forms exist only at high pressures. Polymorphism is more the rule than the exception among solids. Where it occurs, a phase diagram has triple points in addition to the usual solid–liquid–vapor triple point. For example at point D in Figure 12-21, ice I, ice III, and liquid H_2O are in equilibrium at $-22.0\ °C$ and 2045 atm. Note that the fusion curves for the forms of ice other than ice I have *positive* slopes. Thus, the triple point with ice VI, ice VII, and liquid water is at 81.6 °C and 21,700 atm.

PHASES AND PHASE TRANSITIONS

Changes of State animation

What's the difference between a phase and a state of matter? These terms tend to be used synonymously, but there is a small distinction between them. As we have already noted, there are just *three* states of matter: solid, liquid, and gas. A *phase* is any sample of matter with definite composition and uniform properties that is distinguishable from other phases with which it is in contact. Thus, we can describe liquid water in equilibrium with its vapor as a two-phase mixture. The liquid is one phase and the gas, or vapor, is the other. In this case, the phases (liquid and gas) are the same as the states of matter present (liquid and gas).

We can describe the equilibrium mixture at the triple point D in Figure 12-21 as a *three-phase* mixture, even though only *two* states of matter are present (solid and liquid). Two of the phases are in the solid state—the polymorphic forms ice I and ice III. For mixtures of two or more components, different phases may exist in the liquid state as well as in the solid state. For example, most mixtures of triethylamine, $N(CH_2CH_3)_3$, and water at 25 °C separate into two physically distinct liquid phases. One is a saturated solution of triethylamine in water and the other, a saturated solution of water in triethylamine. Because the pressure–temperature diagrams we have been describing can accommodate all the phases in a system, we call them *phase* diagrams. We call the crossing of a two-phase curve in a phase diagram a *phase transition*.

Listed below are six common names assigned to phase transitions.

melting (s $\longrightarrow$ l)	freezing (l $\longrightarrow$ s)
vaporization (l $\longrightarrow$ g)	condensation (g $\longrightarrow$ l)
sublimation (s $\longrightarrow$ g)	deposition (g $\longrightarrow$ s)

Following are two useful generalizations about the changes that occur when crossing a two-phase equilibrium curve in a phase diagram.

- From lower to higher temperatures along a *constant-pressure* line (an isobar), enthalpy *increases*. (Heat is absorbed.)
- From lower to higher pressures along a *constant-temperature* line (an isotherm), volume *decreases*. (The phase at the higher pressure has the higher density.)

▶ Because ice(I) is less dense than $H_2O(l)$, the fusion curve OD in Figure 12-21 has a negative slope.

The second generalization helps us to understand why a fusion curve usually has a positive slope. Typical behavior is for a solid to have a greater density than the corresponding liquid. Example 12-5 illustrates how we can use a phase diagram to describe the phase transitions that a substance can undergo.

Ice I	$H_2O(l)$
At point P	At point Q

EXAMPLE 12-5

Interpreting a Phase Diagram. A sample of ice is maintained at 1 atm and at a temperature represented by point P in Figure 12-21. Describe what happens when **(a)** the temperature is raised, at constant pressure, to point R, and **(b)** the pressure is raised, at constant temperature, to point Q. The sketches in Figure 12-22 suggest the conditions at points P, Q, and R.

Solution

(a) When the temperature reaches a point on the fusion curve OD (0 °C), ice begins to melt. The temperature remains constant as ice is converted to liquid. When melting is complete, the temperature again increases. No vapor appears in the cylinder until the temperature reaches 100 °C, at which point the vapor pressure is 1 atm. When all the liquid has vaporized, the temperature is again free to rise to a final value of R.

(b) Because solids are not very compressible, very little change occurs until the pressure reaches the point of intersection of the constant-temperature line PQ with the fusion curve OD. Here melting begins. A significant *decrease* in volume occurs (about 10%) as ice is converted to liquid water. After melting, additional pressure produces very little change because liquids are not very compressible.

Practice Example A: With as much detail as possible, describe the phase changes that would occur if a sample of water represented by point R in Figure 12-21 were brought first to point P and then to point Q.

Practice Example B: Draw a sketch showing the condition prevailing along the line PR when 1.00 mol of water has been brought to the point where exactly one-half of it has vaporized. Compare this to the condition at point R in Figure 12-22, assuming that this is also based on 1.00 mol of water. For example, is the volume of the system the same as that in Figure 12-22? If not, is it larger or smaller, and by how much? Assume that the temperature at point R is the same as the critical temperature of water and that water vapor behaves as an ideal gas.

$H_2O(g)$

At point R

▲ FIGURE 12-22
Example 12-5 illustrated
A sample of pure water is confined in a cylinder by a freely moving piston surmounted by weights to establish the confining pressure. Sketched here are conditions at the points labeled P, Q, and R in Figure 12-21. The transition from point P to Q is accomplished by changing the pressure at constant temperature (isothermal). The transition from point P to R is accomplished by changing the temperature at constant pressure (isobaric).

CONCEPT ASSESSMENT ✓

One method of restoring water-damaged books after a fire in a library is by "freeze drying" them in evacuated chambers. Describe how this method might work.

12-5 VAN DER WAALS FORCES

Because helium forms no stable chemical bonds, we might expect it to remain a gas right down to 0 K. Although helium remains gaseous to very low temperatures, it does condense to a liquid at 4 K and freeze to a solid (at 25 atm pressure) at 1 K. These data suggest that intermolecular forces, even though very weak, must exist among He atoms. If the temperature is sufficiently low, these forces overcome thermal agitation and cause helium to condense. In this section, we will examine the types of intermolecular forces known collectively as **van der Waals forces**. The intermolecular forces contributing to the term n^2a/V^2 in the van der Waals equation for nonideal gases (equation 6.26) are of this type.

INSTANTANEOUS AND INDUCED DIPOLES

In describing electronic structures, we speak of electron charge density, or the probability that an electron is in a certain region at a given time. One probability is that at some particular instant—purely by chance—electrons are concentrated in one region of an atom or molecule. This displacement of electrons causes a normally nonpolar species to become momentarily polar.

▲ **FIGURE 12-23**
The phenomenon of induction
The attraction of a balloon to a surface is a commonplace example of induction. The balloon is charged by rubbing, and the charged balloon induces an opposite charge on the surface. (See also Appendix B).

An *instantaneous dipole* is formed. That is, the molecule has an instantaneous dipole moment. After this, electrons in a neighboring atom or molecule may be displaced to also produce a dipole. This is a process of induction (Fig. 12-23), and the newly formed dipole is called an *induced dipole*.

Taken together, these two events lead to an intermolecular force of attraction (Fig. 12-24). We can call this an instantaneous dipole–induced dipole attraction, but the names more commonly used are **dispersion force** and **London force**. (In 1928, Fritz London offered a theoretical explanation of these forces.)

Polarizability is the term used to describe the tendency for charge separation to occur in a molecule. The greater this tendency, the more polarizable the molecule is said to be. Polarizability increases with increased numbers of electrons, and the number of electrons increases with increased molecular mass. Also, in large molecules, some electrons, being farther from atomic nuclei, are less firmly held. These electrons are more easily displaced, and the polarizability of the molecule increases. Because dispersion forces become stronger as polarizability increases, molecules attract each other more strongly, with the result that melting points and boiling points of covalent substances generally increase with increasing molecular mass. For instance, helium, with a molecular (atomic) mass of 4 u, has a boiling point of 4 K, whereas radon (atomic mass, 222 u) has a boiling point of 211 K. The melting points and boiling points of the halogens increase in a similar way in the series F_2, Cl_2, Br_2, I_2 (recall Table 9.5).The strength of dispersion forces also depends on *molecular shape*. Electrons in elongated molecules are more easily displaced than are those in small, compact, symmetrical molecules; the elongated molecules are more polarizable. Two substances with identical numbers and kinds of atoms but different molecular shapes (*isomers*) may have different properties. This idea is illustrated in Figure 12-25.

KEEP IN MIND ▶
that a bond dipole results from the separation of centers of positive and negative charge in a covalent bond, that a resultant dipole moment, μ, is a summation of bond dipoles taking into account their magnitudes and directions, and that a *polar* molecule (Section 10-7) is one that has a permanent resultant dipole moment.

(a)   (b)   (c)

▲ **FIGURE 12-24**
Instantaneous and induced dipoles
(a) In the *normal condition*, a nonpolar molecule has a symmetrical charge distribution. **(b)** In the *instantaneous condition*, a displacement of the electronic charge produces an instantaneous dipole with a charge separation represented as $\delta+$ and $\delta-$. **(c)** In an *induced dipole*, the instantaneous dipole on the left induces a charge separation in the molecule on the right. The result is a dipole–dipole attraction.

(a) Neopentane
bp = 9.5 °C

(b) Pentane
bp = 36.1 °C

The SI unit for dipole moment is the Debye (D), introduced mainly because in MKS units the values of the dipole moment are very small numbers.

▲ **FIGURE 12-25**
Molecular shapes and polarizability
The elongated pentane molecule is more easily polarized than is the compact neopentane molecule. Intermolecular forces are stronger in pentane than they are in neopentane. As a result, pentane boils at a higher temperature than neopentane.

▲ **FIGURE 12-26**
Dipole–dipole interactions
Dipoles tend to arrange themselves with the positive end of one dipole pointed toward the negative end of a neighboring dipole. Ordinarily, thermal motion upsets this orderly array. Nevertheless, this tendency for dipoles to align themselves can affect physical properties, such as the melting points of solids and the boiling points of liquids.

DIPOLE–DIPOLE INTERACTIONS

In a *polar* substance, the molecules have permanent dipole moments, so the molecules tend to line up with the positive end of one dipole directed toward the negative ends of neighboring dipoles (Fig. 12-26). This additional partial ordering of molecules can cause a substance to persist as a solid or liquid at temperatures higher than otherwise expected. Consider N_2, O_2, and NO. There are no electronegativity differences in N_2 and O_2, and both substances are nonpolar. In NO, on the other hand, there is an electronegativity difference, and the molecule has a slight dipole moment. Considering only dispersion forces, we would expect the boiling point of NO(l) to be intermediate to those of N_2(l) and O_2(l), but in the comparison below, we see that it is not. NO(l) has the highest boiling point of the three.

N_2	NO	O_2
$\mu = 0$ (nonpolar)	$\mu = 0.153$ D (polar)	$\mu = 0$ (nonpolar)
mol. mass = 28 u	mol. mass = 30 u	mol. mass = 32 u
bp = 77.34 K	bp = 121.39 K	bp = 90.19 K

▲ **Electrostatic potential map of NO**
The permanent dipole of NO illustrated.

▲ **Butane and acetone**
The lower diagrams are electrostatic potential diagrams for butane and acetone. The red color indicates regions of high negative electrostatic potential.

EXAMPLE 12-6

Comparing Physical Properties of Polar and Nonpolar Substances. Which would you expect to have the higher boiling point, the hydrocarbon fuel butane, C_4H_{10}, or the organic solvent acetone, $(CH_3)_2CO$?

Solution

Ordinarily, the first clue comes in a comparison of molecular masses. However, because the two substances have the same molecular mass (58 u), we have to look elsewhere for a factor on which to base our prediction.

Point out that molecular solids are held together by forces that are much weaker than their actual molecular bonds. Water has a heat of melting of 6 kJ mol^{-1}, while the H—O bond energy is 495 kJ mol^{-1}.

The next consideration is the polarity of the molecules. The electronegativity difference between C and H is so small that we generally expect hydrocarbons to be nonpolar. The acetone molecule contains an O atom, and we do expect a strong carbon-to-oxygen bond dipole. At times, it is helpful to sketch the structure of a molecule to see whether symmetrical features cause bond dipoles to cancel. However, this is not necessary for the acetone molecule because only the C=O bond has a large bond dipole, and this cannot be offset by other bond dipoles. Acetone must have a resultant dipole moment and is therefore a polar molecule. Given two substances with the same molecular mass, one polar and one nonpolar, we expect the polar substance—acetone—to have the higher boiling point. (The measured boiling points are butane, −0.5 °C; acetone, 56.2 °C.)

Practice Example A: Which of the following substances would you expect to have the highest boiling point: C_3H_8, CO_2, CH_3CN? Explain.

Practice Example B: Arrange the following in the expected order of increasing boiling point: C_8H_{18}, $CH_3CH_2CH_2CH_3$, $(CH_3)_3CH$, C_6H_5CHO, SO_3 (octane, butane, isobutane, benzaldehyde, and sulfur trioxide, respectively).

SUMMARY OF VAN DER WAALS FORCES

When assessing the importance of van der Waals forces, consider the following statements.

- *Dispersion (London) forces exist between all molecules.* They involve displacements of all the electrons in molecules, and they increase in strength with increasing molecular mass. The forces also depend on molecular shapes.

- *Forces associated with permanent dipoles* involve displacements of electron pairs in bonds rather than in molecules as a whole. These forces are found only in substances with resultant dipole moments (polar molecules). Their existence *adds* to the effect of dispersion forces also present.

- *When comparing substances of roughly comparable molecular masses,* dipole forces can produce significant differences in properties such as melting point, boiling point, and enthalpy of vaporization.

- *When comparing substances of widely different molecular masses,* dispersion forces are usually more significant than dipole forces.

▶ In our discussion of London forces, we use molar mass only as a guide to the number of electrons present in a molecule; the forces holding a molecule in a liquid are not gravitational in nature.

Let's see how these statements relate to the data in Table 12.5, which includes a rough breakdown of van der Waals forces into dispersion forces and forces due to dipoles. HCl and F_2 have comparable molecular masses, but because HCl is polar, it has a significantly larger ΔH_{vap} and a higher boiling point. Within the series HCl, HBr, and HI, molecular mass increases sharply and ΔH_{vap} and boiling points increase in the order HCl < HBr < HI. The more polar nature of HCl and HBr relative to HI is not sufficient to reverse the trends produced by the increasing molecular masses—dispersion forces are the predominant intermolecular forces.

	Molecular Mass, u	Dipole Moment, D	Van der Waals Forces		ΔH_{vap}, kJ mol^{-1}	Boiling Point, K
			% Dispersion	% Dipole		
F_2	38.00	0	100	0	6.86	85.01
HCl	36.46	1.08	81.4	18.6	16.15	188.11
HBr	80.92	0.82	94.5	5.5	17.61	206.43
HI	127.91	0.44	99.5	0.5	19.77	237.80

TABLE 12.5 Intermolecular Forces and Properties of Selected Substances

EXAMPLE 12-7

Relating Intermolecular Forces and Physical Properties. Arrange the following substances in the order in which you would expect their boiling points to increase: CCl_4, Cl_2, $ClNO$, N_2.

Solution

Three of the substances are nonpolar. For these, the strengths of dispersion forces, and hence the boiling points, should increase with increasing molecular mass, that is, $N_2 < Cl_2 < CCl_4$. ClNO has a molecular mass (65.5 u) comparable to that of Cl_2 (70.9 u), but the ClNO molecule is polar (bond angle $\approx 120°$). This suggests stronger intermolecular forces and a higher boiling point for ClNO than for Cl_2. We should not expect the boiling point of ClNO to be higher than that of CCl_4, however, because of the large difference in their molecular masses (65.5 u compared with 154 u). The expected order is $N_2 < Cl_2 < ClNO < CCl_4$. (The observed boiling points are 77.3, 239.1, 266.7, and 349.9 K, respectively.)

Practice Example A: Arrange the following in the expected order of increasing boiling point: Ne, He, Cl_2, $(CH_3)_2CO$, O_2, O_3.

Practice Example B: Following are some values of ΔH_{vap} for several liquids at their normal boiling points: H_2, 0.92 kJ mol^{-1}; CH_4, 8.16 kJ mol^{-1}; C_6H_6, 31.0 kJ mol^{-1}; CH_3NO_2, 34.0 kJ mol^{-1}. Explain the differences among these values.

CONCEPT ASSESSMENT ✓

Explain why CCl_4 has a higher boiling point than CH_3Cl, despite the polarity of CH_3Cl.

12-6   HYDROGEN BONDING

Figure 12-27, in which the boiling points of a series of similar compounds are plotted as a function of molecular mass, demonstrates some features that we cannot explain by the types of intermolecular forces considered to this point.

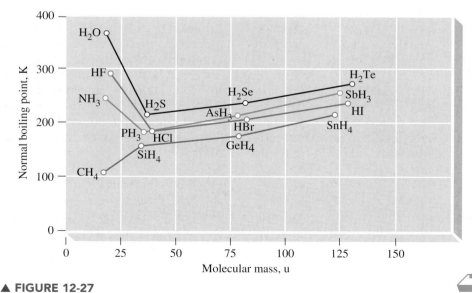

▲ **FIGURE 12-27**
Comparison of boiling points of some hydrides of the elements of groups 14, 15, 16, and 17
The values for NH_3, H_2O, and HF are unusually high compared with those of other members of their groups.

▲ **FIGURE 12-28**
Hydrogen bonding in gaseous hydrogen fluoride
In gaseous hydrogen fluoride, many of the HF molecules are associated into cyclic $(HF)_6$ structures of the type pictured here. Each H atom is bonded to one F atom by a single covalent bond (—) and to another F atom through a hydrogen bond (···).

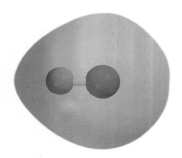

▲ Electrostatic potential map of HF

Hydrogen Bonding activity

$$H \diagdown_{\delta-} \quad_{\delta+} \quad_{\delta-} \\ O \cdots H{-}O$$
H   H

▲ Hydrogen bonding between H_2O molecules

This article describes a classroom activity where students investigate the hydrogen bonds present in water using K'Nex toy components: Schultz, Emeric. *J. Chem. Educ.* **2005:** *82,* 400A.

The hydrogen compounds (hydrides) of the group 14 elements display normal behavior; that is, the boiling points increase regularly as the molecular mass increases. But there are three striking exceptions in groups 15, 16, and 17. The boiling points of NH_3, H_2O, and HF are as high or higher than those of any other hydride in their group—not lowest, as we might expect. A special type of intermolecular force causes this exceptional behavior, as we see for hydrogen fluoride in Figure 12-28. The main points established in the figure are outlined below.

1. The alignment of HF dipoles places a H atom between two F atoms. Because of the very small size of the H atom, the dipoles come close together and produce strong *dipole–dipole* attractions.

2. Although a H atom is covalently bonded to one F atom, it is also weakly bonded to the F atom of a nearby HF molecule. This occurs through a lone pair of electrons on the F atom. Each H atom acts as a bridge between two F atoms.

3. The bond angle between two F atoms bridged by a H atom (that is, the angle F—HF···F) is about 180°.

The type of intermolecular force just described is called a hydrogen bond, although it is simply an electrostatic attraction and not an actual chemical bond like a covalent bond. In a **hydrogen bond** a H atom is covalently bonded to a highly electronegative atom, which attracts electron density away from the H nucleus. This in turn allows the H nucleus, a proton, to be simultaneously attracted to a lone pair of electrons on a highly electronegative atom in a neighboring molecule.

Hydrogen bonds are possible only with certain hydrogen-containing compounds because all atoms other than H have inner-shell electrons to shield their nuclei from attraction by lone-pair electrons of nearby atoms. Only F, O, and N easily meet the requirements for hydrogen-bond formation. Weak hydrogen bonding is occasionally encountered between a H atom of one molecule and a Cl or S atom in a neighboring molecule. Compared to other intermolecular forces, hydrogen bonds are relatively strong; their energies are of the order of 15 to 40 kJ mol^{-1}. By contrast, single covalent bonds are much stronger still—greater than 150 kJ mol^{-1}. (See Table 10.3 for further comparisons.)

HYDROGEN BONDING IN WATER

Ordinary water is certainly the most common substance in which hydrogen bonding occurs. Figure 12-29 shows how one water molecule is held to four neighbors in a tetrahedral arrangement by hydrogen bonds. In ice, hydrogen bonds hold the water molecules in a rigid but rather open structure. As ice melts, only a fraction of the hydrogen bonds are broken. One indication of this is the relatively low heat of fusion of ice (6.01 kJ mol^{-1}). It is much less than we would expect if all the hydrogen bonds were to break during melting.

The open structure of ice shown in Figure 12-29(b) gives ice a low density. When ice melts, some of the hydrogen bonds are broken. This allows the water molecules to be more compactly arranged, accounting for the increase in density when ice melts. That is, the number of H_2O molecules per unit volume is greater in the liquid than in the solid.

▲ FIGURE 12-29
Hydrogen bonding in water
(a) Each water molecule is linked to four others through hydrogen bonds. The arrangement is tetrahedral. Each H atom is situated along a line joining two O atoms, but closer to one O atom (100 pm) than to the other (180 pm). **(b)** For the crystal structure of ice, H atoms lie between pairs of O atoms, again closer to one O atom than to the other. (Molecules behind the plane of the page are light blue.) O atoms are arranged in bent hexagonal rings arranged in layers. This characteristic pattern is similar to the hexagonal shapes of snowflakes. **(c)** In the liquid, water molecules have hydrogen bonds to only some of their neighbors. This allows the water molecules to pack more densely in the liquid than in the solid.

As liquid water is heated above the melting point, hydrogen bonds continue to break. The molecules become even more closely packed, and the density of the liquid water continues to increase. Liquid water attains its maximum density at 3.98 °C. Above this temperature, the water behaves in a "normal" fashion: Its density decreases as temperature increases. The unusual freezing-point behavior of water explains why a freshwater lake freezes from the top down. When the water temperature falls below 4 °C, the denser water sinks to the bottom of the lake and the colder surface water freezes. The ice over the top of the lake then tends to insulate the water below from further heat loss. This allows fish to survive the winter in a lake that has been frozen over. Without hydrogen bonding, all lakes would freeze from the bottom up; and fish, small bottom-feeding animals, and aquatic plants would not survive the winter. The density relationship between liquid water and ice is compared with the more common liquid–solid density relationship in Figure 12-30.

OTHER PROPERTIES AFFECTED BY HYDROGEN BONDING

Water is one example of a substance whose properties are affected by hydrogen bonding. There are numerous others. In acetic acid, CH_3COOH, pairs of molecules tend to join together into *dimers* (double molecules), both in the liquid and vapor states (Fig. 12-31). Not all the hydrogen bonds are disrupted when liquid acetic acid vaporizes, and as a result, the heat of vaporization is abnormally low.

▲ Hydrogen bonding between NH₃ molecules

▲ FIGURE 12-30
Solid and liquid densities compared
The sight of ice cubes floating on liquid water (left) is a familiar one; ice is less dense than liquid water. The more common situation, however, is that of paraffin wax (right). Solid paraffin is denser than the liquid and sinks to the bottom of the beaker.

▲ **FIGURE 12-31**
An acetic acid dimer
Electrostatic potential maps
showing hydrogen bonding.

Certain trends in viscosity can also be explained by hydrogen bonding. In alcohols, the H atom in a —OH group in one molecule can form a hydrogen bond to the O atom in a neighboring alcohol molecule. An alcohol molecule with two —OH groups (a *diol*) has more possibilities for hydrogen-bond formation than a comparable alcohol with a single —OH group. Having stronger intermolecular forces, we expect the diol to flow more slowly, that is, to have a greater viscosity, than the simple alcohol. When still more —OH groups are present (*polyols*), we expect a further increase in viscosity. These comparisons are illustrated by the three common alcohols below. (The unit cP is a centipoise. The SI unit of viscosity is $1 \text{ N s m}^{-2} = 10 \text{ P.}$)

Ethyl alcohol	Ethylene glycol	Glycerol
(ethanol)	(1,2-ethanediol)	(1,2,3-propanetriol)
at 20 °C: 1.20 cP	at 20 °C: 19.9 cP	at 20 °C: 1490 cP

Intermolecular and *Intramolecular* Hydrogen Bonding

All the examples of hydrogen bonding presented to this point have involved an intermolecular force *between two molecules*, and this is called an *intermolecular hydrogen bond*. Another possibility occurs in molecules with a H atom covalently bonded to one highly electronegative atom (for example, O or N) and with another highly electronegative atom nearby in the same molecule. This type of hydrogen bonding *within a molecule* is called *intramolecular hydrogen bonding*. As shown in the molecular model of salicylic acid in the margin, an intermolecular hydrogen bond (represented by a dotted line) joins the —OH group to the doubly bonded oxygen atom of the —COOH group on the same molecule. To underscore the importance of molecular geometry in establishing

▲ Electrostatic potential map of salicylic acid showing intramolecular hydrogen bonding. The double bond character of certain bonds are not shown in the ball and stick model.

▲ There is no intramolecular hydrogen bonding in *para*-hydroxy-benzoic acid.

the conditions necessary for intramolecular hydrogen bonding, we need only turn to an isomer of salicylic acid called *para*-hydroxybenzoic acid. In this molecule, the H atom of the —COOH group is too close to the doubly bonded O atom of the same group to form a hydrogen bond, and the H atom of the —OH group on the opposite side of the molecule is too far away. Intramolecular hydrogen bonding does not occur in this situation.

Hydrogen Bonding in Living Matter

Some chemical reactions in living matter involve complex structures such as proteins and DNA, and in these reactions certain bonds must be easily broken and re-formed. Hydrogen bonding is the only type of bonding with energies of just the right magnitude to allow this, as we will discover in Chapter 27. We will also find that both intra- and intermolecular hydrogen bonding is involved in these complex structures.

Hydrogen bonding seems to provide an answer to the puzzle of how some trees are able to grow to great heights. In Chapter 6 (page 181), we learned that atmospheric pressure is capable of pushing a column of water to a maximum height of only about 10 m—other factors must be involved in transporting water to the tops of redwood trees up to 100 m tall. In the next chapter, we will learn about osmotic pressure and its ability to force water through membranes, but hydrogen bonding seems also to be a factor in transporting water in trees. Thin columns of water (in xylem, a plant tissue) extend from the roots to the leaves in the very tops of trees. In these columns, the water molecules are hydrogen-bonded to one another, with each water molecule acting like a link in a cohesive chain. When one water molecule evaporates from a leaf, another molecule in the chain moves to take its place and all the other molecules are pulled up the chain. Ultimately, a new water molecule joins the chain in the root system.

▲ Hydrogen bonding between guanine (left) and cytosine (right) in DNA

This article describes a demonstration that can be performed to show how intermolecular forces determine the shape of DNA molecules: Bruist, Michael F. *J. Chem. Educ.* 1998: *75*, 53.

▲ Sequoia trees
The mystery of how these trees can bring water to leaves that are hundreds of feet up may be explained by hydrogen bonding.

CONCEPT ASSESSMENT ✓

What are the types of intermolecular interactions in $CH_3CH_2NH_2(l)$, and which is the strongest?

12-7 Network Covalent Solids and Ionic Solids

In most covalent substances, intermolecular forces are quite weak compared with the bonds between atoms within molecules. This is why covalent substances of low molecular mass (those with weak dispersion forces) are generally gaseous at room temperature. Others, usually of somewhat higher molecular masses (with stronger dispersion forces), are liquids. Still others are solids with moderately low melting points. An example of such a trend are the room-temperature states at 1 atm pressure of chlorine (a gas), bromine (a liquid), and iodine (a solid).

Network Covalent Solids

In a few substances, known as **network covalent solids**, covalent bonds extend throughout a crystalline solid. In these cases, the entire crystal is held together by strong forces. Consider, for example, two of the allotropic forms in which pure carbon occurs—diamond and graphite.

Diamond, Graphite, and Fullerene models

▶ **FIGURE 12-32**
The diamond structure
(a) A portion of the Lewis structure.
(b) The crystal structure shows each carbon atom bonded to four others in a tetrahedral fashion. The segment of the entire crystal shown here is called a unit cell.

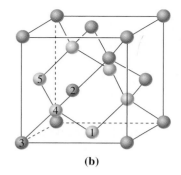

(a)   **(b)**

KEEP IN MIND ▶
that four bonds directed from a central atom to the corners of a tetrahedron correspond to the sp^3 hybridization scheme.

▶ Another silicon-containing network covalent solid is ordinary silica—silicon dioxide, SiO_2.

142 pm

335 pm

▲ **FIGURE 12-33**
The graphite structure

▲ **Graphite conducts electricity**
Delocalized electrons in graphite allow the conduction of electricity. In this photo, pencil "lead," a mixture of graphite and clay, is used as electrodes to complete the circuit. The beaker contains a solution of ions that carry the current between the pencil electrodes.

Diamond. Figure 12-32 shows one way that carbon atoms can bond one to another in a very extensive array or crystal. The two-dimensional Lewis structure (Fig. 12-32a) is useful only in suggesting that the bonding scheme involves ever increasing numbers of C atoms leading to a giant molecule. It does not give any insight into the three-dimensional structure of the molecule. For this, we need the portion of the crystal shown in Figure 12-32(b). Each atom is bonded to four others. Atoms 1, 2, and 3 lie in a plane, with atom 4 above the plane. Atoms 1, 2, 3, and 5 define a tetrahedron with atom 4 at its center. When viewed from a particular direction, a nonplanar hexagonal arrangement of carbon atoms (gray) is also seen.

If silicon atoms are substituted for half the carbon atoms in this structure, the resulting structure is that of silicon carbide (carborundum). Both diamond and silicon carbide are extremely hard, and this accounts for their extensive use as abrasives. In fact, diamond is the hardest substance known. To scratch or break diamond or silicon carbide crystals, covalent bonds must be broken. These two materials are also nonconductors of electricity and do not melt or sublime except at very high temperatures. SiC sublimes at 2700 °C, and diamond melts above 3500 °C.

Graphite. Carbon atoms can bond together to produce a solid with properties very different from those of diamond. In graphite, bonding involves the orbital set $sp^2 + p$. The three sp^2 orbitals are directed in a plane at angles of 120 °, and the p orbitals overlap in the manner described for carbon atoms in benzene, C_6H_6 (see Figure 11-27). Thus, the p electrons are *delocalized*—that is, not restricted to the region between two C atoms but shared among many C atoms within a plane of C atoms. This type of bonding produces the crystal structure shown in Figure 12-33. Each carbon atom forms strong covalent bonds with three neighboring carbon atoms in the same plane, giving rise to layers of carbon atoms in a hexagonal arrangement. Bonding within layers is strong, but the intermolecular forces between layers are the much weaker van der Waals forces. We can see this through bond distances. The C—C bond distance within a layer is 142 pm (compared with 139 pm in benzene); between layers, it is 335 pm.

Its unique crystal structure gives graphite some distinctive properties. Because bonding between layers is weak, the layers can glide over one another rather easily. As a result, graphite is a good lubricant, either in dry form or in an oil suspension.* If a mild pressure is applied to a piece of graphite, layers of the graphite flake off; this is what happens when we use a graphite pencil. Also, because the p electrons are delocalized, they migrate through the planes of carbon atoms when an electric field is applied; graphite conducts electricity. An important use of graphite is as electrodes in batteries and in industrial electrolysis. Diamond is not an electrical conductor because all of its valence electrons are localized or permanently fixed into single covalent bonds.

*The lubricating properties of graphite also appear to depend on the presence of oxygen molecules between the layers of carbon atoms. When graphite is strongly heated in a vacuum, it becomes a much poorer lubricant.

OTHER ALLOTROPES OF CARBON

In 1985, the first of what is now known to be an extensive series of allotropes of carbon was discovered. In experiments designed to mimic conditions found near red-giant stars, a number of carbon-containing molecules were discovered and characterized through mass spectroscopy. The strongest peak in the mass spectrum came at 720 u, corresponding to the molecule C_{60}. For a time, proposing a plausible structure for this molecule proved to be a challenge. Neither diamond- nor graphite-type structures could account for a molecule with 60 carbon atoms because "dangling" bonds would remain at the edges of the structures. The structure that was finally proposed, and confirmed by X-ray crystallography, is that of a *truncated icosohedron*—a three-dimensional figure composed of 12 pentagonal and 20 hexagonal faces, with a carbon atom at each of its 60 vertices (Fig. 12-34). This figure resembles a soccer ball and also certain geodesic domes. In fact, the resemblance to the geodesic dome led first to the proposed name "buckminsterfullerenes," then simply, *fullerenes*, and finally the colloquial expression "buckyballs." (The geodesic dome is an architectural form pioneered by R. Buckminster Fuller.) Since 1985, many other fullerenes have been discovered, including C_{70}, C_{74}, and C_{82}. Fullerenes can also form compounds, some by attaching atoms or groups of atoms to their surfaces, others by encasing an atom inside the fullerene structure. To date, several thousand fullerene compounds have been prepared.

Research on fullerenes has led to the discovery of a related type of carbon allotrope—*nanotubes*. A nanotube can be thought of as a two-dimensional array of hexagonal rings of carbon atoms, which is called a graphene sheet. An analogous macroscopic structure is a sheet of chicken wire. Now imagine rolling the graphene sheet into a cylinder (something that a section cut from a roll of chicken wire seems to do so naturally). Finally, cap off each end of the cylindrical graphene sheet with a fullerene (Fig. 12-35). The diameters of these tubes are of the order of a few nanometers (hence the name *nano*tube). Their lengths can vary from a few nanometers to a micrometer or more. Nanotubes possess unusual electronic and mechanical properties that offer the promise of some applications in the macroscopic world and probably many more in the submicroscopic world of *nanotechnology*. For example, nanotubes might one day be used to channel molecules into the interior of cells.

The following article discusses laboratory experiments that can be performed with buckmisterfullerene: Hildebrand, Achim, et al. *J. Chem. Educ.* **1996:** *73*, 1066.

(a)   (b)   (c)   (d)

▲ **FIGURE 12-34**
Fullerenes
(a) An icosahedron, a shape formed by 20 equilateral triangles. Five triangles meet at each of the 12 vertices. **(b)** Truncating or cutting off a vertex reveals a new pentagonal face. **(c)** The truncated icosahedron. Twelve pentagons have replaced the original 12 vertices, and the 20 equilateral triangles have been replaced by 20 hexagons. **(d)** The C_{60} molecule.

▲ **FIGURE 12-35**
Nanotubes
(a) Ball-and-stick model of a small nanotube. (b) A bundle of single-wall nanotubes.

IONIC SOLIDS

When predicting properties of an ionic solid, we often face this question: How difficult is it to break up an ionic crystal and separate its ions? This question is addressed by the *lattice energy* of a crystal. Let us define **lattice energy** as the energy given off when separated *gaseous* ions—positive and negative—come together to form *one mole* of a *solid* ionic compound. Lattice energies can be useful in making predictions about the melting points and water solubilities of ionic compounds. We will examine how to calculate lattice energies in Section 12-9. At times, however, we need to make only *qualitative* comparisons of *interionic forces*, and the following generalization works quite well.

> The attractive force between a pair of oppositely charged ions increases with increased charge on the ions and with decreased ionic sizes.

This idea is based on Coulomb's law (Appendix B) and illustrated in Figure 12-36.

For most ionic compounds, lattice energies are great enough that ions do not readily detach themselves from the crystal and pass into the gaseous state. Ionic solids do not sublime at ordinary temperatures. We can melt ionic solids by supplying enough thermal energy to disrupt the crystalline lattice. In general, the higher the lattice energy of an ionic compound, the higher is its melting point.

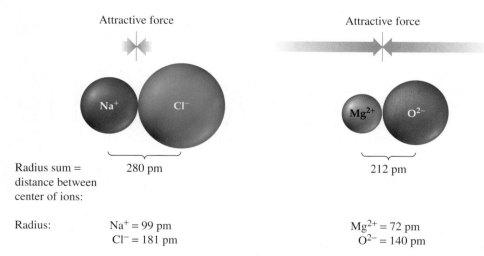

Radius sum = distance between center of ions: 280 pm   212 pm

Radius: Na^+ = 99 pm Mg^{2+} = 72 pm
                 Cl^- = 181 pm O^{2-} = 140 pm

▲ **FIGURE 12-36**
Interionic forces of attraction
Because of the higher charges on the ions and the closer proximity of their centers, the interionic attractive force between Mg^{2+} and O^{2-} is about seven times as great as between Na^+ and Cl^-.

The energy required to break up an ionic crystal when it dissolves results from the interaction of ions in the crystal with molecules of the solvent. The extent to which an ionic solid dissolves in a solvent, however, depends only in part on the lattice energy of the ionic solid. As a rough rule, though, the lower the lattice energy, the greater the quantity of an ionic solid that can be dissolved in a given quantity of solvent.

EXAMPLE 12-8

Predicting Physical Properties of Ionic Compounds. Which has the higher melting point, KI or CaO?

Solution

Ca^{2+} and O^{2-} are more highly charged than K^+ and I^-. Also, Ca^{2+} is smaller than K^+, and O^{2-} is smaller than I^-. We would expect the interionic forces in crystalline CaO to be much larger than in KI. CaO should have the higher melting point. (The observed melting points are 677 °C for KI and 2590 °C for CaO.)

Practice Example A: Cite one ionic compound that you would expect to have a lower melting point than KI and one with a higher melting point than CaO.

Practice Example B: Which would you expect to have the greater solubility in water, NaI or $MgCl_2$? Explain.

12-8 CRYSTAL STRUCTURES

Crystals, solid structures having plane surfaces, sharp edges, and regular geometric shapes, have aroused interest from earliest times, whether as ice, rock salt, quartz, or gemstones. Yet, only in relatively recent times have we come to a fundamental understanding of the crystalline state. This understanding started with the invention of the optical microscope and was greatly expanded following the discovery of X-rays. The key idea, now supported by countless experiments, is that the regularity observed in crystals at the macroscopic level is due to an underlying regular pattern in the arrangement of atoms, ions, or molecules.

CRYSTAL LATTICES

You can probably think of a number of situations in which you have had to deal with repeating patterns in one or two dimensions. These might include projects like sewing a decorative border on a piece of material, wallpapering a room, or creating a design with floor tiles. The structures of crystals, however, must be described through *three*-dimensional patterns. These patterns are outlined against a framework called a *lattice* comprising the intersections of three sets of parallel planes. Figure 12-37 shows the special case for a lattice in which the planes are equidistant and mutually perpendicular (intersecting at 90° angles). This is called a *cubic* lattice, and it can be used to describe a number of crystals. For other crystals, the appropriate lattice may involve planes that are not equidistant or that intersect at angles other than 90°. In all, there are seven possibilities for crystal lattices, but we will emphasize only the cubic lattice.

Lattice planes intersect to produce three-dimensional figures having six faces arranged in three sets of parallel planes. These figures are called *parallelepipeds*. In Figure 12-37, the parallelepipeds are cubes. A parallelepiped called the **unit cell** can be used to generate the entire lattice by replicating it along the three perpendicular directions. (Consider a two-dimensional analogy: A single floor tile is like a unit cell and, wherever the first tile is placed, the entire floor can be covered by adding identical tiles in the two perpendicular directions from the initial one.) Where possible, we arrange the three-dimensional space lattice so

Bring to class a few minerals and crystals to show the distinctive shapes.

Explain to the students that almost all the properties of crystals can be derived from the periodicity of the structure.

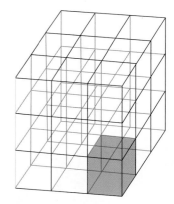

▲ **FIGURE 12-37**
The cubic lattice
One parallelepiped formed by the intersection of mutually perpendicular planes is shaded in green— it is a cube. An endless lattice can be generated by simple displacements of the green cube in the three perpendicular directions (that is, left and right, up and down, and forward and backward).

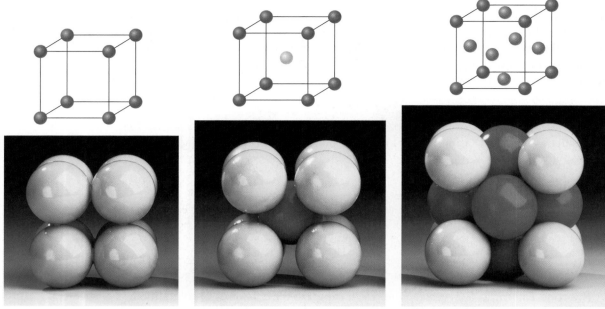

Simple cubic   Body-centered cubic   Face-centered cubic

▲ **FIGURE 12-38**
Unit cells in the cubic crystal system
In the line-and-ball drawings in the top row, only the centers of spheres (atoms) are shown at their respective positions in the unit cells. The space-filling models in the bottom row show contacts between spheres (atoms). In the simple cubic cell, spheres come into contact along each edge. In the body-centered cubic (bcc) cell, contact of the spheres is along the cube diagonal. In the face-centered cubic (fcc) cell, contact is along the diagonal of each face. The spheres shown here are identical atoms; color is used only for emphasis.

Models of unit cells can be made of Styrofoam balls. Packing of planes of balls can be used to illustrate the cubic close packing arrangements.

 Cubic packing (Figure 12-38a) is not a closest packing. Neither is the body-centered arrangement as the central atom forces the cubic packing apart. For cubic cells, only the ccp and hcp arrangements result from close packing.

Unit Cells activity

that the centers of the structural particles of the crystal (atoms, ions, or molecules) are situated at lattice points. If a unit cell has structural particles only at its corners, it is called a *primitive* or simple unit cell, because it is the simplest unit cell we can consider. But some unit cells have more structural particles than those found at its corners. In the **body-centered cubic (bcc)** structure, there is a structural particle at the center of the cube as well as at each corner of the unit cell. In a **face-centered cubic (fcc)** structure, there is a structural particle at the center of each face as well as at each corner. These unit cells are shown in Figure 12-38.

CLOSEST PACKED STRUCTURES

Unlike boxes, which can be stacked to fill all space, when spheres are stacked together, there must always be some unfilled space. In some arrangements, however, the spheres come into as close contact as possible, and the volume of the holes, or voids, is at a minimum. These arrangements are known as closest packed structures and are the basis of a number of crystal structures.

To analyze the closest packed structures in Figure 12-39(a), imagine one layer of spheres, layer A (red), in which each sphere is in contact with six others arranged in a hexagonal fashion around it. Among the spheres, there are holes. The hole between three spheres resembling a triangle is called a *trigonal hole* (Fig. 12-39b). Once the first sphere is placed in the next layer, layer B (yellow), the entire pattern for that layer is fixed. Again, there are holes in layer B, but the holes are of two different types. *Tetrahedral holes* fall directly over *spheres* in layer A, and *octahedral holes* fall directly over *holes* in layer A (Fig. 12-39b).

▲ A closest packed pyramid of cannonballs. Oranges at a fruit stand are often packed in hexagonal closest packed pyramids so that they will not slip.

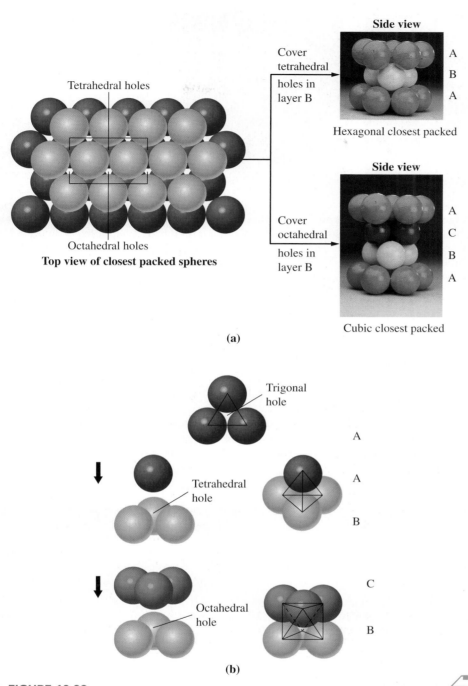

This article describes the use of pom pons to illustrate cubic crystal structures: Cady, Susan G. *J. Chem. Educ.* **1997:** *74, 794.*

Side view

Cover tetrahedral holes in layer B

A
B
A

Hexagonal closest packed

Side view

Cover octahedral holes in layer B

A
C
B
A

Cubic closest packed

(a)

Tetrahedral holes

Octahedral holes
Top view of closest packed spheres

Trigonal hole

A

Tetrahedral hole

A

B

Octahedral hole

C

B

(b)

▲ **FIGURE 12-39**
Closest packed structures
(a) Spheres in layer A are red. Those in layer B are yellow, and in layer C, blue. **(b)** The holes in closest packed structures. The trigonal hole is formed by three spheres in one of the layers. The tetrahedral hole is formed when a sphere in the upper layer sits in the dimple of the lower layer. The octahedral hole is formed between two groups of three spheres in two layers.

There are two possibilities for C, the third layer (Fig. 12-39a). In one arrangement, called **hexagonal closest packed (hcp)**, all the tetrahedral holes are covered. Layer C is identical to layer A, and the structure begins to repeat itself. In the other arrangement, called **cubic closest packed**, all the octahedral holes are covered. The spheres in layer C (blue) are out of line with those in layer A. Only when the fourth layer is added does the structure begin to repeat itself.

The hexagonal unit cell is hard for students to visualize and a model of this can show them how to see this cell.

▲ **FIGURE 12-40**
A face-centered cubic unit cell for the cubic closest packing of spheres
The 14 spheres on the left are extracted from a larger array of spheres in a cubic closest packed structure. The two middle layers each have six atoms; the top and bottom layers, one. Rotation of the group of 14 spheres reveals the fcc unit cell (right).

(a)

(b)

▲ **FIGURE 12-41**
The hexagonal closest packed (hcp) crystal structure
(a) A unit cell is highlighted in heavy black lines. The atoms that are part of that cell are joined in solid lines. Note that the unit cell is a parallelepiped, but not a cube. Three adjoining unit cells are also shown. The highlighted unit cell and broken-line regions together show the layering (ABA) described in Figure 12-39.
(b) The hexagonal prism showing parts of the shared spheres at the corners and the single sphere at the center of the unit cell.

Study Figure 12-40 and you will see that the cubic closest packed structure has a face-centered cubic unit cell. The unit cell of the hexagonal closest packed structure is shown in Figure 12-41. In both the hcp and fcc structures, holes account for only 25.96% of the total volume. Another possibility in which spheres are closely packed but not in a closest-packed arrangement has a body-centered cubic unit cell. In this structure, holes account for 31.98% of the total volume. The best examples of crystal structures based on the packing of spheres are found among the metals. Some examples are listed in Table 12.6.

TABLE 12.6   Some Features of Crystal Structures in Metals

	Coordination Number	Number of Atoms per Unit Cell	Examples
Hexagonal closest packed (hcp)	12	2	Cd, Mg, Ti, Zn
Face-centered cubic (fcc)	12	4	Al, Cu, Pb, Ag
Body-centered cubic (bcc)	8	2	Fe, K, Na, W

COORDINATION NUMBER AND NUMBER OF ATOMS PER UNIT CELL

In crystals with atoms as their structural units, each atom is in contact with several others. For example, can you see in Figure 12-38 that the center atom in the bcc unit cell is in contact with each corner atom? The number of atoms with which a given atom is in contact is called its *coordination number*. For the bcc structure, this is 8; for the fcc and hcp structures, the coordination number is 12. The easiest way to visualize the coordination number 12 is from the layering of spheres described in Figure 12-39. Each sphere is in contact with *six* others in the same layer, *three* in the layer above, and *three* in the layer below.

Although it takes nine atoms to draw the bcc unit cell, it is wrong to conclude that the unit cell consists of nine atoms. As shown in Figure 12-42(a), only the center atom belongs *entirely* to the bcc unit cell. The other atoms are shared with other unit cells. The corner atoms are shared among eight adjoining unit cells. Only one-eighth of each corner atom should be thought

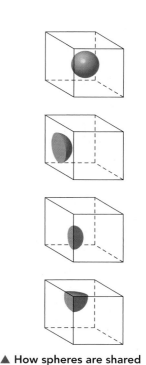

▲ Illustrating the coordination number for the hcp and ccp structures

of as belonging entirely to a given unit cell (Fig. 12-42b). Thus, the eight corner atoms collectively contribute the equivalent of *one* atom to the unit cell. The total number of atoms in a bcc unit cell, then, is *two* [that is, $1 + \left(8 \times \frac{1}{8}\right)$]. For the hcp unit cell of Figure 12-41, we also get *two* atoms per unit cell if we use the correct counting procedure. The corner atoms account for $\frac{1}{8} \times 8 = 1$ atom, and the central atom belongs entirely to the unit cell. In the fcc unit cell, the corner atoms account for $\frac{1}{8} \times 8 = 1$ atom, and those in the center of the faces for $\frac{1}{2} \times 6 = 3$ atoms. The fcc unit cell contains *four* atoms (Fig. 12-42c). The simple cubic unit cell contains only *one* atom per unit cell (Fig. 12-42d).

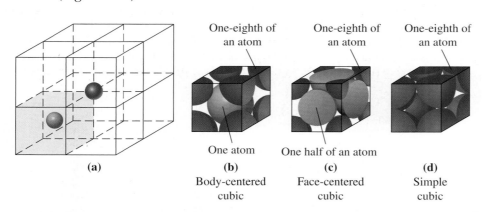

One-eighth of an atom | One-eighth of an atom | One-eighth of an atom

One atom | One half of an atom

(a) | **(b)** Body-centered cubic | **(c)** Face-centered cubic | **(d)** Simple cubic

▲ **FIGURE 12-42**
Apportioning atoms among cubic unit cells
(a) Eight unit cells are outlined. Attention is directed to the blue-shaded unit cell. For clarity, only the centers of two atoms are pictured. The atom in the center of the blue cell belongs entirely to that cell. The corner atom is seen to be shared by all eight unit cells. **(b)** The shared spheres of a body-centered unit cell. **(c)** The shared spheres of a face-centered unit cell. **(d)** The shared spheres of a simple cubic unit cell. The spheres shown here are identical atoms; color is used only for emphasis.

▲ How spheres are shared between or among unit cells

X-RAY DIFFRACTION

We can see macroscopic objects using visible light and our eyes. To "see" how atoms, ions, or molecules are arranged in a crystal requires light of much shorter wavelength. When a beam of X-rays encounters atoms, the X-rays interact with electrons in the atoms and the original beam is scattered in all directions. The pattern of this scattered radiation is related to the distribution of electronic charge in the atoms and/or molecules. The scattered X-rays can produce a visible pattern, as on a photographic film, and it is then possible to infer the microscopic structure of the substance from this visible pattern. How successful we are in making inferences depends on the amount of the scattered radiation recovered, that is, on how much "information" is gathered.

Point out that crystal structures are also studied by neutron diffraction and electron diffraction (electron microscope), so that X rays are not the only means of determining crystal structures.

Are You Wondering . . .

How to calculate the volume of the holes in a structure?

To illustrate this, consider the bcc structure. The ratio of the occupied volume to the unit cell volume is

$$f_v = \frac{\text{volume of spheres in unit cell}}{\text{volume of unit cell}}$$

If the radius of the atom is r, the volume of a sphere is $(4/3)\pi r^3$, and by the construction shown in Figure 12-45 the cube edge l is $r(4/\sqrt{3})$. So that, based on two complete spheres in the unit cell, we have

$$f_v = \frac{2 \times (4/3)\pi r^3}{[r(4/\sqrt{3})]^3} = 0.6802$$

Thus, 68.02% of the unit cell is occupied and 31.98% of the unit cell is empty. Note also that this percentage of empty space is the same regardless of the radius of the sphere.

▶ The X-ray diffraction method was originated by Max von Laue (Nobel Prize, 1914), but carried further by the Braggs. William Lawrence Bragg was only 25 years old when he and his father, William Henry Bragg, won the Nobel Prize in 1915.

The power of the X-ray diffraction method has been greatly increased by the use of high-speed computers to process vast amounts of X-ray data.

Figure 12-43 suggests a method of scattering X-rays from a crystal. X-ray data can be explained by a geometric analysis proposed by W. H. Bragg and W. L. Bragg in 1912 and illustrated in Figure 12-44. The figure shows two rays in a monochromatic (single-wavelength) X-ray beam, labeled *a* and *b*. Wave *a* is diffracted, or scattered, by one plane of atoms or ions in a crystal and wave *b* from the next plane below. Wave *b* travels a greater distance than wave *a*.

▲ **FIGURE 12-43**
Diffraction of X-rays by a crystal
In X-ray diffraction, the scattering is usually from no more than 20 planes deep in a crystal.

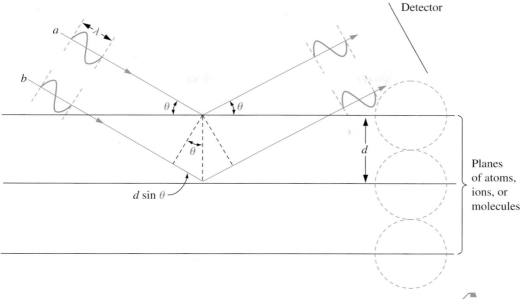

▲ **FIGURE 12-44**
Determination of crystal structure by X-ray diffraction
The two triangles outlined by dashed lines are identical. The hypotenuse of each triangle is equal to the interatomic distance, d. The side opposite the angle θ thus has a length of $d \sin \theta$. Wave b travels farther than wave a by the distance $2d \sin \theta$.

The additional distance is $2d \sin \theta$. The intensity of the scattered radiation will be greatest if waves a and b reinforce each other, that is, if their crests and troughs line up. To satisfy this requirement, the additional distance traveled by wave b must be an integral multiple of the wavelength of the X-rays.

$$n\lambda = 2d \sin \theta \tag{12.5}$$

From the measured angle θ yielding the maximum intensity for the scattered X-rays, and the X-ray wavelength (λ), we can calculate the spacing (d) between atomic planes. With different orientations of the crystal, we can determine atomic spacings and electron densities for different directions through the crystal, in short, the crystal structure.

Once a crystal structure is known, certain other properties can be determined by calculation. Example 12-9 shows the determination of a metallic radius, and Example 12-10 estimates the density of a crystalline solid. For both of these calculations, we need to sketch, or in some way visualize, a unit cell of the crystal. In particular, we need to see which atoms are in direct contact.

$l = 287$ pm

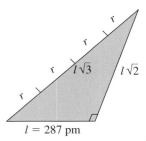

$l = 287$ pm

▲ **FIGURE 12-45**
Determination of the atomic radius of iron— Example 12-9 illustrated
The right triangle must conform to the Pythagorean formula $a^2 + b^2 = c^2$. That is, with l as an edge of the cube, $(l)^2 + (l\sqrt{2})^2 = (l\sqrt{3})^2$, or $(l)^2 + 2(l)^2 = 3(l)^2$.

EXAMPLE 12-9

Using X-Ray Data to Determine an Atomic Radius. At room temperature, iron crystallizes in a bcc structure. By X-ray diffraction, the edge of the cubic cell corresponding to Figure 12-45 is found to be 287 pm. What is the radius of an iron atom?

Solution

Nine atoms are associated with a bcc unit cell. One atom is located at each of the eight corners of the cube and one at the center. The three atoms along a diagonal through the cube are in contact. The length of the cube diagonal (the distance from the farthest upper-right corner to the nearest lower-left corner) is four times the atomic radius. Also shown in Figure 12-45 is the fact that the diagonal of a cube is equal to $\sqrt{3} \times l$. The length of an edge, l, is what is given.

$$4r = l\sqrt{3} \qquad r = \frac{\sqrt{3} \times 287 \text{ pm}}{4} = \frac{1.732 \times 287 \text{ pm}}{4} = 124 \text{ pm}$$

Practice Example A: Potassium crystallizes in the bcc structure. What is the length of the unit cell in this structure? Use the metallic radius of potassium given in Figure 9-8.

Practice Example B: Aluminum crystallizes in an fcc structure. Given that the atomic radius of Al is 143.1 pm, what is the volume of a unit cell?

EXAMPLE 12-10

Relating Density to Crystal Structure Data. Use data from Example 12-9, together with the molar mass of Fe and the Avogadro constant, to calculate the density of iron.

Solution

In Example 12-9, we saw that the length of a unit cell is $l = 287$ pm $= 287 \times 10^{-12}$ m $= 2.87 \times 10^{-8}$ cm. The volume of the unit cell is $V = l^3 = (2.87 \times 10^{-8})^3$ cm^3 $= 2.36 \times 10^{-23}$ cm^3.

From Table 12.6, we find that there are *two* Fe atoms per bcc unit cell. We need the mass of these two atoms, and the key to getting this is a conversion factor based on the fact that 1 mol Fe $= 6.022 \times 10^{23}$ Fe atoms $= 55.85$ g Fe.

$$m = 2 \text{ Fe atoms} \times \frac{55.85 \text{ g Fe}}{6.022 \times 10^{23} \text{ Fe atoms}} = 1.855 \times 10^{-22} \text{ g Fe}$$

Density is the ratio of mass to volume.

$$\text{density of Fe} = \frac{m}{V} = \frac{1.855 \times 10^{-22} \text{ g Fe}}{2.36 \times 10^{-23} \text{ cm}^3} = 7.86 \text{ g Fe cm}^{-3}$$

Practice Example A: Use the result of Practice Example 12-9A, the molar mass of K and the Avogadro constant to calculate the density of potassium.

Practice Example B: Use the result of Practice Example 12-9B, the molar mass of Al and its density (2.6984 g cm^{-3}) to evaluate the Avogadro constant, N_A.

[*Hint:* From the volume of a unit cell and the density of Al, you can determine the mass of a unit cell. Knowing the number of Al atoms in the fcc unit cell, you can determine the mass per Al atom.]

KEEP IN MIND ▶
that the type of unit cell adopted by a metal can be deduced by using the experimental density and experimentally determined cell edge length.

CONCEPT ASSESSMENT ✓

Suppose a first-order diffraction is observed at an angle θ for a particular plane of atoms using X-rays of wavelength λ. In order to observe a second-order diffraction from the same plane of atoms at the same angle θ, the wavelength of the X-rays must be a multiple of λ. What is that multiple?

IONIC CRYSTAL STRUCTURES

If we try to apply the packing-of-spheres model to an ionic crystal, we run into two complications: (1) Some of the ions are positively charged and some are negatively charged, and (2) the cations and anions are of different sizes. What we can expect, however, is that oppositely charged ions will come into close proximity. Generally we think of them as being in contact. Like-charged ions, because of mutual repulsions, are not in direct contact. We can think of some ionic crystals as a fairly closely packed arrangement of ions of one type with holes filled by ions of the opposite charge. The relative sizes of cations and anions are important in establishing a particular packing arrangement.

A common arrangement in binary ionic solids is the cubic closest packed arrangement. Very often one of the ions, usually the anion, can be viewed as adopting the cubic closest packed structure while the cation fits in one of the holes between the closest-packed spheres. The three types of holes of the cubic closest packed structure—trigonal, tetrahedral, and octahedral—are shown in Figure 12-46. The size of the holes is related to the radius, R, of the anions used to form the structure. Figure 12-47 shows a cross section through an octahedral hole. The radius of the cation, r, that can just fit into the hole can be found using the Pythagorean formula, as follows.

$$(2R)^2 + (2R)^2 = (2R + 2r)^2$$

$$2\sqrt{2}\,R = 2R + 2r$$

$$\left(2\sqrt{2} - 2\right)R = 2r$$

$$\left(\sqrt{2} - 1\right)R = r$$

$$r = 0.414R$$

Similar calculations can be used for tetrahedral and trigonal holes, for which $r = 0.225\,R$ and $r = 0.155\,R$, respectively. These calculations show that in the cubic closest packed structure, the octahedral hole is bigger than the tetrahedral hole.

Another arrangement adopted by binary ionic solids is the simple cubic arrangement. The simple cubic arrangement is not a closest packed structure and has larger holes than the cubic closest packed arrangement. The simple cubic structure has a cubic hole at the center of the unit cell. The size of the cubic hole is $r = 0.732\,R$; of the cubic unit cells considered here, this is the largest hole.

Which hole does the cation occupy in a closest-packed array of anions? The cation occupies a hole that maximizes the attractions between the cation and anion and minimizes the repulsions between the anions. This can be accomplished by accommodating cations into holes that are slightly smaller than the actual size of the ion. This pushes the anions of the closest packed array slightly apart, reducing repulsions, while the anion and cation are in contact, maximizing attractions. Therefore, if a cation is to occupy a tetrahedral hole, the ion should be bigger than the tetrahedral hole but smaller than the octahedral hole; that is,

$$0.225\,R_{\text{anion}} < r_{\text{cation}} < 0.414\,R_{\text{anion}}$$

or in terms of the *radius ratio* of the cation (r) to the anion (R)

$$0.225 < (r_{\text{cation}}/R_{\text{anion}}) < 0.414$$

Similarly, if a cation is to occupy an octahedral hole, the radii will be governed by the radius ratio inequality

$$0.414 < (r_{\text{cation}}/R_{\text{anion}}) < 0.732$$

where the upper limit of the inequality corresponds to the hole in a simple cubic lattice. When the cation is too large, that is, bigger than $0.732\,R$, the anions adopt a simple cubic structure which allows the cation to be accommodated in the cubic hole of the lattice.

(a) Trigonal hole

(b) Tetrahedral hole

(c) Octahedral hole

▲ **FIGURE 12-46**
Holes in a face-centered cubic unit cell
(a) The trigonal hole is formed by two face-centered spheres and one corner sphere. **(b)** The tetrahedral hole is formed by three face-centered spheres and one corner sphere. **(c)** The octahedral hole is formed by all six face-centered spheres in the cube.

◀ **FIGURE 12-47**
Cross section of an octahedral hole

To summarize, if

$0.225 < (r_{\text{cation}}/R_{\text{anion}}) < 0.414$ tetrahedral hole of fcc array of anions occupied by the cation

$0.414 < (r_{\text{cation}}/R_{\text{anion}}) < 0.732$ octahedral hole of fcc array of anions occupied by the cation

$0.732 < (r_{\text{cation}}/R_{\text{anion}})$ cubic hole of simple cubic array of anions occupied by the cation

The criteria given here provide a useful way of rationalizing the structures of binary ionic solids. However, as with all simplified models, we must be aware of the limitations of the model. In developing the criteria given, we have assumed that there are no interactions other than coulombic attractions between the ions. The criteria will fail if this is not the case. Nonetheless we will find the criteria to be very useful.

In defining a unit cell of an ionic crystal we must choose a unit cell that

- by translation in three dimensions, generates the entire crystal
- is consistent with the formula of the compound
- indicates the coordination numbers of the ions

Unit cells of crystalline NaCl and CsCl are pictured in Figures 12-48 and 12-49, respectively. We can investigate these structures for their consistency with the formula of the compound and the type of hole the cation occupies.

The radius ratio for NaCl is

$$\frac{r_{\text{Na}^+}}{R_{\text{Cl}^-}} = \frac{99 \text{ pm}}{181 \text{ pm}} = 0.55$$

KEEP IN MIND ▶
that a cubic closest packed array of spheres produces a face-centered cubic unit cell.

We expect Na$^+$ ions to occupy the octahedral holes of the cubic closest packed arrays of Cl$^-$ ions. The sodium chloride unit cell is shown in Figure 12-48. To establish the formula of the compound, we must apportion the 27 ions in Figure 12-48 among the unit cell and its neighboring unit cells. Recall from Figure 12-42 on how this apportioning is done. Each Cl$^-$ ion in a corner position is shared by *eight* unit cells, and each Cl$^-$ in the center of a face is shared by *two* unit cells. This leads to a total number of Cl$^-$ ions in the unit cell of $\left(8 \times \frac{1}{8}\right) + \left(6 \times \frac{1}{2}\right) = 1 + 3 = 4$. There are 2 Na$^+$ ions along the edges of the unit cell, and each edge is shared by *four* unit cells. The Na$^+$ ion in the very center of the unit cell belongs entirely to that cell. Thus, the total number of

▶ **FIGURE 12-48**
The sodium chloride unit cell
For clarity, only the centers of the ions are shown. Oppositely charged ions are actually in contact. We can think of this structure as an fcc lattice of Cl$^-$ ions, with Na$^+$ ions filling the octahedral holes.

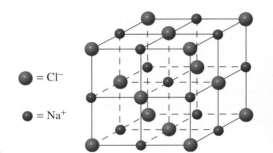

● = Cl$^-$

● = Na$^+$

▶ **FIGURE 12-49**
The cesium chloride unit cell
The Cs$^+$ ion is in the center of the cube, with Cl$^-$ ions at the corners. In reality, each Cl$^-$ is in contact with the Cs$^+$ ion. An alternative unit cell has Cl$^-$ at the center and Cs$^+$ at the corners.

● = Cl$^-$

● = Cs$^+$

Are You Wondering . . .

Why we don't select one of the smaller cubes in Figure 12-48 as the unit cell of NaCl?

There are eight smaller cubes in the unit cell, each of which has a Na^+ ion at four of the corners and a Cl^- ion at the other four. Such a cube is consistent with the formula NaCl but will not generate the entire lattice by simple displacements. Move any one of these cubes to the adjoining cube in any direction, and a Na^+ ion takes the position where a Cl^- ion should be.

Na^+ ions in a unit cell is $\left(12 \times \frac{1}{4}\right) + (1 \times 1) = 3 + 1 = 4$. The unit cell has the equivalent of $4\,Na^+$ and $4\,Cl^-$ ions. The ratio of Na^+ to Cl^- is $4:4 = 1:1$, corresponding to the formula NaCl.

To establish the coordination number in an ionic crystal, count the number of nearest neighbor ions of opposite charge to any given ion in the crystal. In NaCl, each Na^+ is surrounded by *six* Cl^- ions. The coordination numbers of both Na^+ and Cl^- are *six*. By contrast, the coordination numbers of Cs^+ and Cl^- in Figure 12-49 are *eight*. The difference in the structure of CsCl from that of NaCl can be accounted for in terms of the radius ratio for this compound.

$$\frac{r_{Cs^+}}{R_{Cl^-}} = \frac{169\ \text{pm}}{181\ \text{pm}} = 0.934$$

We expect from the radius ratio inequalities above that the Cs^+ ion will occupy a cubic hole in a simple cubic lattice of Cl^- ions. This unit cell is in accord with the one-to-one ratio of Cs^+ to Cl^- ions since there is one Cs^+ in the center of the unit cell and $8 \times \left(\frac{1}{8}\right)\ Cl^-$ ions at the corners.

EXAMPLE 12-11

Relating Ionic Radii and the Dimensions of a Unit Cell of an Ionic Crystal. The ionic radii of Na^+ and Cl^- in NaCl are 99 and 181 pm, respectively. What is the length of the unit cell of NaCl?

Solution

Again, the key to solving this problem lies in understanding geometric relationships in the unit cell. Along each edge of the unit cell (see Figure 12-48), two Cl^- ions are in contact with one Na^+. The edge length is equal to the radius of one Cl^- plus the diameter of Na^+, plus the radius of another Cl^-. That is,

$$\begin{aligned}
\text{Length} &= (r_{Cl^-}) + (r_{Na^+}) + (r_{Na^+}) + (r_{Cl^-}) \\
&= 2(r_{Na^+}) + 2(r_{Cl^-}) \\
&= (2 \times 99) + (2 \times 181) = 560\ \text{pm}
\end{aligned}$$

Practice Example A: The ionic radius of Cs^+ is 167 pm. Use Figure 12-49 and information in Examples 12-9 and 12-11 to determine the length of the unit cell of CsCl.

Practice Example B: Use the length of the unit cell of NaCl obtained in Example 12-11, together with the molar mass of NaCl and the Avogadro constant, to estimate the density of NaCl.

Ionic compounds of the type $M^{2+}X^{2-}$ (for example, MgO, BaS, CaO) may form crystals of the NaCl type. However, if the cation is small enough, as in the case of Zn^{2+}, it can occupy the tetrahedral holes. The radius ratio for ZnS is 0.35, so to satisfy the stoichiometry only half of the tetrahedral holes (there are

Find examples of CaF_2, TiO_2 and ZnS to show the fluorite, rutile, and zinc blend structures.

$\bigcirc$ = S^{2-} $\bullet$ = Zn^{2+}

(a) Unit cell of ZnS, the zinc blend structure

$\bigcirc$ = Ca^{2+} $\bullet$ = F^-

(b) Unit cell of CaF_2, the fluorite structure

$\bigcirc$ = Ti^{4+} $\bullet$ = O^{2-}

(c) Unit cell of TiO_2, the rutile structure

▶ **FIGURE 12-50**
Some unit cells of greater complexity

eight of them) are occupied, to correspond to the four S^{2-} forming the face-centered cubic array (Fig. 12-50). For substances with the formulas MX_2 or M_2X, the crystal structures are more complex. Because the cations and anions occur in unequal numbers, the crystals have *two* coordination numbers, one for the cation and another for the anion.

In CaF_2 (the fluorite structure), there are twice as many fluoride ions as calcium ions (Fig. 12-50b). The coordination number of Ca^{2+} is *eight*, and that of F^- is *four*. This is easiest to see by looking at the Ca^{2+} ion in the middle of a face. There are four F^- ions within the unit cell that are nearest neighbors. In addition, the four F^- ions in the next unit cell (the one that shares the face-centered Ca^{2+} ion) are also nearest neighbors. This gives a coordination number of eight for the Ca^{2+}. The F^- ions each have one corner Ca^{2+} ion and three face-centered Ca^{2+} ions as nearest neighbors, giving a coordination number of four. In TiO_2 (the rutile structure, Figure 12-50c), Ti^{4+} has a coordination number of *six* and O^{2-}, *three*. In this structure, two of the O^{2-} ions are within the interior of the cell, two are in the top face, and two in the bottom face of the cell. Ti^{4+} ions are at the corners and the center of the cell.

CONCEPT ASSESSMENT: ✓

Buckminsterfullerene C_{60} crystallizes in a face-centered cubic array. If potassium atoms fill all the tetrahedral and octahedral holes, what is the formula of the resulting compound?

TYPES OF CRYSTALLINE SOLIDS: A SUMMARY

In this section, we have emphasized crystal structures composed of metal atoms and those composed of ions. But the structural particles of crystalline solids can be atoms, ions, or molecules. To picture a crystal structure having molecules as its structural units, consider solid methane, CH_4. The crystal

TABLE 12.7   Characteristics of Crystalline Solids

Type	Structural Particles	Intermolecular Forces	Typical Properties	Examples
Metallic	Cations and delocalized electrons	Metallic bonds	Hardness varies from soft to very hard; melting point varies from low to very high; lustrous; ductile; malleable; very good conductors of heat and electricity	Na, Mg, Al, Fe, Sn, Cu, Ag, W
Ionic	Cations and anions	Electrostatic attractions	Hard; moderate to very high melting points; nonconductors as solids, but good electric conductors as liquids; many are soluble in polar solvents like water	NaCl, MgO, $NaNO_3$
Network covalent	Atoms	Covalent bonds	Most are very hard and either sublime or melt at very high temperatures; most are nonconductors of electricity	C (diamond), C (graphite), SiC, AlN, SiO_2
Molecular *Nonpolar*	Atoms or nonpolar molecules	Dispersion forces	Soft; extremely low to moderate melting points (depending on molar mass); sublime in some cases; soluble in some nonpolar solvents	He, Ar, H_2, CO_2, CCl_4, CH_4, I_2
Polar	Polar molecules	Dispersion forces and dipole–dipole attractions	Low to moderate melting points; soluble in some polar and some nonpolar solvents	$(CH_3)_2O$, $CHCl_3$, HCl
Hydrogen-Bonded	Molecules with H bonded to N, O, or F	Hydrogen bonds	Low to moderate melting points; soluble in some hydrogen-bonded solvents and some polar solvents	H_2O, NH_3

structure is fcc, which means that the unit cell has a CH_4 molecule at each corner and at the center of each face. Each CH_4 molecule occupies a volume equivalent to a sphere with a radius of 228 pm. Substances that adopt fcc structures are relatively uncommon. Most complex molecules adopt less symmetric unit cells, but a further discussion of this matter is beyond the scope of this text.

The intermolecular forces operating among the structural units of a crystal may be metallic bonds, interionic attractions, van der Waals forces, hydrogen bonds, or covalent bonds. Table 12.7 lists the basic types of crystalline solids, the intermolecular forces within them, some of their characteristic properties, and examples of each.

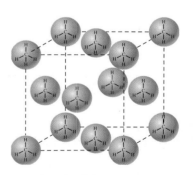

▲ **A sketch of the unit cell of methane**
The unit cell of methane is a face-centered cubic array of CH_4 molecules. In the diagram, the spheres containing the methane molecules are meant to emphasize the fcc array of molecules.

12-9   ENERGY CHANGES IN THE FORMATION OF IONIC CRYSTALS

The concept of lattice energy, which we introduced qualitatively in Section 12-7, is most useful when stated in quantitative terms. It is difficult, however, to calculate a lattice energy directly. The problem is that oppositely charged ions attract one another and like-charged ions repel one another, and these interactions must be considered at the same time. More commonly, lattice energy is determined *indirectly* through an application of Hess's law known as the Born–Fajans–Haber cycle, named after its originators Max Born, Kasimir Fajans, and Fritz Haber. The crux of the method is to design a sequence of steps in which enthalpy changes are known for all the steps but one—the step in which a crystal lattice is formed from gaseous ions.

Carter, Alan A. "Simplified Mathematical Model for Calculating the Lattice Energies of Binary Group I and Group II Ionic Compounds: Using Solver to Estimate the Empirical Constants." *J. Chem. Educ.* **2000**: *77*, 1081 (August 2000).

▶ **FIGURE 12-51**
Enthalpy diagram for the formation of an ionic crystal
Shown here is a five-step sequence for the formation of one mole of NaCl(s) from its elements in their standard states. The sum of the five enthalpy changes gives $\Delta H_f^\circ[\text{NaCl(s)}]$. The equivalent one-step reaction for the formation of NaCl(s) directly from Na(s) and $Cl_2(g)$ is shown in color. (The vertical arrows representing ΔH values are not to scale.)

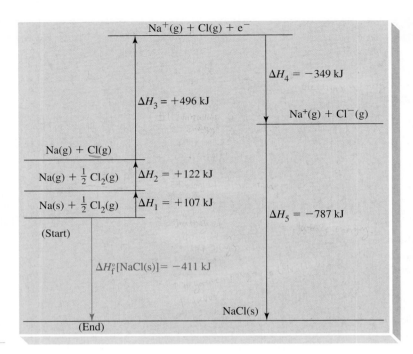

✓ NaCl has a lattice energy of about $\frac{1}{4}$ that of MgO. This is because the coulombic attraction between the ions is proportional to $(-1)(+1)$ in the former and $(-2)(+2)$ in the latter.

Figure 12-51 illustrates a five-step method for finding the lattice energy of NaCl.

Step 1. Sublime one mole of solid Na.

Step 2. Dissociate 0.5 mole of $Cl_2(g)$ into one mole of Cl(g).

Step 3. Ionize one mole of Na(g) to $Na^+(g)$.

Step 4. Convert one mole of Cl(g) to $Cl^-(g)$.

Step 5. Allow the $Na^+(g)$ and $Cl^-(g)$ to form one mole of NaCl(s).

The overall change in these five steps is the same as the reaction in which NaCl(s) is formed from its elements in their standard states—that is, $\Delta H_{\text{overall}} = \Delta H_f^\circ[\text{NaCl(s)}]$. From Appendix D, we see that $\Delta H_f^\circ[\text{NaCl(s)}] = -411 \text{ kJ mol}^{-1}$, so in the following setup, the lattice energy of NaCl is the only unknown.

1. $\quad$ Na(s) $\longrightarrow$ Na(g) $\qquad$ $\Delta H_1 = \Delta H_{\text{sublimation}} = +107$ kJ

2. $\quad$ $\frac{1}{2}Cl_2(g) \longrightarrow$ Cl(g) $\qquad$ $\Delta H_2 = \frac{1}{2}$Cl—Cl bond energy $= +122$ kJ

3. $\quad$ Na(g) $\longrightarrow$ $Na^+(g) + e^-$ $\quad$ $\Delta H_3 = 1^{\text{st}}$ ioniz. energy $= +496$ kJ

4. $\quad$ Cl(g) $+ e^- \longrightarrow Cl^-(g)$ $\qquad$ $\Delta H_4 =$ electron affinity of Cl $= -349$ kJ

5. $\quad$ $Na^+(g) + Cl^-(g) \longrightarrow$ NaCl(s) $\qquad$ $\Delta H_5 =$ lattice energy of NaCl $= ?$

▶ A commonly used convention defines lattice energy in terms of the breakup of a crystal rather than its formation. By that convention, all lattice energies are positive quantities and $\Delta H_5 = -(\text{lattice energy})$.

overall: $\qquad$ Na(s) $+ \frac{1}{2}Cl_2(g) \longrightarrow$ NaCl(s)

$$\Delta H_{\text{overall}} = -411 \text{ kJ} = \Delta H_1 + \Delta H_2 + \Delta H_3 + \Delta H_4 + \Delta H_5$$

$$-411 \text{ kJ} = 107 \text{ kJ} + 122 \text{ kJ} + 496 \text{ kJ} - 349 \text{ kJ} + \Delta H_5$$

$$\Delta H_5 = \text{lattice energy} = (-411 - 107 - 122 - 496 + 349)\text{kJ} = -787 \text{ kJ}$$

One way to use the concept of lattice energy is in making predictions about the possibility of synthesizing ionic compounds. In Example 12-12, we predict the likelihood of obtaining the compound MgCl(s) by evaluating its enthalpy of formation.

EXAMPLE 12-12

Relating Enthalpy of Formation, Lattice Energy, and Other Energy Quantities. With the following data, calculate ΔH_f° per mol MgCl(s): Enthalpy of sublimation of 1 mol Mg(s): +146 kJ; enthalpy of dissociation of $\frac{1}{2}$ mol $Cl_2(g)$: +122 kJ; first ionization energy of 1 mol Mg(g): +738 kJ; electron affinity of 1 mol Cl(g): −349 kJ; lattice energy of 1 mol MgCl(s): −676 kJ.

Solution

In this case the lattice energy (ΔH_5) is known, and the unknown is $\Delta H_{overall}$, which is the enthalpy of formation of MgCl(s).

$$Mg(s) \longrightarrow Mg(g) \qquad\qquad \Delta H_1 = +146 \text{ kJ}$$

$$\frac{1}{2}Cl_2(g) \longrightarrow Cl(g) \qquad\qquad \Delta H_2 = +122 \text{ kJ}$$

$$Mg(g) \longrightarrow Mg^+(g) + e^- \qquad \Delta H_3 = +738 \text{ kJ}$$

$$Cl(g) + e^- \longrightarrow Cl^-(g) \qquad\qquad \Delta H_4 = -349 \text{ kJ}$$

$$Mg^+(g) + Cl^-(g) \longrightarrow MgCl(s) \qquad \Delta H_5 = -676 \text{ kJ}$$

$$overall: \qquad Mg(s) + \frac{1}{2}Cl_2(g) \longrightarrow MgCl(s)$$

$$\Delta H_{overall} = \Delta H_f^\circ[MgCl(s)] = \Delta H_1 + \Delta H_2 + \Delta H_3 + \Delta H_4 + \Delta H_5$$

$$= 146 \text{ kJ} + 122 \text{ kJ} + 738 \text{ kJ} - 349 \text{ kJ} - 676 \text{ kJ} = -19 \text{ kJ}$$

Practice Example A: The enthalpy of sublimation of cesium is 78.2 kJ mol^{-1}, and $\Delta H_f^\circ[CsCl(s)] = -442.8$ kJ mol^{-1}. Use these values, together with other data from the text, to calculate the lattice energy of CsCl(s).

Practice Example B: Given the following data, together with data included in Example 12-12, calculate ΔH_f° per mol $CaCl_2(s)$: Enthalpy of sublimation of Ca(s), +178.2 kJ mol^{-1}; first ionization energy of Ca(g), +590 kJ mol^{-1}; second ionization energy of Ca(g), +1145 kJ mol^{-1}; lattice energy of $CaCl_2(s)$, −2223 kJ mol^{-1}.

Example 12-12 suggests that we can obtain MgCl(s) as a stable compound—it has a slightly negative enthalpy of formation. Why have we been writing $MgCl_2$ all this time instead of MgCl? You might think that because MgCl has a Mg-to-Cl ratio of 1:1 and $MgCl_2$ has a ratio of 1:2, MgCl should form if Mg(s) reacts with a limited amount of $Cl_2(g)$. But this is not the case. No matter how limited the amount of $Cl_2(g)$ available, the only compound that forms is $MgCl_2$. To understand this, repeat the calculation of Example 12-12 for the formation of $MgCl_2(s)$, and you will obtain an enthalpy of formation that is very much more negative than that for MgCl(s) (see Exercise 75). Even though the energy requirement to produce Mg^{2+} is larger than to produce Mg^+, the lattice energy is very much greater for $MgCl_2(s)$ than for MgCl(s). This is because the *doubly* charged Mg^{2+} ions exert a much stronger force on Cl^- ions than do *singly* charged Mg^+ ions. The reaction between Mg and Cl atoms does not stop at MgCl but continues on to the more stable $MgCl_2$.

Is $NaCl_2$ a stable compound? Here, the answer is no. The additional lattice energy associated with $NaCl_2$ over NaCl is not nearly enough to compensate for the very high second ionization energy of sodium (see Exercise 103).

◄ The flashlight provides enough radiant energy to slightly raise the temperature of this liquid crystalline material. As their temperature changes, the liquid crystals undergo a change in color. This effect can be used to make liquid crystal thermometers.

The acronym LCD needs little introduction. Most people know that this term stands for liquid crystal display and that such displays are found in many places—calculators, watches and clocks, thermometers, and many more. After a study of this chapter, though, "liquid crystal" sounds like a contradiction. Liquids are one state of matter, and crystals are something we associate with another state of matter—solids. Liquid crystals, discovered as laboratory curiosities about 100 years ago, are forms of matter that are intermediate between the liquid and solid state. Liquid crystals have the fluid properties of liquids and the optical properties of solids.

Liquid crystals are observed most commonly in organic compounds that have cylindrically shaped (rodlike) molecules with masses of 200 to 500 u and lengths four to eight times their diameters. Potentially, this represents about 0.5% of all organic compounds.

In the *nematic* (meaning thread-like) form of the liquid crystalline state, the rod-like molecules are arranged in a parallel fashion. They are free to move in all directions, but they can rotate only on their long axes. (Imagine the ways in which you might move a particular pencil in a box of loosely packed pencils.) In the *smectic* (meaning grease-like) form, rod-like molecules are arranged in layers, with the long axes of the molecules perpendicular to the planes of the layers. The molecular motions possible here are a translation within, but not between, layers and a rotation about the long axis. The *cholesteric* form is related to the smectic form, but the orientation in each layer is different from that in the layer above and below. These three forms of liquid crystals are illustrated in Figure 12-52.

In a cholesteric structure, each particular orientation is repeated over a span of several layers. The distance between planes with molecules in the same orientation is a distinctive feature of a cholesteric liquid crystal. Certain properties of light reflected by a liquid crystal depend on this characteristic distance. For example, because this distance is very temperature sensitive, the reflected light

Summary

12-1 Intermolecular Forces and Some Properties of Liquids—Surface tension, the energy required to extend the surface of a liquid, and **viscosity**, a liquid's resistance to flow, are properties related to intermolecular forces. Familiar phenomena such as drop shape, meniscus formation, and capillary action depend on surface tension. Specifically, these phenomena are influenced by the balance between **cohesive forces**, intermolecular forces between molecules in a liquid, and **adhesive forces**, intermolecular forces between liquid molecules and a surface.

12-2 Vaporization of Liquids: Vapor Pressure—Vapor pressure, the pressure exerted by a vapor in equilibrium with a liquid, is a measure of the volatility of a liquid and is related to the strength of intermolecular forces. The conversion of a liquid to a vapor is called **vaporization**, or **evaporation**; the reverse process is called **condensation**. The dependence of vapor pressure on temperature is represented by a **vapor pressure curve** (Fig. 12-9) and can be expressed in the **Clausius–Clapeyron equation** (12.2). When the pressure exerted by the escaping molecules from the surface of the liquid equals the pressure exerted by the molecules in the atmosphere, **boiling** is said to occur. The **normal boiling point** is the temperature at which the vapor pressure of the liquid equals 1 atm. The **critical point** is the condition of temperature and pressure at which a liquid and its vapor become indistinguishable (Fig. 12-11).

12-3 Some Properties of Solids—When crystalline solids are heated, a temperature is reached where the solid state is converted to a liquid—**melting** occurs. The temperature at which this occurs is the **melting point**. When liquids are cooled, the crystalline material will form during the process of **freezing**, and the temperature at which this occurs is the **freezing point**. Under certain conditions solids can directly convert into the vapor by the process of **sublimation**. The reverse process is called **deposition**. Among the properties of a solid affected by intermolecular forces are its sublimation (vapor) pressure and its melting point.

12-4 Phase Diagrams—A phase diagram (Figs. 12-18 to 12-21) is a graphical plot of conditions under which solids, liquids, and gases (vapors) exist, as single phases or as two or more phases in equilibrium with one another. Especially significant points on a phase diagram are the **triple point** (where all three phases coexist), melting changes color with changing temperature. This phenomenon is the basis of liquid crystal temperature-sensing devices, which can detect temperature changes as small as 0.01 °C.

The orientation of molecules in a thin film of nematic liquid crystals is easily altered by pressure and by an electric field. The altered orientation affects the optical properties of the film, such as causing the film to become opaque. Suppose electrodes are arranged in certain patterns (say, in the shape of numbers). When an electric field is imposed through these electrodes onto a thin film of liquid crystals, the patterns of the electrodes become visible. This principle is used in liquid crystal display devices.

Liquid crystals occur widely in living matter. Cell membranes and certain tissues have structures that can be described as liquid crystalline. Hardening of the arteries is caused by the deposition of liquid crystalline compounds of cholesterol. Liquid crystalline properties have also been identified in various synthetic polymers, such as Kevlar® fiber.

(a) Orientation of molecules in liquid

Smectic liquid crystal

Nematic liquid crystal

Cholesteric liquid crystal

(b) Orientation of molecules in liquid crystals

◀ **FIGURE 12-52**
The liquid crystalline state

point, boiling point, and critical point. Some substances can exist in different forms in the solid state; such behavior is called **polymorphism** (Fig. 12-21).

12-5 Van der Waals Forces—The intermolecular forces that occur between molecules are collectively known as **van der Waals forces**. The most common intermolecular forces of attraction are those between instantaneous and induced dipoles (**dispersion forces**, or **London forces**). The magnitudes of dispersion forces depend on how easily electron displacements within molecules cause a temporary imbalance of electron charge distribution, that is, on the **polarizability** of the molecule. In polar substances, there are also dipole–dipole forces.

12-6 Hydrogen Bonding—Some hydrogen-containing substances exhibit significant intermolecular attractions called **hydrogen bonds**, in which H atoms bonded to highly electronegative atoms—N, O, or F—in a molecule are simultaneously attracted to other highly electronegative atoms in the same molecule or in different molecules. Hydrogen bonding has a profound effect on physical properties such as boiling points (Fig. 12-27) and is a vital intermolecular force in living systems.

12-7 Network Covalent Solids and Ionic Solids—In **network covalent solids**, chemical bonds extend throughout a crystalline structure. For these substances, the chemical bonds are themselves intermolecular forces. **Lattice energy** is the energy released when separated gaseous ions come together to form one mole of an ionic solid.

12-8 Crystal Structures—Some crystal structures can be described in terms of the packing of spheres. Depending on the way in which the spheres are packed, different **unit cells** are obtained (Fig. 12-37). The hexagonal unit cell is obtained with **hexagonal closest packed (hcp)** spheres; a **face-centered cubic (fcc)** unit cell is obtained with **cubic closest packed** spheres (Figs. 12-39 and 12-40). A **body-centered cubic (bcc)** (Fig. 12-38) unit cell is found in some cases where spheres are not packed as closely as in the hcp and fcc structures. The dimensions of the unit cell can be determined by X-ray diffraction, and these dimensions can be used in calculating atomic radii and densities. An important consideration with ionic crystals is that the ions are not all of the same size or charge. Ionic crystals can often be viewed as an array of anions with the cations fitting in the holes within the anion array.

12-9 Energy Changes in the Formation of Ionic Crystals—Lattice energies of ionic crystals can be related to certain atomic and thermodynamic properties by means of the Born–Fajans–Haber cycle (Fig. 12-51).

Integrative Example

Use data from the table of physical properties of hydrazine, N_2H_4, to calculate the partial pressure of $N_2H_4(g)$ when a container filled with an equilibrium mixture of $N_2H_4(g)$ and $N_2H_4(l)$ at 25.0 °C is cooled to the temperature of an ice-water bath.

Property	Value
Freezing point	2.0 °C
Boiling point	113.5 °C
Critical temperature	380 °C
Critical pressure	145.4 atm
Enthalpy of fusion	12.66 kJ mol^{-1}
Heat capacity of liquid	98.84 J mol^{-1} °C^{-1}
Density of liquid at 25.0 °C	1.0036 g mL^{-1}
Vapor pressure at 25.0 °C	14.4 Torr

Strategy

At a temperature below its freezing point of 2.0 °C, the hydrazine will be present as a solid in equilibrium with its vapor. We are seeking the sublimation pressure of $N_2H_4(s)$ at the melting point of ice, 0 °C. At its freezing point of 2.0 °C, the hydrazine coexists in three phases—liquid, solid, and vapor. We must first determine the vapor pressure of hydrazine at 2.0 °C. Then we can then use the Clausius–Clapeyron equation (12.2) to calculate the vapor (sublimation) pressure at 0 °C. Our principal task will be to identify the data needed to apply the Clausius–Clapeyron equation, three times in all, as detailed in the stepwise solution to the problem.

Solution

To determine a value of ΔH_{vap}, choose the vapor pressure data at 25.0 °C for T_1 and P_1 and at the normal boiling point for T_2 and P_2 for substitution into equation (12.2).

$$\ln\frac{P_2}{P_1} = \frac{\Delta H_{vap}}{R}\left(\frac{1}{T_1} - \frac{1}{T_2}\right)$$

$$\ln\frac{760\ \text{Torr}}{14.4\ \text{Torr}} = \frac{\Delta H_{vap}}{8.3145\ \text{J mol}^{-1}\,\text{K}^{-1}} \times \left(\frac{1}{298.2\ \text{K}} - \frac{1}{386.7\ \text{K}}\right) = 3.967$$

$$\Delta H_{vap} = \frac{8.3145\ \text{J mol}^{-1}\,\text{K}^{-1} \times 3.967}{(0.003353 - 0.002586)\text{K}^{-1}} = 4.30 \times 10^4\ \text{J mol}^{-1}$$

Return to the Clausius–Clapeyron equation (12.2) using the value of ΔH_{vap} just obtained. Also use the same data as in the first calculation for T_1 and P_1, but now with $T_2 = 2.0 + 273.15 = 275.2$ K and P_2 as an unknown. Solve the equation for P_2.

$$\ln\frac{P_2}{14.4} = \frac{4.30 \times 10^4\ \text{J mol}^{-1}}{8.3145\ \text{J mol}^{-1}\,\text{K}^{-1}} \times \left(\frac{1}{298.2\ \text{K}} - \frac{1}{275.2\ \text{K}}\right)$$

$$= 5.17 \times 10^3 \times (-2.80 \times 10^{-4}) = -1.45$$

$$P_2/14.4 = e^{-1.45} = 0.235$$

$$P_2 = 0.235 \times 14.4 = 3.38\ \text{Torr}$$

We now have the triple point data for hydrazine. The triple point temperature is 2.0 °C (275.2 K) and the triple point pressure is 3.38 Torr. In our final application of equation (12.2), we use those data as T_2 and P_2. The temperature T_1 is 0 °C (273.2 K) and the unknown sublimation pressure is P_1. The enthalpy change needed in this final calculation must be the enthalpy of sublimation, which is

$$\Delta H_{sub} = \Delta H_{fus} + \Delta H_{vap}$$

$$= \left(12.66\frac{\text{kJ}}{\text{mol}} \times \frac{1000\ \text{J}}{1\ \text{kJ}}\right) + 4.30 \times 10^4\ \text{J mol}^{-1} = 5.57 \times 10^4\ \text{J mol}^{-1}$$

Finally, we substitute these data into equation (12.2) and solve for P_1, the sublimation pressure of hydrazine at 0 °C.

$$\ln\frac{3.38\ \text{Torr}}{P_1} = \frac{5.57 \times 10^4\ \text{J mol}^{-1}}{8.3145\ \text{J mol}^{-1}\,\text{K}^{-1}} \times \left(\frac{1}{273.2} - \frac{1}{275.2}\right)\text{K}^{-1}$$

$$\ln\frac{3.38\ \text{Torr}}{P_1} = 6.70 \times 10^3 \times 2.66 \times 10^{-5} = 0.178$$

$$\frac{3.38\ \text{Torr}}{P_1} = e^{0.178} = 1.19$$

$$P_1 = \frac{3.38\ \text{Torr}}{1.19} = 2.84\ \text{Torr}$$

Assessment

Observe that, compared to the vapor pressure at 25 °C (14.4 Torr), the calculated triple point pressure (3.38 Torr) is smaller; and the sublimation pressure at 0 °C (2.84 Torr) is smaller still. This is certainly the trend expected for the three values. In the three situations in which equation (12.2) is used, the first one is the most subject to error because the difference between T_2 and T_1 is 89 °C, while in the other two it is 23 °C and 2 °C, respectively. Both ΔH_{vap} and ΔH_{sub} are undoubtedly temperature-dependent.

Exercises

Surface Tension; Viscosity

1. Silicone oils are used in water repellents for treating tents, hiking boots, and similar items. Explain how they function.
2. Surface tension, viscosity, and vapor pressure are all related to intermolecular forces. Why do surface tension and viscosity decrease with temperature, whereas vapor pressure increases with temperature?
3. Is there any scientific basis for the colloquial expression, "slower than molasses in January"? Explain.
4. A television commercial claims that a product makes water "wetter." Can there be any basis to this claim? Explain.

Vaporization

5. As a liquid evaporated from an open container, its temperature was observed to remain roughly constant. When the same liquid evaporated from a thermally insulated container (a vacuum bottle or Dewar flask), its temperature was observed to drop. How would you account for this difference?
6. Explain why vaporization occurs only at the surface of a liquid until the boiling point temperature is reached. That is, why does vapor not form throughout the liquid at all temperatures?
7. The enthalpy of vaporization of benzene, $C_6H_6(l)$, is 33.9 kJ mol^{-1} at 298 K. How many liters of $C_6H_6(g)$, measured at 298 K and 95.1 mmHg, are formed when 1.54 kJ of heat is absorbed by $C_6H_6(l)$ at a constant temperature of 298 K?
8. A vapor volume of 1.17 L forms when a sample of liquid acetonitrile, CH_3CN, absorbs 1.00 kJ of heat at its normal boiling point (81.6 °C and 1 atm). What is ΔH_{vap} in kilojoules per mole of CH_3CN?
9. Use data from the Integrative Example (page 518) to determine how much heat is required to convert 25.00 mL of liquid hydrazine at 25.0 °C to hydrazine vapor at its normal boiling point.
10. How much heat is required to raise the temperature of 215 g $CH_3OH(l)$ from 20.0 to 30.0 °C and then vaporize it at 30.0 °C? Use data from Table 12.1 and a molar heat capacity of $CH_3OH(l)$ of 81.1 J mol^{-1} K^{-1}.
11. How many liters of $CH_4(g)$, measured at 23.4 °C and 768 mmHg, must be burned to provide the heat needed to vaporize 3.78 L of water at 100 °C? $\Delta H_{combustion} = -8.90 \times 10^2$ kJ mol^{-1} CH_4. For $H_2O(l)$ at 100 °C, $d = 0.958$ g cm^{-3}, and $\Delta H_{vap} = 40.7$ kJ mol^{-1}.
12. A 50.0-g piece of iron at 152 °C is dropped into 20.0 g $H_2O(l)$ at 89 °C in an open, thermally insulated container. How much water would you expect to vaporize, assuming no water splashes out? The specific heats of iron and water are 0.45 and 4.21 J g^{-1} $°C^{-1}$, respectively, and $\Delta H_{vap} = 40.7$ kJ mol^{-1} H_2O.

Vapor Pressure and Boiling Point

13. From Figure 12-9, estimate (a) the vapor pressure of C_6H_7N at 100 °C; (b) the normal boiling point of C_7H_8.
14. Use data in Figure 12-13 to estimate (a) the normal boiling point of aniline; (b) the vapor pressure of diethyl ether at 25 °C.
15. Equilibrium is established between $Br_2(l)$ and $Br_2(g)$ at 25.0 °C. A 250.0-mL sample of the vapor weighs 0.486 g. What is the vapor pressure of bromine at 25.0 °C, in millimeters of mercury?
16. The density of acetone vapor in equilibrium with liquid acetone, $(CH_3)_2CO$, at 32 °C is 0.876 g L^{-1}. What is the vapor pressure of acetone at 32 °C, expressed in kilopascals?
17. A double boiler is used when a careful control of temperature is required in cooking. Water is boiled in an outside container to produce steam, and the steam condenses on the outside walls of an inner container in which cooking occurs. (A related laboratory device is called a steam bath.) (a) How is heat energy conveyed to the food to be cooked in a double boiler? (b) What is the maximum temperature that can be reached in the inside container?
18. One popular demonstration in chemistry labs is performed by boiling a small quantity of water in a metal can (such as a used soda can), picking up the can with tongs and quickly submerging it upside down in cold water. The can collapses with a loud and satisfying pop. Give an explanation of this crushing of the can. (Note: If you try this demonstration, do not heat the can over an open flame.)
19. Pressure cookers achieve a high cooking temperature to speed the cooking process by heating a small amount of water under a constant pressure. If the pressure is set at 2 atm, what is the boiling point of the water? Use information from Table 12.2.

20. Use data from Table 12.2 to estimate **(a)** the boiling point of water in Santa Fe, New Mexico, if the prevailing atmospheric pressure is 640 mmHg; **(b)** the prevailing atmospheric pressure at Lake Arrowhead, California, if the observed boiling point of water is 94 °C.

21. A 25.0-L volume of He(g) at 30.0 °C is passed through 6.220 g of liquid aniline ($C_6H_5NH_2$) at 30.0 °C. The liquid remaining after the experiment weighs 6.108 g. Assume that the He(g) becomes saturated with aniline vapor and that the total gas volume and temperature remain constant. What is the vapor pressure of aniline at 30.0 °C?

22. A 7.53-L sample of N_2(g) at 742 mmHg and 45.0 °C is bubbled through CCl_4(l) at 45.0 °C. Assuming the gas becomes saturated with CCl_4(g), what is the volume of the resulting gaseous mixture, if the total pressure remains at 742 mmHg and the temperature remains at 45 °C? The vapor pressure of CCl_4 at 45 °C is 261 mmHg.

23. Some vapor pressure data for Freon-12, CCl_2F_2, once a common refrigerant, are −12.2 °C, 2.0 atm; 16.1 °C, 5.0 atm; 42.4 °C, 10.0 atm; 74.0 °C, 20.0 atm. Also, bp = −29.8 °C, T_c = 111.5 °C, P_c = 39.6 atm. Use these data to plot the vapor pressure curve of Freon-12. What approximate pressure would be required in the compressor of a refrigeration system to convert Freon-12 vapor to liquid at 25 °C?

24. A 10.0-g sample of liquid water is sealed in a 1515-mL flask and allowed to come to equilibrium with its vapor at 27 °C. What is the mass of H_2O(g) present when equilibrium is established? Use vapor pressure data from Table 12.2.

The Clausius–Clapeyron Equation

25. Cyclohexanol has a vapor pressure of 10.0 mmHg at 56.0 °C and 100.0 mmHg at 103.7 °C. Calculate its enthalpy of vaporization, ΔH_{vap}.

26. The vapor pressure of methyl alcohol is 40.0 mmHg at 5.0 °C. Use this value and other information from the text to estimate the normal boiling point of methyl alcohol.

27. The normal boiling point of acetone, an important laboratory and industrial solvent, is 56.2 °C and its ΔH_{vap} is 25.5 kJ mol^{-1}. At what temperature does acetone have a vapor pressure of 375 mmHg?

28. The vapor pressure of trichloromethane (chloroform) is 40.0 Torr at −7.1 °C. Its enthalpy of vaporization is 29.2 kJ mol^{-1}. Calculate its normal boiling point.

29. Benzaldehyde, C_6H_5CHO, has a normal boiling point of 179.0 °C and a critical point at 422 °C and 45.9 atm. Estimate its vapor pressure at 100.0 °C.

30. With reference to Figure 12-13, which is the more volatile liquid, benzene or toluene? At approximately what temperature does the less volatile liquid have the same vapor pressure as the more volatile one at 65 °C?

Critical Point

31. Which substances listed in Table 12.3 can exist as liquids at room temperature (about 20 °C)? Explain.

32. Can SO_2 be maintained as a liquid under a pressure of 100 atm at 0 °C? Can liquid methane be obtained under the same conditions?

Melting and Freezing

33. The normal melting point of copper is 1357 K, and ΔH_{fus} of Cu is 13.05 kJ mol^{-1}. **(a)** How much heat, in kilojoules, is evolved when a 3.78-kg sample of molten Cu freezes? **(b)** How much heat, in kilojoules, must be absorbed at 1357 K to melt a bar of copper that is 75 cm × 15 cm × 12 cm? (Assume d = 8.92 g/cm^3 for Cu.)

34. An ice calorimeter measures quantities of heat by the quantity of ice melted. How many grams of ice would be melted by the heat released in the complete combustion of 1.35 L of propane gas, C_3H_8(g), measured at 25.0 °C and 748 mmHg?
[*Hint:* What is the standard molar enthalpy of combustion of C_3H_8(g)?]

States of Matter and Phase Diagrams

35. An 80.0-g piece of Dry Ice, CO_2(s), is placed in a 0.500-L container, and the container is sealed. If this container is held at 25 °C, what state(s) of matter must be present? [*Hint:* Refer to Table 12.3 and Figure 12-19.]

36. Sketch a plausible phase diagram for hydrazine (N_2H_4) from the following data: triple point (2.0 °C and 3.4 mmHg), the normal melting point (2 °C), the normal boiling point (113.5 °C), and the critical point (380 °C and 145 atm). The density of the liquid is less than that of the solid. Label significant data points on this diagram. Are there any features of the diagram that remain uncertain? Explain.

37. Describe what happens to the following samples in situations like those pictured in Figure 12-22. Be as specific as you can about the temperatures and pressures at which changes occur.
(a) A sample of water is heated from −20 to 200 °C at a constant pressure of 600 Torr.
(b) The pressure on a sample of iodine is increased from 90 mmHg to 100 atm at a constant temperature of 114 °C.
(c) A sample of carbon dioxide at 35 °C is cooled to −100 °C at a constant pressure of 50 atm.
[*Hint:* Refer also to Table 12.3.]

38. Shown here is a portion of the phase diagram for phosphorus.
(a) Indicate the phases present in the regions labeled (?).
(b) A sample of solid red phosphorus cannot be melted by heating in a container open to the atmosphere. Explain why this is so.
(c) Trace the phase changes that occur when the pressure on a sample is reduced from point A to B, at constant temperature.

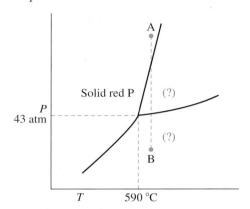

39. A 0.240-g sample of $H_2O(l)$ is sealed into an evacuated 3.20-L flask. What is the pressure of the vapor in the flask if the temperature is **(a)** 30.0 °C; **(b)** 50.0 °C; **(c)** 70.0 °C?

40. A 2.50-g sample of $H_2O(l)$ is sealed in a 5.00-L flask at 120.0 °C.
(a) Show that the sample exists completely as vapor.
(b) Estimate the temperature to which the flask must be cooled before liquid water condenses.

41. Use appropriate phase diagrams and data from Table 12.3 to determine whether any of the following is likely to occur naturally at or near Earth's surface anywhere on Earth: **(a)** $CO_2(s)$; **(b)** $CH_4(l)$; **(c)** $SO_2(g)$; **(d)** $I_2(l)$; **(e)** $O_2(l)$. Explain.

42. Trace the phase changes that occur as a sample of $H_2O(g)$, originally at 1.00 mmHg and −0.10 °C, is compressed at constant temperature until the pressure reaches 100 atm.

43. To an insulated container with 100.0 g $H_2O(l)$ at 20.0 °C, 175 g steam at 100.0 °C and 1.65 kg of ice at 0.0 °C are added.
(a) What mass of ice remains unmelted after equilibrium is established?
(b) What *additional* mass of steam should be introduced into the insulated container to just melt all of the ice?

44. A 54-cm^3 ice cube at −25.0 °C is added to a thermally insulated container with 400.0 mL $H_2O(l)$ at 32.0 °C. What will be the final temperature in the container and what state(s) of matter will be present? (Specific heats: $H_2O(s)$, 2.01 J g^{-1} °C^{-1}; $H_2O(l)$, 4.18 J g^{-1} °C^{-1}. Densities: $H_2O(s)$, 0.917 g/cm^3; $H_2O(l)$, 0.998 g/cm^3. Also, ΔH_{fus} of ice = 6.01 kJ mol^{-1}.)

45. You decide to cool a can of soda pop quickly in the freezer compartment of a refrigerator. When you take out the can, the soda pop is still liquid; but when you open the can, the soda pop immediately freezes. Explain why this happens.

46. Why is the triple point of water (ice–liquid–vapor) a better fixed point for establishing a thermometric scale than either the melting point of ice or the boiling point of water?

Intermolecular Forces

47. For each of the following substances describe the importance of dispersion (London) forces, dipole–dipole interactions, and hydrogen bonding: **(a)** HCl; **(b)** Br_2; **(c)** ICl; **(d)** HF; **(e)** CH_4.

48. When another atom or group of atoms is substituted for one of the hydrogen atoms in benzene, C_6H_6, the boiling point changes. Explain the order of the following boiling points: C_6H_6, 80 °C; C_6H_5Cl, 132 °C; C_6H_5Br, 156 °C; C_6H_5OH, 182 °C.

49. Arrange the liquids represented through the following molecular models in the expected order of increasing viscosity at 25 °C.

(a)   **(b)**   **(c)**   **(d)**

50. Arrange the liquids represented by the following molecular models in the expected order of increasing normal boiling point.

(a)   **(b)**   **(c)**   **(d)**

51. One of the following substances is a liquid at room temperature, whereas the others are gaseous: CH_3OH; C_3H_8; N_2; N_2O. Which do you think is the liquid? Explain.

52. In which of the following compounds do you think that intramolecular hydrogen bonding is an important factor: **(a)** $CH_3CH_2CH_2CH_3$; **(b)** $HOOCCH_2CH_2$ CH_2CH_2COOH; **(c)** CH_3COOH; **(d)** *ortho*-phthalic acid? Explain.

ortho-Phthalic acid

Network Covalent Solids

53. Based on data presented in the text, would you expect diamond or graphite to have the greater density? Explain.
54. Diamond is often used as a cutting medium in glass cutters. What property of diamond makes this possible? Could graphite function as well?
55. Silicon carbide, SiC, crystallizes in a form similar to diamond, whereas boron nitride, BN, crystallizes in a form similar to graphite.

    (a) Sketch the SiC structure as in Figure 12-32(b).
    (b) Propose a bonding scheme for BN.
56. Are the fullerenes network covalent solids? What makes them different from diamond and graphite? It has been shown that carbon can form chains in which every other carbon atom is bonded to the next carbon atom by a triple bond. Is this allotrope of carbon a network covalent solid? Explain.

Ionic Bonding and Properties

57. The melting points of NaF, NaCl, NaBr, and NaI are 988, 801, 755, and 651 °C, respectively. Are these data consistent with ideas developed in Section 12-7? Explain.
58. Use Coulomb's law (see Appendix B) to verify the conclusion concerning the relative strengths of the attractive forces in the ion pairs Na^+Cl^- and $Mg^{2+}O^{2-}$ presented in Figure 12-36.

Crystal Structures

59. Explain why there are *two* arrangements for the closest packing of spheres rather than a single one.
60. Argon, copper, sodium chloride, and carbon dioxide all crystallize in the fcc structure. How can this be when their physical properties are so different?
61. For the two-dimensional lattice shown here,

    ment of circles pictured here, what percentage of the area remains uncovered?

63. Tungsten has a body-centered cubic crystal structure. Using a metallic radius of 139 pm for the W atom, calculate the density of tungsten.
64. Magnesium crystallizes in the hcp arrangement shown in Figure 12-41. The dimensions of the unit cell are height, 520 pm; length on an edge, 320 pm. Calculate the density of Mg(s), and compare with the measured value of 1.738 g/cm³.
65. Polonium (Po) is the largest member of group 16 and is the only element known to take on the simple cubic crystal system. The distance between nearest neighbor Po atoms in this structure is 335 pm.

    (a) What is the diameter of a Po atom?
    (b) What is the density of Po metal?
    (c) At what angle (in degrees) to the parallel faces of the Po unit cells would first-order diffraction be observed when using X-rays of wavelength 1.785×10^{-10} m?
66. Germanium has a cubic unit cell with a side edge of 565 pm. The density of germanium is 5.36 g/cm³. What is the crystal system adopted by germanium?

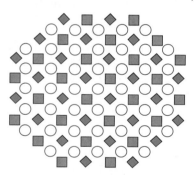

    (a) identify a unit cell.
    (b) How many of each of the following elements are in the unit cell: ◆, ■, and ○?
    (c) Indicate some simpler units than the unit cell, and explain why they cannot function as a unit cell.
62. As we saw in Section 12-8, stacking spheres always leaves open space. Consider the corresponding situation in two dimensions: Squares can be arranged to cover all the area, but circles cannot. For the arrange-

Ionic Crystal Structures

67. Show that the unit cells for CaF_2 and TiO_2 in Figure 12-50 are consistent with their formulas.
68. Using methods similar to Examples 12-10 and 12-11, calculate the density of CsCl. Use 169 pm as the radius of Cs^+.
69. The crystal structure of magnesium oxide, MgO, is of the NaCl type (Fig. 12-48). Use this fact, together with ionic radii from Figure 9-8, to establish the following.
    (a) the coordination numbers of Mg^{2+} and O^{2-};
    (b) the number of formula units in the unit cell;
    (c) the length and volume of a unit cell;
    (d) the density of MgO.

70. Potassium chloride has the same crystal structure as NaCl. Careful measurement of the internuclear distance between K^+ and Cl^- ions gave a value of 314.54 pm. The density of KCl is 1.9893 g/cm³. Use these data to evaluate the Avogadro constant, N_A.
71. Use data from Figure 9-8 to predict the type of cubic unit cell adopted by (a) CaO; (b) CuCl; (c) LiO_2 (the radius of the O_2^- ion is 128 pm).
72. Use data from Figure 9-8 to predict the type of cubic unit cell adopted by (a) BaO; (b) CuI; (c) LiS_2 (the radius of the S_2^- ion is 198 pm).

Lattice Energy

73. *Without doing calculations,* indicate how you would expect the lattice energies of LiCl(s), KCl(s), RbCl(s), and CsCl(s) to compare with the value of -787 kJ mol^{-1} determined for NaCl(s) on page 514. [*Hint:* Assume that the enthalpies of sublimation of the alkali metals are comparable in value. What atomic properties from Chapter 9 should you compare?]

74. Determine the lattice energy of KF(s) from the following data: $\Delta H_f^\circ[\text{KF(s)}] = -567.3$ kJ mol^{-1}; enthalpy of sublimation of K(s), 89.24 kJ mol^{-1}; enthalpy of dissociation of F_2(g), 159 kJ mol^{-1} F_2; I_1 for K(g), 418.9 kJ mol^{-1}; EA for F(g), -328 kJ mol^{-1}.

75. Refer to Example 12-12. Together with data given there, use the data here to calculate ΔH_f° for 1 mol $MgCl_2$(s). Explain why you would expect $MgCl_2$ to be a much more stable compound than MgCl. (Second ionization energy of Mg, $I_2 = 1451$ kJ mol^{-1}; lattice energy of $MgCl_2$(s) $= -2526$ kJ mol^{-1} $MgCl_2$.)

76. In ionic compounds with certain metals, hydrogen exists as the hydride ion, H$^-$. Determine the electron affinity of hydrogen; that is, ΔH for the process H(g) + e$^-$ → H$^-$(g). To do so, use data from Section 12-9; the bond energy of H_2(g) from Table 10.3; -812 kJ mol^{-1} NaH for the lattice energy of NaH(s); and -57 kJ mol^{-1} NaH for the enthalpy of formation of NaH(s).

Integrative and Advanced Exercises

77. When a wax candle is burned, the fuel consists of *gaseous* hydrocarbons appearing at the end of the candle wick. Describe the phase changes and processes by which the solid wax is ultimately consumed.

78. The normal boiling point of water is 100.00 °C and the enthalpy of vaporization at this temperature is $\Delta H_{vap} = 40.657$ kJ mol^{-1}. What would be the boiling point of water if it were based on a pressure of 1 bar instead of the standard atm?

79. The normal boiling point of isooctane (a gasoline component with a high octane rating) is 99.2 °C, and its ΔH_{vap} is 35.76 kJ mol^{-1}. Because isooctane and water have nearly identical boiling points, will they have nearly equal vapor pressures at room temperature? If not, which would you expect to be more volatile? Explain.

80. A supplier of cylinder gases warns customers to determine how much gas remains in a cylinder by weighing the cylinder and comparing this mass to the original mass of the full cylinder. In particular, the customer is told not to try to estimate the mass of gas available from the measured gas pressure. Explain the basis of this warning. Are there cases where a measurement of the gas pressure *can* be used as a measure of the remaining available gas? If so, what are they?

81. Use the following data and data from Appendix D to determine the quantity of heat needed to convert 15.0 g of solid mercury at -50.0 °C to mercury vapor at 25 °C. Specific heats: Hg(s), 24.3 J mol^{-1} K^{-1}; Hg(l), 28.0 J mol^{-1} K^{-1}. Melting point of Hg(s), -38.87 °C. Heat of fusion, 2.33 kJ mol^{-1}.

82. To vaporize 1.000 g water at 20 °C requires 2447 J of heat. At 100 °C, 10.00 kJ of heat will convert 4.430 g H_2O(l) to H_2O(g). Do these observations conform to your expectations? Explain.

83. Estimate how much heat is absorbed when 1.00 g of Instant Car Kooler vaporizes. Comment on the effectiveness of this spray in cooling the interior of a car. Assume the spray is 10% C_2H_5OH(aq) by mass, the temperature is 55 °C, the heat capacity of air is 29 J mol^{-1} K^{-1}, and use ΔH_{vap} data from Table 12.1.

84. Because solid *p*-dichlorobenzene, $C_6H_4Cl_2$, sublimes rather easily, it has been used as a moth repellent. From the data given, estimate the sublimation pressure of $C_6H_4Cl_2$(s) at 25 °C. For $C_6H_4Cl_2$: mp = 53.1 °C; vapor pressure of $C_6H_4Cl_2$(l) at 54.8 °C is 10.0 mmHg: $\Delta H_{fus} = 17.88$ kJ mol^{-1}; $\Delta H_{vap} = 72.22$ kJ mol^{-1}.

85. A 1.05-mol sample of H_2O(g) is compressed into a 2.61-L flask at 30.0 °C. Describe the point(s) in Figure 12-21 representing the final condition.

86. One handbook lists the sublimation pressure of *solid* benzene as a function of *Kelvin* temperature, T, as log P (mmHg) $= 9.846 - 2309/T$. Another handbook lists the vapor pressure of *liquid* benzene as a function of *Celsius* temperature, t, as log P (mmHg) $= 6.90565 - 1211.033/(220.790 + t)$. Use these equations to estimate the normal melting point of benzene, and compare your result with the listed value of 5.5 °C.

87. By the method used to graph Figure 12-13, plot ln P versus $1/T$ for liquid white phosphorus, and estimate (a) its normal boiling point and (b) its enthalpy of vaporization, ΔH_{vap}, in kJ mol^{-1}. Vapor pressure data: 76.6 °C, 1 mmHg; 128.0 °C, 10 mmHg; 166.7 °C, 40 mmHg; 197.3 °C, 100 mmHg; 251.0 °C, 400 mmHg.

88. Assume that a skater has a mass of 80 kg and that his skates make contact with 2.5 cm^2 of ice. (a) Calculate the pressure in atm exerted by the skates on the ice. (b) If the melting point of ice decreases by 1.0 °C for every 125 atm of pressure, what would be the melting point of the ice under the skates?

89. Estimate the boiling point of water in Leadville, Colorado, elevation 3170 m. To do this, use the barometric formula relating pressure and altitude: $P = P_0 \times 10^{-Mgh/2.303\,RT}$ (where P = pressure in atm; $P_0 = 1$ atm; g = acceleration due to gravity; molar mass of air, $M = 0.02896$ kg mol^{-1}; $R = 8.3145$ J mol^{-1} K^{-1}; and T is the Kelvin temperature). Assume the air temperature is 10.0 °C and that $\Delta H_{vap} = 41$ kJ mol^{-1} H_2O.

90. Inspection of the straight-line graphs in Figure 12-13 suggests that the graphs for benzene and water intersect at a point that falls off the page. At this point, the two liquids have the same vapor pressure. Estimate the temperature and the vapor pressure at this point by a calculation based on data obtainable from the graphs.

91. A cylinder containing 151 lb Cl_2 has an inside diameter of 10 in and a height of 45 in. The gas pressure is 100 psi (1 atm = 14.7 psi) at 20 °C. Cl_2 melts at −103 °C, boils at 35 °C, and has its critical point at 144 °C and 76 atm. In what state(s) of matter does the Cl_2 exist in the cylinder?

92. In acetic acid vapor, some molecules exist as monomers and some as dimers (see Figure 12-31). If the density of the vapor at 350 K and 1 atm is 3.23 g/L, what percentage of the molecules must exist as dimers? Would you expect this percent to increase or decrease with temperature?

93. A 685-mL sample of Hg(l) at 20 °C is added to a large quantity of liquid N_2 kept at its boiling point in a thermally insulated container. What mass of N_2(l) is vaporized as the Hg is brought to the temperature of the liquid N_2? For the specific heat of Hg(l) from 20 to −39 °C use 0.138 J g^{-1} $°C^{-1}$, and for Hg(s) from −39 to −196 °C, 0.126 J g^{-1} $°C^{-1}$. The density of Hg(l) is 13.6 g/mL, its melting point is −39 °C, and its enthalpy of fusion is 2.30 kJ mol^{-1}. The boiling point of N_2(l) is −196 °C, and its ΔH_{vap} is 5.58 kJ mol^{-1}.

94. Sketched here are two hypothetical phase diagrams for a substance, but neither of these diagrams is possible. Indicate what is wrong with each of them.

 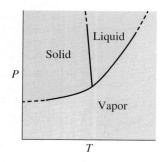

95. A chemistry handbook lists the following equation for the vapor pressure of NH_3(l) as a function of temperature. What is the normal boiling point of NH_3(l)?

$$\log_{10} P(\text{mmHg}) = 9.95028 - 0.003863T - \frac{1473.17}{T}$$

96. The triple point temperature of bismuth is 544.5 K and the normal boiling point is 1832 K. Imagine that a 1.00 mol sample of bismuth is heated at a constant rate of 1.00 kJ min^{-1} in an apparatus in which the sample is maintained under a constant pressure of 1 atm. In the manner shown in Figure 12-15 and as much to scale as possible, that is in terms of times and temperatures, sketch the heating curve that would be obtained in heating the sample from 300 K to 2000 K. Use the following data. ΔH_{fus} = 10.9 kJ mol^{-1} Bi(s); ΔH_{vap} = 151.5 kJ mol^{-1} Bi(l); average molar heat capacities, in J mol^{-1} K^{-1}, 28 for Bi(s), 31 for Bi(l), and 21 for Bi(g). [*Hint:* Under the conditions described, no vapor appears until the normal boiling point is reached.]

97. The crystal structure of lithium sulfide (Li_2S), is pictured here. The length of the unit cell is 5.88 × 10^2 pm. For this structure, determine

(a) the coordination numbers of Li^+ and S^{2-};
(b) the number of formula units in the unit cell;
(c) the density of Li_2S.

98. Refer to Figures 12-44 and 12-48. Suppose that the two planes of ions pictured in Figure 12-44 correspond to the top and middle planes of ions in the NaCl unit cell in Figure 12-48. If the X-rays used have a wavelength of 154.1 pm, at what angle θ would the diffracted beam have its greatest intensity? [*Hint:* Use $n = 1$ in equation (12.5).]

99. Use the analyses of a bcc structure on page 506 and the fcc structure in Exercise 126 to determine the percent voids in the packing-of-spheres arrangement found in the fcc crystal structure.

100. One way to describe ionic crystal structures is in terms of cations filling voids among closely packed anions. Show that in order for cations to fill the tetrahedral voids in a close packed arrangement of anions, the radius ratio of cation, r_c, to anion, r_a, must fall between the following limits $0.225 < r_c:r_a < 0.414$.

101. Use the unit cell of diamond in Figure 12-32(b) and a carbon-to-carbon bond length of 154.45 pm, together with other relevant data from the text, to calculate the density of diamond.

102. The enthalpy of formation of NaI(s) is −288 kJ mol^{-1}. Use this value, together with other data in the text, to calculate the lattice energy of NaI(s). [*Hint:* Use data from Appendix D also.]

103. Show that the formation of $NaCl_2$(s) is very unfavorable; that is, $\Delta H_f^\circ[NaCl_2(s)]$ is a large *positive* quantity. To do this, use data from Section 12-9 and assume that the lattice energy for $NaCl_2$ would be about the same as that of $MgCl_2$, −2.5 × 10^3 kJ mol^{-1}.

104. We cannot measure the second electron affinity of oxygen directly.

$$O^-(g) + e^- \rightarrow O^{2-}(g) \qquad EA_2 = ?$$

The O^{2-} ion can exist in the solid state, however, where the high energy requirement for its formation is offset by the large lattice energies of ionic oxides. **(a)** Show that EA_2 can be calculated from the enthalpy of formation and lattice energy of MgO(s), enthalpy of sublimation of Mg(s), ionization energies of Mg, bond energy of O_2, and EA_1 for O(g). **(b)** The lattice energy of MgO is −3925 kJ mol^{-1}. Combine this with other values in the text to estimate EA_2 for oxygen.

105. A crystalline solid contains three types of ions, Na^+, O^{2-}, and Cl^-. The solid is made up of cubic unit cells that have O^{2-} ions at each corner, Na^+ ions at the center of each face, and Cl^- ions at the center of the cells. What is the chemical formula of the compound? What are the coordination numbers for the O^{2-} and Cl^- ions? If the length of one edge of the unit cell is a, what is the shortest distance from the center of a Na^+ ion to the center of an O^{2-} ion? Similarly, what is the shortest distance from the center of a Cl^- ion to the center of an O^{2-} ion?

106. A certain mineral has a cubic unit cell with calcium at each corner, oxygen at the center of each face, and titanium at its body center. What is the formula of the mineral? An alternate way of drawing the unit cell has calcium at the center of each cubic unit cell. What are the positions of titanium and oxygen in such a representation of the unit cell? How many oxygen atoms surround a particular titanium atom in either representation?

107. Calculate the radius ratio (r_+/r_-) for CaF_2. Suggest an alternative structure to that shown in Figure 12-50 that better conforms to the radius ratio you compute.

Feature Problems

108. In a capillary rise experiment, the height (h) to which a liquid rises depends on the density (d) and surface tension (γ) of the liquid and the radius of the capillary (r). The equation relating these quantities and the acceleration due to gravity (g) is $h = 2\gamma/dgr$. The sketch provides data obtained with ethanol. What is the surface tension of ethanol?

$\rightarrow| \ |\leftarrow r = 0.50$ mm

$h = 1.1$ cm

$d = 0.789$ g/mL

109. We have learned that the enthalpy of vaporization of a liquid is generally a function of temperature. If we wish to take this temperature variation into account, we cannot use the Clausius–Clapeyron equation in the form given in the text (that is, equation 12.2). Instead, we must go back to the differential equation upon which the Clausius–Clapeyron equation is based and reintegrate it into a new expression. Our starting point is the following equation describing the rate of change of vapor pressure with temperature in terms of the enthalpy of vaporization, the difference in molar volumes of the vapor (V_g), and liquid (V_l), and the temperature.

$$\frac{dP}{dT} = \frac{\Delta H_{vap}}{T(V_g - V_l)}$$

Because in most cases the volume of one mole of vapor greatly exceeds the molar volume of liquid, we can treat the V_l term as if it were zero. Also, unless the vapor pressure is unusually high, we can treat the vapor as if it were an ideal gas; that is, for one mole of vapor, $PV = RT$. Make appropriate substitutions into the above expression, and separate the P and dP terms from the T and dT terms. The appropriate substitution for ΔH_{vap} means expressing it as a function of temperature. Finally, integrate the two sides of the equation between the limits P_1 and P_2 on one side and T_1 and T_2 on the other.

(a) Derive an equation for the vapor pressure of $C_2H_4(l)$ as a function of temperature, if $\Delta H_{vap} = 15,971 + 14.55\ T - 0.160\ T^2$ (in J mol^{-1}).

(b) Use the equation derived in (a), together with the fact that the vapor pressure of $C_2H_4(l)$ at 120 K is 10.16 Torr, to determine the normal boiling point of ethylene.

110. All solids contain defects or imperfections of structure or composition. Defects are important because they influence properties, such as mechanical strength. Two common types of defects are a missing ion in an otherwise perfect lattice, and the slipping of an ion from its normal site to a hole in the lattice. The holes discussed in this chapter are often called *interstitial sites*, since the holes are in fact interstices in the array of spheres. The two types of defects described here are called *point defects* because they occur within specific sites. In the 1930s, two solid-state physicists, W. Schottky and J. Fraenkel, studied the two types of point defects: A Schottky defect corresponds to a missing ion in a lattice, while a Fraenkel defect corresponds to an ion that is displaced into an interstitial site.

(a) An example of a Schottky defect is the absence of a Na^+ ion in the NaCl structure. The absence of a Na^+ ion means that a Cl^- ion must also be absent to preserve electrical neutrality. If one NaCl unit is missing per unit cell, does the overall stoichiometry change, and what is the change in density?

(b) An example of a Fraenkel defect is the movement of a Ag^+ ion to a tetrahedral interstitial site from its normal octahedral site in AgCl, which has a structure like NaCl. Does the overall stoichiometry of the compound change, and do you expect the density to change?

(c) Titanium monoxide (TiO) has a sodium chloride-like structure. X-ray diffraction data show that the edge length of the unit cell is 418 pm. The density of the crystal is 4.92 g/cm^3. Do the data indicate the presence of vacancies? If so, what type of vacancies?

111. In an ionic crystal lattice each cation will be attracted by anions next to it and repulsed by cations near it. Consequently the coulomb potential leading to the lattice energy depends on the type of crystal. To get the total lattice energy you must sum all of the electrostatic interactions on a given ion. The general form of the electrostatic potential is

$$V = \frac{Q_1 Q_2 e^2}{d_{12}}$$

where Q_1 and Q_2 are the charges on ions 1 and 2, d_{12} is the distance between them in the crystal lattice. and e is the charge on the electron.

(a) Consider the linear "crystal" shown below.

The distance between the centers of adjacent spheres is R. Assume that the blue sphere and the green spheres are cations and that the red spheres are anions. Show that the total electrostatic energy is

$$V = -\frac{Q^2 e^2}{d} \times \ln 2$$

(b) In general, the electrostatic potential in a crystal can be written as

$$V = -k_M \frac{Q^2 e^2}{R}$$

where k_M is a geometric constant, called the Madelung constant, for a particular crystal system under consideration. Now consider the NaCl crystal structure and let R be the distance between the centers of sodium and chloride ions. Show that by considering three layers of nearest neighbors to a central chloride ion, k_M is given by

$$k_M = \left(6 - \frac{12}{\sqrt{2}} + \frac{8}{\sqrt{3}} - \frac{6}{\sqrt{4}} \cdots \right)$$

(c) Carry out the same calculation for the CsCl structure. Are the Madelung constants the same?

Self-Assessment Exercises

112. In your own words, define or explain the following terms or symbols: (a) ΔH_{vap}; (b) T_c; (c) instantaneous dipole; (d) coordination number; (e) unit cell.

113. Briefly describe each of the following phenomena or methods: (a) capillary action; (b) polymorphism; (c) sublimation; (d) supercooling; (e) determining the freezing point of a liquid from a cooling curve.

114. Explain the important distinctions between each pair of terms: (a) adhesive and cohesive forces; (b) vaporization and condensation; (c) triple point and critical point; (d) face-centered and body-centered cubic unit cell; (e) tetrahedral and octahedral hole.

115. The magnitude of one of the following properties must always increase with temperature; that one is (a) surface tension; (b) density; (c) vapor pressure; (d) ΔH_{vap}.

116. Of the compounds HF, CH_4, CH_3OH, N_2H_4, and $CHCl_3$, hydrogen bonding is an important intermolecular force in (a) none of these; (b) two of these; (c) three of these; (d) all but one of these; (e) all of these.

117. A metal that crystallizes in the body-centered cubic (bcc) structure has a crystal coordination number of (a) 6; (b) 8; (c) 12; (d) any even number between 4 and 12.

118. A unit cell of an ionic crystal (a) shares some ions with other unit cells; (b) is the same as the formula unit; (c) is any portion of the crystal that has a cubic shape; (d) must contain the same number of cations and anions.

119. If the triple point pressure of a substance is greater than 1 atm, which two of the following conclusions are valid?
(a) The solid and liquid states of the substance cannot coexist at equilibrium.
(b) The melting point and boiling point of the substance are identical.
(c) The liquid state of the substance cannot exist.

(d) The liquid state cannot be maintained in a beaker open to air at 1 atm pressure.
(e) The melting point of the solid must be greater than 0 °C.
(f) The gaseous state at 1 atm pressure cannot be condensed to the solid at the triple point temperature.

120. In each of the following pairs, which would you expect to have the higher boiling point? (a) C_7H_{16} or $C_{10}H_{22}$; (b) C_3H_8 or $(CH_3)_2O$; (c) CH_3CH_2SH or CH_3CH_2OH.

121. One of the substances is out of order in the following list based on increasing boiling point. Identify it, and put it in its proper place: N_2, O_3, F_2, Ar, Cl_2. Explain your reasoning.

122. Arrange the following substances in the expected order of increasing melting point: KI, Ne, K_2SO_4, C_3H_8, CH_3CH_2OH, MgO, $CH_2OHCHOHCH_2OH$.

123. Is it possible to obtain a sample of ice from liquid water without ever putting the water in a freezer or other enclosure at a temperature below 0 °C? If so, how might this be done?

124. The phenomena in Figure 12-11 will be seen at the critical temperature only if the proper amount of liquid is placed in the sealed tube initially. Why should this be the case? What would you expect to see if too little liquid was present initially? If too much liquid was present?

125. The following data are given for CCl_4. Normal melting point, −23 °C; normal boiling point, 77 °C; density of liquid 1.59 g/mL; $\Delta H_{fus} = 3.28$ kJ mol^{-1}; vapor pressure at 25 °C, 110 Torr.
(a) What phases—solid, liquid, and/or gas—are present if 3.50 g CCl_4 is placed in a closed 8.21-L container at 25 °C?
(b) How much heat is required to vaporize 2.00 L of $CCl_4(l)$ at its normal boiling point?

126. The fcc unit cell is a cube with atoms at each of the corners and in the center of each face, as shown here. Copper has the fcc crystal structure. Assume an atomic radius of 128 pm for a Cu atom.

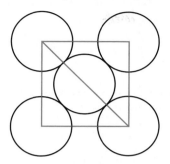

(a) What is the length of the unit cell of Cu?
(b) What is the volume of the unit cell?
(c) How many atoms belong to the unit cell?
(d) What percentage of the volume of the unit cell is occupied?
(e) What is the mass of a unit cell of copper?
(f) Calculate the density of copper.

127. Construct a concept map representing the different types of intermolecular forces and their origin.

128. Construct a concept map using the ideas of packing of spheres and the structure of metal and ionic crystals.

129. Construct a concept map showing the ideas contained in a phase diagram.

 # eMedia Exercises

130. Mixtures of liquids can at times be heated to separate the mixture into its individual components. **(a)** Making use of the **Equilibrium Vapor Pressure** simulation (*Activebook 12-2*), suggest the role of vapor pressure in this process. **(b)** Which two liquids in this simulation would be the easiest to separate? **(c)** Which two liquids would be the most difficult to separate? The separation of liquids by fractional distillation is discussed in Chapter 13.

131. In the **Vapor Pressure vs. Temperature** animation (*Activebook 12-2*), the equation relating vapor pressure and temperature is graphed. If actual data of pressure and temperature were given, describe how you would experimentally determine the constants A and B for different substances.

132. View the **Graphite, Diamond, and C_{60}** models of carbon (*Activebook 12-7*). Rotate the structure to view the directional nature of bonding in each form. Mechanical properties such as hardness can be related to the atomic scale bonding geometry. From these representations, suggest an order of increasing hardness for the three forms of carbon and justify your ordering with a discussion of local bonding in the solid.

133. View the animations of the cubic systems in the **Unit Cells** activity (*Activebook 12-8*). **(a)** Assuming that all the atoms in these structures have the same radius, which structure has the largest unit cell dimension? **(b)** Why aren't they the same?

 # eLaboratory Exercises

These exercises allow students to apply the concepts and skills for this chapter in the simulated laboratory of Virtual ChemLab. Worksheets for each of these exercises are found in the Virtual ChemLab Workbook in your MediaPak.

134. *(VCL 12-1) Heat of Vaporization of Water*
A graph of the vapor pressure of a liquid as a function of temperature has a characteristic shape that can be represented fairly accurately with the *Clausius–Clapeyron* equation. In this assignment you will measure the vapor pressure of water at several temperatures and use these data to estimate the heat of vaporization of water using the *Clausius–Clapeyron* equation.

135. *(VCL 12-2) The Boiling Point of Water at High Altitude*
The relationship between the equilibrium vapor pressure of a liquid or solid and temperature is given by the *Clausius–Clapeyron* equation. In this assignment you will measure the vapor pressure of water at a given temperature and use these data and the *Clausius–Clapeyron* equation to calculate the boiling point of water on the top of Mt. Denali in Alaska.

136. *(VCL 12-3) Heat of Fusion of Water*
The molar heat of fusion for a substance, ΔH_{fus}, is the heat required to transform one mole of the substance from the solid phase into the liquid phase. In this assignment you will use a simple coffee-cup calorimeter and a thermometer to measure the molar heat of fusion for water.

13

SOLUTIONS AND THEIR PHYSICAL PROPERTIES

The dissolving of a cube of sugar (sucrose) is seen here as swirls of a higher-density sucrose solution falling through the lower-density water.

Residents of cold climate regions know they must add antifreeze to the water in the cooling system of an automobile in the winter. The antifreeze–water mixture has a much lower freezing point than does pure water. In this chapter we will learn why.

To restore body fluids to a dehydrated individual by intravenous injection, pure water cannot be used. A solution with just the right value of a physical property known as osmotic pressure is necessary, and this requires a solution of a particular concentration of solutes. Again, in this chapter we will learn why.

Altogether, we will explore several solution properties whose values depend on solution concentration. Our emphasis will be on describing solution phenomena and their applications and explaining these phenomena at the molecular level.

13-1 TYPES OF SOLUTIONS: SOME TERMINOLOGY

In Chapters 1 and 4 we learned that a solution is a *homogeneous mixture*. It is *homogeneous* because its composition and properties are uniform, and it is a *mixture* because it contains two or more substances

TABLE 13.1 Some Common Solutions	
Solution	**Components**
Gaseous solutions	
Air	N_2, O_2, and several others
Natural gas	CH_4, C_2H_6, and several others
Liquid solutions	
Seawater	H_2O, NaCl, and many others
Vinegar	H_2O, $HC_2H_3O_2$ (acetic acid)
Soda pop	H_2O, CO_2, $C_{12}H_{22}O_{11}$ (sucrose), and several others
Solid solutions	
Yellow brass	Cu, Zn
Palladium–Hydrogen	Pd, H_2

 Remind students that air is 78% nitrogen, 21% oxygen and 1% other gases.

in proportions that can be varied. The **solvent** is the component that is present in the greatest quantity or that determines the state of matter in which a solution exists. Other solution components, called **solutes**, are said to be dissolved in the solvent. A *concentrated* solution has a relatively large quantity of dissolved solute(s), and a *dilute* solution has only a small quantity. Consider solutions containing sucrose (cane sugar) as one of the solutes in the solvent water: Pancake syrup is a concentrated solution, whereas a sweetened cup of coffee is much more dilute.

Although liquid solutions are most common, solutions can exist in gaseous and solid states as well. For instance, the U.S. five-cent coin, the nickel, is a solid solution of 75% Cu and 25% Ni. Solid solutions with a metal as the solvent are also called *alloys*.* Table 13.1 lists a few common solutions.

13-2 SOLUTION CONCENTRATION

In Chapters 4 and 5 we learned that to describe a solution fully we must know its *concentration*—a measure of the quantity of solute in a given quantity of solvent (or solution). The concentration unit we stressed in those chapters was molarity. In this section, we describe several methods of expressing concentration, each of which serves a different purpose.

MASS PERCENT, VOLUME PERCENT, AND MASS/VOLUME PERCENT

If we dissolve 5.00 g NaCl in 95.0 g H_2O, we get 100.0 g of a solution that is 5.00% NaCl, by *mass*. Mass percent is widely used in industrial chemistry. Thus, we might read that the action of 78% H_2SO_4(aq) on phosphate rock [3 $Ca_3(PO_4)_2 \cdot CaF_2$] produces 46% H_3PO_4(aq).

Because liquid volumes are so easily measured, some solutions are prepared on a *volume* percent basis. For example, a handbook lists a freezing point of −15.6 °C for a methyl alcohol–water antifreeze solution that is 25.0% CH_3OH, by volume. This solution is prepared by dissolving 25.0 mL CH_3OH(l) for every 100.0 mL of aqueous solution.

Another possibility is to express the *mass* of solute and *volume* of solution. An aqueous solution with 0.9 g NaCl in 100.0 mL of solution is said to be 0.9% NaCl (*mass/volume*). Mass/volume percent is extensively used in the medical and pharmaceutical fields.

---

*The term *alloy* can also apply to certain heterogeneous mixtures, such as the common two-phase solid mixture of lead and tin known as *solder*, or to intermetallic compounds, such as the silver–tin compound Ag_3Sn that, in the past, was mixed with mercury in *dental amalgam*.

KEEP IN MIND ▶
that 1 ppm = 1 mg/L,
1 ppb = 1 μg/L, and
1 ppt = 1 ng/L.

PARTS PER MILLION, PARTS PER BILLION, AND PARTS PER TRILLION

In solutions where the mass or volume percent of a component is very low, we often switch to other units to describe solution concentration. For example, 1 mg solute/L solution amounts to only 0.001 g/L. A solution that is this dilute will have the same density as water, approximately 1 g/mL; therefore, the solution concentration is 0.001 g solute/1000 g solution, which is the same as 1 g solute/1,000,000 g solution. We can describe the solute concentration more succinctly as 1 *part per million* (**ppm**). For a solution with only 1 μg solute/L solution, the situation is 1×10^{-6} g solute/1000 g solution, or 1.0 g solute/1×10^9 g solution. Here, the solute concentration is 1 *part per billion* (**ppb**). If the solute concentration is only 1 ng solute/L solution, the concentration is 1 *part per trillion* (**ppt**).

Because these terms are widely used in environmental reporting, they may be more familiar than other units that chemists use. For example, a consumer in California might read in an annual water quality report from the municipal water department that the maximum contaminant level allowed for nitrate ion is 45 ppm and for carbon tetrachloride, 0.5 ppb.

MOLE FRACTION AND MOLE PERCENT

To relate certain physical properties (such as vapor pressure) to solution concentration, we need a unit in which all solution components are expressed on a mole basis. We can do this with the mole fraction. The *mole fraction* of component i, designated x_i, is the fraction of all the molecules in a solution that are of type i. The mole fraction of component j is x_j, and so on. The mole fraction of a solution component is defined as

$$x_i = \frac{\text{amount of component } i \text{ (in moles)}}{\text{total amount of all solution components (in moles)}}$$

The sum of the mole fractions of all the solution components is 1.

$$x_i + x_j + x_k + \cdots = 1$$

The *mole percent* of a solution component is the percent of all the molecules in solution that are of a given type. Mole percents are mole fractions multiplied by 100%.

MOLARITY

In Chapters 4 and 5, we introduced molarity to provide a conversion factor relating the amount of solute and the volume of solution. We used it in various stoichiometric calculations. As we learned at that time,

$$\text{molarity (M)} = \frac{\text{amount of solute (in moles)}}{\text{volume of solution (in liters)}}$$

MOLALITY

Suppose we prepare a solution at 20 °C by using a volumetric flask calibrated at 20 °C. Then suppose we warm this solution to 25 °C. As the temperature increases from 20 to 25 °C, the amount of solute remains constant, but the solution volume increases slightly (by about 0.1%). The number of moles of solute per liter—the molarity—*decreases* slightly (by about 0.1%). This temperature dependence of molarity can be a problem in experiments demanding a high precision. That is, the solution might be used at a temperature different from the one at which it was prepared, and so its molarity is not exactly the one written on the label. A concentration unit that is *independent* of temperature, and also proportional to mole fraction in dilute solutions, is **molality** (*m*)—the number of moles of solute per kilogram of *solvent* (not of solution). A solution in which 1.00 mol of urea, $CO(NH_2)_2$, is dissolved in 1.00 kg of water is described as a 1.00 molal solution and designated as 1.00 *m* $CO(NH_2)_2$. Molality is defined as

$$\text{molality (}m\text{)} = \frac{\text{amount of solute (in moles)}}{\text{mass of solvent (in kilograms)}}$$

The concentration of a solution is expressed in several different ways in Example 13-1. The calculation in Example 13-2 is perhaps more typical: A concentration is converted from one unit (molarity) to another (mole fraction).

EXAMPLE 13-1

Expressing a Solution Concentration in Various Units. An ethanol–water solution is prepared by dissolving 10.00 mL of ethanol, C_2H_5OH ($d = 0.789$ g/mL), in a sufficient volume of water to produce 100.0 mL of a solution with a density of 0.982 g/mL (Fig. 13-1). What is the concentration of ethanol in this solution expressed as **(a)** volume percent; **(b)** mass percent; **(c)** mass/volume percent; **(d)** mole fraction; **(e)** mole percent; **(f)** molarity; **(g)** molality?

Solution

(a) Volume percent ethanol

$$\text{volume percent ethanol} = \frac{10.00 \text{ mL ethanol}}{100.0 \text{ mL solution}} \times 100\% = 10.00\%$$

(b) Mass percent ethanol

$$\text{mass ethanol} = 10.00 \text{ mL ethanol} \times \frac{0.789 \text{ g ethanol}}{1.00 \text{ mL ethanol}}$$

$$= 7.89 \text{ g ethanol}$$

$$\text{mass soln} = 100.0 \text{ mL soln} \times \frac{0.982 \text{ g soln}}{1.0 \text{ mL solution}} = 98.2 \text{ g soln}$$

$$\text{mass percent ethanol} = \frac{7.89 \text{ g ethanol}}{98.2 \text{ g solution}} \times 100\% = 8.03\%$$

(c) Mass/volume percent ethanol

$$\text{mass/volume percent ethanol} = \frac{7.89 \text{ g ethanol}}{100.0 \text{ mL solution}} \times 100\% = 7.89\%$$

(d) Mole fraction of ethanol
Convert the mass of ethanol from part (b) to an amount in moles.

$$? \text{ mol } C_2H_5OH = 7.89 \text{ g } C_2H_5OH \times \frac{1 \text{ mol } C_2H_5OH}{46.07 \text{ g } C_2H_5OH}$$

$$= 0.171 \text{ mol } C_2H_5OH$$

Determine the mass of water present in 100.0 mL of solution.

$$98.2 \text{ g soln} - 7.89 \text{ g ethanol} = 90.3 \text{ g water}$$

Convert the mass of water to the number of moles present.

$$? \text{ mol } H_2O = 90.3 \text{ g } H_2O \times \frac{1 \text{ mol } H_2O}{18.02 \text{ g } H_2O} = 5.01 \text{ mol } H_2O$$

$$x_{C_2H_5OH} = \frac{0.171 \text{ mol } C_2H_5OH}{0.171 \text{ mol } C_2H_5OH + 5.01 \text{ mol } H_2O} = \frac{0.171}{5.18} = 0.0330$$

(e) Mole percent ethanol

$$\text{mole percent } C_2H_5OH = x_{C_2H_5OH} \times 100\% = 0.0330 \times 100\% = 3.30\%$$

(f) Molarity of ethanol
Divide the number of moles of ethanol from part (d) by the solution volume, 100.0 mL = 0.1000 L.

$$\text{molarity} = \frac{0.171 \text{ mol } C_2H_5OH}{0.1000 \text{ L soln}} = 1.71 \text{ M } C_2H_5OH$$

— 10.00 mL C_2H_5OH

Volumetric Flask

— 100.0 mL —

Water

Ethanol–water solution:
$d = 0.982$ g/mL

▲ **FIGURE 13-1**
Preparation of an ethanol–water solution— Example 13-1 illustrated
A 10.00-mL sample of C_2H_5OH is added to some water in the volumetric flask. The solution is mixed, and more water is added to bring the total volume to 100.0 mL.

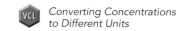
Converting Concentrations to Different Units

(g) Molality of ethanol
First, convert the mass of water present in 100.0 mL of solution [from part (d)] to the unit kg.

$$? \text{ kg H}_2\text{O} = 90.3 \text{ g H}_2\text{O} \times \frac{1 \text{ kg H}_2\text{O}}{1000 \text{ g H}_2\text{O}} = 0.0903 \text{ kg H}_2\text{O}$$

Use this result and the number of moles of C_2H_5OH from part (d) to establish the molality.

$$\text{molality} = \frac{0.171 \text{ mol C}_2\text{H}_5\text{OH}}{0.0903 \text{ kg H}_2\text{O}} = 1.89 \text{ } m \text{ C}_2\text{H}_5\text{OH}$$

Practice Example A: A solution that is 20.0% ethanol, by volume, is found to have a density of 0.977 g/mL. Use this fact, together with data from Example 13-1, to determine the mass percent ethanol in the solution.

Practice Example B: A 11.3-mL sample of CH_3OH ($d = 0.793$ g/mL) is dissolved in enough water to produce 75.0 mL of a solution with a density of 0.980 g/mL. What is the solution concentration expressed as **(a)** mole fraction H_2O; **(b)** molarity of CH_3OH; **(c)** molality of CH_3OH?

EXAMPLE 13-2

Converting Molarity to Mole Fraction. Laboratory ammonia is 14.8 M NH_3(aq) with a density of 0.8980 g/mL. What is x_{NH_3} in this solution?

Solution

In this problem we note that no volume of solution is stated, suggesting that our calculation can be based on any fixed volume of our choice. A convenient volume to work with is one liter. We need to determine the number of moles of NH_3 and of H_2O in one liter of the solution.

Find the number of moles of NH_3 using the definition of molarity.

$$\text{moles of NH}_3 = 1.00 \text{ L} \times \frac{14.8 \text{ mol NH}_3}{1 \text{ L}} = 14.8 \text{ mol NH}_3$$

For moles of H_2O, first find mass of the solution using solution density.

$$\text{mass of soln} = 1000.0 \text{ mL soln} \times \frac{0.8980 \text{ g soln}}{1.0 \text{ mL solution}} = 898.0 \text{ g soln}$$

Then use moles of NH_3 and molar mass to find the mass of NH_3.

$$\text{mass of NH}_3 = 14.8 \text{ mol NH}_3 \times \frac{17.03 \text{ g NH}_3}{1 \text{ mol NH}_3} = 252 \text{ g NH}_3$$

Find the mass of H_2O by subtracting the mass of NH_3 from the solution mass.

$$\text{mass of H}_2\text{O} = 898.0 \text{ g soln} - 252 \text{ g NH}_3 = 646 \text{ g H}_2\text{O}$$

Find moles of H_2O by multiplying by the inverse of the molar mass for H_2O.

$$\text{moles of H}_2\text{O} = 646 \text{ g H}_2\text{O} \times \frac{1 \text{ mol H}_2\text{O}}{18.02 \text{ g H}_2\text{O}} = 35.8 \text{ mol H}_2\text{O}$$

Find the mole fraction of ammonia x_{NH_3} by dividing moles NH_3 by the total number of moles of NH_3 and H_2O in the solution.

$$x_{NH_3} = \frac{14.8 \text{ mol NH}_3}{14.8 \text{ mol NH}_3 + 35.8 \text{ mol H}_2\text{O}} = 0.292$$

Practice Example A: A 16.00% aqueous solution of glycerol, $C_3H_5(OH)_3$, by mass, has a density of 1.037 g/mL. What is the mole fraction of $C_3H_5(OH)_3$ in this solution?

Practice Example B: A 10.00% aqueous solution of sucrose, $C_{12}H_{22}O_{11}$, by mass, has a density of 1.040 g/mL. What is **(a)** the molarity; **(b)** the molality; and **(c)** the mole fraction of $C_{12}H_{22}O_{11}$, in this solution?

CONCEPT ASSESSMENT ✓

Which of the several concentration units described in Section 13-2 are temperature-dependent and which are not? Explain.

13-3 INTERMOLECULAR FORCES AND THE SOLUTION PROCESS

If there is even a little water in the fuel tank of an automobile, the engine will misfire. This problem would not occur if water were soluble in gasoline. Why does water not form solutions with gasoline? We can often understand a process if we analyze its energy requirements; this approach can help us to explain why some substances mix to form solutions and others do not. In this section, we focus on the behavior of molecules in solution, specifically on intermolecular forces and their contribution to the energy required for the dissolution process.

ENTHALPY OF SOLUTION

In the formation of some solutions, heat is given off to the surroundings; in other cases, heat is absorbed. An enthalpy of solution, ΔH_{soln}, can be rather easily measured—for example, in the coffee-cup calorimeter of Figure 7-6—but why should some solution processes be exothermic, whereas others are endothermic?

Let's think in terms of a three-step approach to ΔH_{soln}. First, solvent molecules must be separated from one another to make room for the solute molecules. Some energy is required to overcome the forces of attraction between solvent molecules. As a result, this step should be an endothermic one: $\Delta H > 0$. Second, the solute molecules must be separated from one another. This step, too, will take energy and should be endothermic. Finally, we can imagine that we allow the separated solvent and solute molecules to be attracted to one another. These attractions will bring the molecules closer together and energy should be released. This is an exothermic step: $\Delta H < 0$. The enthalpy of solution is the sum of the three enthalpy changes just described, and depending on their relative values, ΔH_{soln} is either positive (endothermic) or negative (exothermic). This three-step process is summarized by equation (13.1) and Figure 13-2.

(a)	pure solvent	$\longrightarrow$ separated solvent molecules	$\Delta H_a > 0$
(b)	pure solute	$\longrightarrow$ separated solute molecules	$\Delta H_b > 0$
(c)	separated solvent and solute molecules	$\longrightarrow$ solution	$\Delta H_c < 0$

Overall: pure solvent + pure solute $\longrightarrow$ solution

$$\Delta H_{soln} = \Delta H_a + \Delta H_b + \Delta H_c \qquad (13.1)$$

◀ **FIGURE 13-2**
Enthalpy diagram for solution formation
The solution process can be endothermic (blue arrow), exothermic (red arrow), or has $\Delta H_{soln} = 0$ (black arrow), depending on the magnitude of the enthalpy change in the mixing step.

Remind students the difference between *intermolecular* and *intramolecular* forces.

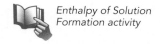

VCL Enthalpy of Solution: NH_4NO_3

Enthalpy of Solution Formation activity

Remind students that bond breaking processes are endothermic and bond forming processes are exothermic.

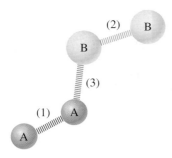

▲ FIGURE 13-3
Intermolecular forces in a solution
The intermolecular forces of attraction, represented here by springs, are between:
(1) solvent molecules, A–A;
(2) solute molecules, B–B; and (3) solvent and solute molecules, A–B.

INTERMOLECULAR FORCES IN MIXTURES

We see from equation (13.1) that the magnitude and sign of ΔH_{soln} depends on the values of the three terms ΔH_a, ΔH_b, and ΔH_c. These, in turn, depend on the strengths of the *three* kinds of intermolecular forces of attraction represented in Figure 13-3. Four possibilities for the relative strengths of these intermolecular forces are described in the discussion that follows.

1. If the intermolecular forces of attraction shown in Figure 13-3 are of the same type and of equal strength, the solute and solvent molecules mix randomly. A homogeneous mixture or solution results. Because properties of solutions of this type can generally be predicted from the properties of the pure components, they are called **ideal solutions**. There is no overall enthalpy change in the formation of an ideal solution from its components, and $\Delta H_{soln} = 0$. This means that ΔH_c in equation (13.1) is equal in magnitude and opposite in sign to the sum of ΔH_a and ΔH_b. Many mixtures of liquid hydrocarbons fit this description, or very nearly so (Fig. 13-4).

2. If forces of attraction between unlike molecules *exceed* those between like molecules, a solution also forms. The properties of such solutions generally cannot be predicted, however, and they are called *nonideal solutions*. Interactions between solute and solvent molecules (ΔH_c) release more heat than the heat absorbed to separate the solvent and solute molecules ($\Delta H_a + \Delta H_b$). The solution process is exothermic ($\Delta H_{soln} < 0$). Solutions of acetone and chloroform fit this type. As suggested by Figure 13-5, weak hydrogen bonding occurs between the two kinds of molecules, but the conditions for hydrogen bonding are not met in either of the pure liquids alone.*

3. If forces of attraction between solute and solvent molecules are *somewhat weaker* than between molecules of the same kind, complete mixing may still occur, but the solution formed is *nonideal*. The solution has a higher enthalpy than the pure components, and the solution process is endothermic. This type of behavior is observed in mixtures of carbon disulfide (CS_2), a nonpolar liquid, and acetone, a polar liquid. In these mixtures, the acetone molecules are attracted to other acetone molecules by dipole–dipole interactions and hence show a preference for other acetone molecules as neighbors. A possible explanation of how a solution process can be endothermic and still occur is found on page 538.

4. Finally, if forces of attraction between unlike molecules are *much weaker* than those between like molecules, the components remain segregated in a *heterogeneous mixture*. Dissolution does not occur to any significant extent. In a mixture of water and octane (a constituent of gasoline), strong hydrogen bonds hold water molecules together in clusters. The nonpolar

This article describes a laboratory experiment where students determine and compare the properties of ideal and nonideal solutions: Marshall, David B. et al. *J. Chem. Educ.* **1987**: *64*, 369.

▶ FIGURE 13-4
Two components of a nearly ideal solution
Think of the —CH_3 group in toluene **(b)** as a small "bump" on the planar benzene ring **(a)**. Substances with similar molecular structures have similar intermolecular forces of attraction.

(a)   **(b)**

*In most cases, H atoms bonded to C atoms cannot participate in hydrogen bonding. In a molecule like $CHCl_3$, however, the three Cl atoms have a strong electron-withdrawing effect on electrons in the C—H bond ($\mu = 1.01$ D). The H atom is then attracted to a lone pair of electrons on the O atom of $(CH_3)_2CO$ (but not to Cl atoms in other $CHCl_3$ molecules).

$$
\begin{array}{ccc}
\quad\text{Cl} & & \text{CH}_3 \\
\quad| & & | \\
\text{Cl}-\text{C}-\text{H}\cdots\text{O}=\text{C} \\
\quad| & & | \\
\quad\text{Cl} & & \text{CH}_3
\end{array}
$$

◀ **FIGURE 13-5**
Intermolecular force between unlike molecules leading to a nonideal solution
Hydrogen bonding between $CHCl_3$ (chloroform) and $(CH_3)_2CO$ (acetone) molecules produces forces of attraction between unlike molecules that exceed those between like molecules.

octane molecules cannot exert a strong attractive force on the water molecules, and the two liquids do not mix. Thus, we now have an answer to the question posed at the beginning of this section of why water does not dissolve in gasoline or vice versa.

As an oversimplified summary of the four cases described in the preceding paragraphs, we can say that "like dissolves like." That is, substances with similar molecular structures are likely to exhibit similar intermolecular forces of attraction and to be soluble in one another. Substances with dissimilar structures are likely not to form solutions. Of course, in many cases, parts of the structures may be similar and parts may be dissimilar. Then it is a matter of trying to establish which are the more important parts, a matter we explore in Example 13-3.

Remember that "like dissolves like."

EXAMPLE 13-3

Using Intermolecular Forces to Predict Solution Formation. Predict whether or not a solution will form in each of the following mixtures and whether the solution is likely to be ideal. **(a)** ethyl alcohol, CH_3CH_2OH, and water (HOH); **(b)** the hydrocarbons hexane, $CH_3(CH_2)_4CH_3$, and octane, $CH_3(CH_2)_6CH_3$; **(c)** octyl alcohol, $CH_3(CH_2)_6CH_2OH$, and water (HOH).

◀ **KEEP IN MIND**
that ideal or nearly ideal solutions are not too common. They require the solvent and solute(s) to be quite similar in structure.

Solution

(a) If we think of water as H—OH, ethyl alcohol is similar to water. (Just substitute the group CH_3CH_2— for one of the H atoms in water.) Both molecules meet the requirements of hydrogen bonding as an important intermolecular force. The strengths of the hydrogen bonds between like molecules and between unlike molecules are likely to differ, however. We should expect ethyl alcohol and water to form *nonideal* solutions.

(b) In hexane, the carbon chain is six atoms long, and in octane it is eight. Both substances are virtually nonpolar, and intermolecular attractive forces (of the dispersion type) should be quite similar both in the pure liquids and in the solution. We expect a solution to form and it should be nearly *ideal*.

▶ Butyl alcohol, $CH_3CH_2CH_2CH_2OH$, has a limited solubility in water (9 grams per 100 grams of water). The aqueous solubilities of alcohols fall off fairly rapidly as the hydrocarbon chain length increases beyond four.

Remind students that the enthalpy of solution for acetone-carbon disulfide is positive and therefore endothermic.

(c) At first sight, this case may seem similar to (a), with the substitution of a hydrocarbon group for a H atom in H—OH. Here, however, the carbon chain is *eight* members long. This long carbon chain is much more important than the terminal —OH group in establishing the physical properties of octyl alcohol. Viewed from this perspective, octyl alcohol and water are quite *dissimilar*. We do not expect a solution to form.

Practice Example A: Which of the following organic compounds do you think is most readily soluble in water? Explain.

(a) Toluene   **(b)** Oxalic acid   **(c)** Benzaldehyde

Practice Example B: In which solvent is solid iodine likely to be more soluble, water or carbon tetrachloride? Explain.

Are You Wondering . . .

What is the nature of intermolecular forces in a mixture of carbon disulfide and acetone?

Carbon disulfide is a nonpolar molecule, so in the pure substance the only intermolecular forces are weak London dispersion forces; carbon disulfide is a volatile liquid. Acetone is a polar molecule, and in the pure substance dipole–dipole forces are strong. Acetone is somewhat less volatile than carbon disulfide. In a solution of acetone in carbon disulfide (case 3 on page 534), the dipoles of acetone molecules polarize carbon disulfide molecules, giving rise to *dipole–induced dipole* interactions.

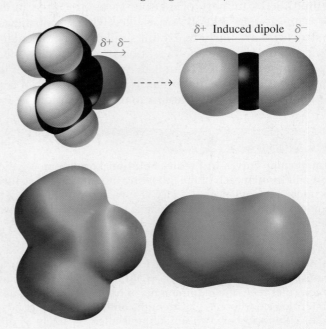

The dipole–induced dipole forces between acetone and carbon disulfide molecules are weaker than the dipole–dipole interactions among acetone molecules, causing the acetone molecules to be relatively less stable in their solutions with carbon disulfide than they are in pure acetone. As a result, acetone–carbon disulfide mixtures are nonideal solutions.

FORMATION OF IONIC SOLUTIONS

To assess the energy requirements for the formation of aqueous solutions of ionic compounds, we turn to the process pictured in Figure 13-6. Water dipoles are shown clustered around ions at the surface of a crystal. The negative ends of water dipoles are pointed toward the positive ions, and the positive ends of water dipoles toward negative ions. If these ion–dipole forces of attraction are strong enough to overcome the interionic forces of attraction in the crystal, dissolving will occur. Moreover, these ion–dipole forces also persist in the solution. An ion surrounded by a cluster of water molecules is said to be *hydrated*. Energy is *released* when ions become hydrated. The greater the hydration energy compared with the energy needed to separate ions from the ionic crystal, the more likely that the ionic solid will dissolve in water.

We can again use a *hypothetical* three-step process to describe the dissolution of an ionic solid. The energy requirement to dissociate a mole of an ionic solid into separated gaseous ions, an endothermic process, is the *negative* of the lattice energy. Energy is released in the next two steps—hydration of the gaseous cations and anions. The enthalpy of solution is the sum of these three ΔH values, described below for NaCl.

◄ We discussed lattice energy in Section 12-9.

$$NaCl(s) \longrightarrow Na^+(g) + Cl^-(g) \qquad \Delta H_1 = (-\text{lattice energy of NaCl}) > 0$$

$$Na^+(g) \xrightarrow{H_2O} Na^+(aq) \qquad \Delta H_2 = (\text{hydration energy of } Na^+) < 0$$

$$Cl^-(g) \xrightarrow{H_2O} Cl^-(aq) \qquad \Delta H_3 = (\text{hydration energy of } Cl^-) < 0$$

$$NaCl(s) \xrightarrow{H_2O} Na^+(aq) + Cl^-(aq) \qquad \Delta H_{\text{soln}} = \Delta H_1 + \Delta H_2 + \Delta H_3 \approx +5 \text{ kJ/mol}$$

Heats of solution: One should always add sulfuric acid slowly to water rather than the other way around. This should be explained in terms of the differential and integral heats of solution.

The dissolution of sodium chloride in water is *endothermic*, and this is also the case for the vast majority (about 95%) of soluble ionic compounds. Why does NaCl dissolve in water if the process is endothermic? It might appear that an endothermic process would not occur due to the increase in enthalpy.

Dissolution of NaCl in Water animation

A common misconception is that endothermic process cannot be spontaneous.

▲ **FIGURE 13-6**
An ionic crystal dissolving in water
Clustering of water dipoles around the surface of the ionic crystal and the formation of hydrated ions in solution are the key factors in the dissolution process.

Because NaCl does actually dissolve in water, there must be another factor involved. In fact, *two* factors must be considered in determining whether a process will occur spontaneously. Enthalpy change is only one of them. The other factor, called *entropy* (see page 782), concerns the natural tendency for microscopic particles—atoms, ions, or molecules—to spread themselves out in the space available to them. The dispersed condition of the microscopic particles in NaCl(aq) compared with pure NaCl(s) and H_2O(l) offsets the +5 kJ/mol increase in enthalpy in the solution process. In summary, if the hypothetical three-step process for solution formation is *exothermic*, we expect dissolution to occur; but we also expect a solution to form for an endothermic solution process, as long as ΔH_{soln} is not too large.

13-4 SOLUTION FORMATION AND EQUILIBRIUM

In the previous section, we described what happens at the molecular (microscopic) level when solutions form. In this section, we will describe solution formation in terms of phenomena that we can actually observe, that is, a macroscopic view.

Figure 13-7 suggests what happens when a solid solute and liquid solvent are mixed. At first, only dissolution occurs, but soon the reverse process of crystallization becomes increasingly important; and some dissolved atoms, ions, or molecules return to the undissolved state. When dissolution and crystallization occur at the same rate, the solution is in a state of dynamic equilibrium. The quantity of dissolved solute remains constant with time, and the solution is said to be a **saturated solution**. The concentration of the saturated solution is called the **solubility** of the solute in the given solvent. Solubility varies with temperature, and a solubility–temperature graph is called a *solubility curve*. Some typical solubility curves are shown in Figure 13-8.

If, in preparing a solution, we start with less solute than would be present in the saturated solution, the solute completely dissolves, and the solution is an **unsaturated solution**. On the other hand, suppose we prepare a saturated solution at one temperature and then change the temperature to a value at which the solubility is lower (this generally means a lower temperature). Usually, the excess solute crystallizes from solution, but occasionally all the solute may remain in solution. In these cases, because the quantity of solute is greater than in a saturated solution, the solution is said to be a **supersaturated**

▶ In some solutions, the solute and solvent are miscible (dissolve) in all proportions. The solution never becomes saturated. Ethyl alcohol–water solutions are an example of this.

(a)

(b)

(c)

▲ **FIGURE 13-7**
Formation of a saturated solution
The lengths of the arrows represent the rate of dissolution (↑) and the rate of crystallization (↓). **(a)** When solute is first placed in the solvent, only dissolution occurs. **(b)** After a time, the rate of crystallization becomes significant. **(c)** The solution is saturated when the rates of dissolution and crystallization become equal.

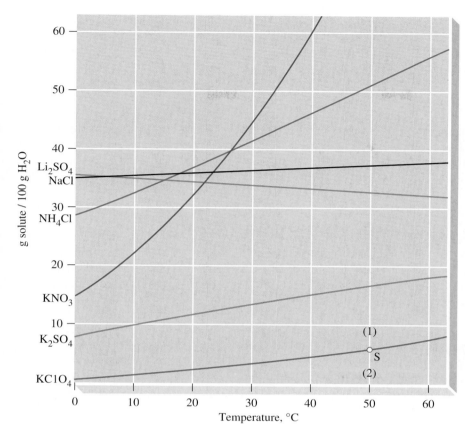

◀ **FIGURE 13-8**
Aqueous solubility of several salts as a function of temperature
Solubilities can be expressed in many ways: molarities, mass percent, or, as in this figure, grams of solute per 100 g H_2O. For each solubility curve (as shown here for $KClO_4$), points on the curve (S) represent saturated solutions. Regions above the curve (1) correspond to supersaturated solutions and below the curve (2), to unsaturated solutions.

solution. A supersaturated solution is unstable, and if a few crystals of solute are added to serve as particles on which crystallization can occur, the excess solute crystallizes. Figure 13-8 shows how unsaturated and supersaturated solutions can be represented with a solubility curve.

SOLUBILITY AS A FUNCTION OF TEMPERATURE

As a general observation, the solubilities of ionic substances (about 95% of them) *increase* with increasing temperature. Exceptions to this generalization tend to be found among compounds containing the anions SO_3^{2-}, SO_4^{2-}, AsO_4^{3-}, and PO_4^{3-}.

In Chapter 15, we will learn to predict how an equilibrium condition changes with such variables as temperature and pressure by using an idea known as *Le Châtelier's principle*. One statement of the principle is that heat added to a system at equilibrium stimulates the heat-absorbing, or endothermic, reaction. This suggests that when $\Delta H_{soln} > 0$, raising the temperature stimulates dissolving and *increases* the solubility of the solute. Conversely, if $\Delta H_{soln} < 0$ (exothermic), the solubility *decreases* with increasing temperature. In this case, crystallization—being endothermic—is favored over dissolving.

We must be careful in applying the relationship we just described. The particular value of ΔH_{soln} that establishes whether solubility increases or decreases with increased temperature is that associated with dissolving a small quantity of solute in a solution that is already very nearly saturated. In some cases, this heat effect is altogether different from what is observed when a solute is added to the pure solvent. For example, when NaOH is dissolved in water, there is a sharp increase in temperature—an *exothermic* process.

▲ **FIGURE 13-9**
Recrystallization of KNO_3
Colorless crystals of KNO_3
separated from an aqueous
solution of KNO_3 and $CuSO_4$
(an impurity). The pale blue
color of the solution is produced by Cu^{2+}, which remains in solution.

Explain that in growing
crystals such as $CuSO_4$, it is
important to have a clean,
dust-free solution to start with.
Heat up the solution and dissolve
as much solid as possible and then
cool the sample. If dirt or dust is
present, crystals form throughout
the whole beaker. If clean,
however, then it is possible to
create a supersaturated solution
from which one large crystal will
form by hanging a small crystal in
the solution.

KEEP IN MIND ▶

that fractional crystallization
works best when (1) the
quantities of impurities are
small and (2) the solubility
curve of the desired
solute rises steeply with
temperature.

This fact suggests that the solubility of NaOH in water should decrease as the
temperature is raised. What is observed, though, is that the solubility of
NaOH in water *increases* with increased temperature. This is because when a
small quantity of NaOH is added to a solution that is already nearly saturated,
heat is *absorbed*, not evolved.*

FRACTIONAL CRYSTALLIZATION

Compounds synthesized in chemical reactions are generally impure, but the
fact that the solubilities of most solids increase with increased temperature
provides the basis for one simple method of purification. Usually, the impure
solid consists of a high proportion of the desired compound and lesser proportions of the impurities. Suppose that both the compound and its impurities
are soluble in a particular solvent and that we prepare a concentrated solution
at a high temperature. Then we let the concentrated solution cool. At lower
temperatures, the solution becomes saturated in the desired compound. The
excess compound crystallizes from solution. The impurities remain in solution
because the temperature is still too high for these to crystallize.† This method
of purifying a solid, called **fractional crystallization**, or **recrystallization**, is
pictured in Figure 13-9. Example 13-4 illustrates how solubility curves can be
used to predict the outcome of a fractional crystallization.

EXAMPLE 13-4

Applying Solubility Data in Fractional Crystallization. A solution is prepared by
dissolving 95 g NH_4Cl in 200.0 g H_2O at 60 °C. **(a)** What mass of NH_4Cl will recrystallize when the solution is cooled to 20 °C? **(b)** How might we improve the yield of
NH_4Cl?

Solution

(a) Figure 13-8 shows that the solubility of NH_4Cl at 20 °C is 37 g
$NH_4Cl/100$ g H_2O. The quantity of NH_4Cl in the saturated solution at
20 °C is

$$200.0 \text{ g } H_2O \times \frac{37 \text{ g } NH_4Cl}{100 \text{ g } H_2O} = 74 \text{ g } NH_4Cl$$

The mass of NH_4Cl recrystallized is $95 - 74 = 21$ g NH_4Cl.

(b) The yield of NH_4Cl in (a) is rather poor—21 g out of 95 g, or 22%. We can
do better: (1) The solution at 60 °C, although concentrated, is not saturated. A saturated solution at 60 °C has 55 g $NH_4Cl/100$ g H_2O. Thus, the
95 g NH_4Cl requires less than 200.0 g H_2O to make a saturated solution.
At 20 °C, a smaller quantity of saturated solution would contain less
NH_4Cl than in (a), and the yield of recrystallized NH_4Cl would be
greater. (2) Instead of cooling the solution to 20 °C, we might cool it to 0
°C. Here the solubility of NH_4Cl is less than at 20 °C, and more solid
would recrystallize. (3) Still another possibility is to start with a solution
at a temperature higher than 60 °C, say closer to 100 °C. The mass of
water needed for the saturated solution would be less than at 60 °C. Note
that options (1) and (3) both require changing the conditions by using a
different amount of water from that originally specified.

Practice Example A: Calculate the quantity of NH_4Cl that would be obtained if
suggestions (1) and (2) in Example 13-4 (b) were followed.

[*Hint:* Use data from Figure 13-8. What mass of water is needed to produce a
saturated solution containing 95 g NH_4Cl at 60 °C?]

---

*The solid in equilibrium with saturated NaOH(aq) over a range of temperatures around 25 °C
is $NaOH \cdot H_2O(s)$. It is actually the temperature dependence of the solubility of this hydrate that
we have been discussing.
†This is the usual behavior, but at times, one or more impurities may form a solid solution with
the compound being recrystallized. In these cases simple recrystallization does not work as a
method of purification.

Practice Example B: Use Figure 13-8 to examine the solubility curves for the three potassium salts: $KClO_4$, K_2SO_4, and KNO_3. If saturated solutions of these salts at 40 °C are cooled to 20 °C, rank the salts in order of highest percent yield for the recrystallization.

13-5 SOLUBILITIES OF GASES

Why does a freshly opened can of soda pop fizz, and why does the soda go flat after a time? To answer questions like these requires an understanding of the solubilities of gases. As discussed in this section, the effect of temperature on the solubility of gases is generally different from that on solid solutes. Additionally, the pressure of a gas strongly affects its solubility.

EFFECT OF TEMPERATURE

We cannot make an all-inclusive generalization about the effect of temperature on the solubilities of gases in solvents. It is certainly true, though, that the solubilities of most gases in water *decrease* with an increase in temperature. This is true of $N_2(g)$ and $O_2(g)$—the major components of air—and of air itself (Fig. 13-10). This fact helps to explain why many types of fish can survive only in cold water. There is not enough dissolved air (oxygen) in warm water to sustain them.

For solutions of gases in organic solvents, the situation is often the reverse of that just described; that is, gases may become more soluble at higher temperatures. The solubility behavior of the noble gases in water is more complex. The solubility of each gas decreases with an increase in temperature, reaching a minimum at a certain temperature; then the solubility trend reverses direction, with the gas becoming more soluble with an increase in temperature. For example, for helium at 1 atm pressure, this minimum solubility in water comes at 35 °C.

▲ **FIGURE 13-10**
Effect of temperature on the solubilities of gases
Dissolved air is released as water is heated, even at temperatures well below the boiling point.

EFFECT OF PRESSURE

Pressure affects the solubility of a gas in a liquid much more than does temperature. The English chemist William Henry (1775–1836) found that *the solubility of a gas increases with increasing pressure*. A mathematical statement of **Henry's law** is

$$C = k \cdot P_{gas} \qquad (13.2)$$

  Simply take a bottle of a soft drink and open it. Have one warm and the other cold. Notice how the carbon dioxide is less soluble in the warm drink than the cold drink.

Henry's Law animation

In this equation, C represents the solubility of a gas in a particular solvent at a fixed temperature, P_{gas} is the partial pressure of the gas above the solution, and k is a proportionality constant. To evaluate the proportionality constant k, we need to have one measurement of the solubility of the gas at a known pressure and temperature. For example, the aqueous solubility of $N_2(g)$ at 0 °C and 1.00 atm is 23.54 mL N_2 per liter. The Henry's law constant, k, is

$$k = \frac{C}{P_{gas}} = \frac{23.54 \text{ mL } N_2/L}{1.00 \text{ atm}}$$

Suppose we wish to increase the solubility of the $N_2(g)$ to a value of 100.0 mL N_2 per liter. Equation (13.2) suggests that to do so, we must increase the pressure of $N_2(g)$ above the solution. That is,

$$P_{N_2} = \frac{C}{k} = \frac{100.0 \text{ mL } N_2/L}{(23.54 \text{ mL } N_2/L)/1.00 \text{ atm}} = 4.25 \text{ atm}$$

At times, we are required to change the units used to express a gas solubility at the same time that the pressure is changed. This variation is illustrated in Example 13-5.

It is possible to store many liters of $CO_2(g)$ in each liter of a carbonated drink. Oxygen dissolves sufficiently well in water for fish to live. However, when the decomposition of organic matter in water [as measured by the biological oxygen demand (BOD)] depletes the oxygen level, fish life may be threatened. Discuss diver's bends, which results from rapid expulsion of $N_2(g)$ dissolved in blood.

EXAMPLE 13-5

Using Henry's Law. At 0 °C and an O_2 pressure of 1.00 atm, the aqueous solubility of $O_2(g)$ is 48.9 mL O_2 per liter. What is the molarity of O_2 in a saturated water solution when the O_2 is under its normal partial pressure in air, 0.2095 atm?

Solution

Think of this as a two-part problem. (1) Determine the molarity of the saturated O_2 solution at 0 °C and 1 atm. (2) Use Henry's law in the manner just outlined.

Determine the molarity of O_2 at 0 °C when P_{O_2} = 1 atm.

$$\text{molarity} = \frac{0.0489 \text{ L O}_2 \times \dfrac{1 \text{ mol O}_2}{22.4 \text{ L O}_2 \text{ (STP)}}}{1 \text{ L soln}} = 2.18 \times 10^{-3} \text{ M O}_2$$

Evaluate the Henry's law constant.

$$k = \frac{C}{P_{\text{gas}}} = \frac{2.18 \times 10^{-3} \text{ M O}_2}{1.00 \text{ atm}}$$

Apply Henry's law.

$$C = k \times P_{\text{gas}} = \frac{2.18 \times 10^{-3} \text{ M O}_2}{1.00 \text{ atm}} \times 0.2095 \text{ atm} = 4.57 \times 10^{-4} \text{ M O}_2$$

Practice Example A: Use data from Example 13-5 to determine the partial pressure of O_2 above an aqueous solution at 0 °C known to contain 5.00 mg O_2 per 100.0 ml of solution.

Practice Example B: A handbook lists the solubility of carbon monoxide in water at 0 °C and 1 atm pressure as 0.0354 mL CO per milliliter of H_2O. What pressure of CO(g) must be maintained above the solution to obtain 0.0100 M CO?

▲ The unopened bottle of soda water is under a high pressure of $CO_2(g)$. When a similar bottle is opened, the pressure quickly drops and some of the $CO_2(g)$ is released from solution (bubbles).

We can rationalize Henry's law as follows: In a saturated solution, the rate of evaporation of gas molecules from solution and the rate of condensation of gas molecules into the solution are equal. Both of these rates depend on the number of molecules per unit volume. With increasing pressure on the system, the number of molecules per unit volume in the gaseous state increases (through an increase in the gas pressure), and the number of molecules per unit volume must also increase in the solution (through an increase in concentration). Figure 13-11 illustrates this rationalization.

We see a practical application of Henry's law in carbonated beverages. The dissolved gas is carbon dioxide, and the higher the gas pressure maintained above the soda pop, the more CO_2 that dissolves. When a bottle of soda is opened, some gas is released. As the gas pressure above the solution drops, dissolved CO_2 is expelled, usually fast enough to cause fizzing. In sparkling wines, the dissolved CO_2 is also under pressure, but rather than being added artificially as in soda pop, the CO_2 is produced by a fermentation process within the bottle.

▶ **FIGURE 13-11**
Effect of pressure on the solubility of a gas
The concentration of dissolved gas (suggested by the depth of color) is proportional to the pressure of the gas above the solution (suggested by the density of the dots).

Deep-sea diving provides us with still another example of Henry's law. Divers must carry a supply of air to breathe while underwater. If they are to stay submerged for any period of time, they must breathe compressed air. High-pressure air, however, is much more soluble in the blood and other body fluids than is air at normal pressures. When a diver returns to the surface, excess dissolved $N_2(g)$ is released as tiny bubbles from body fluids. When the ascent to the surface is made too quickly, N_2 diffuses out of the blood too quickly, causing severe pain in the limbs and joints, probably by interfering with the nervous system. This dangerous condition, known as "the bends," can be avoided if the diver ascends very slowly or spends time in a decompression chamber. Another effective method is to substitute a helium–oxygen mixture for compressed air. Helium is less soluble in blood than is nitrogen.

Henry's law (equation 13.2) fails for gases at high pressures; it also fails if the gas ionizes in water or reacts with water. For example, at 20 °C and with $P_{HCl} = 1$ atm, a saturated solution of HCl(aq) is about 20 M. But to prepare 10 M HCl, we do not need to maintain $P_{HCl} = 0.5$ atm above the solution, nor is $P_{HCl} = 0.05$ atm above 1 M HCl. We cannot even detect HCl(g) above 1 M HCl by its odor. The reason we cannot is that HCl ionizes in aqueous solutions, and in dilute solutions there are almost no molecules of HCl.

$$HCl\,(g) \xrightarrow{\;H_2O\;} H^+(aq) + Cl^-(aq)$$

Henry's law applies only to equilibrium between molecules of a gas and the same *molecules* in solution.

▲ To avoid the painful and dangerous condition of the bends, divers must not surface too quickly from great depths.

CONCEPT ASSESSMENT ✔

Do you think that Henry's law works better for solutions of HCl(g) in benzene, C_6H_6, than it does for solutions of HCl(g) in water? If so, why?

This article uses Henry's law to explain the noise associated with "cracking" knuckles: Kimbrough, Doris R. *J. Chem. Educ.* **1999:** *76*, 1509.

13-6 VAPOR PRESSURES OF SOLUTIONS

Separating compounds from one another is a task that chemists commonly face. If the compounds are volatile liquids, this separation often can be achieved by *distillation*. To understand how distillation works, we need to know something about the vapor pressures of solutions. This knowledge will also enable us to deal with other important solution properties, such as boiling points, freezing points, and osmotic pressures.

To simplify the following discussion we will consider only solutions with two components, solvent A and solute B. In the 1880s, the French chemist F. M. Raoult found that a dissolved solute *lowers* the vapor pressure of the solvent. **Raoult's law** states that the partial pressure exerted by solvent vapor above an ideal solution, P_A, is the product of the mole fraction of solvent in the solution, x_A, and the vapor pressure of the pure solvent at the given temperature, P_A°.

$$P_A = x_A P_A^\circ \tag{13.3}$$

Raoult's Law activity

Equation (13.3) relates to Raoult's observation that a dissolved solute lowers the vapor pressure of the solvent because, if $x_A + x_B = 1.00$, x_A must be less than 1.00, and P_A must be smaller than P_A°. Strictly speaking, Raoult's law applies only to ideal solutions and to all volatile components of the solutions. However, even in nonideal solutions, the law often works reasonably well for the *solvent* in *dilute* solutions, for example, solutions in which $x_{solv} > 0.98$. A more detailed discussion of Raoult's law requires the notion of entropy, which was briefly mentioned on page 538. Rather than attempt the explanation now, however, we will wait until Section 19-3, after we have said more about entropy.

CONCEPT ASSESSMENT ✓

An alternative statement of Raoult's law is that the fractional lowering of the vapor pressure of the solvent, $(P_A^\circ - P_A)/P_A^\circ$, is equal to the mole fraction of solute(s), x_B. Show that this statement is equivalent to equation (13.3).

EXAMPLE 13-6

Predicting Vapor Pressures of Ideal Solutions. The vapor pressures of pure benzene and pure toluene at 25 °C are 95.1 and 28.4 mmHg, respectively. A solution is prepared in which the mole fractions of benzene and toluene are both 0.500. What are the partial pressures of the benzene and toluene above this solution? What is the total vapor pressure?

Solution

We saw in Figure 13-4 that benzene–toluene solutions should be ideal. We expect Raoult's law to apply to both solution components.

▶ Because the mole fractions of the two components are both 0.500, the total vapor pressure is just the average of the vapor pressures of the two components. This is a very special case, however.

$$P_{benz} = x_{benz} P_{benz}^\circ = 0.500 \times 95.1 \text{ mmHg} = 47.6 \text{ mmHg}$$

$$P_{tol} = x_{tol} P_{tol}^\circ = 0.500 \times 28.4 \text{ mmHg} = 14.2 \text{ mmHg}$$

$$P_{total} = P_{benz} + P_{tol} = 47.6 \text{ mmHg} + 14.2 \text{ mmHg} = 61.8 \text{ mmHg}$$

Practice Example A: The vapor pressure of pure hexane and pentane at 25 °C are 149.1 mmHg and 508.5 mmHg, respectively. If a hexane–pentane solution has a mole fraction of hexane of 0.750, what are the vapor pressures of hexane and pentane above the solution? What is the total vapor pressure?

Practice Example B: Calculate the vapor pressures of benzene, C_6H_6, and toluene, C_7H_8, and the total pressure at 25 °C above a solution with equal *masses* of the two liquids. Use the vapor pressure data given in Example 13-6.

EXAMPLE 13-7

Calculating the Composition of Vapor in Equilibrium with a Liquid Solution. What is the composition of the vapor in equilibrium with the benzene–toluene solution of Example 13-6?

Solution

The ratio of each partial pressure to the total pressure is the mole fraction of that component in the vapor. (This is another application of equation 6.17.) The mole-fraction composition of the vapor is

$$x_{benz} = \frac{P_{benz}}{P_{total}} = \frac{47.6 \text{ mmHg}}{61.8 \text{ mmHg}} = 0.770$$

$$x_{tol} = \frac{P_{tol}}{P_{total}} = \frac{14.2 \text{ mmHg}}{61.8 \text{ mmHg}} = 0.230$$

Practice Example A: What is the composition of the vapor in equilibrium with the hexane–pentane solution described in Practice Example 13-6A?

Practice Example B: What is the composition of the vapor in equilibrium with the benzene–toluene solution described in Practice Example 13-6B?

LIQUID–VAPOR EQUILIBRIUM: IDEAL SOLUTIONS

The results of Examples 13-6 and 13-7, together with similar data for other benzene–toluene solutions, are plotted in Figure 13-12. This figure consists of four lines—three straight and one curved—spanning the entire concentration range.

The red line shows how the vapor pressure of benzene varies with the solution composition. Because benzene in benzene–toluene solutions obeys Raoult's law, the red line has the equation $P_{benz} = x_{benz}P^{\circ}_{benz}$. The blue line shows how the vapor pressure of toluene varies with solution composition and indicates that toluene also obeys Raoult's law. The dashed black line shows how the *total* vapor pressure varies with the solution composition. Can you see that each pressure on this black line is the sum of the pressures on the two straight lines that lie below it? Thus, point 3 represents the total vapor pressure (point 1 + point 2) of a benzene–toluene solution in which $x_{benz} = 0.500$ (recall Example 13-6).

As we calculated in Example 13-7, the vapor in equilibrium with a solution in which $x_{benz} = 0.500$ is richer still in benzene. The vapor has $x_{benz} = 0.770$ (point 4). The line joining points 3 and 4 is called a *tie line*. Imagine establishing a series of tie lines throughout the composition range. The vapor ends of these tie lines can be joined to form the green curve in Figure 13-12. From the relative placement of the liquid and vapor curves, we see that for ideal solutions of two components, *the vapor phase is richer in the more volatile component than is the liquid phase.*

> In general, the properties of an ideal binary liquid follow a direct (linear) relationship with mole fraction. This is seen with Raoult's law.

CONCEPT ASSESSMENT ✓

Describe a case in which the liquid and vapor curves in a diagram such as Figure 13-12 would converge into a single curve. Is such a case likely to exist?

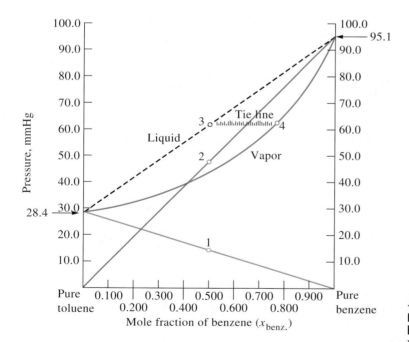

Vapor pressure of benzene
Vapor pressure of toluene
- - - - - - **Total vapor pressure (and liquid composition)**
Vapor composition

◀ **FIGURE 13-12**
Liquid–vapor equilibrium for benzene–toluene mixtures at 25 °C
In this diagram, partial pressures and the total pressure of the vapor are plotted as a function of the solution and vapor compositions.

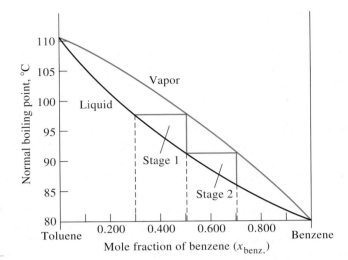

▶ **FIGURE 13-13**
Liquid–vapor equilibrium for benzene–toluene mixtures at 1 atm
In this diagram, the normal boiling points of solutions are plotted as a function of solution and vapor compositions.

FRACTIONAL DISTILLATION

Let's look at liquid–vapor equilibrium in benzene–toluene mixtures in a somewhat different way. Instead of plotting vapor pressures as a function of the solution and vapor compositions, let's plot normal boiling temperature—the temperature at which the *total* vapor pressure of the solution is 1 atm. The resulting graph is shown in Figure 13-13. This graph is useful in explaining **fractional distillation**, a procedure for separating volatile liquids from one another.

Notice that the graph starts at a high temperature—110.6 °C, the boiling point of toluene—and ends at a lower temperature—80.0 °C, the boiling point of benzene. This is the reverse of the situation in Figure 13-12. Also, the vapor curve lies above the liquid curve in Figure 13-13, not below, as is the case in Figure 13-12.

Figure 13-13 indicates that a benzene–toluene solution with $x_{benz} = 0.30$ boils at a temperature of 98.6 °C and is in equilibrium with a vapor in which $x_{benz} = 0.51$. Imagine extracting some of this vapor and cooling it to the point where it condenses to a liquid. The new liquid will have $x_{benz} = 0.51$ and represents the conclusion of stage 1 in Figure 13-13. Now imagine repeating the process, that is, vaporizing a solution with $x_{benz} = 0.51$ and condensing the vapor. The new liquid at the end of stage 2 has $x_{benz} = 0.71$. By repeating the cycle, the vapor becomes progressively richer in benzene. As pictured in Figure 13-14,

KEEP IN MIND ▶

that the placement of the two curves in liquid–vapor equilibrium diagrams is such that the vapor is richer in the more volatile component than is the liquid. The more volatile component is the one with the higher vapor pressure or lower boiling point.

▶ **FIGURE 13-14**
Fractional distillation
The fractionating column is packed with glass beads or stainless steel turnings. Initially, as vapor rises from the pot and encounters these cooler objects, it condenses to a liquid. As the beads or turnings heat up, the liquid–vapor equilibrium front moves progressively up the column. Soon, liquid–vapor equilibrium occurs throughout the column, but with the equilibrium temperature changing continuously from the hottest regions at the bottom of the column to the coolest at the top. The vapor emerging from the top of the column is condensed to a liquid in the water-cooled condenser. The first fraction collected contains the most volatile component (lowest boiling point). Later fractions are less volatile liquids. The least volatile (highest boiling point) components remain as a residue in the distillation pot.

boiling solutions in equilibrium with vapor can be spread out over a long column, called a *fractionating column*, in which the equilibrium temperatures range from lowest at the top of the column to highest at the bottom. The most volatile component in the solution emerges from the top of the column as a vapor that is condensed to a liquid and removed. The least volatile component concentrates in the pot at the bottom of the column. Fractional distillation of a solution of many volatile components, such as petroleum, can be carried out in such a way that the components are withdrawn from the top of the column and condensed, one by one.

LIQUID–VAPOR EQUILIBRIUM: NONIDEAL SOLUTIONS

We cannot construct a liquid–vapor equilibrium diagram for nonideal solutions in the simple manner illustrated in Figure 13-12. For example, vapor pressures in acetone–chloroform solutions are *lower* than we would predict for ideal solutions and boiling temperatures are correspondingly *higher*. In acetone–carbon disulfide solutions, on the other hand, vapor pressures are higher than predicted and boiling temperatures are correspondingly lower. In Figure 13-5, we saw that the forces of attraction between unlike molecules are greater than those between like molecules in acetone–chloroform mixtures. It is not unreasonable to expect the components in such solutions to show a reduced tendency to vaporize and to have lower-than-predicted vapor pressures. With acetone–carbon disulfide solutions, the situation is the reverse: Forces of attraction between unlike molecules are weaker than between like molecules. This leads to greater tendencies for vaporization and higher vapor pressures than predicted by Raoult's law.

If the departures from ideal solution behavior are sufficiently great, some solutions may have vapor pressures that pass through either a maximum or a minimum in vapor-pressure-composition graphs. Correspondingly, their boiling points pass through either a minimum or maximum in boiling-point-composition graphs. The solutions corresponding to these maxima or minima boil at a constant temperature and produce a vapor having the *same* composition as the liquid. These solutions are called **azeotropes**. The boiling-point diagram of a minimum boiling-point azeotrope is illustrated in Figure 13-15.

One of the most familiar azeotropes consists of 96.0% ethanol (C_2H_5OH) and 4.0% water, by mass, and has a boiling point of 78.174 °C. Pure ethanol has a boiling point of 78.3 °C. Dilute ethanol–water solutions can be distilled to produce the azeotrope, but the remaining water cannot be removed by ordinary distillation. As a result, most ethanol used in the laboratory or in industry is only 96.0% C_2H_5OH. To obtain absolute, or 100%, C_2H_5OH requires special measures.

▲ Fractional distillation is used in many industrial processes.

Point out that laboratory-grade 100% ethyl alcohol is obtained by distillation with benzene. Trace amounts of benzene are present, and benzene is both highly toxic and a carcinogen, and it should never be consumed. On the other hand, when ethyl alcohol is distilled from water, it is not possible to get more than 95% pure alcohol.

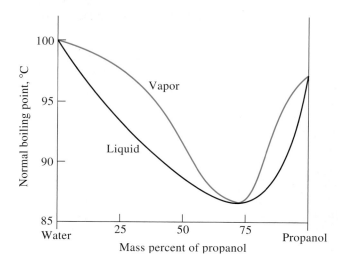

◀ **FIGURE 13-15**
A minimum boiling-point azeotrope
A solution of propanol in water having 71.69% $CH_3CH_2CH_2OH$ by mass—an azeotrope—has a lower boiling point than any other solution of these two components. In fractional distillation, solutions having *less* than 71.69% of the alcohol yield the azeotrope and water as ultimate products. Solutions with *more* than 71.69% of the alcohol yield the azeotrope and propanol. In each case, the azeotrope is drawn off through the condenser (Fig. 13-14), and the other component remains in the pot.

13-7   OSMOTIC PRESSURE

Up to this point in the chapter, the emphasis has been on solutions containing a volatile solvent and volatile solute. Another common type of solution is one with a volatile solvent, such as water, but one or more *nonvolatile* solutes, such as glucose, sucrose, or urea. Raoult's law still applies to the solvent in such solutions—the vapor pressure of the solvent is lowered.

Figure 13-16(a) pictures two aqueous solutions of a nonvolatile solute within the same enclosure. They are labeled A and B. The curved arrow indicates that water vaporizes from A and condenses into B. What is the driving force behind this? It must be that the vapor pressure of H_2O above A is greater than that above B. Solution A is more dilute; it has a higher mole fraction of H_2O. How long will this transfer of water continue? Solution A becomes more concentrated as it loses water, and solution B becomes more dilute as it gains water. When the mole fraction of H_2O is the same in both solutions, the *net* transfer of H_2O stops.

A related phenomenon occurs when $CaCl_2 \cdot 6\,H_2O(s)$ is exposed to air (Fig. 13-16b). Water vapor from the air condenses on the solid, and the solid begins to dissolve, a phenomenon known as *deliquescence*. For a solid to deliquesce, the partial pressure of water vapor in the air must be greater than the vapor pressure of water above a saturated aqueous solution of the solid. This requirement is often met for certain solids under conditions of appropriate relative humidity. The deliquescence of $CaCl_2 \cdot 6\,H_2O$ occurs when the relative humidity exceeds 32%. (Relative humidity was described on page 213.)

Like the case just described, Figure 13-17 also pictures the flow of solvent molecules. Here, however, the flow is not through the vapor phase. An aqueous sucrose (sugar) solution in a long glass tube is separated from pure water by a semipermeable membrane (permeable to water only). Water molecules

▶ **FIGURE 13-16**
Observing the direction of flow of water vapor
(a) Water passes, as vapor, from the more dilute solution (higher mole fraction of H_2O) to the more concentrated solution. **(b)** Water vapor in air condenses onto solid calcium chloride hexahydrate, $CaCl_2 \cdot 6\,H_2O$. The liquid water dissolves some of the solid. The eventual result could be an unsaturated solution.

(a)   (b)

▶ **FIGURE 13-17**
Osmosis
Water molecules pass through pores in the membrane and create a pressure within the funnel that causes the solution to rise and overflow. After a time, the solution inside the funnel becomes more dilute and the pure water outside becomes a sucrose solution. Liquid flow stops when the compositions of the solutions separated by the membrane have become nearly equal.

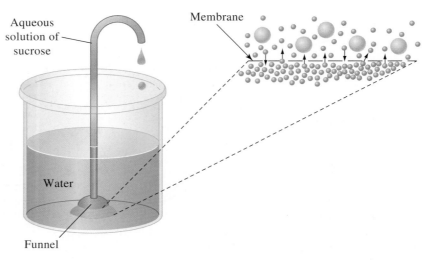

can pass through the membrane in either direction, and they do. But because the concentration of water molecules is greater in the pure water than in the solution, there is a net flow from the pure water into the solution. This net flow, called **osmosis**, causes the solution to rise in the tube. The more concentrated the sucrose solution, the higher the solution level rises.

Semipermeable Membrane activity

◄ Semipermeable membranes are materials containing submicroscopic holes, such as a pig's bladder, parchment, or cellophane. The holes permit the passage of solvent molecules but not those of the solute.

CONCEPT ASSESSMENT ✔

Describe the similarities and differences between the phenomena depicted in Figures 13-16(a) and 13-17.

Applying a pressure to the sucrose solution slows down the net flow of water across the membrane into the solution. With a sufficiently high pressure, the net influx of water can be stopped altogether. The necessary pressure to stop osmotic flow is called the **osmotic pressure** of the solution. For a 20% sucrose solution, this pressure is about 15 atm. The magnitude of osmotic pressure depends only on the number of solute particles per unit volume of solution. It does not depend on the identity of the solute. Properties of this sort, whose values depend only on the concentration of solute particles in solution and *not* on what the solute is, are called **colligative properties**. The following equation works quite well for calculating osmotic pressures of *dilute* solutions of nonelectrolytes. The osmotic pressure is represented by the symbol π, R is the gas constant (0.08206 L atm mol^{-1} K^{-1}); and T is the Kelvin temperature. The term n represents the amount of solute (in moles), and V is the volume (in liters) of solution. Notice that this equation is similar to the equation for the ideal gas law. In this case, however, it is convenient to rearrange terms to yield equation (13.4). The ratio, n/V, then, is the *molarity* of the solution, represented by the symbol M.

🔔 If you can get an intact sausage skin, fill it with a concentrated sugar solution and suspend it, like a balloon, in water. The sausage skin should expand and eventually burst. (Do NOT suggest the old experiment of pouring salt on a slug!)

✔ Vapor-pressure lowering, as expressed through Raoult's law for ideal solutions, is also a colligative property.

$$\pi V = nRT$$

$$\pi = \frac{n}{V}RT = \text{M} \times RT \qquad (13.4)$$

Osmosis and Osmotic Pressure animation

◄ The adjustment required to apply equation (13.4) to electrolyte solutions is discussed in Section 13-9.

EXAMPLE 13-8

Calculating Osmotic Pressure. What is the osmotic pressure at 25 °C of an aqueous solution that is 0.0010 M $C_{12}H_{22}O_{11}$ (sucrose)?

Solution

We just need to substitute the data into equation (13.4).

$$\pi = \frac{0.0010 \text{ mol} \times 0.08206 \text{ L atm mol}^{-1}\text{K}^{-1} \times 298 \text{ K}}{1 \text{ L}}$$

$$\pi = 0.024 \text{ atm (18 mmHg)}$$

Practice Example A: What is the osmotic pressure at 25 °C of an aqueous solution that contains 1.50 g $C_{12}H_{22}O_{11}$ in 125 mL of solution?

Practice Example B: What mass of urea [$CO(NH_2)_2$] would you dissolve in 225 mL of solution to obtain an osmotic pressure of 0.015 atm at 25 °C?

Determination of Molar Mass activity

The pressure difference of 18 mmHg that we calculated in Example 13-8 is easy to measure. (It corresponds to a solution height of about 25 cm.) This means that we can easily use the measurement of osmotic pressure for determining molar masses when we are dealing with very dilute solutions or solutes with high molar masses (or both). Example 13-9 shows how osmotic pressure measurements can be used to determine molar mass.

📖 This article describes the construction and use of a simple device to demonstrate osmosis: Morse, Joseph G. *J. Chem. Educ.* **1999**: *76*, 64.

EXAMPLE 13-9

Establishing a Molar Mass from a Measurement of Osmotic Pressure. A 50.00-mL sample of an aqueous solution contains 1.08 g of human serum albumin, a blood-plasma protein. The solution has an osmotic pressure of 5.85 mmHg at 298 K. What is the molar mass of the albumin?

Solution

Express osmotic pressure in atmospheres.

$$\pi = 5.85 \text{ mmHg} \times \frac{1 \text{ atm}}{760 \text{ mmHg}} = 7.70 \times 10^{-3} \text{ atm}$$

Modify the basic equation for osmotic pressure, by showing moles of solute (n) as the mass of solute (m) divided by its molar mass (M), and solve for M.

$$\pi V = nRT \qquad \pi V = \frac{m}{M} RT \qquad M = \frac{mRT}{\pi V}$$

Obtain the value of M by substituting the given data into the last equation above, ensuring that units cancel to yield g/mol as the unit for M.

$$M = \frac{1.08 \text{ g} \times 0.08206 \text{ L atm mol}^{-1} \text{ K}^{-1} \times 298 \text{ K}}{7.70 \times 10^{-3} \text{ atm} \times 0.0500 \text{ L}} = 6.86 \times 10^4 \text{ g/mol}$$

Practice Example A: Creatinine is a by-product of nitrogen metabolism and can be used to provide an indication of renal function. A 4.04-g sample of creatinine is dissolved in enough water to make 100.0 mL of solution. The osmotic pressure of the solution is 8.73 mmHg at 298 K. What is the molar mass of creatinine?

Practice Example B: What would be the osmotic pressure of a solution containing 2.12 g of human serum albumin in 75.00 mL of water at 37.0 °C? Use the molar mass determined in Example 13-9.

▲ **FIGURE 13-18**
Desalination of saltwater by reverse osmosis
The membrane is permeable to water but not to ions.
The normal flow of water is from side A to side B. If a pressure is exerted on side B that exceeds the osmotic pressure of the saltwater, a net flow of water occurs in the *reverse* direction—from the saltwater to the pure water. The lengths of the arrows suggest the magnitudes of the flow of water molecules in each direction.

PRACTICAL APPLICATIONS

Some of the best examples of osmosis are those associated with living organisms. For instance, if red blood cells are placed in pure water, the cells expand and eventually burst as a result of water that enters through osmosis. The osmotic pressure associated with the fluid inside the cell is equivalent to that of 0.92% (mass/volume) NaCl(aq). Thus, if cells are placed in a sodium chloride (saline) solution of this concentration, there is no net flow of water through the cell membrane, and the cell remains stable. Such a solution is said to be *isotonic*. If cells are placed in a solution with a concentration greater than 0.92% NaCl, water flows out of the cells, and the cells shrink. Such a solution is said to be *hypertonic*. If the NaCl concentration is less than 0.92%, the solution is *hypotonic*, and water flows into the cells. Fluids that are intravenously injected into patients to combat dehydration or to supply nutrients must be adjusted so that they are isotonic with blood. The osmotic pressure of the fluids must be the same as that of 0.92% (mass/volume) NaCl.

One recent application of osmosis goes to the very definition of osmotic pressure. Suppose in the device shown in Figure 13-18, we apply a pressure to the right side (side B) that is less than the osmotic pressure of the saltwater. The net flow of water molecules through the membrane will be from side A to side B, and

▶ A red blood cell in a hypertonic solution (left), an isotonic solution (center), and a hypotonic solution (right).

ordinary osmosis occurs. If we apply a pressure greater than the osmotic pressure to side B, we can cause a net flow of water in the *reverse* direction, from the saltwater into the pure water. This is the condition known as **reverse osmosis**. Reverse osmosis can be used in the *desalination* of seawater to supply drinking water for emergency situations or as an actual source of municipal water. Another application of reverse osmosis is the removal of dissolved materials from industrial or municipal wastewater before it is discharged into the environment.

▲ A small reverse-osmosis unit used to desalinize seawater.

13-8   FREEZING-POINT DEPRESSION AND BOILING-POINT ELEVATION OF NONELECTROLYTE SOLUTIONS

In Section 13-6 we examined the lowering of the vapor pressure of a solvent produced by a dissolved solute. Vapor pressure lowering is not measured as frequently as certain properties directly related to it. In Figure 13-19 the blue curves represent the vapor pressure, fusion, and sublimation curves in the phase diagram for a pure solvent. The red curves represent the vapor pressure and fusion curves of the solvent in a solution. The sublimation curve for the solid solvent that freezes from the solution is shown in purple. Two assumptions are implicit in Figure 13-19. One is that the solute is nonvolatile, the other is that the solid that freezes from a solution is pure solvent. For many mixtures, these requirements are easily met.*

The vapor pressure curve of the solution (red) intersects the sublimation curve at a lower temperature than is the case for the pure solvent. The solid–liquid fusion curve, because it originates at the intersection of the sublimation and vapor pressure curves, is also displaced to lower temperatures. Now recall how we establish normal melting points and boiling points in a phase diagram. They are the temperatures at which a line at $P = 1$ atm intersects the fusion and vapor pressure curves, respectively. Four points of intersection are highlighted in Figure 13-19—the freezing points and the boiling points of the pure solvent and of the solvent in a solution. The freezing point of the solvent in solution is *depressed*, and the boiling point is *elevated*.

The extent to which the freezing point is lowered or the boiling point raised is proportional to the mole fraction of solute (just as is vapor pressure lowering). In *dilute* solutions, the solute mole fraction is proportional to its molality, and so we can write

 Boiling Point Elevation and Freezing Point Depression activity

 Freezing Point Depression

 Boiling Point Elevation

$$\Delta T_f = -K_f \times m \tag{13.5}$$
$$\Delta T_b = K_b \times m \tag{13.6}$$

In Figure 13-19, the solid and vapor free energies do not change upon the addition of a solute to the liquid phase. However, adding solute to the liquid does lower the free energy of the solution. Hence, to reestablish equilibrium, the S–L and the L–V curves shift to respectively lower and higher T. This can be thought of as an example of Le Châtelier's principle.

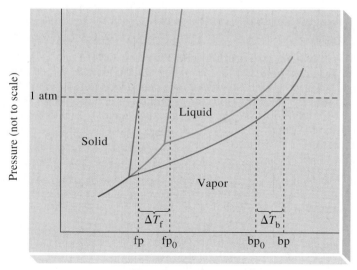

Temperature (not to scale)

◀ **FIGURE 13-19**
Vapor-pressure lowering by a nonvolatile solute
The normal freezing point and normal boiling point of the pure solvent are fp_0 and bp_0, respectively. The corresponding points for the solution are fp and bp. The freezing-point depression, ΔT_f, and the boiling-point elevation, ΔT_b, are indicated. Because the solute is assumed to be insoluble in the solid solvent, the sublimation curve of the solvent is unaffected by the presence of solute in the liquid solution phase. That is, the sublimation curve is the same for the two phase diagrams.

*Actually, the equation for freezing-point depression (13.5) applies even if the solute is volatile.

TABLE 13.2   Freezing-Point Depression and Boiling-Point Elevation Constants[a]

Solvent	Normal Freezing Point, °C	K_f, °C m^{-1}	Normal Boiling Point, °C	K_b, °C m^{-1}
Acetic acid	16.6	3.90	118	3.07
Benzene	5.53	5.12	80.10	2.53
Nitrobenzene	5.7	8.1	210.8	5.24
Phenol	41	7.27	182	3.56
Water	0.00	1.86	100.0	0.512

[a]Values correspond to freezing-point depressions and boiling-point elevations, in degrees Celsius, due to 1 mol of solute particles dissolved in 1 kg of solvent in an ideal solution.

KEEP IN MIND ▶

that freezing-point depression (ΔT_f) is defined as $T - T_f$, where T is the freezing point of the solution and T_f is the freezing point of the pure solvent, and similarly the boiling-point elevation (ΔT_b) is defined as $T - T_b$ where T_b is the boiling point of the pure solvent. So the need for the negative sign in equation (13.5) is evident.

In these equations, ΔT_f and ΔT_b are the freezing-point depression and boiling-point elevation, respectively; m is the solute molality; and K_f and K_b are proportionality constants. The value of K_f depends on the melting point, enthalpy of fusion, and molar mass of the solvent. The value of K_b depends on the boiling point, enthalpy of vaporization, and molar mass of the solvent. The units of K_f and K_b are °C m^{-1}, and you can think of their values as representing the freezing-point depression and boiling-point elevation for a 1 m solution. In practice, though, equations (13.5) and (13.6) often fail for solutions as concentrated as 1 m. Table 13.2 lists some typical values of K_f and K_b.

Historically, chemists have used the group of colligative properties—vapor pressure lowering, freezing-point depression, boiling-point elevation, and osmotic pressure—for molecular mass determinations. In Example 13-9, we showed how this could be accomplished with osmotic pressure. Example 13-10 shows how freezing-point depression can be used to determine a molar mass and, with other information, a molecular formula. To help you understand how this is done, we present a three-step procedure in the form of answers to three separate questions. In other cases, you should be prepared to work out your own stepwise procedure.

CONCEPT ASSESSMENT ✓

In what important way would Figure 13-19 change if it were based on the phase diagram of water rather than for the general case shown? Would a boiling-point elevation and a freezing-point depression still be expected?

 Molar Mass Determination by Freezing Point Depression

Molar Mass Determination by Boiling Point Elevation

This article describes a laboratory experiment where the molecular mass of urea is determined using boiling-point elevation: Thomas, N .C., Saisuwan, P. *J. Chem. Educ.* **1990:** *67*, 971.

EXAMPLE 13-10

Establishing a Molecular Formula with Freezing-Point Data. Nicotine, extracted from tobacco leaves, is a liquid completely miscible with water at temperatures below 60 °C. **(a)** What is the *molality* of nicotine in an aqueous solution that starts to freeze at −0.450 °C? **(b)** If this solution is obtained by dissolving 1.921 g of nicotine in 48.92 g H_2O, what must be the molar mass of nicotine? **(c)** Combustion analysis shows nicotine to consist of 74.03% C, 8.70% H, and 17.27% N, by mass. What is the molecular formula of nicotine?

Solution

(a) We can establish the molality of the nicotine by using equation (13.5) with the value of K_f for water listed in Table 13.2. Note that $T_f = -0.450$ °C, and that $\Delta T_f = -0.450$ °C − 0.000 °C = −0.450 °C.

$$\text{molality} = \frac{\Delta T_f}{-K_f} = \frac{-0.450 \text{ °C}}{-1.86 \text{ °C } m^{-1}} = 0.242 \ m$$

(b) Here we can use the definition of molality, but with a known molality (0.242 m) and an unknown molar mass of solute (M). The number of moles of solute is simply 1.921 g M^{-1}.

$$\text{molality} = \frac{1.921 \text{ g } M^{-1}}{0.04892 \text{ kg water}} = 0.242 \text{ mol (kg water)}^{-1}$$

$$M = \frac{1.921 \text{ g}}{(0.04892 \times 0.242) \text{ mol}} = 162 \text{ g/mol}$$

(c) To establish the empirical formula of nicotine, we need to use the method of Example 3-5. This calculation is left as an exercise for you to do. The result you should obtain is C_5H_7N. The formula mass based on this empirical formula is 81 u. The molecular mass obtained from the molar mass in part (b) is exactly twice this value—162 u. The molecular formula is twice C_5H_7N, or $C_{10}H_{14}N_2$.

Practice Example A: Vitamin B_2, riboflavin, is soluble in water. If 0.833 g of riboflavin is dissolved in 18.1 g H_2O, the resulting solution has a freezing point of -0.227 °C. **(a)** What is the molality of the solution? **(b)** What is the molar mass of riboflavin? **(c)** What is the molecular formula of riboflavin if combustion analysis shows it to consist of 54.25% C, 5.36% H, 25.51% O, and 14.89% N?

Practice Example B: An aqueous solution that is 0.205 m urea $[CO(NH_2)_2]$ is found to boil at 100.025 °C. Is the prevailing barometric pressure above or below 760.0 mmHg?

[*Hint:* At what temperature should the solution begin to boil if atmospheric pressure is 760.0 mmHg?]

Molar mass determination by freezing-point depression or boiling-point elevation has its limitations. Equations (13.5) and (13.6) apply only to dilute solutions of nonelectrolytes, usually much less than 1 m. This requires the use of special thermometers so that temperatures can be measured very precisely, say to ±0.001 °C. Because boiling points depend on barometric pressure, precise measurements require that pressure be held constant. As a consequence, boiling-point elevation is not much used. The precision of the freezing-point depression method can be improved by using a solvent with a larger K_f value than that of water. For example, for cyclohexane $K_f = 20.0$ °C m^{-1} and for camphor $K_f = 37.7$ °C m^{-1}.

◀ The adjustment required to apply these equations to electrolyte solutions is discussed in Section 13-9.

PRACTICAL APPLICATIONS

The typical automobile antifreeze is ethylene glycol, $C_2H_4(OH)_2$. It is a good idea to leave the ethylene glycol–water mixture in the cooling system at all times to provide all-weather protection. In summer, the ethylene glycol helps by raising the boiling point of water and preventing the cooling system from boiling over.

This article describes a melting point depression experiment using iodine and sulfur: DeMeo, Stephen. *J. Chem. Educ.* **1994**: *71*, 796.

▲ A typical aircraft deicer is propylene glycol, $CH_3CHOHCH_2OH$, diluted with water and applied as a hot, high-pressure spray.

▲ Water sprayed on citrus fruit releases its heat of fusion as it freezes into a layer of ice that acts as a thermal insulator. For a time, the temperature remains at 0 °C. The juice of the fruit, having a freezing point below 0 °C, is protected from freezing.

▲ Lowering the freezing point of water on roads.

In colder climates, using salt on roads produces two moles of particles for every one mole of salt. Although salt causes corrosion to automobiles, the roads, and the conduits buried under the roads, this substantial cost is offset by the dramatic reduction in death and injury, as well as fewer automobile repairs.

▶ Later in this section, we explain why the experimentally determined i for 0.0100 m NaCl is 1.94 instead of 2.

Citrus growers faced with an impending freeze know they must take preventive measures only if the temperature drops below 0 °C by several degrees. The juice in the fruit has enough dissolved solutes to lower the freezing point by a degree or two. The growers also know they must protect lemons sooner than oranges because lemons have a lower concentration of dissolved solutes (sugars) than do oranges.

Salts such as NaCl can be used to prepare a *slush bath*, a mixture used to cool or freeze something. One example is the mixture of ice and NaCl(s) used to freeze ice cream in a home ice-cream maker. Because the slush bath is at a temperature well below 0 °C, it is easy to freeze the sugar-and-milk mixture that makes up the ice cream. NaCl is also useful for deicing roads. It is effective in melting ice at temperatures as low as −21 °C (−6 °F). This is the lowest freezing point of a NaCl(aq) solution.

CONCEPT ASSESSMENT ✓

Why do you suppose that the freezing point of NaCl(aq) is depressed no further than −21 °C, regardless of how much more NaCl(s) is added to water?

13-9 SOLUTIONS OF ELECTROLYTES

The discussion of the electrical conductivities of solutions in Section 5-1 retraced some of the work done by the Swedish chemist Svante Arrhenius for his doctoral dissertation (1883). Prevailing opinion at the time was that ions form only with the passage of electric current. Arrhenius, however, reached the conclusion that ions exist in a solid substance and become dissociated from each other when the solid dissolves in water. Such is the case with NaCl, for example. In other cases, as with HCl, ions do not exist in the substance but are formed when it dissolves in water. In any case, electricity is not required to produce ions.

Although Arrhenius developed his theory of electrolytic dissociation to explain the electrical conductivities of solutions, he was able to apply it more widely. One of his first successes came in explaining certain anomalous values of colligative properties described by the Dutch chemist Jacobus van't Hoff (1852–1911).

ANOMALOUS COLLIGATIVE PROPERTIES

Certain solutes produce a greater effect on colligative properties than expected. For example, consider a 0.0100 m aqueous solution. The predicted freezing-point depression of this solution is

$$\Delta T_f = -K_f \times m = -1.86 \text{ °C } m^{-1} \times 0.0100 \text{ } m = -0.0186 \text{ °C}$$

We expect the solution to have a freezing point of −0.0186 °C. If the 0.0100 m solution is 0.0100 m urea, the measured freezing point is just about −0.0186 °C. If the solution is 0.0100 m NaCl, however, the measured freezing point is about −0.0361 °C.

Van't Hoff defined the factor i as the ratio of the measured value of a colligative property to the expected value if the solute is a nonelectrolyte. For 0.0100 m NaCl,

$$i = \frac{\text{measured } \Delta T_f}{\text{expected } \Delta T_f} = \frac{-0.0361 \text{ °C}}{-1.86 \text{ °C } m^{-1} \times 0.0100 \text{ } m} = 1.94$$

Arrhenius's theory of electrolytic dissociation allows us to explain different values of the van't Hoff factor i for different solutes. For solutes such as urea, glycerol, and sucrose (all nonelectrolytes), $i = 1$. For a strong electrolyte such as NaCl, which produces *two* moles of ions in solution per mole of solute dissolved, we would expect the effect on freezing-point depression to be twice as great as for a nonelectrolyte. We would expect that $i = 2$. Similarly, for $MgCl_2$,

Are You Wondering . . .

If there is a molecular interpretation of the freezing-point depression of a solvent by a solute?

When the solid and liquid phases of a pure substance coexist at a particular temperature, two processes occur. First, liquid molecules that collide with the solid sometimes are captured and added to the solid phase. At the same time, molecules on the surface of the solid sometimes become detached and enter the liquid phase. There is a state of dynamic equilibrium in which, at any given time, the number of molecules leaving the surface of the solid matches the number of molecules that enter the solid from the liquid phase. There is no net change even though individual molecules continue to move back and forth between the phases.

Now, imagine adding a solute to the liquid coexisting with its solid phase. In the solution formed above the solid phase, solute molecules replace some of the solvent molecules, and as a consequence, a given volume of solution contains a smaller number of solvent molecules than does the same volume of pure solvent. The dynamic equilibrium between liquid and solid solvent that existed in the pure solvent is disrupted since fewer solvent molecules in the liquid can get to the surface of the solid in a given time. The rate at which molecules leave the liquid phase is reduced and is no longer equal to the rate at which molecules leave the pure solid phase. However, cooling the solution restores the dynamic equilibrium because it simultaneously reduces the number of molecules that have sufficient energy to break away from the surface of the solid and increases the number of molecules in the liquid phase with sufficiently low kinetic energy to be captured by the solid. The lowered equilibrium temperature corresponds to the freezing-point depression.

Although this kinetic-molecular interpretation of freezing-point depression is an appealing one, the phenomenon is better described by the thermodynamic concept of entropy, which we will introduce in Chapter 19.

▲ **Svante Arrhenius (1859–1927)**
At the time Arrhenius was awarded the Nobel Prize in chemistry (1903), his results were described thus: "Chemists would not recognize them as chemistry; nor physicists as physics. They have in fact built a bridge between the two." The field of physical chemistry had its origins in Arrhenius's work.

| Equilibrium at freezing point of solvent | Equilibrium disrupted by solute added to solvent | Equilibrium restored at a lower temperature |

▲ Molecular view of freezing-point depression. The addition of solute to the liquid solvent does not change the rate of escape of molecules from the solid phase, but it does decrease the rate at which solvent molecules can enter the solid phase. The dynamic equilibrium between solid and liquid solvent is disrupted, and can be re-established only at a lower temperature.

 This article explains that *entropy change* is the reason for the vapor pressure lowering observed when a nonvolatile solute is added to a solvent: Peckham, Gavin D. *J. Chem. Educ.* **1998:** *75*, 787.

our expectation would be that $i = 3$. For the weak acid $HC_2H_3O_2$ (acetic acid), which is only slightly ionized in aqueous solution, we expect i to be slightly larger than one but not nearly equal to two.

This discussion suggests that equations (13.4), (13.5), and (13.6) should all be rewritten in the form

$$\pi = i \times M \times RT$$
$$\Delta T_f = -i \times K_f \times m$$
$$\Delta T_b = i \times K_b \times m$$

If these equations are used for nonelectrolytes, simply substitute $i = 1$. For strong electrolytes, predict a value of i as suggested in Example 13-11.

Pure water does not conduct electricity. So why should you be careful with electricity when near water? It is not the water, but the electrolytes that are dissolved in water.

EXAMPLE 13-11

Predicting Colligative Properties for Electrolyte Solutions. Predict the freezing point of aqueous 0.00145 m $MgCl_2$.

Solution

First determine the value of i for $MgCl_2$. We can do this by writing an equation to represent the dissociation of $MgCl_2$(s).

$$MgCl_2(s) \xrightarrow{H_2O} Mg^{2+}(aq) + 2 Cl^-(aq)$$

Because *three* moles of ions are obtained per mole of formula units dissolved, we expect the value $i = 3$.

Now use the expression

$$
\begin{aligned}
\Delta T_f &= -i \times K_f \times m \\
&= -3 \times 1.86\,°C\ m^{-1} \times 0.00145\ m \\
&= -0.0081\ °C
\end{aligned}
$$

The predicted freezing point is $-0.0081\ °C$.

Practice Example A: What is the expected osmotic pressure of a 0.0530 M $MgCl_2$ solution at 25 °C?

Practice Example B: You wish to prepare an aqueous solution that has a freezing point of -0.100 °C. How many milliliters of 12.0 M HCl would you use to prepare 250.0 mL of such a solution?

[*Hint:* Note that in a dilute aqueous solution, molality and molarity are essentially numerically equal.]

▶ Because the value of i for $MgCl_2$ is not exactly 3, we are not justified in carrying more than one or two significant figures in our answer.

(a)

(b)

▲ **FIGURE 13-20**
Interionic attractions in aqueous solution
(a) A positive ion in aqueous solution is surrounded by a shell of negative ions.
(b) A negative ion attracts positive ions to its immediate surroundings.

INTERIONIC ATTRACTIONS

Despite its initial successes, there were apparent deficiencies in Arrhenius's theory. The electrical conductivities of concentrated solutions of strong electrolytes are not as great as expected, and values of the van't Hoff factor i depend on the solution concentrations, as shown in Table 13.3. For strong electrolytes that exist completely in ionic form in aqueous solutions, we would expect $i = 2$ for NaCl, $i = 3$ for $MgCl_2$, and so on, regardless of the solution concentration.

These difficulties can be resolved with a theory of electrolyte solutions proposed by Peter Debye and Erich Hückel in 1923. This theory continues to view strong electrolytes as existing only in ionic form in aqueous solution, but the ions in solution *do not behave independently of one another*. Instead, each cation is surrounded by a cluster of ions in which anions predominate, and each anion is surrounded by a cluster in which cations predominate. In short, each ion is enveloped by an *ionic atmosphere* with a net charge opposite its own (Fig. 13-20).

TABLE 13.3 Variation of the van't Hoff Factor, i, with Solution Molality

Solute	Molality, m					
	1.0	0.10	0.010	0.0010	$\cdots$	Inf. dil.[a]
NaCl	1.81	1.87	1.94	1.97	$\cdots$	2
$MgSO_4$	1.09	1.21	1.53	1.82	$\cdots$	2
$Pb(NO_3)_2$	1.31	2.13	2.63	2.89	$\cdots$	3

[a]The limiting values: $i = 2, 2$, and 3 are reached when the solution is infinitely dilute. Note that a solute whose ions are singly charged (for example, NaCl) approaches its limiting value more quickly than does a solute whose ions carry higher charges. Interionic attractions are greater in solutes with more highly charged ions.

Are You Wondering . . .

How much you need to know about activities?

First, it is worth noting that in sufficiently dilute solutions, activity coefficients approximate one: Activities and stoichiometric concentrations are the same. In doing calculations, we will work only with stoichiometric concentrations because a quantitative treatment of activity coefficients is beyond the scope of this text. Mainly, you should be aware of the distinction between activity and stoichiometric concentration because it helps to explain a number of chemical phenomena, as we shall see again in a few other instances in the text.

In an electric field, the mobility of each ion is reduced because of the attraction or drag exerted by its ionic atmosphere. Similarly, the magnitudes of colligative properties are reduced. This explains why, for example, the value of i for 0.010 m NaCl is 1.94 rather than 2.00. What we can say is that each type of ion in an aqueous solution has two "concentrations." One is called the *stoichiometric concentration* and is based on the amount of solute dissolved. The other is the "effective" concentration, called the *activity*, which takes into account interionic attractions. Stoichiometric calculations of the type presented in Chapters 4 and 5 can be made with great accuracy using stoichiometric concentrations. However, no calculations involving solution properties are 100% accurate if stoichiometric concentrations are used. Activities are needed instead. The activity of a solution is related to its stoichiometric concentration through a factor called an *activity coefficient*. We will discuss the importance of activities in more detail in Chapters 14 and 19.

13-10   COLLOIDAL MIXTURES

In a mixture of sand and water, the sand (silica, SiO_2) quickly settles to the bottom of the container. Yet mixtures can be prepared containing up to 40% by mass of SiO_2, and the silica may remain dispersed in the aqueous medium for many years. In these mixtures, the silica is *not* present as ions or molecules. Rather, much larger particles of silica are present, though they are still submicroscopic in size. The mixture is said to be a **colloid**. To be classified *colloidal*, a material must have one or more of its dimensions (length, width, or thickness) in the approximate range of 1–1000 nm. If all the dimensions are smaller than 1 nm, the particles are of molecular size. If all the dimensions exceed 1000 nm, the particles are of ordinary, or macroscopic, size (even if they are visible only under a microscope). One method of determining whether a mixture is a true solution or a colloid is illustrated in Figure 13-21. When light passes through a true solution, an observer viewing from a direction perpendicular to the light

Point out that colloids are extremely important to the food industry. Gelatins are colloids, and many foods are colloidal mixtures on which the food industry spends considerable research effort to prevent their separation.

This article describes a demonstration of the Tyndall effect using an overhead projector: Goldsmith, Robert B. *J. Chem. Educ.* **1988:** *65, 623.*

◄ **FIGURE 13-21**
The Tyndall effect
The flashlight beam is not visible as it passes through a true solution (left), but it is readily seen as it passes through the colloidal dispersion of Fe_2O_3 (right).

▲ FIGURE 13-22
Surface of SiO₂ particle in colloidal silica
The points made in this simplified drawing are: (1) The SiO₂ particles are hydrated; (2) OH⁻ ions are preferentially adsorbed on the surface; (3) in the immediate vicinity of the particle, negative ions outnumber positive ions and the particle carries a net negative charge. Not illustrated here are the facts that some of the negative charge comes from silicate anions (for example, SiO_3^{2-}), and as a whole, the solution in which these particles are found is electrically neutral.

beam sees no light. In a colloidal dispersion, light is scattered in many directions and is readily seen. This effect, first studied by John Tyndall in 1869, is known as the *Tyndall effect.* A common example is the scattering of light by dust particles in a flashlight beam.

The particles in colloidal silica have a spherical shape. Some colloidal particles are rod-shaped, and some, like gamma globulin in human blood plasma, have a disc-like shape. Thin films, like an oil slick on water, are colloidal. And some colloids, such as cellulose fibers, are randomly coiled filaments.

What keeps the SiO₂ particles suspended in colloidal silica? The most important factor is that the surfaces of the particles *adsorb,* or attach to themselves, ions from the solution, and they preferentially adsorb one type of ion over others. In the case of SiO₂, the preferred ions that are adsorbed are OH⁻ (see Figure 13-22). As a result, the particles acquire a net negative charge. Having like charges, the particles repel one another. These mutual repulsions overcome the force of gravity, and the particles remain suspended indefinitely.

Although electric charge can be important in stabilizing a colloid, a high concentration of ions can also bring about the *coagulation,* or precipitation, of a colloid (Fig. 13-23). The ions responsible for the coagulation are those carrying a charge opposite to that on the colloidal particles. *Dialysis,* a process similar to osmosis, can be used to remove excess ions from a colloidal mixture. As suggested by Figure 13-24, molecules of solvent and molecules or ions of solute pass through a semipermeable membrane, but the much larger colloidal particles do not. In some cases, the process is more effective when carried out in an electric field. In *electrodialysis,* ions are attracted out of a colloidal mixture by an electrode carrying the opposite charge. A human kidney dialyzes blood, a colloidal mixture, to remove excess electrolytes produced by metabolic processes. Certain diseases cause the kidneys to lose this ability, but a dialysis machine, external to the body, can function for the kidneys.

Membrane

● Colloidal particles
• Other solute particles

◀ FIGURE 13-23
Coagulation of colloidal iron oxide
On the left is red colloidal hydrous Fe₂O₃, obtained by adding FeCl₃(aq) to boiling water. When a few drops of Al₂(SO₄)₃(aq) are added, the suspended particles rapidly coagulate into a precipitate of Fe₂O₃(s), as shown on right.

◀ FIGURE 13-24
The principle of dialysis
Water molecules, other solute molecules, and dissolved ions are all free to pass through the pores of the membrane (for example, a film of cellophane) in either direction. The direction of net flow of these species depends on their relative concentrations on either side of the membrane. Colloidal particles, however, cannot pass through the pores of the membrane.

TABLE 13.4 Some Common Types of Colloids

Dispersed Phase	Dispersion Medium	Type	Examples
Solid	Liquid	Sol	Clay sols,[a] colloidal silica, colloidal gold
Liquid	Liquid	Emulsion	Oil in water, milk, mayonnaise
Gas	Liquid	Foam	Soap and detergent suds, whipped cream, meringues
Solid	Gas	Aerosol[b]	Smoke, dust-laden air[c]
Liquid	Gas	Aerosol[b]	Fog, mist (as in aerosol products)
Solid	Solid	Solid sol	Ruby glass, certain natural and synthetic gems, blue rock salt, black diamond
Liquid	Solid	Solid emulsion	Opal, pearl
Gas	Solid	Solid foam	Pumice, lava, volcanic ash

[a]In water purification, it is sometimes necessary to precipitate clay particles or other suspended colloidal materials. This is often done by treating the water with an appropriate electrolyte. Clay sols are suspected of adsorbing organic substances, such as pesticides, and distributing them in the environment.
[b]Smogs are complex materials that are at least partly colloidal. The suspended particles are both solid and liquid. Other constituents of smog are molecular, for example, sulfur oxides, nitrogen oxides, and ozone.
[c]The bluish haze of tobacco smoke and the brilliant sunsets in desert regions are both attributable to the scattering of light by colloidal particles suspended in air.

Table 13.4 lists some common colloids, and as so aptly put by Wilder Bancroft, an American pioneer in the field of colloid chemistry, ". . . colloid chemistry is essential to anyone who really wishes to understand . . . oils, greases, soaps, . . . glue, starch, adhesives, . . . paints, varnishes, lacquers, . . . cream, butter, cheese, . . . cooking, washing, dyeing, . . . colloid chemistry is the chemistry of life."

▲ **Hemodialysis**
An artificial kidney machine cleaning the blood of patients with impaired kidney function.

Summary

13-1 Types of Solutions: Some Terminology—In a solution, the **solvent**—usually the component present in greatest amount—determines the state of matter in which the solution exists (Table 13.1). A **solute** is a solution component dissolved in the solvent. Dilute solutions contain relatively small amounts of solute and concentrated solutions, large amounts.

13-2 Solution Concentration—Any description of the composition of a solution must indicate the quantities of solute and solvent (or solution) present. Solution concentrations expressed as mass percent, volume percent, and mass/volume percent all have practical importance, as do the units, parts per million (**ppm**), parts per billion (**ppb**), and parts per trillion (**ppt**). However, the more fundamental concentration units are mole fraction, molarity, and molality. Molarity (moles of solute per liter of solution) is temperature dependent, but mole fraction and **molality** (moles of solute per kilogram of solvent) are not.

13-3 Intermolecular Forces and the Solution Process—Predictions about whether two substances will mix to form a solution involve knowledge of intermolecular forces between like and unlike molecules (Figs. 13-2 and

13-3). This approach makes it possible to identify an **ideal solution**, one whose properties can be predicted from properties of the individual solution components. Most solutions are nonideal.

13-4 Solution Formation and Equilibrium—Generally, a solvent has a limited ability to dissolve a solute. A solution containing the maximum amount of solute possible is a **saturated solution**. A solution with less than this maximum amount is an **unsaturated solution**. Under certain conditions a solution can be prepared that contains more solute than a normal saturated solution; such solutions are called **supersaturated**. **Solubility** refers to the concentration of solute in a saturated solution and depends on temperature. Graphs of solute solubility versus temperature (Fig. 13-8) can be used to devise conditions for recovering a pure solute from a solution of several solutes through **fractional crystallization** (**recrystallization**) (Fig. 13-9).

13-5 Solubilities of Gases—The solubilities of gases depend on pressure as well as temperature, and many familiar phenomena are related to gas solubilities. **Henry's law** (equation 13.2) relates the concentration of a gas in solution to its pressure above the solution.

◀ A chromatogram obtained in a laboratory drug test.

Chromatography is a technique for separating the components of a mixture present in one phase, called the *mobile phase*, as it moves relative to another phase, called the *stationary phase*. As originally conceived by the Russian botanist Mikhail Tsvett in 1903, the method is based on the ability of a column of finely powdered solid material, such as Al_2O_3 (the stationary phase), to *adsorb* substances from a solution (the mobile phase) allowed to trickle through it. In general, the attractive forces at the solid surface differ for different species in the solution. The substances that the solid adsorbs most strongly move through the stationary phase much more slowly than do those that are not so strongly adsorbed. This means that, although the various solution components start out together, they soon become separated when in contact with the stationary phase. Tsvett used this method to separate plant pigments into colored components. His column developed bands of color, and he named this separation technique **chromatography**.

(Coincidentally, in Greek, *chromatography* means "written in color," and in Russian, *tsvett* means color.)

You can demonstrate chromatography in a very simple way by replicating the experiment pictured in Figure 1-5c-d (page 7). Use a strip of chemistry filter paper (or a paper filter for an automatic coffee maker) as the stationary phase. Water is the mobile phase. Start the demonstration by placing a drop of black ink in the center of the paper strip just above the water level. Water is drawn up the paper by capillary action, dissolving the colored components of the ink as it passes through the ink spot. The components then become separated, based on differences in the strengths of the intermolecular forces between them and the cellulose in the paper.

Tsvett's method remained largely unknown until it was reintroduced by biochemists in the 1930s. This first form of chromatography is known as *adsorption chromatography*. In 1942, Archer Martin and Richard Synge used a liquid adsorbed on a solid as the stationary phase, and another liquid immiscible with the stationary phase as the mobile phase. With this technique, called *liquid–liquid partition chromatography*, the components being separated distribute themselves between the two liquid phases. In 1952, Martin and A. T. James substituted a gas for the liquid mobile phase and thus introduced *gas–liquid partition chromatography*. The effectiveness of liquid–liquid partition chromatography was greatly increased in the 1970s through the use of smaller particles for the solid support and pumps to force the mobile phase through the stationary phase under high pressure. This method is known as *high performance liquid chromatography* (HPLC). More recently, methods have been

---

13-6 Vapor Pressures of Solutions—The vapor pressure of a solution depends on the vapor pressures of its pure components. If the solution is ideal, **Raoult's law** (equation 13.3) can be used to calculate the solution vapor pressure. Liquid–vapor equilibrium curves showing either solution vapor pressures (Fig. 13-12) or solution boiling points (Fig. 13-13) as a function of solution composition help us to visualize **fractional distillation**, a common method of separating the volatile components of a solution. Such curves also illustrate the formation of azeotropes in some nonideal solutions. **Azeotropes** are solutions that boil at a constant temperature and produce vapor of the same composition as the liquid; they have boiling points that in some cases are greater than the boiling points of the pure components and in some cases, less (Fig. 13-15).

13-7 Osmotic Pressure—**Osmosis** is the spontaneous flow of solvent through a semipermeable membrane separating two solutions of different concentration. The net flow is from the less to the more concentrated solution (Fig. 13-17). Osmotic flow can be stopped by applying a pressure, called the **osmotic pressure**, to the more concentrated solution. In **reverse osmosis**, the direction of flow is

reversed by applying a pressure that exceeds the osmotic pressure to the more concentrated solution. Both osmosis and reverse osmosis have important practical applications. Osmotic pressure can be calculated with a simple relationship (equation 13.4) resembling the ideal gas equation. **Colligative properties** are certain properties that depend only on the concentration of solute particles in a solution, and not on the identity of the solute. Vapor-pressure lowering (Section 13-6) is one such property, and osmotic pressure is another.

13-8 Freezing-Point Depression and Boiling-Point Elevation of Nonelectrolyte Solutions—Freezing-point depression and boiling-point elevation (Fig. 13-19) are colligative properties having many familiar practical applications. For reasonably dilute solutions, their values are proportional to the molality of the solution (equations 13.5 and 13.6). The proportionality constants are K_f and K_b, respectively (Table 13.2). Historically, freezing-point depression was a common method for determining molar masses.

13-9 Solutions of Electrolytes—Calculating colligative properties of electrolyte solutions is more difficult than for solutions of nonelectrolytes. The solute particles in electrolyte solutions are ions or ions and molecules. Calculadeveloped that use supercritical fluids as the mobile phases—*supercritical fluid chromatography* (SFC). With the various chromatographic techniques now available, it is possible to separate components in solid, liquid, or gaseous mixtures of organic, inorganic, or biological compounds and to detect components in the range of parts per billion or even parts per trillion. The effectiveness of chromatography is even greater when the chromatograph is combined with another instrument. For example, in the combination of gas chromatography and mass spectrometry (GC–MS), the effluent from the gas chromatograph column is passed into a mass spectrometer for analysis. Figure 13-25 is a *chromatogram*—the data output—of a gas chromatography experiment.

◄ **FIGURE 13-25**
A typical gas chromatogram
The times plotted here are called *retention times*. A retention time for a component in a mixture is the time that elapses between injection of the sample into the chromatographic column and the appearance of that component at the detector. In the hydrocarbon mixture represented here, retention times tend to increase with increasing molecular mass of the components because intermolecular forces of the dispersion type also increase with increasing molecular mass.

tions using equations (13.5) and (13.6) must be based on the total number of particles present, and the van't Hoff factor is introduced into these equations to reflect this number. In all but the most dilute solutions, composition must be in terms of activities—effective concentrations that take into account interionic forces.

13-10 Colloidal Mixtures—Colloids are an important intermediate state between a true solution and a heterogeneous mixture. Colloidal mixtures are responsible for some unusual phenomena (Fig. 13-21) and are encountered in a broad range of contexts, from fluids in living organisms to pollutants in large air masses (Table 13.4).

Integrative Example

A 50.00-g sample of a solution of naphthalene $[C_{10}H_8(s)]$ in benzene $[C_6H_6(l)]$ has a freezing point of 4.45 °C. Calculate the mass percent $C_{10}H_8$ and the boiling point of this solution.

Strategy

Equation (13.5) relates freezing-point depression to the molality of a solution, but we will have to devise an algebraic method that yields the mass of each solution component and consequently the mass percent composition. The boiling point of the solution can be determined with a minimum of calculation through equation (13.6).

Solution

Substitute data for benzene from Table 13.2 ($K_f = 5.12$ °C m^{-1}, fp = 5.53 °C) and the measured freezing point of the solution into equation (13.5), to obtain

$$\Delta T_f = -K_f \times m$$
$$(4.45 - 5.53) \text{ °C} = -5.12 \text{ kg mol}^{-1} \text{ °C} \times m$$
$$1.08 = 5.12 \text{ kg mol}^{-1} \times m$$

Express the molality of the solution in terms of the masses of naphthalene, x, and benzene, y, and the molar mass, 128.2 g $C_{10}H_8$/mol.

$$m = \dfrac{\dfrac{x \text{ g } C_{10}H_8}{128.2 \text{ g } C_{10}H_8/\text{mol}}}{y \text{ g } C_6H_6 \times 1 \text{ kg}/1000 \text{ g } C_6H_6}$$

Since $x + y = 50.00$ g, the above expression reduces to

$$m = \dfrac{(x/128.2)}{(50.00 - x)/1000} \text{ mol kg}^{-1}$$

Now, substituting this expression of m into the expression derived from equation (13.5), we obtain

$$1.08 = 5.12 \times \dfrac{(x/128.2)}{(50.00 - x)/1000}$$

which we solve for x, the mass of naphthalene in grams.

$$\dfrac{1.08 \times 128.2}{5.12 \times 1000} = \dfrac{x}{50.00 - x}$$

$$0.0270 = \dfrac{x}{50.00 - x}$$

$$1.0270x = 0.0270 \times 50.00$$

$$x = 1.31$$

The mass percent naphthalene in the solution is

$$\%C_{10}H_8 = \dfrac{1.31 \text{ g } C_{10}H_8}{50.00 \text{ g soln}} \times 100\% = 2.62\%$$

A simple way to find the boiling point of the solution is to first solve equation (13.5) for the molality of the solution.

$$\text{molality} = \dfrac{\Delta T_f}{-K_f} = \dfrac{-1.08 \text{ °C}}{-5.12 \text{ °C } m^{-1}} = 0.211 \text{ } m$$

Because the molality at the boiling point is the same as at the freezing point, substitute 0.211 m into equation (13.6) and solve for ΔT_b.

$$\Delta T_b = K_b \times m = 2.53 \text{ °C } m^{-1} \times 0.211 \text{ } m = 0.534 \text{ °C}$$

The boiling point of the solution is 0.534 °C higher than the normal boiling point of benzene (80.10 °C), that is,

$$80.10 \text{ °C} + 0.53 \text{ °C} = 80.63 \text{ °C}$$

Assessment
The mass of solution can easily be determined to the nearest 0.01 g and expressed with four significant figures. The freezing point of the solution can also be established to the nearest 0.01 °C with good precision. However, the freezing point depression (−1.08 °C), the difference between two numbers of comparable magnitude, is valid only to about one part per hundred. Although significant-figure rules permit three significant figures in the remainder of the calculation, the actual precision of the calculated quantities is still only about one part per hundred. The final estimate of the boiling point (80.63 °C) seems reasonably good since it required expressing ΔT_b only to two significant figures. We assume that the 0.211 m solution is dilute enough and close enough to ideal in behavior to make equations (13.5) and (13.6) applicable.

Exercises

Homogeneous and Heterogeneous Mixtures

1. Which of the following do you expect to be most water soluble, and why? $C_{10}H_8$(s), NH_2OH(s), C_6H_6(l), $CaCO_3$(s).
2. Which one of the following do you expect to be moderately soluble both in water and in benzene [C_6H_6(l)], and why? **(a)** butyl alcohol, C_4H_9OH; **(b)** naphthalene, $C_{10}H_8$; **(c)** hexane, C_6H_{14}; **(d)** NaCl(s).
3. Substances that dissolve in water generally do not dissolve in benzene. Some substances are moderately soluble in both solvents, however. One of the following is such a substance. Which do you think it is and why?

(a) *para*-Dichlorobenzene
(a moth repellent)

(b) Salicyl alcohol
(a local anesthetic)

(c) Diphenyl
(a heat transfer agent)

(d) Hydroxyacetic acid
(used in textile dyeing)

4. Some vitamins are water soluble and some are fat soluble. (Fats are substances whose molecules have long hydrocarbon chains.) The structural formulas of two vitamins are shown here—one is water soluble and one is fat soluble. Identify which is which, and explain your reasoning.

Vitamin C

Vitamin E

5. Two of the substances listed here are highly soluble in water, two are only slightly soluble in water, and two are insoluble in water. Indicate the situation you expect for each one.

(a) iodoform, CHI_3

(b) benzoic acid,

(c) formic acid,

(d) butyl alcohol, $CH_3CH_2CH_2CH_2OH$

(e) chlorobenzene,

(f) propylene glycol, $CH_3CHOHCH_2OH$

6. Benzoic acid, C_6H_5COOH, is much more soluble in $NaOH(aq)$ than it is in pure water. Can you suggest a reason for this? The structural formula for benzoic acid is given in Exercise 5(b).

7. In light of the factors outlined on page 537, which of the following ionic fluorides would you expect to be most water soluble on a moles-per-liter basis: MgF_2, NaF, KF, CaF_2? Explain your reasoning.

8. Explain the observation that all metal nitrates are water soluble but many metal sulfides are not. Among metal sulfides, which would you expect to be most soluble?

Percent Concentration

9. A saturated aqueous solution of NaBr at 20 °C contains 116 g $NaBr/100$ g H_2O. Express this composition in the more conventional percent by mass, that is, as grams of NaBr per 100 grams of solution.

10. An aqueous solution with density 0.988 g/mL at 20 °C is prepared by dissolving 12.8 mL $CH_3CH_2CH_2OH$ ($d = 0.803$ g/mL) in enough water to produce 75.0 mL of solution. What is the percent $CH_3CH_2CH_2OH$ expressed as **(a)** percent by volume; **(b)** percent by mass; **(c)** percent (mass/volume)?

11. A certain brine has 3.87% NaCl by mass. A 75.0-mL sample weighs 76.9 g. How many liters of this solution should be evaporated to dryness to obtain 725 kg NaCl?

12. You are asked to prepare 125.0 mL of 0.0321 M $AgNO_3$. How many grams would you need of a sample known to be 99.81% $AgNO_3$ by mass?

13. According to Example 13-1, the mass percent ethanol in a particular aqueous solution is less than the volume percent in the same solution. Explain why this is

also true for *all* aqueous solutions of ethanol. Would it be true of all ethanol solutions, regardless of the other component? Explain.

14. Blood cholesterol levels are generally expressed as milligrams of cholesterol per deciliter of blood. What is the approximate mass percent cholesterol in a blood sample having a cholesterol level of 176? Why can you not give a more precise answer?

15. A certain vinegar is 6.02% acetic acid ($HC_2H_3O_2$) by mass. How many grams of $HC_2H_3O_2$ are contained in a 355-mL bottle of vinegar? Assume a density of 1.01 g/mL.

16. 6.00 M sulfuric acid, $H_2SO_4(aq)$, has a density of 1.338 g/mL. What is the percent by mass of sulfuric acid in this solution?

17. The sulfate ion level in a municipal water supply is given as 46.1 ppm. What is $[SO_4^{2-}]$ in this water?

18. A water sample is found to have 9.4 ppb of chloroform, $CHCl_3$. How many grams of $CHCl_3$ would be found in a glassful (250 mL) of this water?

Molarity

19. An aqueous solution is 6.00% methanol (CH_3OH) by mass, with $d = 0.988$ g/mL. What is the molarity of CH_3OH in this solution?

20. A typical commercial grade aqueous phosphoric acid is 75% H_3PO_4 by mass and has a density of 1.57 g/mL. What is the molarity of H_3PO_4 in this solution?

21. How many milliliters of the ethanol–water solution described in Example 13-1 should be diluted with water to produce 825 mL of 0.235 M C_2H_5OH?

22. A 30.00%-by-mass solution of nitric acid, HNO_3, in water has a density of 1.18 g/cm³ at 20 °C. What is the molarity of HNO_3 in this solution?

Molality

23. What is the molality of *para*-dichlorobenzene in a solution prepared by dissolving 2.65 g $C_6H_4Cl_2$ in 50.0 mL benzene ($d = 0.879$ g/mL)?
24. What is the molality of the sulfuric acid solution described in Exercise 16?
25. How many grams of iodine, I_2, must be dissolved in 725 mL of carbon disulfide, CS_2 ($d = 1.261$ g/mL), to produce a 0.236 m solution?
26. How many grams of water would you add to 1.00 kg of 1.38 m $CH_3OH(aq)$ to reduce the molality to 1.00 m CH_3OH?

27. An aqueous solution is 34.0% H_3PO_4 by mass and has a density of 1.209 g/mL. What are the molarity and molality of this solution?
28. A 10.00%-by-mass solution of ethanol, C_2H_5OH, in water has a density of 0.9831 g/mL at 15 °C and 0.9804 g/mL at 25 °C. Calculate the molality of the ethanol–water solution at these two temperatures. Does the molality differ at the two temperatures (that is, at 15 and 25 °C)? Would you expect the molarities to differ? Explain.

Mole Fraction, Mole Percent

29. A solution is prepared by mixing 1.28 mol C_7H_{16}, 2.92 mol C_8H_{18}, and 2.64 mol C_9H_{20}. What is the **(a)** mole fraction and **(b)** mole percent of each component of the solution?
30. Calculate the mole fraction of solute in the following aqueous solutions: **(a)** 21.7% C_2H_5OH, by mass; **(b)** 0.684 m $CO(NH_2)_2$ (urea).
31. Calculate the mole fraction of the solute in the following aqueous solutions: **(a)** 0.112 M $C_6H_{12}O_6$ ($d = 1.006$ g/mL); **(b)** 3.20% ethanol, by volume ($d = 0.993$ g/mL; pure C_2H_5OH, $d = 0.789$ g/mL).

32. Refer to Example 13-1. How many grams of C_2H_5OH must be added to 100.0 mL of the solution described in part (d) to increase the mole fraction of C_2H_5OH to 0.0525?
33. How many milliliters of glycerol, $C_3H_8O_3$ ($d = 1.26$ g/mL), must be added per kilogram of water to produce a solution with 4.85 mol % $C_3H_8O_3$?
34. Two aqueous solutions of sucrose, $C_{12}H_{22}O_{11}$, are mixed. One solution is 0.1487 M $C_{12}H_{22}O_{11}$ and has $d = 1.018$ g/mL; the other is 10.00% $C_{12}H_{22}O_{11}$ by mass and has $d = 1.038$ g/mL. Calculate the mole percent $C_{12}H_{22}O_{11}$ in the mixed solution.

Solubility Equilibrium

35. Refer to Figure 13-8 and determine the molality of NH_4Cl in a saturated aqueous solution at 40 °C.
36. Refer to Figure 13-8 and estimate the temperature at which a saturated aqueous solution of $KClO_4$ is 0.200 m.
37. A solution of 20.0 g $KClO_4$ in 500.0 g of water is brought to a temperature of 40 °C.
    (a) Refer to Figure 13-8 and determine whether the solution is unsaturated or supersaturated at 40 °C.
    (b) Approximately what mass of $KClO_4$, in grams, must be added to saturate the solution (if originally

unsaturated), or what mass of $KClO_4$ can be crystallized (if originally supersaturated)?
38. One way to recrystallize a solute from a solution is to change the temperature. Another way is to evaporate solvent from the solution. A 335-g sample of a saturated solution of $KNO_3(s)$ in water is prepared at 25.0 °C. If 55 g H_2O is evaporated from the solution at the same time as the temperature is reduced from 25.0 to 0.0 °C, what mass of $KNO_3(s)$ will recrystallize? (Refer to Figure 13-8.)

Solubility of Gases

39. Under an $O_2(g)$ pressure of 1.00 atm, 28.31 mL of $O_2(g)$ dissolves in 1.00 L H_2O at 25 °C. What will be the molarity of O_2 in the saturated solution at 25 °C when the O_2 pressure is 3.86 atm? (Assume that the solution volume remains at 1.00 L.)
40. Using data from Exercise 39, determine the molarity of O_2 in an aqueous solution at equilibrium with air at normal atmospheric pressure. The volume percent of O_2 in air is 20.95%.
    [*Hint:* Recall equation (6.17).]
41. Most natural gas consists of about 90% methane, CH_4. Assume that the solubility of natural gas at 20 °C and 1 atm gas pressure is about the same as that of CH_4, 0.02 g/kg water. If a sample of natural gas under a pressure of 20 atm is kept in contact with 1.00×10^3 kg of water, what mass of natural gas will dissolve?

42. At 1.00 atm, the solubility of O_2 in water is 2.18×10^{-3} M at 0 °C and 1.26×10^{-3} M at 25 °C. What volume of $O_2(g)$, measured at 25 °C and 1.00 atm, is expelled when 515 mL of water saturated with O_2 is heated from 0 to 25 °C?
43. The aqueous solubility at 20 °C of Ar at 1.00 atm is equivalent to 33.7 mL Ar(g), measured at STP, per liter of water. What is the molarity of Ar in water that is saturated with air at 1.00 atm and 20 °C? Air contains 0.934% Ar by volume. Assume that the volume of water does not change when it becomes saturated with air.
44. The aqueous solubility of CO_2 at 20 °C and 1.00 atm is equivalent to 87.8 mL $CO_2(g)$, measured at STP, per 100 mL of water. What is the molarity of CO_2 in water that is at 20 °C and saturated with air at 1.00 atm? The volume percent of CO_2 in air is 0.0360%. Assume that the volume of the water does not change when it becomes saturated with air.

45. Henry's law can be stated this way: The mass of a gas dissolved by a given quantity of solvent at a fixed temperature is directly proportional to the pressure of the gas. Show how this statement is related to equation (13.2).

46. Another statement of Henry's law is: At a fixed temperature, a given quantity of liquid dissolves the same volume of gas at all pressures. What is the connection between this statement and the one given in Exercise 45? Under what conditions is this second statement not valid?

Raoult's Law and Liquid–Vapor Equilibrium

47. What are the partial and total vapor pressures of a solution obtained by mixing 35.8 g benzene, C_6H_6, and 56.7 g toluene, C_7H_8, at 25 °C? At 25 °C the vapor pressure of C_6H_6 = 95.1 mmHg; the vapor pressure of C_7H_8 = 28.4 mmHg.

48. Determine the composition of the vapor above the benzene–toluene solution described in Exercise 47.

49. Calculate the vapor pressure at 25 °C of a solution containing 165 g of the *nonvolatile* solute, glucose, $C_6H_{12}O_6$, in 685 g H_2O. The vapor pressure of water at 25 °C is 23.8 mmHg.

50. Calculate the vapor pressure at 20 °C of a saturated solution of the *nonvolatile* solute, urea, $CO(NH_2)_2$, in methanol, CH_3OH. The solubility is 17 g urea/100 mL methanol. The density of methanol is 0.792 g/mL, and its vapor pressure at 20 °C is 95.7 mmHg.

51. Styrene, used in the manufacture of polystyrene plastics, is made by the extraction of hydrogen atoms from ethylbenzene. The product obtained contains about 38% styrene (C_8H_8) and 62% ethylbenzene (C_8H_{10}), by mass. The mixture is separated by fractional distillation at 90 °C. Determine the composition of the vapor in equilibrium with this 38%–62% mixture at 90 °C. The vapor pressure of ethylbenzene is 182 mmHg and that of styrene is 134 mmHg.

52. Calculate $x_{C_6H_6}$ in a benzene–toluene liquid solution that is in equilibrium at 25 °C with a vapor phase that contains 62.0 mol % C_6H_6. (Use data from Exercise 47.)

53. A benzene–toluene solution with x_{benz} = 0.300 has a normal boiling point of 98.6 °C. The vapor pressure of pure toluene at 98.6 °C is 533 mmHg. What must be the vapor pressure of pure benzene at 98.6 °C? (Assume ideal solution behavior.)

54. The two NaCl(aq) solutions pictured are at the same temperature.

NaCl(s)

Solution 1   Solution 2

(a) Above which solution is the vapor pressure of water, P_{H_2O}, greater? Explain.
(b) Above one of these solutions, the vapor pressure of water, P_{H_2O}, remains *constant*, even as water evaporates from solution. Which solution is this? Explain.
(c) Which of these solutions has the higher boiling point? Explain.

Osmotic Pressure

55. A 0.72-g sample of polyvinyl chloride (PVC) is dissolved in 250.0 mL of a suitable solvent at 25 °C. The solution has an osmotic pressure of 1.67 mmHg. What is the molar mass of the PVC?

56. Verify that a 20% aqueous solution by mass of sucrose ($C_{12}H_{22}O_{11}$) would rise to a height of about 150 m in an apparatus of the type pictured in Figure 13-17.

57. When the stems of cut flowers are held in concentrated NaCl(aq), the flowers wilt. In a similar solution a fresh cucumber shrivels up (becomes pickled). Explain the basis of these phenomena.

58. Some fish live in saltwater environments and some in freshwater, but in either environment they need water to survive. Saltwater fish drink water, but freshwater fish do not. Explain this difference between the two types of fish.

59. In what volume of water must 1 mol of a nonelectrolyte be dissolved if the solution is to have an osmotic pressure of 1 atm at 273 K? Which of the gas laws does this result resemble?

60. The molecular mass of hemoglobin is 6.86×10^4 u. What mass of hemoglobin must be present per 100.0 mL of a solution to exert an osmotic pressure of 7.25 mmHg at 25 °C?

61. At 25 °C a 0.50-g sample of polyisobutylene (a polymer used in synthetic rubber) in 100.0 mL of benzene solu-

tion has an osmotic pressure that supports a 5.1-mm column of solution (d = 0.88 g/mL). What is the molar mass of the polyisobutylene? (For Hg, d = 13.6 g/mL.)

62. Use the concentration of an isotonic saline solution, 0.92% NaCl (mass/volume), to determine the osmotic pressure of blood at body temperature, 37.0 °C.
[*Hint:* Assume that NaCl is completely dissociated in aqueous solutions.]

63. What approximate pressure is required in the reverse osmosis depicted in Figure 13-18 if the saltwater contains 2.5% NaCl, by mass?
[*Hint:* Assume that NaCl is completely dissociated in aqueous solutions. Also, assume a temperature of 25 °C.]

64. The two solutions pictured here are separated by a semipermeable membrane that permits only the passage of water molecules. In what direction will a net flow of water occur, that is, from left to right or right to left?

? ←——H_2O

H_2O ——→ ?

14.0 g $C_3H_8O_3$ in 55.2 mL solution

17.2 g $C_{12}H_{22}O_{11}$ in 62.5 mL solution

Freezing-Point Depression and Boiling-Point Elevation

65. 1.10 g of an unknown compound reduces the freezing point of 75.22 g benzene from 5.53 to 4.92 °C. What is the molar mass of the compound?

66. The freezing point of a 0.010 m aqueous solution of a nonvolatile solute is −0.072 °C. What would you expect the normal boiling point of this same solution to be?

67. Adding 1.00 g of benzene, C_6H_6, to 80.00 g cyclohexane, C_6H_{12}, lowers the freezing point of the cyclohexane from 6.5 to 3.3 °C.
    (a) What is the value of K_f for cyclohexane?
    (b) Which is the better solvent for molar mass determinations by freezing-point depression, benzene or cyclohexane? Explain.

68. The boiling point of water at 749.2 mmHg is 99.60 °C. What mass percent sucrose ($C_{12}H_{22}O_{11}$) should be present in an aqueous sucrose solution to raise the boiling point to 100.00 °C at this pressure?

69. A compound is 42.9% C, 2.4% H, 16.7% N, and 38.1% O, by mass. Addition of 6.45 g of this compound to 50.0 mL benzene, C_6H_6 ($d = 0.879$ g/mL), lowers the freezing point from 5.53 to 1.37 °C. What is the molecular formula of this compound?

70. Nicotinamide is a water-soluble vitamin important in metabolism. A deficiency in this vitamin results in the debilitating condition known as pellagra. Nicotinamide is 59.0% C, 5.0% H, 22.9% N, 13.1% O, by mass. Addition of 3.88 g of nicotinamide to 30.0 mL nitrobenzene, $C_6H_5NO_2$ ($d = 1.204$ g/mL), lowers the freezing point from 5.7 to −1.4 °C. What is the molecular formula of this compound?

71. Thiophene (fp = −38.3; bp = 84.4 °C) is a sulfur-containing hydrocarbon sometimes used as a solvent in place of benzene. Combustion of a 2.348-g sample of thiophene produces 4.913 g CO_2, 1.005 g H_2O, and 1.788 g SO_2. When a 0.867-g sample of thiophene is dissolved in 44.56 g of benzene (C_6H_6), the freezing point is lowered by 1.183 °C. What is the molecular formula of thiophene?

72. Coniferin is a glycoside (a derivative of a sugar) found in conifers such as fir trees. When a 1.205-g sample of coniferin is subjected to combustion analysis (recall Section 3-3), the products are 0.698 g H_2O and 2.479 g CO_2. A 2.216-g sample is dissolved in 48.68 g H_2O, and the normal boiling point of this solution is found to be 100.068 °C. What is the molecular formula of coniferin?

73. Cooks often add some salt to water before boiling it. Some people say this helps the cooking process by raising the boiling point of the water. Others say not enough salt is usually added to make any noticeable difference. Approximately how many grams of NaCl must be added to a liter of water at 1 atm pressure to raise the boiling point by 2 °C? Is this a typical amount of salt that you might add to cooking water?

74. An important test for the purity of an organic compound is to measure its melting point. Usually, if the compound is not pure, it begins to melt at a *lower* temperature than the pure compound.
    (a) Why is this the case, rather than the melting point being higher in some cases and lower in others?
    (b) Are there any conditions under which the melting point of the impure compound is *higher* than that of the pure compound? Explain.

Strong Electrolytes, Weak Electrolytes, and Nonelectrolytes

75. Predict the approximate freezing points of 0.10 m solutions of the following solutes dissolved in water:
    (a) $CO(NH_2)_2$ (urea); (b) NH_4NO_3; (c) HCl; (d) $CaCl_2$; (e) $MgSO_4$; (f) C_2H_5OH (ethanol); (g) $HC_2H_3O_2$ (acetic acid).

76. Calculate the van't Hoff factors of the following weak electrolyte solutions:
    (a) 0.050 m $HCHO_2$, which begins to freeze at −0.0986 °C;
    (b) 0.100 M HNO_2, which has a hydrogen ion (and nitrite ion) concentration of 6.91×10^{-3} M.

77. NH_3(aq) conducts electric current only weakly. The same is true for acetic acid, $HC_2H_3O_2$(aq). When these solutions are mixed, however, the resulting solution conducts electric current very well. Propose an explanation.

78. An isotonic solution is described as 0.92% NaCl (mass/volume). Would this also be the required concentration for isotonic solutions of other salts, such as KCl, $MgCl_2$, or $MgSO_4$? Explain.

Integrative and Advanced Exercises

79. A typical root beer contains 0.13% of a 75% H_3PO_4 solution by mass. How many milligrams of phosphorus are contained in a 12-oz can of this root beer? Assume a solution density of 1.00 g/mL; also, 1 oz = 29.6 mL.

80. Water and phenol are completely miscible at temperatures above 66.8 °C, but only partially miscible at temperatures below 66.8 °C. In a mixture prepared at 29.6 °C from 50.0 g water and 50.0 g phenol, 32.8 g of a phase consisting of 92.50% water and 7.50% phenol by mass is obtained. This is a saturated solution of phenol in water. What is the mass percent of water in the second phase—a saturated solution of water in phenol? What is the mole fraction of phenol in the mixture at temperatures above 66.8 °C?

81. An aqueous solution has 109.2 g KOH/L solution. The solution density is 1.09 g/mL. Your task is to use 100.0 mL of this solution to prepare 0.250 m KOH. What mass of which component, KOH or H_2O, would you add to the 100.0-mL of solution?

82. The term "proof," still used to describe the ethanol content of alcoholic beverages, originated in seventeenth-century England. A sample of whiskey was poured on gunpowder and set afire. If the gunpowder ignited after the whiskey had burned off, this "proved" that the whiskey had not been watered down. The minimum ethanol content for a positive test was about 50%, by volume. The 50% ethanol solution became known as "100 proof." Thus, an 80-proof whiskey would be 40% CH_3CH_2OH by volume. Listed in the table below are some data for several aqueous solutions of ethanol. *With a minimum amount of calculation*, determine which of the solutions are more than 100 proof. Assume that the density of pure ethanol is 0.79 g/mL.

Molarity of Ethanol, M	Density of Solution, g/mL
4.00	0.970
5.00	0.963
6.00	0.955
7.00	0.947
8.00	0.936
9.00	0.926
10.00	0.913

83. Four aqueous solutions of acetone, CH_3COCH_3, are prepared at different concentrations: (a) 0.100% CH_3COCH_3, by mass; (b) 0.100 M CH_3COCH_3; (c) 0.100 m CH_3COCH_3; and (d) $\chi_{acetone} = 0.100$. Estimate the highest partial pressure of water at 25 °C to be found in the equilibrium vapor above these solutions. Also, estimate the lowest freezing point to be found among these solutions.

84. A solid mixture consists of 85.0% KNO_3 and 15.0% K_2SO_4, by mass. A 60.0-g sample of this solid is added to 130.0 g of water at 60 °C. Refer to Figure 13-8.
(a) Will all the solid dissolve at 60 °C?
(b) If the resulting solution is cooled to 0 °C, what mass of KNO_3 should crystallize?
(c) Will K_2SO_4 also crystallize at 0 °C?

85. Suppose you have available 2.50 L of a solution ($d = 0.9767$ g/mL) that is 13.8% ethanol (C_2H_5OH), by mass. From this solution you would like to make the *maximum* quantity of ethanol–water antifreeze solution that will offer protection to −2.0 °C. Would you add more ethanol or more water to the solution? What mass of liquid would you add?

86. Hydrogen chloride is a colorless gas, yet when a bottle of concentrated hydrochloric acid [HCl(conc aq)] is opened, mist-like fumes are often seen to escape from the bottle. How do you account for this?

87. Use the following information to confirm that the triple point temperature of water is about 0.0098 °C.
(a) The slope of the fusion curve of water in the region of the normal melting point of ice (Fig. 12-21) is −0.00750 °C/atm.

(b) The solubility of air in water at STP is 0.02918 mL of air per mL of water.

88. Stearic acid ($C_{18}H_{36}O_2$) and palmitic acid ($C_{16}H_{32}O_2$) are common fatty acids. Commercial grades of stearic acid usually contain palmitic acid as well. A 1.115-g sample of a commercial-grade stearic acid is dissolved in 50.00 mL benzene ($d = 0.879$ g/mL). The freezing point of the solution is found to be 5.072 °C. The freezing point of pure benzene is 5.533 °C, and K_f for benzene is 5.12 °C m^{-1}. What is the mass percent of palmitic acid in the stearic acid sample?

89. At a constant temperature of 25.00 °C, a current of dry air was passed through pure water and then through a drying tube, D_1, followed by passage through 1.00 m sucrose and another drying tube, D_2. After the experiment, D_1 had gained 11.7458 g in mass and D_2, 11.5057 g. Given that the vapor pressure of water is 23.76 mmHg at 25.00 °C, (a) what was the vapor pressure lowering in the 1.00 m sucrose, and (b) what was the expected lowering?

90. Nitrobenzene, $C_6H_5NO_2$, and benzene, C_6H_6, are completely miscible in each other. Other properties of the two liquids are *nitrobenzene*: fp = 5.7 °C, $K_f = 8.1$ °C m^{-1}; *benzene*: fp = 5.5 °C, $K_f = 5.12$ °C m^{-1}. It is possible to prepare *two different* solutions with these two liquids having a freezing point of 0.0 °C. What are the compositions of these two solutions, expressed as mass percent nitrobenzene?

91. Refer to Figure 13-16(a). Initially, solution A contains 0.515 g urea, $CO(NH_2)_2$, dissolved in 92.5 g H_2O; solution B contains 2.50 g sucrose, $C_{12}H_{22}O_{11}$, dissolved in 85.0 g H_2O. What are the compositions of the two solutions when equilibrium is reached, that is, when the two have the same vapor pressure?

92. In Figure 13-17, why does the net transfer of water stop when the two solutions are of *nearly* equal concentrations rather than of *exactly* equal concentrations?

93. Shown below is a typical cooling curve for an aqueous solution. Why is there no straight-line portion comparable to that seen in the cooling curve for pure water in Figure 12-14?

94. Suppose that 1.00 mg of gold is obtained in a colloidal dispersion in which the gold particles are spherical, with a radius of 1.00×10^2 nm. (The density of gold is 19.3 g/cm^3.)
(a) What is the total surface area of the particles?
(b) What is the surface area of a single cube of gold of mass 1.00 mg?

95. At 20 °C, liquid benzene has a density of 0.879 g/cm^3; liquid toluene, 0.867 g/cm^3. Assume ideal solutions.
    (a) Calculate the densities of solutions containing 20, 40, 60, and 80 volume percent benzene.
    (b) Plot a graph of density versus volume percent composition.
    (c) Write an equation that relates the density (d) to the volume percent benzene (V) in benzene–toluene solutions at 20 °C.

96. The two compounds whose structures are depicted here are isomers. When derived from petroleum, they always occur mixed together. *meta*-Xylene is used in aviation fuels and in the manufacture of dyes and insecticides. The principal use of *para*-xylene is in the manufacture of polyester resins and fibers (for example, Dacron). Comment on the effectiveness of fractional distillation as a method of separating these two xylenes. What other method(s) might be used to separate them?

    meta-xylene   para-xylene
    fp, 47.9 °C   fp, 13.3 °C
    bp, 139.1 °C   bp, 138.4 °C
    d, 0.864 g/mL   d, 0.861 g/mL

97. Instructions on a container of Prestone® (ethylene glycol; fp, −12.6 °C, bp, 197.3 °C) give the following volumes of Prestone to be used in protecting a 12-qt cooling system against freeze-up at different temperatures (the remaining liquid is water): 10 °F, 3 qt; 0 °F, 4 qt; −15 °F, 5 qt; −34 °F, 6 qt. Since the freezing point of the coolant is successively lowered by using more Prestone, why not use even more than 6 qt of Prestone (and proportionately less water) to ensure the maximum protection against freezing?

98. Demonstrate that
    (a) for a *dilute aqueous* solution, the numerical value of the molality is essentially equal to that of the molarity.
    (b) In a *dilute* solution, the solute mole fraction is proportional to the molality.
    (c) In a *dilute aqueous* solution, the solute mole fraction is proportional to the molarity.

99. At 25 °C and under an O$_2$(g) pressure of 1 atm, the solubility of O$_2$(g) in water is 28.31 mL/1.00 L H$_2$O. At 25 °C and under an N$_2$(g) pressure of 1 atm, the solubility of N$_2$(g) in water is 14.34 mL/1.00 L H$_2$O. The composition of the atmosphere is 78.08% N$_2$ and 20.95% O$_2$, by volume. What is the composition of air dissolved in water expressed as volume percents of N$_2$ and O$_2$?

100. We noted in Figure 13-13 that the liquid and vapor curves taken together outline a lens-shaped region when the normal boiling points of benzene–toluene solutions are plotted as a function of mole fraction of benzene. That is, unlike Figure 13-12, the liquid curve is not a straight line. Use data from Figure 13-13 and show by calculation that this should be the case.

101. A saturated solution prepared at 70 °C contains 32.0 g CuSO$_4$ per 100.0 g solution. A 335-g sample of this solution is then cooled to 0 °C and CuSO$_4 \cdot$ 5 H$_2$O crystallizes out. If the concentration of a saturated solution at 0 °C is 12.5 g CuSO$_4$/100 g soln, what mass of CuSO$_4 \cdot$ 5 H$_2$O would be obtained?
    [*Hint:* Note that the solution composition is stated in terms of CuSO$_4$ and that the solid that crystallizes is the hydrate CuSO$_4 \cdot$ 5 H$_2$O.]

Feature Problems

102. Cinnamaldehyde is the chief constituent of cinnamon oil, which is obtained from the twigs and leaves of cinnamon trees grown in tropical regions. Cinnamon oil is used in the manufacture of food flavorings, perfumes, and cosmetics. The normal boiling point of cinnamaldehyde, C$_9$H$_8$O, is 246.0 °C, but at this temperature it begins to decompose. As a result, cinnamaldehyde cannot be easily purified by ordinary distillation. A method that can be used instead is *steam distillation*. A heterogeneous mixture of cinnamaldehyde and water is heated until the sum of the vapor pressures of the two liquids is equal to barometric pressure. At this point, the temperature remains constant as the liquids vaporize. The mixed vapor condenses to produce two immiscible liquids; one liquid is essentially pure water and the other, pure cinnamaldehyde. The following vapor pressures of cinnamaldehyde are given: 1 mmHg at 76.1 °C; 5 mmHg at 105.8 °C; and 10 mmHg at 120.0 °C. Vapor pressures of water are given in Table 13.2.
    (a) What is the approximate temperature at which the steam distillation occurs?
    (b) The proportions of the two liquids condensed from the vapor is *independent* of the composition of the boiling mixture, as long as both liquids are present in the boiling mixture. Explain why this is so.
    (c) Which of the two liquids, water or cinnamaldehyde, condenses in the greater quantity, by mass? Explain.

103. The phase diagram shown is for mixtures of HCl and H$_2$O at a pressure of 1 atm. The red curve represents the normal boiling points of solutions of

HCl(aq) of various mole fractions. The blue curve represents the compositions of the vapors in equilibrium with boiling solutions.

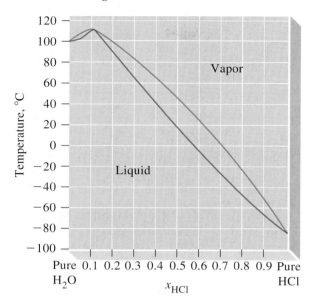

(a) As a solution containing $x_{HCl} = 0.50$ begins to boil, will the vapor have a mole fraction of HCl equal to, less than, or greater than 0.50? Explain.
(b) In the boiling of a pure liquid, there is no change in composition. However, as a solution of HCl(aq) boils in an open container, the composition changes. Explain why this is so.
(c) One particular solution (the azeotrope) is an exception to the observation stated in part (b); that is, its composition remains *unchanged* during boiling. What are the approximate composition and boiling point of this solution?
(d) A 5.00-mL sample of the azeotrope ($d = 1.099$ g/mL) requires 30.32 mL of 1.006 M NaOH for its titration in an acid–base reaction. Use these data to determine a more precise value of the composition of the azeotrope, expressed as the mole fraction of HCl.

104. The laboratory device pictured is called a *desiccator*. It can be used to maintain a constant relative humidity within an enclosure. The material(s) used to control the relative humidity are placed in the bottom compartment, and the substance being subjected to a controlled relative humidity is placed on the platform in the container.

(a) If the material in the bottom compartment is a saturated solution of NaCl(aq) in contact with NaCl(s), what will be the approximate relative humidity in the container at a temperature of 20 °C? Obtain the solubility of NaCl from Figure 13-8 and vapor pressure data for water from Table 12.2; use the definition of Raoult's law from page 543 and that of relative humidity from page 213; assume that the NaCl is completely dissociated into its ions.
(b) If the material placed on the platform is dry $CaCl_2 \cdot 6\,H_2O(s)$, will the solid deliquesce? Explain. [*Hint:* Recall the discussion on page 548.]
(c) To maintain $CaCl_2 \cdot 6\,H_2O(s)$ in the dry state in a desiccator, should the substance in the saturated solution in the bottom compartment be one with a high or a low water solubility? Explain.

105. Every year, oral rehydration therapy (ORT)—the feeding of an electrolyte solution—saves the lives of countless children worldwide who become severely dehydrated as a result of diarrhea. One requirement of the solution used is that it be *isotonic* with human blood.
(a) One definition of an isotonic solution given in the text is that it have the same osmotic pressure as 0.92% NaCl(aq) (mass/volume). Another definition is that the solution have a freezing point of −0.52 °C. Show that these two definitions are in reasonably close agreement given that we are using solution concentrations rather than activities.
(b) Use the freezing-point definition from part (a) to show that an ORT solution containing 3.5 g NaCl, 1.5 g KCl, 2.9 g $Na_3C_6H_5O_7$ (sodium citrate), and 20.0 g $C_6H_{12}O_6$ (glucose) per liter meets the requirement of being isotonic.
[*Hint:* Which of the solutes are nonelectrolytes, and which are strong electrolytes?]

Self-Assessment Exercises

106. In your own words, define or explain the following terms or symbols: **(a)** x_B; **(b)** P_A°; **(c)** K_f; **(d)** i; **(e)** activity.

107. Briefly describe each of the following ideas or phenomena: **(a)** Henry's law; **(b)** freezing-point depression; **(c)** recrystallization; **(d)** hydrated ion; **(e)** deliquescence.

108. Explain the important distinctions between each pair of terms: **(a)** molality and molarity; **(b)** ideal and nonideal solution; **(c)** unsaturated and supersaturated solution; **(d)** fractional crystallization and fractional distillation; **(e)** osmosis and reverse osmosis.

109. An aqueous solution is 0.010 M CH_3OH. The concentration of this solution is also very nearly **(a)** 0.010% CH_3OH (mass/volume); **(b)** 0.010 m CH_3OH; **(c)** $x_{CH_3OH} = 0.010$; **(d)** 0.990 M H_2O.

110. The most likely of the following mixtures to be an ideal solution is **(a)** $NaCl–H_2O$; **(b)** $CH_3CH_2OH–C_6H_6$; **(c)** $C_7H_{16}–H_2O$; **(d)** $C_7H_{16}–C_8H_{18}$.

111. The solubility of a nonreactive gas in water increases with **(a)** an increase in gas pressure; **(b)** an increase in temperature; **(c)** increases in both temperature and pressure; **(d)** an increase in the volume of gas in equilibrium with the available water.

112. Of the following aqueous solutions, the one with the lowest freezing point is **(a)** 0.010 m $MgSO_4$; **(b)** 0.011 m NaCl; **(c)** 0.018 m CH_3CH_2OH; **(d)** 0.0080 m $MgCl_2$.

113. An ideal liquid solution has two volatile components. In the vapor in equilibrium with the solution, the mole fractions of the components are **(a)** both 0.50; **(b)** equal, but not necessarily 0.50; **(c)** not very likely to be equal; **(d)** 1.00 for the solvent and 0.00 for the solute.

114. A solution prepared by dissolving 1.12 mol NH_4Cl in 150.0 g H_2O is brought to a temperature of 30 °C. Use Figure 13-8 to determine whether the solution is unsaturated or whether excess solute will crystallize.

115. NaCl(aq) isotonic with blood is 0.92% NaCl (mass/volume). For this solution, what is **(a)** $[Na^+]$; **(b)** the total molarity of ions; **(c)** the osmotic pressure at 37 °C; **(d)** the approximate freezing point? (Assume that the solution has a density of 1.005 g/mL.)

116. A solution ($d = 1.159$ g/mL) is 62.0% glycerol, $C_3H_8O_3$, and 38.0% H_2O, by mass. Determine **(a)** the molarity of $C_3H_8O_3$ with H_2O as the solvent; **(b)** the molarity of H_2O with $C_3H_8O_3$ as the solvent; **(c)** the molality of H_2O in $C_3H_8O_3$; **(d)** the mole fraction of $C_3H_8O_3$; **(e)** the mole percent of H_2O.

117. Which aqueous solution from the column on the right has the property listed on the left? Explain your choices.

Property	Solution
1. lowest electrical conductivity	**(a)** 0.10 m KCl(aq)
2. lowest boiling point	**(b)** 0.15 m $C_{12}H_{22}O_{11}$(aq)
3. highest vapor pressure of water at 25 °C	**(c)** 0.10 m CH_3COOH(aq)
4. lowest freezing point	**(d)** 0.05 m NaCl

118. Using the method of concept mapping presented in Appendix E, construct a concept map showing the relationships among the various concentration units presented in Section 13-2.

119. Construct a concept map for the relationships that exist among the colligative properties of Sections 13-6, 13-7, 13-8, and 13-9.

 ## eMedia Exercises

120. In the **Dissolution of NaCl in Water** animation (*Activebook 13-3*), **(a)** what types of intermolecular forces compete in the solvation of this ionic compound? **(b)** How would the solution process be influenced by a change in the polarity of the solvent? **(c)** What insight does this observation give you into the saying, "like dissolves like"?

121. In the **Enthalpy of Solution Formation** activity (*Activebook 13-3*), the dissolution of five different compounds in water is illustrated. The dissolution of some compounds show a temperature rise, while the dissolution of others show a temperature fall. **(a)** Account for the different behaviors with a discussion of the intermolecular forces at play in the process. **(b)** What trend can you discern by comparing this series of compounds?

122. The diffusion of water through a semipermeable membrane is illustrated in the **Semipermeable Membrane** activity (*Activebook 13-7*). **(a)** In terms of molecular motion, how would this behavior be influenced by an increase in the temperature of the system? **(b)** What is the quantitative relationship between temperature and the osmotic pressure of a solution?

123. In the **Boiling Point Elevation and Freezing Point Depression** activity for electrolyte solutions (*Activebook 13-8*), **(a)** which of the compounds illustrated gives rise to the greatest change in boiling point? **(b)** Why does this compound have that characteristic?

 ## eLaboratory Exercises

These exercises allow students to apply the concepts and skills for this chapter in the simulated laboratory of Virtual ChemLab. Worksheets for each of these exercises are found in the Virtual ChemLab Workbook in your MediaPak.

124. *(VCL 13-1) Creating a Solution of Known Molarity* In this assignment you will weigh out a sample of baking soda ($NaHCO_3$) and create a solution of known molarity.

125. *(VCL 13-2) Creating a Solution of Known Molality* In this assignment you will weigh out a sample of solid NH_4Cl and create a solution of known molality.

126. *(VCL 13-3) Converting Concentrations to Different Units* Occasionally, when making solutions in the laboratory, it is convenient to make a solution with a certain concentration unit, such as molarity, and

then convert the concentration to a different unit. In this assignment you will make a sodium bicarbonate (baking soda) solution of a certain molarity and then convert that concentration to molality, mass percent, and mole fraction.

127. *(VCL 13-4) Enthalpy of Solution: NH₄NO₃*

Have you ever used one of those "instant cold packs" that looks like a plastic bag filled with liquid? If you hit the bag and shake it up, it gets extremely cold, but why does it do that? The liquid inside the cold pack is water, and in the water is another plastic bag or tube containing NH_4NO_3. When you hit the cold pack, it breaks the tube so that the water mixes with the NH_4NO_3. The dissolving of a salt, such as NH_4NO_3, in water is called dissolution, and the heat associated with the dissolving process is called the enthalpy of solution. In this problem you will take a sample of NH_4NO_3, dissolve it in water, and from measuring the change in temperature, calculate the enthalpy of solution for NH_4NO_3.

128. *(VCL 13-5) Freezing-Point Depression*

If you dissolve a substance such as ordinary table salt (NaCl) in water, the freezing point of the water will decrease relative to the freezing point of the pure water. This property is used to melt the snow or ice on roads during the winter or to make home-made ice cream. In this assignment you will dissolve a sample of NaCl in water, add some ice, and then measure the freezing-point depression.

129. *(VCL 13-6) Boiling-Point Elevation*

If you dissolve a substance such as ordinary table salt (NaCl) in water, the boiling point of the water will increase relative to the boiling point of the pure water. In this assignment you will dissolve a sample of NaCl in water and measure the boiling point elevation for the solution.

130. *(VCL 13-7) Molar Mass Determination by Freezing-Point Depression*

If you dissolve a substance such as ordinary table salt (NaCl) in water, the freezing point of the water will decrease relative to the freezing point of the pure water. You can use this property to calculate the molar mass of an unknown. In this assignment you will dissolve a sample of NaCl in water, measure the freezing point depression for the solution, and then calculate the molar mass for NaCl as if it were an unknown.

131. *(VCL 13-8) Molar Mass Determination by Boiling-Point Elevation*

If you dissolve a substance such as ordinary table salt (NaCl) in water, the boiling point of the water will increase relative to the boiling point of the pure water. You can use this property to calculate the molar mass of an unknown. In this assignment you will dissolve a sample of NaCl in water, measure the boiling-point elevation for the solution, and then calculate the molar mass for NaCl as if it were an unknown.

132. *(VCL 13-9) Changes in the Boiling Point*

If you dissolve a substance such as ordinary table salt (NaCl) in water, the boiling point of the water will increase relative to the boiling point of the pure water. In this assignment you will dissolve a sample of NaCl in water and observe what happens when you continue to boil the water until the water boils away.

CHEMICAL KINETICS

CONTENTS

Although stable at room temperature, ammonium dichromate decomposes very rapidly once ignited. The rates of chemical reactions and the effect of temperature on those rates are among several key concepts explored in this chapter.

Rocket fuel is designed to give a rapid release of gaseous products and energy to provide a rocket maximum thrust. Milk is stored in a refrigerator to slow down the chemical reactions that cause it to spoil. Current strategies to reduce the rate of deterioration of the ozone layer seek to deprive the ozone-consuming reaction cycle of key intermediates that come from chlorofluorocarbons (CFCs). These examples illustrate the importance of the rates of chemical reactions. Moreover, how fast a reaction occurs depends on the reaction mechanism—the step-by-step molecular pathway leading from reactants to products. Thus, *chemical kinetics* concerns how rates of chemical reactions are measured, how they can be predicted, and how reaction-rate data are used to deduce probable reaction mechanisms.

The chapter begins with a discussion of the meaning of a rate of reaction and some ideas about measuring rates of reaction. This is followed by the introduction of mathematical equations, called rate laws, that relate the rates of reactions to the concentrations of the reactants. Finally, with this information as background, rate laws are related to plausible reaction mechanisms, which are a central focus of this chapter.

14-1 THE RATE OF A CHEMICAL REACTION

Rate, or speed, refers to something that happens in a unit of time. A car traveling at 60 mph, for example, covers a distance of 60 miles in one hour. For chemical reactions, the rate of reaction describes how fast the concentration of a reactant or product changes with time.

To illustrate, let's consider the reaction that begins immediately after the ions Fe^{3+} and Sn^{2+} are simultaneously introduced into an aqueous solution.

$$2\,Fe^{3+}(aq) + Sn^{2+}(aq) \longrightarrow 2\,Fe^{2+}(aq) + Sn^{4+}(aq) \qquad (14.1)$$

Suppose that 38.5 s after the reaction starts, $[Fe^{2+}]$ is found to be 0.0010 M. During the period of time, $\Delta t = 38.5$ s, the *change* in concentration of Fe^{2+}, which we can designate as $\Delta[Fe^{2+}]$, is $\Delta[Fe^{2+}] = 0.0010\,M - 0 = 0.0010\,M$. The *average* rate at which Fe^{2+} is formed in this interval is the change in concentration of Fe^{2+} divided by the change in time.

◀ Recall that the symbol [ ] means "the molarity of." Also, Δ means "the change in," that is, the final value minus the initial value.

$$\text{rate of formation of } Fe^{2+} = \frac{\Delta[Fe^{2+}]}{\Delta t} = \frac{0.0010\,M}{38.5\,s} = 2.6 \times 10^{-5}\,M\,s^{-1}$$

How has the concentration of Sn^{4+} changed during the 38.5 s we were monitoring the Fe^{2+}? Can you see that in 38.5 s, $\Delta[Sn^{4+}]$ will be 0.00050 M $- 0 = 0.00050$ M? Because only *one* Sn^{4+} ion is produced for every *two* Fe^{2+} ions, the buildup of $[Sn^{4+}]$ will be only one-half that of $[Fe^{2+}]$. Consequently the rate of formation of Sn^{4+} is 1.3×10^{-5} mole per liter per second.

$$\text{rate of formation of } Sn^{4+} = 1.3 \times 10^{-5}\,M\,s^{-1}$$

We can also follow the course of the reaction by monitoring the concentrations of the starting reactants. Thus, the amount of Fe^{3+} consumed is the same as the amount of Fe^{2+} produced. The *change* in concentration of Fe^{3+} is $\Delta[Fe^{3+}] = -0.0010$ M. The average rate at which Fe^{3+} disappears in the reaction is given by the expression

$$\text{rate of disappearance of } Fe^{3+} = \frac{\Delta[Fe^{3+}]}{\Delta t} = \frac{-0.0010\,M}{38.5\,s} = -2.6 \times 10^{-5}\,M\,s^{-1}$$

The rate of disappearance is a *negative* quantity because concentration decreases with time—the concentration at the end of a time period is less than it was at the start of the period. In the same way that we related the rate of formation of Sn^{4+} to that of Fe^{2+}, we can relate the rate of disappearance of Sn^{2+} to that of Fe^{3+}. That is, the rate of disappearance of Sn^{2+} is half that of Fe^{3+}, giving

$$\text{rate of disappearance of } Sn^{2+} = -1.3 \times 10^{-5}\,M\,s^{-1}$$

When we refer to the rate of reaction (14.1), which of the four quantities described here should we use? To avoid confusion in this matter, the International Union of Pure and Applied Chemistry (IUPAC) recommends that we use a *general* rate of reaction, which, for the hypothetical reaction represented by the balanced equation,

$$a\text{A} + b\text{B} \longrightarrow g\text{G} + h\text{H}$$

is

$$\text{rate of reaction} = -\frac{1}{a}\frac{\Delta[A]}{\Delta t} = -\frac{1}{b}\frac{\Delta[B]}{\Delta t} = \frac{1}{g}\frac{\Delta[G]}{\Delta t} = \frac{1}{h}\frac{\Delta[H]}{\Delta t} \qquad (14.2)$$

In this expression, we take the *negative* values of rates of disappearance, positive values of rates of formation, and *divide* all rates by the appropriate stoichiometric coefficients from the balanced equation. The result is a single, positive-valued quantity that we call the **rate of reaction**. Thus, for reaction (14.1) we can write

$$\text{rate of reaction} = -\frac{1}{2}\frac{\Delta[Fe^{3+}]}{\Delta t} = -\frac{\Delta[Sn^{2+}]}{\Delta t}$$

$$= \frac{1}{2}\frac{\Delta[Fe^{2+}]}{\Delta t} = \frac{\Delta[Sn^{4+}]}{\Delta t} = 1.3 \times 10^{-5}\,M\,s^{-1}$$

EXAMPLE 14-1

Expressing the Rate of a Reaction. Suppose that at some point in the reaction

$$A + 3B \longrightarrow 2C + 2D$$

[B] = 0.9986 M, and that 13.20 min later [B] = 0.9746 M. What is the average rate of reaction during this time period, expressed in M s^{-1}?

Solution

The rate of disappearance of B is the *change* in molarity, Δ[B], divided by the time interval, Δt, over which this change occurs Δ[B] = 0.9746 M − 0.9986 M = −0.0240 M; Δt = 13.20 min, and

$$\text{rate of reaction} = -\frac{1}{3}\frac{\Delta[B]}{\Delta t} = -\frac{1}{3} \times \frac{-0.0240\ M}{13.20\ min} = 6.06 \times 10^{-4}\ M\ min^{-1}$$

To express the rate of reaction in moles per liter per second, we must convert from min^{-1} to s^{-1}. We can do this with the conversion factor 1 min/60 s.

$$\text{rate of reaction} = 6.06 \times 10^{-4}\ M\ min^{-1} \times \frac{1\ min}{60\ s} = 1.01 \times 10^{-5}\ M\ s^{-1}$$

Alternatively, we could have converted 13.20 min to 792 s and used Δt = 792 s in evaluating the rate of reaction.

Practice Example A: At some point in the reaction 2 A + B $\longrightarrow$ C + D, [A] = 0.3629 M. At a time 8.25 min later [A] = 0.3187 M. What is the average rate of reaction during this time interval, expressed in M s^{-1}?

Practice Example B: In the reaction 2 A $\longrightarrow$ 3 B, [A] drops from 0.5684 M to 0.5522 M in 2.50 min. What is the average rate of formation of B during this time interval, expressed in M s^{-1}?

Two of the more recent articles in the *Journal of Chemical Education* describing demonstrations and experiments involving the kinetics of hydrogen peroxide decomposition are Vetter, T. A., Colombo, D. P., Jr. *J. Chem. Educ.* 2003: *80*, 788 and Abramovitch, D. A. et al. *J. Chem. Educ.* 2003: *80*, 790.

CONCEPT ASSESSMENT ✓

In the reaction of gaseous nitrogen and hydrogen to form gaseous ammonia, what are the relative rates of disappearance of the two reactants? How is the rate of formation of the product related to the rates of disappearance of the reactants?

14-2 MEASURING REACTION RATES

To determine a rate of reaction, we need to measure changes in concentration over time. A change in time can be measured with a stopwatch or other timing device, but how do we measure concentration changes during a chemical reaction? Also, why is the term *average* used in referring to a rate of reaction? These are two of the questions that are answered in this section.

FOLLOWING A CHEMICAL REACTION

A 3% aqueous solution of hydrogen peroxide is a common antiseptic. Its antiseptic action results from the release of $O_2(g)$ as the H_2O_2 decomposes. $O_2(g)$ escapes from the $H_2O_2(aq)$, and ultimately the reaction goes to completion.*

$$H_2O_2(aq) \longrightarrow H_2O(l) + \frac{1}{2}O_2(g) \qquad (14.3)$$

KEEP IN MIND ▶

that according to expression (14.2), the rate of this reaction can be expressed either as −rate of disappearance of H_2O_2 or 2 × rate of formation of $O_2(g)$.

---

*Although reaction (14.3) goes to completion, it does so very slowly. Generally, a catalyst is used to speed up the reaction. We describe the catalysis in this reaction in Section 14-11. When $H_2O_2(aq)$ is applied to an open wound, the enzyme catalase in blood catalyzes its decomposition.

We can follow the progress of the reaction by focusing either on the formation of $O_2(g)$ or on the disappearance of H_2O_2. For example, we can

- Measure the volumes of $O_2(g)$ produced at different times and relate these volumes to decreases in concentration of H_2O_2 (Fig. 14-1).

- Remove small samples of the reaction mixture from time to time, and analyze these samples for their H_2O_2 content. One way to do this is by titration with $KMnO_4$ in acidic solution. The net ionic equation for this oxidation–reduction reaction is

$$2 \, MnO_4^-(aq) + 5 \, H_2O_2(aq) + 6 \, H^+(aq) \longrightarrow 2 \, Mn^{2+}(aq) + 8 \, H_2O(l) + 5 \, O_2(g) \quad (14.4)$$

Table 14.1 lists typical data for the decomposition of H_2O_2, and Figure 14-2 displays comparable data graphically.

RATE OF REACTION EXPRESSED AS CONCENTRATION CHANGE OVER TIME

Some data extracted from Figure 14-2 are listed in Table 14.2 (in blue). Column III lists the molarities of H_2O_2 at the times shown in column I. Column II lists the *arbitrary* time interval between data points—400 s. Column IV reports the concentration changes that occur for each 400-s interval. The rates of reaction, expressed as the negative of the rate of disappearance of H_2O_2, are shown in column V. The data show that the reaction rate is not constant—the lower the remaining concentration of H_2O_2, the more slowly the reaction proceeds.

▲ **FIGURE 14-1**
Experimental setup for determining the rate of decomposition of H_2O_2
Oxygen gas given off by the reaction mixture is trapped, and its volume is measured in the gas buret. The amount of H_2O_2 consumed and the remaining concentration of H_2O_2 can be calculated from the measured volume of $O_2(g)$.

TABLE 14.1
Decomposition of H_2O_2

Time, s	[H_2O_2], M
0	2.32
200	2.01
400	1.72
600	1.49
1200	0.98
1800	0.62
3000	0.25

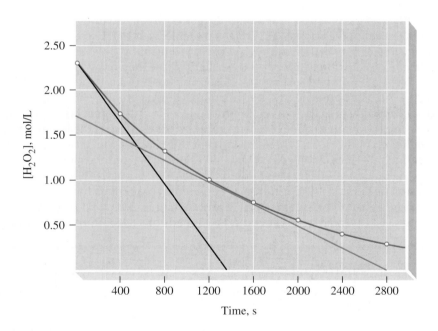

▲ **FIGURE 14-2**
Graphical representation of kinetic data for the reaction:

$$H_2O_2(aq) \longrightarrow H_2O(l) + \frac{1}{2}O_2(g)$$

This is the usual form in which concentration–time data are plotted. Reaction rates are determined from the slopes of the tangent lines. The blue line has a slope of $-1.70 \, M/2800 \, s = -6.1 \times 10^{-4} \, M \, s^{-1}$. The slope of the black line and its relation to the initial rate of reaction are described in Example 14-2.

TABLE 14.2   Decomposition of H_2O_2—Derived Rate Data

I	II	III	IV	V
Time, s	Δt, s	$[H_2O_2]$, M	$\Delta[H_2O_2]$, M	Reaction Rate $-\Delta[H_2O_2]/\Delta t$, M s^{-1}
0		2.32		
	400		−0.60	15.0×10^{-4}
400		1.72		
	400		−0.42	10.5×10^{-4}
800		1.30		
	400		−0.32	8.0×10^{-4}
1200		0.98		
	400		−0.25	6.3×10^{-4}
1600		0.73		
	400		−0.19	4.8×10^{-4}
2000		0.54		
	400		−0.15	3.8×10^{-4}
2400		0.39		
	400		−0.11	2.8×10^{-4}
2800		0.28		

RATE OF REACTION EXPRESSED AS THE SLOPE OF A TANGENT LINE

When the rate of reaction is expressed as $-\Delta[H_2O_2]/\Delta t$, the result is an *average* value for the time interval Δt. For example, in the interval from 1200 to 1600 s, the rate averages 6.3×10^{-4} M s^{-1} (fourth entry in column V of Table 14.2). This can be thought of as the reaction rate at about the middle of the interval—1400 s. We could just as well have chosen $\Delta t = 200$ s in Table 14.2. In this case, to obtain the rate of reaction at $t = 1400$ s, we would use concentration data at $t = 1300$ s and $t = 1500$ s. The rate of reaction would be slightly less than 6.3×10^{-4} M s^{-1}. The smaller the time interval used, the closer the result is to the actual rate at $t = 1400$ s. As Δt approaches 0 s, the rate of reaction approaches the *negative of the slope of the tangent line* to the curve of Figure 14-2. The rate of reaction determined from the slope of a tangent line to a concentration–time curve is the **instantaneous rate of reaction** at the point where the tangent line touches the curve. The best estimate of the rate of reaction of H_2O_2 at 1400 s, then, is from the slope of the blue tangent line in Figure 14-2: $-(-6.1 \times 10^{-4}$ M s$^{-1}) = 6.1 \times 10^{-4}$ M s^{-1}.

To better understand the difference between average and instantaneous reaction rates, think of taking a 108-mi highway trip in 2.00 h. The *average* speed is 54.0 mph. The *instantaneous* speed is the speedometer reading at any instant.

▶ Your instantaneous speed can result in a speeding ticket even if the average speed never exceeds the speed limit.

Are You Wondering . . .

How to differentiate between the average rate of reaction and the instantaneous rate?

If you are familiar with differential calculus, you probably know the answer. If the rate of reaction (14.3) is written as

$$\lim_{\Delta t \longrightarrow 0} \frac{-\Delta[H_2O_2]}{\Delta t}$$

the delta quantities can be replaced by the differentials $d[H_2O_2]$ and dt, leading to the expression

$$\frac{-d[H_2O_2]}{dt}$$

Thus, the delta notation (not taken to the limit of $\Delta t \longrightarrow 0$) signifies an *average* rate and the differential notation, an *instantaneous* rate.

INITIAL RATE OF REACTION

Sometimes we simply want to find the rate of reaction when the reactants are first brought together—the **initial rate of reaction**. This rate can be obtained from the tangent line to the concentration–time curve at $t = 0$. An alternative way is to measure the concentration of the chosen reactant as soon as possible after mixing, in this way obtaining Δ[reactant] for a very short time interval (Δt) at essentially $t = 0$. These two approaches give the same result if the time interval used is limited to that in which the tangent line and the concentration–time curve practically coincide. In Figure 14-2, this condition occurs for about the first 200 s.

EXAMPLE 14-2

Determining and Using an Initial Rate of Reaction. From the data in Table 14.1 and Figure 14-2 for the decomposition of H_2O_2, **(a)** determine the initial rate of reaction, and **(b)** $[H_2O_2]_t$ at $t = 100$ s.

Solution

(a) To determine the initial rate of reaction from the slope of the tangent line, use the intersections of the black tangent line with the axes: $t = 0$, $[H_2O_2] = 2.32$ M; $t = 1360$ s, $[H_2O_2] = 0$.

$$\text{initial rate of reaction} = -(\text{slope of tangent line}) = \frac{-(0 - 2.32)\text{ M}}{(1360 - 0)\text{ s}}$$

$$= 1.71 \times 10^{-3} \text{ M s}^{-1}$$

An alternative method is to use data from Table 14.1: $[H_2O_2] = 2.32$ M at $t = 0$ and $[H_2O_2] = 2.01$ M at $t = 200$ s.

$$\text{initial rate} = \frac{-\Delta[H_2O_2]}{\Delta t} = \frac{-(2.01 - 2.32)\text{ M}}{200 \text{ s}}$$

$$= 1.6 \times 10^{-3} \text{ M s}^{-1}$$

The agreement between the two methods is fairly good, although it might be better if the time interval were less than 200 s. Of the two results, the one based on the tangent line is presumably more precise because it is expressed with more significant figures. On the other hand, the reliability of the tangent line depends on how carefully the tangent line is constructed.

◀ Another reason for favoring a graphical method is that it tends to minimize the effect of errors that may be found in individual data points.

(b) We assume that the rate determined in (a) remains essentially constant for at least 100 s. Because

$$\text{rate of reaction} = \frac{-\Delta[H_2O_2]}{\Delta t}$$

then

$$1.71 \times 10^{-3} \text{ M s}^{-1} = \frac{-\Delta[H_2O_2]}{100 \text{ s}}$$

$$-(1.71 \times 10^{-3} \text{ M s}^{-1})(100 \text{ s}) = \Delta[H_2O_2] = [H_2O_2]_t - [H_2O_2]_0$$

$$-1.71 \times 10^{-1} \text{ M} = [H_2O_2]_t - 2.32 \text{ M}$$

$$[H_2O_2]_t = 2.32 \text{ M} - 0.17 \text{ M} = 2.15 \text{ M}$$

Practice Example A: For reaction (14.3), determine **(a)** the *instantaneous* rate of reaction at 2400 s and **(b)** $[H_2O_2]$ at 2450 s.

[*Hint:* Assume that the instantaneous rate of reaction at 2400 s holds constant for the next 50 s.]

Practice Example B: Use data *only* from Table 14.2 to determine $[H_2O_2]$ at $t = 100$ s. Compare this value to the one calculated in Example 14-2(b). Explain the reason for the difference.

CONCEPT ASSESSMENT ✓

As shown later in the chapter, for certain reactions the initial and instantaneous rates of reaction are equal throughout the course of the reaction. What must be the shape of the concentration–time graph for such a reaction?

14-3 EFFECT OF CONCENTRATION ON REACTION RATES: THE RATE LAW

One of the goals in a chemical kinetics study is to derive an equation that can be used to predict the relationship between the rate of reaction and the concentrations of reactants. Such an experimentally determined equation is called a **rate law**, or **rate equation**.

Consider the hypothetical reaction

$$a\text{A} + b\text{B} \cdots \longrightarrow g\text{G} + h\text{H} \cdots \qquad (14.5)$$

where $a, b, \ldots$ stand for coefficients in the balanced equation. We can often express the rate of such a reaction as*

$$\text{rate of reaction} = k[\text{A}]^m[\text{B}]^n \cdots \qquad (14.6)$$

The terms $[\text{A}]$, $[\text{B}], \ldots$ represent reactant molarities. The required exponents, $m, n, \ldots$ are generally small, positive whole numbers, although in some cases they may be zero, fractional, and/or negative. They must be determined by experiment and are generally *not* related to stoichiometric coefficients $a, b, \ldots$. That is, often $m \neq a$, $n \neq b$, and so on.

The term *order* is related to the exponents in the rate law and is used in two ways: (1) If $m = 1$, we say that the reaction is *first order in A*. If $n = 2$, the reaction is *second order in B*, and so on. (2) The *overall* **order of reaction** is the sum of all the exponents: $m + n + \cdots$. The proportionality constant k relates the rate of reaction to reactant concentrations and is called the **rate constant** of the reaction. Its value depends on the specific reaction, the presence of a catalyst (if any), and the temperature. *The larger the value of k, the faster a reaction goes.* The order of the reaction establishes the general form of the rate law and the appropriate units of k (that is, depending on the values of the exponents).

With the rate law for a reaction, we can

- calculate rates of reaction for known concentrations of reactants
- derive an equation that expresses a reactant concentration as a function of time

But how do we establish the rate law? We need to use *experimental* data of the type described in Section 14-2. The method we describe next works especially well.

METHOD OF INITIAL RATES

As its name implies, this method requires us to work with *initial* rates of reaction. As an example, let's look at a specific reaction: that between mercury(II) chloride and oxalate ion.

$$2\,\text{HgCl}_2(\text{aq}) + \text{C}_2\text{O}_4{}^{2-}(\text{aq}) \longrightarrow 2\,\text{Cl}^-(\text{aq}) + 2\,\text{CO}_2(\text{g}) + \text{Hg}_2\text{Cl}_2(\text{s}) \qquad (14.7)$$

---

*We assume that reaction (14.5) goes to completion. If it is reversible, the rate equation is more complex than (14.6). Even for reversible reactions, though, equation (14.6) applies to the *initial* rate of reaction because in the early stages of the reaction there are not enough products for a significant reverse reaction to occur.

TABLE 14.3	Kinetic Data for the Reaction: $2\,HgCl_2 + C_2O_4^{2-} \longrightarrow 2\,Cl^- + 2\,CO_2 + Hg_2Cl_2$		
Experiment	[HgCl₂], M	[C₂O₄²⁻], M	Initial rate, M min⁻¹
1	$[HgCl_2]_1 = 0.105$	$[C_2O_4^{2-}]_1 = 0.15$	1.8×10^{-5}
2	$[HgCl_2]_2 = 0.105$	$[C_2O_4^{2-}]_2 = 0.30$	7.1×10^{-5}
3	$[HgCl_2]_3 = 0.052$	$[C_2O_4^{2-}]_3 = 0.30$	3.5×10^{-5}

The tentative rate law that we can write for this reaction is

$$\text{rate of reaction} = k[HgCl_2]^m[C_2O_4^{2-}]^n \qquad (14.8)$$

We can follow the reaction by measuring the quantity of $Hg_2Cl_2(s)$ formed as a function of time. Some representative data are given in Table 14.3, which we can assume are based on either the rate of formation of Hg_2Cl_2 or the rate of disappearance of $C_2O_4^{2-}$. In Example 14-3, we will use some of these data to illustrate the method of initial rates.

EXAMPLE 14-3

Establishing the Order of a Reaction by the Method of Initial Rates. Use data from Table 14.3 to establish the order of reaction (14.7) with respect to $HgCl_2$ and $C_2O_4^{2-}$ and also the overall order of the reaction.

Solution

We need to determine the values of m and n in equation (14.8). In comparing Experiment 2 with Experiment 3, note that $[HgCl_2]$ is essentially doubled ($0.105\,\text{M} \approx 2 \times 0.052\,\text{M}$) while $[C_2O_4^{2-}]$ is held constant (at 0.30 M). Note also that $R_2 = 2 \times R_3$ ($7.1 \times 10^{-5} \approx 2 \times 3.5 \times 10^{-5}$). Rather than use the actual concentrations and rates in the following rate equation, let's work with their symbolic equivalents.

$$R_2 = k \times [HgCl_2]_2^m \times [C_2O_4^{2-}]_2^n = k \times (2 \times [HgCl_2]_3)^m \times [C_2O_4^{2-}]_3^n$$

$$R_3 = k \times [HgCl_2]_3^m \times [C_2O_4^{2-}]_3^n$$

$$\frac{R_2}{R_3} = \frac{2 \times R_3}{R_3} = 2 = \frac{k \times 2^m \times [HgCl_2]_3^m \times [C_2O_4^{2-}]_3^n}{k \times [HgCl_2]_3^m \times [C_2O_4^{2-}]_3^n} = 2^m$$

In order that $2^m = 2$, $m = 1$.

To determine the value of n, we can form the ratio R_2/R_1. Now, $[C_2O_4^{2-}]$ is doubled and $[HgCl_2]$ is held constant. This time, let's use actual concentrations instead of symbolic equivalents. Also, we now have the value $m = 1$.

$$R_2 = k \times [HgCl_2]_2^1 \times [C_2O_4^{2-}]_2^n = k \times (0.105)^1 \times (2 \times 0.15)^n$$

$$R_1 = k \times [HgCl_2]_1^1 \times [C_2O_4^{2-}]_1^n = k \times (0.105)^1 \times (0.15)^n$$

$$\frac{R_2}{R_1} = \frac{7.1 \times 10^{-5}}{1.8 \times 10^{-5}} \approx 4 = \frac{k \times (0.105)^1 \times 2^n \times (0.15)^n}{k \times (0.105)^1 \times (0.15)^n} = 2^n$$

In order that $2^n = 4$, $n = 2$.

In summary, the reaction is *first* order in $HgCl_2$ ($m = 1$), *second* order in $C_2O_4^{2-}$ ($n = 2$), and *third* order overall ($m + n = 1 + 2 = 3$).

Practice Example A: The decomposition of N_2O_5 is given by the following equation:

$$2\,N_2O_5 \longrightarrow 4\,NO_2 + O_2$$

At an initial $[N_2O_5] = 3.15$ M, the initial rate of reaction $= 5.45 \times 10^{-5}\,\text{M s}^{-1}$, and when $[N_2O_5] = 0.78$ M, the initial rate of reaction $= 1.35 \times 10^{-5}\,\text{M s}^{-1}$. Determine the order of this decomposition reaction.

Practice Example B: Consider a hypothetical Experiment 4 in Table 14.3, in which the initial conditions are $[HgCl_2]_4 = 0.025$ M and $[C_2O_4^{2-}]_4 = 0.045$ M. Predict the initial rate of reaction.

We made an important observation in Example 14-3: If a reaction is *first order* in one of the reactants, doubling the initial concentration of that reactant causes the initial rate of reaction to double. Following is the general effect of *doubling* the initial concentration of a particular reactant (with other reactant concentrations held constant).

> Note that rates that are too fast for traditional methods of analysis are followed by spectroscopic methods.

- *Zero order* in the reactant—there is *no effect* on the initial rate of reaction.
- *First order* in the reactant—the initial rate of reaction *doubles*.
- *Second order* in the reactant—the initial rate of reaction *quadruples*.
- *Third order* in the reactant—the initial rate of reaction *increases eightfold*.

As previously mentioned, the order of a reaction, as indicated through the rate law, establishes the units of the rate constant, k. That is, if on the left side of the rate law the rate of reaction has the units M (time)$^{-1}$, on the right side, the units of k must provide for the cancellations that also lead to M (time)$^{-1}$. Thus, for the rate law established in Example 14-3,

rate law: rate of reaction $= k \times [HgCl_2] \times [C_2O_4{}^{2-}]^2$

units: M min^{-1} M^{-2} min^{-1} M   M^2

Once we have the exponents in a rate equation, we can determine the value of the rate constant, k. To do this, all we need is the rate of reaction corresponding to known initial concentrations of reactants, as illustrated in Example 14-4.

EXAMPLE 14-4

Using the Rate Law. Use the results of Example 14-3 and data from Table 14.3 to establish the value of k in the rate law (14.8).

Solution

We can use data from any one of the three experiments of Table 14.3, together with the values $m = 1$ and $n = 2$. First, we solve equation (14.8) for k.

$$k = \frac{R_1}{[HgCl_2][C_2O_4{}^{2-}]^2} = \frac{1.8 \times 10^{-5} \text{ M min}^{-1}}{0.105 \text{ M} \times (0.15)^2 \text{ M}^2}$$

$$= 7.6 \times 10^{-3} \text{ M}^{-2} \text{ min}^{-1}$$

> Remind students that the value of k calculated in Example 14-4 and the data presented in Table 14.3 vary with temperature.

Practice Example A: A reaction has the rate law: rate $= k[A]^2[B]$. When $[A] = 1.12$ M and $[B] = 0.87$ M, the rate of reaction $= 4.78 \times 10^{-2}$ M s^{-1}. What is the value of the rate constant, k?

Practice Example B: What is the rate of reaction (14.7) at the point where $[HgCl_2] = 0.050$ M and $[C_2O_4{}^{2-}] = 0.025$ M?

KEEP IN MIND ▶

that if the rate data in Table 14.3 were based on the disappearance of $HgCl_2$ instead of $C_2O_4{}^{2-}$, R_1 in this setup would be twice as great. Then k for the general rate of reaction would have to be based on $-\frac{1}{2} \times$ (rate of disappearance of $HgCl_2$).

CONCEPT ASSESSMENT ✓

The rate of decomposition of gaseous acetaldehyde, CH_3CHO, to gaseous methane and carbon monoxide is found to increase by a factor of 2.83 when the initial concentration of acetaldehyde is doubled. What is the order of this reaction?

14-4   ZERO-ORDER REACTIONS

An overall **zero-order reaction** has a rate law in which the sum of the exponents, $m + n \cdots$ is equal to 0. As an example, let's take a reaction in which a single reactant A decomposes to products.

$$A \longrightarrow \text{products}$$

Zero-order reactions are not nearly as common as first-order and second-order reactions. A demonstration of a zero-order reaction is described in Hindmarsh, K., House, Donald A. *J. Chem. Educ.* **1996:** 73, 585.

Are You Wondering . . .

About the difference between the rate of a reaction and the rate *constant* of a reaction?

Many students have difficulty with this distinction. Remember, a *rate of reaction* tells how the amount of a reactant or product changes with time and is usually expressed as moles per liter per time. A rate of reaction can be established through an expression of the type $-\Delta[A]/\Delta t$, from a tangent to a concentration–time curve, and by calculation from a rate law. In most cases, the rate of a reaction strongly depends on reactant concentrations and therefore changes continuously during a reaction.

The *rate constant* of a reaction (*k*) relates the rate of a reaction to reactant concentrations. Generally, it is not itself a rate of reaction, but it can be used it to calculate rates of reaction. Once the value of *k* at a given temperature has been established, *this value stays fixed* for the given reaction, regardless of the reactant concentrations. Whereas the units of rates of reaction do not depend on the order of a reaction, those of *k* do, as we shall see in this and the following two sections.

◀ The dependence of *k* on temperature is discussed in Section 14-9.

If the reaction is zero order, the rate law is

$$\text{rate of reaction} = k[A]^0 = k = \text{constant} \qquad (14.9)$$

Other features of this zero-order reaction are

- The concentration–time graph is a straight line with a *negative* slope (Fig. 14-3).
- The rate of reaction, which is equal to *k* and remains constant throughout the reaction, is the *negative* of the slope of this line.
- The units of *k* are the same as the units of the rate of a reaction: mol L^{-1} (time)$^{-1}$, for example, mol $L^{-1} s^{-1}$ or $M s^{-1}$.

Equation (14.9) is the rate law for a zero-order reaction. Another useful equation, called an **integrated rate law**, expresses the concentration of a reactant as a function of time. This equation can be established rather easily from the graph in Figure 14-3. Let's start with the general equation for a straight line

$$y = mx + b$$

and substitute $y = [A]_t$ (the concentration of A at some time *t*); $x = t$ (time); $b = [A]_0$ (the initial concentration of A at time $t = 0$); and $m = -k$ (*m*, the slope of the straight line, is obtained as indicated in the caption to Figure 14-3).

$$[A]_t = -kt + [A]_0 \qquad (14.10)$$

▲ **FIGURE 14-3**
A zero-order reaction: A ⟶ products
The initial concentration of the reactant A is $[A]_0$, that is, $[A] = [A]_0$ at $t = 0$. [A] decreases in concentration until the reaction stops. This occurs at the time, t_f, where $[A] = 0$. The slope of the line is $(0 - [A]_0)/(t_f - 0) = -[A]_0/t_f$. The rate constant is the *negative* of the slope: $k = -\text{slope} = [A]_0/t_f$.

◀ Perhaps the most important examples of zero-order reactions are found in the action of enzymes. Enzyme-catalyzed reactions are discussed in Section 14-11.

Are You Wondering . . .

If the term "integrated" rate law has anything to do with integral calculus?

Not surprisingly, it does. The rate of reaction in a rate law such as (14.9) is an *instantaneous* rate, which we learned in the "Are You Wondering" on page 576, can be represented through differentials. When $-d[A]/dt$ is substituted for the rate of reaction in the rate law for a zero-order reaction, we get this equation, $-d[A]/dt = k$. We can separate the differentials to obtain $d[A] = -kdt$. At this point we can apply the calculus procedure of integration to obtain, successively, the following expressions. The final one is the integrated rate law for a zero-order reaction (14.10).

$$\int_{[A]_0}^{[A]_t} d[A] = -k \int_0^t dt, \qquad [A]_t - [A]_0 = -kt, \qquad [A]_t = -kt + [A]_0 \qquad (14.10)$$

14-5 FIRST-ORDER REACTIONS

An overall **first-order reaction** has a rate law in which the sum of the exponents, $m + n \cdots$ is equal to 1. A particularly common type of first-order reaction, and the only type we will consider, is one in which a single reactant decomposes into products. Reaction (14.3), the decomposition of H_2O_2 that we described in Section 14-2, is a first-order reaction.

$$H_2O_2(aq) \longrightarrow H_2O(l) + \frac{1}{2}O_2(g)$$

The rate of reaction depends on the concentration of H_2O_2 raised to the *first* power, that is,

$$\text{rate of reaction} = k[H_2O_2] \tag{14.11}$$

It is easy to establish that reaction (14.3) is first order by the method of initial rates, but there are also other ways of recognizing a first-order reaction.

AN INTEGRATED RATE LAW FOR A FIRST-ORDER REACTION

Let us begin our discussion of first-order reactions as we did zero-order reactions, by examining a hypothetical reaction

$$A \longrightarrow \text{products}$$

for which the rate law is

$$\text{rate of reaction} = k[A] \tag{14.12}$$

We can obtain the *integrated* rate law for this first-order reaction by applying the calculus technique of *integration* to equation (14.12). The result of this derivation (shown in the Are You Wondering feature on page 583) is

$$\ln \frac{[A]_t}{[A]_0} = -kt \quad \text{or} \quad \ln[A]_t = -kt + \ln[A]_0 \tag{14.13}$$

$[A]_t$ is the concentration of A at time t, $[A]_0$ is its concentration at $t = 0$, and k is the rate constant. Because the logarithms of numbers are dimensionless (have no units), the product $-k \times t$ must also be dimensionless. This means that the unit of k in a first-order reaction is $(\text{time})^{-1}$, such as s^{-1} or $\min^{-1}$. Equation (14.13) is that of a straight line.

$$\underbrace{\ln[A]_t}_{y} = \underbrace{(-k)}_{}\underbrace{t}_{} + \underbrace{\ln[A]_0}_{b}$$
$$\qquad\qquad y \quad = \quad m \cdot x \ + \quad b$$

Equation of straight line

An easy test for a first-order reaction is to plot the natural logarithm of a reactant concentration versus time and see if the graph is linear. The data from Table 14.1 are plotted in Figure 14-4, and the rate constant k is derived from the slope of the line: $k = -\text{slope} = -(-7.30 \times 10^{-4}\,s^{-1}) = 7.30 \times 10^{-4}\,s^{-1}$. An alternative, nongraphical approach, illustrated in Practice Example 14-5B, is to substitute data points into equation (14.13) and solve for k.

EXAMPLE 14-5

Using the Integrated Rate Law for a First-Order Reaction. $H_2O_2(aq)$, initially at a concentration of 2.32 M, is allowed to decompose. What will $[H_2O_2]$ be at $t = 1200$ s? Use $k = 7.30 \times 10^{-4}\,s^{-1}$ for this first-order decomposition.

Solution

We have values for three of the four terms in equation (14.13)

$k = 7.30 \times 10^{-4}\,s^{-1}$ $\qquad$ $t = 1200$ s

$[H_2O_2]_0 = 2.32$ M $\qquad$ $[H_2O_2]_t = ?$

First-Order Process animation

☑ Most processes in nature follow first-order chemical kinetics. If you had a bank that compounded interest continuously, then your funds would grow exponentially.

KEEP IN MIND ▶

that the scatter experimental data on a straight-line graph often make a value of k calculated from equation (14.13) less reliable than a value obtained from the slope of the straight line.

Progress of Reaction activity

☑ Point out the meaning of the situation when the points do not lie on a straight line in Figure 14-4.

◀ **FIGURE 14-4**
Test for a first-order reaction: Decomposition of H_2O_2(aq)
Plot of ln H_2O_2 versus t. The data are based on Table 14.1 and are listed below. The slope of the line is used in the text.

t, s	H_2O_2, M	ln[H_2O_2]
0	2.32	0.842
200	2.01	0.698
400	1.72	0.542
600	1.49	0.399
1200	0.98	−0.020
1800	0.62	−0.48
3000	0.25	−1.39

which we substitute into the expression

$$\ln[H_2O_2]_t = -kt + \ln[H_2O_2]_0$$
$$= -(7.30 \times 10^{-4}\ s^{-1} \times 1200\ s) + \ln 2.32$$
$$= \qquad -0.876 \qquad + 0.842 = -0.034$$
$$[H_2O_2]_t = e^{-0.034} = 0.967\ M$$

This calculated value agrees well with the experimentally determined value of 0.98 M.

◀ To find the number whose natural logarithm is −0.034, raise e to the −0.034 power.

Practice Example A: The reaction A ⟶ 2 B + C is first order. If the initial [A] = 2.80 M and $k = 3.02 \times 10^{-3}\ s^{-1}$, what is the value of [A] after 325 s?

Practice Example B: Use data tabulated in Figure 14-4, together with equation (14.13), to show that the decomposition of H_2O_2 is a first-order reaction.

[*Hint:* Use a pair of data points for [H_2O_2]$_0$ and [H_2O_2]$_t$ and their corresponding times to solve for k. Repeat this calculation using other sets of data. How should the results compare?]

Are You Wondering . . .

How to obtain the integrated rate law for a first-order reaction?

In differential form, the rate law for the reaction A ⟶ product is $d[A]/dt = -k[A]$ Separation of the differentials leads to the expression $d[A]/[A] = -kdt$ Integration of this expression between the limits [A]$_0$ at time $t = 0$ and [A]$_t$ at time t is indicated through the expression

$$\int_{[A]_0}^{[A]_t} \frac{d[A]}{[A]} = -k \int_0^t dt, \qquad \text{yielding} \ \ln \frac{[A]_t}{[A]_0} = -kt$$

The result of the integration is the integrated rate law.

$$\ln \frac{[A]_t}{[A]_0} = -kt \qquad (14.13)$$

This article describes a classroom demonstration that can be used to calculate the rate order of the iodine clock reaction: Creary, X., Morris, K. M. *J. Chem. Educ.* **1999:** *76*, 530.

Although until now we have used only molar concentrations in kinetics equations, we can sometimes work directly with the masses of reactants. Another possibility is to work with a fraction of reactant consumed, as is done in the concept of half-life.

The **half-life** of a reaction is the time required for one-half of a reactant to be consumed. It is the time during which the amount of reactant or its concentration decreases to one-half of its initial value. That is, at $t = t_{1/2}$, $[A]_t = \frac{1}{2}[A]_0$. At this time, equation (14.13) takes the form

$$\ln \frac{[A]_t}{[A]_0} = \ln \frac{\frac{1}{2}[A]_0}{[A]_0} = \ln \frac{1}{2} = -\ln 2 = -k \times t_{1/2}$$

Some students might have heard about half-life in relation to radioactive decay. Point out that radioactive decay is a first-order process.

$$t_{1/2} = \frac{\ln 2}{k} = \frac{0.693}{k} \qquad (14.14)$$

For the decomposition of $H_2O_2(aq)$, the reaction described in Section 14-2, we conclude that the half-life is

$$t_{1/2} = \frac{0.693}{7.30 \times 10^{-4}\,s^{-1}} = 9.49 \times 10^2\,s = 949\,s$$

Equation (14.14) indicates that *the half-life is constant for a first-order reaction.* Thus, regardless of the value of $[A]_0$ at the time we begin to follow a reaction, at $t = t_{1/2}$, $[A] = \frac{1}{2}[A]_0$. After *two* half-lives, that is, at $t = 2 \times t_{1/2}$, $[A] = \frac{1}{2} \times \frac{1}{2}[A]_0 = \frac{1}{4}[A]_0$. At $t = 3 \times t_{1/2}$, $[A] = \frac{1}{8}[A]_0$, and so on.

Point out that half-life is constant for first-order reactions but not constant for zero-order or second-order reactions. For a zero-order reaction half life decreases with decreasing reactant concentration. For a second-order reaction half-life increases with decreasing reactant concentration.

The constancy of the half-life and its independence of the initial concentration can be used as a test for a first-order reaction. Try it with the simple concentration–time graph of Figure 14-2. That is, starting with $[H_2O_2] = 2.32\,M$ at $t = 0$, at what time is $[H_2O_2] \approx 1.16\,M$, $\approx 0.58\,M$, $\approx 0.29\,M$? Starting with $[H_2O_2] = 1.50\,M$ at $t = 600\,s$, at what time is $[H_2O_2] = 0.75\,M$?

As illustrated in Example 14-6, a first-order reaction can also be described in terms of the percent of a reactant consumed or remaining.

EXAMPLE 14-6

Expressing Fraction (or Percent) of Reactant Consumed in a First-Order Reaction. Use a value of $k = 7.30 \times 10^{-4}\,s^{-1}$ for the first-order decomposition of $H_2O_2(aq)$ to determine the percent H_2O_2 that has decomposed in the first 500.0 s after the reaction begins.

Solution

The ratio $[H_2O_2]_t/[H_2O_2]_0$ represents the fractional part of the initial amount of H_2O_2 that remains *unreacted* at time t. Our problem is to evaluate this ratio at $t = 500.0\,s$.

$$\ln \frac{[H_2O_2]_t}{[H_2O_2]_0} = -kt = -7.30 \times 10^{-4}\,s^{-1} \times 500.0\,s = -0.365$$

$$\frac{[H_2O_2]_t}{[H_2O_2]_0} = e^{-0.365} = 0.694 \qquad \text{and} \qquad [H_2O_2]_t = 0.694[H_2O_2]_0$$

The fractional part of the H_2O_2 remaining is 0.694, or 69.4%. The percent of H_2O_2 that has decomposed is $100.0\% - 69.4\% = 30.6\%$.

Practice Example A: Consider the first-order reaction A $\longrightarrow$ products, with $k = 2.95 \times 10^{-3}\,s^{-1}$. What percent of A remains after 150 s?

Practice Example B: At what time after the start of the reaction is a sample of $H_2O_2(aq)$ two-thirds decomposed? $k = 7.30 \times 10^{-4}\,s^{-1}$?

REACTIONS INVOLVING GASES

For gaseous reactions, rates are often measured in terms of gas pressures. For the hypothetical reaction, $A(g) \longrightarrow$ products, the initial partial pressure, $(P_A)_0$, and the partial pressure at some time t, $(P_A)_t$, are related through the expression

$$\ln \frac{(P_A)_t}{(P_A)_0} = -kt \qquad (14.15)$$

To see how this equation is derived, start with the ideal gas equation written for reactant A: $P_A V = n_A RT$. Note that the ratio n_A/V is the same as [A]. So, $[A]_0 = (P_A)_0/RT$ and $[A]_t = (P_A)_t/RT$. Substitute these terms into equation (14.13), and note that the RT terms cancel in the numerator and denominator and leave the simple ratio $(P_A)_t/(P_A)_0$.

Di-t-butyl peroxide (DTBP) is used as a catalyst in the manufacture of polymers. In the gaseous state, DTBP decomposes into acetone and ethane by a first-order reaction.

$$\underset{\text{DTBP}}{C_8H_{18}O_2(g)} \longrightarrow \underset{\text{acetone}}{2\,C_3H_6O(g)} + \underset{\text{ethane}}{C_2H_6(g)} \qquad (14.16)$$

Partial pressures of DTBP are plotted as a function of time in Figure 14-5, and the half-life of the reaction is indicated.

As shown in the Are You Wondering feature on page 586, the partial pressure of the reactant DTBP can be obtained from two experimentally determined quantities: the initial pressure P_0, and the total pressure P_{total}.

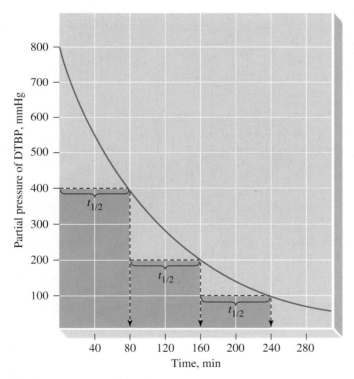

▲ **FIGURE 14-5**
Decomposition of di-t-butyl peroxide (DTBP) at 147 °C
The decomposition reaction is described through equation (14.16). In this graph of the partial pressure of DTBP as a function of time, three successive half-life periods of 80 min each are indicated. This constancy of the half-life is proof that the reaction is first order.

Are You Wondering . . .

How the partial pressure can be obtained experimentally in a reaction involving gases?

In the study of a reaction like the decomposition of DTBP, the *total* pressure is typically measured as a function of time. At any time t, the total pressure is

$$(P_{total})_t = (P_{DTBP})_t + (P_{acetone})_t + (P_{ethane})_t$$

If the initial pressure of DTBP is P_0, then using the stoichiometry of the balanced chemical equation, the partial pressure of DTBP is $P_{DTBP} = (P_0 - P_{ethane})$ since for every mole of DTBP that decomposes, a mole of ethane is produced. The partial pressure of acetone is $P_{acetone} = 2 P_{ethane}$, again using the stoichiometry of the reaction. The total pressure is then given by

$$P_{total} = (P_0 - P_{ethane}) + 2 P_{ethane} + P_{ethane} = P_0 + 2 P_{ethane}$$

and

$$P_{ethane} = \frac{P_{total} - P_0}{2}$$

So that

$$P_{DTBP} = (P_0 - P_{ethane}) = \frac{2 P_0 - (P_{total} - P_0)}{2} = \frac{3 P_0 - P_{total}}{2}.$$

▶ Note that the total pressure in reaction (14.16) increases from P_0 at the start of the reaction to $3 P_0$ when P_{DTBP} has fallen to zero.

EXAMPLE 14-7

Applying First-Order Kinetics to a Reaction Involving Gases. Reaction (14.16) is started with pure DTBP at 147 °C and 800.0 mmHg pressure in a flask of constant volume. **(a)** What is the value of the rate constant k? **(b)** At what time will the partial pressure of DTBP be 50.0 mmHg?

Solution

(a) From Figure 14-5, we see that $t_{1/2} = 8.0 \times 10^1$ min. For a first-order reaction, $t_{1/2} = 0.693/k$, or

$$k = 0.693/t_{1/2} = 0.693/8.0 \times 10^1 \text{ min} = 8.7 \times 10^{-3} \text{ min}^{-1}$$

(b) A DTBP partial pressure of 50.0 mmHg is $\frac{1}{16}$ of the starting pressure of 800.0 mmHg, that is, $P_{DTBP} = \left(\frac{1}{2}\right)^4 \times 800.0 = 50.0$ mmHg. The reaction must go through *four* half-lives; $t = 4 \times t_{1/2} = 4 \times 8.0 \times 10^1$ min = 3.2×10^2 min.

Practice Example A: Start with DTBP at a pressure of 800.0 mmHg at 147 °C. What will be the pressure of DTBP at $t = 125$ min, if $t_{1/2} = 8.0 \times 10^1$ min?

[*Hint:* Because 125 min is not an exact multiple of the half-life, you must use equation (14.15). Can you see that the answer is between 200 and 400 mmHg?]

Practice Example B: Use data from Table 14.4 to determine **(a)** the partial pressure of ethylene oxide, and **(b)** the total gas pressure after 30.0 h in a reaction vessel at 415 °C if the initial partial pressure of $(CH_2)_2O(g)$ is 782 mmHg.

EXAMPLES OF FIRST-ORDER REACTIONS

▶ We will explore radioactive decay in some detail in Chapter 25.

One of the most familiar examples of a first-order process is radioactive decay. For example, the radioactive isotope iodine-131, used in treating thyroid disorders, has a half-life of 8.04 days. Whatever number of iodine-131 atoms are in a sample at a given moment, there will be half that number in 8.04 days; one-quarter of that number in $8.04 + 8.04 = 16.08$ days; and so on. The rate constant for the decay is $k = 0.693/t_{1/2}$, and in equation (14.13) we can use numbers of atoms, that is, N_t for $[A]_t$ and N_0 for $[A]_0$. Table 14.4 lists several examples of first-order processes. Note the great range of values of $t_{1/2}$ and k. The processes range from very slow to ultrafast.

TABLE 14.4   Some Typical First-Order Processes

Process	Half-Life, $t_{1/2}$	Rate Constant k, s^{-1}
Radioactive decay of $^{238}_{92}U$	4.51×10^9 yr	4.87×10^{-18}
Radioactive decay of $^{14}_{6}C$	5.73×10^3 yr	3.83×10^{-12}
Radioactive decay of $^{32}_{15}P$	14.3 d	5.61×10^{-7}
$C_{12}H_{22}O_{11}(aq) + H_2O(l) \xrightarrow{15\,°C} C_6H_{12}O_6(aq) + C_6H_{12}O_6(aq)$ sucrose glucose fructose	8.4 h	2.3×10^{-5}
$(CH_2)_2O(g) \xrightarrow{415\,°C} CH_4(g) + CO(g)$ ethylene oxide	56.3 min	2.05×10^{-4}
$2\,N_2O_5(g) \xrightarrow[45\,°C]{\text{in } CCl_4} 2\,N_2O_4(g) + O_2(g)$	18.6 min	6.21×10^{-4}
$HC_2H_3O_2(aq) \longrightarrow H^+(aq) + C_2H_3O_2^-(aq)$	8.9×10^{-7} s	7.8×10^5

CONCEPT ASSESSMENT ✓

Without doing calculations, sketch **(a)** concentration versus time plots for two first-order reactions, one having a large k and the other a small k, and **(b)** ln k versus time plots for the same two situations. Describe the similarities and differences between the two plots in each case.

14-6   SECOND-ORDER REACTIONS

An overall **second-order reaction** has a rate law with the sum of the exponents, $m + n \cdots$, equal to 2. As with zero- and first-order reactions, our discussion will be limited to reactions involving the decomposition of a single reactant

$$A \longrightarrow \text{products}$$

that follow the rate law

$$\text{rate of reaction} = k[A]^2 \qquad (14.17)$$

Again, our primary interest will be in the integrated rate law that is derived from the rate law. This proves to be the equation of a straight-line graph.

$$\frac{1}{[A]_t} = kt + \frac{1}{[A]_0} \qquad (14.18)$$

Figure 14-6 is a plot of $1/[A]_t$ against time. The slope of the line is k, and the intercept is $1/[A]_0$. From the graph, we can see that the units of k must be the *reciprocal* of concentration divided by time: $M^{-1}/(\text{time})$ or $M^{-1}(\text{time})^{-1}$—for example, $M^{-1}\,s^{-1}$ or $M^{-1}\,min^{-1}$. We can reach this same conclusion by determining the units of k that produce the required units for the rate of a reaction, that is, moles per liter per time. From equation (14.17):

rate law:	rate of reaction $= k \times [A]^2$
units:	$M\,\text{time}^{-1}$ $M^{-1}\,\text{time}^{-1}\,M^2$

For the half-life of the second-order reaction $A \longrightarrow$ products, we can substitute $t = t_{1/2}$ and $[A] = \frac{1}{2}[A]_0$ into equation (14.18).

$$\frac{1}{[A]_0/2} = kt_{1/2} + \frac{1}{[A]_0}; \qquad \frac{2}{[A]_0} = kt_{1/2} + \frac{1}{[A]_0} \qquad \text{and} \qquad t_{1/2} = \frac{1}{k[A]_0} \qquad (14.19)$$

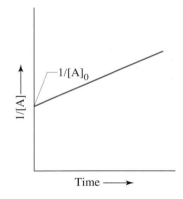

▲ **FIGURE 14-6**
A straight-line plot for the second-order reaction $A \longrightarrow$ products
The reciprocal of the concentration, $1/[A]$, is plotted against time. As the reaction proceeds, [A] decreases and $1/[A]$ increases in a linear fashion. The slope of the line is the rate constant k.

First- and Second-Order Reactions activity

From equation (14.19), we see that the half-life depends on both the rate constant *and* the initial concentration $[A]_0$. The *half-life is not constant.* Its value depends on the concentration of reactant at the start of each half-life interval. Because the starting concentration is always one-half that of the previous half-life, each successive half-life is twice as long as the one before it.

PSEUDO-FIRST-ORDER REACTIONS

At times, it is possible to simplify the kinetic study of complex reactions by getting them to behave like reactions of a lower order. Then their rate laws become easier to work with. Consider the hydrolysis of ethyl acetate, which is second order overall.

$$CH_3COOC_2H_5 + H_2O \longrightarrow CH_3COOH + C_2H_5OH$$

ethyl acetate   acetic acid   ethanol

Suppose we follow the hydrolysis of 1 L of aqueous 0.01 M ethyl acetate to completion. $[CH_3COOC_2H_5]$ decreases from 0.01 M to essentially zero. This means that 0.01 mol $CH_3COOC_2H_5$ is consumed, and along with it, 0.01 mol H_2O. Now consider what happens to the molarity of the H_2O. Initially, the solution contains about 1000 g H_2O, or about 55.5 mol H_2O. When the reaction is completed, there is still 55.5 mol H_2O (that is, $55.5 - 0.01 \approx 55.5$). The molarity of the water remains essentially constant throughout the reaction—55.5 M. The rate of reaction does not appear to depend on $[H_2O]$. So, the reaction appears to be *zero* order in H_2O, *first* order in $CH_3COOC_2H_5$, and *first* order overall. A second-order reaction that is made to behave like a first-order reaction by holding one reactant concentration constant is called a *pseudo*-first-order reaction. We can treat the reaction with the methods of first-order reaction kinetics. Other reactions of higher order can be made to behave like reactions of lower order under certain conditions. Thus, a third-order reaction might be converted to pseudo-second order or even to pseudo-first order.

▶ The rate constant obtained from a study using an excess of one reactant, sometimes called Ostwald's isolation method after the kineticist who invented it, is a pseudo-rate constant and is concentration-dependent.

Are You Wondering . . .

How we obtain the integrated rate law for the second-order reaction A $\longrightarrow$ products?

In differential form, the rate law for the reaction A $\longrightarrow$ products, is $d[A]/dt = -k[A]^2$.
Separation of the differentials leads to the expression $d[A]/[A]^2 = -kdt$.
Integration of this expression between the limits $[A]_0$ at time $t = 0$ and $[A]_t$ at time t is indicated through the expression

$$\int_{[A]_0}^{[A]_t} \frac{d[A]}{[A]^2} = -\int_0^t kdt$$

The result of the integration is the integrated rate law.

$$-\frac{1}{[A]_t} + \frac{1}{[A]_0} = -kt \quad \text{or} \quad \frac{1}{[A]_t} = kt + \frac{1}{[A]_0} \qquad (14.18)$$

The emphasis has been on reaction rates that approach equilibrium. In a vast number of chemical processes, however, equilibrium is not a desirable condition. For example, processes within cells are cyclic and oscillate. These reactions are not considered here, but are of great importance in the study of chemical kinetics.

14-7 REACTION KINETICS: A SUMMARY

Let's pause briefly to review what we have learned about rates of reaction, rate constants, and reaction orders. Although a problem often can be solved in several different ways, these approaches are generally most direct.

1. To calculate a rate of reaction when the rate law is known, use this expression: rate of reaction $= k[A]^m[B]^n \cdots$

TABLE 14.5   Reaction Kinetics: A Summary for the Hypothetical Reaction A ⟶ Products

Order	Rate Law	Integrated Rate Equation	Straight Line	k =	Units of k	Half-life
0	Rate = k	$[A]_t = -kt + [A]_0$	$[A]$ v. time	$-$slope	mol L^{-1} s^{-1}	$[A]_0/2k$
1	Rate = $k[A]$	$\ln[A]_t = -kt + \ln[A]_0$	$\ln[A]$ v. time	$-$slope	s^{-1}	$0.693/k$
2	Rate = $k[A]^2$	$\dfrac{1}{[A]_t} = kt + \dfrac{1}{[A]_0}$	$\dfrac{1}{[A]}$ v. time	slope	L mol^{-1} s^{-1}	$\dfrac{1}{k[A]_0}$

2. To determine a rate of reaction when the rate law is not given, use
   - the slope of an appropriate tangent line to the graph of [A] versus t
   - the expression $-\Delta[A]/\Delta t$, with a short time interval Δt
3. To determine the order of a reaction, use one of the following methods.
   - Use the method of initial rates if the experimental data are given in the form of reaction rates at different initial concentrations.
   - Find the graph of rate data that yields a straight line (Table 14.5).
   - Test for the constancy of the half-life (good only for first-order).
   - Substitute rate data into integrated rate laws to find the one that gives a constant value of k.
4. To find the rate constant k for a reaction, use one of the following methods.
   - Obtain k from the slope of a straight-line graph.
   - Substitute concentration–time data into the appropriate integrated rate law.
   - Obtain k from the half-life of the reaction (good only for a first-order reaction).
5. To relate reactant concentrations and times, use the appropriate integrated rate law after first determining k.

EXAMPLE 14-8

Graphing Data to Determine the Order of a Reaction. The data listed in Table 14.6 were obtained for the decomposition reaction, A ⟶ products. **(a)** Establish the order of the reaction. **(b)** What is the rate constant, k? **(c)** What is the half-life, $t_{1/2}$, if $[A]_0 = 1.00$ M?

TABLE 14.6   Kinetic Data for Example 14-8

Time, min	[A], M	ln [A]	1/[A]
0	1.00	0.00	1.00
5	0.63	−0.46	1.6
10	0.46	−0.78	2.2
15	0.36	−1.02	2.8
25	0.25	−1.39	4.0

▲ FIGURE 14-7
Testing for the order of a reaction—Example 14-8 illustrated
The straight-line plot is obtained for 1/[A] versus t, graph (3). The reaction is second order.

Solution

(a) Plot the following three graphs.
   1. [A] versus time. (If a straight line, reaction is zero order.)
   2. ln[A] versus time. (If a straight line, reaction is first order.)
   3. 1/[A] versus time. (If a straight line, reaction is second order.)

These graphs are plotted in Figure 14-7. The reaction is second order.

(b) The slope of graph 3 in Figure 14-7 is

$$k = \frac{(4.00 - 1.00)\ \text{L/mol}}{25\ \text{min}} = 0.12\ \text{M}^{-1}\ \text{min}^{-1}$$

(c) According to equation (14.19),

$$t_{1/2} = \frac{1}{k[\text{A}]_0} = \frac{1}{0.12\ \text{M}^{-1}\ \text{min}^{-1} \times 1.00\ \text{M}} = 8.3\ \text{min}$$

Practice Example A: In the decomposition reaction B $\longrightarrow$ products, the following data are obtained: $t = 0$ s, $[\text{B}] = 0.88$ M; $t = 25$ s, 0.74 M; $t = 50$ s, 0.62 M; $t = 75$ s, 0.52 M; $t = 100$ s, 0.44 M; $t = 150$ s, 0.31 M; $t = 200$ s, 0.22 M; $t = 250$ s, 0.16 M. What are the order of this reaction and its rate constant k?

Practice Example B: The following data are obtained for the reaction A $\longrightarrow$ products: $t = 0$ min, $[\text{A}] = 0.250$ M; $t = 4.22$ min, $[\text{A}] = 0.210$ M; $t = 6.60$ min, $[\text{A}] = 0.188$ M; $t = 10.61$ min, $[\text{A}] = 0.150$ M; $t = 14.48$ min, $[\text{A}] = 0.114$ M; $t = 18.00$ min, $[\text{A}] = 0.083$ M. What are the order of this reaction and its rate constant, k?

Are You Wondering . . .

If you can determine the order of a reaction just from a single graph of [A] versus time?

You can for reactions of the type A $\longrightarrow$ products and orders limited to zero, first, and second. If the [A] versus t graph is a straight line, the reaction is *zero order*. If the graph is not linear, apply the half-life test, as in Figure 14-5. If $t_{1/2}$ is constant, the reaction is *first order*. If the half-life is not constant, the reaction is *second order*. (For a second-order reaction, you will find that the half-life *doubles* for every successive half-life period.)

14-8   THEORETICAL MODELS FOR CHEMICAL KINETICS

Practical aspects of reaction kinetics—rate laws, rate constants—can be described without considering the behavior of individual molecules. However, insight into the processes involved requires examination at the molecular level. For example, experiments show that the decomposition of H_2O_2 is first order, but *why* is this so? The remainder of the chapter considers the theoretical aspects of chemical kinetics that help answer such questions.

COLLISION THEORY

In our discussion of kinetic-molecular theory in Chapter 6 our emphasis was on molecular speeds. A further aspect of the theory with relevance to chemical kinetics is **collision frequency**—the number of molecular collisions per unit time. In a typical reaction involving gases, the calculated collision frequency is of the order of 10^{30} collisions per second. If each collision yielded product molecules, the rate of reaction would be about 10^6 M s^{-1}, an extremely rapid rate. The typical gas-phase reaction would go essentially to completion in a fraction of a second. Gas-phase reactions generally proceed at a much slower rate, perhaps on the order of 10^{-4} M s^{-1}. This must mean that, generally, *only a fraction of the collisions among gaseous molecules lead to chemical reaction*. This is a reasonable conclusion; we should not expect every collision to result in a reaction.

✓ Not all collisions are effective in causing a reaction. The average time between collisions in a gas at STP is about 10^{-10} s and the time that the collision is actually taking place is about 10^{-13} s.

◀ **FIGURE 14-8**
Distribution of molecular kinetic energies
At both temperatures, the fraction of all molecules having kinetic energies in excess of the value marked by the heavy black arrow is small. (Note the shaded areas on the right.) At the higher temperature T_2 (red), however, this fraction is considerably larger than at the lower temperature T_1 (blue).

For a reaction to occur following a collision between molecules, there must be a redistribution of energy that puts enough energy into certain key bonds to break them. We would not expect two slow-moving molecules to bring enough kinetic energy into their collision to permit bond breakage. We would expect two fast-moving molecules to do so, however, or perhaps one extremely fast molecule colliding with a slow-moving one. The **activation energy** of a reaction is the minimum energy above the average kinetic energy that molecules must bring to their collisions for a chemical reaction to occur.

The kinetic-molecular theory can be used to establish the fraction of all the molecules in a mixture that possess certain kinetic energies. The results of this calculation are depicted in Figure 14-8. On this graph, a hypothetical energy is noted and the fraction of all molecules having energies in excess of this value is identified. Let's assume that these are the molecules whose molecular collisions are most likely to lead to chemical reaction. The rate of a reaction, then, depends on the product of the collision frequency *and* the fraction of these "activated" molecules—in other words, on how often molecules with sufficient kinetic energy to react are likely to collide with each other. Because the fraction of high-energy molecules is generally so small, the rate of reaction is usually much smaller than the collision frequency. Moreover, the *higher* the activation energy of a reaction, the *smaller* is the fraction of energetic collisions and the slower the reaction.

Another factor that can strongly affect the rate of a reaction is the *orientation* of molecules at the time of their collision. In a reaction in which two hydrogen atoms combine to form a hydrogen molecule (see margin) no bonds are broken and a H—H bond forms

$$H\cdot + \cdot H \longrightarrow H_2$$

The H atoms are spherically symmetrical, and all approaches of one H atom to another prior to collision are equivalent. Orientation is *not* a factor, and the reaction occurs about as rapidly as the atoms collide. On the other hand, orientation of the colliding molecules is a crucial matter in the reaction of N_2O and NO, represented here in an equation highlighting chemical bonds.

$$N\equiv N-O + N=O \longrightarrow N\equiv N + O-N\overset{\displaystyle O}{\diagup} \qquad (14.20)$$

The fundamental changes that occur during a successful collision are that the N—O bond in N_2O breaks and a new O—N bond is established to the NO molecule. As a result of the collision, the molecules N_2 and NO_2 are formed. As suggested by Figure 14-9, a favorable collision requires the N atom of the NO molecule to strike the O atom of N_2O during a collision. Other orientations, such as the N atom of NO striking the terminal N atom of N_2O, do not produce a reaction. The number of unfavorable collisions in the reaction mixture exceeds the number of favorable ones.

Analogies to help explain collision theory are described in Piepgrass, K. W. *J. Chem. Educ.* **1998:** *75,* 724 and a simulation to help explain collision theory is described in Evenson, A. *J. Chem. Educ.* **2002:** *79,* 822.

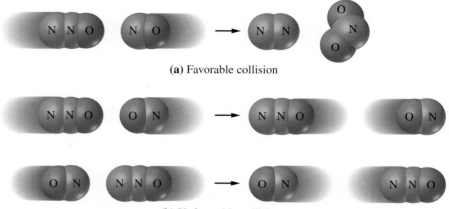

(a) Favorable collision

(b) Unfavorable collisions

▶ **FIGURE 14-9**
Molecular collisions and chemical reactions
(a) A favorable collision between N_2O and NO molecules, resulting in the products N_2 and NO_2.
(b) Two unfavorable collisions between N_2O and NO molecules; no reaction follows the collisions.

Molecular Collisions activity

Modern Raman laser spectroscopic methods can occur in the femtosecond (10^{-15}) time scale. This allows all motions, except electronic transitions, to be frozen. Such techniques are used to study activated complexes.

TRANSITION STATE THEORY

In a theory proposed by Henry Eyring (1901–1981) and others, special emphasis is placed on a hypothetical species believed to exist in a transitory state that lies between the reactants and the products. We call this state the **transition state**, and the hypothetical species, the **activated complex**. The activated complex, formed through collisions, either dissociates back into the original reactants or forms product molecules. We can represent an activated complex for reaction (14.20) in this way.

$$N\equiv N—O + N=O \rightleftharpoons N\equiv N\cdots O\cdots N{\overset{O}{\diagdown}} \longrightarrow N\equiv N + O—N{\overset{O}{\diagdown}}$$

reactants   activated complex   products

In the reactants, there is no bond between the O atom of N_2O and the N atom of NO. In the activated complex, the O atom has been partially removed from the N_2O molecule and partially joined to the NO molecule, as indicated by the *partial bonds* ($\cdots$). The formation of the activated complex is a reversible process. Once formed, some molecules of the activated complex may dissociate back into the reactants, but others may dissociate into the product molecules, where the partial bond of the O atom in N_2O has been completely severed and the partial bond between the O atom and NO has become a complete bond.

Figure 14-10, called a reaction profile, is a graphical way of looking at activation energy. In a **reaction profile**, energies are plotted on the vertical axis against a quantity called "progress of reaction" on the horizontal axis. Think of the progress of reaction as representing the extent of the reaction. That is, the reaction starts with reactants on the left, progresses through a transition state, and ends with products on the right.

The difference in energies between the reactants and products is ΔH for the reaction. Reaction (14.20) is an exothermic reaction with $\Delta H = -139$ kJ. The difference in energy between the activated complex and the reactants, 209 kJ, is the *activation energy* of the reaction. Thus, a large energy barrier separates the reactants from the products, and only very energetic molecules can pass over this barrier. Figure 14-11 suggests an analogy to activation energy and the reaction profile.

Figure 14-10 describes both the forward reaction and its reverse—the reaction of N_2 and NO_2 to form N_2O and NO. The activation energy for the reverse reaction is 348 kJ; this reverse reaction is highly endothermic. Figure 14-10 also illustrates two useful ideas. (1) The enthalpy change of a reaction is equal to the difference in activation energies of the forward and reverse reactions. (2) For an *endothermic* reaction, the activation energy must be equal to or greater than the enthalpy of reaction (and usually it is greater).

KEEP IN MIND ▶
that the difference in potential energy between reactants and product is ΔU of a reaction. For this reaction $\Delta U = \Delta H$ because the number of product gas molecules is equal to the number of reactant gas molecules. As we learned in Chapter 7, even when this is not the case, the differences between ΔU and ΔH are usually quite small.

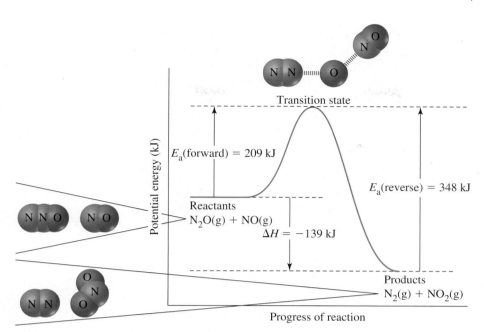

▲ **FIGURE 14-10**
A reaction profile for the reaction

$$N_2O(g) + NO(g) \longrightarrow N_2(g) + NO_2(g)$$

This simplified reaction profile traces energy changes during the course of reaction (14.20). The reactant and product molecules are depicted by the molecular models, as is the activated complex.

▲ **FIGURE 14-11**
An analogy for a reaction profile and activation energy
A hike (red path) is taken from the valley on the left (reactants) over the ridge to the valley on the right (products). The ridge above the starting point corresponds to the transition state. It is probably the height of this ridge (activation energy) more than anything else that determines how many people are willing to take the hike, regardless of the fact that it is all downhill on the other side.

Attempts at purely theoretical predictions of rate constants have not been very successful. The principal value of reaction-rate theories is to help us explain experimentally observed reaction-rate data. For example, in the next section we will see how the concept of activation energy enters into a discussion of the effect of temperature on reaction rates.

CONCEPT ASSESSMENT ✓

Indicate whether the following conditions can exist for a chemical reaction: **(a)** $\Delta H < 0 < E_a$; **(b)** $0 < \Delta H < E_a$; **(c)** $0 < E_a < \Delta H$; **(d)** $0 = \Delta H < E_a$; **(e)** $E_a < \Delta H < 0$. Where the conditions can exist, describe the reaction profile.

14-9   THE EFFECT OF TEMPERATURE ON REACTION RATES

From practical experience, we expect chemical reactions to go faster at higher temperatures. To speed up the biochemical reactions involved in cooking, we raise the temperature, and to slow down other reactions, we lower the temperature—as in refrigerating milk to prevent it from souring.

In 1889, Svante Arrhenius demonstrated that the rate constants of many chemical reactions vary with temperature in accordance with the expression

$$k = Ae^{-E_a/RT} \tag{14.21}$$

By taking the natural logarithm of both sides of this equation, we obtain the following expression.

$$\ln k = -\frac{E_a}{RT} + \ln A$$

✓ Point out that both exothermic *and* endothermic reactions go faster at higher temperatures.

◄ This equation indicates that a rate constant *increases* as the temperature *increases* and as the activation energy *decreases*.

▶ This is the same technique used for the Clausius–Clapeyron equation on page 481 and illustrated in Appendix A-4.

Rates of Reaction simulation

A graph of ln k versus $1/T$ is a straight line, thus giving us a graphical method for determining the activation energy of a reaction, as shown in Figure 14-12. We can also derive a useful variation of the equation by writing it twice—each time for a different value of k and the corresponding temperature—and then eliminating the constant ln A. The result, also called the Arrhenius equation, is

$$\ln \frac{k_2}{k_1} = \frac{E_a}{R}\left(\frac{1}{T_1} - \frac{1}{T_2}\right) \tag{14.22}$$

In equation (14.22)* T_2 and T_1 are two Kelvin temperatures; k_2 and k_1 are the rate constants at these temperatures; and E_a is the activation energy in joules per mole. R is the gas constant expressed as 8.3145 J mol^{-1} K^{-1}.

Equation (14.22) can be rewritten in several ways.

$$\ln \frac{k_2}{k_1} = -\frac{E_a}{R}\left(\frac{1}{T_2} - \frac{1}{T_1}\right) = -\frac{E_a}{R}\left(\frac{T_1 - T_2}{T_2 T_1}\right) = \frac{E_a}{R}\left(\frac{T_2 - T_1}{T_2 T_1}\right)$$

▲ **FIGURE 14-12**
Temperature dependence of the rate constant k for the reaction

$$N_2O_5 \text{ (in CCl}_4\text{)} \longrightarrow N_2O_4 \text{ (in CCl}_4\text{)} + \frac{1}{2}O_2(g)$$

Data are plotted as follows, for the representative point in black.

$$t = 25\,°C = 298\,K$$
$$1/T = 1/298 = 0.00336 = 3.36 \times 10^{-3}\,K^{-1}$$
$$k = 3.46 \times 10^{-5}\,s^{-1}; \ln k = \ln 3.46 \times 10^{-5} = -10.272$$

To evaluate E_a,

$$\text{slope of line} = -E_a/R = -1.2 \times 10^4\,K$$
$$E_a = 8.3145\,J\,mol^{-1}\,K^{-1} \times 1.2 \times 10^4\,K$$
$$= 1.0 \times 10^5\,J/mol = 1.0 \times 10^2\,kJ/mol$$

(A more precise plot yields a value of $E_a = 106$ kJ/mol. The arrow points to data referred to in Example 14-9.)

---

*To see that this expression is dimensionally correct, note that on the right side the units in the numerator are J mol^{-1} (for E_a) and K^{-1} (for the quantity in parentheses) and that in the denominator the units are J mol^{-1} K^{-1} (for R). Cancellation yields a dimensionless quantity on the right, to match the dimensionless logarithmic term on the left.

The first form brings out the minus sign and reverses the T_1 and T_2, and the next two combine the fractions within the parentheses. Also, the equation can be written in exponential form.

$$\frac{k_2}{k_1} = e^{-\frac{E_a}{R}\left(\frac{1}{T_2} - \frac{1}{T_1}\right)}$$

Which equation is used is a matter of calculational convenience.

EXAMPLE 14-9

Applying the Arrhenius Equation. Use data from Figure 14-12 to determine the temperature at which $t_{1/2}$ for the first-order decomposition of N_2O_5 in CCl_4 is 2.00 h.

Solution

First, find the rate constant k corresponding to a 2.00-h half-life. For a *first-order reaction*,

$$k = \frac{\ln 2}{t_{1/2}} = \frac{0.693}{2.00 \text{ h}} = \frac{0.693}{7200 \text{ s}} = 9.63 \times 10^{-5} \text{ s}^{-1}$$

Now, the temperature at which $k = 9.63 \times 10^{-5} \text{ s}^{-1}$ can be determined in two ways:

Graphical Method. The temperature at which $\ln k = \ln 9.63 \times 10^{-5} = -9.248$ is marked by the red arrow in Figure 14-12. The value of $1/T$ corresponding to $\ln k = -9.248$ is $1/T = 3.28 \times 10^{-3} \text{ K}^{-1}$, which means that

$$T = \left(\frac{1}{3.28 \times 10^{-3} K^{-1}}\right) = 305 \text{ K} = 32 \text{ °C}$$

Using Equation (14.22). Take T_2 to be the temperature at which $k = k_2 = 9.63 \times 10^{-5} \text{ s}^{-1}$. T_1 is some other temperature at which a value of k is known. Suppose we take $T_1 = 298 \text{ K}$ and $k_1 = 3.46 \times 10^{-5} \text{ s}^{-1}$, a point referred to in the caption of Figure 14-12. The activation energy is 106 kJ/mol $= 1.06 \times 10^5$ J/mol (the more precise value given in Figure 14-12). Now we can solve equation (14.22) for T_2. (For simplicity, we have omitted units below, but the temperature is obtained in kelvins.)

$$\ln \frac{k_2}{k_1} = \frac{E_a}{R}\left(\frac{1}{T_1} - \frac{1}{T_2}\right)$$

$$\ln \frac{9.63 \times 10^{-5}}{3.46 \times 10^{-5}} = \frac{1.06 \times 10^5}{8.3145}\left(\frac{1}{298} - \frac{1}{T_2}\right)$$

$$1.024 = 1.27 \times 10^4\left(0.00336 - \frac{1}{T_2}\right) = 42.7 - \frac{1.27 \times 10^4}{T_2}$$

$$\frac{1.27 \times 10^4}{T_2} = 42.7 - 1.024 = 41.7$$

$$T_2 = \frac{(1.27 \times 10^4)}{41.7} = 305 \text{ K}$$

Practice Example A: What is the half-life of the first-order decomposition of N_2O_5 at 75.0 °C? Use data from Example 14-9.

Practice Example B: At what temperature will it take 1.50 h for two-thirds of a sample of N_2O_5 in CCl_4 to decompose in Example 14-9?

Arrhenius established equation (14.22) by fitting experimental data into his equation. This was before the collision theory of chemical reactions had been developed, but his equation is consistent with the collision theory. In the preceding section, we discussed the importance of (1) the frequency of molecular collisions, (2) the fraction of collisions energetic enough to produce a reaction, and (3) the need for favorable orientations during collisions. Let's represent the collision frequency by the symbol Z_0. From kinetic-molecular theory, the

▲ Both the rate of chirping of tree crickets and the flashing of fireflies roughly double for a 10 °C temperature rise. This corresponds to an activation energy of about 50 kJ/mol and suggests that the physiological processes governing these phenomena involve chemical reactions.

fraction of sufficiently energetic collisions proves to be $e^{-E_a/RT}$. The probability of favorable orientations of colliding molecules is p. In collision theory, the rate constant of a reaction can be expressed as the product of these three terms. If the product $Z_0 \times p$ is replaced by the term A, collision theory yields a result identical to Arrhenius's experimentally determined equation.

$$k = Z_0 \cdot p \cdot e^{-E_a/RT} = Ae^{-E_a/RT}$$

CONCEPT ASSESSMENT ✓

Without doing calculations, use a ln k versus $1/T$ graph to explain whether the rate of change of the rate constant with temperature is affected more strongly by a low or high energy of activation.

14-10   REACTION MECHANISMS

$NO_2(g)$ is known to play a key role in the formation of photochemical smog (see page 601), but it is unlikely that very much of this gas is formed in the atmosphere by the direct reaction

$$2\,NO(g) + O_2(g) \longrightarrow 2\,NO_2(g) \qquad (14.23)$$

For this reaction to occur in a single step in the manner suggested by equation (14.23), *three* molecules would have to collide simultaneously, or very nearly so. A three-molecule collision is an unlikely event. The reaction appears to follow a different mechanism or pathway. One of the main purposes in determining rate laws of chemical reactions is to relate them to probable reaction mechanisms.

A **reaction mechanism** is a step-by-step detailed description of a chemical reaction. Each step in a mechanism is called an **elementary process**, which describes any molecular event that significantly alters a molecule's energy or geometry or produces a new molecule. Two requirements of a plausible reaction mechanism are that it must

- be consistent with the stoichiometry of the overall reaction
- account for the *experimentally determined* rate law

In this section, we will first explore the nature of elementary processes and then apply these processes to two simple types of reaction mechanisms.

ELEMENTARY PROCESSES

The characteristics of elementary processes are as follows:

1. Elementary processes are either **unimolecular**—a process in which a single molecule dissociates—or **bimolecular**—a process involving the collision of two molecules. A *termolecular* process, which would involve the simultaneous collision of three molecules, is relatively rare as an elementary process.

2. The exponents of the concentration terms in the rate law for an elementary process are the *same* as the stoichiometric coefficients in the balanced equation for the process. (Note that this is unlike the case of the overall rate law, for which the exponents are *not* necessarily related to the stoichiometric coefficients in the overall equation.)

3. Elementary processes are reversible, and some may reach a condition of equilibrium in which the rates of the forward and reverse processes are equal.

Although much progress has been made in the theoretical understanding of reaction mechanisms, by far most of the data and rate constants are obtained experimentally.

 Bimolecular Reaction animation

This article describes a classroom activity that demonstrates reaction mechanisms and rate-determining steps: Jennings, L. D., Keller, S. W. *J. Chem. Educ.* **2005**: *82*, 549.

4. Certain species are produced in one elementary process and consumed in another. In a proposed reaction mechanism, such intermediates must not appear in either the overall chemical equation or the overall rate law.

5. One elementary process may occur much more slowly than all the others, and in some cases may determine the rate of the overall reaction. Such a process is called the **rate-determining step** (Fig. 14-13).

Keep these characteristics in mind as we will apply them in our analysis of different mechanisms below.

A MECHANISM WITH A SLOW STEP FOLLOWED BY A FAST STEP

The reaction between gaseous iodine monochloride and gaseous hydrogen produces iodine and hydrogen chloride as gaseous products.

$$H_2(g) + 2\,ICl(g) \longrightarrow I_2(g) + 2\,HCl(g)$$

The experimentally determined rate law for this reaction is

$$\text{rate of reaction} = k[H_2][ICl]$$

Let's begin with a mechanism that seems plausible, such as the following two-step mechanism.

(1) Slow: $H_2 + ICl \longrightarrow HI + HCl$
(2) Fast: $HI + ICl \longrightarrow I_2 + HCl$

Overall: $H_2 + 2\,ICl \longrightarrow I_2 + 2\,HCl$

This scheme seems plausible for two reasons: (1) The sum of the two steps yields the experimentally observed *overall* reaction. (2) As we have noted, unimolecular and bimolecular elementary processes are most plausible, and each step in the above mechanism is bimolecular. Because each step is an elementary process, we can write

$$\text{rate (1)} = k_1[H_2][ICl] \qquad \text{and} \qquad \text{rate (2)} = k_2[HI][ICl]$$

Now, note that our mechanism proposes that step (1) occurs slowly but step (2) occurs rapidly. This suggests that HI is consumed in the second step just as fast as it is formed in the first. The first step is the rate-determining step, and the rate of the overall reaction is governed just by the rate at which HI is formed in this first step, that is, by rate (1). This explains why the observed rate law for the net reaction is rate of reaction = $k[H_2][ICl]$. The proposed mechanism gives a rate law that is in agreement with experiment, as it should if we have made a reasonable proposal.

The species HI is called a **reaction intermediate**, and it does not occur in the experimental rate law. In this case, the intermediate species is a well-known stable molecule. Often, when postulating mechanisms, we have to invoke less well-known and less stable species; and in these instances, we have to rely on the chemical reasonableness of the basic assumptions. The presence of a reaction intermediate leads to a slightly more complicated reaction profile. The reaction profile for the two steps in the proposed mechanism is shown in Figure 14-14. We see that there are two transition states and one reaction intermediate. The activation energy for the first step is greater than that for the second step, which we would expect if the first step in the reaction mechanism is the slowest. It is important to understand the difference between a transition state (activated complex) and a reaction intermediate. The transition state represents the highest energy structure involved in a reaction (or step in a mechanism). While transition states exist only momentarily and can never be isolated, reaction intermediates can sometimes be isolated. Transition states have *partially formed bonds*, whereas reaction intermediates have *fully formed bonds*.

▲ **FIGURE 14-13**
The San Ysidro/Tijuana border station: An analogy for a rate-determining step
Note the tie-up of traffic on the Mexican side of the border (top) and the relatively few cars on the United States side (bottom). This station is a bottleneck and hence the rate-determining part of the trip by car from Tijuana, Mexico, to San Diego, California, two cities located only about a dozen miles apart.

Remind students that a transition state is not a "real" species. It is only hypothetical.

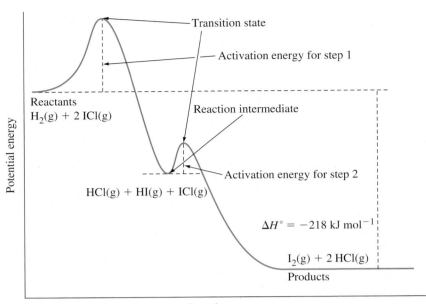

A MECHANISM WITH A FAST REVERSIBLE FIRST STEP FOLLOWED BY A SLOW STEP

The rate law for the reaction of NO(g) and O_2(g)

$$2\,NO(g) + O_2(g) \longrightarrow 2\,NO_2(g) \tag{14.23}$$

is found to be

$$\text{rate of reaction} = k[NO]^2[O_2] \tag{14.24}$$

Even though it is consistent with this rate law, we have already noted that the one-step *termolecular* mechanism suggested by equation (14.23) is highly improbable. Let's explore instead the following mechanism.

$$\textit{Fast:} \qquad 2\,NO(g) \underset{k_2}{\overset{k_1}{\rightleftharpoons}} N_2O_2(g) \tag{14.25}$$

$$\textit{Slow:} \quad \underline{N_2O_2(g) + O_2(g) \xrightarrow{\ k_3\ } 2\,NO_2(g)} \tag{14.26}$$

$$\textit{Overall:} \quad 2\,NO(g) + O_2(g) \longrightarrow 2\,NO_2(g) \tag{14.23}$$

In this mechanism, there is a rapid equilibrium as the first step, but some of the N_2O_2 is slowly drawn off and consumed in the second, slow step. The rate law for the slow, or *rate-determining*, step (14.26) is

$$\text{rate of reaction} = k_3[N_2O_2][O_2] \tag{14.27}$$

Because N_2O_2 is an *intermediate*, however, we must eliminate it from the rate law. We are told that the first step of the mechanism consists of a fast reversible reaction, so we can assume that this step progresses rapidly to equilibrium. If this is the case, the forward and reverse rates of reaction in the first step become equal and we write

$$\text{rate of forward reaction} = \text{rate of reverse reaction}$$

$$k_1[NO]^2 = k_2[N_2O_2]$$

Now, let us arrange this equation into an expression having a ratio of rate constants on one side and a ratio of concentration terms on the other. Also, we can replace the ratio of rate constants by a single constant, which we will represent as K_1.

$$K_1 = \frac{k_1}{k_2} = \frac{[N_2O_2]}{[NO]^2}$$

Students often have trouble relating their math courses to science courses. If they wonder why, you might have to solve systems of differential equations (sophomore level); then the study of reaction mechanisms is a good motivator.

The above expression is known as an equilibrium constant expression; the numerical constant, K_1, is an equilibrium constant. Next, we rearrange the expression to solve for the term $[N_2O_2]$.

$$[N_2O_2] = K_1[NO]^2$$

Then, substituting this into equation (14.27) we obtain the experimentally observed rate law.

$$\text{rate of reaction} = k_3[N_2O_2][O_2] = k_3K_1[NO]^2[O_2]$$

The experimentally observed rate constant, k, is related to the other constants in the proposed mechanism, as follows:

$$k = k_3K_1 = \frac{k_1}{k_2} \times k_3$$

The type of mechanism described here with a *rapid pre-equilibrium* is a very common mechanism, and is to be expected when the overall stoichiometry suggests an unlikely termolecular collision.

We have just shown that the proposed mechanism is consistent with (a) the reaction stoichiometry and (b) the experimentally determined rate law. Whether this mechanism is the actual reaction path, we cannot say, however. All that we can say is that it is *plausible*; it has not been ruled out by kinetics.

◀ Equilibrium constant expressions are of fundamental importance throughout chemistry. Here, we see their significance in chemical kinetics. In Chapter 15, we describe the experimental basis of equilibrium constant expressions and their application to the stoichiometry of reversible reactions. In Chapter 19, we explore their thermodynamic basis.

EXAMPLE 14-10

Testing a Reaction Mechanism. An alternative mechanism of the reaction $2\,NO(g) + O_2(g) \longrightarrow 2\,NO_2(g)$ follows. Show that this mechanism is consistent with the rate law (14.24).

Fast: $\quad NO(g) + O_2(g) \underset{k_2}{\overset{k_1}{\rightleftharpoons}} NO_3(g)$

Slow: $\quad \underline{NO_3(g) + NO(g) \overset{k_3}{\longrightarrow} 2\,NO_2(g)}$

Overall: $\quad 2\,NO(g) + O_2(g) \longrightarrow 2\,NO_2(g)$

Solution

The rate equation for the rate-determining step is

$$\text{rate of reaction} = k_3[NO_3][NO]$$

Eliminate $[NO_3]$, by assuming that the pre-equilibrium is rapidly established.

$$\text{rate of forward reaction} = \text{rate of reverse reaction}$$
$$k_1[NO][O_2] = k_2[NO_3]$$

Rearrange previous equation to develop an expression for an equilibrium constant (K) in terms of the rate constants k_1 and k_2,

$$K = \frac{k_1}{k_2} = \frac{[NO_3]}{[NO][O_2]}$$

Rearrange this expression for K to solve for $[NO_3]$.

$$[NO_3] = K[NO][O_2]$$

Finally, substitute the value of $[NO_3]$ into the rate equation to obtain the observed rate law (equation 14.24).

$$\text{rate} = k_3[NO_3][NO]$$
$$\text{rate of reaction} = k_3K[NO]^2[O_2] = k_3\frac{k_1}{k_2}[NO]^2[O_2] = k[NO]^2[O_2] \quad (14.24)$$

Practice Example A: In a proposed two-step mechanism for the reaction $CO(g) + NO_2(g) \longrightarrow CO_2(g) + NO(g)$, the second, fast step is $NO_3(g) + CO(g) \longrightarrow NO_2(g) + CO_2(g)$. What must be the *slow* step? What would you expect the rate law of the reaction to be? Explain.

Practice Example B: Show that the proposed mechanism for the reaction $2\,NO_2(g) + F_2(g) \longrightarrow 2\,NO_2F(g)$ is plausible. The rate of reaction is rate $= k[NO_2][F_2]$.

Fast: $\quad NO_2(g) + F_2(g) \rightleftharpoons NO_2F_2(g)$

Slow: $\quad NO_2F_2(g) \longrightarrow NO_2F(g) + F(g)$

Fast: $\quad F(g) + NO_2(g) \longrightarrow NO_2F(g)$

THE STEADY-STATE APPROXIMATION

The reaction mechanisms considered so far have had one particular rate-determining step, and the rate law of the reaction could be deduced from the rate of this step after the relationships for the concentrations of any intermediates were established. In complex multistep reaction mechanisms, however, more than one step may control the rate of a reaction.

To illustrate, let's reconsider the first mechanism presented for the reaction of nitric oxide with oxygen, but this time we will make no assumptions about the relative rates of the steps in the mechanism. The proposed mechanism is

$$NO + NO \xrightarrow{k_1} N_2O_2$$

$$N_2O_2 \xrightarrow{k_2} NO + NO$$

$$N_2O_2 + O_2 \xrightarrow{k_3} 2\,NO_2$$

For clarity, the first, reversible reaction is written as two forward steps.

We choose one of the steps of the mechanism that provides a convenient relationship to the observed rate of reaction. In this case, we will use the third step, since it involves the disappearance of O_2. Therefore, the rate of the reaction from this mechanism is

$$\text{rate of reaction} = k_3[N_2O_2][O_2] \tag{14.27}$$

KEEP IN MIND ▶

that if the rate of change of the concentration of a substance is zero, then the concentration of that substance is constant.

As before, the intermediate N_2O_2 must be eliminated from this rate law. We can do this by assuming that the $[N_2O_2]$ reaches a *steady-state condition* in which N_2O_2 is produced and consumed at equal rates. That is, $[N_2O_2]$ remains constant throughout most of the reaction. We can use the steady-state assumption to express $[N_2O_2]$ in terms of $[NO]$.

$$\Delta[N_2O_2]/\Delta t = \text{rate of formation of } N_2O_2 + \text{rate of disappearance of } N_2O_2 = 0$$

$$\text{rate of formation of } N_2O_2 = -(\text{rate of disappearance of } N_2O_2)$$

The rate of disappearance of N_2O_2 is made up of two parts—the reverse step of equation (14.25) and the forward step of (14.26)—so we write

$$\text{rate of disappearance of } N_2O_2 = -(k_3[N_2O_2][O_2] + k_2[N_2O_2])$$

The two rates for the steps depleting the concentration of N_2O_2 have been added; the minus sign signifies a decrease in concentration. Now, as dictated by the steady-state assumption, the negative of the rate of disappearance of N_2O_2 is equated with the rate of appearance of N_2O_2, which is $k_1[NO]^2$.

$$k_1[NO]^2 = k_2[N_2O_2] + k_3[N_2O_2][O_2] = [N_2O_2](k_2 + k_3[O_2])$$

Rearranging to solve for $[N_2O_2]$, we have

$$[N_2O_2] = \frac{k_1[NO]^2}{(k_2 + k_3[O_2])}$$

We now substitute this into equation (14.27) to obtain

$$\text{rate} = k_3[O_2][N_2O_2] = k_3[O_2]\left(\frac{k_1[NO]^2}{(k_2 + k_3[O_2])}\right)$$

or

> Note that this rate does not follow the usual *n*th order reaction rate law as seen in Table 14.5.

$$\text{rate} = \frac{k_1 k_3[O_2][NO]^2}{(k_2 + k_3[O_2])}$$

So, this is the rate law for the proposed mechanism based on our steady-state analysis. This rate law is more complicated than the observed rate law. What happened? In carrying out the steady-state calculation, we did not make any assumptions about the relative rates of the three steps in the mechanism.

If we now make the assumption that the rate of disappearance of N_2O_2 in the second step of the proposed mechanism is greater than the rate of disappearance of N_2O_2 in the third step of the proposed mechanism, then

$$k_2[N_2O_2] > k_3[N_2O_2][O_2]$$

which means

$$k_2 > k_3[O_2]$$

and

$$k_2 + k_3[O_2] \cong k_2$$

so that

$$[N_2O_2] = \frac{k_1[NO]^2}{k_2}$$

If we substitute this value of $[N_2O_2]$ into the rate equation (14.27) and replace k_1k_3/k_2 by k, we obtain for the overall reaction

$$\text{rate of reaction} = \frac{k_1k_2}{k_2}[NO]^2[O_2] = k[NO]^2[O_2] \tag{14.24}$$

The result of a steady-state analysis of any mechanism in which no rate-determining step can be identified will often be a complicated rate law. The use of this type of rate law is illustrated in the section on enzyme catalysis later in this chapter.

SMOG—AN ENVIRONMENTAL PROBLEM WITH ROOTS IN CHEMICAL KINETICS

About 100 years ago, a new word entered the English language—**smog**. It referred to a condition, common in London, in which a combination of *smoke* and *fog* obscured visibility and produced health hazards (including death). These conditions are often associated with heavy industry, and this type of smog is now called *industrial* smog.

A more familiar form of air pollution commonly thought of as smog results from the action of sunlight on the products of combustion. Chemical reactions brought about by light are called *photochemical* reactions, and the smog formed primarily as a result of photochemical reactions is photochemical smog. This type of smog is associated with high-temperature combustion processes, such as those that occur in internal combustion engines. Because the combustion of motor fuels takes place in air rather than in pure oxygen, oxides of nitrogen, principally $NO(g)$, are inevitably found in the exhaust from motor vehicles. Other products found in the exhaust are hydrocarbons (unburned gasoline) and partially oxidized hydrocarbons. These, then, are the starting materials—the precursors—of photochemical smog.

Many substances have been identified in smoggy air, including NO, NO_2, O_3 (ozone, an allotrope of oxygen introduced on page 391 and discussed further in Section 22-3), and a variety of organic compounds derived from gasoline hydrocarbons. Ozone is very reactive and is largely responsible for the breathing difficulties that some people experience during smog episodes. Another noxious substance found in smog is an organic compound known as peroxyacetyl nitrate (PAN). PAN is a powerful lacrimator—that is, it causes tear formation in the eyes. Photochemical smog components cause heavy crop damages (to oranges, for example) and the deterioration of rubber goods. And, of course, the best-known symbol of photochemical smog is the hazy brown air that results in reduced visibility (Fig. 14-15).

Chemists who have been studying photochemical smog formation over the past several decades have determined that certain precursors are converted to the observable smog components through the action of sunlight. Because the chemical reactions involved are very complex and still not totally understood, we will give only a very brief, simplified reaction mechanism showing how photochemical smog is formed.

◀ Air quality in London has been greatly improved by control measures such as elimination of coal as a household fuel, introduced after a severe smog episode in 1952.

▲ **FIGURE 14-15**
Smog in Mexico City
At times, the topographical features, climatic conditions, traffic congestion, and heavy industrial pollution combine to create severe smog conditions in Mexico City.

Smog formation begins with NO(g), produced by reaction (14.28).

$$N_2(g) + O_2(g) \xrightarrow{\Delta} 2\,NO(g) \quad (14.28)$$

NO(g) is subsequently converted to $NO_2(g)$, which then absorbs ultraviolet radiation from sunlight and decomposes.

$$NO_2 + \text{sunlight} \longrightarrow NO + O \quad (14.29)$$

This is followed by a reaction forming ozone, O_3.

$$O + O_2 \longrightarrow O_3 \quad (14.30)$$

Catalytic Destruction of Stratospheric Ozone animation

Thus, a large buildup of ozone in photochemical smog requires a plentiful source of NO_2. At one time, this source was believed to be reaction (14.31).

$$2\,NO + O_2 \longrightarrow 2\,NO_2 \quad (14.31)$$

It is now well established, however, that reaction (14.31) occurs much too slowly to yield the required levels of NO_2 in photochemical smog. Instead, NO is rapidly converted to NO_2 when it reacts with O_3,

$$O_3 + NO \longrightarrow O_2 + NO_2 \quad (14.32)$$

Even though reaction (14.32) accounts for the formation of NO_2, it leads to the destruction of ozone. Thus, photochemical smog formation cannot occur just through the reaction sequence: (14.28), (14.29), (14.30), and (14.31). The ozone would be consumed as quickly as it was formed, and there would be no ozone buildup at all.

It is now known that organic compounds, particularly unburned hydrocarbons in automotive exhaust, provide a pathway for the conversion of NO to NO_2. The reaction sequence that follows involves some highly reactive molecular fragments. Recall (page 393) that these fragments are known as *free radicals* and are represented by formulas written with a bold dot. RH represents a hydrocarbon molecule, and R· is a free-radical fragment of a hydrocarbon molecule. Oxygen atoms, fragments of the O_2 molecule, are also represented as free radicals, as are hydroxyl groups, fragments of the H_2O molecule.

$$RH + O\cdot \longrightarrow R\cdot + \cdot OH$$
$$RH + \cdot OH \longrightarrow R\cdot + H_2O$$
$$R\cdot + O_2 \longrightarrow RO_2\cdot$$
$$RO_2\cdot + NO \longrightarrow RO\cdot + NO_2$$

The final step in this reaction mechanism accounts for the rapid conversion of NO to NO_2 that seems essential to smog formation.

The role of NO_2 in the formation of the smog component PAN is suggested by the equation

$$\underset{}{\overset{O}{\overset{\|}{CH_3C}}}{-}O{-}O\cdot + NO_2 \longrightarrow \underset{\text{PAN}}{\overset{O}{\overset{\|}{CH_3C}}}{-}O{-}ONO_2$$

The details of smog formation have been worked out in part through the use of smog chambers. By varying experimental conditions in these chambers, scientists have been able to create polluted atmospheres very similar to smog. For example, they have found that if hydrocarbons are omitted from the starting materials in the smog chamber, no ozone is formed. The reaction scheme just proposed is consistent with this observation. Figure 14-16 gives a typical result from a smog chamber.

To control smog, automobiles are now provided with *catalytic converters*. CO and hydrocarbons are oxidized to CO_2 and H_2O in the presence of an oxidation catalyst such as platinum or palladium metal. NO must be reduced to N_2, and this requires a reduction catalyst. A dual-catalyst system uses both types of catalysts. Alternatively, the air–fuel ratio of the engine is set to produce some CO and unburned hydrocarbons; these then act as reducing agents to reduce NO to N_2.

$$2\,CO(g) + 2\,NO(g) \longrightarrow 2\,CO_2(g) + N_2(g)$$

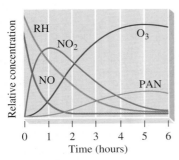

▲ **FIGURE 14-16**
Smog component profile
Data from a smog chamber show how the concentrations of smog components change with time. For example, the concentrations of hydrocarbon (RH) and nitrogen monoxide (NO) fall continuously, whereas that of nitrogen dioxide (NO_2) rises to a maximum and then drops off. The concentrations of ozone (O_3) and peroxyacetyl nitrate (PAN) build up more slowly. Any reaction scheme proposed to explain smog formation must be consistent with observations such as these. Under actual smog conditions, the pattern of concentration changes shown here repeats itself on a daily basis.

Next, the exhaust gases are passed through an oxidation catalyst to oxidize the remaining hydrocarbons and CO to CO_2 and H_2O. Future smog-control measures may include the use of alternative fuels, such as methanol or hydrogen, and the development of electric-powered automobiles.

14-11   CATALYSIS

A reaction can generally be made to go faster by increasing the temperature. Another way to speed up a reaction is to use a catalyst. A **catalyst** provides an alternative reaction pathway of lower activation energy. The catalyst participates in a chemical reaction but does not itself undergo a permanent change. As a result, the formula of a catalyst does not appear in the overall chemical equation (its formula is generally placed over the reaction arrow).

The success of a chemical process often hinges on finding the right catalyst, as in the manufacture of nitric acid. By conducting the oxidation of $NH_3(g)$ very quickly (less than 1 ms) in the presence of a Pt–Rh catalyst, $NO(g)$ can be obtained as a product instead of $N_2(g)$. The formation of $HNO_3(aq)$ from $NO(g)$ then follows easily.

In this section, the two basic types of catalysis—homogeneous and heterogeneous—are described first. This is followed by discussions of the catalyzed decomposition of $H_2O_2(aq)$ and the biological catalysts called enzymes.

HOMOGENEOUS CATALYSIS

Figure 14-17 shows reaction profiles for the decomposition of formic acid (HCOOH). In the uncatalyzed reaction, a H atom must be transferred from one part of the formic acid molecule to another, shown by the arrow. Then a C—O bond breaks. Because the energy requirement for this atom transfer is high, the activation energy is high and the reaction is slow. In the acid-catalyzed decomposition of formic acid, a hydrogen ion from solution attaches itself to the O atom that is singly bonded to the C atom to form $(HCOOH_2)^+$. The C—O bond breaks, and a H atom attached to a carbon atom in the intermediate species $(HCO)^+$ is released to the solution as H^+.

▲ **FIGURE 14-17**
An example of homogeneous catalysis
The activation energy is lowered in the presence of H^+, a catalyst for the decomposition of HCOOH.

This catalyzed reaction pathway does not require a H atom to be transferred within the formic acid molecule. It has a lower activation energy than does the uncatalyzed reaction and proceeds at a faster rate. Because the reactants and products of this reaction are all present throughout the solution, or homogeneous mixture, this type of catalysis is called **homogeneous catalysis**.

HETEROGENEOUS CATALYSIS

Many reactions can be catalyzed by allowing them to occur on an appropriate solid surface. Essential reaction intermediates are found on the surface. This type of catalysis is called **heterogeneous catalysis** because the catalyst is present in a different phase of matter than are the reactants and products. Catalytic activity is associated with many transition elements and their compounds. The precise mechanism of heterogeneous catalysis is not totally understood, but in many cases the availability of electrons in d orbitals in surface atoms may play a role.

Surface Reaction—
Hydrogenation animation,
Catalysis movie

A key feature of heterogeneous catalysis is that reactants from a gaseous or solution phase are adsorbed, or attached, to the surface of the catalyst. Not all surface atoms are equally effective for catalysis; those that are effective are called **active sites**. Basically, heterogeneous catalysis involves (1) *adsorption* of reactants; (2) *diffusion* of reactants along the surface; (3) *reaction* at an active site to form adsorbed product; and (4) *desorption* of the product.

An interesting reaction is the oxidation of CO to CO_2 and the reduction of NO to N_2 in automotive exhaust gases as a smog-control measure. Figure 14-18 shows how this reaction is thought to occur on the surface of rhodium metal in a catalytic converter. In general, the reaction profile for a surface-catalyzed reaction resembles that shown in Figure 14-19.

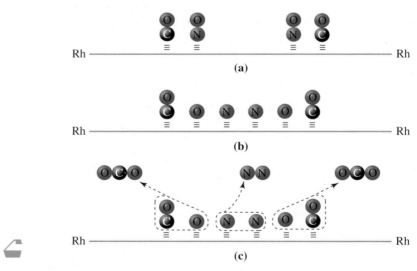

▲ **FIGURE 14-18**
Heterogeneous catalysis in the reaction

$$2\,CO\ +\ 2\,NO\ \xrightarrow{\text{Rh}}\ 2\,CO_2\ +\ N_2$$

(a) Molecules of CO and NO are adsorbed on the rhodium surface. **(b)** The adsorbed NO molecules dissociate into adsorbed N and O atoms. **(c)** Adsorbed CO molecules and O atoms combine to form CO_2 molecules, which desorb into the gaseous state. Two N atoms combine and are desorbed as a N_2 molecule.

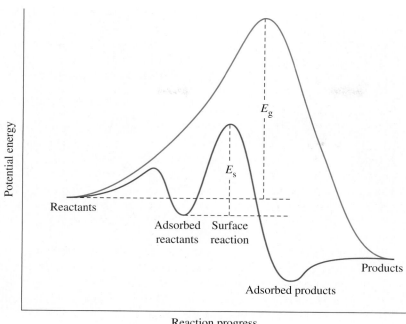

▲ **FIGURE 14-19**
Reaction profile for a surface-catalyzed reaction
In the reaction profile (blue) for the surface-catalyzed reaction, the activation energy
for the reaction step, E_s, is considerably less than in the reaction profile (red) for the
uncatalyzed gas-phase reaction, E_g.

THE CATALYZED DECOMPOSITION OF HYDROGEN PEROXIDE

As previously noted (see the footnote on page 574), the decomposition of
$H_2O_2(aq)$ is a slow reaction and generally must be catalyzed. Iodide ion is a good
catalyst that seems to function by means of the following two-step mechanism.

Slow: $H_2O_2 + I^- \longrightarrow OI^- + H_2O$

Fast: $H_2O_2 + OI^- \longrightarrow H_2O + I^- + O_2(g)$

Overall: $2\,H_2O_2 \longrightarrow 2\,H_2O + O_2(g)$

As required for a catalyzed reaction, the formula of the catalyst does not
appear in the overall equation. Neither does the intermediate species OI^-. The
rate of reaction of H_2O_2 is determined by the rate of the slow first step.

$$\text{rate of reaction of } H_2O_2 = k[H_2O_2][I^-] \qquad (14.33)$$

Because I^- is constantly regenerated, its concentration is constant throughout
a given reaction. If the product of the constant terms $k[I^-]$ is replaced by a new
constant, k', the rate law can be rewritten as

$$\text{rate of reaction of } H_2O_2 = k'[H_2O_2] \qquad (14.34)$$

Equation (14.33) indicates that the rate of decomposition of $H_2O_2(aq)$ is
affected by the initial concentration of I^-. For each initial concentration of I^-,
we obtain a different rate constant, k', in equation (14.34).

We have just described the homogeneous catalysis of the decomposition of
hydrogen peroxide. The decomposition can also be catalyzed by heterogeneous catalysis, as seen on page 606.

Remind students that
although catalysts are not
in the overall chemical
equation, they do participate in
the chemical reaction and do
appear in the mechanism.

▶ The decomposition of hydrogen peroxide, H_2O_2, to H_2O and O_2 is a highly exothermic reaction that is strongly catalyzed by platinum metal.

▶ Many people lose the ability to produce lactase when they become adults. In such cases, lactose passes through the small intestine into the colon, where it ferments and may cause severe gastric disturbances.

ENZYMES AS CATALYSTS

Unlike platinum, which catalyzes a wide variety of reactions, the catalytic action of high molar mass proteins known as **enzymes** is very specific. For example, in the digestion of milk, lactose, a more complex sugar, breaks down into two simpler ones, glucose and galactose. This occurs in the presence of the enzyme *lactase*.

$$\text{lactose} \xrightarrow{\text{lactase}} \text{glucose} + \text{galactose}$$
$$\text{``milk sugar''}$$

Biochemists describe enzyme activity with the "lock-and-key" model (Fig. 14-20). The reacting substance, the **substrate** (S), attaches itself to the enzyme (E) at a particular point called an *active site* to form the enzyme–substrate complex (ES). The complex decomposes to form products (P) and regenerate the enzyme.

$$E + S \underset{k_{-1}}{\overset{k_1}{\rightleftharpoons}} ES$$

$$ES \xrightarrow{k_2} E + P$$

▲ A computer graphics representation of the enzyme phosphoglycerate kinase (carbon backbone shown as blue ribbon). A molecule of ATP, the substrate, is shown in green.

▲ **FIGURE 14-20**
Lock-and-key model of enzyme action
(a) The substrate attaches itself to an active site on an enzyme molecule. **(b)** Reaction occurs. **(c)** Product molecules detach themselves from the site, freeing the enzyme molecule to attach another molecule of substrate. The substrate and enzyme must have complementary structures to produce a complex, hence the term *lock-and-key*.

Most human enzyme-catalyzed reactions proceed fastest at about 37 °C (body temperature). If the temperature is raised much higher than that, the structure of the enzyme changes, the active sites become distorted, and the catalytic activity is lost.

Determining the rates of enzyme-catalyzed reactions is an important part of enzyme studies. Figure 14-21, a plot of reaction rate against substrate concentration, illustrates what we generally observe. Along the rising portion of the graph, the rate of reaction is proportional to the substrate concentration, [S]. The reaction is first order: rate of reaction = k[S]. At high substrate concentrations, the rate is independent of [S]. The reaction follows a zero-order rate equation: rate of reaction = k.

This behavior can be understood in terms of the three-step mechanism given above. The rate at which the product appears, which is often called the velocity (V) of the reaction by biochemists, is given by

$$\text{rate of production of } P = V = k_2[\text{ES}]$$

To proceed further, we need an expression for the enzyme–substrate complex, and we can get this by applying the steady-state approximation to the concentration of the enzyme–substrate complex.

$$\text{rate of formation of ES} = \text{rate of destruction of ES}$$

$$k_1[\text{E}][\text{S}] = (k_{-1} + k_2)[\text{ES}] \tag{14.35}$$

We can solve this equation for [ES], but the solution contains the concentration of free enzyme E, which is unknown. However, we do know the *total* concentration of enzyme in an experiment, [E_0]. Then, by the condition known as *material balance*, we have

$$[\text{E}_0] = [\text{E}] + [\text{ES}]$$

Solving this equation for [E] and substituting the result into equation (14.35), we get

$$k_1[\text{S}]([\text{E}_0] - [\text{ES}]) = (k_{-1} + k_2)[\text{ES}]$$

$$[\text{ES}] = \frac{k_1[\text{E}_0][\text{S}]}{(k_{-1} + k_2) + k_1[\text{S}]}$$

for the concentration of the enzyme–substrate complex. Substituting this value into the rate of reaction, we get

$$V = \frac{k_2 k_1[\text{E}_0][\text{S}]}{(k_{-1} + k_2) + k_1[\text{S}]}$$

This equation can be put into a more convenient form by dividing the numerator and denominator by k_1 and replacing a ratio of rate constants by the single constant K_M.

$$K_M = \frac{k_{-1} + k_2}{k_1}$$

Our final result is

$$V = \frac{k_2[\text{E}_0][\text{S}]}{K_M + [\text{S}]} \tag{14.36}$$

Now, let's test whether the reaction velocity V, given by equation (14.36), depends on the substrate concentration in the manner suggested by Figure 14-21. At sufficiently low concentrations of S, we have the inequality

$$K_M \gg [\text{S}]$$

We can ignore [S] with respect to K_M in the denominator and obtain the following for the reaction velocity.

$$V = \frac{k_2}{K_M}[\text{E}_0][\text{S}]$$

▲ **FIGURE 14-21**
Effect of substrate concentration on the rate of an enzyme reaction

◄ The reaction mechanism outlined here was proposed by Michaelis and Menten in 1913, accounting for the subscript M in the constant K_M.

▲ The main thrusters that provide the energy to put the space shuttle into orbit are powered by the controlled combustion of hydrogen and oxygen.

At times, only a fine line separates combustion reactions and explosions. The typical explosion is a self-sustaining combustion reaction that proceeds at an ever-increasing rate and cannot be stopped until the reactants are consumed. An understanding of the mechanisms of combustion and explosion reactions can help us to achieve the one and avoid the other.

A dramatic contrast can be seen in the reaction

$$2\,H_2 + O_2 \longrightarrow 2\,H_2O$$

When it is carried out in a controlled fashion, this reaction provides the energy and thrust needed to propel the space shuttle into orbit.

One type of explosion, called a *thermal* explosion, occurs because the exothermic heat of a reaction cannot be conducted away from the reaction mixture fast enough. The temperature of the reaction mixture rises, and with the increase in temperature, the rate constant increases unchecked. Another cause of explosive reactions is found in the *branched-chain* mechanism, outlined here in simplified form for the hydrogen–oxygen reaction.

Because the total enzyme concentration is constant, the rate law is first order with respect to substrate, as observed experimentally.

The other limiting case is that in which the velocity of the reaction becomes independent of substrate concentration. At sufficiently high concentrations of substrate,

$$[S] \gg K_M$$

and

$$V = k_2[E_0]$$

Here, for a chosen concentration of enzyme, the reaction velocity is constant and is the maximum reaction velocity attainable for the particular enzyme. This velocity corresponds to the experimentally observed plateau at high substrate concentrations in a plot such as Figure 14-21. Thus, there is a satisfactory agreement between the predictions of the postulated mechanism and the experimental results. As is typical of the scientific method, postulated mechanisms are continually tested by subsequent experiment and modified when necessary.

Are You Wondering . . .

Why the reaction order of an enzyme reaction changes from first to zero order, depending on substrate concentration?

This situation is much like what you experience in a fast-food take-out restaurant. The order clerks are like active sites, and the customers are like substrate molecules. When the restaurant is relatively empty (low [S]), the rate at which orders are placed depends on the number of people present. When the restaurant is crowded, with customers waiting in lines, orders are placed at essentially a constant rate, which depends on the number of order clerks, not the number of patrons.

Initiation:

(1) $H_2 + O_2 \longrightarrow HO_2\cdot + H\cdot$

Propagation:

(2) $HO_2\cdot + H_2 \longrightarrow HO\cdot + H_2O$

(3) $HO\cdot + H_2 \longrightarrow H\cdot + H_2O$

Branching:

(4) $H\cdot + O_2 \longrightarrow O\cdot + HO\cdot$

(5) $O\cdot + H_2 \longrightarrow HO\cdot + H\cdot$

Termination:

(6) $O\cdot + O\cdot + M \longrightarrow O_2 + M^*$

etc.

As we have learned previously (page 393), a *free radical* is a highly reactive molecular fragment with one or more unpaired electrons. Free radicals are produced in reactions such as step (1) above. In steps (2) and (3), for each free radical consumed, a molecule of the product H_2O is formed, together with another free radical. These steps continue the "chain" of reaction and are called *propagation* steps.

In steps (4) and (5), a free radical and a molecule combine to form *two* new free radicals—the chain branches. As more and more branches are produced in the chain of reaction, more and more free radicals are produced, and the reaction quickly becomes explosive.

One method of preventing a combustion reaction from becoming explosive is to keep the concentration of one of the reactants very low (*lean*). The rate of reaction is slowed down because of this low concentration of the lean reactant. Another method is to introduce into the reaction mixture a species M that can remove energy from free radicals and cause them to combine, as in the *termination* step (6). Energy from the excited species M^* is dissipated without the further formation of free radicals. Also, a species M can be chosen that reacts with free radicals; this again reduces their number. Still another way to avoid explosions is to keep the gaseous mixture at a low pressure. Then, many of the free radicals formed are able to migrate to the walls of the container without undergoing further reaction. At the walls, the free radicals lose energy and combine in reactions similar to step (6). At higher pressures, however, the free radicals are more likely to collide with molecules of the reactants before they reach the container walls. Here again, an explosion rather than a steady combustion is the likely result.

Summary

14-1 Rate of a Chemical Reaction—The **rate of reaction** reflects the rate of change in the concentrations of the reactants and products of a reaction. A *general rate of reaction* (equation 14.2) is defined so that the same value is obtained no matter which reactant or product serves as the basis of kinetic measurements.

14-2 Measuring Reaction Rates—An **initial rate of reaction** is the rate measured over a short time interval at the start of a reaction. An **instantaneous rate of reaction** is assessed over an infinitesimal time interval at any point in the reaction, often through the slope of a tangent line to a graph of concentration versus time (Fig. 14-2). Reaction rates measured over longer time intervals are simply *average* rates, since in almost all cases reaction rates continuously decrease as a reaction proceeds.

14-3 Effect of Concentration on Reaction Rates: The Rate Law—The relationship between the rate of a reaction and the concentrations of the reactants is called the **rate law** (**rate equation**) (equation 14.6); it has the form: rate of reaction $= k[A]^m[B]^n \cdots$. The **order of a reaction** refers to the exponents $m, n, \ldots$ in the rate law. If $m = 2$, the reaction is second order in A; if $n = 1$, the reaction is first order in B; and so on. The *overall order* of a reaction is given by the sum $m + n + \cdots$. One method of establishing the rate law of a reaction is by the *method of initial rates*. The **rate constant** relates the rate of reaction to reactant concentrations.

14-4 Zero-Order Reactions—A reaction having $m + n + \cdots = 0$ is a **zero-order reaction** (equation 14.9). A useful equation expressing concentration of a reactant as a function of time is called an **integrated rate law** (equation 14.10). A plot of concentration as a function of time for the zero-order reaction $A \longrightarrow$ products is a straight line with a slope of $-k$ (Fig. 14-3).

14-5 First-Order Reactions—A reaction having $m + n + \cdots = 1$ is a **first-order reaction** (equations 14.12 and 14.13). A graph of $\ln[A]$ versus time for the first-order reaction $A \longrightarrow$ products is a straight line with a slope of $-k$ (Fig. 14-4). The **half-life** of a reaction is the time required for the amount of a reactant to be reduced to one-half its initial value. For a first-order reaction, the half-life is a constant (equation 14.14). Many important reactions are first-order processes, including the decay of radioactive nuclides (Table 14.4).

14-6 Second-Order Reactions—A reaction having $m + n + \cdots = 2$ is a **second-order reaction** (equations 14.17 and 14.18). A graph of $1/[A]$ versus time for the second-order reaction, $A \longrightarrow$ products, is a straight line with a slope of k (Fig. 14-6). For a second-order reaction, the half-life is *not* constant; each successive half-life period is twice as long as the one preceding it (equation 14.19).

Some second-order reactions, called pseudo-first-order reactions, can be treated as first-order if one of the reactants is present at such a high concentration that its concentration remains essentially constant during the reaction.

14-7 Reaction Kinetics: A Summary—A helpful summary of some basic ideas of reaction kinetics can be found on pages 588 to 590 and in Table 14.5.

14-8 Theoretical Models for Chemical Kinetics—The rate of reaction depends on the frequency of molecular collisions (**collision frequency**), the proportion of molecules having energies in excess of the **activation energy** (Fig. 14-8) and proper orientation of molecules for effective collisions (Fig. 14-9). A **reaction profile** (Fig. 14-10) traces the progress of a reaction, highlighting the energy states of the reactants, the products, and the **activated complex**, a hypothetical transitory species that exists in a high-energy **transition state** between reactants and products.

14-9 The Effect of Temperature on Reaction Rates—The principal basis for describing the effect of temperature on the rate of a chemical reaction is the Arrhenius equation (14.21) or a variant of it (14.22). A graph of $\ln k$ versus $1/T$ is linear, with the slope of the line equal to $-E_a/R$ (Fig. 14-12).

14-10 Reaction Mechanisms—A **reaction mechanism** is a step-by-step description of a chemical reaction consisting of a series of **elementary processes**. Rate laws are written for the elementary processes and combined into a rate law for the overall reaction. To be plausible, the reaction mechanism must be consistent with the stoichiometry of the overall reaction and its experimentally determined rate law.

The most common elementary processes are **unimolecular** (one molecule dissociates) and **bimolecular** (two molecules collide). Some of the species in elementary processes may be **reaction intermediates**, species produced in one elementary process and consumed in another. One of the elementary processes may be the **rate-determining step**. When a single rate-determining step cannot be identified, the mechanism can often be established by the *steady-state approximation*. Reaction mechanisms can also be depicted through reaction profiles (Fig. 14-14).

Photochemical **smog** forms through the action of sunlight on the combustion products of internal combustion engines. The mechanism of its formation has been extensively studied by the methods of chemical kinetics.

14-11 Catalysis—A **catalyst** changes a reaction mechanism to one with a lower activation energy, thereby speeding up the overall reaction, but the catalyst is not itself changed by the reaction. In **homogeneous catalysis**, the catalytic reaction occurs within a single phase (Fig. 14-17). In **heterogeneous catalysis**, the catalytic action occurs on a surface separating two phases (Figs. 14-18 and 14-19). In biochemical reactions, the catalysts are high-molecular-mass proteins called **enzymes**. The reactant, called the **substrate**, attaches to the **active site** on the enzyme, where reaction occurs (Fig. 14-20). The rate of an enzyme-catalyzed reaction can be calculated with an equation (14.36) based on a generally accepted mechanism of enzyme catalysis.

Integrative Example

Peroxyacetyl nitrate (PAN) is an air pollutant produced in photochemical smog by the reaction of hydrocarbons, oxides of nitrogen, and sunlight. PAN is unstable and dissociates into peroxyacetyl radicals and $NO_2(g)$. Its presence in polluted air is like a reservoir for NO_2 storage.

$$\underset{\text{PAN}}{CH_3\overset{\displaystyle O}{\overset{\|}{C}}OONO_2} \longrightarrow \underset{\substack{\text{peroxyacetyl} \\ \text{radical}}}{CH_3\overset{\displaystyle O}{\overset{\|}{C}}OO\cdot} + NO_2$$

The first-order decomposition of PAN has a half-life of 35 h at 0 °C and 30.0 min at 25 °C. At what temperature will a sample of air containing 5.0×10^{14} PAN molecules per liter decompose at the rate of 1.0×10^{12} PAN molecules per liter per minute?

Strategy

This problem, which requires four principal tasks, is centered on the relationship between rate constants and temperature (equation 14.22) and between a rate constant and the rate of a reaction (equation 14.6). Specifically, we will need to (1) convert the two half-lives to values of k; (2) use those values of k and their related temperatures to determine the activation energy of the reaction; (3) find the value of k corresponding to the decomposition rate specified; and (4) calculate the temperature at which k has the value determined in (3).

Solution

Determine the value of k at 0 °C for the first-order reaction.

$$k = 0.693/t_{1/2}$$

$$k = \frac{0.693}{35 \text{ h}} \times \frac{1 \text{ h}}{60 \text{ min}} = 3.3 \times 10^{-4} \text{ min}^{-1}$$

At 25 °C,

$$k = \frac{0.693}{30.0 \text{ min}} = 2.31 \times 10^{-2} \text{ min}^{-1}$$

To determine the activation energy of the reaction, substitute these data

$k_2 = 2.31 \times 10^{-2} \text{ min}^{-1}; T_2 = 25 \text{ °C} = 298 \text{ K}$

$k_1 = 3.3 \times 10^{-4} \text{ min}^{-1}; T_1 = 0 \text{ °C} = 273 \text{ K}$

into equation (14.22)

$$\ln \frac{k_2}{k_1} = \frac{E_a}{R}\left(\frac{1}{T_1} - \frac{1}{T_2}\right)$$

$$\ln \frac{2.31 \times 10^{-2} \text{ min}^{-1}}{3.3 \times 10^{-4} \text{ min}^{-1}} = \frac{E_a}{8.3145 \text{ J mol}^{-1} \text{ K}^{-1}} \times \left(\frac{1}{273 \text{ K}} - \frac{1}{298 \text{ K}}\right)$$

$$= \frac{E_a}{8.3145 \text{ J mol}^{-1}} (0.00366 - 0.00336) = 4.25$$

$$E_a = \frac{8.3145 \text{ J mol}^{-1} \times 4.25}{0.00030} \times 1.2 \times 10^5 \text{ J mol}^{-1}$$

Because the reaction is first order, the rate law is rate = k[PAN], which can be rearranged to give

$$k = \text{rate}/[\text{PAN}]$$

Because mol/L and molecules/L are related through the Avogadro constant, [PAN] can be expressed as molecules/L.

$$k = \frac{\text{rate of reaction}}{[\text{PAN}]} = \frac{1.0 \times 10^{12} \text{ molecules L}^{-1} \text{ min}^{-1}}{5.0 \times 10^{14} \text{ molecules L}^{-1}}$$

$$= 2.0 \times 10^{-3} \text{ min}^{-1}$$

To determine the unknown temperature, choose one of the known combinations of k and T as k_2 and T_2. For example,

$$k_2 = 2.31 \times 10^{-2} \text{ min}^{-1}; T_2 = 298 \text{ K}$$

The unknown combination is

$$k_1 = 2.0 \times 10^{-3} \text{ min}^{-1}; T_1 = ?$$

Substitute these values into equation (14.22), together with the known value, $E_a = 1.2 \times 10^5 \text{ J mol}^{-1}$ to obtain

$$\ln \frac{2.31 \times 10^{-2} \text{ min}^{-1}}{2.0 \times 10^{-3} \text{ min}^{-1}} = \frac{1.2 \times 10^5 \text{ J mol}^{-1}}{8.3145 \text{ J mol}^{-1} \text{ K}^{-1}} \times \left(\frac{1}{T_1} - \frac{1}{298}\right) \text{K}^{-1}$$

$$\ln 12 = 1.4 \times 10^4 \left(\frac{1}{T_1} - 3.36 \times 10^{-3}\right)$$

$$2.5 = \frac{1.4 \times 10^4}{T_1} - 47$$

$$50 T_1 = 1.4 \times 10^4$$

$$T_1 = 2.8 \times 10^2 \text{ K}$$

Assessment

The best check on the reasonableness of the final answer is to note that, based on the values: $k = 3.3 \times 10^{-4} \text{ min}^{-1}$ at 273 K and $k = 2.31 \times 10^{-2} \text{ min}^{-1}$ at 298 K, the temperature at which $k = 2.0 \times 10^{-3} \text{ min}^{-1}$ should be somewhere between 273 K and 298 K. Our result is just that: 2.8×10^2 K.

Exercises

Rates of Reactions

1. In the reaction 2 A + B ⟶ C + 3 D, reactant A is found to disappear at the rate of $6.2 \times 10^{-4} \text{ M s}^{-1}$. **(a)** What is the rate of reaction at this point? **(b)** What is the rate of disappearance of B? **(c)** What is the rate of formation of D?

2. From Figure 14-2 estimate the rate of reaction at **(a)** $t = 800$ s; **(b)** the time at which $[\text{H}_2\text{O}_2] = 0.50$ M.

3. In the reaction A ⟶ products, [A] is found to be 0.485 M at $t = 71.5$ s and 0.474 M at $t = 82.4$ s. What is the average rate of the reaction during this time interval?

4. In the reaction A ⟶ products, at $t = 0$, [A] = 0.1565 M. After 1.00 min, [A] = 0.1498 M, and after 2.00 min, [A] = 0.1433 M.
   (a) Calculate the average rate of the reaction during the first minute and during the second minute.
   (b) Why are these two rates not equal?

5. In the reaction A ⟶ products, 4.40 min after the reaction is started, [A] = 0.588 M. The rate of reaction at this point is rate = $-\Delta[\text{A}]/\Delta t = 2.2 \times 10^{-2} \text{ M min}^{-1}$. Assume that this rate remains constant for a short period of time.
   (a) What is [A] 5.00 min after the reaction is started?
   (b) At what time after the reaction is started will [A] = 0.565 M?

6. Refer to Experiment 2 of Table 14.3 and to reaction (14.7) and rate law (14.8). Exactly 1.00 h after the reaction is started, what are **(a)** $[\text{HgCl}_2]$ and **(b)** $[\text{C}_2\text{O}_4^{2-}]$ in the mixture?

7. For the reaction A + 2 B ⟶ 2 C, the rate of reaction is $1.76 \times 10^{-5} \text{ M s}^{-1}$ at the time when [A] = 0.3580 M.
   (a) What is the rate of formation of C?
   (b) What will [A] be 1.00 min later?
   (c) Assume the rate remains at $1.76 \times 10^{-5} \text{ M s}^{-1}$. How long would it take for [A] to change from 0.3580 to 0.3500 M?

8. If the rate of reaction (14.3) is $5.7 \times 10^{-4}\,M\,s^{-1}$, what is the rate of production of $O_2(g)$ from 1.00 L of the $H_2O_2(aq)$, expressed as **(a)** mol $O_2\,s^{-1}$; **(b)** mol $O_2\,min^{-1}$; **(c)** mL $O_2(STP)\,min^{-1}$?

9. In the reaction $A(g) \longrightarrow 2\,B(g) + C(g)$, the *total* pressure increases while the *partial* pressure of A(g) decreases. If the initial pressure of A(g) in a vessel of constant volume is 1.000×10^3 mmHg,
(a) what will be the total pressure when the reaction has gone to completion?
(b) What will be the total gas pressure when the partial pressure of A(g) has fallen to 8.00×10^2 mmHg?

10. At 65 °C, the half-life for the first-order decomposition of $N_2O_5(g)$ is 2.38 min.

$$N_2O_5(g) \longrightarrow 2\,NO_2(g) + \frac{1}{2}O_2(g)$$

If 1.00 g of N_2O_5 is introduced into an evacuated 15-L flask at 65 °C,
(a) What is the initial partial pressure, in mmHg, of $N_2O_5(g)$?
(b) What is the partial pressure, in mmHg, of $N_2O_5(g)$ after 2.38 min?
(c) What is the total gas pressure, in mmHg, after 2.38 min?

Method of Initial Rates

11. The initial rate of the reaction $A + B \longrightarrow C + D$ is determined for different initial conditions, with the results listed in the table.
(a) What is the order of reaction with respect to A and to B?
(b) What is the overall reaction order?
(c) What is the value of the rate constant, k?

Expt	[A], M	[B], M	Initial rate, $M\,s^{-1}$
1	0.185	0.133	3.35×10^{-4}
2	0.185	0.266	1.35×10^{-3}
3	0.370	0.133	6.75×10^{-4}
4	0.370	0.266	2.70×10^{-3}

12. For the reaction $A + B \longrightarrow C + D$, the following initial rates of reaction were found. What is the rate law for this reaction?

Expt	[A], M	[B], M	Initial Rate, $M\,min^{-1}$
1	0.50	1.50	4.2×10^{-3}
2	1.50	1.50	1.3×10^{-2}
3	3.00	3.00	5.2×10^{-2}

13. The following rates of reaction were obtained in three experiments with the reaction $2\,NO(g) + Cl_2(g) \longrightarrow 2\,NOCl(g)$.

Expt	Initial [NO], M	Initial [Cl$_2$], M	Initial Rate of Reaction, $M\,s^{-1}$
1	0.0125	0.0255	2.27×10^{-5}
2	0.0125	0.0510	4.55×10^{-5}
3	0.0250	0.0255	9.08×10^{-5}

What is the rate law for this reaction?

14. The following data are obtained for the initial rates of reaction in the reaction $A + 2\,B + C \longrightarrow 2\,D + E$.

Expt	[A], M	[B], M	[C], M	Initial Rate
1	1.40	1.40	1.00	R_1
2	0.70	1.40	1.00	$R_2 = \dfrac{1}{2} \times R_1$
3	0.70	0.70	1.00	$R_3 = \dfrac{1}{4} \times R_2$
4	1.40	1.40	0.50	$R_4 = 16 \times R_3$
5	0.70	0.70	0.50	$R_5 = ?$

(a) What are the reaction orders with respect to A, B, and C?
(b) What is the value of R_5 in terms of R_1?

First-Order Reactions

15. One of the following statements is true and the other is false regarding the first-order reaction $2\,A \longrightarrow B + C$. Identify the true statement and the false one, and explain your reasoning.
(a) The rate of the reaction decreases as more and more of B and C form.
(b) The time required for one-half of substance A to react is directly proportional to the quantity of A present initially.

16. One of the following statements is true and the other is false regarding the first-order reaction $2\,A \longrightarrow B + C$. Identify the true statement and the false one, and explain your reasoning.
(a) A graph of [A] versus time is a straight line.
(b) The rate of the reaction is one-half the rate of disappearance of A.

17. The first-order reaction $A \longrightarrow$ products has $t_{1/2} = 180$ s.
(a) What percent of a sample of A remains *unreacted* 900 s after a reaction has been started?
(b) What is the rate of reaction when [A] = 0.50 M?

18. The reaction $A \longrightarrow$ products is first order in A. Initially, [A] = 0.800 M; and after 54 min, [A] = 0.100 M.
(a) At what time is [A] = 0.025 M?
(b) What is the rate of reaction when [A] = 0.025 M?

19. The reaction $A \longrightarrow$ products is first order in A.
(a) If 1.60 g A is allowed to decompose for 38 min, the mass of A remaining undecomposed is found to be 0.40 g. What is the half-life, $t_{1/2}$, of this reaction?
(b) Starting with 1.60 g A, what is the mass of A remaining undecomposed after 1.00 h?

20. In the first-order reaction A $\longrightarrow$ products, [A] = 0.816 M initially and 0.632 M after 16.0 min.
(a) What is the value of the rate constant, k?
(b) What is the half-life of this reaction?
(c) At what time will [A] = 0.235 M?
(d) What will [A] be after 2.5 h?

21. In the first-order reaction A $\longrightarrow$ products, it is found that 99% of the original amount of reactant A decomposes in 137 min. What is the half-life, $t_{1/2}$, of this decomposition reaction?

22. The half-life of the radioactive isotope phosphorus-32 is 14.3 days. How long does it take for a sample of phosphorus-32 to lose 99% of its radioactivity?

23. Acetoacetic acid, CH_3COCH_2COOH, a reagent used in organic synthesis, decomposes in acidic solution, producing acetone and $CO_2(g)$.

$$CH_3COCH_2COOH(aq) \longrightarrow CH_3COCH_3(aq) + CO_2(g)$$

This first-order decomposition has a half-life of 144 min.
(a) How long will it take for a sample of acetoacetic acid to be 65% decomposed?
(b) How many liters of $CO_2(g)$, measured at 24.5 °C and 748 Torr, are produced as a 10.0-g sample of CH_3COCH_2COOH decomposes for 575 min? [Ignore the aqueous solubility of $CO_2(g)$.]

24. The following first-order reaction occurs in $CCl_4(l)$ at 45 °C: $N_2O_5 \longrightarrow N_2O_4 + \dfrac{1}{2}O_2(g)$. The rate constant is $k = 6.2 \times 10^{-4}\ s^{-1}$. An 80.0-g sample of N_2O_5 in $CCl_4(l)$ is allowed to decompose at 45 °C.
(a) How long does it take for the quantity of N_2O_5 to be reduced to 2.5 g?
(b) How many liters of O_2, measured at 745 mmHg and 45 °C, are produced up to this point?

25. For the reaction A $\longrightarrow$ products, the following data give [A] as a function of time: t = 0 s, [A] = 0.600 M; 100 s, 0.497 M; 200 s, 0.413 M; 300 s, 0.344 M; 400 s, 0.285 M; 600 s, 0.198 M; 1000 s, 0.094 M.
(a) Show that the reaction is first order.
(b) What is the value of the rate constant, k?
(c) What is [A] at t = 750 s?

26. The decomposition of dimethyl ether at 504 °C is

$$(CH_3)_2O(g) \longrightarrow CH_4(g) + H_2(g) + CO(g)$$

The following data are partial pressures of dimethyl ether (DME) as a function of time: t = 0 s, P_{DME} = 312 mmHg; 390 s, 264 mmHg; 777 s, 224 mmHg; 1195 s, 187 mmHg; 3155 s, 78.5 mmHg.
(a) Show that the reaction is first order.
(b) What is the value of the rate constant, k?
(c) What is the total gas pressure at 390 s?
(d) What is the total gas pressure when the reaction has gone to completion?
(e) What is the total gas pressure at t = 1000 s?

Reactions of Various Orders

Three different sets of data of [A] versus time are given in the following table for the reaction A $\longrightarrow$ products. [*Hint:* There are several ways of arriving at answers for each of the following six questions.]

Data for Exercises 27–32

	I		II		III
Time, s	[A], M	Time, s	[A], M	Time, s	[A], M
0	1.00	0	1.00	0	1.00
25	0.78	25	0.75	25	0.80
50	0.61	50	0.50	50	0.67
75	0.47	75	0.25	75	0.57
100	0.37	100	0.00	100	0.50
150	0.22			150	0.40
200	0.14			200	0.33
250	0.08			250	0.29

27. Which of these sets of data corresponds to a (a) zero-order, (b) first-order, (c) second-order reaction?

28. What is the value of the rate constant k of the zero-order reaction?

29. What is the approximate half-life of the first-order reaction?

30. What is the approximate initial rate of the second-order reaction?

31. What is the approximate rate of reaction at t = 75 s for the (a) zero-order, (b) first-order, (c) second-order reaction?

32. What is the approximate concentration of A remaining after 110 s in the (a) zero-order, (b) first-order, (c) second-order reaction?

33. The reaction A + B $\longrightarrow$ C + D is second order in A and zero order in B. The value of k is 0.0103 $M^{-1}\ min^{-1}$. What is the rate of this reaction when [A] = 0.116 M and [B] = 3.83 M?

34. A reaction is 50% complete in 30.0 min. How long after its start will the reaction be 75% complete if it is (a) first order; (b) zero order?

35. The decomposition of HI(g) at 700 K is followed for 400 s, yielding the following data: at t = 0, [HI] = 1.00 M; at t = 100 s, [HI] = 0.90 M; at t = 200 s, [HI] = 0.81 M; t = 300 s, [HI] = 0.74 M; at t = 400 s, [HI] = 0.68 M. What are the reaction order and the rate constant for the reaction:

$$HI(g) \longrightarrow \frac{1}{2}H_2(g) + \frac{1}{2}I_2(g)?$$ Write the rate law for the reaction at 700 K.

36. For the disproportionation of *p*-toluenesulfinic acid,

$$3\ ArSO_2H \longrightarrow ArSO_2SAr + ArSO_3H + H_2O$$

(where Ar = p-$CH_3C_6H_4$—), the following data were obtained: t = 0 min, [$ArSO_2H$] = 0.100 M; 15 min, 0.0863 M; 30 min, 0.0752 M; 45 min, 0.0640 M; 60 min, 0.0568 M; 120 min, 0.0387 M; 180 min, 0.0297 M; 300 min, 0.0196 M.
(a) Show that this reaction is second order.
(b) What is the value of the rate constant, k?
(c) At what time would [$ArSO_2H$] = 0.0500 M?
(d) At what time would [$ArSO_2H$] = 0.0250 M?
(e) At what time would [$ArSO_2H$] = 0.0350 M?

37. For the reaction A $\longrightarrow$ products, the following data were obtained: $t = 0$ s, $[A] = 0.715$ M; 22 s, 0.605 M; 74 s, 0.345 M; 132 s, 0.055 M. **(a)** What is the order of this reaction? **(b)** What is the half-life of the reaction?

38. The following data were obtained for the dimerization of 1,3-butadiene, $2\ C_4H_6(g) \longrightarrow C_8H_{12}(g)$, at 600 K: $t = 0$ min, $[C_4H_6] = 0.0169$ M; 12.18 min, 0.0144 M; 24.55 min, 0.0124 M; 42.50 min, 0.0103 M; 68.05 min, 0.00845 M.
    (a) What is the order of this reaction?
    (b) What is the value of the rate constant, k?
    (c) At what time would $[C_4H_6] = 0.00423$ M?
    (d) At what time would $[C_4H_6] = 0.0050$ M?

39. For the reaction A $\longrightarrow$ products, the data tabulated below are obtained.
    (a) Determine the initial rate of reaction (that is, $-\Delta[A]/\Delta t$) in each of the two experiments.
    (b) Determine the order of the reaction.

First Experiment	
$[A] = 1.512$ M	$t = 0$ min
$[A] = 1.490$ M	$t = 1.0$ min
$[A] = 1.469$ M	$t = 2.0$ min

Second Experiment	
$[A] = 3.024$ M	$t = 0$ min
$[A] = 2.935$ M	$t = 1.0$ min
$[A] = 2.852$ M	$t = 2.0$ min

40. For the reaction A $\longrightarrow$ 2 B + C, the following data are obtained for $[A]$ as a function of time: $t = 0$ min, $[A] = 0.80$ M; 8 min, 0.60 M; 24 min, 0.35 M; 40 min, 0.20 M.
    (a) By suitable means, establish the order of the reaction.
    (b) What is the value of the rate constant, k?
    (c) Calculate the rate of formation of B at $t = 30$ min.

41. In three different experiments, the following results were obtained for the reaction A $\longrightarrow$ products: $[A]_0 = 1.00$ M, $t_{1/2} = 50$ min; $[A]_0 = 2.00$ M, $t_{1/2} = 25$ min; $[A]_0 = 0.50$ M, $t_{1/2} = 100$ min. Write the rate equation for this reaction, and indicate the value of k.

42. Ammonia decomposes on the surface of a hot tungsten wire. Following are the half-lives that were obtained at 1100 °C for different initial concentrations of NH_3: $[NH_3]_0 = 0.0031$ M, $t_{1/2} = 7.6$ min; 0.0015 M, 3.7 min; 0.00068 M, 1.7 min. For this decomposition reaction, what is **(a)** the order of the reaction; **(b)** the rate constant, k?

43. The half-lives of both zero-order and second-order reactions depend on the initial concentration, as well as on the rate constant. In one case, the half-life gets longer as the initial concentration increases, and in the other it gets shorter. Which is which, and why isn't the situation the same for both?

44. Consider three hypothetical reactions, A $\longrightarrow$ products, all having the same numerical value of the rate constant k. One of the reactions is zero order, one is first order, and one is second order. What must be the initial concentration $[A]_0$ if **(a)** the zero- and first-order; **(b)** the zero- and second-order; **(c)** the first- and second-order reactions are to have the same half-life?

Collision Theory; Activation Energy

45. Explain why
    (a) A reaction rate cannot be calculated from the collision frequency alone;
    (b) The rate of a chemical reaction may increase dramatically with temperature, whereas the collision frequency increases much more slowly;
    (c) The addition of a catalyst to a reaction mixture can have such a pronounced effect on the rate of a reaction, even if the temperature is held constant.

46. If even a tiny spark is introduced into a mixture of $H_2(g)$ and $O_2(g)$, a highly exothermic explosive reaction occurs. Without the spark, the mixture remains unreacted indefinitely.
    (a) Explain this difference in behavior.
    (b) Why is the nature of the reaction independent of the size of the spark?

47. For the reversible reaction A + B $\rightleftharpoons$ C + D, the enthalpy change of the forward reaction is +21 kJ/mol. The activation energy of the forward reaction is 84 kJ/mol.
    (a) What is the activation energy of the reverse reaction?
    (b) In the manner of Figure 14-10, sketch the reaction profile of this reaction.

48. By an appropriate sketch, indicate why there is some relationship between the enthalpy change and the activation energy for an endothermic reaction but not for an exothermic reaction.

49. By inspection of the reaction profile for the reaction A to D given below, answer the following questions.

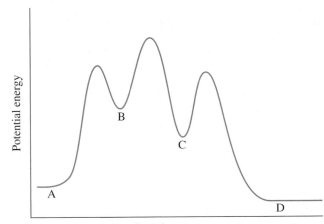

(a) How many intermediates are there in the reaction?
(b) How many transition states are there?
(c) Which is the fastest step in the reaction?
(d) What is the reactant in the rate-determining step?
(e) Is the first step of the reaction exothermic or endothermic?
(f) Is the overall reaction exothermic or endothermic?

50. By inspection of the reaction profile for the reaction A to D given below answer the following questions.

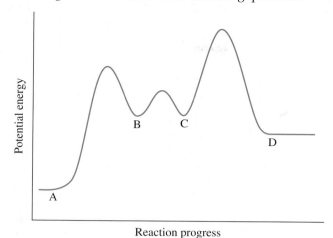

(a) How many intermediates are there in the reaction?
(b) How many transition states are there?
(c) Which is the fastest step in the reaction?
(d) What is the reactant in the rate-determining step?
(e) Is the first step of the reaction exothermic or endothermic?
(f) Is the overall reaction exothermic or endothermic?

Effect of Temperature on Rates of Reaction

51. The rate constant for the reaction $H_2(g) + I_2(g) \longrightarrow 2 HI(g)$ has been determined at the following temperatures: 599 K, $k = 5.4 \times 10^{-4} M^{-1} s^{-1}$; 683 K, $k = 2.8 \times 10^{-2} M^{-1} s^{-1}$. Calculate the activation energy for the reaction.

52. At what temperature will the rate constant for the reaction in Exercise 51 have the value $k = 5.0 \times 10^{-3} M^{-1} s^{-1}$?

53. A treatise on atmospheric chemistry lists the following rate constants for the decomposition of PAN described in the Integrative Example on page 610: 0 °C, $k = 5.6 \times 10^{-6} s^{-1}$; 10 °C, $k = 3.2 \times 10^{-5} s^{-1}$; 20 °C, $k = 1.6 \times 10^{-4} s^{-1}$; 30 °C, $k = 7.6 \times 10^{-4} s^{-1}$.
(a) Construct a graph of $\ln k$ versus $1/T$.
(b) What is the activation energy, E_a, of the reaction?
(c) Calculate the half-life of the decomposition reaction at 40 °C.

54. The reaction $C_2H_5I + OH^- \longrightarrow C_2H_5OH + I^-$ was studied in an ethanol (C_2H_5OH) solution, and the following rate constants were obtained: 15.83 °C, $k = 5.03 \times 10^{-5}$; 32.02 °C, 3.68×10^{-4}; 59.75 °C, 6.71×10^{-3}; 90.61 °C, 0.119 $M^{-1} s^{-1}$.
(a) Determine E_a for this reaction by a graphical method.
(b) Determine E_a by the use of equation (14.22).
(c) Calculate the value of the rate constant k at 100.0 °C.

55. The first-order reaction A $\longrightarrow$ products has a half-life, $t_{1/2}$, of 46.2 min at 25 °C and 2.6 min at 102 °C.
(a) Calculate the activation energy of this reaction.
(b) At what temperature would the half-life be 10.0 min?

56. For the first-order reaction

$$N_2O_5(g) \longrightarrow 2 NO_2(g) + \frac{1}{2}O_2(g)$$

$t_{1/2} = 22.5$ h at 20 °C and 1.5 h at 40 °C.
(a) Calculate the activation energy of this reaction.
(b) If the Arrhenius constant $A = 2.05 \times 10^{13} s^{-1}$, determine the value of k at 30 °C.

57. A commonly stated rule of thumb is that reaction rates double for a temperature increase of about 10 °C. (This rule is very often wrong.)
(a) What must be the approximate activation energy for this statement to be true for reactions at about room temperature?
(b) Would you expect this rule of thumb to apply at room temperature for the reaction profiled in Figure 14-10? Explain.

58. Concerning the rule of thumb stated in Exercise 57, estimate how much faster cooking occurs in a pressure cooker with the vapor pressure of water at 2.00 atm instead of in water under normal boiling conditions. [*Hint:* Refer to Table 12.2.]

Catalysis

59. The following statements about catalysis are not stated as carefully as they might be. What slight modifications would you make in them?
(a) A catalyst is a substance that speeds up a chemical reaction but does not take part in the reaction.
(b) The function of a catalyst is to lower the activation energy for a chemical reaction.

60. The following substrate concentration [S] versus time data were obtained during an enzyme-catalyzed reaction: $t = 0$ min, [S] = 1.00 M; 20 min, 0.90 M; 60 min, 0.70 M; 100 min, 0.50 M; 160 min, 0.20 M. What is the order of this reaction with respect to S in the concentration range studied?

61. What are the similarities and differences between the catalytic activity of platinum metal and of an enzyme?

62. Certain gas-phase reactions on a heterogeneous catalyst are first order at low gas pressures and zero order at high pressures. Can you suggest a reason for this?

63. The graph shows the effect of enzyme concentration on the rate of an enzyme reaction. What reaction conditions are necessary to account for this graph?

64. The graph shows the effect of temperature on enzyme activity. Explain why the graph has the general shape shown. For human enzymes, at what temperature would you expect the maximum in the curve to appear?

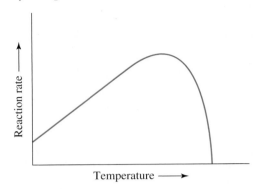

Reaction Mechanisms

65. We have used the terms *order of a reaction* and *molecularity of an elementary process* (that is, unimolecular, bimolecular). What is the relationship, if any, between these two terms?

66. According to collision theory, chemical reactions occur through molecular collisions. A unimolecular elementary process in a reaction mechanism involves dissociation of a *single* molecule. How can these two ideas be compatible? Explain.

67. The reaction $2 NO + 2 H_2 \longrightarrow N_2 + 2 H_2O$ is second order in [NO] and first order in $[H_2]$. A *three-step* mechanism has been proposed. The first, fast step is the elementary process given as equation (14.25) on page 598. The third step, also fast, is $N_2O + H_2 \longrightarrow N_2 + H_2O$. Propose an entire three-step mechanism, and show that it conforms to the experimentally determined reaction order.

68. The mechanism proposed for the reaction of $H_2(g)$ and $I_2(g)$ to form HI(g) consists of a fast reversible first step involving $I_2(g)$ and I(g), followed by a slow step. Propose a two-step mechanism for the reaction $H_2(g) + I_2(g) \longrightarrow 2 HI(g)$, which is known to be first order in H_2 and first order in I_2.

69. The reaction $2 NO + Cl_2 \longrightarrow 2 NOCl$ has the rate law: rate of reaction = $k[NO]^2[Cl_2]$. Propose a two-step mechanism for this reaction consisting of a fast reversible first step, followed by a slow step.

70. A simplified rate law for the reaction $2 O_3(g) \longrightarrow 3 O_2(g)$ is

$$\text{rate} = k = \frac{[O_3]^2}{[O_2]}$$

For this reaction, propose a two-step mechanism that consists of a fast, reversible first step, followed by a slow second step.

Integrative and Advanced Exercises

71. Suppose that the reaction in Example 14-8 is first order with a rate constant of 0.12 min^{-1}. Starting with $[A]_0 = 1.00$ M, will the curve for [A] versus t for the first-order reaction cross the curve for the second-order reaction at some time after $t = 0$? Will the two curves cross if $[A]_0 = 2.00$ M? In each case, if the curves are found to cross, at what time will this happen?

72. $[A]_t$ as a function of time for the reaction A $\longrightarrow$ products is plotted in the graph shown here. Use data from this graph to determine **(a)** the order of the reaction; **(b)** the rate constant, k; **(c)** the rate of the reaction at $t = 3.5$ min, using the results of parts (a) and (b); **(d)** the rate of the reaction at $t = 5.0$ min, from the slope of the tangent line; **(e)** the initial rate of the reaction.

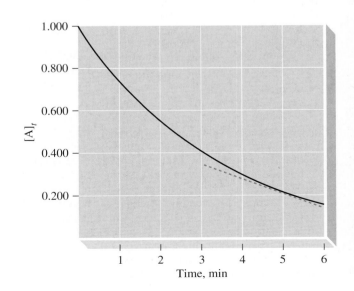

73. Exactly 300 s after decomposition of $H_2O_2(aq)$ begins (reaction 14.3), a 5.00-mL sample is removed and immediately titrated with 37.1 mL of 0.1000 M $KMnO_4$. What is $[H_2O_2]$ at this 300-s point in the reaction?

74. Use the method of Exercise 73 to determine the volume of 0.1000 M $KMnO_4$ required to titrate 5.00-mL samples of $H_2O_2(aq)$ for each of the entries in Table 14.1. Plot these volumes of $KMnO_4(aq)$ as a function of time, and show that from this graph you can get the same rate of reaction at 1400 s as that obtained in Figure 14-2.

75. The initial rate of reaction (14.3) is found to be $1.7 \times 10^{-3}\,M\,s^{-1}$. Assume that this rate holds for 2 minutes. Start with 175 mL of 1.55 M $H_2O_2(aq)$ at $t = 0$. How many milliliters of $O_2(g)$, measured at 24 °C and 757 mmHg, are released from solution in the first minute of the reaction?

76. We have seen that the unit of k depends on the overall order of a reaction. Derive a general expression for the units of k for a reaction of any overall order, based on the order of the reaction (o) and the units of concentration (M) and time (s).

77. At room temperature (20 °C), milk turns sour in about 64 hours. In a refrigerator at 3 °C, milk can be stored three times as long before it sours. **(a)** Estimate the activation energy of the reaction that causes the souring of milk. **(b)** How long should it take milk to sour at 40 °C?

78. Hydroxide ion is involved in the mechanism of the following reaction but is not consumed in the overall reaction.

$$OCl^- + I^- \xrightarrow{OH^-} OI^- + Cl^-$$

(a) From the data given, determine the order of the reaction with respect to OCl^-, I^-, and OH^-.
(b) What is the overall reaction order?
(c) Write the rate equation, and determine the value of the rate constant, k.

$[OCl^-]$, M	$[I^-]$, M	$[OH^-]$, M	Rate Formation OI^-, $M\,s^{-1}$
0.0040	0.0020	1.00	4.8×10^{-4}
0.0020	0.0040	1.00	5.0×10^{-4}
0.0020	0.0020	1.00	2.4×10^{-4}
0.0020	0.0020	0.50	4.6×10^{-4}
0.0020	0.0020	0.25	9.4×10^{-4}

79. The half-life for the first-order decomposition of nitramide, $NH_2NO_2(aq) \longrightarrow N_2O(g) + H_2O(l)$, is 123 min at 15 °C. If 165 mL of a 0.105 M NH_2NO_2 solution is allowed to decompose, how long must the reaction proceed to yield 50.0 mL of $N_2O(g)$ collected over water at 15 °C and a barometric pressure of 756 mmHg? (The vapor pressure of water at 15 °C is 12.8 mmHg.)

80. The decomposition of ethylene oxide at 690 K is monitored by measuring the *total* gas pressure as a function of time. The data obtained are $t = 10$ min, $P_{tot} = 139.14$ mmHg; 20 min, 151.67 mmHg; 40 min, 172.65 mmHg; 60 min, 189.15 mmHg; 100 min, 212.34 mmHg; 200 min, 238.66 mmHg; ∞, 249.88 mmHg. What is the order of the reaction $(CH_2)_2O(g) \longrightarrow CH_4(g) + CO(g)$?

81. Refer to Example 14-7. For the decomposition of di-*t*-butyl peroxide (DTBP), determine the time at which the *total* gas pressure is 2100 mmHg.

82. The following data are for the reaction $2\,A + B \longrightarrow$ products. Establish the order of this reaction with respect to A and to B.

Expt 1, [B] = 1.00 M		Expt 2, [B] = 0.50 M	
Time, min	[A], M	Time, min	[A], M
0	1.000×10^{-3}	0	1.000×10^{-3}
1	0.951×10^{-3}	1	0.975×10^{-3}
5	0.779×10^{-3}	5	0.883×10^{-3}
10	0.607×10^{-3}	10	0.779×10^{-3}
20	0.368×10^{-3}	20	0.607×10^{-3}

83. Show that the following mechanism is consistent with the rate law established for the iodide–hypochlorite reaction in Exercise 78.

Fast: $\quad OCl^- + H_2O \underset{k_2}{\overset{k_1}{\rightleftharpoons}} HOCl + OH^-$

Slow: $\quad I^- + HOCl \xrightarrow{k_3} HOI + Cl^-$

Fast: $\quad HOI + OH^- \underset{k_5}{\overset{k_4}{\rightleftharpoons}} H_2O + OI^-$

84. In the hydrogenation of a compound containing a carbon-to-carbon triple bond, two products are possible, as in the reaction

$$CH_3-C\equiv C-CH_3 + H_2 \longrightarrow$$

The amount of each product can be controlled by using an appropriate catalyst. The Lindlar catalyst is a *heterogeneous* catalyst that produces only one of these products. Which product, I or II, do you think is produced and why? Draw a sketch of how the reaction might occur.

85. Derive a plausible mechanism for the following reaction in aqueous solution, $Hg_2^{2+} + Tl^{3+} \longrightarrow 2\,Hg^{2+} + Tl^+$, for which the observed rate law is: rate $= k[Hg_2^{2+}][Tl^{3+}]/[Hg^{2+}]$.

86. The following three-step mechanism has been proposed for the reaction of chlorine and chloroform.

(1) $Cl_2(g) \underset{k_{-1}}{\overset{k_1}{\rightleftharpoons}} 2\,Cl(g)$

(2) $Cl(g) + CHCl_3(g) \xrightarrow{k_2} HCl(g) + CCl_3(g)$

(3) $CCl_3(g) + Cl(g) \xrightarrow{k_3} CCl_4(g)$

The numerical values of the rate constants for these steps are $k_1 = 4.8 \times 10^3$; $k_{-1} = 3.6 \times 10^3$; $k_2 = 1.3 \times 10^{-2}$; $k_3 = 2.7 \times 10^2$. Derive the rate law and the magnitude of k for the overall reaction.

87. For the reaction $A \longrightarrow$ products, derive the integrated rate law and an expression for the half-life if the reaction is third order.

88. The reaction A + B $\longrightarrow$ products is first order in A, first order in B, and second order overall. Consider that the starting concentrations of the reactants are $[A]_0$ and $[B]_0$, and that x represents the decrease in these concentrations at the time t. That is, $[A]_t = [A]_0 - x$ and $[B]_t = [B]_0 - x$. Show that the integrated rate law for this reaction can be expressed as shown below.

$$\ln \frac{[A]_0 \times [B]_t}{[B]_0 \times [A]_t} = ([B]_0 - [A]_0) \times kt$$

89. The rate of the reaction

$$2\, CO(g) \longrightarrow CO_2(g) + C(s)$$

was studied by injecting $CO(g)$ into a reaction vessel and measuring the total pressure at constant volume.

P_{total} (Torr)	Time (s)
250	0
238	398
224	1002
210	1801

What is the rate constant of this reaction?

90. The kinetics of the decomposition of phosphine at 950 K

$$4\, PH_3(g) \longrightarrow P_4(g) + 6\, H_2(g)$$

was studied by injecting $PH_3(g)$ into a reaction vessel and measuring the total pressure at constant volume.

P_{total} (Torr)	Time (s)
100	0
150	40
167	80
172	120

What is the rate constant of this reaction?

91. The rate of an enzyme-catalyzed reaction can be slowed down by the presence of an inhibitor (I) that reacts with the enzyme in a rapid equilibrium process.

$$E + I \rightleftharpoons EI$$

By adding this step to the mechanism for enzyme catalysis on page 607, determine the effect of adding the concentration $[I_0]$ on the rate of an enzyme-catalyzed reaction.

92. By taking the reciprocal of both sides of equation 14.36, obtain an expression for $1/V$. Using the resulting equation, suggest a strategy for determining the Michaelis–Menten constant, K_M, and the value of k_2.

93. The following mechanism can be used to account for the change in apparent order of unimolecular reactions, such as the conversion of cyclopropane (A) into propene (P), where A^* is an energetic form of cyclopropane that can either react or return to unreacted cyclopropane.

$$A + A \underset{k_{-1}}{\overset{k_1}{\rightleftharpoons}} A^* + A$$

$$A^* \xrightarrow{k_2} P$$

Show that at low pressures of cyclopropane the rate law is second order in A and at high pressures it is first order in A.

94. You wish to test the following proposed mechanism for the oxidation of HBr.

$$HBr + O_2 \xrightarrow{k_1} HOOBr$$

$$HOOBr + HBr \xrightarrow{k_2} 2\, HOBr$$

$$HOBr + HBr \xrightarrow{k_3} H_2O + Br_2$$

You find that the rate is first order with respect to HBr and to O_2. You cannot detect HOBr among the products.
(a) If the proposed mechanism is correct, which must be the rate-determining step?
(b) Can you prove the mechanism from these observations?
(c) Can you disprove the mechanism from these observations?

Feature Problems

95. Benzenediazonium chloride decomposes by a first-order reaction in water, yielding $N_2(g)$ as one product.

$$C_6H_5N_2Cl \longrightarrow C_6H_5Cl + N_2(g)$$

The reaction can be followed by measuring the volume of $N_2(g)$ as a function of time. The data in the table were obtained for the decomposition of a 0.071 M solution at 50 °C, where $t = \infty$ corresponds to the completed reaction.

Time, min	$N_2(g)$, mL	Time, min	$N_2(g)$, mL
0	0	18	41.3
3	10.8	21	44.3
6	19.3	24	46.5
9	26.3	27	48.4
12	32.4	30	50.4
15	37.3	∞	58.3

(a) Convert the information given here into a table with one column for time and the other for $[C_6H_5N_2Cl]$.

(b) Construct a table similar to Table 14.2, in which the time interval is $\Delta t = 3$ min.

(c) Plot graphs similar to Figure 14-2, showing both the formation of $N_2(g)$ and the disappearance of $C_6H_5N_2Cl$ as a function of time.

(d) From the graph of part (c), determine the rate of reaction at $t = 21$ min, and compare your result with the reported value of 1.1×10^{-3} M min^{-1}.

(e) Determine the initial rate of reaction.

(f) Write the rate law for the first-order decomposition of $C_6H_5N_2Cl$, and estimate a value of k based on the rate determined in parts (d) and (e).

(g) Determine $t_{1/2}$ for the reaction by estimation from the graph of the rate data and by calculation.

(h) At what time would the decomposition of the sample be three-fourths complete?

(i) Plot $\ln[C_6H_5N_2Cl]$ versus time, and show that the reaction is indeed first order.

(j) Determine k from the slope of the graph of part (i).

96. The object is to study the kinetics of the reaction between peroxodisulfate and iodide ions.

(a) $S_2O_8^{2-}(aq) + 3\,I^-(aq) \longrightarrow$

$$2\,SO_4^{2-}(aq) + I_3^-(aq)$$

The I_3^- formed in reaction (a) is actually a complex of iodine, I_2, and iodide ion, I^-. Thiosulfate ion, $S_2O_3^{2-}$, also present in the reaction mixture, reacts with I_3^- just as fast as it is formed.

(b) $2\,S_2O_3^{2-}(aq) + I_3^-(aq) \longrightarrow S_4O_6^{2-} + 3\,I^-(aq)$

When all of the thiosulfate ion present initially has been consumed by reaction (b), a third reaction occurs between $I_3^-(aq)$ and starch, which is also present in the reaction mixture.

(c) $I_3^-(aq) + \text{starch} \longrightarrow \text{blue complex}$

The rate of reaction (a) is inversely related to the time required for the blue color of the starch–iodine complex to appear. That is, the faster reaction (a) proceeds, the more quickly the thiosulfate ion is consumed in reaction (b), and the sooner the blue color appears in reaction (c). One of the photographs shows the initial colorless solution and an electronic timer set at $t = 0$; the other photograph shows the very first appearance of the blue complex (after 49.89 s). Tables I and II list some actual student data obtained in this study.

TABLE I

Reaction conditions at 24 °C: 25.0 mL of the $(NH_4)_2S_2O_8(aq)$ listed, 25.0 mL of the KI(aq) listed, 10.0 mL of 0.010 M $Na_2S_2O_3(aq)$, and 5.0 mL starch solution are mixed. The time is that of the first appearance of the starch–iodine complex.

Experiment	Initial Concentrations, M		Time, s
	$(NH_4)_2S_2O_8$	KI	
1	0.20	0.20	21
2	0.10	0.20	42
3	0.050	0.20	81
4	0.20	0.10	42
5	0.20	0.050	79

TABLE II

Reaction conditions: those listed in Table I for Experiment 4, but at the temperatures listed.

Experiment	Temperature, °C	Time, s
6	3	189
7	13	88
8	24	42
9	33	21

(a) Use the data in Table I to establish the order of reaction (a) with respect to $S_2O_8^{2-}$ and to I^-. What is the overall reaction order?
[*Hint:* How are the times required for the blue complex to appear related to the actual rates of reaction?]

(b) Calculate the initial rate of reaction in Experiment 1, expressed in M s^{-1}.
[*Hint:* You must take into account the dilution that occurs when the various solutions are mixed, as well as the reaction stoichiometry indicated by equations (a), (b), and (c).]

(c) Calculate the value of the rate constant, k, based on experiments 1 and 2.

(d) Calculate the rate constant, k, for the four different temperatures in Table II.

(e) Determine the activation energy, E_a, of the peroxodisulfate–iodide ion reaction.

(f) The following mechanism has been proposed for reaction (a). The first step is slow, and the others are fast.

$$I^- + S_2O_8^{2-} \longrightarrow IS_2O_8^{3-}$$
$$IS_2O_8^{3-} \longrightarrow 2\,SO_4^{2-} + I^+$$
$$I^+ + I^- \longrightarrow I_2$$
$$I_2 + I^- \longrightarrow I_3^-$$

Show that this mechanism is consistent with both the stoichiometry and the rate law of reaction (a). Explain why it is reasonable to expect the first step in the mechanism to be slower than the others.

Self-Assessment Exercises

97. In your own words, define or explain the following terms or symbols: **(a)** $[A]_0$; **(b)** k; **(c)** $t_{1/2}$; **(d)** zero-order reaction; **(e)** catalyst.

98. Briefly describe each of the following ideas, phenomena, or methods: **(a)** the method of initial rates; **(b)** activated complex; **(c)** reaction mechanism; **(d)** heterogeneous catalysis; **(e)** rate-determining step.

99. Explain the important distinctions between each pair of terms: **(a)** first-order and second-order reactions; **(b)** rate law and integrated rate law; **(c)** activation energy and enthalpy of reaction; **(d)** elementary process and overall reaction; **(e)** enzyme and substrate.

100. The rate equation for the reaction $2\,A + B \longrightarrow C$ is found to be rate $= k[A][B]$. For this reaction, we can conclude that **(a)** the unit of $k = s^{-1}$; **(b)** $t_{1/2}$ is constant; **(c)** the value of k is independent of the values of $[A]$ and $[B]$; **(d)** the rate of formation of C is twice the rate of disappearance of A.

101. A first-order reaction, $A \longrightarrow$ products, has a half-life of 75 s, from which we can draw two conclusions. Of the following, those two are **(a)** the reaction goes to completion in 150 s; **(b)** the quantity of A remaining after 150 s is half of what remains after 75 s; **(c)** the same quantity of A is consumed for every 75 s of the reaction; **(d)** one-quarter of the original quantity of A is consumed in the first 37.5 s of the reaction; **(e)** twice as much A is consumed in 75 s when the initial amount of A is doubled; **(f)** the amount of A consumed in 150 s is twice as much as is consumed in 75 s.

102. A first order reaction $A \longrightarrow$ products has a half-life of 13.9 min. The rate at which this reaction proceeds when $[A] = 0.40\,M$ is **(a)** $0.020\ \text{mol L}^{-1}\,\text{min}^{-1}$; **(b)** $5.0 \times 10^{-2}\ \text{mol L}^{-1}\,\text{min}^{-1}$; **(c)** $8.0\ \text{mol L}^{-1}\,\text{min}^{-1}$; **(d)** $0.125\ \text{mol L}^{-1}\,\text{min}^{-1}$.

103. The reaction $A \longrightarrow$ products is second order. The initial rate of decomposition of A when $[A]_0 = 0.50\,M$ is **(a)** the same as the initial rate for any other value of $[A]_0$; **(b)** half as great as when $[A]_0 = 1.00\,M$; **(c)** five times as great as when $[A]_0 = 0.10\,M$; **(d)** four times as great as when $[A]_0 = 0.25\,M$.

104. The rate of a chemical reaction generally increases rapidly, even for small increases in temperature, because of a rapid increase in **(a)** collision frequency; **(b)** fraction of reactant molecules with very high kinetic energies; **(c)** activation energy; **(d)** average kinetic energy of the reactant molecules.

105. For the reaction $A + B \longrightarrow 2\,C$, which proceeds by a single-step bimolecular elementary process, **(a)** $t_{1/2} = 0.693/k$; **(b)** rate of appearance of C $=$ $-$rate of disappearance of A; **(c)** rate of reaction $= k[A][B]$; **(d)** $\ln[A]_t = -kt + \ln[A]_0$.

106. In the first-order decomposition of substance A the following concentrations are found at the indicated times: $t = 0$ s, $[A] = 0.88\,M$; $t = 50$ s, $[A] = 0.62\,M$; $t = 100$ s, $[A] = 0.44\,M$; $t = 150$ s, $[A] = 0.31\,M$. Calculate the instantaneous rate of decomposition at $t = 100$ s.

107. A reaction is 50% complete in 30.0 min. How long after its start will the reaction be 75% complete if it is **(a)** first order; **(b)** zero order?

108. A kinetic study of the reaction $A \longrightarrow$ products yields the data: $t = 0$ s, $[A] = 2.00\,M$; 500 s, 1.00 M; 1500 s, 0.50 M; 3500 s, 0.25 M. *Without performing detailed calculations*, determine the order of this reaction and indicate your method of reasoning.

109. For the reaction $A \longrightarrow$ products the following data are obtained.

Experiment 1		Experiment 2	
$[A] = 1.204\,M$	$t = 0$ min	$[A] = 2.408\,M$	$t = 0$ min
$[A] = 1.180\,M$	$t = 1.0$ min	$[A] = ?$	$t = 1.0$ min
$[A] = 0.602\,M$	$t = 35$ min	$[A] = ?$	$t = 30$ min

(a) Determine the initial rate of reaction in Experiment 1.
(b) If the reaction is second order, what will be $[A]$ at $t = 1.0$ min in Experiment 2?
(c) If the reaction is first order, what will be $[A]$ at 30 min in Experiment 2?

110. For the reaction $A + 2\,B \longrightarrow C + D$, the rate law is rate of reaction $= k[A][B]$.
(a) Show that the following mechanism is consistent with the stoichiometry of the overall reaction and with the rate law.

$$A + B \longrightarrow I \quad \text{(slow)}$$
$$I + B \longrightarrow C + D \quad \text{(fast)}$$

(b) Show that the following mechanism is consistent with the stoichiometry of the overall reaction, but *not* with the rate law.

$$2\,B \underset{k_2}{\overset{k_1}{\rightleftharpoons}} B_2 \quad \text{(fast)}$$
$$A + B_2 \overset{k_3}{\longrightarrow} C + D \quad \text{(slow)}$$

111. Using the method presented in Appendix E, construct a concept map illustrating the concepts in Sections 14–8 and 14–9.

 # eMedia Exercises

112. In the animation describing a **First-Order Process** (*Activebook 14-5*), the half-life of the reaction is illustrated. **(a)** How does this relationship between time and concentration differ from that of zero- and second-order processes? **(b)** What is the ratio between the half-life and quarter-life (the time required for the concentration to fall to 75% of its initial value) for a first-order process?

113. The influence of reaction conditions and energetics is simulated in the **Rates of Reactions** simulation found in *Activebook 14-9*. **(a)** What set of adjustable conditions in this simulation favors the greatest rate of reaction? What set of conditions favors the lowest rate of reaction? **(b)** What is the general relationship between ΔH_{rxn} and reaction rate? Under what conditions will endothermic reactions proceed at an appreciable rate?

114. The reaction of OH^- and CH_3Cl is illustrated in the **Bimolecular Reaction** animation (*Activebook 14-10*). **(a)** Identify the transition state or activated complex in this reaction. **(b)** Describe the hybridization of the central carbon atom as a reactant, activated complex, and product. What does this tell you about the stability of the transition state?

115. The reaction of hydrogen and ethylene over an alloy surface is illustrated in the **Surface Reaction—Hydrogenation** animation (*Activebook 14-11*). **(a)** Write out a balanced chemical equation describing this reaction. Where does the metal surface appear in this equation? **(b)** What is the primary role that the metal surface plays in the reaction? Why would this process proceed more slowly in the absence of the metal catalyst?

15

PRINCIPLES OF CHEMICAL EQUILIBRIUM

There are many demonstrations that show equilibrium: roll a marble in a parabolic clear dish to show the establishment of physical equilibrium; pour $AgNO_3$ into ordinary tap water, and the chloride ion in the water will precipitate out leaving the water cloudy; burn a match, and when it goes out, equilibrium is established. Point out that equilibrium in chemical reactions is obtained by minimizing the free energy (see Chapter 19).

✓ Point out that equilibrium is less common than nonequilibrium. For example, your heart and other biochemical processes are oscillating back and forth in cycles. We certainly don't want our hearts to come to equilibrium.

A vital natural reaction is in progress in the lightning bolt seen here: $N_2(g) + O_2(g) \rightleftharpoons 2 NO(g)$. Usually this reversible reaction does not occur to any significant extent in the forward direction, but in the high-temperature lightning bolt it does. At equilibrium at high temperatures, measurable conversion of $N_2(g)$ and $O_2(g)$ to $NO(g)$ occurs. In this chapter we study the equilibrium condition in a reversible reaction and the factors affecting it.

Until now, we have stressed reactions that go to completion and the concepts of stoichiometry that allow us to calculate the outcomes of such reactions. We have made occasional references to situations involving both a forward and a reverse reaction—*reversible reactions*—but in this chapter, we will look at them in a detailed and systematic way.

Our emphasis will be on the equilibrium condition reached when forward and reverse reactions proceed at the same rate. Our main tool in dealing with equilibrium will be the equilibrium constant. We will begin with some key relationships involving equilibrium constants; then we will make qualitative predictions about the condition of equilibrium; and finally we will do various equilibrium calculations. As we will discover throughout the remainder of the text, the equilibrium condition plays a role in numerous natural phenomena and affects the methods used to produce many important industrial chemicals.

15-1   DYNAMIC EQUILIBRIUM

Let's begin by describing three simple physical and one chemical phenomena that will help us to establish the core attribute of a system at **equilibrium**—two opposing processes take place at equal rates.

1. When a liquid vaporizes within a closed container, after a time, vapor molecules condense to the liquid state at the same rate at which liquid molecules vaporize. Even though molecules continue to pass back and forth between liquid and vapor (a *dynamic* process), the pressure exerted by the vapor remains constant with time. *The vapor pressure of a liquid is a property resulting from an equilibrium condition.*

2. When a solute is added to a solvent, the system may reach a point at which the rate of dissolution is just matched by the rate at which dissolved solute crystallizes—that is, the solution is saturated. Even though solute particles continue to pass back and forth between the saturated solution and the undissolved solute, the concentration of dissolved solute remains constant. *The solubility of a solute is a property resulting from an equilibrium condition.*

3. When an aqueous solution of iodine, I_2, is shaken with pure carbon tetrachloride, $CCl_4(l)$, the I_2 molecules move into the CCl_4 layer. As the concentration of I_2 builds up in the CCl_4, the rate of return of I_2 to the water layer becomes significant. When I_2 molecules pass between the two liquids at equal rates—a condition of dynamic equilibrium—the concentration of I_2 in each layer remains constant. At this point, the concentration of I_2 in the CCl_4 is about 85 times greater than in the H_2O (Fig. 15-1). The ratio of concentrations of a solute in two immiscible solvents is called the distribution coefficient. *The distribution coefficient, which represents the partitioning of a solute between two immiscible solvents, is a property resulting from an equilibrium condition.*

4. When gaseous phosphorus pentachloride is heated, it decomposes to phosphorus trichloride and chlorine gases: $PCl_5(g) \longrightarrow PCl_3(g) + Cl_2(g)$. Consider a sample of $PCl_5(g)$ initially exerting a pressure of 1.0 atm in a closed container at 250 °C. The gas pressure in the container first rises rapidly and then ever more slowly, reaching a maximum, unchanging pressure of 1.7 atm. Because two moles of gas are produced for each mole of $PCl_5(g)$ that decomposes, if the reaction went to completion the final pressure would have been 2.0 atm. We conclude that *the decomposition of PCl_5 is a reversible reaction that reaches an equilibrium condition.*

The properties in the first three situations just described—vapor pressure, solubility, and distribution coefficient—are examples of physical equilibria. The fourth situation is an example of chemical equilibrium. All four are described through a general quantity known as an *equilibrium constant*, the subject of the next section.

15-2   THE EQUILIBRIUM CONSTANT EXPRESSION

Methanol (methyl alcohol) is synthesized from a carbon monoxide–hydrogen mixture called synthesis gas. This reaction is likely to become increasingly important as methanol and its mixtures with gasoline find greater use as motor fuels. Methanol has a high octane rating, and its combustion produces much less air pollution than does gasoline.

Methanol synthesis is a *reversible* reaction, which means that at the same time $CH_3OH(g)$ is being formed,

$$CO(g) + 2 H_2(g) \longrightarrow CH_3OH(g) \tag{15.1}$$

it decomposes in the reverse reaction

$$CH_3OH(g) \longrightarrow CO(g) + 2 H_2(g) \tag{15.2}$$

Dynamic Equilibrium animation

Paiva, João C. M., Victor M. S. Gil. "The Complexity of Teaching and Learning Chemical Equilibrium." *J. Chem. Educ.* **2000**: 77, 1560 (December 2000).

Silverstein, Todd P. "Equilibrium: A Teaching/Learning Activity." *J. Chem. Educ.* **2000**: 77, 1410 (November 2000).

The two opposing processes operate at the microscopic level.

(a)   **(b)**

▲ **FIGURE 15-1**
Dynamic equilibrium in a physical process
(a) A yellow-brown saturated solution of I_2 in water (top layer) is brought into contact with colorless $CCl_4(l)$ (bottom layer). **(b)** I_2 molecules distribute themselves between the H_2O and CCl_4. When equilibrium is reached, $[I_2]$ in the CCl_4 (violet, bottom layer) is about 85 times greater than in the water (colorless, top layer).

▲ Methanol is actively being considered as an alternative fuel to gasoline.

Are You Wondering . . .

How we know that an equilibrium is dynamic—that forward and reverse reactions continue even after equilibrium is reached?

Suppose we have an equilibrium mixture of AgI(s) and its saturated aqueous solution.

$$AgI(s) \rightleftharpoons AgI(satd\ aq)$$

Now let's add to this mixture some saturated solution of AgI made from AgI containing radioactive iodine-131 as iodide ion, as illustrated in Figure 15-2. If both the forward and reverse processes stopped at equilibrium, radioactivity would be confined to the solution. What we find, though, is that radioactivity shows up in the solid in contact with the saturated solution. Over time, the radioactive "hot" spots distribute themselves throughout the solution and undissolved solid. The only way this can happen is if the dissolving of the solid solute and its crystallization from the saturated solution continue indefinitely. The equilibrium condition is *dynamic*.

Saturated solution only added to beaker

(a)

(b)

▲ **FIGURE 15-2**
Dynamic equilibrium illustrated
(a) A saturated solution of radioactive AgI is added to a saturated solution of AgI. **(b)** The radioactive iodide ions distribute themselves throughout the solution and the solid AgI, showing that the equilibrium is dynamic.

Initially, only the forward reaction (15.1) occurs, but as soon as some CH_3OH forms, the reverse reaction (15.2) begins. With passing time, the forward reaction slows because of the decreasing concentrations of CO and H_2 and the reverse reaction speeds up as more CH_3OH accumulates. Eventually, the forward and reverse reactions proceed at equal rates, and the reaction mixture reaches a condition of dynamic equilibrium, which we can represent with a double arrow $\rightleftharpoons$.

$$CO(g) + 2\,H_2(g) \rightleftharpoons CH_3OH(g) \qquad (15.3)$$

TABLE 15.1   Three Approaches to Equilibrium in the Reaction[a]
$CO(g) + 2 H_2(g) \rightleftharpoons CH_3OH(g)$

	CO(g)	H₂(g)	CH₃OH(g)
Experiment 1			
Initial amounts, mol	1.000	1.000	0.000
Equilibrium amounts, mol	0.911	0.822	0.0892
Equilibrium concentrations, mol/L	0.0911	0.0822	0.00892
Experiment 2			
Initial amounts, mol	0.000	0.000	1.000
Equilibrium amounts, mol	0.753	1.506	0.247
Equilibrium concentrations, mol/L	0.0753	0.151	0.0247
Experiment 3			
Initial amounts, mol	1.000	1.000	1.000
Equilibrium amounts, mol	1.380	1.760	0.620
Equilibrium concentrations, mol/L	0.138	0.176	0.0620

The concentrations printed in blue are used in the calculations in Table 15.2.
[a] Reaction carried out in a 10.0-L flask at 483 K.

> Point out to students that the equilibrium state can be obtained by starting with any combination of reactants and/or products.

One consequence of the equilibrium condition is that the amounts of the reactants and products remain constant with time. These equilibrium amounts, however, depend on the quantities of reactants and products present initially. For example, Table 15.1 lists data for three hypothetical experiments. All three experiments are conducted in a 10.0-L flask at 483 K. In the first experiment, only CO and H_2 are present initially; in the second, only CH_3OH; and in the third, CO, H_2, and CH_3OH. The data from Table 15.1 are plotted in Figure 15-3, and from these graphs we see that

- in no case is any reacting species completely consumed;
- in all three cases the equilibrium amounts of reactants and products appear to have nothing in common.

Silverstein, Todd P. "The Real Reason Why Oil and Water Don't Mix." *J. Chem. Educ.* **1998:** *75,* 116 (January 1998).

Jordan, A. D. "Liquid-Liquid Equilibrium: Verification of the Lever Rule." *J. Chem. Educ.* **2000:** *77,* 395 (March 2000).

Harrison, J. A., Buckley, P. D. "Simulating Dynamic Equilibria: A Class Experiment." *J. Chem. Educ.* **2000:** *77,* 1013 (August 2000).

Chemical Equilibrium activity

t_e = time for equilibrium to be reached
—— mol CO
—— mol H₂
—— mol CH₃OH

◀ FIGURE 15-3
Three approaches to equilibrium in the reaction

$CO(g) + 2 H_2(g) \rightleftharpoons CH_3OH(g)$

The initial and equilibrium amounts for each of these three cases are listed in Table 15.1. t_e = time for equilibrium to be reached.

TABLE 15.2

Expt	Trial 1: $\dfrac{[CH_3OH]}{[CO][H_2]}$	Trial 2: $\dfrac{[CH_3OH]}{[CO](2 \times [H_2])}$	Trial 3: $\dfrac{[CH_3OH]}{[CO][H_2]^2}$
1	$\dfrac{0.00892}{0.0911 \times 0.0822} = 1.19$	$\dfrac{0.00892}{0.0911 \times (2 \times 0.0822)} = 0.596$	$\dfrac{0.00892}{0.0911 \times (0.0822)^2} = 14.5$
2	$\dfrac{0.0247}{0.0753 \times 0.151} = 2.17$	$\dfrac{0.0247}{0.0753 \times (2 \times 0.151)} = 1.09$	$\dfrac{0.0247}{0.0753 \times (0.151)^2} = 14.4$
3	$\dfrac{0.0620}{0.138 \times 0.176} = 2.55$	$\dfrac{0.0620}{0.138 \times (2 \times 0.176)} = 1.280$	$\dfrac{0.0620}{0.138 \times (0.176)^2} = 14.5$

Equilibrium concentration data are from Table 15.1. In Trial 1, the equilibrium concentration of CH_3OH is placed in the numerator and the product of the equilibrium concentrations, $[CO][H_2]$, in the denominator. In Trial 2, each concentration is multiplied by its stoichiometric coefficient. In Trial 3, each concentration is raised to a power equal to its stoichiometric coefficient. Trial 3 has essentially the same value for each experiment. This value is the equilibrium constant K_c.

In the three experiments, point out that Table 15.1 is consistent with the equilibrium concentrations of the two reactants and the one product in Figure 15-3. Put the equilibrium concentrations into the equilibrium expression (15.4) to show that this equation is satisfied.

The representation of the equilibrium expression in terms of concentrations is only valid at low concentrations, usually less than a few moles per liter.

Stress that "equilibrium" means equal rates of forward and reverse reactions, *not* equal concentrations of reactants and products.

Although it is not obvious from a cursory inspection of the data, a particular ratio involving equilibrium concentrations of product and reactants has a constant value, independent of how the equilibrium is reached. This ratio, which is central to the study of chemical equilibrium, can be derived theoretically using concepts presented later in the text, but it can also be established empirically, that is, by trial and error. Three reasonable attempts at formulating the desired ratio for reaction (15.3) are outlined in Table 15.2, and the ratio that works is identified.

For the methanol synthesis reaction, the ratio of equilibrium concentrations in the following equation has a constant value of 14.5 at 483 K.

$$K = \left(\frac{[CH_3OH]}{[CO]([H_2])^2} \right)_{eq} = 14.5 \qquad (15.4)$$

This ratio is called the **equilibrium constant expression** and its numerical value is the **equilibrium constant**.

THE EQUILIBRIUM CONSTANT AND ACTIVITIES

Let's think about expression (15.4) for a moment. We have shown that we obtain a numerical value of 14.5 by substituting equilibrium concentrations from Table 15.2 (Trial 3) into the equilibrium constant expression. But what happened to the units? The numerator in expression (15.4) has the unit $mol\ L^{-1}$ and the denominator, $mol^3\ L^{-3}$. The resultant unit to accompany the numerical value looks like it should be $L^2\ mol^{-2}$. In later chapters we will encounter several expressions that require the logarithm of an equilibrium constant, but we can only take the logarithms of dimensionless numbers, *not* of numbers that carry units. We took the easy way out in equation (15.4) by just "dropping" the troublesome units. But there is a more satisfactory way to eliminate the units.

We need to replace equation (15.4) by the following expression

$$K = \left(\frac{a_{CH_3OH}}{a_{CO}(a_{H_2})^2} \right)_{eq} = 14.5 \qquad (15.5)$$

where a represents the *activity* of each reactant or product denoted through a subscript formula. **Activity**, a thermodynamic concept introduced by G. N. Lewis,[*] is the dimensionless ratio $[X]/c°$, where $[X]$ represents a particular concentration and $c°$ corresponds to the concentration in a chosen reference state. Our usual choice of reference state for a substance in solution is a concentration of one mole per liter ($1\ mol\ L^{-1}$). For gases, activity can also be expressed as the dimensionless ratio, $P/P°$, where P is a particular partial

[*]G. N. Lewis and M. Randall, *Thermodynamics*, McGraw Hill, New York, 1923.

pressure and $P°$ is the partial pressure in the reference state; and our usual choice of $P°$ is 1 bar (essentially equal to 1 atm). Pure solids and pure liquids are assigned activities of 1.

Now, by returning to the methanol-synthesis example, let us establish the relationship between an equilibrium constant expressed in activities and the corresponding one expressed in concentrations. We begin by writing the activity of each species, using the [ ] symbol for the equilibrium concentration and c^0 for the concentration in the reference state.

$$a_{CH_3OH} = \frac{[CH_3OH]}{c°}$$

$$a_{CO} = \frac{[CO]}{c°}$$

$$a_{H_2} = \frac{[H_2]}{c°}$$

Then we choose the value $c° = 1 \text{ mol L}^{-1}$, substitute these relationships into the equilibrium constant expression (15.5), and we have

$$K = \left(\frac{\frac{[CH_3OH]}{c°}}{\frac{[CO]}{c°}\left(\frac{[H_2]}{c°}\right)^2} \right)_{eq} = (c°)^2 \left(\frac{[CH_3OH]}{[CO]([H_2])^2} \right)_{eq} = 14.5 \qquad (15.6)$$

Notice that we have arrived at exactly the expression in equation (15.4)! In this case, however, the unwanted units have been properly cancelled rather than just conveniently dropped; that is, $L^2 \text{ mol}^{-2}$ inside the large parentheses is cancelled by $\text{mol}^2 \text{ L}^{-2}$ on the outside.

Here is another reason for basing equilibrium constants on activities: Under conditions where gases do not obey the ideal gas law (Section 6-9) or solutions depart from ideal behavior (Section 13-3), equilibrium constant values may vary with total concentration or pressure. This problem is eliminated when activities are used. As we learned in Section 13-9, activities are "effective" or "active" concentrations. In this text we will generally assume that systems are ideal, and that activities can be replaced by concentrations or partial pressures.

> Point out to students that the equilibrium constant "14.5" calculated for the methanol synthesis reaction is specific to a 483 K reaction temperature.

> ◀ **KEEP IN MIND**
> that any concentrations substituted into an equilibrium constant expression, or obtained from it, must be *equilibrium* concentrations.

EXAMPLE 15-1

Relating Equilibrium Concentrations of Reactants and Products. These equilibrium concentrations are measured in reaction (15.3) at 483 K: [CO] = 1.03 M and [CH₃OH] = 1.56 M. What is the equilibrium concentration of H₂?

Solution

Write the equilibrium constant expression in terms of activities

$$K = \left(\frac{a_{CH_3OH}}{a_{CO}(a_{H_2})^2} \right)_{eq} = 14.5$$

Assume that the reaction conditions are such that the activities can be replaced by their concentration values, allowing concentration units to be canceled as in expression (15.6).

$$K = \left(\frac{[CH_3OH]}{[CO]([H_2])^2} \right)_{eq} = 14.5$$

Substitute the known equilibrium concentrations into the equilibrium constant expression (15.6).

$$K = \frac{[CH_3OH]}{[CO][H_2]^2} = \frac{1.56}{1.03[H_2]^2} = 14.5$$

Solve for the unknown concentration, [H₂]. (An implicit calculation to restore the concentration unit is $[H_2] = a^{H_2} \times c° = 0.322 \times 1.00 \text{ M} = 0.322 \text{ M}$.)

$$[H_2]^2 = \frac{1.56}{1.03 \times 14.5} = 0.104$$

$$[H_2] = \sqrt{0.104} = 0.322 \text{ M}$$

Practice Example A: In another experiment, equal concentrations of CH₃OH and CO are found at equilibrium in reaction (15.3). What must be the equilibrium concentration of H₂?

Practice Example B: At a certain temperature, $K = 1.8 \times 10^4$ for the reaction $N_2(g) + 3 H_2(g) \rightleftharpoons 2 NH_3(g)$. If the equilibrium concentrations of N₂ and NH₃ are 0.015 M and 2.00 M, respectively, what is the equilibrium concentration of H₂?

A GENERAL EXPRESSION FOR K

Before proceeding to other matters, let us emphasize that the equilibrium constant expression for the methanol synthesis reaction summarized through expression (15.6) is just a specific example of a more general case. For the hypothetical, generalized reaction

$$a\text{A} + b\text{B} \cdots \rightleftharpoons g\text{G} + h\text{H} \cdots$$

The equilibrium constant expression has the form

$$K = \frac{(a_\text{G})^g (a_\text{H})^h \cdots}{(a_\text{A})^a (a_\text{B})^b \cdots} = \frac{[\text{G}]^g [\text{H}]^h \cdots}{[\text{A}]^a [\text{B}]^b \cdots} \tag{15.7}$$

The *numerator* of an equilibrium constant expression is the product of the activities of the species on the *right* side of the equation ($a_\text{G}, a_\text{H}, \ldots$), with each activity raised to a power given by the stoichiometric coefficient ($g, h, \ldots$). The *denominator* is the product of the activities of the species on the *left* side of the equation ($a_\text{A}, a_\text{B}, \ldots$), and again, with each activity raised to a power given by the stoichiometric coefficient ($a, b, \ldots$). As previously noted, where equilibrium systems are sufficiently close to ideal in their behavior, equilibrium concentrations are acceptable approximations to true activities.

The numerical value of an equilibrium constant, K, depends on the particular reaction and on the temperature. We will explore the significance of these numerical values in Section 15-4.

CONCEPT ASSESSMENT

Consider a hypothetical reaction in which one molecule, A, is converted to its isomer, B, that is, the reversible reaction A $\rightleftharpoons$ B. Start with a flask containing 54 molecules of A, represented by open circles. Convert the appropriate number of open circles to filled circles to represent the isomer B and portray the equilibrium condition if $K = 0.02$. Repeat the process for $K = 0.5$ and then for $K = 1$.

Are You Wondering . . .

If there is a relationship between the equilibrium constant and rate constants?

Given the requirement that the rates of the forward and reverse reactions become equal at equilibrium, it seems that there should be a relationship. The rate laws for the forward and reverse reactions include numerical constants (rate constants) and concentration terms raised to powers. Moreover, if we set the rate equations equal to one another at equilibrium, we should be able to derive an expression involving a ratio of concentration terms (raised to powers) and a ratio of constants. A major difficulty, however, is that the exponents of the concentration terms in the equilibrium constant expression must be the same as the coefficients in the balanced equation, whereas the exponents in rate laws are generally *not* the same as these coefficients. The trick to discovering the relationship between rate constants and an equilibrium constant is to work with the detailed mechanism for the reaction in the manner outlined in Exercise 83. Still, it is generally easier to obtain K directly from measurements on equilibrium conditions than to attempt a calculation based on rate constants. Moreover, in Chapters 19 and 20 we will learn about much more direct measurements and calculations leading to values of equilibrium constants.

15-3 RELATIONSHIPS INVOLVING EQUILIBRIUM CONSTANTS

Before assessing an equilibrium situation, it may be necessary to make some preliminary calculations or decisions to get the appropriate equilibrium constant expression. This section presents some useful ideas in working with equilibrium constants.

RELATIONSHIP OF K TO THE BALANCED CHEMICAL EQUATION

We must always make certain that the expression for K matches the corresponding balanced equation. In doing so, the following hold true.

- When we *reverse* an equation, we *invert* the value of K.
- When we *multiply* the coefficients in a balanced equation by a common factor $(2, 3, \dots)$, we raise the equilibrium constant to the *corresponding power* $(2, 3, \dots)$.
- When we *divide* the coefficients in a balanced equation by a common factor $(2, 3, \dots)$, we take the *corresponding root* of the equilibrium constant (square root, cube root, $\dots$).

Suppose that in discussing the synthesis of CH_3OH from CO and H_2, we had written the reverse of equation (15.3)—that is,

$$CH_3OH(g) \rightleftharpoons CO(g) + 2\,H_2(g) \qquad K' = ?$$

Now, according to the generalized equilibrium constant expression (15.7), we should write

$$K' = \frac{[CO][H_2]^2}{[CH_3OH]} = \frac{1}{\dfrac{[CH_3OH]}{[CO][H_2]^2}} = \frac{1}{K} = \frac{1}{14.5} = 0.0690$$

In the preceding expression, the terms printed in blue are the equilibrium constant expression and K value originally written as expression (15.4). We see that $K' = 1/K$.

Suppose that for a certain application we want an equation based on synthesizing *two* moles of $CH_3OH(g)$.

$$2\,CO(g) + 4\,H_2(g) \rightleftharpoons 2\,CH_3OH(g) \qquad K'' = ?$$

Here, $K'' = K^2$. That is,

$$K'' = \frac{[CH_3OH]^2}{[CO]^2[H_2]^4} = \left(\frac{[CH_3OH]}{[CO][H_2]^2}\right)^2 = (K)^2 = (14.5)^2 = 2.10 \times 10^2$$

EXAMPLE 15-2

Relating K to the Balanced Chemical Equation. The following K value is given at 298 K for the synthesis of $NH_3(g)$ from its elements.

$$N_2(g) + 3\,H_2(g) \rightleftharpoons 2\,NH_3(g) \qquad K = 3.6 \times 10^8$$

What is the value of K at 298 K for the following reaction?

$$NH_3(g) \rightleftharpoons \frac{1}{2}N_2(g) + \frac{3}{2}H_2(g) \qquad K = ?$$

Solution

First, reverse the given equation. This puts $NH_3(g)$ on the left side of the equation, where we need it.

$$2\,NH_3(g) \rightleftharpoons N_2(g) + 3\,H_2(g)$$

The equilibrium constant K' becomes

$$K' = 1/(3.6 \times 10^8) = 2.8 \times 10^{-9}$$

Then, to base the equation on 1 mol $NH_3(g)$, divide all coefficients by 2.

$$NH_3(g) \rightleftharpoons \frac{1}{2}N_2(g) + \frac{3}{2}H_2(g)$$

This requires the square root of K'.

$$K = \sqrt{2.8 \times 10^{-9}} = 5.3 \times 10^{-5}$$

Practice Example A: Use data from Example 15-2 to determine the value of K at 298 K for the reaction

$$\frac{1}{3}N_2(g) + H_2(g) \rightleftharpoons \frac{2}{3}NH_3(g)$$

Practice Example B: For the reaction $NO(g) + \frac{1}{2}O_2(g) \rightleftharpoons NO_2(g)$ at 184 °C, $K = 7.5 \times 10^2$. What is the value of K at 184 °C for the reaction $2\,NO_2(g) \rightleftharpoons 2\,NO(g) + O_2(g)$?

CONCEPT ASSESSMENT ✓

Can you conclude whether the numerical value of K for the reaction $2\,ICl(g) \rightleftharpoons I_2(g) + Cl_2(g)$ is greater or less than the numerical value of K for the reaction $ICl(g) \rightleftharpoons \frac{1}{2}I_2(g) + \frac{1}{2}Cl_2(g)$? Explain.

COMBINING EQUILIBRIUM CONSTANT EXPRESSIONS

In Section 7-7, through Hess's law, we showed how to combine a series of equations into a single overall equation. The enthalpy change of the overall reaction was obtained by adding together the enthalpy changes of the individual reactions. A similar procedure can be used with equilibrium constants, but with this important difference:

> When individual equations are combined (that is, added), their equilibrium constants are *multiplied* to obtain the equilibrium constant for the overall reaction.

Suppose we seek the equilibrium constant for the reaction

$$N_2O(g) + \frac{1}{2}O_2(g) \rightleftharpoons 2\,NO(g) \qquad K = ? \tag{15.8}$$

and know the K values of these two equilibria.

$$N_2(g) + \frac{1}{2}O_2(g) \rightleftharpoons N_2O(g) \qquad K = 2.7 \times 10^{-18} \tag{15.9}$$

$$N_2(g) + O_2(g) \rightleftharpoons 2\,NO(g) \qquad K = 4.7 \times 10^{-31} \tag{15.10}$$

Equation (15.8) is obtained by reversing equation (15.9) and adding it to (15.10). This requires that we also take the *reciprocal* of the K value of equation (15.9).

(a)
$$N_2O(g) \rightleftharpoons N_2(g) + \frac{1}{2}O_2(g) \qquad K(a) = 1/(2.7 \times 10^{-18})$$
$$= 3.7 \times 10^{17}$$

(b)
$$N_2(g) + O_2(g) \rightleftharpoons 2\,NO(g) \qquad K(b) = 4.7 \times 10^{-31}$$

Overall: $N_2O(g) + \frac{1}{2}O_2(g) \rightleftharpoons 2\,NO(g) \qquad K(\text{overall}) = ?$

The overall equation is expression (15.8), and according to the general expression (15.7),

$$K(\text{overall}) = \frac{[NO]^2}{[N_2O][O_2]^{1/2}} = \underbrace{\frac{[N_2][O_2]^{1/2}}{[N_2O]}}_{K(a)} \times \underbrace{\frac{[NO]^2}{[N_2][O_2]}}_{K(b)} = K(a) \times K(b)$$

$$= 3.7 \times 10^{17} \times 4.7 \times 10^{-31} = 1.7 \times 10^{-13}$$

CONCEPT ASSESSMENT ✓

You wish to calculate K for the reaction

$$CH_4(g) + 2\,H_2O(g) \rightleftharpoons CO_2(g) + 4\,H_2(g)$$

and you have available a K value for the reaction

$$CO_2(g) + H_2(g) \rightleftharpoons CO(g) + H_2O(g)$$

What additional K value do you need, assuming that all K values are at the same temperature?

Point out that the reaction of sulfur dioxide with oxygen gas to form sulfur trioxide is a reaction that takes place in the atmosphere. This results in the formation of sulfuric acid which contributes to acid rain.

EQUILIBRIA INVOLVING GASES: THE EQUILIBRIUM CONSTANTS, K_c AND K_p

Mixtures of gases are as much solutions as are mixtures in a liquid solvent. Thus, concentrations in a gaseous mixture can be expressed on a mole-per-liter basis, and this is what we have done in writing K expressions using concentration units for our reference state. In order to describe gaseous reactants and products through their partial pressures in atmospheres, which is commonly done, we need to switch our reference state. We will do this next.

A key step in the manufacture of sulfuric acid is the following reversible reaction.

$$2\,SO_2(g) + O_2(g) \rightleftharpoons 2\,SO_3(g) \tag{15.11}$$

Since all of the reaction species are in the gas phase it seems reasonable to use a partial-pressure reference state. We begin by writing the equilibrium constant expression in terms of activities

$$K = \left(\frac{(a_{SO_3})^2}{(a_{SO_2})^2 a_{O_2}}\right)_{eq} \tag{15.12}$$

where the activities are

$$a_{SO_2} = \frac{P_{SO_2}}{P°}; \qquad a_{O_2} = \frac{P_{O_2}}{P°}; \qquad a_{SO_3} = \frac{P_{SO_3}}{P°}$$

The reference-state partial pressure is $P° = 1$ bar, which we will take to be essentially the same as 1 atm. Substituting these relationships into equation (15.12), we obtain

$$K_p = \left(\frac{\left(\frac{P_{SO_3}}{P°}\right)^2}{\left(\frac{P_{SO_2}}{P°}\right)^2 \frac{P_{O_2}}{P°}}\right)_{eq} = P°\left(\frac{(P_{SO_3})^2}{(P_{SO_2})^2 P_{O_2}}\right)_{eq} \tag{15.13}$$

As expected, the equilibrium constant is dimensionless. To designate that a partial-pressure reference state was used we add the subscript "p" to the equilibrium constant, that is, by writing K_p.

To establish the equilibrium constant based on concentrations, we first use the ideal gas law, $PV = nRT$, to relate gas concentrations and partial pressures

$$[SO_2] = \frac{n}{V} = \frac{P_{SO_2}}{RT}; \qquad [O_2] = \frac{n}{V} = \frac{P_{O_2}}{RT}; \qquad [SO_3] = \frac{n}{V} = \frac{P_{SO_3}}{RT}$$

and then express activities in terms of those concentrations, where the reference state is $c° = 1$ mol L^{-1}.

$$a_{SO_2} = \frac{[SO_2]}{c°} = \frac{\frac{P_{SO_2}}{RT}}{c°}; \qquad a_{O_2} = \frac{[O_2]}{c°} = \frac{\frac{P_{O_2}}{RT}}{c°}; \qquad a_{SO_3} = \frac{[SO_3]}{c°} = \frac{\frac{P_{SO_3}}{RT}}{c°}$$

Substituting into the equilibrium constant expression (15.12), we obtain

$$K_p = P° \left(\frac{(P_{SO_3})^2}{(P_{SO_2})^2 P_{O_2}} \right)_{eq} = P° \left(\frac{([SO_3]RT)^2}{([SO_2]RT)^2 [O_2]RT} \right)_{eq} = \frac{P°}{RT} \left(\frac{[SO_3]^2}{[SO_2]^2 [O_2]} \right)_{eq} \qquad (15.14)$$

As expected the final expression is dimensionless. Because we have designated that the reference state is based on $c° = 1$ mol L^{-1}, we can attach the subscript "c" to the equilibrium constant, K_c, which is the ratio of concentrations in the final parenthetical term of expression (15.14). Finally, observe that (15.14) has a *different* value than (15.13). This result is not wrong. It simply stems from a difference in the reference state in the two cases. In working with equilibrium constant expressions, therefore, it is important to state the experimental conditions and the reference state clearly. Choosing and defining a reference state is an important concept that we will see again in our discussion of thermodynamics in Chapter 19.

Eliminating the reference-state terms having a value of 1, the relationship between K_p and K_c for reaction (15.11) is

$$K_p = K_c(RT)^{-1} \qquad (15.15)$$

If we carried out a similar derivation for the general reaction,

$$aA(g) + bB(g) + \cdots \rightleftharpoons gG(g) + hH(g) + \cdots$$

the result would be

$$K_p = K_c(RT)^{\Delta n_{gas}} \qquad (15.16)$$

where Δn_{gas} is the difference in the stoichiometric coefficients of *gaseous* products and reactants; that is, $\Delta n_{gas} = (g + h + \cdots) - (a + b + \cdots)$. In reaction (15.11), $\Delta n_{gas} = 2 - (2 + 1) = -1$, which is what we used in equation (15.15).

In summary, although we do not use units for the equilibrium constants, we do need to use the correct dimensionless values of concentrations or pressures for terms within equilibrium constant expressions. These are *molarity* for K_c expressions and pressures in *atmospheres* for K_p expressions. These choices then require that we use a value of $R = 0.08206$ L atm mol^{-1} K^{-1} in equation (15.16).

EXAMPLE 15-3

Illustrating the Dependence of K on the Reference State. Complete the calculation of K_p for reaction (15.11) knowing that $K_c = 2.8 \times 10^2$ (at 1000 K).

Solution

Write the equation relating the two equilibrium constants with different reference states.

$$K_c = RT \times K_p$$

Rearrange the expression to obtain the quantity desired, K_p.

$$K_p = \frac{K_c}{RT}$$

Substitute the given data and solve.

$$K_p = \frac{2.8 \times 10^2}{0.08206 \times 1000} = 3.4$$

Practice Example A: For the reaction $2\,NH_3(g) \rightleftharpoons N_2(g) + 3\,H_2(g)$ at 298 K, $K_c = 2.8 \times 10^{-9}$. What is the value of K_p for this reaction?

Practice Example B: At 1065 °C, for the reaction $2\,H_2S(g) \rightleftharpoons 2\,H_2(g) + S_2(g)$, $K_p = 1.2 \times 10^{-2}$. What is the value of K_c for the reaction $H_2(g) + \frac{1}{2}S_2(g) \rightleftharpoons H_2S(g)$ at 1065 °C?

EQUILIBRIA INVOLVING PURE LIQUIDS AND SOLIDS

Up to this point in the chapter, all our examples have involved gaseous reactions. In subsequent chapters, we will emphasize equilibria in aqueous solutions. Gas-phase reactions and reactions in aqueous solution are *homogeneous* reactions: They occur within a single phase. Let's extend our coverage now to include reactions involving one or more condensed phases—solids and liquids—in contact with a gas or solution phase. These are called *heterogeneous* reactions. One of the most important ideas about heterogeneous reactions is that

> Equilibrium constant expressions *do not* contain concentration terms for solid or liquid phases of a single component (that is, for pure solids and liquids).

We can think about this statement in either of two ways: (1) An equilibrium constant expression includes terms only for reactants and products whose concentrations and/or partial pressures *can change* during a chemical reaction. The concentration of the single component within a pure solid or liquid phase *cannot change*. (2) Alternatively, recall that the activities of pure liquids and solids are set equal to 1; thus the effect on the numerical value of the equilibrium constant is the same as not including terms for pure solids and liquids at all.

The water–gas reaction, used to make combustible gases from coal, has reacting species in both gaseous and solid phases.

$$C(s) + H_2O(g) \rightleftharpoons CO(g) + H_2(g)$$

Although solid carbon must be present for the reaction to occur, the equilibrium constant expression contains terms only for the species in the homogeneous gas phase: H_2O, CO, and H_2.

$$K_c = \frac{a_{CO}a_{H_2}}{a_{C(s)}a_{H_2O}} = \frac{[CO][H_2]}{[H_2O]}$$

The activity of solid carbon is $a_{C(s)} = 1$, and we have implicitly divided through each of the remaining concentrations by the reference-state concentration, $c^0 = 1$ mol L^{-1}, to obtain a dimensionless K_c.

The decomposition of calcium carbonate (limestone) is also a heterogeneous reaction. The equilibrium constant expression contains just a single term.

$$CaCO_3(s) \rightleftharpoons CaO(s) + CO_2(g) \qquad K_c = [CO_2] \qquad (15.17)$$

We can write K_p for reaction (15.17) by using equation (15.16), with $\Delta n_{gas} = 1$.

$$K_p = P_{CO_2} \qquad and \qquad K_p = K_c(RT) \qquad (15.18)$$

Equation (15.18) indicates that the equilibrium pressure of $CO_2(g)$ in contact with $CaCO_3(s)$ and $CaO(s)$ is a constant equal to K_p. Its value is *independent* of the quantities of $CaCO_3$ and CaO (as long as both solids are present). Figure 15-4 offers a conceptualization of this decomposition reaction.

◀ Still another way to think about solids and liquids is through their densities. Density, the mass per unit volume of a substance, can be expressed in moles per liter by converting the unit volume from milliliter to liter and dividing the mass in grams by the molar mass. The resultant molar density (mol/L) is a concentration term and, at a fixed temperature, is a constant that would be incorporated in the K_c value.

Of course, the relationship between concentration and pressure for gases is based here on the ideal gas law: $PV = n_{gas}RT$, or $[gas] = (n_{gas}/V) = P/RT$.

Drop two pieces of limestone, one large and the other small, into a dilute solution of HCl, seal the beakers, and leave them until next class. Some carbon dioxide will be seen bubbling off. By the next class, the reaction will have stopped. Point out that the pressure of CO_2 in both beakers is the same, but one piece of limestone is still bigger than the other. That is, the concentration of CO_2 does not depend upon the amount of solid present. An improvement of the experiment would be to attach the two closed vessels to a U-tube manometer to show the pressures are equal. Relate this to Figure 15-4.

(a) **(b)**

◀ **FIGURE 15-4**
Equilibrium in the reaction

$$CaCO_3(s) \rightleftharpoons CaO(s) + CO_2(g)$$

(a) Decomposition of $CaCO_3(s)$ upon heating in a closed vessel yields a few granules of CaO(s), together with $CO_2(g)$, which soon exerts its equilibrium partial pressure. **(b)** Introduction of additional $CaCO_3(s)$ and/or more CaO(s) has no effect on the partial pressure of the $CO_2(g)$, which remains the same as in (a).

One of our examples in Section 15-1 was liquid–vapor equilibrium. This is a physical equilibrium because no chemical reactions are involved. Consider the liquid–vapor equilibrium for water.

$$H_2O(l) \rightleftharpoons H_2O(g)$$

$$K_c = [H_2O(g)] \qquad K_p = P_{H_2O} \qquad K_p = K_c RT$$

So, equilibrium vapor pressures such as P_{H_2O} are just values of K_p. As we have seen before, these values do *not* depend on the quantities of liquid or vapor at equilibrium, as long as some of each is present.

EXAMPLE 15-4

Writing Equilibrium Constant Expressions for Reactions Involving Pure Solids or Liquids. At equilibrium in the following reaction at 60 °C, the partial pressures of the gases are found to be $P_{HI} = 3.65 \times 10^{-3}$ atm and $P_{H_2S} = 9.96 \times 10^{-1}$ atm. What is the value of K_p for the reaction?

$$H_2S(g) + I_2(s) \rightleftharpoons 2 HI(g) + S(s) \qquad K_p = ?$$

Solution

Write the equilibrium constant expression in terms of activities. Note that activities for the iodine and sulfur are not included, since the activity of a pure solid is 1.

$$K = \frac{(a_{HI})^2}{(a_{H_2S})}$$

Substitute partial pressures for the activities into the equilibrium constant expression.

$$K_p = \frac{(P_{HI})^2}{(P_{H_2S})}$$

Substitute the given equilibrium data into the equilibrium constant expression.

$$K_p = \frac{(3.65 \times 10^{-3})^2}{9.96 \times 10^{-1}} = 1.34 \times 10^{-5}$$

Practice Example A: Teeth are made principally from the mineral hydroxyapatite, $Ca_5(PO_4)_3OH$, which can be dissolved in acidic solution such as that produced by bacteria in the mouth. The reaction that occurs is $Ca_5(PO_4)_3OH(s) + 4 H^+(aq) \rightleftharpoons 5 Ca^{2+}(aq) + 3 HPO_4^{2-}(aq) + H_2O(l)$. Write the equilibrium constant expression K_c for this reaction.

Practice Example B: The steam–iron process is used to generate $H_2(g)$, mostly for use in hydrogenating oils. Iron metal and steam [$H_2O(g)$] react to produce $Fe_3O_4(s)$ and $H_2(g)$. Write expressions for K_c and K_p for this reversible reaction. How are the values of K_c and K_p related to each other? Explain.

15-4 THE MAGNITUDE OF AN EQUILIBRIUM CONSTANT

Point out the huge range of values that equilibrium constants can take.

In principle, every chemical reaction has an equilibrium constant, but often the constants are not used. Why is this so? Table 15.3 lists equilibrium constants for several reactions mentioned in this chapter or previously in the text. The first of these reactions is the synthesis of H_2O from its elements. We have always assumed that this reaction goes to completion, that is, that the reverse reaction is negligible and the overall reaction proceeds only in the forward direction. If a reaction goes to completion, one (or more) of the reactants is used up. A term in the *denominator* of the equilibrium constant expression approaches *zero* and makes the value of the equilibrium constant very large. A very large numerical value of K signifies that the forward reaction, as written, *goes to completion* or very nearly so. Because the value of K_p for the water synthesis reaction is 1.4×10^{83}, we are entirely justified in saying that the reaction goes to completion at 298 K.

Equilibrium Constant activity

TABLE 15.3 Equilibrium Constants of Some Common Reactions	
Reaction	Equilibrium constant, K_p
$2 H_2(g) + O_2(g) \rightleftharpoons 2 H_2O(l)$	1.4×10^{83} at 298 K
$CaCO_3(s) \rightleftharpoons CaO(s) + CO_2(g)$	1.9×10^{-23} at 298 K 1.0 at about 1200 K
$2 SO_2(g) + O_2(g) \rightleftharpoons 2 SO_3(g)$	3.4 at 1000 K
$C(s) + H_2O(g) \rightleftharpoons CO(g) + H_2(g)$	1.6×10^{-21} at 298 K 10.0 at about 1100 K

If the equilibrium constant is so large, why is a mixture of hydrogen and oxygen gases stable at room temperature? The value of the equilibrium constant relates to thermodynamic stability: $H_2O(l)$ is much more thermodynamically stable than a mixture of $H_2(g)$ and $O_2(g)$ because it lies at a lower energy state. As noted in Chapter 14, however, the rate of a chemical reaction is strongly governed by the activation energy, E_a. Because E_a is very high for the synthesis of $H_2O(l)$ from $H_2(g)$ and $O_2(g)$, the rate of reaction is inconsequential at 298 K. To get the reaction to occur at a measurable rate, we must either raise the temperature or use a catalyst. A chemist would say that the synthesis of $H_2O(l)$ at 298 K is a *kinetically* controlled reaction (as opposed to *thermodynamically* controlled).

From Table 15.3, we see that K_p for the decomposition of $CaCO_3(s)$ (limestone) is very small at 298 K (only 1.9×10^{-23}). To account for a very small numerical value of an equilibrium constant, the *numerator* must be very small (approaching zero). A very small numerical value of K signifies that the forward reaction, as written, *does not occur to any significant extent*. Although limestone does not decompose at ordinary temperatures, the partial pressure of $CO_2(g)$ in equilibrium with $CaCO_3(s)$ and $CaO(s)$ increases with temperature. It becomes 1 atm at about 1200 K. An important application of this decomposition reaction is in the commercial production of quicklime (CaO).

The conversion of $SO_2(g)$ and $O_2(g)$ to $SO_3(g)$ at 1000 K has an equilibrium constant such that we expect significant amounts of both reactants and products to be present at equilibrium (see Table 15.3). Both the forward and reverse reactions are important. A similar situation exists for the reaction of $C(s)$ and $H_2O(g)$ at 1100 K, but not at 298 K where the forward reaction does not occur to any significant extent ($K_p = 1.6 \times 10^{-21}$).

In light of the several cases from Table 15.3, we can conclude that

> A reaction is most likely to reach a state of equilibrium in which significant quantities of both reactants and products are present if the numerical value of K is *neither very large nor very small*, as a very rough approximation, in the range of about 10^{-10} to 10^{10}.

Thus, we see that equilibrium calculations are not required for all reactions. At times, we can use simple stoichiometric calculations to determine the outcome of a reaction, and in some cases there may be no reaction at all.

The products formed in a reaction under *kinetic control* are determined by reaction rates. The products formed in a reaction under *thermodynamic control* will depend on the stability of the products.

Equilibrium constants usually vary in value to a large extent with temperature.

CONCEPT ASSESSMENT ✓

Why is having a balanced equation a necessary condition for predicting the outcome of a chemical reaction, but often not a sufficient condition?

15-5   THE REACTION QUOTIENT, Q: PREDICTING THE DIRECTION OF NET CHANGE

Let's return briefly to the set of three experiments that we discussed in Section 15-2, involving the reaction

$$CO(g) + 2\,H_2(g) \rightleftharpoons CH_3OH(g) \qquad K_c = 14.5$$

Experiment 1 starts with just the reactants, CO and H_2. An overall, or net, change has to occur in which some CH_3OH forms. Only in this way can an equilibrium condition be reached in which all reacting species are present. We say that a net change occurs in the *forward* direction (*to the right*).

Experiment 2 starts with just the product, CH_3OH. Here, some of the CH_3OH must decompose back to CO and H_2 before equilibrium can be established. We say that a net change occurs in the *reverse* direction (*to the left*).

Experiment 3 starts with all the reacting species present: CO, H_2, and CH_3OH. In this system, it is not obvious in what direction a net change occurs to establish equilibrium.

The ability to predict the direction of net change in establishing equilibrium is important for two reasons.

- At times we do not need detailed equilibrium calculations. We may need only a qualitative description of the changes that occur in establishing equilibrium from a given set of initial conditions.

- In some equilibrium calculations, it is helpful to determine the direction of net change as a first step.

For any set of *initial* activities in a reaction mixture, we can set up a ratio of activities having the same form as the equilibrium constant expression. This ratio is called the **reaction quotient** and is designated Q. For a hypothetical generalized reaction, the reaction quotient, first written in terms of activities, and then as concentrations assuming a concentration reference state, is

$$Q = \frac{(a_{init})^g (a_{init})^h \cdots}{(a_{init})^a (a_{init})^b \cdots} \qquad Q_c = \frac{[G]_{init}^g [H]_{init}^h \cdots}{[A]_{init}^a [B]_{init}^b \cdots} \qquad (15.19)$$

If $Q = K$, a reaction is at equilibrium, but our primary interest in the relationship between Q and K is for a reaction mixture that is not at equilibrium. To see what this relationship is, let's turn again to the experiments in Table 15.1.

In Experiment 1, the initial concentrations of CO and H_2 are 1.000 mol/10.0 L = 0.100 M. Initially there is no CH_3OH. The value of Q_c is

$$Q_c = \frac{[CH_3OH]_{init}}{[CO]_{init}[H_2]_{init}^2} = \frac{0}{(0.100)(0.100)^2} = 0 \qquad (15.20)$$

We know that a net reaction occurs *to the right*, producing some CH_3OH. As it does, the numerator in expression (15.20) increases, the denominator decreases, and the value of Q_c increases; eventually $Q_c = K_c$.

If $Q_c < K_c$, a net change occurs from left to right (the direction of the forward reaction).

In Experiment 2, the initial concentration of CH_3OH is 1.000 mol/10.0 L = 0.100 M. Initially, there is no CO or H_2. The value of Q_c is

$$Q_c = \frac{[CH_3OH]_{init}}{[CO]_{init}[H_2]_{init}^2} = \frac{0.100}{0 \times 0} = \infty \qquad (15.21)$$

We know that a net reaction occurs *to the left*, producing some CO and H_2. As it does, the numerator in expression (15.21) decreases, the denominator increases, and the value of Q_c decreases; eventually $Q_c = K_c$.

If $Q_c > K_c$, a net change occurs from right to left (the direction of the reverse reaction).

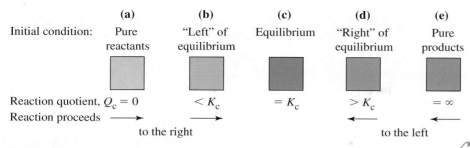

▲ **FIGURE 15-5**
Predicting the direction of net change in a reversible reaction
Five possibilities for the relationship of initial and equilibrium conditions are shown. From Table 15.1 and Figure 15-3, Experiment 1 corresponds to initial condition (a); Experiment 2 to condition (e); and Experiment 3 to (d). The situation in Example 15-5 also corresponds to condition (d).

Now let us turn to a case where direction of net change is not immediately obvious. In Experiment 3, the initial concentrations of all three species are $1.000 \ mol/10.0 \ L = 0.100 \ M$. The value of Q_c is

$$Q_c = \frac{[CH_3OH]_{init}}{[CO]_{init}[H_2]_{init}^2} = \frac{0.100}{(0.100)(0.100)^2} = 100$$

Because $Q_c > K_c$ (100 compared with 14.5), a net change occurs in the *reverse direction*. Note that you can verify this conclusion from Figure 15-3. The amounts of CO and H_2 at equilibrium are greater than they were initially, and the amount of CH_3OH is less.

The criteria for predicting the direction of a net chemical change in a reversible reaction are summarized in Figure 15-5 and applied in Example 15-5.

EXAMPLE 15-5

Predicting the Direction of a Net Chemical Change in Establishing Equilibrium. To increase the yield of $H_2(g)$ in the water–gas reaction—the reaction of $C(s)$ and $H_2O(g)$ to form $CO(g)$ and $H_2(g)$—a follow-up reaction called the "water–gas shift reaction" is generally used. In this reaction, some of the $CO(g)$ of the water gas is replaced by $H_2(g)$.

$$CO(g) + H_2O(g) \rightleftharpoons CO_2(g) + H_2(g)$$

$K_c = 1.00$ at about 1100 K. The following amounts of substances are brought together and allowed to react at this temperature: 1.00 mol CO, 1.00 mol H_2O, 2.00 mol CO_2, and 2.00 mol H_2. Compared with their initial amounts, which of the substances will be present in a greater amount and which in a lesser amount when equilibrium is established?

Solution

Our task is to determine the direction of net change by evaluating Q_c. Write down the expression for Q_c.

$$Q_c = \frac{[CO_2][H_2]}{[CO][H_2O]}$$

Substitute concentrations into the expression for Q_c, by assuming an arbitrary volume V (which cancels out in the calculation).

$$Q_c = \frac{(2.00/V)(2.00/V)}{(1.00/V)(1.00/V)} = 4.00$$

Compare Q_c to K_c.

$$4.00 > 1.00$$

Because $Q_c > K_c$ (that is, $4.00 > 1.00$), a net change occurs to the *left*. When equilibrium is established, the amounts of CO and H_2O will be greater than the initial quantities and the amounts of CO_2 and H_2 will be less.

Practice Example A: In Example 15-5, equal masses of CO, H_2O, CO_2, and H_2 are mixed at a temperature of about 1100 K. When equilibrium is established, which substance(s) will show an increase in quantity and which will show a decrease compared with the initial quantities?

Practice Example B: For the reaction $PCl_5(g) \rightleftharpoons PCl_3(g) + Cl_2(g)$, $K_c = 0.0454$ at 261 °C. If a vessel is filled with these gases such that the initial partial pressures are $P_{PCl_3} = 2.19 \ atm$, $P_{Cl_2} = 0.88 \ atm$, $P_{PCl_5} = 19.7 \ atm$, in which direction will a net change occur?

CONCEPT ASSESSMENT ✓

A mixture of 1.00 mol each of CO(g), H_2O(g), and CO_2(g) is placed in a 10.0-L flask at a temperature at which K_p = 10.0 in the reaction

$$CO(g) + H_2O(g) \rightleftharpoons CO_2(g) + H_2(g)$$

When equilibrium is established, **(a)** the amount of H_2(g) will be 1.00 mol; **(b)** the amounts of all reactants and products will be greater than 1.00 mol; **(c)** the amounts of all reactants and products will be less than 1.00 mol; **(d)** the amount of CO_2(g) will be greater than 1.00 mol and the amounts of CO(g), H_2O(g), and H_2(g) will be less than 1.00 mol; **(e)** the amounts of reactants and products cannot be predicted and can only be determined by analyzing the equilibrium mixture.

15-6 ALTERING EQUILIBRIUM CONDITIONS: LE CHÂTELIER'S PRINCIPLE

At times, we want only to make qualitative statements about a reversible reaction: the direction of a net change, whether the amount of a substance will have increased or decreased when equilibrium is reached, and so on. Also, we may not have the data needed for a quantitative calculation. In these cases, we can use a statement attributed to the French chemist Henri Le Châtelier (1884). **Le Châtelier's principle** is hard to state unambiguously, but its essential meaning is stated here.

> When an equilibrium system is subjected to a change in temperature, pressure, or concentration of a reacting species, the system responds by attaining a new equilibrium that *partially* offsets the impact of the change.

As we will see in the examples that follow, it is generally not difficult to predict the outcome of changing one or more variables in a system at equilibrium.

EFFECT OF CHANGING THE AMOUNTS OF REACTING SPECIES ON EQUILIBRIUM

Let's return to reaction (15.11)

$$2\,SO_2(g) + O_2(g) \rightleftharpoons 2\,SO_3(g) \qquad K_c = 2.8 \times 10^2 \text{ at } 1000 \text{ K}$$

▶ $2\,SO_2(g) + O_2(g) \rightleftharpoons 2\,SO_3(g)$

Suppose we start with certain equilibrium amounts of SO_2, O_2, and SO_3, as suggested by Figure 15-6(a). Now let's create a disturbance in the equilibrium mixture by forcing an additional 1.00 mol SO_3 into the 10.0-L flask (Fig. 15-6b). How will the amounts of the reacting species change to reestablish equilibrium?

According to Le Châtelier's principle, if the system is to partially offset an action that increases the equilibrium concentration of one of the reacting species, it must do so by favoring the reaction in which that species is consumed. In this case, this is the *reverse* reaction—conversion of some of the added SO_3 to SO_2 and O_2. In the new equilibrium, there are greater amounts of all the substances than in the original equilibrium, but the additional amount of SO_3 is less than the 1.00 mol that was added.

Another way to look at the matter is to evaluate the reaction quotient immediately after adding the SO_3.

Original equilibrium	*Immediately following disturbance*
$Q_c = \dfrac{[SO_3]}{[SO_2]^2[O_2]} = K_c$	$Q_c = \dfrac{[SO_3]}{[SO_2]^2[O_2]} > K_c$

Le Châtelier's Principle movie

▲ **FIGURE 15-6**
Changing equilibrium conditions by changing the amount of a reactant

$$2 SO_2(g) + O_2(g) \rightleftharpoons 2 SO_3(g), \, K_c = 2.8 \times 10^2 \text{ at } 1000 \text{ K}$$

(a) The original equilibrium condition. **(b)** Disturbance caused by adding 1.00 mol SO_3. **(c)** The new equilibrium condition. The amount of SO_3 in the new equilibrium mixture, 1.46 mol, is greater than the original 0.68 mol but it is not as great as immediately after the addition of 1.00 mol SO_3. The effect of adding SO_3 to an equilibrium mixture is *partially* offset when equilibrium is restored.

Adding any quantity of SO_3 to a constant-volume equilibrium mixture makes Q_c larger than K_c. A net change occurs in the direction that reduces $[SO_3]$, that is, to the left, or in the reverse direction. Notice that reaction in the reverse direction increases $[SO_2]$ and $[O_2]$, further decreasing the value of Q_c.

EXAMPLE 15-6

Applying Le Châtelier's Principle: Effect of Adding More of a Reactant to an Equilibrium Mixture. Predict the effect of adding more $H_2(g)$ to a constant-volume equilibrium mixture of N_2, H_2, and NH_3.

$$N_2(g) + 3 H_2(g) \rightleftharpoons 2 NH_3(g)$$

Solution

Increasing $[H_2]$ stimulates the forward reaction and a shift in the equilibrium condition to the right. However, only a portion of the added H_2 is consumed in this reaction. When equilibrium is reestablished, there will be more H_2 than was present originally, and also more NH_3, but the amount of N_2 will be *smaller*. Some of the original N_2 must be consumed in converting some of the added H_2 to NH_3.

Practice Example A: Given the reaction $2 CO(g) + O_2(g) \rightleftharpoons 2 CO_2(g)$, what is the effect of adding $O_2(g)$ to a constant-volume equilibrium mixture?

Practice Example B: Calcination of limestone (decomposition by heating), $CaCO_3(s) \rightleftharpoons CaO(s) + CO_2(g)$, is the commercial source of quicklime, $CaO(s)$. After this equilibrium has been established in a constant-temperature, constant-volume container, what is the effect on the equilibrium amounts of materials caused by *adding* some **(a)** $CaO(s)$; **(b)** $CO_2(g)$; **(c)** $CaCO_3(s)$?

EFFECT OF CHANGES IN PRESSURE OR VOLUME ON EQUILIBRIUM

There are three ways to change the pressure of a constant-temperature equilibrium mixture.

1. **Add or remove a gaseous reactant or product.** The effect of these actions on the equilibrium condition is simply that due to adding or removing a reaction component, as described previously.

2. **Add an inert gas to the constant-volume reaction mixture.** This has the effect of increasing the *total* pressure, but the partial pressures of the reacting species are all unchanged. An inert gas added to a constant-volume equilibrium mixture has no effect on the equilibrium condition.

3. **Change the pressure by changing the volume of the system.** Decreasing the volume of the system increases the pressure, and increasing the system volume decreases the pressure. Thus, the effect of this type of pressure change is simply that of a volume change.

Let's explore the third situation first. Consider, again, the formation of $SO_3(g)$ from $SO_2(g)$ and $O_2(g)$.

$$2\,SO_2(g) + O_2(g) \rightleftharpoons 2\,SO_3(g) \qquad K_c = 2.8 \times 10^2 \text{ at } 1000\text{ K}$$

The equilibrium mixture in Figure 15-7(a) has its volume reduced to one-tenth of its original value by increasing the external pressure. To see how the equilibrium amounts of the gases change, let's first rearrange the equilibrium constant expression to the form

$$K_c = \frac{[SO_3]^2}{[SO_2]^2[O_2]} = \frac{(n_{SO_3}/V)^2}{(n_{SO_2}/V)^2(n_{O_2}/V)} = \frac{(n_{SO_3})^2}{(n_{SO_2})^2(n_{O_2})} \times V = 2.8 \times 10^2 \quad (15.22)$$

From equation (15.22), we see that if V is *reduced* by a factor of 10, the ratio

$$\frac{(n_{SO_3})^2}{(n_{SO_2})^2(n_{O_2})}$$

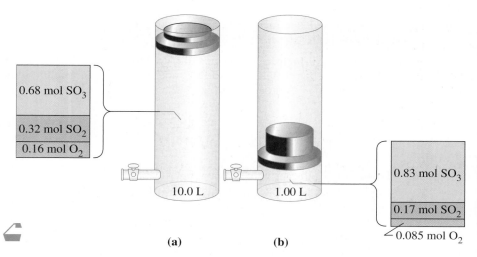

▲ **FIGURE 15-7**
Effect of pressure change on equilibrium in the reaction

$$2\,SO_2(g) + O_2(g) \rightleftharpoons 2\,SO_3(g)$$

An increase in external pressure causes a decrease in the reaction volume and a shift in equilibrium "to the right." (See Exercise 65 for a calculation of the new equilibrium amounts.)

must *increase* by a factor of 10. In this way, the value of K_c is restored, as it must be to restore equilibrium. There is only one way in which the ratio of moles of gases will increase in value: The number of moles of SO_3 must increase, and the numbers of moles of SO_2 and O_2 must decrease. The equilibrium shifts in the direction producing more SO_3—to the right.

Notice that three moles of *gas* on the left produce two moles of *gas* on the right in reaction (15.11). When compared at the same temperature and pressure, two moles of $SO_3(g)$ occupy a smaller volume than does a mixture of two moles of $SO_2(g)$ and one mole of $O_2(g)$. Given this fact and the observation from equation (15.22) that a decrease in volume favors the production of additional SO_3, we can formulate a statement that is especially easy to apply.

> When the volume of an equilibrium mixture of gases is *reduced*, a net change occurs in the direction that produces *fewer moles of gas*. When the volume is *increased*, a net change occurs in the direction that produces *more moles of gas*.

Figure 15-7 suggests a way of decreasing the volume of gaseous mixture at equilibrium—by increasing the external pressure. One way to increase the volume is to lower the external pressure. Another way is to transfer the equilibrium mixture from its original container to one of larger volume. A third method is to add an inert gas at *constant pressure*; the volume of the mixture must increase to make room for the added gas. The effect on the equilibrium, however, is the same for all three methods: Equilibrium shifts in the direction of the reaction producing the greater number of moles of gas.

Equilibria between condensed phases are not affected much by changes in external pressure because solids and liquids are not easily compressible. Also, we cannot assess whether the forward or reverse reaction is favored by these changes by examining only the chemical equation.

NO_2—N_2O_4
Equilibrium animation

◀ **KEEP IN MIND**
that an inert gas has no effect on an equilibrium condition if the gas is added to a system maintained at constant volume, but it can have an effect if added at constant pressure.

EXAMPLE 15-7

Applying Le Châtelier's Principle: The Effect of Changing Volume. An equilibrium mixture of $N_2(g)$, $H_2(g)$, and $NH_3(g)$ is transferred from a 1.50-L flask to a 5.00-L flask. In which direction does a net change occur to restore equilibrium?

$$N_2(g) + 3\,H_2(g) \rightleftharpoons 2\,NH_3(g)$$

Solution

When the gaseous mixture is transferred to the larger flask, the partial pressure of each gas and the total pressure drop. Whether we think in terms of a decrease in pressure or an increase in volume, we reach the same conclusion. Equilibrium shifts in such a way as to produce a larger number of moles of gas. Some of the NH_3 originally present decomposes back to N_2 and H_2. A net change occurs in the direction of the reverse reaction—to the left—in restoring equilibrium.

Practice Example A: The reaction $N_2O_4(g) \rightleftharpoons 2\,NO_2(g)$ is at equilibrium in a 3.00-L cylinder. What would be the effect on the concentrations of $N_2O_4(g)$ and $NO_2(g)$ if the pressure were doubled (that is, cylinder volume decreased to 1.50 L)?

Practice Example B: How is the equilibrium amount of $H_2(g)$ produced in the water–gas shift reaction affected by changing the total gas pressure or the system volume? Explain.

$$CO(g) + H_2O(g) \rightleftharpoons CO_2(g) + H_2(g)$$

Remind students that the pressure of a particular gas inside a container remains unchanged even if an inert gas is added to the container as long as the volume of the container is not changed. Review Dalton's Law of Partial Pressures.

The following reaction is brought to equilibrium at 700 °C.

$$2 H_2S(g) + CH_4(g) \rightleftharpoons CS_2(g) + 4 H_2(g)$$

Indicate whether each of the following statements is true, false, or not possible to evaluate from the information given.

(a) If the equilibrium mixture is allowed to expand into an evacuated larger container, the mole fraction of H_2 will increase.

(b) If several moles of $Ar(g)$ are forced into the reaction container, the amounts of H_2S and CH_4 will increase.

(c) If the equilibrium mixture is cooled to 100 °C, the mole fractions of the four gases will likely change.

(d) If the equilibrium mixture is forced into a slightly smaller container, the partial pressures of the four gases will all increase.

EFFECT OF TEMPERATURE ON EQUILIBRIUM

 Temperature Dependence of Equilibrium animation

We can think of changing the temperature of an equilibrium mixture in terms of adding heat (raising the temperature) or removing heat (lowering the temperature). According to Le Châtelier's principle, adding heat favors the reaction in which heat is absorbed (*endothermic* reaction). Removing heat favors the reaction in which heat is evolved (*exothermic* reaction). Stated in terms of changing temperature,

> *Raising the temperature* of an equilibrium mixture shifts the equilibrium condition in the direction of the *endothermic* reaction. *Lowering the temperature* causes a shift in the direction of the *exothermic* reaction.

✓ Note that an exothermic reaction is aided by lowering the temperature and an endothermic reaction is aided by raising the temperature. You can then point out the difference between the system and the surroundings.

✓ Remind students not to confuse shifts in equilibrium with changes in reaction rates that result from temperature changes. Equilibria of exothermic and endothermic reactions will shift *differently* when temperatures are increased, but the rates of exothermic and endothermic reactions *both increase* with increasing temperature.

✓ Stress to students that changing the temperature of a reaction will result in a shift of the equilibrium and a *new* equilibrium constant.

The principal effect of temperature on equilibrium is in changing the value of the equilibrium constant. In Chapter 19, we will learn how to calculate equilibrium constants as a function of temperature. For now, we will limit ourselves to making qualitative predictions.

EXAMPLE 15-8

Applying Le Châtelier's Principle: Effect of Temperature on Equilibrium. Consider the reaction

$$2 SO_2(g) + O_2(g) \rightleftharpoons 2 SO_3(g) \qquad \Delta H° = -197.8 \text{ kJ}$$

Will the amount of $SO_3(g)$ formed from given amounts of $SO_2(g)$ and $O_2(g)$ be greater at high or low temperatures?

Solution

Raising the temperature favors the endothermic reaction, the *reverse* reaction. Lowering the temperature favors the forward (exothermic) reaction. Therefore, an equilibrium mixture would have a higher concentration of SO_3 at lower temperatures. The conversion of SO_2 to SO_3 is favored at *low* temperatures.

Practice Example A: The reaction $N_2O_4(g) \rightleftharpoons 2 NO_2(g)$ has $\Delta H° = +57.2$ kJ. Will the amount of $NO_2(g)$ formed from $N_2O_4(g)$ be greater at high or low temperatures?

Practice Example B: The enthalpy of formation of NH_3 is $\Delta H_f°[NH_3(g)] = -46.11$ kJ/mol NH_3. Will the concentration of NH_3 in an equilibrium mixture with its elements be greater at 100 or at 300 °C? Explain.

▲ Sulfuric acid is produced from SO_3

$$SO_3(g) + H_2O(l) \rightleftharpoons H_2SO_4(aq)$$

The catalyst used to speed up the conversion of SO_2 to SO_3 in the commercial production of sulfuric acid is $V_2O_5(s)$.

EFFECT OF A CATALYST ON EQUILIBRIUM

Adding a catalyst to a reaction mixture speeds up both the forward and reverse reactions. Equilibrium is achieved more rapidly, but the equilibrium amounts are unchanged by the catalyst. Consider again reaction (15.11)

$$2\,SO_2(g) + O_2(g) \rightleftharpoons 2\,SO_3(g) \qquad K_c = 2.8 \times 10^2 \text{ at } 1000 \text{ K}$$

For a given set of reaction conditions, the equilibrium amounts of SO_2, O_2, and SO_3 have fixed values. This is true whether the reaction is carried out by a slow homogeneous reaction, catalyzed in the gas phase, or conducted as a heterogeneous reaction on the surface of a catalyst. Stated another way, the presence of a catalyst does not change the numerical value of the equilibrium constant.

We now have two thoughts about a catalyst to reconcile: one from the preceding chapter and one from this discussion.

- A catalyst changes the mechanism of a reaction to one with a lower activation energy.
- A catalyst has no effect on the condition of equilibrium in a reversible reaction.

Taken together, these two statements must mean that an equilibrium condition is *independent* of the reaction mechanism. Thus, even though equilibrium has been described in terms of opposing reactions occurring at equal rates, we do not have to be concerned with the kinetics of chemical reactions to work with the equilibrium concept. This observation is still another indication that the equilibrium constant is a thermodynamic quantity, as we shall describe more fully in Chapter 19.

CONCEPT ASSESSMENT ✓

Two students are performing the same experiment in which an endothermic reaction rapidly attains a condition of equilibrium. Student A does the reaction in a beaker resting on the surface of the lab bench while student B holds the beaker in which the reaction occurs. Assuming that all other environmental variables are the same, which student should end up with more product? Explain.

Good Web sites for equilibrium calculations: http://www.chem.vt.edu/RVGS/ACT/notes/chem-eqm.html (noncommercial); http://stokes.lance.colcostate.edu/tools/equil.html (noncommercial).

Nitrogen Dioxide and Dinitrogen Tetroxide movie

Leenson, I. A. "Approaching Equilibrium in the N_2O_4—NO_2 System: A Common Mistake in Textbooks." *J. Chem. Educ.* **2000:** 77, 1652 (December 2000).

15-7 EQUILIBRIUM CALCULATIONS: SOME ILLUSTRATIVE EXAMPLES

We are now ready to tackle the problem of describing, in quantitative terms, the condition of equilibrium in a reversible reaction. Part of the approach we use may seem unfamiliar at first—it has an algebraic look to it. But as you adjust to this "new look," do not lose sight of the fact that we continue to use some familiar and important ideas—molar masses, molarities, and stoichiometric factors from the balanced equation, for example.

The five numerical examples that follow apply the general equilibrium principles described earlier in the chapter. The first four involve gases, while the fifth deals with equilibrium in an aqueous solution. (The study of equilibria in aqueous solutions is the principal topic of the next three chapters.) Each example includes a brief section labeled "comments," which is printed on a yellow background. Think of the comments as the basic methodology of equilibrium calculations. You may want to refer back to these comments from time to time while you are studying later chapters.

Example 15-9 is relatively straightforward. It demonstrates how to determine the equilibrium constant of a reaction when the equilibrium concentrations of the reactants and products are known.

EXAMPLE 15-9

Determining a Value of K_c from the Equilibrium Quantities of Substances. Dinitrogen tetroxide, $N_2O_4(l)$, is an important component of rocket fuels—for example, as an oxidizer of liquid hydrazine in the Titan rocket. At 25 °C, N_2O_4 is a colorless gas that partially dissociates into NO_2, a red-brown gas. The color of an equilibrium mixture of these two gases depends on their relative proportions, which in turn depends on the temperature (Fig. 15-8).

Equilibrium is established in the reaction $N_2O_4(g) \rightleftharpoons 2 NO_2(g)$ at 25 °C. The quantities of the two gases present in a 3.00-L vessel are 7.64 g N_2O_4 and 1.56 g NO_2. What is the value of K_c for this reaction?

(a)   (b)

▲ **FIGURE 15-8**
The equilibrium $N_2O_4(g) \rightleftharpoons 2 NO_2(g)$
(a) At dry ice temperatures, N_2O_4 exists as a solid. The gas in equilibrium with the solid is mostly colorless N_2O_4, with only a trace of brown NO_2.
(b) When warmed to room temperature and above, the N_2O_4 melts and vaporizes. The proportion of $NO_2(g)$ at equilibrium increases over that at low temperatures, and the equilibrium mixture of $N_2O_4(g)$ and $NO_2(g)$ has a red-brown color.

▲ **The Lewis structures of N_2O_4 and $NO_2(g)$**
Nitrogen dioxide is a free radical that combines exothermically to form dinitrogen tetroxide.

Use these examples to point out the importance of significant figures.

Solution

Convert the mass of N_2O_4 to moles.	$\text{mol } N_2O_4 = 7.64 \text{ g } N_2O_4 \times \dfrac{1 \text{ mol } N_2O_4}{92.01 \text{ g } N_2O_4} = 8.303 \times 10^{-2} \text{ mol}$
Convert moles of N_2O_4 to mol/L.	$[N_2O_4] = \dfrac{8.303 \times 10^2 \text{ mol}}{3.00 \text{ L}} = 0.0277 \text{ M}$
Convert the mass of NO_2 to moles.	$\text{mol } NO_2 = 1.56 \text{ g } NO_2 \times \dfrac{1 \text{ mol } NO_2}{46.01 \text{ g } NO_2} = 3.391 \times 10^{-2} \text{ mol}$
Convert moles of NO_2 to mol/L.	$[NO_2] = \dfrac{3.391 \times 10^{-2}}{3.00 \text{ L}} = 0.0113 \text{ M}$
Write the equilibrium constant expression, substitute the equilibrium concentrations, and solve for K_c.	$K_c = \dfrac{[NO_2]^2}{[N_2O_4]} = \dfrac{(0.0113)^2}{(0.0277)} = 4.61 \times 10^{-3}$

Practice Example A: Equilibrium is established in a 3.00-L flask at 1405 K for the reaction $2 H_2S(g) \rightleftharpoons 2 H_2(g) + S_2(g)$. At equilibrium, there is 0.11 mol $S_2(g)$, 0.22 mol $H_2(g)$, and 2.78 mol $H_2S(g)$. What is the value of K_c for this reaction?

Practice Example B: Equilibrium is established at 25 °C in the reaction $N_2O_4(g) \rightleftharpoons 2 NO_2(g)$, $K_c = 4.61 \times 10^{-3}$. If $[NO_2] = 0.0236$ M in a 2.26-L flask, how many grams of N_2O_4 are also present?

Comments

1. The quantities required in an equilibrium constant expression, K_c, are equilibrium *concentrations* in *moles per liter*, not simply equilibrium amounts in moles or masses in grams. You will find it helpful to organize all the equilibrium data and carefully label each item.

Example 15-10 is somewhat more involved than Example 15-9. We are still interested in determining the equilibrium constant for a reaction, but we do not have the same sort of information as in Example 15-9. We are given the initial concentrations of all the reactants and products, but the equilibrium concentration of only one substance. This case requires a little algebra and some careful bookkeeping. We will introduce a tabular system, sometimes called an **ICE table**, for keeping track of changing concentrations of reactants and products. The table contains the **i**nitial, **c**hange in, and **e**quilibrium concentration of each species. It is a helpful device that we will use throughout the next three chapters.

EXAMPLE 15-10

Determining a Value of K_p from Initial and Equilibrium Amounts of Substances: Relating K_c and K_p The equilibrium condition for $SO_2(g)$, $O_2(g)$, and $SO_3(g)$ is important in sulfuric acid production. When a 0.0200-mol sample of SO_3 is introduced into an evacuated 1.52-L vessel at 900 K, 0.0142 mol SO_3 is present at equilibrium. What is the value of K_p for the dissociation of $SO_3(g)$ at 900 K?

Silverstein, Todd P. "Graphing Calculator Strategies for Solving Chemical Equilibrium Problems." *J. Chem. Educ.* **2000:** *77*, 1120. (September 2000).

$$2 SO_3(g) \rightleftharpoons 2 SO_2(g) + O_2(g) \qquad K_p = ?$$

Solution

Let's first determine K_c and then convert to K_p by using equation (15.16). In the ICE table on page 646, the key term leading to the other data is the change in amount of SO_3: In progressing from 0.0200 mol SO_3 to 0.0142 mol SO_3, 0.0058 mol SO_3 is dissociated. The *negative* sign (-0.0058 mol) indicates that this amount of SO_3 is consumed in establishing equilibrium. In the row labeled "changes," the changes in amounts of SO_2 and O_2 must be related to the change in amount of SO_3. For this, we use the stoichiometric coefficients from the balanced equation: 2, 2, and 1. That is, *two* moles of SO_2 and *one* mole of O_2 are produced for every *two* moles of SO_3 that dissociate.

The reaction:	$2 SO_3(g)$	$\rightleftharpoons$	$2 SO_2(g)$	$+$	$O_2(g)$
initial amounts:	0.0200 mol		0.00 mol		0.00 mol
changes:	-0.0058 mol		$+0.0058$ mol		$+0.0029$ mol
equil amounts:	0.0142 mol		0.0058 mol		0.0029 mol

$$[SO_3] = \frac{0.0142 \text{ mol}}{1.52 \text{ L}}; \qquad [SO_2] = \frac{0.0058 \text{ mol}}{1.52 \text{ L}}; \qquad [O_2] = \frac{0.0029 \text{ mol}}{1.52 \text{ L}}$$

$$[SO_3] = 9.34 \times 10^{-3} \text{ M}; \qquad [SO_2] = 3.8 \times 10^{-3} \text{ M}; \qquad [O_2] = 1.9 \times 10^{-3} \text{ M}$$

$$K_c = \frac{[SO_2]^2[O_2]}{[SO_3]^2} = \frac{(3.8 \times 10^{-3})^2(1.9 \times 10^{-3})}{(9.34 \times 10^{-3})^2} = 3.1 \times 10^{-4}$$

$$K_p = K_c(RT)^{\Delta n_{gas}} = 3.1 \times 10^{-4}(0.0821 \times 900)^{(2+1)-2}$$

$$= 3.1 \times 10^{-4}(0.0821 \times 900)^1 = 2.3 \times 10^{-2}$$

Practice Example A: A 5.00-L evacuated flask is filled with 1.86 mol NOBr. At equilibrium at 25 °C, there is 0.082 mol of Br_2 present. Determine K_c and K_p for the reaction $2 NOBr(g) \rightleftharpoons 2 NO(g) + Br_2(g)$.

Practice Example B: 0.100 mol SO_2 and 0.100 mol O_2 are introduced into an evacuated 1.52-L flask at 900 K. When equilibrium is reached, the amount of SO_3 found is 0.0916 mol. Use these data to determine K_p for the reaction $2 SO_3(g) \rightleftharpoons 2 SO_2(g) + O_2(g)$.

Comments

2. The chemical equation for a reversible reaction serves both to establish the form of the equilibrium constant expression and to provide the conversion factors (stoichiometric factors) to relate the equilibrium quantity of one species to equilibrium quantities of the others.

3. For equilibria involving gases, you can use either K_c or K_p. In general, if the data given involve amounts of substances and volumes, it is easier to work with K_c. If data are given as partial pressures, then work with K_p. Whether working with K_c or K_p or the relationship between them, you must always base these expressions on the given chemical equation, not on equations you may have used in other situations.

The methods used in Examples 15-9 and 15-10 are summarized in Figure 15-9. Example 15-11 demonstrates that we can often determine several pieces of useful information about an equilibrium system from just the equilibrium constant and the reaction equation.

EXAMPLE 15-11

Determining Equilibrium Partial and Total Pressures from a Value of K_p. Ammonium hydrogen sulfide, $NH_4HS(s)$, used as a photographic developer, is unstable and dissociates at room temperature.

$$NH_4HS(s) \rightleftharpoons NH_3(g) + H_2S(g) \qquad K_p = 0.108 \text{ at } 25 \text{ °C}$$

A sample of $NH_4HS(s)$ is introduced into an evacuated flask at 25 °C. What is the total gas pressure at equilibrium?

Solution

Write out the equilibrium constant expression in terms of pressures.

$$K_p = (P_{NH_3})(P_{H_2S}) = 0.108$$

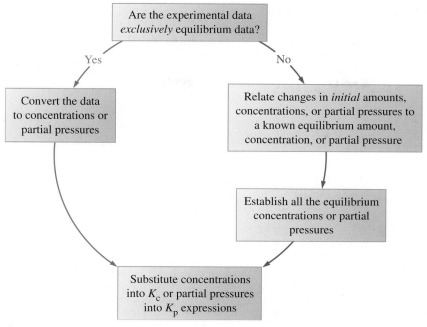

▲ **FIGURE 15-9**
Determining K_c or K_p from experimental data

K_p for this reaction is just the product of the equilibrium partial pressures of $NH_3(g)$ and $H_2S(g)$, each stated in atmospheres. (There is no term for NH_4HS because it is a solid.) Because these gases are produced in equimolar amounts, $P_{NH_3} = P_{H_2S}$.

$$K_p = (P_{NH_3})(P_{H_2S}) = (P_{NH_3})(P_{NH_3}) = (P_{NH_3})^2 = 0.108$$

Find P_{NH_3}. (Note that the unit atm appears because in the equilibrium expression the reference pressure $P°$ was implicitly included.)

$$P_{NH_3} = \sqrt{0.108} = 0.329 \text{ atm} \qquad P_{H_2S} = P_{NH_3} = 0.329 \text{ atm}$$

The total pressure is

$$P_{tot} = P_{NH_3} + P_{H_2S} = 0.329 \text{ atm} + 0.329 \text{ atm} = 0.658 \text{ atm}$$

Practice Example A: Sodium hydrogen carbonate (baking soda) decomposes at elevated temperatures and is one of the sources of $CO_2(g)$ when this compound is used in baking.

$$2\, NaHCO_3(s) \rightleftharpoons Na_2CO_3(s) + H_2O(g) + CO_2(g) \qquad K_p = 0.231 \text{ at } 100\,°C$$

What is the partial pressure of $CO_2(g)$ when this equilibrium is established starting with $NaHCO_3(s)$?

Practice Example B: If enough additional $NH_3(g)$ is added to the flask in Example 15-11 to raise its partial pressure to 0.500 atm at equilibrium, what will be the *total* gas pressure when equilibrium is reestablished?

Comments

4. When using K_p expressions, look for relationships among partial pressures of the reactants. If you need to relate the total pressure to the partial pressures of the reactants, you should be able to do this with some equations presented in Chapter 6 (for example, equations 6.15, 6.16, and 6.17).

Example 15-12 brings back the ICE format, but with a twist. This time the known values include the equilibrium constant and an initial amount of the reactant, but no information is given about the equilibrium amount of the reactant or the product. That means that we do not know how much the initial value will change. We show this by using an "x" in that part of the table. The setup will be quite algebraic; in fact, we must use the quadratic formula to obtain a solution.

EXAMPLE 15-12

Calculating Equilibrium Concentrations from Initial Conditions. A 0.0240-mol sample of $N_2O_4(g)$ is allowed to come to equilibrium with $NO_2(g)$ in a 0.372-L flask at 25 °C. Calculate the amount of N_2O_4 present at equilibrium (Fig. 15-10).

$$N_2O_4(g) \rightleftharpoons 2 NO_2(g) \qquad K_c = 4.61 \times 10^3 \text{ at } 25 \text{ °C}$$

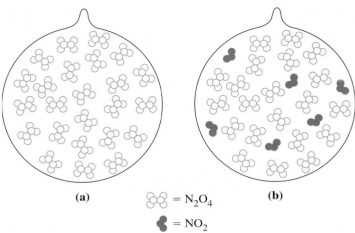

(a) = N_2O_4 (b)

 = NO_2

▲ **FIGURE 15-10**
Equilibrium in the reaction

$$N_2O_4(g) \rightleftharpoons 2 NO_2(g)$$

at 25 °C—Example 15-12 illustrated
Each "molecule" illustrated represents 0.001 mol. **(a)** Initially, the bulb contains 0.024 mol N_2O_4, represented by 24 "molecules." **(b)** At equilibrium, some "molecules" of N_2O_4 have dissociated to NO_2. The 21 "molecules" of N_2O_4 and 6 of NO_2 correspond to 0.021 mol N_2O_4 and 0.006 mol NO_2 at equilibrium.

Solution

We need to determine the amount of N_2O_4 that dissociates to establish equilibrium. For the first time, we introduce an algebraic unknown, x. Suppose we let x = the number of moles of N_2O_4 that dissociate. In the following ICE table, we enter the value $-x$ into the row labeled "changes." The amount of NO_2 produced is $+2x$ because the stoichiometric coefficient of NO_2 is 2 and that of N_2O_4 is 1.

The reaction:	$N_2O_4(g)$	$\rightleftharpoons$	$2 NO_2(g)$
initial amounts:	0.0240 mol		0.00 mol
changes:	$-x$ mol		$+2x$ mol
equil amounts:	$(0.0240 - x)$ mol		$2x$ mol
equil concns:	$[N_2O_4] = (0.0240 - x \text{ mol})/0.372 \text{ L}$		$[NO_2] = 2x \text{ mol}/0.372 \text{ L}$

$$K_c = \frac{[NO_2]^2}{[N_2O_4]} = \frac{\left(\dfrac{2x}{0.372}\right)^2}{\left(\dfrac{0.0240 - x}{0.372}\right)} = \frac{4x^2}{0.372(0.0240 - x)} = 4.61 \times 10^{-3}$$

$$4x^2 = 4.12 \times 10^{-5} - (1.71 \times 10^{-3})x$$

$$x^2 + (4.28 \times 10^{-4})x - 1.03 \times 10^{-5} = 0$$

$$x = \frac{-4.28 \times 10^{-4} \pm \sqrt{(4.28 \times 10^{-4})^2 + 4 \times 1.03 \times 10^{-5}}}{2}$$

$$= \frac{-4.28 \times 10^{-4} \pm \sqrt{(1.83 \times 10^{-7}) + 4.12 \times 10^{-5}}}{2}$$

Most students can solve a quadratic equation, but few of us can solve polynomials greater than a quadratic. Suggest to the students that if they get an equation that is a cubic or higher degree equation, it is likely that it will simplify by using an approximation.

▶ For a discussion of quadratic equations, see Appendix A.

▶ The symbol $\pm$ signifies that there are two possible roots. In this problem, x must be a *positive* quantity smaller than 0.0240.

$$x = \frac{-4.28 \times 10^{-4} \pm \sqrt{4.14 \times 10^{-5}}}{2}$$

$$= \frac{-4.28 \times 10^{-4} \pm 6.43 \times 10^{-3}}{2}$$

$$= \frac{-4.28 \times 10^{-4} + 6.43 \times 10^{-3}}{2} = \frac{6.00 \times 10^{-3}}{2}$$

$$= 3.00 \times 10^{-3} \text{ mol } N_2O_4$$

The amount of N_2O_4 at equilibrium is $(0.0240 - x) = (0.0240 - 0.0030) = 0.0210 \text{ mol } N_2O_4$.

Practice Example A: If 0.150 mol $H_2(g)$ and 0.200 mol $I_2(g)$ are introduced into a 15.0-L flask at 445 °C and allowed to come to equilibrium, how many moles of HI(g) will be present?

$$H_2(g) + I_2(g) \rightleftharpoons 2\,HI(g) \qquad K_c = 50.2 \text{ at } 445\,°C$$

Practice Example B: Suppose the equilibrium mixture of Example 15-12 is transferred to a 10.0-L flask. **(a)** Will the equilibrium amount of N_2O_4 increase or decrease? Explain. **(b)** Calculate the number of moles of N_2O_4 in the new equilibrium condition.

Comments

5. When you need to introduce an algebraic unknown, x, into an equilibrium calculation, follow these steps.

- Introduce x into the ICE setup in the row labeled "changes."
- Decide which change to label as x, that is, the amount of a reactant consumed or of a product formed. Usually, we base this on the species that has the smallest stoichiometric coefficient in the balanced chemical equation.
- Use stoichiometric factors to relate the other changes to x (that is, $2x$, $3x, \ldots$).
- Consider that equilibrium amounts = initial amounts + "changes." (If you have assigned the correct signs to the changes, equilibrium amounts will also be correct.)
- After substitutions have been made into the equilibrium constant expression, the equation will often be a quadratic equation in x, which you can solve by the quadratic formula. Occasionally you may encounter a higher-degree equation. Appendix A-3 outlines a straightforward method of dealing with these.

Our final example is similar to the previous one, but with this slight complication: Initially, we don't know whether a net change occurs to the right or to the left to establish equilibrium. We can find out, though, by using the reaction quotient, Q_c, and proceeding in the manner suggested in Figure 15-11. Also, because the reactants and products are in solution, we can work exclusively with concentrations in formulating the K_c expression.

EXAMPLE 15-13

Using the Reaction Quotient, Q_c, in an Equilibrium Calculation. Solid silver is added to a solution with these initial concentrations: $[Ag^+] = 0.200$ M, $[Fe^{2+}] = 0.100$ M, and $[Fe^{3+}] = 0.300$ M. The following reversible reaction occurs.

$$Ag^+(aq) + Fe^{2+}(aq) \rightleftharpoons Ag(s) + Fe^{3+}(aq) \qquad K_c = 2.98$$

What are the ion concentrations when equilibrium is established?

Determine the direction of net change by comparing Q and K

Let x = change in amount, concentration, or partial pressure of one reactant or product to reach equilibrium

Relate changes in amounts, concentrations, or partial pressures of other reactants or products to the chosen x

Express equilibrium amounts, concentrations, partial pressures in terms of x

Substitute equilibrium concentrations or partial pressures into K_c or K_p expression; solve for x; substitute the value of x into any equation in which x appeared to find the desired quantities

Tabulate these data in an ICE table

▲ FIGURE 15-11
Determining equilibrium concentrations and partial pressures

Solution

Because all reactants and products are present initially, we need to use the reaction quotient Q_c to determine the direction in which a net change occurs.

$$Q_c = \frac{[Fe^{3+}]}{[Ag^+][Fe^{2+}]} = \frac{0.300}{(0.200)(0.100)} = 15.0$$

Because Q_c (15.0) is larger than K_c (2.98), a net change must occur in the direction of the reverse reaction, *to the left*. Let's define x as the change in molarity of Fe^{3+}. Because the net change occurs *to the left*, we designate the changes for the species on the left side of the equation as positive and those on the right side as negative. The relevant data are tabulated as follows.

The reaction:	$Ag^+(aq)$	+	$Fe^{2+}(aq)$	$\rightleftharpoons$	$Ag(s) + Fe^{3+}(aq)$
Initial concns:	0.200 M		0.100 M		0.300 M
changes:	$+x$ M		$+x$ M		$-x$ M
equil concns:	$(0.200 + x)$ M		$(0.100 + x)$ M		$(0.300 - x)$ M

$$K_c = \frac{[Fe^{3+}]}{[Ag^+][Fe^{2+}]} = \frac{(0.300 - x)}{(0.200 + x)(0.100 + x)} = 2.98$$

This equation, which is solved in Appendix A-3, is a quadratic equation for which the acceptable root is $x = 0.11$. To obtain the equilibrium concentrations, we substitute this value of x into the terms shown in the table of data.

$$[Ag^+]_{equil} = 0.200 + 0.11 = 0.31 \text{ M}$$

$$[Fe^{2+}]_{equil} = 0.100 + 0.11 = 0.21 \text{ M}$$

$$[Fe^{3+}]_{equil} = 0.300 - 0.11 = 0.19 \text{ M}$$

CHECK: If we have done the calculation correctly, we should obtain a value very close to that given for K_c when we substitute the *calculated* equilibrium concentrations into the reaction quotient, Q_c. We do.

$$Q_c = \frac{[Fe^{3+}]}{[Ag^+][Fe^{2+}]} = \frac{(0.19)}{(0.31)(0.21)} = 2.9 \qquad (K_c = 2.98)$$

Practice Example A: Excess $Ag(s)$ is added to 1.20 M $Fe^{3+}(aq)$. Given that

$$Ag^+(aq) + Fe^{2+}(aq) \rightleftharpoons Ag(s) + Fe^{3+}(aq) \qquad K_c = 2.98$$

what are the equilibrium concentrations of the species in solution?

Practice Example B: A solution is prepared with $[V^{3+}] = [Cr^{2+}] = 0.0100$ M and $[V^{2+}] = [Cr^{3+}] = 0.150$ M. The following reaction occurs.

$$V^{3+}(aq) + Cr^{2+}(aq) \rightleftharpoons V^{2+}(aq) + Cr^{3+}(aq) \qquad K_c = 7.2 \times 10^2$$

What are the ion concentrations when equilibrium is established?

[*Hint:* The algebra can be greatly simplified by extracting the square root of both sides of an equation at the appropriate point.]

> After making an approximation, it is always necessary to check its validity by substituting the approximate value back into the equation and verifying the 5% rule.

KEEP IN MIND ▶

that if one or more of the substances appearing in Q_c (or Q_p) is not present initially, a net change must occur to produce some of the substance(s). You need to compare Q_c (or Q_p) with K_c (or K_p) only if *all* the substances appearing in these expressions are present initially.

Comments

6. It is sometimes helpful to compare the reaction quotient Q to the equilibrium constant K to determine the direction of the net change.

7. In many equilibrium calculations—often those in aqueous solutions—you can work with molarities directly, without having to work with moles of reactants and solution volumes.

8. Where possible, check your calculation, for instance, by substituting *calculated* equilibrium concentrations into the reaction quotient Q to see if its numerical value is close to that of K.

Summary

15-1 Dynamic Equilibrium—Equilibrium is the condition in which the forward and reverse reaction rates of reversible processes are equal. Chemical and physical processes in equilibrium are dynamic by nature.

15-2 The Equilibrium Constant Expression—This condition of dynamic equilibrium is described through an **equilibrium constant expression**. The form of the equilibrium constant expression is established from the balanced chemical equation using **activities** to express the "effective" concentrations (equation 15.7). The numerical value obtained from the equilibrium constant expression is referred to as the **equilibrium constant**, K. Equilibrium constants are unitless.

15-3 Relationships Involving Equilibrium Constants—When the equation for a reversible reaction is written in the reverse order, the equilibrium constant expression and the value of K are both inverted from their original form. When two or more reactions are coupled together, the equilibrium constant for the overall reaction is the product of the K values of the individual reactions. The equilibrium constant of a reaction can have different values depending on the reference state used. For K_c a concentration reference state is used, while for K_p, a pressure reference state is used. The relationship between K_c and K_p is given by equation (15.16).

15-4 The Magnitude of an Equilibrium Constant—The magnitude of the equilibrium constant can be used to determine the outcome of a reaction. For large values of K the reaction goes to completion, with all reactants converted to products. A very small equilibrium constant, for example, a large negative power of ten, indicates that practically none of the reactants have been converted to products. Finally, equilibrium constants of an intermediate value, for example, between 10^{-10} and 10^{10}, indicate that some of the reactants have been converted to products.

15-5 The Reaction Quotient, Q: Predicting the Direction of Net Change—The **reaction quotient**, Q (equation 15.19), has the same form as the equilibrium constant expression; however, its numerical value is determined using the initial reaction activities. A comparison of the reaction quotient with the equilibrium constant makes it possible to predict the direction of net change leading to equilibrium (Fig. 15-5). If $Q < K$, the forward reaction is favored, meaning that when equilibrium is established the amounts of products will have increased and the amounts of reactants will have decreased. If $Q > K$, the reverse reaction is favored until equilibrium is established. If $Q = K$, neither the forward nor reverse reaction is favored. The initial conditions are in fact equilibrium conditions.

15-6 Altering Equilibrium Conditions: Le Châtelier's Principle—**Le Châtelier's principle** is used to make qualitative predictions of the effects of different variables on an equilibrium condition. This principle describes how an equilibrium condition is modified, or "shifts," in response to the addition or removal of reactants or changes in reaction volume, external pressure, or temperature. Catalysts, by speeding up the forward and reverse reactions equally, have no effect on an equilibrium condition.

15-7 Equilibrium Calculations: Some Illustrative Examples—For quantitative equilibrium calculations, a few basic principles and algebraic techniques are required. A useful method employs a tabular system, called an **ICE table**, for keeping track of the *initial* concentrations of the reactants and products, *changes* in these concentrations, and the *equilibrium* concentrations.

Integrative Example

In the manufacture of ammonia, the chief source of hydrogen gas is the following reaction for the reforming of methane at high temperatures.

$$CH_4(g) + 2\,H_2O(g) \rightleftharpoons CO_2(g) + 4\,H_2(g) \tag{15.23}$$

The following data are also given.

(a) $CO(g) + H_2O(g) \rightleftharpoons CO_2(g) + H_2(g)$ $\Delta H° = -40$ kJ; $K_c = 1.4$ at 1000 K

(b) $CO(g) + 3\,H_2(g) \rightleftharpoons H_2O(g) + CH_4(g)$ $\Delta H° = -230$ kJ; $K_c = 190$ at 1000 K

At 1000 K, 1.00 mol each of CH_4 and H_2O are allowed to come to equilibrium in a 10.0-L vessel. Calculate the number of moles of H_2 present at equilibrium. Would the yield of H_2 increase if the temperature were raised above 1000 K?

Strategy

First, we should assemble the data needed to solve this problem. The amounts of substances and a reaction volume are given, so we should be able to work with a K_c expression. However, because the K_c value for the reaction of interest is not given, we will have to derive this value by combining the two equations for which data are given. This will yield values of both K_c and ΔH for the reaction of interest.

To calculate the number of moles of H_2 at equilibrium we can use the ICE method, and to assess the effect of temperature on the equilibrium yield of H_2 we can apply Le Châtelier's principle.

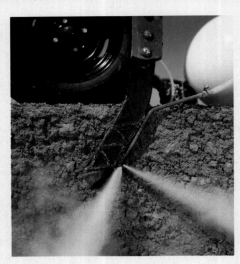

▲ Use of liquid ammonia as a fertilizer by direct injection into the soil.

Nitrogen is an element essential both in living things and in industry. The atmosphere contains a vast pool of elemental nitrogen, but most organisms cannot use nitrogen in that form. Instead, they require certain nitrogen-containing compounds. The conversion of elemental atmospheric nitrogen to nitrogen compounds is called *nitrogen fixation*, and in nature, this process is carried out only by certain types of bacteria. Nitrogen fixation is part of the nitrogen cycle, which is the path of nitrogen through the environment and a variety of living organisms and back into the environment. A simplified version of the nitrogen cycle is depicted in Figure 15-12, which shows that elemental nitrogen from the atmosphere is fixed, becomes part of plants, animals, and other organisms, and is then returned to the atmosphere. The numbers in parentheses refer to the various parts of the cycle described below.

A few leguminous plants, such as beans, peas, and alfalfa, have bacteria residing on their roots that convert elemental nitrogen from the air into compounds used to make plant protein (1). Plants also convert nitrates in the soil to proteins (5). Animals obtain their protein-building nitrogen by feeding on plants and/or other animals (2). The decay of plant and animal proteins produces ammonia (3). Through a series of bacterial actions, ammonia is converted to nitrites and nitrates (4). Denitrifying bacteria decompose nitrites and nitrates, returning N_2O and N_2 to the atmosphere, thus completing the cycle (6). Some atmospheric nitrogen is converted to nitrates during electrical storms (1a).

Reversible chemical reactions play an important role in the nitrogen cycle. One example is the reaction of $N_2(g)$ and $O_2(g)$ to form $NO(g)$.

$$N_2(g) + O_2(g) \rightleftharpoons 2\,NO(g)$$

$$K_P = 4.7 \times 10^{-31} \text{ at } 298 \text{ K}$$

$$= 1.3 \times 10^{-4} \text{ at } 1800 \text{ K}$$

The reaction does not occur to any measurable extent at 298 K, but at 1800 K the situation is a little different. An equilibrium mixture of $N_2(g)$ and $O_2(g)$ at 1800 K

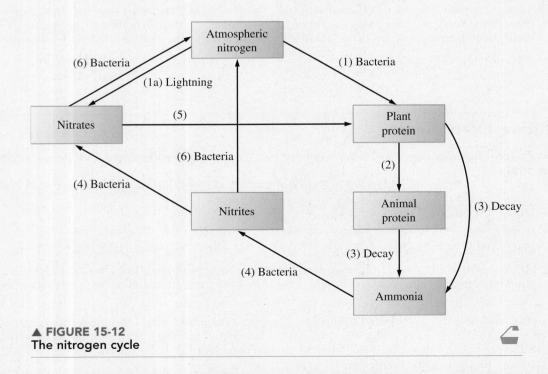

▲ **FIGURE 15-12**
The nitrogen cycle

▲ During electrical storms, $N_2(g)$ and $O_2(g)$ combine to produce small quantities of $NO(g)$ in a reversible chemical reaction.

contains about 1 or 2% $NO(g)$. $NO(g)$ is introduced into the nitrogen cycle through this high-temperature reaction occurring naturally in lightning flashes during thunderstorms and artificially in high-temperature combustion processes, as in internal combustion engines. Further reactions account for the formation of $HNO_3(aq)$ in rainstorms and the introduction of nitrates into the soil.

$$2\,NO(g) + O_2(g) \longrightarrow 2\,NO_2(g)$$
$$3\,NO_2(g) + H_2O(l) \longrightarrow 2\,HNO_3(aq) + NO(g)$$

Ammonia is an important industrial chemical. Its synthesis is achieved by the following reaction.

$$N_2(g) + 3\,H_2(g) \rightleftharpoons 2\,NH_3(g)$$

$$\Delta H^\circ = -92.22\;\text{kJ} \qquad K_p = 6.2 \times 10^5 \text{ at 298 K}$$

Since ammonia can be converted by soil bacteria to nitrites and nitrates that can be used by plants, one of the principal uses of artificial NH_3 is as a fertilizer that is injected directly into the soil. NH_3 is also used in the production of other nitrogen compounds, such as urea, hydrazine, ammonium sulfate, ammonium nitrate, ammonium dihydrogen phosphate, and ammonium hydrogen phosphate. Several of these compounds are used as fertilizers, and others are used in the manufacture of explosives, pharmaceuticals, and plastics. So much nitrogen is now being fixed artificially that fixed nitrogen is accumulating in the environment somewhat faster than it is being returned to the atmosphere. This causes environmental problems such as the buildup of nitrates in groundwater.

Let us look at the commercial synthesis of ammonia, called the Haber–Bosch process, from the standpoint of chemical equilibrium and kinetics. In the synthesis reaction, two moles of gaseous product are formed for every four moles of gaseous reactants. Carrying out the reaction at high pressure favors the production of NH_3. Because the forward reaction is exothermic, the equilibrium yield

of NH_3 is greatest at low temperatures. Thus, the optimum conditions for the equilibrium production of NH_3 is greatest at low temperatures. Thus, the optimum conditions for the equilibrium production of NH_3 are *high pressures* and *low temperatures*. However, these "optimum" conditions do not take into account the rate of reaction.

Although the equilibrium production of NH_3 is favored at low temperatures, equilibrium is achieved so slowly that the synthesis is not feasible at those temperatures. One way to speed up the reaction is to raise the temperature, even though doing so decreases the equilibrium concentration of NH_3. Another way is to use a catalyst. The usual industrial operating conditions are a temperature of about 550 °C, pressures ranging from 150 to 350 atm, and a catalyst—usually iron in the presence of Al_2O_3, MgO, CaO, and K_2O. Figure 15-13 suggests the dramatic difference between the theoretical optimum conditions and the actual operating conditions.

Another essential feature of the Haber–Bosch method is to remove NH_3 as it forms. This is done by liquefying the $NH_3(g)$. In fact, the mixture need not be brought to equilibrium at all, and nearly 100% conversion of N_2 and H_2 to NH_3 is achieved.

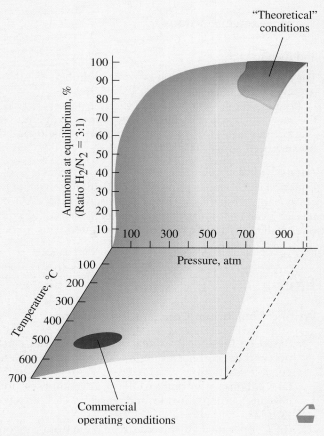

▲ FIGURE 15-13
Equilibrium conversion of $N_2(g)$ and $H_2(g)$ to $NH_3(g)$ as a function of temperature and pressure

Solution

We combine equations (a) and (b) to obtain the data needed in this problem.

(a) $\quad CO(g) + H_2O(g) \rightleftharpoons CO_2(g) + H_2(g) \qquad \Delta H = -40 \text{ kJ} \quad K_c = 1.4$

(b) $\quad \underline{CH_4(g) + H_2O(g) \rightleftharpoons CO(g) + 3 H_2(g) \qquad \Delta H = 230 \text{ kJ} \quad K_c = 1/190}$

Overall: $\quad CH_4(g) + 2 H_2O(g) \rightleftharpoons CO_2(g) + 4 H_2(g) \qquad \Delta H = 190 \text{ kJ} \quad K_c = 1.4/190 = 7.4 \times 10^{-3}$

Next we set up an ICE table in which x represents the number of moles of CH_4 consumed in reaching equilibrium.

The reaction:	$CH_4(g)$	+	$2 H_2O(g)$	$\rightleftharpoons$	$CO_2(g)$	+	$4 H_2(g)$
initial amounts:	1.00 mol		1.00 mol		0.00 mol		0.00 mol
changes:	$-x$ mol		$-2x$ mol		x mol		$4x$ mol
equil amounts:	$(1.00 - x)$ mol		$(1.00 - 2x)$ mol		x mol		$4x$ mol
equil concns, M:	$(1.00 - x)/10.0$		$(1.00 - 2x)/10.0$		$x/10.0$		$4x/10.0$

Now we set up K_c and make substitutions into the expression.

$$K_c = \frac{[CO_2][H_2]^4}{[CH_4][H_2O]^2}$$

$$= \frac{(x/10.0)(4x/10.0)^4}{[(1.00 - x)/10.0][(1.00 - 2x)/10.0]^2}$$

$$= \frac{x(4x)^4}{100(1.00 - x)(1.00 - 2x)^2} = 7.4 \times 10^{-3}$$

The above equation reduces to

$$256x^5 = 0.74[(1.00 - x)(1.00 - 2x)^2]$$

and then to

$$256x^5 - 0.74[(1.00 - x)(1.00 - 2x)^2] = 0 \qquad (15.24)$$

The solution to this equation is $x = 0.23$ mol. The number of moles of H_2 at equilibrium is $4x = 0.92$ mol.

Because the reaction is endothermic ($\Delta H = 190$ kJ), the forward reaction is favored at higher temperatures. The equilibrium yield of H_2 will increase if the temperature is raised above 1000 K.

Assessment

Equation (15.24) looks impossibly difficult to solve, but it is not. It can be solved for x rather simply by the method of successive approximations. This is done in Appendix A-3, equation (A.2). An important clue as to the possible range of values for x can be found in the ICE table. Note that the equilibrium amount of $H_2O(g)$ is $1.00 - 2x$, meaning that $x < 0.50$, or else all of the $H_2O(g)$ would be consumed. This marks a good place to start the approximations.

Exercises

Writing Equilibrium Constant Expressions

1. Based on these descriptions, write a balanced equation and the corresponding K_c expression for each reversible reaction.
   (a) Carbonyl fluoride, $COF_2(g)$, decomposes into gaseous carbon dioxide and gaseous carbon tetrafluoride.
   (b) Copper metal displaces silver(I) ion from aqueous solution, producing silver metal and an aqueous solution of copper(II) ion.
   (c) Peroxodisulfate ion, $S_2O_8{}^{2-}$, oxidizes iron(II) ion to iron(III) ion in aqueous solution and is itself reduced to sulfate ion.

2. Based on these descriptions, write a balanced equation and the corresponding K_p expression for each reversible reaction.
   (a) Oxygen gas oxidizes gaseous ammonia to gaseous nitrogen and water vapor.
   (b) Hydrogen gas reduces gaseous nitrogen dioxide to gaseous ammonia and water vapor.
   (c) Nitrogen gas reacts with the solid sodium carbonate and carbon to produce solid sodium cyanide and carbon monoxide gas.

3. Write equilibrium constant expressions, K_c, for the reactions

(a) $2\,NO(g) + O_2(g) \rightleftharpoons 2\,NO_2(g)$

(b) $Zn(s) + 2\,Ag^+(aq) \rightleftharpoons Zn^{2+}(aq) + 2\,Ag(s)$

(c) $Mg(OH)_2(s) + CO_3^{2-}(aq) \rightleftharpoons$
$$MgCO_3(s) + 2\,OH^-(aq)$$

4. Write equilibrium constant expressions, K_p, for the reactions
   (a) $CS_2(g) + 4\,H_2(g) \rightleftharpoons CH_4(g) + 2\,H_2S(g)$

   (b) $Ag_2O(s) \rightleftharpoons 2\,Ag(s) + \frac{1}{2}O_2(g)$

   (c) $2\,NaHCO_3(s) \rightleftharpoons$
   $$Na_2CO_3(s) + CO_2(g) + H_2O(g)$$

5. Write an equilibrium constant, K_c, for the formation from its gaseous elements of **(a)** 1 mol HF(g); **(b)** 2 mol $NH_3(g)$; **(c)** 2 mol $N_2O(g)$ **(d)** 1 mol $ClF_3(l)$.

6. Write an equilibrium constant, K_p, for the formation from its gaseous elements of **(a)** 1 mol NOCl(g); **(b)** 2 mol $ClNO_2(g)$; **(c)** 1 mol $N_2H_4(g)$; **(d)** 1 mol $NH_4Cl(s)$.

7. Determine values of K_c from the K_p values given.
   (a) $SO_2Cl_2(g) \rightleftharpoons SO_2(g) + Cl_2(g)$
   $$K_p = 2.9 \times 10^{-2} \text{ at } 303\text{ K}$$
   (b) $2\,NO(g) + O_2(g) \rightleftharpoons 2\,NO_2(g)$
   $$K_p = 1.48 \times 10^4 \text{ at } 184\,°C$$
   (c) $Sb_2S_3(s) + 3\,H_2(g) \rightleftharpoons 2\,Sb(s) + 3\,H_2S(g)$
   $$K_p = 0.429 \text{ at } 713\text{ K}$$

8. Determine the values of K_p from the K_c values given.
   (a) $N_2O_4(g) \rightleftharpoons 2\,NO_2(g)$
   $$K_c = 4.61 \times 10^{-3} \text{ at } 25\,°C$$
   (b) $2\,CH_4(g) \rightleftharpoons C_2H_2(g) + 3\,H_2(g)$
   $$K_c = 0.154 \text{ at } 2000\text{ K}$$
   (c) $2\,H_2S(g) + CH_4(g) \rightleftharpoons 4\,H_2(g) + CS_2(g)$
   $$K_c = 5.27 \times 10^{-8} \text{ at } 973\text{ K}$$

9. The vapor pressure of water at 25 °C is 23.8 mmHg. Write K_p for the vaporization of water, with pressures in atmospheres. What is the value of K_c for the vaporization process?

10. If $K_c = 5.12 \times 10^{-3}$ for the equilibrium established between liquid benzene and its vapor at 25 °C, what is the vapor pressure of C_6H_6 at 25 °C, expressed in millimeters of mercury?

11. Determine K_c for the reaction
$$\frac{1}{2}N_2(g) + \frac{1}{2}O_2(g) + \frac{1}{2}Br_2(g) \rightleftharpoons NOBr(g)$$
from the following information (at 298 K).
$$2\,NO(g) \rightleftharpoons N_2(g) + O_2(g) \quad K_c = 2.1 \times 10^{30}$$
$$NO(g) + \frac{1}{2}Br_2(g) \rightleftharpoons NOBr(g) \quad K_c = 1.4$$

12. Given the equilibrium constant values
$$N_2(g) + \frac{1}{2}O_2(g) \rightleftharpoons N_2O(g) \quad K_c = 2.7 \times 10^{-18}$$
$$N_2O_4(g) \rightleftharpoons 2\,NO_2(g) \quad K_c = 4.6 \times 10^{-3}$$
$$\frac{1}{2}N_2(g) + O_2(g) \rightleftharpoons NO_2(g) \quad K_c = 4.1 \times 10^{-9}$$

Determine a value of K_c for the reaction
$$2\,N_2O(g) + 3\,O_2(g) \rightleftharpoons 2\,N_2O_4(g)$$

13. Use the following data to estimate a value of K_p at 1200 K for the reaction $2\,H_2(g) + O_2(g) \rightleftharpoons 2\,H_2O(g)$
$$C(graphite) + CO_2(g) \rightleftharpoons 2\,CO(g) \quad K_c = 0.64$$
$$CO_2(g) + H_2(g) \rightleftharpoons CO(g) + H_2O(g) \quad K_c = 1.4$$
$$C(graphite) + \frac{1}{2}O_2(g) \rightleftharpoons CO(g) \quad K_c = 1 \times 10^8$$

14. Determine K_c for the reaction $N_2(g) + O_2(g) + Cl_2(g) \rightleftharpoons 2\,NOCl(g)$, given the following data at 298 K.
$$\frac{1}{2}N_2(g) + O_2(g) \rightleftharpoons NO_2(g) \quad K_p = 1.0 \times 10^{-9}$$
$$NOCl(g) + \frac{1}{2}O_2(g) \rightleftharpoons NO_2Cl(g) \quad K_p = 1.1 \times 10^2$$
$$NO_2(g) + \frac{1}{2}Cl_2(g) \rightleftharpoons NO_2Cl(g) \quad K_p = 0.3$$

Experimental Determination of Equilibrium Constants

15. 1.00×10^{-3} mol PCl_5 is introduced into a 250.0-mL flask, and equilibrium is established at 284 °C: $PCl_5(g) \rightleftharpoons PCl_3(g) + Cl_2(g)$. The quantity of $Cl_2(g)$ present at equilibrium is found to be 9.65×10^{-4} mol. What is the value of K_c for the dissociation reaction at 284 °C?

16. A mixture of 1.00 g H_2 and 1.06 g H_2S in a 0.500-L flask comes to equilibrium at 1670 K: $2\,H_2(g) + S_2(g) \rightleftharpoons 2\,H_2S(g)$. The equilibrium amount of $S_2(g)$ found is 8.00×10^{-6} mol. Determine the value of K_p at 1670 K.

17. The two common chlorides of phosphorus, PCl_3 and PCl_5, both important in the production of other phos-

phorus compounds, coexist in equilibrium through the reaction
$$PCl_3(g) + Cl_2(g) \rightleftharpoons PCl_5(g)$$
At 250 °C, an equilibrium mixture in a 2.50-L flask contains 0.105 g PCl_5, 0.220 g PCl_3, and 2.12 g Cl_2. What are the values of **(a)** K_c and **(b)** K_p for this reaction at 250 °C?

18. A 0.682-g sample of ICl(g) is placed in a 625-mL reaction vessel at 682 K. When equilibrium is reached between the ICl(g) and $I_2(g)$ and $Cl_2(g)$ formed by its dissociation, 0.0383 g I_2 is present. What is K_c for this reaction?

Equilibrium Relationships

19. Equilibrium is established at 1000 K, where $K_c = 281$ for the reaction $2\,SO_2(g) + O_2(g) \rightleftharpoons 2\,SO_3(g)$. The equilibrium amount of $O_2(g)$ in a 0.185-L flask is 0.00247 mol. What is the ratio of $[SO_2]$ to $[SO_3]$ in this equilibrium mixture?

20. For the dissociation of $I_2(g)$ at about 1200 °C, $I_2(g) \rightleftharpoons 2\,I(g)$, $K_c = 1.1 \times 10^{-2}$. What volume flask should we use if we want 0.37 mol I to be present for every 1.00 mol I_2 at equilibrium?

21. In the Ostwald process for oxidizing ammonia, a variety of products is possible—N_2, N_2O, NO, and NO_2—depending on the conditions. One possibility is

$$NH_3(g) + \frac{5}{4}O_2(g) \rightleftharpoons NO(g) + \frac{3}{2}H_2O(g)$$

$$K_p = 2.11 \times 10^{19} \text{ at 700 K}$$

For the decomposition of NO_2 at 700 K,

$$NO_2(g) \rightleftharpoons NO(g) + \frac{1}{2}O_2(g) \quad K_p = 0.524$$

(a) Write a chemical equation for the oxidation of $NH_3(g)$ to $NO_2(g)$.
(b) Determine K_p for the chemical equation you have written.

22. At 2000 K, $K_c = 0.154$ for the reaction $2\,CH_4(g) \rightleftharpoons C_2H_2(g) + 3\,H_2(g)$. If a 1.00-L equilibrium mixture at 2000 K contains 0.10 mol each of $CH_4(g)$ and $H_2(g)$,
(a) what is the mole fraction of $C_2H_2(g)$ present?
(b) Is the conversion of $CH_4(g)$ to $C_2H_2(g)$ favored at high or low pressures?
(c) If the equilibrium mixture at 2000 K is transferred from a 1.00-L flask to a 2.00-L flask, will the number of moles of $C_2H_2(g)$ increase, decrease, or remain unchanged?

23. An equilibrium mixture at 1000 K contains 0.276 mol H_2, 0.276 mol CO_2, 0.224 mol CO, and 0.224 mol H_2O.

$$CO_2(g) + H_2(g) \rightleftharpoons CO(g) + H_2O(g)$$

(a) Show that for this reaction, K_c is independent of the reaction volume, V.
(b) Determine the value of K_c and K_p.

24. For the reaction $CO(g) + H_2O(g) \rightleftharpoons CO_2(g) + H_2(g)$, $K_p = 23.2$ at 600 K. Explain which of the following situations might be found at equilibrium:
(a) $P_{CO} = P_{H_2O} = P_{CO_2} = P_{H_2}$; (b) $P_{H_2}/P_{H_2O} = P_{CO_2}/P_{CO}$; (c) $(P_{CO_2})(P_{H_2}) = (P_{CO})(P_{H_2O})$; (d) $P_{CO_2}/P_{H_2O} = P_{H_2}/P_{CO}$.

Direction and Extent of Chemical Change

25. Can a mixture of 2.2 mol O_2, 3.6 mol SO_2, and 1.8 mol SO_3 be maintained indefinitely in a 7.2-L flask at a temperature at which $K_c = 100$ in this reaction? Explain.

$$2\,SO_2(g) + O_2(g) \rightleftharpoons 2\,SO_3(g)$$

26. Is a mixture of 0.0205 mol $NO_2(g)$ and 0.750 mol $N_2O_4(g)$ in a 5.25-L flask at 25 °C at equilibrium? If not, in which direction will the reaction proceed—toward products or reactants?

$$N_2O_4(g) \rightleftharpoons 2\,NO_2(g) \quad K_c = 4.61 \times 10^{-3} \text{ at 25 °C}$$

27. In the reaction $2\,SO_2(g) + O_2(g) \rightleftharpoons 2\,SO_3(g)$, 0.455 mol SO_2, 0.183 mol O_2, and 0.568 mol SO_3 are introduced simultaneously into a 1.90-L vessel at 1000 K.
(a) Is this mixture at equilibrium?
(b) If not, in which direction will a net change occur?

28. In the reaction $CO(g) + H_2O(g) \rightleftharpoons CO_2(g) + H_2(g)$, $K = 31.4$ at 588 K. Equal masses of each reactant and product are brought together in a reaction vessel at 588 K.
(a) Can this mixture be at equilibrium?
(b) If not, in which direction will a net change occur?

29. A mixture consisting of 0.150 mol H_2 and 0.150 mol I_2 is brought to equilibrium at 445 °C in a 3.25-L flask. What are the equilibrium amounts of H_2, I_2, and HI?

$$H_2(g) + I_2(g) \rightleftharpoons 2\,HI(g) \quad K_c = 50.2 \text{ at 445 °C}$$

30. Starting with 0.280 mol $SbCl_3$ and 0.160 mol Cl_2, how many moles of $SbCl_5$, $SbCl_3$, and Cl_2 are present when equilibrium is established at 248 °C in a 2.50-L flask?

$$SbCl_5(g) \rightleftharpoons SbCl_3(g) + Cl_2(g)$$

$$K_c = 2.5 \times 10^{-2} \text{ at 248 °C}$$

31. Starting with 0.3500 mol CO(g) and 0.05500 mol $COCl_2(g)$ in a 3.050-L flask at 668 K, how many moles of $Cl_2(g)$ will be present at equilibrium?

$$CO(g) + Cl_2(g) \rightleftharpoons COCl_2(g)$$

$$K_c = 1.2 \times 10^3 \text{ at 668 K}$$

32. 1.00 g *each* of CO, H_2O, and H_2 are sealed in a 1.41-L vessel and brought to equilibrium at 600 K. How many grams of CO_2 will be present in the equilibrium mixture?

$$CO(g) + H_2O(g) \rightleftharpoons CO_2(g) + H_2(g) \quad K_c = 23.2$$

33. Equilibrium is established in a 2.50-L flask at 250 °C for the reaction

$$PCl_5(g) \rightleftharpoons PCl_3(g) + Cl_2(g) \quad K_c = 3.8 \times 10^{-2}$$

How many moles of PCl_5, PCl_3, and Cl_2 are present at equilibrium, if
(a) 0.550 mol each of PCl_5 and PCl_3 are initially introduced into the flask?
(b) 0.610 mol PCl_5 alone is introduced into the flask?

34. For the following reaction, $K_c = 2.00$ at 1000 °C.

$$2\,COF_2(g) \rightleftharpoons CO_2(g) + CF_4(g)$$

If a 5.00-L mixture contains 0.145 mol COF_2, 0.262 mol CO_2, and 0.074 mol CF_4 at a temperature of 1000 °C,
(a) Will the mixture be at equilibrium?
(b) If the gases are not at equilibrium, in what direction will a net change occur?
(c) How many moles of each gas will be present at equilibrium?

35. In the following reaction, $K_c = 4.0$.

$$C_2H_5OH + CH_3COOH \rightleftharpoons CH_3COOC_2H_5 + H_2O$$

A reaction is allowed to occur in a mixture of 17.2 g C_2H_5OH, 23.8 g CH_3COOH, 48.6 g $CH_3COOC_2H_5$, and 71.2 g H_2O.
(a) In what direction will a net change occur?
(b) How many grams of each substance will be present at equilibrium?

36. The N_2O_4–NO_2 equilibrium mixture in the flask on the left in the figure is allowed to expand into the evacuated flask on the right. What is the composition of the gaseous mixture when equilibrium is reestablished in the system consisting of the two flasks?

$$N_2O_4(g) \rightleftharpoons 2\,NO_2(g) \quad K_c = 4.61 \times 10^{-3} \text{ at } 25\,°C$$

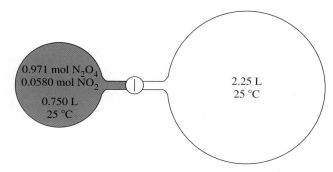

0.971 mol N_2O_4
0.0580 mol NO_2

0.750 L
25 °C

2.25 L
25 °C

37. Formamide, used in the manufacture of pharmaceuticals, dyes, and agricultural chemicals, decomposes at high temperatures.

$$HCONH_2(g) \rightleftharpoons NH_3(g) + CO(g)$$

$$K_c = 4.84 \text{ at } 400\,K$$

If 0.186 mol $HCONH_2(g)$ dissociates in a 2.16-L flask at 400 K, what will be the *total* pressure at equilibrium?

38. A mixture of 1.00 mol $NaHCO_3(s)$ and 1.00 mol $Na_2CO_3(s)$ is introduced into a 2.50-L flask in which the partial pressure of CO_2 is 2.10 atm and that of $H_2O(g)$ is 715 mmHg. When equilibrium is established at 100 °C, will the partial pressures of $CO_2(g)$ and $H_2O(g)$ be greater or less than their initial partial pressures? Explain.

$$2\,NaHCO_3(s) \rightleftharpoons Na_2CO_3(s) + CO_2(g) + H_2O(g)$$

$$K_p = 0.23 \text{ at } 100\,°C$$

39. Cadmium metal is added to 0.350 L of an aqueous solution in which $[Cr^{3+}] = 1.00$ M. What are the concentrations of the different ionic species at equilibrium? What is the minimum mass of cadmium metal required to establish this equilibrium?

$$2\,Cr^{3+}(aq) + Cd(s) \rightleftharpoons 2\,Cr^{2+}(aq) + Cd^{2+}(aq)$$

$$K_c = 0.288$$

40. Lead metal is added to 0.100 M $Cr^{3+}(aq)$. What are $[Pb^{2+}]$, $[Cr^{2+}]$, and $[Cr^{3+}]$ when equilibrium is established in the reaction?

$$Pb(s) + 2\,Cr^{3+}(aq) \rightleftharpoons Pb^{2+}(aq) + 2\,Cr^{2+}(aq)$$

$$K_c = 3.2 \times 10^{-10}$$

41. One sketch below represents an initial nonequilibrium mixture in the reversible reaction

$$SO_2(g) + Cl_2(g) \rightleftharpoons SO_2Cl_2(g) \quad K_c = 4.0$$

Which of the other three sketches best represents an equilibrium mixture? Explain.

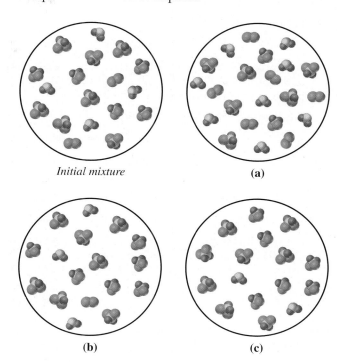

Initial mixture   **(a)**

(b)   **(c)**

42. One sketch below represents an initial nonequilibrium mixture in the reversible reaction

$$2\,NO(g) + Br_2(g) \rightleftharpoons 2\,NOBr(g) \quad K_c = 3.0$$

Which of the other three sketches best represents an equilibrium mixture? Explain.

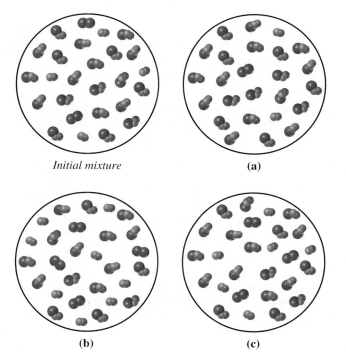

Initial mixture   **(a)**

(b)   **(c)**

Partial Pressure Equilibrium Constant, K_p

43. Refer to Example 15-4. $H_2S(g)$ at 747.6 mmHg pressure and a 1.85-g sample of $I_2(s)$ are introduced into a 725-mL flask at 60 °C. What will be the total pressure in the flask at equilibrium?

$$H_2S(g) + I_2(s) \rightleftharpoons 2\,HI(g) + S(s)$$

$$K_p = 1.34 \times 10^5 \text{ at } 60\,°C$$

44. A sample of $NH_4HS(s)$ is placed in a 2.58-L flask containing 0.100 mol $NH_3(g)$. What will be the total gas pressure when equilibrium is established at 25 °C?

$$NH_4HS(s) \rightleftharpoons NH_3(g) + H_2S(g)$$

$$K_p = 0.108 \text{ at } 25\,°C$$

45. The following reaction is used in some self-contained breathing devices as a source of $O_2(g)$.

$$4\,KO_2(s) + 2\,CO_2(g) \rightleftharpoons 2\,K_2CO_3(s) + 3\,O_2(g)$$

$$K_p = 28.5 \text{ at } 25\,°C$$

Suppose that a sample of $CO_2(g)$ is added to an evacuated flask containing $KO_2(s)$ and equilibrium is established. If the equilibrium partial pressure of $CO_2(g)$ is found to be 0.0721 atm, what are the equilibrium partial pressure of $O_2(g)$ and the total gas pressure?

46. Concerning the reaction in Exercise 45, if $KO_2(s)$ and $K_2CO_3(s)$ are maintained in contact with air at 1.00 atm and 25 °C, in which direction will a net change occur to establish equilibrium? Explain. [*Hint:* Recall equation (6.17) and the composition of air (Table 6.3.)]

47. 1.00 mol *each* of CO and Cl_2 are introduced into an evacuated 1.75-L flask, and the following equilibrium is established at 668 K.

$$CO(g) + Cl_2(g) \longrightarrow COCl_2(g) \qquad K_p = 22.5$$

For this equilibrium, calculate **(a)** the partial pressure of $COCl_2(g)$; **(b)** the total gas pressure.

48. For the reaction $2\,NO_2(g) \rightleftharpoons 2\,NO(g) + O_2(g)$, $K_c = 1.8 \times 10^{-6}$ at 184 °C. What is the value of K_p for this reaction at 184 °C?

$$NO(g) + \frac{1}{2}O_2(g) \rightleftharpoons NO_2(g)$$

Le Châtelier's Principle

49. Continuous removal of one of the products of a chemical reaction has the effect of causing the reaction to go to completion. Explain this fact in terms of Le Châtelier's principle.

50. We can represent the freezing of $H_2O(l)$ at 0 °C as H_2O $(l, d = 1.00\ \text{g/cm}^3) \rightleftharpoons H_2O(s, d = 0.92\ \text{g/cm}^3)$. Explain why increasing the pressure on ice causes it to melt. Is this the behavior you expect for solids in general? Explain.

51. Explain how each of the following affects the amount of H_2 present in an equilibrium mixture in the reaction

$$3\,Fe(s) + 4\,H_2O(g) \rightleftharpoons Fe_3O_4(s) + 4\,H_2(g)$$

$$\Delta H° = -150 \text{ kJ}$$

(a) Raising the temperature of the mixture; **(b)** introducing more $H_2O(g)$; **(c)** doubling the volume of the container holding the mixture; **(d)** adding an appropriate catalyst.

52. In the gas phase, iodine reacts with cyclopentene (C_5H_8) by a free radical mechanism to produce cyclopentadiene (C_5H_6) and hydrogen iodide. Explain how each of the following affects the amount of $HI(g)$ present in the equilibrium mixture in the reaction

$$I_2(g) + C_5H_8(g) \rightleftharpoons C_5H_6(g) + 2\,HI(g)$$

$$\Delta H° = 92.5 \text{ kJ}$$

(a) Raising the temperature of the mixture; **(b)** introducing more $C_5H_6(g)$; **(c)** doubling the volume of the container holding the mixture; **(d)** adding an appropriate catalyst; **(e)** adding an inert gas such as He to a constant-volume reaction mixture.

53. The reaction $N_2(g) + O_2(g) \rightleftharpoons 2\,NO(g)$, $\Delta H° = +181$ kJ, occurs in high-temperature combustion processes carried out in air. Oxides of nitrogen produced from the nitrogen and oxygen in air are intimately involved in the production of photochemical smog. What effect does increasing the temperature have on **(a)** the equilibrium production of $NO(g)$; **(b)** the rate of this reaction?

54. Use data from Appendix D to determine whether the forward reaction is favored by high temperatures or low temperatures.

(a) $PCl_3(g) + Cl_2(g) \rightleftharpoons PCl_5(g)$
(b) $SO_2(g) + 2\,H_2S(g) \rightleftharpoons 2\,H_2O(g) + 3\,S(s)$
(c) $2\,N_2(g) + 3\,O_2(g) + 4\,HCl(g) \rightleftharpoons$
$$4\,NOCl(g) + 2\,H_2O(g)$$

55. If the volume of an equilibrium mixture of $N_2(g)$, $H_2(g)$, and $NH_3(g)$ is reduced by doubling the pressure, will P_{N_2} have increased, decreased, or remained the same when equilibrium is reestablished? Explain.

$$N_2(g) + 3\,H_2(g) \rightleftharpoons 2\,NH_3(g)$$

56. For the reaction

$$A(s) \rightleftharpoons B(s) + 2\,C(g) + \frac{1}{2}D(g) \qquad \Delta H° = 0$$

(a) Will K_p increase, decrease, or remain constant with temperature? Explain.
(b) If a *constant-volume* mixture at equilibrium at 298 K is heated to 400 K and equilibrium reestablished, will the number of moles of $D(g)$ increase, decrease, or remain constant? Explain.

57. What effect does increasing the volume of the system have on the equilibrium condition in each of the following reactions?
    (a) $C(s) + H_2O(g) \rightleftharpoons CO(g) + H_2(g)$
    (b) $Ca(OH)_2(s) + CO_2(g) \rightleftharpoons CaCO_3(s) + H_2O(g)$
    (c) $4 NH_3(g) + 5 O_2(g) \rightleftharpoons 4 NO(g) + 6 H_2O(g)$
58. For which of the following reactions would you expect the extent of the forward reaction to increase with increasing temperatures? Explain.

(a) $NO(g) \rightleftharpoons \frac{1}{2}N_2(g) + \frac{1}{2}O_2(g)$ $\quad \Delta H° = -90.2 \text{ kJ}$

(b) $SO_3(g) \rightleftharpoons SO_2(g) + \frac{1}{2}O_2(g)$ $\quad \Delta H° = +98.9 \text{ kJ}$

(c) $N_2H_4(g) \rightleftharpoons N_2(g) + 2 H_2(g)$ $\quad \Delta H° = -95.4 \text{ kJ}$

(d) $COCl_2(g) \rightleftharpoons CO(g) + Cl_2(g)$ $\quad \Delta H° = +108.3 \text{ kJ}$

Integrative and Advanced Exercises

59. Explain why the percent of molecules that dissociate into atoms in reactions of the type $I_2(g) \rightleftharpoons 2 I(g)$ *always* increases with an increase in temperature.
60. A 1.100-L flask at 25 °C and 1.00 atm pressure contains $CO_2(g)$ in contact with 100.0 mL of a saturated aqueous solution in which $[CO_2(aq)] = 3.29 \times 10^{-2}$ M.
    (a) What is the value of K_c at 25 °C for the equilibrium $CO_2(g) \rightleftharpoons CO_2(aq)$?
    (b) If 0.01000 mol of radioactive $^{14}CO_2$ is added to the flask, how many moles of the $^{14}CO_2$ will be found in the gas phase and in the aqueous solution when equilibrium is reestablished?
    [*Hint:* The radioactive $^{14}CO_2$ distributes itself between the two phases in exactly the same manner as the nonradioactive $^{12}CO_2$.]
61. Refer to Example 15-13. Suppose that 0.100 L of the equilibrium mixture is diluted to 0.250 L with water. What will be the new concentrations when equilibrium is reestablished?
62. In the equilibrium described in Example 15-12, the percent dissociation of N_2O_4 can be expressed as

    $$\frac{3.00 \times 10^{-3} \text{ mol } N_2O_4}{0.0240 \text{ mol } N_2O_4 \text{ initially}} \times 100\% = 12.5\%$$

    What must be the total pressure of the gaseous mixture if $N_2O_4(g)$ is to be 10.0% dissociated at 298 K?

    $$N_2O_4 \rightleftharpoons 2 NO_2(g) \quad K_p = 0.113 \text{ at } 298 \text{ K}$$

63. Starting with $SO_3(g)$ at 1.00 atm, what will be the total pressure when equilibrium is reached in the following reaction at 700 K?

    $$2 SO_3(g) \rightleftharpoons 2 SO_2(g) + O_2(g) \quad K_p = 1.6 \times 10^{-5}$$

64. A sample of air with a mole ratio of N_2 to O_2 of 79:21 is heated to 2500 K. When equilibrium is established in a closed container with air initially at 1.00 atm, the mole percent of NO is found to be 1.8%. Calculate K_p for the reaction.

    $$N_2(g) + O_2(g) \rightleftharpoons 2 NO(g)$$

65. Derive, by calculation, the equilibrium amounts of SO_2, O_2, and SO_3 listed in (a) Figure 15-6(c); (b) Figure 15-7(b).
66. The decomposition of salicylic acid to phenol and carbon dioxide was carried out at 200.0 °C, a temperature at which the reactant and products are all gaseous. A 0.300-g sample of salicylic acid was introduced into a 50.0-mL reaction vessel, and equilibrium was established. The equilibrium mixture was rapidly cooled to condense salicylic acid and phenol as solids; the $CO_2(g)$ was collected over mercury and its volume was measured at 20.0 °C and 730 mmHg. In two identical experiments, the volumes of $CO_2(g)$ obtained were 48.2 and 48.5 mL, respectively. Calculate K_p for this reaction.

67. One of the key reactions in the gasification of coal is the methanation reaction, in which methane is produced from synthesis gas—a mixture of CO and H_2.

    $$CO(g) + 3 H_2(g) \rightleftharpoons CH_4(g) + H_2O(g)$$

    $$\Delta H = -230 \text{ kJ}; K_c = 190 \text{ at } 1000 \text{ K}$$

    (a) Is the equilibrium conversion of synthesis gas to methane favored at higher or lower temperatures? Higher or lower pressures?
    (b) Assume you have 4.00 mol of synthesis gas with a 3:1 mol ratio of $H_2(g)$ to $CO(g)$ in a 15.0-L flask. What will be the mole fraction of $CH_4(g)$ at equilibrium at 1000 K?
68. A sample of pure $PCl_5(g)$ is introduced into an evacuated flask and allowed to dissociate.

    $$PCl_5(g) \rightleftharpoons PCl_3(g) + Cl_2(g)$$

    If the fraction of PCl_5 molecules that dissociate is denoted by α, and if the total gas pressure is P, show that

    $$K_p = \frac{\alpha^2 P}{1 - \alpha^2}$$

69. Nitrogen dioxide obtained as a cylinder gas is always a mixture of $NO_2(g)$ and $N_2O_4(g)$. A 5.00-g sample obtained from such a cylinder is sealed in a 0.500-L flask at 298 K. What is the mole fraction of NO_2 in this mixture?

    $$N_2O_4(g) \rightleftharpoons 2 NO_2(g) \quad K_c = 4.61 \times 10^{-3}$$

70. What is the apparent molar mass of the gaseous mixture that results when $COCl_2(g)$ is allowed to dissociate at 395 °C and a total pressure of 3.00 atm?

    $$COCl_2(g) \rightleftharpoons CO(g) + Cl_2(g)$$

    $$K_p = 4.44 \times 10^{-2} \text{ at } 395 \text{ °C}$$

    Think of the apparent molar mass as the molar mass of a hypothetical single gas that is equivalent to the gaseous mixture.

71. Show that in terms of mole fractions of gases and *total* gas pressure the equilibrium constant expression for

$$N_2(g) + 3 H_2(g) \rightleftharpoons 2 NH_3(g)$$

is

$$K_p = \frac{(x_{NH_3})^2}{(x_{N_2})(x_{H_2})^2} \times \frac{1}{(P_{tot})^2}$$

72. For the synthesis of ammonia at 500 K, $N_2(g) + 3 H_2(g) \rightleftharpoons 2 NH_3(g)$, $K_p = 9.06 \times 10^{-2}$. Assume that N_2 and H_2 are mixed in the mole ratio 1:3 and that the total pressure is maintained at 1.00 atm. What is the mole percent NH_3 at equilibrium? [*Hint:* Use the equation from Exercise 71.]

73. A mixture of $H_2S(g)$ and $CH_4(g)$ in the mole ratio 2:1 was brought to equilibrium at 700 °C and a total pressure of 1 atm. On analysis, the equilibrium mixture was found to contain 9.54×10^{-3} mol H_2S. The CS_2 present at equilibrium was converted successively to H_2SO_4 and then to $BaSO_4$; 1.42×10^{-3} mol $BaSO_4$ was obtained. Use these data to determine K_p at 700 °C for the reaction

$$2 H_2S(g) + CH_4(g) \rightleftharpoons CS_2(g) + 4 H_2(g)$$

$$K_p \text{ at } 700 °C = ?$$

74. A solution is prepared having these initial concentrations: $[Fe^{3+}] = [Hg_2^{2+}] = 0.5000$ M; $[Fe^{2+}] = [Hg^{2+}] = 0.03000$ M. The following reaction occurs among the ions at 25 °C.

$$2 Fe^{3+}(aq) + Hg_2^{2+}(aq) \rightleftharpoons 2 Fe^{2+}(aq) + 2 Hg^{2+}(aq)$$

$$K_c = 9.14 \times 10^{-6}$$

What will be the ion concentrations at equilibrium?

75. Refer to the Integrative Example. A gaseous mixture is prepared containing 0.100 mol each of $CH_4(g)$, $H_2O(g)$, $CO_2(g)$, and $H_2(g)$ in a 5.00-L flask. Then the mixture is allowed to come to equilibrium at 1000 K in reaction (15.23). What will be the equilibrium amount, in moles, of each gas?

76. Concerning the reaction in Exercise 22 and the situation described in part (c) of that exercise, will the mole fraction of $C_2H_2(g)$ increase, decrease, or remain unchanged when equilibrium is reestablished? Explain.

77. The formation of nitrosyl chloride is given by the following equation: $2 NO(g) + Cl_2(g) \rightleftharpoons 2 NOCl(g)$; $K_c = 4.6 \times 10^4$ at 298 K. In a 1.50-L flask, there are 4.125 mol of NOCl and 0.1125 mol of Cl_2 present at equilibrium (298 K).
    (a) Determine the partial pressure of NO at equilibrium.
    (b) What is the total pressure of the system at equilibrium?

78. At 500 K, a 10.0-L equilibrium mixture contains 0.424 mol N_2, 1.272 mol H_2, and 1.152 mol NH_3. The mixture is quickly chilled to a temperature at which the NH_3 liquefies, and the $NH_3(l)$ is completely removed. The 10.0-L gaseous mixture is then returned to 500 K, and equilibrium is reestablished. How many moles of $NH_3(g)$ will be present in the new equilibrium mixture?

$$N_2(g) + 3 H_2(g) \rightleftharpoons 2 NH_3 \qquad K_c = 152 \text{ at } 500 \text{ K}$$

79. Recall the formation of methanol from synthesis gas, the reversible reaction with which we began our discussion of the equilibrium constant expression (page 623).

$$CO(g) + 2 H_2(g) \rightleftharpoons CH_3OH(g)$$

$$K_c = 14.5 \text{ at } 483 \text{ K}$$

A particular synthesis gas consisting of 35.0 mole percent $CO(g)$ and 65.0 mole percent $H_2(g)$ at a total pressure of 100.0 atm at 483 K is allowed to come to equilibrium. Determine the partial pressure of $CH_3OH(g)$ in the equilibrium mixture.

Feature Problems

80. A classic experiment in equilibrium studies dating from 1862 involved the reaction in solution of ethanol (C_2H_5OH) and acetic acid (CH_3COOH) to produce ethyl acetate and water.

$$C_2H_5OH + CH_3COOH \rightleftharpoons CH_3COOC_2H_5 + H_2O$$

The reaction can be followed by analyzing the equilibrium mixture for its acetic acid content.

$$2 CH_3COOH(aq) + Ba(OH)_2(aq) \rightleftharpoons$$
$$Ba(CH_3COO)_2(aq) + 2 H_2O(l)$$

In one experiment, a mixture of 1.000 mol acetic acid and 0.5000 mol ethanol is brought to equilibrium. A sample containing exactly one-hundredth of the equilibrium mixture requires 28.85 mL 0.1000 M $Ba(OH)_2$ for its titration. Calculate the equilibrium constant, K_c, for the ethanol–acetic acid reaction based on this experiment.

81. The decomposition of $HI(g)$ is represented by the equation

$$2 HI(g) \rightleftharpoons H_2(g) + I_2(g)$$

$HI(g)$ is introduced into five identical 400-cm³ glass bulbs, and the five bulbs are maintained at 623 K. Each bulb is opened after a period of time and analyzed for I_2 by titration with 0.0150 M $Na_2S_2O_3(aq)$.

$$I_2(aq) + 2 Na_2S_2O_3(aq) \longrightarrow$$
$$Na_2S_4O_6(aq) + 2 NaI(aq)$$

Data for this experiment are provided in the table below. What is the value of K_c at 623 K?

Bulb Number	Initial Mass of HI(g), g	Time Bulb Opened (h)	Volume 0.0150 M $Na_2S_2O_3$ Required for Titration (in mL)
1	0.300	2	20.96
2	0.320	4	27.90
3	0.315	12	32.31
4	0.406	20	41.50
5	0.280	40	28.68

82. In one of Fritz Haber's experiments to establish the conditions required for the ammonia synthesis reaction, pure $NH_3(g)$ was passed over an iron catalyst at 901 °C and 30.0 atm. The gas leaving the reactor was bubbled through 20.00 mL of a HCl(aq) solution. In this way, the $NH_3(g)$ present was removed by reaction with HCl. The remaining gas occupied a volume of 1.82 L at STP. The 20.00 mL of HCl(aq) through which the gas had been bubbled required 15.42 mL of 0.0523 M KOH for its titration. Another 20.00-mL sample of the same HCl(aq) through which no gas had been bubbled required 18.72 mL of 0.0523 M KOH for its titration. Use these data to obtain a value of K_p at 901 °C for the reaction $N_2(g) + 3 H_2(g) \rightleftharpoons 2 NH_3(g)$.

83. The following is an approach to establishing a relationship between the equilibrium constant and rate constants mentioned in the Are You Wondering feature on page 628.
    - Work with the detailed mechanism for the reaction.
    - Use the principle of microscopic reversibility, the idea that every step in a reaction mechanism is reversible. (In the presentation of elementary reactions in Chapter 14, we treated some reaction steps as reversible and others as going to completion. However, as noted in Table 15.3, every reaction has an equilibrium constant even though a reaction is generally considered to go to completion if its equilibrium constant is very large.)
    - Use the idea that when equilibrium is attained in an overall reaction, it is also attained in each step of its mechanism. Moreover, we can write an equilibrium constant expression for each step in the mechanism, similar to what we did with the steady-state assumption in describing reaction mechanisms.
    - Combine the K_c expressions for the elementary steps into a K_c expression for the overall reaction. The numerical value of the overall K_c can thereby be expressed as a ratio of rate constants, k.

    Use this approach to establish the equilibrium constant expression for the overall reaction,
    $$H_2(g) + I_2(g) \rightleftharpoons 2 HI(g)$$
    The mechanism of the reaction appears to be the following:

    Fast: $\qquad\qquad I_2(g) \rightleftharpoons 2 I(g)$

    Slow: $\qquad 2 I(g) + H_2(g) \rightleftharpoons 2 HI(g)$

Self-Assessment Exercises

84. In your own words, define or explain the following terms or symbols: **(a)** K_p; **(b)** Q_c; **(c)** Δn_{gas}.

85. Briefly describe each of the following ideas or phenomena: **(a)** dynamic equilibrium; **(b)** direction of a net chemical change; **(c)** Le Châtelier's principle; **(d)** effect of a catalyst on equilibrium.

86. Explain the important distinctions between each pair of terms: **(a)** reaction that goes to completion and reversible reaction; **(b)** K_c and K_p; **(c)** reaction quotient (Q) and equilibrium constant expression (K); **(d)** homogeneous and heterogeneous reaction.

87. In the reversible reaction $H_2(g) + I_2(g) \rightleftharpoons 2 HI(g)$, an initial mixture contains 2 mol H_2 and 1 mol I_2. The amount of HI expected at equilibrium is **(a)** 1 mol; **(b)** 2 mol; **(c)** less than 2 mol; **(d)** more than 2 mol but less than 4 mol.

88. Equilibrium is established in the reaction $2 SO_2(g) + O_2(g) \rightleftharpoons 2 SO_3(g)$ at a temperature where $K_c = 100$. If the number of moles of $SO_3(g)$ in the equilibrium mixture is the same as the number of moles of $SO_2(g)$, **(a)** the number of moles of $O_2(g)$ is also equal to the number of moles of $SO_2(g)$; **(b)** the number of moles of $O_2(g)$ is half the number of moles of SO_2; **(c)** $[O_2]$ may have any of several values; **(d)** $[O_2] = 0.010$ M.

89. The volume of the reaction vessel containing an equilibrium mixture in the reaction $SO_2Cl_2(g) \rightleftharpoons SO_2(g) + Cl_2(g)$ is increased. When equilibrium is reestablished, **(a)** the amount of Cl_2 will have increased; **(b)** the amount of SO_2 will have decreased; **(c)** the amounts of SO_2 and Cl_2 will have remained the same; **(d)** the amount of SO_2Cl_2 will have increased.

90. For the reaction $2 NO_2(g) \rightleftharpoons 2 NO(g) + O_2(g)$, $K_c = 1.8 \times 10^{-6}$ at 184 °C. At 184 °C, the value of K_c for the reaction $NO(g) + \frac{1}{2}O_2(g) \rightleftharpoons NO_2(g)$ is **(a)** 0.9×10^6; **(b)** 7.5×10^2; **(c)** 5.6×10^5; **(d)** 2.8×10^5.

91. For the dissociation reaction $2 H_2S(g) \rightleftharpoons 2 H_2(g) + S_2(g)$, $K_p = 1.2 \times 10^{-2}$ at 1065 °C. For this same reaction at 1000 K, **(a)** K_c is less than K_p; **(b)** K_c is greater than K_p; **(c)** $K_c = K_p$; **(d)** whether K_c is less than, equal to, or greater than K_p depends on the total gas pressure.

92. The following data are given at 1000 K: $CO(g) + H_2O(g) \rightleftharpoons CO_2(g) + H_2(g)$; $\Delta H° = -42$ kJ; $K_c = 0.66$. After an initial equilibrium is established in a 1.00-L container, the equilibrium amount of H_2 can be increased by **(a)** adding a catalyst; **(b)** increasing the temperature; **(c)** transferring the mixture to a 10.0-L container; **(d)** in some way other than (a), (b), or (c).

93. Equilibrium is established in the reversible reaction $2 A + B \rightleftharpoons 2 C$. The equilibrium concentrations are $[A] = 0.55$ M, $[B] = 0.33$ M, $[C] = 0.43$ M. What is the value of K_c for this reaction?

94. The Deacon process for producing chlorine gas from hydrogen chloride is used in situations where HCl is available as a by-product from other chemical processes.
    $$4 HCl(g) + O_2(g) \rightleftharpoons 2 H_2O(g) + 2 Cl_2(g)$$
    $$\Delta H° = -114 \text{ kJ}$$

    A mixture of HCl, O_2, H_2O, and Cl_2 is brought to equilibrium at 400 °C. What is the effect on the equilibrium amount of $Cl_2(g)$ if
    (a) additional $O_2(g)$ is added to the mixture at constant volume;
    (b) HCl(g) is removed from the mixture at constant volume;
    (c) the mixture is transferred to a vessel of twice the volume;
    (d) a catalyst is added to the reaction mixture;
    (e) the temperature is raised to 500 °C?

95. An equilibrium mixture of SO_2, SO_3, and O_2 gases is maintained in a 2.05-L flask at a temperature at which $K_c = 35.5$ for the reaction

$$2\,SO_2(g) + O_2(g) \rightleftharpoons 2\,SO_3(g)$$

    (a) If the numbers of moles of SO_2 and SO_3 in the flask are equal, how many moles of O_2 are present?

    (b) If the number of moles of SO_3 in the flask is twice the number of moles of SO_2, how many moles of O_2 are present?

96. Using the method in Appendix E, construct a concept map of Section 15-6, illustrating the shift in equilibrium due to the various stresses.

---

eMedia Exercises

97. After viewing the **Dynamic Equilibrium** animation of equilibrium through a physical change (*Activebook 15-1*), describe the influence of temperature on rates of change.

98. After viewing the **Chemical Equilibrium** activity (*Activebook 15-2*), estimate the value of the equilibrium constant of the reaction depicted. What information did you use to make this estimate?

99. (a) Describe how the stoichiometry of the reaction in the **Chemical Equilibrium** activity (*Activebook 15-2*) influences the values of concentrations at equilibrium. (b) If the initial concentrations of both reactants are doubled in this exercise, does this change the value of the equilibrium constant? (c) Does this change, if any, affect the concentration of the product at equilibrium?

100. Using equal initial concentrations of reactant and product in the **Equilibrium Constant** activity (*Activebook 15-4*), describe how the value of the equilibrium constant is related to the concentration of the product once equilibrium has been reached.

101. (a) What would be the change in the results seen in the **NO_2–N_2O_4 Equilibrium** animation (*Activebook 15-6*) if the pressure were *decreased* by a factor of two instead of increased? (b) Given that this forward reaction is exothermic, what would be the effect on the ratio of the NO_2 and N_2O_4 concentrations by increasing the temperature of the system?

16

ACIDS AND BASES

CONTENTS

Use litmus paper to test various home products, like lemon juice, vinegar, cleaning fluids, mouthwash, etc. Supply litmus paper to students and ask them to make a list of common household fluids and categorize them as acid, base, or neutral.

Citrus fruit derives its acidic qualities from citric acid, $H_3C_6H_5O_7$, a type of acid (polyprotic) discussed in Section 16-6. Another important constituent of citrus fruit is ascorbic acid, or vitamin C (page 563), a dietary requirement to prevent scurvy. (FoodPix/Getty Images, Inc.–FoodPix)

The general public is familiar with the concepts of acids and bases. The environmental problem of acid rain is a popular topic in newspapers and magazines, and television commercials mention pH in relation to such products as deodorants, shampoos, and antacids.

Chemists have been classifying substances as acids and bases for a long time. Antoine Lavoisier thought that the common element in all acids was oxygen, a fact conveyed by its name. (Oxygen means "acid former" in Greek). In 1810, Humphry Davy showed that hydrogen instead is the element that acids have in common. In 1884, Svante Arrhenius developed the theory of acids and bases that we introduced in Chapter 5. There we emphasized the stoichiometry of acid–base reactions.

Some of the topics we will study in this chapter are modern acid–base theories, factors affecting the strengths of acids and bases, the pH scale, and the calculation of ion concentrations in solutions of weak acids and bases. At the end of the chapter, we bring some of these ideas together in a discussion of acid rain.

663

Descriptions of acids and bases become more general, less restrictive, as one moves from the Arrhenius theory, to the Brønsted–Lowry theory, to the Lewis theory.

Introduction to Aqueous Acids and Introduction to Aqueous Bases animations

▲ A holdover of the Arrhenius theory. Although there is no compelling evidence that NH_4OH molecules exist in $NH_3(aq)$, solutions are commonly labeled as if they do.

16-1   ARRHENIUS THEORY: A BRIEF REVIEW

Some aspects of the behavior of acids and bases can be explained adequately with the theory developed by Arrhenius as part of his studies of electrolytic dissociation (Section 13-9). Arrhenius proposed that in aqueous solutions, strong electrolytes exist only in the form of ions, whereas weak electrolytes exist partly as ions and partly as molecules. When the acid HCl dissolves in water, the HCl molecules ionize completely, yielding hydrogen ions, H^+, as one of the products.

$$HCl(g) \xrightarrow{H_2O} H^+(aq) + Cl^-(aq)$$

When the base NaOH dissolves in water, the Na^+ and OH^- ions in the solid become dissociated from one another through the action of H_2O molecules (see Figure 13-6).

$$NaOH(s) \longrightarrow Na^+(aq) + OH^-(aq)$$

The neutralization reaction of HCl and NaOH can be represented with the ionic equation

$$\underset{\text{an acid}}{H^+(aq) + Cl^-(aq)} + \underset{\text{a base}}{Na^+(aq) + OH^-(aq)} \longrightarrow \underset{\text{a salt}}{Na^+(aq) + Cl^-(aq)} + \underset{\text{water}}{H_2O(l)}$$

or, perhaps better still, with the net ionic equation

$$\underset{\text{an acid}}{H^+(aq)} + \underset{\text{a base}}{OH^-(aq)} \longrightarrow \underset{\text{water}}{H_2O(l)} \tag{16.1}$$

Equation (16.1) illustrates an essential idea of the Arrhenius theory: *A neutralization reaction involves the combination of hydrogen ions and hydroxide ions to form water.*

Despite its early successes and continued usefulness, the Arrhenius theory does have limitations. One of the most glaring is in its treatment of the weak base ammonia, NH_3. The Arrhenius theory suggests that all bases contain OH^-. Where is the OH^- in NH_3? To get around this difficulty, chemists began to think of aqueous solutions of NH_3 as containing the compound ammonium hydroxide, NH_4OH, which as a weak base is partially ionized into NH_4^+ and OH^- ions:

$$NH_3(g) + H_2O(l) \longrightarrow NH_4OH(aq)$$
$$NH_4OH(aq) \rightleftharpoons NH_4^+(aq) + OH^-(aq)$$

The problem with this formulation is that there is no compelling evidence that NH_4OH exists in aqueous solutions. We should always question a hypothesis or theory that postulates the existence of hypothetical substances. As we shall see in Section 16-2, the essential failure of the Arrhenius theory is in not recognizing the key role of the *solvent* in the ionization of a solute.

KEEP IN MIND ▶

that a "proton donor" is a donor of H^+ ions. That is, a hydrogen atom consists of one proton and one electron, and the hydrogen ion, H^+, is simply a proton.

16-2   BRØNSTED–LOWRY THEORY OF ACIDS AND BASES

In 1923, J. N. Brønsted in Denmark and T. M. Lowry in Great Britain independently proposed a new acid–base theory. According to their theory, an acid is a **proton donor** and a base is a **proton acceptor**. To describe the behavior of ammonia as a base, which we found difficult to do with the Arrhenius theory, we can write

$$\underset{\text{base}}{NH_3} + \underset{\text{acid}}{H_2O} \longrightarrow NH_4^+ + OH^- \tag{16.2}$$

In reaction (16.2), H_2O acts as an *acid*. It gives up a proton, H^+, which is taken up by NH_3, a *base*. As a result of this transfer, the polyatomic ions NH_4^+ and OH^- are formed—the same ions produced by the ionization of the hypothetical NH_4OH of the Arrhenius theory. Because NH_3 is a weak base, we need also to consider the reverse of reaction (16.2). In the reverse reaction, NH_4^+ is an acid and OH^- is a base.

$$NH_4^+ + OH^- \longrightarrow NH_3 + H_2O \qquad (16.3)$$
$$\text{acid} \qquad \text{base}$$

The conventional way to represent a reversible reaction is to use the double arrow notation. In identifying the species in this reversible ionization reaction, we have used the number "1" for the related pair NH_3 and NH_4^+ and the number "2" for the related pair H_2O and OH^-.

$$NH_3 + H_2O \rightleftharpoons NH_4^+ + OH^- \qquad (16.4)$$
$$\text{base(1)} \quad \text{acid(2)} \qquad \text{acid(1)} \quad \text{base(2)}$$

An acid and a base that are related to each other as the pair NH_3/NH_4^+ or the pair H_2O/OH^- in reaction (16.4) are referred to as a *conjugate pair*. Thus, when considering an NH_3 molecule as a base, an NH_4^+ ion is the **conjugate acid** of NH_3. Similarly, in reaction (16.4) H_2O is an acid and OH^- is its **conjugate base**. Figure 16-1 illustrates the proton transfer involved in the forward and reverse reactions of (16.4).

On the basis of what we learned in Chapter 15, we might write as the equilibrium constant expression for reaction (16.4)

$$K_c = \frac{[NH_4^+][OH^-]}{[NH_3][H_2O]}$$

In aqueous ammonia, however, H_2O molecules are present in such overwhelming numbers compared with NH_3 molecules and the ions NH_4^+ and OH^-, that water, the solvent, is essentially a pure liquid with an activity of one (recall page 633). For this reason, the equilibrium constant expression we want does not include the term $[H_2O]$.

$$K_b = \frac{[NH_4^+][OH^-]}{[NH_3]} = 1.8 \times 10^{-5}$$

The equilibrium constant K_b is called the **base ionization constant**.

The ionization of acetic acid can be expressed as

$$HC_2H_3O_2 + H_2O \rightleftharpoons C_2H_3O_2^- + H_3O^+$$
$$\text{acid(1)} \quad \text{base(2)} \qquad \text{base(1)} \quad \text{acid(2)}$$

Brønsted–Lowry theory is not restricted to the dissociation of acids and bases in water, but is valid for any solvent.

Conjugate Acids and Bases activity

◀ **KEEP IN MIND**
that in designating conjugate pairs, it does not matter which conjugate pair we call (1) and which we call (2). Nor does it matter in what order the acid and base are written on each side of the equation.

This article discusses the use of a conjugate acid–base chart to teach about conjugate acid–base pairs and the relative strengths of acids and bases: Treptow, R. S. *J. Chem. Educ.* **1986**: 63, 938.

◀ The conventional use of curved arrows is to highlight the role of electrons in reaction mechanisms, as will be seen in Sections 16-9 and 26-11. The arrows used here in portraying Brønsted-Lowry acid-base reactions are unrelated to reaction mechanisms; they simply suggest the destinations of donated protons.

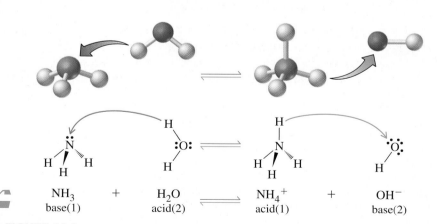

▲ **FIGURE 16-1**
Brønsted–Lowry acid–base reaction: weak base
The arrows represent the proton transfer in reaction (16.4). The red arrows represent the forward reaction; the blue arrows, the reverse reaction. Because NH_4^+ is a stronger acid than H_2O and OH^- is a stronger base than NH_3, the reverse reaction proceeds to a greater extent than does the forward reaction. Hence, NH_3 is only slightly ionized.

▼ The Lewis structure of the hydronium ion is

$$\begin{bmatrix} H-\ddot{O}-H \\ | \\ H \end{bmatrix}^{+}$$

▲ **FIGURE 16-2**
A hydrated hydronium ion
This species, $H_{11}O_5^{+}$, consists of a central H_3O^{+} ion hydrogen-bonded to four H_2O molecules.

▶ The term *amphiprotic* is similar to the term *amphoteric*, which indicates the ability of a substance to behave as both an acid and a base. Amphiprotic conveys the notion of proton transfer embodied in the Brønsted–Lowry theory of acids and bases.

Here, acetate ion, $C_2H_3O_2^{-}$, is the conjugate base of the acid $HC_2H_3O_2$. This time, H_2O acts as a base. Its conjugate acid is the **hydronium ion, H_3O^{+}**. We first discussed the formation of the hydronium ion in Chapter 5 (page 145). Because the simple H^{+} ion is tiny, the positive charge of this ion is concentrated in a very small region; the ion has a high positive charge density. We should expect H^{+} ions (protons) to seek out centers of negative charge with which to bond. When a H^{+} ion attaches to a lone pair of electrons in an O atom in H_2O, the resulting hydronium ion forms hydrogen bonds with several water molecules (Fig. 16-2). Figure 16-3 illustrates the proton transfer involved in the forward and reverse reactions of the ionization of acetic acid.

Using the same approach as for $NH_3(aq)$, the ionization of acetic acid can be described in the following way.

$$K_a = \frac{[C_2H_3O_2^{-}][H_3O^{+}]}{[HC_2H_3O_2]} = 1.8 \times 10^{-5}$$

The equilibrium constant K_a is called the **acid ionization constant**. (The fact that K_a of acetic acid and K_b of ammonia have the same value is just a coincidence.)

We can represent the ionization of HCl in the same way that we did for acetic acid. In this case, however, because K_a is so large (about 10^6), we can treat the ionization of HCl as a reaction that goes to completion. We denote this by writing the ionization equation with a single arrow.

$$HCl + H_2O \longrightarrow Cl^{-} + H_3O^{+} \tag{16.5}$$

Figure 16-4 illustrates the proton transfer involved in the complete ionization of hydrochloric acid.

In Example 16-1, we identify acids and bases in some typical acid–base reactions. In working through this example, notice the following additional features: (1) Any species that is an acid according to the Arrhenius theory is also an acid according to the Brønsted–Lowry theory; the same is true of bases. (2) Certain species, even though they do not contain the OH group, produce OH^{-} in aqueous solution—for example, OCl^{-}. As such, they are Brønsted–Lowry bases. (3) The Brønsted–Lowry theory accounts for substances that can act either as an acid or a base; such substances are said to be **amphiprotic**. The Arrhenius theory does not account for the behavior of amphiprotic substances.

| $HC_2H_3O_2$ | + | H_2O | ⇌ | $C_2H_3O_2^{-}$ | + | H_3O^{+} |
| acid(1) | | base(2) | | base(1) | | acid(2) |

▲ **FIGURE 16-3**
Brønsted–Lowry acid–base reaction: weak acid
The arrows represent the proton transfer in the ionization of acetic acid. The red arrows represent the forward reaction; the blue arrows, the reverse reaction. Because H_3O^{+} is a stronger acid than $HC_2H_3O_2$ and $C_2H_3CO^{-}$ is a stronger base than H_2O, the reverse reaction proceeds to a greater extent than does the forward reaction. Hence, $HC_2H_3O_2$ is only slightly ionized.

$$\text{H}_2\text{O} \quad + \quad \text{HCl} \quad \longrightarrow \quad \text{H}_3\text{O}^+ \quad + \quad \text{Cl}^-$$

base(1)   acid(2)   acid(1)   base(2)

▲ **FIGURE 16-4**
Brønsted–Lowry acid–base reaction: strong acid
The red arrows represent the proton transfer in the ionization of hydrochloric acid. Because H_3O^+ is a weaker acid than HCl and Cl^- is a much weaker base than H_2O, the forward reaction proceeds almost to completion. Hence, HCl is essentially completely ionized.

EXAMPLE 16-1

Identifying Brønsted–Lowry Acids and Bases and Their Conjugates. For each of the following, identify the acids and bases in both the forward and reverse reactions in the manner shown in equation (16.4).

(a) $HClO_2 + H_2O \rightleftharpoons ClO_2^- + H_3O^+$

(b) $OCl^- + H_2O \rightleftharpoons HOCl + OH^-$

(c) $NH_3 + H_2PO_4^- \rightleftharpoons NH_4^+ + HPO_4^{2-}$

(d) $HCl + H_2PO_4^- \rightleftharpoons Cl^- + H_3PO_4$

Solution

Consider $HClO_2$ in reaction (a). It gives up a proton, H^+, to become ClO_2^-. Therefore, $HClO_2$ is an acid, and ClO_2^- is its conjugate base. Now consider H_2O. It takes the proton from $HClO_2$ and becomes H_3O^+. Thus, H_2O is a base, and H_3O^+ is its conjugate acid. In reaction (b), OCl^- is a base and gains a proton from water. OH^- produced in this reaction is the conjugate base of H_2O. Taken together, reactions (a) and (b) show that H_2O is amphiprotic. Reactions (c) and (d) illustrate the same for $H_2PO_4^-$.

(a) $HClO_2 + H_2O \rightleftharpoons ClO_2^- + H_3O^+$
     acid(1)   base(2)   base(1)   acid(2)

(b) $OCl^- + H_2O \rightleftharpoons HOCl + OH^-$
     base(1)   acid(2)   acid(1)   base(2)

(c) $NH_3 + H_2PO_4^- \rightleftharpoons NH_4^+ + HPO_4^{2-}$
     base(1)   acid(2)   acid(1)   base(2)

(d) $HCl + H_2PO_4^- \rightleftharpoons Cl^- + H_3PO_4$
     acid(1)   base(2)   base(1)   acid(2)

Practice Example A: For each of the following reactions, identify the acids and bases in both the forward and reverse directions.

(a) $HF + H_2O \rightleftharpoons F^- + H_3O^+$

(b) $HSO_4^- + NH_3 \rightleftharpoons SO_4^{2-} + NH_4^+$

(c) $C_2H_3O_2^- + HCl \rightleftharpoons HC_2H_3O_2 + Cl^-$

Practice Example B: Of the following species, one is acidic, one is basic, and one is amphiprotic in their reactions with water: HNO_2, PO_4^{3-}, HCO_3^-. Write the *four* equations needed to represent these facts.

CONCEPT ASSESSMENT ✓

Is it appropriate to describe each of the following as a conjugate acid/base pair? Explain. **(a)** HCO_3^-/CO_3^{2-}; **(b)** HSO_3^-/SO_4^{2-}; **(c)** $H_2CO_3/H_2C_2O_4$.

Junquera, E., Aicart E., "An Easy and Fast Experiment for the Determination of the Equilibrium Constants of an Acid-Base Pair, Free and Complexed with a Molecular Receptor." *J. Chem. Educ.* **2000**: *77*, 1215 (September 2000).

The ionization of HCl in aqueous solution (reaction 16.5) goes to completion because HCl is a strong acid; it readily gives up protons to H_2O. At the same time, Cl^- ion, the conjugate base of HCl, has very little tendency to take a proton from H_3O^+; Cl^- is a very weak base. This observation suggests the generalization that follows.

> In an acid–base reaction, the favored direction of the reaction is from the stronger to the weaker member of a conjugate acid–base pair.

Here the Arrhenius and Brønsted–Lowry theories should be compared and contrasted.

With this generalization, we can predict that the neutralization of HCl by OH^- should go to completion.

$$HCl + OH^- \longrightarrow Cl^- + H_2O$$
$$\text{acid(1)} \quad \text{base(2)} \qquad \text{base(1)} \quad \text{acid(2)}$$
$$\text{strong} \quad \text{strong} \qquad \text{weak} \quad \text{weak}$$

And we would predict that the following reaction should occur almost exclusively in the *reverse* direction.

$$H_2O + I^- \longleftarrow OH^- + HI$$
$$\text{acid(1)} \quad \text{base(2)} \qquad \text{base(1)} \quad \text{acid(2)}$$
$$\text{weak} \quad \text{weak} \qquad \text{strong} \quad \text{strong}$$

▶ The acid–base strengths listed in Table 16.1 are the result of experiments carried out by many chemists.

To be able to apply the generalization more broadly, though, we need a tabulation of acid and base strengths, such as that in Table 16.1. The strongest acids are at the top of the column on the left, and the strongest bases are at the bottom of the column on the right. It is important to note that *the stronger an acid, the weaker its conjugate base.*

TABLE 16.1   Relative Strengths of Some Common Brønsted–Lowry Acids and Bases

	Acid		Conjugate Base	
↑ Increasing acid strength	Perchloric acid	$HClO_4$	Perchlorate ion	ClO_4^-	↓ Increasing base strength
	Hydroiodic acid	HI	Iodide ion	I^-	
	Hydrobromic acid	HBr	Bromide ion	Br^-	
	Hydrochloric acid	HCl	Chloride ion	Cl^-	
	Sulfuric acid	H_2SO_4	Hydrogen sulfate ion	HSO_4^-	
	Nitric acid	HNO_3	Nitrate ion	NO_3^-	
	Hydronium ion[a]	H_3O^+	Water[a]	H_2O	
	Hydrogen sulfate ion	HSO_4^-	Sulfate ion	SO_4^{2-}	
	Nitrous acid	HNO_2	Nitrite ion	NO_2^-	
	Acetic acid	$HC_2H_3O_2$	Acetate ion	$C_2H_3O_2^-$	
	Carbonic acid	H_2CO_3	Hydrogen carbonate ion	HCO_3^-	
	Ammonium ion	NH_4^+	Ammonia	NH_3	
	Hydrogen carbonate ion	HCO_3^-	Carbonate ion	CO_3^{2-}	
	Water	H_2O	Hydroxide ion	OH^-	
	Methanol	CH_3OH	Methoxide ion	CH_3O^-	
	Ammonia	NH_3	Amide ion	NH_2^-	

[a]The hydronium ion–water combination refers to the ease with which a proton is passed from one water molecule to another; that is, $H_3O^+ + H_2O \rightleftharpoons H_2O + H_3O^+$

Both HCl and $HClO_4$ are strong acids because H_2O is a sufficiently strong base to take protons from either acid in a reaction that goes to completion. Because both HCl and $HClO_4$ react to completion with water, yielding H_3O^+ (the strongest acid possible in water), the solvent water is said to have a *leveling effect* on these two acids. That is, we cannot say which is the stronger acid of the two in water. How can we say, then, as we indicate in Table 16.1, that $HClO_4$ is a stronger acid than HCl?

To determine whether $HClO_4$ or HCl is the stronger acid, we need to use a solvent that is a weaker base than water—a solvent that will take protons from the stronger of the two acids more readily than from the weaker one. In the solvent $(C_2H_5)_2O$, diethyl ether, $HClO_4$ is completely ionized, but HCl is only partially ionized. Thus, $HClO_4$ is a stronger acid than is HCl.

$$HClO_4 + C_2H_5{-}\overset{\displaystyle ..}{\underset{\displaystyle ..}{O}}{-}C_2H_5 \longrightarrow ClO_4^- + [C_2H_5{-}\overset{\displaystyle H}{\underset{\displaystyle ..}{O}}{-}C_2H_5]^+$$

$$HCl + C_2H_5{-}\overset{\displaystyle ..}{\underset{\displaystyle ..}{O}}{-}C_2H_5 \rightleftharpoons Cl^- + [C_2H_5{-}\overset{\displaystyle H}{\underset{\displaystyle ..}{O}}{-}C_2H_5]^+$$

Continually stress that stronger acids have weaker conjugate bases, and that weaker acids have stronger conjugate bases.

16-3   SELF-IONIZATION OF WATER AND THE pH SCALE

Even when it is pure, water contains a very low concentration of ions that can be detected in precise electrical conductivity measurements. The ions form as a result of the amphiprotic nature of water; some water molecules donate protons and others accept protons. In the **self-ionization** (or *autoionization*) of water, for each H_2O molecule that acts as an acid, another H_2O molecule acts as a base, and hydronium (H_3O^+) and hydroxide (OH^-) ions are formed. The reaction is reversible, and in the reverse reaction, H_3O^+ releases a proton to OH^-. The reverse reaction is far more significant than the forward reaction. *Equilibrium is displaced far to the left.* In reaction (16.6), acid(1) and base(2) are *much* stronger than are acid(2) and base(1).

Self-Ionization of Water animation

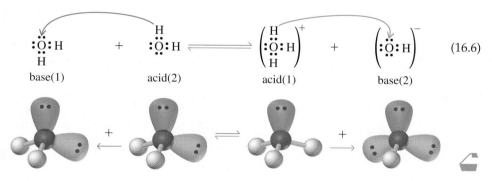

$$\begin{array}{ccccccc} \underset{\text{base(1)}}{:\!\overset{\displaystyle H}{\underset{\displaystyle H}{O}}\!:\!H} & + & \underset{\text{acid(2)}}{:\!\overset{\displaystyle H}{O}\!:\!H} & \rightleftharpoons & \underset{\text{acid(1)}}{\left(:\!\overset{\displaystyle H}{\underset{\displaystyle H}{O}}\!:\!H\right)^+} & + & \underset{\text{base(2)}}{\left(:\!\overset{\displaystyle ..}{O}\!:\!H\right)^-} \end{array} \quad (16.6)$$

Again, we follow the approach we used in writing equilibrium constants for the ionization of NH_3 and $HC_2H_3O_2$, namely we assume an activity of one for H_2O molecules and replace activities of other species by their molarities. For the self-ionization of water

$$H_2O + H_2O \rightleftharpoons H_3O^+ + OH^-$$

we can write

$$K = [H_3O^+][OH^-]$$

Equation (16.6) indicates that $[H_3O^+]$ and $[OH^-]$ are equal in pure water. There are several experimental methods of determining these concentrations. All lead to this result.

A common error is that K_w is the equilibrium constant for water. Strictly speaking, it is the ionic product. The equilibrium constant $K_c = [H_3O^+][OH^-]/[H_2O]$ which at 25 °C has the value of $10^{-14}/55.55 = 1.8 \times 10^{-16}$. In Chapter 19, we see that
$$K = (a_{H_3O^+})(a_{OH^-})/(a_{H_2O})^2$$
$$= 1.0 \times 10^{-14}$$

At 25 °C in pure water: $[H_3O^+] = [OH^-] = 1.0 \times 10^{-7}$ M van Lubeck, Henk. "Why Not Replace pH and pOH by Just One Real Acidity Grade, AG?" *J. Chem. Educ.* **1999:** *76,* 892 (July 1999).

Acids and Bases activity

KEEP IN MIND ▶

that this definition of pH is one of the few scientific expressions that uses logarithms to the base 10 (log) rather than natural logarithms (ln).

▶ The determination of logarithms and inverse logarithms (antilogarithms) is discussed in Appendix A. Significant figure rules for logarithms are also presented there.

K_w activity

A common mistake is to think that the value of K_w (1.0×10^{14}) is only valid for neutral solutions.

The equilibrium condition for the self-ionization of water is called the **ion product of water**. It is symbolized as K_w. At 25 °C,

$$K_w = [H_3O^+][OH^-] = 1.0 \times 10^{-14} \tag{16.7}$$

Since K_w is an equilibrium constant, the product of the concentrations of the hydronium and hydroxide ions must always equal 10^{-14}. If the concentration of H_3O^+ is increased by the addition of an acid, then the concentration of OH^- must decrease to maintain the value of K_w. If the concentration of OH^- is increased by the addition of a base, then the concentration of H_3O^+ must decrease. Equation (16.7) connects the concentrations of H_3O^+ and OH^- and applies to *all* aqueous solutions, not just to pure water, as we shall see shortly.

pH AND pOH

Because their product in an aqueous solution is only 1.0×10^{-14}, we expect $[H_3O^+]$ and $[OH^-]$ also to be small. Typically, they are less than 1 M—often very much less. Exponential notation is useful in these situations; for example, $[H_3O^+] = 2.2 \times 10^{-13}$ M. But we now want to consider an even more convenient way to describe hydronium and hydroxide ion concentrations.

In 1909, the Danish biochemist Søren Sørensen proposed the term **pH** to refer to the "potential of hydrogen ion." He defined pH as the *negative of the logarithm of* [H⁺]. Restated in terms of $[H_3O^+]$,*

$$pH = -\log[H_3O^+] \tag{16.8}$$

Thus, in a solution that is 0.0025 M HCl,

$$[H_3O^+] = 2.5 \times 10^{-3} \text{ M} \quad \text{and} \quad pH = -\log(2.5 \times 10^{-3}) = 2.60$$

To determine the $[H_3O^+]$ that corresponds to a particular pH value, we do an inverse calculation. In a solution with pH = 4.50,

$$\log[H_3O^+] = -4.50 \quad \text{and} \quad [H_3O^+] = 10^{-4.50} = 3.2 \times 10^{-5} \text{ M}$$

The quantity **pOH** can be defined as:

$$pOH = -\log[OH^-] \tag{16.9}$$

Still another useful expression can be derived by taking the *negative logarithm* of the K_w expression (written for 25 °C) and introducing the symbol pK_w.

$$K_w = [H_3O^+][OH^-] = 1.0 \times 10^{-14}$$
$$-\log K_w = -(\log[H_3O^+][OH^-]) = -\log(1.0 \times 10^{-14})$$
$$pK_w = -(\log[H_3O^+] + \log[OH^-]) = -(-14.00)$$
$$= -\log[H_3O^+] - \log[OH^-] = 14.00$$

$$pK_w = pH + pOH = 14.00 \tag{16.10}$$

An aqueous solution with $[H_3O^+] = [OH^-]$ is said to be *neutral*. In pure water at 25 °C, $[H_3O^+] = [OH^-] = 1.0 \times 10^{-7}$ M and pH = 7.00. Thus at 25 °C, all aqueous solutions with pH = 7.00 are neutral. If the pH is less than 7.00, the solution is *acidic*; if the pH is greater than 7.00, the solution is *basic*, or alkaline. Equation 16.10 is a restatement of the interrelationship between $[H_3O^+]$, $[OH^-]$, and K_w in terms of pH, pOH, and pK_w. If we know the value of either $[H_3O^+]$ or $[OH^-]$, we can calculate the value of the other (Fig. 16-5).

---

*Strictly speaking, we should use the *activity* of H_3O^+, $a_{H_3O^+}$, a dimensionless quantity. But we will not use activities here, just as we did not use them in Chapter 15. We will substitute the numerical value of the molarity of H_3O^+ for its activity and recognize that some pH calculations may be only approximations.

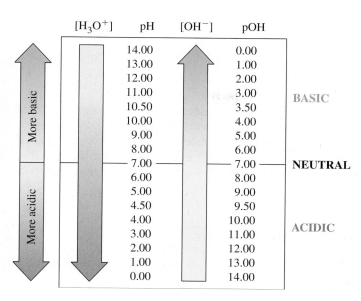

Set up a pH meter and show the effect of slowly adding HCl to water, and then slowly adding NaOH to water.

◀ **FIGURE 16-5**
Relating [H₃O⁺], pH, [OH⁻], and pOH
In aqueous solutions, the sum of the pH and pOH values always gives $pK_w = 14$ because of the self-ionization equilibrium of water.

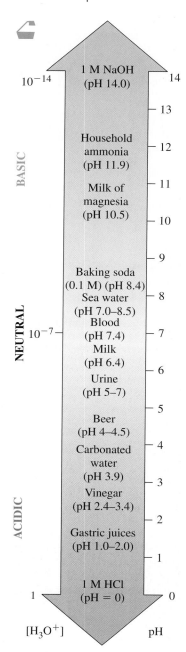

▲ **FIGURE 16-6**
The pH scale and pH values of some common materials
The scale shown here ranges from pH 0 to pH 14. Slightly negative pH values, perhaps to about −1 (corresponding to $[H_3O^+] \approx 10$ M), are possible. Also possible are pH values up to about 15 (corresponding to $[OH^-] \approx 10$ M). For practical purposes, however, the pH scale is useful only in the range $2 < pH < 12$, because the molarities of H_3O^+ and OH^- in concentrated acids and bases may differ significantly from their true activities.

CONCEPT ASSESSMENT ✔

Figure 16-5 indicates that pH and pOH *decrease* as [H⁺] and [OH⁻] increase. If pH and pOH were defined as pH = log[H₃O⁺] and pOH = log[OH⁻], pH and pOH would *increase* as [H⁺] and [OH⁻] increase. Why do you suppose that this alternate definition was not adopted? Logarithmic functions appear frequently in chemistry (for example, in chemical kinetics and thermodynamics), but these are based on natural logarithms, ln. Why do you suppose that the definitions pH = −ln[H₃O⁺] and pOH = −ln[OH⁻] were not adopted?

The pH values of a number of materials are depicted in Figure 16-6. These values and the many examples in this chapter and the next should familiarize you with the pH concept. Later, we will consider two methods for measuring pH: by means of acid–base indicators (Section 17-3) and electrical measurements (Section 20-4).

EXAMPLE 16-2

Relating [H₃O⁺], [OH⁻], pH, and pOH. In a laboratory experiment, students measured the pH of samples of rainwater and household ammonia. Determine **(a)** [H₃O⁺] in the rainwater, with pH measured at 4.35; **(b)** [OH⁻] in the ammonia, with pH measured at 11.28.

Solution

(a) By definition, pH = −log[H₃O⁺], or

$$\log[H_3O^+] = -pH = -4.35$$
$$[H_3O^+] = 10^{-4.35} = 4.5 \times 10^{-5} \text{ M}$$

(b) First, determine pOH with equation (16.10).

$$pOH = 14.00 - pH = 14.00 - 11.28 = 2.72$$

Now, use the definition pOH = −log[OH⁻].

$$\log[OH^-] = -pOH = -2.72$$
$$[OH^-] = 10^{-2.72} = 1.9 \times 10^{-3} \text{ M}$$

Practice Example A: Students found that a yogurt sample had a pH of 2.85. What are the [H⁺] and [OH⁻] of the yogurt?

Practice Example B: The pH of a solution of HCl in water is found to be 2.50. What volume of water would you add to 1.00 L of this solution to raise the pH to 3.10?

Most students consider strong acids to be more dangerous than strong bases, but strong bases can cause serious burns and should be treated with as much care as acids.

Here one should point out that the dilution of strong acids and bases is usually exothermic. One should never add water to concentrated strong acids and bases (particularly sulfuric acid) as the heat of dilution will boil the water and spatter concentrated acid.

Aqueous Acids and Bases animation

Students have a difficult time recognizing strong and weak acids and bases. Tell students that essentially all acids and bases not listed in Table 16.2 are weak.

16-4 STRONG ACIDS AND STRONG BASES

As equation (16.5) indicated, the ionization of HCl in dilute aqueous solutions

$$HCl + H_2O \longrightarrow Cl^- + H_3O^+$$

goes essentially to completion.* In contrast, equation (16.6) suggested that the self-ionization of water occurs only to a very slight extent. As a result, we conclude that in calculating $[H_3O^+]$ in an aqueous solution of a strong acid, the strong acid is the only significant source of H_3O^+. The contribution due to the self-ionization of water can generally be ignored *unless the solution is extremely dilute*.

EXAMPLE 16-3

Calculating Ion Concentrations in an Aqueous Solution of a Strong Acid. Calculate $[H_3O^+]$, $[Cl^-]$, and $[OH^-]$ in 0.015 M HCl(aq).

Solution
We can assume that HCl is completely ionized and is the sole source of H_3O^+ in solution. Therefore,

$$[H_3O^+] = 0.015 \text{ M}$$

Furthermore, because one Cl^- ion is produced for every H_3O^+ ion,

$$[Cl^-] = [H_3O^+] = 0.015 \text{ M}$$

To calculate $[OH^-]$, we must use the following facts.

1. All the OH^- is derived from the self-ionization of water, per reaction (16.6).
2. $[OH^-]$ and $[H_3O^+]$ must have values consistent with K_w for water.

$$K_w = [H_3O^+][OH^-] = 1.0 \times 10^{-14}$$

$$(0.015)[OH^-] = 1.0 \times 10^{-14}$$

$$[OH^-] = \frac{1.0 \times 10^{-14}}{1.5 \times 10^{-2}} = 0.67 \times 10^{-12} = 6.7 \times 10^{-13} \text{ M}$$

Practice Example A: A 0.0025 M solution of HI(aq) has $[H_3O^+]$ = 0.0025 M. Calculate the $[I^-]$, $[OH^-]$, and pH of the solution.

Practice Example B: If 535 mL of *gaseous* HCl, at 26.5 °C and 747 mmHg, is dissolved in enough water to prepare 625 mL of solution, what is the pH of this solution?

TABLE 16.2
The Common Strong Acids and Strong Bases

Acids	Bases
HCl	LiOH
HBr	NaOH
HI	KOH
$HClO_4$	RbOH
HNO_3	CsOH
H_2SO_4[a]	$Mg(OH)_2$
	$Ca(OH)_2$
	$Sr(OH)_2$
	$Ba(OH)_2$

[a]H_2SO_4 ionizes in two distinct steps. It is a strong acid only in its first ionization (see page 684).

The common strong bases are ionic hydroxides. When these bases dissolve in water, H_2O molecules completely dissociate the cations and anions (OH^-) of the base from each other. The self-ionization of water, because it occurs to so very limited an extent, is an inconsequential source of OH^-. This means that in calculating $[OH^-]$ in an aqueous solution of a strong base, the strong base is the only significant source of OH^- *unless the solution is extremely dilute*.

As noted in Chapter 5, the number of common strong acids and strong bases is quite small. Try to memorize the listing in Table 16.2.

*In very concentrated aqueous solutions, HCl does not exist exclusively as the separated ions H_3O^+ and Cl^-. One indication of this is that we can smell HCl in the vapor above such solutions.

EXAMPLE 16-4

Calculating the pH of an Aqueous Solution of a Strong Base. Calcium hydroxide (slaked lime), $Ca(OH)_2$, is the cheapest strong base available. It is generally used for industrial operations in which a high concentration of OH^- is not required. $Ca(OH)_2(s)$ is soluble in water only to the extent of 0.16 g $Ca(OH)_2/100.0$ mL solution at 25 °C. What is the pH of saturated $Ca(OH)_2(aq)$ at 25 °C?

Solution

First, we need to express the solubility of $Ca(OH)_2$ on a molar basis.

$$\text{molarity} = \frac{0.16 \text{ g Ca(OH)}_2 \times \dfrac{1 \text{ mol Ca(OH)}_2}{74.1 \text{ g Ca(OH)}_2}}{0.1000 \text{ L}} = 0.022 \text{ M Ca(OH)}_2$$

Next, we can relate the molarity of OH^- to the molarity of $Ca(OH)_2$.

$$[OH^-] = \frac{0.022 \text{ mol Ca(OH)}_2}{1 \text{ L}} \times \frac{2 \text{ mol OH}^-}{1 \text{ mol Ca(OH)}_2} = 0.044 \text{ M OH}^-$$

Now we can calculate the pOH and, from it, the pH.

$$pOH = -\log[OH^-] = -\log 0.044 = 1.36$$
$$pH = 14.00 - pOH = 14.00 - 1.36 = 12.64$$

Practice Example A: Milk of magnesia is a saturated solution of $Mg(OH)_2$. Its solubility is 9.63 mg $Mg(OH)_2/100.0$ mL solution at 20 °C. What is the pH of saturated $Mg(OH)_2$ at 20 °C?

Practice Example B: Calculate the pH of an aqueous solution that is 3.00% KOH, by mass, and has a density of 1.0242 g/mL.

◀ A common error is to assume that you have calculated the pH when in fact you have found the pOH. Thus, the pH cannot be 1.36. The solution must be *basic*; it must have pH > 7. Use qualitative reasoning to avoid simple errors.

Are You Wondering . . .

How to calculate $[H_3O^+]$ in an extremely dilute solution of a strong acid?

The method of Example 16-3 won't work for calculating the pH of a solution as dilute as 1.0×10^{-8} M HCl. We would write $[H_3O^+] = 1.0 \times 10^{-8}$ M, and pH = 8.00. But how can a solution of a strong acid, no matter how dilute, have a pH greater than 7? The difficulty is that at this extreme dilution, we must consider two sources of H_3O^+. The sources of H_3O^+ and the ion concentrations from both sources are indicated as follows:

$$H_2O + H_2O \rightleftharpoons H_3O^+ + OH^-$$

Molarity: x x

$$HCl + H_2O \longrightarrow H_3O^+ + Cl^-$$

Molarity: 1.0×10^{-8} 1.0×10^{-8}

To satisfy the K_w expression for water in this solution, we use equation (16.7) to get

$$[H_3O^+][OH^-] = x(x + 1.0 \times 10^{-8}) = 1.0 \times 10^{-14}$$

This expression rearranges to the quadratic form

$$x^2 + (1.0 \times 10^{-8}x) - (1.0 \times 10^{-14}) = 0$$

The solution to this equation is $x = 9.5 \times 10^{-8}$ M. Therefore, we combine $[H_3O^+]$ from both sources to get $[H_3O^+] = (9.5 \times 10^{-8}) + (1.0 \times 10^{-8}) = 1.05 \times 10^{-7}$ M, and pH = 6.98.

From this result, we conclude that the pH is slightly less than 7, as expected for a very dilute acid, and that the self-ionization of water contributes nearly ten times as much hydronium ion to the solution as does the strong acid.

Equilibrium Constant activity

Silverstein, Todd P. "Weak vs Strong Acids and Bases: The Football Analogy." *J. Chem. Educ.* **2000:** *77*, 849 (July 2000).

☑ Weak acids are vital to biological processes. Weak acids are more interesting than strong acids that simply dissociate 100%. It is the partial dissociation of weak acids that makes them interesting and useful.

☑ Remind students that equilibrium constants (and therefore pK_a and pK_b values) vary with temperature.

☑ The $pK = -\log K$ is introduced so that very large and very small numbers that arise for K can be more easily handled.

16-5   WEAK ACIDS AND WEAK BASES

Figure 16-7 illustrates two ways of showing that ionization has occurred in an aqueous solution of an acid: One is by the color of an acid–base indicator; the other, the response of a pH meter. The pink color of the solution in Figure 16-7 tells us the pH of 0.1 M HCl is *less than 1.2*. The pH meter registers a value of 1.20, about what we expect for a strong acid solution with $[H_3O^+]$ approximately equal to 0.1 M. The yellow color of the solution in Figure 16-7 indicates that the pH of 0.1 M $HC_2H_3O_2$ (acetic acid) is *2.8 or greater*. The pH meter registers 2.80.

So we see that two acids can have the same molarity but different pH values. The acid's molarity simply indicates what was put into the solution, but $[H_3O^+]$ and pH depend on what *happens* in the solution. In both solutions, some self-ionization of water occurs, but this reaction is negligible. Ionization of HCl, a strong acid, can be assumed to go to completion, as indicated in equation (16.5). As we previously noted, ionization of $HC_2H_3O_2$, a weak acid, is a reversible reaction that reaches a condition of equilibrium.*

$$HC_2H_3O_2 + H_2O \rightleftharpoons H_3O^+ + C_2H_3O_2^- \tag{16.11}$$

The equilibrium constant expression for reaction (16.11) is

$$K_a = \frac{[H_3O^+][C_2H_3O_2^-]}{[HC_2H_3O_2]} = 1.8 \times 10^{-5} \tag{16.12}$$

Just as pH is a convenient shorthand designation related to $[H_3O^+]$, pK is related to an equilibrium constant. That is, **$pK = -\log K$**. Thus, for acetic acid,

$$pK_a = -\log K_a = -\log(1.8 \times 10^{-5}) = -(-4.74) = 4.74$$

As with other equilibrium constants, the larger the value of K_a (or K_b for a base), the farther the equilibrium condition lies in the direction of the forward reaction. And the more extensive the ionization, the greater are the concentrations of the ions produced. Ionization constants must be determined *by experiment*.

▲ **FIGURE 16-7**
Strong and weak acids compared
The color of thymol blue indicator, which is present in both solutions, depends on the pH of the solution.

$$\textbf{pH} < \textbf{1.2} < \textbf{pH} < \textbf{2.8} < \textbf{pH}$$
red   orange   yellow

The principle of the pH meter is discussed in Section 20-4. (Left) 0.1 M HCl has pH ≈ 1. (Right) 0.1 M $HC_2H_3O_2$ has pH ≈ 2.8.

---

*We have been writing ionization equations in the form: acid(1) + base(2) $\rightleftharpoons$ base(1) + acid(2). Here we have written acid(1) + base(2) $\rightleftharpoons$ acid(2) + base(1) to highlight H_3O^+, the species that is usually the subject of a calculation.

TABLE 16.3   Ionization Constants of Some Weak Acids and Weak Bases in Water at 25 °C

	Ionization Equilibrium	Ionization Constant K	pK
Acid		$K_a =$	p$K_a =$
Iodic acid	$HIO_3 + H_2O \rightleftharpoons H_3O^+ + IO_3^-$	1.6×10^{-1}	0.80
Chlorous acid	$HClO_2 + H_2O \rightleftharpoons H_3O^+ + ClO_2^-$	1.1×10^{-2}	1.96
Chloroacetic acid	$HC_2H_2ClO_2 + H_2O \rightleftharpoons H_3O^+ + C_2H_2ClO_2^-$	1.4×10^{-3}	2.85
Nitrous acid	$HNO_2 + H_2O \rightleftharpoons H_3O^+ + NO_2^-$	7.2×10^{-4}	3.14
Hydrofluoric acid	$HF + H_2O \rightleftharpoons H_3O^+ + F^-$	6.6×10^{-4}	3.18
Formic acid	$HCHO_2 + H_2O \rightleftharpoons H_3O^+ + CHO_2^-$	1.8×10^{-4}	3.74
Benzoic acid	$HC_7H_5O_2 + H_2O \rightleftharpoons H_3O^+ + C_7H_5O_2^-$	6.3×10^{-5}	4.20
Hydrazoic acid	$HN_3 + H_2O \rightleftharpoons H_3O^+ + N_3^-$	1.9×10^{-5}	4.72
Acetic acid	$HC_2H_3O_2 + H_2O \rightleftharpoons H_3O^+ + C_2H_3O_2^-$	1.8×10^{-5}	4.74
Hypochlorous acid	$HOCl + H_2O \rightleftharpoons H_3O^+ + OCl^-$	2.9×10^{-8}	7.54
Hydrocyanic acid	$HCN + H_2O \rightleftharpoons H_3O^+ + CN^-$	6.2×10^{-10}	9.21
Phenol	$HOC_6H_5 + H_2O \rightleftharpoons H_3O^+ + C_6H_5O^-$	1.0×10^{-10}	10.00
Hydrogen peroxide	$H_2O_2 + H_2O \rightleftharpoons H_3O^+ + HO_2^-$	1.8×10^{-12}	11.74
Base		$K_b =$	p$K_b =$
Diethylamine	$(C_2H_5)_2NH + H_2O \rightleftharpoons (C_2H_5)_2NH_2^+ + OH^-$	6.9×10^{-4}	3.16
Ethylamine	$C_2H_5NH_2 + H_2O \rightleftharpoons C_2H_5NH_3^+ + OH^-$	4.3×10^{-4}	3.37
Ammonia	$NH_3 + H_2O \rightleftharpoons NH_4^+ + OH^-$	1.8×10^{-5}	4.74
Hydroxylamine	$HONH_2 + H_2O \rightleftharpoons HONH_3^+ + OH^-$	9.1×10^{-9}	8.04
Pyridine	$C_5H_5N + H_2O \rightleftharpoons C_5H_5NH^+ + OH^-$	1.5×10^{-9}	8.82
Aniline	$C_6H_5NH_2 + H_2O \rightleftharpoons C_6H_5NH_3^+ + OH^-$	7.4×10^{-10}	9.13

Acid strength →

Base strength →

A few ionization constants for weak acids and weak bases are listed in Table 16.3. A more extensive listing is given in Appendix D.

IDENTIFYING WEAK ACIDS AND BASES

A large number of weak acids have the same structural feature as acetic acid: that is, a —COOH group as part of the molecule. This *carboxyl group* is a common feature of many organic acids, including such biologically important acids as lactic acid and all the amino acids, including glycine. We will use a number of carboxylic acids as examples in this and later chapters.

In general, to distinguish a weak acid from a strong acid, you need recall only that the half-dozen strong acids listed in Table 16.2 are the most common strong acids. Unless you are informed to the contrary, assume that any acid not listed in Table 16.2 is a weak acid.

At first glance, weak bases seem more difficult to identify than weak acids: There is no distinctive element such as H written first in the formula. Yet, if you study the bases in Table 16.3, you will see that all but one of them (pyridine) can be viewed as an ammonia molecule in which some other group (—C_6H_5, —C_2H_5, —OH, or —CH_3) has been substituted for one of the H atoms. The substitution of a methyl group, —CH_3, for a H atom is suggested in the following structural formulas.

Lactic acid

▲ Lactic acid, $CH_3CH(OH)COOH$.

Glycine

▲ Glycine, NH_2CH_2COOH.

Ammonia   Methylamine

▲ Pyridine, C_5H_5N.

We can represent the ionization of methylamine in this way.

$$H_3C-\overset{..}{\underset{H}{N}}-H \;+\; H-\overset{..}{\underset{..}{O}}: \rightleftharpoons \left[H_3C-\overset{H}{\underset{H}{N}}-H \right]^+ \;+\; \left[H-\overset{..}{\underset{..}{O}}: \right]^-$$

base   acid   acid   base

The ionization constant expression is

$$K_b = \frac{[CH_3NH_3^+][OH^-]}{[CH_3NH_2]} = 4.2 \times 10^{-4} \tag{16.13}$$

Not all weak bases contain N. Yet, so many of them do that the similarity to NH_3 outlined here is well worth remembering. These weak bases derived from ammonia are known as *amines*.

ILLUSTRATIVE EXAMPLES

For some students, solution equilibrium calculations are among the most challenging in general chemistry. At times, the difficulty is in sorting out what is relevant to a given problem. The number of types of calculations seems very large, although in fact it is quite limited. The key to solving solution equilibrium problems is to be able to imagine what is going on. Here are some questions to ask yourself.

- Which are the principal species in solution?
- What are the chemical reactions that produce them?
- Can some reactions (for example, the self-ionization of water) be ignored?
- Can you make any assumptions that allow you to simplify the equilibrium calculations?
- What is a reasonable answer to the problem? For instance, should the final solution be acidic (pH < 7) or basic (pH > 7)?

In short, first think through a problem *qualitatively*. At times, you may not even have to do a calculation. Next, organize the relevant data in a clear, logical manner. In this way, many problems that at first appear new to you will take on a familiar pattern. Look for other helpful hints as you proceed through this chapter and the following two chapters.

VCL *Ionization Constants of Weak Acids*

▲ Butyric acid, $CH_3CH_2CH_2COOH$.

EXAMPLE 16-5

Determining a Value of K_a from the pH of a Solution of a Weak Acid. Butyric acid, $HC_4H_7O_2$, is used to make compounds employed in artificial flavorings and syrups. A 0.250 M aqueous solution of $HC_4H_7O_2$ is found to have a pH of 2.72. Determine K_a for butyric acid.

$$HC_4H_7O_2 + H_2O \rightleftharpoons H_3O^+ + C_4H_7O_2^- \qquad K_a = ?$$

Solution

For $HC_4H_7O_2$, K_a is likely to be much larger than K_w. Therefore, we can assume that self-ionization of water is unimportant and that ionization of the butyric acid is the only source of H_3O^+. Let's treat the situation as if $HC_4H_7O_2$ first dissolves in molecular form, and then the molecules ionize until equilibrium is reached. That is, write the balanced chemical equation and use it as the basis for an ICE table, as discussed in Chapter 15 (page 645). We will represent the concentrations of H_3O^+ and $C_4H_7O_2^-$ at equilibrium as x M.

$$HC_4H_7O_2 + H_2O \rightleftharpoons H_3O^+ + C_4H_7O_2^-$$

initial concns:	0.250 M	—	—
changes:	$-x$ M	$+x$ M	$+x$ M
equil concns:	$(0.250 - x)$ M	x M	x M

But x is *not* unknown. It is the $[H_3O^+]$ in solution, which we can determine from the pH.

$$\log[H_3O^+] = -pH = -2.72$$
$$[H_3O^+] = 10^{-2.72} = 1.9 \times 10^{-3} = x$$

Now we can solve the following expression for K_a, substituting in the known value for x.

$$K_a = \frac{[H_3O^+][C_4H_7O_2^-]}{[HC_4H_7O_2]} = \frac{x \cdot x}{0.250 - x}$$

$$= \frac{(1.9 \times 10^{-3})(1.9 \times 10^{-3})}{0.250 - (1.9 \times 10^{-3})} = 1.5 \times 10^{-5}$$

Notice that our original assumption was correct: K_a is much larger than K_w.

Practice Example A: Hypochlorous acid, HOCl, is used in water treatment and as a disinfectant in swimming pools. A 0.150 M solution of HOCl has a pH of 4.18. Determine K_a for hypochlorous acid.

Practice Example B: The much-abused drug cocaine is an alkaloid. Alkaloids are noted for their bitter taste, an indication of their basic properties. Cocaine, $C_{17}H_{21}O_4N$, is soluble in water to the extent of 0.17 g/100 mL solution, and a saturated solution has a pH = 10.08. What is the value of K_b for cocaine?

$$C_{17}H_{21}O_4N + H_2O \rightleftharpoons C_{17}H_{21}O_4NH^+ + OH^- \qquad K_b = ?$$

◀ For a weak base, $[OH^-]$ and the molarity of a cation appear in the numerator of the K_b expression.

Example 16-6 presents a common problem involving weak acids and weak bases: calculating the pH of a solution of known molarity. The calculation invariably involves a quadratic equation, but very often we can make a simplifying assumption that leads to a shortcut that saves both time and effort.

EXAMPLE 16-6

Calculating the pH of a Weak Acid Solution. Show by calculation that the pH of 0.100 M $HC_2H_3O_2$ should be about the value shown on the pH meter in Figure 16-7; that is, pH ≈ 2.8.

Solution

Here, we know that K_a is much larger than K_w. Let's again treat the situation as if $HC_2H_3O_2$ first dissolves in molecular form and then ionizes until equilibrium is reached. In this case, the quantity x is an unknown that must be obtained by an algebraic solution.

✓ Students at first always think that x is small, and so it is for weak acids and bases. It is a good idea at some point to reverse a weak acid dissociation, in which case x is large and cannot be neglected. The trick is to substitute $y = 1 - x$ and then y turns out to be small and can be safely neglected.

$$HC_2H_3O_2 + H_2O \rightleftharpoons H_3O^+ + C_2H_3O_2^-$$

initial concns:	0.100 M	—	—
changes:	$-x$ M	$+x$ M	$+x$ M
equil concns:	$(0.100 - x)$ M	x M	x M

$$K_a = \frac{[H_3O^+][C_2H_3O_2^-]}{[HC_2H_3O_2]} = \frac{x \cdot x}{0.100 - x} = 1.8 \times 10^{-5}$$

▲ Fluoroacetic acid,
CH_2FCOOH.

▲ Acetylsalicylic acid,
$C_6H_4(OOCCH_3)COOH$.

We could solve this equation by using the quadratic formula, but let's instead make a simplifying assumption that is often valid. Assume that x is very small compared with 0.100. That is, assume that $(0.100 - x) \approx 0.100$.

$$x^2 = 0.100 \times 1.8 \times 10^{-5} = 1.8 \times 10^{-6}$$
$$x = [H_3O^+] = \sqrt{1.8 \times 10^{-6}} = 1.3 \times 10^{-3} \, M$$

Now, we must check our assumption: $0.100 - 0.0013 = 0.099 \approx 0.100$. Our assumption is good to about 1 part per 100 (1%) and is valid for a calculation involving two or three significant figures.

Finally,

$$pH = -\log[H_3O^+] = -\log(1.3 \times 10^{-3}) = -(-2.89) = 2.89$$

Practice Example A: Substituting halogen atoms for hydrogen atoms bound to carbon increases the strength of carboxylic acids. Show that the pH of 0.100 M $HC_2H_2FO_2$, fluoroacetic acid, is lower than that calculated in Example 16-6 for 0.100 M $HC_2H_3O_2$.

$$HC_2H_2FO_2 + H_2O \rightleftharpoons H_3O^+ + C_2H_2FO_2^- \qquad K_a = 2.6 \times 10^{-3}$$

Practice Example B: Acetylsalicylic acid, $HC_9H_7O_4$, is the active component in aspirin. This acid is the cause of the stomach upset some people get when taking aspirin. Two extra-strength aspirin tablets, each containing 500 mg of acetylsalicylic acid, are dissolved in 325 mL of water. What is the pH of this solution?

$$HC_9H_7O_4 + H_2O \rightleftharpoons H_3O^+ + C_9H_7O_4^- \qquad K_a = 3.3 \times 10^{-4}$$

EXAMPLE 16-7

Dealing with the Failure of a Simplifying Assumption. What is the pH of a solution that is 0.00250 M $CH_3NH_2(aq)$? For methylamine, $K_b = 4.2 \times 10^{-4}$.

Solution

We can begin by describing the ionization equilibrium in the customary format.

$$CH_3NH_2 + H_2O \rightleftharpoons CH_3NH_3^+ + OH^-$$

	$CH_3NH_2 + H_2O \rightleftharpoons$	$CH_3NH_3^+$	OH^-
initial concns:	0.00250 M	—	—
changes:	$-x$ M	$+x$ M	$+x$ M
equil concns:	$(0.00250 - x)$ M	x M	x M

$$K_b = \frac{[CH_3NH_3^+][OH^-]}{[CH_3NH_2]} = \frac{x \cdot x}{0.00250 - x} = 4.2 \times 10^{-4}$$

Now let's assume that x is very much less than 0.00250 and that $0.00250 - x \approx 0.00250$.

$$\frac{x^2}{0.00250} = 4.2 \times 10^{-4} \qquad x^2 = 1.1 \times 10^{-6} \qquad [OH^-] = x = 1.0 \times 10^{-3} \, M$$

The value of x is nearly half as large as 0.00250—too large to ignore.

$$\frac{0.0010}{0.00250} \times 100\% = 40\%$$

Our assumption failed, so we must use an exact method. This means using the *quadratic* formula.

$$\frac{x^2}{0.00250 - x} = 4.2 \times 10^{-4}$$
$$x^2 + (4.2 \times 10^{-4}x) - (1.1 \times 10^{-6}) = 0$$
$$x = \frac{(-4.2 \times 10^{-4}) \pm \sqrt{(4.2 \times 10^{-4})^2 + 4 \times 1.1 \times 10^{-6}}}{2}$$
$$x = [OH^-] = \frac{(-4.2 \times 10^{-4}) \pm (2.1 \times 10^{-3})}{2} = 8.4 \times 10^{-4} \, M$$
$$pOH = -\log[OH^-] = -\log(8.4 \times 10^{-4}) = 3.08$$
$$pH = 14.00 - pOH = 14.00 - 3.08 = 10.92$$

KEEP IN MIND ▶

that the relationship pH + pOH = pK can be used because the equilibria
$$CH_3NH_2 + H_2O \rightleftharpoons$$
$$CH_3NH_3^+ + OH^-$$
$$H_2O + H_2O \rightleftharpoons$$
$$H_3O^+ + OH^-$$
are satisfied simultaneously. That is, the same value of $[OH^-]$ goes into the equilibrium expressions for both reactions.

Practice Example A: What is the pH of 0.015 M $HC_2H_2FO_2(aq)$?

$$HC_2H_2FO_2 + H_2O \rightleftharpoons H_3O^+ + C_2H_2FO_2^- \qquad K_a = 2.6 \times 10^{-3}$$

Practice Example B: Piperidine is a base found in small amounts in black pepper. What is the pH of 315 mL of an aqueous solution containing 114 mg piperidine?

$$C_5H_{11}N + H_2O \rightleftharpoons C_5H_{11}NH^+ + OH^- \qquad K_b = 1.6 \times 10^{-3}$$

▲ Piperidine, $C_5H_{10}NH$.

Are You Wondering . . .

How to calculate the pH of a very dilute solution of a weak acid?

Think of this as a companion question to the one posed in the Are You Wondering feature on page 673, except here the acid in question is weak (represented as HA) rather than strong. The initial approach is similar: Write two equations representing the sources of H_3O^+, and indicate the concentrations of various species in the solution.

$$H_2O + H_2O \rightleftharpoons H_3O^+ + OH^-$$

Molarity: $\qquad\qquad\qquad\qquad\qquad x \qquad\quad x$

$$HA + H_2O \rightleftharpoons H_3O^+ + A^-$$

Molarity: $\qquad M - y \qquad\qquad y \qquad\quad y$

Our ultimate objective is to determine $[H_3O^+]$ in the solution, and this is $x + y$. From $[H_3O^+]$, we can easily get the pH.

Our principal task is to solve a pair of equations simultaneously for x and y. The two equations are

$$K_w = [H_3O^+][OH^-] = (x + y) \times x = 1.0 \times 10^{-14}$$

$$K_a = \frac{[H_3O^+][A^-]}{[HA]} = \frac{(x + y) \times y}{(M - y)}$$

Note the following three points in these equations. (1) There can be only one value of $[H_3O^+]$ in the solution, and it is this value $(x + y)$ that appears in each equation. (2) The stoichiometric concentration of the acid is M (its molarity), and its *equilibrium* concentration is $[HA] = M - y$. The numerical value of M depends on the particular case considered. (3) Similarly, the numerical value of K_a depends on the particular case. When we solve the K_a expression for x, we obtain

$$x = \frac{K_a(M - y)}{y} - y \quad \text{and} \quad x + y = \frac{K_a(M - y)}{y}$$

And when we substitute these values of x and $x + y$ into the K_w equation, we get

$$K_w = \frac{K_a(M - y)}{y} \times \left(\frac{K_a(M - y)}{y} - y \right) = 1.0 \times 10^{-14}$$

The value of y satisfying this equation is not difficult to obtain by the method of successive approximations, illustrated in Appendix A.

The solution of this problem is left for you to do (see Exercise 85), but you will find that for 1.0×10^{-5} M HCN ($K_a = 6.2 \times 10^{-10}$), $y \cong 4.8 \times 10^{-8}$, $(x + y) \cong 1.3 \times 10^{-7}$, and pH $\cong 6.90$. This certainly seems like a reasonable pH for a very dilute solution of a weak acid in water—just below the neutral pH of 7.00.

Finally, we can use the results of the previous discussion to establish a criterion for ignoring the self-ionization of water in calculations. When we do this, we are assuming that $y \gg x$, so that $y \approx x + y$, and $yx \approx (x + y)x = [H_3O^+][OH^-] = K_w$. Also, if $y \gg x$, then $y^2 \gg K_w$. For what values of y can we say that $y \gg x$? Let's take the maximum value of x consistent with ignoring the self-ionization of water to be $1/100$ of y which, as shown below, means that $[H_3O^+]$ must be greater than 10^{-6} M.

$$y^2 > y \times x = y \times \frac{y}{100} = K_w = 1 \times 10^{-14}$$

$$y^2 > 1 \times 10^{-12} \quad \text{and} \quad y > 1 \times 10^{-6}$$

In acid–base calculations, we should first use the simplifying assumptions (ignore K_w and assume that [HA] can be replaced by the molarity of the acid). Then check the answer to see whether $[H_3O^+]$ is greater than 1×10^{-6} M and the 5% criterion presented below is also met.

CONCEPT ASSESSMENT ✓

Is it possible for a weak acid solution to have a lower pH than a strong acid solution? If not, why not? If it is possible, under what conditions?

MORE ON SIMPLIFYING ASSUMPTIONS

The usual simplifying assumption is that of treating a weak acid or weak base as though it remains essentially non-ionized (so that $M - x \approx M$). In general, this assumption will work if the molarity of the weak acid, M_A, or that of the weak base, M_B, exceeds the value of K_a or K_b by a factor of at least 100. That is,

$$\frac{M_A \text{ (or } M_B)}{K_a \text{ (or } K_b)} > 100$$

In any case, it is important to test the validity of any assumption that you make. If the assumption is good to within a few percent (say, less than 5%), then it is generally valid. In Example 16-6, the simplifying assumption was good to about 1%, but in Example 16-7 it was off by 40%.

PERCENT IONIZATION

The extent of ionization of a weak acid or weak base can be described in terms of the degree of ionization or percent ionization. It is convenient to introduce the generic symbol HA for any weak acid, and A^- as the conjugate base of the acid HA.

For the ionization $HA + H_2O \rightleftharpoons H_3O^+ + A^-$, the degree of ionization is the fraction of the acid molecules that ionize. Thus, if in 1.00 M HA, ionization produces $[H_3O^+] = [A^-] = 0.05$ M, the degree of ionization = 0.05 M/1.00 M = 0.05. **Percent ionization** gives the proportion of ionized molecules on a percentage basis.

$$\text{percent ionization} = \frac{\text{molarity of } H_3O^+ \text{ derived from HA}}{\text{initial molarity of HA}} \times 100\% \quad (16.14)$$

A weak acid with a degree of ionization of 0.05 has a percent ionization of 5%.

Figure 16-8 compares percent ionization and solution molarity for a weak acid and a strong acid. Example 16-8 shows by calculation that the percent ionization of a weak acid or a weak base *increases* as the solution becomes *more dilute*, a fact that we can also demonstrate by a simple analysis of the ionization reaction

$$HA + H_2O \rightleftharpoons H_3O^+ + A^-$$

At equilibrium, n_{HA} moles of the acid HA, $n_{H_3O^+}$ moles of H_3O^+, and n_{A^-} moles of A^- are present in a volume of V liters. The K_a expression is

$$K_a = \frac{[H_3O^+][A^-]}{[HA]} = \frac{(n_{H_3O^+}/V)(n_{A^-}/V)}{n_{HA}/V} = \frac{(n_{H_3O^+})(n_{A^-})}{n_{HA}} \times \frac{1}{V}$$

When we dilute the solution, V increases, $1/V$ decreases, and the ratio $(n_{H_3O^+})(n_{A^-})/n_{HA}$ must increase to maintain the constant value of K_a. In turn, $n_{H_3O^+}$ and n_{A^-} must increase and n_{HA} must decrease, signifying an increase in the percent ionization.

◀ **FIGURE 16-8**
Percent ionization of an acid as a function of concentration
Over the concentration range shown, HCl, a strong acid, is essentially 100% ionized. The percent ionization of $HC_2H_3O_2$, a weak acid, increases from about 4% in 0.010 M to essentially 100% when the solution is extremely dilute. Note that in extremely dilute solutions, the two acids would have virtually the same pH.

EXAMPLE 16-8

Determining Percent Ionization as a Function of Weak Acid Concentration.
What is the percent ionization of acetic acid in 1.0 M, 0.10 M, and 0.010 M $HC_2H_3O_2$?

Solution

Use the ICE format to describe 1.0 M $HC_2H_3O_2$:

$$HC_2H_3O_2 + H_2O \rightleftharpoons H_3O^+ + C_2H_3O_2^-$$

initial concns:	1.0 M	—	—
changes:	$-x$ M	$+x$ M	$+x$ M
equil concns:	$(1.0 - x)$ M	x M	x M

We need to calculate $x = [H_3O^+] = [C_2H_3O_2^-]$. In doing so, let's make the usual assumption: $1.0 - x \approx 1.0$.

$$K_a = \frac{[H_3O^+][C_2H_3O_2^-]}{[HC_2H_3O_2]} = \frac{x \cdot x}{1.0 - x} = \frac{x^2}{1.0} = 1.8 \times 10^{-5}$$

$$x = [H_3O^+] = [C_2H_3O_2^-] = \sqrt{1.8 \times 10^{-5}} = 4.2 \times 10^{-3} \text{ M}$$

The percent ionization of 1.0 M $HC_2H_3O_2$ is

$$\textit{% ionization} = \frac{[H_3O^+]}{[HC_2H_3O_2]} \times 100\% = \frac{4.2 \times 10^{-3} \text{ M}}{1.0 \text{ M}} \times 100\% = 0.42\%$$

The calculations for 0.10 M $HC_2H_3O_2$ and 0.010 M $HC_2H_3O_2$ are very similar and yield the results

0.10 M $HC_2H_3O_2$ is 1.3% ionized; 0.010 M $HC_2H_3O_2$ is 4.2% ionized.

Practice Example A: What is the percent ionization of hydrofluoric acid in 0.20 M HF and in 0.020 M HF?

Practice Example B: An 0.0284 M aqueous solution of lactic acid, a substance that accumulates in the blood and muscles during physical activity, is found to be 6.7% ionized. Determine K_a for lactic acid.

$$HC_3H_5O_3 + H_2O \rightleftharpoons H_3O^+ + C_3H_5O_3^- \qquad K_a = ?$$

16-6 POLYPROTIC ACIDS

All the acids listed in Table 16.3 are weak *monoprotic acids*, meaning that their molecules have only one ionizable H atom, even though several of these acids contain more than one H atom. But some acids have more than one ionizable

▲ Phosphoric acid, H_3PO_4.

TABLE 16.4 Ionization Constants of Some Polyprotic Acids

Acid	Ionization Equilibria	Ionization Constants, K	pK
Hydrosulfuric[a]	$H_2S + H_2O \rightleftharpoons H_3O^+ + HS^-$	$K_{a_1} = 1.0 \times 10^{-7}$	p$K_{a_1} = 7.00$
	$HS^- + H_2O \rightleftharpoons H_3O^+ + S^{2-}$	$K_{a_2} = 1 \times 10^{-19}$	p$K_{a_2} = 19.0$
Carbonic[b]	$H_2CO_3 + H_2O \rightleftharpoons H_3O^+ + HCO_3^-$	$K_{a_1} = 4.4 \times 10^{-7}$	p$K_{a_1} = 6.36$
	$HCO_3^- + H_2O \rightleftharpoons H_3O^+ + CO_3^{2-}$	$K_{a_2} = 4.7 \times 10^{-11}$	p$K_{a_2} = 10.33$
Phosphoric	$H_3PO_4 + H_2O \rightleftharpoons H_3O^+ + H_2PO_4^-$	$K_{a_1} = 7.1 \times 10^{-3}$	p$K_{a_1} = 2.15$
	$H_2PO_4^- + H_2O \rightleftharpoons H_3O^+ + HPO_4^{2-}$	$K_{a_2} = 6.3 \times 10^{-8}$	p$K_{a_2} = 7.20$
	$HPO_4^{2-} + H_2O \rightleftharpoons H_3O^+ + PO_4^{3-}$	$K_{a_3} = 4.2 \times 10^{-13}$	p$K_{a_3} = 12.38$
Sulfurous[c]	$H_2SO_3 + H_2O \rightleftharpoons H_3O^+ + HSO_3^-$	$K_{a_1} = 1.3 \times 10^{-2}$	p$K_{a_1} = 1.89$
	$HSO_3^- + H_2O \rightleftharpoons H_3O^+ + SO_3^{2-}$	$K_{a_2} = 6.2 \times 10^{-8}$	p$K_{a_2} = 7.21$
Sulfuric[d]	$H_2SO_4 + H_2O \rightleftharpoons H_3O^+ + HSO_4^-$	$K_{a_1} = $ very large	p$K_{a_1} < 0$
	$HSO_4^- + H_2O \rightleftharpoons H_3O^+ + SO_4^{2-}$	$K_{a_2} = 1.1 \times 10^{-2}$	p$K_{a_2} = 1.96$

Acid strength

[a]The value for K_{a_2} of H_2S most commonly found in older literature is about 1×10^{-14}, but current evidence suggests that the value is considerably smaller.

[b]H_2CO_3 cannot be isolated. It is in equilibrium with H_2O and dissolved CO_2. The value given for K_{a_1} is actually for the reaction

$$CO_2(aq) + 2 H_2O \rightleftharpoons H_3O^+ + HCO_3^-$$

Generally, aqueous solutions of CO_2 are treated *as if* the $CO_2(aq)$ were first converted to H_2CO_3, followed by ionization of the H_2CO_3.

[c]H_2SO_3 is a hypothetical, nonisolatable species. The value listed for K_{a_1} is actually for the reaction

$$SO_2(aq) + 2 H_2O \rightleftharpoons H_3O^+ + HSO_3^-$$

[d]H_2SO_4 is completely ionized in the first step.

H atom per molecule. These are **polyprotic acids**. Table 16.4 lists ionization constants for several polyprotic acids. Additional listings can be found in Appendix D. We will focus on phosphoric acid, H_3PO_4.

PHOSPHORIC ACID

Phosphoric acid, H_3PO_4, ranks second only to sulfuric acid among the important commercial acids. Annual production of H_3PO_4 in the United States typically exceeds 10 million tons. Its principal use is in the manufacture of phosphate fertilizers. In addition, various sodium, potassium, and calcium phosphates are used in the food industry.

The H_3PO_4 molecule has *three* ionizable H atoms; it is a *triprotic acid*. It ionizes in three steps. For each step, we can write an ionization equation and an acid ionization constant expression with a distinctive value of K_a.

A common error that students make is to assume that the $[H_3O^+]$ is the same for all three dissociations. In fact, the pH is dominated by only the first dissociation as seen from the different K_a values here. This is only true, of course, for weak acids. The examples here illustrate the points well.

(1) $\quad H_3PO_4 + H_2O \rightleftharpoons H_3O^+ + H_2PO_4^- \quad K_{a_1} = \dfrac{[H_3O^+][H_2PO_4^-]}{[H_3PO_4]} = 7.1 \times 10^{-3}$

(2) $\quad H_2PO_4^- + H_2O \rightleftharpoons H_3O^+ + HPO_4^{2-} \quad K_{a_2} = \dfrac{[H_3O^+][HPO_4^{2-}]}{[H_2PO_4^-]} = 6.3 \times 10^{-8}$

(3) $\quad HPO_4^{2-} + H_2O \rightleftharpoons H_3O^+ + PO_4^{3-} \quad K_{a_3} = \dfrac{[H_3O^+][PO_4^{3-}]}{[HPO_4^{2-}]} = 4.2 \times 10^{-13}$

There is a ready explanation for the relative magnitudes of the ionization constants—that is, for the fact that $K_{a_1} > K_{a_2} > K_{a_3}$. When ionization occurs in step (1), a proton (H^+) moves away from an ion with a 1− charge ($H_2PO_4^-$). In step (2), the proton moves away from an ion with a 2− charge (HPO_4^{2-}), a more difficult separation. As a result, the ionization constant in the second step is smaller than that in the first. Ionization is more difficult still in step (3).

We can make three key statements about the ionization of phosphoric acid, as illustrated in Example 16-9.

1. K_{a_1} is so much larger than K_{a_2} and K_{a_3} that essentially all the H_3O^+ is produced in the first ionization step.

2. So little of the $H_2PO_4^-$ forming in the first ionization step ionizes any further that we can assume $[H_2PO_4^-] = [H_3O^+]$ in the solution.

3. $[HPO_4^{2-}] \approx K_{a_2}$, regardless of the molarity of the acid.*

Although statement (1) seems essential if statements (2) and (3) are to be valid, it is not as crucial as might first appear. Even for polyprotic acids whose K_a values do not differ greatly between successive ionizations, H_3O^+ is often still determined almost exclusively by the K_{a_1} expression, and statements (2) and (3) remain valid. As long as the polyprotic acid is weak in its first ionization step, the concentration of the anion produced in this step will be so much less than the molarity of the acid that additional $[H_3O^+]$ produced in the second ionization remains negligible.

EXAMPLE 16-9

Calculating Ion Concentrations in a Polyprotic Acid Solution. For a 3.0 M H_3PO_4 solution, calculate **(a)** $[H_3O^+]$; **(b)** $[H_2PO_4^-]$; **(c)** $[HPO_4^{2-}]$; and **(d)** $[PO_4^{3-}]$.

Solution

(a) Because K_{a_1} is so much larger than K_{a_2}, let's assume that all the H_3O^+ forms in the *first* ionization step. This is equivalent to thinking of H_3PO_4 as though it were a monoprotic acid, ionizing only in the first step.

$$H_3PO_4 + H_2O \rightleftharpoons H_3O^+ + H_2PO_4^-$$

initial concns:	3.0 M	—	—
changes:	$-x$ M	$+x$ M	$+x$ M
after first ionization:	$(3.0 - x)$ M	x M	x M

Following the usual assumption that x is much smaller than 3.0 and that $3.0 - x \approx 3.0$, we obtain

$$K_{a_1} = \frac{[H_3O^+][H_2PO_4^-]}{[H_3PO_4]} = \frac{x \cdot x}{(3.0 - x)} = \frac{x^2}{3.0} = 7.1 \times 10^{-3}$$

$$x^2 = 0.021 \qquad x = [H_3O^+] = 0.14 \text{ M}$$

◀ In the assumption $3.0 - x \approx 3.0$, $x = 0.14$, which is 4.7% of 3.0. This is about the maximum error that can be tolerated for an acceptable assumption.

(b) From part (a), $x = [H_2PO_4^-] = [H_3O^+] = 0.14$ M.

(c) To determine $[H_3O^+]$ and $[H_2PO_4^-]$, we assumed that the second ionization is insignificant. Here we must consider the second ionization, no matter how slight; otherwise we would have no source of the ion HPO_4^{2-}. We can represent the second ionization, as shown in the following table. *Note especially how the results of the first ionization enter in.* We start with a solution in which $[H_2PO_4^-] = [H_3O^+] = 0.14$ M.

$$H_2PO_4^- + H_2O \rightleftharpoons H_3O^+ + HPO_4^{2-}$$

from first ionization:	0.14 M	0.14 M	—
changes:	$-y$ M	$+y$ M	$+y$ M
after second ionization:	$(0.14 - y)$ M	$(0.14 + y)$ M	yM

---

*If we assume that $[H_2PO_4^-] = [H_3O^+]$, the second ionization expression reduces to

$$\frac{\cancel{[H_3O^+]}[HPO_4^{2-}]}{\cancel{[H_2PO_4^-]}} = K_{a_2}$$

▶ The fact that the concentration of anion produced in the second ionization step of a polyprotic acid is equal to K_a can be used to get this result directly.

If we assume that y is much smaller than 0.14, then $(0.14 + y) \approx (0.14 - y) \approx 0.14$.

We then get

$$K_{a_2} = \frac{[H_3O^+][HPO_4{}^{2-}]}{[H_2PO_4{}^-]} = \frac{(0.14 + y)(y)}{(0.14 - y)} = \frac{(0.14)(y)}{(0.14)} = 6.3 \times 10^{-8}$$

$$y = [HPO_4{}^{2-}] = 6.3 \times 10^{-8} \text{ M}$$

Note that the assumption is valid.

(d) The $PO_4{}^{3-}$ ion forms only in the third ionization step. When we write this acid ionization constant expression, we see that we have already calculated the ion concentrations other than $[PO_4{}^{3-}]$. We can simply solve the K_{a_3} expression for $[PO_4{}^{3-}]$.

$$K_{a_3} = \frac{[H_3O^+][PO_4{}^{3-}]}{[HPO_4{}^{2-}]} = \frac{0.14 \times [PO_4{}^{3-}]}{6.3 \times 10^{-8}} = 4.2 \times 10^{-13}$$

$$[PO_4{}^{3-}] = \frac{4.2 \times 10^{-13} \times 6.3 \times 10^{-8}}{0.14} = 1.9 \times 10^{-19} \text{ M}$$

Practice Example A: Malonic acid, $HOOCCH_2COOH$, is a diprotic acid used in the manufacture of barbiturates.

$$HOOCCH_2COOH + H_2O \rightleftharpoons H_3O^+ + HOOCCH_2COO^- \qquad K_{a_1} = 1.4 \times 10^{-3}$$

$$HOOCCH_2COO^- + H_2O \rightleftharpoons H_3O^+ + {}^-OOCCH_2COO^- \qquad K_{a_2} = 2.0 \times 10^{-6}$$

Calculate $[H_3O^+]$, $[HOOCCH_2COO^-]$, and $[{}^-OOCCH_2COO^-]$ in a 1.00 M solution of malonic acid.

Practice Example B: Oxalic acid, found in the leaves of rhubarb and other plants, is a diprotic acid.

$$H_2C_2O_4 + H_2O \rightleftharpoons H_3O^+ + HC_2O_4{}^- \qquad K_{a_1} = ?$$

$$HC_2O_4{}^- + H_2O \rightleftharpoons H_3O^+ + C_2O_4{}^{2-} \qquad K_{a_2} = ?$$

An aqueous solution that is 1.05 M $H_2C_2O_4$ has pH = 0.67. The free oxalate ion concentration in this solution is $[C_2O_4{}^{2-}] = 5.3 \times 10^{-5}$ M. Determine K_{a_1} and K_{a_2} for oxalic acid.

A Somewhat Different Case: H_2SO_4

Sulfuric acid differs from most polyprotic acids in this important respect: It is a *strong* acid in its first ionization and a *weak* acid in its second. Ionization is complete in the first step, which means that in most $H_2SO_4(aq)$ solutions, $[H_2SO_4] \approx 0$ M. Thus, if a solution is 0.50 M H_2SO_4, we can treat it as though it were 0.50 M H_3O^+ and 0.50 M $HSO_4{}^-$ initially. Then we can determine the extent to which ionization of $HSO_4{}^-$ produces additional H_3O^+ and $SO_4{}^{2-}$.

▲ Sulfuric acid, H_2SO_4.

EXAMPLE 16-10

Calculating Ion Concentrations in Sulfuric Acid Solutions: Strong Acid Ionization Followed by Weak Acid Ionization. Calculate $[H_3O^+]$, $[HSO_4{}^-]$, and $[SO_4{}^{2-}]$ in 0.50 M H_2SO_4.

Solution

Let us use an approach similar to that of Example 16-9.

	H_2SO_4 + H_2O	$\longrightarrow$ H_3O^+	+ $HSO_4{}^-$
initial concn:	0.50 M	—	—
changes:	−0.50 M	+0.50 M	+0.50 M
after first ionization:	≈ 0	0.50 M	0.50 M

$$HSO_4^- + H_2O \rightleftharpoons H_3O^+ + SO_4^{2-}$$

from first ionization:	0.50 M	0.50 M	—
changes:	$-x$ M	$+x$ M	$+x$ M
after second ionization:	$(0.50 - x)$ M	$(0.50 + x)$ M	xM

We need to deal only with the ionization constant expression for K_{a_2}. If we assume that x is much smaller than 0.50, then $(0.50 + x) \approx (0.50 - x) \approx 0.50$ and

$$K_{a_2} = \frac{[H_3O^+][SO_4^{2-}]}{[HSO_4^-]} = \frac{(0.50 + x) \cdot x}{(0.50 - x)} = \frac{0.50 \cdot x}{0.50} = 1.1 \times 10^{-2}$$

Our results, then, are

$$[H_3O^+] = 0.50 + x = 0.51 \text{ M}; \quad [HSO_4^-] = 0.50 - x = 0.49 \text{ M}$$

$$[SO_4^{2-}] = x = K_{a_2} = 0.011 \text{ M}$$

Practice Example A: Calculate $[H_3O^+]$, $[HSO_4^-]$, and $[SO_4^{2-}]$ in 0.20 M H_2SO_4.

Practice Example B: Calculate $[H_3O^+]$, $[HSO_4^-]$, and $[SO_4^{2-}]$ in 0.020 M H_2SO_4.

[*Hint:* Is the assumption that $[HSO_4^-] = [H_3O^+]$ valid?]

A GENERAL APPROACH TO SOLUTION EQUILIBRIUM CALCULATIONS

Suppose we were required to determine the stoichiometric molarity of the H_2SO_4(aq) that is required to produce a solution with pH = 2.15. We could start by determining the hydronium ion concentration in the solution: $[H_3O^+] = 10^{-pH} = 10^{-2.15} = 7.1 \times 10^{-3}$ M. What next? We cannot follow the approach used in Example 16-6 because H_2SO_4 is not a monoprotic acid. Instead, we have to use a method like that outlined in the Are You Wondering features on pages 673 and 679. An alternative approach worth considering has the appeal of getting us on the right track for all kinds of solution equilibrium calculations. That method has the following format.

1. Identify the species present in any significant amount in the solution (excluding H_2O molecules). Consider the concentrations of these species as unknowns.

2. Write equations that include these species. The number of equations involving these species should match the number of unknowns. The equations are of three types.
   (a) equilibrium constant expressions
   (b) material balance equations
   (c) an electroneutrality condition

3. Solve the system of equations for the unknowns.

Let's apply this approach to the H_2SO_4(aq) solution mentioned in the first sentence of this section.

Possible Species:

$$\cancel{H_2SO_4}, H_3O^+, HSO_4^-, SO_4^{2-}, \cancel{OH^-}$$

We can eliminate H_2SO_4 because its ionization goes to completion in the first step. We can also eliminate OH^- because $[OH^-]$ is exceedingly small in an *acidic* solution that has a pH = 2.15.

Unknowns:

$$\cancel{[H_3O^+]}, [HSO_4^-], [SO_4^{2-}], \text{ and M [the molarity of the } H_2SO_4(aq)]$$

Point out that calculations like this are not as complicated when performed for other polyprotic acids (phosphoric acid, carbonic acid, etc.) because essentially all the hydronium ion forms after the first ionization of these acids.

We can eliminate $[H_3O^+]$ because we essentially know its value from the outset. A pH = 2.15 corresponds to $[H_3O^+]$ = 0.0071 M. Thus, we are left with three unknowns, and we need three equations.

Equations:

(a) The K_a expression for the ionization $HSO_4^- + H_2O \rightleftharpoons H_3O^+ + SO_4^{2-}$ is

$$K_{a_2} = \frac{[H_3O^+][SO_4^{2-}]}{[HSO_4^-]} = 1.1 \times 10^{-2}$$

(b) The following material balance equation accounts for the fact that the sum of the concentrations of the sulfur-containing species must equal the stoichiometric molarity of the $H_2SO_4(aq)$.

$$[HSO_4^-] + [SO_4^{2-}] = M$$

(c) The electroneutrality condition simply verifies that the solution carries no net charge. The sum of the positive charges must equal the sum of the negative charges. We can sum these charges on a mol/liter basis. For example, because there is one positive charge for every H_3O^+ ion, the number of moles per liter of positive charge is the same as the number of moles per liter of H_3O^+, 0.0071 M. We multiply $[SO_4^{2-}]$ by *two* because each SO_4^{2-} ion carries two units of negative charge.

$$[H_3O^+] = [HSO_4^-] + (2 \times [SO_4^{2-}]) = 0.0071$$

Solving the Equations:

Solve equation (c) for $[HSO_4^-]$: $[HSO_4^-] = 0.0071 - 2[SO_4^{2-}]$. Substitute this result, together with $[H_3O^+] = 0.0071$, into equation (a) and obtain the expression

$$\frac{0.0071 \times [SO_4^{2-}]}{0.0071 - 2[SO_4^{2-}]} = 1.1 \times 10^{-2}$$

KEEP IN MIND ▶
that although this method gives you a quick way to set up a solution equilibrium calculation, more information may be needed for you to arrive at an answer without undue effort. For example, answers to the general questions posed on page 676 may point the way to simplifying the algebraic solution.

Solve this equation to find that $[SO_4^{2-}]$ = 0.0027 M. Then substitute this result into equation (c) to obtain $[HSO_4^-]$ = 0.0017 M. Finally, according to equation (b), $[HSO_4^-] + [SO_4^{2-}]$ = 0.0044 M. The required molarity is 0.0044 M H_2SO_4.

Check:

There are usually ways to check the reasonableness of an answer obtained by this method. In this case, we can easily determine the possible pH range for 0.0044 M H_2SO_4. If the acid ionized only in the first step, $[H_3O^+]$ = 0.0044 M (pH = 2.36); if the second ionization step also went to completion, $[H_3O^+]$ = 0.0088 M (pH = 2.06). The observed pH, 2.15, falls squarely in this range.

The alternative method outlined here is ideal for computerized calculation. Moreover, because the additional manipulations required to convert stoichiometric concentrations to activities can be incorporated into the calculations, the solutions obtained are generally both more accurate and more readily obtained than are those derived by traditional methods.

16-7   IONS AS ACIDS AND BASES

In our discussion to this point, we have emphasized the behavior of electrically neutral molecules as acids (for example, HCl, $HC_2H_3O_2$, H_3PO_4) or as bases (for example, NH_3, CH_3NH_2). We have also seen, however, that ions can act as acids or bases. For instance, in the second and subsequent ionization steps of a polyprotic acid, an anion acts as an acid.

$$H_2PO_4^- + H_2O \rightleftharpoons H_3O^+ + HPO_4^{2-} \qquad K = K_{a_2} = 6.3 \times 10^{-8}$$

Now let's think about how each of the following can be described as an acid–base reaction.

$$NH_4^+ + H_2O \rightleftharpoons NH_3 + H_3O^+ \qquad (16.15)$$

acid(1)   base(2)   base(1)   acid(2)

$$C_2H_3O_2^- + H_2O \rightleftharpoons HC_2H_3O_2 + OH^- \qquad (16.16)$$

base(1)   acid(2)   acid(1)   base(2)

In reaction (16.15), NH_4^+ is an *acid*, giving up a proton to water, a *base*. Equilibrium in this reaction is described by means of the *acid ionization constant* of the ammonium ion, NH_4^+.

$$K_a = \frac{[NH_3][H_3O^+]}{[NH_4^+]} = ? \qquad (16.17)$$

Two of the concentration terms in equation (16.17)—$[NH_3]$ and $[NH_4^+]$—are the same as in the K_b expression for NH_3, the conjugate base of NH_4^+. It seems that K_a for NH_4^+ and K_b for NH_3 should bear some relationship to each other, and they do. The easiest way to see this is to multiply both the numerator and denominator of (16.17) by $[OH^-]$. The product $[H_3O^+] \times [OH^-]$ is the ion product of water, K_w, shown in red. The other terms, shown in blue, represent the *inverse* of K_b for NH_3. The value obtained, 5.6×10^{-10}, is the missing value of K_a in expression (16.17).

$$K_a = \frac{[NH_3][H_3O^+][OH^-]}{[NH_4^+][OH^-]} = \frac{K_w}{K_b} = \frac{1.0 \times 10^{-14}}{1.8 \times 10^{-5}} = 5.6 \times 10^{-10}$$

The result we just obtained is an important consequence of the Brønsted–Lowry theory.

> The product of the ionization constants of an acid and its conjugate base equals the ion product of water.

$$K_a \text{ (acid)} \times K_b \text{ (its conjugate base)} = K_w$$
$$K_b \text{ (base)} \times K_a \text{ (its conjugate acid)} = K_w \qquad (16.18)$$

In reaction (16.16), $C_2H_3O_2^-$ acts as a *base* by taking a proton from water, an *acid*. Here, equilibrium is described by means of the *base ionization constant* of the acetate ion, $C_2H_3O_2^-$. With expression (16.18) we can evaluate K_b.

$$K_b = \frac{[HC_2H_3O_2][OH^-]}{[C_2H_3O_2^-]} = \frac{K_w}{K_a(HC_2H_3O_2)} = \frac{1.0 \times 10^{-14}}{1.8 \times 10^{-5}} = 5.6 \times 10^{-10}$$

In many tabulations of ionization constants, only K_a values are listed, whether for neutral molecules or for ions. Equation (16.18) can be used to obtain the values of their conjugates.

CONCEPT ASSESSMENT ✓

A handbook that lists only pK_a values for weak electrolytes has the following entry for 1,2-ethanediamine, $NH_2CH_2CH_2NH_2$: $pK_1 = 6.85(+2)$; $pK_2 = 9.92(+1)$. Interpret this handbook entry. That is, write equations for the ionization reactions to which these pK values apply. What are the corresponding values of the base ionization constants K_{b_1} and K_{b_2}?

HYDROLYSIS

In pure water at 25 °C, $[H_3O^+] = [OH^-] = 1.0 \times 10^{-7}$ M and pH = 7.00. *Pure water is pH neutral.* When NaCl dissolves in water at 25 °C, complete dissociation into Na^+ and Cl^- ions occurs, and the pH of the solution remains 7.00. We can represent this fact with the equation

$$Na^+ + Cl^- + H_2O \longrightarrow \text{no reaction}$$

▲ **FIGURE 16-9**
Ions as acids and bases
Each of these 1 M solutions contains bromthymol blue indicator, which has the
following colors:

pH < 7	pH = 7	pH > 7
yellow	green	blue

(Left) $NH_4Cl(aq)$ is acidic. (Center) $NaCl(aq)$ is neutral. (Right) $NaC_2H_3O_2(aq)$ is basic.

 This article discusses the acidity of positive metal ions: Hawkes, Stephen J. *J. Chem. Educ.* **1996:** *73*, 516.

As shown in Figure 16-9, when NH_4Cl is added to water, the pH falls below 7. This means that $[H_3O^+] > [OH^-]$ in the solution. A reaction producing H_3O^+ must occur.

$$Cl^- + H_2O \longrightarrow \text{no reaction}$$

$$NH_4^+ + H_2O \rightleftharpoons NH_3 + H_3O^+$$

The reaction between NH_4^+ and H_2O is fundamentally no different from other acid–base reactions. A reaction between an ion and water, however, is often called a **hydrolysis** reaction. We say that ammonium ion *hydrolyzes* (and chloride ion does not).

When sodium acetate is dissolved in water, the pH rises above 7 (see Figure 16-9). This means that $[OH^-] > [H_3O^+]$ in the solution. Here, acetate ion hydrolyzes.

$$Na^+ + H_2O \longrightarrow \text{no reaction}$$

$$C_2H_3O_2^- + H_2O \rightleftharpoons HC_2H_3O_2 + OH^-$$

THE pH OF SALT SOLUTIONS

We are now in a position to make both qualitative predictions and quantitative calculations concerning the pH values of aqueous solutions of salts. Whichever of these tasks is called for, note that hydrolysis takes place only if there is a chemical reaction producing a weak acid or weak base. The following generalizations are useful.

Acid-Base Classification of Salts

- Salts of strong bases and strong acids (for example, NaCl) *do not hydrolyze*: for the solution, pH = 7.
- Salts of strong bases and *weak* acids (for example, $NaC_2H_3O_2$) *hydrolyze*: pH > 7. (The *anion* acts as a *base*.)
- Salts of *weak* bases and strong acids (for example, NH_4Cl) *hydrolyze*: pH < 7. (The *cation* acts as an *acid*.)
- Salts of *weak* bases and *weak* acids (for example, $NH_4C_2H_3O_2$) *hydrolyze*. (The cations are acids, and the anions are bases. Whether the solution is acidic or basic, however, depends on the relative values of K_a and K_b for the ions.)

EXAMPLE 16-11

Making Qualitative Predictions About Hydrolysis Reactions. Predict whether each of the following solutions is acidic, basic, or pH neutral: **(a)** NaOCl(aq); **(b)** KCl(aq); **(c)** NH_4NO_3(aq).

Ranking Salt Solutions by pH

Solution

(a) The ions present are Na^+, which does not hydrolyze, and OCl^-, which does. OCl^- is the conjugate base of HOCl and forms a basic solution.

$$OCl^- + H_2O \rightleftharpoons HOCl + OH^-$$

(b) Neither K^+ nor Cl^- hydrolyzes. KCl(aq) is neutral—that is, pH = 7.

(c) NH_4^+ hydrolyzes, but NO_3^- does not (HNO_3 is a strong acid).

$$NH_4^+ + H_2O \rightleftharpoons NH_3 + H_3O^+$$

In this case, $[H_3O^+] > [OH^-]$, and the solution is acidic.

Practice Example A: Predict whether each of the following 1.0 M solutions is acidic, basic, or pH neutral: **(a)** $CH_3NH_3^+NO_3^-$(aq); **(b)** NaI(aq); **(c)** $NaNO_2$(aq).

Practice Example B: An aqueous solution containing $H_2PO_4^-$ has a pH of about 4.7. Write equations for *two* reactions of $H_2PO_4^-$ with water, and explain which reaction occurs to the greater extent.

CONCEPT ASSESSMENT ✔

Write a chemical equation showing how a particular type of ion can act as both an acid and a base in aqueous solution. Will the resulting solution be acidic, basic, or pH neutral?

EXAMPLE 16-12

Evaluating Ionization Constants for Hydrolysis Reactions. Both sodium nitrite, $NaNO_2$, and sodium benzoate, $NaC_7H_5O_2$, are used as food preservatives. If solutions of these two salts have the same molarity, which solution will have the *higher* pH?

Solution

Each of these substances is the salt of a strong base (NaOH) and a *weak acid*. The anions should ionize as *bases*, making their solutions somewhat basic.

$$NO_2^- + H_2O \rightleftharpoons HNO_2 + OH^- \qquad K_b(NO_2^-) = ?$$
$$C_7H_5O_2^- + H_2O \rightleftharpoons HC_7H_5O_2 + OH^- \qquad K_b(C_7H_5O_2^-) = ?$$

Our task is to determine the K_b values, neither of which is listed in a table in this chapter. Table 16.3 does list K_a for the conjugate acids, however. Equation (16.18) can be used to write

$$K_b \text{ of } NO_2^- = \frac{K_w}{K_a(HNO_2)} = \frac{1.0 \times 10^{-14}}{7.2 \times 10^{-4}} = 1.4 \times 10^{-11}$$

$$K_b \text{ of } C_7H_5O_2^- = \frac{K_w}{K_a(HC_7H_5O_2)} = \frac{1.0 \times 10^{-14}}{6.3 \times 10^{-5}} = 1.6 \times 10^{-10}$$

The K_b of $C_7H_5O_2^-$ is about 10 times larger than the K_b of NO_2^-. The benzoate ion can be expected to hydrolyze to a somewhat greater extent than the nitrite ion and to give a solution with a higher $[OH^-]$. A sodium benzoate solution should be more basic and have a higher pH than a sodium nitrite solution of the same concentration.

Practice Example A: The organic bases cocaine ($pK_b = 8.41$) and codeine ($pK_b = 7.95$) react with hydrochloric acid to form salts (similar to the formation of NH_4Cl by the reaction of NH_3 and HCl). If solutions of the following salts have the same molarity, which solution would have the higher pH: cocaine hydrochloride, $C_{17}H_{21}O_4NH^+Cl^-$, or codeine hydrochloride, $C_{18}H_{21}ClO_3NH^+Cl^-$?

Practice Example B: Predict whether the solution NH_4CN(aq) is acidic, basic, or neutral; and explain the basis of your prediction.

▶ Solutions containing cyanide ion must be handled with extreme caution. They should be handled only in a fume hood by an operator wearing protective clothing.

EXAMPLE 16-13

Calculating the pH of a Solution in Which Hydrolysis Occurs. Sodium cyanide, NaCN, is extremely poisonous, but it has very useful applications in gold and silver metallurgy and in the electroplating of metals. Aqueous solutions of cyanides are especially hazardous if they become acidified, because toxic hydrogen cyanide gas, HCN(g), is released. Are NaCN(aq) solutions normally acidic, basic, or pH neutral? What is the pH of 0.50 M NaCN(aq)?

Solution

Na^+ does not hydrolyze, but as represented below, CN^- does hydrolyze, producing a basic solution. In the tabulation of the concentrations of the species involved in the hydrolysis reaction, let $[OH^-] = x$.

$$CN^- + H_2O \rightleftharpoons HCN + OH^-$$

initial concns:	0.50 M	—	—
changes:	$-x$ M	$+x$ M	$+x$ M
equil concns:	$(0.50 - x)$ M	x M	x M

Use equation (16.18) to obtain a value of K_b.

$$K_b = \frac{K_w}{K_a(HCN)} = \frac{1.0 \times 10^{-14}}{6.2 \times 10^{-10}} = 1.6 \times 10^{-5}$$

Now return to the tabulated data.

$$K_b = \frac{[HCN][OH^-]}{[CN^-]} = \frac{x \cdot x}{0.50 - x} = \frac{x^2}{0.50 - x} = 1.6 \times 10^{-5}$$

▶ The symbol $\ll$ means "much less than."

▶ The value of x: 2.8×10^{-3} is less than 1% of 0.500 M, so our assumption is valid.

Assume: $x \ll 0.50$ and $0.50 - x \approx 0.50$.

$$x^2 = 0.50 \times 1.6 \times 10^{-5} = 0.80 \times 10^{-5} = 8.0 \times 10^{-6}$$
$$x = [OH^-] = (8.0 \times 10^{-6})^{1/2} = 2.8 \times 10^{-3}$$
$$pOH = -\log[OH^-] = -\log(2.8 \times 10^{-3}) = 2.55$$
$$pH = 14.00 - pOH = 14.00 - 2.55 = 11.45$$

Practice Example A: Sodium fluoride, NaF, is found in some toothpaste formulations as an anticavity agent. What is the pH of 0.10 M NaF(aq)?

Practice Example B: The pH of an aqueous solution of NaCN is 10.38. What is $[CN^-]$ in this solution?

16-8 MOLECULAR STRUCTURE AND ACID–BASE BEHAVIOR

We have now dealt with a number of aspects of acid–base chemistry, both qualitatively and quantitatively. Yet some very fundamental questions still remain to be answered, such as these: Why is HCl a strong acid, whereas HF is a weak acid? Why is acetic acid (CH_3COOH) a stronger acid than ethanol (CH_3CH_2OH) but a weaker acid than chloroacetic acid ($ClCH_2COOH$)?

These questions involve relative acid strengths. In this section, we will examine the relationship between molecular structure and the strengths of acids and bases.

▶ Many molecular structures can be viewed on computers and shown in class using the 3-D viewer called Chime (the web version of Rasmol). This can be obtained for no charge from http://www.mdlchime.com/chime/ (commercial site).

STRENGTHS OF BINARY ACIDS

Because the behavior of acids requires the loss of a proton through bond breakage, acid strength and bond strength appear to be related. To relate the acidities of the HX binary acids to the mere breaking of the H—X bond is an oversimplification, however. For one thing, bond energies are based on the dissociation of gaseous species, and here we are dealing with the ionization of species in solution. Nevertheless, it is true that, in general, the stronger the H—X bond, the *weaker* the acid is, and that strong bonds are characterized by short bond lengths and high bond-dissociation energies. For the binary acids of group 17, bond lengths *decrease* and bond-dissociation energies *increase* in the following order:

	HI		**HBr**		**HCl**		**HF**
bond length:	160.9	>	141.4	>	127.4	>	91.7 pm
bond dissociation energy:	297	<	368	<	431	<	569 kJ/mol

and acid strengths *decrease* in the order

$$K_a = \underbrace{10^9 > 10^8 > 1.3 \times 10^6}_{\text{strong}} > \underbrace{6.6 \times 10^{-4}}_{\text{weak}}$$

with the labels **HI   HBr   HCl   HF** above.

That HF is a weaker acid than the other hydrogen halides is expected, but that it should be so much weaker has always seemed an anomaly. Explanations of this behavior center on the tendency for hydrogen bonding in HF (recall Figure 12-28). For example, in HF(aq), ion pairs are held together by strong hydrogen bonds, which keeps the concentration of free H_3O^+ from being as large as otherwise expected.

$$HF + H_2O \longrightarrow (^-F \cdots H_3O^+) \rightleftharpoons H_3O^+ + F^-$$
$$\text{ion pair}$$

When we compare the strengths of binary acids within a *period*, bond polarity proves to be the dominant factor. The greater the electronegativity difference (ΔEN) in the bond H—X, the more polar is the bond. Thus, the loss of H^+ to a base occurs more readily from a polar bond, where partial ionic charges already exist, than from a nonpolar bond.

	CH$_4$		**NH$_3$**		**H$_2$O**		**HF**
ΔEN:	0.4	<	0.9	<	1.4	<	1.9

CH_4 and NH_3 do not have acidic properties in water. The acidity of H_2O is very limited ($K_w = 1.0 \times 10^{-14}$), but HF is an acid of moderate strength ($K_a = 6.6 \times 10^{-4}$).

STRENGTHS OF OXOACIDS

To describe the relative strengths of oxoacids, we must focus on the attraction of electrons from the O—H bond toward the central atom. The following factors promote this electron withdrawal from O—H bonds: (1) a high electronegativity (EN) of the central atom and (2) a large number of terminal O atoms in the acid molecule.

◀ The term *oxoacid* was defined in Chapter 3.

Neither HOCl nor HOBr has a terminal O atom. The major difference between the two acids is one of electronegativity—Cl is slightly more electronegative than Br. As expected, HOCl is more acidic than HOBr.

$$H—\ddot{O}—\ddot{C}l\!:$$
$$EN_{Cl} = 3.0$$
$$K_a = 2.9 \times 10^{-8}$$

$$H—\ddot{O}—\ddot{B}r\!:$$
$$EN_{Br} = 2.8$$
$$K_a = 2.1 \times 10^{-9}$$

To compare the acid strengths of H_2SO_4 and H_2SO_3, we must look beyond the central atom, which is S in each acid.

A highly electronegative terminal O atom tends to withdraw electrons from the O—H bonds, weakening the bonds and increasing the acidity of the molecule. Because H_2SO_4 has *two* terminal O atoms to only one in H_2SO_3, the electron-withdrawing effect is greater in H_2SO_4. As a result, H_2SO_4 is a stronger acid than H_2SO_3.

STRENGTHS OF ORGANIC ACIDS

Perez, G. V., Perez A. L., "Organic Acids without a Carboxylic Acid Functional Group." *J. Chem. Educ.* **2000:** 77, 910 (July 2000).

This discussion of the relationship between molecular structure and acid strength concludes with a brief consideration of some organic compounds. Consider first the case of acetic acid and ethanol. Both have an O—H group bonded to a carbon atom, but acetic acid is a much stronger acid than ethanol.

acetic acid
$K_a = 1.8 \times 10^{-5}$

ethanol
$K_a = 1.3 \times 10^{-16}$

Review the concept of resonance. Compounds or ions with more resonance structures are more stable.

One possible explanation for the large difference in acidity of these two compounds is that the highly electronegative terminal O atom in acetic acid withdraws electrons from the O—H bond. The bond is weakened, and a proton (H^+) is more readily taken from a molecule of the acid by a base. A more satisfactory explanation focuses on the anions formed in the ionization.

acetate ion   ethoxide ion

There are two plausible structures for the acetate ion. These structures suggest that each carbon-to-oxygen bond is a "$\frac{3}{2}$" bond and that each O atom carries "$\frac{1}{2}$" unit of negative charge. In short, the excess unit of negative charge in CH_3COO^- is spread out. This arrangement reduces the ability of either O atom to attach a proton and makes acetate ion only a weak Brønsted–Lowry base. In ethoxide ion, conversely, the unit of negative charge is localized on the single O atom. Ethoxide ion is a much stronger base than is acetate ion. The stronger the conjugate base, the weaker the corresponding acid.

The length of the carbon chain in a carboxylic acid has little effect on the acid strength, as in a comparison of acetic acid and octanoic acid.

CH_3COOH
acetic acid
$K_a = 1.8 \times 10^{-5}$

$CH_3(CH_2)_6COOH$
octanoic acid
$K_a = 1.3 \times 10^{-5}$

Yet, other atoms or groups of atoms substituted onto the carbon chain may strongly affect acid strength. If a Cl atom is substituted for one of the H atoms that is bonded to carbon in acetic acid, the result is chloroacetic acid.

$$\begin{array}{c}
\quad\;\; \text{Cl} \quad\; \text{O} \\
\quad\;\; | \quad\;\; \| \\
\text{H}-\text{C}-\text{C}-\text{O}-\text{H} \\
\quad\;\; | \\
\quad\;\; \text{H}
\end{array}$$

chloroacetic acid
$K_a = 1.4 \times 10^{-3}$

The highly electronegative Cl atom helps draw electrons away from the O—H bond. The O—H bond is weakened, the proton is lost more readily, and the acid is a stronger acid than acetic acid. This effect falls off rapidly as the distance increases between the substituted atom or group and the O—H bond in an organic acid.

Example 16-14 illustrates some of the factors affecting acid strength that are discussed in this section.

EXAMPLE 16-14

Identifying Factors That Affect the Strengths of Acids. Explain which member of each of the following pairs is the stronger acid.

(a) (I) H—O—P—O—H   or (II) :O—Cl—O—H
with :O: above P and :O—H below; with :O: above Cl

(b) (I) :Cl—C—C—C—O—H   or (II) H—C—C—C—O—H

Solution

(a) Phosphoric acid, H_3PO_4, has four O atoms to the three in $HClO_3$, but it is the number of *terminal* O atoms that we must consider, not just the total number of O atoms in the molecule. $HClO_3$ has *two* terminal O atoms and H_3PO_4 has *one*. Also, the Cl atom (EN = 3.0) is considerably more electronegative than the P atom (EN = 2.1). These facts point to chloric acid (II) as being the stronger of the two acids. ($K_a \approx 5 \times 10^2$ for $HClO_3$ and $K_{a_1} = 7.1 \times 10^{-3}$ for H_3PO_4.)

(b) The Cl atom withdraws electrons more strongly when it is directly adjacent to the carboxyl group. Compound (II), 2-chloropropanoic acid ($K_a = 1.4 \times 10^{-3}$), is a stronger acid than compound (I), 3-chloropropanoic acid ($K_a = 1.0 \times 10^{-4}$).

Practice Example A: Explain which is the stronger acid, HNO_3 or $HClO_4$; CH_2FCOOH or $CH_2BrCOOH$.

[*Hint:* Draw plausible Lewis structures.]

Practice Example B: Explain which is the stronger acid, H_3PO_4 or H_2SO_3; CCl_3CH_2COOH or CCl_2FCH_2COOH.

[*Hint:* Draw plausible Lewis structures.]

STRENGTHS OF AMINES AS BASES

The fundamental factor affecting the strength of an amine as a base concerns the ability of the lone pair of electrons on the N atom to bind a proton taken from an acid. When an atom or group of atoms more electronegative than H replaces one of the H atoms of NH_3, the electronegative group withdraws electron density from the N atom. The lone-pair electrons cannot bind a proton as strongly, and the base is weaker. Thus, bromamine, in which the electronegative Br atom is attached to the amine group (NH_2), is a *weaker* base than ammonia.

H—N: Br—N:
ammonia   bromamine
$pK_b = 4.74$ $NH_2Br, pK_b = 7.61$

Hydrocarbon chains have no electron-withdrawing ability. When they are attached to the amine group, the pK_b values are lower than for ammonia due to the electron-donating ability of CH_3 and CH_2CH_3.

ammonia   methylamine   ethylamine
$pK_b = 4.74$ $CH_3NH_2, pK_b = 3.38$ $CH_3CH_2NH_2, pK_b = 3.37$

An additional electron-withdrawing effect is seen in amines that are based on the benzene ring or related structures. Such amines are called *aromatic* amines. Cyclohexylamine, $C_6H_{11}NH_2$, is based on cyclohexane, C_6H_{12}, which is a six-carbon alkane that forms a ring rather than a chain. Aniline, $C_6H_5NH_2$, is based on benzene, C_6H_6, which is a six-carbon ring molecule with unsaturation in the carbon-to-carbon bonds. The electrons associated with this unsaturation are said to be *delocalized*. As suggested by the following structures, to some extent even the lone-pair electrons of the NH_2 group participate in the "spreading out" of delocalized electrons. (The curved arrows suggest the progressive movement of electrons around the ring.)

> ✓ Note that these are actually resonance Lewis structures.

The withdrawal of electron charge density from the NH_2 group causes aniline to be a much weaker base than is cyclohexylamine. (H atoms bonded to ring carbon atoms are not shown in the following structures.)

cyclohexylamine, $pK_b = 3.36$ aniline, $pK_b = 9.13$

> ✓ The pK_b for *meta*-chloroaniline is 10.66.

Replacement of a ring-bound H atom in aniline with an atom or group that has a high electronegativity causes even more electron density to be drawn away from the NH_2 group, further reducing the base strength. Also, the closer this ring substituent is to the NH_2 group, the greater is the effect.

para-chloroaniline, $pK_b = 10.01$ *ortho*-chloroaniline, $pK_b = 11.36$

CONCEPT ASSESSMENT ✓

Would you expect pK_a of *ortho*-chlorophenol to be greater than, less than, or nearly the same as that of phenol? Explain.

phenol, pK_a = 10.00   *ortho*-chlorophenol, pK_a = ?

16-9   LEWIS ACIDS AND BASES

In the previous section, we presented ideas about the molecular structures of acids and bases. In 1923, G. N. Lewis proposed an acid–base theory closely related to bonding and structure. The Lewis acid–base theory is not limited to reactions involving H^+ and OH^-: It extends acid–base concepts to reactions in gases and in solids. It is especially important in describing certain reactions between organic molecules.

A **Lewis acid** is a species (an atom, ion, or molecule) that is an *electron-pair acceptor*, and a **Lewis base** is a species that is an *electron-pair donor*. A reaction between a Lewis acid (A) and a Lewis base (B:) results in the formation of a covalent bond between them. The product of a Lewis acid–base reaction is called an **adduct** (or *addition compound*). The reaction can be represented as

$$B: + A \longrightarrow B:A$$

where B:A is the adduct. The formation of a covalent chemical bond by one species donating a pair of electrons to another is called *coordination*, and the bond joining the Lewis acid and Lewis base is called a *coordinate covalent bond* (see page 377). *Lewis acids* are species with vacant orbitals that can accommodate electron pairs; *Lewis bases* are species that have lone-pair electrons available for sharing.

By these definitions, OH^-, a Brønsted–Lowry base, is also a Lewis base because lone-pair electrons are present on the O atom. So too is NH_3 a Lewis base. HCl, conversely, is not a Lewis acid: It is not an electron-pair acceptor. We can think of HCl as producing H^+, however, and H^+ is a Lewis acid. H^+ forms a coordinate covalent bond with an available electron pair.

Species with an incomplete valence shell are Lewis acids. When the Lewis acid forms a coordinate covalent bond with a Lewis base, the octet is completed. A good example of octet completion is the reaction of BF_3 and NH_3.

The reaction of lime (CaO) with sulfur dioxide is an important reaction for reducing SO_2 emissions from coal-fired power plants. This reaction between a solid and a gas underscores that Lewis acid–base reactions can occur in all states of matter. The small curved red arrow in reaction (16.19) suggests that an electron pair in the Lewis structure is rearranged.

$$Ca^{2+} :\overset{..}{\underset{..}{O}}:^{2-} + \quad \overset{\overset{..}{O}:}{\underset{\overset{..}{O}:}{S:}} \quad \longrightarrow \quad Ca^{2+} \left[:\overset{..}{\underset{..}{O}} - \overset{\overset{..}{O}:}{\underset{\overset{..}{O}:}{S:}} \right]^{2-} \qquad (16.19)$$

Lewis Acid–Base Theory animation

☑ Organic chemistry is dominated by Lewis acid–base reactions. This section also introduces the arrow pushing mechanisms that students will use in organic chemistry.

◀ Bonding in the $H_3N—BF_3$ adduct can be described by the overlap of sp^3 orbitals on the N and B atoms, with the two electrons donated by the N atom.

▲ **FIGURE 16-10**
The Lewis structure of $[Al(H_2O)_6]^{3+}$ and a ball-and-stick representation

▲ **FIGURE 16-12**
Acidic properties of hydrated metal ions
The yellow color of bromthymol blue indicator in $Al_2(SO_4)_3$(aq) denotes that the solution is acidic. The pH meter gives a more precise indication of the pH.

An important application of the Lewis acid–base theory involves the formation of *complex ions*. Complex ions are polyatomic ions that contain a central metal ion to which other ions or small molecules are attached. *Hydrated metal ions* form in aqueous solution because the water acts as a Lewis base and the metal ion as a Lewis acid. The water molecules attach themselves to the metal ion by means of coordinate covalent bonds. Thus, for example, when anhydrous $AlCl_3$ is added to water, the resultant solution becomes hot because of the heat evolved in the formation of the hydrated metal ion $[Al(H_2O)_6]^{3+}$(aq) (Fig. 16-10).

The interaction between the metal ion and the water molecules is so strong that when the salt is crystallized from the solution, the water molecules crystallize along with the metal ion, forming the hydrated metal salt $AlCl_3 \cdot 6\ H_2O$. In aqueous solution, the hydrated metal ions can act as Brønsted acids. For instance, the hydrolysis of hydrated Al^{3+} is given by

$$[Al(H_2O)_6]^{3+} + H_2O \rightleftharpoons [Al(OH)(H_2O)_5]^{2+} + H_3O^+$$

In the hydrated metal ion, the OH bond in a water molecule becomes weakened. This happens because, in forming the coordinate covalent bond with the O atom of the water, the metal ion causes electron density to be drawn toward it; hence, electron density is drawn away from the OH bond. As a consequence, the coordinated H_2O molecule can donate a H^+ to a solvent H_2O molecule (Fig. 16-11). The H_2O molecule that has ionized is converted to OH^-, which remains attached to the Al^{3+}; the charge on the complex ion is reduced from 3+ to 2+. The extent of ionization of $[Al(H_2O)_6]^{3+}$, measured by its K_a value and as pictured in Figure 16-12, is essentially the same as that of acetic acid ($K_a = 1.8 \times 10^{-5}$). Many other metal ions hydrolyze, especially the transition metal ions. These and other hydrated metal ions acting as acids are discussed in later chapters.

Complex ions can also form between transition metal ions and other Lewis bases, such as NH_3. For instance, Zn^{2+} combines with NH_3 to form the complex ion $[Zn(NH_3)_4]^{2+}$. The central Zn^{2+} ion accepts electrons from the Lewis base NH_3. to form coordinate covalent bonds; it is a Lewis acid. We will discuss the application of Lewis acid–base theory to complex ions in Chapter 24.

$$Al(H_2O)_6{}^{3+} + H_2O \rightleftharpoons [Al(OH)(H_2O)_5]^{2+} + H_3O^+$$

▲ **FIGURE 16-11**
Hydrolysis of $[Al(H_2O)_6]^{3+}$ to produce H_3O^+
An uncoordinated water molecule removes a proton from a coordinated water molecule.

EXAMPLE 16-15

Identifying Lewis Acids and Bases. According to the Lewis theory, each of the following is an acid–base reaction. Which species is the acid and which is the base?

(a) $BF_3 + F^- \longrightarrow BF_4{}^-$

(b) OH^-(aq) $+ CO_2$(aq) $\longrightarrow HCO_3{}^-$(aq)

Are You Wondering . . .

Why Na$^+$(aq) does not act as an acid in aqueous solution?

Whether an aqueous solution of a metal ion is acidic depends on two principal factors. The first is the amount of charge on the cation; the second is the size of the ion. The greater the charge on the cation, the greater is the ability of the metal ion to draw electron density away from the O—H bond in a H_2O molecule in its hydration sphere, favoring the release of a H^+ ion. The smaller the cation, the more highly concentrated is the positive charge. Hence, for a given positive charge, the smaller the cation, the more acidic the solution.

The ratio of the charge on the cation to the volume of the cation is called the *charge density*.

$$\text{charge density} = \frac{\text{ionic charge}}{\text{ionic volume}}$$

The greater its charge density, the more effective a metal ion is at pulling electron density from the O—H bond and the more acidic is the hydrated cation. A highly concentrated positive charge on a small cation is better able to pull electron density from the O—H bond than is a less concentrated positive charge on a larger cation.

Thus the small (53 pm ionic radius), highly charged Al^{3+} ion produces acidic solutions, but the larger (99 pm) Na$^+$ cation, with a charge of just 1+, does not increase the concentration of H_3O^+. In fact, none of the group 1 cations produces appreciably acidic solutions, and only Be^{2+} of the group 2 elements is small enough to do so ($pK_a = 5.4$).

Solution

(a) In BF_3, the B atom has a vacant orbital and an incomplete octet. The fluoride ion has an outer-shell octet of electrons. BF_3 is the electron-pair acceptor—the acid. F^- is the electron-pair donor—the base.

(b) We have already identified OH^- as a Lewis base, so we might suspect that it is the base and that CO_2(aq) is the Lewis acid. The following Lewis structures show this to be so. As in reaction (16.19), a rearrangement of an electron pair at one of the double bonds is also required, as indicated by the red arrow.

Carbon Dioxide Behaves as an Acid in Water movie

Practice Example A: Identify the Lewis acids and bases in these reactions.

(a) $BF_3 + NH_3 \longrightarrow F_3BNH_3$

(b) $Cr^{3+} + 6\,H_2O \longrightarrow [Cr(H_2O)_6]^{3+}$

Practice Example B: Identify the Lewis acids and bases in these reactions.

(a) $Al(OH)_3 + OH^- \longrightarrow [Al(OH)_4]^-$

(b) $SnCl_4 + 2\,Cl^- \longrightarrow [SnCl_6]^{2-}$

CONCEPT ASSESSMENT ✓

Liquid bromine in the presence of iron(III) tribromide forms a bromonium:iron(III) tribromide adduct. Propose a plausible mechanism for adduct formation and identify the Lewis acid and Lewis base. [*Hint:* What is the iron(III) electron configuration?]

◄ On the left is a marble statue of George Washington as it appeared in 1935. On the right is the same statue 59 years later. The effects of acid rain are clearly evident.

Pure water has pH = 7, but not rainwater—it is acidic. The natural pH of rainwater should be about 5.6. In recent years, however, the pH of rainfall in northeastern United States has averaged about 4.5. Some rainfall has been found to be even more acidic than that; in one episode on the West Coast in 1982, the pH of fog was 1.7. Let us briefly consider both the natural sources of acidity in rainwater and how human activities have contributed to acid rain.

$CO_2(g)$ is an acidic oxide. Although H_2CO_3 cannot be isolated, it is customary to consider that CO_2 reacts with water to form carbonic acid. The acidity of rainwater arises mostly through the first ionization step of this acid.

Summary

16-1 Arrhenius Theory—The central concept in Arrhenius theory describes a neutralization reaction as the combination of hydrogen ions and hydroxide ions to form water (expression 16.1). A major failing of this theory is that it does not account for the key role of the solvent in the ionization of a solute.

16-2 Brønsted–Lowry Theory of Acids and Bases—The Brønsted–Lowry theory describes an acid as a **proton donor** and a base as a **proton acceptor**. In an acid–base reaction, a base takes a proton (H^+) from an acid. In general, acid–base reactions are reversible, but equilibrium is displaced in the direction from the *stronger* acids and bases to their *weaker* conjugates. The **conjugate base** (A^-) is derived from the acid HA while the **conjugate acid** (HB^+) is derived from the base (B). The combinations of HA/A^- and B/HB^+ are known as conjugate acid–base pairs. The conjugate acid of the base H_2O is the **hydronium ion**, H_3O^+. The equilibrium constants representing the ionization of an acid or a base in water are commonly referred to as the **acid ionization constant** and **base ionization constant**, respectively. Certain substances, for example water, are said to be **amphiprotic**. They can act as an acid or base.

16-3 Self-Ionization of Water and the pH Scale—In pure water and in aqueous solutions, **self-ionization** of the water occurs to a very slight extent, producing H_3O^+ and OH^-, as described by the equilibrium constant K_w, known as the **ion product of water** (expression 16.7). The designations **pH** (expression 16.8) and **pOH** (expression 16.9) are often used to describe the concentrations of H_3O^+ and OH in aqueous solutions.

16-4 Strong Acids and Strong Bases—In aqueous solutions, strong acids ionize completely to produce H_3O^+, and strong bases dissociate completely to produce OH^-. Common strong acids and bases are given in Table 16.2 and can be easily memorized.

16-5 Weak Acids and Weak Bases—The ionizations of weak acids and weak bases are reversible reactions, and the extent of their ionization can be related to the ionization constants K_a and K_b or their logarithmic equivalents $pK_a = -\log K_a$ and $pK_b = -\log K_b$ (Table 16.3). Another method used to indicate the degree of ionization is **percent ionization** (expression 16.14). The acidity of many weak acids is associated with the carboxylic acid group, —COOH (page 95). Weak bases typically contain one or more nitrogen atoms. Calculations involving ionization equilibria are in many ways similar to those introduced in Chapter 15, although some additional considerations are necessary for polyprotic acids.

16-6 Polyprotic Acids—**Polyprotic acids** are acids with more than one ionizable H atom that undergo a stepwise ionization and have a different ionization constant, K_{a_1}, $K_{a_2}, \ldots$, for each ionization step.

16-7 Ions as Acids and Bases—In reactions between ions and water—**hydrolysis** reactions—the ions react as weak acids or weak bases. The pH of salt solutions depends on the anions and/or cations present. Anions from weak acids lead to solutions with pH > 7 while cations from weak bases lead to pH < 7.

$$CO_2(g) + H_2O \longrightarrow H_2CO_3$$
$$H_2CO_3 + H_2O \rightleftharpoons H_3O^+ + HCO_3^-$$
$$K_{a_1} = 4.4 \times 10^{-7}$$

Rainwater in equilibrium with atmospheric $CO_2(g)$ at its normal partial pressure of 0.0037 atm has a pH of about 5.6.

$NO(g)$ is formed in lightning storms through the high-temperature reaction of $N_2(g)$ and $O_2(g)$ in air. This reaction is followed by the oxidation of $NO(g)$ to $NO_2(g)$ in air. Nitric acid forms by the reaction

$$3\ NO_2(g) + H_2O(l) \longrightarrow 2\ HNO_3(aq) + NO(g)$$

To some extent, then, naturally produced nitric acid contributes to the acidity of rain. More important, though, is $HNO_3(aq)$ derived from artificial sources of $NO(g)$—primarily, high-temperature combustion processes in air, such as those that occur in automobile engines and power plants. In southern California, for example, where the oxides of nitrogen are implicated in the formation of photochemical smog, HNO_3 is a major contributor to acid rain. On average, nitric acid accounts for about one-quarter of the acidity of acid rain.

$SO_2(g)$ is normally only a trace constituent of the atmosphere, being produced mostly by biological decay and volcanic activity. Artificial sources of $SO_2(g)$ are substantial, however, and they create higher-than-normal concentrations in many areas. The chief source of SO_2 is the combustion of sulfur-containing coal (up to 8% S) in electric power plants. Another source is the extraction of certain metals from their sulfide ores. In the atmosphere, $SO_2(g)$ can be oxidized by any of several routes to $SO_3(g)$, and SO_3 is the acid anhydride of sulfuric acid. Sulfuric acid accounts for well over one-half of the acidity of acid rain.

Some effects of acid rain are clearly visible in urban areas, particularly in the degradation of statues, monuments, and buildings made of sandstone, limestone, or marble. In India, acidic air pollutants from nearby industrial plants threaten to destroy the Taj Mahal, the famous marble mausoleum that is more than 350 years old. The most serious ecological effects, though, are on forests and on freshwater lakes and streams. Fish and other aquatic life may be killed in acidic lakes. To maintain healthy forests, the soil must furnish certain nutrients while it immobilizes other species, such as Al^{3+}, that interfere with the nutritional cycle of trees. Acidic rainwater typically leaches important nutrients from the soil and at the same time frees up or mobilizes undesirable soil species.

Measures to reduce $SO_2(g)$ and $NO(g)$ emissions include the use of low-sulfur fuels, the control of combustion temperatures to reduce $NO(g)$ emissions, and the trapping of offending flue gases by various means.

16-8 Molecular Structure and Acid–Base Behavior— Molecular composition and structure are the keys to determining whether a substance is acidic, basic, or amphiprotic. In addition, molecular structure affects whether an acid or base is strong or weak. In assessing acid strength, for example, factors that affect the strength of the bond that must be broken to release H^+ must be considered. In assessing base strength, factors that affect the ability of lone-pair electrons to bind a proton are of primary concern.

16-9 Lewis Acids and Bases— The Lewis acid–base theory views an electron-pair acceptor as a **Lewis acid** and an electron-pair donor as a **Lewis base**. The addition compound of a Lewis acid–base reaction is referred to as an **adduct**. The theory is most useful in situations that cannot be described by means of proton transfers, for example, in reactions involving gases and solids and in reactions between organic compounds (considered in Chapter 26).

Integrative Example

Bromoacetic acid, $BrCH_2COOH$, has $pK_a = 2.902$. Calculate the expected values of **(a)** the freezing point of 0.0500 M $BrCH_2COOH(aq)$ and **(b)** the osmotic pressure at 25 °C of 0.00500 M $BrCH_2COOH(aq)$.

Strategy

Freezing point and osmotic pressure are both colligative properties. As we saw in Chapter 13, the values of these properties depend on the total concentrations of particles (molecules and ions) in a solution, but not on the identity of those particles. We can use the ICE method for equilibrium calculations (Chapter 15) to determine the total concentrations of particles (molecules and ions) in a weak electrolyte solution, as we learned to do in this chapter. Once we have those results we can turn to equations (13.5) and (13.4) to do the calculations required in parts (a) and (b).

Solution

A good place to begin is to convert the pK_a for bromoacetic acid to K_a.

$$pK_a = 2.902 = -\log K_a$$
$$K_a = 10^{-2.902} = 1.25 \times 10^{-3}$$

Next, write the equation for the reversible ionization reaction and the equilibrium constant expression.

$$BrCH_2COOH + H_2O \rightleftharpoons H_3O^+ + BrCH_2COO^-$$
$$K_a = \frac{[H_3O^+][BrCH_2COO^-]}{[BrCH_2COOH]} = 1.25 \times 10^{-3}$$

(a) Enter the relevant data into the ICE format under the equation for the ionization reaction.

$$BrCH_2COOH + H_2O \rightleftharpoons H_3O^+ + BrCH_2COO^-$$

initial concns:	0.0500 M	—	—
changes:	$-x$ M	$+x$ M	$+x$ M
equil concs:	$(0.0500 - x)$ M	x M	x M

The equilibrium constant expression based on these data is

$$K_a = \frac{[H_3O^+][BrCH_2COO^-]}{[BrCH_2COOH]} = \frac{x \cdot x}{0.0500 - x} = 1.25 \times 10^{-3}$$

Solve for x.

$$x^2 + 1.25 \times 10^{-3}x - 6.25 \times 10^{-5} = 0$$

$$x = \frac{-1.25 \times 10^{-3} \pm \sqrt{(1.25 \times 10^{-3})^2 + 4 \times 6.25 \times 10^{-5}}}{2}$$

$$x = \frac{-1.25 \times 10^{-3} \pm 1.59 \times 10^{-2}}{2} = 7.3 \times 10^{-3} \text{ M}$$

The total concentration of molecules and ions at equilibrium is

$$(0.0500 - x) \text{ M} + x \text{ M} + x \text{ M} = (0.0500 + x) \text{ M} = 0.0573 \text{ M}$$

Assuming that 0.0573 M = 0.0573 m, the freezing point depression of water caused by 0.0573 mol/L of particles is

$$\Delta T_f = -K_f \times m = -1.86 \text{ °C } m^{-1} \times 0.0573 \ m = -0.107 \text{ °C}$$

The freezing point of 0.0500 M $BrCH_2COOH(aq)$ is 0.107 °C below the freezing point of water (0.000 °C), that is, −0.107 °C.

(b) Enter the relevant data into the ICE format under the equation for the ionization reaction.

$$BrCH_2COOH + H_2O \rightleftharpoons H_3O^+ + BrCH_2COO^-$$

initial concns:	0.00500 M	—	—
changes:	$-x$ M	$+x$ M	$+x$ M
equil concs:	$(0.00500 - x)$ M	x M	x M

The equilibrium constant expression based on these data is

$$K_a = \frac{[H_3O^+][BrCH_2COO^-]}{[BrCH_2COOH]} = \frac{x \cdot x}{0.00500 - x} = 1.25 \times 10^{-3}$$

Solve for x.

$$x^2 + 1.25 \times 10^{-3}x - 6.25 \times 10^{-6} = 0$$

$$x = \frac{-1.25 \times 10^{-3} \pm \sqrt{(1.25 \times 10^{-3})^2 + 4 \times 6.25 \times 10^{-6}}}{2}$$

$$x = \frac{-1.25 \times 10^{-3} \pm 5.15 \times 10^{-3}}{2} = 1.95 \times 10^{-3} \text{ M}$$

The total concentration of molecules and ions at equilibrium is

$$(0.00500 - x) \text{ M} + x \text{ M} + x \text{ M} = (0.00500 + x) \text{ M} = 0.00695 \text{ M}$$

At 25.00 °C, the osmotic pressure of an aqueous solution with 0.00695 mol/L of particles (molecules and ions) is

$$\pi = M \times RT = 0.00695 \text{ mol L}^{-1} \times 0.08206 \text{ L atm mol}^{-1} \text{ K}^{-1} \times$$
$$298.15 \text{ K} = 0.170 \text{ atm}$$

Assessment

The pK_a is stated more precisely than in most previous equilibrium calculations, and this permitted us to carry three significant figures rather than the usual two in most of the calculation. The assumption in part (a) that 0.0573 M = 0.0573 m is reasonable for a dilute aqueous solution with a density of essentially 1.00 g/mL. The mass of solvent (water) in one liter of solution is very close to one kilogram, so that molarity (mol solute/L solution) and molality (mol solute/kg solvent) are essentially the same. The calculation in part (b) could have been done more easily by assuming that the concentration of solute particles would be just 10% of that in part (a), that is, 0.00573 M compared to 0.0573 M. However, this would have been a false assumption. Because the percent ionization of the acid is a function of its concentration, the total particle concentration in part (b) was about 12% of that found in part (a), not 10%.

Exercises

Brønsted–Lowry Theory of Acids and Bases

1. According to the Brønsted–Lowry theory, label each of the following as an acid or a base. **(a)** HNO_2; **(b)** OCl^-; **(c)** NH_2^-; **(d)** NH_4^+; **(e)** $CH_3NH_3^+$

2. Write the formula of the conjugate base in the reaction of each acid with water. **(a)** HIO_3; **(b)** C_6H_5COOH; **(c)** HPO_4^{2-}; **(d)** $C_2H_5NH_3^+$

3. For each of the following, identify the acids and bases involved in both the forward and reverse directions.
   (a) $HOBr + H_2O \rightleftharpoons OBr^- + H_3O^+$
   (b) $HSO_4^- + H_2O \rightleftharpoons SO_4^{2-} + H_3O^+$
   (c) $HS^- + H_2O \rightleftharpoons H_2S + OH^-$
   (d) $C_6H_5NH_3^+ + OH^- \rightleftharpoons C_6H_5NH_2 + H_2O$

4. Which of the following species are *amphiprotic* in aqueous solution? For such a species, write one equation showing it acting as an acid, and another equation showing it acting as a base. OH^-, NH_4^+, H_2O, HS^-, NO_2^-, HCO_3^-, HBr

5. With which of the following bases will the ionization of acetic acid, $HC_2H_3O_2$, proceed furthest toward completion (to the right): **(a)** H_2O; **(b)** NH_3; **(c)** Cl^-; **(d)** NO_3^-? Explain your answer.

6. In a manner similar to equation (16.6), represent the self-ionization of the following liquid solvents: **(a)** NH_3; **(b)** HF; **(c)** CH_3OH; **(d)** $HC_2H_3O_2$; **(e)** H_2SO_4.

7. With the aid of Table 16.1, predict the direction (forward or reverse) favored in each of the following acid–base reactions.
   (a) $NH_4^+ + OH^- \rightleftharpoons H_2O + NH_3$
   (b) $HSO_4^- + NO_3^- \rightleftharpoons HNO_3 + SO_4^{2-}$
   (c) $CH_3OH + C_2H_3O_2^- \rightleftharpoons HC_2H_3O_2 + CH_3O^-$

8. With the aid of Table 16.1, predict the direction (forward or reverse) favored in each of the following acid–base reactions.
   (a) $HC_2H_3O_2 + CO_3^{2-} \rightleftharpoons HCO_3^- + C_2H_3O_2^-$
   (b) $HNO_2 + ClO_4^- \rightleftharpoons HClO_4 + NO_2^-$
   (c) $H_2CO_3 + CO_3^{2-} \rightleftharpoons HCO_3^- + HCO_3^-$

Strong Acids, Strong Bases, and pH

9. Calculate $[H_3O^+]$ and $[OH^-]$ for each solution: **(a)** 0.00165 M HNO_3; **(b)** 0.0087 M KOH; **(c)** 0.00213 M $Sr(OH)_2$; **(d)** 5.8×10^{-4} M HI.

10. What is the pH of each of the following solutions? **(a)** 0.0045 M HCl; **(b)** 6.14×10^{-4} M HNO_3; **(c)** 0.00683 M NaOH; **(d)** 4.8×10^{-3} M $Ba(OH)_2$

11. Calculate $[H_3O^+]$ and pH in saturated $Ba(OH)_2(aq)$, which contains 3.9 g $Ba(OH)_2 \cdot 8\,H_2O$ per 100 mL of solution.

12. A saturated aqueous solution of $Ca(OH)_2$ has a pH of 12.35. What is the solubility of $Ca(OH)_2$, expressed in milligrams per 100 mL of solution?

13. What is $[H_3O^+]$ in a solution obtained by dissolving 205 mL HCl(g), measured at 23 °C and 751 mmHg, in 4.25 L of aqueous solution?

14. What is the pH of the solution obtained when 125 mL of 0.606 M NaOH is diluted to 15.0 L with water?

15. How many milliliters of concentrated HCl(aq) (36.0% HCl by mass, $d = 1.18$ g/mL) are required to produce 12.5 L of a solution with pH = 2.10?

16. How many milliliters of a 15.0%, by mass solution of KOH(aq) ($d = 1.14$ g/mL) are required to produce 25.0 L of a solution with pH = 11.55?

17. What volume of 6.15 M HCl(aq) is required to exactly neutralize 1.25 L of 0.265 M $NH_3(aq)$?

$$NH_3(aq) + H_3O^+(aq) \longrightarrow NH_4^+(aq) + H_2O$$

18. A 28.2-L volume of HCl(g), measured at 742 mmHg and 25.0 °C, is dissolved in water. What volume of $NH_3(g)$, measured at 762 mmHg and 21.0 °C, must be absorbed by the same solution to neutralize the HCl?

19. 50.00 mL of 0.0155 M HI(aq) is mixed with 75.00 mL of 0.0106 M KOH(aq). What is the pH of the final solution?

20. 25.00 mL of a $HNO_3(aq)$ solution with a pH of 2.12 is mixed with 25.00 mL of a KOH(aq) solution with a pH of 12.65. What is the pH of the final solution?

Weak Acids, Weak Bases, and pH

(Use data from Table 16.3 as necessary.)

21. What are the $[H_3O^+]$ and pH of 0.143 M HNO_2?

22. What are the $[H_3O^+]$ and pH of 0.085 M $C_2H_5NH_2$?

23. For the ionization of phenylacetic acid,

$$HC_8H_7O_2 + H_2O \rightleftharpoons H_3O + C_8H_7O_2^-$$
$$K_a = 4.9 \times 10^{-5}$$

   (a) What is $[C_8H_7O_2^-]$ in 0.186 M $HC_8H_7O_2$?
   (b) What is the pH of 0.121 M $HC_8H_7O_2$?

24. A 625-mL sample of an aqueous solution containing 0.275 mol propionic acid, $HC_3H_5O_2$, has $[H_3O^+] = 0.00239$ M. What is the value of K_a for propionic acid?

$$HC_3H_5O_2 + H_2O \rightleftharpoons H_3O^+ + C_3H_5O_2^- \quad K_a = ?$$

25. Fluoroacetic acid occurs in gifblaar, one of the most poisonous of all plants. A 0.318 M solution of the acid is found to have a pH = 1.56. Calculate K_a of fluoroacetic acid.

$$CH_2FCOOH(aq) + H_2O \rightleftharpoons$$
$$H_3O^+(aq) + CH_2FCOO^-(aq) \quad K_a = ?$$

26. Caproic acid, $HC_6H_{11}O_2$, found in small amounts in coconut and palm oils, is used in making artificial flavors. A saturated aqueous solution of the acid contains 11 g/L and has pH = 2.94. Calculate K_a for the acid.

$$HC_6H_{11}O_2 + H_2O \rightleftharpoons H_3O^+ + C_6H_{11}O_2^- \quad K_a = ?$$

27. What mass of benzoic acid, $HC_7H_5O_2$, would you dissolve in 350.0 mL of water to produce a solution with a pH = 2.85?

$$HC_7H_5O_2 + H_2O \rightleftharpoons H_3O^+ + C_7H_5O_2^-$$
$$K_a = 6.3 \times 10^{-5}$$

28. What must be the molarity of an aqueous solution of trimethylamine, $(CH_3)_3N$, if it has a pH = 11.12?

$$(CH_3)_3N + H_2O \rightleftharpoons (CH_3)_3NH^+ + OH^-$$
$$K_b = 6.3 \times 10^{-5}$$

29. What are $[H_3O^+]$, $[OH^-]$, pH, and pOH of 0.55 M $HClO_2$?

30. What are $[H_3O^+]$, $[OH^-]$, pH, and pOH of 0.386 M CH_3NH_2?

31. The solubility of 1-naphthylamine, $C_{10}H_7NH_2$, a substance used in the manufacture of dyes, is given in a handbook as 1 g per 590 g H_2O. What is the approximate pH of a saturated aqueous solution of 1-naphthylamine?

$$C_{10}H_7NH_2 + H_2O \rightleftharpoons C_{10}H_7NH_3^+ + OH^-$$
$$pK_b = 3.92$$

32. A saturated aqueous solution of o-nitrophenol, $HOC_6H_4NO_2$, has pH = 4.53. What is the solubility of o-nitrophenol in water, in grams per liter?

$$HOC_6H_4NO_2 + H_2O \rightleftharpoons H_3O^+ + {}^-OC_6H_4NO_2$$
$$pK_a = 7.23$$

33. A particular vinegar is found to contain 5.7% acetic acid, $HC_2H_3O_2$, by mass. What mass of this vinegar should be diluted with water to produce 0.750 L of a solution with pH = 4.52?

34. A particular household ammonia solution ($d = 0.97$ g/mL) is 6.8% NH_3 by mass. How many milliliters of this solution should be diluted with water to produce 625 mL of a solution with pH = 11.55?

35. A 275-mL sample of vapor in equilibrium with 1-propylamine at 25.0 °C is removed and dissolved in 0.500 L H_2O. For 1-propylamine, $pK_b = 3.43$ and v.p. = 316 Torr.
    (a) What should be the pH of the aqueous solution?
    (b) How many mg of NaOH dissolved in 0.500 L of water give the same pH?

36. One handbook lists a value of 9.5 for pK_b of quinoline, C_9H_7N, a weak base used as a preservative for anatomical specimens and to make dyes. Another handbook lists the solubility of quinoline in water at 25 °C as 0.6 g/100 mL. Use this information to calculate the pH of a saturated solution of quinoline in water.

37. The sketch on the far left represents the $[H_3O^+]$ present in an acetic acid solution of molarity M. If the molarity of the solution is doubled, which of the sketches on the right best represents the resulting solution?

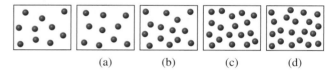

              (a)   (b)   (c)   (d)

38. The sketch on the far left represents the $[OH^-]$ present in an ammonia solution of molarity M. If the solution is diluted to half its original molarity, which of the sketches on the right best represents the resulting solution?

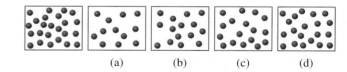

              (a)   (b)   (c)   (d)

Percent Ionization

39. What is the (a) degree of ionization and (b) percent ionization of propionic acid in a solution that is 0.45 M $HC_3H_5O_2$?

$$HC_3H_5O_2 + H_2O \rightleftharpoons H_3O^+ + C_3H_5O_2^-$$
$$pK_a = 4.89$$

40. What is the (a) degree of ionization and (b) percent ionization of ethylamine, $C_2H_5NH_2$, in an 0.85 M aqueous solution?

41. What must be the molarity of an aqueous solution of NH_3 if it is 4.2% ionized?

42. What must be the molarity of an acetic acid solution if it has the same percent ionization as 0.100 M $HC_3H_5O_2$ (propionic acid, $K_a = 1.3 \times 10^{-5}$)?

43. Continuing the dilutions described in Example 16-8, should we expect the percent ionization to be 13% in 0.0010 M $HC_2H_3O_2$ and 42% in 0.00010 M $HC_2H_3O_2$? Explain.

44. What is the (a) degree of ionization and (b) percent ionization of trichloroacetic acid in a 0.035 M $HC_2Cl_3O_2$ solution?

$$HC_2Cl_3O_2 + H_2O \rightleftharpoons H_3O^+ + C_2Cl_3O_2^-$$
$$pK_a = 0.52$$

Polyprotic Acids

(Use data from Table 16.4 as necessary.)

45. Explain why $[PO_4^{3-}]$ in 1.00 M H_3PO_4 is *not* simply $\frac{1}{3}[H_3O^+]$, but much, much less than $\frac{1}{3}[H_3O^+]$.

46. Cola drinks have a phosphoric acid content that is described as "from 0.057 to 0.084% of 75% phosphoric acid, by mass." Estimate the pH range of cola drinks corresponding to this range of H_3PO_4 content.

47. Determine $[H_3O^+]$, $[HS^-]$, and $[S^{2-}]$ for the following $H_2S(aq)$ solutions: **(a)** 0.075 M H_2S; **(b)** 0.0050 M H_2S; **(c)** 1.0×10^{-5} M H_2S.

48. For 0.045 M H_2CO_3, a weak diprotic acid, calculate **(a)** $[H_3O^+]$, **(b)** $[HCO_3^-]$, and **(c)** $[CO_3^{2-}]$. Use data from Table 16.4 as necessary.

49. Calculate $[H_3O^+]$, $[HSO_4^-]$, and $[SO_4^{2-}]$ in **(a)** 0.75 M H_2SO_4; **(b)** 0.075 M H_2SO_4; **(c)** 7.5×10^{-4} M H_2SO_4. [*Hint:* Check any assumptions that you make.]

50. Adipic acid, $HOOC(CH_2)_4COOH$, is among the top 50 manufactured chemicals in the United States (nearly 1 million tons annually). Its chief use is in the manufacture of nylon. It is a *diprotic* acid having $K_{a_1} = 3.9 \times 10^{-5}$ and $K_{a_2} = 3.9 \times 10^{-6}$. A saturated solution of adipic acid is about 0.10 M $HOOC(CH_2)_4$ $COOH$. Calculate the concentration of each ionic species in this solution.

51. The antimalarial drug quinine, $C_{20}H_{24}O_2N_2$, is a *diprotic base* with a water solubility of 1.00 g/1900 mL of solution.
    (a) Write equations for the ionization equilibria corresponding to $pK_{b_1} = 6.0$ and $pK_{b_2} = 9.8$.
    (b) What is the pH of saturated aqueous quinine?

52. For hydrazine, N_2H_4, $pK_{b_1} = 6.07$ and $pK_{b_2} = 15.05$. Draw a structural formula for hydrazine, and write equations to show the ionization of hydrazine in two distinctive steps. Calculate the pH of 0.245 M $N_2H_4(aq)$.

Ions as Acids and Bases (Hydrolysis)

53. Complete the following equations in those instances in which a reaction (hydrolysis) will occur. If no reaction occurs, so state.
    (a) $NH_4^+(aq) + NO_3^-(aq) + H_2O \longrightarrow$
    (b) $Na^+(aq) + NO_2^-(aq) + H_2O \longrightarrow$
    (c) $K^+(aq) + C_7H_5O_2^-(aq) + H_2O \longrightarrow$
    (d) $K^+(aq) + Cl^-(aq) + Na^+(aq) + I^-(aq) + H_2O \longrightarrow$
    (e) $C_6H_5NH_3^+(aq) + Cl^-(aq) + H_2O \longrightarrow$

54. From data in Table 16.3, determine **(a)** K_a for $C_5H_5NH^+$; **(b)** K_b for CHO_2^-; **(c)** K_b for $C_6H_5O^-$.

55. Predict whether a solution of each of the following salts is acidic, basic, or pH neutral: **(a)** KCl; **(b)** KF; **(c)** $NaNO_3$; **(d)** $Ca(OCl)_2$; **(e)** NH_4NO_2.

56. Arrange the following 0.010 M solutions in order of *increasing* pH: $NH_3(aq)$, $HNO_3(aq)$, $NaNO_2(aq)$, $HC_2H_3O_2(aq)$, $NaOH(aq)$, $NH_4C_2H_3O_2(aq)$, $NH_4ClO_4(aq)$.

57. What is the pH of an aqueous solution that is 0.089 M NaOCl?

58. What is the pH of an aqueous solution that is 0.123 M NH_4Cl?

59. Sorbic acid, $HC_6H_7O_2$ ($pK_a = 4.77$), is widely used in the food industry as a preservative. For example, its potassium salt (potassium sorbate) is added to cheese to inhibit the formation of mold. What is the pH of 0.37 M $KC_6H_7O_2(aq)$?

60. Pyridine, C_5H_5N ($pK_b = 8.82$), forms a salt, pyridinium chloride, as a result of a reaction with HCl. Write an ionic equation to represent the hydrolysis of the pyridinium ion, and calculate the pH of 0.0482 M $C_5H_5NH^+Cl^-(aq)$.

61. For each of the following ions, write two equations—one showing its ionization as an acid and the other as a base: **(a)** HSO_3^-; **(b)** HS^-; **(c)** HPO_4^-. Then use data from Table 16.4 to predict whether each ion makes the solution acidic or basic.

62. Suppose you wanted to produce an aqueous solution of pH = 8.65 by dissolving one of the following salts in water. Which salt would you use, and at what molarity? **(a)** NH_4Cl; **(b)** $KHSO_4$; **(c)** KNO_2; **(d)** $NaNO_3$.

Molecular Structure and Acid–Base Behavior

63. Predict which is the stronger acid: **(a)** $HClO_2$ or $HClO_3$; **(b)** H_2CO_3 or HNO_2; **(c)** H_2SiO_3 or H_3PO_4. Explain.

64. Explain why trichloroacetic acid, CCl_3COOH, is a stronger acid than acetic acid, CH_3COOH.

65. Which is the stronger acid of each of the following pairs of acids? Explain your reasoning. **(a)** HBr or HI; **(b)** HOClO or HOBr; **(c)** $I_3CCH_2CH_2COOH$ or $CH_3CH_2CCl_2COOH$.

66. Indicate which of the following is the *weakest* acid, and give reasons for your choice: HBr; $CH_2ClCOOH$; CH_3CH_2COOH; CH_2FCH_2COOH; CI_3COOH.

67. From the following bases, select the one with the *smallest* K_b and the one with the *largest* K_b, and give reasons for your choices.

    (a) **(b)**

    (c) $CH_3CH_2CH_2NH_2$ **(d)** $N\equiv CCH_2NH_2$

68. For the molecular models shown, write the formula of the species that is the most acidic and the one that is most basic, and give reasons for your choices.

(a)   (b)   (c)   (d)

Lewis Theory of Acids and Bases

69. Indicate whether each of the following is a Lewis acid or base. **(a)** OH^-; **(b)** $(C_2H_5)_3B$; **(c)** CH_3NH_2

70. Each of the following is a Lewis acid–base reaction. Which reactant is the acid, and which is the base? Explain.
   (a) $SO_3 + H_2O \longrightarrow H_2SO_4$
   (b) $Zn(OH)_2(s) + 2\,OH^-(aq) \longrightarrow [Zn(OH)_4]^{2-}(aq)$

71. The three following reactions are acid–base reactions according to the Lewis theory. Draw Lewis structures, and identify the Lewis acid and Lewis base in each reaction.
   (a) $B(OH)_3 + OH^- \longrightarrow [B(OH)_4]^-$
   (b) $N_2H_4 + H_3O^+ \longrightarrow N_2H_5^+ + H_2O$
   (c) $(C_2H_5)_2O + BF_3 \longrightarrow (C_2H_5)_2OBF_3$

72. $CO_2(g)$ can be removed from confined quarters (such as a spacecraft) by allowing it to react with an alkali metal hydroxide. Show that this is a Lewis acid–base reaction. For example,
   $$CO_2(g) + LiOH(s) \longrightarrow LiHCO_3(s)$$

73. The molecular solid $I_2(s)$ is only slightly soluble in water but will dissolve to a much greater extent in an aqueous solution of KI, because the I_3^- anion forms.

Write an equation for the formation of the I_3^- anion, and indicate the Lewis acid and Lewis base.

74. The following very strong acids are formed by the reactions indicated:
   $$HF + SbF_5 \longrightarrow HSbF_6$$
   (called "super acid," hexafluoroantimonic acid)
   $$HF + BF_3 \longrightarrow HBF_4$$
   (tetrafluoroboric acid)
   (a) Identify the Lewis acids and bases.
   (b) To which atom is the H atom bonded in each acid?

75. Use Lewis structures to diagram the following reaction in the manner of reaction (16.19).
   $$H_2O + SO_2 \longrightarrow H_2SO_3$$
   Identify the Lewis acid and Lewis base.

76. Use Lewis structures to diagram the following reaction in the manner of reaction (16.19).
   $$2\,NH_3 + Ag^+ \longrightarrow [Ag(NH_3)_2]^+$$
   Identify the Lewis acid and Lewis base.

Integrative and Advanced Exercises

77. The Brønsted–Lowry theory can be applied to acid–base reactions in nonaqueous solvents, where the relative strengths of acids and bases can differ from what they are in aqueous solutions. Indicate whether each of the following would be an acid, a base, or amphiprotic in pure liquid acetic acid, $HC_2H_3O_2$, as a solvent. **(a)** $C_2H_3O_2^-$; **(b)** H_2O; **(c)** $HC_2H_3O_2$; **(d)** $HClO_4$.
   [*Hint:* Refer to Table 16.1.]

78. The pH of saturated $Sr(OH)_2(aq)$ is found to be 13.12. A 10.0-mL sample of saturated $Sr(OH)_2(aq)$ is diluted to 250.0 mL in a volumetric flask. A 10.0-mL sample of the diluted $Sr(OH)_2(aq)$ is transferred to a beaker, and some water is added. The resulting solution requires 25.1 mL of a HCl solution for its titration. What is the molarity of this HCl solution?

79. Several approximate pH values are marked on the following pH scale.

Some of the following solutions can be matched to one of the approximate pH values marked on the scale; others cannot. For solutions that can be matched to a pH value, identify each solution and its pH value. Identify the solutions that cannot be matched, and give reasons why matches are not possible. **(a)** 0.010 M H_2SO_4; **(b)** 1.0 M NH_4Cl; **(c)** 0.050 M KI; **(d)** 0.0020 M CH_3NH_2; **(e)** 1.0 M NaOCl; **(f)** 0.10 M C_6H_5OH; **(g)** 0.10 M HOCl; **(h)** 0.050 M $HC_2H_2ClO_2$; **(i)** 0.050 M $HCHO_2$

80. Show that when $[H_3O^+]$ is reduced to half its original value, the pH of a solution increases by 0.30 unit, *regardless of the initial pH*. Is it also true that when any solution is diluted to half its original concentration, the pH increases by 0.30 unit? Explain.

81. Explain why $[H_3O^+]$ in a strong acid solution *doubles* as the total acid concentration doubles, whereas in a weak acid solution, $[H_3O^+]$ increases only by about a factor of $\sqrt{2}$.

82. Use data from Appendix D to determine whether the ion product of water, K_w, increases, decreases, or remains unchanged with increasing temperature.

83. From the observation that 0.0500 M vinylacetic acid has a freezing point of -0.096 °C, determine K_a for this acid.

$$HC_4H_5O_2 + H_2O \rightleftharpoons H_3O^+ + C_4H_5O_2^- \quad K_a = ?$$

84. You are asked to prepare a 100.0-mL sample of a solution with a pH of 5.50 by dissolving the appropriate amount of a solute in water with pH = 7.00. Which of these solutes would you use, and in what quantity? Explain your choice. **(a)** 15 M $NH_3(aq)$; **(b)** 12 M $HCl(aq)$; **(c)** $NH_4Cl(s)$; **(d)** glacial (pure) acetic acid, $HC_2H_3O_2$.

85. Determine the pH of **(a)** 1.0×10^{-5} M HCN and **(b)** 1.0×10^{-5} M $C_6H_5NH_2$ (aniline).

86. The solubility of $CO_2(g)$ in H_2O at 25 °C and under a $CO_2(g)$ pressure of 1 atm is 1.45 g CO_2/L. Air contains 0.037% CO_2, by volume. Use this information, together with data from Table 16.4, to show that rainwater saturated with CO_2 has a pH $\approx$ 5.6 (referred to in the Focus On feature on page 698 as the normal pH for rainwater).

[*Hint:* Recall Henry's law. What is the partial pressure of $CO_2(g)$ in air?]

87. It is possible to write simple equations to relate pH, pK, and molarities (M) of various solutions. Three such equations are shown here.

Weak acid: $\quad pH = \dfrac{1}{2}pK_a - \dfrac{1}{2}\log M$

Weak base: $\quad pH = 14.00 - \dfrac{1}{2}pK_b + \dfrac{1}{2}\log M$

Salt of weak acid (pK_a) and strong base: $\quad pH = 14.00 - \dfrac{1}{2}pK_w + \dfrac{1}{2}pK_a + \dfrac{1}{2}\log M$

(a) Derive these three equations, and point out the assumptions involved in the derivations.
(b) Use these equations to determine the pH of 0.10 M $HC_2H_3O_2(aq)$, 0.10 M $NH_3(aq)$, and 0.10 M $NaC_2H_3O_2(aq)$. Verify that the equations give correct results by determining these pH values in the usual way.

88. A handbook lists the following formula for the percent ionization of a weak acid.

$$\% \text{ ionized} = \frac{100}{1 + 10^{(pK - pH)}}$$

(a) Derive this equation. What assumptions must you make in this derivation?

(b) Use the equation to determine the percent ionization of a formic acid solution, $HCOOH(aq)$, with a pH of 2.50.
(c) A 0.150 M solution of propionic acid has a pH of 2.85. What is K_a for propionic acid?

$$HC_3H_5O_2 + H_2O \rightleftharpoons H_3O^+ + C_3H_5O_2^- \quad K_a = ?$$

89. Often the following generalization applies to oxoacids with the formula $EO_m(OH)_n$ (where E is the central atom): If $m = 0$, $K_a \approx 10^{-7}$; if $m = 1$, $K_a \approx 10^{-2}$; if $m = 2$, K_a is large; and if $m = 3$, K_a is very large.
(a) Show that this generalization works well for the oxoacids of chlorine: HOCl, pK_a = 7.52; HOClO, pK_a = 1.92; $HOClO_2$, pK_a = -3; $HOClO_3$; pK_a = -8.
(b) Estimate the value of K_{a_1} for H_3AsO_4.
(c) Write a Lewis structure for hypophosphorous acid, H_3PO_2, for which pK_a = 1.1.

90. Oxalic acid, HOOCCOOH, a weak diprotic acid, has pK_{a_1} = 1.25 and pK_{a_2} = 3.81. A related diprotic acid, suberic acid, $HOOC(CH_2)_8COOH$ has pK_{a_1} = 4.21 and pK_{a_2} = 5.40. Offer a plausible reason as to why the *difference* between pK_{a_1} and pK_{a_2} is so much greater for oxalic acid than for suberic acid.

91. Here is a way to test the validity of the statement made on page 683 in conjunction with the three key ideas governing the ionization of polyprotic acids. Determine the pH of 0.100 M succinic acid in two ways: first by assuming that H_3O^+ is produced only in the first ionization step, and then by allowing for the possibility that some H_3O^+ is also produced in the second ionization step. Compare the results, and discuss the significance of your finding.

$$H_2C_4H_4O_4 + H_2O \rightleftharpoons H_3O^+ + HC_4H_4O_4^-$$
$$K_{a_1} = 6.2 \times 10^{-5}$$

$$HC_4H_4O_4^- + H_2O \rightleftharpoons H_3O^+ + C_4H_4O_4^{2-}$$
$$K_{a_2} = 2.3 \times 10^{-6}$$

92. What mass of acetic acid, $HC_2H_3O_2$, must be dissolved per liter of aqueous solution if the solution is to have the same freezing point as 0.150 M $HC_2H_2ClO_2$ (chloroacetic acid)?

93. What is the pH of a solution that is 0.68 M H_2SO_4 and 1.5 M $HCHO_2$ (formic acid)?

94. An aqueous solution of two weak acids has a stoichiometric molarity, M, in each acid. If one acid has a K_a value twice as large as the other, show that the pH of the solution is given by the equation pH = $-\frac{1}{2}\log 3$ M K_a. Assume that the criteria for the simplifying assumption on page 680 are met.

95. Use the concept of hybrid orbitals to describe the bonding in the strong acids given in Exercise 74.

96. Phosphorous acid is listed in Appendix D as a *di*protic acid. Propose a Lewis structure for phosphorous acid that is consistent with this fact.

Feature Problems

97. Maleic acid is a carbon–hydrogen–oxygen compound used in dyeing and finishing fabrics and as a preservative of oils and fats. In a combustion analysis, a 1.054-g sample of maleic acid yields 1.599 g CO_2 and 0.327 g H_2O. In a freezing-point depression experiment, a 0.615-g sample of maleic acid dissolved in 25.10 g of glacial acetic acid, $CH_3COOH(l)$ (which has the freezing-point depression constant $K_f = 3.90 \,°C \, m^{-1}$ and in which maleic acid does not ionize), lowers the freezing point by 0.82 °C. In a titration experiment, a 0.4250-g sample of maleic acid is dissolved in water and requires 34.03 mL of 0.2152 M KOH for its complete neutralization. The pH of a 0.215-g sample of maleic acid dissolved in 50.00 mL of aqueous solution is found to be 1.80.
(a) Determine the empirical and molecular formulas of maleic acid.
[*Hint:* Which experiment(s) provide the necessary data?]
(b) Use the results of part (a) and the titration data to rewrite the molecular formula to reflect the number of ionizable H atoms in the molecule.
(c) Given that the ionizable H atom(s) is(are) associated with the carboxyl group(s), write the plausible condensed structural formula of maleic acid.
(d) Determine the ionization constant(s) of maleic acid. If the data supplied are insufficient, indicate what additional data would be needed.
(e) Calculate the expected pH of a 0.0500 M aqueous solution of maleic acid. Indicate any assumptions required in this calculation.

98. In Example 16-7, rather than use the quadratic formula to solve the quadratic equation, we could have proceeded in the following way. Substitute the value yielded by our failed assumption—$x = 0.0010$—into the *denominator* of the quadratic equation; that is, use $(0.00250 - 0.0010)$ as the value of $[CH_3NH_2]$ and solve for a new value of x. Use this second value of x to reevaluate $[CH_3NH_2]$: $[CH_3NH_2] = (0.00250 - \text{second value of } x)$. Solve the simple quadratic equation for a third value of x, and so on. After three or four trials, you will find that the value of x no longer changes. This is the answer you are seeking.
(a) Complete the calculation of the pH of 0.00250 M CH_3NH_2 by this method, and show that the result is the same as that obtained by using the quadratic formula. **(b)** Use this method to determine the pH of 0.500 M $HClO_2$.

99. Apply the general method for solution equilibrium calculations outlined on page 685 to determine the pH values of the following solutions. In applying the method, look for valid assumptions that may simplify the numerical calculations.
(a) a solution that is 0.315 M $HC_2H_3O_2$ and 0.250 M $HCHO_2$
(b) a solution that contains 1.55 g CH_3NH_2 and 12.5 g NH_3 in 375 mL
(c) 1.0 M $NH_4CN(aq)$

Self-Assessment Exercises

100. In your own words, define or explain the following terms or symbols: **(a)** K_w; **(b)** pH; **(c)** pK_a; **(d)** hydrolysis; **(e)** Lewis acid.

101. Briefly describe each of the following ideas or phenomena: **(a)** conjugate base; **(b)** percent ionization of an acid or base; **(c)** self-ionization; **(d)** amphiprotic behavior.

102. Explain the important distinctions between each pair of terms: **(a)** Brønsted–Lowry acid and base; **(b)** $[H_3O^+]$ and pH; **(c)** K_a for NH_4^+ and K_b for NH_3; **(d)** leveling effect and electron-withdrawing effect.

103. Of the following, the amphiprotic ion is **(a)** HCO_3^-; **(b)** CO_3^{2-}; **(c)** NH_4^+; **(d)** $CH_3NH_3^+$; **(e)** ClO_4^-.

104. The pH in 0.10 M $CH_3CH_2COOH(aq)$ must be **(a)** equal to $[H_3O^+]$ in 0.10 M $HNO_2(aq)$; **(b)** less than the pH in 0.10 M $HI(aq)$; **(c)** greater than the pH in 0.10 M $HBr(aq)$; **(d)** equal to 1.0.

105. In 0.10 M $CH_3NH_2(aq)$, **(a)** $[H_3O^+] = 0.10$ M; **(b)** $[OH^-] = 0.10$ M; **(c)** pH < 7; **(d)** pH < 13.

106. The reaction of $CH_3COOH(aq)$ proceeds furthest toward completion with a base when that base is **(a)** H_2O; **(b)** $CH_3NH_3^+$; **(c)** NH_4^+; **(d)** Cl^-; **(e)** CO_3^{2-}.

107. In 0.10 M $H_2SO_4(aq)$, $[H_3O^+]$ is equal to **(a)** 0.050 M; **(b)** 0.10 M; **(c)** 0.11 M; **(d)** 0.20 M.

108. For $H_2SO_3(aq)$, $K_{a_1} = 1.3 \times 10^{-2}$ and $K_{a_2} = 6.3 \times 10^{-8}$. In 0.10 M $H_2SO_3(aq)$, **(a)** $[HSO_3^-] = 0.013$ M;

(b) $[SO_3^{2-}] = 6.3 \times 10^{-8}$ M; **(c)** $[H_3O^+] = 0.10$ M; **(d)** $[H_3O^+] = 0.013$ M; **(e)** $[SO_3^{2-}] = 0.036$ M.

109. What is the pH of the solution obtained by mixing 24.80 mL of 0.248 M HNO_3 and 15.40 mL of 0.394 M KOH?

110. How many milliters of a concentrated acetic acid solution (35.0% $HC_2H_3O_2$ by mass; $d = 1.044$ g/mL) must be diluted with water to produce 12.5 L of solution with pH 3.25?

111. Determine the pH of 2.05 M $NaC_2H_2ClO_2$. (Use data from Table 16.3, as necessary.)

112. Several aqueous solutions are prepared. *Without consulting any tables in the text*, arrange these ten solutions in order of *increasing* pH: 1.0 M NaBr, 0.05 M $HC_2H_3O_2$, 0.05 M NH_3, 0.02 M $KC_2H_3O_2$, 0.05 M $Ba(OH)_2$, 0.05 M H_2SO_4, 0.10 M HI, 0.06 M NaOH, 0.05 M NH_4Cl, and 0.05 M $HC_2H_2ClO_2$ (that is, $CH_2ClCOOH$).

113. A solution is found to have pH = 5 × pOH. Is this solution acidic or basic? What is $[H_3O^+]$ in the solution? Which of the following could be the solute in this solution: NH_3, $HC_2H_3O_2$, or $NH_4C_2H_3O_2$, and what would be its molarity?

114. Appendix E describes a useful study aid known as concept mapping. Using the method presented in Appendix E, construct a concept map that summarizes the material discussed in Section 16-8.

eMedia Exercises

115. In the **Self-Ionization of Water** animation, the ionization process is shown with an unrealistically high concentration of the products (*Activebook 16-3*). **(a)** According to the known value of K_w at 25 °C, estimate how many ions would be present in the field of view of the animation. **(b)** Estimate what the value of K_w would be if, in fact, the animation as shown were accurately depicting the concentrations of ions produced by self-ionization.

116. (a) In the **Aqueous Acids and Bases** animation (*Activebook 16-4*), write a balanced chemical equation for each of the reactions depicted. **(b)** In which reaction(s) is dynamic equilibrium an accurate description of the final state? **(c)** Which species are best described by the Arrhenius theory? **(d)** Which are best described by Brønsted–Lowry theory? **(e)** Which can be described by both theories?

117. (a) Using the **Equilibrium Constant** activity (*Activebook 16-5*), estimate the ranges of equilibrium constants that are typical of weak acids. **(b)** At roughly what value of K_a would the acid be more accurately described as a strong acid? **(c)** What is the corresponding percent ionization at this K_a value?

118. In the **Lewis Acid–Base Theory** animation (*Activebook 16-9*), three different species are identified as Lewis bases. **(a)** Identify these bases and the molecular trait that distinguishes them as Lewis bases. **(b)** How does this description differ from the other acid and base characterizations given earlier in the chapter? **(c)** Would any of these species also be classified as Arrhenius or Brønsted–Lowry bases?

 # eLaboratory Exercises

These exercises allow students to apply the concepts and skills for this chapter in the simulated laboratory of Virtual ChemLab. Worksheets for each of these exercises are found in the Virtual ChemLab Workbook in your MediaPak.

119. *(VCL 16-1) Ionization Constants of Weak Acids*
An acid–base indicator is usually a weak acid with a characteristic color in the protonated and deprotonated forms. In this assignment you will monitor the color of an acetic acid solution containing *bromocresol green* as an indicator as the pH is changed, and estimate the ionization constant, K_a, for the indicator.

120. *(VCL 16-2) Acid–Base Classification of Salts*
In this assignment you will be asked to classify aqueous solutions of salts as to whether they are acidic, basic, or neutral. This is most easily done by first identifying how both the cation and anion affect the pH of the solution and then combine the effects. After predicting the acid–base properties of these salts, you will then test your predictions in the laboratory.

121. *(VCL 16-3) Ranking Salt Solutions by pH*
In this assignment you will be asked to rank a set of aqueous solutions of acids, bases, and salts in order of increasing pH of the solutions. After ranking these solutions, you will then test your predictions in the laboratory.

17 ADDITIONAL ASPECTS OF ACID–BASE EQUILIBRIA

CONTENTS

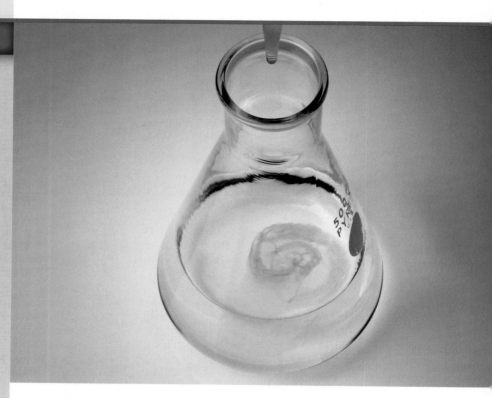

NaOH(aq) is slowly added to an aqueous solution containing HCl(aq) and the indicator phenolphthalein. The indicator color changes from colorless to red as the pH changes from 8.0 to 10.0. The equivalence point of the neutralization is reached when the solution turns a lasting pink (the pink seen here disappears when the flask is swirled to mix the reactants). The selection of indicators for acid-base titrations is one of the topics considered in this chapter.

In our study of acid rain (page 698), we learned that a very small amount of atmospheric $CO_2(g)$ dissolves in rainwater. Yet this amount is sufficient to lower the pH of rainwater by nearly 2 units. And when acid-forming air pollutants, such as SO_2, SO_3, and NO_2, also dissolve in rainwater, it becomes even more acidic. A chemist would say that water has no "buffer capacity"—that is, its pH changes sharply when even small quantities of acids or bases are dissolved in it.

One of the main topics of this chapter is buffer solutions—solutions that can resist a change in pH when acids or bases are added to them. We will consider how such solutions are prepared, how they maintain a nearly constant pH, and how they are used. At the end of the chapter, we will consider perhaps the most important buffer system to humans: the buffer system that maintains the constant pH of blood.

A second topic that we shall explore is acid–base titrations. Here, our aim will be to calculate how pH changes during a titration. We can use this information to select an appropriate indicator for a titration and to determine, in general, which acid–base titrations work well and which do not. For the most part, we will find the calculations in this chapter to be extensions of those in Chapter 16.

17-1   COMMON-ION EFFECT IN ACID–BASE EQUILIBRIA

The questions answered in Chapter 16 were mostly of the type, "What is the pH of 0.10 M $HC_2H_3O_2$, of 0.10 M NH_3, of 0.10 M H_3PO_4, of 0.10 M NH_4Cl?" In each of these cases, we think of dissolving a *single* substance in aqueous solution and determining the concentrations of the species present at equilibrium. In most situations in this chapter, a solution of a weak acid or weak base initially contains a second source of one of the ions produced in the ionization of the acid or base. The added ions are said to be *common* to the weak acid or weak base. The presence of a common ion can have some important consequences.

SOLUTIONS OF WEAK ACIDS AND STRONG ACIDS

Consider a solution that is at the same time 0.100 M $HC_2H_3O_2$ and 0.100 M HCl. We can write separate equations for the ionizations of the acids, one weak and the other strong, and indicate the expected concentrations of molecules and ions in the solution.

$$HC_2H_3O_2 \ + \ H_2O \ \rightleftharpoons \ H_3O^+ \ + \ C_2H_3O_2^- \qquad K_a = 1.8 \times 10^{-5}$$
$$(0.100 - x) \text{ M} \qquad\qquad\qquad x \text{ M} \qquad x \text{ M}$$

$$HCl \ + \ H_2O \ \longrightarrow \ H_3O^+ \ + \ Cl^-$$
$$0.100 \text{ M} \qquad 0.100 \text{ M}$$

Of course, there can be only a single concentration of H_3O^+ in the solution, and this must be $[H_3O^+] = (0.100 + x)$ M. Because H_3O^+ is formed in both ionization processes, we say that it is a *common ion*. The weak acid–strong acid mixture described here is pictured in Figure 17-1. Although it might seem that the pH would be lower than 1.0, the figure indicates that this is not the case.

Concentrations of the species present in this mixture of a weak acid and a strong acid are calculated in Example 17-1, followed by comments on the significance of the result.

▲ FIGURE 17-1
A weak acid–strong acid mixture
The solution pictured is 0.100 M $HC_2H_3O_2$ and 0.100 M HCl. The reading on the pH meter (1.0) indicates that essentially all the H_3O^+ comes from the strong acid HCl. The red color of the solution is that of thymol blue indicator. Compare this photo with Figure 16-7, in which the separate acids are shown.

EXAMPLE 17-1

Demonstrating the Common-Ion Effect: A Solution of a Weak Acid and a Strong Acid. **(a)** Determine $[H_3O^+]$ and $[C_2H_3O_2^-]$ in 0.100 M $HC_2H_3O_2$. **(b)** Then determine these same quantities in a solution that is 0.100 M in both $HC_2H_3O_2$ and HCl.

Solution

(a) This calculation was done in Example 16-6 (page 677). We found that in 0.100 M $HC_2H_3O_2$, $[H_3O^+] = [C_2H_3O_2^-] = 1.3 \times 10^{-3}$ M.

(b) Instead of writing two separate ionization equations, as we did just prior to this example, let's write only the ionization equation for $HC_2H_3O_2$ and enter information about the common ion, H_3O^+, in the following format.

 The common-ion effect is not restricted to weak acids and weak bases. Buffers are the most important examples of the common-ion effect in weak acids and weak bases.

 The common-ion effect is an example of Le Châtelier's principle.

	$HC_2H_3O_2$	+	H_2O	$\rightleftharpoons$	H_3O^+	+	$C_2H_3O_2^-$
initial concns:							
weak acid:	0.100 M				—		—
strong acid:	—				0.100 M		—
changes:	$-x$ M				$+x$ M		$+x$ M
equil concns:	$(0.100 - x)$ M				$(0.100 + x)$ M		x M

KEEP IN MIND ▶
that by the criterion
$M_a > 100 K_a$ (see page 680),
we expect this assumption
to be valid. Actually, the assumption is even better than
in Example 17-6 because the
ionization of the weak acid is
suppressed by the presence of
the common ion, H_3O^+.

As is customary, we begin with the assumption that x is very small compared with 0.100. Thus, $0.100 - x \approx 0.100 + x \approx 0.100$.

$$K_a = \frac{[H_3O^+][C_2H_3O_2^-]}{[HC_2H_3O_2]} = \frac{(0.100 + x) \cdot x}{0.100 - x} = \frac{\cancel{0.100} \cdot x}{\cancel{0.100}} = 1.8 \times 10^{-5}$$

$$x = [C_2H_3O_2^-] = 1.8 \times 10^{-5} \, M \quad 0.100 + x = [H_3O^+] = 0.100 \, M$$

Practice Example A: Determine $[H_3O^+]$ and $[HF]$ in 0.500 M HF. Then determine these concentrations in a solution that is 0.100 M HCl and 0.500 M HF.

Practice Example B: How many drops of 12 M HCl would you add to 1.00 L of
0.100 M $HC_2H_3O_2$ to make $[C_2H_3O_2^-] = 1.0 \times 10^{-4}$ M? Assume that 1 drop =
0.050 mL and that the volume of solution remains 1.00 L after the 12 M HCl is diluted.

[*Hint:* What must be the $[H_3O^+]$ in the solution?]

Now we see the consequence of adding a strong acid (HCl) to a weak
acid ($HC_2H_3O_2$): The concentration of the anion $[C_2H_3O_2^-]$ is greatly reduced. Between parts (a) and (b) of Example 17-1, $[C_2H_3O_2^-]$ is lowered
from 1.3×10^{-3} M to 1.8×10^{-5} M—almost a 100-fold decrease. Another
way to state this result is through Le Châtelier's principle (see Chapter 15,
page 638). Increasing the concentration of one of the *products* of a reaction—
the common ion—shifts the equilibrium condition in the *reverse* direction.
The **common-ion effect** is the suppression of the ionization of a weak electrolyte caused by adding more of an ion that is a product of this ionization.
The common-ion effect of H_3O^+ on the ionization of acetic acid is suggested
as follows.

*Common-Ion Effect
animation*

When a strong acid supplies the common ion H_3O^+,
the equilibrium shifts to form more $HC_2H_3O_2$.

Added H_3O^+

$$HC_2H_3O_2 \; + \; H_2O \; \rightleftharpoons \; H_3O^+ \; + \; C_2H_3O_2^- \quad K_a = 1.8 \times 10^{-5}$$

Equilibrium shifts to form
more $HC_2H_3O_2$

The ionization of a weak base such as NH_3 is suppressed when a strong
base such as NaOH is added. Here, OH^- is the common ion, and its increased
concentration shifts the equilibrium to the left.

When a strong base supplies the common ion OH^-,
the equilibrium shifts to form more NH_3.

Added OH^-

$$NH_3 \; + \; H_2O \; \rightleftharpoons \; NH_4^+ \; + \; OH^- \quad K_b = 1.8 \times 10^{-5}$$

Equilibrium shifts to
form more NH_3

SOLUTIONS OF WEAK ACIDS AND THEIR SALTS

The salt of a weak acid is a strong electrolyte—its ions become completely dissociated from one another in aqueous solution. One of the ions, the *anion*, is an ion common to the ionization equilibrium of the weak acid. The presence of this common ion suppresses the ionization of the weak acid. For example, we can represent the effect of acetate salts on the acetic acid equilibrium as

When a salt supplies the common anion $C_2H_3O_2^-$, the equilibrium shifts to form more $HC_2H_3O_2$.

$$NaC_2H_3O_2(aq) \longrightarrow Na^+ + C_2H_3O_2^-$$

Added $C_2H_3O_2^-$

$$HC_2H_3O_2 + H_2O \rightleftharpoons H_3O^+ + C_2H_3O_2^- \qquad K_a = 1.8 \times 10^{-5}$$

Equilibrium shifts to form more $HC_2H_3O_2$

The common-ion effect of acetate ion on the ionization of acetic acid is depicted in Figure 17-2 and demonstrated in Example 17-2. In solving common-ion problems such as Example 17-2, assume that ionization of the weak acid (or base) does not begin until both the weak acid (or base) and its salt have been placed in solution. Then consider that ionization occurs until equilibrium is reached.

(a)   (b)

▲ **FIGURE 17-2**
A mixture of a weak acid and its salt
Bromphenol blue indicator is present in both solutions. Its color dependence on pH is

pH < 3.0 < pH < 4.6 < pH

yellow   green   blue-violet

(a) 0.100 M $HC_2H_3O_2$ has a calculated pH of 2.89, but **(b)** if the solution is also 0.100 M in $NaC_2H_3O_2$, the calculated pH is 4.74. (The readability of the pH meters used here is 0.1 unit, and their accuracy is probably somewhat less than that. The discrepancy between 4.74 and the 4.9 value shown here is a result.)

EXAMPLE 17-2

Demonstrating the Common-Ion Effect: A Solution of a Weak Acid and a Salt of That Weak Acid. Calculate $[H_3O^+]$ and $[C_2H_3O_2^-]$ in a solution that is 0.100 M in both $HC_2H_3O_2$ and $NaC_2H_3O_2$.

Solution

The setup shown here is very similar to that in Example 17-1(b), except that $NaC_2H_3O_2$ is the source of the common ion.

	$HC_2H_3O_2$	+	H_2O	$\rightleftharpoons$	H_3O^+	+	$C_2H_3O_2^-$
initial concns:							
weak acid:	0.100 M				—		—
salt:	—				—		0.100 M
changes:	$-x$ M				$+x$ M		$+x$ M
equil concns:	$(0.100 - x)$ M				x M		$(0.100 + x)$ M

Because the salt suppresses the ionization of $HC_2H_3O_2$, we expect $[H_3O^+] = x$ to be very small and $0.100 - x \approx 0.100 + x \approx 0.100$. This proves to be a valid assumption.

$$K_a = \frac{[H_3O^+][C_2H_3O_2^-]}{[HC_2H_3O_2]} = \frac{x \cdot (0.100 + x)}{0.100 - x} = \frac{x \cdot \cancel{0.100}}{\cancel{0.100}} = 1.8 \times 10^{-5}$$

$$x = [H_3O^+] = 1.8 \times 10^{-5}\,M \qquad 0.100 + x = [C_2H_3O_2^-] = 0.100\,M$$

As in Example 17-1, ionization of $HC_2H_3O_2$ is reduced about 100-fold. This time the large decrease in concentration is that of H_3O^+.

Practice Example A: Calculate $[H_3O^+]$ and $[CHO_2^-]$ in a solution that is 0.100 M $HCHO_2$ and 0.150 M $NaCHO_2$.

Practice Example B: What mass of $NaC_2H_3O_2$ should be added to 1.00 L of 0.100 M $HC_2H_3O_2$ to produce a solution with pH = 5.00? Assume that the volume remains 1.00 L.

Point out that when concentrations of a weak acid and its conjugate base are the same, $K_a = [H_3O^+]$ and pH = pK_a.

(a)   **(b)**

▲ **FIGURE 17-3**
A mixture of a weak base and its salt
Thymolphthalein indicator is blue if pH > 10 and colorless if pH < 10. **(a)** The pH of 0.100 M NH_3 is above 10 (calculated value: 11.11). **(b)** If the solution is also 0.100 M NH_4Cl, the pH drops below 10 (calculated value: 9.26). The ionization of NH_3 is suppressed in the presence of added NH_4^+. $[OH^-]$ decreases, $[H_3O^+]$ increases, and the pH is lowered.

SOLUTIONS OF WEAK BASES AND THEIR SALTS

The common-ion effect of a salt of a weak base is similar to the weak acid–anion situation just described. The suppression of the ionization of NH_3 by the common *cation*, NH_4^+, is pictured in Figure 17-3 and represented as follows.

When a salt supplies the common cation NH_4^+, the equilibrium shifts to form more NH_3.

$$NH_4Cl(aq) \longrightarrow NH_4^+ + Cl^-$$

Added NH_4^+

$$NH_3 + H_2O \rightleftharpoons NH_4^+ + OH^- \quad K_b = 1.8 \times 10^{-5}$$

Equilibrium shifts to form more NH_3

CONCEPT ASSESSMENT ✓

Without doing detailed calculations, determine which of the following will *raise* the pH when added to 1.00 L of 0.100 M NH_3(aq): **(a)** 0.010 mol NH_4Cl(s); **(b)** 0.010 mol $(CH_3CH_2)_2NH$(l); **(c)** 0.010 mol HCl(g); **(d)** 1.00 L of 0.050 M NH_3(aq); **(e)** 1.00 g $Ca(OH)_2$(s). For NH_3, $pK_b = 4.74$; for $(CH_3CH_2)_2NH$, $pK_b = 3.16$.

17-2   BUFFER SOLUTIONS

Figure 17-4 illustrates a statement made in the chapter introduction: Pure water has no buffer capacity. There are some acqueous solutions, however, called **buffer** (or buffered) **solutions**, whose pH values change only very slightly on the addition of small amounts of either an acid or a base.

What buffer solutions require are two components; one component is able to neutralize acids, and the other is able to neutralize bases. But the two components must not neutralize each other. This requirement rules out mixtures of a strong acid and a strong base. Instead, common buffer solutions are described as combinations of

- a weak acid and its conjugate base, or
- a weak base and its conjugate acid

To show that such mixtures function as buffer solutions, let's consider a solution that has the equilibrium concentrations $[HC_2H_3O_2] = [C_2H_3O_2^-]$. As summarized in expression (17.1), in this solution $[H_3O^+] = K_a = 1.8 \times 10^{-5}$ M.

$$K_a = \frac{[H_3O^+][C_2H_3O_2^-]}{[HC_2H_3O_2]} = 1.8 \times 10^{-5}$$

$$[H_3O^+] = K_a \times \frac{[HC_2H_3O_2]}{[C_2H_3O_2^-]} = 1.8 \times 10^{-5} \text{ M} \qquad (17.1)$$

As a result, pH $= -\log[H_3O^+] = -\log K_a = -\log 1.8 \times 10^{-5} = 4.74$.

Now, imagine adding a *small* amount of a strong acid to this buffer solution. A reaction occurs in which a *small* amount of the base $C_2H_3O_2^-$ is converted to its conjugate acid $HC_2H_3O_2$.

$$C_2H_3O_2^- + H_3O^+ \longrightarrow HC_2H_3O_2 + H_2O$$

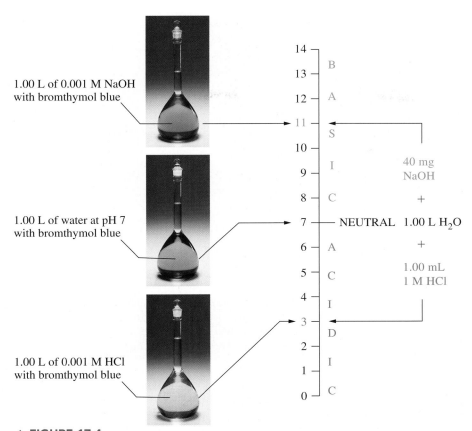

▲ FIGURE 17-4
Pure water has no buffering ability
Bromthymol blue indicator is blue at pH > 7, green at pH = 7, and yellow at
pH < 7. Pure water has pH = 7.0. The addition of 0.001 mol H_3O^+ (1.00 mL of
1 M HCl) to 1.00 L water produces $[H_3O^+]$ = 0.001 M and pH = 3.0. The addition of
0.001 mol OH^- (40 mg NaOH) to 1.00 L of water produces $[OH^-]$ = 0.001 M and
pH = 11.0.

After the neutralization of the added H_3O^+, we find that in expression (17.1)
$[HC_2H_3O_2]$ has increased *slightly* and $[C_2H_3O_2^-]$ has decreased *slightly*. The
ratio $[HC_2H_3O_2]/[C_2H_3O_2^-]$ is only *slightly* greater than 1, and $[H_3O^+]$ has
barely changed. The buffer solution has resisted a change in pH following the
addition of a small amount of acid; the pH remains close to the original 4.74.

Next, imagine adding a *small* amount of a strong base to the original buffer
solution with $[HC_2H_3O_2]$ = $[C_2H_3O_2^-]$. A reaction occurs in which a *small*
amount of the weak acid $HC_2H_3O_2$ is converted to its conjugate base $C_2H_3O_2^-$.

$$HC_2H_3O_2 + OH^- \longrightarrow C_2H_3O_2^- + H_2O$$

Here we find that $[C_2H_3O_2^-]$ has increased *slightly*, and $[HC_2H_3O_2]$ has decreased *slightly*. The ratio $[HC_2H_3O_2]/[C_2H_3O_2^-]$ is only *slightly* smaller than
1, and again $[H_3O^+]$ has barely changed. The buffer solution has resisted a
change in pH following the addition of a small amount of base; again, the pH
remains close to the original 4.74. The variation of the concentration of the
weak acid and its conjugate base are illustrated in Figure 17-5.

Later in this section, we will be more specific about what constitutes *small*
additions of an acid or a base and *slight* changes in the concentrations of the
buffer components and pH. Also, we will discover that an acetic acid–sodium
acetate buffer is good only for maintaining a nearly constant pH in a range of
about 2 pH units centered on a pH = pK_a = 4.74. A buffer solution that maintains a nearly constant pH outside this range requires different buffer components, as suggested in Example 17-3.

Most students will correctly
assume that the pH of the
acetic acid-acetate ion buffer
will increase slightly when a strong
base is added and decrease slightly
when a strong acid is added.

Reproduce the experiment
shown in Figure 17-3. Use
thymolphthalein indicator in an
unbuffered and a buffered solution
of aqueous ammonia. Add a small
amount of HCl to the unbuffered
solution and watch the indicator
change rapidly from blue to
colorless. Do the same for the
buffered solution and see that the
blue (base) color persists. You can
also use a pH meter rather than
the indicator.

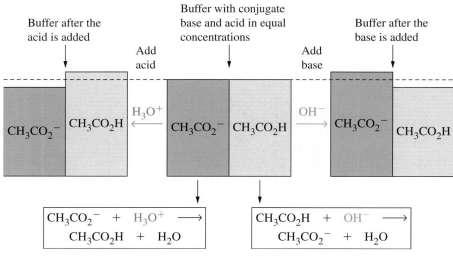

▲ **FIGURE 17-5**
How a buffer works
Acetate ion, the conjugate base of acetic acid, acts as a proton sink when strong acid is added. In this way, the ratio [conjugate base]/[acid] is kept approximately constant, so there is a minimal change in pH. Similarly, acetic acid acts as a proton donor when strong base is added, keeping the ratio [conjugate base]/[acid] approximately constant and minimizing the change in pH.

EXAMPLE 17-3

Predicting Whether a Solution Is a Buffer Solution. Show that an NH_3–NH_4Cl solution is a buffer solution. Over what pH range would you expect it to function?

Solution

To show that a solution has buffer properties, first identify a component in the solution that neutralizes acids and a component that neutralizes bases. In this case, these components are NH_3 and NH_4^+, respectively.

$$NH_3 + H_3O^+ \longrightarrow NH_4^+ + H_2O$$
$$NH_4^+ + OH^- \longrightarrow NH_3 + H_2O$$

In *all* aqueous solutions containing NH_3 and NH_4^+, we know that

$$NH_3 + H_2O \rightleftharpoons NH_4^+ + OH^- \quad \text{and}$$

$$K_b = \frac{[NH_4^+][OH^-]}{[NH_3]} = 1.8 \times 10^{-5}$$

If a solution has approximately equal concentrations of NH_4^+ and NH_3, then $[OH^-] \approx 1.8 \times 10^{-5}$ M; pOH $\approx$ 4.74; and pH $\approx$ 9.26. Ammonia–ammonium chloride solutions are *basic* buffer solutions that function over the approximate pH range of 8 to 10.

Practice Example A: Describe how a mixture of a strong acid (such as HCl) and the salt of a weak acid (such as $NaC_2H_3O_2$) can be a buffer solution.

[*Hint*: What is the reaction that produces $HC_2H_3O_2$?]

Practice Example B: Describe how a mixture of NH_3 and HCl can result in a buffer solution.

Buffer Solutions activity

We commonly need to calculate the pH of a buffer solution. At a minimum, such a calculation requires use of the ionization constant expression for a weak acid or weak base. Aspects of solution stoichiometry may also be required.

In Example 17-4, we first determine the stoichiometric concentrations of the buffer components. Then we perform an equilibrium calculation in the same fashion as in Examples 17-1 and 17-2.

EXAMPLE 17-4

Calculating the pH of a Buffer Solution. What is the pH of a buffer solution prepared by dissolving 25.5 g $NaC_2H_3O_2$ in a sufficient volume of 0.550 M $HC_2H_3O_2$ to make 500.0 mL of the buffer?

Solution

First, we must determine the molarity of $C_2H_3O_2^-$ corresponding to 25.5 g $NaC_2H_3O_2$ in 500.0 mL of solution.

$$\text{amount of } C_2H_3O_2^- = 25.5 \text{ g } NaC_2H_3O_2 \times \frac{1 \text{ mol } NaC_2H_3O_2}{82.04 \text{ g } NaC_2H_3O_2}$$

$$\times \frac{1 \text{ mol } C_2H_3O_2^-}{1 \text{ mol } NaC_2H_3O_2}$$

$$= 0.311 \text{ mol } C_2H_3O_2^-$$

$$[C_2H_3O_2^-] = \frac{0.311 \text{ mol } C_2H_3O_2^-}{0.500 \text{ L}} = 0.622 \text{ M } C_2H_3O_2^-$$

Equilibrium Calculation:

	$HC_2H_3O_2$	+	H_2O	$\rightleftharpoons$	H_3O^+	+	$C_2H_3O_2^-$
initial concns:							
weak acid:	0.550 M				—		—
salt:	—				—		0.622 M
changes:	$-x$ M				$+x$ M		$+x$ M
equil concns:	$(0.550 - x)$ M				$+x$ M		$(0.622 + x)$ M

Let's assume that x is very small, so $0.550 - x \approx 0.550$ and $0.622 + x \approx 0.622$. We will find this assumption to be valid.

$$K_a = \frac{[H_3O^+][C_2H_3O_2^-]}{[HC_2H_3O_2]} = \frac{(x)(0.622)}{0.550} = 1.8 \times 10^{-5}$$

$$x = [H_3O^+] = \frac{0.550}{0.622} \times 1.8 \times 10^{-5} = 1.6 \times 10^{-5}$$

$$\text{pH} = -\log[H_3O^+] = -\log(1.6 \times 10^{-5}) = 4.80$$

CHECK: We have seen that pH = pK_a = 4.74 when acetic acid and acetate ion are present in equal concentrations. Here the concentration of the conjugate *base* (acetate ion) is greater than that of the acetic acid. The solution should be somewhat more basic (less acidic) than pH = 4.74. A pH of 4.80 is a reasonable answer.

Practice Example A: What is the pH of a buffer solution prepared by dissolving 23.1 g $NaCHO_2$ in a sufficient volume of 0.432 M $HCHO_2$ to make 500.0 mL of the buffer?

Practice Example B: A handbook states that to prepare 100.0 mL of a particular buffer solution, mix 63.0 mL of 0.200 M $HC_2H_3O_2$ with 37.0 mL of 0.200 M $NaC_2H_3O_2$. What is the pH of this buffer?

An important point worth noting in Example 17-4 is that if a solution is to be an effective buffer, the assumptions $(M - x) \approx M$ and $(M + x) \approx M$ will always be valid. That is, the *equilibrium* concentrations of the buffer components will be very nearly the same as their *stoichiometric* concentrations. As a result, in Example 17-4 we could have gone directly from the stoichiometric concentrations of the buffer components to the expression

$$K_a = \frac{[H_3O^+][C_2H_3O_2^-]}{[HC_2H_3O_2]} = \frac{[H_3O^+](0.622)}{0.550} = 1.8 \times 10^{-5}$$

without setting up the ICE table. This procedure can be formalized through the special equation that is introduced next.

The history and limitations of the Henderson-Hasselbalch equation are discussed in this article: Po, H. N., Senozan, N. M. *J. Chem. Educ.* **2001:** *78*, 1499.

Calculating pH Using Henderson-Hasselbalch Equation activity

AN EQUATION FOR BUFFER SOLUTIONS: THE HENDERSON–HASSELBALCH EQUATION

Although we can continue to use the format demonstrated in Example 17-4 for buffer calculations, it is often useful to describe a buffer solution by means of an equation known as the **Henderson–Hasselbalch equation**. Biochemists and molecular biologists commonly use this equation. To derive this variation of the ionization constant expression, let's consider a mixture of a hypothetical weak acid, HA (such as $HC_2H_3O_2$), and its salt, NaA (such as $NaC_2H_3O_2$). We start with the familiar expressions

$$HA + H_2O \rightleftharpoons H_3O^+ + A^-$$

$$K_a = \frac{[H_3O^+][A^-]}{[HA]}$$

and rearrange the right side of the K_a expression to obtain

$$K_a = [H_3O^+] \times \frac{[A^-]}{[HA]}$$

Next, we take the *negative logarithm* of each side of this equation.

$$-\log K_a = -\log[H_3O^+] - \log\frac{[A^-]}{[HA]}$$

Now, recall that $pH = -\log[H_3O^+]$ and that $pK_a = -\log K_a$, which gives

$$pK_a = pH - \log\frac{[A^-]}{[HA]}$$

Solve for pH by rearranging the equation.

$$pH = pK_a + \log\frac{[A^-]}{[HA]}$$

A^- is the conjugate base of the weak acid HA, so we can write the more general equation (17.2), the Henderson–Hasselbalch equation.

$$pH = pK_a + \log\frac{[\text{conjugate base}]}{[\text{acid}]} \qquad (17.2)$$

When the [conjugate base] = [acid] then $pH = pK_a$. When we get to titrations, an indicator is chosen to change color at $pH = pK_a$ of the indicator.

To apply this equation to an acetic acid–sodium acetate buffer, we use pK_a for $HC_2H_3O_2$ and these concentrations: $[HC_2H_3O_2]$ for [acid] and $[C_2H_3O_2^-]$ for [conjugate base]. To apply it to an ammonia–ammonium chloride buffer, we use pK_a for NH_4^+ and these concentrations: $[NH_4^+]$ for [acid] and $[NH_3]$ for [conjugate base].

Equation (17.2) is useful only when we can substitute *stoichiometric* or initial concentrations for equilibrium concentrations to give

$$pH = pK_a + \log\frac{[\text{conjugate base}]_{\text{initial}}}{[\text{acid}]_{\text{initial}}}$$

KEEP IN MIND ▶

that the Henderson–Hasselbalch equation is very useful, but should probably not be committed to memory; it is easy to get the conjugate base and acid terms inverted. It is most important to understand the principles that lead to this equation, thereby avoiding the pitfalls of using the equation incorrectly or when it is not valid.

thus avoiding the need to set up an ICE table. This constraint places important limitations on the equation's validity, however. Later, we will see that there are also conditions that must be met if a mixture is to be an effective buffer solution. Although the following rules may be overly restrictive in some cases, a reasonable approach to the twin concerns of effective buffer action and the validity of equation (17.2) is to ensure that

1. the ratio [conjugate base]/[acid] is within the limits

$$0.10 < \frac{[\text{conjugate base}]}{[\text{acid}]} < 10 \qquad (17.3)$$

2. the molarity of each buffer component exceeds the value of K_a by a factor of at least 100

Viewed another way, equation (17.2) works only for cases in which the assumption $M - x \approx M$ is valid. If a quadratic equation is required to solve the equilibrium constant expression, equation (17.2) will likely fail.

PREPARING BUFFER SOLUTIONS

Suppose we need a buffer solution with pH = 5.09. Equation (17.2) suggests two alternatives. One is to find a weak acid, HA, that has $pK_a = 5.09$ and prepare a solution with equal molarities of the acid and its salt.

$$pH = pK_a + \log\frac{[A^-]}{[HA]} = 5.09 + \log 1 = 5.09$$

Although this alternative is simple in concept, generally, it is not practical. We are not likely to find a readily available, water-soluble weak acid with exactly $pK_a = 5.09$. The second alternative, summarized in the margin, is to use a cheap, common weak acid such as acetic acid, $HC_2H_3O_2(pK_a = 4.74)$, and establish an appropriate ratio of $[C_2H_3O_2^-]/[HC_2H_3O_2]$ to obtain a pH of 5.09. Example 17-5 demonstrates this second alternative.

Select a weak acid with a pK_a close to the desired pH.

↓

Calculate the necessary ratio
$$\frac{[\text{conjugate base}]}{[\text{acid}]}$$
to give the desired pH.

↓

Calculate the necessary concentrations of conjugate base and acid.

▲ One procedure follow in making a buffer solution with a desired pH.

EXAMPLE 17-5

Preparing a Buffer Solution of a Desired pH. What mass of $NaC_2H_3O_2$ must be dissolved in 0.300 L of 0.25 M $HC_2H_3O_2$ to produce a solution with pH = 5.09? (Assume that the solution volume remains constant at 0.300 L.)

Solution

Equilibrium among the buffer components is expressed by the equation

$$HC_2H_3O_2 + H_2O \rightleftharpoons H_3O^+ + C_2H_3O_2^- \qquad K_a = 1.8 \times 10^{-5}$$

and by the ionization constant expression for acetic acid.

$$K_a = \frac{[H_3O^+][C_2H_3O_2^-]}{[HC_2H_3O_2]} = 1.8 \times 10^{-5}$$

Each of the three concentration terms appearing in a K_a expression should be an equilibrium concentration. The $[H_3O^+]$ corresponding to a pH of 5.09 is the equilibrium concentration. For $[HC_2H_3O_2]$, we will assume that the equilibrium concentration is equal to the stoichiometric or initial concentration. The value of $[C_2H_3O_2^-]$ that we calculate with the K_a expression is the equilibrium concentration, and we will assume that it is also the same as the stoichiometric concentration. Thus, we assume that neither the ionization of $HC_2H_3O_2$ to form $C_2H_3O_2^-$ nor the hydrolysis of $C_2H_3O_2^-$ to form $HC_2H_3O_2$ produces much of a difference between the stoichiometric (initial) and equilibrium concentrations of the buffer components. These assumptions work well if the conditions stated in expression (17.3) are met. The relevant concentration terms, then, are

$$[H_3O^+] = 10^{-pH} = 10^{-5.09} = 8.1 \times 10^{-6} \text{ M}$$
$$[HC_2H_3O_2] = 0.25 \text{ M}$$
$$[C_2H_3O_2^-] = ?$$

The required acetate ion concentration in the buffer solution is

$$[C_2H_3O_2^-] = K_a \times \frac{[HC_2H_3O_2]}{[H_3O^+]} = 1.8 \times 10^{-5} \times \frac{0.25}{8.1 \times 10^{-6}} = 0.56 \text{ M}$$

We complete the calculation of the mass of sodium acetate with some familiar ideas of solution stoichiometry.

$$\text{mass} = 0.300 \text{ L} \times \frac{0.56 \text{ mol } C_2H_3O_2^-}{1 \text{ L}} \times \frac{1 \text{ mol } NaC_2H_3O_2}{1 \text{ mol } C_2H_3O_2^-}$$

$$\times \frac{82.0 \text{ g } NaC_2H_3O_2}{1 \text{ mol } NaC_2H_3O_2} = 14 \text{ g } NaC_2H_3O_2$$

Point out that if you insert $[H_3O^+]$, $[HC_2H_3O_2]$ and $[C_2H_3O_2^-]$ from Example 17-5 into equation (17.2) you get a pH = 5.09.

Practice Example A: How many grams of $(NH_4)_2SO_4$ must be dissolved in 0.500 L of 0.35 M NH_3 to produce a solution with pH = 9.00? (Assume that the solution volume remains at 0.500 L.)

Practice Example B: In Practice Example 17-3A, we established that an appropriate mixture of a strong acid and the salt of a weak acid is a buffer solution. Show that a solution made by adding 33.05 g $NaC_2H_3O_2 \cdot 3\ H_2O(s)$ to 300 mL of 0.250 M HCl should have pH $\approx$ 5.1.

In Example 17-5, we achieved the desired ratio of $[C_2H_3O_2^-]/[HC_2H_3O_2]$ by adding 14 g of sodium acetate to the previously prepared 0.25 M $HC_2H_3O_2$ solution. This is a common method of obtaining a buffer solution. Other methods are sometimes useful as well. Sufficient NaOH(aq) could be added to $HC_2H_3O_2(aq)$ to neutralize the acid partially, *producing* $C_2H_3O_2^-$ as a product. Or enough $NaC_2H_3O_2(s)$ could be added to HCl(aq) to convert all the HCl to $HC_2H_3O_2$ and leave some $C_2H_3O_2^-$ in excess. As we saw in Chapter 16, amines are weak bases, so an aqueous mixture of an amine and its conjugate acid is a buffer solution. Buffer solutions based on amines can be prepared in ways analogous to those based on weak acids. The methods available for making buffer solutions are summarized in Figure 17-6.

CALCULATING pH CHANGES IN BUFFER SOLUTIONS

To calculate how the pH of a buffer solution changes when small amounts of a strong acid or base are added, we must first use *stoichiometric* principles to establish how much of one buffer component is consumed and how much of the other component is produced. Then the new concentrations of weak acid (or weak base) and its salt can be used to calculate the pH of the buffer solution.

> ☑ This is a difficult set of conditions to memorize. You may want simply to emphasize the six possibilities and not the details.

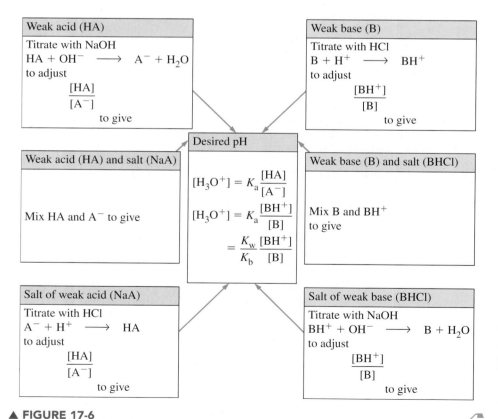

▲ **FIGURE 17-6**
Six methods for preparing buffer solutions
Depending on the pH range required and the type of experiment the buffer is to be used for, either a weak acid or a weak base can be used to prepare a buffer solution.

▲ FIGURE 17-7
Calculation of the new pH of a buffer after strong acid or base is added
The stoichiometric and equilibrium parts of the calculation are indicated. This scheme can also be applied to the conjugate acid–base pair BH^+/B, where B is a base.

Essentially, this problem is solved in two steps. First, we assume that the neutralization reaction proceeds *to completion* and determine new stoichiometric concentrations. Then these new stoichiometric concentrations are substituted into the equilibrium constant expression and the expression is solved for $[H_3O^+]$, which is converted to pH. This method is applied in Example 17-6 and illustrated in Figure 17-7.

EXAMPLE 17-6

Calculating pH Changes in a Buffer Solution. What are the effects on the pH of adding **(a)** 0.0060 mol HCl and **(b)** 0.0060 mol NaOH to 0.300 L of a buffer solution that is 0.250 M $HC_2H_3O_2$ and 0.560 M $NaC_2H_3O_2$?

Solution

To judge the effect of adding either (a) acid or (b) base on the pH of the buffer, the value we must keep in mind is the pH of the original buffer. This value can be obtained by using equation (17.2).

$$pH = pK_a + \log\frac{[C_2H_3O_2^-]}{[HC_2H_3O_2]}$$

$$= 4.74 + \log\frac{0.560}{0.250} = 4.74 + 0.35 = 5.09$$

(a) Stoichiometric Calculation: Let's convert all concentrations to amounts in moles, and assume that the neutralization goes to completion. Essentially, this is a limiting reactant calculation, but perhaps simpler than many of those in Chapter 4. In neutralizing the added H_3O^+, 0.0060 mol $C_2H_3O_2^-$ is converted to 0.0060 mol $HC_2H_3O_2$.

◄ KEEP IN MIND
that $[HC_2H_3O_2] = 0.250$ M and $[C_2H_3O_2^-] = 0.560$ M are *stoichiometric* concentrations. The corresponding *equilibrium* concentrations are $0.250 - x$ and $0.560 + x$, where $x = [H_3O^+]$. The stoichiometric concentrations can be substituted for the equilibrium concentrations because x is very small.

	$C_2H_3O_2^-$	+	H_3O^+	$\longrightarrow$	$HC_2H_3O_2$	+	H_2O
original buffer:	$\dfrac{0.300\ L \times 0.560\ M}{0.168\ mol}$				$\dfrac{0.300\ L \times 0.250\ M}{0.750\ mol}$		
add:			0.0060 mol				
changes:	−0.0060 mol		−0.0060 mol		+0.0060 mol		
final buffer:							
amounts:	0.162 mol		(?)		0.0810 mol		
concns:	$\dfrac{0.162\ mol/0.300\ L}{0.540\ M}$		(?)		$\dfrac{0.0810\ mol/0.300\ L}{0.270\ M}$		

Equilibrium Calculation: We can redetermine the pH with equation (17.2), using the new equilibrium concentrations.

$$pH = pK_a + \log\frac{[C_2H_3O_2^-]}{[HC_2H_3O_2]}$$

$$= 4.74 + \log\frac{0.540}{0.270} = 4.74 + 0.30 = 5.04$$

This addition of 0.0060 mol HCl *lowers* the pH from 5.09 to 5.04; this is only a small change in pH.

(b) Stoichiometric Calculation: In neutralizing the added OH^-, 0.0060 mol $HC_2H_3O_2$ is converted to 0.0060 mol $C_2H_3O_2^-$. The calculation of the new stoichiometric concentrations is shown on the last line of the following table.

	$HC_2H_3O_2$	+	OH^-	$\longrightarrow$	$C_2H_3O_2^-$	+	H_2O
original buffer:	$\dfrac{0.300\ L \times 0.250\ M}{0.0750\ mol}$				$\dfrac{0.300\ L \times 0.560\ M}{0.168\ mol}$		
add:			0.0060 mol				
changes:	−0.0060 mol		−0.0060 mol		+0.0060 mol		
final buffer:							
amounts:	0.0690 mol		(?)		0.174 mol		
concns:	$\dfrac{0.0690\ mol/0.300\ L}{0.230\ M}$		(?)		$\dfrac{0.174\ mol/0.300\ L}{0.580\ M}$		

Equilibrium Calculation: This is the same type of calculation as in part (a), but with slightly different concentrations.

$$pH = 4.74 + \log\frac{0.580}{0.230} = 4.74 + 0.40 = 5.14$$

The addition of 0.0060 mol OH^- *raises* the pH from 5.09 to 5.14—another small change.

CHECK: The most important factors to confirm in a buffer calculation are that the magnitude of the pH change is small and that the change occurs in the correct direction: *lowering* of the pH by an acid and *raising* of the pH by a base. The results are indeed reasonable.

Practice Example A: A 1.00-L volume of buffer is made with concentrations of 0.350 M $NaCHO_2$ (sodium formate) and 0.550 M $HCHO_2$ (formic acid). **(a)** What is the initial pH? **(b)** What is the pH after the addition of 0.0050 mol HCl(aq)? (Assume that the volume remains 1.00 L.) **(c)** What would be the pH after the addition of 0.0050 mol NaOH to the original buffer?

Practice Example B: How many milliliters of 6.0 M HNO_3 would you add to 300.0 mL of the buffer solution of Example 17-6 to change the pH from 5.09 to 5.03?

Urbansky, E. T., Schock, M. R. "Understanding, Deriving, and Computing Buffer-Capacity." *J. Chem. Educ.* **2000:** *77*, 1640 (December 2000).

✓ Dilute and concentrated buffers will have the same pH, but as mentioned in the next section, a given volume of a dilute buffer will have a lower buffer capacity than the same volume of a more concentrated buffer.

Perhaps you have already noticed a way to simplify the calculation in Example 17-6. Because the buffer components are always present in the same solution of volume V, the numbers of moles can be substituted directly into equation (17.2) without regard for the particular value of V. Thus, in Example 17-6(b),

$$pH = 4.74 + \log\frac{[C_2H_3O_2^-]}{[HC_2H_3O_2]} = 4.74 + \log\frac{0.174\ \cancel{mol}/\cancel{V}}{0.0690\ \cancel{mol}/\cancel{V}} = 4.74 + 0.40 = 5.14$$

This expression is also consistent with the observation that, on dilution, buffer solutions resist pH changes. Diluting a buffer solution means increasing its volume V by adding water. This action produces the same change in the numerator and the denominator of the ratio [conjugate base]/[acid]. The ratio itself remains unchanged, as does the pH.

BUFFER CAPACITY AND BUFFER RANGE

It is not difficult to see that if we add more than 0.0750 mol OH⁻ to the buffer solution described in Example 17-6, the 0.0750 mol $HC_2H_3O_2$ will be completely converted to 0.0750 mol $C_2H_3O_2^-$. An excess of OH⁻ will remain, and the solution will become rather strongly basic.

Buffer capacity refers to the amount of acid or base that a buffer can neutralize before its pH changes appreciably. In general, the maximum buffer capacity exists when the concentrations of a weak acid and its conjugate base are kept *large* and *approximately equal to each other*. The **buffer range** is the pH range over which a buffer effectively neutralizes added acids and bases and maintains a fairly constant pH. As equation (17.2) suggests,

$$pH = pK_a + \log\frac{[\text{conjugate base}]}{[\text{acid}]}$$

when the ratio [conjugate base]/[acid] = 1, $pH = pK_a$. When the ratio falls to 0.10, the pH *decreases* by 1 pH unit from pK_a because log 0.10 = −1. If the ratio increases to a value of 10, the pH *increases* by 1 unit because log 10 = 1. For practical purposes, this range of 2 pH units is the maximum range to which a buffer solution should be exposed. For acetic acid–sodium acetate buffers, the effective range is about pH 3.7–5.7; for ammonia–ammonium chloride buffers, it is about pH 8.3–10.3.

APPLICATIONS OF BUFFER SOLUTIONS

An important example of a buffered system is that found in blood, which must be maintained at a pH of 7.4 in humans. We will consider the buffering of blood in the Focus On feature at the end of this chapter. But buffers have other important applications, too.

Protein studies often must be performed in buffered media because the structures of protein molecules, including the magnitude and kind of electric charges they carry, depend on the pH (see Section 27-4). The typical enzyme is a protein capable of catalyzing a biochemical reaction, so enzyme activity is closely linked to protein structure and hence to pH. Most enzymes in the body have their maximum activity between pH 6 and pH 8. Studying enzyme activity in the laboratory usually means working with media buffered in this pH range.

The control of pH is often important in industrial processes. For example, in the mashing of barley malt, the first step of making beer, the pH of the solution must be maintained at 5.0 to 5.2, so that the protease and peptidase enzymes can hydrolyze the proteins from the barley. The inventor of the pH scale, Søren Sørensen, was a research scientist in a brewery.

We will consider the importance of buffer solutions in solubility/precipitation processes in Chapter 18.

 Our eyes can see an indicator color change over a range of about 2 pH units.

◀ **KEEP IN MIND**
that as a rule of thumb, the amounts of the buffer components should be at least ten times greater than the amount of acid or base to be neutralized.

◀ The buffer range for the ammonia–ammonium chloride solution is based on the pK_a of NH_4^+, 9.26.

▲ A master brewer inspecting wort temperature and pH in the making of beer.

17-3 ACID–BASE INDICATORS

An **acid–base indicator** is a substance whose color depends on the pH of the solution to which it is added. Several of the photographs in this and the preceding chapter have shown acid–base indicators in use. The indicator chosen depended on just how acidic or basic the solution was. In this section, we will consider how an acid–base indicator works and how an appropriate indicator is selected for a pH measurement.

Acid–base indicators exist in two forms: (1) a weak acid, represented symbolically as HIn and having one color, and (2) its conjugate base, represented as In⁻ and having a different color. When just a small amount of indicator is added to a solution, the indicator does not affect the pH of the solution. Instead, the ionization equilibrium of the indicator is itself affected by the prevailing [H_3O^+] in solution.

$$\underset{\text{acid color}}{\text{HIn}} + H_2O \rightleftharpoons H_3O^+ + \underset{\text{base color}}{\text{In}^-}$$

Two of the most important biological buffers are the phosphate and bicarbonate buffer systems. Proteins and nucleotides also function as buffers on the cellular level.

Acid-base indicators can be obtained from many plant sources. Indicators found in several fruits and vegetables are discussed in Mebane, R. C., Rybolt, T. R. *J. Chem. Educ.* **1985:** *62,* 285.

▶ The acid "color" of a few indicators is colorless.

Collect as many of the indicators in Figure 17-8 as you can and put a few drops into beakers containing acid and base to confirm the indicator colors.

Natural Indicators movie

From Le Châtelier's principle, we see that *increasing* [H_3O^+] in a solution displaces the equilibrium to the left, increasing the proportion of HIn and hence the acid color. *Decreasing* [H_3O^+] in a solution displaces the equilibrium to the right, increasing the proportion of In^- and hence the base color. The color of the solution depends on the relative proportions of the acid and base. The pH of the solution can be related to these relative proportions and to the pK_a of the indicator by means of an equation similar to equation (17.2).

$$\text{pH} = pK_{HIn} + \log\frac{[In^-]}{[HIn]} \tag{17.4}$$

In general, if 90% or more of an indicator is in the form HIn, the solution will take on the acid color. If 90% or more is in the form In^-, the solution takes on the base (or anion) color. If the concentrations of HIn and In^- are about equal, the indicator is in the process of changing from one form to the other and has an intermediate color. The complete change in color occurs over a range of about *2 pH units*, with pH = pK_{HIn} at about the middle of the range. The colors and pH ranges of several acid–base indicators are shown in Figure 17-8. A summary of these ideas is presented in Table 17.1, and an example of their use is given below.

Bromthymol blue, $pK_{HIn} = 7.1$

pH < 6.1 (yellow)   pH ≈ 7.1 (green)   pH > 8.1 (blue)

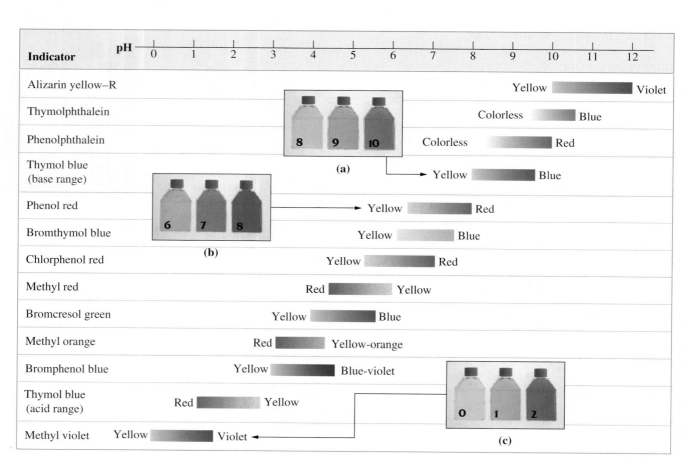

▲ **FIGURE 17-8**
pH and color changes for some common acid–base indicators
The indicators pictured and the pH values at which they change color are **(a)** thymol blue (pH 8–10); **(b)** phenol red (pH 6–8); and **(c)** methyl violet (pH 0–2).

TABLE 17.1	pH and the Colors of Acid–Base Indicators	
Acid Color	**Intermediate Color**	**Base Color**
$[In^-]/[HIn] < 0.10$	$[In^-]/[HIn] \approx 1$	$[In^-]/[HIn] > 10$
$pH < pK_{HIn} + \log 0.10$	$pH \approx pK_{HIn} + \log 1$	$pH > pK_{HIn} + \log 10$
$pH < pK_{HIn} - 1$	$pH \approx pK_{HIn}$	$pH > pK_{HIn} + 1$

An acid–base indicator is usually prepared as a solution (in water, ethanol, or some other solvent). In acid–base titrations, a few drops of the indicator solution are added to the solution being titrated. In other applications, porous paper is impregnated with an indicator solution and dried. When this paper is moistened with the solution being tested, it acquires a color determined by the pH of the solution. This paper is usually called *pH test paper*.

CONCEPT ASSESSMENT ✓

Starting with about 10 mL of dilute NaCl(aq) containing a couple drops of phenol red indicator, what color would the solution be for each of the following actions: **(a)** first 10 drops of 1.0 M HCl(aq) are added to the solution; **(b)** next 15 drops of 1.0 M CH$_3$COONa(aq) are added to solution (a); **(c)** then one drop of 1.0 M KOH(aq) is added to solution (b); and **(d)** 10 more drops of 1.0 M KOH(aq) are added to solution (c).

APPLICATIONS

Acid–base indicators are most useful when only an approximate pH determination is needed. For example, they are used in soil-testing kits to establish the approximate pH of soils. Soils are usually acidic in regions of high rainfall and heavy vegetation, and they are alkaline in more arid regions. The pH can vary considerably with local conditions, however. If a soil is found to be too acidic for a certain crop, its pH can be raised by adding slaked lime [Ca(OH)$_2$]. To reduce the pH of a soil, organic matter might be added.

In swimming pools, chlorinating agents are most effective at a pH of about 7.4. At this pH, the growth of algae is avoided, and the corrosion of pool plumbing is minimized. Phenol red (see Figure 17-8) is a common indicator used in testing swimming pool water. If chlorination is carried out with Cl$_2$(g), the pool water becomes acidic as a result of the reaction of Cl$_2$ with H$_2$O: Cl$_2$ + 2 H$_2$O $\longrightarrow$ H$_3$O$^+$ + Cl$^-$ + HOCl. In this case, a basic substance such as sodium carbonate is used to raise the pH. Another widely used chlorinating agent is sodium hypochlorite, NaOCl(aq), made by the reaction of Cl$_2$(g) with excess NaOH(aq): Cl$_2$ + 2 OH$^-$ $\longrightarrow$ Cl$^-$ + OCl$^-$ + H$_2$O. The excess NaOH raises the pH of the pool water. The pH is adjusted by adding an acid such as HCl or H$_2$SO$_4$.

▲ Testing swimming pool water for its chlorine content and pH.

Find a titration curve simulator you like and do some in class. Encourage the students to investigate these pages on their own.

 Acid–Base Titration animation

 Predicting the Equivalence Point

17-4   NEUTRALIZATION REACTIONS AND TITRATION CURVES

As we learned in the discussion of the stoichiometry of titration reactions (Section 5-7), the **equivalence point** of a neutralization reaction is the point at which both acid and base have been consumed and *neither* is in excess.

In a titration, one of the solutions to be neutralized—say, the acid—is placed in a flask or beaker, together with a few drops of an acid–base indicator. The other solution (the base) used in a titration is added from a buret and is called the **titrant**. The titrant is added to the acid, first rapidly and then drop by drop, up to the equivalence point (recall Figure 5-10). The equivalence point is located by noting the color change of the acid–base indicator.

Good web pages for simulation of titration curves:
http://yip5.chem.wfu.edu/yip/java/ (noncommercial);
http://www.attotron.com/pub/pctitr.htm (commercial);
http://michele.usc.edu/java/acidbase/acidbase.html (noncommercial);
http://www.chm.davidson.edu/java/titrate/titrate.html (noncommercial).

Barnum, Dennis W. "Predicting Acid-Base Titration Curves without Calculations." *J. Chem. Educ.* **1999:** *76*, 938 (July 1999).

de Levie, Robert A. "General Simulator for Acid-Base Titrations." *J. Chem. Educ.* **1999:** *76*, 1987 (July 1999).

This article discusses using the sense of smell to determine titration endpoints using olfactory acid-base indicators: Neppel, K., et al. *J. Chem. Educ.* **2005:** *82*, 607.

Study of Acid–Base Titrations: Monoprotic Acids

The point in a titration at which the indicator changes color is called the **end point** of the indicator. The end point must match the equivalence point of the neutralization. That is, if the indicator's end point is near the equivalence point of the neutralization, the color change marked by that end point will signal the attainment of the equivalence point. This match can be achieved by use of an indicator whose color change occurs over a pH range that includes the pH of the equivalence point.

A graph of pH versus volume of titrant (the solution in the buret) is called a **titration curve**. Titration curves are most easily constructed by measuring the pH during a titration with a pH meter and plotting the data with a recorder. In this section we will emphasize calculating the pH at various points in a titration. These calculations will serve as a review of aspects of acid–base equilibria considered earlier in this chapter and in the preceding chapter.

THE MILLIMOLE

In a typical titration, the volume of solution delivered from a buret is less than 50 mL (usually about 20–25 mL). The molarity of the solution used for the titration is generally less than 1 M. The typical amount of OH^- (or H_3O^+) delivered from the buret during a titration is only a few thousandths of a mole—for example, 5.00×10^{-3} mol. In calculations it is often easier to work with millimoles instead of moles. The symbol **mmol** stands for a **millimole**, which is one thousandth of a mole, or 10^{-3} mol.

Recall from Chapter 4 that molarity is defined as the number of moles per liter. We can use an alternative definition of molarity by converting from moles to millimoles and from liters to milliliters.

$$M = \frac{mol}{L} = \frac{mol/1000}{L/1000} = \frac{mmol}{mL}$$

Thus, the expression from Chapter 4 that the amount of solute is the product of molarity and solution volume (page 122) can be based either on mol/L × L = mol or on mmol/mL × mL = mmol.

TITRATION OF A STRONG ACID WITH A STRONG BASE

Suppose that 25.00 mL of 0.100 M HCl (a strong acid) is placed in a small flask or beaker and that 0.100 M NaOH (a strong base) is added to it from a buret. The pH of the accumulated solution can be calculated at different points in the titration, and these pH values can be plotted against the volume of NaOH added. From this titration curve we can establish the pH at the equivalence point and identify an appropriate indicator for the titration. Some typical calculations are outlined in Example 17-7.

EXAMPLE 17-7

Calculating Points on a Titration Curve: Strong Acid Titrated with a Strong Base. What is the pH at each of the following points in the titration of 25.00 mL of 0.100 M HCl with 0.100 M NaOH?

(a) before the addition of any NaOH (*initial pH*)

(b) after the addition of 24.00 mL 0.100 M NaOH (*before equiv point*)

(c) after the addition of 25.00 mL 0.100 M NaOH (*at equiv point*)

(d) after the addition of 26.00 mL 0.100 M NaOH (*beyond equiv point*)

Solution

First, let's write the titration equation in the ionic and net ionic form.

Ionic form: $H_3O^+(aq) + Cl^-(aq) + Na^+(aq) + OH^-(aq) \longrightarrow$
$$Na^+(aq) + Cl^-(aq) + 2 H_2O(l)$$

Net ionic form: $H_3O^+(aq) + OH^-(aq) \longrightarrow 2\,H_2O(l)$

(a) Before any NaOH is added, we are dealing with 0.100 M HCl. This solution has $[H_3O^+] = 0.100$ M and pH = 1.00.

(b) The number of millimoles of H_3O^+ to be titrated is

$$25.00\ \text{mL} \times \frac{0.100\ \text{mmol}\ H_3O^+}{1\ \text{mL}} = 2.50\ \text{mmol}\ H_3O^+$$

The number of millimoles of OH^- present in 24.00 mL of 0.100 M NaOH is

$$24.00\ \text{mL} \times \frac{0.100\ \text{mmol}}{1\ \text{mL}} = 2.40\ \text{mmol}\ OH^-$$

Now we can represent the net ionic equation of the neutralization reaction in a familiar format.

	H_3O^+	$+$	OH^-	$\longrightarrow$	$2\,H_2O$
initially present:	2.50 mmol		—		
add:			2.40 mmol		
changes:	−2.40 mmol		−2.40 mmol		
after reaction:	0.10 mmol		≈0		

The remaining 0.10 mmol of H_3O^+ is present in 49.00 mL of solution (25.00 mL original + 24.00 mL added base).

$$[H_3O^+] = \frac{0.10\ \text{mmol}\ H_3O^+}{49.00\ \text{mL}} = 2.0 \times 10^{-3}\ \text{M}$$

$$\text{pH} = -\log[H_3O^+] = -\log(2.0 \times 10^{-3}) = 2.70$$

(c) The equivalence point is the point at which the HCl is completely neutralized and no excess NaOH is present. As seen in the ionic form of the equation for the neutralization reaction, the solution at the equivalence point is simply NaCl(aq). And, as we learned in Section 16-7, because neither Na^+ nor Cl^- hydrolyzes in water, pH = 7.00.

(d) To determine the pH of the solution beyond the equivalence point, we can return to the format in (b), except that now OH^- is in excess. The amount of OH^- added is $26.00\ \text{mL} \times 0.100\ \text{mmol/L} = 26.0\ \text{mmol}$.

	H_3O^+	$+$	OH^-	$\longrightarrow$	$2\,H_2O$
initially present:	2.50 mmol		—		
add:			2.60 mmol		
changes:	−2.50 mmol		−2.50 mmol		
after reaction:	≈0		0.10 mmol		

The excess 0.10 mmol of NaOH is present in 51.00 mL of solution (25.00 mL original acid + 26.00 mL added base). The concentration of OH^- in this solution is

$$[OH^-] = \frac{0.10\ \text{mmol}\ OH^-}{51.00\ \text{mL}} = 2.0 \times 10^{-3}\ \text{M}$$

$$\text{pOH} = -\log(2.0 \times 10^{-3}) = 2.70 \qquad \text{pH} = 14.00 - 2.70 = 11.30$$

Practice Example A: For the titration of 25.00 mL of 0.150 M HCl with 0.250 M NaOH, calculate **(a)** the initial pH; **(b)** the pH when neutralization is 50.0% complete; **(c)** the pH when neutralization is 100.0% complete; and **(d)** the pH when 1.00 mL of NaOH is added beyond the equivalence point.

Practice Example B: For the titration of 50.00 mL of 0.00812 M $Ba(OH)_2$ with 0.0250 M HCl, calculate **(a)** the initial pH; **(b)** the pH when neutralization is 50.0% complete; **(c)** the pH when neutralization is 100.0% complete.

Titration Data

mL NaOH(aq)	pH
0.00	1.00
10.00	1.37
20.00	1.95
22.00	2.19
24.00	2.70
25.00	7.00
26.00	11.30
28.00	11.75
30.00	11.96
40.00	12.36
50.00	12.52

▲ **FIGURE 17-9**

Titration curve for the titration of a strong acid with a strong base—25.00 mL of 0.100 M HCl with 0.100 M NaOH

All indicators whose color ranges fall along the steep portion of the titration curve are suitable for this titration. Thymol blue changes color too soon; alizarin yellow-R, too late.

Titration simulation

Use Figure 17-9 to point out the difference between the equivalence point and the end point in a titration.

Figure 17-9 presents pH versus volume data and the titration curve for the HCl–NaOH titration. From this figure, we can establish these principal features of the titration curve for the titration of a *strong acid with a strong base*.

- The pH has a low value at the beginning of the titration.
- The pH changes slowly until just before the equivalence point.
- At the equivalence point, the pH rises very sharply, perhaps by 6 units for an addition of only 0.10 mL (2 drops) of base.
- Beyond the equivalence point, the pH again rises only slowly.
- Any acid–base indicator whose color changes in the pH range from about 4 to 10 is suitable for this titration.

In the titration of a strong base with a strong acid, we can obtain a titration curve essentially identical to Figure 17-9 by plotting pOH against volume of titrant (the strong acid). Also, we can make a set of statements similar to those listed above, except that pOH would be substituted for pH. Alternatively, if pH is plotted against volume of titrant (the strong acid), the titration curve looks like Figure 17-9 flipped over from top to bottom, as shown in Figure 17-10.

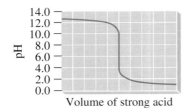

▲ **FIGURE 17-10**

Titration curve for the titration of a strong base with a strong acid

If you are certain with your concentrations, you can take a beaker containing (dilute) HCl and another containing exactly the same number of moles of dilute NaOH. Pour the two together and show that the pH = 7. If you stress the importance of being careful, you can taste the result which, of course, will taste like salty water.

TITRATION OF A WEAK ACID WITH A STRONG BASE

Several important differences exist between the titration of a weak acid with a strong base and a strong acid with a strong base, but one feature is *unchanged* when we compare the two titrations.

For equal volumes of acid solutions of the same molarity, the volume of base required to titrate to the equivalence point is independent of the strength of the acid.

▲ **FIGURE 17-11**
Titration curve for the titration of a weak acid with a strong base—25.00 mL of 0.100 M $HC_2H_3O_2$ with 0.100 M NaOH
Phenolphthalein is a suitable indicator for this titration, but methyl red is not. When exactly half of the acid is neutralized, $[HC_2H_3O_2] = [C_2H_3O_2^-]$ and $pH = pK_a = 4.74$.

We can think of the neutralization of a weak acid such as $HC_2H_3O_2$ as involving the direct transfer of protons from $HC_2H_3O_2$ molecules to OH^- ions. In the neutralization of a strong acid, the protons are transferred from H_3O^+ ions. In either case, the acid and base react in a $1:1$ mole ratio.

$$HC_2H_3O_2 + OH^- \longrightarrow H_2O + C_2H_3O_2^-$$
$$H_3O^+ + OH^- \longrightarrow H_2O + H_2O'$$

Calculations for the titration of a weak acid with a strong base can be divided into a stoichiometric part and an equilibrium part to take into account the partial ionization of the weak acid. The calculation strategy is analogous to that adopted when we considered the addition of a strong base to a buffer solution. In Example 17-8 and in Figure 17-11, we consider the titration of 25.00 mL of 0.100 M $HC_2H_3O_2$ with 0.100 M NaOH.

EXAMPLE 17-8

Calculating Points on a Titration Curve: Weak Acid Titrated with a Strong Base.
What is the pH at each of the following points in the titration of 25.00 mL of 0.100 M $HC_2H_3O_2$ with 0.100 M NaOH?

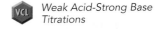
Weak Acid-Strong Base Titrations

   (a) before the addition of any NaOH (*initial pH*)
   (b) after the addition of 10.00 mL 0.100 M NaOH (*before equiv point*)
   (c) after the addition of 12.50 mL 0.100 M NaOH (*half-neutralization*)
   (d) after the addition of 25.00 mL 0.100 M NaOH (*equiv point*)
   (e) after the addition of 26.00 mL 0.100 M NaOH (*beyond equiv point*)

Solution

   (a) The initial $[H_3O^+]$ is obtained by the calculation in Example 16-6 (page 677). $pH = -\log(1.3 \times 10^{-3}) = 2.89$.
   (b) The number of millimoles of $HC_2H_3O_2$ to be neutralized is

$$25.00 \text{ mL} \times \frac{0.100 \text{ mmol } HC_2H_3O_2}{1 \text{ mL}} = 2.50 \text{ mmol } HC_2H_3O_2$$

At this point in the titration, the number of millimoles of OH^- added is

$$10.00 \text{ mL} \times \frac{0.100 \text{ mmol } OH^-}{1 \text{ mL}} = 1.00 \text{ mmol } OH^-$$

The total solution volume = 25.00 mL original acid + 10.00 mL added base = 35.00 mL. We enter this information at appropriate points into the following setup.

Stoichiometric Calculation:

	$HC_2H_3O_2$	+	OH^-	$\longrightarrow$	$C_2H_2O_2^-$	+	H_2O
initially present:	2.50 mmol		—		—		
add:			1.00 mmol				
changes:	−1.00 mmol		−1.00 mmol		+1.00 mmol		
after reaction:							
mmol:	1.50 mmol				1.00 mmol		
concns:	1.50 mmol/35.00 mL		≈ 0		1.00 mmol/35.00 mL		
	0.0429 M				0.0286 M		

Equilibrium Calculation: The most direct approach is to recognize that the acetic acid–sodium acetate solution is a buffer solution whose pH can be calculated with the Henderson–Hasselbalch equation. Use of that equation is justified for two reasons: (1) The ratio: $[C_2H_3O_2^-]/[HC_2H_3O_2] = 0.0286/0.0429 = 0.667$ (satisfying the requirement on page 716 that it be between 0.10 and 10), and (2) $[C_2H_3O_2^-]$ and $[HC_2H_3O_2]$ exceed $K_a(1.8 \times 10^{-5})$ by the factors 1.6×10^3 and 2.4×10^3 respectively (satisfying the requirement on page 680 that the factor exceed 100). So

$$pH = pK_a + \log\frac{[A^-]}{[HA]} = 4.74 + \log\frac{0.0286}{0.0429} = 4.74 - 0.18 = 4.56$$

Simpler still would be to substitute the numbers of millimoles of $C_2H_3O_2^-$ and $HC_2H_3O_2$ directly into the Henderson–Hasselbalch equation, without converting to molarities. That is,

$$pH = pK_a + \log\frac{[A^-]}{[HA]}$$

$$= 4.74 + \log\frac{1.00 \text{ mmol}/V}{1.50 \text{ mmol}/V} = 4.74 - 0.18 = 4.56$$

(c) When we have added 12.50 mL of 0.100 M NaOH, we have added $12.50 \times 0.100 = 1.25$ mmol OH^-. As the following setup shows, this is enough base to neutralize exactly *half* of the acid.

	$HC_2H_3O_2$	+	OH^-	$\longrightarrow$	$C_2H_3O_2^-$	+	H_2O
initially present:	2.50 mmol		—		—		
add:			1.25 mmol				
changes:	−1.25 mmol		−1.25 mmol		+1.25 mmol		
after reaction:	1.25 mmol				1.25 mmol		

Again, applying the Henderson–Hasselbalch equation, we get

$$pH = pK_a + \log\frac{[C_2H_3O_2^-]}{[HC_2H_3O_2]}$$

$$= 4.74 + \log\frac{1.25 \text{ mmol}/V}{1.25 \text{ mmol}/V} = 4.74 + \log 1 = 4.74$$

(d) At the equivalence point, neutralization is complete and 2.50 mmol $NaC_2H_3O_2$ has been produced in 50.00 mL of solution, leading to 0.500 M $NaC_2H_3O_2$. The question becomes, "What is the pH of 0.500 M $NaC_2H_3O_2$?" To answer this question, we must recognize that $C_2H_3O_2^-$ hydrolyzes (and Na^+ does not). The hydrolysis reaction and value of K_b are

KEEP IN MIND ▶
that the Henderson–Hasselbalch equation (equation 17.2) might be inaccurate in the very early stages of the titration and near the equivalence point. In the first instance, $[C_2H_3O_2^-]/[HC_2H_3O_2] < 0.10$; in the second instance, $[C_2H_3O_2^-]/[HC_2H_3O_2] > 10$.

Titration Data

mL NaOH(aq)	pH
0.00	2.89
5.00	4.14
10.00	4.57
12.50	4.74
15.00	4.92
20.00	5.35
24.00	6.12
25.00	8.72
26.00	11.30
30.00	11.96
40.00	12.36
50.00	12.52

$$C_2H_3O_2^- + H_2O \rightleftharpoons HC_2H_3O_2 + OH^-$$

$$K_b = \frac{K_w}{K_a} = \frac{1.0 \times 10^{-14}}{1.8 \times 10^{-5}} = 5.6 \times 10^{-10}$$

With a format similar to that used in the hydrolysis calculation of Example 16-13 (page 690), we obtain the following expression, where $x = [OH^-]$ and $x \ll 0.0500$.

$$K_b = \frac{[HC_2H_3O_2]}{[C_2H_3O_2^-]} = \frac{x \cdot x}{0.500 - x} = 5.6 \times 10^{-10}$$

$$x^2 = 2.8 \times 10^{-11} \qquad x = [OH^-] = 5.3 \times 10^{-6} \text{ M}$$

$$pOH = -\log(5.3 \times 10^{-6}) = 5.28$$

$$pH = 14.00 - pOH = 14.00 - 5.28 = 8.72$$

(e) The amount of OH^- added is 26.00 mL $\times$ 0.100 mmol/mL = 2.60 mmol. The volume of solution is 25.00 mL acid + 26.00 mL base = 51.00 mL. The 2.60 mmol OH^- neutralizes the 2.50 mmol of available acid, and 0.10 mmol OH^- remains in *excess*. Beyond the equivalence point, the pH of the solution is determined by the excess *strong* base.

$$[OH^-] = \frac{0.10 \text{ mmol } OH^-}{51.00 \text{ mL}} = 2.0 \times 10^{-3} \text{ M}$$

$$pOH = -\log(2.0 \times 10^{-3}) = 2.70 \qquad pH = 14.00 - 2.70 = 11.30$$

Practice Example A: A 20.00-mL sample of 0.150 M HF solution is titrated with 0.250 M NaOH. Calculate **(a)** the initial pH and the pH when neutralization is **(b)** 25.0%, **(c)** 50.0%, **(d)** 100.0% complete.

[*Hint:* What is the initial amount of HF, and what amount remains unneutralized at the points in question?]

Practice Example B: For the titration of 50.00 mL of 0.106 M NH_3 with 0.225 M HCl, calculate **(a)** the initial pH and the pH when neutralization is **(b)** 25.0% complete; **(c)** 50.0% complete; **(d)** 100.0% complete.

Here are the principal features of the titration curve for a weak acid titrated with a strong base (Fig. 17-11).

1. The initial pH is higher (less acidic) than in the titration of a strong acid. (The weak acid is only partially ionized.)

2. There is an initial rather sharp increase in pH at the start of the titration. (The anion produced by the neutralization of the weak acid is a common ion that reduces the extent of ionization of the acid.)

3. Over a long section of the curve preceding the equivalence point, the pH changes only gradually. (Solutions corresponding to this portion of the curve are buffer solutions.)

4. Because $[HA] = [A^-]$ at the point of half-neutralization, $pH = pK_a$.

5. At the equivalence point, $pH > 7$. (The conjugate base of a weak acid hydrolyzes, producing OH^-.)

6. Beyond the equivalence point, the titration curve is identical to that of a strong acid with a strong base. (In this portion of the titration, the pH is established entirely by the concentration of unreacted OH^-.)

7. The steep portion of the titration curve at the equivalence point occurs over a relatively short pH range (from about pH 7 to pH 10).

8. The selection of indicators available for the titration is more limited than in a strong acid–strong base titration. (Indicators that change color below pH 7 cannot be used.)

▶ **FIGURE 17-12**
Constructing the titration curve for a weak acid with a strong base
The calculations needed to plot this graph, illustrated in Example 17-8, can be divided into *four* types.

1. pH of a pure weak acid (initial pH)
2. pH of a buffer solution of a weak acid and its salt (over a broad range before the equivalence point)
3. pH of a salt solution undergoing hydrolysis (equivalence point)
4. pH of a solution of a strong base (over a broad range beyond the equivalence point)

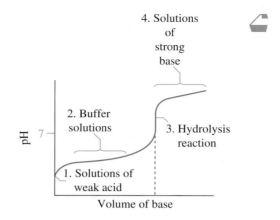

As illustrated in Example 17-8 and suggested by Figure 17-12, the necessary calculations for a weak acid–strong base titration curve are of four distinct types, depending on the portion of the titration curve being described. One type of titration that generally cannot be performed successfully is that of a weak acid with a weak base (or vice versa). The equivalence point cannot be located precisely because the change in pH with volume of titrant is too gradual.

CONCEPT ASSESSMENT ✓

To raise the pH of 1.00 L of 0.50 M HCl(aq) *significantly*, which of the following would you add to the solution and why? **(a)** 0.50 mol $HC_2H_3O_2$; **(b)** 1.00 mol NaCl; **(c)** 0.60 mol $NaC_2H_3O_2$; **(d)** 0.40 mol NaOH

TITRATION OF A WEAK POLYPROTIC ACID

▶ This stepwise neutralization is observed only if successive ionization constants ($K_{a_1}, K_{a_2}, \dots$) differ significantly in magnitude (for example, by a factor of 10^3 or more). Otherwise, the second neutralization step begins before the first step is completed, and so on.

The most striking evidence that a polyprotic acid ionizes in distinct steps comes by way of its titration curve. For a polyprotic acid, we expect to see a separate equivalence point for each acidic hydrogen. Thus, we expect to see three equivalence points when H_3PO_4 is titrated with NaOH(aq). In the neutralization of phosphoric acid by sodium hydroxide, essentially all the H_3PO_4 molecules are first converted to the salt, NaH_2PO_4. Then all the NaH_2PO_4 is converted to Na_2HPO_4; and finally the Na_2HPO_4 is converted to Na_3PO_4.

Are You Wondering . . .

How to calculate the pH values at various points on the titration curve in Figure 17-13?

The pH of the initial 0.100 M H_3PO_4 can be calculated with the K_{a_1} expression of H_3PO_4 (recall Example 16-9). For the slowly rising portion of the curve before the first equivalence point, the predominant species are H_3PO_4 and $H_2PO_4^-$, acting as a buffer solution. For this portion of the curve, we can calculate the pH by using equation (17.2). Thus, halfway to the first equivalence point, where $[H_3PO_4] = [H_2PO_4^-]$, pH = pK_{a_1}. Between the first and second equivalence points, the predominant species are $H_2PO_4^-$ and HPO_4^{2-}, and calculations can be based on the K_{a_2} expression. At the midway point for this section of the curve, pH = pK_{a_2}. Beyond the second equivalence point, the predominant species are HPO_4^{2-} and PO_4^{3-}. Although pH calculations can be made in this region, titrations are generally not carried this far (for reasons stated in the text). The calculations required at the equivalence points are described in Section 17-5.

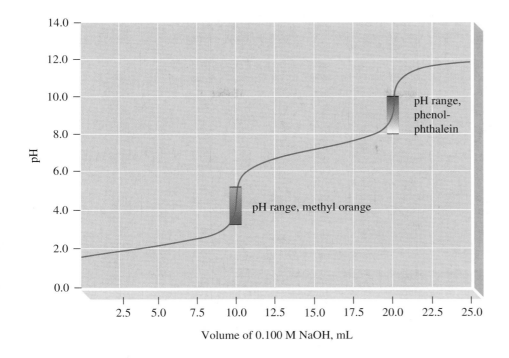

Volume of 0.100 M NaOH, mL

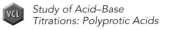

◀ **FIGURE 17-13**
Titration of a weak polyprotic acid—10.0 mL of 0.100 M H_3PO_4 with 0.100 M NaOH
A 10.0-mL volume of 0.100 M NaOH is required to reach the first equivalence point. The additional volume of 0.100 M NaOH required to reach the second equivalence point is also 10.0 mL.

The titration of 10.0 mL of 0.100 M H_3PO_4 with 0.100 M NaOH is pictured in Figure 17-13. Notice that the first two equivalence points come at equal intervals on the volume axis, at 10.0 mL and at 20.0 mL. Although we expect a third equivalence point at 30.0 mL, it is not realized in this titration. The pH of the strongly hydrolyzed Na_3PO_4 solution at the third equivalence point—approaching pH 13—is higher than can be reached by adding 0.100 M NaOH to water. $Na_3PO_4(aq)$ is nearly as basic as the NaOH(aq) used in the titration (as we shall see in Section 17-5).

Let's focus on a few details of this titration. For each mole of H_3PO_4, 1 mol NaOH is required to reach the first equivalence point. At this first equivalence point, the solution is essentially $NaH_2PO_4(aq)$. This is an *acidic* solution because $K_{a_2} > K_b$ for $H_2PO_4^-$: the reaction that produces H_3O^+ predominates over the one that produces OH^-.

$$H_2PO_4^- + H_2O \rightleftharpoons H_3O^+ + HPO_4^{2-} \qquad K_{a_2} = 6.3 \times 10^{-8}$$
$$H_2PO_4^- + H_2O \rightleftharpoons H_3PO_4 + OH^- \qquad K_b = 1.4 \times 10^{-12}$$

The pH at the equivalence point falls within the pH range over which the color of methyl orange indicator changes from red to orange.

An additional mole of NaOH is required to convert 1 mol $H_2PO_4^-$ to 1 mol HPO_4^{2-}. At this second equivalence point in the titration of H_3PO_4, the solution is *basic* because $K_b > K_{a_3}$ for HPO_4^{2-}.

$$HPO_4^{2-} + H_2O \rightleftharpoons H_2PO_4^- + OH^- \qquad K_b = 1.6 \times 10^{-7}$$
$$HPO_4^{2-} + H_2O \rightleftharpoons H_3O^+ + PO_4^{3-} \qquad K_{a_3} = 4.2 \times 10^{-13}$$

Phenolphthalein is an appropriate indicator for this equivalence point; the color of this indicator changes from colorless to light pink.

VCL *Study of Acid–Base Titrations: Polyprotic Acids*

CONCEPT ASSESSMENT ✓

Sketch the titration curve for 1,2-ethanediamine, $NH_2CH_2CH_2NH_2(aq)$, with HCl(aq) and label all important points on the titration curve. For 1,2-ethanediamine, $pK_{b_1} = 4.08$; $pK_{b_2} = 7.15$.

17-5 SOLUTIONS OF SALTS OF POLYPROTIC ACIDS

In discussing the neutralization of phosphoric acid by a strong base, we found that the first equivalence point should come in a somewhat acidic solution and the second in a mildly basic solution. We reasoned that the third equivalence point could be reached only in a strongly basic solution. The pH at this third equivalence point is not difficult to calculate. It corresponds to that of $Na_3PO_4(aq)$, and PO_4^{3-} can ionize (hydrolyze) only as a base.

$$PO_4^{3-} + H_2O \rightleftharpoons HPO_4^{2-} + OH^- \qquad K_b = K_w/K_{a_3}$$

$$= \frac{1.0 \times 10^{-14}}{4.2 \times 10^{-13}}$$

$$= 2.4 \times 10^{-2}$$

EXAMPLE 17-9

Determining the pH of a Solution Containing the Anion (A^{n-}) of a Polyprotic Acid. Sodium phosphate, Na_3PO_4, is an ingredient of some preparations used to clean painted walls before they are repainted. What is the pH of 1.0 M $Na_3PO_4(aq)$?

Solution

In the usual fashion, we can write

$$PO_4^{3-} + H_2O \rightleftharpoons HPO_4^{2} + OH^- \qquad K_b = 2.4 \times 10^{-2}$$

initial concns:	1.0 M	—	—
changes:	$-x$ M	$+x$ M	$+x$ M
equil concns:	$(1.0 - x)$ M	x M	x M

$$K_b = \frac{[HPO_4^{2-}][OH^-]}{[PO_4^{3-}]} = \frac{x \cdot x}{1.0 - x} = 2.4 \times 10^{-2}$$

Because K_b is quite large, we should not expect the usual simplifying assumption to work here. That is, x is *not* very much smaller than 1.0. Solution of the quadratic equation $x^2 + 0.024x - 0.024 = 0$ yields $x = [OH^-] = 0.14$ M. Thus,

$$pOH = -\log[OH^-] = -\log 0.14 = +0.85$$

$$pH = 14.00 - 0.85 = 13.15$$

Practice Example A: Calculate the pH of an aqueous solution that is 1.0 M Na_2CO_3.
[*Hint:* Use data from Table 16.4.]

Practice Example B: Calculate the pH of an aqueous solution that is 0.500 M Na_2SO_3.
[*Hint:* Use data from Table 16.4.]

▶ Sodium phosphate is often sold under the name *trisodium phosphate* (TSP). Anyone working with TSP should wear protective gloves. Fats and greases, including those in human skin, are solubilized in strongly basic solutions.

▶ The ratio $M_b/K_b = 1.0/0.024 = 42$. This value is smaller than the minimum value of 100 that we have been using as the usual criterion.

It is more difficult to calculate the pH values of $NaH_2PO_4(aq)$ and $Na_2HPO_4(aq)$ than of $Na_3PO_4(aq)$. This is because with both $H_2PO_4^-$ and HPO_4^{2-}, two equilibria must be considered *simultaneously*: ionization as an acid and ionization as a base (hydrolysis). For solutions that are reasonably concentrated (say, 0.10 M or greater), the pH values prove to be *independent* of the solution concentration. Shown here (with pK_a values from Table 16.4) are general expressions, printed in blue, and their application to $H_2PO_4^-(aq)$ and $HPO_4^{2-}(aq)$:

$$\text{for } H_2PO_4^-: \qquad pH = \frac{1}{2}(pK_{a_1} + pK_{a_2}) = \frac{1}{2}(2.15 + 7.20) = 4.68 \qquad (17.5)$$

$$\text{for } HPO_4^{2-}: \qquad pH = \frac{1}{2}(pK_{a_2} + pK_{a_3}) = \frac{1}{2}(7.20 + 12.38) = 9.79 \qquad (17.6)$$

Are You Wondering . . .

How to derive equations (17.5) and (17.6)?

Here is good place to use the general problem-solving method introduced in Section 16-6 (page 685). Consider a solution of NaH_2PO_4, of molarity M. The principal concentrations that we must account for are $[Na^+]$, $[H_3O^+]$, $[H_3PO_4]$, $[H_2PO_4^-]$, $[HPO_4^{2-}]$, and $[OH^-]$. Of these, two have very simple values: $[Na^+] = M$, and $[OH^-] = K_w/[H_3O^+]$. Additionally, we can write the following equations.

1. *Acid Ionization:* $H_2PO_4^- + H_2O \rightleftharpoons H_3O^+ + HPO_4^{2-}$

$$K_{a_2} = \frac{[H_3O^+][HPO_4^{2-}]}{[H_2PO_4^-]}$$

2. *Hydrolysis:* $H_2PO_4^- + H_2O \rightleftharpoons H_3PO_4 + OH^-$

$$K_b = K_w/K_{a_1} = \frac{[H_3PO_4][OH^-]}{[H_2PO_4^-]}$$

3. *Material Balance:* The total concentration of the phosphorus-containing species is the stoichiometric molarity, M.
    $[H_3PO_4] + [H_2PO_4^-] + [HPO_4^{2-}] = M$

4. *Electroneutrality Condition:* $[H_3O^+] + [Na^+] = [H_2PO_4^-] + (2 \times [HPO_4^{2-}])$. However, since $[Na^+] = M$, we can also write $[H_3O^+] = [H_2PO_4^-] + (2 \times [HPO_4^{2-}]) - M$.

Solving the set of equations: Begin by substituting equation (3) into equation (4).

$$[H_3O^+] = [H_2PO_4^-] + (2 \times [HPO_4^{2-}]) - [H_3PO_4] - [H_2PO_4^-] - [HPO_4^{2-}]$$

$$= [HPO_4^{2-}] - [H_3PO_4]$$

To continue from here, rearrange equation (1) to obtain $[HPO_4^{2-}]$ in terms of $[H_3O^+]$, $[H_2PO_4^-]$, and K_{a_2}; then rearrange equation (2) to obtain $[H_3PO_4]$ in terms of $[H_3O^+]$, $[H_2PO_4^-]$, and K_{a_1}. Next, substitute the results into the expression, $[H_3O^+] = [HPO_4^{2-}] - [H_3PO_4]$. At this point, you will have an equation in terms of $[H_3O^+]$, $[H_2PO_4^-]$, K_{a_1}, and K_{a_2}. Assume that $[H_2PO_4^-] \approx M$, and you will get an equation from which you can derive equation (17.5). The remainder of this derivation and the derivation of equation (17.6) are left for you to do (see Exercise 79).

17-6   ACID–BASE EQUILIBRIUM CALCULATIONS: A SUMMARY

In this and the preceding chapter, we have considered a variety of acid–base equilibrium calculations. When you are faced with a new problem-solving situation, you might find it helpful to relate the new problem to a type that you have encountered before. It is best not to rely exclusively on "labeling" a problem, however. Some problems might not fit a recognizable category. Instead, keep in mind some principles that apply regardless of the particular problem, as suggested by these questions.

1. **Which species are potentially present in solution, and how large are their concentrations likely to be?**
    In a solution containing similar amounts of HCl and $HC_2H_3O_2$, the only significant *ionic* species are H_3O^+ and Cl^-. HCl is a completely ionized strong acid, and in the presence of a strong acid, the weak acid $HC_2H_3O_2$ is only very slightly ionized because of the common-ion effect. In a mixture containing similar amounts of two *weak* acids of similar strengths, such as $HC_2H_3O_2$ and HNO_2, each acid partially ionizes. All of these

◀ Extreme hyperventilation is needed to compensate for the very low partial pressures of O_2 encountered by high-altitude mountain climbers. This hyperventilation leads to the condition called alkalosis. The blood pH of climbers reaching the summit of Mt. Everest (8848 m = 29,028 ft) without supplemental oxygen can rise to 7.7 or 7.8. (John W. Finley/John W. Finley)

Among the conditions that can lead to *acidosis*, a condition in which the pH of blood decreases below normal, are heart failure, kidney failure, diabetes, persistent diarrhea, and a long-term high-protein diet. Prolonged, extensive exercise also can produce a temporary acidosis. *Alkalosis*, a condition of an increased pH of blood, may occur as a result of severe vomiting, hyperventilation, or exposure to high altitudes (altitude sickness).

One characteristic of blood that we rarely think about is its pH. Yet, maintaining the proper pH in blood and in intracellular fluids is crucial not only to human health but to life itself, primarily because the functioning of enzymes is sharply pH-dependent. The normal pH of blood is 7.4. Severe illness or death can result from sustained variations of just a few tenths of a pH unit from this normal value.

BLOOD AS A BUFFERED SOLUTION
Human blood has a high buffer capacity. The addition of 0.01 mol HCl to 1 L of blood lowers the pH from 7.4 only to 7.2. The same amount of HCl added to a saline (NaCl) solution isotonic with blood lowers the pH from 7.0 to 2.0. The saline solution has no buffer capacity.

Point out to the students that body temperature is 37 °C and at that temperature K_w does not equal 1.0×10^{-14}. Refer them to Exercise 83 on page 743.

concentrations would be significant: $[HC_2H_3O_2]$, $[C_2H_3O_2^-]$, $[HNO_2]$, $[NO_2^-]$, and $[H_3O^+]$. In a solution containing phosphoric acid or a phosphate salt (or both), H_3PO_4, $H_2PO_4^-$, HPO_4^{2-}, PO_4^{3-}, OH^-, H_3O^+, and possibly other cations might be present. If the solution is simply $H_3PO_4(aq)$, however, the only species present in significant concentrations are those associated with the first ionization: H_3PO_4, H_3O^+, and $H_2PO_4^-$. If the solution is instead described as $Na_3PO_4(aq)$, the significant species are Na^+, PO_4^{3-}, and the ions associated with the hydrolysis of PO_4^{3-}, that is, HPO_4^{2-} and OH^-.

2. **Are reactions possible among any of the solution components; if so, what is their stoichiometry?**

    Suppose that you are asked to calculate $[OH^-]$ in a solution that is prepared to be 0.10 M NaOH and 0.20 M NH_4Cl. Before you answer that $[OH^-]$ = 0.10 M, consider whether a solution can be *simultaneously* 0.10 M in OH^- and 0.20 M in NH_4^+. It cannot; any solution containing both NH_4^+ and OH^- must also contain NH_3. The OH^- and NH_4^+ react in a 1:1 mole ratio until OH^- is almost totally consumed:

    $$NH_4^+ + OH^- \longrightarrow NH_3 + H_2O$$

    You are now dealing with the buffer solution 0.10 M NH_3–0.10 M NH_4^+.

3. **Which equilibrium equations apply to the particular situation? Which are the most significant?**

    One equation that applies to all acids and bases in aqueous solutions is $K_w = [H_3O^+][OH^-] = 1.0 \times 10^{-14}$. In many calculations, however, this equation is not significant compared with others. One situation in which it *is* significant is in calculating $[OH^-]$ in an *acidic* solution or $[H_3O^+]$ in a *basic* solution. After all, an acid does not produce OH^-, and a base does not produce H_3O^+. Another situation in which K_w is likely to be significant is in a solution with a pH near 7.

Several factors are involved in the control of blood pH. A particularly important one is the ratio of dissolved HCO_3^- (hydrogen carbonate ion) to H_2CO_3 (carbonic acid). Even though $CO_2(g)$ is only partially converted to H_2CO_3 when it dissolves in water, we generally treat the solution as if this conversion were complete. Moreover, although H_2CO_3 is a weak *diprotic* acid, we deal only with the first ionization step in the carbonic acid–hydrogen carbonate buffer system: H_2CO_3 is the weak acid, and HCO_3^- is the conjugate base.

$$CO_2(g) + H_2O \longrightarrow H_2CO_3(aq)$$
$$H_2CO_3 + H_2O \rightleftharpoons H_3O^+ + HCO_3^-$$
$$K_{a_1} = 4.4 \times 10^{-7}$$

Carbon dioxide enters the bloodstream from tissues as the by-product of metabolic reactions. In the lungs, $CO_2(g)$ is exchanged for $O_2(g)$, which the blood then transports throughout the body.

Using equation (17.2), a value of $pK_a = -\log(4.4 \times 10^{-7}) = 6.4$, and a normal blood pH of 7.4, we can write

$$pH = 7.4 = 6.4 + 1.0$$
$$= pK_{a_1} + \log\frac{[HCO_3^-]}{[H_2CO_3]}$$
$$= 6.4 + \log\left(\frac{10}{1}\right)$$

The large ratio of $[HCO_3^-]$ to $[H_2CO_3]$ (10:1) seems to place this buffer somewhat outside the range of its maximum buffer capacity. (Recall the discussion of buffer capacity on page 721.) The situation is rather complex, but some of the factors involved are listed below.

1. The need to neutralize excess acid (lactic acid produced by exercise) is generally greater than the need to neutralize excess base. The high proportion of HCO_3^- helps in this regard.

2. If additional H_2CO_3 is needed to neutralize excess alkalinity, $CO_2(g)$ in the lungs can be reabsorbed to build up the H_2CO_3 content of the blood.

3. Other components, such as some plasma proteins and the phosphate buffer system, $H_2PO_4^- - HPO_4^{2-}$, contribute to maintaining the pH of blood at 7.4.

Often you will find that the ionization equilibrium with the largest K value is the most significant, but this will not always be the case. The amounts of the various species in solution are also an important consideration. When one drop of 1.00 M H_3PO_4 ($K_{a_1} = 7.1 \times 10^{-3}$) is added to 1.00 L of 0.100 M $HC_2H_3O_2$ ($K_a = 1.8 \times 10^{-5}$), the acetic acid ionization is most important in establishing the pH of the solution. The solution contains far more acetic acid than it does phosphoric acid.

CONCEPT ASSESSMENT ✓

A solution is formed by mixing 200.0 mL of 0.100 M KOH with 100.0 mL of a solution that is both 0.200 M in CH_3COOH and 0.050 M in HI. *Without doing detailed calculations*, identify in the final solution **(a)** all the solute species present, **(b)** the two most abundant solute species, and **(c)** the two least abundant species.

Summary

17-1 Common-Ion Effect in Acid–Base Equilibria—The ionization of a weak electrolyte is suppressed by the addition of an ion that is the product of the ionization and is known as the **common-ion effect**. This effect is a manifestation of Le Châtelier's principle, introduced in Chapter 15.

17-2 Buffer Solutions—Solutions that resist changes in pH upon the addition of small amounts of an acid or base are referred to as **buffer solutions**. The finite amount of acid or base that a buffer solution can neutralize is known as the **buffer capacity**, while the pH range over which the

buffer solution neutralizes the added acid or base is referred to as **buffer range**. Pure water has no buffer capacity (Fig. 17-4). Key to the functioning of a buffer solution is the presence of either a weak acid and its conjugate base or a weak base and its conjugate acid (Fig. 17-5). Calculating the pH of a buffer solution can be accomplished using the ICE method developed in Chapter 15 or by application of the **Henderson–Hasselbalch equation** (expression 17.2). Determination of the pH of a buffer solution after the addition of a strong acid or base requires a stoichiometric calculation followed by an equilibrium calculation (Fig. 17-7).

17-3 Acid–Base Indicators—Substances whose colors depend on the pH of a solution are known as **acid–base indicators**. Acid–base indicators exist in solution as a weak acid (HIn) and its conjugate base (In$^-$). Each form has a different color and the proportions of the two forms determine the color of the solution, which in turn depends on the pH of the solution. The pH range over which an acid–base indicator changes color is determined by the K_a of the specific indicator (Fig. 17-8).

17-4 Neutralization Reactions and Titration Curves—As described in Chapter 5, the concentration of an acidic or basic solution of unknown concentration can be determined by titration with a base or acid of precisely known concentration. In this process a precisely measured volume of the solution of known concentration, the **titrant**, is added through a buret into a precisely measured quantity of the "unknown" contained in a beaker or flask. Typically, the amounts of reactants in a titration are of the order of 10^{-3} mol, that is, **millimoles (mmol)**. A **titration curve** is a graph of a measured property of the reaction mixture as a function of the volume of titrant added—pH for an acid–base titration (Fig. 17-9). The point at which neither

reactant is in excess in a titration is known as the **equivalence point**. The **end point** of an acid–base titration can be located through the change in color of an indicator. The indicator must be chosen such that its color change occurs as close to the equivalence point as possible. Strong acid–strong base titration curves (Figs. 17-9 and 17-10) are different from weak acid–strong base titration curves (Fig. 17-11). The two main differences are seen in the latter type, a buffer region and a hydrolysis reaction at the equivalence point (Fig. 17-12).

17-5 Solutions of Salts of Polyprotic Acids—Calculating the pH of solutions containing the salts of polyprotic acids is made difficult by the fact that two or more equilibria occur simultaneously. Yet for certain solutions, the calculations can be reduced to a simple form (expressions 17.5 and 17.6).

17-6 Acid–Base Equilibrium Calculations: A Summary—As a general summary of acid–base equilibrium calculations, the essential factors are identifying all the species in solution, their concentrations, the possible reactions between them, and the stoichiometry and equilibrium constants of those reactions.

Integrative Example

The structural formula shown is *para*-hydroxybenzoic acid, a weak diprotic acid used as a food preservative. Titration of 25.00 mL of a dilute aqueous solution of this acid requires 16.24 mL of 0.0200 M NaOH to reach the first equivalence point. The measured pH after the addition of 8.12 mL of the base is 4.57; after 16.24 mL, the pH is 7.02. Determine the values of pK_{a_1} and pK_{a_2} of *para*-hydroxybenzoic acid and the pH values for the two equivalence points in the titration.

Strategy

This is a titration of a polyprotic weak acid with a strong base, and the titration curve for this problem should look very similar to Figure 17-13. In the titration of a weak acid by a strong base we know that at the point of half-neutralization, pH = pK_a and therefore pK_{a_1} should be the pH at 8.12 mL. For pK_{a_2}, we will use expression 17.5 since at this point in the titration we will have an aqueous solution of HOC$_6$H$_4$COONa, which is a salt of a polyprotic acid. The pH of the first equivalence point is given and to find the pH of the second equivalence point we must perform an ICE calculation similar to the one in Example 16-13.

Solution

The volume of base needed to reach the first equivalence point is 16.24 mL; at this point, the pH = 7.02. A volume of 8.12 mL is needed to half-neutralize the acid in its first ionization step; at this point the pH = pK_{a_1}, that is, $pK_{a_1} = 4.57$.

At the first equivalence point, the solution is HOC$_6$H$_4$COONa(aq) with pH = 7.02. Recognizing this as the salt produced in neutralizing a polyprotic acid in its first ionization, we use equation (17.5) to solve for pK_{a_2}. That is, the pH of an aqueous solution of the ion $H\overset{\cdot}{O}C_6H_6COO^-$ is given by the expression

$$pH = \tfrac{1}{2}(pK_{a_1} + pK_{a_2}) = \tfrac{1}{2}(4.57 + pK_{a_2}) = 7.02$$

$$pK_{a_2} = (2 \times 7.02) - 4.57 = 9.47$$

Determining the pH at the second equivalence point involves additional calculations. We begin by noting that at the second equivalence point the solution is one of NaOC$_6$H$_4$COONa. The pH of the solution is established by the hydrolysis of $^-$OC$_6$H$_4$COO$^-$.

$$^-OC_6H_4COO^- + H_2O \rightleftharpoons HOC_6H_4COO^- + OH^-$$

$$K_b = K_w/K_{a_2}$$

To evaluate K_b, let's first obtain K_{a_2} from pK_{a_2}.

$$pK_{a_2} = -\log K_{a_2} = 9.47 \text{ and } K_{a_2} = 10^{-9.47} = 3.4 \times 10^{-10}$$
$$K_b = K_w/K_{a_2} = 1.0 \times 10^{-14}/3.4 \times 10^{-10} = 2.9 \times 10^{-5}$$

We can get the pH of this solution by first calculating $[OH^-]$ and pOH. However, to do this, we still need one more piece of data—the molarity of the $NaOC_6H_4COONa(aq)$. We can get this from data for titration to the first equivalence point.

$$? \text{ mmol } OH^- = 16.24 \text{ mL} \times 0.0200 \text{ mmol}$$
$$OH^-/mL = 0.325 \text{ mmol } OH^-$$
$$? \text{ mmol } HOC_6H_4COOH = 0.325 \text{ mmol } OH^- \times 1 \text{ mmol}$$
$$HOC_6H_4COOH/mmol \; OH^- = 0.325 \text{ mmol } HOC_6H_4COOH$$

The amount of $^-OC_6H_4COO^-$ at the second equivalence point is the same as the amount of acid at the start of the titration.

$$0.325 \text{ mmol } ^-OC_6H_4COO^-$$

The volume of solution at the second equivalence point is

$$25.00 \text{ mL} + 16.24 \text{ mL} + 16.24 \text{ mL} = 57.48 \text{ mL}.$$

Thus,

$$[^-OC_6H_4COO^-] = 0.325 \text{ mmol } ^-OC_6H_4COO^-/57.48 \text{ mL}$$
$$= 5.65 \times 10^{-3} \text{ M}.$$

Now we can return to the hydrolysis equation and the expression for K_b, using the method of Example 16-13.

$$^-OC_6H_4COO^- + H_2O \rightleftharpoons HOC_6H_4COO^- + OH^-$$

	$^-OC_6H_4COO^-$	$HOC_6H_4COO^-$	OH^-
initial concns:	5.65×10^{-3} M	—	—
changes:	$-x$ M	$+x$ M	$+x$ M
equil concns:	$(5.65 \times 10^{-3} - x)$ M	x M	x M

$$K_b = \frac{x \cdot x}{(5.65 \times 10^{-3} - x)} = 2.9 \times 10^{-5}$$

The solution to this quadratic equation is $x = [OH^-] = 3.9 \times 10^{-4}$, corresponding to pOH = 3.41 and pH = 10.59.

Assessment

The polyprotic acid, *para*-hydroxybenzoic acid, has two functional groups, a carboxylic acid and a phenolic group. Each group has an ionizable proton. Given just two basic pieces of titration data, we used concepts from this and the preceding chapter to determine the pK_a values for both ionizable groups as well as the pH at the two equivalence points. As a check, note that the pK_a values of these groups are comparable to the values for their parent compounds, acetic acid and phenol (see Table 16.3).

Exercises

The Common-Ion Effect

(*Use data from Table 16.3 as necessary.*)

1. For a solution that is 0.275 M $HC_3H_5O_2$ (propionic acid, $K_a = 1.3 \times 10^{-5}$) and 0.0892 M HI, calculate **(a)** $[H_3O^+]$; **(b)** $[OH^-]$; **(c)** $[C_3H_5O_2^-]$; **(d)** $[I^-]$.

2. For a solution that is 0.164 M NH_3 and 0.102 M NH_4Cl, calculate **(a)** $[OH^-]$; **(b)** $[NH_4^+]$; **(c)** $[Cl^-]$; **(d)** $[H_3O^+]$.

3. Calculate the *change* in pH that results from adding **(a)** 0.100 mol $NaNO_2$ to 1.00 L of 0.100 M $HNO_2(aq)$; **(b)** 0.100 mol $NaNO_3$ to 1.00 L of 0.100 M $HNO_3(aq)$. Why are the changes not the same? Explain.

4. In Example 16-8, we calculated the percent ionization of $HC_2H_3O_2$ in **(a)** 1.0 M; **(b)** 0.10 M; and **(c)** 0.010 M $HC_2H_3O_2$ solutions. Recalculate those percent ionizations if each solution also contains 0.10 M $NaC_2H_3O_2$. Explain why the results are different from those of Example 16-8.

5. Calculate $[H_3O^+]$ in a solution that is **(a)** 0.035 M HCl and 0.075 M HOCl; **(b)** 0.100 M $NaNO_2$ and 0.0550 M HNO_2; **(c)** 0.0525 M HCl and 0.0768 M $NaC_2H_3O_2$.

6. Calculate $[OH^-]$ in a solution that is **(a)** 0.0062 M $Ba(OH)_2$ and 0.0105 M $BaCl_2$; **(b)** 0.315 M $(NH_4)_2SO_4$ and 0.486 M NH_3; **(c)** 0.196 M NaOH and 0.264 M NH_4Cl.

Buffer Solutions

(Use data from Tables 16.3 and 16.4 as necessary.)

7. What concentration of formate ion, $[CHO_2^-]$, should be present in 0.366 M $HCHO_2$ to produce a buffer solution with pH = 4.06?

$$HCHO_2 + H_2O \rightleftharpoons H_3O^+ + CHO_2^-$$
$$K_a = 1.8 \times 10^{-4}$$

8. What concentration of ammonia, $[NH_3]$, should be present in a solution with $[NH_4^+] = 0.732$ M to produce a buffer solution with pH = 9.12? For NH_3, $K_b = 1.8 \times 10^{-5}$.

9. Calculate the pH of a buffer that is
   (a) 0.012 M $HC_7H_5O_2(K_a = 6.3 \times 10^{-5})$ and 0.033 M $NaC_7H_5O_2$;
   (b) 0.408 M NH_3 and 0.153 M NH_4Cl.

10. Lactic acid, $HC_3H_5O_3$, is found in sour milk. A solution containing 1.00 g $NaC_3H_5O_3$ in 100.0 mL of 0.0500 M $HC_3H_5O_3$ has a pH = 4.11. What is K_a of lactic acid?

11. Indicate which of the following aqueous solutions are buffer solutions, and explain your reasoning.
    [*Hint:* Consider any reactions that might occur between solution components.]
    (a) 0.100 M NaCl
    (b) 0.100 M NaCl–0.100 M NH_4Cl
    (c) 0.100 M CH_3NH_2–0.150 M $CH_3NH_3^+Cl^-$
    (d) 0.100 M HCl–0.050 M $NaNO_2$
    (e) 0.100 M HCl–0.200 M $NaC_2H_3O_2$
    (f) 0.100 M $HC_2H_3O_2$–0.125 M $NaC_3H_5O_2$

12. The $H_2PO_4^-$–HPO_4^{2-} combination plays a role in maintaining the pH of blood.
    (a) Write equations to show how a solution containing these ions functions as a buffer.
    (b) Verify that this buffer is most effective at pH 7.2.
    (c) Calculate the pH of a buffer solution in which $[H_2PO_4^-] = 0.050$ M and $[HPO_4^{2-}] = 0.150$ M.
    [*Hint:* Focus on the second step of the phosphoric acid ionization.]

13. What is the pH of a solution obtained by adding 1.15 mg of aniline hydrochloride ($C_6H_5NH_3^+Cl^-$) to 3.18 L of 0.105 M aniline ($C_6H_5NH_2$)?
    [*Hint:* Check any assumptions that you make.]

14. What is the pH of a solution prepared by dissolving 8.50 g of aniline hydrochloride ($C_6H_5NH_3^+Cl^-$) in 750 mL of 0.125 M aniline, ($C_6H_5NH_2$)? Would this solution be an effective buffer? Explain.

15. You wish to prepare a buffer solution with pH = 9.45.
    (a) How many grams of $(NH_4)_2SO_4$ would you add to 425 mL of 0.258 M NH_3 to do this? Assume that the solution's volume remains constant.
    (b) Which buffer component, and how much (in grams), would you add to 0.100 L of the buffer in part (a) to change its pH to 9.30? Assume that the solution's volume remains constant.

16. You prepare a buffer solution by dissolving 2.00 g each of benzoic acid, $HC_7H_5O_2$, and sodium benzoate, $NaC_7H_5O_2$, in 750.0 mL of water.
    (a) What is the pH of this buffer? Assume that the solution's volume is 750.0 mL.
    (b) Which buffer component, and how much (in grams), would you add to the 750.0 mL of buffer solution to change its pH to 4.00?

17. If 0.55 mL of 12 M HCl is added to 0.100 L of the buffer solution in Exercise 15(a), what will be the pH of the resulting solution?

18. If 0.35 mL of 15 M NH_3 is added to 0.750 L of the buffer solution in Exercise 16(a), what will be the pH of the resulting solution?

19. You are asked to prepare a buffer solution with a pH of 3.50. The following solutions, all 0.100 M, are available to you: $HCHO_2$, $HC_2H_3O_2$, H_3PO_4, $NaCHO_2$, $NaC_2H_3O_2$, and NaH_2PO_4. Describe how you would prepare this buffer solution.
    [*Hint:* What volumes of which solutions would you use?]

20. You are asked to reduce the pH of the 0.300 L of buffer solution in Example 17-5 from 5.09 to 5.00. How many milliliters of which of these solutions would you use: 0.100 M NaCl, 0.150 M HCl, 0.100 M $NaC_2H_3O_2$, 0.125 M NaOH? Explain your reasoning.

21. Given 1.00 L of a solution that is 0.100 M $HC_3H_5O_2$ and 0.100 M $KC_3H_5O_2$,
    (a) Over what pH range will this solution be an effective buffer?
    (b) What is the buffer capacity of the solution? That is, how many millimoles of strong acid or strong base can be added to the solution before any significant change in pH occurs?

22. Given 125 mL of a solution that is 0.0500 M CH_3NH_2 and 0.0500 M $CH_3NH_3^+Cl^-$,
    (a) Over what pH range will this solution be an effective buffer?
    (b) What is the buffer capacity of the solution? That is, how many millimoles of strong acid or strong base can be added to the solution before any significant change in pH occurs?

23. A solution of volume 75.0 mL contains 15.5 mmol $HCHO_2$ and 8.50 mmol $NaCHO_2$.
    (a) What is the pH of this solution?
    (b) If 0.25 mmol $Ba(OH)_2$ is added to the solution, what will be the pH?
    (c) If 1.05 mL of 12 M HCl is added to the original solution, what will be the pH?

24. A solution of volume 0.500 L contains 1.68 g NH_3 and 4.05 g $(NH_4)_2SO_4$.
    (a) What is the pH of this solution?
    (b) If 0.88 g NaOH is added to the solution, what will be the pH?
    (c) How many milliliters of 12 M HCl must be added to 0.500 L of the original solution to change its pH to 9.00?

25. A handbook lists various procedures for preparing buffer solutions. To obtain a pH = 9.00, the handbook says to mix 36.00 mL of 0.200 M NH_3 with 64.00 mL of 0.200 M NH_4Cl.
    (a) Show by calculation that the pH of this solution is 9.00.
    (b) Would you expect the pH of this solution to remain at pH = 9.00 if the 100.00 mL of buffer solution were diluted to 1.00 L? To 1000 L? Explain.
    (c) What will be the pH of the original 100.00 mL of buffer solution if 0.20 mL of 1.00 M HCl is added to it?

(d) What is the maximum volume of 1.00 M HCl that can be added to 100.00 mL of the original buffer solution so that the pH does not drop below 8.90?

26. An acetic acid–sodium acetate buffer can be prepared by the reaction

$$C_2H_3O_2{}^- + H_3O^+ \longrightarrow HC_2H_3O_2 + H_2O$$

(from $NaC_2H_3O_2$)   (from HCl)

(a) If 12.0 g $NaC_2H_3O_2$ is added to 0.300 L of 0.200 M HCl, what is the pH of the resulting solution?
(b) If 1.00 g $Ba(OH)_2$ is added to the solution in part (a), what is the new pH?
(c) What is the maximum mass of $Ba(OH)_2$ that can be neutralized by the buffer solution of part (a)?
(d) What is the pH of the solution in part (a) following the addition of 5.50 g $Ba(OH)_2$?

Acid–Base Indicators

(Use data from Tables 16.3 and 16.4 as necessary.)

27. A handbook lists the following data:

Indicator	K_{HIn}	Color Change Acid → Anion
Bromphenol blue	1.4×10^{-4}	yellow → blue
Bromcresol green	2.1×10^{-5}	yellow → blue
Bromthymol blue	7.9×10^{-8}	yellow → blue
2,4-Dinitrophenol	1.3×10^{-4}	colorless → yellow
Chlorphenol red	1.0×10^{-6}	yellow → red
Thymolphthalein	1.0×10^{-10}	colorless → blue

(a) Which of these indicators change color in acidic solution, which in basic solution, and which near the neutral point?
(b) What is the approximate pH of a solution if bromcresol green indicator turns green? if chlorphenol red turns orange?

28. With reference to the indicators listed in Exercise 27, what would be the color of each combination?
(a) 2,4-dinitrophenol in 0.100 M HCl(aq)
(b) chlorphenol red in 1.00 M NaCl(aq)
(c) thymolphthalein in 1.00 M NH_3(aq)
(d) bromcresol green in seawater (recall Figure 17-8)

29. In the use of acid–base indicators,
(a) Why is it generally sufficient to use a *single* indicator in an acid–base titration, but often necessary to use *several* indicators to establish the approximate pH of a solution?
(b) Why must the quantity of indicator used in a titration be kept as small as possible?

30. The indicator methyl red has a $pK_{HIn} = 4.95$. It changes from red to yellow over the pH range from 4.4 to 6.2.

(a) If the indicator is placed in a buffer solution of pH = 4.55, what percent of the indicator will be present in the acid form, HIn, and what percent will be present in the base or anion form, In^-?
(b) Which form of the indicator has the "stronger" (that is, more visible) color—the acid (red) form or base (yellow) form? Explain.

31. Phenol red indicator changes from yellow to red in the pH range from 6.6 to 8.0. *Without making detailed calculations*, state what color the indicator will assume in each of the following solutions: (a) 0.10 M KOH; (b) 0.10 M $HC_2H_3O_2$; (c) 0.10 M NH_4NO_3; (d) 0.10 M HBr; (e) 0.10 M NaCN; (f) 0.10 M $HC_2H_3O_2$–0.10 M $NaC_2H_3O_2$.

32. Thymol blue indicator has *two* pH ranges. It changes color from red to yellow in the pH range from 1.2 to 2.8, and from yellow to blue in the pH range from 8.0 to 9.6. What is the color of the indicator in each of the following situations?
(a) The indicator is placed in 350.0 mL of 0.205 M HCl.
(b) To the solution in part (a) is added 250.0 mL of 0.500 M $NaNO_2$
(c) To the solution in part (b) is added 150.0 mL of 0.100 M NaOH.
(d) To the solution in part (c) is added 5.00 g $Ba(OH)_2$.

33. In the titration of 10.00 mL of 0.04050 M HCl with 0.01120 M $Ba(OH)_2$ in the presence of the indicator 2,4-dinitrophenol, the solution changes from colorless to yellow when 17.90 mL of the base has been added. What is the approximate value of pK_{HIn} for 2,4-dinitrophenol? Is this a good indicator for the titration?

34. Solution (a) is 100.0 mL of 0.100 M HCl and solution (b) is 150.0 mL of 0.100 M $NaC_2H_3O_2$. A few drops of thymol blue indicator are added to each solution. What is the color of each solution? What is the color of the solution obtained when these two solutions are mixed?

Neutralization Reactions

35. A 25.00-mL sample of H_3PO_4(aq) requires 31.15 mL of 0.2420 M KOH for titration to the second equivalence point. What is the molarity of the H_3PO_4(aq)?

36. A 20.00-mL sample of H_3PO_4(aq) requires 18.67 mL of 0.1885 M NaOH for titration from the first to the second equivalence point. What is the molarity of the H_3PO_4(aq)?

37. Two aqueous solutions are mixed: 50.0 mL of 0.0150 M H_2SO_4 and 50.0 mL of 0.0385 M NaOH. What is the pH of the resulting solution?

38. Two solutions are mixed: 100.0 mL of HCl(aq) with pH 2.50 and 100.0 mL of NaOH(aq) with pH 11.00. What is the pH of the resulting solution?

Titration Curves

39. Calculate the pH at the points in the titration of 25.00 mL of 0.160 M HCl when **(a)** 10.00 mL and **(b)** 15.00 mL of 0.242 M KOH have been added.

40. Calculate the pH at the points in the titration of 20.00 mL of 0.275 M KOH when **(a)** 15.00 mL and **(b)** 20.00 mL of 0.350 M HCl have been added.

41. Calculate the pH at the points in the titration of 25.00 mL of 0.132 M HNO_2 when **(a)** 10.00 mL and **(b)** 20.00 mL of 0.116 M NaOH have been added. For HNO_2, $K_a = 7.2 \times 10^{-4}$.

$$HNO_2 + OH^- \rightleftharpoons H_2O + NO_2^-$$

42. Calculate the pH at the points in the titration of 20.00 mL of 0.318 M NH_3 when **(a)** 10.00 mL and **(b)** 15.00 mL of 0.475 M HCl have been added. For NH_3, $K_b = 1.8 \times 10^{-5}$.

$$NH_3(aq) + HCl(aq) \rightleftharpoons NH_4^+(aq) + Cl^-(aq)$$

43. Explain why the volume of 0.100 M NaOH required to reach the equivalence point in the titration of 25.00 mL of 0.100 M HA is the same regardless of whether HA is a strong or a weak acid, yet the pH at the equivalence point is not the same.

44. Explain whether the equivalence point of each of the following titrations should be below, above, or at pH 7: **(a)** $NaHCO_3(aq)$ titrated with NaOH(aq); **(b)** HCl(aq) titrated with NH_3(aq); **(c)** KOH(aq) titrated with HI(aq).

45. Sketch the titration curves of the following mixtures. Indicate the initial pH and the pH corresponding to the equivalence point. Indicate the volume of titrant required to reach the equivalence point, and select a suitable indicator from Figure 17-8.
(a) 25.0 mL of 0.100 M KOH with 0.200 M HI
(b) 10.0 mL of 1.00 M NH_3 with 0.250 M HCl

46. Determine the following characteristics of the titration curve for 20.0 mL of 0.275 M NH_3(aq) titrated with 0.325 M HI(aq).
(a) the initial pH
(b) the volume of 0.325 M HI(aq) at the equivalence point
(c) the pH at the half-neutralization point
(d) the pH at the equivalence point

47. In the titration of 20.00 mL of 0.175 M NaOH, calculate the number of milliliters of 0.200 M HCl that must be added to reach a pH of **(a)** 12.55, **(b)** 10.80, **(c)** 4.25. [*Hint:* Solve an algebraic equation in which the number of milliliters is x. Which reactant is in excess at each pH?]

48. In the titration of 25.00 mL of 0.100 M $HC_2H_3O_2$, calculate the number of milliliters of 0.200 M NaOH that must be added to reach a pH of **(a)** 3.85, **(b)** 5.25, **(c)** 11.10. [*Hint:* Solve an algebraic equation in which the number of milliliters is x. Which reactant is in excess at each pH?]

49. Sketch a titration curve (pH versus mL of titrant) for each of the following three hypothetical weak acids when titrated with 0.100 M NaOH. Select suitable indicators for the titrations from Figure 17-8. [*Hint:* Select a few key points at which to estimate the pH of the solution.]
(a) 10.00 mL of 0.100 M HX; $K_a = 7.0 \times 10^{-3}$
(b) 10.00 mL of 0.100 M HY; $K_a = 3.0 \times 10^{-4}$
(c) 10.00 mL of 0.100 M HZ; $K_a = 2.0 \times 10^{-8}$

50. Sketch a titration curve (pH versus mL of titrant) for each of the following hypothetical weak bases when titrated with 0.100 M HCl. (Think of these bases as involving the substitution of organic groups, R, for one of the H atoms of NH_3.) Select suitable indicators for the titrations from Figure 17-8. [*Hint:* Select a few key points at which to estimate the pH of the solution.]
(a) 10.00 mL of 0.100 M RNH_2; $K_b = 1 \times 10^{-3}$
(b) 10.00 mL of 0.100 M $R'NH_2$; $K_b = 3 \times 10^{-6}$
(c) 10.00 mL of 0.100 M $R''NH_2$; $K_b = 7 \times 10^{-8}$

51. For the titration of 25.00 mL of 0.100 M NaOH with 0.100 M HCl, calculate the pOH at a few representative points in the titration, sketch the titration curve of pOH versus volume of titrant, and show that it has exactly the same form as Figure 17-9. Then, using this curve and the simplest method possible, sketch the titration curve of pH versus volume of titrant.

52. For the titration of 25.00 mL 0.100 M NH_3 with 0.100 M HCl, calculate the pOH at a few representative points in the titration, sketch the titration curve of pOH versus volume of titrant, and show that it has exactly the same form as Figure 17-11. Then, using this curve and the simplest method possible, sketch the titration curve of pH versus volume of titrant.

Salts of Polyprotic Acids

(Use data from Table 16.4 or Appendix D as necessary.)

53. Is a solution that is 0.10 M Na_2S(aq) likely to be acidic, basic, or pH neutral? Explain.

54. Is a solution of sodium dihydrogen citrate, NaH_2Cit, likely to be acidic, basic, or neutral? Explain. Citric acid, H_3Cit, is $H_3C_6H_5O_7$.

55. Sodium phosphate, Na_3PO_4, is made commercially by first neutralizing phosphoric acid with sodium carbonate to obtain Na_2HPO_4. The Na_2HPO_4 is further neutralized to Na_3PO_4 with NaOH.
(a) Write net ionic equations for these reactions.
(b) Na_2CO_3 is a much cheaper base than is NaOH. Why do you suppose that NaOH must be used as well as Na_2CO_3 to produce Na_3PO_4?

56. Both sodium hydrogen carbonate (sodium bicarbonate) and sodium hydroxide can be used to neutralize acid spills. What is the pH of 1.00 M $NaHCO_3$(aq) and of 1.00 M NaOH(aq)? On a per-liter basis, do these two solutions have an equal capacity to neutralize acids? Explain. On a per-gram basis, do the two solids, $NaHCO_3$(s) and NaOH(s), have an equal capacity to neutralize acids? Explain. Why do you suppose that $NaHCO_3$ is often preferred to NaOH in neutralizing acid spills?

57. The pH of a solution of 19.5 g of malonic acid in 0.250 L is 1.47. The pH of a 0.300 M solution of sodium hydrogen malonate is 4.26. What are the values of K_{a_1} and K_{a_2} for malonic acid?

Malonic acid

58. The ionization constants of *ortho*-phthalic acid are $K_{a_1} = 1.1 \times 10^{-3}$ and $K_{a_2} = 3.9 \times 10^{-6}$.
1. $H_2C_8H_4O_4 + H_2O \rightleftharpoons H_3O^+ + HC_8H_4O_4^-$
2. $HC_8H_4O_4^- + H_2O \rightleftharpoons H_3O^+ + C_8H_4O_4^{2-}$

What are the pH values of the following aqueous solutions: **(a)** 0.350 M potassium hydrogen *ortho*-phthalate; **(b)** a solution containing 36.35 g potassium *ortho*-phthalate per liter?

ortho-Phthalic acid

General Acid–Base Equilibria

59. What stoichiometric concentration of the indicated substance is required to obtain an aqueous solution with the pH value shown: **(a)** $Ba(OH)_2$ for pH = 11.88; **(b)** $HC_2H_3O_2$ in 0.294 M $NaC_2H_3O_2$ for pH = 4.52?

60. What stoichiometric concentration of the indicated substance is required to obtain an aqueous solution with the pH value shown: **(a)** aniline, $C_6H_5NH_2$, for pH = 8.95; **(b)** NH_4Cl for pH = 5.12?

61. Using appropriate equilibrium constants but *without doing detailed calculations*, determine whether a solution can be simultaneously
(a) 0.10 M NH_3 and 0.10 M NH_4Cl, with pH = 6.07
(b) 0.10 M $NaC_2H_3O_2$ and 0.058 M HI
(c) 0.10 M KNO_2 and 0.25 M KNO_3
(d) 0.050 M $Ba(OH)_2$ and 0.65 M NH_4Cl
(e) 0.018 M $HC_7H_5O_2$ and 0.018 M $NaC_7H_5O_2$, with pH = 4.20

(f) 0.68 M KCl, 0.42 M KNO_3, 1.2 M NaCl, and 0.55 M $NaC_2H_3O_2$, with pH = 6.4

62. This single equilibrium equation applies to different phenomena described in this or the preceding chapter.

$$HC_2H_3O_2 + H_2O \rightleftharpoons H_3O^+ + C_2H_3O_2^-$$

Of these four phenomena, ionization of pure acid, common-ion effect, buffer solution, and hydrolysis, indicate which occurs if
(a) $[H_3O^+]$ and $[HC_2H_3O_2]$ are high, but $[C_2H_3O_2^-]$ is very low.
(b) $[C_2H_3O_2^-]$ is high, but $[HC_2H_3O_2]$ and $[H_3O^+]$ are very low.
(c) $[HC_2H_3O_2]$ is high, but $[H_3O^+]$ and $[C_2H_3O_2^-]$ are low.
(d) $[HC_2H_3O_2]$ and $[C_2H_3O_2^-]$ are high, but $[H_3O^+]$ is low.

Integrative and Advanced Exercises

63. Sodium hydrogen sulfate, $NaHSO_4$, is an acidic salt with a number of uses, such as metal pickling (removal of surface deposits). $NaHSO_4$ is made by the reaction of H_2SO_4 with NaCl. To determine the percent NaCl impurity in $NaHSO_4$, a 1.016-g sample is titrated with NaOH(aq); 36.56 mL of 0.225 M NaOH is required.
(a) Write the net ionic equation for the neutralization reaction.
(b) Determine the percent NaCl in the sample titrated.
(c) Select a suitable indicator(s) from Figure 17-8.

64. You are given 250.0 mL of 0.100 M $HC_3H_5O_2$ (propionic acid, $K_a = 1.35 \times 10^{-5}$). You wish to adjust its pH by adding an appropriate solution. What volume would you add of **(a)** 1.00 M HCl to lower the pH to 1.00; **(b)** 1.00 M $NaC_3H_5O_3$ to raise the pH to 4.00; **(c)** water to raise the pH by 0.15 unit?

65. Even though the carbonic acid–hydrogen carbonate buffer system is crucial to the maintenance of the pH of blood, it has no practical use as a laboratory buffer solution. Can you think of a reason(s) for this? [*Hint:* Refer to data in Exercise 86 of Chapter 16.]

66. Thymol blue in its acid range is not a suitable indicator for the titration of HCl by NaOH. Suppose that a student uses thymol blue by mistake in the titration of Figure 17-9 and that the indicator end point is taken to be pH = 2.0.
(a) Would there be a sharp color change, produced by the addition of a single drop of NaOH(aq)?
(b) Approximately what percent of the HCl remains unneutralized at pH = 2.0?

67. Rather than calculate the pH for different volumes of titrant, a titration curve can be established by calculating the volume of titrant required to reach certain pH values. Determine the volumes of 0.100 M NaOH required to reach the following pH values in the titration of 20.00 mL of 0.150 M HCl: pH = **(a)** 2.00; **(b)** 3.50; **(c)** 5.00; **(d)** 10.50; **(e)** 12.00. Then plot the titration curve.

68. Use the method of Exercise 67 to determine the volume of titrant required to reach the indicated pH values in the following titrations.
(a) 25.00 mL of 0.250 M NaOH titrated with 0.300 M HCl; pH = 13.00, 12.00, 10.00, 4.00, 3.00
(b) 50.00 mL of 0.0100 M benzoic acid ($HC_7H_5O_2$) titrated with 0.0500 M KOH: pH = 4.50, 5.50, 11.50 ($K_a = 6.3 \times 10^{-5}$)

69. A buffer solution can be prepared by starting with a weak acid, HA, and converting some of the weak acid to its salt (for example, NaA) by titration with a strong base. The *fraction* of the original acid that is converted to the salt is designated f.
(a) Derive an equation similar to equation (17.2) but expressed in terms of f rather than concentrations.
(b) What is the pH at the point in the titration of phenol, HOC_6H_5, at which $f = 0.27$ (pK_a of phenol = 10.00)?

70. You are asked to prepare a KH_2PO_4–Na_2HPO_4 solution that has the same pH as human blood, 7.40.
(a) What should be the ratio of concentrations $[HPO_4^{2-}]/[H_2PO_4^-]$ in this solution?
(b) Suppose you have to prepare 1.00 L of the solution described in part (a) and that this solution must be isotonic with blood (have the same osmotic pressure as blood). What masses of KH_2PO_4 and of $Na_2HPO_4 \cdot 12H_2O$ would you use?
[*Hint:* Refer to the definition of isotonic on page 550. Recall that a solution of NaCl with 9.2 g NaCl/L solution is isotonic with blood, and assume that NaCl is completely ionized in aqueous solution.]

71. You are asked to bring the pH of 0.500 L of 0.500 M $NH_4Cl(aq)$ to 7.00. How many drops (1 drop = 0.05 mL) of which of the following solutions would you use: 10.0 M HCl or 10.0 M NH_3?

72. Because an acid–base indicator is a weak acid, it can be titrated with a strong base. Suppose you titrate 25.00 mL of a 0.0100 M solution of the indicator *p*-nitrophenol, $HC_6H_4NO_3$, with 0.0200 M NaOH. The pK_a of *p*-nitrophenol is 7.15, and it changes from colorless to yellow in the pH range from 5.6 to 7.6.
(a) Sketch the titration curve for this titration.
(b) Show the pH range over which *p*-nitrophenol changes color.
(c) Explain why *p*-nitrophenol cannot serve as its own indicator in this titration.

73. The neutralization of NaOH by HCl is represented in equation (1), and the neutralization of NH_3 by HCl in equation (2).
(1) $OH^- + H_3O^+ \rightleftharpoons 2\,H_2O$ K = ?
(2) $NH_3 + H_3O^+ \rightleftharpoons NH_4^+ + H_2O$ K = ?
(a) Determine the equilibrium constant K for each reaction.
(b) Explain why each neutralization reaction can be considered to go to completion.

74. The titration of a weak acid by a weak base is not a satisfactory procedure because the pH does not increase sharply at the equivalence point. Demonstrate this fact by sketching a titration curve for the neutralization of 10.00 mL of 0.100 M $HC_2H_3O_2$ with 0.100 M NH_3.

75. At times, a salt of a weak base can be titrated by a strong base. Use appropriate data from the text to sketch a titration curve for the titration of 10.00 mL of 0.0500 M $C_6H_5NH_3^+Cl^-$ with 0.100 M NaOH.

76. Sulfuric acid is a diprotic acid, strong in the first ionization step and weak in the second ($K_{a_2} = 1.1 \times 10^{-2}$). By using appropriate calculations, determine whether it is feasible to titrate 10.00 mL of 0.100 M H_2SO_4 to two distinct equivalence points with 0.100 M NaOH.

77. Carbonic acid is a weak diprotic acid (H_2CO_3) with $K_{a_1} = 4.43 \times 10^{-7}$ and $K_{a_2} = 4.73 \times 10^{-11}$. The equivalence points for the titration come at approximately pH 4 and 9. Suitable indicators for use in titrating carbonic acid or carbonate solutions are methyl orange and phenolphthalein.
(a) Sketch the titration curve that would be obtained in titrating a sample of $NaHCO_3(aq)$ with 1.00 M HCl.
(b) Sketch the titration curve for $Na_2CO_3(aq)$ with 1.00 M HCl.
(c) What volume of 0.100 M HCl is required for the complete neutralization of 1.00 g $NaHCO_3(s)$?
(d) What volume of 0.100 M HCl is required for the complete neutralization of 1.00 g $Na_2CO_3(s)$?
(e) A sample of NaOH contains a small amount of Na_2CO_3. For titration to the phenolphthalein end point, 0.1000 g of this sample requires 23.98 mL of 0.1000 M HCl. An additional 0.78 mL is required to reach the methyl orange end point. What is the percent Na_2CO_3, by mass, in the sample?

78. Piperazine is a diprotic weak base used as a corrosion inhibitor and an insecticide. Its ionization is described by the following equations.

$HN(C_4H_8)\,NH + H_2O \rightleftharpoons$
$\qquad [HN(C_4H_8)\,NH_2]^+ + OH^- \quad pK_{b_1} = 4.22$

$[HN(C_4H_8)\,NH_2]^+ + H_2O \rightleftharpoons$
$\qquad [H_2N(C_4H_8)\,NH_2]^{2+} + OH^- \quad pK_{b_2} = 8.67$

The piperazine used commercially is a hexahydrate, $C_4H_{10}N_2 \cdot 6H_2O$. A 1.00-g sample of this hexahydrate is dissolved in 100.0 mL of water and titrated with 0.500 M HCl. Sketch a titration curve for this titration, indicating **(a)** the initial pH; **(b)** the pH at the half-neutralization point of the first neutralization; **(c)** the volume of HCl(aq) required to reach the first equivalence point; **(d)** the pH at the first equivalence point; **(e)** the pH when the second step of the neutralization is half completed; **(f)** the pH at the half-neutralization point of the second neutralization; **(g)** the volume of HCl(aq) required to reach the second equivalence point; **(h)** the pH at the second equivalence point.

79. Complete the derivation of equation (17.5) outlined in the Are You Wondering feature on page 733. Then derive equation (17.6).

80. Explain why equation (17.5) fails when applied to dilute solutions—for example, when you calculate the pH of 0.010 M NaH_2PO_4.
[*Hint:* Refer also to Exercise 79.]

81. A solution is prepared that is 0.150 M $HC_2H_3O_2$ and 0.250 M $NaCHO_2$.
   (a) Show that this is a buffer solution.
   (b) Calculate the pH of this buffer solution.
   (c) What is the final pH if 1.00 L of 0.100 M HCl is added to 1.00 L of this buffer solution?

82. A series of titrations of lactic acid, $CH_3CH(OH)COOH$ ($pK_a = 3.86$) is planned. About 1.00 mmol of the acid will be titrated with NaOH(aq) to a final volume of about 100 mL at the equivalence point. **(a)** Which acid–base indicator from Figure 17-8 would you select for the titration? To assist in locating the equivalence point in the titration, a buffer solution is to be prepared having the same pH as that at the equivalence point. A few drops of the indicator in this buffer will produce the color to be matched in the titrations. **(b)** Which of the following combinations would be suitable for the buffer solutions: $HC_2H_3O_2$–$C_2H_3O_2^-$, $H_2PO_4^-$–HPO_4^{2-}, or NH_4^+–NH_3? **(c)** What ratio of conjugate base to acid is required in the buffer?

83. Hydrogen peroxide, H_2O_2, is a somewhat stronger acid than water. Its ionization is represented by the equation

$$H_2O_2 + H_2O \rightleftharpoons H_3O^+ + HO_2^-$$

In 1912, the following experiments were performed to obtain an approximate value of pK_a for this ionization at 0 °C. A sample of H_2O_2 was shaken together with a mixture of water and 1-pentanol. The mixture settled into two layers. At equilibrium, the hydrogen peroxide had distributed itself between the two layers such that the water layer contained 6.78 times as much H_2O_2 as the 1-pentanol layer. In a second experiment, a sample of H_2O_2 was shaken together with 0.250 M NaOH(aq) and 1-pentanol. At equilibrium, the concentration of H_2O_2 was 0.00357 M in the 1-pentanol layer and 0.259 M in the aqueous layer. In a third experiment, a sample of H_2O_2 was brought to equilibrium with a mixture of 1-pentanol and 0.125 M NaOH(aq); the concentrations of the hydrogen peroxide were 0.00198 M in the 1-pentanol and 0.123 M in

the aqueous layer. For water at 0 °C, $pK_w = 14.94$. Find an approximate value of pK_a for H_2O_2 at 0 °C. [Hint: The hydrogen peroxide concentration in the aqueous layers is the total concentration of H_2O_2 and HO_2^-. Assume that the 1-pentanol solutions contain no ionic species.]

84. Sodium ammonium hydrogen phosphate, $NaNH_4HPO_4$, is a salt in which one of the ionizable H atoms of H_3PO_4 is replaced by Na^+, another is replaced by NH_4^+, and the third remains in the anion HPO_4^{2-}. Calculate the pH of 0.100 M $NaNH_4HPO_4$(aq).
   [Hint: You can use the general method introduced on page 685. First, identify all the species that could be present and the equilibria involving these species. Then identify the two equilibrium expressions that will predominate and eliminate all the species whose concentrations are likely to be negligible. At that point, only a few algebraic manipulations are required.]

85. Consider a solution containing two weak monoprotic acids with dissociation constants K_{HA} and K_{HB}. Find the charge balance equation for this system, and use it to derive an expression that gives the concentration of H_3O^+ as a function of the concentrations of HA and HB and the various constants.

86. Calculate the pH of a solution that is 0.050 M acetic acid and 0.010 M phenylacetic acid.

87. A very common buffer agent used in the study of biochemical processes is the weak base TRIS, $(HOCH_2)_3CNH_2$, which has a pK_b of 5.91 at 25 °C. A student is given a sample of the hydrochloride of TRIS together with standard solutions of 10 M NaOH and HCl.
   (a) Using TRIS, how might the student prepare 1 L of a buffer of pH = 7.79?
   (b) In one experiment, 30 mmol of protons are released into 500 mL of the buffer prepared in part (a). Is the capacity of the buffer sufficient? What is the resulting pH?
   (c) Another student accidentally adds 20 mL of 10 M HCl to 500 mL of the buffer solution prepared in part (a). Is the buffer ruined? If so, how could the buffer be regenerated?

Feature Problems

88. The graph on the right, which is related to a titration curve, shows the fraction (f) of the stoichiometric amount of acetic acid present as non-ionized $HC_2H_3O_2$ and as acetate ion, $C_2H_3O_2^-$, as a function of the pH of the solution containing these species.
   (a) Explain the significance of the point at which the two curves cross. What are the fractions and the pH at that point?
   (b) Sketch a comparable set of curves for carbonic acid, H_2CO_3.
   [Hint: How many carbonate-containing species should appear in the graph? How many points of intersection should there be? at what pH values?]
   (c) Sketch a comparable set of curves for phosphoric acid, H_3PO_4.
   [Hint: How many phosphate-containing species should appear in the graph? How many points of intersection should there be? at what pH values?]

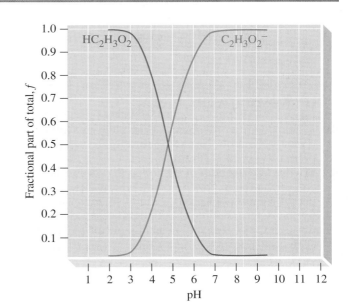

89. In some cases, the titration curve for a mixture of *two* acids has the same appearance as that for a single acid; in other cases it does not.
(a) Sketch the titration curve (pH versus volume of titrant) for the titration with 0.200 M NaOH of 25.00 mL of a solution that is 0.100 M in HCl and 0.100 M in HNO_3. Does this curve differ in any way from what would be obtained in the titration of 25.00 mL of 0.200 M HCl with 0.200 M NaOH? Explain.
(b) The titration curve shown was obtained when 10.00 mL of a solution containing both HCl and H_3PO_4 was titrated with 0.216 M NaOH. From this curve, determine the stoichiometric molarities of both the HCl and the H_3PO_4.

(c) A 10.00-mL solution that is 0.0400 M H_3PO_4 and 0.0150 M NaH_2PO_4 is titrated with 0.0200 M NaOH. Sketch the titration curve.

90. Amino acids contain both an acidic carboxylic acid group (—COOH) and a basic amino group (—NH_2). The amino group can be *protonated* (that is, it has an extra proton attached) in a strongly acidic solution. This produces a diprotic acid of the form H_2A^+, as exemplified by the protonated amino acid alanine.

Protonated alanine

The protonated amino acid has two ionizable protons that can be titrated with OH^-.

$$^+H_3NCHCOH \xrightarrow{OH^-} {}^+H_3NCHCO^- \xrightarrow{OH^-} H_2NCHCO^-$$

| protonated form of alanine (H_2A^+) | neutral form of alanine (HA) | anionic form of alanine (A^-) |

For the —COOH group, $pK_{a_1} = 2.34$; for the —NH_3^+ group, $pK_{a_2} = 9.69$. Consider the titration of a 0.500 M solution of alanine hydrochloride with 0.500 M NaOH solution. What is the pH of **(a)** the 0.500 M alanine hydrochloride; **(b)** the solution at the first half-neutralization point; **(c)** the solution at the first equivalence point?

The dominant form of alanine present at the first equivalence point is electrically neutral despite the positive charge and negative charge it possesses. The point at which the neutral form is produced is called the *isoelectric point*. Confirm that the pH at the isoelectric point is

$$pH = \frac{1}{2}(pK_{a_1} + pK_{a_2})$$

What is the pH of the solution **(d)** halfway between the first and second equivalence points? **(e)** at the second equivalence point?
(f) Calculate the pH values of the solutions when the following volumes of the 0.500 M NaOH have been added to 50 mL of the 0.500 M alanine hydrochloride solution: 10.0 mL, 20.0 mL, 30.0 mL, 40.0 mL, 50.0 mL, 60.0 mL, 70.0 mL, 80.0 mL, 90.0 mL, 100.0 mL, and 110.0 mL.
(g) Sketch the titration curve for the 0.500 M solution of alanine hydrochloride, and label significant points on the curve.

Self-Assessment Exercises

91. In your own words, define or explain the following terms or symbols: **(a)** mmol; **(b)** HIn; **(c)** equivalence point of a titration; **(d)** titration curve.

92. Briefly describe each of the following ideas, phenomena, or methods: **(a)** the common-ion effect; **(b)** the use of a buffer solution to maintain a constant pH; **(c)** the determination of pK_a of a weak acid from a titration curve; **(d)** the measurement of pH with an acid–base indicator.

93. Explain the important distinctions between each pair of terms: **(a)** buffer capacity and buffer range; **(b)** hydrolysis and neutralization; **(c)** first and second equivalence points in the titration of a weak diprotic acid; **(d)** equivalence point of a titration and end point of an indicator.

94. Write equations to show how each of the following buffer solutions reacts with a small added amount of a strong acid or a strong base: **(a)** $HCHO_2$–$KCHO_2$; **(b)** $C_6H_5NH_2$–$C_6H_5NH_3^+Cl^-$; **(c)** KH_2PO_4–Na_2HPO_4.

95. Sketch the titration curves that you would expect to obtain in the following titrations. Select a suitable indicator for each titration from Figure 17-8.
    (a) $NaOH(aq)$ titrated with $HNO_3(aq)$
    (b) $NH_3(aq)$ titrated with $HCl(aq)$
    (c) $HC_2H_3O_2(aq)$ titrated with $KOH(aq)$
    (d) $NaH_2PO_4(aq)$ titrated with $KOH(aq)$

96. A 25.00-mL sample of 0.0100 M $HC_7H_5O_2$ ($K_a = 6.3 \times 10^{-5}$) is titrated with 0.0100 M $Ba(OH)_2$. Calculate the pH **(a)** of the initial acid solution; **(b)** after the addition of 6.25 mL of 0.0100 M $Ba(OH)_2$; **(c)** at the equivalence point; **(d)** after the addition of a total of 15.00 mL of 0.0100 M $Ba(OH)_2$.

97. To *repress* the ionization of formic acid, $HCHO_2(aq)$, which of the following should be added to the solution? **(a)** NaCl; **(b)** NaOH; **(c)** $NaCHO_2$; **(d)** $NaNO_3$

98. To *increase* the ionization of formic acid, $HCHO_2(aq)$, which of the following should be added to the solution? **(a)** NaCl; **(b)** $NaCHO_2$; **(c)** H_2SO_4; **(d)** $NaHCO_3$

99. To convert $NH_4^+(aq)$ to $NH_3(aq)$, **(a)** add H_3O^+; **(b)** raise the pH; **(c)** add $KNO_3(aq)$; **(d)** add NaCl.

100. The effect of adding 0.001 mol KOH to 1.00 L of a solution that is 0.10 M NH_3–0.10 M NH_4Cl is to **(a)** raise the pH very slightly; **(b)** lower the pH very slightly; **(c)** raise the pH by several units; **(d)** lower the pH by several units.

101. The most acidic of the following 0.10 M salt solutions is **(a)** Na_2S; **(b)** $NaHSO_4$; **(c)** $NaHCO_3$; **(d)** Na_2HPO_4.

102. If an indicator is to be used in an acid–base titration having an equivalence point in the pH range 8 to 10, the indicator must **(a)** be a weak base; **(b)** have $K_a = 1 \times 10^{-9}$; **(c)** ionize in two steps; **(d)** be added to the solution only after the solution has become alkaline.

103. Indicate whether you would expect the equivalence point of each of the following titrations to be below, above, or at pH 7. Explain your reasoning. **(a)** $NaHCO_3(aq)$ is titrated with $NaOH(aq)$; **(b)** $HCl(aq)$ is titrated with $NH_3(aq)$; **(c)** $KOH(aq)$ is titrated with HI(aq).

104. Using the method presented in Appendix E, construct a concept map relating the concepts in Sections 17-2, 17-3, and 17-4.

 ## eMedia Exercises

105. In the **Common-Ion Effect** animation (*Activebook 17-1*), the influence of adding a second salt to solution is shown. **(a)** What are the requirements on the second ionic compound if it is to have an effect on the existing equilibrium? **(b)** What would be the influence of removing one of the ions present in the initial solution?

106. Explore the **Buffer Solutions** activity (*Activebook 17-2*). **(a)** Determine the buffer capacity (in terms of moles of an added component) of an acetic acid–sodium acetate buffer containing 0.10 M of each component. **(b)** What is the effect on the buffer capacity if the initial concentrations of the buffer components are increased?

107. The titration of an acidic solution with a base is shown in the **Acid–Base Titration** animation (*Activebook 17-4*). **(a)** In stoichiometric terms, describe why there is a change in slope of the titration curve as the reaction progresses. **(b)** How many regions of the curve with roughly constant slope are present? **(c)** Why are the slopes dramatically different between these regions?

 ## eLaboratory Exercises

These exercises allow students to apply the concepts and skills for this chapter in the simulated laboratory of Virtual ChemLab. Worksheets for each of these exercises are found in the Virtual ChemLab Workbook in your MediaPak.

108. *(VCL 17-1) Predicting the Equivalence Point*
    To make a titration more efficient and more accurate, it is often important to be able to predict the equivalence point for the titration. In this assignment you will be given 0.3000 M HCl and 0.3000 M NaOH. You will predict the equivalence point and then perform the titration to check your prediction.

109. *(VCL 17-2) Predicting the Equivalence Point*
    To make a titration more efficient and more accurate, it is often important to be able to predict the equivalence point for the titration. In this assignment you will be given 0.1276 M HCl and 0.1475 M NaOH. You will predict the equivalence point and then perform the titration to check your prediction.

110. *(VCL 17-3) Predicting the Equivalence Point*
    To make a titration more efficient and more accurate, it is often important to be able to predict the equivalence point for the titration. In this assignment you will be given 0.1033 M CH_3COOH (acetic acid, or HAc) and 0.1104 M NaOH. You will predict the equivalence point and then perform the titration to check your prediction.

111. *(VCL 17-4) Study of Acid–Base Titrations: Monoprotic Acids*
    Titrations provide a method of quantitatively measuring the concentration of an unknown solution. In an acid–base titration this is done by delivering a titrant of known concentration into an analyte of known volume. (The concentration of an unknown titrant can also be determined by titration with an analyte of known concentration and volume.) Titration curves (graphs of volume versus pH)

have characteristic shapes. By comparison, the graph can be used to determine the strength or weakness of an acid or base. The equivalence point of the titration, or the point where the analyte has been completely consumed by the titrant, is identified by the point where the pH changes rapidly over a small volume of titrant delivered. In this assignment you will observe this titration curve by titrating the strong acid HCl with the strong base NaOH.

112. **(VCL 17-5) Weak Acid–Strong Base Titrations**
In this assignment you will observe a titration curve associated with a weak acid and strong base by titrating the acid CH_3COOH (acetic acid) with the base NaOH. You will also predict the pH at the equivalence point, validate your prediction experimentally, and calculate the equilibrium constant for the neutralization reaction.

113. **(VCL 17-6) Strong Acid–Weak Base Titrations**
In this assignment you will observe a titration curve associated with a strong acid and weak base by titrating the weak base $NaHCO_3$ (baking soda) with the strong acid HCl. You will also predict the pH at the equivalence point, validate your prediction experimentally, and calculate the equilibrium constant for the neutralization reaction.

114. **(VCL 17-7) Weak Acid–Weak Base Titrations**
In this assignment you will observe a titration curve associated with a weak acid and weak base by titrat-

ing the acid CH_3COOH (acetic acid) with the weak base NH_3. You will also predict the pH at the equivalence point, validate your prediction experimentally, and calculate the equilibrium constant for the neutralization reaction.

115. **(VCL 17-8) Study of Acid–Base Titrations: Polyprotic Acids**
Titrations provide a method of quantitatively measuring the concentration of an unknown solution. The equivalence point of the titration, or the point where the analyte has been completely consumed by the titrant, is identified by the point where the pH changes rapidly over a small volume of titrant delivered. For polyprotic acids, there will be multiple equivalence points. In this assignment you will observe a polyprotic acid titration curve by titrating the acid H_2SO_3 with the strong base NaOH.

116. **(VCL 17-9) Acid–Base Standardization**
In this assignment you will determine the molarity of an unknown solution of NaOH by titrating against a primary standard, potassium hydrogen phthalate (KHP).

117. **(VCL 17-10) Analysis of Baking Soda**
In this assignment you will determine the mass percent of an unknown sample of baking soda ($NaHCO_3$) by titrating with an NaOH solution of known concentration.

18

SOLUBILITY AND COMPLEX-ION EQUILIBRIA

Stalactite and stalagmite formations in a cavern in the Yunnan Province, People's Republic of China. Stalactites and stalagmites are formed from calcium salts deposited as underground water seeps into the cavern and evaporates.

The dissolution and precipitation of limestone ($CaCO_3$) underlie a variety of natural phenomena, such as the formation of limestone caverns. Whether a solution containing Ca^{2+} and CO_3^{2-} ions undergoes precipitation depends on the concentrations of these ions. In turn, the CO_3^{2-} ion concentration depends on the pH of the solution. To develop a better understanding of the conditions under which $CaCO_3$ dissolves or precipitates, we must consider equilibrium relationships between Ca^{2+} and CO_3^{2-}, and between CO_3^{2-}, H_3O^+, and HCO_3^-. This requirement suggests a need to combine ideas about acid–base equilibria from Chapters 16 and 17 with ideas about the new types of equilibria to be introduced in this chapter.

Silver chloride is a familiar precipitate in the general chemistry laboratory, yet it does *not* precipitate from a solution that has a moderate to high concentration of $NH_3(aq)$. The silver ion and ammonia combine instead to form a species, called a *complex ion*, that remains in solution. Complex-ion formation and equilibria involving complex ions are additional topics discussed in this chapter.

747

18-1 SOLUBILITY PRODUCT CONSTANT, K_{sp}

There are many easy demonstrations that can be performed to show the formation of precipitates. Add $AgNO_3$ to a NaCl solution. The white precipitate AgCl forms immediately. Add KI to the white precipitate and it immediately turns yellow as the solubility of AgI (yellow) is less than AgCl (white). Add NH_3 to the AgCl precipitate; it immediately dissolves through formation of the complex ion $[Ag(NH_3)_2]^+$.

Solubility Product Constant activity

Point out that solubility products vary with temperature.

Gypsum ($CaSO_4 \cdot 2\,H_2O$) is a calcium mineral that is slightly soluble in water. Groundwater that comes into contact with gypsum often contains some dissolved calcium sulfate. This water cannot be used for certain applications, such as in evaporative cooling systems in power plants because the calcium sulfate might precipitate from the water and block pipes. The equilibrium between Ca^{2+}(aq) and $SO_4{}^{2-}$(aq) and undissolved $CaSO_4$(s) can be represented as

$$CaSO_4(s) \rightleftharpoons Ca^{2+}(aq) + SO_4{}^{2-}(aq)$$

We can write the equilibrium constant expression for this equilibrium as we learned to do in Chapter 15 (page 626)—that is,

$$K = \frac{a_{Ca^{2+}}a_{SO_4{}^{2-}}}{a_{CaSO_4}}$$

The activity of a pure solid is 1. Because the concentrations of the ions are very small, we can set their activities equal to their molar concentrations. With these substitutions, we obtain expression (18.1).

$$K_{sp} = [Ca^{2+}][SO_4{}^{2-}] = 9.1 \times 10^{-6} \text{ (at 25 °C)} \tag{18.1}$$

The **solubility product constant**, K_{sp}, is the constant for the equilibrium established between a solid solute and its ions in a saturated solution. Table 18.1 lists several K_{sp} values and the solubility equilibria to which they apply.

TABLE 18.1 Several Solubility Product Constants at 25 °C[a]		
Solute	**Solubility Equilibrium**	**K_{sp}**
Aluminum hydroxide	$Al(OH)_3(s) \rightleftharpoons Al^{3+}(aq) + 3\,OH^-(aq)$	1.3×10^{-33}
Barium carbonate	$BaCO_3(s) \rightleftharpoons Ba^{2+}(aq) + CO_3{}^{2-}(aq)$	5.1×10^{-9}
Barium sulfate	$BaSO_4(s) \rightleftharpoons Ba^{2+}(aq) + SO_4{}^{2-}(aq)$	1.1×10^{-10}
Calcium carbonate	$CaCO_3(s) \rightleftharpoons Ca^{2+}(aq) + CO_3{}^{2-}(aq)$	2.8×10^{-9}
Calcium fluoride	$CaF_2(s) \rightleftharpoons Ca^{2+}(aq) + 2\,F^-(aq)$	5.3×10^{-9}
Calcium sulfate	$CaSO_4(s) \rightleftharpoons Ca^{2+}(aq) + SO_4{}^{2-}(aq)$	9.1×10^{-6}
Chromium(III) hydroxide	$Cr(OH)_3(s) \rightleftharpoons Cr^{3+}(aq) + 3\,OH^-(aq)$	6.3×10^{-31}
Iron(III) hydroxide	$Fe(OH)_3(s) \rightleftharpoons Fe^{3+}(aq) + 3\,OH^-(aq)$	4×10^{-38}
Lead(II) chloride	$PbCl_2(s) \rightleftharpoons Pb^{2+}(aq) + 2\,Cl^-(aq)$	1.6×10^{-5}
Lead(II) chromate	$PbCrO_4(s) \rightleftharpoons Pb^{2+}(aq) + CrO_4{}^{2-}(aq)$	2.8×10^{-13}
Lead(II) iodide	$PbI_2(s) \rightleftharpoons Pb^{2+}(aq) + 2\,I^-(aq)$	7.1×10^{-9}
Magnesium carbonate	$MgCO_3(s) \rightleftharpoons Mg^{2+}(aq) + CO_3{}^{2-}(aq)$	3.5×10^{-8}
Magnesium fluoride	$MgF_2(s) \rightleftharpoons Mg^{2+}(aq) + 2\,F^-(aq)$	3.7×10^{-8}
Magnesium hydroxide	$Mg(OH)_2(s) \rightleftharpoons Mg^{2+}(aq) + 2\,OH^-(aq)$	1.8×10^{-11}
Magnesium phosphate	$Mg_3(PO_4)_2(s) \rightleftharpoons 3\,Mg^{2+}(aq) + 2\,PO_4{}^{3-}(aq)$	1×10^{-25}
Mercury(I) chloride	$Hg_2Cl_2(s) \rightleftharpoons Hg_2{}^{2+}(aq) + 2\,Cl^-(aq)$	1.3×10^{-18}
Silver bromide	$AgBr(s) \rightleftharpoons Ag^+(aq) + Br^-(aq)$	5.0×10^{-13}
Silver carbonate	$Ag_2CO_3(s) \rightleftharpoons 2\,Ag^+(aq) + CO_3{}^{2-}(aq)$	8.5×10^{-12}
Silver chloride	$AgCl(s) \rightleftharpoons Ag^+(aq) + Cl^-(aq)$	1.8×10^{-10}
Silver chromate	$Ag_2CrO_4(s) \rightleftharpoons 2\,Ag^+(aq) + CrO_4{}^{2-}(aq)$	1.1×10^{-12}
Silver iodide	$AgI(s) \rightleftharpoons Ag^+(aq) + I^-(aq)$	8.5×10^{-17}
Strontium carbonate	$SrCO_3(s) \rightleftharpoons Sr^{2+}(aq) + CO_3{}^{2-}(aq)$	1.1×10^{-10}
Strontium sulfate	$SrSO_4(s) \rightleftharpoons Sr^{2+}(aq) + SO_4{}^{2-}(aq)$	3.2×10^{-7}

[a] A more extensive listing of K_{sp} values is given in Appendix D.

EXAMPLE 18-1

Writing Solubility Product Constant Expressions for Slightly Soluble Solutes. Write the solubility product constant expression for the solubility equilibrium of

(a) Calcium fluoride, CaF_2 (one of the substances used when a fluoride treatment is applied to teeth) and

(b) Copper arsenate, $Cu_3(AsO_4)_2$ (used as an insecticide and fungicide).

Solution

The K_{sp} expression is formulated for the ionic species appearing in the equation for the solubility equilibrium. This equation is written for one mole of the slightly soluble solute. That is, the coefficient "1" is understood for the slightly soluble solute. The coefficients for the ions in solution are whatever is needed to balance the equation. The coefficients then establish the powers to which the ion concentrations are raised in the K_{sp} expression.

(a) $CaF_2(s) \rightleftharpoons Ca^{2+}(aq) + 2\,F^-(aq)$ $K_{sp} = [Ca^{2+}][F^-]^2$

(b) $Cu_3(AsO_4)_2(s) \rightleftharpoons 3\,Cu^{2+}(aq) + 2\,AsO_4{}^{3-}(aq)$

$$K_{sp} = [Cu^{2+}]^3[AsO_4{}^{3-}]^2$$

Practice Example A: Write the solubility product constant expression for (a) $MgCO_3$ (one of the components of dolomite, a form of limestone), and (b) Ag_3PO_4 (used in photographic emulsions).

Practice Example B: A handbook lists $K_{sp} = 1 \times 10^{-7}$ for calcium hydrogen phosphate, a substance used in dentifrices and as an animal feed supplement. Write (a) the equation for the solubility equilibrium and (b) the solubility product constant expression for this slightly soluble solute.

▲ Some calcium salts, such as calcium fluoride and calcium hydrogen phosphate, have beneficial uses, but another calcium salt, calcium oxalate (CaC_2O_4), can be harmful. The photo is a scanning electron microscope image of calcium oxalate crystals, a common type of kidney stone that can form in the human kidney.

CONCEPT ASSESSMENT ✓

A large excess of $MgF_2(s)$ is maintained in contact with 1.00 L of pure water to produce a saturated solution of MgF_2. When an additional 1.00 L of pure water is added to the mixture and equilibrium reestablished, compared to the original saturated solution, will $[Mg^{2+}]$ be (a) the same; (b) twice as large; (c) half as large; (d) some unknown fraction of the original $[Mg^{2+}]$? Explain.

18-2 RELATIONSHIP BETWEEN SOLUBILITY AND K_{sp}

Is there a relationship between the solubility product constant, K_{sp}, of a solute and the solute's *molar solubility*—its molarity in a saturated aqueous solution? As shown in Examples 18-2 and 18-3, there is a definite relationship between them. As discussed in Section 18-4, calculations involving K_{sp} are generally more subject to error than are those involving other equilibrium constants, but the results are suitable for many purposes. In Example 18-2, we start with an experimentally determined solubility and obtain a value of K_{sp}.

Martin, R. Bruce. "Solubility and Solubility Products." *J. Chem. Educ.* **2000**: *77*, 1558 (December 2000).

Clark, R. W., Bonicamp J. M., "Solubility and Solubility Products." *J. Chem. Educ.* **2000**: *77*, 1558 (December 2000).

EXAMPLE 18-2

Calculating K_{sp} of a Slightly Soluble Solute from Its Solubility. A handbook lists the aqueous solubility of $CaSO_4$ at 25 °C as 0.20 g $CaSO_4$/100 mL. What is the K_{sp} of $CaSO_4$ at 25 °C?

$$CaSO_4(s) \rightleftharpoons Ca^{2+}(aq) + SO_4{}^{2-}(aq)   K_{sp} = ?$$

Solution

We need to construct a conversion pathway that begins with finding $[Ca^{2+}]$ and $[SO_4{}^{2-}]$, which we can then substitute into the K_{sp} expression.

g $CaSO_4$/100 mL $\longrightarrow$ mol $CaSO_4$/L $\longrightarrow$

$[Ca^{2+}]$ and $[SO_4{}^{2-}] \longrightarrow K_{sp}$

The first step is to convert the mass of $CaSO_4$ in a 100-mL volume to molar solubility. This is accomplished using the inverse of the molar mass of $CaSO_4$ and replacing 100 mL with 0.100 L.

$$mol\ CaSO_4/L\ satd\ soln = \frac{0.20\ g\ CaSO_4}{0.100\ L\ soln} \times \frac{1\ mol\ CaSO_4}{136\ g\ CaSO_4}$$

$$= 0.015\ M\ CaSO_4$$

Using stoichiometric ratios (shown in blue) determine $[Ca^{2+}]$ and $[SO_4{}^{2-}]$.

$$[Ca^{2+}] = \frac{0.015\ mol\ CaSO_4}{1\ L} \times \frac{1\ mol\ Ca^{2+}}{1\ mol\ CaSO_4} = 0.015\ M$$

$$[SO_4{}^{2-}] = \frac{0.015\ mol\ CaSO_4}{1\ L} \times \frac{1\ mol\ SO_4{}^{2-}}{1\ mol\ CaSO_4} = 0.015\ M$$

Substitute these ion concentrations into the solubility product expression.

$$K_{sp} = [Ca^{2+}][SO_4{}^{2-}] = (0.015)(0.015) = 2.3 \times 10^{-4}$$

Practice Example A: A handbook lists the aqueous solubility of AgOCN as 7 mg/100 mL at 20 °C. What is the K_{sp} of AgOCN at 20 °C?

Practice Example B: A handbook lists the aqueous solubility of lithium phosphate at 18 °C as 0.034 g Li_3PO_4/100 mL soln. What is the K_{sp} of Li_3PO_4 at 18 °C?

▲ The rather large discrepancy between the result in Example 18-2 and the K_{sp} value in equation (18.1) is explained on page 754.

Euler, W. B., Kirschenbaum, L. J., Ruekberg B. "Determination of K_{sp} for the Dissolution of Calcium Hydroxide in Water: A General Chemistry Experiment." *J. Chem. Educ.* **2000:** 77, 1039 (August 2000).

▲ Barium sulfate, $BaSO_4$, is a good absorber of X-rays. As a component of a "barium milk shake," $BaSO_4$ coats the intestinal tract so that this soft tissue will show up when X-rayed. Even though Ba^{2+}(aq) is poisonous, $BaSO_4$(s) is harmless because its aqueous solubility is very low.

The "inverse" of Example 18-2 is the calculation of the solubility of a solute from its K_{sp} value. When this is done, as in Example 18-3, the result is always a molar solubility—a molarity. Additional conversions are required to obtain solubility in units other than moles per liter, as in Practice Example 18-3B.

EXAMPLE 18-3

Calculating the Solubility of a Slightly Soluble Solute from Its K_{sp} Value. Lead(II) iodide, PbI_2, is a dense, golden yellow, "insoluble" solid used in bronzing and in ornamental work requiring a golden color (such as mosaic gold). Calculate the molar solubility of lead(II) iodide in water at 25 °C, given that its $K_{sp} = 7.1 \times 10^{-9}$.

Solution

The solubility equilibrium equation

$$PbI_2(s) \rightleftharpoons Pb^{2+}(aq) + 2\,I^-(aq)$$

shows that for each mole of PbI_2 that dissolves, *one* mole of Pb^{2+} and *two* moles of I^- appear in solution. If we let s represent the number of moles of PbI_2 dissolved per liter of saturated solution, we have,

$$[Pb^{2+}] = s \quad \text{and} \quad [I^-] = 2s$$

These concentrations must also satisfy the K_{sp} expression.

$$K_{sp} = [Pb^{2+}][I^-]^2 = (s)(2s)^2 = 7.1 \times 10^{-9}$$

$$4s^3 = 7.1 \times 10^{-9}$$

$$s^3 = 1.8 \times 10^{-9}$$

$$s = (1.8 \times 10^{-9})^{1/3} = 1.2 \times 10^{-3}$$

$$= \text{molar solubility of } PbI_2 = 1.2 \times 10^{-3}\ M$$

Practice Example A: The K_{sp} of $Cu_3(AsO_4)_2$ at 25 °C is 7.6×10^{-36}. What is the molar solubility of $Cu_3(AsO_4)_2$ in H_2O at 25 °C?

Practice Example B: How many milligrams of $BaSO_4$ are dissolved in a 225-mL sample of saturated $BaSO_4$(aq)? $K_{sp} = 1.1 \times 10^{-10}$.

Are You Wondering . . .

When comparing molar solubilities, is a solute with a larger value of K_{sp} always more soluble than one with a smaller value?

If the solutes being compared are of the same type (all of the type MX, MX_2, $M_2X, \ldots$), their molar solubilities will be related in the same way as their K_{sp} values. That is, the solute with the largest K_{sp} value will have the greatest molar solubility. Thus, AgCl ($K_{sp} = 1.8 \times 10^{-10}$) is more soluble than AgBr ($K_{sp} = 5.0 \times 10^{-13}$). For these particular solutes, the molar solubility is $s = \sqrt{K_{sp}}$.

If the solutes are *not* of the same type, you'll have to calculate, or at least estimate, each molar solubility and compare the results. Thus, even though its solubility product constant is smaller, Ag_2CrO_4 ($K_{sp} = 1.1 \times 10^{-12}$) is more soluble than AgCl ($K_{sp} = 1.8 \times 10^{-10}$). For Ag_2CrO_4, the molar solubility is $s = (K_{sp}/4)^{1/3}$ $= 6.5 \times 10^{-5}$ M, whereas for AgCl, it is $s = \sqrt{K_{sp}} = 1.3 \times 10^{-5}$ M.

> This article discusses a laboratory demonstration of the common-ion effect: Koubek, E. *J. Chem. Educ.* **1993:** *70*, 155.

18-3   COMMON-ION EFFECT IN SOLUBILITY EQUILIBRIA

In Examples 18-2 and 18-3, the ions in the saturated solutions came from a single source, the pure solid solute. Suppose that to the saturated solution of PbI_2 in Example 18-3, we add some I^-—a *common ion*—from a source such as KI(aq). The situation is similar to our first encounter with the common-ion effect in Chapter 17.

According to Le Châtelier's principle, an equilibrium mixture responds to a forced increase in the concentration of one of its reactants by shifting in the direction in which that reactant is consumed. In the lead(II) iodide solubility equilibrium, addition of the common ion, I^-, causes the reverse reaction to be favored, leading to a new equilibrium.

> *Common-Ion Effect animation*

The addition of the common ion shifts the equilibrium of a slightly soluble ionic compound toward the undissolved compound, causing more to precipitate. Thus, the solubility of the compound is reduced.

> The solubility of a slightly soluble ionic compound is lowered in the presence of a second solute that furnishes a common ion.

The common-ion effect is illustrated in Figure 18-1, and it is applied quantitatively in Example 18-4.

EXAMPLE 18-4

Calculating the Solubility of a Slightly Soluble Solute in the Presence of a Common Ion. What is the molar solubility of PbI_2 in 0.10 M KI(aq)?

Solution

To solve this problem, let's set up an ICE table with s instead of x to represent changes in concentrations. Think of producing a saturated solution of PbI_2, but instead of using pure water as the solvent, we will use 0.10 M KI(aq). Thus, we begin

Here K^+ does not take part in the process and is generally not included in the solubility equations. Such ions must always be present to ensure electrical neutrality of the solution. These ions are sometimes called "spectator ions."

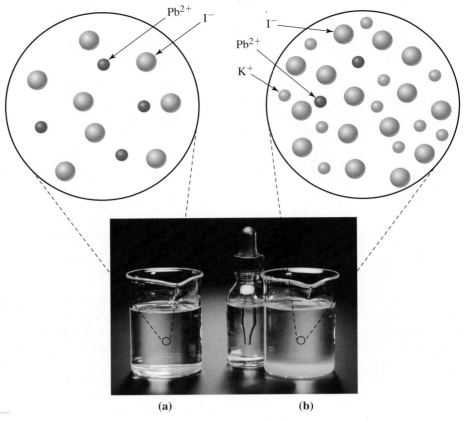

▶ **FIGURE 18-1**
The common-ion effect in solubility equilibrium
(a) A clear saturated solution of lead(II) iodide from which excess undissolved solute has been filtered off. **(b)** When a small volume of a concentrated solution of KI (containing the common ion, I^-) is added, a small quantity of $PbI_2(s)$ precipitates. A common ion reduces the solubility of a sparingly soluble solute.

(a)   **(b)**

with $[I^-] = 0.10$ M. Now let s represent the amount of PbI_2, in moles, that dissolves to produce 1 L of saturated solution. The additional concentrations appearing in this solution are s mol Pb^{2+}/L and $2s$ mol I^-/L.

$$PbI_2(s) \rightleftharpoons Pb^{2+}(aq) + 2\,I^-(aq)$$

initial concns, M:		0.10
from PbI_2, M:	s	$2s$
equil concns, M:	s	$(0.10 + 2s)$

The usual K_{sp} relationship must be satisfied.

$$K_{sp} = [Pb^{2+}][I^-]^2 = (s)(0.10 + 2s)^2 = 7.1 \times 10^{-9}$$

To simplify the solution to this equation, let's assume that s is much smaller than 0.10 M, so that $0.10 + 2s \approx 0.10$.

$$s(0.10)^2 = 7.1 \times 10^{-9}$$

$$s = \frac{7.1 \times 10^{-9}}{(0.10)^2} = 7.1 \times 10^{-7} \text{ M}$$

Our assumption is well justified: 7.1×10^{-7} is much smaller than 0.10, and

$$s = \text{molar solubility of } PbI_2 = 7.1 \times 10^{-7} \text{ M}$$

Practice Example A: What is the molar solubility of PbI_2 in 0.10 M $Pb(NO_3)_2(aq)$?

[*Hint:* To which ion concentration should the solubility be related?]

Practice Example B: What is the molar solubility of $Fe(OH)_3$ in a buffered solution with pH = 8.20?

The solubility of PbI_2 in the presence of 0.10 M I^-, as calculated in Example 18-4, is about 2000 times less than its value in pure water (Example 18-3). If you work out Practice Example 18-4A, you will see that the effect of added Pb^{2+} in reducing the solubility of PbI_2 is not as striking as that of I^-, but it is significant nevertheless.

A typical error in problems such as Example 18-4 is to double the common-ion concentration—that is, to write $[I^-] = (2 \times 0.10)$ M instead of $[I^-] = 0.10$ M. While it is true that in *any* aqueous solution of PbI_2, the $[I^-]$ derived from PbI_2 is *twice* the molarity of the PbI_2, the $[I^-]$ that comes from a soluble strong electrolyte is determined only by the molarity of the strong electrolyte. Thus, $[I^-]$ in 0.10 M KI(aq) is 0.10 M. In 0.10 M KI(aq) that is also saturated with PbI_2, the *total* $[I^-] = (0.10 + 2s)$ M. In short, no relationship exists between the stoichiometry of the dissolution of PbI_2, which requires a factor of 2 in establishing $[I^-]$, and that of KI, which does not.

18-4   LIMITATIONS OF THE K_{sp} CONCEPT

We have repeatedly used the term *slightly soluble* in describing the solutes for which we have written K_{sp} expressions. You might wonder if we can write K_{sp} expressions for moderately or highly soluble ionic compounds, such as NaCl, KNO_3, and NaOH. The answer is yes, but the K_{sp} must be based on ion *activities* rather than on concentrations. In ionic solutions of moderate to high concentrations, activities and concentrations are generally far from equal (recall Section 13-9). For example, in 0.1 M KCl(aq) the activity is roughly 24% of the molarity. If we cannot use molarities in place of activities, much of the simplicity of the solubility product concept is lost. Thus, K_{sp} values are usually limited to slightly soluble (essentially insoluble) solutes, and ion molarities are used in place of activities. In addition, the K_{sp} concept has several other limitations, which are discussed in the following sections.

THE DIVERSE ("UNCOMMON") ION EFFECT: THE SALT EFFECT

We have explored the effect of common ions on a solubility equilibrium, but what effect do ions different from those involved in the equilibrium have on solute solubilities? The effect of "uncommon" or *diverse* ions is not as striking as the common-ion effect. Moreover, uncommon ions tend to increase rather than decrease solubility. As the total ionic concentration of a solution increases, interionic attractions become more important. Activities (effective concentrations) become smaller than the stoichiometric or measured concentrations. For the ions involved in the solution process, this means that higher concentrations must appear in solution before equilibrium is established—the *solubility increases*. Figure 18-2 compares the effects of common ions and uncommon ions.

The diverse ion effect is more commonly called the **salt effect**. As a result of the salt effect, the numerical value of a K_{sp} based on molarities will vary depending on the ionic atmosphere. Most tabulated values of K_{sp} are based on activities rather than on molarities, thus avoiding the problem of the salt effect.

INCOMPLETE DISSOCIATION OF SOLUTE INTO IONS

In performing calculations involving K_{sp} values and solubilities, we have assumed that all the dissolved solute appears in solution as separated cations and anions. However, this assumption is often not valid. The solute might not be 100% ionic, and some of the solute might enter solution in molecular form. Alternatively, some ions in solution might join together into **ion pairs**. An ion pair is two oppositely charged ions that are held together by the electrostatic attraction between the ions. For example, in a saturated solution of magnesium fluoride, although most of the solute exists as Mg^{2+} and F^- ions, some exists as the ion pair MgF^+.

Point out that the difference between stoichiometric concentration and effective concentration increases as more solute is dissolved in the solvent. There are no interactions between solute particles in an ideal solution where stoichiometric and effective concentrations are equal. These interactions increase as more solute is dissolved.

This article discusses a laboratory experiment which investigates common-ion and salt effects: Marzzacco, Charles J. *J. Chem. Educ.* **1998**: 75, 1628.

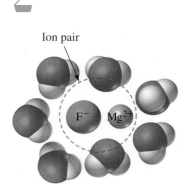

▲ An ion pair, MgF^+, in a magnesium fluoride aqueous solution.

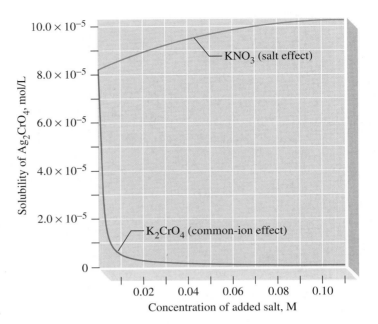

▶ **FIGURE 18-2**
Comparison of the common-ion effect and the salt effect on the molar solubility of Ag_2CrO_4

The presence of CrO_4^{2-} ions, derived from $K_2CrO_4(aq)$, reduces the solubility of Ag_2CrO_4 by a factor of about 35 over the concentration range shown (from 0 to 0.10 M added salt). Over the same concentration range, the solubility of Ag_2CrO_4 is increased by the presence of the uncommon, or diverse, ions from KNO_3, but only by about 25%.

To the extent that a solution contains cations and anions of a solute as ion pairs, the concentrations of the dissociated ions are reduced from the stoichiometric expectations. Thus, although the measured solubility of MgF_2 is about 4×10^{-3} M, we cannot safely assume that $[Mg^{2+}] = 4 \times 10^{-3}$ M, and that $[F^-] = 8 \times 10^{-3}$ M, because some of the Mg^{2+} and F^- ions are involved in ion pairing. This means that additional solute must be present for the product of ion concentrations to equal K_{sp} of the solute, making the true solubility of the solute greater than otherwise expected on the basis of K_{sp}.

The degree of ion-pair formation increases as mutual electrostatic attraction of the anion and cation increases. Hence, ion-pair formation is increasingly likely when the cations or anions in solution carry multiple charges (for example, Mg^{2+} or SO_4^{2-}).

Simultaneous Equilibria

The reversible reaction between a solid solute and its ions in aqueous solution is never the sole process occurring. At the very least, the self-ionization of water also occurs, although we can generally ignore it. Other equilibrium processes that may occur include reactions between solute ions and other solution species. Two possibilities are acid–base reactions (Section 18-7) and complex-ion formation (Section 18-8). Calculations based on the K_{sp} expression may be in error if we fail to take into account other equilibrium processes that occur simultaneously with solution equilibrium.

Assessing the Limitations of K_{sp}

Let's assess the importance of the effects discussed in this section, some of which apply to $CaSO_4$. Recall that in Example 18-2 we calculated K_{sp} for $CaSO_4$ on the basis of its measured solubility. Our result was $K_{sp} = 2.3 \times 10^{-4}$. This value is about 25 times larger than the value listed in Table 18.1, which is $K_{sp} = 9.1 \times 10^{-6}$.

These conflicting results for $CaSO_4$ are understandable. The K_{sp} value listed in Table 18.1 is based on ion activities, whereas the K_{sp} value calculated from the experimentally determined solubility is based on ion concentrations, assuming complete dissociation of the solute into ions and no ion-pair formation. We will continue to substitute molarities for activities of ions, and the case of $CaSO_4$ simply suggests that some of our results, although of the appropriate general magnitude (that is, within a factor of 10 or 100), may not be highly accurate. These order-of-magnitude results, however, still allow us to make some correct predictions and to apply the K_{sp} concept in useful ways.

18-5 CRITERIA FOR PRECIPITATION AND ITS COMPLETENESS

Silver iodide is a light-sensitive compound used in photographic film and also in cloud seeding to produce rain. Its solubility equilibrium and K_{sp} are represented as

$$AgI(s) \rightleftharpoons Ag^+(aq) + I^-(aq)$$

$$K_{sp} = [Ag^+][I^-] = 8.5 \times 10^{-17}$$

Suppose we mix solutions of $AgNO_3(aq)$ and $KI(aq)$ to obtain a mixed solution that has $[Ag^+] = 0.010$ M and $[I^-] = 0.015$ M. Is this solution unsaturated, saturated, or supersaturated?

Recall the reaction quotient, Q, that was introduced in Chapter 15. It has the same form as an equilibrium constant expression but uses initial concentrations rather than equilibrium concentrations. Initially,

$$Q_{sp} = [Ag^+]_{init} \times [I^-]_{init} = (0.010)(0.015) = 1.5 \times 10^{-4} > K_{sp}$$

The fact that $Q_{sp} > K_{sp}$ indicates that the concentrations of Ag^+ and I^- are already higher than they would be in a saturated solution and that a net change should occur to the left. The solution is *supersaturated*. As is generally the case with supersaturated solutions, excess AgI should precipitate from solution. If we had found $Q_{sp} < K_{sp}$, the solution would have been *unsaturated*. No precipitate would form from such a solution.

When applied to solubility equilibria, Q_{sp} is generally called the **ion product** because its form is that of the product of ion concentrations raised to appropriate powers. The criteria for determining whether ions in a solution will combine to form a precipitate require us to compare the ion product with K_{sp}.

- Precipitation *should occur* if $Q_{sp} > K_{sp}$.
- Precipitation *cannot occur* if $Q_{sp} < K_{sp}$.
- A solution is just saturated if $Q_{sp} = K_{sp}$.

These criteria are illustrated in Figure 18-3 and Example 18-5. The example emphasizes the important point that *any possible dilutions must be considered before the criteria for precipitation are applied.*

EXAMPLE 18-5

Applying the Criteria for Precipitation of a Slightly Soluble Solute. Three drops of 0.20 M KI are added to 100.0 mL of 0.010 M $Pb(NO_3)_2$. Will a precipitate of lead(II) iodide form? (Assume 1 drop = 0.05 mL.)

$$PbI_2(s) \rightleftharpoons Pb^{2+}(aq) + 2\,I^-(aq) \qquad K_{sp} = 7.1 \times 10^{-9}$$

(a)

(b)

▲ **FIGURE 18-3**
Applying the criteria for precipitation from solution—Example 18-5 illustrated
(a) When three drops of 0.20 M KI are first added to 100.0 mL of 0.010 M $Pb(NO_3)_2$, a precipitate forms because K_{sp} is exceeded in the immediate vicinity of the drops. **(b)** When the KI becomes uniformly mixed in the $Pb(NO_3)_2(aq)$, K_{sp} is no longer exceeded and the precipitate redissolves. The criteria for precipitation must be applied *after* dilution has occurred.

KEEP IN MIND ▶
that any possible dilutions must be considered *before* the criteria for precipitation are applied.

Precipitation Reactions movie

▶ One method of maintaining a constant pH during a precipitation is to carry out the precipitation from a buffer solution.

Solution

We need to compare the product $[Pb^{2+}][I^-]^2$ formulated for the initial concentrations with the K_{sp} for PbI_2. For $[Pb^{2+}]$ we can simply use 0.010 M. For $[I^-]$, however, we must consider the great reduction in concentration that occurs when the three drops of 0.20 M KI are diluted to 100.0 mL.

Dilution Calculation:

$$\text{amount } I^- = 3 \text{ drops} \times \frac{0.05 \text{ mL}}{1 \text{ drop}} \times \frac{1 \text{ L}}{1000 \text{ mL}} \times \frac{0.20 \text{ mol KI}}{L}$$

$$\times \frac{1 \text{ mol } I^-}{1 \text{ mol KI}} = 3 \times 10^{-5} \text{ mol } I^-$$

$$[I^-] = \frac{3 \times 10^{-5} \text{ mol } I^-}{0.1000 \text{ L}} = 3 \times 10^{-4} \text{ M}$$

Applying Precipitation Criteria:

$$Q_{sp} = [Pb^{2+}][I^-]^2 = (0.010)(3 \times 10^{-4})^2 = 9 \times 10^{-10}$$

Because a Q_{sp} of 9×10^{-10} is *smaller than* a K_{sp} of 7.1×10^{-9}, we conclude that $PbI_2(s)$ should *not* precipitate.

Practice Example A: Three drops of 0.20 M KI are added to 100.0 mL of a 0.010 M solution of $AgNO_3$. Will a precipitate of silver iodide form?

Practice Example B: We saw in Example 18-5 that a 3-drop volume of 0.20 M KI is insufficient to cause precipitation in 100.0 mL of 0.010 M $Pb(NO_3)_2$. What minimum number of drops would be required to produce the first precipitate?

Precipitation of a solute is considered to be complete only if the amount of solute remaining in solution is very small. An arbitrary rule of thumb is that precipitation is complete if 99.9% or more of a particular ion has precipitated, leaving less than 0.1% of the ion in solution. In Example 18-6, we will calculate the concentration of Mg^{2+} that remains in a solution from which $Mg(OH)_2(s)$ has precipitated. We will compare this remaining $[Mg^{2+}]$ to the initial $[Mg^{2+}]$ to determine the completeness of the precipitation.

EXAMPLE 18-6

Assessing the Completeness of a Precipitation Reaction. The first step in a commercial process in which magnesium is obtained from seawater involves precipitating Mg^{2+} as $Mg(OH)_2(s)$. The magnesium ion concentration in seawater is about 0.059 M. If a seawater sample is treated so that its $[OH^-]$ is maintained at 2.0×10^{-3} M, **(a)** what will be $[Mg^{2+}]$ remaining in solution when precipitation stops ($K_{sp} = 1.8 \times 10^{-11}$)? **(b)** Is the precipitation of $Mg(OH)_2(s)$ complete under these conditions?

Solution

(a) There is no question that precipitation will occur, because the ion product $Q_{sp} = [Mg^{2+}][OH^-]^2 = (0.059)(2.0 \times 10^{-3})^2 = 2.4 \times 10^{-7}$ exceeds K_{sp}. Precipitation of $Mg(OH)_2(s)$ will continue as long as the ion product exceeds K_{sp}, but will stop when that product is equal to K_{sp}. At the point at which the ion product equals K_{sp}, whatever $[Mg^{2+}]$ is in solution remains in solution.

$$[Mg^{2+}][OH^-]^2 = [Mg^{2+}](2.0 \times 10^{-3})^2 = 1.8 \times 10^{-11} = K_{sp}$$

$$[Mg^{2+}]_{\text{remaining}} = \frac{1.8 \times 10^{-11}}{(2.0 \times 10^{-3})^2} = 4.5 \times 10^{-6} \text{ M}$$

(b) $[Mg^{2+}]$ in seawater is reduced from 0.059 M to 4.5×10^{-6} M as a result of the precipitation reaction. Expressed as a percentage,

$$\%[Mg^{2+}]_{\text{remaining}} = \frac{4.5 \times 10^{-6} \text{ M}}{0.059 \text{ M}} \times 100\% = 0.0076\%$$

Because less than 0.1% of the Mg^{2+} remains, we conclude that precipitation is essentially complete.

Practice Example A: A typical Ca^{2+} concentration in seawater is 0.010 M. Will the precipitation of $Ca(OH)_2$ be complete from a seawater sample in which $[OH^-]$ is maintained at 0.040 M?

Practice Example B: What $[OH^-]$ should be maintained in a solution if, after precipitation of Mg^{2+} as $Mg(OH)_2(s)$, the remaining Mg^{2+} is to be at a level of $1\ \mu g\ Mg^{2+}/L$?

Are You Wondering . . .

What conditions favor completeness of precipitation?

The key factors in determining whether the target ion is essentially completely removed from solution in a precipitation are (1) the value of K_{sp}, (2) the initial concentration of the target ion, and (3) the concentration of the common ion. In general, completeness of precipitation is favored by

- *a very small value of K_{sp}.* (The concentration of the target ion remaining in solution will be very small.)
- *a high initial concentration of the target ion.* (The concentration of the target ion remaining in solution will be only a very small fraction of the initial value.)
- *a concentration of common ion much larger than that of the target ion.* (The common-ion concentration will remain nearly constant during the precipitation.)

18-6   FRACTIONAL PRECIPITATION

If a large excess of $AgNO_3(s)$ is added to a solution containing the ions CrO_4^{2-} and Br^-, a mixed precipitate of $Ag_2CrO_4(s)$ and $AgBr(s)$ is obtained. There is a method of adding $AgNO_3$, however, that will cause $AgBr(s)$ to precipitate but leave CrO_4^{2-} in solution. That method is fractional precipitation.

Fractional precipitation is a technique in which two or more ions in solution, each capable of being precipitated by the same reagent, are separated by the proper use of that reagent: *One ion is precipitated, while the other(s) remains in solution.* The primary condition for a successful fractional precipitation is that there be a significant difference in the solubilities of the substances being separated. (Usually this means a significant difference in their K_{sp} values.) The key to the technique is the slow addition of a concentrated solution of the precipitating reagent to the solution from which precipitation is to occur, as from a buret (Fig. 18-4).

Example 18-7 considers the separation of $CrO_4^{2-}(aq)$ and $Br^-(aq)$ through the use of $Ag^+(aq)$.

◀ Fractional precipitation is also called *selective precipitation*.

◀ **FIGURE 18-4**
Fractional precipitation—Example 18-7 illustrated
(a) $AgNO_3(aq)$ is slowly added to a solution that is 0.010 M in Br^- and 0.010 M in CrO_4^{2-}. **(b)** Essentially all the Br^- has precipitated as pale yellow $AgBr(s)$, with $[Br^-]$ in solution = 5.0×10^{-8} M. Red-brown $Ag_2CrO_4(s)$ is just about to precipitate.

$AgNO_3$ solution

$[CrO_4^{2-}] = [Br^-]$
$= 0.010$ M

$[Ag^+] = 1.0 \times 10^{-5}$ M
$[CrO_4^{2-}] = 0.010$ M
$[Br^-] = 5.0 \times 10^{-8}$ M

$AgBr(s)$

(a)   **(b)**

EXAMPLE 18-7

Separating Ions by Fractional Precipitation. $AgNO_3(aq)$ is slowly added to a solution that has $[CrO_4^{2-}] = 0.010$ M and $[Br^-] = 0.010$ M.

(a) Show that AgBr(s) should precipitate before $Ag_2CrO_4(s)$ does.

(b) When $Ag_2CrO_4(s)$ begins to precipitate, what is $[Br^-]$ remaining in solution?

(c) Is complete separation of $Br^-(aq)$ and $CrO_4^{2-}(aq)$ by fractional precipitation feasible?

Solution

The necessary data are the solubility equilibrium equations and the K_{sp} values of Ag_2CrO_4 and AgBr.

$$Ag_2CrO_4(s) \rightleftharpoons 2\,Ag^+(aq) + CrO_4^{2-}(aq) \qquad K_{sp} = 1.1 \times 10^{-12}$$

$$AgBr(s) \rightleftharpoons Ag^+(aq) + Br^-(aq) \qquad K_{sp} = 5.0 \times 10^{-13}$$

(a) The required values of $[Ag^+]$ for precipitation to start are

AgBr ppt: $\qquad Q_{sp} = [Ag^+][Br^-] = [Ag^+](0.010) = 5.0 \times 10^{-13} = K_{sp}$

$$[Ag^+] = 5.0 \times 10^{-11} \text{ M}$$

Ag_2CrO_4 ppt: $\quad Q_{sp} = [Ag^+]^2[CrO_4^{2-}] = [Ag^+]^2(0.010)$

$$= 1.1 \times 10^{-12} = K_{sp}$$

$$[Ag^+]^2 = 1.1 \times 10^{-10} \quad \text{and} \quad [Ag^+] = 1.0 \times 10^{-5} \text{ M}$$

Because the $[Ag^+]$ required to start the precipitation of AgBr(s) is much less than that for $Ag_2CrO_4(s)$, AgBr(s) precipitates first. As long as AgBr(s) is forming, the silver ion concentration can only slowly approach the value required for the precipitation of $Ag_2CrO_4(s)$.

(b) As AgBr(s) precipitates, $[Br^-]$ gradually decreases, and this permits $[Ag^+]$ to increase. When $[Ag^+]$ reaches 1.0×10^{-5} M, precipitation of $Ag_2CrO_4(s)$ begins. To determine $[Br^-]$ at the point at which $[Ag^+] = 1.0 \times 10^{-5}$ M, we use K_{sp} for AgBr and solve for $[Br^-]$.

$$K_{sp} = [Ag^+][Br^-] = (1.0 \times 10^{-5})[Br^-] = 5.0 \times 10^{-13}$$

$$[Br^-] = \frac{5.0 \times 10^{-13}}{1.0 \times 10^{-5}} = 5.0 \times 10^{-8} \text{ M}$$

(c) Before $Ag_2CrO_4(s)$ begins to precipitate, $[Br^-]$ will have been reduced from 1.0×10^{-2} M to 5.0×10^{-8} M. Essentially, all the Br^- will have precipitated from solution as AgBr(s), whereas the CrO_4^{2-} remains in solution. Fractional precipitation is feasible for separating mixtures of Br^- and CrO_4^{2-}.

Practice Example A: $AgNO_3(aq)$ is slowly added to a solution with $[Cl^-] = 0.115$ M and $[Br^-] = 0.264$ M. What percent of the Br^- remains unprecipitated at the point at which AgCl(s) begins to precipitate?

$$\text{AgCl:} \quad K_{sp} = 1.8 \times 10^{-10} \qquad \text{AgBr:} \quad K_{sp} = 5.0 \times 10^{-13}$$

Practice Example B: A solution has $[Ba^{2+}] = [Sr^{2+}] = 0.10$ M. Use data from Appendix D to choose the best precipitating agent to separate these two ions. What is the concentration of the first ion to precipitate when the second ion begins to precipitate?

Make a precipitate of AgCl and show that adding HNO_3 will not dissolve the precipitate. Silver acetate, however, can be dissolved by adding HNO_3.

Are You Wondering . . .

How the titration illustrated in Figure 18-4 and Example 18-7 might be carried out?

That is, how can we stop the titration just as $Ag_2CrO_4(s)$ begins to precipitate? One possibility, suggested in Figure 18-4, is to look for a color change in the precipitate from pale yellow (AgBr) to red-brown (Ag_2CrO_4). A more effective method is to follow $[Ag^+]$ during the titration. $[Ag^+]$ increases very rapidly between the points at which AgBr has finished precipitating and Ag_2CrO_4 is about to begin. We will discuss an electrometric method of determining very low ion concentrations in Chapter 20.

CONCEPT ASSESSMENT ✔

In the fractional precipitation pictured in Figure 18-4 and described in Example 18-7, no mention was made of the concentration of the $AgNO_3(aq)$ used. Is this concentration immaterial? Explain.

18-7   SOLUBILITY AND pH

The pH of a solution can affect the solubility of a salt to a large degree. That is especially true when the anion of the salt is the conjugate base of a weak acid or the base OH^- itself. An interesting example is the highly insoluble $Mg(OH)_2(s)$, which, when suspended in water, is the popular antacid known as milk of magnesia. Hydroxide ions from the dissolved magnesium hydroxide react with hydronium ions (in stomach acid) to form water.

$$Mg(OH)_2(s) \rightleftharpoons Mg^{2+}(aq) + 2\,OH^-(aq) \tag{18.2}$$

$$OH^-(aq) + H_3O^+(aq) \longrightarrow 2\,H_2O(l) \tag{18.3}$$

According to Le Châtelier's principle, we expect reaction (18.2) to be displaced to the right—that is, additional $Mg(OH)_2$ would dissolve to replace OH^- ions drawn off by the neutralization reaction (18.3). The overall net ionic equation can be obtained by doubling equation (18.3) and adding it to equation (18.2). At the same time, we can apply the method of combining equilibrium constants (page 630). The result is

$$Mg(OH)_2(s) \rightleftharpoons Mg^{2+}(aq) + \cancel{2\,OH^-(aq)} \qquad K_{sp} = 1.8 \times 10^{-11}$$

$$\underline{\cancel{2\,OH^-(aq)} + 2\,H_3O^+(aq) \rightleftharpoons 4\,H_2O(l) \qquad\qquad K' = 1/K_w^{\,2} = 1.0 \times 10^{28}}$$

$$Mg(OH)_2(s) + 2\,H_3O^+ \rightleftharpoons Mg^{2+}(aq) + 4\,H_2O(l) \tag{18.4}$$

$$K = K_{sp}/K_w^{\,2} = 1.8 \times 10^{-11} \times 1.0 \times 10^{28} = 1.8 \times 10^{17}$$

The large value of K for reaction (18.4) indicates that the reaction goes essentially to completion and that $Mg(OH)_2$ is highly soluble in acidic solutions.

Other slightly soluble solutes having basic anions (such as $ZnCO_3$, MgF_2, and CaC_2O_4) also become more soluble in acidic solutions. For these solutes, we can write overall net ionic equations for solubility equilibria and corresponding K values based on K_{sp} for the solutes and K_a for the conjugate acids of the anions.

Although $Mg(OH)_2$ is soluble in acidic solution, in moderately or strongly basic solutions it is not. In Example 18-8, we calculate $[OH^-]$ in a solution of the weak base NH_3 and then use the criteria for precipitation to see if $Mg(OH)_2(s)$ will precipitate. In Example 18-9, we determine how to adjust $[OH^-]$ to prevent precipitation of $Mg(OH)_2(s)$. This adjustment is made by adding NH_4^+ to the $NH_3(aq)$, thereby converting it to a buffer solution.

▲ Milk of magnesia, an aqueous suspension of $Mg(OH)_2(s)$.

Dissolution of $Mg(OH)_2$ by Acid animation

✓ In general, a water-insoluble salt of a weak acid can be dissolved by acid, but not the water-insoluble salt of a strong acid.

✓ Remind students that equilibrium constant expressions can be combined. See Section 15.3.

EXAMPLE 18-8

Determining Whether a Precipitate Will Form in a Solution in Which There Is Also an Ionization Equilibrium. Should $Mg(OH)_2(s)$ precipitate from a solution that is 0.010 M $MgCl_2$ and also 0.10 M NH_3?

Solution

The key here is in understanding that $[OH^-]$ is established by the ionization of $NH_3(aq)$.

$$NH_3(aq) + H_2O(l) \rightleftharpoons NH_4^+(aq) + OH^-(aq) \qquad K_b = 1.8 \times 10^{-5}$$

If we set this up in the usual way, the equilibrium values are $x = [NH_4^+] = [OH^-]$ and $[NH_3] = (0.10 - x) \approx 0.10$. Then we obtain

$$K_b = \frac{[NH_4^+][OH^-]}{[NH_3]} = \frac{x \cdot x}{0.10} = 1.8 \times 10^{-5}$$

$$x^2 = 1.8 \times 10^{-6} \qquad x = [OH^-] = 1.3 \times 10^{-3}\,M$$

Now we can rephrase the original question: Should $Mg(OH)_2(s)$ precipitate from a solution in which $[Mg^{2+}] = 1.0 \times 10^{-2}$ M and $[OH^-] = 1.3 \times 10^{-3}$ M? We must compare the ion product, Q_{sp}, with K_{sp}.

$$Q_{sp} = [Mg^{2+}][OH^-]^2 = (1.0 \times 10^{-2})(1.3 \times 10^{-3})^2$$

$$= 1.7 \times 10^{-8} > K_{sp} = 1.8 \times 10^{-11}$$

Precipitation should occur.

Practice Example A: Should $Mg(OH)_2(s)$ precipitate from a solution that is 0.010 M $MgCl_2(aq)$ and also 0.10 M $NaC_2H_3O_2$? $K_{sp} = [Mg(OH)_2] = 1.8 \times 10^{-11}$; $K_a(HC_2H_3O_2) = 1.8 \times 10^{-5}$.

[*Hint:* What equilibrium expression establishes $[OH^-]$ in the solution?]

Practice Example B: Will a precipitate of $Fe(OH)_3$ form from a solution that is 0.013 M Fe^{3+} in a buffer solution that is 0.150 M $HC_2H_3O_2$ and 0.250 M $NaC_2H_3O_2$?

EXAMPLE 18-9

Controlling an Ion Concentration, Either to Cause Precipitation or to Prevent It. What $[NH_4^+]$ must be maintained to prevent precipitation of $Mg(OH)_2(s)$ from a solution that is 0.010 M $MgCl_2$ and 0.10 M NH_3?

Solution

The maximum value of the ion product, Q_{sp}, before precipitation occurs is 1.8×10^{-11}, the value of K_{sp} for $Mg(OH)_2$. This fact allows us to determine the maximum concentration of OH^- that can be tolerated.

$$[Mg^{2+}][OH^-]^2 = (1.0 \times 10^{-2})[OH^-]^2 = 1.8 \times 10^{-11}$$

$$[OH^-]^2 = 1.8 \times 10^{-9}$$

$$[OH^-] = 4.2 \times 10^{-5}\,M$$

Next let's determine what $[NH_4^+]$ must be present in 0.10 M NH_3 to maintain $[OH^-] = 4.2 \times 10^{-5}$ M.

$$NH_3(aq) + H_2O(l) \rightleftharpoons NH_4^+(aq) + OH^-(aq) \qquad K_b = 1.8 \times 10^{-5}$$

$$K_b = \frac{[NH_4^+][OH^-]}{[NH_3]} = \frac{[NH_4^+](4.2 \times 10^{-5})}{0.10} = 1.8 \times 10^{-5}$$

$$[NH_4^+] = \frac{0.10 \times 1.8 \times 10^{-5}}{4.2 \times 10^{-5}} = 0.043\,M$$

To keep the $[OH^-]$ at 4.2×10^{-5} M *or less*, and thus prevent the precipitation of $Mg(OH)_2(s)$, $[NH_4^+]$ should be maintained at 0.043 M *or greater*.

Point out to students that in Example 18-9, the addition of NH_4^+ causes a shift to the left in the ionization reaction of NH_3. This shift consumes OH^- which works to prevent precipitation of $Mg(OH)_2$.

Practice Example A: What minimum $[NH_4^+]$ must be present to prevent precipitation of $Mn(OH)_2(s)$ from a solution that is 0.0050 M $MnCl_2$ and 0.025 M NH_3? For $Mn(OH)_2$, $K_{sp} = 1.9 \times 10^{-13}$.

Practice Example B: What is the molar solubility of $Mg(OH)_2(s)$ in a solution that is 0.250 M NH_3 and 0.100 M NH_4Cl?

[*Hint:* Use equation (18.4).]

CONCEPT ASSESSMENT ✔

Determine $[Mg^{2+}]$ in a saturated solution of $Mg(OH)_2$ at **(a)** pH = 10.00 and **(b)** pH = 5.00. Is each of these a plausible quantity? Explain.

18-8   EQUILIBRIA INVOLVING COMPLEX IONS

As shown in Figure 18-5, when moderately concentrated $NH_3(aq)$ is added to a saturated solution of silver chloride in contact with undissolved $AgCl(s)$, the solid dissolves. The key to this dissolving action is that Ag^+ ions from AgCl combine with NH_3 molecules to form the ions $[Ag(NH_3)_2]^+$, which, together with Cl^- ions, remain in solution as the soluble compound $Ag(NH_3)_2Cl$.

$$AgCl(s) + 2\,NH_3(aq) \longrightarrow [Ag(NH_3)_2]^+(aq) + Cl^-(aq) \qquad (18.5)$$

Here $[Ag(NH_3)_2]^+$ is called a complex ion, and $Ag(NH_3)_2Cl$ is called a coordination compound. A **complex ion** is a polyatomic cation or anion composed of a central metal ion to which other groups (molecules or ions) called *ligands* are bonded. **Coordination compounds** are substances containing complex ions. It helps to think of reaction (18.5) as involving two simultaneous equilibria.

$$AgCl(s) \rightleftharpoons Ag^+(aq) + Cl^-(aq) \qquad (18.6)$$

$$Ag^+(aq) + 2\,NH_3(aq) \rightleftharpoons [Ag(NH_3)_2]^+(aq) \qquad (18.7)$$

The equilibrium in reaction (18.7) is shifted far to the right—$[Ag(NH_3)_2]^+$ is a stable complex ion. The equilibrium concentration of $Ag^+(aq)$ in (18.7) is kept so low that the ion product $[Ag^+][Cl^-]$ fails to exceed K_{sp} and AgCl remains in solution. Let's first apply additional qualitative reasoning of this sort in Example 18-10. Then we can turn to some of the quantitative calculations that are also possible.

Take a range of anhydrous transition metal compounds of copper, ($CuSO_4$), nickel ($NiCl_2$), chromium, and zinc. Note the colors of the compounds. Dissolve the compounds in water and note the colors again. Add ammonia to the beakers to show the deep blues, greens, reds, and violet colors produced. Experiment by adding other complexing agents such as EDTA, KCN, ethylenediamine, etc., noting the rapid changes of colors when one complexing agent (ligand) replaces another.

A coordination compound,
$[Co(NH_3)_6]Cl_3]$

Complex cation	Anions
$[Co(NH_3)_6]^{3+}$	$3\,Cl^-$

Central ion / Ligands

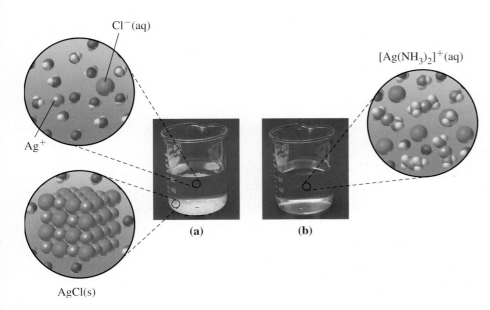

$Cl^-(aq)$

Ag^+

$AgCl(s)$

(a)   **(b)**

$[Ag(NH_3)_2]^+(aq)$

◀ **FIGURE 18-5**
Complex-ion formation: dissolution of AgCl(s) in $NH_3(aq)$
(a) A saturated solution of silver chloride in contact with excess $AgCl(s)$. **(b)** When $NH_3(aq)$ is added, the excess $AgCl(s)$ dissolves through the formation of the complex ion $[Ag(NH_3)_2]^+$.

▲ FIGURE 18-6
Reprecipitating AgCl(s)
The reagent being added
to the solution containing
$[Ag(NH_3)_2]^+$ and Cl^- is
$HNO_3(aq)$. H_3O^+ from the
acid reacts with $NH_3(aq)$ to
form $NH_4^+(aq)$.
As a result, equilibrium
between $[Ag(NH_3)_2]^+$, Ag^+,
and NH_3 is upset. The
complex ion is destroyed,
$[Ag^+]$ quickly rises to the
point at which K_{sp} for AgCl
is exceeded, and a
precipitate forms.

EXAMPLE 18-10

Predicting Reactions Involving Complex Ions. Predict what will happen if nitric acid is added to a solution of $[Ag(NH_3)_2]Cl$ in $NH_3(aq)$.

Solution

Nitric acid neutralizes free NH_3 in the solution. Because $HNO_3(aq)$ is a strong acid, we represent it as being completely ionized and write only the net ionic equation.

$$H_3O^+(aq) + NH_3(aq) \longrightarrow NH_4^+(aq) + H_2O(l)$$

To replace free NH_3 lost in this neutralization, equilibrium in reaction (18.7) shifts to the *left*. As a result, $[Ag^+]$ increases. When $[Ag^+]$ increases to the point at which the ion product $[Ag^+][Cl^-]$ exceeds K_{sp}, AgCl(s) precipitates (Fig. 18-6).

Practice Example A: Copper(II) ion forms both an insoluble hydroxide and the complex ion $[Cu(NH_3)_4]^{2+}$. Write equations to represent the expected reaction when **(a)** $CuSO_4(aq)$ and $NaOH(aq)$ are mixed; **(b)** an excess of $NH_3(aq)$ is added to the product of part (a); and **(c)** an excess of $HNO_3(aq)$ is added to the product of part (b).

Practice Example B: Zinc(II) ion forms both an insoluble hydroxide and the complex ions $[Zn(OH)_4]^{2-}$ and $[Zn(NH_3)_4]^{2+}$. Write four equations to represent the reactions of **(a)** $NH_3(aq)$ with $ZnSO_4(aq)$, followed by **(b)** enough $HNO_3(aq)$ to make the product of part (a) acidic; **(c)** enough $NaOH(aq)$ to make the product of part (b) slightly basic; **(d)** enough $NaOH(aq)$ to make the product of part (c) strongly basic.

To describe the ionization of a weak acid, we use the ionization constant K_a. For a solubility equilibrium, we use the solubility product constant K_{sp}. The equilibrium constant that is used to deal with a complex-ion equilibrium is called the formation constant. The **formation constant, K_f,** of a complex ion is the equilibrium constant describing the formation of a complex ion from a central ion and its attached groups. For reaction (18.7) this equilibrium constant expression is

$$K_f = \frac{[[Ag(NH_3)_2]^+]}{[Ag^+][NH_3]^2} = 1.6 \times 10^7$$

Table 18.2 lists some representative formation constants, K_f.

TABLE 18.2   Formation Constants for Some Complex Ions[a]

Complex Ion	Equilibrium Reaction[b]	K_f
$[Co(NH_3)_6]^{3+}$	$Co^{3+} + 6\,NH_3 \rightleftharpoons [Co(NH_3)_6]^{3+}$	4.5×10^{33}
$[Cu(NH_3)_4]^{2+}$	$Cu^{2+} + 4\,NH_3 \rightleftharpoons [Cu(NH_3)_4]^{2+}$	1.1×10^{13}
$[Fe(CN)_6]^{4-}$	$Fe^{2+} + 6\,CN^- \rightleftharpoons [Fe(CN)_6]^{4-}$	1×10^{37}
$[Fe(CN)_6]^{3-}$	$Fe^{3+} + 6\,CN^- \rightleftharpoons [Fe(CN)_6]^{3-}$	1×10^{42}
$[PbCl_3]^-$	$Pb^{2+} + 3\,Cl^- \rightleftharpoons [PbCl_3]^-$	2.4×10^1
$[Ag(NH_3)_2]^+$	$Ag^+ + 2\,NH_3 \rightleftharpoons [Ag(NH_3)_2]^+$	1.6×10^7
$[Ag(CN)_2]^-$	$Ag^+ + 2\,CN^- \rightleftharpoons [Ag(CN)_2]^-$	5.6×10^{18}
$[Ag(S_2O_3)_2]^{3-}$	$Ag^+ + 2\,S_2O_3^{2-} \rightleftharpoons [Ag(S_2O_3)_2]^{3-}$	1.7×10^{13}
$[Zn(NH_3)_4]^{2+}$	$Zn^{2+} + 4\,NH_3 \rightleftharpoons [Zn(NH_3)_4]^{2+}$	4.1×10^8
$[Zn(CN)_4]^{2-}$	$Zn^{2+} + 4\,CN^- \rightleftharpoons [Zn(CN)_4]^{2-}$	1×10^{18}
$[Zn(OH)_4]^{2-}$	$Zn^{2+} + 4\,OH^- \rightleftharpoons [Zn(OH)_4]^{2-}$	4.6×10^{17}

[a] A more extensive tabulation is given in Appendix D.
[b] Tabulated here are *overall* formation reactions and the corresponding *overall* formation constants. In Section 24-8, we describe the formation of complex ions in a *stepwise* fashion and introduce formation constants for individual steps.

Point out that KCN is a deadly poison because cyanide ion forms a stronger complex with the iron in hemoglobin than does oxygen. Hence all the oxygen is replaced by cyanide and the victim suffocates.

This articles discusses the synthesis of cobalt coordination compounds in the general chemistry laboratory: Williams, G. M. et al. *J. Chem. Educ.* **1989:** *66*, 1043.

One feature that distinguishes K_f from most other equilibrium constants previously considered is that K_f values are usually *large* numbers. This fact can affect the way we approach certain calculations. With large K values, it is sometimes convenient to solve a problem in two steps. First, assume that the forward reaction goes to completion; second, assume that a small change occurs in the reverse direction to establish the equilibrium. This approach is demonstrated in Example 18-11.

EXAMPLE 18-11

Determining Whether a Precipitate Will Form in a Solution Containing Complex Ions. A 0.10-mol sample of $AgNO_3$ is dissolved in 1.00 L of 1.00 M NH_3. If 0.010 mol NaCl is added to this solution, will AgCl(s) precipitate?

Solution
Let's begin by assuming that because the value of K_f for $[Ag(NH_3)_2]^+$ is very large, the following reaction initially goes to completion, with the results shown.

$$Ag^+(aq) + 2\,NH_3(aq) \longrightarrow [Ag(NH_3)_2]^+(aq)$$

	$Ag^+(aq)$	$2\,NH_3(aq)$	$[Ag(NH_3)_2]^+(aq)$
initial concns, M:	0.10	1.00	
changes, M:	−0.10	−0.20	+0.10
after reaction, M:	≈0	0.80	0.10

However, the concentration of uncomplexed silver ion, though very small, is not zero. To determine the value of $[Ag^+]$, let's start with $[[Ag(NH_3)_2]^+]$ and $[NH_3]$ in solution and establish $[Ag^+]$ at equilibrium.

$$Ag^+ + 2\,NH_3 \rightleftharpoons [Ag(NH_3)_2]^+$$

	Ag^+	$2\,NH_3$	$[Ag(NH_3)_2]^+$
initial concns, M:		0.80	0.10
changes, M:	$+x$	$+2x$	$-x$
equil concns, M:	x	$0.80 + 2x$	$0.10 - x$

When substituting into the following expression, we make the assumption that $x \ll 0.10$, which we will find to be the case.

$$\frac{[[Ag(NH_3)_2]^+]}{[Ag^+][NH_3]^2} = \frac{0.10 - x}{x(0.80 + 2x)^2} \approx \frac{0.10}{x(0.80)^2} = 1.6 \times 10^7$$

$$x = [Ag^+] = \frac{0.10}{(1.6 \times 10^7)(0.80)^2} = 9.8 \times 10^{-9}\ M$$

Finally, we must compare $Q_{sp} = [Ag^+][Cl^-]$ with K_{sp} for AgCl (that is, 1.8×10^{-10}). $[Ag^+]$ is the value of x that we just calculated. Because the solution contains 0.010 mol NaCl/L, $[Cl^-] = 0.010\ M = 1.0 \times 10^{-2}\ M$, and

$$Q_{sp} = (9.8 \times 10^{-9})(1.0 \times 10^{-2}) = 9.8 \times 10^{-11} < 1.8 \times 10^{-10}$$

AgCl will not precipitate.

Practice Example A: Will AgCl(s) precipitate from 1.50 L of a solution that is 0.100 M $AgNO_3$ and 0.225 M NH_3 if 1.00 mL of 3.50 M NaCl is added?

[*Hint:* What are $[Ag^+]$ and $[Cl^-]$ immediately after the addition of the 1.00 mL of 3.50 M NaCl? Take into account the dilution of the NaCl(aq), but assume the total volume remains at 1.50 L.]

Practice Example B: A solution is prepared that is 0.100 M in $Pb(NO_3)_2$ and 0.250 M in the ethylenediaminetetraacetate anion, $EDTA^{4-}$. Together, Pb^{2+} and $EDTA^{4-}$ form the complex ion $[PbEDTA]^{2-}$. If the solution is also made 0.10 M in I^-, will $PbI_2(s)$ precipitate? For PbI_2, $K_{sp} = 7.1 \times 10^{-9}$; for $[PbEDTA]^{2-}$, $K_f = 2 \times 10^{18}$.

Just as some precipitation reactions can be controlled by using a buffer solution (Example 18-9), precipitation from a solution of complex ions can be controlled by fixing the concentration of the complexing agent. Such a case is demonstrated for AgCl in Example 18-12.

EXAMPLE 18-12

Controlling a Concentration to Cause or Prevent Precipitation from a Solution of Complex Ions. What is the *minimum* concentration of NH_3 needed to prevent AgCl(s) from precipitating from 1.00 L of a solution containing 0.10 mol $AgNO_3$ and 0.010 mol NaCl?

Solution

The $[Cl^-]$ that must be maintained in solution is 1.0×10^{-2} M. If no precipitation is to occur, $[Ag^+][Cl^-] \leq K_{sp}$.

$$[Ag^+](1.0 \times 10^{-2}) \leq K_{sp} = 1.8 \times 10^{-10} \qquad [Ag^+] \leq 1.8 \times 10^{-8} \text{ M}$$

Thus, the maximum concentration of *uncomplexed* Ag^+ in solution is 1.8×10^{-8} M. This means that essentially all the Ag^+ (0.10 mol/L) must be tied up (complexed) in the complex ion $[Ag(NH_3)_2]^+$. We need to solve the expression at the right for $[NH_3]$.

$$K_f = \frac{[[Ag(NH_3)_2]^+]}{[Ag^+][NH_3]^2} = \frac{1.0 \times 10^{-1}}{1.8 \times 10^{-8}[NH_3]^2} = 1.6 \times 10^7$$

$$[NH_3]^2 = \frac{1.0 \times 10^{-1}}{1.8 \times 10^{-8} \times 1.6 \times 10^7} = 0.35 \qquad [NH_3] = 0.59 \text{ M}$$

The concentration just calculated is that of *free, uncomplexed* NH_3. Considering as well the 0.20 mol NH_3/L complexed in the 0.10 M $[Ag(NH_3)_2]^+$, we see that the total concentration of NH_3(aq) required is

$$[NH_3]_{tot} = 0.59 \text{ M} + 0.20 \text{ M} = 0.79 \text{ M}$$

Practice Example A: What $[NH_3]_{tot}$ is necessary to keep AgCl from precipitating from a solution that is 0.13 M $AgNO_3$ and 0.0075 M NaCl?

Practice Example B: What minimum concentration of thiosulfate ion, $S_2O_3^{2-}$, should be present in 0.10 M $AgNO_3$(aq) so that AgCl(s) does not precipitate when the solution is also made 0.010 M in Cl^-? For AgCl, $K_{sp} = 1.8 \times 10^{-10}$; for $[Ag(S_2O_3)_2]^{3-}$, $K_f = 1.7 \times 10^{13}$.

On page 761, there is a qualitative description of how the solubility of AgCl increases in the presence of NH_3(aq). Example 18-13 shows how to calculate the actual solubility of AgCl in NH_3(aq).

EXAMPLE 18-13

Determining the Solubility of a Solute When Complex Ions Form. What is the molar solubility of AgCl in 0.100 M NH_3(aq)?

Solution

As we have already seen, equation (18.5) describes the solubility equilibrium.

$$AgCl(s) + 2\,NH_3(aq) \rightleftharpoons [Ag(NH_3)_2]^+(aq) + Cl^-(aq) \qquad (18.5)$$

Let's base our calculation on the equilibrium constant K for reaction (18.5). There are two ways to obtain this value. By one method, equation (18.5) is written as the sum of equations (18.6) and (18.7) on page 761. Then its K value is obtained as the product of a K_{sp} and a K_f.

$$AgCl(s) \rightleftharpoons Ag^+(aq) + Cl^-(aq) \qquad K_{sp} = 1.8 \times 10^{-10}$$
$$\underline{Ag^+(aq) + 2\,NH_3(aq) \rightleftharpoons [Ag(NH_3)_2]^+(aq) \qquad\qquad K_f = 1.6 \times 10^7}$$
$$AgCl(s) + 2\,NH_3(aq) \rightleftharpoons [Ag(NH_3)_2]^+(aq) + Cl^-(aq)$$

$$K = K_{sp} \times K_f = 1.8 \times 10^{-10} \times 1.6 \times 10^7 = 2.9 \times 10^{-3}$$

By a second method, the equilibrium constant expression for reaction (18.5) is written first, and then the numerator and denominator are multiplied by $[Ag^+]$.

$$K = \frac{[Ag(NH_3)_2^+][Cl^-]}{[NH_3]^2} = \frac{\textcolor{red}{[Ag(NH_3)_2^+]}\textcolor{blue}{[Cl^-][Ag^+]}}{\textcolor{red}{[NH_3]^2[Ag^+]}} = K_f \times K_{sp} = 2.9 \times 10^{-3}$$

The expression printed in red is K_f for $[Ag(NH_3)_2]^+$; the one in blue is K_{sp} for AgCl. The K value for reaction (18.5) is the product of the two.

According to equation (18.5), if s mol AgCl/L dissolves (the molar solubility), the expected concentrations of $[Ag(NH_3)_2]^+$ and Cl^- are also equal to s.

$$AgCl(s) + 2\,NH_3(aq) \rightleftharpoons [Ag(NH_3)_2]^+(aq) + Cl^-(aq)$$

initial concns, M:	0.100		
changes, M:	$-2s$	$+s$	$+s$
equil concns, M:	$(0.100 - 2s)$	s	s

$$K = \frac{[[Ag(NH_3)_2]^+][Cl^-]}{[NH_3]^2} = \frac{s \cdot s}{(0.100 - 2s)^2} = \left(\frac{s}{0.100 - 2s}\right)^2 = 2.9 \times 10^{-3}$$

We can solve this equation by taking the square root of both sides.

$$\frac{s}{0.100 - 2s} = \sqrt{2.9 \times 10^{-3}} = 5.4 \times 10^{-2}$$

$$s = 5.4 \times 10^{-3} - 0.11s$$

$$1.11s = 5.4 \times 10^{-3}$$

$$s = 4.9 \times 10^{-3}$$

The molar solubility of AgCl(s) in 0.100 M NH_3(aq) is 4.9×10^{-3} M.

NOTE: The usual simplifying assumption, that is, $(0.100 - 2s) \approx 0.100$, would not have worked well in this calculation. The value of s obtained would have been 5.4×10^{-3} M, and $0.100 - (2 \times 0.0054) \neq 0.100$. Also, the molar solubility is actually the *total* concentration of silver in solution: $[Ag^+] + [[Ag(NH_3)_2]^+]$. Only when K_f is large and the concentration of complexing agent sufficiently high can we ignore the concentration of uncomplexed metal ion, as was the case here.

Practice Example A: What is the molar solubility of $Fe(OH)_3$ in a solution containing 0.100 M $C_2O_4^{2-}$? For $[Fe(C_2O_4)_3]^{3-}$, $K_f = 2 \times 10^{20}$.

Practice Example B: *Without doing detailed calculations,* show that the order of *decreasing* solubility in 0.100 M NH_3(aq) should be AgCl > AgBr > AgI.

CONCEPT ASSESSMENT ✔

The measured molar solubility of AgCl in water is 1.3×10^{-5} M. In the presence of Cl^-(aq) as a common ion at different concentrations, the measured solubilities of AgCl are as listed below.

$[Cl^-]$, M:	0.0039	0.036	0.35	1.4	2.9	3.8
Solubility of AgCl, M:	7.2×10^{-7}	1.9×10^{-6}	1.7×10^{-5}	1.8×10^{-4}	1.0×10^{-2}	2.5×10^{-2}

Give a plausible explanation for the trends in the molar solubilities of the AgCl.

18-9   QUALITATIVE CATION ANALYSIS

In *qualitative analysis*, we determine what substances are present in a mixture but *not* their quantities. An analysis that aims at identifying the cations present in a mixture is called **qualitative cation analysis**. Qualitative cation analysis is not as important a method as it once was, because now most qualitative and quantitative analyses are done with instruments. Its current value is in the wealth of examples it provides of precipitation (and dissolution) equilibria, acid–base equilibria, and oxidation–reduction reactions. Also, in the general chemistry laboratory it offers the challenge of unraveling a mystery—solving a qualitative analysis "unknown."

Woodfield, B. F. et al. The *Virtual ChemLab* Project: A "Realistic and Sophisticated Simulation of Inorganic Qualitative Analysis." *J. Chem. Educ.* **2004:** *81,* 1672.

Oliver-Hoyo, M. et al. "Qualitative Analysis of Fourteen White Solids and Two Mixtures Using Household Chemicals." *J. Chem. Educ.* **2001:** *78,* 1475.

Kirschenbaum, L. J. et al. "An Alternative Confirmatory Test for Silver Ion in Qualitative Analysis." *J. Chem. Educ.* **2001:** *78,* 1524.

▲ **FIGURE 18-7**
Outline of a qualitative cation analysis
Various aspects of this scheme are described in the text. A sample containing all 25 cations can be separated into five groups by the indicated reagents.

▶ In the Hg_2^{2+} ion, a covalent bond links a Hg atom to a Hg^{2+} ion.

Today, wet chemistry is not performed using these qualitative cation analysis techniques. Even so, at the introductory level, knowledge of the groups and the differing solubility criteria is useful background information for students.

In the scheme in Figure 18-7, about 25 common cations are divided into five groups, depending on differing solubilities of their compounds. The first cations separated, Pb^{2+}, Hg_2^{2+}, and Ag^+, are those with insoluble *chlorides.* The reagent used is HCl(aq). All other cations remain in solution because their chlorides are soluble. After the chloride group precipitate is removed, the remaining solution is treated with H_2S in an acidic medium. Under these conditions, a group of sulfides precipitates. They are known as the hydrogen sulfide group. Next, the solution containing the remaining cations is treated with H_2S in a buffer mixture of ammonia and ammonium ion, yielding a mixture of insoluble hydroxides and sulfides.

This group is called the ammonium sulfide group. The sulfide of aluminum(III) and chromium(III) are unstable, reacting with water to form the hydroxides.

Treatment of the ammonium sulfide group filtrate with CO_3^{2-} yields the fourth group precipitate, which consists of the carbonates of Mg^{2+}, Ca^{2+}, Sr^{2+}, and Ba^{2+}. It is called the carbonate group because the aqueous carbonate anion is the key reagent. At the end of this series of precipitations, the resulting solution contains only Na^+, K^+, and NH_4^+, all of whose common salts are water soluble.

In this section, we will discuss the chemistry of the chloride and sulfide groups. The chemistry of metal carbonates is discussed in Chapter 21.

Are You Wondering . . .

How to test for the presence of Na^+, K^+, and NH_4^+ cations?

 Identification of Cations in Solution: Flame Tests

Kvaran, Á., Haraldsson, Á. Hr., Sigfusson T. I., "Spectroscopy of Flames: Luminescence Spectra of Reactive Intermediates." *J. Chem. Educ.* **2000:** *77*, 1345 (October 2000).

McKelvy, George M. "Flame Tests That Are Portable, Storable, and Easy To Use." *J. Chem. Educ.* **1998:** *75*, 55 (January 1998).

Tests by precipitation are difficult because the salts of these cations exhibit near-universal solubility. Both Na^+ and K^+ ions are most easily detected with a flame test. When a solution containing sodium ions is brought into contact with a flame, the characteristic orange-yellow color of the emission spectrum of sodium ions is observed. For potassium ions, a pale violet color results. To detect the presence of NH_4^+, we use the fact that the ammonium ion is the conjugate acid of the weak volatile base ammonia. Heating some of the original solution (not the final solution, which contains NH_4^+ ions added in the fractional precipitation scheme) with excess strong base will liberate ammonia.

$$NH_4^+(aq) + OH^- \longrightarrow NH_3(g) + H_2O(l)$$

The NH_3 is detected by its characteristic odor and its effect on the color of an acid–base indicator such as litmus.

(a)   (b)

▲ Flame colors of **(a)** sodium and **(b)** potassium.

CATION GROUP 1: THE CHLORIDE GROUP

If a precipitate forms when a solution is treated with HCl(aq), one or more of the following cations must be present: Pb^{2+}, Hg_2^{2+}, Ag^+. To establish the presence or absence of each of these three cations, the chloride group precipitate is filtered off and subjected to further testing.

Of the three chlorides in the group precipitate, $PbCl_2(s)$ is the most soluble; its K_{sp} is much larger than those of AgCl and Hg_2Cl_2. When the precipitate is washed with hot water, a sufficient quantity of $PbCl_2$ dissolves to permit a test for Pb^{2+} in the solution. In this test, a lead compound less soluble than $PbCl_2$, such as lead(II) chromate, precipitates (Fig. 18-8).

$$Pb^{2+}(aq) + CrO_4^{2-}(aq) \longrightarrow PbCrO_4(s)$$

The portion of the chloride group precipitate that is insoluble in hot water is then treated with $NH_3(aq)$. Two things happen. One is that any AgCl(s) present dissolves and forms the complex ion $[Ag(NH_3)_2^+]$, as described by equation (18.5).

$$AgCl(s) + 2 NH_3(aq) \longrightarrow [Ag(NH_3)_2]^+(aq) + Cl^-(aq)$$

At the same time, any $Hg_2Cl_2(s)$ present undergoes an oxidation–reduction reaction. One of the products of the reaction is finely divided black mercury. A black color is common for finely divided metals.

$$Hg_2Cl_2(s) + 2 NH_3(aq) \longrightarrow \underbrace{Hg(l) + HgNH_2Cl(s)}_{\text{dark gray}} + NH_4^+(aq) + Cl^-(aq)$$

(a)   (b)   (c)

▲ **FIGURE 18-8**
Chloride group precipitates
(a) Group 1 precipitate: a mixture of $PbCl_2$ (white), Hg_2Cl_2 (white), and AgCl (white). **(b)** Test for Hg_2^{2+}: a mixture of Hg (black) and $HgNH_2Cl$ (white). **(c)** Test for Pb^{2+}: a yellow precipitate of $PbCrO_4(s)$.

 Identification of Cations in Solution: Ag^+, Hg_2^{2+}, Pb^{2+}

The appearance of a dark gray mixture of black mercury and white $HgNH_2Cl$ [mercury(II) amidochloride] is the qualitative analysis confirmation of mercury(I) ion (see Figure 18-8).

When the solution from reaction (18.5) is acidified with $HNO_3(aq)$, any silver ion present precipitates as $AgCl(s)$. This is the reaction predicted in Example 18-10 and pictured in Figure 18-6.

CONCEPT ASSESSMENT ✓

A qualitative analysis chloride group unknown forms a white precipitate with HCl(aq). The precipitate is treated with hot water, yielding a solution that gives a yellow precipitate with $K_2CrO_4(aq)$. There is no change in color when the undissolved portion of the precipitate is treated with $NH_3(aq)$. Indicate for each chloride group cation whether it is present or absent, or about which there is some doubt.

 Identification of Cations in Solution: Co^{2+}, Cr^{3+}, Cu^{2+}

IIdentification of Cations in Solution: Ba^{2+}, Sr^{2+}, Ca^{2+}, Mg^{2+}

Identification of Cations in Solution: Co^{2+}, Cu^{2+}, Ni^{2+}

▶ $H_2S(g)$ has a familiar rotten egg odor, especially noticeable in volcanic areas and near sulfur hot springs. It can cause nausea and headaches at levels of 10 ppm in air, and it can produce paralysis or death at levels of 100 ppm. The gas is detectable by its odor at levels of 1 ppm, although exposure to the gas soon deadens the sense of smell.

CATION GROUPS 2 AND 3: EQUILIBRIA INVOLVING HYDROGEN SULFIDE

Figure 18-7 suggests that aqueous hydrogen sulfide (hydrosulfuric acid) is the key reagent in the analysis of cation groups 2 and 3. In aqueous solution, H_2S is a *weak diprotic acid*.

$$H_2S(aq) + H_2O(l) \rightleftharpoons H_3O^+(aq) + HS^-(aq) \qquad K_{a_1} = 1.0 \times 10^{-7}$$

$$HS^-(aq) + H_2O(l) \rightleftharpoons H_3O^+(aq) + S^{2-}(aq) \qquad K_{a_2} = 1 \times 10^{-19}$$

The extremely small value of K_{a_2} suggests that sulfide ion is a very strong base, as seen in the following hydrolysis reaction and K_b value.

$$S^{2-} + H_2O \rightleftharpoons HS^- + OH^- \qquad K_b = K_w/K_{a_2}$$

$$= (1.0 \times 10^{-14})/(1 \times 10^{-19}) = 1 \times 10^5$$

The hydrolysis of S^{2-} should go nearly to completion, which means that very little S^{2-} can exist in an aqueous solution and that sulfide ion is probably not the precipitating agent for sulfides.

One way to handle the precipitation and dissolution of sulfide precipitates is to restrict the discussion to acidic solutions. Then we can write an equilibrium constant expression in which the concentration terms for HS^- and S^{2-} are eliminated. This approach is reasonable because most sulfide separations are carried out in acidic solution.

Consider (1) the solubility equilibrium equation for PbS written to reflect hydrolysis of S^{2-}, (2) an equation written for the reverse of the first ionization of H_2S, and (3) an equation that is the reverse of the self-ionization of water. These three equations can be combined into an overall equation that shows the dissolving of PbS(s) in an acidic solution. The equilibrium constant for this overall equation is generally referred to as K_{spa}.*

(1) $PbS(s) + H_2O(l) \rightleftharpoons Pb^{2+}(aq) + HS^-(aq) + OH^-(aq)$ $K_{sp} = 3 \times 10^{-28}$

(2) $H_3O^+(aq) + HS^-(aq) \rightleftharpoons H_2S(aq) + H_2O(l)$ $1/K_{a_1} = 1/1.0 \times 10^{-7}$

(3) $H_3O^+(aq) + OH^-(aq) \rightleftharpoons H_2O(l) + H_2O(l)$ $1/K_w = 1/1.0 \times 10^{-14}$

Overall: $PbS(s) + 2 H_3O^+(aq) \rightleftharpoons Pb^{2+}(aq) + H_2S(aq) + 2 H_2O(l)$ $K_{spa} = ?$

▶ $PbCl_2$ is sufficiently soluble that enough Pb^{2+} ions from cation group 1 remain in solution to precipitate again as PbS(s) in cation group 2.

$$K_{spa} = \frac{K_{sp}}{K_{a_1} \times K_w} = \frac{3 \times 10^{-28}}{(1.0 \times 10^{-7})(1.0 \times 10^{-14})} = 3 \times 10^{-7}$$

---

*See Myers, R. J. *J. Chem. Educ.* "The new low value for the second dissociation constant for H_2S: Its history, its best value, and its impact on the teaching of sulfide equilibria." **1986**: 63, 687.

Example 18-14 illustrates the use of K_{spa} in the type of calculation needed to sort the sulfides into two qualitative analysis groups. Pb^{2+} is in qualitative analysis cation group 2, and Fe^{2+} is in group 3. The conditions cited in the example are those generally used.

EXAMPLE 18-14

Separating Metal Ions by Selective Precipitation of Metal Sulfides. Show that PbS(s) will precipitate but FeS(s) will not precipitate from a solution that is 0.010 M in Pb^{2+}, 0.010 M in Fe^{2+}, saturated in H_2S (0.10 M H_2S), and maintained with $[H_3O^+] = 0.30$ M. For PbS, $K_{spa} = 3 \times 10^{-7}$; for FeS, $K_{spa} = 6 \times 10^2$.

◄ **KEEP IN MIND**
that the value of K_{spa} of FeS can be derived from K_{sp} of FeS (6×10^{-19}) by the method outlined for PbS.

Solution

We must determine whether, for the stated conditions, equilibrium is displaced in the forward or reverse direction in reactions of the type

$$MS(s) + 2\,H_3O^+(aq) \rightleftharpoons M^{2+}(aq) + H_2S(aq) + 2\,H_2O(l) \qquad (18.8)$$

where M represents either Pb or Fe. In each case, we can compare the Q_{spa} expression to the appropriate K_{spa} value for reaction (18.8). If $Q_{spa} > K_{spa}$, a net change will occur to the *left* and MS(s) will precipitate. If $Q_{spa} < K_{spa}$, a net change will occur to the *right*. In this case, some of the metal sulfide will actually dissolve in the solution, and no precipitation will occur.

$$Q_{spa} = \frac{[M^{2+}][H_2S]}{[H_3O^+]^2} = \frac{0.010 \times 0.10}{(0.30)^2} = 1.1 \times 10^{-2}$$

For PbS: Q_{spa} of $1.1 \times 10^{-2} > K_{spa}$ of 3×10^{-7}. PbS(s) will precipitate.
For FeS: Q_{spa} of $1.1 \times 10^{-2} < K_{spa}$ of 6×10^2. FeS(s) will not precipitate.

Practice Example A: Show that $Ag_2S(s)$ ($K_{spa} = 6 \times 10^{-30}$) should precipitate and that FeS(s) ($K_{spa} = 6 \times 10^2$) should not precipitate from a solution that is 0.010 M Ag^+ and 0.020 M Fe^{2+}, but otherwise under the same conditions as in Example 18-14.

Practice Example B: What is the minimum pH of a solution that is 0.015 M Fe^{2+} and saturated in H_2S (0.10 M) from which FeS(s) ($K_{spa} = 6 \times 10^2$) can be precipitated?

CONCEPT ASSESSMENT ✔

Both Cu^{2+} and Ag^+ are present in the same aqueous solution. Explain which of the following reagents would work best in separating these ions, precipitating one and leaving the other in solution: $(NH_4)_2CO_3(aq)$, $HNO_3(aq)$, $H_2S(aq)$, $HCl(aq)$, $NH_3(aq)$, or $NaOH(aq)$.

DISSOLVING METAL SULFIDES

In the qualitative cation analysis, it is necessary to both precipitate and redissolve sulfides. Here, we look at several methods of dissolving metal sulfides. One way to increase the solubility of any sulfide is to allow it to react with an acid, as equation (18.8) suggests. According to Le Châtelier's principle, the solubility increases as the solution is made more acidic—equilibrium is shifted to the right. As a result, some water-insoluble sulfides, such as FeS, are readily soluble in strongly acidic solutions. Others, such as PbS and HgS, cannot be dissolved in acidic solutions because their K_{sp} values are too low. In these cases, $[H_3O^+]$ cannot be made high enough to force reaction (18.8) very far to the right.

Another way to promote the dissolving of metal sulfides is to use an *oxidizing* acid such as $HNO_3(aq)$. In this case, sulfide ion is oxidized to elemental sulfur and the free metal ion appears in solution, as in the dissolving of CuS(s).

$$3\,CuS(s) + 8\,H^+(aq) + 2\,NO_3^-(aq) \longrightarrow$$

$$3\,Cu^{2+}(aq) + 3\,S(s) + 2\,NO(g) + 4\,H_2O(l) \quad (18.9)$$

A fossilized chambered nautilus, a marine animal that forms its shell by precipitating calcium carbonate.

Although most of Earth's minerals have formed by cooling of molten material called magma, a few have been produced by precipitation processes. For example, warm seawater is nearly saturated in Ca^{2+} and HCO_3^- ions and can yield the mineral *calcite* ($CaCO_3$) by precipitation.

$$Ca^{2+}(aq) + 2\,HCO_3^-(aq) \longrightarrow$$

$$CaCO_3(s) + H_2O(l) + CO_2(g)$$

Chemical precipitation, however, is not the principal source of calcite deposits in the ocean. Most calcite and related carbonate deposits originate from the biological precipitation of minerals to form the shells of certain marine organisms. These organisms can extract Ca^{2+} and HCO_3^- ions from seawater and concentrate them in solution in specialized cells. The organisms then secrete crystals of $CaCO_3$ to build the shells within which they live.

Some organisms secrete harder materials than carbonates and use them to form bones and teeth. Human bones and tooth enamel, for example, are made principally of the mineral *hydroxyapatite*, $Ca_5(PO_4)_3OH$. Hydroxyapatite is somewhat soluble in acidic solutions, and this property

To render the $Cu^{2+}(aq)$ more visible, it is converted to the deeply colored complex ion $[Cu(NH_3)_4]^{2+}(aq)$ in a reaction in which NH_3 molecules replace H_2O molecules in a complex ion (Fig. 18-9).

$$[(Cu(H_2O)_4]^{2+}(aq) + 4\,NH_3(aq) \longrightarrow [Cu(NH_3)_4]^{2+}(aq) + 4\,H_2O(l)$$

pale blue   deep violet

A few metal sulfides dissolve in a basic solution with a high concentration of HS^-, just as acidic oxides dissolve in solutions with a high concentration of OH^-. This property is used to advantage in separating the eight sulfides of cation group 2, the hydrogen sulfide group, into two subgroups. The subgroup consisting of HgS, PbS, CuS, CdS, and Bi_2S_3 remains unchanged after treatment with an alkaline solution with an excess of HS^-, but As_2S_3, SnS_2, and Sb_2S_3 dissolve.

▲ FIGURE 18-9

Complex-ion formation: A test for $Cu^{2+}(aq)$

Dilute $CuSO_4(aq)$ (left) derives its pale blue color from the complex ions $[Cu(H_2O)_4]^{2+}$. When $NH_3(aq)$ is added (here labeled "conc ammonium hydroxide"), the color changes to a deep violet, signaling the presence of $[Cu(NH_3)_4]^{2+}$ (right). The deep violet color is detectable at much lower concentrations than the pale blue; the formation of $[Cu(NH_3)_4]^{2+}$ is a sensitive test for the presence of Cu^{2+}.

is a matter of concern in good dental health. Bacteria in the mouth produce acids from food trapped between teeth. These acids cause tooth enamel to dissolve through reactions such as

$$Ca_5(PO_4)_3OH(s) + 4\,H_3O^+(aq) \longrightarrow$$
$$5\,Ca^{2+}(aq) + 3\,HPO_4{}^{2-}(aq) + 5\,H_2O(l)$$

If it proceeds unchecked, dissolution of tooth enamel, referred to as *demineralization*, results in the formation of cavities. Fortunately, the removal of the bacteria and food particles from teeth by brushing and flossing is one effective strategy for combating tooth decay.

Another strategy is to alter the composition of the tooth enamel to make it more resistant to attack by acids. *Fluorapatite*, $Ca_5(PO_4)_3F$, is less soluble in acids than is hydroxyapatite because F^- is a weaker base than OH^-. Brushing the teeth with a fluoride-containing toothpaste sets up a competitive equilibrium that results in the conversion of some hydroxyapatite to fluorapatite, a process called *remineralization*.

$$Ca_5(PO_4)_3OH(s) + F^-(aq) \rightleftharpoons$$
$$Ca_5(PO_4)_3F(s) + OH^-(aq) \quad (18.10)$$

In addition to its lower solubility in acids, fluorapatite forms crystals that pack more densely than do crystals of hydroxyapatite, making the fluorapatite structure less porous and more resistant to penetration by acidic solutions.

Another source of fluoride ions for promoting the remineralization reaction (18.10) is drinking water. Some groundwater is naturally fluoridated, but many communities fluoridate drinking water by adding a soluble fluoride, enough to raise the F^- concentration in the water to about 1 ppm.

The same replacement of OH^- by F^- as described for fighting tooth decay occurs in the fossilization of bones and in natural deposits of hydroxyapatite. Fluoride ions in groundwater promote reaction (18.10). As a result, phosphate rock, used in the manufacture of phosphorus and phosphorus-containing fertilizers, is a mixture of $Ca_5(PO_4)_3OH$ and $Ca_5(PO_4)_3F$. As a further consequence, industrial operations that use phosphate rock as a source of phosphorus invariably generate large quantities of CaF_2 as an unwanted by-product. Ancient bones recovered by archeologists are composed almost entirely of fluorapatite. The fossilized (remineralized) bones retain the form of the original bones, including nicks, cuts, and breaks, and thus preserve a record of the life of the original animal.

Summary

18-1 Solubility Product Constant, K_{sp}—The equilibrium constant for the equilibrium between a solid ionic solute and its ions in a saturated aqueous solution is expressed through the **solubility product constant, K_{sp}** (expression 18.1, Table 18.1).

18-2 Relationship Between Solubility and K_{sp}—A solute's molarity in a saturated aqueous solution is known as its molar solubility. Molar solubility and K_{sp} are related to each other in a way that makes it possible to calculate one when the other is known.

18-3 Common-Ion Effect in Solubility Equilibria—The solubility of a slightly soluble ionic solute is greatly reduced in an aqueous solution containing an ion in common with the solubility equilibrium—a common ion.

18-4 Limitations of the K_{sp} Concept—The solubility product concept is most useful for slightly soluble ionic solutes, and especially in cases where activities can be replaced by molar concentrations. Moderately or highly soluble ionic compounds require the use of activities. The presence of common ions reduces the solubility of a slightly soluble ionic solute, generally to a significant degree.

Other factors also affect solute solubility. The presence of uncommon or diverse ions generally increases solute solubility, an effect called the **salt effect**. Solute activities, and hence solute solubilities, are strongly influenced by interionic attractions, which become especially significant at higher concentrations and for highly charged ions. Dissociation of ionic solutes may not be 100% complete, leading to the formation of **ion pairs** which act as single units, such as MgF^+ in $MgF_2(aq)$.

18-5 Criteria for Precipitation and Its Completeness—To determine whether a slightly soluble solute will precipitate from a solution, the **ion product, Q_{sp},** is compared to the solubility product constant, K_{sp}. Q_{sp} is based on the initial ion concentrations in a solution. K_{sp}, on the other hand, is based on the equilibrium ion concentrations in a saturated solution. If $Q_{sp} > K_{sp}$, precipitation will occur; if $Q_{sp} < K_{sp}$, the solution will remain unsaturated. When $Q_{sp} = K_{sp}$, the solution is just saturated.

18-6 Fractional Precipitation—A comparison of K_{sp} values is a factor in determining the feasibility of **fractional precipitation**, a process in which one ionic species is removed by precipitation while others remain in solution.

18-7 Solubility and pH—The solubility of a slightly soluble solute is affected by pH if the anion is OH^- or derived from a weak acid. The solubility increases as the pH is lowered or decreases as the pH is raised. This can be illustrated through Le Châtelier's principle. Also, an equilibrium constant for the dissolution reaction can be obtained by combining the solubility equilibrium equation and the ionization equilibrium equation of the weak electrolyte.

18-8 Equilibria Involving Complex Ions—A **complex ion** is a polyatomic ion composed of a central metal ion bonded to two or more molecules or ions called ligands. The formation of a complex ion is an equilibrium process with an equilibrium constant called the **formation constant, K_f**. In general, if the formation constant is large, the concentration of uncomplexed metal ion in equilibrium with the complex ion is very small. Complex-ion formation can render certain insoluble materials quite soluble in appropriate aqueous solutions, such as AgCl in $NH_3(aq)$. A complex ion is either a cation or an anion depending upon the particular central metal ion and the particular ligands. When a complex ion and an oppositely charged ion combine they form a **coordination compound**.

18-9 Qualitative Cation Analysis—Precipitation, acid–base, oxidation–reduction, and complex-ion formation reactions are all used extensively in **qualitative cation analysis**. Such an analysis can provide a rapid means of determining the presence or absence of certain cations in an unknown material.

Integrative Example

Lime (quicklime), CaO, is obtained from the high-temperature decomposition of limestone ($CaCO_3$). Quicklime is the cheapest source of basic substances, but it is water insoluble. It does react with water, however, producing $Ca(OH)_2$ (slaked lime). Unfortunately, $Ca(OH)_2(s)$ has limited solubility, so it cannot be used to prepare aqueous solutions of high pH.

$$Ca(OH)_2(s) \rightleftharpoons Ca^{2+}(aq) + 2\,OH^-(aq) \qquad K_{sp} = 5.5 \times 10^{-6}$$

When $Ca(OH)_2(s)$ reacts with a *soluble* carbonate, such as $Na_2CO_3(aq)$, however, the solution produced has a much higher pH. Equilibrium is displaced to the right in reaction (18.11) because $CaCO_3$ is much less soluble than $Ca(OH)_2$.

$$Ca(OH)_2(s) + CO_3^{2-}(aq) \rightleftharpoons CaCO_3(s) + 2\,OH^-(aq) \tag{18.11}$$

Assume an initial $[CO_3^{2-}] = 1.0$ M in reaction (18.11), and show that the equilibrium pH should indeed be higher than that in saturated $Ca(OH)_2(aq)$.

Strategy

(1) Determine the pH of the saturated $Ca(OH)_2(aq)$. (2) Find the equilibrium constant, K, for reaction (18.11). (3) Calculate the equilibrium $[OH^-]$ in reaction (18.11). (4) Convert $[OH^-]$ to pOH and then to pH. Compare the pH in steps (1) and (4).

Solution

Write the K_{sp} expression for $Ca(OH)_2$. Let s be the molar solubility, so the $[OH^-] = 2s$.

$$K_{sp} = [Ca^{2+}][OH^-]^2 = (s)(2s)^2 = 4s^3 = 5.5 \times 10^{-6}$$
$$s = (5.5 \times 10^{-6}/4)^{1/3} = 0.011 \text{ M}$$
$$[OH^-] = 2s = 0.022 \text{ M}$$

Calculate the pOH.

$$pOH = -\log[OH^-] = -\log 0.022$$

Determine the pH from the pOH by subtracting pOH from 14.00.

$$pOH = 1.66 \quad pH = 14.00 - pOH = 14.00 - 1.66 = 12.34$$

Combine solubility equilibrium equations for $Ca(OH)_2$ and $CaCO_3$ to obtain the net ionic equation (18.11).

$$Ca(OH)_2(s) \rightleftharpoons Ca^{2+}(aq) + 2\,OH^-(aq) \qquad K_{sp} = 5.5 \times 10^{-6}$$
$$Ca^{2+}(aq) + CO_3^{2-}(aq) \rightleftharpoons CaCO_3(s) \qquad 1/K_{sp} = 1/(2.8 \times 10^{-9})$$
$$Ca(OH)_2(s) + CO_3^{2-}(aq) \rightleftharpoons CaCO_3(s) + 2\,OH^-(aq) \tag{18.11}$$

Use the K_{sp} values of $Ca(OH)_2$ and $CaCO_3$ to obtain the overall K.

$$K = \frac{K_{sp}[Ca(OH)_2]}{K_{sp}[CaCO_3]}$$
$$K = 5.5 \times 10^{-6}/2.8 \times 10^{-9} = 2.0 \times 10^3$$

Next, calculate the equilibrium $[OH^-]$ in reaction (18.11), starting with $[CO_3^{2-}] = 1.0$ M, and proceeding in the familiar fashion to obtain a quadratic equation. The solution, to two significant figures, is

	$Ca(OH)_2(s)$ +	$CO_3^{2-}(aq)$	$\rightleftharpoons$	$CaCO_3(s)$ +	$2\,OH^-(aq)$
initial concns, M:		1.0			≈ 0
changes, M:		$-x$			$+2x$
equil concns, M:		$1.0 - x$			$2x$

$$K = \frac{[OH^-]^2}{[CO_3^{2-}]} = \frac{(2x)^2}{(1.0 - x)} = 2.0 \times 10^3$$
$$4x^2 + (2.0 \times 10^3)x - 2.0 \times 10^3 = 0$$
$$x = 1.0 \text{ M}$$

From the value of x, obtain [OH$^-$], pOH, and pH.

$$[OH^-] = 2x = 2.0 \text{ M}$$
$$pOH = -\log[OH^-] = -\log 2.0 = -0.30$$
$$pH = 14.00 - pOH = 14.00 + 0.30 = 14.30$$

Assessment

We have succeeded in showing that the solution produced by reaction (18.11) has a higher pH than that found in saturated Ca(OH)$_2$(aq), that is, a pH of 14.30 compared to 12.34. An interesting aspect of this calculation concerns solution of the quadratic equation $4x^2 + (2.0 \times 10^3)x - 2.0 \times 10^3 = 0$. By using the quadratic formula with no rounding of intermediate results, the value of $x = 0.998$, which rounds off to 1.0. Alternatively, note that by assuming that $x = 1.0$, the second and third terms of the equation cancel, yielding the result $4(1.0^2) + (2.0 \times 10^3)(1.0) - 2.0 \times 10^3 = 4.0$. We conclude that x must be very slightly less than 1.0. A value of $x = 0.998$ on the left side of the equation yields the result -0.016, very close to the 0 required for an exact solution.

Exercises   (Use data from Chapters 16 and 18 and Appendix D, as needed.)

K_{sp} and Solubility

1. Write K_{sp} expressions for the following equilibria. For example, for the reaction AgCl(s) $\rightleftharpoons$ Ag$^+$(aq) + Cl$^-$(aq), $K_{sp} = [Ag^+][Cl^-]$.
    (a) Ag$_2$SO$_4$(s) $\rightleftharpoons$ 2 Ag$^+$(aq) + SO$_4{}^{2-}$(aq)
    (b) Ra(IO$_3$)$_2$(s) $\rightleftharpoons$ Ra^{2+}(aq) + 2 IO$_3{}^-$(aq)
    (c) Ni$_3$(PO$_4$)$_2$(s) $\rightleftharpoons$ 3 Ni^{2+}(aq) + 2 PO$_4{}^{3-}$(aq)
    (d) PuO$_2$CO$_3$(s) $\rightleftharpoons$ PuO$_2{}^{2+}$(aq) + CO$_3{}^{2-}$(aq)

2. Write solubility equilibrium equations that are described by the following K_{sp} expressions. For example, $K_{sp} = [Ag^+][Cl^-]$ represents AgCl(s) $\rightleftharpoons$ Ag$^+$(aq) + Cl$^-$(aq).
    (a) $K_{sp} = [Fe^{3+}][OH^-]^3$
    (b) $K_{sp} = [BiO^+][OH^-]$
    (c) $K_{sp} = [Hg_2{}^{2+}][I^-]^2$
    (d) $K_{sp} = [Pb^{2+}]^3[AsO_4{}^{3-}]^2$

3. The following K_{sp} values are found in a handbook. Write the solubility product expression to which each one applies. For example, $K_{sp}(AgCl) = [Ag^+][Cl^-] = 1.8 \times 10^{-10}$.
    (a) $K_{sp}(CrF_3) = 6.6 \times 10^{-11}$
    (b) $K_{sp}[Au_2(C_2O_4)_3] = 1 \times 10^{-10}$
    (c) $K_{sp}[Cd_3(PO_4)_2] = 2.1 \times 10^{-33}$
    (d) $K_{sp}(SrF_2) = 2.5 \times 10^{-9}$

4. Calculate the aqueous solubility, in moles per liter, of each of the following.
    (a) BaCrO$_4$, $K_{sp} = 1.2 \times 10^{-10}$
    (b) PbBr$_2$, $K_{sp} = 4.0 \times 10^{-5}$
    (c) CeF$_3$, $K_{sp} = 8 \times 10^{-16}$
    (d) Mg$_3$(AsO$_4$)$_2$, $K_{sp} = 2.1 \times 10^{-20}$

5. Arrange the following solutes in order of increasing molar solubility in water: AgCN, AgIO$_3$, AgI, AgNO$_2$, Ag$_2$SO$_4$. Explain your reasoning.

6. Which of the following saturated aqueous solutions would have the highest [Mg^{2+}]: (a) MgCO$_3$; (b) MgF$_2$; (c) Mg$_3$(PO$_4$)$_2$? Explain.

7. Fluoridated drinking water contains about 1 part per million (ppm) of F$^-$. Is CaF$_2$ sufficiently soluble in water to be used as the source of fluoride ion for the fluoridation of drinking water? Explain.
    [*Hint:* Think of 1 ppm as signifying 1 g F$^-$ per 10^6 g solution.]

8. In the qualitative cation analysis procedure, Bi^{3+} is detected by the appearance of a white precipitate of bismuthyl hydroxide, BiOOH(s):

    $$\text{BiOOH(s)} \rightleftharpoons \text{BiO}^+\text{(aq)} + \text{OH}^-\text{(aq)}$$
    $$K_{sp} = 4 \times 10^{-10}$$

    Calculate the pH of a saturated aqueous solution of BiOOH.

9. A solution is saturated with magnesium palmitate [Mg(C$_{16}$H$_{31}$O$_2$)$_2$, a component of bathtub ring] at 50 °C. How many milligrams of magnesium palmitate will precipitate from 965 mL of this solution when it is cooled to 25 °C? For Mg(C$_{16}$H$_{31}$O$_2$)$_2$, $K_{sp} = 4.8 \times 10^{-12}$ at 50 °C and 3.3×10^{-12} at 25 °C.

10. A 725-mL sample of a saturated aqueous solution of calcium oxalate, CaC$_2$O$_4$, at 95 °C is cooled to 13 °C. How many milligrams of calcium oxalate will precipitate? For CaC$_2$O$_4$, $K_{sp} = 1.2 \times 10^{-8}$ at 95 °C and 2.7×10^{-9} at 13 °C.

11. A 25.00-mL sample of a clear *saturated* solution of PbI$_2$ requires 13.3 mL of a certain AgNO$_3$(aq) for its titration. What is the molarity of this AgNO$_3$(aq)?

    $$\text{I}^-\text{(satd PbI}_2\text{)} + \text{Ag}^+\text{(from AgNO}_3\text{)} \longrightarrow \text{AgI(s)}$$

12. A 250-mL sample of saturated CaC$_2$O$_4$(aq) requires 4.8 mL of 0.00134 M KMnO$_4$(aq) for its titration in an acidic solution. What is the value of K_{sp} for CaC$_2$O$_4$ obtained with these data? In the titration reaction, C$_2$O$_4{}^{2-}$ is oxidized to CO$_2$ and MnO$_4{}^-$ is reduced to Mn^{2+}.

13. To precipitate as Ag$_2$S(s), all the Ag$^+$ present in 338 mL of a saturated solution of AgBrO$_3$ requires 30.4 mL of H$_2$S(g) measured at 23 °C and 748 mmHg. What is K_{sp} for AgBrO$_3$?

14. Excess $Ca(OH)_2(s)$ is shaken with water to produce a saturated solution. A 50.00-mL sample of the clear satu- rated solution is withdrawn and requires 10.7 mL of 0.1032 M HCl for its titration. What is K_{sp} for $Ca(OH)_2$?

The Common-Ion Effect

15. Calculate the molar solubility of $Mg(OH)_2$ ($K_{sp} = 1.8 \times 10^{-11}$) in (a) pure water; (b) 0.0862 M $MgCl_2$; (c) 0.0355 M KOH(aq).
16. How would you expect the presence of each of the fol- lowing solutes to affect the molar solubility of $CaCO_3$ in water: (a) Na_2CO_3; (b) HCl; (c) $NaHSO_4$? Explain.
17. Describe the effects of the salts KI and $AgNO_3$ on the solubility of AgI in water.
18. Describe the effect of the salt KNO_3 on the solubility of AgI in water, and explain why it is different from the effects noted in Exercise 17.
19. A 0.150 M Na_2SO_4 solution that is saturated with Ag_2SO_4 has $[Ag^+] = 9.7 \times 10^{-3}$ M. What is the value of K_{sp} for Ag_2SO_4 obtained with these data?
20. If 100.0 mL of 0.0025 M $Na_2SO_4(aq)$ is saturated with $CaSO_4$, how many grams of $CaSO_4$ would be present in the solution?
    [Hint: Does the usual simplifying assumption hold?]
21. What $[Pb^{2+}]$ should be maintained in $Pb(NO_3)_2(aq)$ to produce a solubility of 1.5×10^{-4} mol PbI_2/L when $PbI_2(s)$ is added?

22. What $[I^-]$ should be maintained in KI(aq) to produce a solubility of 1.5×10^{-5} mol PbI_2/L when $PbI_2(s)$ is added?
23. Can the solubility of Ag_2CrO_4 be lowered to 5.0×10^{-8} mol Ag_2CrO_4/L by using CrO_4^{2-} as the common ion? by using Ag^+? Explain.
24. A handbook lists the K_{sp} values 1.1×10^{-10} for $BaSO_4$ and 5.1×10^{-9} for $BaCO_3$. When 0.50 M $Na_2CO_3(aq)$ is added to saturated $BaSO_4(aq)$, a precipitate of $BaCO_3(s)$ forms. How do you account for this fact, given that $BaCO_3$ has a larger K_{sp} than does $BaSO_4$?
25. A particular water sample that is saturated in CaF_2 has a Ca^{2+} content of 115 ppm (that is, 115 g Ca^{2+} per 10^6 g of water sample). What is the F^- ion content of the water in ppm?
26. Assume that, to be visible to the unaided eye, a pre- cipitate must weigh more than 1 mg. If you add 1.0 mL of 1.0 M NaCl(aq) to 100.0 mL of a clear saturated aqueous AgCl solution, will you be able to see AgCl(s) precipitated as a result of the common-ion effect? Explain.

Criteria for Precipitation from Solution

27. Will precipitation of $MgF_2(s)$ occur if a 22.5-mg sample of $MgCl_2 \cdot 6\,H_2O$ is added to 325 mL of 0.035 M KF?
28. Will $PbCl_2(s)$ precipitate when 155 mL of 0.016 M KCl(aq) are added to 245 mL of 0.175 M $Pb(NO_3)_2(aq)$?
29. What is the minimum pH at which $Cd(OH)_2(s)$ will precipitate from a solution that is 0.0055 M in $Cd^{2+}(aq)$?
30. What is the minimum pH at which $Cr(OH)_3(s)$ will precipitate from a solution that is 0.086 M in $Cr^{3+}(aq)$?
31. Will precipitation occur in the following cases?
    (a) 0.10 mg NaCl is added to 1.0 L of 0.10 M $AgNO_3(aq)$.
    (b) One drop (0.05 mL) of 0.10 M KBr is added to 250 mL of a saturated solution of AgCl.
    (c) One drop (0.05 mL) of 0.0150 M NaOH(aq) is added to 3.0 L of a solution with 2.0 mg Mg^{2+} per liter.
32. The electrolysis of $MgCl_2(aq)$ can be represented as

$$Mg^{2+}(aq) + 2\,Cl^-(aq) + 2\,H_2O(l) \longrightarrow$$

$$Mg^{2+}(aq) + 2\,OH^-(aq) + H_2(g) + Cl_2(g)$$

The electrolysis of a 315-mL sample of 0.185 M $MgCl_2$ is continued until 0.652 L $H_2(g)$ at 22 °C and 752 mmHg has been collected. Will $Mg(OH)_2(s)$ pre- cipitate when electrolysis is carried to this point?
    [Hint: Notice that $[Mg^{2+}]$ remains constant through- out the electrolysis, but $[OH^-]$ increases.]
33. Determine whether 1.50 g $H_2C_2O_4$ (oxalic acid: $K_{a_1} = 5.2 \times 10^{-2}$, $K_{a_2} = 5.4 \times 10^{-5}$) can be dissolved in 0.200 L of 0.150 M $CaCl_2$ without the formation of $CaC_2O_4(s)$ ($K_{sp} = 1.3 \times 10^{-9}$).
34. If 100.0 mL of a clear saturated solution of Ag_2SO_4 is added to 250.0 mL of a clear saturated solution of $PbCrO_4$, will any precipitate form?
    [Hint: Take into account the dilutions that occur. What are the possible precipitates?]

Completeness of Precipitation

35. When 200.0 mL of 0.350 M $K_2CrO_4(aq)$ are added to 200.0 mL of 0.0100 M $AgNO_3(aq)$, what percentage of the Ag^+ is left unprecipitated?
36. What percentage of the original Ag^+ remains in solu- tion when 175 mL 0.0208 M $AgNO_3$ is added to 250 mL 0.0380 M K_2CrO_4?
37. If a constant $[Cl^-] = 0.100$ M is maintained in a solu- tion in which the initial $[Pb^{2+}] = 0.065$ M, what per-

centage of the Pb^{2+} will remain in solution after $PbCl_2(s)$ precipitates? What $[Cl^-]$ should be main- tained to ensure that only 1.0% of the Pb^{2+} remains unprecipitated?
38. The ancient Romans added calcium sulfate to wine to clarify it and to remove dissolved lead. What is the maximum $[Pb^{2+}]$ that might be present in wine to which calcium sulfate has been added?

Fractional Precipitation

39. Assume that the seawater sample described in Example 18-6 contains approximately 440 g Ca^{2+} per metric ton (1 metric ton = 10^3 kg; density of seawater = 1.03 g/mL).
(a) Should $Ca(OH)_2(s)$ precipitate from seawater under the stated conditions, that is, with $[OH^-]$ = 2.0×10^{-3} M?
(b) Is the separation of Ca^{2+} from Mg^{2+} in seawater feasible?

40. Which one of the following solutions can be used to separate the cations in an aqueous solution in which $[Ba^{2+}] = [Ca^{2+}] = 0.050$ M: 0.10 M NaCl(aq), 0.05 M Na_2SO_4(aq), 0.001 M NaOH(aq), or 0.50 M Na_2CO_3(aq)? Explain why.

41. KI(aq) is slowly added to a solution with $[Pb^{2+}]$ = $[Ag^+] = 0.10$ M. For PbI_2, $K_{sp} = 7.1 \times 10^{-9}$; for AgI, $K_{sp} = 8.5 \times 10^{-17}$.
(a) Which precipitate should form first, PbI_2 or AgI?
(b) What $[I^-]$ is required for the *second* cation to begin to precipitate?
(c) What concentration of the first cation to precipitate remains in solution at the point at which the second cation begins to precipitate?
(d) Can Pb^{2+}(aq) and Ag^+(aq) be effectively separated by fractional precipitation of their iodides?

42. A solution is 0.010 M in both CrO_4^{2-} and SO_4^{2-}. To this solution, 0.50 M $Pb(NO_3)_2$(aq) is slowly added.
(a) Which anion will precipitate first from solution?
(b) What is $[Pb^{2+}]$ at the point at which the second anion begins to precipitate?
(c) Are the two anions effectively separated by this fractional precipitation?

43. An aqueous solution that 2.00 M in $AgNO_3$ is slowly added from a buret to an aqueous solution that is 0.0100 M in Cl^- and 0.250 M in I^-.
(a) Which ion, Cl^- or I^-, is the first to precipitate?
(b) When the second ion begins to precipitate, what is the remaining concentration of the first ion?
(c) Is the separation of Cl^- and I^- feasible by fractional precipitation in this solution?

44. $AgNO_3$(aq) is slowly added to a solution that is 0.250 M NaCl and also 0.0022 M KBr.
(a) Which anion will precipitate first, Cl^- or Br^-?
(b) What is $[Ag^+]$ at the point at which the second anion begins to precipitate?
(c) Can the Cl^- and Br^- be separated effectively by this fractional precipitation?

Solubility and pH

45. Which of the following solids is (are) more soluble in an acidic solution than in pure water: KCl, $MgCO_3$, FeS, $Ca(OH)_2$, or C_6H_5COOH? Explain.

46. Which of the following solids is (are) more soluble in a basic solution than in pure water: $BaSO_4$, $H_2C_2O_4$, $Fe(OH)_3$, $NaNO_3$, or MnS? Explain.

47. The solubility of $Mg(OH)_2$ in a particular buffer solution is 0.65 g/L. What must be the pH of the buffer solution?

48. To 0.350 L of 0.150 M NH_3 is added 0.150 L of 0.100 M $MgCl_2$. How many grams of $(NH_4)_2SO_4$ should be present to prevent precipitation of $Mg(OH)_2$(s)?

49. For the equilibrium

$$Al(OH)_3(s) \rightleftharpoons Al^{3+}(aq) + 3\,OH^-(aq)$$

$$K_{sp} = 1.3 \times 10^{-33}$$

(a) What is the *minimum pH* at which $Al(OH)_3$(s) will precipitate from a solution that is 0.075 M in Al^{3+}?
(b) A solution has $[Al^{3+}] = 0.075$ M and $[HC_2H_3O_2]$ = 1.00 M. What is the maximum quantity of $NaC_2H_3O_2$ that can be added to 250.0 mL of this solution before precipitation of $Al(OH)_3$(s) begins?

50. Will the following precipitates form under the given conditions?
(a) PbI_2(s), from a solution that is 1.05×10^{-3} M HI, 1.05×10^{-3} M NaI, and 1.1×10^{-3} M $Pb(NO_3)_2$.
(b) $Mg(OH)_2$(s), from 2.50 L of 0.0150 M $Mg(NO_3)_2$ to which is added 1 drop (0.05 mL) of 6.00 M NH_3.
(c) $Al(OH)_3$(s) from a solution that is 0.010 M in Al^{3+}, 0.010 M $HC_2H_3O_2$, and 0.010 M $NaC_2H_3O_2$.

Complex-Ion Equilibria

51. $PbCl_2$(s) is considerably more soluble in HCl(aq) than in pure water, but its solubility in HNO_3(aq) is not much different from what it is in water. Explain this difference in behavior.

52. Which of the following would be most effective, and which would be least effective, in reducing the concentration of the complex ion $[Zn(NH_3)_4]^{2+}$ in a solution: HCl, NH_3, or NH_4Cl? Explain your choices.

53. In a solution that is 0.0500 M in $[Cu(CN)_4]^{3-}$ and 0.80 M in free CN^-, the concentration of Cu^+ is 6.1×10^{-32} M. Calculate K_f of $[Cu(CN)_4]^{3-}$.

$$Cu^+(aq) + 4\,CN^-(aq) \rightleftharpoons [Cu(CN)_4]^{3-}(aq) \quad K_f = ?$$

54. Calculate $[Cu^{2+}]$ in a 0.10 M $CuSO_4$(aq) solution that is also 6.0 M in free NH_3.

$$Cu^{2+}(aq) + 4\,NH_3(aq) \rightleftharpoons [Cu(NH_3)_4]^{2+}(aq)$$

$$K_f = 1.1 \times 10^{13}$$

55. Can the following ion concentrations be maintained in the same solution without a precipitate forming: $[[Ag(S_2O_3)_2]^{3-}] = 0.048$ M, $[S_2O_3^{2-}] = 0.76$ M, and $[I^-] = 2.0$ M?

56. A solution is 0.10 M in *free* NH_3, 0.10 M in NH_4Cl, and 0.015 M in $[Cu(NH_3)_4]^{2+}$. Will $Cu(OH)_2$(s) precipitate from this solution? K_{sp} of $Cu(OH)_2$ is 2.2×10^{-20}.

57. A 0.10-mol sample of $AgNO_3(s)$ is dissolved in 1.00 L of 1.00 M NH_3. How many grams of KI can be dissolved in this solution without a precipitate of $AgI(s)$ forming?

58. A solution is prepared that has $[NH_3] = 1.00$ M and $[Cl^-] = 0.100$ M. How many grams of $AgNO_3$ can be dissolved in 1.00 L of this solution without a precipitate of $AgCl(s)$ forming?

Precipitation and Solubilities of Metal Sulfides

59. Can Fe^{2+} and Mn^{2+} be separated by precipitating $FeS(s)$ and not $MnS(s)$? Assume $[Fe^{2+}] = [Mn^{2+}] = [H_2S] = 0.10$ M. Choose a $[H_3O^+]$ that ensures maximum precipitation of $FeS(s)$ but not $MnS(s)$. Will the separation be complete? For FeS, $K_{spa} = 6 \times 10^2$; for MnS, $K_{spa} = 3 \times 10^7$.

60. A solution is 0.05 M in Cu^{2+}, in Hg^{2+}, and in Mn^{2+}. Which sulfides will precipitate if the solution is made to be 0.10 M $H_2S(aq)$ and 0.010 M $HCl(aq)$? For CuS, $K_{spa} = 6 \times 10^{-16}$; for HgS, $K_{spa} = 2 \times 10^{-32}$; for MnS, $K_{spa} = 3 \times 10^7$.

61. A buffer solution is 0.25 M $HC_2H_3O_2$–0.15 M $NaC_2H_3O_2$, saturated in H_2S (0.10 M), and with $[Mn^{2+}] = 0.15$ M.
    (a) Show that MnS will *not* precipitate from this solution (for MnS, $K_{spa} = 3 \times 10^7$).

    (b) Which buffer component would you increase in concentration, and to what minimum value, to ensure that precipitation of MnS(s) begins? Assume that the concentration of the other buffer component is held constant.
    [*Hint:* Recall equation (18.8).]

62. The following expressions pertain to the precipitation or dissolving of metal sulfides. Use information about the qualitative cation analysis scheme to predict whether a reaction proceeds to a significant extent in the forward direction and what the products are in each case.
    (a) $Cu^{2+}(aq) + H_2S$ (satd aq) $\longrightarrow$
    (b) $Mg^{2+}(aq) + H_2S$ (satd aq) $\xrightarrow{0.3\,M\,HCl}$
    (c) $PbS(s) + HCl$ (0.3 M) $\longrightarrow$
    (d) $ZnS(s) + HNO_3(aq) \longrightarrow$

Qualitative Cation Analysis

63. Suppose you did a group 1 qualitative cation analysis and treated the chloride precipitate with $NH_3(aq)$ without first treating it with hot water. What might you observe, and what valid conclusions could you reach about cations present, cations absent, and cations in doubt?

64. Show that in qualitative cation analysis group 1, if you obtain 1.00 mL of saturated $PbCl_2(aq)$ at 25 °C, sufficient Pb^{2+} should be present to produce a precipitate of $PbCrO_4(s)$. Assume that you use 1 drop (0.05 mL) of 1.0 M K_2CrO_4 for the test.

65. The addition of $HCl(aq)$ to a solution containing several different cations produces a white precipitate. The filtrate is removed and treated with $H_2S(aq)$ in 0.3 M

HCl. No precipitate forms. Which of the following conclusions is (are) valid? Explain.
    (a) Ag^+ or Hg_2^{2+} (or both) is probably present.
    (b) Mg^{2+} is probably not present.
    (c) Pb^{2+} is probably not present.
    (d) Fe^{2+} is probably not present.

66. Write net ionic equations for the following qualitative cation analysis procedures.
    (a) precipitation of $PbCl_2(s)$ from a solution containing Pb^{2+}
    (b) dissolution of $Zn(OH)_2(s)$ in a solution of $NaOH(aq)$
    (c) dissolution of $Fe(OH)_3(s)$ in $HCl(aq)$
    (d) precipitation of $CuS(s)$ from an acidic solution of Cu^{2+} and H_2S

Integrative and Advanced Exercises

(Use data from Chapters 16 and 18 and Appendix D as needed.)

67. A particular water sample has 131 ppm of $CaSO_4$ (131 g $CaSO_4$ per 10^6 g water). If this water is boiled in a teakettle, approximately what fraction of the water must be evaporated before $CaSO_4(s)$ begins to precipitate? Assume that the solubility of $CaSO_4(s)$ does not change much in the temperature range 0 to 100 °C.

68. A handbook lists the solubility of $CaHPO_4$ as 0.32 g $CaHPO_4 \cdot 2\,H_2O/L$ and lists $K_{sp} = 1 \times 10^{-7}$.

$$CaHPO_4(s) \rightleftharpoons Ca^{2+}(aq) + HPO_4^{2-}(aq)$$

$$K_{sp} = 1 \times 10^{-7}$$

(a) Are these data consistent? (That is, are the molar solubilities the same when derived in two different ways?)
(b) If there is a discrepancy, how do you account for it?

69. A 50.0-mL sample of 0.0152 M $Na_2SO_4(aq)$ is added to 50.0 mL of 0.0125 M $Ca(NO_3)_2(aq)$. What percentage of the Ca^{2+} remains unprecipitated?

70. What percentage of the Ba^{2+} in solution is precipitated as $BaCO_3(s)$ if equal volumes of 0.0020 M $Na_2CO_3(aq)$ and 0.0010 M $BaCl_2(aq)$ are mixed?

71. Determine the molar solubility of lead(II) azide, $Pb(N_3)_2$, in a buffer solution with $pH = 3.00$, given that

$$Pb(N_3)_2(s) \rightleftharpoons Pb^{2+}(aq) + 2\,N_3^-(aq)$$

$$K_{sp} = 2.5 \times 10^{-9}$$

$$HN_3(aq) + H_2O(l) \rightleftharpoons H_3O^+(aq) + N_3^-(aq)$$

$$K_a = 1.9 \times 10^{-5} \times$$

72. Calculate the molar solubility of $Mg(OH)_2$ in 1.00 M $NH_4Cl(aq)$.

73. The chief compound in marble is $CaCO_3$. Marble has been widely used for statues and ornamental work on buildings, including the Taj Mahal shown below (see also page 699). However, marble is readily attacked by acids. Determine the solubility of marble (that is, $[Ca^{2+}]$ in a saturated solution) in **(a)** normal rainwater of $pH = 5.6$; **(b)** acid rainwater of $pH = 4.20$. Assume that the overall reaction that occurs is

$$CaCO_3(s) + H_3O^+(aq) \rightleftharpoons$$

$$Ca^{2+}(aq) + HCO_3^-(aq) + H_2O(l)$$

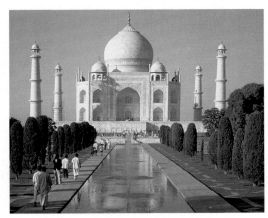

74. What is the solubility of MnS, in grams per liter, in a buffer solution that is 0.100 M $HC_2H_3O_2$ − 0.500 M $NaC_2H_3O_2$? For MnS, $K_{spa} = 3 \times 10^7$.

75. Write net ionic equations for each of the following observations.
    (a) When concentrated $CaCl_2(aq)$ is added to $Na_2HPO_4(aq)$, a white precipitate forms that is 38.7% Ca by mass.
    (b) When a piece of dry ice, $CO_2(s)$, is placed in a clear dilute solution of limewater $[Ca(OH)_2(aq)]$, bubbles of gas evolve. At first, a white precipitate forms, but then it redissolves.

76. Concerning the reactions described in Exercise 75(b),
    (a) Will the same observations be made if $Ca(OH)_2(aq)$ is replaced by $CaCl_2(aq)$? Explain.

    (b) Show that the white precipitate will redissolve if the $Ca(OH)_2(aq)$ is about 0.005 M, but not if the solution is saturated.

77. Reaction (18.11), described in the Integrative Example, is called a *carbonate transposition*. In such a reaction, anions of a slightly soluble compound (for example, hydroxides and sulfates) are obtained in a sufficient concentration in aqueous solution that they can be identified by qualitative analysis tests. Suppose that 3 M Na_2CO_3 is used and that an anion concentration of 0.050 M is sufficient for its detection. Predict whether carbonate transposition will be effective for detecting **(a)** SO_4^{2-} from $BaSO_4(s)$; **(b)** Cl^- from $AgCl(s)$; **(c)** F^- from $MgF_2(s)$.

78. For the titration in Example 18-7, verify the assertion in the Are You Wondering feature on page 759 that $[Ag^+]$ increases very rapidly between the point at which AgBr has finished precipitating and Ag_2CrO_4 is about to begin.

79. Aluminum compounds are soluble in acidic solution, where aluminum(III) exists as the complex ion $[Al(H_2O)_6]^{3+}$, which is generally represented simply as $Al^{3+}(aq)$. They are also soluble in basic solutions, where the aluminum(III) is present as the complex ion $[Al(OH)_4]^-$. At certain intermediate pH values, the concentration of aluminum(III) that can exist in solution is at a minimum. Thus, a plot of the total concentration of aluminum(III) in solution as a function of pH yields a U-shaped curve. Demonstrate that this is the case with a few calculations.

80. The solubility of AgCN(s) in 0.200 M $NH_3(aq)$ is 8.8×10^{-6} mol/L. Calculate K_{sp} for AgCN.

81. The solubility of $CdCO_3(s)$ in 1.00 M KI(aq) is 1.2×10^{-3} mol/L. Given that K_{sp} of $CdCO_3$ is 5.2×10^{-12}, what is K_f for $[CdI_4]^{2-}$?

82. Use K_{sp} for $PbCl_2$ and K_f for $[PbCl_3]^-$ to determine the molar solubility of $PbCl_2$ in 0.10 M HCl(aq).
    [*Hint:* What is the total concentration of lead species in solution?]

83. A mixture of $PbSO_4(s)$ and $PbS_2O_3(s)$ is shaken with pure water until a saturated solution is formed. Both solids remain in excess. What is $[Pb^{2+}]$ in the saturated solution? For $PbSO_4$, $K_{sp} = 1.6 \times 10^{-8}$; for PbS_2O_3, $K_{sp} = 4.0 \times 10^{-7}$.

84. Use the method of Exercise 83 to determine $[Pb^{2+}]$ in a saturated solution in contact with a mixture of $PbCl_2(s)$ and $PbBr_2(s)$.

85. A 2.50-g sample of $Ag_2SO_4(s)$ is added to a beaker containing 0.150 L of 0.025 M $BaCl_2$.
    (a) Write an equation for any reaction that occurs.
    (b) Describe the final contents of the beaker—that is, the masses of any precipitates present and the concentrations of the ions in solution.

Feature Problems

86. In an experiment to measure K_{sp} of $CaSO_4$ [Masterman, D. *J. Chem. Educ.* **1987**: *64*, 409], a saturated solution of $CaSO_4(aq)$ is poured into the ion-exchange column pictured (and described in Chapter 21). As the solution passes through the column, Ca^{2+} is retained by the ion-exchange medium and H_3O^+ is released; two H_3O^+ ions appear in the effluent solution for every Ca^{2+} ion. As the drawing suggests, a 25.00-mL sample is added to the column, and the effluent is collected and diluted to 100.0 mL in a volumetric flask.

A 10.00-mL portion of the diluted solution requires 8.25 mL of 0.0105 M NaOH for its titration. Use these data to obtain a value of K_{sp} for $CaSO_4$.

87. In the *Mohr titration*, $Cl^-(aq)$ is titrated with $AgNO_3(aq)$ in solutions that are at about pH = 7. Thus, it is suitable for determining the chloride ion content of drinking water. The indicator used in the titration is $K_2CrO_4(aq)$. A red-brown precipitate of $Ag_2CrO_4(s)$ forms after all the Cl^- has precipitated. The titration reaction is $Ag^+(aq) + Cl^-(aq) \longrightarrow AgCl(s)$. At the equivalence point of the titration, the titration mixture consists of $AgCl(s)$ and a solution having neither Ag^+ nor Cl^- in excess. Also, no $Ag_2CrO_4(s)$ is present, but it forms immediately after the equivalence point.
    (a) How many milliliters of 0.01000 M $AgNO_3(aq)$ are required to titrate 100.0 mL of a municipal water sample having 29.5 mg Cl^-/L?
    (b) What is $[Ag^+]$ at the equivalence point of the Mohr titration?
    (c) What is $[CrO_4^{2-}]$ in the titration mixture to meet the requirement of no precipitation of $Ag_2CrO_4(s)$ until immediately after the equivalence point?
    (d) Describe the effect on the results of the titration if $[CrO_4^{2-}]$ were (1) greater than that calculated in part (c) or (2) less than that calculated?

(e) Do you think the Mohr titration would work if the reactants were exchanged—that is, with $Cl^-(aq)$ as the titrant and $Ag^+(aq)$ in the sample being analyzed? Explain.

88. The accompanying drawing suggests a series of manipulations starting with saturated $Mg(OH)_2(aq)$. Calculate $[Mg^{2+}(aq)]$ at each of the lettered stages.
    (a) 0.500 L of saturated $Mg(OH)_2(aq)$ is in contact with $Mg(OH)_2(s)$.
    (b) 0.500 L of H_2O is added to the 0.500 L of solution in part (a), and the solution is vigorously stirred. Undissolved $Mg(OH)_2(s)$ remains.
    (c) 100.0 mL of the clear solution in part (b) is removed and added to 0.500 L of 0.100 M HCl(aq).
    (d) 25.00 mL of the clear solution in part (b) is removed and added to 250.0 mL of 0.065 M $MgCl_2(aq)$.
    (e) 50.00 mL of the clear solution in part (b) is removed and added to 150.0 mL of 0.150 M KOH(aq).

Self-Assessment Exercises

89. In your own words, define the following terms or symbols: (a) K_{sp}; (b) K_f; (c) Q_{sp}; (d) complex ion.
90. Briefly describe each of the following ideas, methods, or phenomena: (a) common-ion effect in solubility equilibrium; (b) fractional precipitation; (c) ion-pair formation; (d) qualitative cation analysis.
91. Explain the important distinction between each pair of terms: (a) solubility and solubility product constant; (b) common-ion effect and salt effect; (c) ion pair and ion product.
92. Pure water is saturated with slightly soluble PbI_2. Which of the following is a correct statement concerning the lead ion concentration in the solution, and what is wrong with the others? (a) $[Pb^{2+}] = [I^-]$; (b) $[Pb^{2+}] = K_{sp}$ of PbI_2; (c) $[Pb^{2+}] = \sqrt{K_{sp}}$ of PbI_2; (d) $[Pb^{2+}] = 0.5[I^-]$.

93. Adding 1.85 g Na_2SO_4 to 500.0 mL of saturated aqueous $BaSO_4$: (a) reduces $[Ba^{2+}]$; (b) reduces $[SO_4^{2-}]$; (c) increases the solubility of $BaSO_4$; (d) has no effect.
94. The slightly soluble solute Ag_2CrO_4 is *most* soluble in (a) pure water; (b) 0.10 M K_2CrO_4; (c) 0.25 M KNO_3; (d) 0.40 M $AgNO_3$.
95. Cu^{2+} and Pb^{2+} are both present in an aqueous solution. To precipitate one of the ions and leave the other in solution, add (a) $H_2S(aq)$; (b) $H_2SO_4(aq)$; (c) $HNO_3(aq)$; (d) $NH_4NO_3(aq)$.
96. All but two of the following solutions yield a precipitate when the solution is also made 2.00 M in NH_3. Those two are (a) $MgCl_2(aq)$; (b) $FeCl_3(aq)$; (c) $(NH_4)_2SO_4(aq)$; (d) $Cu(NO_3)_2(aq)$; (e) $Al_2(SO_4)_3(aq)$.
97. To increase the molar solubility of $CaCO_3(s)$ in a saturated aqueous solution, add (a) ammonium chloride; (b) sodium carbonate; (c) ammonia; (d) more water.

98. The best way to ensure complete precipitation from saturated $H_2S(aq)$ of a metal ion, M^{2+}, as its sulfide, MS(s), is to **(a)** add an acid; **(b)** increase $[H_2S]$ in the solution; **(c)** raise the pH; **(d)** heat the solution.

99. Which of the following solids are likely to be more soluble in acidic solution and which in basic solution? Which are likely to have a solubility that is independent of pH? Explain. **(a)** $H_2C_2O_4$; **(b)** $MgCO_3$; **(c)** CdS; **(d)** KCl; **(e)** $NaNO_3$; **(f)** $Ca(OH)_2$.

100. Both Mg^{2+} and Cu^{2+} are present in the same aqueous solution. Which of the following reagents would work best in separating these ions, precipitating one and leaving the other in solution: NaOH(aq), HCl(aq), $NH_4Cl(aq)$, or $NH_3(aq)$? Explain your choice.

101. Will $Al(OH)_3(s)$ precipitate from a buffer solution that is 0.45 M $HC_2H_3O_2$ and 0.35 M $NaC_2H_3O_2$ and also 0.275 M in $Al^{3+}(aq)$? For $Al(OH)_3$, $K_{sp} = 1.3 \times 10^{-33}$; for $HC_2H_3O_2$, $K_a = 1.8 \times 10^{-5}$.

102. Will AgI(s) precipitate from a solution with $[[Ag(CN)_2]^-] = 0.012$ M, $[CN^-] = 1.05$ M, and $[I^-] = 2.0$ M? For AgI, $K_{sp} = 8.5 \times 10^{-17}$; for $[Ag(CN)_2]^-$, $K_f = 5.6 \times 10^{18}$.

103. Without performing detailed calculations, indicate whether either of the following compounds is appreciably soluble in $NH_3(aq)$: **(a)** CuS, $K_{sp} = 6.3 \times 10^{-36}$; **(b)** $CuCO_3$, $K_{sp} = 1.4 \times 10^{-10}$. Also use the fact that K_f for $[Cu(NH_3)_4]^{2+}$ is 1.1×10^{13}.

104. Appendix E describes a useful study aid known as concept mapping. Using the methods presented in Appendix E, construct a concept map that links the various factors affecting the solubility of slightly soluble solutes.

 ## eMedia Exercises

105. In the **Common-Ion Effect** animation (*Activebook 18-3*), the concentration of the solvated ions is affected by the addition of a second ionic salt. Identify other salts that would alter the equilibrium concentrations, and explain how they do so.

106. The formation of AgI is depicted in the **Precipitation Reactions** movie (*Activebook 18-5*). **(a)** How do you recognize this as a precipitate? **(b)** From what you observe in the movie, what do you learn about the relative concentrations of the Ag^+ and I^- ions in the initial solution?

107. **(a)** Write an ionic equilibrium constant expression for the net ionic reaction seen in the **Dissolution of $Mg(OH)_2$ by Acid** animation (*Activebook 18-7*). **(b)** From this relationship, describe in qualitative terms the pH dependence of the solubility of $Mg(OH)_2$.

108. Use the data represented in the **Solubility Products of Ionic Compounds** activity (*Activebook 18-9*) to write a specific set of precipitation rules for the aluminum cation.

 ## eLaboratory Exercises

These exercises allow students to apply the concepts and skills for this chapter in the simulated laboratory of Virtual ChemLab. Worksheets for each of these exercises are found in the Virtual ChemLab Workbook in your MediaPak.

109. *(VCL 18-1) Identification of Cations in Solution: Flame Tests*
The process of determining the composition of a sample by conducting chemical tests is called qualitative analysis. By using the appropriate tests and applying logic, the identities of the ions present in an unknown solution can be determined. A qualitative analysis scheme is typically made up of a systematic set of chemical reactions where a certain subset of the ions present in the solution are selectively precipitated and removed. The colors of the precipitates and solutions provide the means to identify the ions present. Flame tests are also used to identify certain ions that are difficult to identify chemically. In this assignment you will learn how flame tests are used to identify the cations Na^+ and K^+. As you complete this analysis, remember that careful observation and logical reasoning are the keys to a successful qualitative analysis.

110. *(VCL 18-2) Identification of Cations in Solution: Ag^+, Hg_2^{2+}, Pb^{2+}*
In this assignment you will learn the basics of a qualitative analysis scheme by performing an analysis on a mixture of Ag^+, Hg_2^{2+}, and Pb^{2+}.

111. *(VCL 18-3) Identification of Cations in Solution: Co^{2+}, Cr^{2+}, Cu^{2+}*
In this assignment you will learn the basics of a qualitative analysis scheme by performing an analysis on a mixture of Co^{2+}, Cr^{3+}, and Cu^{2+}.

112. *(VCL 18-4) Identification of Cations in Solution: Ba^{2+}, Sr^{2+}, Ca^{2+}, Mg^{2+}*
In this assignment you will need to develop your own qualitative analysis scheme to separate and identify the group 2 cations Ba^{2+}, Sr^{2+}, Ca^{2+}, and Mg^{2+}.

113. *(VCL 18-5) Identification of Cations in Solution: Co^{2+}, Cu^{2+}, Ni^{2+}*
In this assignment you will need to develop your own qualitative analysis scheme to separate and identify the transition-metal cations Co^{2+}, Cu^{2+}, and Ni^{2+}.

19 SPONTANEOUS CHANGE: ENTROPY AND FREE ENERGY

CONTENTS

Thermodynamics originated in the early nineteenth century in attempts to improve the efficiency of steam engines. However, the laws of thermodynamics are widely useful throughout the field of chemistry and in biology as well, as we discover in this chapter.

In Chapter 15, we noted that the reaction of nitrogen and oxygen gases, which does not occur appreciably in the forward direction at room temperature, produces significant equilibrium amounts of NO(g) at *high* temperatures.

$$N_2(g) + O_2(g) \rightleftharpoons 2\,NO(g)$$

Another reaction involving oxides of nitrogen is the conversion of NO(g) to NO_2(g):

$$2\,NO(g) + O_2(g) \rightleftharpoons 2\,NO_2(g)$$

This reaction, unlike the first, yields its greatest equilibrium amounts of NO_2(g) at *low* temperatures.

What is there about these two reactions that causes the forward reaction of one to be favored at high temperatures but the forward reaction of the other to be favored at low temperatures? Our primary objective in this chapter is to develop concepts to help us answer questions like this. This chapter, taken together with ideas from Chapter 7, shows the great power of thermodynamics to provide explanations of many chemical phenomena.

19-1 SPONTANEITY: THE MEANING OF SPONTANEOUS CHANGE

Most of us have played with spring-wound toys, whether a toy automobile, top, or music box. In every case, once the wound-up toy is released, it keeps running until the stored energy in the spring has been released; then the toy stops. The toy never rewinds itself. Human intervention is necessary (winding by hand). The running down of a wound-up spring is an example of a *spontaneous* process. The rewinding of the spring is a *nonspontaneous* process. Let's explore the scientific meaning of these two terms.

A **spontaneous process** is a process that occurs in a system left to itself; once started, no action from outside the system (external action) is necessary to make the process continue. Conversely, a **nonspontaneous process** will not occur *unless* some external action is continuously applied. Consider the rusting of an iron pipe exposed to the atmosphere. Although the process occurs only slowly, it does so continuously. As a result, the amount of iron decreases and the amount of rust increases until a final state of equilibrium is reached in which essentially all the iron has been converted to iron(III) oxide. We say that the reaction

$$4 \, Fe(s) + 3 \, O_2(g) \longrightarrow 2 \, Fe_2O_3(s)$$

is *spontaneous*. Now consider the reverse situation: the extraction of pure iron from iron(III) oxide. We should not say that the process is impossible, but it is certainly *nonspontaneous*. In fact, this nonspontaneous reverse process is involved in the manufacture of iron from iron ore.

We will consider specific quantitative criteria for spontaneous change later in the chapter, but even now we can identify some spontaneous processes intuitively. For example, in the neutralization of NaOH(aq) with HCl(aq), the net change that occurs is

$$H_3O^+(aq) + OH^-(aq) \longrightarrow 2 \, H_2O(l)$$

There is very little tendency for the reverse reaction (self-ionization) to occur, so the neutralization reaction is a spontaneous reaction. The melting of ice, however, is spontaneous at temperatures above 0 °C but nonspontaneous below 0 °C.

From our discussion of spontaneity to this point, we can reach these conclusions.

- If a process is spontaneous, the reverse process is nonspontaneous.

- Both spontaneous and nonspontaneous processes are possible, but only spontaneous processes will occur *without intervention*. Nonspontaneous processes require the system to be acted on by an external agent.

We would like to do more, however. We want to be able to predict whether the forward or the reverse direction is the direction of spontaneous change in a process, so we need a criterion for spontaneous change. To begin, let's look to mechanical systems for a clue. A ball rolls downhill, and water flows to a lower level. A common feature of these processes is that *potential energy decreases*.

For chemical systems, the property analogous to the potential energy of a mechanical system is the internal energy (U) or the closely related property enthalpy (H). In the 1870s, P. Berthelot and J. Thomsen proposed that the direction of spontaneous change is the direction in which the enthalpy of a system decreases. In a system in which enthalpy decreases, heat is given off by the system to the surroundings. Bertholet and Thomsen concluded that exothermic reactions should be spontaneous. In fact, many exothermic processes are spontaneous, but some are not. Also, some endothermic reactions *are* spontaneous.

▲ When the spring powering this mechanical toy unwinds, the toy stops moving. The spring cannot spontaneously rewind.

◀ Spontaneous: "proceeding from natural feeling or native tendency without external constraint...; developing without apparent external influence, force, cause, or treatment." *Merriam-Webster's Collegiate Dictionary*, on-line, 2000.

 The amount of steel destroyed each year by rust is approximately equal to 10% of the world's annual production.

 Spontaneous vs Nonspontaneous activity

▲ The melting of an ice cube occurs spontaneously at temperatures above 0 °C.

✓ No change takes place for a system at equilibrium until some mechanism is provided to couple it to the surroundings. For example, gasoline is stable until an engine converts its chemical energy to heat and work. The engine provides the coupling to the surroundings.

(a) Initial condition

(b) After expansion into vacuum

▲ **FIGURE 19-1**
Expansion of an ideal gas into a vacuum
(a) Initially, an ideal gas is confined to the bulb on the left at 1.00 atm pressure. **(b)** When the stopcock is opened, the gas expands into the identical bulb on the right. The final condition is one in which the gas is equally distributed between the two bulbs at a pressure of 0.50 atm.

KEEP IN MIND ▶

that U and H are related as follows: $H = U + PV$, and $\Delta H = \Delta U + \Delta(PV)$. For a fixed amount of an ideal gas at a constant temperature, $PV = $ constant, $\Delta(PV) = 0$, and $\Delta H = \Delta U$.

Mixing of Gases activity

Jansen, Michael P. "The Cost of Converting a Gasoline-Powered Vehicle to Propane. A Practical Review Problem for Senior High School or Introductory Chemistry." *J. Chem. Educ.* **2000:** *77,* 1578 (December 2000).

Take two dice and show that rolling a 7 is most common (1/6 chance) and a 2 or 12 least common (1/36). For 10 dice, the chance of all ten showing a 1 is 1 in 60 million! The random roll is most likely and dominates the process. Use this to convince students that the random states dominate and the ordered states can be ignored.

Thus, we cannot predict whether a process is spontaneous from its enthalpy change alone. Here are three examples of spontaneous, *endothermic* processes.

- the melting of ice at room temperature
- the evaporation of liquid diethyl ether from an open beaker
- the dissolving of ammonium nitrate in water

We will have to look to thermodynamic functions other than enthalpy change (ΔH) as criteria for spontaneous change.

CONCEPT ASSESSMENT ✔

Is it correct to say that a spontaneous process is a fast process and a nonspontaneous process is a very slow one? Explain.

19-2 THE CONCEPT OF ENTROPY

To continue our search for criteria for spontaneous change, consider Figure 19-1, which depicts two identical glass bulbs joined by a stopcock. Initially, the bulb on the left contains an ideal gas at 1.00 atm pressure, and the bulb on the right is evacuated. When the valve is opened, the gas immediately expands into the evacuated bulb. After this expansion, the molecules are dispersed throughout the apparatus, with essentially equal numbers of molecules in both bulbs and a pressure of 0.50 atm. What causes this spontaneous expansion of the gas at a constant temperature?

One of the characteristics of an ideal gas is that its internal energy (U) does not depend on the gas pressure, but only on the temperature. Therefore, in this expansion $\Delta U = 0$. Also, the enthalpy change is zero: $\Delta H = 0$. This means that the expansion is not caused by the system dropping to a lower energy state. A convenient mental image to "explain" the expansion is that the gas molecules tend to spread out into the larger volume available to them at the reduced pressure. A more fundamental description of the underlying cause is that, for the same total energy, in the expanded volume there are more available translational energy levels among which the gas molecules can be distributed. The tendency is for the energy of the system to spread out over a larger number of energy levels.

A similar situation—the mixing of ideal gases—is depicted in Figure 19-2. In this case, the two bulbs initially are filled with different ideal gases at 1.00 atm. When the stopcock is opened, the gases mix. The resulting change is essentially that of the expansion of the ideal gas pictured in Figure 19-1, but twice over. That is, each gas expands into the new volume available to it, without regard for the other gas (recall Dalton's law of partial pressures, page 198). Again, each expanded gas has more translational energy levels available to its molecules—the energy of the system has spread out. And again, the internal energy and enthalpy of the system are not changed by the expansion.

ENTROPY

The thermodynamic property related to the way in which the energy of a system is distributed among the available microscopic energy levels is called **entropy**.

The greater the number of configurations of the microscopic particles (atoms, ions, molecules) among the energy levels in a particular state of a system, the greater the entropy of the system.

Entropy is denoted by the symbol S. Like internal energy and enthalpy, entropy is a function of state (see page 239). It has a unique value for a system whose temperature, pressure, and composition are specified. The **entropy change**, ΔS, is the difference in entropy between two states of a system, and it also has a unique value.

In the gas expansion of Figure 19-1, the entropy of the gas *increases* and $\Delta S > 0$. In the mixing of gases as carried out in Figure 19-2, entropy also increases, a fact that we can represent symbolically.

$$A(g) + B(g) \longrightarrow \text{mixture of A(g) and B(g)}$$

$$\Delta S = S_{\text{mix of gases}} - [S_{A(g)} + S_{B(g)}] > 0$$

Because both of these expansions occur spontaneously and neither is accompanied by a change in internal energy or enthalpy, it seems possible that *increases in entropy underlie spontaneous processes*. This is a proposition that we will have to examine more closely later, but let's accept it tentatively for now.

THE BOLTZMANN EQUATION FOR ENTROPY

The connection between macroscopic changes, such as the mixing of gases, and the microscopic nature of matter was enunciated by Ludwig Boltzmann. The conceptual breakthrough that Boltzmann made was to associate the number of energy levels in the system with the number of ways of arranging the particles (atoms, ions, or molecules) in these energy levels. The microscopic energy levels are also called *states*, and the particular way a number of particles is distributed among these states is called a *microstate*. The more states a given number of particles can occupy, the more microstates the system has. The more microstates that exist, the greater the entropy. Boltzmann derived the relationship

$$S = k \ln W \tag{19.1}$$

where S is the entropy, k is the Boltzmann constant, and W is the number of microstates. We can think of the Boltzmann constant as the gas constant per molecule; that is, $k = R/N_A$. (Although we didn't specifically introduce k in the discussion of kinetic–molecular theory, R/N_A appears in equation 6.21.) The number of microstates, W, is the number of ways that the atoms or molecules can be positioned in the states available and still give rise to the same total energy. Each permissible arrangement of the particles constitutes one of the microstates, so W is the total number of microstates that correspond to the same energy.

How can we use Boltzmann's equation to think about the distribution of microscopic particles among the energy levels of a system? Let's consider again the particle-in-a-box model for a matter wave (page 301). Specifically, we can use the equation $E_W = n^2 h^2 / 8mL^2$ to calculate a few energy levels for a matter wave in a one-dimensional box. Representative energy levels are shown in the energy-level diagrams in Figure 19-3a for a particle in boxes of lengths L, $2L$, and $3L$. We see the following relationship between the length of the box and the number of levels: L, *three* levels; $2L$, *six* levels; and $3L$, *nine* levels. As the boundaries of the box are expanded, the number of available energy levels increases and the separation between levels decreases. Extending this model to three-dimensional space and large numbers of gas molecules, we find less crowding of molecules into a limited number of energy levels when the pressure of the gas drops and the molecules expand into a larger volume. Thus, there is a greater spreading of the energy, and the entropy increases.

We can use the same particle-in-a-box model to understand the effect of raising the temperature of a substance on the entropy of the system. We will consider a gas, but our conclusions are equally valid for a liquid or solid. At low temperatures, the molecules have a low energy, and the gas molecules can occupy only a few of the energy levels; the value of W is small, and the entropy is

(a) Before mixing

(b) After mixing

Gas A   Gas B

▲ **FIGURE 19-2**
The mixing of ideal gases
The total volume of the system and the total gas pressure remain fixed. The net change is that **(a)** before mixing, each gas is confined to half of the total volume (a single bulb) at a pressure of 1.00 atm, and **(b)** after mixing, each gas has expanded into the total volume (both bulbs) and exerts a partial pressure of 0.50 atm.

▲ **A bust marking Ludwig Boltzmann's tomb in Vienna**
Boltzmann's famous equation is inscribed on the tomb. At the time of Boltzmann's death, the term "log" was used for both natural logarithms and logarithms to the base ten; the symbol "ln" had not yet been adopted.

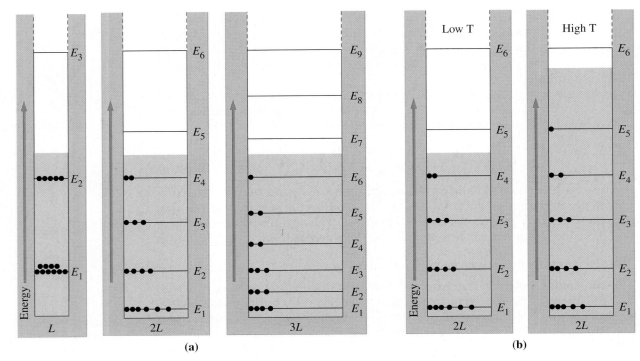

▲ FIGURE 19-3
Energy levels for a particle in a one-dimensional box
(a) The energy levels of a particle in a box become more numerous and closer together as the length of the box increases. The range of thermally accessible levels is indicated by the tinted band. The solid circles signify a system consisting of 15 particles. Each drawing represents a single microstate of the system. Can you see that as the box length increases there are many more microstates available to the particles? As the number of possible microstates for a given total energy increases, so does the entropy. **(b)** More energy levels become accessible in a box of fixed length as the temperature is raised. Because the average energy of the particles also increases, the internal energy and entropy both increase as the temperature is raised.

Sattar, Simeen. "Thermodynamics of Mixing Real Gases." *J. Chem. Educ.* **2000**: 77, 1361 (October 2000).

✓ Note that when $W = 1$, $S = 0$. This can only happen at absolute zero. Noting this fact can prepare students for the third law of thermodynamics and the observation of residual entropy at $T = 0$ K.

✓ The number of accessible states, W, is determined by the properties of a system. When a process takes place, the coupling must make the system larger; hence W must increase as the system spontaneously moves to a different equilibrium.

low. As the temperature is raised, the energy of the molecules increases and the molecules have access to a larger number of energy levels. Thus the number of accessible microstates (W) increases and the entropy rises (Fig. 19-3b).

In summary, the state of a thermodynamic system can be described in two ways: the macroscopic description, in terms of state functions P, V, and T; and the microscopic description, requiring a knowledge of the position and velocity of every particle (atom or molecule) in the system. Boltzmann's equation provides the connection between the two.

ENTROPY CHANGE

An entropy change is based on two measurable quantities: heat (q) and temperature (T). Both of these factors affect the availability of energy levels to the microscopic particles of a system. The following equation relates these factors to an entropy change,

$$\Delta S = \frac{q_{\text{rev}}}{T} \tag{19.2}$$

where T is the Kelvin temperature. Notice that ΔS is directly proportional to the quantity of heat because the more energy added to a system (as heat), the greater the number of energy levels available to the microscopic particles. Raising the temperature also increases the availability of energy levels, but for a given quantity of heat the proportional increase in number of energy levels is greatest at low temperatures. That is why ΔS is inversely proportional to the Kelvin temperature.

Are You Wondering . . .

If there is a natural way to incorporate the notion of infinitesimal changes in deriving equation (19.2)?

The infinitesimal change in entropy, dS, that accompanies an infinitesimal reversible heat flow, dq_{rev}, is $dS = dq_{rev}/T$. Now imagine the change in a system from state 1 to state 2 is carried out in a series of such infinitesimal reversible steps. Summation of all these infinitesimal quantities through the calculus technique of integration yields ΔS.

$$\Delta S = \int \frac{dq_{rev}}{T}$$

If the change of state is isothermal (carried out at constant temperature), we can write

$$\Delta S = \int \frac{dq_{rev}}{T} = \frac{1}{T} \int dq_{rev} = \frac{q_{rev}}{T}$$

and we have recovered the definition of entropy change in (19.2).

Starting with equivalent expressions for dq_{rev}, ΔS can be related to other system properties. For the isothermal, reversible expansion of an ideal gas, $dq_{rev} = -dw_{rev}$, leading to equation (19.10) on page 798, which describes ΔS in terms of gas volumes. For a reversible change in temperature, $dq_{rev} = C_P\, dT$, which leads to the entropy change for a change in temperature (see Exercise 86).

Equation (19.2) appears simple, but it is not. If S is to be a function of state, ΔS for a system must be independent of the path by which heat is lost or gained. Conversely, because the value of q ordinarily depends on the path chosen (recall page 243), equation (19.2) holds only for a carefully defined path. The path must be *reversible*, that is, $q = q_{rev}$. As we learned in Chapter 7, a reversible process can be made to reverse its direction when just an infinitesimal change in the opposite direction is made in a system property (review Figure 7-12). Because q has the unit J and $1/T$ has the unit K^{-1}, the unit of entropy change, ΔS, is J/K, or JK^{-1}.

 Lattice Vibrations activity

In some instances, it is difficult to construct mental pictures to assess how the entropy of a system changes during a process. However, in many cases, an increase or decrease in the accessibility of energy levels for the microscopic particles of a system parallels an increase or decrease in the *number* of microscopic particles and the *space* available to them. As a consequence, we can often make qualitative predictions about entropy change by focusing on those two factors. Let's test this idea by considering again the three spontaneous, endothermic processes listed at the conclusion of Section 19-1 and illustrated in Figure 19-4.

In the melting of ice, a crystalline solid is replaced by a less structured liquid. Molecules that were relatively fixed in position in the solid, being limited to vibrational motion, are now free to move about a bit. The molecules have gained some translational and rotational motion. The number of accessible microscopic energy levels has increased, and so has the entropy.

In the vaporization process, a liquid is replaced by the even less structured gas. Molecules in the gaseous state, because they can move within a large free volume, have many more accessible energy levels than do those in the liquid state. In the gas, energy can be spread over a much greater number of microscopic energy levels than in the liquid. The entropy of the gaseous state is much higher than that of the liquid state.

In the dissolving of ammonium nitrate in water, for example, a crystalline solid and a pure liquid are replaced by a mixture of ions and water molecules in the liquid (solution) state. This situation is somewhat more involved than the first two because some decrease in entropy is associated with the clustering of water molecules around the ions due to ion–dipole forces. The increase in

Concerning reversible processes, draw an isotherm on a P–V plot. If the system moves from one state to another such that the system remains on the isotherm, the process is reversible. If the ideal gas law is not obeyed, then the system moves off the isotherm as it starts its irreversible process, and returns to the isotherm when completed. This is quite easy to draw and makes the distinction between reversible and irreversible processes easier to grasp.

Solid → Liquid

(a) Melting: $S_{\text{liquid}} > S_{\text{solid}}$

Liquid → Vapor

(b) Vaporization: $S_{\text{vapor}} > S_{\text{liquid}}$

 FIGURE 19-4
Three processes in which entropy increases
Each of the processes pictured—**(a)** the melting of a solid, **(b)** the evaporation of a liquid, and **(c)** the dissolving of a solute—results in an increase in entropy. For part (c), the generalization works best for nonelectrolyte solutions, in which ion–dipole forces do not exist.

Solute   +   Solvent   →   Solution

(c) Dissolving: $S_{\text{soln}} > (S_{\text{solvent}} + S_{\text{solute}})$

Enthalpy of Solution Formation activity

Craig, N. C. "Campbell's Rule for Estimating Entropy Changes in Gas-Producing and Gas-Consuming Reactions and Related Generalizations about Entropies and Enthalpies" *J. Chem. Educ.* **2003:** *80,* 1432.

Lambert, F. L. "Entropy Is Simple, Qualitatively" *J. Chem. Educ.* **2002:** *79,* 1241.

Jensen, W. B. "Entropy and Constraint of Motion" *J. Chem. Educ.* **2004:** *81,* 639.

entropy that accompanies the destruction of the solid's crystalline lattice predominates, however, and for the overall dissolution process, $\Delta S > 0$. In each of the three spontaneous, endothermic processes discussed here, the increase in entropy ($\Delta S > 0$) outweighs the fact that heat must be absorbed ($\Delta H > 0$), and each process is spontaneous.

In summary, there are four situations that generally produce an *increase* in entropy.

- Pure liquids or liquid solutions are formed from solids.
- Gases are formed from either solids or liquids.
- The number of molecules of gas increases as a result of a chemical reaction.
- The temperature of a substance increases. (Increased temperature means an increased number of accessible energy levels for the increased molecular motion, whether it be vibrational motion of atoms or ions in a solid, or translational and rotational motion of molecules in a liquid or gas.)

We apply these generalizations in Example 19-1.

Estimation of Entropy Changes activity

EXAMPLE 19-1

Making Qualitative Predictions of Entropy Changes in Chemical Processes.
Predict whether each of the following processes involves an increase or decrease in entropy or whether the outcome is uncertain.

(a) The decomposition of ammonium nitrate (a fertilizer and a highly explosive compound): $2 \, NH_4NO_3(s) \longrightarrow 2 \, N_2(g) + 4 \, H_2O(g) + O_2(g)$.

(b) The conversion of SO_2 to SO_3 (a key step in the manufacture of sulfuric acid): $2 \, SO_2(g) + O_2(g) \longrightarrow 2 \, SO_3(g)$.

(c) The extraction of sucrose from cane sugar juice: $C_{12}H_{22}O_{11}(aq) \longrightarrow C_{12}H_{22}O_{11}(s)$

(d) The "water gas shift" reaction (involved in the gasification of coal): $CO(g) + H_2O(g) \longrightarrow CO_2(g) + H_2(g)$.

Solution

(a) Here, a solid yields a large quantity of gas. Entropy increases.

(b) Three moles of gaseous reactants produce two moles of gaseous products. The loss of one mole of gas indicates a loss of volume available to a smaller number of gas molecules. This loss reduces the number of possible configurations for the molecules in the system and the number of accessible microscopic energy levels. Entropy decreases.

(c) The sucrose molecules are reduced in mobility and in the number of forms in which their energy can be stored when they leave the solution and arrange themselves into a crystalline state. Entropy decreases.

(d) The entropies of the four gases are likely to be different because their molecular structures are different. The number of moles of gases is the same on both sides of the equation, however, so the entropy change is likely to be small if the temperature is constant. On the basis of just the generalizations listed on page 786, we cannot determine whether entropy increases or decreases.

Practice Example A: Predict whether entropy increases or decreases in each of the following reactions. (a) The Claus process for removing H_2S from natural gas: $2 H_2S(g) + SO_2(g) \longrightarrow 3 S(s) + 2 H_2O(g)$; (b) the decomposition of mercury(II) oxide: $2 HgO(s) \longrightarrow 2 Hg(l) + O_2(g)$.

Practice Example B: Predict whether entropy increases or decreases or whether the outcome is uncertain in each of the following reactions. (a) $Zn(s) + Ag_2O(s) \longrightarrow ZnO(s) + 2 Ag(s)$; (b) the chlor-alkali process, $2 Cl^-(aq) + 2 H_2O(l) \xrightarrow{\text{electrolysis}} 2 OH^-(aq) + H_2(g) + Cl_2(g)$.

CONCEPT ASSESSMENT ✔

Figure 19-1 illustrates a spontaneous process through the expansion of an ideal gas into an evacuated bulb. Use the one-dimensional particle-in-a-box model to represent the initial condition of Figure 19-1. Use a second particle-in-a-box model to represent the system after expansion into the vacuum. Use these models to explain on a microcopic basis why this expansion is spontaneous.

[*Hint:* Assume that the volume of the bulbs is analogous to the length of the box.]

19-3   EVALUATING ENTROPY AND ENTROPY CHANGES

The difficulty of calculating an entropy change with equation (19.2) was mentioned on page 785. The emphasis then shifted to making qualitative predictions about entropy changes. In this section we will see that in a few instances a simple direct calculation of ΔS is possible. Also, we will find that, unlike the case with internal energy and enthalpy, it is possible to determine *absolute* entropy values.

PHASE TRANSITIONS

In the equilibrium between two phases, the exchange of heat can be carried out reversibly, and the quantity of heat proves to be equal to the enthalpy change for the transition, ΔH_{tr}. In this case, equation (19.2) can be written as

$$\Delta S_{tr} = \frac{\Delta H_{tr}}{T_{tr}} \qquad (19.3)$$

Rather than use the general symbol "tr" to represent a transition, we can be more specific about just which phases are involved, such as "fus" for the melting of a solid and "vap" for the vaporization of a liquid. If the transitions involve standard-state conditions (1 bar $\cong$ 1 atm pressure), we also use the degree sign (°). Thus for the melting (fusion) of ice at its normal melting point,

$$H_2O(s, 1 \text{ atm}) \rightleftharpoons H_2O(l, 1 \text{ atm}) \qquad \Delta H_{fus}^\circ = 6.02 \text{ kJ at } 273.15 \text{ K}$$

the standard entropy change is

$$\Delta S_{fus}^\circ = \frac{\Delta H_{fus}^\circ}{T_{mp}} = \frac{6.02 \text{ kJ mol}^{-1}}{273.15 \text{ K}} = 2.20 \times 10^{-2} \text{ kJ mol}^{-1} \text{ K}^{-1}$$
$$= 22.0 \text{ J mol}^{-1} \text{ K}^{-1}$$

Entropy changes depend on the quantities of substances involved and are usually expressed on a per-mole basis.

Brown, R. J. C., Brown, R. F. C. "Melting Point and Molecular Symmetry." *J. Chem. Educ.* **2000:** *77*, 724 (June 2000).

Remind students that enthalpy change varies with temperature. However, in most cases these changes are ignored as discussed later on in this chapter.

◀ **KEEP IN MIND**
that the normal melting point and normal boiling point are determined at 1 atm pressure. The difference between 1 atm and the standard state pressure of 1 bar is so small that we can usually ignore it.

Are You Wondering . . .

If the thermodynamic entropy (equation 19.2), $\Delta S = q_{rev}/T$, can be derived from the statistical entropy (equation 19.1), $S = k \ln W$?

It can, but a rigorous derivation is very complex. However, by using a system of evenly spaced energy levels for the surroundings, a simplified derivation can be shown. Consider just two energy levels from the numerous energy levels representing the surroundings. Now, as suggested in Figure 19-5, construct two states, **A** and **B,** which are the most probable initial state (state **A**) and final state (state **B**) after the addition of an infinitesimal amount of heat (q_{rev}).

The temperature of **B** is slightly higher than the temperature of **A**. The amount of heat (q) used is just the energy difference ($\Delta \varepsilon$) between the two levels and therefore a single particle jumps from level **i** to level **j**. The number of **A** microstates, W_A, is almost exactly the same as the number of **B** microstates, W_B. The entropy change for the surroundings is

$$\Delta S_{sur} = k \ln \left(\frac{W_B}{W_A} \right)$$

However the ratio of probabilities is related to the population of each state as shown in the following relationship

$$\frac{W_B}{W_A} = \frac{n_i}{n_j + 1} \approx \frac{n_i}{n_j}$$

Boltzmann derived the following distribution law

$$\frac{n_j}{n_i} = e^{-\Delta \varepsilon / kT}$$

which relates the population of level i to that of level j. We use this to determine the entropy change of the surroundings along with the substitution of q_{rev} for $\Delta \varepsilon$.

$$\Delta S_{sur} = k \ln \left(\frac{W_B}{W_A} \right) = k \ln \left(e^{q_{rev}/kT} \right) = k \frac{q_{rev}}{kT} = \frac{q_{rev}}{T}$$

We have shown the relationship of the statistical entropy (equation 19.1) to the thermodynamic entropy (equation 19.2) to be true for the entropy change of the surroundings; however, this can be shown to hold for the system as well.

▶ **FIGURE 19-5**
Energy levels and populations representing the initial state of the surroundings (State A) and the state of the surroundings (State B) upon the addition of a quantity of heat (q). The spacing between the energy levels is $\Delta \varepsilon$. The populations of the energy levels are indicated by n_i and n_j.

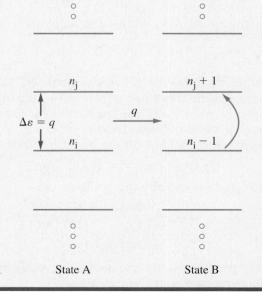

EXAMPLE 19-2

Determining the Entropy Change for a Phase Transition. What is the standard molar entropy for the vaporization of water at 373 K given that the standard molar enthalpy of vaporization is 40.7 kJ mol^{-1}?

Solution

Although a chemical equation is not necessary, writing one can help us see the process for which we seek the value of ΔS°_{vap}.

$$H_2O(l, 1\ atm) \rightleftharpoons H_2O(g, 1\ atm) \qquad \Delta H^\circ_{vap} = 40.7\ kJ/mol\ H_2O$$

$$\Delta S^\circ_{vap} = ?$$

$$\Delta S^\circ_{vap} = \frac{\Delta H^\circ_{vap}}{T_{bp}} = \frac{40.7\ kJ\ mol^{-1}}{373\ K} = 0.109\ kJ\ mol^{-1}K^{-1}$$

$$= 109\ J\ mol^{-1}\ K$$

Practice Example A: What is the standard molar entropy of vaporization, ΔS°_{vap}, for CCl_2F_2, a chlorofluorocarbon that once was heavily used in refrigeration systems? Its normal boiling point is $-29.79\ °C$, and $\Delta H^\circ_{vap} = 20.2\ kJ\ mol^{-1}$.

Practice Example B: The entropy change for the transition from solid rhombic sulfur to solid monoclinic sulfur at $95.5\ °C$ is $\Delta S^\circ_{tr} = 1.09\ J\ mol^{-1}\ K^{-1}$. What is the standard molar enthalpy change, ΔH°_{tr}, for this transition?

A useful generalization known as **Trouton's rule** states that for many liquids at their normal boiling points, the standard molar *entropy of vaporization* has a value of about 87 J mol^{-1} K^{-1}.

$$\Delta S^\circ_{vap} = \frac{\Delta H^\circ_{vap}}{T_{bp}} \approx 87\ J\ mol^{-1}\ K^{-1} \qquad (19.4)$$

For instance, the values of ΔS°_{vap} for benzene (C_6H_6) and octane (C_8H_{18}) are 87.1 and 86.2 J mol^{-1} K^{-1}, respectively. If the increased accessibility of microscopic energy levels produced in transferring one mole of molecules from liquid to vapor at 1 atm pressure is roughly comparable for different liquids, then we should expect similar values of ΔS°_{vap}.

Instances in which Trouton's rule fails are also understandable. In water and in ethanol, for example, hydrogen bonding among molecules produces a lower entropy than would otherwise be expected in the liquid state. Consequently, the entropy increase in the vaporization process is greater than normal, and so $\Delta S^\circ_{vap} > 87$ J mol^{-1} K^{-1}.

The entropy concept helps explain Raoult's law (Section 13-6). Recall that for an ideal solution, $\Delta H_{soln} = 0$ and intermolecular forces of attraction are the same as in the pure liquid solvent (page 533). Thus, we expect the molar ΔH_{vap} to be the same whether vaporization of solvent occurs from an ideal solution or from the pure solvent at the same temperature. So, too, should ΔS_{vap} be the same because $\Delta S_{vap} = \Delta H_{vap}/T$. When one mole of solvent is transferred from liquid to vapor at the equilibrium vapor pressure P°, entropy increases by the amount ΔS_{vap}. As shown in Figure 19-6, because the entropy of the ideal solution is greater than that of the pure solvent, the entropy of the vapor produced by the vaporization of solvent from the ideal solution is also greater than the entropy of the vapor obtained from the pure solvent. For the vapor above the solution to have the higher entropy, its molecules must have a greater number of accessible microscopic energy levels. In turn, the vapor must be present in a larger volume and, hence, must be at a lower pressure than the vapor coming from the pure solvent. This relationship corresponds to Raoult's law: $P_A = x_A P^\circ_A$.

Phase transitions are good examples of almost reversible processes at the melting or boiling points. For example, at the melting point of water heat slowly moves between the system and surroundings and either freezes or melts the water. If the temperature is above or below the melting point, then one phase is favored over the other.

◄ We found the value of ΔS°_{vap} for water at 373 K to be 109 J mol^{-1} K^{-1} in Example 19-2.

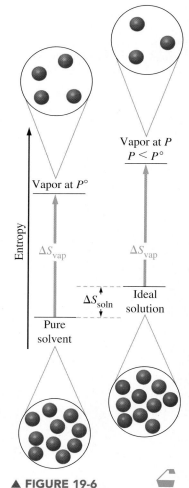

▲ **FIGURE 19-6**
An entropy-based rationale of Raoult's law
If ΔS_{vap} has the same value for vaporization from the pure solvent and from an ideal solution, the equilibrium vapor pressure is lower above the solution: $P < P^\circ$.

▶ **FIGURE 19-7**
Molar entropy as a function of temperature
The standard molar entropy of methyl chloride, $CHCl_3$, is plotted at various temperatures from 0 to 300 K, with the phases noted. The vertical segment between the solid and liquid phases corresponds to ΔS_{fus}; the other vertical segment, to ΔS_{vap}. By the third law of thermodynamics, an entropy of *zero* is expected at 0 K. Experimental methods cannot be carried to that temperature, however, so an extrapolation is required.

Temperature Dependence of Entropy simulation

ABSOLUTE ENTROPIES

To establish an *absolute* value of the entropy of a substance, we look for a condition in which the substance is in its lowest possible energy state, called the *zero-point energy*. The entropy of this state is taken to be zero. Then we evaluate entropy changes as the substance is brought to other conditions of temperature and pressure. We add together these entropy changes and obtain a numerical value of the absolute entropy. The principle that permits this procedure is the **third law of thermodynamics**, which can be stated as follows:

> The entropy of a pure perfect crystal at 0 K is zero.

Figure 19-7 illustrates the method outlined in the preceding paragraph for determining absolute entropy as a function of temperature. Where phase transitions occur, equation (19.3) is used to evaluate the corresponding entropy changes. Over temperature ranges in which there are no transitions, $\Delta S°$ values are obtained from measurements of specific heats as a function of temperature.

The absolute entropy of one mole of a substance in its standard state is called the **standard molar entropy**, $S°$. Standard molar entropies of a number of substances at 25 °C are tabulated in Appendix D. To use these values to calculate the entropy change of a reaction, we use an equation with a familiar form (recall equation 7.21).

$$\Delta S° = \left[\sum \nu_p S°(\text{products}) - \sum \nu_r S°(\text{reactants}) \right] \qquad (19.5)$$

The symbol $\sum$ means "the sum of," and the terms added are the products of the standard molar entropies and the corresponding stoichiometric coefficients, ν. Example 19-3 shows how to use this equation.

EXAMPLE 19-3

Calculating Entropy Changes from Standard Molar Entropies. Use data from Appendix D to calculate the standard molar entropy change for the conversion of nitrogen monoxide to nitrogen dioxide (a step in the manufacture of nitric acid).

$$2\,NO(g) + O_2(g) \longrightarrow 2\,NO_2(g) \qquad \Delta S°_{298\,K} = ?$$

Solution

Equation (19.5) takes the form

$$\Delta S^\circ = 2S^\circ_{NO_2(g)} - 2S^\circ_{NO(g)} - S^\circ_{O_2(g)}$$

$$= (2 \times 240.1) - (2 \times 210.8) - 205.1 = -146.5 \text{ J K}^{-1}$$

Some qualitative reasoning can be applied as a useful check on this calculation. Because three moles of gaseous reactants produce only two moles of gaseous products, the entropy should decrease; that is, ΔS° should be negative.

Practice Example A: Use data from Appendix D to calculate the standard molar entropy change for the synthesis of ammonia from its elements.

$$N_2(g) + 3 H_2(g) \longrightarrow 2 NH_3(g) \qquad \Delta S^\circ_{298 \text{ K}} = ?$$

Practice Example B: N_2O_3 is an unstable oxide that readily decomposes. The decomposition of 1.00 mol of N_2O_3 to nitrogen monoxide and nitrogen dioxide at 25 °C is accompanied by the entropy change $\Delta S^\circ = 138.5 \text{ J K}^{-1}$. What is the standard molar entropy of $N_2O_3(g)$ at 25 °C?

Example 19-3 used the standard molar entropies of $NO_2(g)$ and $NO(g)$. Why is the value for $NO_2(g)$, 240.1 J mol^{-1} K^{-1}, greater than that of $NO(g)$, 210.8 J mol^{-1} K^{-1}? Entropy increases when a substance absorbs heat (recall that $\Delta S = q_{rev}/T$), and some of this heat goes into raising the average translational kinetic energies of molecules. But there are other ways for heat energy to be used. One possibility, pictured in Figure 19-8, is that the vibrational energies of molecules can be increased. In the *diatomic* molecule $NO(g)$, only one type of vibration is possible; in the *triatomic* molecule $NO_2(g)$, *three* types are possible. Because there are more possible ways of distributing energy among NO_2 molecules than among NO molecules, $NO_2(g)$ has a higher molar entropy than does $NO(g)$ at the same temperature. Thus the following statement should be added to the generalizations about entropy on page 786.

- In general, the more complex their molecules (that is, the greater the number of atoms present), the greater the molar entropies of substances.

▲ FIGURE 19-8
Vibrational energy and entropy
The movement of atoms is suggested by the arrows. **(a)** The NO molecule has only one type of vibrational motion, whereas **(b)** the NO_2 molecule has three. This difference helps account for the fact that the molar entropy of $NO_2(g)$ is greater than that of $NO(g)$.

◀ In general, at low temperatures, because the quanta of energy are so small, translational energies are most important in establishing the entropy of gaseous molecules. As the temperature increases and the quanta of energy become larger, first rotational energies become important, and finally, at still higher temperatures, vibrational modes of motion start to contribute to the entropy.

Methane, CH_4
$S^\circ = 186.3 \text{ J mol}^{-1} \text{ K}^{-1}$

Ethane, C_2H_6
$S^\circ = 229.6 \text{ J mol}^{-1} \text{ K}^{-1}$

Propane, C_3H_8
$S^\circ = 270.3 \text{ J mol}^{-1} \text{ K}^{-1}$

19-4 CRITERIA FOR SPONTANEOUS CHANGE: THE SECOND LAW OF THERMODYNAMICS

In Section 19-2, we came to the tentative conclusion that processes in which the entropy of a system increases should be spontaneous and that processes in which entropy decreases should be nonspontaneous. But this statement can present difficulties, for example, how to explain the spontaneous freezing of water at $-10\ °C$. Because crystalline ice has a lower molar entropy than does liquid water, the freezing of water is a process for which entropy *decreases*. The way out of this dilemma is to recognize that *two* entropy changes must always be considered simultaneously—the entropy change of the system itself and the entropy change of the surroundings. The criteria for spontaneous change must be based on the sum of the two, called the entropy change of the "universe":

$$\Delta S_{\text{total}} = \Delta S_{\text{universe}} = \Delta S_{\text{system}} + \Delta S_{\text{surroundings}} \quad (19.6)$$

Although it is beyond the scope of this discussion to verify the following expression, the expression provides the basic criterion for spontaneous change. In a spontaneous change,

$$\Delta S_{\text{univ}} = \Delta S_{\text{sys}} + \Delta S_{\text{surr}} > 0 \quad (19.7)$$

Equation (19.7) is one way of stating the **second law of thermodynamics**. Another way is through the following statement.

> All spontaneous processes produce an increase in the entropy of the universe.

According to expression (19.7), if a process produces positive entropy changes in both the system and its surroundings, the process is surely spontaneous. And if both these entropy changes are negative, the process is just as surely nonspontaneous. If one of the entropy changes is positive, and the other negative, whether the sum of the two is positive or negative depends on the relative magnitudes of the two changes. The freezing of water produces a negative entropy change in the system, but in the surroundings, which absorb heat, the entropy change is positive. As long as the temperature is below $0\ °C$, the entropy of the surroundings increases more than the entropy of the system decreases. Because the *total* entropy change is positive, the freezing of water below $0\ °C$ is indeed spontaneous.

FREE ENERGY AND FREE ENERGY CHANGE

We could use expression (19.7) as the basic criterion for spontaneity (spontaneous change), but it would be very difficult to apply. To evaluate a total entropy change (ΔS_{univ}), we always have to evaluate ΔS for the surroundings. At best, this process is tedious, and in many cases it is not even possible, because we cannot figure out all the interactions between a system and its surroundings. Surely it is preferable to have a criterion that can be applied *to the system itself*, without having to worry about changes in the surroundings.

To develop this new criterion, let us explore a hypothetical process conducted at constant temperature and pressure and with work limited to pressure–volume work. This process is accompanied by a heat effect, q_p, which is equal to ΔH for the system (ΔH_{sys}) as seen in Section 7-6. The heat effect experienced by the surroundings is the *negative* of that for the system: $q_{\text{surr}} = -q_p = -\Delta H_{\text{sys}}$. Furthermore, if the hypothetical surroundings are large enough, the path by which heat enters or leaves the surroundings can be made *reversible*. That is, the quantity of heat can be made to produce only an infinitesimal change in the temperature of the surroundings. In this case, according to equation (19.2), the entropy change in the surroundings is $\Delta S_{\text{surr}} = -\Delta H_{\text{sys}}/T.^*$ Now substitute this value of ΔS_{surr} into equation (19.6), then multiply by T to obtain

$$T\,\Delta S_{\text{univ}} = T\,\Delta S_{\text{sys}} - \Delta H_{\text{sys}} = -(\Delta H_{\text{sys}} - T\,\Delta S_{\text{sys}})$$

Finally, multiply by -1 (change signs).

$$-T\,\Delta S_{\text{univ}} = \Delta H_{\text{sys}} - T\,\Delta S_{\text{sys}} \quad (19.8)$$

---

*We cannot similarly substitute $\Delta H_{\text{sys}}/T$ for ΔS_{sys}. A process that occurs spontaneously is generally far removed from an equilibrium condition and is therefore *irreversible*. We cannot substitute q for an irreversible process into equation (19.2).

Margin notes:

☑ Calculate a residual entropy for, say, one mole of CO. Carbon monoxide has a small dipole and it freezes with some residual order. That is, rather than a lattice at $T = 0\ K$ of ... COCOCOCO ..., some molecules are flipped ... COOCOCOCCO .... Each CO can be either CO or OC in the lattice, so there is a residual order of $W = (2)^N$ giving a residual entropy of $S = k\ln(2)^N = kN\ln 2 = R\ln 2$, where R is the gas constant. This agrees quite well with experimental results.

⚗ Many aspects of free energy can be illustrated by water falling and pooling at various levels. Construct an apparatus with glass bowls that you can cascade water into and over. This analogy is often helpful for students to visualize spontaneous processes: Variations in the height of the falling water, equilibrium, maintenance of production (flow), and local pooling can all be easily followed and related to free energy.

This is the significance of equation (19.8). The right side of this equation has terms involving *only the system*. On the left side appears the term ΔS_{univ}, which embodies the criterion for spontaneous change, that for a spontaneous process, $\Delta S_{univ} > 0$.

Equation (19.8) is generally cast in a somewhat different form which requires a new thermodynamic function, variously called the Gibbs energy or the **free energy**, *G*. The free energy for a system is defined by the equation

$$G = H - TS$$

The **free energy change**, ΔG, for a process at constant *T* is

$$\Delta G = \Delta H - T\,\Delta S \qquad (19.9)$$

In equation (19.9), all the terms apply to measurements *on the system*. All reference to the surroundings has been eliminated. Also, when we compare equations (19.8) and (19.9), we get

$$\Delta G = -T\,\Delta S_{univ}$$

Now, by noting that ΔG is *negative* when ΔS_{univ} is *positive*, we have our final criterion for spontaneous change based on properties of only the system itself.

For a process occurring at constant *T* and *P*, these statements hold true.

- If $\Delta G < 0$ (*negative*), the process is *spontaneous*.
- If $\Delta G > 0$ (*positive*), the process is *nonspontaneous*.
- If $\Delta G = 0$ (*zero*), the process is *at equilibrium*.

Evaluation of the units in equation (19.9) shows that free energy is indeed an energy term. ΔH has the unit joules (J), and the product $T\,\Delta S$ has the units K × J/K = J. ΔG is the difference in two quantities with units of energy.

▲ **J. Willard Gibbs (1839–1903)—a great "unknown" scientist of the United States**
Gibbs, a Yale University professor of mathematical physics, spent most of his career without recognition, partly because his work was abstract and partly because his important publications were in little-read journals. Yet today, Gibbs's ideas serve as the basis of most of chemical thermodynamics.

APPLYING THE FREE ENERGY CRITERIA FOR SPONTANEOUS CHANGE

Later, we will look at quantitative applications of equation (19.9), but for now we can use the equation to make some qualitative predictions. Altogether there are four possibilities for ΔG on the basis of the signs of ΔH and ΔS. These possibilities are outlined in Table 19.1 and demonstrated in Example 19-4.

If ΔH is *negative* and ΔS is *positive*, the expression $\Delta G = \Delta H - T\,\Delta S$ is negative at all temperatures. The process is spontaneous at all temperatures. This corresponds to the situation noted previously in which both ΔS_{sys} and ΔS_{surr} are positive and ΔS_{univ} is also positive.

Unquestionably, if a process is accompanied by an *increase* in enthalpy (heat is absorbed) and a *decrease* in entropy, ΔG is positive at all temperatures and the process is nonspontaneous. This corresponds to a situation in which both ΔS_{sys} and ΔS_{surr} are negative and ΔS_{univ} is also negative.

◀ Sometimes the term "$T\,\Delta S$" is referred to as "organizational energy," because ΔS is related to the way the energy of a system is distributed among the available energy levels.

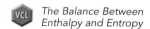 *The Balance Between Enthalpy and Entropy*

TABLE 19.1   Criteria for Spontaneous Change: $\Delta G = \Delta H - T\Delta S$

Case	ΔH	ΔS	ΔG	Result	Example
1.	−	+	−	spontaneous at all temp.	$2\,N_2O(g) \longrightarrow 2\,N_2(g) + O_2(g)$
2.	−	−	$\begin{cases} - \\ + \end{cases}$	spontaneous at low temp. nonspontaneous at high temp.	$H_2O(l) \longrightarrow H_2O(s)$
3.	+	+	$\begin{cases} + \\ - \end{cases}$	nonspontaneous at low temp. spontaneous at high temp.	$2\,NH_3(g) \longrightarrow N_2(g) + 3\,H_2(g)$
4.	+	−	+	nonspontaneous at all temp.	$3\,O_2(g) \longrightarrow 2\,O_3(g)$

▶ For cases 2 and 3, there is a particular temperature at which a process switches from being spontaneous to being nonspontaneous. Section 19-6 explains how to determine such a temperature.

The questionable cases are those in which the entropy and enthalpy factors work in opposition—that is, with ΔH and ΔS *both* negative or *both* positive. In these cases, whether a reaction is spontaneous or not (that is, whether ΔG is negative or positive) depends on temperature. In general, if a reaction has negative values for both ΔH and ΔS, it is spontaneous at *lower* temperatures, whereas if ΔH and ΔS are both positive, the reaction is spontaneous at *higher* temperatures.

EXAMPLE 19-4

Using Enthalpy and Entropy Changes to Predict the Direction of Spontaneous Change. Under what temperature conditions would the following reactions occur spontaneously?

(a) $2 NH_4NO_3(s) \longrightarrow 2 N_2(g) + 4 H_2O(g) + O_2(g)$ $\Delta H° = -236.0$ kJ

(b) $I_2(g) \longrightarrow 2 I(g)$

Solution

▶ Only because of the high activation energy for the $NH_4NO_3(s)$ decomposition reaction does $NH_4NO_3(s)$ exist at all.

(a) The reaction is exothermic, and in Example 19-1(a) we concluded that $\Delta S > 0$ because large quantities of gases are produced. With $\Delta H < 0$ and $\Delta S > 0$, this reaction should be spontaneous at all temperatures (case 1 of Table 19.1).

(b) Because one mole of gaseous reactant produces two moles of gaseous product, we expect entropy to increase. But what is the sign of ΔH? We could calculate ΔH from enthalpy of formation data, but there is no need to. In the reaction, covalent bonds in $I_2(g)$ are broken and no new bonds are formed. Because energy is absorbed to break bonds, ΔH must be positive. With $\Delta H > 0$ and $\Delta S > 0$, case 3 in Table 19.1 applies. ΔH is larger than $T \Delta S$ at low temperatures, and the reaction is nonspontaneous. At high temperatures, the $T \Delta S$ term becomes larger than ΔH, ΔG becomes negative, and the reaction is spontaneous.

✓ Changes in enthalpy and entropy vary with temperature, but the differences can be ignored at small temperature intervals. The temperature dependence of free energy change is overwhelmed by the T factor in equation (19.9).

Practice Example A: Which of the four cases in Table 19.1 would apply to each of the following reactions:

(a) $N_2(g) + 3 H_2(g) \longrightarrow 2 NH_3(g)$, $\Delta H° = -92.22$ kJ;

(b) $2 C(graphite) + 2 H_2(g) \longrightarrow C_2H_4(g)$, $\Delta H° = 52.26$ kJ?

Practice Example B: Under what temperature conditions would the following reactions occur spontaneously? **(a)** The decomposition of calcium carbonate into calcium oxide and carbon dioxide. **(b)** The "roasting" of zinc sulfide in oxygen to form zinc oxide and sulfur dioxide. This exothermic reaction releases 439.1 kJ for every mole of zinc sulfide that reacts.

▶ A related observation is that only a small fraction of the mass of the universe is in molecular form.

Example 19-4(b) illustrates why there is an upper temperature limit for the stabilities of chemical compounds. No matter how positive the value of ΔH for dissociation of a molecule into its atoms, the term $T \Delta S$ will eventually exceed ΔH in magnitude as the temperature increases. Known temperatures range from near absolute zero to the interior temperatures of stars (about 3×10^7 K). Molecules exist only at limited temperatures (up to about 1×10^4 K or about 0.03% of this total temperature range).

The method of Example 19-4 is adequate for making predictions about the sign of ΔG, but we will also want to use equation (19.9) to calculate numerical values. We will do that in Section 19-5.

Are You Wondering . . .

What the term *free energy* signifies?

We might think that the quantity of energy available to do work in the surroundings as a result of a chemical process is $-\Delta H$. This would be the same as the quantity of heat that an exothermic reaction releases to the surroundings. (In thinking along those lines, we would say that an endothermic reaction is incapable of doing work.) However, that quantity of heat must be adjusted for the heat requirement in producing the entropy change in the system ($q_{rev} = T\,\Delta S$). If an exothermic reaction is accompanied by an *increase* in entropy, the amount of energy available to do work in the surroundings is *greater* than $-\Delta H$. If entropy *decreases* in the exothermic reaction, the amount of energy available to do work is *less* than $-\Delta H$. But notice that in either case, this amount of energy is equal to $-\Delta G$. Thus, the amount of work that can be extracted from a chemical process is $-\Delta G$, so the Gibb's function G is called the *free energy function*. Notice also that this interpretation of free energy allows for the possibility of work being done in an endothermic process if $T\,\Delta S$ exceeds ΔH. In Chapter 20, we will see how the free energy change of a reaction can be converted to electrical work. In any case, do not think of free energy as being "free." Costs are always involved in tapping an energy source.

> Ask the students why is it called *free* energy— the explanation here gives the reason.

19-5   STANDARD FREE ENERGY CHANGE, $\Delta G°$

Because free energy is related to enthalpy ($G = H - TS$), we cannot establish absolute values of G any more than we can for H. We must work with free energy changes, ΔG. We will find a special use for the free energy change corresponding to reactants and products in their standard states—the **standard free energy change**, $\Delta G°$. The standard state conventions were introduced and applied to enthalpy change in Chapter 7.

The **standard free energy of formation**, $\Delta G_f°$, is the free energy change for a reaction in which a substance in its standard state is formed from its elements in their reference forms in their standard states. And, as was the case when we established enthalpies of formation in Section 7-8, this definition leads to values of *zero* for the free energies of formation of the elements in their reference forms at a pressure of 1 bar. Other free energies of formation are related to this condition of zero and are generally tabulated per mole of substance (see Appendix D).

Some additional relationships involving free energy changes are similar to those presented for enthalpy in Section 7-7: (1) ΔG changes sign when a process is reversed; and (2) ΔG for an overall process can be obtained by summing the ΔG values for the individual steps. The two expressions that follow are useful in calculating $\Delta G°$ values, depending on the data available. We can use the first expression at any temperature for which $\Delta H°$ and $\Delta S°$ values are known. We can use the second expression only at temperatures at which $\Delta G_f°$ values are known. The only temperature at which tabulated data are commonly given is 298.15 K. The first expression is applied in Example 19-5 and Practice Example 19-5A, and the second expression in Practice Example 19-5B.

$$\Delta G° = \Delta H° - T\Delta S°$$

$$\Delta G° = \left[\sum \nu_p\,\Delta G_f°(\text{products}) - \sum \nu_r\,\Delta G_f°(\text{reactants}) \right]$$

> ◄ KEEP IN MIND
> that a pressure of 1 bar is very nearly the same as 1 atm. The difference in these two pressures on the values of properties is generally so small that we can use the two pressure units almost interchangeably.

> Many substances do not exist at the standard conditions that define their free energy. This does not matter since we can calculate the standard free energy from nonstandard conditions. Dealing with nonstandard conditions is discussed on page 797. Free energies are listed under standard conditions for ease and conciseness.

EXAMPLE 19-5

Calculating $\Delta G°$ for a Reaction. Determine $\Delta G°$ at 298.15 K for the reaction

$$2\,NO(g) + O_2(g) \longrightarrow 2\,NO_2(g) \quad \text{(at 298.15 K)} \qquad \Delta H° = -114.1 \text{ kJ}$$
$$\Delta S° = -146.5 \text{ J K}^{-1}$$

Solution

Because we have values of $\Delta H°$ and $\Delta S°$, the most direct method of calculating $\Delta G°$ is to use the expression $\Delta G° = \Delta H° - T\,\Delta S°$. In doing so, we must first convert all the data to a common energy unit (for instance, kJ).

$$\Delta G° = -114.1 \text{ kJ} - (298.15 \text{ K} \times -0.1465 \text{ kJ K}^{-1})$$
$$= -114.1 \text{ kJ} + 43.68 \text{ kJ}$$
$$= -70.4 \text{ kJ}$$

Practice Example A: Determine $\Delta G°$ at 298.15 K for the reaction $4\,Fe(s) + 3\,O_2(g) \longrightarrow 2\,Fe_2O_3(s)$. $\Delta H° = -1648$ kJ and $\Delta S° = -549.3$ J K^{-1}.

Practice Example B: Determine $\Delta G°$ for the reaction in Example 19-5 by using data from Appendix D. Compare the two results.

This example says that all the reactants and products are maintained at 25 °C and 1 atm pressure. Under these conditions, the free energy change is −70.4 kJ for oxidizing two moles of NO to two moles of NO₂. To do this, it is necessary to replenish the NO so as to maintain the standard conditions.

19-6 FREE ENERGY CHANGE AND EQUILIBRIUM

We have seen that $\Delta G < 0$ for spontaneous processes and that $\Delta G > 0$ for nonspontaneous processes. If $\Delta G = 0$, the forward and reverse processes show an equal tendency to occur, and the system is at *equilibrium*. At this point, even an infinitesimal change in one of the system variables (such as temperature or pressure) will cause a net change to occur. But if a system at equilibrium is left undisturbed, no net change occurs with time.

Let's consider the hypothetical process outlined in Figure 19-9. If we start at the left-hand side of the figure, we see that ΔH exceeds $T\,\Delta S$ and that ΔG is positive; the process is *nonspontaneous*. The magnitude of ΔG decreases with increasing temperature. At the right-hand side of the figure, $T\,\Delta S$ exceeds ΔH and ΔG is negative; the process is *spontaneous*. At the temperature at which the two lines intersect, $\Delta G = 0$ and the system is at equilibrium.

For the vaporization of water, *with both liquid and vapor in their standard states* (which means that $\Delta G = \Delta G°$), the intersection of the two lines in Figure 19-9 is at $T = 373.15$ K (100.00 °C). That is, for the vaporization of water at 1 atm,

$$H_2O(l, 1 \text{ atm}) \rightleftharpoons H_2O(g, 1 \text{ atm}) \qquad \Delta G° = 0 \text{ at } 373.15 \text{ K}$$

▶ **FIGURE 19-9**
Free energy change as a function of temperature
The value of ΔG is given by the distance between the two lines; that is, $\Delta G = \Delta H - T\,\Delta S$. In this illustration, both ΔH and ΔS have positive values at all temperatures. If ΔH is greater than the $T\,\Delta S$ value, $\Delta G > 0$ and the reaction is *nonspontaneous*. If ΔH is less than $T\,\Delta S$, $\Delta G < 0$ and the reaction is *spontaneous*. At equilibrium, $\Delta G = 0$; this occurs at the temperature at which the two lines intersect. An assumption made here is that ΔH and ΔS are essentially independent of temperature.

(a)

(b)

(c)

▲ **FIGURE 19-10**
Liquid–vapor equilibrium and the direction of spontaneous change
(a) For the vaporization of water at 298.15 K and 1 atm, $H_2O(l, 1 \text{ atm}) \longrightarrow$ $H_2O(g, 1 \text{ atm})$, $\Delta G° = 8.590$ kJ. The direction of spontaneous change is the *condensation* of $H_2O(g)$. **(b)** At 298.15 K and 23.76 mmHg, the liquid and vapor are in equilibrium and $\Delta G° = 0$. **(c)** At 298.15 K and 10 mmHg, the vaporization of $H_2O(l)$ occurs spontaneously: $H_2O(l, 10 \text{ mmHg}) \longrightarrow H_2O(g, 10 \text{ mmHg})$, and $\Delta G < 0$.

At 25 °C, the $\Delta H°$ line lies above the $T \Delta S$ line in Figure 19-9. This means that $\Delta G° > 0$.

$$H_2O(l, 1 \text{ atm}) \longrightarrow H_2O(g, 1 \text{ atm}) \qquad \Delta G° = +8.590 \text{ kJ at } 298.15 \text{ K}$$

The positive value of $\Delta G°$ does not mean that vaporization of water will not occur. From common experience, we know that water spontaneously evaporates at room temperature. What the positive value means is that liquid water will not spontaneously produce $H_2O(g)$ at 1 atm pressure at 25 °C. Instead, $H_2O(g)$ is produced with a vapor pressure that is less than 1 atm pressure. The equilibrium vapor pressure of water at 25 °C is 23.76 mmHg = 0.03126 atm; that is,

$$H_2O(l, 0.03126 \text{ atm}) \rightleftharpoons H_2O(g, 0.03126 \text{ atm}) \qquad \Delta G = 0$$

Figure 19-10 offers a schematic summary of ideas concerning the transition between liquid and gaseous water at 25 °C.

CONCEPT ASSESSMENT ✔

Redraw Figure 19-9 for case 2 in Table 19.1. How does your drawing compare with Figure 19-9? State the similarities and differences.

RELATIONSHIP OF $\Delta G°$ TO ΔG FOR NONSTANDARD CONDITIONS

If you think about the situation just described for the vaporization of water, there is not much value in describing equilibrium in a process in terms of its $\Delta G°$ value. At only one temperature are the reactants in their standard states in equilibrium with products in their standard states; that is, at only one temperature does $\Delta G° = 0$. We want to be able to describe equilibrium for a variety of conditions, typically *nonstandard* conditions. Many reactions, such as processes occurring under physiological conditions, take place under nonstandard conditions. How, under such circumstances, can a biochemist decide which processes are spontaneous? For this we need to work with ΔG, not $\Delta G°$.

To obtain the relationship between ΔG and $\Delta G°$, we will consider a reaction between ideal gas molecules. We assume this is the case in the reaction of nitrogen with hydrogen to produce ammonia.

$$N_2(g) + 3 H_2(g) \rightleftharpoons 2 NH_3(g)$$

◀ Here, we have used a standard-state pressure of 1 atm. See Feature Problem 88 for an appraisal of this matter using a standard-state pressure of 1 bar.

◀ The liquid–vapor equilibrium represented here is out of contact with the atmosphere. In the presence of the atmosphere, the pressure on the liquid would be barometric pressure, whereas that of the vapor would remain essentially unchanged at 0.03126 atm.

Water droplets in the atmosphere frequently become supercooled because of the absence of a dust particle upon which to nucleate. As soon as the supercooled droplet finds a bit of dust it is immediately and spontaneously converted to ice.

Erné, B. H. "Thermodynamics of Water Superheated in the Microwave Oven." *J. Chem. Educ.* **2000:** *77*, 1309 (October 2000).

The expressions for ΔG and $\Delta G°$ are $\Delta G = \Delta H - T\,\Delta S$ and $\Delta G° = \Delta H° - T\,\Delta S°$, respectively. First consider how the enthalpy terms ΔH and $\Delta H°$ are related for an ideal gas. The enthalpy of an ideal gas is a function of temperature only; it is independent of pressure. Thus, under any mixing conditions for an ideal gas, $\Delta H = \Delta H°$. We can write

$$\Delta G = \Delta H° - T\,\Delta S \qquad \text{(ideal gas)}$$

We now need to obtain a relationship between ΔS and $\Delta S°$. To do so, we consider the isothermal expansion of an ideal gas for which $q = -w$ and $\Delta U = 0$. If the expansion occurs reversibly (recall Figure 7-12), the work of expansion for one mole of an ideal gas is given by an equation derived in Feature Problem 108 in Chapter 7.

$$w = -RT\ln\frac{V_f}{V_i} \qquad \text{(reversible, isothermal)}$$

The reversible, isothermal heat of expansion is

$$q_{rev} = -w = RT\ln\frac{V_f}{V_i}$$

From equation (19.2), we obtain the entropy change for the isothermal expansion of one mole of an ideal gas.

$$\Delta S = \frac{q_{rev}}{T} = R\ln\frac{V_f}{V_i} \qquad (19.10)$$

Using equation (19.10), we can now evaluate the entropy of an ideal gas under any conditions of pressure. From the ideal gas equation, we know that the volume of an ideal gas is inversely proportional to the pressure, so we can recast equation (19.10) as

$$\Delta S = S_f - S_i = R\ln\frac{V_f}{V_i} = R\ln\frac{P_i}{P_f} = -R\ln\frac{P_f}{P_i}$$

where P_i and P_f are the initial and final pressures, respectively. If we set $P_i = 1$ bar and designate P_i as $P°$ and S_i as $S°$, we obtain for the entropy at any pressure P

$$S = S° - R\ln\frac{P}{P°} = S° - R\ln\frac{P}{1} = S° - R\ln P \qquad (19.11)$$

Now, let's return to the ammonia synthesis reaction and calculate the entropy change for that reaction. We begin by applying equation (19.11) to each of the three gases.

$$S_{NH_3} = S°_{NH_3} - R\ln P_{NH_3} \qquad S_{N_2} = S°_{N_2} - R\ln P_{N_2} \qquad S_{H_2} = S°_{H_2} - R\ln P_{H_2}$$

Then we substitute the above values into the equation $\Delta S = 2S_{NH_3} - S_{N_2} - 3S_{H_2}$ to obtain

$$\Delta S = 2S°_{NH_3} - 2R\ln P_{NH_3} - S°_{N_2} + R\ln P_{N_2} - 3S°_{H_2} + 3R\ln P_{H_2}$$

By rearranging the terms, we get

$$\Delta S = 2S°_{NH_3} - S°_{N_2} - 3S°_{H_2} - 2R\ln P_{NH_3} + R\ln P_{N_2} + 3R\ln P_{H_2}$$

and, since the first three terms on the right-hand side of the above equation represent $\Delta S°$, we have

$$\Delta S = \Delta S° - 2R\ln P_{NH_3} + R\ln P_{N_2} + 3R\ln P_{H_2}$$

$$\Delta S = \Delta S° - R\ln P^2_{NH_3} + R\ln P_{N_2} + R\ln P^3_{H_2}$$

$$\Delta S = \Delta S° + R\ln\frac{P_{N_2}P^3_{H_2}}{P^2_{NH_3}}$$

Are You Wondering . . .

If there is a microscopic approach to obtaining equation (19.10)?

To do this, we use the ideas of Ludwig Boltzmann. Consider an ideal gas at an initial volume V_i and allow the gas to expand isothermally to a final volume V_f. Using the Boltzmann equation, we find that for the change in entropy,

$$\Delta S = S_f - S_i = k \ln W_f - k \ln W_i$$

$$\Delta S = k \ln \frac{W_f}{W_i}$$

where k is the Boltzmann constant, S_i and S_f are the initial and final entropies, respectively, and W_i and W_f are the number of microstates for the initial and final macroscopic states of the gas, respectively. We must now obtain a value for the ratio W_f/W_i. To do that, suppose that there is only a single gas molecule in a container. The number of microstates available to this single molecule should be proportional to the number of positions where the molecule can be and, hence, to the volume of the container. That is also true for each molecule in a system of N_A particles—Avogadro's number of particles. The number of microstates available to the whole system is

$$W_{total} = W_{particle\ 1} \times W_{particle\ 2} \times W_{particle\ 3} \times \cdots$$

Because the number of microstates for each particle is proportional to the volume V of the container, the number of microstates for N_A (Avogadro's number) ideal gas molecules is

$$W \propto V^{N_A}$$

Thus, the ratio of the microstates for isothermal expansion is

$$\frac{W_f}{W_i} = \left(\frac{V_f}{V_i} \right)^{N_A}$$

We can now calculate ΔS as follows:

$$\Delta S = k \ln \frac{W_f}{W_i} = k \ln \left(\frac{V_f}{V_i} \right)^{N_A} = N_A k \ln \left(\frac{V_f}{V_i} \right) = R \ln \left(\frac{V_f}{V_i} \right)$$

where R is the ideal gas constant. This equation, which gives the entropy change for the expansion of one mole of ideal gas, is simply equation (19.10).

Finally, we can write the equation for ΔG by substituting the expression for ΔS into the equation

$$\Delta G = \Delta H° - T\,\Delta S \qquad \qquad (ideal\ gas)$$

This leads to

$$\Delta G = \Delta H° - T\,\Delta S° - RT \ln \frac{P_{N_2} P^3{}_{H_2}}{P^2{}_{NH_3}}$$

$$\Delta G = \underbrace{\Delta H° - T\,\Delta S°} + RT \ln \frac{P^2{}_{NH_3}}{P_{N_2} P^3{}_{H_2}}$$

$$\Delta G = \Delta G° + RT \ln \frac{P^2{}_{NH_3}}{P_{N_2} P^3{}_{H_2}}$$

To simplify, we designate the quotient in the logarithmic term as the *reaction quotient* Q (recall page 636).

$$\Delta G = \Delta G° + RT \ln Q \qquad \qquad (19.12)$$

 Free Energy and Reaction Mixture activity

Equation (19.12) is the relationship between ΔG and $\Delta G°$ that we have been seeking in this section, and we see that the key term in the equation is the reaction quotient formulated for the actual, nonstandard conditions. We can use equation (19.12) to decide on the spontaneity of a reaction under any conditions of composition, provided that the temperature and pressure at which we observe the reaction are constant. We turn now to describing how the standard Gibbs free energy change is related to the equilibrium constant.

RELATIONSHIP OF $\Delta G°$ TO THE EQUILIBRIUM CONSTANT K

We encounter an interesting situation when we apply equation (19.12) to a reaction at equilibrium. We have learned that at equilibrium $\Delta G = 0$, and in Chapter 15 we saw that if a system is at equilibrium, $Q = K_c$ or $Q = K_p$, or, more generally, $Q = K$. So, we can write that, *at equilibrium*,

$$\Delta G = \Delta G° + RT \ln K = 0$$

which means that

$$\Delta G° = -RT \ln K \qquad (19.13)$$

If we have a value of $\Delta G°$ at a given temperature, we can use equation (19.13) to calculate an equilibrium constant K. This means that the tabulation of thermodynamic data in Appendix D can serve as a direct source of countless equilibrium constant values at 298.15 K.

We need to say a few words about the units required in equation (19.13). Because logarithms can be taken of dimensionless numbers only, K has no units; neither does $\ln K$. The right-hand side of equation (19.13) has the unit of "RT": $J \, mol^{-1} \, K^{-1} \times K = J \, mol^{-1}$. $\Delta G°$, on the left-hand side of the equation, must have the same unit: $J \, mol^{-1}$. The "mol^{-1}" part of this unit means "per mole of reaction." One mole of reaction is simply the reaction based on the stoichiometric coefficients chosen for the balanced equation. When a $\Delta G°$ value is accompanied by a chemical equation, the "mol^{-1}" portion of the unit is often dropped, but there are a few times when we need it, as for the proper cancellation of units in equation (19.13).

CRITERIA FOR SPONTANEOUS CHANGE: OUR SEARCH CONCLUDED

The graphs plotted in Figure 19-11 represent the culmination of our quest for criteria for spontaneous change. Unfortunately, to construct these plots in all their detail is beyond the scope of this text. However, we can rationalize their general shape on the basis of two ideas: (1) Every chemical reaction consists of both a forward and a reverse reaction, even if one of these occurs only to a very slight extent. (2) The direction of spontaneous change in both the forward and reverse reactions is the direction in which free energy decreases ($\Delta G < 0$). As a consequence, free energy reaches a minimum at some point between the left-hand and right-hand sides of the graph. This minimum is the equilibrium point in the reaction.

Now consider the vertical distance between the two end points of the graph; this distance represents $\Delta G°$ of the reaction. If, as in Figure 19-11(a), $\Delta G°$ of a reaction is small, either positive or negative, the equilibrium condition is one in which significant amounts of both reactants and products will be found. If $\Delta G°$ is a *large, positive* quantity, as in Figure 19-11(b), the equilibrium point lies far to the left—that is, very close to the reactants side. We can say that the reaction occurs hardly at all. If $\Delta G°$ is a *large, negative* quantity, as in Figure 19-11(c), the equilibrium point lies far to the right—that is, very close to the products side. We can say that the reaction goes essentially to completion. Table 19.2 summarizes the conclusions of this discussion, gives approximate magnitudes to the terms *small* and *large*, and relates $\Delta G°$ values to values of K.

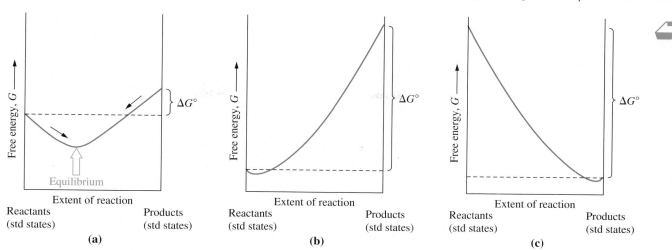

▲ **FIGURE 19-11**

Free energy change, equilibrium, and the direction of spontaneous change
Free energy is plotted against the extent of reaction for a hypothetical reaction. $\Delta G°$ is the difference between the standard molar free energies of formation of products and reactants. The equilibrium point lies somewhere between pure reactants and pure products. **(a)** $\Delta G°$ is small, so the equilibrium mixture lies about midway between the two extremes of pure products or reactants in their standard states. The effect of nonstandard conditions can be deduced from the slope of the curve. Mixtures with $Q > K$ are to the right of the equilibrium point, and undergo spontaneous change in the direction of lower free energy, eventually coming to equilibrium. Similarly, mixtures with $Q < K$ are to the left of the equilibrium point and spontaneously yield more products before reaching equilibrium. **(b)** $\Delta G°$ is large and positive, so the equilibrium point lies close to the extreme of pure reactants in their standard states. Consequently, very little reaction takes place before equilibrium is reached. **(c)** $\Delta G°$ is large and negative, so the equilibrium point lies close to the extreme of pure products in their standard states; the reaction goes essentially to completion.

Free Energy and Chemical Equilibrium activity

See the note on page 796. Here the system starts at standard conditions and runs down to equilibrium because the reactants are not replenished. At equilibrium there is no driving force for the reaction, so there is no further reaction and the free energy must be at a minimum.

NO₂–N₂O₄ Equilibrium animation

$\Delta G°$	K	Significance
TABLE 19.2 Significance of the Magnitude of $\Delta G°$ (at 298 K)		
+200 kJ/mol	9.1×10^{-36}	No reaction
+100	3.0×10^{-18}	
+50	1.7×10^{-9}	
+10	1.8×10^{-2}	
+1.0	6.7×10^{-1}	
0	1.0	Equilibrium calculation is necessary
−1.0	1.5	
−10	5.6×10^{1}	
−50	5.8×10^{8}	
−100	3.3×10^{17}	Reaction goes to completion
−200	1.1×10^{35}	

The huge range of values of the equilibrium constant are seen to arise from the natural logarithm term. Choose a few reasonable values of the free energy, both negative and positive, to illustrate this fact.

$\Delta G°$ AND ΔG: PREDICTING THE DIRECTION OF CHEMICAL CHANGE

We have considered both $\Delta G°$ and ΔG in relation to the spontaneity of chemical reactions, and this is a good time to summarize some ideas about them.

$\Delta G < 0$ signifies that a reaction or process is spontaneous in the forward direction (to the right) for the stated conditions.

$\Delta G° < 0$ signifies that the forward reaction is spontaneous when reactants and products are in their standard states. It further signifies that $K > 1$, whatever the initial concentrations or pressures of reactants and products.

$\Delta G = 0$ signifies that the reaction is at equilibrium under the stated conditions.

$\Delta G° = 0$ signifies that the reaction is at equilibrium when reactants and products are in their standard states. It further signifies that $K = 1$, which can occur only at a particular temperature.

$\Delta G > 0$ signifies that the reaction or process is nonspontaneous in the forward direction under the stated conditions.

$\Delta G° > 0$ signifies that the forward reaction is nonspontaneous when reactants and products are in their standard states. It further signifies that $K < 1$, whatever the initial concentrations or pressures of reactants and products.

$\Delta G = \Delta G°$ only when all reactants and products are in their standard states. Otherwise, $\Delta G = \Delta G° + RT \ln Q$.

THE THERMODYNAMIC EQUILIBRIUM CONSTANT: ACTIVITIES

When we derived the equation $\Delta G = \Delta G° + RT \ln Q$, we used the relationship given in equation (19.11),

$$S = S° - R \ln \frac{P}{P°} = S° - R \ln \frac{P}{1}$$

where for a gas, we defined a standard state of 1 bar, the reference state for values of entropy. The ratio $P/P°$ is dimensionless, which is essential for a term appearing in a logarithm. At the time, we were considering a gas-phase reaction, but we must be able to discuss reactions in solutions also, so we need a more general approach. For this, we need to return to the concept of *activity* introduced in Section 15-2, which requires us to write

$$S = S° - R \ln a$$

where a is the activity, defined as

$$a = \frac{\text{the effective concentration of a substance in the system}}{\text{the effective concentration of that substance in a standard reference state}}$$

In a gas-phase reaction, we express pressure in bars and take the reference state to be 1 bar. In this way and as expected, activity is a dimensionless quantity.

In extending the activity concept to solutions, we define the reference state as a 1 M solution, so the activity of a substance is the numerical value of its molarity. Thus, the activity of protons in a 0.1 M solution of HCl in water is

$$a_{H^+} = \frac{0.1\ M}{1\ M} = 0.1$$

Another situation that we have encountered is that of a heterogeneous equilibrium, such as

$$CaCO_3(s) \rightleftharpoons CaO(s) + CO_2(g)$$

Recall that we choose the pure solids as the reference states, but the effective concentrations of the $CaCO_3(s)$ and $CaO(s)$ in the system are also those of the pure solids. Consequently, the activity of a solid is unity. This conclusion agrees with our observation in Figure 15-3 that the addition of either $CaO(s)$ or $CaCO_3(s)$ to an equilibrium mixture of $CaCO_3(s)$, $CO_2(g)$, and $CaO(s)$ has no effect on the pressure of $CO_2(g)$. The activities of $CaO(s)$ and $CaCO_3(s)$ are constant (unity).

KEEP IN MIND ▶

that the ideal gas equation $PV = nRT$ can be rewritten as $(n/V) = [\text{concentration}] = (P/RT)$ so that pressure is an effective concentration.

KEEP IN MIND ▶

that the precise definition of pH is

$$pH = -\log a_{H^+}$$
$$= -\log \left(\frac{[H^+]M}{1\ M} \right)$$
$$= -\log [H^+]$$

By using this definition of activity, we remove the units and can employ the log term in a correct manner.

Are You Wondering . . .

How to deal with activities under nonideal conditions?

For nonideal conditions, we sweep all deviations from ideality into an experimentally determined correction factor called the *activity coefficient*, γ. Thus, for real (nonideal) systems, we write

For a gas:	$a_G = \gamma P_G$
For a solute:	$a_X = \gamma [X]$
For a pure solid or liquid:	$a_L = a_S = 1$

More advanced treatments of this topic show how γ is related to the composition of the system. For dilute solutions or near ideal gases, we will assume that $\gamma = 1$. However, keep in mind that the results we obtain are limited by the validity of this assumption.

In summary, we can make these statements.

- *For pure solids and liquids:* The activity $a = 1$. The reference state is the pure solid or liquid.

- *For gases:* With ideal gas behavior assumed, the activity is replaced by the numerical value of the gas pressure in bars. The reference state is the gas at 1 bar at the temperature of interest. Thus, the activity of a gas at 0.50 bar pressure is $a = (0.50 \text{ bar})/(1 \text{ bar}) = 0.50$. (Recall also, that 1 bar of pressure is almost identical to 1 atm.)

- *For solutes in aqueous solution:* With ideal solution behavior assumed (for example, no interionic attractions), the activity is replaced by the numerical value of the molarity. The reference state is a 1 M solution. Thus, the activity of the solute in a 0.25 M solution is $a = (0.25 \text{ M})/(1 \text{ M}) = 0.25$.

When an equilibrium expression is written in terms of activities, the equilibrium constant is called the **thermodynamic equilibrium constant**. The thermodynamic equilibrium constant is dimensionless and thus appropriate for use in equation (19.13).

Thermodynamic equilibrium constants, K, are sometimes identical to K_c and K_p values, as in parts (a) and (b) of Example 19-6. In other instances, as in part (c), this is not the case. In working through Example 19-6, keep in mind that the sole reason for writing thermodynamic equilibrium constants in this text is to get the proper value to use in equation (19.13). Note that the reaction quotient Q must also be written in the same manner as K when used in equation (19.12), as demonstrated in Example 19-7.

EXAMPLE 19-6

Writing Thermodynamic Equilibrium Constant Expressions. For the following reversible reactions, write thermodynamic equilibrium constant expressions, making appropriate substitutions for activities. Then equate K to K_c or K_p, where this can be done.

(a) The water gas reaction

$$C(s) + H_2O(g) \rightleftharpoons CO(g) + H_2(g)$$

(b) Formation of a saturated aqueous solution of lead(II) iodide, a very slightly soluble solute

$$PbI_2(s) \rightleftharpoons Pb^{2+}(aq) + 2\,I^-(aq)$$

(c) Oxidation of sulfide ion by oxygen gas (used in removing sulfides from wastewater, as in pulp and paper mills)

$$O_2(g) + 2\,S^{2-}(aq) + 2\,H_2O(l) \rightleftharpoons 4\,OH^-(aq) + 2\,S_8(s)$$

Solution

In each case, once we have made the appropriate substitutions for activities, if all terms are molarities, the thermodynamic equilibrium constant is the same as K_c. If all terms are partial pressures, $K = K_p$. If both molarities *and* partial pressures appear in the expression, however, the equilibrium constant expression can be designated only as K.

(a) The activity of solid carbon is 1. Partial pressures are substituted for the activities of the gases.

$$K = \frac{a_{CO(g)}}{a_{C(s)}a_{H_2O(g)}} = \frac{(P_{CO})(P_{H_2})}{(P_{H_2O})} = \frac{(P_{CO})(P_{H_2})}{(P_{H_2O})} = K_p$$

(b) The activity of solid lead(II) iodide is 1. Molarities are substituted for activities of the ions in aqueous solution.

$$K = \frac{a_{Pb^{2+}(aq)}a^2_{I^-(aq)}}{a_{PbI_2(s)}} = [Pb^{2+}][I^-]^2 = K_c = K_{sp}$$

(c) The activity of both the solid sulfur and the liquid water is 1. Molarities are substituted for the activities of $OH^-(aq)$ and $S^{2-}(aq)$. The partial pressure of $O_2(g)$ is substituted for its activity. Thus, the resulting K is neither a K_c nor a K_p.

$$K = \frac{a^4_{OH^-(aq)}a^2_{S(s)}}{a_{O_2(g)}a^2_{S^{2-}(aq)}a^2_{H_2O(l)}} = \frac{[OH^-]^4 \cdot (1)^2}{P_{O_2} \cdot [S^{2-}]^2 \cdot (1)^2} = \frac{[OH^-]^4}{P_{O_2} \cdot [S^{2-}]^2}$$

Practice Example A: Write thermodynamic equilibrium constant expressions for each of the following reactions. Relate these to K_c or K_p where appropriate.

(a) $Si(s) + 2 Cl_2(g) \rightleftharpoons SiCl_4(g)$

(b) $Cl_2(g) + H_2O(l) \rightleftharpoons HOCl(aq) + H^+(aq) + Cl^-(aq)$

Practice Example B: Write a thermodynamic equilibrium constant expression to represent the reaction of solid lead(II) sulfide with aqueous nitric acid to produce solid sulfur, a solution of lead(II) nitrate, and nitrogen monoxide gas. Base the expression on the balanced net ionic equation for the reaction.

EXAMPLE 19-7

Assessing Spontaneity for Nonstandard Conditions. For the decomposition of 2-propanol to form propanone (acetone) and hydrogen,

$$(CH_3)_2CHOH(g) \rightleftharpoons (CH_3)_2CO(g) + H_2(g)$$

the equilibrium constant is 0.444 at 452 K. Is this reaction spontaneous under standard conditions? Will the reaction be spontaneous when the partial pressures of 2-propanol, propanone, and hydrogen are 0.1 bar, respectively?

Solution

In each case, we first must obtain the value of $\Delta G°$, which we can get from equation (19.13).

$$\Delta G° = -RT \ln K = -8.3145 \text{ J mol}^{-1} \text{ K}^{-1} \times 452 \text{ K} \times \ln(0.444)$$
$$= 3.05 \times 10^3 \text{ J mol}^{-1}$$

This result enables us to state categorically that the reaction will not proceed spontaneously if all reactants and products are in their standard states—that is, with the partial pressures of reactants and products at 1 bar.

To determine whether the reaction is spontaneous under the nonstandard-state conditions given, we must calculate ΔG. We first write Q in terms of activities and then substitute the partial pressures of the gases for the activities of the gases.

$$Q = \frac{a_{(CH_3)_2CO}a_{H_2}}{a_{(CH_4)_2CHOH}} = \frac{P_{(CH_3)_2CO}P_{H_2}}{P_{(CH_3)_2CHOH}}$$

Then use this expression in equation (19.12).

$$\Delta G = \Delta G° + RT \ln\frac{P_{(CH_3)_2CO}P_{H_2}}{P_{(CH_3)_2CHOH}}$$

$$= 3.05 \times 10^3 \, J \, mol^{-1} + \left(8.3145 \, J \, mol^{-1} \, K^{-1} \times 452 \, K \times \ln\frac{0.1 \times 0.1}{1} \right)$$

$$= -1.43 \times 10^4 \, J \, mol^{-1}$$

The value of ΔG is negative, so we can conclude that under this second set of conditions the reaction should proceed spontaneously. Remember, however, that thermodynamics says nothing about the rate of the reaction, only that the reaction will proceed in its own good time!

Practice Example A: Use the data in Appendix D to decide whether the following reaction is spontaneous under standard conditions at 298.15 K.

$$N_2O_4(g) \longrightarrow 2 \, NO_2(g)$$

Practice Example B: If a gaseous mixture of N_2O_4 and NO_2, both at a pressure of 0.5 bar, is introduced into a previously evacuated vessel, which of the two gases will spontaneously convert into the other at 298.15 K?

We have now acquired all the tools with which to perform one of the most practical calculations of chemical thermodynamics: *determining the equilibrium constant for a reaction from tabulated data.* Example 19-8, which demonstrates this application, uses thermodynamic properties of ions in aqueous solution as well as of compounds. An important idea to note about the thermodynamic properties of ions is that they are relative to $H^+(aq)$, which, by convention, is assigned values of *zero* for $\Delta H_f°$, $\Delta G_f°$, and $S°$. This means that entropies listed for ions are not absolute entropies, as they are for compounds. Negative values of $S°$ simply denote an entropy less than that of $H^+(aq)$.

EXAMPLE 19-8

Calculating the Equilibrium Constant of a Reaction from the Standard Free Energy Change. Determine the equilibrium constant at 298.15 K for the dissolution of magnesium hydroxide in an acidic solution.

$$Mg(OH)_2(s) + 2 \, H^+(aq) \rightleftharpoons Mg^{2+}(aq) + 2 \, H_2O(l)$$

Solution

The key to solving this problem is to find a value of $\Delta G°$ and then to use the expression $\Delta G° = -RT \ln K$. We can obtain $\Delta G°$ from standard free energies of formation listed in Appendix D. Note that because its value is zero, the term $\Delta G_f°[H^+(aq)]$ is not included.

$$\Delta G° = 2 \, \Delta G_f°[H_2O(l)] + \Delta G_f°[Mg^{2+}(aq)] - \Delta G_f°[Mg(OH)_2(s)]$$

$$= 2(-237.1 \, kJ \, mol^{-1}) + (-454.8 \, kJ \, mol^{-1}) - (-833.5 \, kJ \, mol^{-1})$$

Now solve for $\ln K$ and K.

$$\Delta G° = -RT \ln K = -95.5 \, kJ \, mol^{-1} = -95.5 \times 10^3 \, J \, mol^{-1}$$

$$\ln K = \frac{-\Delta G°}{RT} = \frac{-(-95.5 \times 10^3 \, J \, mol^{-1})}{8.3145 \, J \, mol^{-1} \, K^{-1} \times 298.15 \, K} = 38.5$$

$$K = e^{38.5} = 5 \times 10^{16}$$

The value of K obtained here is the thermodynamic equilibrium constant. According to the conventions we have established, the activities of both $Mg(OH)_2(s)$ and $H_2O(l)$ are 1, and molarities can be substituted for the activities of the ions.

$$K = \frac{a_{Mg^{2+}(aq)}a^2_{H_2O(l)}}{a_{Mg(OH)_2(s)}a^2_{H^+(aq)}} = \frac{[Mg^{2+}]}{[H^+]^2} = K_c = 5 \times 10^{16}$$

Practice Example A: Determine the equilibrium constant at 298.15 K for $AgI(s) \rightleftharpoons Ag^+(aq) + I^-(aq)$. Compare your answer to the K_{sp} for AgI in Appendix D.

Practice Example B: At 298.15 K, should manganese dioxide react to an appreciable extent with 1 M HCl(aq), producing manganese(II) ion in solution and chlorine gas?

When a question requires the use of thermodynamic properties, it is a good idea to think qualitatively about the problem before diving into calculations. The dissolution of $Mg(OH)_2(s)$ in acidic solution considered in Example 19-8 is an acid–base reaction that was used as an example in Chapter 18 to illustrate the effect of pH on solubility. It was also mentioned in Chapter 5 as the basis for using milk of magnesia as an antacid. We should certainly expect the reaction to be spontaneous. This means that the value of K should be large, which we found to be the case. If we had made an error in sign in our calculation (an easy thing to do using the expression $\Delta G° = -RT \ln K$), we would have obtained $K = 2 \times 10^{-17}$. But we would have seen immediately that this is the wrong answer. This erroneous value suggests a reaction in which the concentration of products is extremely low at equilibrium.

The data listed in Appendix D are for 25 °C. Thus, values of $\Delta G°$ and K obtained with these data are also at 25 °C. Most chemical reactions are carried out at temperatures other than 25 °C, however. In Section 19-7, we will learn how to calculate values of equilibrium constants at various temperatures.

19-7 $\Delta G°$ AND K AS FUNCTIONS OF TEMPERATURE

In general, equilibrium constants for exothermic reactions will be lower at higher temperatures and higher at lower temperatures. Alternatively, equilibrium constants for endothermic reactions are lower at lower temperatures and higher at higher temperatures. This is seen by evaluating equation 19.15.

In Chapter 15, we used Le Châtelier's principle to make qualitative predictions of the effect of temperature on an equilibrium condition. We can now describe a *quantitative* relationship between the equilibrium constant and temperature. In the method illustrated in Example 19-9, we assume that $\Delta H°$ is practically independent of temperature. Although absolute entropies depend on temperature, we assume that the entropy *change* $\Delta S°$ for a reaction is also independent of temperature. Yet, the term "$T\Delta S$" is strongly temperature-dependent because of the temperature factor T. As a result, $\Delta G°$, which is equal to $\Delta H° - T \Delta S°$, is also dependent on temperature.

EXAMPLE 19-9

Determining the Relationship Between an Equilibrium Constant and Temperature by Using Equations for Free Energy Change. At what temperature will the equilibrium constant for the formation of NOCl(g) be $K = K_p = 1.00 \times 10^3$? Data for this reaction at 25 °C are

$$2 NO(g) + Cl_2(g) \rightleftharpoons 2 NOCl(g)$$

$$\Delta G° = -40.9 \text{ kJ mol}^{-1} \qquad \Delta H = -77.1 \text{ kJ mol}^{-1}$$

$$\Delta S° = -121.3 \text{ J mol}^{-1} \text{ K}^{-1}$$

Solution

To determine an unknown temperature from a known equilibrium constant, we need an equation in which both of these terms appear. The required equation is $\Delta G° = -RT \ln K$. However, to solve for the unknown temperature, we need the value of $\Delta G°$ at that temperature. We know the value of $\Delta G°$ at 25 °C (-40.9 kJ mol^{-1}), but we also know that this value will be different at other temperatures. We can assume, however, that the values of $\Delta H°$ and $\Delta S°$ will not change much with temperature. This means that we can obtain a value of $\Delta G°$ from the equation $\Delta G° = \Delta H° - T\,\Delta S°$, where T is the *unknown* temperature and the values of $\Delta H°$ and $\Delta S°$ are those at 25 °C. Now we have two equations that we can set equal to each other. That is,

$$\Delta G° = \Delta H° - T\,\Delta S° = -RT \ln K$$

We can gather the terms with T on the right,

$$\Delta H° = T\,\Delta S° - RT \ln K = T(\Delta S° - R \ln K)$$

and solve for T.

$$T = \frac{\Delta H°}{\Delta S° - R \ln K}$$

Now substitute values for $\Delta H°$, $\Delta S°$, R, and $\ln K$.

$$T = \frac{-77.1 \times 10^3 \text{ J mol}^{-1}}{-121.3 \text{ J mol}^{-1}\text{ K}^{-1} - [8.3145 \text{ J mol}^{-1}\text{ K}^{-1} \times \ln (1.00 \times 10^3)]}$$

$$= \frac{-77.1 \times 10^3 \text{ J mol}^{-1}}{-121.3 \text{ J mol}^{-1}\text{ K}^{-1} - (8.3145 \times 6.908) \text{ J mol}^{-1}\text{ K}^{-1}}$$

$$= \frac{-77.1 \times 10^3 \text{ J mol}^{-1}}{-178.7 \text{ J mol}^{-1}\text{ K}^{-1}} = 431K$$

Although the answer shows three significant figures, the final result should probably be rounded to just two significant figures. The assumption we made about the constancy of $\Delta H°$ and $\Delta S°$ is probably no more valid than that.

Practice Example A: At what temperature will the formation of $NO_2(g)$ from $NO(g)$ and $O_2(g)$ have $K_p = 1.50 \times 10^2$? For the reaction $2\,NO(g) + O_2(g) \rightleftharpoons 2\,NO_2(g)$ at 25 °C, $\Delta H° = -114.1$ kJ mol^{-1} and $\Delta S° = -146.5$ J mol^{-1} K^{-1}.

Practice Example B: For the reaction $2\,NO(g) + Cl_2(g) \rightleftharpoons 2\,NOCl(g)$, what is the value of K at **(a)** 25 °C; **(b)** 75 °C? Use data from Example 19-9. [*Hint:* The solution to part (a) can be done somewhat more simply than that for (b).]

An alternative to the method outlined in Example 19-9 is to relate the equilibrium constant and temperature directly, without specific reference to a free energy change. We start with the same two expressions as in Example 19-9,

$$-RT \ln K = \Delta G° = \Delta H° - T\,\Delta S°$$

and divide by $-RT$.

$$\ln K = \frac{-\Delta H°}{RT} + \frac{\Delta S°}{R} \qquad (19.14)$$

If we assume that $\Delta H°$ and $\Delta S°$ are constant, equation (19.14) describes a straight line with a slope of $-\Delta H°/R$ and a y-intercept of $\Delta S°/R$. Table 19.3 lists equilibrium constants as a function of the reciprocal of Kelvin temperature for

TABLE 19.3 Equilibrium Constants, K_p, for the Reaction $2\,SO_2(g) + O_2(g) \rightleftharpoons 2\,SO_3(g)$ at Several Temperatures

T, K	$1/T$, K^{-1}	K_p	$\ln K_p$
800	12.5×10^{-4}	9.1×10^2	6.81
850	11.8×10^{-4}	1.7×10^2	5.14
900	11.1×10^{-4}	4.2×10^1	3.74
950	10.5×10^{-4}	1.0×10^1	2.30
1000	10.0×10^{-4}	3.2×10^0	1.16
1050	9.52×10^{-4}	1.0×10^{-4}	0.00
1100	9.09×10^{-4}	3.9×10^{-1}	-0.94
1170	8.5×10^{-4}	1.2×10^{-1}	-2.12

▶ **FIGURE 19-12**
Temperature dependence of the equilibrium constant K_p for the reaction

$$2\,SO_2(g) + O_2(g) \rightleftharpoons 2\,SO_3(g)$$

This graph can be used to establish the enthalpy of reaction, $\Delta H°$ (see equation 19.14).

$$\text{slope} = \Delta H°/R = 2.2 \times 10^4 \text{ K}$$
$$\Delta H° = -8.3145 \text{ J mol}^{-1}\text{ K}^{-1} \times 2.2 \times 10^4 \text{ K}$$
$$= -1.8 \times 10^5 \text{ J mol}^{-1}$$
$$= -1.8 \times 10^2 \text{ kJ mol}^{-1}$$

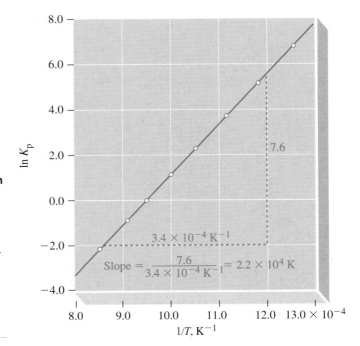

the reaction of $SO_2(g)$ and $O_2(g)$ that forms $SO_3(g)$. The ln K_p and $1/T$ data from Table 19.3 are plotted in Figure 19-12 and yield the expected straight line.

Now we can follow the procedure used in Appendix A-4 to derive the Clausius–Clapeyron equation. We can write equation (19.14) twice, for two different temperatures and with the corresponding equilibrium constants. Then, if we subtract one equation from the other, we obtain the result shown here,

$$\ln\frac{K_2}{K_1} = \frac{\Delta H°}{R}\left(\frac{1}{T_1} - \frac{1}{T_2}\right) \tag{19.15}$$

where T_2 and T_1 are two Kelvin temperatures; K_2 and K_1 are the equilibrium constants at those temperatures; $\Delta H°$ is the enthalpy of reaction, expressed in J mol^{-1}; and R is the gas constant, expressed as 8.3145 J mol^{-1} K^{-1}. Jacobus van't Hoff (1852–1911) derived equation (19.15), which is often referred to as the *van't Hoff equation*.

KEEP IN MIND ▶
that the Clausius–Clapeyron equation (12.2) is just a special case of equation (19.15) in which the equilibrium constants are equilibrium vapor pressures and $\Delta H° = \Delta H_{vap}$.

EXAMPLE 19-10

Relating Equilibrium Constants and Temperature Through the van't Hoff Equation. Use data from Table 19.3 and Figure 19-12 to estimate the temperature at which $K_p = 1.0 \times 10^6$ for the reaction

$$2\,SO_2(g) + O_2(g) \rightleftharpoons 2\,SO_3(g)$$

▶ For simplicity, we have dropped the units in this setup, but you should be able to show that units cancel properly.

Solution

Select one known temperature and equilibrium constant from Table 19.3 and the enthalpy change of the reaction, $\Delta H°$, from Figure 19-12. The data to be substituted into equation (19.15) are $T_1 = ?$, $K_1 = 1.0 \times 10^6$; $T_2 = 800$ K, $K_2 = 9.1 \times 10^2$; and $\Delta H° = -1.8 \times 10^5$ J mol^{-1}.

$$\ln\frac{K_2}{K_1} = \frac{\Delta H°}{R}\left(\frac{1}{T_1} - \frac{1}{T_2}\right)$$

$$\ln\frac{9.1 \times 10^2}{1.0 \times 10^6} = \frac{-1.8 \times 10^5}{8.3145}\left(\frac{1}{T_1} - \frac{1}{800}\right)$$

$$-7.00 = -2.2 \times 10^4\left(\frac{1}{T_1} - \frac{1}{800}\right)$$

$$\frac{-7.00}{-2.2 \times 10^4} + \frac{1}{800} = \frac{1}{T_1}$$

$$\frac{1}{T_1} = (3.2 \times 10^{-4}) + (1.25 \times 10^{-3}) = 1.57 \times 10^{-3}$$

$$T_1 = \frac{1}{1.57 \times 10^{-3}} = 6.37 \times 10^2 \text{ K}$$

Practice Example A: Estimate the temperature at which $K_p = 5.8 \times 10^{-2}$ for the reaction in Example 19-10. Use data from Table 19.3 and Figure 19-12.

Practice Example B: What is the value of K_p for the reaction $2\,SO_2(g) + O_2(g) \rightleftharpoons 2\,SO_3(g)$ at 235 °C? Use data from Table 19.3, Figure 19-12, and the van't Hoff equation (19.15).

CONCEPT ASSESSMENT ✓

The normal boiling point of water is 100 °C. At 120 °C and 1 atm, is ΔH or $T\,\Delta S$ greater for the vaporization of water?

19-8   COUPLED REACTIONS

We have seen two ways to obtain product from a nonspontaneous reaction: (1) Change the reaction conditions to ones that make the reaction spontaneous (mostly by changing the temperature), and (2) carry out the reaction by electrolysis. But there is a third way also. Combine a pair of reactions, one with a positive ΔG and one with a negative ΔG, to obtain a spontaneous overall reaction. Such paired reactions are called **coupled reactions**. Consider the extraction of a metal from its oxide.

When copper(I) oxide is heated to 673 K, no copper metal is obtained. The decomposition of Cu_2O to form products in their standard states (for instance, $P_{O_2} = 1.00$ bar) is nonspontaneous at 673 K.

$$Cu_2O(s) \xrightarrow{\Delta} 2\,Cu(s) + \frac{1}{2}O_2(g) \qquad \Delta G°_{673K} = +125 \text{ kJ} \qquad (19.16)$$

Suppose this nonspontaneous decomposition reaction is coupled with the partial oxidation of carbon to carbon monoxide—a spontaneous reaction. The overall reaction (19.17), because it has a negative value of $\Delta G°$, is spontaneous when reactants and products are in their standard states.

$$Cu_2O(s) \longrightarrow 2\,Cu(s) + \frac{1}{2}O_2(g) \qquad \Delta G°_{673\,K} = +125 \text{ kJ}$$

$$C(s) + \frac{1}{2}O_2(g) \longrightarrow CO(g) \qquad \Delta G°_{673\,K} = -175 \text{ kJ}$$

$$Cu_2O(s) + C(s) \longrightarrow 2\,Cu(s) + CO(g) \qquad \Delta G°_{673\,K} = -50 \text{ kJ} \qquad (19.17)$$

 Reduction of CuO movie

In general chemistry, simple examples of reactions are generally used. In fact, in almost all interesting cases, one reaction is coupled to another, and so forth. No better example exists than the complex cycles of coupled chemical reactions in biological processes, such as illustrated in the Focus On feature.

▲ Mitochondria and endoplasmic reticulum
A colorized scanning electron micrograph of mitochondria (blue) and rough endoplasmic reticulum (yellow) in a pancreatic cell. Mitochondria are the powerhouses of the cell. They oxidize sugars and fats, producing energy for the conversion of ADP to ATP. Rough endoplasmic reticulum is a network of folded membranes covered with protein-synthesizing ribosomes (small dots).

An important example of coupled reactions in living organisms involves the breakdown of glucose ($C_6H_{12}O_6$) accompanied by the conversion of adenosine diphosphate (ADP) to adenosine triphosphate (ATP)* in the mitochondria of cells (Fig. 19-13). ATP serves as an energy-storage compound that is broken down to ADP, which releases energy that can be used in cell processes. For example, it is used in the ribosomes to produce proteins. The ATP-forming reaction

$$ADP^{3-} + HPO_4{}^{2-} + H^+ \longrightarrow ATP^{4-} + H_2O$$

$$\Delta G = -9.2 \text{ kJ mol}^{-1}$$

Adenosine$-$O$-$P$-$O$-$P$-$O$^-$
(ADP^{3-})

Adenosine$-$O$-$P$-$O$-$P$-$O$-$P$-$O$^-$
(ATP^{4-})

is spontaneous under standard conditions at 37 °C, so why does the cell need to use glucose to make ATP? The answer is that cells do not operate with $[H^+] = 1$ M as required by standard conditions; in fact, the pH in a cell is about 7. When we estimate ΔG for the reaction at that pH and assume all other species are at 1.0 M (still far from actuality), we get

$$\Delta G = \Delta G° + RT \ln \left(\frac{a_{ATP} a_{H_2O}}{a_{ADP} a_{P_i} a_{H^+}} \right)$$

Note that reactions (19.16) and (19.17) are not the same, even though each has Cu(s) as a product. The purpose of coupled reactions, then, is to produce a spontaneous overall reaction by combining two other processes: one nonspontaneous and one spontaneous. Many metallurgical processes employ coupled reactions, especially those that use carbon or hydrogen as reducing agents.

To sustain life, organisms must synthesize complex molecules from simpler ones. If carried out as single-step reactions, these syntheses would generally be accompanied by increases in enthalpy, decreases in entropy, and increases in free energy—in short, they would be nonspontaneous and would not occur. In living organisms, changes in temperature and electrolysis are not viable options for dealing with nonspontaneous processes. Here, coupled reactions are crucial, as described in the Focus On feature.

*The structural formulas for ADP^{3-} and ATP^{4-} are in accord with the discussion of expanded valence shells on page 394. Often, these structures are written with one P-to-O double bond per phosphate unit.

where P_i is a common abbreviation for HPO_4^{2-}. We now use $a_{ATP} = a_{ADP} = a_{P_i} = a_{H_2O} = 1$ and $a_{H^+} = 10^{-7}$ to obtain

$$\Delta G = -9.2 \text{ kJ mol}^{-1} + 41.6 \text{ kJ mol}^{-1} = +32.4 \text{ kJ mol}^{-1}$$

In biochemistry, this value of ΔG is called the *biological standard state*, designated $\Delta G^{\circ\prime}$. Thus, we can write

$$\Delta G = \Delta G^{\circ\prime} + RT \ln \left(\frac{a_{ATP} a_{H_2O}}{a_{ADP} a_{P_i} ([H^+]/10^{-7})} \right)$$

Note that the proton concentration is divided by 10^{-7} to give the activity because we have revised our definition of standard state.

Under standard biochemical conditions, the conversion of ADP to ATP is *not spontaneous*. Consequently, in cells this conversion must be coupled with another reaction to provide the necessary energy. The reaction, in the absence of oxygen (the anaerobic conditions inside a cell), is *glycolysis*—a metabolic process that converts glucose to the lactate anion. This reaction has a biochemical standard

Gibbs energy change of -218 kJ mol^{-1}. In the cell, the coupling of this conversion involves ten chemical reactions that are enzyme-catalyzed and form 2 moles of ATP. The overall process can be represented by two steps.

glucose $\longrightarrow$ 2 lactate$^-$ + 2 H$^+$ $\Delta G^{\circ\prime} = -218 \text{ kJ mol}^{-1}$

2 ADP^{3-} + 2 HPO$_4^{2-}$ + 2 H$^+$ $\longrightarrow$ 2 ATP^{4-} + 2 H$_2$O

$\Delta G^{\circ\prime} = 2 \times 32.4 = 64.8 \text{ kJ mol}^{-1}$

glucose + 2 ADP^{3-} + 2 HPO$_4^{2-}$ $\longrightarrow$

2 lactate$^-$ + 2 ATP^{4-} + 2 H$_2$O $\Delta G^{\circ\prime} = -153 \text{ kJ mol}^{-1}$

The overall reaction is therefore spontaneous. The coupling of the partial oxidation of glucose by way of glycolysis is spontaneous and provides a source of ATP. The ATP is then used in the formation of proteins. That is, the reaction

ATP^{4-} + H$_2$O $\longrightarrow$ ADP^{3-} + HPO$_4^{2-}$ + H$^+$

$$\Delta G^{\circ} = -32.4 \text{ kJ mol}^{-1}$$

is coupled with a nonspontaneous reaction to produce a protein in a ribosome as suggested by Figure 19-13.

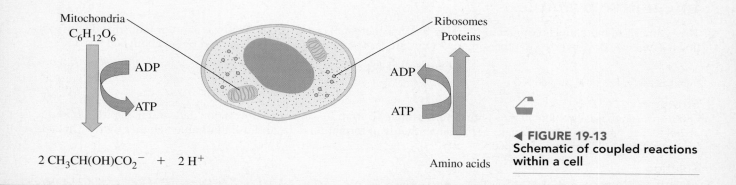

Mitochondria
$C_6H_{12}O_6$

ADP

ATP

2 CH$_3$CH(OH)CO$_2^-$ + 2 H$^+$

Ribosomes
Proteins

ADP

ATP

Amino acids

◀ **FIGURE 19-13**
Schematic of coupled reactions within a cell

Summary

19-1 Spontaneity: The Meaning of Spontaneous Change—A process that proceeds without need of external intervention is said to be a **spontaneous process**. A **nonspontaneous process** cannot occur without external intervention. A process that is spontaneous in one direction is nonspontaneous in the reverse direction. Some spontaneous processes are exothermic, others are endothermic so that criteria other than enthalpy change are needed to define spontaneity.

19-2 The Concept of Entropy—**Entropy** is a thermodynamic property related to the distribution of a system's energy among the available microscopic energy levels. Boltzmann's formula (equation 19.1) illustrates the relationship between entropy and the number of microstates of a system. The thermodynamic definition of an **entropy**

change is of a quantity of heat (q_{rev}) divided by a Kelvin temperature (equation 19.2), and having the units $J\,K^{-1}$. The quantity of heat released (or absorbed) during the process must be from a reversible process in order for the entropy change to be path-independent.

19-3 Evaluating Entropy and Entropy Changes—The **third law of thermodynamics** states that the entropy of a pure, perfect crystal at 0 K is zero. Thus there are absolute entropies, unlike internal energy and enthalpy. The entropy of a substance in its standard state is called **standard molar entropy**, S°. Standard molar entropies of reactants and products can be used to calculate standard entropy changes in chemical reactions (equation 19.5). Another important entropy-related relationship is **Trouton's rule**, which states that the standard entropy of vaporization at the normal boiling point is approximately constant at $87 \, \text{J mol}^{-1} \, \text{K}^{-1}$ (equation 19.4).

19-4 Criteria for Spontaneous Change: The Second Law of Thermodynamics—The basic criterion for spontaneous change is that the entropy change of the universe, which is the sum of the entropy change of the system plus that of the surroundings (equation 19.6), must be greater than zero (equation 19.7). This statement is known as the **second law of thermodynamics**. An equivalent criterion applied to the system alone is based on a thermodynamic function known as the Gibbs energy, G, or the **free energy**. The **free energy change**, ΔG, is the enthalpy change for the system (ΔH) minus the product of the temperature and entropy change for the system ($T \, \Delta S$) (equation 19.9). Table 19.1 summarizes the criteria for spontaneous change based on free energy change.

19-5 Standard Free Energy Change, $\Delta G°$—The **standard free energy change**, $\Delta G°$, is based on the conversion of reactants in their standard states to products in their standard states. Tabulated free energy data are usually **standard molar free energies of formation**, $\Delta G_f°$, and usually at 298.15 K.

19-6 Free Energy Change and Equilibrium—The relationship between the standard free energy change and the equilibrium constant for a reaction is $\Delta G° = -RT \ln K$. The constant, K, is called a **thermodynamic equilibrium constant**. It is based on the activities of reactants and products, but these activities can be related to solution molarities and gas partial pressures by means of a few simple conventions.

19-7 $\Delta G°$ and K as Functions of Temperature—By starting with the relationship between standard free energy change and the equilibrium constant, the van't Hoff equation—relating the equilibrium constant and temperature—can be written. With this equation, tabulated data at 25 °C can be used to determine equilibrium constants not just at 25 °C but at other temperatures as well.

19-8 Coupled Reactions—Nonspontaneous processes can be made spontaneous by coupling them with spontaneous reactions and by taking advantage of the state function property of G. **Coupled reactions**, that is, paired reactions that yield a spontaneous overall reaction, occur in metallurgical processes and in biochemical transformations.

Integrative Example

The synthesis of methanol is of great importance because methanol can be used directly as a motor fuel, mixed with gasoline for fuel use, or converted to other organic compounds. The synthesis reaction, carried out at about 500 K, is

$$CO(g) + 2 \, H_2(g) \rightleftharpoons CH_3OH(g)$$

What is the value of K_p at 500 K?

Strategy

Our approach to this problem begins with determining $\Delta G°$ from free energy of formation data and using $\Delta G°$ to find K_p at 298 K. The next step is to calculate $\Delta H°$ from enthalpy of formation data, and use this value together with K_p at 298 K in expression (19.15) to find K_p at 500 K.

Solution

Write the equation for methanol synthesis; place free energy of formation data from Appendix D under formulas in the equation, and use these data to calculate $\Delta G°$ at 298 K.

$$\begin{array}{cccc} & CO(g) & + \; 2 \, H_2(g) & \rightleftharpoons CH_3OH(g) \\ \Delta G_f°, \text{kJ mol}^{-1} & -137.2 & 0 & -162.0 \end{array}$$

$\Delta G° = 1 \, \text{mol CH}_3\text{OH} \times (-162.0 \, \text{kJ/mol CH}_3\text{OH})$
$\qquad\qquad -1 \, \text{mol CO} \times (-137.2 \, \text{kJ/mol CO}) = -24.8 \, \text{kJ}$

To calculate K_p at 298 K, use $\Delta G°$ at 298 K, written as $-24.8 \times 10^3 \, \text{J mol}^{-1}$, in the expression $\Delta G° = -RT \ln K_p$.

$$\ln K_p = -\Delta G°/RT = \frac{-(-24.8 \times 10^3 \, \text{J mol}^{-1})}{8.3145 \, \text{J mol}^{-1} \, \text{K}^{-1} \times 298 \, \text{K}} = 10.0$$

$$K_p = e^{10.0} = 2.2 \times 10^4$$

To determine $\Delta H°$ at 298 K, use standard enthalpy of formation data from Appendix D, applied in the same manner as was previously used for $\Delta G°$.

$$\begin{array}{cccc} & CO(g) & + \; 2 \, H_2(g) & \rightleftharpoons CH_3OH(g) \\ \Delta H_f°, \text{kJ mol}^{-1} & -110.5 & 0 & -200.7 \end{array}$$

$\Delta H° = 1 \, \text{mol CH}_3\text{OH} \times (-200.7 \, \text{kJ/mol CH}_3\text{OH})$
$\qquad\qquad -1 \, \text{mol CO} \times (-110.5 \, \text{kJ/mol CO}) = -90.2 \, \text{kJ}$

Use the van't Hoff equation with $K_p = 2.2 \times 10^4$ at 298 K and $\Delta H° = -90.2 \times 10^3 \, \text{J mol}^{-1}$. Solve for K_p at 500 K.

$$\ln \frac{K_p}{2.2 \times 10^4} = \frac{-90.2 \times 10^3 \, \text{J mol}^{-1}}{8.3145 \, \text{J mol}^{-1} \, \text{K}^{-1}} \left(\frac{1}{298 \, \text{K}} - \frac{1}{500 \, \text{K}} \right)$$

$$= -14.7$$

$$\frac{K_p}{2.2 \times 10^4} = e^{-14.7} = 4 \times 10^{-7} \qquad K_p = 9 \times 10^{-3}$$

Assessment

We have been successful in determining the equilibrium constant for the synthesis of methanol at 500 K using tabulated thermodynamic data and the van't Hoff equation. Note that increasing the temperature favors the reverse reaction, as we should expect from Le Châtelier's principle. That is, an increase in temperature in a reversible reaction favors the heat absorbing (endothermic) reaction. Here, the forward reaction is exothermic and the reverse reaction is endothermic.

Exercises

Spontaneous Change and Entropy

1. Indicate whether each of the following changes represents an increase or decrease in entropy in a system, and explain your reasoning: **(a)** the freezing of ethanol; **(b)** the sublimation of Dry Ice; **(c)** the burning of a rocket fuel.

2. Arrange the entropy changes of the following processes, all at 25 °C, in the expected order of increasing ΔS, and explain your reasoning: **(a)** $H_2O(l, 1\ atm) \longrightarrow H_2O(g, 1\ atm)$; **(b)** $CO_2(s, 1\ atm) \longrightarrow CO_2(g, 10\ mmHg)$; **(c)** $H_2O(l, 1\ atm) \longrightarrow H_2O(g, 10\ mmHg)$.

3. Use ideas from this chapter to explain this famous remark attributed to Rudolf Clausius (1865): "Die Energie der Welt ist konstant; die Entropie der Welt strebt einem Maximum zu." ("The energy of the world is constant; the entropy of the world increases toward a maximum.")

4. Comment on the difficulties of solving environmental pollution problems from the standpoint of entropy changes associated with the formation of pollutants and with their removal from the environment.

5. Indicate whether the entropy of the system would increase or decrease in each of the following reactions. If you cannot be certain simply by inspecting the equation, explain why.
   (a) $CCl_4(l) \longrightarrow CCl_4(g)$
   (b) $CuSO_4 \cdot 3\ H_2O(s) + 2\ H_2O(g) \longrightarrow$
   $$CuSO_4 \cdot 5\ H_2O(s)$$

   (c) $SO_3(g) + H_2(g) \longrightarrow SO_2(g) + H_2O(g)$
   (d) $H_2S(g) + O_2(g) \longrightarrow H_2O(g) + SO_2(g)$
   (not balanced)

6. Which substance in each of the following pairs would have the greater entropy? Explain.
   (a) at 75 °C and 1 atm: 1 mol $H_2O(l)$ or 1 mol $H_2O(g)$
   (b) at 5 °C and 1 atm: 50.0 g Fe(s) or 0.80 mol Fe(s)
   (c) 1 mol Br_2 (l, 1 atm, 8 °C) or 1 mol Br_2 (s, 1 atm, -8 °C)
   (d) 0.312 mol SO_2 (g, 0.110 atm, 32.5 °C) or 0.284 mol O_2 (g, 15.0 atm, 22.3 °C)

7. For each of the following reactions, indicate whether ΔS for the reaction should be positive or negative. If it is not possible to determine the sign of ΔS from the information given, indicate why.
   (a) $CaO(s) + H_2O(l) \longrightarrow Ca(OH)_2(s)$
   (b) $2\ HgO(s) \longrightarrow 2\ Hg(l) + O_2(g)$
   (c) $2\ NaCl(l) \longrightarrow 2\ Na(l) + Cl_2(g)$
   (d) $Fe_2O_3(s) + 3\ CO(g) \longrightarrow 2\ Fe(s) + 3\ CO_2(g)$
   (e) $Si(s) + 2\ Cl_2(g) \longrightarrow SiCl_4(g)$

8. By analogy to ΔH_f° and ΔG_f° how would you define entropy of formation? Which would have the largest entropy of formation: $CH_4(g)$, $CH_3CH_2OH(l)$, or $CS_2(l)$? First make a qualitative prediction; then test your prediction with data from Appendix D.

Phase Transitions

9. In Example 19-2, we dealt with ΔH_{vap}° and ΔS_{vap}° for water at 100 °C.
   (a) Use data from Appendix D to determine values for these two quantities at 25 °C.
   (b) From your knowledge of the structure of liquid water, explain the differences in ΔH_{vap}° values and in ΔS_{vap}° values between 25 °C and 100 °C.

10. Pentane is one of the most volatile of the hydrocarbons in gasoline. At 298.15 K, the following enthalpies of formation are given for pentane: $\Delta H_f^\circ[C_5H_{12}(l)] = -173.5\ kJ\ mol^{-1}$; $\Delta H_f^\circ[C_5H_{12}(g)] = -146.9\ kJ\ mol^{-1}$.
   (a) Estimate the normal boiling point of pentane.
   (b) Estimate ΔG° for the vaporization of pentane at 298 K.
   (c) Comment on the significance of the sign of ΔG° at 298 K.

11. Which of the following substances would obey Trouton's rule most closely: HF, $C_6H_5CH_3$ (toluene), or CH_3OH (methanol)? Explain your reasoning.

12. Estimate the normal boiling point of bromine, Br_2, in the following way: Determine ΔH_{vap}° for Br_2 from data in Appendix D. Assume that ΔH_{vap}° remains constant and that Trouton's rule is obeyed.

13. In what temperature range can the following equilibrium be established? Explain.

    $$H_2O(l, 0.50\ atm) \rightleftharpoons H_2O(g, 0.50\ atm)$$

14. Refer to Figures 12-19 and 19-9. Which has the lowest free energy at 1 atm and -60 °C: solid, liquid, or gaseous carbon dioxide? Explain.

Free Energy and Spontaneous Change

15. Which of the following changes in a thermodynamic property would you expect to find for the reaction $Br_2(g) \longrightarrow 2\,Br(g)$ *at all temperatures:* **(a)** $\Delta H < 0$; **(b)** $\Delta S > 0$; **(c)** $\Delta G < 0$; **(d)** $\Delta S < 0$? Explain.

16. If a reaction can be carried out only by electrolysis, which of the following changes in a thermodynamic property *must* apply: **(a)** $\Delta H > 0$; **(b)** $\Delta S > 0$; **(c)** $\Delta G = \Delta H$; **(d)** $\Delta G > 0$? Explain.

17. Indicate which of the four cases in Table 19.1 applies to each of the following reactions. If you are unable to decide from only the information given, state why.
    (a) $PCl_3(g) + Cl_2(g) \longrightarrow PCl_5(g) \quad \Delta H^\circ = -87.9\ kJ$
    (b) $CO_2(g) + H_2(g) \longrightarrow CO(g) + H_2O(g)$
    $\Delta H^\circ = +41.2\ kJ$
    (c) $NH_4CO_2NH_2(s) \longrightarrow 2\,NH_3(g) + CO_2(g)$
    $\Delta H^\circ = +159.2\ kJ$

18. Indicate which of the four cases in Table 19.1 applies to each of the following reactions. If you are unable to decide from only the information given, state why.
    (a) $H_2O(g) + \frac{1}{2}O_2(g) \longrightarrow H_2O_2(g)$
    $\Delta H^\circ = +105.5\ kJ$

(b) $C_6H_6(l) + \frac{15}{2}O_2(g) \longrightarrow 6\,CO_2(g) + 3\,H_2O(g)$
$\Delta H^\circ = -3135\ kJ$

(c) $NO(g) + \frac{1}{2}Cl_2(g) \longrightarrow NOCl(g)$
$\Delta H^\circ = -38.54\ kJ$

19. For the mixing of ideal gases (see Figure 19-2), explain whether a positive, negative, or zero value is expected for ΔH, ΔS, and ΔG.

20. What values of ΔH, ΔS, and ΔG would you expect for the formation of an ideal solution of liquid components? (Is each value positive, negative, or zero?)

21. Explain why **(a)** some exothermic reactions do not occur spontaneously, and **(b)** some reactions in which the entropy of the system increases do not occur spontaneously.

22. Explain why you would expect a reaction of the type $AB(g) \longrightarrow A(g) + B(g)$ always to be spontaneous at *high* rather than at low temperatures.

Standard Free Energy Change

23. From the data given in the following table, determine ΔS° for the reaction $NH_3(g) + HCl(g) \longrightarrow NH_4Cl(s)$. All data are at 298 K.

	ΔH_f°, kJ mol^{-1}	ΔG_f°, kJ mol^{-1}
$NH_3(g)$	-46.11	-16.48
$HCl(g)$	-92.31	-95.30
$NH_4Cl(s)$	-314.4	-202.9

24. Use data from Appendix D to determine values of ΔG° for the following reactions at 25 °C.
    (a) $C_2H_2(g) + 2\,H_2(g) \longrightarrow C_2H_6(g)$
    (b) $2\,SO_3(g) \longrightarrow 2\,SO_2(g) + O_2(g)$
    (c) $Fe_3O_4(s) + 4\,H_2(g) \longrightarrow 3\,Fe(s) + 4\,H_2O(g)$
    (d) $2\,Al(s) + 6\,H^+(aq) \longrightarrow 2\,Al^{3+}(aq) + 3\,H_2(g)$

25. At 298 K, for the reaction $2\,PCl_3(g) + O_2(g) \longrightarrow 2\,POCl_3(l)$, $\Delta H^\circ = -620.2\ kJ$ and the standard molar entropies are $PCl_3(g)$, $311.8\ J\,K^{-1}$; $O_2(g)$, $205.1\ J\,K^{-1}$; and $POCl_3(l)$, $222.4\ J\,K^{-1}$. Determine **(a)** ΔG° at 298 K and **(b)** whether the reaction proceeds spontaneously in the forward or the reverse direction when reactants and products are in their standard states.

26. At 298 K, for the reaction $2\,H^+(aq) + 2\,Br^-(aq) + 2\,NO_2(g) \longrightarrow Br_2(l) + 2\,HNO_2(aq)$, $\Delta H^\circ = -61.6\ kJ$ and the standard molar entropies are $H^+(aq)$, $0\ J\,K^{-1}$; $Br^-(aq)$, $82.4\ J\,K^{-1}$; $NO_2(g)$, $240.1\ J\,K^{-1}$; $Br_2(l)$, $152.2\ J\,K^{-1}$; $HNO_2(aq)$, $135.6\ J\,K^{-1}$. Determine **(a)** ΔG° at 298 K and **(b)** whether the reaction proceeds spontaneously in the forward or the reverse direction when reactants and products are in their standard states.

27. The following standard free energy changes are given for 25 °C.
    (1) $N_2(g) + 3\,H_2(g) \longrightarrow 2\,NH_3(g)$
    $\Delta G^\circ = -33.0\ kJ$

(2) $4\,NH_3(g) + 5\,O_2(g) \longrightarrow 4\,NO(g) + 6\,H_2O(l)$
$\Delta G^\circ = -1010.5\ kJ$

(3) $N_2(g) + O_2(g) \longrightarrow 2\,NO(g)$
$\Delta G^\circ = +173.1\ kJ$

(4) $N_2(g) + 2\,O_2(g) \longrightarrow 2\,NO_2(g)$
$\Delta G^\circ = +102.6\ kJ$

(5) $2\,N_2(g) + O_2(g) \longrightarrow 2\,N_2O(g)$
$\Delta G^\circ = +208.4\ kJ$

Combine the preceding equations, as necessary, to obtain ΔG° values for each of the following reactions.

(a) $N_2O(g) + \frac{3}{2}O_2(g) \longrightarrow 2\,NO_2(g) \qquad \Delta G^\circ = ?$

(b) $2\,H_2(g) + O_2(g) \longrightarrow 2\,H_2O(l) \qquad \Delta G^\circ = ?$

(c) $2\,NH_3(g) + 2\,O_2(g) \longrightarrow N_2O(g) + 3\,H_2O(l)$
$\Delta G^\circ = ?$

Of reactions (a), (b), and (c), which would tend to go to completion at 25 °C, and which would reach an equilibrium condition with significant amounts of all reactants and products present?

28. The following standard free energy changes are given for 25 °C.
    (1) $SO_2(g) + 3\,CO(g) \longrightarrow COS(g) + 2\,CO_2(g)$
    $\Delta G^\circ = -246.4\ kJ$

(2) $CS_2(g) + H_2O(g) \longrightarrow COS(g) + H_2S(g)$
$\Delta G^\circ = -41.5\ kJ$

(3) $CO(g) + H_2S(g) \longrightarrow COS(g) + H_2(g)$
$\Delta G^\circ = +1.4\ kJ$

(4) $CO(g) + H_2O(g) \longrightarrow CO_2(g) + H_2(g)$
$\Delta G^\circ = -28.6\ kJ$

Combine the preceding equations, as necessary, to obtain ΔG° values for the following reactions.

(a) $COS(g) + 2\,H_2O(g) \longrightarrow$
$SO_2(g) + CO(g) + 2\,H_2(g) \qquad \Delta G^\circ = ?$

(b) $COS(g) + 3 H_2O(g) \longrightarrow$
$$SO_2(g) + CO_2(g) + 3 H_2(g) \quad \Delta G° = ?$$
(c) $COS(g) + H_2O(g) \longrightarrow CO_2(g) + H_2S(g)$
$$\Delta G° = ?$$
Of reactions (a), (b), and (c), which is spontaneous in the forward direction when reactants and products are present in their standard states?

29. Write an equation for the combustion of one mole of benzene, $C_6H_6(l)$, and use data from Appendix D to determine $\Delta G°$ at 298 K if the products of the combustion are (a) $CO_2(g)$ and $H_2O(l)$, and (b) $CO_2(g)$ and $H_2O(g)$. Describe how you might determine the *difference* between the values obtained in (a) and (b) without having either to write the combustion equation or to determine $\Delta G°$ values for the combustion reactions.

30. Use molar entropies from Appendix D, together with the following data, to estimate the bond-dissociation energy of the F_2 molecule.
$$F_2(g) \longrightarrow 2 F(g) \quad \Delta G° = 123.9 \text{ kJ}$$
Compare your result with the value listed in Table 10.3.

31. Assess the feasibility of the reaction
$$N_2H_4(g) + 2 OF_2(g) \longrightarrow N_2F_4(g) + 2 H_2O(g)$$
by determining each of the following quantities for this reaction at 25 °C.
(a) $\Delta S°$ (The standard molar entropy of $N_2F_4(g)$ is 301.2 J K^{-1}.)
(b) $\Delta H°$ (Use data from Table 10.3 and F—O and N—F bond energies of 222 and 301 kJ mol^{-1}, respectively.)
(c) $\Delta G°$
Is the reaction feasible? If so, is it favored at high or low temperatures?

32. Solid ammonium nitrate can decompose to dinitrogen oxide gas and liquid water. What is $\Delta G°$ at 298 K? Is the decomposition reaction favored at temperatures above or below 298 K?

The Thermodynamic Equilibrium Constant

33. For one of the following reactions, $K_c = K_p = K$. Identify that reaction. For the other two reactions, what is the relationship between K_c, K_p, and K? Explain.
(a) $2 SO_2(g) + O_2(g) \rightleftharpoons 2 SO_3(g)$
(b) $HI(g) \rightleftharpoons \dfrac{1}{2}H_2(g) + \dfrac{1}{2}I_2(g)$
(c) $NH_4HCO_3(s) \rightleftharpoons NH_3(g) + CO_2(g) + H_2O(l)$

34. $H_2(g)$ can be prepared by passing steam over hot iron: $3 Fe(s) + 4 H_2O(g) \rightleftharpoons Fe_3O_4(s) + 4 H_2(g)$.

(a) Write an expression for the thermodynamic equilibrium constant for this reaction.
(b) Explain why the partial pressure of $H_2(g)$ is independent of the amounts of $Fe(s)$ and $Fe_3O_4(s)$ present.
(c) Can we conclude that the production of $H_2(g)$ from $H_2O(g)$ could be accomplished regardless of the proportions of $Fe(s)$ and $Fe_3O_4(s)$ present? Explain.

Relationships Involving ΔG, $\Delta G°$, Q, and K

35. Use data from Appendix D to determine K_p at 298 K for the reaction $N_2O(g) + \dfrac{1}{2}O_2(g) \rightleftharpoons 2 NO(g)$.

36. Use data from Appendix D to establish for the reaction $2 N_2O_4(g) + O_2(g) \rightleftharpoons 2 N_2O_5(g)$:
(a) $\Delta G°$ at 298 K for the reaction as written;
(b) K_p at 298 K.

37. Use data from Appendix D to determine values at 298 K of $\Delta G°$ and K for the following reactions. (*Note:* The equations are not balanced.)
(a) $HCl(g) + O_2(g) \rightleftharpoons H_2O(g) + Cl_2(g)$
(b) $Fe_2O_3(s) + H_2(g) \rightleftharpoons Fe_3O_4(s) + H_2O(g)$
(c) $Ag^+(aq) + SO_4^{2-}(aq) \rightleftharpoons Ag_2SO_4(s)$

38. In Example 19-1, we were unable to conclude by inspection whether $\Delta S°$ for the reaction $CO(g) + H_2O(g) \longrightarrow CO_2(g) + H_2(g)$ should be positive or negative. Use data from Appendix D to obtain $\Delta S°$ at 298 K.

39. Use thermodynamic data at 298 K to decide in which direction the reaction
$$2 SO_2(g) + O_2(g) \rightleftharpoons 2 SO_3(g)$$
is spontaneous when the partial pressures of SO_2, O_2, and SO_3 are 1.0×10^{-4}, 0.20, and 0.10 atm, respectively.

40. Use thermodynamic data at 298 K to decide in which direction the reaction
$$H_2(g) + Cl_2(g) \rightleftharpoons 2 HCl(g)$$
is spontaneous when the partial pressures of H_2, Cl_2, and HCl are all 0.5 atm.

41. The standard free energy change for the reaction
$$CH_3CO_2H(aq) + H_2O(l) \rightleftharpoons$$
$$CH_3CO_2^-(aq) + H_3O^+(aq)$$
is 27.07 kJ mol^{-1} at 298 K. Use this thermodynamic quantity to decide in which direction the reaction is spontaneous when the concentrations of $CH_3CO_2H(aq)$, $CH_3CO_2^-(aq)$, and $H_3O^+(aq)$ are 0.10 M, 1.0×10^{-3} M, and 1.0×10^{-3} M, respectively.

42. The standard free energy change for the reaction
$$NH_3(aq) + H_2O(l) \rightleftharpoons NH_4^+(aq) + OH^-(aq)$$
is 29.05 kJ mol^{-1} at 298 K. Use this thermodynamic quantity to decide in which direction the reaction is spontaneous when the concentrations of $NH_3(aq)$, $NH_4^+(aq)$, and $OH^-(aq)$ are 0.10 M, 1.0×10^{-3} M, and 1.0×10^{-3} M, respectively.

43. For the reaction $2\,NO(g) + O_2(g) \longrightarrow 2\,NO_2(g)$ all but one of the following equations is correct. Which is *incorrect*, and why? **(a)** $K = K_p$; **(b)** $\Delta S^\circ = (\Delta G^\circ - \Delta H^\circ)/T$; **(c)** $K_p = e^{-\Delta G^\circ/RT}$; **(d)** $\Delta G = \Delta G^\circ + RT \ln Q$.

44. Why is ΔG° such an important property of a chemical reaction, even though the reaction is generally carried out under *nonstandard* conditions?

45. At 1000 K, an equilibrium mixture in the reaction $CO_2(g) + H_2(g) \rightleftharpoons CO(g) + H_2O(g)$ contains 0.276 mol H_2, 0.276 mol CO_2, 0.224 mol CO, and 0.224 mol H_2O.
    (a) What is K_p at 1000 K?
    (b) Calculate ΔG° at 1000 K.
    (c) In which direction would a spontaneous reaction occur if the following were brought together at 1000 K: 0.0750 mol CO_2, 0.095 mol H_2, 0.0340 mol CO, and 0.0650 mol H_2O?

46. For the reaction $2\,SO_2(g) + O_2(g) \rightleftharpoons 2\,SO_3(g)$, $K_c = 2.8 \times 10^2$ at 1000 K.
    (a) What is ΔG° at 1000 K?
    [*Hint:* What is K_p?]
    (b) If 0.40 mol SO_2, 0.18 mol O_2, and 0.72 mol SO_3 are mixed in a 2.50-L flask at 1000 K, in what direction will a net reaction occur?

47. For the following equilibrium reactions, calculate ΔG° at the indicated temperature.
    [*Hint:* How is each equilibrium constant related to a thermodynamic equilibrium constant, K?]
    (a) $H_2(g) + I_2(g) \rightleftharpoons 2\,HI(g)$ $K_c = 50.2$ at 445 °C
    (b) $N_2O(g) + \dfrac{1}{2}O_2(g) \rightleftharpoons 2\,NO(g)$
    $$K_c = 1.7 \times 10^{-13} \text{ at 25 °C}$$
    (c) $N_2O_4(g) \rightleftharpoons 2\,NO_2(g)$
    $$K_c = 4.61 \times 10^{-3} \text{ at 25 °C}$$
    (d) $2\,Fe^{3+}(aq) + Hg_2^{2+}(aq) \rightleftharpoons$
    $$2\,Fe^{2+}(aq) + 2\,Hg^{2+}(aq)$$
    $$K_c = 9.14 \times 10^{-6} \text{ at 25 °C}$$

48. Two equations can be written for the dissolution of $Mg(OH)_2(s)$ in acidic solution.
    $$Mg(OH)_2(s) + 2\,H^+(aq) \rightleftharpoons Mg^{2+}(aq) + 2\,H_2O(l)$$
    $$\Delta G^\circ = -95.5 \text{ kJ mol}^{-1}$$

$$\frac{1}{2}Mg(OH)_2(s) + H^+(aq) \rightleftharpoons \frac{1}{2}Mg^{2+}(aq) + H_2O(l)$$
$$\Delta G^\circ = -47.8 \text{ kJ mol}^{-1}$$

(a) Explain why these two equations have different ΔG° values.
(b) Will K for these two equations be the same or different? Explain.
(c) Will the solubilities of $Mg(OH)_2(s)$ in a buffer solution at pH = 8.5 depend on which of the two equations is used as the basis of the calculation? Explain.

49. At 298 K, $\Delta G_f^\circ[CO(g)] = -137.2$ kJ/mol and $K_p = 6.5 \times 10^{11}$ for the reaction $CO(g) + Cl_2(g) \rightleftharpoons COCl_2(g)$. Use these data to determine $\Delta G_f^\circ[COCl_2(g)]$, and compare your result with the value in Appendix D.

50. Use thermodynamic data from Appendix D to calculate values of K_{sp} for the following sparingly soluble solutes: **(a)** AgBr; **(b)** $CaSO_4$; **(c)** $Fe(OH)_3$.
    [*Hint:* Begin by writing solubility equilibrium expressions.]

51. To establish the law of conservation of mass, Lavoisier carefully studied the decomposition of mercury(II) oxide:
    $$HgO(s) \longrightarrow Hg(l) + \frac{1}{2}O_2(g)$$
    At 25 °C, $\Delta H^\circ = +90.83$ kJ and $\Delta G^\circ = +58.54$ kJ.
    (a) Show that the partial pressure of $O_2(g)$ in equilibrium with $HgO(s)$ and $Hg(l)$ at 25 °C is extremely low.
    (b) What conditions do you suppose Lavoisier used to obtain significant quantities of oxygen?

52. Currently, CO_2 is being studied as a source of carbon atoms for synthesizing organic compounds. One possible reaction involves the conversion of CO_2 to methanol, CH_3OH.
    $$CO_2(g) + 3\,H_2(g) \longrightarrow CH_3OH(g) + H_2O(g)$$
    With the aid of data from Appendix D, determine
    (a) if this reaction proceeds to any significant extent at 25 °C;
    (b) if the production of $CH_3OH(g)$ is favored by raising or lowering the temperature from 25 °C;
    (c) K_p for this reaction at 500 K;
    (d) the partial pressure of $CH_3OH(g)$ at equilibrium if $CO_2(g)$ and $H_2(g)$, each initially at a partial pressure of 1 atm, react at 500 K.

ΔG° and K as Functions of Temperature

53. Use data from Appendix D to establish at 298 K for the reaction:
    $$2\,NaHCO_3(s) \longrightarrow Na_2CO_3(s) + H_2O(l) + CO_2(g)$$
    (a) ΔS°;   **(b)** ΔH°;   **(c)** ΔG°;   **(d)** K.

54. A possible reaction for converting methanol to ethanol is
    $$CO(g) + 2\,H_2(g) + CH_3OH(g) \longrightarrow C_2H_5OH(g) + H_2O(g)$$
    (a) Use data from Appendix D to calculate ΔH°, ΔS°, and ΔG° for this reaction at 25 °C.

(b) Is this reaction thermodynamically favored at high or low temperatures? At high or low pressures? Explain.
(c) Estimate K_p for the reaction at 750 K.

55. What must be the temperature if the following reaction has $\Delta G^\circ = -45.5$ kJ, $\Delta H^\circ = -24.8$ kJ, and $\Delta S^\circ = 15.2$ J K^{-1}?
    $$Fe_2O_3(s) + 3\,CO(g) \longrightarrow 2\,Fe(s) + 3\,CO_2(g)$$

56. Estimate K_p at 100 °C for the reaction $2\,SO_2(g) + O_2(g) \rightleftharpoons 2\,SO_3(g)$. Use data from Table 19.3 and Figure 19-12.

57. The synthesis of ammonia by the Haber process occurs by the reaction $N_2(g) + 3 H_2(g) \rightleftharpoons 2 NH_3(g)$ at 400 °C. Using data from Appendix D and assuming that $\Delta H°$ and $\Delta S°$ are essentially unchanged in the temperature interval from 25 to 400 °C, estimate K_p at 400 °C.

58. Use data from Appendix D to determine **(a)** $\Delta H°$, $\Delta S°$, and $\Delta G°$ at 298 K and **(b)** K_p at 875 K for the water gas shift reaction, used commercially to produce $H_2(g)$: $CO(g) + H_2O(g) \rightleftharpoons CO_2(g) + H_2(g)$. [*Hint:* Assume that $\Delta H°$ and $\Delta S°$ are essentially unchanged in this temperature interval.]

59. In Example 19-10, we used the van't Hoff equation to determine the temperature at which $K_p = 1.0 \times 10^6$ for the reaction $2 SO_2(g) + O_2(g) \rightleftharpoons 2 SO_3(g)$. Obtain another estimate of this temperature with data from Appendix D and equations (19.9) and (19.13). Compare your result with that obtained in Example 19-10.

60. The following equilibrium constants have been determined for the reaction $H_2(g) + I_2(g) \rightleftharpoons 2 HI(g)$: $K_p = 50.0$ at 448 °C and 66.9 at 350 °C. Use these data to estimate $\Delta H°$ for the reaction.

61. For the reaction $N_2O_4(g) \rightleftharpoons 2 NO_2(g)$, $\Delta H° = +57.2$ kJ mol^{-1} and $K_p = 0.113$ at 298 K.
    (a) What is K_p at 0 °C?
    (b) At what temperature will $K_p = 1.00$?

62. Use data from Appendix D and the van't Hoff equation (19.15) to estimate a value of K_p at 100 °C for the reaction $2 NO(g) + O_2(g) \rightleftharpoons 2 NO_2(g)$. [*Hint:* First determine K_p at 25 °C. What is $\Delta H°$ for the reaction?]

63. For the reaction
$$CO(g) + 3 H_2(g) \rightleftharpoons CH_4(g) + H_2O(g),$$
$$K_p = 2.15 \times 10^{11} \text{ at } 200 °C$$
$$K_p = 4.56 \times 10^8 \text{ at } 260 °C$$

determine $\Delta H°$ by using the van't Hoff equation (19.15) and by using tabulated data in Appendix D. Compare the two results, and comment on how good the assumption is that $\Delta H°$ is essentially independent of temperature in this case.

64. Sodium carbonate, an important chemical used in the production of glass, is made from sodium hydrogen carbonate by the reaction
$$2 NaHCO_3(s) \rightleftharpoons Na_2CO_3(s) + CO_2(g) + H_2O(g)$$
Data for the temperature variation of K_p for this reaction are $K_p = 1.66 \times 10^{-5}$ at 30 °C; 3.90×10^{-4} at 50 °C; 6.27×10^{-3} at 70 °C; and 2.31×10^{-1} at 100 °C.
    (a) Plot a graph similar to Figure 19-12, and determine $\Delta H°$ for the reaction.
    (b) Calculate the temperature at which the total gas pressure above a mixture of $NaHCO_3(s)$ and $Na_2CO_3(s)$ is 2.00 atm.

Coupled Reactions

65. Titanium is obtained by the reduction of $TiCl_4(l)$, which in turn is produced from the mineral rutile (TiO_2).
    (a) With data from Appendix D, determine $\Delta G°$ at 298 K for this reaction.
$$TiO_2(s) + 2 Cl_2(g) \longrightarrow TiCl_4(l) + O_2(g)$$
    (b) Show that the conversion of $TiO_2(s)$ to $TiCl_4(l)$, with reactants and products in their standard states, is spontaneous at 298 K if the reaction in (a) is coupled with the reaction
$$2 CO(g) + O_2(g) \longrightarrow 2 CO_2(g)$$

66. Following are some standard free energies of formation, $\Delta G_f°$, per mole of metal oxide at 1000 K: NiO, -115 kJ; MnO, -280 kJ; TiO_2, -630 kJ. The standard free energy of formation of CO at 1000 K is -250 kJ per mol CO. Use the method of coupled reactions (page 809) to determine which of these metal oxides can be reduced to the metal by a spontaneous reaction with carbon at 1000 K and with all reactants and products in their standard states.

Integrative and Advanced Exercises

67. Use data from Appendix D to estimate **(a)** the normal boiling point of mercury and **(b)** the vapor pressure of mercury at 25 °C.

68. Dinitrogen pentoxide, N_2O_5, is a solid with a high vapor pressure. Its vapor pressure at 7.5 °C is 100 mmHg, and the solid sublimes at a pressure of 1.00 atm at 32.4 °C. What is the standard free energy change for the process $N_2O_5(s) \longrightarrow N_2O_5(g)$ at 25 °C?

69. Consider the vaporization of water: $H_2O(l) \longrightarrow H_2O(g)$ at 100 °C, with $H_2O(l)$ in its standard state, but with the partial pressure of $H_2O(g)$ at 2.0 atm. Which of the following statements about this vaporization at 100 °C are true? **(a)** $\Delta G° = 0$, **(b)** $\Delta G = 0$, **(c)** $\Delta G° > 0$, **(d)** $\Delta G > 0$? Explain.

70. At 298 K, 1.00 mol BrCl(g) is introduced into a 10.0-L vessel, and equilibrium is established in the reaction
$$BrCl(g) \rightleftharpoons \frac{1}{2} Br_2(g) + \frac{1}{2} Cl_2(g).$$ Calculate the amounts of each of the three gases present when equilibrium is established.
[*Hint:* Use data from Appendix D as necessary.]

71. Use data from Appendix D and other information from this chapter to estimate the temperature at which the dissociation of $I_2(g)$ becomes appreciable [for example, with the $I_2(g)$ 50% dissociated into I(g) at 1 atm total pressure].

72. The following table shows the enthalpies and free energies of formation of three metal oxides at 25 °C.

	ΔH_f°, kJ mol^{-1}	ΔG_f°, kJ mol^{-1}
PbO(red)	−219.0	−188.9
Ag$_2$O	−31.05	−11.20
ZnO	−348.3	−318.3

(a) Which of these oxides can be most readily decomposed to the free metal and $O_2(g)$?
(b) For the oxide that is most easily decomposed, to what temperature must it be heated to produce $O_2(g)$ at 1.00 atm pressure?

73. The following data are given for the two solid forms of HgI_2 at 298 K.

	ΔH_f°, kJ mol^{-1}	ΔG_f°, kJ mol^{-1}	S°, J mol^{-1} K^{-1}
HgI$_2$(red)	−105.4	−101.7	180.
HgI$_2$(yellow)	−102.9	(?)	(?)

Estimate values for the two missing entries. To do this, assume that for the transition $HgI_2(red) \longrightarrow HgI_2(yellow)$, the values of ΔH° and ΔS° at 25 °C have the same values that they do at the equilibrium temperature of 127 °C.

74. Oxides of nitrogen are produced in high-temperature combustion processes. The essential reaction is $N_2(g) + O_2(g) \rightleftharpoons 2\,NO(g)$. At what approximate temperature will an *equimolar* mixture of $N_2(g)$ and $O_2(g)$ be 1.0% converted to $NO(g)$?
[*Hint:* Use data from Appendix D as necessary.]

75. Use the following data, as appropriate, to estimate the molarity of a saturated aqueous solution of $Sr(IO_3)_2$.

	ΔH_f°, kJ mol^{-1}	ΔG_f°, kJ mol^{-1}	S°, J mol^{-1} K^{-1}
Sr(IO$_3$)$_2$(s)	−1019.2	−855.1	234
Sr^{2+}(aq)	−545.8	−599.5	−32.6
IO$_3^-$(aq)	−221.3	−128.0	118.4

76. A plausible reaction for the production of ethylene glycol (used as antifreeze) is

$$2\,CO(g) + 3\,H_2(g) \longrightarrow CH_2OHCH_2OH(l)$$

The following thermodynamic properties of CH_2OHCH_2OH at 25 °C are given: $\Delta H_f^\circ = -454.8$ kJ mol^{-1} and $\Delta G_f^\circ = -323.1$ kJ mol^{-1}. Use these data, together with values from Appendix D, to obtain a value of S°, the standard molar entropy of $CH_2OHCH_2OH(l)$, at 25 °C.

77. Use the following data

	ΔH_f°, kJ mol^{-1}	ΔG_f°, kJ mol^{-1}	S°, J mol^{-1} K^{-1}
CuSO$_4 \cdot 3\,H_2O$(s)	−1684.3	−1400.0	221.3
CuSO$_4 \cdot H_2O$(s)	−1085.8	−918.1	146.0

together with other data from the text to determine the temperature at which the equilibrium pressure of water vapor above the two solids in the following reaction is 75 Torr.

$$CuSO_4 \cdot 3\,H_2O(s) \rightleftharpoons CuSO_4 \cdot H_2O(s) + 2\,H_2O(g)$$

78. For the dissociation of $CaCO_3(s)$ at 25 °C, $CaCO_3(s) \rightleftharpoons CaO(s) + CO_2(g)$ $\Delta G^\circ = +131$ kJ mol^{-1}. A sample of pure $CaCO_3(s)$ is placed in a flask and connected to an ultrahigh vacuum system capable of reducing the pressure to 10^{-9} mmHg.
(a) Would $CO_2(g)$ produced by the decomposition of $CaCO_3(s)$ at 25 °C be detectable in the vacuum system at 25 °C?
(b) What additional information do you need to determine P_{CO_2} as a function of temperature?
(c) With necessary data from Appendix D, determine the minimum temperature to which $CaCO_3(s)$ would have to be heated for $CO_2(g)$ to become detectable in the vacuum system.

79. Introduced into a 1.50-L flask is 0.100 mol of $PCl_5(g)$; the flask is held at a temperature of 227 °C until equilibrium is established. What is the total pressure of the gases in the flask at this point?

$$PCl_5(g) \rightleftharpoons PCl_3(g) + Cl_2(g)$$

[*Hint:* Use data from Appendix D and appropriate relationships from this chapter.]

80. From the data given in Exercise 64, estimate a value of ΔS° at 298 K for the reaction

$$2\,NaHCO_3(s) \longrightarrow Na_2CO_3(s) + H_2O(g) + CO_2(g)$$

81. The normal boiling point of cyclohexane, C_6H_{12}, is 80.7 °C. Estimate the temperature at which the vapor pressure of cyclohexane is 100.0 mmHg.

82. The term *thermodynamic stability* refers to the sign of ΔG_f°. If ΔG_f° is negative, the compound is stable with respect to decomposition into its elements. Use the data in Appendix D to determine whether $Ag_2O(s)$ is thermodynamically stable at **(a)** 25 °C and **(b)** 200 °C.

83. At 0 °C, ice has a density of 0.917 g mL^{-1} and an absolute entropy of 37.95 J mol^{-1} K^{-1}. At this temperature, liquid water has a density of 1.000 g mL^{-1} and an absolute entropy of 59.94 J mol^{-1} K^{-1}. The pressure corresponding to these values is 1 bar. Calculate ΔG, ΔG°, ΔS°, and ΔH° for the melting of two moles of ice at its normal melting point.

84. The decomposition of the poisonous gas phosgene is represented by the equation $COCl_2(g) \rightleftharpoons CO(g) + Cl_2(g)$. Values of K_p for this reaction are $K_p = 6.7 \times 10^{-9}$ at 99.8 °C and $K_p = 4.44 \times 10^{-2}$ at 395 °C. At what temperature is $COCl_2$ 15% dissociated when the total gas pressure is maintained at 1.00 atm?

85. Use data from Appendix D to estimate the aqueous solubility, in milligrams per liter, of $AgBr(s)$ at 100 °C.

86. The standard molar entropy of solid hydrazine at its melting point of 1.53 °C is 67.15 J mol^{-1} K^{-1}. The enthalpy of fusion is 12.66 kJ mol^{-1}. For $N_2H_4(l)$ in the interval from 1.53 °C to 298.15 K, the molar heat capacity at constant pressure is given by the expression $C_p = 97.78 + 0.0586(T - 280)$. Determine the standard molar entropy of $N_2H_4(l)$ at 298.15 K.
[*Hint:* The heat absorbed to produce an infinitesimal change in the temperature of a substance is $dq_{rev} = C_p\,dT$.]

87. Use the following data to estimate the standard molar entropy of gaseous benzene at 298.15 K; that is, $S°[C_6H_6(g, 1\ atm)]$. For C_6H_6 (s, 1 atm) at its melting point of 5.53 °C, $S°$ is 128.82 J mol^{-1} K^{-1}. The enthalpy of fusion is 9.866 kJ mol^{-1}. From the melting point to 298.15 K, the average heat capacity of liquid benzene is 134.0 J K^{-1} mol^{-1}. The enthalpy of vaporization of $C_6H_6(l)$ at 298.15 K is 33.85 kJ mol^{-1}, and in the vaporization, $C_6H_6(g)$ is produced at a pressure of 95.13 Torr. Imagine that this vapor could be compressed to 1 atm pressure without condensing and while behaving as an ideal gas. Calculate $S°[C_6H_6(g, 1\ atm)]$. [*Hint:* Refer to Exercise 86, and note the following: For infinitesimal quantities, $dS = dq/dT$; for the compression of an ideal gas, $dq = -dw$; and for pressure–volume work, $dw = -P\ dV$.]

Feature Problems

88. A tabulation of more precise thermodynamic data than are presented in Appendix D lists the following values for $H_2O(l)$ and $H_2O(g)$ at 298.15 K, at a standard-state pressure of 1 bar.

	$\Delta H_f°$, kJ mol^{-1}	$\Delta G_f°$, kJ mol^{-1}	$S°$, J mol^{-1} K^{-1}
$H_2O(l)$	−285.830	−237.129	69.91
$H_2O(g)$	−241.818	−228.572	188.825

(a) Use these data to determine, in two different ways, $\Delta G°$ at 298.15 K for the vaporization: H_2O (l, 1 bar) $\rightleftharpoons$ H_2O(g, 1 bar). The value you obtain will differ slightly from that on page 797, because here, the standard state pressure is 1 bar, and there, it is 1 atm.
(b) Use the result of part (a) to obtain the value of K for this vaporization and, hence, the vapor pressure of water at 298.15 K.
(c) The vapor pressure in part (b) is in the unit bar. Convert the pressure to millimeters of mercury.
(d) Start with the value $\Delta G° = 8.590$ kJ, given on page 797, and calculate the vapor pressure of water at 298.15 K in a fashion similar to that in parts (b) and (c). In this way, demonstrate that the results obtained in a thermodynamic calculation do not depend on the convention we choose for the standard-state pressure, as long as we use standard-state thermodynamic data consistent with that choice.
89. The graphs show how $\Delta G°$ varies with temperature for three different oxidation reactions: the oxidations of C(graphite), Zn, and Mg to CO, ZnO, and MgO, respectively. Graphs such as these can be used to show the temperatures at which carbon is an effective reducing agent to reduce metal oxides to the free metals. As a result, such graphs are important to metallurgists. Use these graphs to answer the following questions.
(a) Why can Mg be used to reduce ZnO to Zn at all temperatures, but Zn cannot be used to reduce MgO to Mg at any temperature?
(b) Why can C be used to reduce ZnO to Zn at some temperatures but not at others? At what temperatures can carbon be used to reduce zinc oxide?
(c) Is it possible to produce Zn from ZnO by its direct decomposition without requiring a coupled reaction? If so, at what approximate temperatures might this occur?
(d) Is it possible to decompose CO to C and O_2 in a spontaneous reaction? Explain.

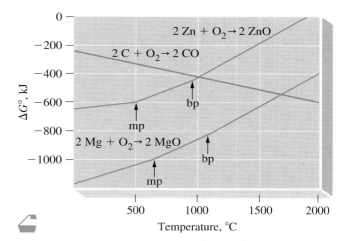

▲ $\Delta G°$ for three reactions as a function of temperature. The reactions are indicated by the equations written above the graphs. The points noted by arrows are the melting points (mp) and boiling points (bp) of zinc and magnesium.

(e) To the set of graphs, add straight lines representing the reactions

$$C(graphite) + O_2(g) \longrightarrow CO_2(g)$$
$$2\ CO(g) + O_2(g) \longrightarrow 2\ CO_2(g)$$

given that the three lines representing the formation of oxides of carbon intersect at about 800°C. [*Hint:* At what other temperature can you relate $\Delta G°$ and temperature?]
The slopes of the three lines described above differ sharply. Explain why this so—that is, explain the slope of each line in terms of principles governing free energy change.
(f) The graphs for the formation of oxides of other metals are similar to the ones shown for Zn and Mg; that is, they all have positive slopes. Explain why carbon is such a good reducing agent for the reduction of metal oxides.
90. In a heat engine, heat (q_h) is absorbed by a working substance (such as water) at a high temperature (T_h). Part of this heat is converted to work (w), and the rest (q_l) is released to the surroundings at the lower temperature (T_l). The *efficiency* of a heat engine is the ratio w/q_h. The second law of thermodynamics establishes the following equation for the maximum efficiency of a heat engine, expressed on a percentage basis.

$$\text{efficiency} = \frac{w}{q_h} \times 100\% = \frac{T_h - T_1}{T_h} \times 100\%$$

In a particular electric power plant, the steam leaving a steam turbine is condensed to liquid water at 41 °C (T_1) and the water is returned to the boiler to be regenerated as steam. If the system operates at 36% efficiency,

(a) What is the minimum temperature of the steam [$H_2O(g)$] used in the plant?

(b) Why is the actual steam temperature probably higher than that calculated in part (a)?

(c) Assume that at T_h the $H_2O(g)$ is in equilibrium with $H_2O(l)$. Estimate the steam pressure at the temperature calculated in part (a).

(d) Is it possible to devise a heat engine with greater than 100 percent efficiency? With 100 percent efficiency? Explain.

91. The free energy available from the complete combustion of 1 mol of glucose to carbon dioxide and water is

$$C_6H_{12}O_6(aq) + 6\,O_2(g) \longrightarrow 6\,CO_2(g) + 6\,H_2O(l)$$
$$\Delta G° = -2870 \text{ kJ mol}^{-1}$$

(a) Under biological standard conditions, compute the maximum number of moles of ATP that could form from ADP and phosphate if all the energy of combustion of 1 mol of glucose could be utilized.

(b) The actual number of moles of ATP formed by a cell under aerobic conditions (that is, in the presence of oxygen) is about 38. Calculate the efficiency of energy conversion of the cell.

(c) Consider these typical physiological conditions.

$$P_{CO_2} = 0.050 \text{ bar; } P_{O_2} = 0.132 \text{ bar;}$$
$$[\text{glucose}] = 1.0 \text{ mg/mL; pH} = 7.0;$$
$$[\text{ATP}] = [\text{ADP}] = [P_i] = 0.00010 \text{ M.}$$

Calculate ΔG for the conversion of 1 mol ADP to ATP and ΔG for the oxidation of 1 mol glucose under these conditions.

(d) Calculate the efficiency of energy conversion for the cell under the conditions given in part (c). Compare this efficiency with that of a diesel engine that attains 78% of the theoretical efficiency operating with $T_h = 1923$ K and $T_1 = 873$ K. Suggest a reason for your result.

[*Hint:* See Problem 90.]

Self-Assessment Exercises

92. In your own words, define the following symbols: **(a)** ΔS_{univ}; **(b)** $\Delta G_f°$; **(c)** K.

93. Briefly describe each of the following ideas, methods, or phenomena: **(a)** absolute molar entropy; **(b)** coupled reactions; **(c)** Trouton's rule; **(d)** evaluation of an equilibrium constant from tabulated thermodynamic data.

94. Explain the important distinctions between each of the following pairs: **(a)** spontaneous and nonspontaneous processes; **(b)** the second and third laws of thermodynamics; **(c)** ΔG and $\Delta G°$.

95. For a process to occur spontaneously, **(a)** the entropy of the system must increase; **(b)** the entropy of the surroundings must increase; **(c)** both the entropy of the system and the entropy of the surroundings must increase; **(d)** the net change in entropy of the system and surroundings considered together must be a positive quantity; **(e)** the entropy of the universe must remain constant.

96. The free energy change of a reaction can be used to assess **(a)** how much heat is absorbed from the surroundings; **(b)** how much work the system does on the surroundings; **(c)** the net direction in which the reaction occurs to reach equilibrium; **(d)** the proportion of the heat evolved in an exothermic reaction that can be converted to various forms of work.

97. The reaction, $2\,Cl_2O(g) \longrightarrow 2\,Cl_2(g) + O_2(g)$ $\Delta H = -161$ kJ, is expected to be **(a)** spontaneous at all temperatures; **(b)** spontaneous at low temperatures, but nonspontaneous at high temperatures; **(c)** nonspontaneous at all temperatures; **(d)** spontaneous at high temperatures only.

98. If $\Delta G° = 0$ for a reaction, it must also be true that **(a)** $K = 0$; **(b)** $K = 1$; **(c)** $\Delta H° = 0$; **(d)** $\Delta S° = 0$; **(e)** the equilibrium activities of the reactants and products do not depend on the initial conditions.

99. Two correct statements about the reversible reaction $N_2(g) + O_2(g) \rightleftharpoons 2\,NO(g)$ are **(a)** $K = K_p$; **(b)** the equilibrium amount of NO increases with an increased total gas pressure; **(c)** the equilibrium amount of NO increases if an equilibrium mixture is transferred from a 10.0-L container to a 20.0-L container; **(d)** $K = K_c$; **(e)** the composition of an equilibrium mixture of the gases is independent of the temperature.

100. Suppose a graph similar to Figure 19-9 were drawn for the process $I_2(s) \longrightarrow I_2(l)$ at 1 atm.
(a) Refer to Figure 12-18 and determine the temperature at which the two lines would intersect.
(b) What would be the value of $\Delta G°$ at this temperature? Explain.

101. *Without performing detailed calculations*, indicate whether any of the following reactions would occur to a measurable extent at 298 K.
(a) Conversion of dioxygen to ozone:
$$3\,O_2(g) \longrightarrow 2\,O_3(g)$$
(b) Dissociation of N_2O_4 to NO_2:
$$N_2O_4(g) \longrightarrow 2\,NO_2(g)$$
(c) Formation of BrCl:
$$Br_2(l) + Cl_2(g) \longrightarrow 2\,BrCl(g)$$

102. Explain briefly why
(a) the change in entropy in a system is not always a suitable criterion for spontaneous change;
(b) $\Delta G°$ is so important in dealing with the question of spontaneous change, even though the conditions employed in a reaction are very often nonstandard.

103. A handbook lists the following standard enthalpies of formation at 298 K for cyclopentane, C_5H_{10}: $\Delta H_f°[C_5H_{10}(l)] = -105.9$ kJ/mol and $\Delta H_f°[C_5H_{10}(g)] = -77.2$ kJ/mol.

(a) Estimate the normal boiling point of cyclopentane.
(b) Estimate $\Delta G°$ for the vaporization of cyclopentane at 298 K.
(c) Comment on the significance of the sign of $\Delta G°$ at 298 K.

104. Consider the reaction $NH_4NO_3(s) \longrightarrow N_2O(g) + 2 H_2O(l)$ at 298 K.
   (a) Is the forward reaction endothermic or exothermic?
   (b) What is the value of $\Delta G°$ at 298 K?
   (c) What is the value of K at 298 K?
   (d) Does the reaction tend to occur spontaneously at temperatures above 298 K, below 298 K, both, or neither?

eMedia Exercises

105. Observe the motion of atoms in the **Mixing of Gases** activity (*Activebook 19-2*). Describe why entropy increases in this process. If the choice of each atom's location in either of the two halves of the system (boxes) is considered a microstate, W, calculate the change in entropy between the initial (separated) and final (mixed) states.

106. **(a)** Describe how temperature causes a change in entropy on the atomic scale in the **Lattice Vibrations** activity (*Activebook 19-2*). **(b)** What is the property of the crystal that represents the degree of its order (or disorder)?

107. **(a)** In the **Temperature Dependence of Entropy** simulation (*Activebook 19-3*), what point of the curve corresponds to the greatest relative increase in entropy? **(b)** How does this relate to the values of enthalpy changes observed at this point, compared to elsewhere on the curve?

108. **(a)** Write out a balanced chemical equation for the reaction illustrated in the **Formation of Aluminum Bromide** movie (*Activebook 19-3*). **(b)** What information is needed to calculate the entropy change associated with this reaction? **(c)** Using the tabulated thermodynamic values in Appendix D, calculate the entropy change that would occur if 25.0 grams of aluminum reacted with an excess of liquid bromine at 298 K.

109. **(a)** In the **NO$_2$–N$_2$O$_4$ Equilibrium** animation (*Activebook 19-6*), under which condition(s) shown will the free energy of the system be greater than the standard free energy? **(b)** Which set of conditions maximizes the free energy of the system?

eLaboratory Exercise

These exercises allow students to apply the concepts and skills for this chapter in the simulated laboratory of Virtual ChemLab. Worksheets for each of these exercises are found in the Virtual ChemLab Workbook in your MediaPak.

110. **(VCL 19-1) The Balance Between Enthalpy and Entropy**
   For chemical reactions, we say a reaction proceeds to the right when ΔG is negative and the reaction proceeds to the left when ΔG is positive. At equilibrium, ΔG is zero. The Gibbs–Helmholtz equation specifies that at constant temperature $\Delta G = \Delta H - T \Delta S$ or, in other words, the sign and size of ΔG are governed by the balance between enthalpic (ΔH) and entropic (ΔS) considerations. In this assignment you will dissolve several different salts in water, measure the resulting temperature changes, and then make some deductions about the thermodynamic driving forces behind the dissolving process.

20

ELECTROCHEMISTRY

CONTENTS

A transit bus fitted with hydrogen–oxygen fuel cells. The use of fuel cells could dramatically reduce urban air pollution. The conversion of chemical energy into electrical energy is one of the main subjects of this chapter.

Huddle, P. A., White, M. D., Rogers, F. "Using a Teaching Model to Correct Known Misconceptions in Electrochemistry." *J. Chem. Educ.* **2000:** *77*, 104 (January 2000).

Sanger, M. J., Greenbowe, T. J. "An Analysis of College Chemistry Textbooks As Sources of Misconceptions and Errors in Electrochemistry." *J. Chem. Educ.* **1999:** *76*, 853 (June 1999).

A conventional gasoline-powered automobile is only about 25% efficient in converting chemical energy into kinetic energy (energy of motion). An electric-powered auto is about three times as efficient. Unfortunately, when automotive technology was first being developed, devices for converting chemical energy to electrical energy did not perform at their intrinsic efficiencies. This fact, together with the availability of high-quality gasoline at a low cost, resulted in the preeminence of the internal combustion automobile. Now, with concern about long-term energy supplies and environmental pollution, there is a renewed interest in electric-powered buses and automobiles.

In this chapter, we will see how chemical reactions can be used to produce electricity and how electricity can be used to cause chemical reactions. The practical applications of electrochemistry are countless, ranging from batteries and fuel cells as electric power sources to the manufacture of key chemicals, the refining of metals, and methods for controlling corrosion. Also important, however, are the theoretical implications. Because electricity involves a flow of electric charge, a study of the relationship between chemistry and electricity gives us additional insight into reactions in which electrons are transferred—*oxidation–reduction reactions.*

20-1   ELECTRODE POTENTIALS AND THEIR MEASUREMENT

The criteria for spontaneous change developed in Chapter 19 apply to reactions of all types—precipitation, acid–base, and oxidation–reduction (redox). We can devise an additional useful criterion for redox reactions, however.

Figure 20-1 shows that a redox reaction occurs between $Cu(s)$ and $Ag^+(aq)$, but not between $Cu(s)$ and $Zn^{2+}(aq)$. Specifically, we see that silver ions are reduced to silver atoms on a copper surface, whereas zinc ions are *not* reduced to zinc atoms on a copper surface. We can say that Ag^+ is more readily reduced than is Zn^{2+}. In this section, we will introduce the *electrode potential*, a property related to these reduction tendencies.

When used in electrochemical studies, a strip of metal, M, is called an **electrode**. An electrode immersed in a solution containing ions of the same metal, M^{n+}, is called a **half-cell**. Two kinds of interactions are possible between metal atoms on the electrode and metal ions in solution (Fig. 20-2):

1. A metal ion M^{n+} from solution may collide with the electrode, gain n electrons from it, and be converted to a metal atom M. *The ion is reduced.*

2. A metal atom M on the surface may lose n electrons to the electrode and enter the solution as the ion M^{n+}. *The metal atom is oxidized.*

An equilibrium is quickly established between the metal and the solution, which can represented as

$$M(s) \xrightleftharpoons[\text{reduction}]{\text{oxidation}} M^{n+}(aq) + ne^- \qquad (20.1)$$

However, any changes produced at the electrode or in the solution as a consequence of this equilibrium are too slight to measure. Instead, measurements must be based on a combination of *two different* half-cells. Specifically, we must measure the tendency for electrons to flow from the electrode of one half-cell to the electrode of the other. Electrodes are classified according to whether oxidation or reduction takes place there. If oxidation takes place, the electrode is called the **anode**. If reduction takes place, the electrode is called the **cathode**.

◄ The term *electrode* is sometimes used for the entire half-cell assembly.

◄ **KEEP IN MIND**
that although $M^{n+}(aq)$ and ne^- appear together on the right-hand side of this expression, only the ion M^{n+} enters the solution. The electrons remain on the electrode, $M(s)$. Free electrons are never found in an aqueous solution.

Formation of Silver Crystals movie

(a)   (b)

◄ **FIGURE 20-1**
Behavior of $Ag^+(aq)$ and $Zn^{2+}(aq)$ in the presence of copper

(a) Copper metal displaces silver ions from colorless $AgNO_3(aq)$ as a deposit of silver metal; the copper enters the solution as blue $Cu^{2+}(aq)$.

$$Cu(s) + 2\,Ag^+(aq) \longrightarrow Cu^{2+}(aq) + 2\,Ag(s)$$

(b) $Cu(s)$ *does not* displace colorless Zn^{2+} from $Zn(NO_3)_2(aq)$.

$$Cu(s) + Zn^{2+}(aq) \longrightarrow \text{no reaction}$$

Oxidation

Reduction

▶ **FIGURE 20-2**
An electrochemical half-cell
The half-cell consists of a metal electrode, M, partially immersed in an aqueous solution of its ions, M^{n+}. (The anions required to maintain electrical neutrality in the solution are not shown.) The situation illustrated here is limited to metals that do not react with water.

Make a solution of about 1 M $AgNO_3$. Cut copper foil into a shape that resembles a Christmas tree. Place the copper in a 1 liter beaker and pour the $AgNO_3$ solution in to submerse the copper. After about 30 minutes, the silver has plated out onto the copper giving the effect of snow on the branches of the tree.

Figure 20-3 depicts a combination of two half-cells, one with a Cu electrode in contact with $Cu^{2+}(aq)$, and the other with an Ag electrode in contact with $Ag^+(aq)$. The two electrodes are joined by wires to an electric meter—here, a *voltmeter*. To complete the electric circuit, the two solutions must also be

1.00 M $Cu(NO_3)_2(aq)$ 1.00 M $AgNO_3(aq)$

Continually stress that electrons flow away from the anode and toward the cathode in voltaic cells.

Emphasize that current is electron flow where as voltage is the force behind the flow.

▲ **FIGURE 20-3**
Measurement of the electromotive force of an electrochemical cell
An electrochemical cell consists of two half-cells with electrodes joined by a wire and solutions joined by a salt bridge. (The ends of the salt bridge are plugged with a porous material that allows ions to migrate but prevents the bulk flow of liquid.) Electrons flow from the Cu electrode, the anode, where oxidation occurs to the Ag electrode, the cathode, where reduction occurs. For precise measurements, the amount of electric current drawn from the cell must be kept very small by means of either a specially designed voltmeter or a device called a potentiometer.

▶ Anions migrate toward the <u>an</u>ode, and <u>cat</u>ions toward the <u>cat</u>hode.

connected electrically. However, because charge is carried through solutions by the migration of *ions*, a wire cannot be used for this connection. The solutions must either be in direct contact through a porous barrier or joined by a third solution in a U-tube called a **salt bridge**. The properly connected combination of two half-cells is called an **electrochemical cell**.

Now, we shall consider the changes that occur in the electrochemical cell in Figure 20-3. As the arrows suggest, Cu atoms release electrons at the anode and enter the $Cu(NO_3)_2(aq)$ as Cu^{2+} ions. Electrons lost by the Cu atoms pass through the wires and the voltmeter to the cathode, where they are gained by Ag^+ ions from the $AgNO_3(aq)$, producing a deposit of metallic silver. Simultaneously, anions (NO_3^-) from the salt bridge migrate into the copper half-cell and neutralize the positive charge of the excess Cu^{2+} ions; cations (K^+) migrate into the silver half-cell and neutralize the negative charge of the excess NO_3^- ions. The overall reaction that occurs as the electrochemical cell spontaneously produces electric current is

Oxidation: $\qquad Cu(s) \longrightarrow Cu^{2+}(aq) + 2\,e^-$

Reduction: $\qquad \underline{2\,\{Ag^+(aq) + e^- \longrightarrow Ag(s)\}}$

Overall: $\qquad Cu(s) + 2\,Ag^+(aq) \longrightarrow Cu^{2+}(aq) + 2\,Ag(s) \qquad$ (20.2)

The reading on the voltmeter (0.460 V) is significant. It is the **cell voltage**, or the *potential difference* between the two half-cells. The unit of cell voltage, **volt (V)**, is the energy per unit charge. Thus, a potential difference of one volt signifies an energy of one joule for every coulomb of charge passing through an electric circuit: $1\,V = 1\,J/C$. We can think of a voltage, or potential difference, as the driving force for electrons; the greater the voltage, the greater the driving force. The flow of water from a higher to a lower level is analogous to this situation. The greater the difference in water levels, the greater the force behind the flow of water. Cell voltage is also called **electromotive force (emf)**, or **cell potential**, and represented by the symbol E_{cell}.

Now let's return to the question raised by Figure 20-1: Why does copper *not* displace Zn^{2+} from solution? In an electrochemical cell consisting of a $Zn(s)/Zn^{2+}(aq)$ half-cell and a $Cu^{2+}(aq)/Cu(s)$ half-cell, electrons flow *from the Zn to the Cu*. The spontaneous reaction in the electrochemical cell in Figure 20-4 is

Oxidation: $\qquad Zn(s) \longrightarrow Zn^{2+}(aq) + 2\,e^-$

Reduction: $\qquad \underline{Cu^{2+}(aq) + 2\,e^- \longrightarrow Cu(s)}$

Overall: $\qquad Zn(s) + Cu^{2+}(aq) \longrightarrow Zn^{2+}(aq) + Cu(s) \qquad$ (20.3)

Because reaction (20.3) is a spontaneous reaction, the displacement of $Zn^{2+}(aq)$ by Cu(s)—the *reverse* of reaction (20.3)—does *not* occur spontaneously. This is the observation made in Figure 20-1. In Section 20-3, we will discuss how to predict the direction of spontaneous change for oxidation–reduction reactions.

◀ KEEP IN MIND

that the overall reaction occurring in the electrochemical cell is identical to what happens in the direct addition of Cu(s) to $Ag^+(aq)$ pictured in Figure 20-1(a).

> ✓ It is a good idea to use the word "potential" in order to describe the drive behind spontaneous redox reactions. Since these are chemical reactions, the description "chemical potential" is natural.

◀ Formulations such as $Zn(s)/Zn^{2+}(aq)$ and $Cu^{2+}(aq)/Cu(s)$ are called *couples* and are often used as abbreviations for half-cells.

Probst, D. A., Henderson, G. "Zinc Electrodes and the Thermodynamics of a Galvanic Cell." *J. Chem. Educ.* **1996**: 73, 962 (October 1996).

Set up an electrochemical cell similar to the diagram. Treat it as a circuit and show that the voltage drops to zero when the salt bridge is removed. Remove other components to emphasize the circuit. Explain how the salt bridge maintains electric neutrality. Note also that the voltage is small in electrochemical circuits.

Voltaic Cells I: The Copper-Zinc Cell animation

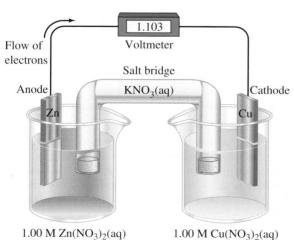

Flow of electrons

1.103

Voltmeter

Salt bridge

Anode

$KNO_3(aq)$

Cathode

Zn

Cu

1.00 M $Zn(NO_3)_2(aq)$ 1.00 M $Cu(NO_3)_2(aq)$

◀ **FIGURE 20-4**

The reaction
$Zn(s) + Cu^{2+}(aq) \longrightarrow Zn^{2+}(aq) + Cu(s)$
in an electrochemical cell

CELL DIAGRAMS AND TERMINOLOGY

Drawing sketches of electrochemical cells, as in Figures 20-3 and 20-4, is helpful, but more often a simpler representation is used. A **cell diagram** shows the components of an electrochemical cell in a symbolic way. We will use the following, generally accepted conventions in writing cell diagrams.

- The anode, the electrode at which *oxidation* occurs, is placed at the *left* side of the diagram.
- The cathode, the electrode at which *reduction* occurs, is placed at the *right* side of the diagram.
- A boundary between different phases (for example, an electrode and a solution) is represented by a *single vertical line* ($|$).
- The boundary between half-cell compartments, commonly a salt bridge, is represented by a *double vertical line* ($\|$). Species in aqueous solution are placed on either side of the double vertical line. Different species within the same solution are separated from each other by a comma.

The cell diagram corresponding to both Figure 20-4 and reaction (20.3) is customarily written as

anode $\longrightarrow$ $\underset{\substack{\text{half-cell} \\ \text{(oxidation)}}}{\text{Zn(s)}|\text{Zn}^{2+}\text{(aq)}}$ $\underset{\substack{\text{salt} \\ \text{bridge}}}{\|}$ $\underset{\substack{\text{half-cell} \\ \text{(reduction)}}}{\text{Cu}^{2+}\text{(aq)}|\text{Cu(s)}}$ $\longleftarrow$ cathode $\quad E_{cell} = 1.103 \text{ V} \quad$ (20.4)
$\underset{\text{cell voltage}}{}$

The electrochemical cells of Figures 20-3 and 20-4 produce electricity as a result of spontaneous chemical reactions; as such, they are called **voltaic**, or **galvanic**, **cells**. In Section 20-7 we will consider *electrolytic cells*—electrochemical cells in which electricity is used to accomplish a nonspontaneous chemical change.

> ▶ Several memory devices have been proposed for the oxidation/anode and reduction/cathode relationships. Perhaps the simplest is that in the oxidation/anode relationship, both terms begin with a vowel: *o/a*; in the reduction/cathode relationship, both begin with a consonant: *r/c*.

> **KEEP IN MIND ▶**
> that the spectator ions are not shown in a cell diagram, but they are present. They pass through the salt bridge to maintain electrical neutrality.

> ✓ Remind students that the spectator ions are not shown, but are there. They pass through the salt bridge to maintain electrical neutrality.

> ✓ A useful mnemonic: oxidation at anode (AN OX); and reduction at cathode (RED CAT).

EXAMPLE 20-1

Representing a Redox Reaction by Means of a Cell Diagram. Aluminum metal displaces zinc(II) ion from aqueous solution.

(a) Write oxidation and reduction half-equations and an overall equation for this redox reaction.

(b) Write a cell diagram for a voltaic cell in which this reaction occurs.

Solution

(a) The term *displaces* means that aluminum goes into solution as Al^{3+}(aq), forcing Zn^{2+}(aq) out of solution as zinc metal. Al is oxidized to Al^{3+}, and Zn^{2+} is reduced to Zn. In writing the overall equation, the coefficients must be adjusted so that equal numbers of electrons are involved in oxidation and in reduction. (This is the half-reaction method of balancing redox equations discussed in Section 5-5.)

Oxidation:	$2 \{ Al(s) \longrightarrow Al^{3+}(aq) + 3 e^- \}$
Reduction:	$3 \{ Zn^{2+}(aq) + 2 e^- \longrightarrow Zn(s) \}$
Overall:	$2 Al(s) + 3 Zn^{2+}(aq) \longrightarrow 2 Al^{3+}(aq) + 3 Zn(s)$

(b) Al(s) is oxidized to Al^{3+}(aq) in the anode half-cell (left), and Zn^{2+}(aq) is reduced to Zn(s) in the cathode half-cell (right).

$$Al(s)|Al^{3+}(aq)\|Zn^{2+}(aq)|Zn(s)$$

Practice Example A: Write the overall equation for the redox reaction that occurs in the voltaic cell $Sc(s)|Sc^{3+}(aq)\|Ag^+(aq)|Ag(s)$.

Practice Example B: Draw a voltaic cell in which silver ion is displaced from solution by aluminum metal. Label the cathode, the anode, and other features of the cell. Show the direction of flow of electrons. Also, indicate the direction of flow of cations and anions from a KNO_3(aq) salt bridge. Write an equation for the half-reaction occurring at each electrode, write a balanced equation for the overall cell reaction, and write a cell diagram.

Are You Wondering . . .

How to ensure that you place the half-cells in the proper order in a cell diagram?

If you guess that a particular electrode is the anode in a voltaic cell, you are simply deciding to connect that electrode to the negative terminal of the voltmeter (and the other electrode to the positive terminal). If you have guessed correctly, you will get a positive reading on the voltmeter. If you get a negative reading on the voltmeter, this signifies that the electrons flow in the direction opposite that of your expectation: What you thought was the anode is actually the cathode, and vice versa. Some voltmeters will register only a positive voltage. In this case, you won't get any meter reading until you switch the connections to the terminals. You can write the cell diagram with the "misplaced" half-cells and a *negative* cell voltage, or you can switch the half-cells and write a *positive* cell voltage.

CONCEPT ASSESSMENT ✓

Add appropriate arrows to Figure 20-4 to show the direction of migration of ions through the electrochemical cell.

20-2   STANDARD ELECTRODE POTENTIALS

Cell voltages—*potential differences* between electrodes—are among the most precise scientific measurements possible. Potentials of individual electrodes, however, cannot be precisely established. If we could make such measurements, cell voltages could be obtained just by subtracting one electrode potential from another. The same result can be achieved by *arbitrarily* choosing a particular half-cell that is assigned an electrode potential of *zero*. Other half-cells can then be compared to this reference. The commonly accepted reference is the standard hydrogen electrode.

The **standard hydrogen electrode** (**SHE**) is depicted in Figure 20-5. The SHE involves equilibrium established on the surface of an inert metal (such as platinum) between H_3O^+ ions from a solution in which they are at unit

◀ This method is comparable to establishing standard enthalpies or free energies of formation on the basis of an arbitrary zero value.

📖 Wuchang, Z., Jiaxing, L., Hebal, S. "On the standard hydrogen electrode (LTE)." *J. Chem. Educ.* **1991**: *68,* 356.

▲ **FIGURE 20-5**
The standard hydrogen electrode (SHE)
Because hydrogen is a gas at room temperature, electrodes cannot be constructed from it. The standard hydrogen electrode consists of a piece of platinum dipped into a solution containing 1 M H^+(aq) with a stream of hydrogen passing over its surface. The platinum does not react but provides a surface for the reduction of H_3O(aq)$^+$ to H_2(g) as well as the reverse oxidation half-reaction.

activity (that is, $a_{H_3O^+} = 1$) and H_2 molecules from the gaseous state at a pressure of 1 bar. The equilibrium reaction produces a particular potential on the metal surface, but this potential is arbitrarily taken to be *zero*.

$$2\,H^+(a = 1) + 2\,e^- \xrightleftharpoons[\text{on Pt}]{} H_2(g, 1\text{ bar}) \qquad E° = 0 \text{ volt (V)} \qquad (20.5)$$

The diagram for this half-cell is

$$Pt|H_2(g, 1\text{ bar})|H^+(a = 1)$$

The two vertical lines signify that three phases are present: solid platinum, gaseous hydrogen, and aqueous hydrogen ion. For simplicity, we will usually write H^+ for H_3O^+, assume that unit activity ($a = 1$) exists at roughly $[H^+] = 1$ M, and replace a pressure of 1 bar by 1 atm.

By international agreement, a **standard electrode potential**, $E°$, measures the tendency for a *reduction* process to occur at an electrode. In all cases, the ionic species are present in aqueous solution at unit activity (approximately 1 M), and gases are at 1 bar pressure (approximately 1 atm). Where no metallic substance is indicated, the potential is established on an inert metallic electrode, such as platinum.

To emphasize that $E°$ refers to a reduction, we will write a reduction couple as a subscript to $E°$, as shown in half-reaction (20.6). The substance being reduced is written on the left of the (slash) sign, and the chief reduction product on the right.

$$Cu^{2+}(1\text{ M}) + 2\,e^- \longrightarrow Cu(s) \qquad E°_{Cu^{2+}/Cu} = ? \qquad (20.6)$$

Cheng, K. L. "A New Concept for pH-Potential Calculations." *J. Chem. Educ.* **1999**: 76, 1029 (July 1999).

To determine the value of $E°$ for a standard electrode such as that to which half-reaction (20.6) applies, we compare it with a standard hydrogen electrode (SHE). In this comparison, the SHE is always taken as the electrode on the *left* of the cell diagram—the anode—and the compared electrode is the electrode on the *right*—the cathode. In the following voltaic cell, the measured potential difference is 0.340 V, with electrons flowing from the H_2 to the Cu electrode.

$$\underset{\text{anode}}{Pt|H_2(g, 1\text{ atm})|H^+(1\text{ M})}||\underset{\text{cathode}}{Cu^{2+}(1\text{ M})|Cu(s)} \qquad E°_{cell} = 0.340 \text{ V} \qquad (20.7)$$

Just as arbitrary reference states are chosen to establish standard free energies of formation, the standard hydrogen electrode is chosen as the basis for standard electrode potentials.

A **standard cell potential**, $E°_{cell}$, is the potential difference, or voltage, of a cell formed from two *standard* electrodes. The *difference* is always taken in the following way:

$$E°_{cell} = \underset{\text{(cathode)}}{E°(\text{right})} - \underset{\text{(anode)}}{E°(\text{left})}$$

Applied to the cell diagram (20.7), we get

$$E°_{cell} = E°_{Cu^{2+}/Cu} - E°_{H^+/H_2} = 0.340 \text{ V}$$
$$= E°_{Cu^{2+}/Cu} - 0 \text{ V} = 0.340 \text{ V}$$
$$E°_{Cu^{2+}/Cu} = 0.340 \text{ V}$$

Standard Reduction Potentials animation

Thus, the standard *reduction* half-reaction can be written as

$$Cu^{2+}(1\text{ M}) + 2\,e^- \longrightarrow Cu(s) \qquad E°_{Cu^{2+}/Cu} = +0.340 \text{ V} \qquad (20.8)$$

The overall reaction occurring in the voltaic cell diagrammed in (20.7) can be represented as

$$H_2(g, 1\text{ atm}) + Cu^{2+}(1\text{ M}) \longrightarrow 2\,H^+(1\text{ M}) + Cu(s) \qquad E°_{cell} = 0.340 \text{ V} \quad (20.9)$$

Cell reaction (20.9) indicates that $Cu^{2+}(1\text{ M})$ is more easily reduced than is $H^+(1\text{ M})$.

Suppose the standard copper electrode in cell diagram (20.7) is replaced by a standard zinc electrode, and the potential difference between the standard hydrogen and zinc electrodes is measured by using the same voltmeter connections as in (20.7). In this case, the voltage is found to be -0.763 V. The negative sign indicates that electrons flow in the direction *opposite* that in

(20.7)—that is, *from* the zinc electrode *to* the hydrogen electrode. Here H^+(1 M) is more easily reduced than is Zn^{2+}(1 M). These findings are represented in the following cell diagram, in which the zinc electrode appears on the *right*.

Voltaic Cells II: The Zinc-Hydrogen Cell animation

$$Pt|H_2(g, 1\ atm)|H^+(1\ M)||Zn^{2+}(1\ M)|Zn(s) \qquad E^\circ_{cell} = -0.763\ V \qquad (20.10)$$

The standard electrode potential for the Zn^{2+}/Zn couple can be written as

$$E^\circ_{cell} = E^\circ(right) - E^\circ(left)$$
$$= E^\circ_{Zn^{2+}/Zn} - 0\ V = -0.763\ V$$
$$E^\circ_{Zn^{2+}/Zn} = -0.763\ V$$

Thus, the standard *reduction* half-reaction is

$$Zn^{2+}(1\ M) + 2\ e^- \longrightarrow Zn(s) \qquad E^\circ_{Zn^{2+}/Zn} = -0.763\ V \qquad (20.11)$$

In summary, the potential of the standard hydrogen electrode is set at exactly 0 V. Any electrode at which a reduction half-reaction shows a *greater* tendency to occur than does the reduction of H^+ (1 M) to H_2 (g, 1 atm) has a *positive* value for its standard electrode potential, E°. Any electrode at which a reduction half-reaction shows a *lesser* tendency to occur than does the reduction of H^+ (1 M) to H_2 (g, 1 atm) has a *negative* value for its standard reduction potential, E°. Comparisons of the standard copper and zinc electrodes to the standard hydrogen electrode are illustrated in Figure 20-6. Table 20.1 on the next page lists some common reduction half-reactions and their standard electrode potentials at 25 °C.

CONCEPT ASSESSMENT ✓

Regarding Figure 20-6, describe any changes in mass that might be detected at the Pt, Cu, and Zn electrodes as electric current passes through the electrochemical cells.

Standard reduction potentials are used throughout this chapter for many purposes. Our first objective will be to calculate standard cell potentials for redox reactions—E°_{cell} values—from standard electrode potentials for half-cell reactions—E° values. The procedure used is illustrated here for reaction (20.3) and cell diagram (20.4). Note that the first three equations are alternative ways of stating the same thing; we will generally not write all of them.

◀ Reaction (20.3) is shown on page 825 and diagram (20.4) on page 826.

$$E^\circ_{cell} = E^\circ(right) - E^\circ(left)$$
$$= E^\circ(cathode) - E^\circ(anode)$$
$$= E^\circ(reduction\ half\text{-}cell) - E^\circ(oxidation\ half\text{-}cell)$$
$$= E^\circ_{Cu^{2+}/Cu} - E^\circ_{Zn^{2+}/Zn}$$
$$= 0.340\ V - (-0.763\ V) = 1.103\ V$$

◀ **KEEP IN MIND**
that the E° values in this formulation are for a reduction half-reaction, regardless whether oxidation or reduction occurs in the half-cell.

◀ **FIGURE 20-6**
Measuring standard electrode potentials
(a) A standard hydrogen electrode is the anode, and copper is the cathode. Contact between the half-cells occurs through a porous plate that prevents bulk flow of the solutions while allowing ions to pass. **(b)** This cell has the same connections as that in part (a), but with zinc substituting for copper. However, the electron flow is opposite that in (a), as noted by the *negative* voltage. (Zinc is the anode.)

▶ A more extensive listing of reduction half-reactions and their potentials is given in Appendix D.

▶ The placement of *oxidizing agents* is as follows: strongest oxidizing agents (F_2, O_3, ...), *left* sides, *top* of the list; weakest oxidizing agents (Li^+, K^+, ...), *left* sides, *bottom* of list. The placement of *reducing agents* is as follows: strongest reducing agents (Li, K, ...), *right* sides, *bottom* of list; weakest reducing agents (F^-, O_2, ...), *right* sides, *top* of list.

Ciparick, Joseph D. "Half cell reactions: Do students ever see them? (TD)." *J. Chem. Educ.* **1991**: *68*, 247.

Some students mistakenly believe that voltaic cells can only be prepared when half reactions with positive standard potentials are combined with half reactions that have negative standard potentials.

TABLE 20.1   Some Selected Standard Electrode (Reduction) Potentials at 25 °C

Reduction Half-Reaction	$E°$, V
Acidic solution	
$F_2(g) + 2\,e^- \longrightarrow 2\,F^-(aq)$	+2.866
$O_3(g) + 2\,H^+(aq) + 2\,e^- \longrightarrow O_2(g) + H_2O(l)$	+2.075
$S_2O_8^{2-}(aq) + 2\,e^- \longrightarrow 2\,SO_4^{2-}(aq)$	+2.01
$H_2O_2(aq) + 2\,H^+(aq) + 2\,e^- \longrightarrow 2\,H_2O(l)$	+1.763
$MnO_4^-(aq) + 8\,H^+(aq) + 5\,e^- \longrightarrow Mn^{2+}(aq) + 4\,H_2O(l)$	+1.51
$PbO_2(s) + 4\,H^+(aq) + 2\,e^- \longrightarrow Pb^{2+}(aq) + 2\,H_2O(l)$	+1.455
$Cl_2(g) + 2\,e^- \longrightarrow 2\,Cl^-(aq)$	+1.358
$Cr_2O_7^{2-}(aq) + 14\,H^+(aq) + 6\,e^- \longrightarrow 2\,Cr^{3+}(aq) + 7\,H_2O(l)$	+1.33
$MnO_2(s) + 4\,H^+(aq) + 2\,e^- \longrightarrow Mn^{2+}(aq) + 2\,H_2O(l)$	+1.23
$O_2(g) + 4\,H^+(aq) + 4\,e^- \longrightarrow 2\,H_2O(l)$	+1.229
$2\,IO_3^-(aq) + 12\,H^+(aq) + 10\,e^- \longrightarrow I_2(s) + 6\,H_2O(l)$	+1.20
$Br_2(l) + 2\,e^- \longrightarrow 2\,Br^-(aq)$	+1.065
$NO_3^-(aq) + 4\,H^+(aq) + 3\,e^- \longrightarrow NO(g) + 2\,H_2O(l)$	+0.956
$Ag^+(aq) + e^- \longrightarrow Ag(s)$	+0.800
$Fe^{3+}(aq) + e^- \longrightarrow Fe^{2+}(aq)$	+0.771
$O_2(g) + 2\,H^+(aq) + 2\,e^- \longrightarrow H_2O_2(aq)$	+0.695
$I_2(s) + 2\,e^- \longrightarrow 2\,I^-(aq)$	+0.535
$Cu^{2+}(aq) + 2\,e^- \longrightarrow Cu(s)$	+0.340
$SO_4^{2-}(aq) + 4\,H^+(aq) + 2\,e^- \longrightarrow 2\,H_2O(l) + SO_2(g)$	+0.17
$Sn^{4+}(aq) + 2\,e^- \longrightarrow Sn^{2+}(aq)$	+0.154
$S(s) + 2\,H^+(aq) + 2\,e^- \longrightarrow H_2S(g)$	+0.14
$2\,H^+(aq) + 2\,e^- \longrightarrow H_2(g)$	0
$Pb^{2+}(aq) + 2\,e^- \longrightarrow Pb(s)$	−0.125
$Sn^{2+}(aq) + 2\,e^- \longrightarrow Sn(s)$	−0.137
$Fe^{2+}(aq) + 2\,e^- \longrightarrow Fe(s)$	−0.440
$Zn^{2+}(aq) + 2\,e^- \longrightarrow Zn(s)$	−0.763
$Al^{3+}(aq) + 3\,e^- \longrightarrow Al(s)$	−1.676
$Mg^{2+}(aq) + 2\,e^- \longrightarrow Mg(s)$	−2.356
$Na^+(aq) + e^- \longrightarrow Na(s)$	−2.713
$Ca^{2+}(aq) + 2\,e^- \longrightarrow Ca(s)$	−2.84
$K^+(aq) + e^- \longrightarrow K(s)$	−2.924
$Li^+(aq) + e^- \longrightarrow Li(s)$	−3.040
Basic solution	
$O_3(g) + H_2O(l) + 2\,e^- \longrightarrow O_2(g) + 2\,OH^-(aq)$	+1.246
$OCl^-(aq) + H_2O(l) + 2\,e^- \longrightarrow Cl^-(aq) + 2\,OH^-(aq)$	+0.890
$O_2(g) + 2\,H_2O(l) + 4\,e^- \longrightarrow 4\,OH^-(aq)$	+0.401
$2\,H_2O(l) + 2\,e^- \longrightarrow H_2(g) + 2\,OH^-(aq)$	−0.828

Example 20-2 predicts $E°_{cell}$ for a new battery system. Example 20-3 uses one known electrode potential and a measured $E°_{cell}$ value to determine an unknown $E°$.

EXAMPLE 20-2

Combining $E°$ Values into $E°_{cell}$ for a Reaction. A new battery system currently under study for possible use in electric vehicles is the zinc–chlorine battery. The overall reaction producing electricity in this cell is $Zn(s) + Cl_2(g) \longrightarrow ZnCl_2(aq)$. What is $E°_{cell}$ of this voltaic cell?

Solution

Equation (20.12) shows that $Zn(s)$ is oxidized and that $Cl_2(g)$ is reduced. It is the overall reaction resulting from the two half-reactions indicated below. The $E°$ values required to establish $E°_{cell}$ for the overall reaction are from Table 20.1.

$$\begin{aligned}
&Reduction: &Cl_2(g) + 2\,e^- &\longrightarrow 2\,Cl^-(aq) \\
&Oxidation: &Zn(s) &\longrightarrow Zn^{2+}(aq) + 2\,e^- \\
\hline
&Overall: &Zn(s) + Cl_2(g) &\longrightarrow Zn^{2+}(aq) + 2\,Cl^-(aq) &(20.12)
\end{aligned}$$

$$\begin{aligned}
E°_{cell} &= E°(\text{reduction half-cell}) - E°(\text{oxidation half-cell}) \\
&= 1.358\,V - (-0.763\,V) = 2.121\,V
\end{aligned}$$

Practice Example A: What is $E°_{cell}$ for the reaction in which $Cl_2(g)$ oxidizes $Fe^{2+}(aq)$ to $Fe^{3+}(aq)$?

$$2\,Fe^{2+}(aq) + Cl_2(g) \longrightarrow 2\,Fe^{3+}(aq) + 2\,Cl^-(aq) \qquad E°_{cell} = \,?$$

Practice Example B: Use data from Table 20.1 to determine $E°_{cell}$ for the redox reaction in which $Fe^{2+}(aq)$ is oxidized to $Fe^{3+}(aq)$ by $MnO_4^-(aq)$ in acidic solution.

Tanis, David O. "Galvanic cells and the standard reduction potential table (F&R)." *J. Chem. Educ.* **1990:** *67*, 602.

EXAMPLE 20-3

Determining an Unknown $E°$ from an $E°_{cell}$ Measurement. Cadmium is found in small quantities wherever zinc is found. Unlike zinc, which in trace amounts is an essential element, cadmium is an environmental poison. To determine cadmium ion concentrations by electrical measurements, we need the standard electrode potential for the Cd^{2+}/Cd electrode. The voltage of the following voltaic cell is measured.

$$Cd(s)|Cd^{2+}(1\,M)\|Cu^{2+}(1\,M)|Cu(s) \qquad E°_{cell} = 0.743\,V$$

What is the standard electrode potential for the Cd^{2+}/Cd electrode?

Solution

We know one half-cell potential and $E°_{cell}$ for the overall redox reaction. We can solve for the unknown standard electrode potential, $E°_{Cd^{2+}/Cd}$.

$$\begin{aligned}
E°_{cell} &= E°(\text{right}) - E°(\text{left}) \\
0.743\,V &= E°_{Cu^{2+}/Cu} - E°_{Cd^{2+}/Cd} \\
&= 0.340\,V - E°_{Cd^{2+}/Cd} \\
E°_{Cd^{2+}/Cd} &= 0.340\,V - 0.743\,V = -0.403\,V
\end{aligned}$$

Practice Example A: In acidic solution, dichromate ion oxidizes oxalic acid, $H_2C_2O_4(aq)$, to $CO_2(g)$ in a reaction with $E°_{cell} = 1.81\,V$.

$$Cr_2O_7^{2-}(aq) + 3\,H_2C_2O_4(aq) + 8\,H^+(aq) \longrightarrow 2\,Cr^{3+}(aq) + 7\,H_2O + 6\,CO_2(g)$$

Use the value of $E°_{cell}$ for this reaction, together with appropriate data from Table 20.1, to determine $E°$ for the $CO_2(g)/H_2C_2O_4(aq)$ electrode.

Practice Example B: In an acidic solution, $O_2(g)$ oxidizes $Cr^{2+}(aq)$ to $Cr^{3+}(aq)$. The $O_2(g)$ is reduced to $H_2O(l)$. $E°_{cell}$ for the reaction is 1.653 V. What is the standard electrode potential for the couple Cr^{3+}/Cr^{2+}?

CONCEPT ASSESSMENT ✓

For the half-cell reaction $ClO_4^-(aq) + 8\,H^+(aq) + 7\,e^- \longrightarrow \frac{1}{2}Cl_2(g) + 4\,H_2O(l)$, what are the standard-state conditions for the reactants and products?

▲ **Michael Faraday (1791–1867)**
Faraday, an assistant to Humphry Davy and often called "Davy's greatest discovery," made many contributions to both physics and chemistry, including systematic studies of electrolysis.

Toma, H. E., Araki, K., Dovidauskas, S. "A Cyclic Voltammetry Experiment Illustrating Redox Potentials, Equilibrium Constants, and Substitution Reactions in Coordination Chemistry." *J. Chem. Educ.* **2000**: *77*, 1351 (October 2000).

✓ Point out that based on equation (20.15) the criterion for a spontaneous reaction is a positive cell potential.

✓ Although students in chemistry have no difficulty with the expression work = force × distance, when dealing with uncharged objects, they have more difficulty with electrical work. Compare a gravitational field to an electric field. Place an object with mass in a gravitational field and it will fall (move to lower potential). Place a charged object in an electric field, and it will move towards the opposite charge. Electric force usually dominates the gravitational force because the charged particles are small and have relatively small mass.

20-3 E_{cell}, ΔG, AND K

When a reaction occurs in a voltaic cell, the cell does work—electrical work. Think of this as the work of moving electric charges. The total work done is the product of three terms: (a) E_{cell}; (b) n, the number of moles of electrons transferred between the electrodes; and (c) the electric charge per mole of electrons, called the **Faraday constant (F)**. The Faraday constant is equal to 96,485 coulombs per mole of electrons (96,485 C/mol e^-). Because the product volt × coulomb = joule, the unit of w_{elec} is joules (J).

$$w_{elec} = nFE_{cell} \qquad (20.13)$$

Expression (20.13) applies only if the cell operates reversibly.* The Are You Wondering feature on page 795 described the amount of available energy (work) that can be derived from a process as equal to $-\Delta G$. Thus,

$$\Delta G = -nFE_{cell} \qquad (20.14)$$

In the special case in which the reactants and products are in their standard states,

$$\Delta G° = -nFE°_{cell} \qquad (20.15)$$

Our primary interest is not in calculating quantities of work but in using expression (20.15) as a means of evaluating free energy changes from measured cell potentials, as illustrated in Example 20-4.

EXAMPLE 20-4

Determining a Free Energy Change from a Cell Potential. Use $E°$ data to determine $\Delta G°$ for the reaction

$$Zn(s) + Cl_2(g, 1\ atm) \longrightarrow ZnCl_2(aq, 1\ M)$$

Solution

This reaction is cell reaction (20.12) occurring in the voltaic cell described in Example 20-2. In this type of problem, the overall equation generally needs to be separated into two half-equations. Then the value of $E°_{cell}$ and the number of moles of electrons (n) involved in the cell reaction can be determined. Refer to Example 20-2 to see that $E°_{cell} = 2.121$ V and $n = 2$ mol e^-. Now use equation (20.15).

$$\Delta G° = -nFE°_{cell} = -\left(2\ mol\ e^- \times \frac{96,485\ C}{1\ mol\ e^-} \times 2.121\ V\right)$$

$$= -4.093 \times 10^5\ J = -409.3\ kJ$$

Practice Example A: Use electrode potential data to determine $\Delta G°$ for the reaction

$$2\ Al(s) + 3\ Br_2(l) \longrightarrow 2\ Al^{3+}(aq, 1\ M) + 6\ Br^-(aq, 1\ M) \qquad \Delta G° = ?$$

Practice Example B: The hydrogen–oxygen fuel cell is a voltaic cell with a cell reaction of $2\ H_2(g) + O_2(g) \longrightarrow 2\ H_2O(l)$. Calculate $E°_{cell}$ for this reaction.

[*Hint:* Use thermodynamic data from Appendix D (Table D-2).]

---

*The meaning of a reversible process was illustrated by Figure 7-12 on page 241. The reversible operation of a voltaic cell requires that electric current be drawn from the cell only very, very slowly.

COMBINING REDUCTION HALF-EQUATIONS

Not only can equation (20.15) be used to determine $\Delta G°$ from $E°_{cell}$, as in Example 20-4, but the calculation can be reversed and an $E°_{cell}$ value determined from $\Delta G°$. Moreover, equation (20.15) can be applied to half-cell reactions and half-cell potentials—that is, to standard electrode potentials, $E°$. That is what we must do, for example, to determine $E°$ for the half-reaction

$$Fe^{3+}(aq) + 3\,e^- \longrightarrow Fe(s)$$

Both in Table 20.1 and in Appendix D, the only entries that deal with Fe(s) and its ions are

$$Fe^{2+}(aq) + 2\,e^- \longrightarrow Fe(s), E° = -0.440 \text{ V} \quad \text{and} \quad Fe^{3+}(aq) + e^- \longrightarrow Fe^{2+}(aq), E° = 0.771 \text{ V}$$

The half-equation we are seeking is simply the sum of these two half-equations, but the $E°$ value we are seeking is *not* the sum of -0.440 V and 0.771 V. What we *can* add together, though, are the $\Delta G°$ values for the two known half-reactions.

$$Fe^{2+}(aq) + 2\,e^- \longrightarrow Fe(s); \qquad \Delta G° = -2 \times F \times (-0.440 \text{ V})$$
$$Fe^{3+}(aq) + e^- \longrightarrow Fe^{2+}(aq); \qquad \Delta G° = -1 \times F \times (0.771 \text{ V})$$
$$\overline{Fe^{3+}(aq) + 3\,e^- \longrightarrow Fe(s); \qquad \Delta G° = (0.880F) \text{ V} - (0.771F) \text{ V} = (0.109F) \text{ V}}$$

Now, to get $E°_{Fe^{3+}/Fe}$, we can again use equation (20.15) and solve for $E°_{Fe^{3+}/Fe}$.

$$\Delta G° = -nFE°_{Fe^{3+}/Fe} = -3FE°_{Fe^{3+}/Fe} = (0.109F) \text{ V}$$
$$E°_{Fe^{3+}/Fe} = (-0.109F/3F) \text{ V} = -0.0363 \text{ V}$$

> Remind students that free energy changes are functions of state and therefore can be combined to determine free energy changes for new reactions.

Are You Wondering . . .

How the procedure for combining two $E°$ values to obtain an unknown $E°_{cell}$ relates to combining two $E°$ values to obtain an unknown $E°$?

We have just seen how to obtain an unknown $E°$ from two known values of $E°$ by working through the expression $\Delta G = -nFE°$. As shown below for a hypothetical displacement reaction, we can similarly calculate an unknown $E°_{cell}$ through the expression $\Delta G° = -nFE°_{cell}$. (Note that for the oxidation half-reaction, $\Delta G°_{ox}$ is simply the negative of the value for the reverse half-reaction, $\Delta G°_{red}$.)

Reduction: $M^{n+}(aq) + n\,e^- \longrightarrow M(s)$ $\Delta G°_{red} = -nFE°_{M^{n+}/M}$

Oxidation: $N(s) \longrightarrow N^{n+}(aq) + n\,e^-$
$$\Delta G°_{ox} = -(\Delta G°_{red}) = -(-nFE°_{N^{n+}/N}) = nFE°_{N^{n+}/N}$$

Overall: $M^{n+}(aq) + N(s) \longrightarrow M(s) + N^{n+}(aq)$
$$\Delta G° = \Delta G°_{red} + \Delta G°_{ox} = -nFE°_{cell} = -nFE°_{M^{n+}/M} + nFE°_{N^{n+}/N}$$

Dividing through the above equation by the term $-nF$, we obtain $E°_{cell}$ as the familiar difference in two electrode potentials.

$$E°_{cell} = E°_{M^{n+}/M} - E°_{N^{n+}/N}$$

We have been able to skip this calculation based on $\Delta G°$ values and proceed straight to the expression

$$E°_{cell} = E°(\text{reduction}) - E°(\text{oxidation})$$

because the term $-nF$ always cancels out. That is, n, the number of electrons, must have the same value for the oxidation and reduction half-reactions and the overall reaction. By contrast, when obtaining an unknown $E°$ from the known $E°$ values, the value for n will not be the same in all three places where it appears, and so we do have to work through the $\Delta G°$ expressions.

> When adding and subtracting half-equations and multiplying by factors to make the equations balance, students may feel that they should multiply the cell potentials like they do enthalpies in Hess's Law. Point out that the cell potential is an intensive quantity, whereas the energy is extensive. This is also seen from the "n" in the equation $\Delta G = -nFE$.

SPONTANEOUS CHANGE IN OXIDATION–REDUCTION REACTIONS

Our main criterion for spontaneous change is that $\Delta G < 0$. According to equation (20.14), however, redox reactions have the property that, if $\Delta G < 0$, then $E_{cell} > 0$. That is, E_{cell} must be *positive* if ΔG is to be negative. Predicting the direction of spontaneous change in a redox reaction is a relatively simple matter using the following ideas:

- If E_{cell} is *positive*, a reaction occurs spontaneously in the *forward* direction for the stated conditions. If E_{cell} is *negative*, the reaction occurs spontaneously in the *reverse* direction for the stated conditions. If $E_{cell} = 0$, the reaction is at equilibrium for the stated conditions.
- If a cell reaction is *reversed*, E_{cell} changes sign.

In the special case in which reactants and products are in their standard states, we work with $\Delta G°$ and $E_{cell}°$ values, as illustrated in Examples 20-5 and 20-6.

EXAMPLE 20-5

Applying the Criterion for Spontaneous Change in a Redox Reaction. Will aluminum metal displace Cu^{2+} ion from aqueous solution? That is, will a spontaneous reaction occur in the forward direction for the following reaction?

$$2 \, Al(s) + 3 \, Cu^{2+}(1 \, M) \longrightarrow 3 \, Cu(s) + 2 \, Al^{3+}(1 \, M)$$

Solution

The cell diagram corresponding to the reaction is $Al(s)|Al^{3+}(aq)\|Cu^{2+}(aq)|Cu(s)$, and $E_{cell}°$ is

$$E_{cell}° = E°(\text{cathode}) - E°(\text{anode})$$
$$= E°_{Cu^{2+}/Cu} - E°_{Al^{3+}/Al}$$
$$= 0.340 \, V - (-1.676 \, V) = 2.016 \, V$$

Because $E_{cell}°$ is positive, the direction of spontaneous change is that of the forward reaction. Al(s) will displace Cu^{2+} from aqueous solution under standard-state conditions.

Practice Example A: Name one metal ion that Cu(s) will displace from aqueous solution, and determine $E_{cell}°$ for the reaction.

Practice Example B: When sodium metal is added to seawater, which has $[Mg^{2+}] = 0.0512 \, M$, no magnesium metal is obtained. According to $E°$ values, should this displacement reaction occur? What reaction does occur?

KEEP IN MIND ▶
that both $E°$ and $E_{cell}°$ are *intensive* properties. They do not depend on the quantities of materials involved, which means that their values are not affected by the way we write the cell reaction. We could just as well have written

$$Al(s) + \frac{3}{2}Cu^{2+}(1 \, M) \longrightarrow$$
$$\frac{3}{2}Cu(s) + Al^{3+}(1 \, M)$$

or $\frac{2}{3}Al(s) + Cu^{2+}(1 \, M) \longrightarrow$
$$Cu(s) + \frac{2}{3}Al^{3+}(1 \, M)$$

Even though we used electrode potentials and cell voltage to predict a spontaneous reaction in Example 20-5, we do not have to carry out the reaction in a voltaic cell. This is an important point to keep in mind. Thus, Cu^{2+} is displaced from aqueous solution simply by adding aluminum metal, as shown in Figure 20-7. Another point, illustrated by Example 20-6, is that qualitative answers to questions concerning redox reactions can be found without going through a complete calculation of $E_{cell}°$.

EXAMPLE 20-6

Making Qualitative Predictions with Electrode Potential Data. Peroxodisulfate salts, such as $Na_2S_2O_8$, are oxidizing agents used in bleaching. Dichromates such as $K_2Cr_2O_7$ have been used as laboratory oxidizing agents. Which is the better oxidizing agent in acidic solution under standard conditions, $S_2O_8^{2-}$ or $Cr_2O_7^{2-}$?

Solution

In a redox reaction, the oxidizing agent is reduced; the greater the tendency for this reduction to occur, the better the oxidizing agent. The reduction tendency, in turn, is measured by the $E°$ value. Because the $E°$ value for the reduction of $S_2O_8^{2-}$(aq) to SO_4^{2-}(aq) (2.01 V) is larger than that for the reduction of $Cr_2O_7^{2-}$(aq) to Cr^{3+}(aq) (1.33 V), $S_2O_8^{2-}$(aq) should be the better oxidizing agent.

▲ FIGURE 20-7
Reaction of Al(s) and Cu^{2+}(aq)
Notice the holes in the foil where Al(s) has dissolved. Notice also the dark deposit of Cu(s) at the bottom of the beaker.

Practice Example A: An inexpensive way to produce peroxodisulfates would be to pass $O_2(g)$ through an acidic solution containing sulfate ion. Is this method feasible under standard conditions?
[*Hint*: What would be the reduction half-reaction?]

Practice Example B: Consider the following observations: (1) Aqueous solutions of Sn^{2+} are difficult to maintain because atmospheric oxygen easily oxidizes Sn^{2+} to Sn^{4+}. (2) One way to preserve the $Sn^{2+}(aq)$ solutions is to add some metallic tin. *Without doing detailed calculations,* explain these two statements by using $E°$ data.

THE BEHAVIOR OF METALS TOWARD ACIDS

In the discussion of redox reactions in Chapter 5, it was noted that most metals react with an acid such as HCl, but that a few do not. This observation can now be explained. When a metal, M, reacts with an acid such as HCl, the metal is oxidized to the metal ion, such as M^{2+}. The reduction involves H^+ being reduced to $H_2(g)$. These ideas can be expressed as

Oxidation:	$M(s) \longrightarrow M^{2+}(aq) + 2\,e^-$
Reduction:	$2\,H^+(aq) + 2\,e^- \longrightarrow H_2(g)$
Overall:	$M(s) + 2\,H^+(aq) \longrightarrow M^{2+}(aq) + H_2(g)$

$$E°_{cell} = E°_{H^+/H_2} - E°_{M^{2+}/M} = 0\,V - E°_{M^{2+}/M} = -E°_{M^{2+}/M}$$

Metals with *negative* standard electrode potentials yield *positive* values of $E°_{cell}$ in the above expression. These are the metals that should displace $H_2(g)$ from acidic solutions. Thus, all the metals listed *below* hydrogen in Table 20.1 (Pb through Li) should react with acids.

In acids such as HCl, HBr, and HI, the oxidizing agent is H^+ (that is, H_3O^+). Certain metals that will not react with HCl will react with an acid in the presence of an *anion* that is a better oxidizing agent than H^+. Nitrate ion is a good oxidizing agent in acidic solution, and silver metal, which does not react with HCl(aq), readily reacts with nitric acid, $HNO_3(aq)$.

$$3\,Ag(s) + NO_3^-(aq) + 4\,H^+(aq) \longrightarrow 3\,Ag^+(aq) + NO(g) + 2\,H_2O \quad E°_{cell} = 0.156\,V$$

THE RELATIONSHIP BETWEEN $E°_{cell}$ AND K

$\Delta G°$ and $E°_{cell}$ were related through equation (20.15). In Chapter 19, $\Delta G°$ and K were related through equation (19.12). The three quantities are thus related in this way.

$$\Delta G° = -RT \ln K = -nFE°_{cell}$$

and therefore,

$$E°_{cell} = \frac{RT}{nF} \ln K \tag{20.16}$$

In equation (20.16), R has a value of $8.3145\,J\,mol^{-1}\,K^{-1}$ and n represents the number of moles of electrons involved in the reaction. If we then specify a temperature of $25\,°C = 298.15\,K$ (the temperature at which electrode potentials are generally determined), the combined terms "RT/F" in equation (20.16) can be replaced by a single constant. This constant has the value $0.025693\,J/C = 0.025693\,V$.

$$E°_{cell} = \frac{RT}{nF} \ln K = \frac{8.3145\,J\,\cancel{mol^{-1}}\,\cancel{K^{-1}} \times 298.15\,\cancel{K}}{n \times 96485\,C\,\cancel{mol^{-1}}} \ln K$$

$$E°_{cell} = \frac{0.025693\,V}{n} \ln K \tag{20.17}$$

Note that any electrochemical cell, if left in a completed circuit, will eventually die as the redox reaction goes to completion. This means that the cell potential will eventually drop to zero. In Chapter 19, the relationship between free energy and equilibrium was established in a similar way.

Equation 20.16 gives the expected result that reactions with equilibrium constants larger than one have a positive standard cell potential.

The relationship between E°_{cell} and K is illustrated in Example 20-7. Also, Figure 20-8 summarizes several important relationships from thermodynamics, equilibrium, and electrochemistry.

▲ **FIGURE 20-8**
A summary of important thermodynamic, equilibrium, and electrochemical relationships under standard conditions

EXAMPLE 20-7

Relating K to E°_{cell} for a Redox Reaction. What is the value of the equilibrium constant K for the reaction between copper metal and iron(III) ions in aqueous solution at 25 °C?

$$Cu(s) + 2 Fe^{3+}(aq) \longrightarrow Cu^{2+}(aq) + 2 Fe^{2+}(aq) \qquad K = ?$$

Solution

First, use data from Table 20.1 to determine E°_{cell}.

$$E^\circ_{cell} = E^\circ(\text{reduction half-cell}) - E^\circ(\text{oxidation half-cell})$$
$$= E^\circ_{Fe^{3+}/Fe^{2+}} - E^\circ_{Cu^{2+}/Cu}$$
$$= 0.771 \text{ V} - 0.340 \text{ V} = 0.431 \text{ V}$$

The number of moles of electrons for the cell reaction is 2.

$$E^\circ_{cell} = 0.431 \text{ V} = \frac{0.02569 \text{ V}}{2} \ln K$$

$$\ln K = \frac{2 \times 0.431 \cancel{V}}{0.02569 \cancel{V}} = 33.6$$

$$K = e^{33.6} = 4 \times 10^{14}$$

Practice Example A: Should the displacement of Cu^{2+} from aqueous solution by Al(s) go to completion? [*Hint:* Base your assessment on the value of K for the displacement reaction. We determined E°_{cell} for this reaction in Example 20-5.]

Practice Example B: Should the reaction of Sn(s) and Pb^{2+}(aq) go to completion? Explain.

CONCEPT ASSESSMENT ✓

Point out that the solid electrodes are not included in the equilibrium expressions for the same reasons that pure phases do not appear in heterogeneous equilibrium expressions.

When two cell reactions with reactants and products in their standard states are compared, one is found to have a negative value of E°_{cell} and the other a positive value. Which cell reaction will proceed toward the formation of more products to establish equilibrium? Will a net cell reaction occur in the other case? If so, how will the equilibrium concentrations compare with the initial concentrations?

20-4 E_{cell} AS A FUNCTION OF CONCENTRATIONS

When we combine standard electrode potentials, we obtain a standard E_{cell}°, such as $E_{cell}^\circ = 1.103$ V for the voltaic cell of Figure 20-4. For the following cell reaction at *nonstandard* conditions, however, the measured E_{cell} is not 1.103 V.

$$Zn(s) + Cu^{2+}(2.0\ M) \longrightarrow Zn^{2+}(0.10\ M) + Cu(s) \qquad E_{cell} = 1.142\ V$$

Experimental measurements of cell potentials are often made for nonstandard conditions; these measurements have great significance, especially for performing chemical analyses.

From Le Châtelier's principle, it would seem that *increasing* the concentration of a reactant (Cu^{2+}) while *decreasing* the concentration of a product (Zn^{2+}) should favor the forward reaction. $Zn(s)$ should displace $Cu^{2+}(aq)$ even more readily than for standard state conditions and $E_{cell} > 1.103$ V. E_{cell} is found to vary linearly with log ($[Zn^{2+}]/[Cu^{2+}]$), as illustrated in Figure 20-9.

It is not difficult to establish the relationship between the cell potential, E_{cell}, and the concentrations of reactants and products. From Chapter 19 we can write equation (19.11).

$$\Delta G = \Delta G^\circ + RT \ln Q$$

For ΔG and ΔG°, we can substitute $-nFE_{cell}$ and $-nFE_{cell}^\circ$, respectively.

$$-nFE_{cell} = -nFE_{cell}^\circ + RT \ln Q$$

Dividing through by $-nF$ gives

$$E_{cell} = E_{cell}^\circ - \frac{RT}{nF} \ln Q$$

This equation was first proposed by Walther Nernst in 1889. It is commonly used by analytical chemists in the form in which Nernst expressed it. The **Nernst equation** can be obtained by switching from natural to common logarithms ($\ln Q = 2.3026 \log Q$).

$$E_{cell} = E_{cell}^\circ - \frac{2.3026\ RT}{nF} \log Q$$

By specifying a temperature of 298.15 K and replacing RT/F by 0.025693 V, as in the development of equation (20.17), we find that the term $2.3026\ RT/F = 2.3026 \times 0.025693$ V $= 0.059161$ V, usually rounded off to 0.0592 V. The final form of the Nernst equation is

$$E_{cell} = E_{cell}^\circ - \frac{0.0592\ V}{n} \log Q \qquad (20.18)$$

In the Nernst equation, we make the usual substitutions into Q: $a = 1$ for the activities of pure solids and liquids, partial pressures (atm) for the activities of gases, and molarities for the activities of solution components. Example 20-8 demonstrates that the Nernst equation makes it possible to calculate E_{cell} for any chosen concentrations, not just for standard conditions.

CONCEPT ASSESSMENT ✔

Describe *two* sets of conditions under which the measured E_{cell} for a reaction is equal to E_{cell}°.

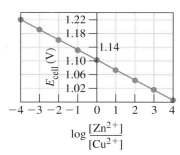

▲ **FIGURE 20-9**
Variation of E_{cell} with ion concentrations
The cell reaction is $Zn(s) + Cu^{2+}(aq) \longrightarrow Zn^{2+}(aq) + Cu(s)$ and has $E_{cell}^\circ = 1.103$ V.

Point out that according to equation (20.18), there are values of Q which result in positive, zero and negative values of E_{cell} (see Example 20-9).

Nernst Equation activity

▲ **Walther Nernst (1864–1941)**
Nernst was only 25 years old when he formulated his equation relating cell voltages and concentrations. He is also credited with proposing the solubility product concept in the same year. In 1906, he announced his "heat theorem," which we now know as the third law of thermodynamics.

Feiner, A.-S., McEvoy, A. J. "The Nernst Equation." *J. Chem. Educ.* **1994:** 71, 493.

EXAMPLE 20-8

Applying the Nernst Equation for Determining E_{cell}. What is the value of E_{cell} for the voltaic cell pictured in Figure 20-10 and diagrammed as follows?

$$Pt|Fe^{2+}(0.10 \text{ M}), Fe^{3+}(0.20 \text{ M})\|Ag^+(1.0 \text{ M})|Ag(s) \qquad E_{cell} = ?$$

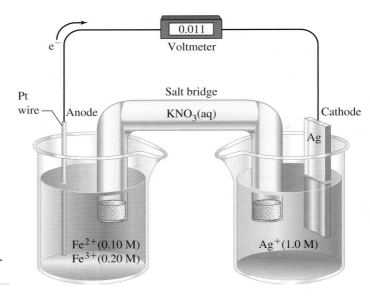

▶ **FIGURE 20-10**
A voltaic cell with nonstandard conditions—Example 20-8 illustrated

Solution

Two steps are required when using the Nernst equation. First, to determine E_{cell}°, use data from Table 20.1 to write

$$E_{cell}^{\circ} = E^{\circ}(\text{cathode}) - E^{\circ}(\text{anode})$$
$$= E_{Ag^+/Ag}^{\circ} - E_{Fe^{3+}/Fe^{2+}}^{\circ} \qquad (20.19)$$
$$= 0.800 \text{ V} - 0.771 \text{ V} = 0.029 \text{ V}$$

Now, to determine E_{cell} for the reaction

$$Fe^{2+}(0.10 \text{ M}) + Ag^+(1.0 \text{ M}) \longrightarrow Fe^{3+}(0.20 \text{ M}) + Ag(s) \quad E_{cell} = ? \quad (20.20)$$

substitute appropriate values into the Nernst equation (20.18), starting with $E_{cell}^{\circ} = 0.029 \text{ V}$ and $n = 1$,

$$E_{cell} = 0.029 \text{ V} - \frac{0.0592 \text{ V}}{1}\log\frac{[Fe^{3+}]}{[Fe^{2+}][Ag^+]}$$

and for concentrations $[Fe^{2+}] = 0.10 \text{ M}$; $[Fe^{3+}] = 0.20 \text{ M}$; $[Ag^+] = 1.0 \text{ M}$.

$$E_{cell} = 0.029 \text{ V} - 0.0592 \text{ V} \times \log\frac{0.20}{0.10 \times 1.0}$$
$$= 0.029 \text{ V} - 0.0592 \text{ V} \times \log 2 = 0.029 \text{ V} - 0.018 \text{ V}$$
$$= 0.011 \text{ V}$$

Practice Example A: Calculate E_{cell} for the following voltaic cell.

$$Al(s)|Al^{3+}(0.36 \text{ M})\|Sn^{4+}(0.086 \text{ M}), Sn^{2+}(0.54 \text{ M})|Pt$$

Practice Example B: Calculate E_{cell} for the following voltaic cell.

$$Pt(s)|Cl_2(1 \text{ atm})|Cl^-(1.0 \text{ M})\|Pb^{2+}(0.050 \text{ M}), H^+(0.10 \text{ M})|PbO_2(s)$$

In Section 20-3, we developed a criterion for spontaneous change ($E_{cell} > 0$), but we used the criterion only with E° data from Table 20.1. Qualitative conclusions reached with E_{cell}° values often hold over a broad range of nonstandard conditions as well. However, when E_{cell}° is within a few hundredths of a volt of zero, it is sometimes necessary to determine E_{cell} for nonstandard conditions in order to apply the criterion for spontaneity of redox reactions, as illustrated in Example 20-9.

EXAMPLE 20-9

Predicting Spontaneous Reactions for Nonstandard Conditions. Will the cell reaction proceed spontaneously as written for the following cell?

$$Sn(s)|Sn^{2+}(0.50 \text{ M})||Pb^{2+}(0.0010 \text{ M})|Pb(s)$$

Solution

To determine E°_{cell} from E° data, we write

$$E^{\circ}_{cell} = E^{\circ}(cathode) - E^{\circ}(anode)$$

$$= E^{\circ}_{Pb^{2+}/Pb} - E^{\circ}_{Sn^{2+}/Sn}$$

$$= -0.125 \text{ V} - (-0.137) \text{ V} = 0.012 \text{ V}$$

Then, to determine E_{cell} for the reaction

$$Sn(s) + Pb^{2+}(0.0010 \text{ M}) \longrightarrow Pb(s) + Sn^{2+}(0.50 \text{ M}) \qquad E_{cell} = ?$$

we substitute the following data into the Nernst equation: $E^{\circ}_{cell} = 0.012 \text{ V}$, $n = 2$, $[Sn^{2+}] = 0.50 \text{ M}$, and $[Pb^{2+}] = 0.0010 \text{ M}$.

$$E_{cell} = 0.012 \text{ V} - \frac{0.0592 \text{ V}}{2} \log \frac{[Sn^{2+}]}{[Pb^{2+}]}$$

$$= 0.012 \text{ V} - 0.0296 \text{ V} \log \frac{0.50}{0.0010} = 0.012 \text{ V} - 0.0296 \text{ V} \log 500$$

$$= 0.012 \text{ V} - 0.080 \text{ V} = -0.068 \text{ V}$$

Because $E_{cell} < 0$, we conclude that the reaction is nonspontaneous as written.

Practice Example A: Will the cell reaction proceed spontaneously as written for the following cell?

$$Cu(s)|Cu^{2+}(0.15 \text{ M})||Fe^{3+}(0.35 \text{ M}), Fe^{2+}(0.25 \text{ M})|Pt(s)$$

Practice Example B: For what ratio of $[Sn^{2+}]/[Pb^{2+}]$ will the cell reaction in Example 20-9 not be spontaneous in either direction?

CONCEPT ASSESSMENT ✓

The following cell is set up under standard-state conditions.

$$Pb(s)|Pb^{2+}||Cu^{2+}|Cu(s) \qquad E^{\circ}_{cell} = 0.47 \text{ V}$$

When sodium sulfate is added to the anode half-cell, formation of a white precipitate is observed, accompanied by a change in the value of E_{cell}. Explain these observations, and predict whether the new E_{cell} is greater or less than E°_{cell}.

CONCENTRATION CELLS

The voltaic cell in Figure 20-11 consists of two hydrogen electrodes. One is a standard hydrogen electrode (SHE), and the other is a hydrogen electrode immersed in a solution of unknown $[H^+]$, less than 1 M. The cell diagram is

$$Pt|H_2(g, 1 \text{ atm})|H^+(x \text{ M})||H^+(1 \text{ M})|H_2(g, 1 \text{ atm})|Pt$$

The reaction occurring in this cell is

Reduction:	$2 H^+(1 \text{ M}) + 2e^- \longrightarrow H_2(g, 1 \text{ atm})$	
Oxidation:	$H_2(g, 1 \text{ atm}) \longrightarrow 2 H^+(x \text{ M}) + 2e^-$	
Overall:	$2 H^+(1 \text{ M}) \longrightarrow 2 H^+(x \text{ M})$	(20.21)

$$E^{\circ}_{cell} = E^{\circ}_{H^+/H_2} - E^{\circ}_{H^+/H_2} = 0 \text{ V}$$

Relate the concentration cell to the driving force behind dilution, such as osmosis. In both cases the concentration difference means that the free energy between two compartments are different, giving rise to a stress.

▶ **FIGURE 20-11**
A concentration cell
The cell consists of two hydrogen electrodes. The electrode on the right is a SHE. Oxidation occurs at the anode on the left, where $[H^+]$ is less than 1 M. The reading on the voltmeter is directly proportional to the pH of the solution in the anode compartment.

The voltaic cell in Figure 20-11 is called a concentration cell. A **concentration cell** consists of two half-cells with *identical electrodes* but different ion concentrations. Because the electrodes are identical, the standard electrode potentials are numerically equal and subtracting one from the other leads to the value $E^\circ_{cell} = 0$. However, because the ion concentrations differ, there is a potential difference between the two half-cells. The spontaneous change in a concentration cell always occurs such that the concentrated solution becomes more dilute, and the dilute solution becomes more concentrated. The final result is as if the solutions were simply mixed. In a concentration cell, however, the natural tendency for entropy to increase in a mixing process is used as a means of producing electricity.

The Nernst equation for reaction (20.21) takes the form

$$E_{cell} = E^\circ_{cell} - \frac{0.0592 \text{ V}}{2} \log \frac{x^2}{1^2}$$

which simplifies to

$$E_{cell} = 0 - \frac{0.0592 \text{ V}}{2} \times 2 \log \frac{x}{1} = -0.0592 \text{ V} \log x$$

Because x is $[H^+]$ in the unknown solution and $-\log x = -\log[H^+] = pH$, the final result is

$$E_{cell} = (0.0592 \text{ pH}) \text{ V} \tag{20.22}$$

where the pH is that of the unknown solution. If an unknown solution has a pH of 3.50, for example, the measured cell voltage in Figure 20-11 will be $E_{cell} = (0.0592 \times 3.50) \text{ V} = 0.207 \text{ V}$.

Constructing and using a hydrogen electrode is difficult. The Pt metal surface must be specially prepared and maintained, gas pressure must be controlled, and the electrode cannot be used in the presence of strong oxidizing or reducing agents. A better approach is to replace the SHE in Figure 20-11 by a different reference electrode and the other hydrogen electrode by a *glass electrode*. A glass electrode is a thin glass membrane enclosing HCl(aq) and a silver wire coated with AgCl(s). When the glass electrode is dipped into a solution, H^+ ions are exchanged across the membrane. The potential established on the silver wire depends on $[H^+]$ in the solution being tested. Glass electrodes are most commonly encountered in laboratory pH meters (Fig. 20-12).

CONCEPT ASSESSMENT ✓

Write a cell diagram for a possible voltaic cell in which the cell reaction is $Cl^-(0.50 \text{ M}) \longrightarrow Cl^-(0.10 \text{ M})$. What would be E_{cell} for this reaction?

◀ **FIGURE 20-12**
A glass electrode and pH meter
The potential of the glass electrode
depends on the hydrogen ion
concentration of the solution being
tested. The difference in potential
between the glass electrode and a
reference electrode is converted
to a pH reading by the meter.

MEASUREMENT OF K_{sp}

The difference in concentration of ions in the two half-cells of a concentration
cell accounts for the observed E_{cell}. It also provides a basis for determining K_{sp}
values for sparingly soluble ionic compounds. Consider the following concentration cell.

$$Ag(s)|Ag^+(satd\ AgI)\|Ag^+(0.100\ M)|Ag \qquad E_{cell} = 0.417\ V$$

At the anode, a silver electrode is placed in a saturated aqueous solution of silver iodide. At the cathode, a second silver electrode is placed in a solution
with $[Ag^+] = 0.100$ M. The two half-cells are connected by a salt bridge, and
the measured cell voltage is 0.417 V (Fig. 20-13). The cell reaction occurring in
this *concentration cell* is

Reduction: $\qquad Ag^+(0.100\ M) + e^- \longrightarrow Ag(s)$

Oxidation: $\qquad\qquad\qquad\qquad Ag(s) \longrightarrow Ag^+(satd\ AgI)$

Overall: $\qquad\quad Ag^+(0.100\ M) \longrightarrow Ag^+(satd\ AgI) \qquad$ (20.23)

The calculation of K_{sp} of silver iodide is completed in Example 20-10.

Thompson, M. L., Kateley,
L. J. "The Nernst Equation:
Determination of Equilibrium
Constants for Complex Ions of
Silver." *J. Chem. Educ.* **1999:** *76*, 95
(January 1999).

Stress that the driving force
in a concentration cell is
to equalize the ion
concentrations in the cell. The
direction of the electron flow
corresponds to this equalization.

◀ **FIGURE 20-13**
**A concentration cell for determining
K_{sp} of AgI**
The silver electrode in the anode
compartment is in contact with a
saturated solution of AgI. In the cathode
compartment, $[Ag^+] = 0.100$ M.

It is quite dramatic to set up a
cell such as shown in Figure
20-13 and add KI to one side. The
AgI immediately precipitates out
and the potential drops.

EXAMPLE 20-10

Using a Voltaic Cell to Determine K_{sp} of a Slightly Soluble Solute. With the data given for reaction (20.23), calculate K_{sp} for AgI.

$$AgI(s) \rightleftharpoons Ag^+(aq) + I^-(aq) \qquad K_{sp} = ?$$

Solution

$[Ag^+]$ in saturated silver iodide solution can be represented as x. The Nernst equation is then applied to reaction (20.23). (To simplify the equations that follow, we have dropped the unit V, which would otherwise appear in several places.)

$$E_{cell} = E_{cell}^{\circ} - \frac{0.0592}{n} \log \frac{[Ag^+]_{satd\ AgI}}{[Ag^+]_{0.100\ M\ soln}}$$

$$= E_{cell}^{\circ} - \frac{0.0592}{1} \log \frac{x}{0.100}$$

$$0.417 = 0 - 0.0592(\log x - \log 0.100)$$

Divide both sides of the equation by 0.0592.

$$\frac{0.417}{0.0592} = -\log x + \log 0.100$$

$$\log x = \log 0.100 - \frac{0.417}{0.0592} = -1.00 - 7.04 = -8.04$$

$$x = [Ag^+] = 10^{-8.04} = 9.1 \times 10^{-9}\ M$$

Because in saturated AgI the concentrations of Ag^+ and I^- are equal,

$$K_{sp} = [Ag^+][I^-] = (9.1 \times 10^{-9})(9.1 \times 10^{-9}) = 8.3 \times 10^{-17}$$

Practice Example A: K_{sp} for AgCl = 1.8×10^{-10}. What would be the measured E_{cell} for the voltaic cell in Example 20-10 if the contents of the anode half-cell were saturated AgCl(aq) and AgCl(s)?

Practice Example B: Calculate the K_{sp} for PbI_2 given the following concentration cell information.

$$Pb(s)|Pb^{2+}(satd\ PbI_2)||Pb^{2+}(0.100\ M)|Pb(s) \qquad E_{cell} = 0.0567\ V$$

20-5 BATTERIES: PRODUCING ELECTRICITY THROUGH CHEMICAL REACTIONS

▶ Batteries are vitally important to modern society. Annual production in developed nations has been estimated at over 10 batteries per person per year.

Smith, M. J., Vincent, C. A. "Structure and Content of Some Primary Batteries." *J. Chem. Educ.* **2001;** *78,* 519.

Batteries activity

Cell phones, laptop computers, and many other devices rely heavily on rechargeable batteries. However, advances in electrochemistry and engineering have not been able to keep up with the demands of the microelectronic industry to deliver the longer life and higher power required.
http://www.howstuffworks.com/battery.htm (non-commercial)
http://www.varta.com/ (commercial)

A **battery** is a device that stores chemical energy for later release as electricity. Some batteries consist of a single voltaic cell with two electrodes and the appropriate electrolyte(s); an example is a flashlight cell. Other batteries consist of two or more voltaic cells joined in series fashion—plus to minus—to increase the total voltage; an example is an automobile battery. In this section, we will consider three types of voltaic cells and the batteries based on them.

- **Primary cells.** The cell reaction in a primary cell is not reversible. When the reactants have been mostly converted to products, no more electricity is produced and a battery employing a primary cell(s) is dead.

- **Secondary cells.** The cell reaction in a secondary cell *can* be reversed by passing electricity through the cell (charging). A battery employing secondary cells can be used through several hundred or more cycles of discharging followed by charging.

- **Flow batteries** and **fuel cells**. Materials (reactants, products, and electrolytes) pass through the battery, which is simply a converter of chemical energy to electric energy.

THE LECLANCHÉ (DRY) CELL

The most common form of voltaic cell is the *Leclanché cell*, invented by the French chemist Georges Leclanché (1839–1882) in the 1860s. Popularly called a *dry cell*, because no free liquid is present, or *flashlight battery*, the Leclanché cell is diagrammed in Figure 20-14. In this cell, oxidation occurs at a zinc anode and reduction at an inert carbon (graphite) cathode. The electrolyte is a moist paste of MnO_2, $ZnCl_2$, NH_4Cl, and carbon black (soot). The maximum cell voltage is 1.55 V. The anode (oxidation) half-reaction is simple.

$$\textit{Oxidation:} \quad Zn(s) \longrightarrow Zn^{2+}(aq) + 2\,e^-$$

The reduction is more complex. Essentially, it involves the reduction of MnO_2 to compounds having Mn in a +3 oxidation state, for example,

$$\textit{Reduction:} \quad 2\,MnO_2(s) + H_2O(l) + 2\,e^- \longrightarrow Mn_2O_3(s) + 2\,OH^-(aq)$$

An acid–base reaction occurs between NH_4^+ (from NH_4Cl) and OH^-.

$$NH_4^+(aq) + OH^-(aq) \longrightarrow NH_3(g) + H_2O(l)$$

A buildup of $NH_3(g)$ around the cathode would disrupt the current because the $NH_3(g)$ adheres to the cathode. That buildup is prevented by a reaction between Zn^{2+} and $NH_3(g)$ to form the complex ion $[Zn(NH_3)_2]^{2+}$, which crystallizes as the chloride salt.

$$Zn^{2+}(aq) + 2\,NH_3(g) + 2\,Cl^-(aq) \longrightarrow [Zn(NH_3)_2]Cl_2(s)$$

The Leclanché cell is a *primary cell*; it cannot be recharged. This cell is cheap to make, but it has some drawbacks. When current is drawn rapidly from the cell, products such as NH_3 build up on the electrodes, causing the voltage to drop. Also, because the electrolyte medium is acidic, zinc metal slowly dissolves.

A superior form of the Leclanché cell is the *alkaline cell*, which uses NaOH or KOH in place of NH_4Cl as the electrolyte. The reduction half-reaction is the same as that shown above, but the oxidation half-reaction involves the formation of $Zn(OH)_2(s)$, which can be thought of as occurring in two steps.

$$Zn(s) \longrightarrow Zn^{2+}(aq) + 2\,e^-$$
$$\underline{Zn^{2+}(aq) + 2\,OH^-(aq) \longrightarrow Zn(OH)_2(s)}$$
$$Zn(s) + 2\,OH^-(aq) \longrightarrow Zn(OH)_2(s) + 2\,e^-$$

The advantages of the alkaline cell are that zinc does not dissolve as readily in a basic (alkaline) medium as in an acidic medium, and the cell does a better job of maintaining its voltage as current is drawn from it.

THE LEAD–ACID (STORAGE) BATTERY

Secondary cells are most commonly encountered joined together in series in the *lead–acid battery*, or *storage battery*, which has been used in automobiles since about 1915 (Fig. 20-15). A storage battery is capable of repeated use because its chemical reactions are reversible. That is, the discharged energy can be restored by supplying electric current to recharge the cells in the battery.

The reactants in a lead–acid cell are spongy lead packed into a lead grid at the anode, red-brown lead(IV) oxide packed into a lead grid at the cathode, and dilute sulfuric acid with about 35% H_2SO_4, by mass. In this strongly acidic medium, the ionization of H_2SO_4 does not go to completion. Both $HSO_4^-(aq)$ and $SO_4^{2-}(aq)$ are present, but $HSO_4^-(aq)$ predominates. The half-reactions and overall reaction are

Reduction: $\quad PbO_2(s) + 3\,H^+(aq) + HSO_4^-(aq) + 2\,e^- \longrightarrow PbSO_4(s) + 2\,H_2O(l)$

Oxidation: $\quad\quad\quad\quad\quad\quad\quad\quad Pb(s) + HSO_4^-(aq) \longrightarrow PbSO_4(s) + H^+(aq) + 2\,e^-$

Overall: $\quad PbO_2(s) + Pb(s) + 2\,H^+(aq) + 2\,HSO_4^-(aq) \longrightarrow 2\,PbSO_4(s) + 2\,H_2O(l)$ (20.24)

$$E_{cell} = E_{PbO_2/PbSO_4} - E_{PbSO_4/Pb} = 1.74\ V - (-0.28\ V) = 2.02\ V$$

When an automobile engine is started, the battery is at first discharged. Once the car is in motion, an alternator powered by the engine constantly recharges the battery. At times, the plates of the battery become coated with

▲ FIGURE 20-14
The Leclanché (dry) cell
The chief components of the cell are a graphite (carbon) rod serving as the cathode, a zinc container serving as the anode, and an electrolyte.

▲ E_{cell}° is an intensive property
The voltage of a dry cell battery does not depend on the size of the battery—all of those pictured here are 1.5 V batteries.

◀ You can think of the half-reactions as occurring in two steps: (1) oxidation of Pb(s) to $Pb^{2+}(aq)$ and reduction of $PbO_2(s)$ to $Pb^{2+}(aq)$, followed by (2) precipitation of $PbSO_4(s)$ at each electrode.

Contrast normal batteries which when left a long time can burst and corrode. This is because the paste used NH_4Cl, which is a salt of a weak base and a strong acid. Hence the zinc case is eventually corroded. In contrast, alkali batteries replace the ammonium chloride with KOH or NaOH which are bases and do not corrode the zinc.

Shearer, Edmund C. "The construction and use of commercial voltaic cell displays in freshman chemistry (TD)." *J. Chem. Educ.* **1990:** *67,* 158.

LeRoux, X., Ottewill, G. A., Walsh, F. C. "The Comparative Performance of Batteries: The Lead-Acid and the Aluminum-Air Cells." *J. Chem. Educ.* **1996:** *73,* 811 (August 1996).

In spite of its usefulness and ability to deliver a strong current, the lead storage battery is also a pollution hazard. All batteries should be disposed of properly and should not be dumped in land fills or garbage disposal sites.

Lead-acid storage batteries are used to power golf carts, wheelchairs and passenger carts in airport terminals.

Treptow, R. S. "The Lead-Acid Battery: Its Voltage in Theory and in Practice." *J. Chem. Educ.* **2002:** *79,* 334.

▲ **FIGURE 20-15**
A lead–acid (storage) cell
The composition of the electrodes is described in the text. The cell reaction that occurs as the cell is discharged is given in equation (20.24). The voltage of the cell is 2.02 V. In this figure, two anode plates are connected in parallel fashion, as are two cathode plates.

$PbSO_4(s)$ and the electrolyte becomes sufficiently diluted with water that the battery must be recharged by connecting it to an external electric source. This forces the reverse of reaction (20.24), a nonspontaneous reaction.

$$2\,PbSO_4(s) + 2\,H_2O(l) \longrightarrow Pb(s) + PbO_2(s) + 2\,H^+(aq) + 2\,HSO_4^-(aq)$$
$$E_{cell} = -2.02 \text{ V}$$

To prevent the anode and cathode from coming into contact with each other, causing a *short circuit*, sheets of an insulating material are used to separate alternating anode and cathode plates. A group of anodes is connected together electrically, as is a group of cathodes. This parallel connection increases the electrode area in contact with the electrolyte solution and increases the current-delivering capacity of the cell. Cells are then joined in a series fashion, positive to negative, to produce a battery. The typical 12 V battery consists of six cells, each cell with a potential of about 2 V.

THE SILVER–ZINC CELL: A BUTTON BATTERY

The cell diagram of a *silver–zinc cell* (Fig. 20-16) is

$$Zn(s), ZnO(s)\,|\,KOH(satd)\,|\,Ag_2O(s), Ag(s)$$

The half-reactions on discharging are

Reduction:	$Ag_2O(s) + H_2O(l) + 2\,e^- \longrightarrow 2\,Ag(s) + 2\,OH^-(aq)$
Oxidation:	$Zn(s) + 2\,OH^-(aq) \longrightarrow ZnO(s) + H_2O(l) + 2\,e^-$
Overall:	$Zn(s) + Ag_2O(s) \longrightarrow ZnO(s) + 2\,Ag(s)$ (20.25)

Because no solution species is involved in the cell reaction, the quantity of electrolyte is very small and the electrodes can be maintained very close together. The cell voltage is 1.8 V, and its storage capacity is six times greater than that of a lead–acid battery of the same size. These characteristics make batteries such as the silver–zinc cell useful in button batteries. These miniature batteries are

◀ **FIGURE 20-16**
A silver–zinc button (miniature) cell

used in watches, hearing aids, and cameras. In addition, silver–zinc batteries fulfill the requirements of spacecraft, satellites, missiles, rockets, space launch vehicles, torpedoes, underwater vehicles, and life-support systems. On the Mars *Pathfinder* mission, the rover and the cruise system were powered by solar cells. The energy storage requirements of the lander were met by modified silver–zinc batteries with about three times the storage capacity of the standard nickel–cadmium rechargeable battery.

Heinhorst, S., Cannon, G. "Nature: Cleaner Fuels for the Future." *J. Chem. Educ.* **2000**: *77*, 810 (July 2000).

THE NICKEL–CADMIUM CELL: A RECHARGEABLE BATTERY

The *nickel–cadmium cell* (or *nicad battery*) is commonly used in cordless electric devices, such as electric shavers and handheld calculators. The anode in this cell is cadmium metal, and the cathode is the Ni(III) compound NiO(OH) supported on nickel metal. The half-cell reactions for a nickel–cadmium battery during discharge are

Reduction: $2\,NiO(OH)(s) + 2\,H_2O(l) + 2\,e^- \longrightarrow 2\,Ni(OH)_2(s) + 2\,OH^-(aq)$

Oxidation: $\underline{\hspace{1.5cm} Cd(s) + 2\,OH^-(aq) \longrightarrow Cd(OH)_2(s) + 2\,e^-}$

Overall: $Cd(s) + 2\,NiO(OH)(s) + 2\,H_2O(l) \longrightarrow 2\,Ni(OH)_2(s) + Cd(OH)_2(s)$

This cell gives a fairly constant voltage of 1.4 V. When the cell is recharged by connection to an external voltage source, the reactions above are reversed. Nickel–cadmium batteries can be recharged many times because the solid products adhere to the surface of the electrodes.

▲ A rechargeable nickel–cadmium cell, or nicad battery.

FUEL CELLS

The two types of cells considered in the remainder of this section fall into the third category mentioned on page 842; they are found in flow batteries.

For most of the twentieth century, scientists explored the possibility of converting the chemical energy of fuels directly to electricity. The essential process in a fuel cell is *fuel + oxygen* $\longrightarrow$ *oxidation products*. The first fuel cells were based on the reaction of hydrogen and oxygen. Figure 20-17 represents such a fuel cell. The overall change is that $H_2(g)$ and $O_2(g)$ in an alkaline medium produce $H_2O(l)$.

Reduction: $O_2(g) + 2\,H_2O(l) + 4\,e^- \longrightarrow 4\,OH^-(aq)$

Oxidation: $\underline{2\,\{H_2(g) + 2\,OH^-(aq) \longrightarrow 2\,H_2O(l) + 2\,e^-\}}$

Overall: $2\,H_2(g) + O_2(g) \longrightarrow 2\,H_2O(l)$ (20.26)

$$E°_{cell} = E°_{O_2/OH^-} - E°_{H_2O/H_2} = 0.401\,V - (-0.828\,V) = 1.229\,V$$

The theoretical maximum energy available as electric energy in any electrochemical cell is the free energy change for the cell reaction, $\Delta G°$. The maximum energy release when a fuel is burned is the enthalpy change, $\Delta H°$. One of the measures used to evaluate a fuel cell is the *efficiency value*, $\varepsilon = \Delta G°/\Delta H°$. For the hydrogen–oxygen fuel cell, $\varepsilon = -474.4\,kJ/-571.6\,kJ = 0.83$.

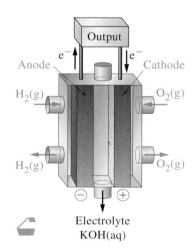

▲ **FIGURE 20-17**
A hydrogen–oxygen fuel cell
A key requirement in fuel cells is porous electrodes that allow for easy access of the gaseous reactants to the electrolyte. The electrodes chosen should also catalyze the electrode reactions.

▲ This Toyota prototype is a fuel-cell-powered electric car producing hydrogen from gasoline.

The day is fast approaching when fuel cells based on the direct oxidation of common fuels will become a reality. For example, the half-reaction and cell reaction for a fuel cell using methane (natural gas) are

Reduction: $2\{O_2(g) + 4H^+ + 4e^- \longrightarrow 2H_2O(l)\}$

Oxidation: $\underline{CH_4(g) + 2H_2O(l) \longrightarrow CO_2(g) + 8H^+ + 8e^-}$

Overall: $CH_4(g) + 2O_2(g) \longrightarrow CO_2(g) + 2H_2O(l)$

$$\Delta H° = -890\text{ kJ} \qquad \Delta G° = -818\text{ kJ} \qquad \varepsilon = 0.92 \qquad (20.27)$$

Although methane fuel cells are still in the research stage, an automobile engine is currently under development in which (1) a liquid hydrocarbon is vaporized; (2) the vaporized fuel is partially oxidized to $CO(g)$; (3) in the presence of a catalyst, steam converts the $CO(g)$ to $CO_2(g)$ and $H_2(g)$; and (4) $H_2(g)$ and air are fed through a fuel cell, producing electric energy.

A fuel cell should actually be called an *energy converter* rather than a battery. As long as fuel and $O_2(g)$ are available, the cell will produce electricity. It does not have the limited capacity of a primary battery or the fixed storage capacity of a secondary battery. Fuel cells based on reaction (20.26) have had their most notable successes as energy sources in space vehicles. (Water produced in the cell reaction is also a valuable product of the fuel cell.)

AIR BATTERIES

In a fuel cell, $O_2(g)$ is the oxidizing agent that oxidizes a fuel such as $H_2(g)$ or $CH_4(g)$. Another kind of flow battery, because it uses $O_2(g)$ from air, is known as an *air battery*. The substance that is oxidized in an air battery is typically a metal.

One heavily studied battery system is the aluminum–air battery in which oxidation occurs at an aluminum anode and reduction at a carbon–air cathode. The electrolyte circulated through the battery is $NaOH(aq)$. Because it is in the presence of a high concentration of OH^-, Al^{3+} produced at the anode forms the complex ion $[Al(OH)_4]^-$. The operation of the battery is suggested by Figure 20-18. The half-reactions and the overall cell reaction are

Reduction: $3\{O_2(g) + 2H_2O(l) + 4e^- \longrightarrow 4OH^-(aq)\}$

Oxidation: $\underline{4\{Al(s) + 4OH^-(aq) \longrightarrow [Al(OH)_4]^-(aq) + 3e^-\}}$

Overall: $4Al(s) + 3O_2(g) + 6H_2O(l) + 4OH^-(aq) \longrightarrow 4[Al(OH)_4]^-(aq)$ (20.28)

The battery is kept charged by feeding chunks of Al and water into it. A typical air battery can power an automobile several hundred miles before refueling is necessary. The electrolyte is circulated outside the battery, where $Al(OH)_3(s)$ is precipitated from the $[Al(OH)_4]^-(aq)$. This $Al(OH)_3(s)$ is collected and can then be converted back to aluminum metal at an aluminum manufacturing facility.

▶ **FIGURE 20-18**
A simplified aluminum–air battery

CONCEPT ASSESSMENT ✓

Why do dry cells and lead–acid cells "run down" during use? Do you think a fuel cell runs down? Explain.

20-6   CORROSION: UNWANTED VOLTAIC CELLS

The reactions occurring in voltaic cells (batteries) are important sources of electricity, but similar reactions also underlie corrosion processes. First, we will consider the electrochemical basis of corrosion, and then we will see how electrochemical principles can be applied to control corrosion.

Figure 20-19(a) demonstrates the basic processes in the corrosion of an iron nail. The nail is embedded in an agar gel in water. The gel contains the common acid–base indicator phenolphthalein and potassium ferricyanide, $K_3[Fe(CN)_6]$. Within hours of starting the experiment, a deep blue precipitate forms at the head and tip of the nail. Along the body of the nail, the agar gel turns pink. The blue precipitate, Turnbull's blue, establishes the presence of iron(II). The pink color is that of phenolphthalein in basic solution. From these observations, we write two simple half-equations.

Corrosion web site: http://www.cp.umist. ac.uk/ (non-commercial)

Reduction: $O_2(g) + 2 H_2O(l) + 4 e^- \longrightarrow 4 OH^-(aq)$

Oxidation: $2 Fe(s) \longrightarrow 2 Fe^{2+}(aq) + 4 e^-$

◄ This and other tests for iron(II) are described more fully in Section 23-5.

The potential difference for these two half-reactions is

$$E°_{cell} = E°_{O_2/OH^-} - E°_{Fe^{2+}/Fe} = 0.401 \text{ V} - (-0.440 \text{ V}) = 0.841 \text{ V}$$

indicating that the corrosion process should be spontaneous when reactants and products are in their standard states. Typically, the corrosion medium has $[OH^-] \ll 1$ M, the reduction half-reaction is even more favorable, and E_{cell} is even greater than 0.841 V. Corrosion is especially significant in acidic solutions, in which the reduction half-reaction is

Muller, Bodo. "Corrosion Inhibitors for Aluminum: Student Experiments." *J. Chem. Educ.* **1995**: *72*, 350.

$$O_2(g) + 4 H^+(aq) + 4 e^- \longrightarrow 2 H_2O(l) \qquad E°_{O_2/H_2O} = 1.229 \text{ V}$$

In the corroding nail of Figure 20-19(a), oxidation occurs at the head and tip. Electrons given up in the oxidation move along the nail and are used to reduce dissolved O_2. The reduction product, OH^-, is detected by the phenolphthalein. In the bent nail in Figure 20-19(b), oxidation occurs at *three* points: the head and tip and also the bend. The nail is preferentially oxidized at these points because the strained metal is more active (more anodic) than the unstrained metal. This situation is similar to the preferential rusting of a dented automobile fender.

Some metals, such as aluminum, form corrosion products that adhere tightly to the underlying metal and protect it from further corrosion. Iron oxide (rust), however, flakes off and constantly exposes fresh surface. This difference

(a)

(b)

(c)

(d)

◄ **FIGURE 20-19**
Demonstration of corrosion and methods of corrosion protection
The pink color results from the indicator phenolphthalein in the presence of base; the dark blue color results from the formation of Turnbull's blue $KFe[Fe(CN)_6]$. Corrosion (oxidation) of the nail occurs at strained regions: **(a)** the head and tip and **(b)** a bend in the nail. **(c)** Contact with zinc protects the nail from corrosion. Zinc is oxidized instead of the iron (forming the faint white precipitate of zinc ferricyanide). **(d)** Copper does not protect the nail from corrosion. Electrons lost in the oxidation half-reaction distribute themselves along the copper wire, as seen by the pink color that extends the full length of the wire.

Prevention of Corrosion animation

(a) Copper-plated iron

(b) Galvanized iron

▲ **FIGURE 20-20**
Protection of iron against electrolytic corrosion
In the *anodic* reaction, the metal that is more easily oxidized loses electrons to produce metal ions. In **(a)**, this is iron; in **(b)**, it is zinc. In the *cathodic* reaction, oxygen gas, which is dissolved in a thin film of water on the metal, is reduced to OH^-. Rusting of iron occurs in (a), but it does not in (b). When iron corrodes, Fe^{2+} and OH^- ions from the half-reactions initiate these further reactions.

$$Fe^{2+} + 2\,OH^- \longrightarrow Fe(OH)_2(s)$$
$$4\,Fe(OH)_2(s) + O_2 + 2\,H_2O \longrightarrow 4\,Fe(OH)_3(s)$$
$$2\,Fe(OH)_3(s) \longrightarrow Fe_2O_3 \cdot H_2O(s) + H_2O(l)$$
$$\text{rust}$$

▲ **Galvanized nails**

Sacrificial Mg anodes

▲ **Magnesium sacrificial anodes**
The small cylindrical bars of magnesium attached to the steel ship provide cathodic protection against corrosion.

in corrosion behavior explains why cans made of iron deteriorate rapidly in the environment, whereas aluminum cans have an almost unlimited lifetime. The simplest method of protecting a metal from corrosion is to cover it with paint or some other protective coating impervious to water, an important reactant and solvent in corrosion processes.

Another method of protecting an iron surface is to plate it with a thin layer of a second metal. Iron can be plated with copper by electroplating or with tin by dipping the iron into molten tin. In either case, the underlying metal is protected as long as the coating remains intact. If the coating is cracked, as when a "tin" can is dented, the underlying iron is exposed and begins to corrode. Iron, being more active than copper and tin, undergoes oxidation; the reduction half-reaction occurs on the plating (Figs. 20-19d and 20-20a).

When iron is coated with zinc (galvanized iron), the situation is different. Zinc is more active than iron. If a break occurs in the zinc plating, the iron is still protected because the zinc is oxidized instead of the iron, and corrosion products protect the zinc from further corrosion (Figs. 20-19c and 20-20b).

Still another method is used to protect large iron and steel objects in contact with water or moist soils—ships, storage tanks, pipelines, plumbing systems. This method involves connecting a chunk of magnesium or some other active metal to the object, either directly or through a wire. Oxidation occurs at the active metal, which slowly dissolves. The iron surface acquires electrons from the oxidation of the active metal; the iron acts as a cathode and supports a *reduction* half-reaction. As long as some of the active metal remains, the iron is protected. This type of protection is called **cathodic protection**, and the active metal is called, appropriately, a *sacrificial anode*. Millions of pounds of magnesium are used annually in the United States in sacrificial anodes.

CONCEPT ASSESSMENT ✓

Of the metals Al, Cu, Ni, and Zn, which could act as a sacrificial anode for iron?

20-7   ELECTROLYSIS: CAUSING NONSPONTANEOUS REACTIONS TO OCCUR

Until now, the emphasis has been on voltaic (galvanic) cells, electrochemical cells in which chemical change is used to produce electricity. Another type of electrochemical cell—the **electrolytic cell**—uses electricity to produce a *nonspontaneous* reaction. The process in which a nonspontaneous reaction is driven by the application of electric energy is called **electrolysis**.

Let's explore the relationship between voltaic and electrolytic cells by returning briefly to the cell shown in Figure 20-4. When the cell functions spontaneously, electrons flow from the zinc to the copper and the overall chemical change in the voltaic cell is

$$Zn(s) + Cu^{2+}(aq) \longrightarrow Zn^{2+}(aq) + Cu(s) \qquad E^\circ_{cell} = 1.103 \text{ V}$$

Now suppose the same cell is connected to an external electric source of voltage greater than 1.103 V (Fig. 20-21). That is, the connection is made so that electrons are forced into the zinc electrode (now the cathode) and removed from the copper electrode (now the anode). The overall reaction in this case is the *reverse* of the voltaic cell reaction, and E°_{cell} is *negative*.

Reduction: $Zn^{2+}(aq) + 2 e^- \longrightarrow Zn(s)$

Oxidation: $\underline{\qquad\qquad\quad Cu(s) \longrightarrow Cu^{2+}(aq) + 2 e^-}$

Overall: $Cu(s) + Zn^{2+}(aq) \longrightarrow Cu^{2+}(aq) + Zn(s)$

$$E^\circ_{cell} = E^\circ_{Zn^{2+}/Zn} - E^\circ_{Cu^{2+}/Cu} = -0.763 \text{ V} - 0.340 \text{ V} = -1.103 \text{ V}$$

Thus, reversing the direction of the electron flow changes the voltaic cell into an electrolytic cell.

PREDICTING ELECTROLYSIS REACTIONS

For the cell in Figure 20-21 to function as an electrolytic cell with reactants and products in their standard states, the external voltage has to exceed 1.103 V. We can make similar calculations for other electrolyses. What actually happens,

◀ **KEEP IN MIND**
that voltaic (galvanic) and electrolytic cells are the two categories subsumed under the more general term: electrochemical cell.

▲ **FIGURE 20-21**
An electrolytic cell
The direction of electron flow is the reverse of that in the voltaic cell of Figure 20-4, and so is the cell reaction. Now the zinc electrode is the *cathode* and the copper electrode, the *anode*. The battery must have a voltage in excess of 1.103 V in order to force electrons to flow in the reverse (nonspontaneous) direction.

Are You Wondering . . .

Why the anode is (+) in an electrolytic cell but (−) in a voltaic cell?

Assigning the terms *anode* and *cathode* is not based on the electrode charges; it is based on the half-reactions at the electrode surfaces. Specifically,

- *Oxidation* always occurs at the *anode* of an electrochemical cell. Because of the buildup of electrons freed in the oxidation half-reaction, the anode of a *voltaic* cell is (−). Because electrons are withdrawn from it, the anode in an *electrolytic* cell is (+). For both cell types, the anode is the electrode from which electrons *exit* the cell.
- *Reduction* always occurs at the cathode of an electrochemical cell. Because of the *removal* of electrons by the reduction half-reaction, the cathode of a *voltaic* cell is (+). Because of the electrons forced onto it, the cathode of an *electrolytic* cell is (−). For both cell types, the cathode is the electrode at which electrons *enter* the cell.

The following table summarizes the relationship between a voltaic cell and an electrolytic cell.

	Voltaic Cell			Electrolytic Cell	
Oxidation:	$A \longrightarrow A^+ + e^-$	Anode (negative)	*Oxidation:*	$B \longrightarrow B^+ + e^-$	Anode (positive)
Reduction:	$B^+ + e^- \longrightarrow B$	Cathode (positive)	*Reduction:*	$A^+ + e^- \longrightarrow A$	Cathode (negative)
Overall:	$A + B^+ \longrightarrow A^+ + B$ $\Delta G < 0$ Spontaneous redox reaction releases energy		*Overall:*	$A^+ + B \longrightarrow A + B^+$ $\Delta G > 0$ Nonspontaneous redox reaction absorbs energy to drive it	
	The system (the cell) does work on the surroundings			The surroundings (the source of energy) do work on the system	

Note that the sign of each electrode in an electrolytic cell is the same as the sign of the battery electrode to which it is attached.

Hoffman, B., Mitchell, E., Roulhac, P., Thomes, M., Stumpo, V. M. "Determination of the Fundamental Electronic Charge via the Electrolysis of Water." *J. Chem. Educ.* **2000:** 77, 95 (January 2000).

Electrolysis of water website: http://www.chem.uiuc. edu/demos/elec.html (non-commercial)
General electrolysis: http://www.encyclopedia.com/ articles/04022.html (commercial)

▶ We have written a *minus* sign in front of the electrode potentials in (20.31) and (20.32) as a way of emphasizing the *oxidation* rather than the reduction tendency.

however, does not always correspond to these calculations. Four complicating factors must be considered:

1. A voltage significantly in excess of the calculated value, an **overpotential**, may be necessary to cause a particular electrode reaction to occur. Overpotentials are needed to overcome interactions at the electrode surface and are particularly common when gases are involved. For example, the overpotential for the discharge of $H_2(g)$ at a mercury cathode is approximately 1.5 V; the overpotential on a platinum cathode is practically zero.

2. Competing electrode reactions may occur. In the electrolysis of *molten* sodium chloride with inert electrodes, only one oxidation and one reduction are possible.

$$\text{Reduction:} \quad 2\,Na^+ + 2\,e^- \longrightarrow 2\,Na(l)$$
$$\text{Oxidation:} \quad 2\,Cl^- \longrightarrow Cl_2(g) + 2\,e^-$$

In the electrolysis of *aqueous* sodium chloride with inert electrodes, there are *two* possible reduction half-reactions and *two* possible oxidation half-reactions.

Reduction:	$2\,Na^+(aq) + 2\,e^- \longrightarrow Na(s)$	$E^\circ_{Na^+/Na} = -2.71\ V$	(20.29)
	$2\,H_2O(l) + 2\,e^- \longrightarrow H_2(g) + 2\,OH^-(aq)$	$E^\circ_{H_2O/H_2} = (-0.83\ V)$	(20.30)
Oxidation:	$2\,Cl^-(aq) \longrightarrow Cl_2(g) + 2\,e^-$	$-E^\circ_{Cl_2/Cl^-} = -(1.36\ V)$	(20.31)
	$2\,H_2O(l) \longrightarrow O_2(g) + 4\,H^+(aq) + 4\,e^-$	$-E^\circ_{O_2/H_2O} = -(1.23\ V)$	(20.32)

Reaction (20.29) can be eliminated as a possible reduction half-reaction: Unless the overpotential for $H_2(g)$ is unusually high, the reduction of Na^+ is far more difficult to accomplish than that of H_2O. This leaves two possibilities for the cell reaction.

Half-reaction (20.30) + half-reaction (20.31):

Reduction: $2\,H_2O(l) + 2\,e^- \longrightarrow H_2(g) + 2\,OH^-(aq)$

Oxidation: $\underline{\qquad 2\,Cl^-(aq) \longrightarrow Cl_2(g) + 2\,e^- \qquad}$

Overall: $2\,Cl^-(aq) + 2\,H_2O(l) \longrightarrow Cl_2(g) + H_2(g) + 2\,OH^-(aq)$ (20.33)

$$E^\circ_{cell} = E^\circ_{H_2O/H_2} - E^\circ_{Cl_2/Cl^-} = -0.83\,V - (1.36\,V) = -2.19\,V$$

Half-reaction (20.30) + half-reaction (20.32):

Reduction: $2\,\{2\,H_2O(l) + 2\,e^- \longrightarrow H_2(g) + 2\,OH^-(aq)\}$

Oxidation: $\underline{\qquad 2\,H_2O(l) \longrightarrow O_2(g) + 4\,H^+(aq) + 4\,e^- \qquad}$

Overall: $2\,H_2O(l) \longrightarrow 2\,H_2(g) + O_2(g)$ (20.34)

$$E^\circ_{cell} = E^\circ_{H_2O/H_2} - E^\circ_{O_2/H_2O} = -0.83\,V - (1.23\,V) = -2.06\,V$$

In the electrolysis of NaCl(aq), $H_2(g)$ is the product expected at the *cathode*. Because cell reactions (20.33) and (20.34) have E°_{cell} values that are so similar, a mixture of $Cl_2(g)$ and $O_2(g)$ would be the expected product at the *anode*. Actually, because of the high overpotential of $O_2(g)$ compared to $Cl_2(g)$, cell reaction (20.33) predominates; $Cl_2(g)$ is essentially the only product at the anode.

3. The reactants very often are in *nonstandard* states. In the industrial electrolysis of NaCl(aq), $[Cl^-] \approx 5.5\,M$, not the unit activity ($[Cl^-] \approx 1\,M$) implied in half-reaction (20.31); therefore $E_{Cl_2/Cl^-} = 1.31\,V$ (*not* 1.36 V). Also, the pH in the anode half-cell is adjusted to 4, not the unit activity ($[H_3O^+] \approx 1\,M$) implied in half-reaction (20.32); hence $E_{O_2/H_2O} = 0.99\,V$ (*not* 1.23 V). The net effect of these nonstandard conditions is to favor the production of O_2 at the anode. In practice, however, the $Cl_2(g)$ obtained contains less than 1% $O_2(g)$, indicating the overpowering effect of the high overpotential of $O_2(g)$. Not surprisingly, the proportion of $O_2(g)$ increases significantly in the electrolysis of very dilute NaCl(aq).

4. The nature of the electrodes matters. An *inert electrode*, such as platinum, provides a surface on which an electrolysis half-reaction occurs, but the reactants themselves must come from the electrolyte solution. An *active electrode* is one that can itself participate in the oxidation or reduction half-reaction. The distinction between inert and active electrodes is explored in Figure 20-22 and Example 20-11.

▲ The electrolysis of water into $H_2(g)$ and $O_2(g)$, shown by bubbles at the electrodes and the gases collecting in the test tubes—twice the volume of $H_2(g)$ as $O_2(g)$.

▲ **FIGURE 20-22**
Predicting electrode reactions in electrolysis—Example 20-11 illustrated
Electrons are forced onto the copper cathode by the external source (battery). Cu^{2+} ions are attracted to the cathode and are reduced to Cu(s). The oxidation half-reaction depends on the metal used for the anode.

Anderson, Guy E. "Small Scale Electrolytic Cells." *J. Chem. Educ.* **1996:** 73, A170 (August 1996).

Electrolysis of Water animation

Are You Wondering . . .

What happens when no electrode reactions seem feasible in an aqueous solution?

Electrolysis requires that an electrolyte be present to carry current through the aqueous solution. If ions of the electrolyte are less easily oxidized and reduced than is water, $H_2O(l)$ will react at each electrode. The combination of half-reactions (20.30) and (20.32) occurs in the electrolysis of water: $2\,H_2O(l) \longrightarrow 2\,H_2(g) + O_2(g)$.

EXAMPLE 20-11

Predicting Electrode Half-Reactions and Overall Reactions in Electrolysis. Refer to Figure 20-22. Predict the electrode reactions and the overall reaction when the anode is made of **(a)** copper and **(b)** platinum.

Solution

In both cases, the reduction of $Cu^{2+}(aq)$ is the only likely reduction process.

$$Reduction: \quad Cu^{2+}(aq) + 2\,e^- \longrightarrow Cu(s) \qquad E^\circ_{Cu^{2+}/Cu} = 0.340 \text{ V}$$

(a) At the anode, $Cu(s)$ can be oxidized to $Cu^{2+}(aq)$, as represented by

$$Oxidation: \quad Cu(s) \longrightarrow Cu^{2+}(aq) + 2\,e^-$$

If the oxidation and reduction half-equations are added, $Cu^{2+}(aq)$ cancels out. The electrolysis reaction is simply

$$Cu(s)[\text{anode}] \longrightarrow Cu(s)[\text{cathode}] \qquad (20.35)$$

$$E^\circ_{cell} = E^\circ_{Cu^{2+}/Cu} - E^\circ_{Cu^{2+}/Cu} = 0.340 \text{ V} - 0.340 \text{ V} = 0$$

Only a very small voltage is needed to overcome the resistance in the electric circuit for this electrolysis. For every Cu atom that enters the solution at the anode, an active electrode, one Cu^{2+} ion deposits as a Cu atom at the cathode. Copper is transferred from the anode to the cathode through the solution as Cu^{2+}, and the concentration of $CuSO_4(aq)$ remains unchanged.

(b) A platinum electrode is inert. It is not easily oxidized. The oxidation of SO_4^{2-} to $S_2O_8^{2-}$ also is not feasible ($-E^\circ_{S_2O_8^{2-}/SO_4^{2-}} = -2.01$ V). The oxidation that occurs most readily is that of H_2O, shown in reaction (20.32).

$$Oxidation: \quad 2\,H_2O(l) \longrightarrow O_2(g) + 4\,H^+(aq) + 4\,e^-$$

$$-E^\circ_{O_2/H_2O} = -1.23 \text{ V}$$

The electrolysis reaction and its E°_{cell} are

$$2\,Cu^{2+}(aq) + 2\,H_2O(l) \longrightarrow 2\,Cu(s) + 4\,H^+(aq) + O_2(g) \qquad (20.36)$$

$$E^\circ_{cell} = E^\circ(\text{reduction half-cell}) - E^\circ(\text{oxidation half-cell})$$

$$= E^\circ_{Cu^{2+}/Cu} - E^\circ_{O_2/H_2O}$$

$$= 0.340 \text{ V} - 1.23 \text{ V} = -0.89 \text{ V}$$

Practice Example A: Use data from Table 20.1 to predict the probable products when Pt electrodes are used in the electrolysis of KI(aq).

Practice Example B: In the electrolysis of $AgNO_3(aq)$, what are the expected electrolysis products if the anode is silver metal and the cathode is platinum?

QUANTITATIVE ASPECTS OF ELECTROLYSIS

We have seen how to calculate the theoretical voltage required for electrolysis. Equally important are calculations of the quantities of reactants consumed and products formed in an electrolysis. For these calculations, we will continue to use stoichiometric factors from the chemical equation, but another factor enters in as well: the quantity of electric charge associated with one mole of electrons. This factor is provided by the Faraday constant, which we can write as

$$1 \text{ mol } e^- = 96{,}485 \text{ C}$$

Generally, electric charge is not measured directly; instead, it is the electric current that is measured. One *ampere* (A) of electric current represents the passage of 1 coulomb of charge per second (C/s). The product of current and time yields the total quantity of charge transferred.

$$\text{charge (C)} = \text{current (C/s)} \times \text{time (s)}$$

To determine the number of moles of electrons involved in an electrolysis reaction, we can write

$$\text{number of mol } e^- = \text{current}\left(\frac{C}{s}\right) \times \text{time (s)} \times \frac{1 \text{ mol } e^-}{96{,}485 \text{ C}}$$

As illustrated in Example 20-12, to determine the mass of a product in an electrolysis reaction, follow this conversion pathway.

$$C/s \longrightarrow C \longrightarrow \text{mol } e^- \longrightarrow \text{mol product} \longrightarrow \text{g product}$$

EXAMPLE 20-12

Calculating Quantities Associated with Electrolysis Reactions. The electrodeposition of copper can be used to determine the copper content of a sample. The sample is dissolved to produce $Cu^{2+}(aq)$, which is electrolyzed. At the cathode, the reduction half-reaction is $Cu^{2+}(aq) + 2\,e^- \longrightarrow Cu(s)$. What mass of copper can be deposited in 1.00 hour by a current of 1.62 A?

Electrolysis Calculation Example activity

Solution

We can think of this as a two-part calculation. First we can determine the number of moles of electrons involved in the electrolysis in the manner outlined above.

$$1.00 \text{ h} \times \frac{60 \text{ min}}{1 \text{ h}} \times \frac{60 \text{ s}}{1 \text{ min}} \times \frac{1.62 \text{ C}}{1 \text{ s}} \times \frac{1 \text{ mol } e^-}{96{,}485 \text{ C}} = 0.0604 \text{ mol } e^-$$

Then we can calculate the mass of Cu(s) produced at the cathode by this number of moles of electrons. The key factor is printed in blue.

$$\text{mass of Cu} = 0.0604 \text{ mol } e^- \times \frac{1 \text{ mol Cu}}{2 \text{ mol } e^-} \times \frac{63.5 \text{ g Cu}}{1 \text{ mol Cu}} = 1.92 \text{ g Cu}$$

Practice Example A: If 12.3 g of Cu is deposited at the cathode of an electrolytic cell after 5.50 h, what was the current used?

Practice Example B: For how long would the electrolysis in Example 20-12 have to be carried out, using Pt electrodes and a current of 2.13 A, to produce 2.62 L $O_2(g)$ at 26.2 °C and 738 mmHg pressure at the anode?

20-8   INDUSTRIAL ELECTROLYSIS PROCESSES

Modern industry could not function in its present form without electrolysis reactions. A number of elements are produced almost exclusively by electrolysis—for example, aluminum, magnesium, chlorine, and fluorine. Among chemical compounds produced industrially by electrolysis are NaOH, $K_2Cr_2O_7$, $KMnO_4$, $Na_2S_2O_8$, and a number of organic compounds.

ELECTROREFINING

The *electrorefining* of metals involves the deposition of pure metal at a cathode, from a solution containing the metal ion. Copper produced by the smelting of copper ores is of sufficient purity for some uses, such as plumbing, but it is not pure enough for applications in which high electrical conductivity is required.

▶ The refining of copper by electrolysis.

☑ Electrorefining: http://www.hydromet-research.com.au/solext/electwin_refine.html (Commercial)

📖 Gorodetsky, M., Singerman, A. "Electroforming: An improvised experiment on electroplating." *J. Chem. Educ.* **1980:** 57, 514.

📖 Gorodetsky, Malka. "Electroplating of polyethylene." *J. Chem. Educ.* **1978:** 55, 66.

📖 Dix, G. F., Hultsch, R. A. "Electroplating with solar energy." *J. Chem. Educ.* **1978:** 55, 259.

Electrolysis simulation and Electroplating movie

For these applications, the copper must be more than 99.5% pure. The electrolysis reaction (20.35) on page 852 is used to obtain such high-purity copper. A chunk of impure copper is the anode and a thin sheet of pure copper is the cathode. During the electrolysis, Cu^{2+} produced at the anode migrates through an aqueous sulfuric acid–copper(II) sulfate solution to the cathode, where it is reduced to Cu(s). The pure copper cathode increases in size as the impure chunk of copper is consumed. As noted in Example 20-11a, the electrolysis is carried out at a low voltage—from 0.15 to 0.30 V. Under these conditions, Ag, Au, and Pt impurities are not oxidized at the anode, and they drop to the bottom of the tank as a sludge called *anode mud*. Sn, Bi, and Sb are oxidized, but they precipitate as oxides or hydroxides; Pb is oxidized but precipitates as $PbSO_4(s)$. As, Fe, Ni, Co, and Zn are oxidized but form water-soluble species. Recovery of Ag, Au, and Pt from the anode mud helps offset the cost of the electrolysis.

ELECTROPLATING

In *electroplating*, one metal is plated onto another, often less expensive, metal by electrolysis. This procedure is done for decorative purposes or to protect the underlying metal from corrosion. Silver-plated flatware, for example, consists of a thin coating of metallic silver on an underlying base of iron. In electroplating, the item to be plated is the cathode in an electrolytic cell. The electrolyte contains ions of the metal to be plated, which are attracted to the cathode, where they are reduced to metal atoms.

In copper plating, the electrolyte is usually copper sulfate. In silver plating, it is commonly $K[Ag(CN)_2](aq)$. The concentration of free silver ion in a solution of the complex ion $[Ag(CN)_2]^-(aq)$ is very low, and electroplating under these conditions promotes a strongly adherent microcrystalline deposit of the metal. Chromium plating is useful for its resistance to corrosion as well as its appearance. Steel can be chromium-plated from an aqueous solution of CrO_3 and H_2SO_4. The plating obtained, however, is thin and porous and tends to develop cracks. In practice, the steel is first plated with a thin coat of copper or nickel, and then the chromium plating is applied. Chromium plating or cadmium plating is used to weatherproof machine parts. Metal plating can even be applied to some plastics. The plastic must first be made electrically conductive—for example, by coating it with graphite powder. Copper plating of plastics has been used to improve the quality of some microelectronic circuit boards. Electroplating is even used, quite literally, to make money. The U.S. penny is no longer copper throughout. A zinc plug is electroplated with a thin coat of copper, and the copper-plated plug is stamped to create a penny.

ELECTROSYNTHESIS

Electrosynthesis is a method of producing substances through electrolysis reactions. It is useful for certain syntheses in which reaction conditions must be carefully controlled. Manganese dioxide occurs naturally as the mineral *pyrolusite*, but small crystal size and lattice imperfections make this material

▲ A rack of metal parts being lifted from the electrolyte solution after electroplating.

inadequate for certain modern applications, such as alkaline batteries. The electrosynthesis of MnO_2 is carried out in a solution of $MnSO_4$ in $H_2SO_4(aq)$. Pure $MnO_2(s)$ is formed by the oxidation of Mn^{2+} at an inert anode such as graphite.

Oxidation: $\quad Mn^{2+}(aq) + 2 H_2O(l) \longrightarrow MnO_2(s) + 4 H^+(aq) + 2 e^-$

The reaction at the cathode is the reduction of H^+ to $H_2(g)$, and the overall electrolysis reaction is

$$Mn^{2+}(aq) + 2 H_2O(l) \longrightarrow MnO_2(s) + 2 H^+(aq) + H_2(g)$$

An example of electrosynthesis in organic chemistry is the reduction of acrylonitrile, $CH_2{=}CH{-}C{\equiv}N$, to adiponitrile, $N{\equiv}C(CH_2)_4C{\equiv}N$, at a lead cathode (chosen because of the high overpotential of H_2 on lead). Oxygen is released at the anode.

Reduction: $\quad 2 CH_2{=}CH{-}C{\equiv}N + 2 H_2O + 2 e^- \longrightarrow$

$$N{\equiv}C(CH_2)_4C{\equiv}N + 2 OH^-$$

The commercial importance of this electrolysis is that adiponitrile can be readily converted to two other compounds: hexamethylenediamine, H_2NCH_2 $(CH_2)_4CH_2NH_2$, and adipic acid, $HOOCCH_2(CH_2)_2CH_2COOH$. These two compounds are the monomers used to make the polymer *Nylon-66* (page 1120).

THE CHLOR–ALKALI PROCESS

On page 851 we described the electrolysis of NaCl(aq) through the reduction half-reaction (20.30) and the oxidation half-reaction (20.31).

$$2 Cl^-(aq) + 2 H_2O(l) \longrightarrow 2 OH^-(aq) + H_2(g) + Cl_2(g) \qquad E^\circ_{cell} = -2.19 \text{ V}$$

When conducted on an industrial scale, this electrolysis is called the *chlor–alkali process*, named after the two principal products: *chlor*ine and the *alkali* NaOH(aq). The chlor–alkali process is one of the most important of all electrolytic processes because of the high value of these products.

In the *diaphragm cell* depicted in Figure 20-23, $Cl_2(g)$ is produced in the anode compartment, and $H_2(g)$ and NaOH(aq) in the cathode compartment. If $Cl_2(g)$ comes in contact with NaOH(aq), the Cl_2 disproportionates into $ClO^-(aq)$, $ClO_3{}^-(aq)$, and $Cl^-(aq)$. The purpose of the diaphragm is to prevent this contact. The NaCl(aq) in the anode compartment is kept at a slightly higher level than that in the cathode compartment. This disparity creates a gradual flow of NaCl(aq) between the compartments and reduces the backflow of NaOH(aq) into the anode compartment. The solution in the cathode compartment,

 Electrosynthesis website:
http://www.electro synthesis.com/ (commercial)

Wagenknecht, John H. "Industrial organic electrosynthesis (SOA-Electrochemistry)." *J. Chem. Educ.* **1983:** *60,* 271.

A Chlor-Alkali website:
http://www.cheresources. com/chloralk.shtml (commercial)

◀ **FIGURE 20-23**
A diaphragm chlor–alkali cell
The anode may be made of graphite or, in more modern technology, specially treated titanium metal. The diaphragm and cathode are generally fabricated as a composite unit consisting of asbestos or an asbestos–polymer mixture deposited on a steel wire mesh. To avoid the use of asbestos, a more modern development substitutes a fluorocarbon mesh for the asbestos.

▲ **FIGURE 20-24**
The mercury-cell chlor–alkali process
The cathode is a layer of Hg(l) that flows along the bottom of the tank. Anodes, at which $Cl_2(g)$ forms, are situated in the NaCl(aq) just above the Hg(l). Sodium formed at the cathode dissolves in the Hg(l), and the sodium amalgam is decomposed with water to produce NaOH(aq) and $H_2(g)$. The regenerated Hg(l) is recycled.

about 10–12% NaOH(aq) and 14–16% NaCl(aq), is concentrated and purified by evaporating some water and crystallizing the NaCl(s). The final product is 50% NaOH(aq), with up to 1% NaCl(aq).

The theoretical voltage required for this electrolysis is 2.19 V. However, as a result of the internal resistance of the cell and overpotentials at the electrodes, a voltage of about 3.5 V is used. The current is kept very high, typically about 1×10^5 A.

The NaOH(aq) produced in a diaphragm cell is not pure enough for certain uses such as rayon manufacture. A higher purity is achieved if electrolysis is carried out in a mercury cell, illustrated in Figure 20-24. This cell takes advantage of the high overpotential for the reduction of $H_2O(l)$ to $H_2(g)$ and $OH^-(aq)$ at a mercury cathode. The reduction that occurs instead is that of $Na^+(aq)$ to Na, which dissolves in Hg(l) to form an amalgam (Na–Hg alloy) with about 0.5% Na by mass.

$$2\,Na^+(aq) + 2\,Cl^-(aq) \longrightarrow 2\,Na(in\ Hg) + Cl_2(g) \qquad E^\circ_{cell} = -3.20\ V$$

When the Na amalgam is removed from the cell and treated with water, NaOH(aq) forms,

$$2\,Na(in\ Hg) + 2\,H_2O(l) \longrightarrow 2\,Na^+(aq) + 2\,OH^-(aq) + H_2(g) + Hg(l)$$

and the liquid mercury is recycled back to the electrolytic cell.

Although the mercury cell has the advantage of producing concentrated high-purity NaOH(aq), it has some disadvantages. The mercury cell requires a higher voltage (about 4.5 V) than does the diaphragm cell (3.5 V) and consumes more electrical energy, about 3400 kWh/ton Cl_2 in a mercury cell, compared with 2500 in a diaphragm cell. Another serious drawback is the need to control mercury effluents to the environment. Mercury losses, which at one time were as high as 200 g Hg per ton Cl_2, have been reduced to about 0.25 g Hg per ton of Cl_2 in older plants and half this amount in new plants.

The ideal chlor–alkali process is one that is energy-efficient and does not use mercury. A type of cell offering these advantages is the *membrane cell*, in which the porous diaphragm of Figure 20-23 is replaced by a cation-exchange membrane, normally made of a fluorocarbon polymer. The membrane permits hydrated cations (Na^+ and H_3O^+) to pass between the anode and cathode compartments but severely restricts the backflow of Cl^- and OH^- ions. As a result, the sodium hydroxide solution produced contains less than 50 ppm chloride ion contaminant.

Summary

20-1 Electrode Potentials and Their Measurement—In an **electrochemical cell** electrons in an oxidation–reduction reaction are transferred at metal strips called **electrodes** and conducted through an external circuit. The oxidation and reduction half-reactions occur in separate regions called **half-cells**. In a half-cell, an electrode is immersed in a solution. The electrodes of the two half-cells are joined by a wire, and an electrical connection between the solutions is also made, as through a **salt bridge** (Fig. 20-3). The cell reaction involves oxidation at one electrode called the **anode** and reduction at the other electrode called the **cathode**. A **voltaic (galvanic) cell** produces electricity from a spontaneous oxidation–reduction reaction. The difference in electric potential between the two electrodes is the **cell voltage**; the unit of cell voltage is the **volt (V)**. The cell voltage is also called the **cell potential** or **electromotive force** (emf) and designated as E_{cell}. A **cell diagram** displays the components of a cell in a symbolic way (expression 20-4).

20-2 Standard Electrode Potentials—The reduction occurring at a **standard hydrogen electrode (SHE)**,
$$2\,H^+(a = 1) + 2\,e^- \xrightarrow{\text{on Pt}} H_2(g, 1 \text{ bar}),$$ is arbitrarily assigned a potential of zero. A half-cell has a **standard electrode potential**, $E°$, in which all reactants and products are at unit activity. A half-cell reaction with a *positive* standard electrode potential ($E°$) occurs more readily than does reduction of H^+ ions at the SHE. A *negative* standard electrode potential signifies a lesser tendency to undergo reduction. The **standard cell potential ($E_{cell}°$)** of a voltaic cell is the *difference* between $E°$ of the cathode and $E°$ of the anode; that is, $E_{cell}° = E°(\text{cathode}) - E°(\text{anode})$.

20-3 E_{cell}, ΔG, and K—Cell voltages based on standard electrode potentials are $E_{cell}°$ values. The electrical work that can be obtained from a cell depends on the number of electrons involved in the cell reaction, the cell potential, and the **Faraday constant (F)**, which is the number of coulombs of charge per mole of electrons—96,485 C/mol e^-. An important relationship exists between $E_{cell}°$ and $\Delta G°$, namely, $\Delta G° = -nFE_{cell}°$. The equilibrium constant of the cell reaction K is related to $E_{cell}°$ through the expression $\Delta G° = -RT \ln K = -nFE_{cell}°$.

20-4 E_{cell} as a Function of Concentrations—In the **Nernst equation**, E_{cell} for nonstandard conditions is related to $E_{cell}°$ and the reaction quotient Q (equation 20.18).

If $E_{cell} > 0$, the cell reaction is spontaneous in the forward direction for the stated conditions; if $E_{cell} < 0$, the forward reaction is *nonspontaneous* for those conditions. A **concentration cell** consists of two half-cells with identical electrodes but different solution concentrations.

20-5 Batteries: Producing Electricity Through Chemical Reactions—An important application of voltaic cells is found in various battery systems. A **battery** stores chemical energy so that it can be released as energy. Batteries consist of one or more voltaic cells and are divided into three major classes: **primary** (Leclanché), **secondary** (lead–acid or silver–zinc), and **flow batteries** or **fuel cells** in which reactants, such as hydrogen and oxygen, are continuously fed into the battery and chemical energy is converted to electric energy.

20-6 Corrosion: Unwanted Voltaic Cells—Electrochemistry plays a key role in corrosion and its control. Oxidation half-reactions produce anodic regions and reduction half-reactions, cathodic regions. **Cathodic protection** is achieved when a more active metal is attached to the metal being protected from corrosion. The more active metal, a "sacrifical" anode, is preferentially oxidized while the protected metal is a cathode at which a harmless reduction half-reaction occurs.

20-7 Electrolysis: Causing Nonspontaneous Reactions to Occur—In **electrolysis**, a nonspontaneous chemical reaction occurs as electrons from an external source are forced to flow in a direction opposite that in which they would flow spontaneously. The electrochemical cell in which electrolysis is conducted is called an **electrolyic cell**. $E°$ values are used to establish the theoretical voltage requirements for an electrolysis. Sometimes, particularly when a gas is liberated at an electrode, the voltage requirement for the electrode reaction exceeds the value of $E°$. The additional voltage requirement is called the **overpotential**. The amounts of reactants and products involved in an electrolysis can be calculated from the amount of electric charge passing through the electrolytic cell. The Faraday constant is featured in these calculations.

20-8 Industrial Electrolysis Processes—Electrolysis has many industrial applications, including electroplating, refining of metals, and production of substances such as $NaOH(aq)$, $H_2(g)$, and $Cl_2(g)$.

Integrative Example

Two electrochemical cells are connected as shown.

Cell A

$Zn(s)|Zn^{2+}(0.85\ M)|\,|Cu^{2+}(1.10\ M)|Cu(s)$

$Zn(s)|Zn^{2+}(1.05\ M)|\,|Cu^{2+}(0.75\ M)|Cu(s)$

Cell B

(a) Do electrons flow in the direction of the red arrows or the blue arrows?

(b) What are the ion concentrations in the half-cells at the point at which current ceases to flow?

◀ A computer-generated model of a portion of a cell membrane. Na^+ and K^+ traverse the membrane through channels. The K^+ channel is blue, and the Na^+ channel is red.

Membrane

$[K^+]_1 > [K^+]_2$
$[Cl^-]_1 > [Cl^-]_2$

$[K^+]_1 = [K^+]_2$
$[Cl^-]_1 = [Cl^-]_2$

(a)

Net negative charge   Net positive charge

$[K^+]_1 > [K^+]_2$
$[Cl^-]_1 > [Cl^-]_2$

Final state

$$\Delta\Phi = \frac{RT}{zF} \ln \frac{[K^+]_2}{[K^+]_1}$$

(b)

Ordinary electrochemical cells consist of metallic conductors immersed in electrolyte solutions. In living systems, there are no metallic conductors. So what is the source of biological electric currents, such as those generated in muscle contraction and neuron activity? The answer is membrane potentials.

When a membrane separates two electrolyte solutions of different concentrations, in general there will be an electrical potential difference across the membrane, but various situations are possible. One possibility is that the membrane is impermeable to the ions and the solvent. In this case, inserting an electrode on each side of the membrane, joining the electrodes with a wire, and joining the solutions with a salt bridge would create a simple concentration cell. The cell potential would be given by the Nernst equation.

Figure 20-25 depicts solutions of KCl separated by a membrane. If the membrane is permeable to both K^+ and Cl^- ions, their concentrations eventually become equal and there is no potential difference (Fig. 20-25a). If, however, the membrane is impermeable to solvent* and permeable only to potassium ions, a net flow of K^+ ions crosses the membrane from the more concentrated side (left-hand side of membrane in Figure 20-25b) to the less concentrated side. As a result, the left side has a negative potential (excess anions) with respect to the right. The effect of this

▲ **FIGURE 20-25**
Generation of membrane potential
(a) Solutions of KCl separated by a membrane that is permeable to both K^+ and Cl^-. **(b)** Solutions of KCl separated by a membrane that is permeable only to K^+. The change in $[K^+]$ is greatly exaggerated for the final state. Actually, $[K^+]_2$ is only slightly greater than $[K^+]_1$.

*This restriction is made so that there will be no complications due to osmotic pressure.

Strategy
The two cells differ only in their ion concentrations, which means that they have the same E°_{cell} value but different E_{cell} values. In part (a), use the Nernst equation (20.18) to determine which cell has the greater E_{cell} value when functioning as a voltaic cell. This will establish the direction that electrons flow. In part (b), write and solve an equation relating ion concentrations to the condition where the two cells have the same voltage but, being connected in opposition to each other, produce no net electric current.

Solution
(a) In each voltaic cell zinc is the anode, copper is the cathode, and the cell reaction is

$$Zn(s) + Cu^{2+}(aq) \longrightarrow Zn^{2+}(aq) + Cu(s)$$

The E_{cell} values are given by the Nernst equation.

$$E_{cell} = E^\circ_{cell} - (0.0592/2) \log[Zn^{2+}]/[Cu^2] \qquad (20.37)$$

potential difference is to prevent more K^+ ions from crossing the membrane. An equilibrium is established when the electric potential difference exactly balances the tendency of the concentrations to become equal. This potential difference is known as the *Nernst potential*, $\Delta\Phi$.

The Gibbs energy difference ΔG_e arising from the potential difference $\Delta\Phi$ is

$$\Delta G_e = zF\Delta\Phi$$

where z is the charge on the permeable ions ($z = 1$ for K^+) and F is the Faraday constant. In Figure 20-25(b), the potential is higher on the right-hand side because more K^+ ions are there than on the left-hand side. Viewed in terms of the K^+ ions on the right side, $\Delta G_e > 0$. Also, an additional Gibbs energy difference arises from the concentration difference between the compartments.

$$\Delta G_c = RT\ln\frac{[K^+]_1}{[K^+]_2}$$

At equilibrium, the net ΔG across the membrane is zero. Therefore,

$$\Delta G = \Delta G_e + \Delta G_c = zF\Delta\Phi + RT\ln\frac{[K^+]_1}{[K^+]_2} = 0$$

Thus, the Nernst potential is given by

$$\Delta\Phi = \frac{RT}{zF}\ln\frac{[K^+]_2}{[K^+]_1}$$

Mammalian muscle cells are freely permeable to K^+ ions but much less permeable to Na^+ and Cl^- ions. Typical concentrations of K^+ ions are $[K^+] = 155$ mM inside the cells and 4.00 mM outside. The Nernst potential at 310 K (37 °C) is

$$\Delta\Phi = \frac{8.3145\ \text{J K}^{-1}\ \text{mol}^{-1} \times 310\ \text{K}}{96{,}500\ \text{C mol}^{-1}}\ln\frac{4}{155}$$

$$= -0.0977\ \text{V} = -97.7\ \text{mV}$$

The contents of each cell in a multicellular organism are separated from other cells by a semipermeable membrane. The potential is negative inside the cell and positive outside. In actual measurements, such potentials are more like -85 mV because there is a certain amount of diffusion of Na^+ and Cl^- ions, and there is also a biological pumping mechanism that does not allow the potential difference to stray too far from a desired value. The potential difference measured is that between the interior and the exterior of the cell and is called the *transmembrane potential*.

Measurements of transmembrane potentials of various cells range from -30 to -100 mV, with the cell interior at a lower potential than the exterior. A typical value for a nerve cell (squid) undergoing no activity—a resting cell—is -70 mV. Nerve cells are permeable to all three ions: K^+, Na^+, and Cl^-. The observed concentrations of these ions are given in Table 20.2, together with the potentials calculated from the Nernst potential equation and the experimental and expected ratios of concentrations.

At a resting potential of -70 mV, Cl^- ion is nearly in equilibrium, but the Na^+ and K^+ are not. From the ratios in the table, we see that Na^+ ions spontaneously flow into the cell and K^+ ions spontaneously flow out. The observed steady-state concentrations of the Na^+ and K^+ are maintained by the cell's active transport processes, which use some metabolic energy to pump the Na^+ out of the cell and K^+ into the cell continuously. The cells maintain the Na^+ and K^+ in a state of nonequilibrium. At equilibrium, nothing happens. A cell that is at equilibrium is dead!

During a nerve impulse, protein activity in the membrane allows Na^+ to enter the cell and K^+ to leave, leading to a change in membrane potential toward $+60$ mV. The cell is said to be *depolarized*. After the peak of 60 mV is reached, the cell returns to its resting potential by pumping the Na^+ ions out and the K^+ ions in. The mechanisms by which cell membranes change their permeability to ions are an area of active research.

TABLE 20.2 Ion Concentrations and Membrane Potentials for a Typical Nerve Cell

Ion	External Concentration, mM	Internal Concentration, mM	Estimated Membrane Potential, mV	Ratio of [ion]$_{\text{ext}}$/[ion]$_{\text{int}}$ Observed	Ratio of [ion]$_{\text{ext}}$/[ion]$_{\text{int}}$ Expected for -70 mV
Na^+	460	49	+57	9:1	1:15
K^+	10	410	-95	1:41	1:15
Cl^-	540	40	-67	14:1	15:1

Note that for Cell A,

$[Zn^{2+}]/[Cu^{2+}] = 0.85\ \text{M}/1.10\ \text{M} < 1$

$\log[Zn^{2+}]/[Cu^{2+}] < 0$, and $E_{\text{cell}} > E_{\text{cell}}^\circ$

For Cell B,

$[Zn^{2+}]/[Cu^{2+}] = 1.05\ \text{M}/0.75\ \text{M} > 1$

$\log[Zn^{2+}]/[Cu^{2+}] > 0$, and $E_{\text{cell}} < E_{\text{cell}}^\circ$

The voltage of Cell A is greater than that of Cell B.

In the connection of the two cells shown in the diagram, Cell A is a *voltaic cell* and Cell B is an *electrolytic cell*. There is an emf from Cell B that resists that of Cell A, but on balance, the electron flow is in the direction of the red arrows.

859

(b) As electrons flow between the two cells, the overall reaction in Cell A causes $[Zn^{2+}]$ to increase, $[Cu^{2+}]$ to decrease, and E_{cell} to decrease. The overall reaction in Cell B causes $[Zn^{2+}]$ to decrease, $[Cu^{2+}]$ to increase, and the back emf to increase. When the back emf from Cell B equals E_{cell} of Cell A, electrons cease to flow.

The cell diagrams when this condition is reached, with x representing *changes* in concentrations, are

Cell A: $Zn(s)|Zn^{2+}(0.85 + x) \, M\|Cu^{2+}(1.10 - x) \, M|Cu(s)$

Cell B: $Zn(s)|Zn^{2+}(1.05 - x) \, M\|Cu^{2+}(0.75 + x) \, M|Cu(s)$

Use equation (20.37) to obtain E_{cell} for each cell.

Cell A: $E_{cell} = E^{\circ}_{cell} - \dfrac{0.0592 \text{ V}}{2} \log \dfrac{(0.85 + x)}{(1.10 - x)}$

Cell B: $E_{cell} = E^{\circ}_{cell} - \dfrac{0.0592 \text{ V}}{2} \log \dfrac{(1.05 - x)}{(0.75 + x)}$

Set the two expressions equal to one another, cancel the terms E°_{cell} and $(0.0592 \text{ V})/2$, to obtain

$\log \dfrac{(0.85 + x)}{(1.10 - x)} = \log \dfrac{(1.05 - x)}{(0.75 + x)}$

Because the logarithms of the quantities on the two sides are equal, so too are the quantities themselves.

$\dfrac{(0.85 + x)}{(1.10 - x)} = \dfrac{(1.05 - x)}{(0.75 + x)}$

The expression to be solved is a quadratic equation

$(0.85 + x)(0.75 + x) = (1.10 - x)(1.05 - x)$

Cancel x^2 on each side

$0.64 + 1.60x + x^2 = 1.16 - 2.15x + x^2$

$0.64 + 1.60x = 1.16 - 2.15x$

Solve to obtain

$3.75x = 0.52$ and $x = 0.14$

When electrons no longer flow, the ion concentrations are as follows:

Cell A: $[Zn^{2+}] = 0.99 \text{ M}; [Cu^{2+}] = 0.96 \text{ M}.$

Cell B: $[Zn^{2+}] = 0.91 \text{ M}; [Cu^{2+}] = 0.89 \text{ M}.$

Assessment

Once the direction of electron flow had been established, it was possible to decide in which cell $[Zn^{2+}]$ would increase and in which cell it would decrease. At equilibrium the two cell potentials became equal. That the calculated equilibrium concentrations are correct can be seen in $0.99/0.96 \approx 0.91/0.89$.

Exercises   *(Use data from Table 20.1 and Appendix D as necessary.)*

Standard Electrode Potentials

1. From the observations listed, estimate the value of E° for the half-reaction $M^{2+}(aq) + 2 e^- \longrightarrow M(s)$.
   (a) The metal M reacts with $HNO_3(aq)$, but not with $HCl(aq)$; M displaces $Ag^+(aq)$, but not $Cu^{2+}(aq)$.
   (b) The metal M reacts with $HCl(aq)$, producing $H_2(g)$, but displaces neither $Zn^{2+}(aq)$ nor $Fe^{2+}(aq)$.
2. You must estimate E° for the half-reaction $In^{3+}(aq) + 3 e^- \longrightarrow In(s)$. You have no electrical equipment, but you do have all of the metals listed in Table 20.1 and aqueous solutions of their ions, as well as In(s) and $In^{3+}(aq)$. Describe the experiments you would perform and the accuracy you would expect in your result.
3. $E^{\circ}_{cell} = 0.201$ V for the reaction

   $3 \, Pt(s) + 12 \, Cl^-(aq) + 2 \, NO_3{}^-(aq) + 8 \, H^+(aq) \longrightarrow$
   $3[PtCl_4]^{2-}(aq) + 2 \, NO(g) + 4 \, H_2O(l)$

   What is E° for the reduction of $[PtCl_4]^{2-}$ to Pt in acidic solution?
4. Given that $E^{\circ}_{cell} = 3.20$ V for the reaction

   $2 \, Na(in \, Hg) + Cl_2(g) \longrightarrow 2 \, Na^+(aq) + 2 \, Cl^-(aq)$

   What is E° for the reduction $2 \, Na^+(aq) + 2 \, e^- \longrightarrow 2 \, Na(in \, Hg)$?
5. Given that E°_{cell} for the aluminum–air battery is 2.71 V, what is E° for the reduction half-reaction $[Al(OH)_4]^-(aq) + 3 e^- \longrightarrow Al(s) + 4 \, OH^-(aq)$? [*Hint:* Refer to cell reaction (20.28).]
6. The theoretical E°_{cell} for the methane–oxygen fuel cell is 1.06 V. What is E° for the reduction half-reaction $CO_2(g) + 8 \, H^+(aq) + 8 \, e^- \longrightarrow CH_4(g) + 2 \, H_2O(l)$? [*Hint:* Refer to cell reaction (20.27).]
7. The sketch is of a voltaic cell consisting of a standard zinc electrode and a standard electrode of a second metal, M. For the reduction half-reaction $Zn^{2+}(1 \, M) + 2 e^- \longrightarrow Zn(s)$, $E^{\circ} = -0.763$ V. For each of the given metals M and measured values of E°_{cell}, determine E° for the reduction half-reaction

   $M^{2+}(1 \, M) + 2 \, e^- \longrightarrow M(s) \qquad E^{\circ} = ?$

   (a) Mn, $E^{\circ}_{cell} = 0.417$ V   **(c)** Ti, $E^{\circ}_{cell} = 0.87$ V
   (b) Po, $E^{\circ}_{cell} = -1.13$ V   **(d)** V, $E^{\circ}_{cell} = 0.37$ V

M²⁺ (1 M)   Zn²⁺ (1 M)

Anode (oxid.)   Cathode (red.)

8. From the data listed, together with data from Table 20.1, determine the quantity indicated.
   (a) $E°_{cell}$ for the reaction $PbO_2(s) + 4 H^+(aq) + 2 Cl^-(aq) \longrightarrow Pb^{2+}(aq) + 2 H_2O(l) + Cl_2(g)$
   (b) $E°$ for the couple Sc^{3+}/Sc, given that $3 Mg(s) + 2 Sc^{3+}(aq) \longrightarrow 3 Mg^{2+}(aq) + 2 Sc(s)$ $E°_{cell} = 0.33$ V
   (c) $E°$ for the couple Cu^{2+}/Cu^+, given that $Cu^+(aq) + Ag^+(aq) \longrightarrow Cu^{2+}(aq) + Ag(s)$ $E°_{cell} = 0.641$ V

Predicting Oxidation–Reduction Reactions

9. According to standard electrode potentials, both sodium and aluminum should displace zinc from an aqueous solution of Zn^{2+}. What is observed, however, is that aluminum does displace Zn^{2+} and sodium does not. Explain this difference in behavior.

10. In the following photograph, copper and zinc strips are joined and immersed in 1 M HCl. What reaction occurs? Why are gas bubbles evident on both metal strips?

11. Assume that all reactants and products are in their standard states, and use data from Table 20.1 to predict whether a spontaneous reaction will occur in the forward direction in each case.
    (a) $Sn(s) + Pb^{2+}(aq) \longrightarrow Sn^{2+}(aq) + Pb(s)$
    (b) $Cu^{2+}(aq) + 2 I^-(aq) \longrightarrow Cu(s) + I_2(s)$
    (c) $4 NO_3^-(aq) + 4 H^+(aq) \longrightarrow$
    $\qquad\qquad 3 O_2(g) + 4 NO(g) + 2 H_2O(l)$
    (d) $O_3(g) + Cl^-(aq) \longrightarrow OCl^-(aq) + O_2(g)$
    $\qquad\qquad\qquad\qquad$ (basic solution)

12. For the reduction half-reaction $Hg_2^{2+}(aq) + 2 e^- \longrightarrow 2 Hg(l)$, $E° = 0.797$ V. Will Hg(l) react with and dissolve in HCl(aq)? in HNO₃(aq)? Explain.

13. Use data from Table 20.1 to predict whether, to any significant extent,
    (a) Mg(s) will displace Pb^{2+} from aqueous solution;
    (b) Sn(s) will react with and dissolve in 1 M HCl;
    (c) SO_4^{2-} will oxidize Sn^{2+} to Sn^{4+} in acidic solution;
    (d) $MnO_4^-(aq)$ will oxidize $H_2O_2(aq)$ to $O_2(g)$ in acidic solution;
    (e) $I_2(s)$ will displace $Br^-(aq)$ to produce $Br_2(l)$.

14. Consider the reaction $Co(s) + Ni^{2+}(aq) \longrightarrow Co^{2+}(aq) + Ni(s)$, with $E°_{cell} = 0.02$ V. If Co(s) is added to a solution with $[Ni^{2+}] = 1$ M, should the reaction go to completion? Explain.

15. Dichromate ion ($Cr_2O_7^{2-}$) in acidic solution is a good oxidizing agent. Which of the following oxidations can be accomplished with dichromate ion in acidic solution? Explain.
    (a) $Sn^{2+}(aq)$ to $Sn^{4+}(aq)$
    (b) $I_2(s)$ to $IO_3^-(aq)$
    (c) $Mn^{2+}(aq)$ to $MnO_4^-(aq)$

16. The standard electrode potential for the reduction of $Eu^{3+}(aq)$ to $Eu^{2+}(aq)$ is -0.43 V. Use the data in Appendix D to determine which of the following is capable of reducing $Eu^{3+}(aq)$ to $Eu^{2+}(aq)$ under standard-state conditions: Al(s), Co(s), $H_2O_2(aq)$, Ag(s), $H_2C_2O_4(aq)$?

17. Predict whether the following metals will react with the acid indicated. If a reaction does occur, write the net ionic equation for the reaction. Assume that reactants and products are in their standard states. (a) Ag in HNO₃(aq); (b) Zn in HI(aq); (c) Au in HNO₃ (for the couple Au^{3+}/Au, $E° = 1.52$ V).

18. Predict whether, to any significant extent,
    (a) Fe(s) will displace $Zn^{2+}(aq)$;
    (b) $MnO_4^-(aq)$ will oxidize $Cl^-(aq)$ to $Cl_2(g)$ in acidic solution;
    (c) Ag(s) will react with 1 M HCl(aq);
    (d) $O_2(g)$ will oxidize $Cl^-(aq)$ to $Cl_2(g)$ in acidic solution.

Voltaic Cells

19. Write cell reactions for the electrochemical cells diagrammed here, and use data from Table 20.1 to calculate $E°_{cell}$ for each reaction.
    (a) $Al(s)|Al^{3+}(aq)||Sn^{2+}(aq)|Sn(s)$
    (b) $Pt(s)|Fe^{2+}(aq), Fe^{3+}(aq)||Ag^+(aq)|Ag(s)$

20. Use the data in Appendix D to calculate the standard cell potential for each of the following reactions. Which reactions will occur spontaneously?
    (a) $H_2(g) + F_2(g) \longrightarrow 2 H^+(aq) + 2 F^-(aq)$
    (b) $Cu(s) + Ba^{2+}(aq) \longrightarrow Cu^{2+}(aq) + Ba(s)$
    (c) $3 Fe^{2+}(aq) \longrightarrow Fe(s) + 2 Fe^{3+}(aq)$
    (d) $Hg(l) + HgCl_2(aq) \longrightarrow Hg_2Cl_2(s)$

21. In each of the following examples, sketch a voltaic cell that uses the given reaction. Label the anode and cathode; indicate the direction of electron flow; write a balanced equation for the cell reaction; and calculate E_{cell}°.
    (a) $Cu(s) + Fe^{3+}(aq) \longrightarrow Cu^{2+}(aq) + Fe^{2+}(aq)$
    (b) $Pb^{2+}(aq)$ is displaced from solution by $Al(s)$
    (c) $Cl_2(g) + H_2O(l) \longrightarrow Cl^-(aq) + O_2(g) + H^+(aq)$
    (d) $Zn(s) + H^+ + NO_3^- \longrightarrow Zn^{2+} + H_2O(l) + NO(g)$

22. Diagram the cell and calculate the value of E_{cell}° for a voltaic cell in which
    (a) $Cl_2(g)$ is reduced to $Cl^-(aq)$ and $Fe(s)$ is oxidized to $Fe^{2+}(aq)$;
    (b) $Ag^+(aq)$ is displaced from solution by $Zn(s)$;
    (c) The cell reaction is $2 Cu^+(aq) \longrightarrow Cu^{2+}(aq) + Cu(s)$;
    (d) $MgBr_2(aq)$ is produced from $Mg(s)$ and $Br_2(l)$.

ΔG°, E_{cell}°, and K

23. Determine the values of ΔG° for the following reactions carried out in voltaic cells.
    (a) $2 Al(s) + 3 Cu^{2+}(aq) \longrightarrow 2 Al^{3+}(aq) + 3 Cu(s)$
    (b) $O_2(g) + 4 I^-(aq) + 4 H^+(aq) \longrightarrow 2 H_2O(l) + 2 I_2(s)$
    (c) $Cr_2O_7^{2-}(aq) + 14 H^+(aq) + 6 Ag(s) \longrightarrow$
    $2 Cr^{3+}(aq) + 6 Ag^+(aq) + 7 H_2O(l)$

24. Write the equilibrium constant expression for each of the following reactions, and determine the value of K at 25 °C. Use data from Table 20.1.
    (a) $Sn^{4+}(aq) + 2 Ag(s) \longrightarrow Sn^{2+}(aq) + 2 Ag^+(aq)$
    (b) $MnO_2(s) + 4 H^+(aq) + 2 Cl^-(aq) \longrightarrow$
    $Mn^{2+}(aq) + 2 H_2O(l) + Cl_2(g)$
    (c) $2 OCl^-(aq) \longrightarrow 2 Cl^-(aq) + O_2(g)$
    (basic solution)

25. For the reaction

    $5 H_2O_2(aq) + 2 Mn^{2+}(aq) \longrightarrow$
    $2 MnO_4^-(aq) + 6 H^+(aq) + 2 H_2O(l)$

    use data from Table 20.1 to determine (a) E_{cell}°; (b) ΔG°; (c) K; (d) whether the reaction goes substantially to completion when the reactants and products are initially in their standard states.

26. For the reaction that occurs in the voltaic cell

    $Fe(s)|Fe^{2+}(aq)||Cr^{3+}(aq), Cr^{2+}(aq)|Pt(s)$

use data from Appendix D to determine (a) the equation for the cell reaction; (b) E_{cell}°; (c) ΔG°; (d) K; (e) whether the reaction goes substantially to completion when the reactants and products are initially in their standard states.

27. For the reaction $2 Cu^+(aq) + Sn^{4+}(aq) \longrightarrow 2 Cu^{2+}(aq) + Sn^{2+}(aq)$, $E_{cell}^{\circ} = -0.0050$ V,
    (a) can a solution be prepared at 298 K that is 0.500 M in each of the four ions?
    (b) If not, in which direction will a reaction occur?

28. For the reaction $2 V^{3+}(aq) + Ni(s) \longrightarrow 2 V^{2+}(aq) + Ni^{2+}(aq)$, $E_{cell}^{\circ} = 0.0020$ V,
    (a) can a solution be prepared at 298 K that has $[V^{2+}] = 0.600$ M and $[V^{3+}] = [Ni^{2+}] = 0.675$ M?
    (b) If not, in which direction will a reaction occur?

29. Use thermodynamic data from Appendix D to calculate a theoretical voltage of the silver–zinc button cell described on page 844.

30. The theoretical voltage of the aluminum–air battery is $E_{cell}^{\circ} = 2.71$ V. Use data from Appendix D and equation (20.28) to determine ΔG_f° for $[Al(OH)_4]^-$.

31. By the method of combining reduction half-equations illustrated on page 833, determine $E_{IrO_2/Ir}^{\circ}$, given that $E_{Ir^{3+}/Ir}^{\circ} = 1.156$ V and $E_{IrO_2/Ir^{3+}}^{\circ} = 0.223$ V.

32. Determine $E_{MoO_2/Mo^{3+}}^{\circ}$, given that $E_{H_2MoO_4/MoO_2}^{\circ} = 0.646$ V and $E_{H_2MoO_4/Mo^{3+}}^{\circ} = 0.428$ V. (See page 833).

Concentration Dependence of E_{cell}—The Nernst Equation

33. A voltaic cell represented by the following cell diagram has $E_{cell} = 1.250$ V. What must be $[Ag^+]$ in the cell?

    $Zn(s)|Zn^{2+}(1.00 M)||Ag^+(x M)|Ag(s)$

34. For the cell pictured in Figure 20-11, what is E_{cell} if the unknown solution in the half-cell on the left (a) has pH = 5.25; (b) is 0.0103 M HCl; (c) is 0.158 M $HC_2H_3O_2$ ($K_a = 1.8 \times 10^{-5}$)?

35. Use the Nernst equation and Table 20.1 to calculate E_{cell} for each of the following cells.
    (a) $Al(s)|Al^{3+}(0.18 M)||Fe^{2+}(0.85 M)|Fe(s)$
    (b) $Ag(s)|Ag^+(0.34 M)||Cl^-(0.098 M)|$
    $Cl_2(g, 0.55 atm)|Pt(s)$

36. Use the Nernst equation and data from Appendix D to calculate E_{cell} for each of the following cells.
    (a) $Mn(s)|Mn^{2+}(0.40 M)||Cr^{3+}(0.35 M),$
    $Cr^{2+}(0.25 M)|Pt(s)$
    (b) $Mg(s)|Mg^{2+}(0.016 M)||[Al(OH)_4]^-(0.25 M),$
    $|OH^-(0.042 M)|Al(s)$

37. Consider the reduction half-reactions listed in Appendix D, and give plausible explanations for the following observations:
    (a) For some half-reactions, E depends on pH; for others, it does not.
    (b) Whenever H^+ appears in a half-equation, it is on the *left* side.
    (c) Whenever OH^- appears in a half-equation, it is on the *right* side.

38. Write an equation to represent the oxidation of $Cl^-(aq)$ to $Cl_2(g)$ by $PbO_2(s)$ in an acidic solution. Will this reaction occur spontaneously in the forward direction if all other reactants and products are in their standard states and (a) $[H^+] = 6.0$ M; (b) $[H^+] = 1.2$ M; (c) pH = 4.25? Explain.

39. If $[Zn^{2+}]$ is maintained at 1.0 M,
    (a) what is the minimum $[Cu^{2+}]$ for which reaction (20.3) is spontaneous in the forward direction?
    (b) Should the displacement of $Cu^{2+}(aq)$ by $Zn(s)$ go to completion? Explain.

40. Can the displacement of $Pb(s)$ from 1.0 M $Pb(NO_3)_2$ be carried to completion by tin metal? Explain.

41. A concentration cell is constructed of two hydrogen electrodes: one immersed in a solution with $[H^+] = 1.0$ M and the other in 0.65 M KOH.
   (a) Determine E_{cell} for the reaction that occurs.
   (b) Compare this value of E_{cell} with $E°$ for the reduction of H_2O to $H_2(g)$ in basic solution, and explain the relationship between them.

42. If the 0.65 M KOH of Exercise 41 is replaced by 0.65 M NH_3,
   (a) will E_{cell} be higher or lower than in the cell with 0.65 M KOH?
   (b) What will be the value of E_{cell}?

43. A voltaic cell is constructed as follows:

$$Ag(s)|Ag^+(\text{satd } Ag_2CrO_4)||Ag^+(0.125\text{ M})|Ag(s)$$

What is the value of E_{cell}? For Ag_2CrO_4, $K_{sp} = 1.1 \times 10^{-12}$.

44. A voltaic cell, with $E_{cell} = 0.180$ V, is constructed as follows:

$$Ag(s)|Ag^+(\text{satd } Ag_3PO_4)||Ag^+(0.140\text{ M})|Ag(s)$$

What is the K_{sp} of Ag_3PO_4?

45. For the voltaic cell,

$$Sn(s)|Sn^{2+}(0.075\text{ M})||Pb^{2+}(0.600\text{ M})|Pb(s)$$

(a) what is E_{cell} initially?
(b) If the cell is allowed to operate spontaneously, will E_{cell} increase, decrease, or remain constant with time? Explain.
(c) What will be E_{cell} when $[Pb^{2+}]$ has fallen to 0.500 M?
(d) What will be $[Sn^{2+}]$ at the point at which $E_{cell} = 0.020$ V?
(e) What are the ion concentrations when $E_{cell} = 0$?

46. For the voltaic cell,

$$Ag(s)|Ag^+(0.015\text{ M})||Fe^{3+}(0.055\text{ M}), Fe^{2+}(0.045\text{ M})|Pt(s)$$

(a) what is E_{cell} initially?
(b) As the cell operates, will E_{cell} increase, decrease, or remain constant with time? Explain.
(c) What will be E_{cell} when $[Ag^+]$ has increased to 0.020 M?
(d) What will be $[Ag^+]$ when $E_{cell} = 0.010$ V?
(e) What are the ion concentrations when $E_{cell} = 0$?

47. Show that the oxidation of $Cl^-(aq)$ to $Cl_2(g)$ by $Cr_2O_7^{2-}(aq)$ in acidic solution, with reactants and products in their standard states, does not occur spontaneously. Explain why it is still possible to use this method to produce $Cl_2(g)$ in the laboratory. What experimental conditions would you use?

48. Refer to the Integrative Example on page 857. Calculate the net voltage of the current entering electrolytic cell B when that cell is first connected to the voltaic cell A.

Batteries and Fuel Cells

49. The iron–chromium redox battery makes use of the reaction

$$Cr^{2+}(aq) + Fe^{3+}(aq) \longrightarrow Cr^{3+}(aq) + Fe^{2+}(aq)$$

occurring at a chromium anode and an iron cathode.
   (a) Write a cell diagram for this battery.
   (b) Calculate the theoretical voltage of the battery.

50. Refer to the discussion of the Leclanché cell (page 843).
   (a) Combine the several equations written for the operation of the Leclanché cell into a single overall equation.
   (b) Given that the voltage of the Leclanché cell is 1.55 V, estimate the electrode potentials, E, for each of the half-reactions. Why are your values only estimates?

51. What is the theoretical standard cell voltage, $E°_{cell}$, of each of the following voltaic cells: **(a)** the hydrogen–oxygen fuel cell described by equation (20.26); **(b)** the zinc–air battery; **(c)** a magnesium–iodine battery?

52. For the alkaline Leclanché cell (page 843),
   (a) write the overall cell reaction.
   (b) Determine $E°_{cell}$ for that cell reaction.

53. One of the advantages of the aluminum–air battery over the iron–air and zinc–air batteries is the greater quantity of charge transferred per unit mass of metal consumed. Show that this is indeed the case. Assume that zinc and iron are oxidized to oxidation state +2 in air batteries.

54. Describe how you might construct batteries with each of the following voltages: **(a)** 0.10 V; **(b)** 2.5 V; **(c)** 10.0 V. Be as specific as you can about the electrodes and solution concentrations you would use, and indicate whether the battery would consist of a single cell or two or more cells connected in series.

Electrochemical Mechanism of Corrosion

55. Refer to Figure 20-19, and describe in words or with a sketch what you would expect to happen in each of the following cases.
   (a) Several turns of copper wire are wrapped around the head and tip of an iron nail.
   (b) A deep scratch is filed at the center of an iron nail.
   (c) A galvanized nail is substituted for the iron nail.

56. When an iron pipe is partly submerged in water, the iron dissolves more readily below the waterline than at the waterline. Explain this observation by relating it to the description of corrosion given in Figure 20-20.

57. Natural gas transmission pipes are sometimes protected against corrosion by the maintainence of a small potential difference between the pipe and an inert electrode buried in the ground. Describe how the method works.

58. In the construction of the Statue of Liberty, a framework of iron ribs was covered with thin sheets of copper less than 2.5 mm thick. A layer of asbestos separated the copper skin and iron framework. Over time, the asbestos wore away and the iron ribs corroded. Some of the ribs lost more than half their mass in the 100 years before the statue was restored. At the same time, the copper skin lost only about 4% of its thickness. Use electrochemical principles to explain these observations.

Electrolysis Reactions

59. How many grams of metal are deposited at the cathode by the passage of 2.15 A of current for 75 min in the electrolysis of an aqueous solution containing (a) Zn^{2+}; (b) Al^{3+}; (c) Ag^+; (d) Ni^{2+}?

60. A quantity of electric charge brings about the deposition of 3.28 g Cu at a cathode during the electrolysis of a solution containing $Cu^{2+}(aq)$. What volume of $H_2(g)$, measured at 28.2 °C and 763 mmHg, would be produced by this same quantity of electric charge in the reduction of $H^+(aq)$ at a cathode?

61. Which of the following reactions occur spontaneously, and which can be brought about only through electrolysis, assuming that all reactants and products are in their standard states? For those requiring electrolysis, what is the *minimum* voltage required?
    (a) $2 H_2O(l) \longrightarrow 2 H_2(g) + O_2(g)$ [in 1 M $H^+(aq)$]
    (b) $Zn(s) + Fe^{2+}(aq) \longrightarrow Zn^{2+}(aq) + Fe(s)$
    (c) $2 Fe^{2+}(aq) + I_2(s) \longrightarrow 2 Fe^{3+}(aq) + 2 I^-(aq)$
    (d) $Cu(s) + Sn^{4+}(aq) \longrightarrow Cu^{2+}(aq) + Sn^{2+}(aq)$

62. An aqueous solution of K_2SO_4 is electrolyzed by means of Pt electrodes.
    (a) Which of the following gases should form at the *anode*: O_2, H_2, SO_2, SO_3? Explain.
    (b) What product should form at the *cathode*? Explain.
    (c) What is the *minimum* voltage required? Why is the actual voltage needed likely to be higher than this value?

63. If a lead storage battery is charged at too high a voltage, gases are produced at each electrode. (It is possible to recharge a lead-storage battery only because of the high overpotential for gas formation on the electrodes.)
    (a) What are these gases?
    (b) Write a cell reaction to describe their formation.

64. A dilute aqueous solution of Na_2SO_4 is electrolyzed between Pt electrodes for 3.75 h with a current of 2.83 A. What volume of gas, saturated with water vapor at 25 °C and at a total pressure of 742 mmHg, would be collected at the *anode*? Use data from Table 12.2, as required.

65. Calculate the quantity indicated for each of the following electrolyses.
    (a) the mass of Zn deposited at the cathode in 42.5 min when 1.87 A of current is passed through an aqueous solution of Zn^{2+}
    (b) the time required to produce 2.79 g I_2 at the anode if a current of 1.75 A is passed through KI(aq)

66. Calculate the quantity indicated for each of the following electrolyses.
    (a) $[Cu^{2+}]$ *remaining* in 425 mL of a solution that was originally 0.366 M $CuSO_4$, after passage of 2.68 A for 282 s and the deposition of Cu at the cathode
    (b) the time required to reduce $[Ag^+]$ in 255 mL of $AgNO_3(aq)$ from 0.196 to 0.175 M by electrolyzing the solution between Pt electrodes with a current of 1.84 A

67. A *coulometer* is a device for measuring a quantity of electric charge. In a silver coulometer, $Ag^+(aq)$ is reduced to Ag(s) at a Pt cathode. If 1.206 g Ag is deposited in 1412 s by a certain quantity of electricity, (a) how much electric charge (in C) must have passed, and (b) what was the magnitude (in A) of the electric current?

68. Electrolysis is carried out for 2.00 h in the following cell. The platinum *cathode*, which has a mass of 25.0782 g, weighs 25.8639 g after the electrolysis. The platinum *anode* weighs the same before and after the electrolysis.
    (a) Write plausible equations for the half-reactions that occur at the two electrodes.
    (b) What must have been the magnitude of the current used in the electrolysis (assuming a constant current throughout)?
    (c) A gas is collected at the anode. What is this gas, and what volume should it occupy if (when dry) it is measured at 23 °C and 755 mmHg pressure?

Integrative and Advanced Exercises

69. Two voltaic cells are assembled in which the following reactions occur.

$$V^{2+}(aq) + VO^{2+}(aq) + 2\,H^+(aq) \longrightarrow$$
$$2\,V^{3+}(aq) + H_2O(l) \qquad E^\circ_{cell} = 0.616\ V$$

$$V^{3+}(aq) + Ag^+(aq) + H_2O(l) \longrightarrow$$
$$VO^{2+}(aq) + 2\,H^+(aq) + Ag(s) \qquad E^\circ_{cell} = 0.439\ V$$

Use these data and other values from Table 20.1 to calculate E° for the half-reaction $V^{3+} + e^- \longrightarrow V^{2+}$.

70. Suppose that a fully charged lead–acid battery contains 1.50 L of 5.00 M H_2SO_4. What will be the concentration of H_2SO_4 in the battery after 2.50 A of current is drawn from the battery for 6.0 h?

71. The energy consumption in electrolysis depends on the product of the charge and the voltage [volt $\times$ coulomb = $V \cdot C$ = J(joules)]. Determine the theoretical energy consumption per 1000 kg Cl_2 produced in a diaphragm chlor–alkali cell (page 855) that operates at 3.45 V. Express this energy in **(a)** kJ; **(b)** kilowatt-hours, kWh.

72. For the half-reaction $Cr^{3+} + e^- \longrightarrow Cr^{2+}$, $E^\circ = -0.424$ V. If excess Fe(s) is added to a solution in which $[Cr^{3+}] = 1.00$ M, what will be $[Fe^{2+}]$ when equilibrium is reached at 298 K?

$$Fe(s) + 2\,Cr^{3+} \rightleftharpoons Fe^{2+} + 2\,Cr^{2+}$$

73. A voltaic cell is constructed based on the following reaction and initial concentrations:

$$Fe^{2+}(0.0050\ M) + Ag^+(2.0\ M) \rightleftharpoons$$
$$Fe^{3+}(0.0050\ M) + Ag(s)$$

Calculate $[Fe^{2+}]$ when the cell reaction reaches equilibrium.

74. To construct a voltaic cell with $E_{cell} = 0.0860$ V, what $[Cl^-]$ must be present in the cathode half-cell to achieve this result?

$$Ag(s)|Ag^+(satd\ AgI)||Ag^+(satd\ AgCl,\ x\ M\ Cl^-)|Ag(s)$$

75. Describe a laboratory experiment that you could perform to evaluate the Faraday constant, F, and then show how you could use this value to determine the Avogadro constant.

76. The hydrazine fuel cell is based on the reaction

$$N_2H_4(aq) + O_2(g) \longrightarrow N_2(g) + 2\,H_2O(l)$$

The theoretical E°_{cell} of this fuel cell is 1.559 V. Use this information and data from Appendix D to calculate a value of ΔG°_f for $[N_2H_4(aq)]$.

77. It is sometimes possible to separate two metal ions through electrolysis. One ion is reduced to the free metal at the cathode, and the other remains in solution. In which of these cases would you expect complete or nearly complete separation: **(a)** Cu^{2+} and K^+; **(b)** Cu^{2+} and Ag^+; **(c)** Pb^{2+} and Sn^{2+}? Explain.

78. Show that for some fuel cells the efficiency value, $\varepsilon = \Delta G^\circ / \Delta H^\circ$, can have a value greater than 1.00. Can you identify one such reaction?
[*Hint:* Use data from Appendix D.]

79. In one type of Breathalyzer (alcohol meter), the quantity of ethanol in a sample is related to the amount of electric current produced by an ethanol–oxygen fuel cell. Use data from Table 20.1 and Appendix D to determine **(a)** E°_{cell} and **(b)** E° for the reduction of $CO_2(g)$ to $CH_3CH_2OH(g)$.

80. You prepare 1.00 L of a buffer solution that is 1.00 M NaH_2PO_4 and 1.00 M Na_2HPO_4. The solution is divided in half between the two compartments of an electrolytic cell. Both electrodes used are Pt. Assume that the only electrolysis is that of water. If 1.25 A of current is passed for 212 min, what will be the pH in each cell compartment at the end of the electrolysis?

81. Assume that the volume of each solution in Figure 20-21 is 100.0 mL. The cell is operated as an electrolytic cell, using a current of 0.500 A. Electrolysis is stopped after 10.00 h, and the cell is allowed to function as a voltaic cell. What is E_{cell} at this point?

82. A common reference electrode consists of a silver wire coated with AgCl(s) and immersed in 1 M KCl.

$$AgCl(s) + e^- \longrightarrow Ag(s) + Cl^-(1\ M)\quad E^\circ = 0.2223\ V$$

(a) What is E°_{cell} when this electrode is a cathode in combination with a standard zinc electrode as an anode?
(b) Cite several reasons why this electrode should be easier to use than a standard hydrogen electrode.
(c) By comparing the potential of this silver–silver chloride electrode with that of the silver–silver ion electrode, determine K_{sp} for AgCl.

83. The electrodes in the following electrochemical cell are connected to a voltmeter as shown. The half-cell on the right contains a standard silver–silver chloride electrode (see Exercise 82). The half-cell on the left contains a silver electrode immersed in 100.0 mL of 1.00×10^{-3} M $AgNO_3(aq)$. A porous plug through which ions can migrate separates the half-cells.
(a) What is the initial reading on the voltmeter?
(b) What is the voltmeter reading after 10.00 mL of 0.0100 M K_2CrO_4 has been added to the half-cell on the left and the mixture has been thoroughly stirred?
(c) What is the voltmeter reading after 10.00 mL of 10.0 M NH_3 has been added to the half-cell described in part (b) and the mixture has been thoroughly stirred?

Voltmeter

Ag(s)

Ag, AgCl(s)

1.00×10^{-3} M $AgNO_3(aq)$ 1.00 M KCl

84. An important source of Ag is recovery as a by-product in the metallurgy of lead. The percentage of Ag in lead was determined as follows. A 1.050-g sample was dissolved in nitric acid to produce $Pb^{2+}(aq)$ and $Ag^+(aq)$. The solution was then diluted to 500.0 mL with water, a Ag electrode was immersed in the solution, and the potential difference between this electrode and a SHE was found to be 0.503 V. What was the percent Ag by mass in the lead metal?

85. A test for completeness of electrodeposition of Cu from a solution of $Cu^{2+}(aq)$ is to add $NH_3(aq)$. A blue color signifies the formation of the complex ion $[Cu(NH_3)_4]^{2+}$ ($K_f = 1.1 \times 10^{13}$). Let 250.0 mL of 0.1000 M $CuSO_4(aq)$ be electrolyzed with a 3.512 A current for 1368 s. At this time, add a sufficient quantity of $NH_3(aq)$ to complex any remaining Cu^{2+} and to maintain a free $[NH_3] = 0.10$ M. If $[Cu(NH_3)_4]^{2+}$ is detectable at concentrations as low as 1×10^{-5} M, should the blue color appear?

86. A solution is prepared by saturating 100.0 mL of 1.00 M $NH_3(aq)$ with AgBr. A silver electrode is immersed in this solution, which is joined by a salt bridge to a standard hydrogen electrode. What will be the measured E_{cell}? Is the standard hydrogen electrode the anode or the cathode?

87. The electrolysis of $Na_2SO_4(aq)$ is conducted in two separate half-cells joined by a salt bridge, as suggested by the cell diagram $Pt|Na_2SO_4(aq)||Na_2SO_4(aq)|Pt$.
   (a) In one experiment, the solution in the anode compartment becomes more acidic and that in the cathode compartment, more basic during the electrolysis. When the electrolysis is discontinued and the two solutions are mixed, the resulting solution has pH = 7. Write half-equations and the overall electrolysis equation.
   (b) In a second experiment, a 10.00-mL sample of an unknown concentration of H_2SO_4 (aq) and a few drops of phenolphthalein indicator are added to the Na_2SO_4 (aq) in the cathode compartment. Electrolysis is carried out with a current of 21.5 mA (milliamperes) for 683 s, at which point, the solution in the cathode compartment acquires a lasting pink color. What is the molarity of the unknown $H_2SO_4(aq)$?

88. A Ni anode and an Fe cathode are placed in a solution with $[Ni^{2+}] = 1.0$ M and then connected to a battery. The Fe cathode has the shape shown. How long must electrolysis be continued with a current of 1.50 A to build a 0.050-mm-thick deposit of nickel on the iron? (Density of nickel = 8.90 g/cm^3.)

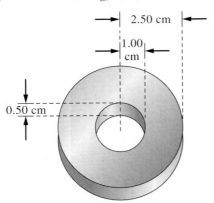

89. Initially, each of the half-cells in Figure 20-21 contained a 100.0-mL sample of solution with an ion concentration of 1.000 M. The cell was operated as an electrolytic cell, with copper as the anode and zinc as the cathode. A current of 0.500 A was used. Assume that the only electrode reactions occurring were those involving Cu/Cu^{2+} and Zn/Zn^{2+}. Electrolysis was stopped after 10.00 h, and the cell was allowed to function as a voltaic cell. What was E_{cell} at that point?

90. Silver tarnish is mainly Ag_2S:

$$Ag_2S(s) + 2\,e^- \longrightarrow 2\,Ag(s) + S^{2-}(aq)$$

$$E° = -0.691 \text{ V}.$$

A tarnished silver spoon is placed in contact with a commercially available metallic product in a glass baking dish. Boiling water, to which some $NaHCO_3$ has been added, is poured into the dish, and the product and spoon are completely covered. Within a short time, the removal of tarnish from the spoon begins.
   (a) What metal or metals are in the product?
   (b) What is the probable reaction that occurs?
   (c) What do you suppose is the function of the $NaHCO_3$?
   (d) An advertisement for the product appears to make two claims: (1) No chemicals are involved, and (2) the product will never need to be replaced. How valid are these claims? Explain.

91. Your task is to determine $E°$ for the reduction of $CO_2(g)$ to $C_3H_8(g)$ in two different ways and to explain why each gives the same result. (a) Consider a fuel cell in which the cell reaction corresponds to the complete combustion of propane gas. Write the half-cell reactions and the overall reaction. Determine $\Delta G°$ and $E°_{cell}$ for the reaction, then obtain $E°_{CO_2/C_3H_8}$. (b) Without considering the oxidation that occurs simultaneously, obtain $E°_{CO_2/C_3H_8}$ directly from tabulated thermodynamic data for the reduction half-reaction.

Feature Problems

92. Consider the following electrochemical cell:

$$Pt(s)|H_2(g, 1\ atm)|H^+(1\ M)||Ag^+(x\ M)|Ag(s)$$

(a) What is E°_{cell}—that is, the cell potential when $[Ag^+] = 1\ M$?

(b) Use the Nernst equation to write an equation for E_{cell} when $[Ag^+] = x$.

(c) Now imagine titrating 50.0 mL of 0.0100 M $AgNO_3$ in the cathode half-cell compartment with 0.0100 M KI. The titration reaction is

$$Ag^+(aq) + I^-(aq) \longrightarrow AgI(s)$$

Calculate $[Ag^+]$ and then E_{cell} after addition of the following volumes of 0.0100 M KI: **(i)** 0.0 mL; **(ii)** 20.0 mL; **(iii)** 49.0 mL; **(iv)** 50.0 mL; **(v)** 51.0 mL; **(vi)** 60.0 mL.

(d) Use the results of part (c) to sketch the titration curve of E_{cell} versus volume of titrant.

93. Ultimately, ΔG°_f values must be based on experimental results; in many cases, these experimental results are themselves obtained from E° values. Early in the twentieth century, G. N. Lewis conceived of an experimental approach for obtaining standard potentials of the alkali metals. This approach involved using a solvent with which the alkali metals do not react. Ethylamine was the solvent chosen. In the following cell diagram, Na(amalg, 0.206%) represents a solution of 0.206% Na in liquid mercury.

1. $Na(s)|Na^+(in\ ethylamine)|Na(amalg, 0.206\%)$

$$E_{cell} = 0.8453\ V$$

Although Na(s) reacts violently with water to produce $H_2(g)$, at least for a short time, a sodium amalgam electrode does not react with water. This makes it possible to determine E_{cell} for the following voltaic cell.

2. $Na(amalg, 0.206\%)|Na^+(1\ M)||H^+(1\ M)|$

$$H_2(g, 1\ atm) \quad E_{cell} = 1.8673\ V$$

(a) Write equations for the cell reactions that occur in the voltaic cells (1) and (2).

(b) Use equation (20.14) to establish ΔG for the cell reactions written in part (a).

(c) Write the overall equation obtained by combining the equations of part (a), and establish ΔG° for this overall reaction.

(d) Use the ΔG° value from part (c) to obtain E°_{cell} for the overall reaction. From this result, obtain $E^\circ_{Na^+/Na}$. Compare your result with the value listed in Appendix D.

94. The following sketch is called an electrode potential diagram. Such diagrams summarize electrode potential data more efficiently than do listings such as that in Appendix D. In this diagram for bromine and its ions in basic solution,

$$BrO_4^- \xrightarrow{\ 1.025\ V\ } BrO_3^-$$

signifies

$$BrO_4^-(aq) + H_2O(l) + 2\ e^- \longrightarrow$$
$$BrO_3^-(aq) + 2\ OH^-(aq), E^\circ_{BrO_4^-/BrO_3^-} = 1.025\ V$$

Similarly,

signifies

$$BrO_3^-(aq) + 3\ H_2O(l) + 6\ e^- \longrightarrow$$
$$Br^-(aq) + 6\ OH^-(aq), E^\circ_{BrO_3^-/Br^-} = 0.584\ V$$

With reference to Appendix D and to the method of determining E° values outlined on page 833, supply the missing data in the following diagram.

Basic solution ($[OH^-] = 1\ M$):

$$BrO_4^- \xrightarrow{\ 1.025\ V\ } BrO_3^- \xrightarrow{\ (?)\ } BrO^- \xrightarrow{\ (?)\ } Br_2 \xrightarrow{\ (?)\ } Br^-$$

with a $(?)$ bracket spanning BrO^- to Br^- and a $0.584\ V$ bracket spanning BrO_3^- to Br^-.

95. Only a tiny fraction of the diffusible ions move across a cell membrane in establishing a Nernst potential (page 859), so there is no detectable concentration change. Consider a typical cell with a volume of $10^{-8}\ cm^3$, a surface area (A) of $10^{-6}\ cm^2$, and a membrane thickness (l) of $10^{-6}\ cm$. Suppose that $[K^+] = 155\ mM$ inside the cell and $[K^+] = 4\ mM$ outside the cell and that the observed Nernst potential across the cell wall is 0.085 V. The membrane acts as a charge-storing device called a *capacitor*, with a *capacitance*, C, given by

$$C = \frac{\varepsilon_0 \varepsilon A}{l}$$

where ε_0 is the *dielectric constant* of a vacuum and the product $\varepsilon_0\varepsilon$ is the dielectric constant of the membrane, having a typical value of $3 \times 8.854 \times 10^{-12}$ $C^2\ N^{-1}\ m^{-2}$ for a biological membrane. The SI unit of capacitance is the *farad*, $1\ F = 1$ coulomb per volt $= 1\ C\ V^{-1} = 1 \times 10^{-3}\ C^2\ N^{-1}\ m^{-1}$.

(a) Determine the capacitance of the membrane for the typical cell described.

(b) What is the net charge required to maintain the observed membrane potential?

(c) How many K^+ ions must flow through the cell membrane to produce the membrane potential?

(d) How many K^+ ions are in the typical cell?

(e) Show that the fraction of the intracellular K^+ ions transferred through the cell membrane to produce the membrane potential is so small that it does not change $[K^+]$ within the cell.

Self-Assessment Exercises

96. In your own words, define the following symbols or terms: **(a)** $E°$; **(b)** F; **(c)** anode; **(d)** cathode.

97. Briefly describe each of the following ideas, methods, or devices: **(a)** salt bridge; **(b)** standard hydrogen electrode (SHE); **(c)** cathodic protection; **(d)** fuel cell.

98. Explain the important distinctions between each pair of terms: **(a)** half-reaction and overall cell reaction; **(b)** voltaic cell and electrolytic cell; **(c)** primary battery and secondary battery; **(d)** E_{cell} and $E°_{cell}$.

99. Of the following statements concerning electrochemical cells, the correct ones are: **(a)** The cathode is the negative electrode in both voltaic and electrolytic cells. **(b)** The function of a salt bridge is to permit the migration of electrons between the half-cell compartments of an electrochemical cell. **(c)** The anode is the negative electrode in a voltaic cell. **(d)** Electrons leave the cell from either the cathode or the anode, depending on what electrodes are used. **(e)** Reduction occurs at the cathode in both voltaic and electrolytic cells. **(f)** If electric current is drawn from a voltaic cell long enough, the cell becomes an electrolytic cell. **(g)** The cell reaction is an oxidation–reduction reaction.

100. For the half-reaction $Hg^{2+}(aq) + 2 e^- \longrightarrow Hg(l)$, $E° = 0.851$ V. This means that **(a)** Hg(l) is more readily oxidized than $H_2(g)$; **(b)** $Hg^{2+}(aq)$ is more readily reduced than $H^+(aq)$; **(c)** Hg(l) will dissolve in 1 M HCl; **(d)** Hg(l) will displace Zn(s) from an aqueous solution of Zn^{2+} ion.

101. The value of $E°_{cell}$ for the reaction $Zn(s) + Pb^{2+}(aq) \longrightarrow Zn^{2+}(aq) + Pb(s)$ is 0.66V. This means that for the reaction $Zn(s) + Pb^{2+}(0.01 M) \longrightarrow Zn^{2+}(0.10 M) + Pb(s)$, E_{cell} equals **(a)** 0.72 V; **(b)** 0.69 V; **(c)** 0.66 V; **(d)** 0.63 V.

102. For the reaction $Co(s) + Ni^{2+}(aq) \longrightarrow Co^{2+}(aq) + Ni(s)$, $E°_{cell} = 0.03$ V. If cobalt metal is added to an aqueous solution in which $[Ni^{2+}] = 1.0$ M, **(a)** the reaction will not proceed in the forward direction at all; **(b)** the displacement of Ni(s) from the $Ni^{2+}(aq)$ will go to completion; **(c)** the displacement of Ni(s) from the solution will proceed to a considerable extent, but the reaction will not go to completion; **(d)** there is no way to predict how far the reaction will proceed.

103. The gas evolved at the *anode* when $K_2SO_4(aq)$ is electrolyzed between Pt electrodes is most likely to be **(a)** O_2; **(b)** H_2; **(c)** SO_2; **(d)** SO_3; **(e)** a mixture of sulfur oxides.

104. The quantity of electric charge that will deposit 4.5 g Al at a cathode will also produce the following volume at STP of $H_2(g)$ from $H^+(aq)$ at a cathode: **(a)** 44.8 L; **(b)** 22.4 L; **(c)** 11.2 L; **(d)** 5.6 L.

105. If a chemical reaction is carried out in a fuel cell, the maximum amount of useful work that can be obtained is **(a)** ΔG; **(b)** ΔH; **(c)** $\Delta G / \Delta H$; **(d)** $T \Delta S$.

106. For the reaction $Zn(s) + H^+(aq) + NO_3^-(aq) \longrightarrow Zn^{2+}(aq) + H_2O(l) + NO(g)$, describe the voltaic cell in which it occurs, label the anode and cathode, use a table of standard electrode potentials to evaluate $E°_{cell}$, and balance the equation for the cell reaction.

107. The following voltaic cell registers an $E_{cell} = 0.108$ V. What is the pH of the unknown solution?

$$Pt|H_2(g, 1\ atm)|H^+(x\ M)\|H^+(1.00\ M)|H_2(g, 1\ atm)|Pt$$

108. $E°_{cell} = -0.0050$ V for the reaction, $2 Cu^+(aq) + Sn^{4+}(aq) \longrightarrow 2 Cu^{2+}(aq) + Sn^{2+}(aq)$.
(a) Can a solution be prepared that is 0.500 M in each of the four ions at 298 K?
(b) If not, in what direction must a net reaction occur?

109. For each of the following combinations of electrodes (A and B) and solutions, indicate
- the overall cell reaction
- the direction in which electrons flow spontaneously (from A to B, or from B to A)
- the magnitude of the voltage read on the voltmeter, V

A	Solution A	B	Solution B
(a) Cu	1.0 M Cu^{2+}	Fe	1.0 M Fe^{2+}
(b) Pt	1.0 M Sn^{2+}/1.0 M Sn^{4+}	Ag	1.0 M Ag^+
(c) Zn	0.10 M Zn^{2+}	Fe	1.0×10^{-3} M Fe^{2+}

110. Use data from Table 20.1, as necessary, to predict the probable products when Pt electrodes are used in the electrolysis of **(a)** $CuCl_2(aq)$; **(b)** $Na_2SO_4(aq)$; **(c)** $BaCl_2(l)$; **(d)** KOH(aq).

111. Using the method presented in Appendix E, construct a concept map showing the relationship between electrochemical cells and thermodynamic properties.

112. Construct a concept map illustrating the relationship between batteries and electrochemical ideas.

113. Construct a concept map illustrating the principles of electrolysis and its industrial applications.

eMedia Exercises

114. The oxidation of zinc metal by two different species is shown in the **Oxidation–Reduction Reactions (Part 2)** animation (*Activebook 20-1*). **(a)** Describe the changes in physical state of the metals in the two reactions. **(b)** If these electrochemical processes were carried out in the laboratory, what would be the macroscopic, visible signs that a reaction is occurring?

115. In the **Voltaic Cells I: The Copper–Zinc Cell** animation (*Activebook 20-1*), two examples of a spontaneous electrochemical reaction are shown. **(a)** Describe the factors that can impede the progress of each reaction. Are they similar for the two examples? **(b)** What do these reactions tell you about the oxidation of copper by an aqueous solution of zinc ions?

116. If the two metal half-cells in the **Standard Reduction Potentials** animation (*Activebook 20-2*) were combined, **(a)** what spontaneous reaction would occur? Write the balanced chemical equation for this reaction. **(b)** Determine the standard cell potential for this spontaneous reaction.

117. Calculate the equilibrium constant of the reaction described in eMedia Exercise 20.116(a). Is the magnitude of the equilibrium constant consistent with your understanding of the spontaneity of the electrochemical reaction? Explain.

118. Calculate the cell potential of the reaction described in eMedia Exercise 20.116(a) under conditions where $[Zn^{2+}] = 0.20$ M and $[Ag^+] = 0.10$ M. Do these conditions favor the oxidation or reduction of zinc?

eLaboratory Exercises

These exercises allow students to apply the concepts and skills for this chapter in the simulated laboratory of Virtual ChemLab. Worksheets for each of these exercises are found in the Virtual ChemLab Workbook in your MediaPak.

119. *(VCL 20-1) Study of Oxidation–Reduction Titrations* Titrations provide a method of quantitatively measuring the concentration of an unknown solution. This is done by delivering a titrant of known concentration into an analyte of known volume. (The concentration of an unknown titrant can also be determined by titration with an analyte of known concentration and volume.) In oxidation–reduction (redox) titrations, the voltage resulting from the mixture of an oxidant and a reductant can be measured as the titration proceeds. The equivalence point of the titration, or the point where the analyte has been completely consumed by the titrant, is identified as the point where the voltage changes rapidly over a small volume of titrant delivered. In this assignment you will observe this titration curve by titrating iron(II) chloride ($FeCl_2$) with potassium permanganate ($KMnO_4$).

120. *(VCL 20-2) Standardization of a Permanganate Solution* In this assignment you will determine the molarity of an unknown solution of potassium permanganate ($KMnO_4$) by titrating against a primary standard, solid arsenic trioxide (As_2O_3).

121. *(VCL 20-3) Analysis of a Iron(II) Chloride Sample* In this assignment you will determine the mass percent of an unknown sample of iron(II) chloride ($FeCl_2$) by titrating with a potassium permanganate ($KMnO_4$) solution of known concentration.

21

CHEMISTRY OF THE MAIN-GROUP ELEMENTS I: GROUPS 1, 2, 13, AND 14

CONTENTS

Some of the dramatic colors seen in fireworks displays are the flame colors of some of the groups 1 and 2 metals. These colors, as we will see, are related to the electronic structures of those metal atoms.

 Fireworks safety website: http://www.fireworksafety.com/ (non-commercial)

The metals we encounter in everyday situations appear to be dense and unreactive. Group 1 elements, the alkali metals, however, have both low densities (some float on water) and are highly reactive, for example, reacting violently with water. Group 2, the alkaline earth metals, are also highly reactive and also less dense than a typical metal, though less reactive (reacting slowly or not at all with water) and denser than the alkali metals (none float on water).

Groups 13 and 14 are the first groups in which both metals and nonmetals are encountered. Boron is the only nonmetal in group 13 and has interesting chemistry because it tends to form molecules with incomplete octets around the central boron atoms. Aluminum is the most abundant of the metals and one of the most widely used. Aluminum production requires prodigious quantities of electricity in a process that is not much more than one hundred years old. The remaining elements of group 13—gallium, indium, and thallium—

are all metals. The chemistry of group 13 is dominated by boron and aluminum, and we will mention the heavier elements only briefly in this chapter. Group 14 contains the nonmetal carbon, the two metalloids silicon and germanium, and the two metals tin and lead. Carbon has the most important chemistry of the group since it occurs in all living systems and we devote two subsequent chapters (25 and 26) to the chemistry of carbon. Silicon is found in numerous minerals, forming many different and interesting oxoanions. In contrast to aluminum, tin and lead can be obtained by chemical reduction, a method used since ancient times.

This chapter and the remaining chapters offer many opportunities to relate new information to principles presented earlier in the text. Ideas of atomic structure, chemical bonding, and thermodynamics will help us to understand the chemical behavior of the elements. Concepts of oxidation–reduction and electrochemistry will help clarify which elements can be obtained from their compounds by chemical reactions and which require electrolysis. Principles of acid–base chemistry and solution equilibria help explain many common natural phenomena, such as the hardness of water. These principles also underlie methods of water softening. We will focus on the links between descriptive facts and the principles of chemistry.

21-1 GROUP 1: THE ALKALI METALS

As Table 21.1 indicates, the group 1 elements, the **alkali metals**, are relatively abundant. Some of their compounds have been known and used since prehistoric times. Yet these elements remained undiscovered until about 200 years ago. The compounds of the alkali metals are difficult to decompose by ordinary chemical means, so discovery of the elements had to await new scientific developments. Sodium (1807) and potassium (1807) were discovered through electrolysis. Cesium (1860) and rubidium (1861) were identified as new elements through their emission spectra. Francium (1939) was isolated in the radioactive decay products of actinium.

Because most alkali metal compounds are water soluble, a number of Li, Na, and K compounds, including chlorides, carbonates, and sulfates, can be obtained from natural brines. A few alkali metal compounds, such as NaCl, KCl, and Na_2CO_3, can be mined as solid deposits. Sodium chloride is also obtained from seawater. An important source of lithium is the mineral *spodumene*, $LiAl(SiO_3)_2$. Rubidium and cesium are obtained as by-products in the processing of lithium ores.

PHYSICAL PROPERTIES OF THE ALKALI METALS

By any measure, the group 1 elements are the most active metals. Table 21.2 lists several of their properties, and a few of these properties are discussed next.

Flame Colors. The energy differences between the valence-shell s and p orbitals of the group 1 metals match those of certain wavelengths of visible light. As a result, when heated in a flame, group 1 compounds produce characteristic flame colors (recall Figure 8-8). For example, when NaCl is vaporized in a flame, ion pairs are converted to gaseous atoms. Na(g) atoms are excited to higher energies, and light with a wavelength of 589 nm (yellow) is emitted as the excited atoms (Na*) revert to their ground-state electron configurations.

$$Na^+Cl^-(g) \longrightarrow Na(g) + Cl(g)$$
$$Na(g) \longrightarrow Na^*(g)$$
$$[Ne]3s^1 \qquad [Ne]3p^1$$
$$Na^*(g) \longrightarrow Na(g) + h\nu \ (589 \ nm; \ yellow)$$

Alkali metal compounds are used in pyrotechnic displays—fireworks.

TABLE 21.1 Abundances of Group 1 Elements		
Elements	Abundances, ppm[a]	Rank
Li	18	35
Na	22,700	7
K	18,400	8
Rb	78	23
Cs	2.6	46
Fr	Trace	—

[a]Grams per 1000 kg of solid crust.

◀ **KEEP IN MIND**
that hydrogen is often placed in group 1 of the periodic table, but this element is not an alkali metal. Francium is an alkali metal, but this highly radioactive metal is so rare that few of its properties have been measured.

▲ The mineral spodumene, $LiAl(SiO_3)_2$.

▲ **The cutting of metallic sodium**
The sodium, an active metal, is covered with a thick oxide coating.

Ciparick, J. D., Jones, R. F. "A variation on the demonstration of the properties of the alkali metals (TD)." *J. Chem. Educ.* **1989:** *66,* 438.

Birmingham, J. F., Jr.; Wood, W. H. "Apparatus for making spectral flames of the alkali and alkaline earth metals." *J. Chem. Educ.* **1936:** *13,* 240.

Dye, James L. "Alkali metal anions. An unusual oxidation state." *J. Chem. Educ.* **1977:** *54,* 332.

Dramatic, but to be done with caution, is to place a small piece of Na metal in water to show the spontaneous combustion of hydrogen produced in the reaction.

Alexander, M. Dale. "Reactions of the alkali metals with water: A novel demonstration (TD)." *J. Chem. Educ.* **1992:** *69,* 418.

Sodium and Potassium in Water and Flame Tests for Metals movies

TABLE 21.2 Some Properties of the Group 1 (Alkali) Metals

	Li	Na	K	Rb	Cs
Atomic number	3	11	19	37	55
Valence-shell electron configuration	$2s^1$	$3s^1$	$4s^1$	$5s^1$	$6s^1$
Atomic (metallic) radius, pm	152	186	227	248	265
Ionic (M^+) radius, pm	59	99	138	149	170
Electronegativity	1.0	0.9	0.8	0.8	0.8
First ionization energy, kJ mol^{-1}	520.2	495.8	418.8	403.0	375.7
Electrode potential $E°$, V[a]	−3.040	−2.713	−2.924	−2.924	−2.923
Melting point, °C	180.54	97.81	63.65	39.05	28.4
Boiling point, °C	1347	883.0	773.9	687.9	678.5
Density, g/cm^3 at 20 °C	0.534	0.971	0.862	1.532	1.873
Hardness[b]	0.6	0.4	0.5	0.3	0.2
Electrical conductivity[c]	17.1	33.2	22.0	12.4	7.76
Flame color	Carmine	Yellow	Violet	Bluish red	Blue
Principal visible emission lines, nm	610,671	589	405,767	780,795	456,459

[a]For the reduction $M^+(aq) + e^- \longrightarrow M(s)$.
[b]Hardness measures the ability of substances to scratch, abrade, or indent one another. On the Mohs scale, ten minerals are ranked by hardness, ranging from that of talc (0) to diamond (10). Other values: wax (0 °C), 0.2; asphalt, 1–2; fingernail, 2.5; copper, 2.5–3; iron, 4–5; chromium, 9. Each substance can scratch only other substances with hardness values lower than its own.
[c]On a scale relative to silver as 100.

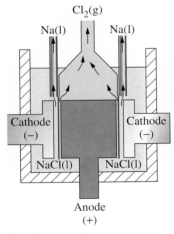

▲ The Downs Cell used for the production of sodium The electrolysis cell shown here is the Downs cell. The electrolyte is molten NaCl(l) to which CaCl₂ has been added to lower the melting point of NaCl(s). Liquid sodium metal forms at the steel cathode and Cl₂(g) forms at the graphite anode. The chlorine and sodium are kept apart by a steel gauze diaphragm.

Properties Influenced by Atomic Sizes. Atoms of the group 1 elements are the largest in their respective periods, and the atomic radii tend to increase from the top to the bottom within this group, as was described in Chapter 9. These large atoms make for a relatively low mass per unit volume—that is, low density. The lighter of the alkali metals (Li, Na, and K) will float on water. The large atomic sizes, together with the fact that each of these atoms has only one valence electron, makes for rather weak metallic bonding. This property, in turn, leads to soft metals with low melting points. A bar of sodium has the consistency of a frozen stick of butter and is easily cut with a knife.

Electrode Potentials. A good indicator of the extreme metallic character of the group 1 elements is their electrode potentials, which are large, negative quantities. The ions $M^+(aq)$ are very difficult to reduce to the metals $M(s)$, and in turn, the metals are very easily oxidized to $M^+(aq)$. All the alkali metals easily displace $H_2(g)$ from water.

$$2\,M(s) + 2\,H_2O(l) \longrightarrow 2\,M^+(aq) + 2\,OH^-(aq) + H_2(g) \tag{21.1}$$

$$E°_{cell} = E°_{H_2O/H_2} - E°_{M^+/M}$$
$$= -0.828\text{ V} - E°_{M^+/M}$$

$$E°_{cell} = 2.212\text{ V (for Li)} \quad 1.885\text{ V (for Na)} \quad 2.096\text{ V (for K)}$$
$$2.096\text{ V (for Rb)} \quad 2.095\text{ V (for Cs)}$$

PRODUCTION AND USES OF THE ALKALI METALS

Lithium and sodium are produced from their molten chlorides by electrolysis. The electrolysis of NaCl(l), for example, is carried out at about 600 °C.

$$2\,NaCl(l) \xrightarrow{\text{electrolysis}} 2\,Na(l) + Cl_2(g) \tag{21.2}$$

The melting point of NaCl is 801 °C, too high a temperature to carry out this electrolysis economically. Adding $CaCl_2$ to the mixture reduces the melting point. [Calcium metal, also produced in the electrolysis, precipitates out from the Na(l) as the liquid metal is cooled. The final product is 99.95% Na.]

Potassium metal is produced by the reduction of molten KCl by liquid sodium.

$$KCl(l) + Na(l) \xrightarrow{850 \,°C} NaCl(l) + K(g) \tag{21.3}$$

Reaction (21.3) is reversible; at low temperatures, most of the KCl(l) is unreacted. At 850 °C, however, the equilibrium is displaced far to the right as K(g) escapes from the molten mixture (an application of Le Châtelier's principle). The K(g) is freed of any Na(g) present by condensation of the vapor, followed by fractional distillation of the liquid metals. Rb and Cs can be produced in much the same way, with Ca metal as the reducing agent.

Because sodium is so reactive, its most important use is as a reducing agent—for example, in obtaining metals such as titanium, zirconium, and hafnium.

$$TiCl_4 + 4\,Na \xrightarrow{\Delta} Ti + 4\,NaCl$$

Another use of sodium metal is as a heat-transfer medium in nuclear reactors. Liquid sodium is especially good for this purpose because it has a low melting point, a high boiling point, and a low vapor pressure. Also, it has better thermal conductivity and a higher specific heat than do most liquid metals. Finally, its low density and low viscosity make it easy to pump. Sodium is also used in

◄ We introduced the symbol $\xrightarrow{\Delta}$ in Chapter 4 (page 113) to indicate that a reaction is carried out at an elevated temperature.

Are You Wondering . . .

Why lithium is the most easily oxidized of the group 1 elements on the basis of $E°$ values but not on the basis of ionization energies?

Being the smallest of the alkali metal atoms, Li has the highest first ionization energy. It is the most difficult to oxidize in the reaction $M(g) \longrightarrow M^+(g) + e^-$. However, oxidation to produce $M^+(aq)$ is a different matter. We can think of it as the overall result of a hypothetical three-step process.

Sublimation:	$M(s) \longrightarrow M(g)$	
Ionization:	$M(g) \longrightarrow M^+(g) + e^-$	
Hydration:	$M^+(g) \longrightarrow M^+(aq)$	
Overall:	$M(s) \longrightarrow M^+(aq) + e^-$	

Thus, to compare tendencies to form $M^+(aq)$ by oxidation of the metals, we must compare tendencies in each of these three steps. Such a comparison shows that Li^+ has an unusually large hydration energy—enough to make $Li^+(aq)$ especially hard to reduce and Li(s) especially easy to oxidize. The large hydration energy is a consequence of the small size of the Li^+ ion, which allows a close approach to surrounding water molecules and strong attractive ion–dipole forces between them (Fig. 21-1).

◄ **FIGURE 21-1**
Hydration of a Li$^+$ ion
Electrostatic forces hold a small number of H_2O molecules around a Li^+ ion in a primary hydration sphere. These molecules, in turn, hold other molecules, but more weakly, in a secondary hydration sphere.

◄ **KEEP IN MIND**
that the more negative the value of $E°$, the more difficult is the reduction but the more easily does the reverse process—the oxidation half-reaction—occur. The value of $E°_{Li^+/Li}$, −3.040 V, comes at the very bottom of a listing of electrode potentials (recall Table 20.1), making Li(s) the easiest substance to oxidize.

▲ An X-ray photograph showing a heart pacemaker powered by a lithium battery.

A list of minerals containing the alkali metals is in House, J. E., House, K. A., *Descriptive Inorganic Chemistry*, Harcourt Academic Press, (2001), p. 158.

sodium vapor lamps, which are very popular for outdoor lighting. Because each lamp uses only a few milligrams of Na, however, the total quantity consumed in this application is rather small.

Lithium metal is used as an alloying agent to make high-strength, low-density alloys with aluminum and with magnesium. These alloys are used in the aerospace and aircraft industries. The use of lithium as an anode in batteries is on the increase, in part because of its ease of oxidation and in part because a small mass of lithium produces a large number of electrons. Only 6.94 g Li (1 mol) needs to be consumed to produce one mole of electrons. Lithium batteries are particularly useful where the installed battery must have high reliability and a long lifetime, as in cardiac pacemakers.

A more recent type of rechargeable lithium battery, used in cell phones, camcorders, and laptop computers, is called a lithium–ion cell. In such a battery, the anode is graphite with lithium atoms incorporated between the layers of C_6 rings. This Li_xC_6 anode exhibits essentially the same electrode potential as lithium itself. The other novel feature of the lithium–ion cell is that Li^+ ions carry charge through an electrolyte to a Li_yCoO_2 cathode, where they take up interstitial positions in the crystal structure. Simultaneously, electrons pass from the anode to the cathode through an external circuit powering the device in which the battery is used. The processes are reversed on recharging.

GROUP 1 COMPOUNDS

Figure 21-2 introduces a useful diagrammatic format for summarizing reaction chemistry. Although this diagram deals with sodium compounds, many of which are discussed in this section, similar diagrams can be constructed for other elements. Such diagrams note a compound of central importance (NaCl in Figure 21-2) and show how several other compounds can be obtained from it. Some of these conversions occur in one step, such as the reaction of NaCl with H_2SO_4 to form Na_2SO_4 (discussed on page 877). Other conversions involve two or more consecutive reactions, as does the preparation of sodium silicate, Na_2SiO_3, for example. The principal reactants required for the conversions are written near the connecting arrows. If a reaction mixture must be heated, a Δ symbol is used to indicate this requirement. The reactions may also produce by-products that are not noted in the diagram.

▲ **FIGURE 21-2**
Preparation of sodium compounds
This is a simple and common method of summarizing the reactions of a compound. Most of these reactions are described in this section. A number of these compounds may be prepared by alternative methods. The conversion of Na_2CO_3 to NaOH (dashed arrow) is no longer of commercial importance.

EXAMPLE 21-1

Writing Chemical Equations from a Summary Diagram of Reaction Chemistry. Propose a method for synthesizing sodium carbonate from sodium chloride.

Solution

Consult Figure 21-2 to find a route from $NaCl$ to Na_2CO_3. One route involves the conversions

$$NaCl \longrightarrow Na_2SO_4 \longrightarrow Na_2S \longrightarrow Na_2CO_3$$

Other necessary reactants (H_2SO_4, C, and $CaCO_3$) are noted. In the following set of equations, we must, as usual, include other reaction products (such as HCl, CO, and CaS).

First, $Na_2SO_4(s)$ is produced from $NaCl(s)$ and concentrated sulfuric acid.

$$2\,NaCl(s) + H_2SO_4(\text{concd aq}) \xrightarrow{\Delta} Na_2SO_4(s) + 2\,HCl(g)$$

Next, the Na_2SO_4 is reduced to Na_2S with carbon.

$$Na_2SO_4(s) + 4\,C(s) \xrightarrow{\Delta} Na_2S(s) + 4\,CO(g)$$

The final step is a reaction between Na_2S and $CaCO_3$.

$$Na_2S(s) + CaCO_3 \xrightarrow{\Delta} CaS(s) + Na_2CO_3(s)$$

Practice Example A: Propose a method for synthesizing sodium nitrate from sodium chloride.

Practice Example B: Propose a method for synthesizing sodium thiosulfate from sodium chloride.

Halides.   All alkali metals react vigorously, sometimes explosively, with halogens to produce ionic halides, the most important of which are NaCl and KCl. Sodium chloride—salt—is the primary sodium compound. In fact, it is the most used of all minerals for the production of chemicals. It is not listed among the top chemicals, however, because it is considered a raw material, not a manufactured chemical. Annual use of NaCl in the United States amounts to about 50 million tons. Salt is used to preserve meat and fish, control ice on roads, and regenerate water softeners. In the chemical industry, NaCl is a source of many chemicals, including sodium metal, chlorine gas, hydrochloric acid, and sodium hydroxide.

Potassium chloride is obtained from naturally occurring brines (concentrated solutions of salts). It is most extensively used in plant fertilizers because potassium is a major essential element for plant growth. KCl is also used as a raw material in the manufacture of KOH, KNO_3, and other industrially important potassium compounds.

Carbonates and Sulfates.   Except for Li_2CO_3, all the alkali metal carbonates are thermally stable compounds. In this and several other ways, lithium and its compounds differ from other members of group 1. The low aqueous solubility of Li_2CO_3 and its instability with respect to the oxide at high temperature resemble the behavior of $MgCO_3$. Such similarities between lithium and

Formation of Sodium Chloride movie

Elson, Jesse. "A bonding parameter. III, Water solubilities and melting points of the alkali halogens." *J. Chem. Educ.* 1969: *46*, 86.

◀ Sea salt (sodium chloride) stacks that have been harvested by evaporation of seawater.

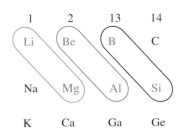

1	2	13	14
Li	Be	B	C
Na	Mg	Al	Si
K	Ca	Ga	Ge

▲ **FIGURE 21-3**
Diagonal relationships
The two elements in each encircled pair exhibit many similar properties.

▶ The term *ash* signifies a product obtained by heating or burning. The earliest alkaline materials (notably, potassium carbonate, *potash*) were extracted from the ashes of burned plants. The first commercial source of *soda ash* was the Leblanc process, featured in Example 21-1.

▲ The mineral *trona*, from Green River, Wyoming, is currently the principal source of Na_2CO_3 in the United States.

Trona website:
http://webmineral.com/
data/Trona.shtml
(commercial)

magnesium are referred to as a **diagonal relationship**. Other diagonal relationships exist between Be and Al and between B and Si (Fig. 21-3). The Li–Mg similarity probably results from the roughly comparable sizes of the Li and Mg atoms and of the Li$^+$ and Mg^{2+} ions.

Lithium carbonate is used in the treatment of individuals who are manic-depressive. Daily dosages of 1–2 g Li_2CO_3 maintain a level of Li$^+$ in the blood of about one millimole per liter. This treatment apparently influences the balance of Na$^+$ and K$^+$, that of Mg^{2+} and Ca^{2+}, or both, across cell membranes.

Sodium carbonate (soda ash) is used primarily in the manufacture of glass. The Na_2CO_3 produced in the United States now comes mostly from natural sources, such as the mineral *trona*, $Na_2CO_3 \cdot NaHCO_3 \cdot nH_2O$, found in dry lakes in California and in immense deposits in western Wyoming. In the past, sodium carbonate was manufactured mostly from NaCl, $CaCO_3$, and NH_3, using a process introduced by the Belgian chemist Ernest Solvay in 1863.

The great success of the *Solvay process* over the synthetic method outlined in Example 21-1 lies in the efficient use of certain raw materials through recycling. An outline of the process is shown in Figure 21-4. The key step involves the reaction of $NH_3(g)$ and $CO_2(g)$ in saturated NaCl(aq). Of the possible ionic compounds that could precipitate from such a mixture (NaCl, NH_4Cl, $NaHCO_3$, and NH_4HCO_3), the least soluble is *sodium hydrogen carbonate* (sodium bicarbonate).

$$Na^+ + Cl^- + NH_3 + CO_2 + H_2O \longrightarrow NaHCO_3(s) + NH_4^+ + Cl^- \quad (21.4)$$

The sodium bicarbonate can be isolated and sold or converted to sodium carbonate by heating.

$$2\,NaHCO_3(s) \xrightarrow{\Delta} Na_2CO_3(s) + H_2O(g) + CO_2(g) \quad (21.5)$$

One noteworthy feature of the Solvay process is that it involves only simple precipitation and acid–base reactions. Another feature is that materials produced in one step are efficiently recycled into a subsequent step. Recycling makes good economic sense: A process that recycles materials minimizes the use of raw materials (an expense in purchasing) and cuts down on the production of by-products (an expense in disposal). Thus, when limestone ($CaCO_3$) is heated to produce the reactant CO_2, the other reaction product, CaO, is also

▲ **FIGURE 21-4**
The Solvay process for the manufacture of NaHCO₃
The main reaction sequence is traced by solid arrows. Recycling reactions are shown by dashed arrows.

used. It is converted to $Ca(OH)_2$, which is then used to convert NH_4Cl (another reaction by-product) to $NH_3(g)$. The $NH_3(g)$ is recycled into the production of ammoniated brine.

The Solvay process has only one ultimate by-product—$CaCl_2$—for which the demand is very limited. In the past, some $CaCl_2$ was used for deicing roads in the winter (page 553) and for dust control on dirt roads in the summer (by means of the deliquescence of $CaCl_2 \cdot 6\,H_2O$, page 548). The bulk of the $CaCl_2$, however, was dumped into local lakes and streams (notably, Onondaga Lake, near Solvay, New York), resulting in extensive environmental contamination. Environmental regulations no longer permit such dumping. Partly due to these regulations, but mainly for economic reasons, natural sources of sodium carbonate have supplanted the Solvay process in the United States. The process is still widely used elsewhere in the world, however.

Sodium sulfate is obtained partly from natural sources, partly from neutralization reactions, and partly through a process discovered by Johann Rudolf Glauber in 1625.

$$H_2SO_4(\text{concd aq}) + NaCl(s) \xrightarrow{\Delta} NaHSO_4(s) + HCl(g)$$

$$NaHSO_4(s) + NaCl(s) \xrightarrow{\Delta} Na_2SO_4(s) + HCl(g)$$

(21.6)

◀ Equations (21.6) are often replaced by the overall equation, $H_2SO_4(\text{concd aq}) + 2\,NaCl(s) \longrightarrow Na_2SO_4(s) + 2\,HCl(g)$.

The strategy behind reactions (21.6) is the production of a *volatile* acid (HCl) by heating one of its salts (NaCl) with a *nonvolatile* acid (H_2SO_4). Several other acids can be produced by similar reactions. The major use of Na_2SO_4 is in the paper industry. For instance, in the kraft process for papermaking, undesirable lignin is removed from wood by digesting the wood in an alkaline solution of Na_2S. Na_2S is produced by the reduction of Na_2SO_4 with carbon.

$$Na_2SO_4(s) + 4\,C(s) \xrightarrow{\Delta} Na_2S(s) + 4\,CO(g)$$

About 100 lb of Na_2SO_4 is required for every ton of paper produced.

Oxides and Hydroxides. The alkali metals react rapidly with oxygen to produce several different ionic oxides. Under appropriate conditions—generally by limiting the supply of oxygen—the oxide, M_2O, can be prepared for each of the alkali metals. Li reacts with excess oxygen to give Li_2O and a small amount of a *peroxide*, M_2O_2—in this case, lithium peroxide, Li_2O_2. Na reacts with excess oxygen to give mostly the peroxide Na_2O_2 and a small amount of Na_2O. K, Rb, and Cs react to form the *superoxides*, MO_2.

$$\left[\ddot{\underset{\cdot\cdot}{O}}\cdot\cdot\right]^{2-} \qquad \left[\ddot{\underset{\cdot\cdot}{O}}\!:\!\ddot{\underset{\cdot\cdot}{O}}\right]^{2-} \qquad \left[\ddot{\underset{\cdot\cdot}{O}}\!:\!\ddot{\underset{\cdot\cdot}{O}}\!:\right]^{-}$$

Oxide ion   Peroxide ion   Superoxide ion

The peroxides contain the O_2^{2-} ion and are fairly stable. Sodium peroxide is used as a bleaching agent and a powerful oxidant. Li_2O_2 and Na_2O_2 are used in emergency breathing devices in submarines and spacecraft because these compounds react with carbon dioxide to produce oxygen.

$$2\,M_2O_2(s) + 2\,CO_2(g) \longrightarrow 2\,M_2CO_3(s) + O_2(g) \qquad (M = Li, Na) \qquad (21.7)$$

KO_2, potassium superoxide, can also be used for this purpose. The oxides, peroxides, and superoxides of the alkali metals react with water to form basic solutions. The reaction of an alkali metal oxide with water is an acid–base reaction that produces the alkali metal hydroxide.

$$Li_2O(s) + H_2O(l) \longrightarrow 2\,LiOH(aq)$$

The peroxide ion reacts with water in a similar manner to produce hydroxide ion and hydrogen peroxide.

$$O_2^{2-}(aq) + 2\,H_2O(l) \longrightarrow 2\,OH^-(aq) + H_2O_2(aq)$$

The hydrogen peroxide then slowly disproportionates into water and oxygen (page 160).

Kirksey, H. G. "Solvay synthesis of sodium hydrogen carbonate. An undergraduate laboratory experiment." *J. Chem. Educ.* **1978:** *55,* 272.

Popular stain removers such as OxiClean contain mixtures of sodium carbonate and sodium percarbonate. An experiment for determining the percentages of these components in stain removers is described in Bracken, J. D. *J. Chem. Educ.* **2005:** *82,* 762.

The superoxide ion reacts with water to give hydroxide ions, hydrogen peroxide, and oxygen.

$$2\,O_2^-(aq) + 2\,H_2O(l) \longrightarrow 2\,OH^-(aq) + H_2O_2(aq) + O_2(g)$$

The hydroxides of the group 1 metals are strong bases because they dissociate to release hydroxide ions in aqueous solution. As we learned in Section 20-8, sodium hydroxide is produced commercially by the electrolysis of NaCl(aq). $Na^+(aq)$ goes through the electrolysis unchanged; $Cl^-(aq)$ is oxidized to $Cl_2(g)$; and H_2O is reduced to $H_2(g)$. KOH and LiOH are made in a similar fashion. Alkali metal hydroxides can also be prepared by the reaction of the group 1 metals with water (equation 21.1). Alkali hydroxides are important in the manufacture of soaps and detergents, described next.

Alkali Metal Detergents and Soaps. A **detergent** is a cleansing agent used primarily because it can emulsify oils. Although the term *detergent* includes common soaps, it is used primarily to describe certain synthetic products, such as sodium lauryl sulfate, whose manufacture involves these conversions.

$$CH_3(CH_2)_{10}CH_2OH \longrightarrow CH_3(CH_2)_{10}CH_2OSO_3H \longrightarrow CH_3(CH_2)_{10}CH_2OSO_3^-\,Na^+$$

lauryl alcohol · · · · · · · · · · · · · · · · lauryl hydrogen sulfate · · · · · · · · · · · · · · · · sodium lauryl sulfate

A **soap** is a specific kind of detergent that is the salt of a metal hydroxide and a fatty acid. An example is the sodium soap of palmitic acid, which we can represent as the product of the reaction of palmitic acid and NaOH.

$$CH_3(CH_2)_{14}-\overset{\displaystyle O}{\overset{\displaystyle \|}{C}}-O-H + Na^+ + OH^- \longrightarrow CH_3(CH_2)_{14}-\overset{\displaystyle O}{\overset{\displaystyle \|}{C}}-O^-\,Na^+ + H_2O \quad (21.8)$$

palmitic acid · sodium palmitate
(a soap)

Nelson, Arthur F. "Potassium soap–soft or hard?" *J. Chem. Educ.* **1948:** *25,* 379.

Snell, Foster D. "Soap and glycerol." *J. Chem. Educ.* **1942:** *19,* 172.

"Soapmaking." *J. Chem. Educ.* **1999:** *76,* 192A (February 1999).

Figure 21-5 illustrates the detergent action of a typical soap: sodium palmitate. Sodium soaps are the familiar hard (bar) soaps. Potassium soaps have low melting points and are soft soaps. Lithium stearate, a soap not seen in

(a)

▶ **FIGURE 21-5**
Structure of soap molecules and their cleaning action
(a) The sodium palmitate molecule has a long nonpolar portion buried in a droplet of oil and a polar head projecting into an aqueous medium. **(b)** Electrostatic attractions between these polar heads and water molecules cause the droplet to be emulsified, or solubilized.

(b)

ordinary household use, thickens oils into greases. These greases have excellent water-repellent and lubricating properties at both high and low temperatures. The greases remain in contact with moving metal parts under conditions in which oil by itself would run off.

CONCEPT ASSESSMENT ✓

Magnesium reacts with nitrogen gas on heating. Only one of the alkali metals exhibits a similar reaction. Which one do you think it is and why? Write balanced equations for both reactions.

21-2 GROUP 2: THE ALKALINE EARTH METALS

As a group, the alkaline earth metals of group 2 are as common as the elements of group 1. Table 21.3 shows that calcium and magnesium are particularly abundant. Even beryllium, the least abundant member of group 2, is accessible because it occurs in deposits of the mineral *beryl*, $Be_3Al_2Si_6O_{18}$. The principal forms in which the other group 2 elements are found are as carbonates, sulfates, and silicates. Radium, like its group 1 neighbor, francium, is a radioactive element found only in trace amounts. Radium is more interesting for its radioactive properties than for its chemical similarities to the other group 2 elements.

Even though the group 2 metal oxides and hydroxides are only very slightly soluble in water, they are basic, or *alkaline*. At one time, insoluble substances that do not decompose on heating were called "earths." This term is the basis of the group 2 name: **alkaline earth metals**.

From a chemical standpoint (for example, in their abilities to react with water and acids and to form ionic compounds), the heavier group 2 metals—Ca, Sr, Ba, and Ra—are nearly as active as the group 1 metals. In terms of certain physical properties (for example, density, hardness, and melting point), all the group 2 elements are more typically metallic than the group 1 elements, as we can see by comparing Tables 21.2 and 21.4.

TABLE 21.3 Abundances of Group 2 Elements

Elements	Abundances, ppm[a]	Rank
Be	2	51
Mg	27,640	6
Ca	46,600	5
Sr	384	15
Ba	390	14
Ra	Trace	—

[a]Grams per 1000 kg of solid crust.

▲ An emerald crystal, which is based on the mineral *beryl*, embedded in a calcite matrix.

Weeks, Mary Elvira. "The discovery of the elements: X. The alkaline earth metals and magnesium and cadmium." *J. Chem. Educ.* **1932:** *9,* 1046.

TABLE 21.4 Some Properties of Group 2 (Alkaline Earth) Metals

	Be	Mg	Ca	Sr	Ba
Atomic number	4	12	20	38	56
Atomic (metallic) radius, pm	111	160	197	215	222
Ionic (M^{2+}) radius, pm	27	72	100	113	136
Electronegativity	1.5	1.2	1.0	1.0	0.9
First ionization energy, kJ mol^{-1}	899.4	737.7	589.7	549.5	502.8
Electrode potential $E°$, V[a]	−1.85	−2.356	−2.84	−2.89	−2.92
Melting point, °C	1278	648.8	839	769	729
Boiling point, °C	2970[b]	1090	1483.6	1383.9	1637
Density, g/cm^3 at 20 °C	1.85	1.74	1.55	2.54	3.60
Hardness[c]	~5	2.0	1.5	1.8	~2
Electrical conductivity[c]	39.7	35.6	40.6	6.90	3.20
Flame color	None	None	Orange-red	Scarlet	Green

[a]For the reduction $M^{2+}(aq) + 2 e^- \longrightarrow M(s)$.
[b]Boiling point at 5 mmHg pressure.
[c]See footnotes b and c of Table 21.2.

A list of minerals containing the alkaline earth metals is in House, J. E., House, K. A., *Descriptive Inorganic Chemistry*, Harcourt Academic Press, (2001), p. 160.

Table 21.4 shows that beryllium is out of step with the other group 2 elements in some of its physical properties. For instance, it has a higher melting point and is much harder than the others. Its chemical properties also differ significantly. For example,

- Be is quite unreactive with air and water;
- BeO does not react with water, whereas the other MO oxides form $M(OH)_2$;
- Be and BeO dissolve in strongly basic solutions to form the ion $[Be(OH)_4]^{2-}$;
- $BeCl_2$ and BeF_2 in the molten state are poor conductors of electricity; they are covalent substances.

The chemical behavior of beryllium can best be related to the small size and high ionization energy of its atoms. Beryllium shows only a limited tendency to form the simple ion Be^{2+}; in fact, its ability to form covalent bonds predominates in the compounds that beryllium forms. For example, while the other oxides of group 2 are basic, BeO is an *amphoteric* oxide, reacting with both strong acids and bases.

$$H_2O(l) + BeO(s) + 2\,H_3O^+(aq) \longrightarrow [Be(H_2O)_4]^{2+}(aq)$$

$$H_2O(l) + BeO(s) + 2\,OH^-(aq) \longrightarrow [Be(OH)_4]^{2-}(aq)$$

▲ Tetrahedral shape of the $[Be(OH_2)_4]^{2+}$ ion.

This behavior is a consequence of beryllium's small ionic size and relatively high ionic charge of 2+. The reaction of beryllium metal with aqueous acids yields hydrogen and ionic compounds such as $BeCl_2 \cdot 4\,H_2O$. In $BeCl_2 \cdot 4\,H_2O$, water molecules are covalently bonded to Be^{2+} ions, producing the complex cations $[Be(OH_2)_4]^{2+}$ which, together with the anions Cl^-, form the crystal lattice. In covalent compounds, Be atoms appear to use hybrid orbitals—sp orbitals in $BeCl_2(g)$ and sp^3 orbitals in $BeCl_2(s)$ (Fig. 21-6).

Feinstein, H. I. "Ignition of magnesium in porcelain." *J. Chem. Educ.* **1982**: *59*, 159.

Driscoll, Jerry A. "Demonstration of burning magnesium and dry ice (TD)." *J. Chem. Educ.* **1978**: *55*, 450.

Wheeler, John C. "Electron Affinities of the Alkaline Earth Metals and the Sign Convention for Electron Affinity." *J. Chem. Educ.* **1997**: *74*, 123 (January 1997).

PRODUCTION AND USES OF THE ALKALINE EARTH METALS

The preferred method of producing the group 2 metals (except Mg) is by reducing their salts with other active metals. Beryl is the natural source of beryllium compounds. This mineral is processed to produce BeF_2, which is then reduced with Mg. Beryllium metal is used as an alloying agent when low density is a primary requirement. Because Be can withstand metal fatigue, an alloy of copper with about 2% Be is used in springs, clips, and electrical contacts. The Be atom does not readily absorb X rays or neutrons, so beryllium is

▶ **FIGURE 21-6**
Covalent bonds in BeCl$_2$
(a) In gaseous $BeCl_2$, discrete molecules exist with the bonding scheme shown.
(b) In solid $BeCl_2$, two Cl atoms are bonded to one Be atom by normal covalent bonds. Two other Cl atoms are bonded by coordinate covalent bonds, using lone-pair electrons of the Cl atoms (bonds shown as arrows). Once formed, these two types of bonds are indistinguishable. $BeCl_2$ units are linked into long, chain-like polymeric molecules as $(BeCl_2)_n$.

$BeCl_2(g)$

(a)

$BeCl_2(s)$

(b)

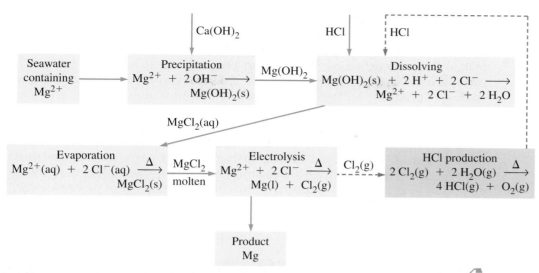

▲ FIGURE 21-7
The Dow process for the production of Mg
The main reaction sequence is traced by solid arrows. The recycling of $Cl_2(g)$ is
shown by dashed arrows.

used to make windows for X-ray tubes and for various components in nuclear
reactors. Beryllium and its compounds are limited in their use, however, because they are toxic. In addition, they are suspected of being carcinogens even
at a level as low as 0.002 ppm in air.

Calcium, strontium, and barium are obtained by the reduction of their oxides with aluminum; Ca and Sr also can be obtained by electrolysis of their
molten chlorides. Calcium metal is used primarily as a reducing agent to prepare, from their oxides or fluorides, other metals such as U, Pu, and most of
the lanthanides. Strontium and barium have limited use in alloys, but some of
their compounds (discussed later) are quite important. Some salts of Sr and Ba
provide vivid colors for pyrotechnic displays.

Magnesium metal is obtained by electrolysis of the molten chloride in the
Dow process. The Dow process is outlined in Figure 21-7, and the electrolysis of
$MgCl_2(l)$ is pictured in Figure 21-8. Like the Solvay process for making
$NaHCO_3$, the Dow process takes advantage of simple chemistry and recycling.

Less dangerous than the
oxidation of Na is the burning
of magnesium ribbon (wear dark
glasses). It burns bright and hot
and is used by war planes as
decoys for heat-seeking missiles.

Strontium lies directly below
calcium in the periodic table
and thus has some similar
properties. For example, before atmospheric testing of nuclear
weapons was banned, ^{90}Sr was
found in milk and in the bones of
some children.

St. Peter, John. "The light
metals: aluminum and
magnesium." *J. Chem. Educ.* **1942:**
19, 556.

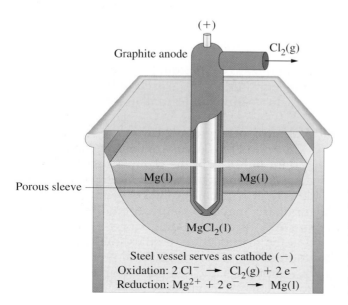

◄ FIGURE 21-8
The electrolysis of molten $MgCl_2$
The electrolyte is a mixture of molten NaCl,
$CaCl_2$, and $MgCl_2$. This mixture has a
lower melting point and higher electrical
conductivity than $MgCl_2$ alone, but if the
voltage is carefully controlled, only Mg^{2+} is
reduced in the electrolysis.

▶ In Example 18-6, we demonstrated that this precipitation goes to completion.

The source of magnesium is seawater or natural brines. The abundance of Mg^{2+} in seawater is about 1350 mg/L. The first step in the Dow process is the precipitation of $Mg(OH)_2(s)$ with slaked lime $[Ca(OH)_2]$ as the source of OH^-. Slaked lime is formed by the reaction of quicklime (CaO) with water. The precipitated $Mg(OH)_2(s)$ is washed, filtered, and dissolved in HCl(aq). The resulting concentrated $MgCl_2(aq)$ is dried by evaporation, melted, and electrolyzed, yielding pure Mg metal and $Cl_2(g)$. The $Cl_2(g)$ is converted to HCl, which is recycled.

Magnesium has a lower density than that of any other metal used for structural purposes. Lightweight objects such as aircraft parts are manufactured from magnesium alloyed with aluminum and other metals. Magnesium is a good reducing agent and is used in a number of metallurgical processes, such as the production of beryllium, as mentioned earlier. The ease with which magnesium is oxidized also underlies its use in sacrificial anodes for corrosion protection (page 848). Magnesium's most spectacular use may be in fireworks.

CONCEPT ASSESSMENT ✓

The good reducing properties of magnesium are illustrated by the fact that the metal burns in an atmosphere of pure carbon dioxide. Write a plausible equation(s) for this reaction.

GROUP 2 COMPOUNDS

The properties of group 2 compounds differ from those of group 1 compounds. In some cases, this difference is attributable to the smaller ionic size and the larger ionic charge of group 2 cations. For example, the lattice energy of $Mg(OH)_2$ is about -3000 kJ mol^{-1}, compared with about -900 kJ mol^{-1} for NaOH. This difference in lattice energy helps account for the ready solubility of NaOH in water up to about 20 M NaOH, and the sparing solubility of $Mg(OH)_2$, with $K_{sp} = 1.8 \times 10^{-11}$. The heavier group 2 hydroxides are somewhat more soluble than $Mg(OH)_2$. Other alkaline earth compounds that are only slightly soluble include the carbonates, fluorides, and oxides. Another common characteristic of alkaline earth compounds is the formation of *hydrates*. Typical hydrates are $MX_2 \cdot 6 H_2O$ (where M = Mg, Ca, or Sr, and X = Cl or Br). As noted earlier, beryllium compounds are rather different from the other group 2 compounds.

Halides. The group 2 metals react directly with the halogens to form halides. Except for those of beryllium, these halides are essentially ionic.

$$M + X_2 \longrightarrow MX_2 \tag{21.9}$$
(M = a group 2 metal, and X = F, Cl, Br, or I)

The halides have varied uses. As an example, $MgCl_2$, in addition to its use in the preparation of magnesium metal, is used in fireproofing wood, in special cements, in ceramics, in treating fabrics, and as a refrigeration brine.

Carbonates and Sulfates. The group 2 carbonates are insoluble in water, as are the sulfates of Ca, Sr, and Ba. Because of this insolubility, these compounds are the most important minerals of the group 2 metals. The most familiar is $CaCO_3$, the principal component of the rock *limestone*. If a limestone contains more than 5% $MgCO_3$, it is usually called dolomitic limestone, or *dolomite*. Some clay, sand, or quartz may also be present in limestone. The primary use of limestone (about 70%) is as a building stone. Among other applications, limestone is used in the manufacture of quicklime and slaked lime, as an ingredient in glass, and as a flux in metallurgical processes. A *flux* is a material that combines with impurities and removes them as a free-flowing liquid—a *slag*—during production of a metal (page 976).

Solubility Products of Ionic Compounds activity

Grube, K., Leffler, A. J. "Synthesis of metal halides (ML)." *J. Chem. Educ.* **1993**: *70,* A204.

Vining, W. J., et al. "Lattice Energetics." *J. Chem. Educ.* **2003**: *80,* 108.

Mossman, D. M., et al. "The Complexometric Determination of Calcium and Magnesium in Limestone Using a Laser Photometer for Endpoint Identification." *J. Chem. Educ.* **1996**: *73,* 82.

Portland cement, another important product of limestone, is a complex mixture of calcium silicates and aluminates. It is produced in long rotary kilns in which mixtures of limestone, clay, and sand are heated to progressively higher temperatures as they slowly move down the inclined kiln. First, moisture and, then, chemically bound water are driven off. This process is followed by decomposition (calcination) of the limestone to $CaO(s)$ and $CO_2(g)$. Finally, the CaO combines with silica (SiO_2) and alumina (Al_2O_3) from the sand and clay to form silicates and aluminates. Pure cement does not have much strength. When mixed with sand, gravel, and water, however, it sets into the familiar rock-like mass called *concrete*. Portland cement is an especially valuable material for building bridge piers and other underwater structures because it hardens even when underwater—it is a *hydraulic* cement.

Pure, white $CaCO_3$ is used in a wide variety of products. For example, it is used in papermaking to impart brightness, opacity, smoothness, and good ink-absorbing qualities to paper. It is particularly suited to newer papermaking processes that produce acid-free (alkaline) paper with an expected shelf life of 300 years or more. $CaCO_3$ is used as a filler in plastics, rubber, floor tiles, putties, and adhesives as well as in foods and cosmetics. It is also used as an antacid and as a dietary supplement for the prevention of osteoporosis, a condition in which the bones become porous and brittle and break easily.

Three steps are required to obtain pure $CaCO_3$ from limestone: (1) thermal decomposition of limestone (called **calcination**), (2) reaction of CaO with water (slaking), and (3) conversion of an aqueous suspension of $Ca(OH)_2(s)$ to precipitated $CaCO_3$ (carbonation).

Calcination: $$CaCO_3(s) \xrightarrow{\Delta} CaO(s) + CO_2(g) \qquad (21.10)$$

Slaking: $$CaO(s) + H_2O(l) \longrightarrow Ca(OH)_2(s) \qquad (21.11)$$

Carbonation: $$Ca(OH)_2(s) + CO_2(g) \xrightarrow{aq} CaCO_3(s) + H_2O(l) \qquad (21.12)$$

Limestone ($CaCO_3$) is also responsible for the beautiful natural formations found in limestone caves. Natural rainwater is slightly acidic due to dissolved $CO_2(g)$ and is essentially a solution of carbonic acid, H_2CO_3.

$$CO_2 + 2H_2O \rightleftharpoons H_3O^+ + HCO_3^- \qquad K_{a_1} = 4.4 \times 10^{-7} \qquad (21.13)$$

$$HCO_3^- + H_2O \rightleftharpoons H_3O^+ + CO_3^{2-} \qquad K_{a_2} = 4.7 \times 10^{-11} \qquad (21.14)$$

Although the carbonates are not very soluble in water, they are bases; thus, they dissolve readily in acidic solutions. As mildly acidic groundwater seeps through limestone beds, insoluble $CaCO_3$ is converted to soluble $Ca(HCO_3)_2$.

$$CaCO_3(s) + H_2O + CO_2 \rightleftharpoons Ca(HCO_3)_2(aq) \qquad K = 2.6 \times 10^{-5} \qquad (21.15)$$

Over time, this dissolving action can produce a large cavity in the limestone bed—a limestone cave. Reaction (21.15) is reversible, however, and evaporation of the solution causes a loss of both water and CO_2 and conversion of $Ca(HCO_3)_2(aq)$ back to $CaCO_3(s)$. This process occurs very slowly. Yet over a period of many years, as $Ca(HCO_3)_2(aq)$ drips from the ceiling of a cave, $CaCO_3(s)$ remains as icicle-like deposits called **stalactites**. Some of the dripping solution may hit the floor of the cave before decomposition occurs; in this way, limestone deposits build up from the floor in formations called **stalagmites**. Eventually, some stalactites and stalagmites grow together into limestone columns (Fig. 21-9).

A feature of the group 2 metal carbonates (MCO_3) that we have already noted for $CaCO_3(s)$ is their decomposition at high temperatures.

$$MCO_3(s) \xrightarrow{\Delta} MO(s) + CO_2(g) \qquad (21.16)$$

This is the chief method of preparing the group 2 metal oxides. The alkali metal carbonates, except Li_2CO_3, do not share this thermal instability. Thus, in the Solvay process (page 876), heating $NaHCO_3$ produces sodium carbonate, Na_2CO_3, but no further decomposition occurs.

▲ The decomposition (calcination) of limestone is carried out in a long rotary kiln, whether for the production of quicklime, CaO, or for the manufacture of Portland cement.

Moyer, Ralph O. "Synthesis and structure of magnesium oxide or calcium oxide. An integrated inorganic-physical experiment." *J. Chem. Educ.* **1975:** 52, 612.

 Stalactites hang from the **top**; stalagmites rise from the **ground**.

▲ FIGURE 21-9
Stalactites and stalagmites

▲ Plaster of Paris castings and the molds used to form them.

Lau, O., et al. "Determination of Free Lime in Clinker and Cement by Iodometry. An Undergraduate Experiment in Redox Titrimetry." *J. Chem. Educ.* **2001:** *78,* 1671.

Another important calcium-containing mineral is *gypsum*, $CaSO_4 \cdot 2\,H_2O$. In the United States, about 50 million tons of gypsum are consumed annually. About half of this is converted to the *hemihydrate* ($\frac{1}{2}$-hydrate), **plaster of Paris**.

$$CaSO_4 \cdot 2\,H_2O(s) \xrightarrow{\Delta} CaSO_4 \cdot \tfrac{1}{2}H_2O(s) + \tfrac{3}{2}H_2O(g) \qquad (21.17)$$

When mixed with water, plaster of Paris reverts to gypsum. Because it expands as it sets, a mixture of plaster of Paris and water is useful in making castings where sharp details of an object must be retained. Plaster of Paris is extensively used in jewelry making and in dental work. The most important application, though, is in producing gypsum wallboard (drywall), which has all but supplanted other interior wall coverings in the construction industry.

Barium sulfate has had important applications in medical imaging because barium is opaque to X rays. Although barium ion is toxic, the compound $BaSO_4$ is so insoluble as to be safe to use as a "barium milkshake" to coat the stomach or upper gastrointestinal tract or in a "barium enema" for the lower tract.

Oxides and Hydroxides.   All the oxides and hydroxides of the group 2 metals, except those of beryllium, are bases. Although it is not very soluble in water, calcium hydroxide is the cheapest commercial strong base. It is used in a variety of applications, such as the Solvay and Dow processes.

The term *lime* is familiar, but you may not be aware that it can refer to several compounds. CaO, called **quicklime**, is produced by the calcination of limestone (reaction 21.10). This reaction is reversible at room temperature; the reverse reaction occurs almost exclusively. So in the calcination of $CaCO_3$, a high temperature must be used and the $CO_2(g)$ produced must be continuously exhausted from the furnace (kiln) in which the reaction occurs. Among the many uses of quicklime are water treatment and the removal of $SO_2(g)$ from the smokestack gases in electric power plants.

$Ca(OH)_2$, called **slaked lime**, is formed by the action of water on CaO (reaction 21.11). A mixture of slaked lime, sand, and water is the familiar mortar used in bricklaying. First, excess water is absorbed by the bricks and then lost by evaporation. In the final setting of the mortar, $CO_2(g)$ from the air reacts with $Ca(OH)_2(s)$ and converts it back to $CaCO_3(s)$. The final form of the mortar is a complex mixture of hydrated calcium carbonate and silicate (from the sand).

$$Ca(OH)_2(s) + CO_2(g) \longrightarrow CaCO_3(s) + H_2O(g) \qquad (21.18)$$

This reaction is general for all group 2 hydroxides. Art conservators have used this reaction to preserve art objects. For example, an aqueous solution of $Ba(NO_3)_2$ is sprayed onto cracking frescos (paintings embedded in plaster). When the solution has had time to fill small cracks and spaces, an aqueous ammonia solution is applied to the surface of the fresco. The ammonia raises the pH of the solution, resulting in formation of $Ba(OH)_2$. As excess water evaporates, carbon dioxide from the air reacts with the barium hydroxide. Insoluble barium carbonate is produced, binding the cracking fresco together and strengthening it without affecting the delicate colors.

CONCEPT ASSESSMENT ✔

Suggest a reason why the hydrated beryllium ion is $[Be(H_2O)_4]^{2+}$, whereas the hydrated magnesium ion is $[Mg(H_2O)_6]^{2+}$.

21-3   IONS IN NATURAL WATERS: HARD WATER

Rainwater is not chemically pure. It contains dissolved atmospheric gases, and once it reaches the ground, some soluble components of soil and rocks are picked up. It may pick up anywhere from a few to perhaps 1000 ppm of dissolved substances. If the water contains ions capable of yielding significant quantities of a precipitate, it is said to be *hard*.

There are two types of hard water: temporary hard water and permanent hard water. **Temporary hard water** contains bicarbonate ion, HCO_3^-. When water containing $HCO_3^-(aq)$ is heated, the bicarbonate ion rapidly decomposes to give CO_3^{2-}, CO_2, and water. The CO_3^{2-} reacts with multivalent cations in the water, forming a mixed precipitate of $CaCO_3$, $MgCO_3$, and rust called *boiler scale*. The principal reaction that occurs is the reverse of reaction (21.15).

The formation of boiler scale can be a very serious problem in steam-driven electric power plants and in boilers producing steam for manufacturing processes. Formation of boiler scale lowers the efficiency of water heaters and can eventually cause a boiler to overheat or even to explode. Closer to home, a buildup of boiler scale can be observed on the inside of containers used for boiling water. Boiler scale can be removed by adding vinegar (acetic acid) to the container and heating.

Water with temporary hardness can be softened at a water treatment plant by adding slaked lime [$Ca(OH)_2$] and filtering off the precipitated metal carbonates. The OH^- reacts with bicarbonate ion to produce water and carbonate ion. The carbonate ion reacts with M^{2+} ion, such as Ca^{2+}, to precipitate a metal carbonate.

$$HCO_3^-(aq) + OH^-(aq) \longrightarrow H_2O(l) + CO_3^{2-}(aq)$$

$$CO_3^{2-}(aq) + M^{2+}(aq) \longrightarrow MCO_3(s)$$

Permanent hard water contains significant concentrations of anions other than HCO_3^-, such as SO_4^{2-}. Adding Na_2CO_3 (washing soda) softens permanent hard water by precipitating cations such as Ca^{2+} and Mg^{2+} as carbonates, leaving an aqueous solution with $Na^+(aq)$. One annoying effect of hard water is encountered in the bath or shower. Water containing Ca^{2+} or Mg^{2+} ions forms a precipitate with soap. This familiar bathtub ring is a mixture of insoluble calcium and magnesium soaps, such as magnesium palmitate [see equation (21.8) for the structure of sodium palmitate, a soluble soap]. Formation of these precipitates also makes it difficult for other soaps or shampoos to foam.

Ion Exchange. One of the best ways to soften water is through **ion exchange**, a process in which the undesirable ions in hard water, typically Ca^{2+}, Mg^{2+}, and Fe^{3+}, are exchanged for ions that are not objectionable, such as Na^+. Ion exchange occurs when the hard water is passed through a column (or bed) containing an ion-exchange material. This material can be either a natural porous sodium aluminosilicate polymer called a *zeolite* or a synthetic resinous material. These polymeric materials ionize to produce two types of ions: *fixed ions*, which remain attached to the polymer surface, and free, or mobile, *counterions*. The counterions are the ones that exchange places with the undesirable ions when a sample of hard water is passed through the resin or zeolite.

Figure 21-10 depicts a resin with negatively charged fixed ions R^- and positively charged counterions. Initially, the counterions in the resin bed are Na^+. When hard water is passed through the bed, the more highly charged Ca^{2+}, Mg^{2+}, and Fe^{3+} displace Na^+ as counterions. Concentrated $NaCl(aq)$ is used to regenerate ion-exchange resins. When present in high concentration, Na^+ can displace multivalent cations and restore an ion-exchange resin to its original condition. The ion-exchange material has an indefinite lifetime.

The only material consumed in water softening by ion exchange is the $NaCl$ required for regenerating the ion-exchange medium. This method of water softening does have the disadvantage that the treated water has a high concentration of Na^+ and would not be appropriate for drinking by a person on a low-sodium diet.

Ion exchange can be used to make *deionized water*, the familiar "DI" water found in chemistry laboratories. Deionized water is used in laboratories because ions present in ordinary tap water may interfere with chemical reactions (by forming precipitates or catalyzing reactions, for example). Deionized

▲ Thick deposits of lime scale on the interior of a household pipe.

▲ A sodium soap is added to soft (distilled) water (*left*) and hard water (*right*). The cloudiness in the beaker on the right is caused by the formation of an insoluble calcium soap by the Ca^{2+} ions in the hard water.

Ceretti, H., Hughes, E. A., Zalts, A. "The Softening of Hard Water and Complexometric Titrations. An Undergraduate Experiment." *J. Chem. Educ.* **1999**: *76*, 1420 (October 1999).

▶ FIGURE 21-10
Ion exchange
The resin shown here is a cation-exchange resin. Multivalent cations (green, Fe^{2+}; yellow, Ca^{2+}) replace Na^+ (orange) at the top of the resin column. By the time the water has reached the bottom of the column, all the multivalent ions have been removed and only Na^+ ions remain as counterions. The exchange can be represented as $2\,NaR + M^{2+} \rightleftharpoons MR_2 + 2\,Na^+$. The reaction occurs in the forward direction during water softening. As expected from Le Châtelier's principle, in the presence of concentrated $NaCl(aq)$, the reverse reaction is favored and the resin is recharged.

Mendes, A. "A Colorful Ion Exchange Experiment." *J. Chem. Educ.* **1999:** *76,* 1538.

Driscoll, J. A. "Visible Ion Exchange Demonstration for Large or Small Lecture Halls." *J. Chem. Educ.* **1996:** *73,* 639.

water is made by first replacing the cations in a water sample with H^+. Then the water is passed through a second ion-exchange column, which exchanges OH^- for all the *anions* present. The H^+ and OH^- combine to form H_2O, resulting in water that is essentially free of all ions.

EXAMPLE 21-2

Determining the Hardness of Water by Ion Exchange. A 25.00-mL sample of hard water is passed through an ion-exchange column in the acid form, HR. The water coming off the column requires 7.59 mL of 0.0133 M NaOH for its titration. What is the hardness of the water, expressed as parts per million of Ca^{2+}?

Solution

First, we assume that Ca^{2+} is the only cation present and that the ion-exchange reaction is

$$Ca^{2+} + 2\,HR \longrightarrow Ca_2R + 2\,H^+$$

Now we can use the titration data to determine the number of millimoles of H^+ that have been replaced by Ca^{2+}. The neutralization reaction is simply $H^+ + OH^- \longrightarrow H_2O$.

$$? \text{ mmol } H^+ = 7.59 \text{ mL} \times \frac{0.0133 \text{ mmol NaOH}}{1 \text{ mL}} \times \frac{1 \text{ mmol } OH^-}{1 \text{ mmol NaOH}} \times \frac{1 \text{ mmol } H^+}{1 \text{ mmol } OH^-}$$

$$= 0.101 \text{ mmol } H^+$$

Next, we can determine the mass of Ca^{2+} present in the 25.00 mL of water. In this conversion, we use the fact that *two* H^+ ions are released into the water for every Ca^{2+} ion retained on the ion-exchange resin.

$$? \text{ mg } Ca^{2+} = 0.101 \text{ mmol } H^+ \times \frac{1 \text{ mmol } Ca^{2+}}{2 \text{ mmol } H^+} \times \frac{40.08 \text{ mg } Ca^{2+}}{1 \text{ mmol } Ca^{2+}} = 2.02 \text{ mg } Ca^{2+}$$

The mass of 25.00 mL of the hard water is 25.0 g, or 25×10^3 mg. The number of milligrams of Ca^{2+} present in 1.00×10^6 mg H_2O is the concentration of Ca^{2+} in parts per million.

$$\text{ppm } Ca^{2+} = 1.00 \times 10^6 \text{ mg } H_2O \times \frac{2.02 \text{ mg } Ca^{2+}}{25,000 \text{ mg } H_2O} = 80.8$$

A list of minerals containing group 13 metals is in House, J. E., House, K. A., *Descriptive Inorganic Chemistry*, Harcourt Academic Press, (2001), p. 190.

Practice Example A: What was the pH of the 25.00-mL sample of water in Example 21-2 as it came off the ion-exchange column and *before* it was titrated with NaOH(aq)?

Practice Example B: A sample of water whose hardness is 185 ppm Ca^{2+} is passed through a cation-exchange resin, and the Ca^{2+} is replaced by Na^+. What is $[Na^+]$ in that water sample?

21-4 GROUP 13: THE BORON FAMILY

The only group 13 element that is almost exclusively nonmetallic in its physical and chemical properties is boron. The remaining members of group 13—Al, Ga, In, and Tl—are metals and will be discussed later in this section.

BORON AND ITS COMPOUNDS

Many boron compounds lack an octet of electrons about the central boron atom, which makes the compounds *electron-deficient*. This deficiency also makes them strong Lewis acids. The electron deficiency of some boron compounds leads to bonding of a type that we have not previously encountered. This type of bonding occurs in the boron hydrides.

Straub, Darel K. "Lewis Structures of Boron Compounds Involving Multiple Bonding." *J. Chem. Educ.* **1995**: 72, 494.

Boron Hydrides. The molecule BH_3 (borane) may exist as a reaction intermediate, but it has not been isolated as a stable compound. The B atom in BH_3 lacks a complete octet—it has only six electrons in its valence shell. The simplest boron hydride that has been isolated is diborane, B_2H_6, but this molecule defies simple description. In the following structural formula, what holds the two borane units together?

$$
\begin{array}{cc}
H & H \\
| & | \\
H{-}B & ? \quad B{-}H \\
| & | \\
H & H \\
\end{array}
$$

(a)

To explain the structure and bonding in B_2H_6, we need new ideas in bonding theory, particularly molecular orbital theory. The problem is this: The B_2H_6 molecule has only *12* valence electrons (three each from the two B atoms, and one each from the six H atoms). The minimum number of valence-shell atomic orbitals required to make a Lewis structure for B_2H_6 resembling that of C_2H_6, however, is *14* (four each from the two B atoms, and one each from the six H atoms).

The currently accepted structure of diborane is illustrated in Figure 21-11. The two B atoms and four of the H atoms lie in the same plane (a plane perpendicular to the plane of the page). The orbitals used by the B atoms to bond these particular four H atoms can be viewed as sp^3. Eight electrons are involved in these four bonds. Four electrons are left to bond the two remaining H atoms to the two B atoms and also to bond the B atoms together. This is accomplished if each of the two H atoms simultaneously bonds to *both* B atoms.

Atom "bridges" are actually fairly common, although we have not had much occasion to deal with them before (see the discussion of Al_2Cl_6, page 893). The B—H—B bridges are unusual, however, in having only *two* electrons shared among *three* atoms. For this reason, these bonds are referred to as *three-center* two-electron bonds.

(b)

(c)

▲ **FIGURE 21-11**
Structure of diborane, B_2H_6
(a) The molecular structure.
(b) Bonding.
(c) Electrostatic potential map.

▲ **FIGURE 21-12**
Structure of pentaborane,
B_5H_9
The boron atoms are joined
by multicenter B—B—B
bonds. Five of the H atoms
are bonded to one B atom
each. The other four H atoms
bridge pairs of B atoms.

▲ Perborate ion

Grimes, R. N. "Boron
Clusters Come of Age."
J. Chem. Educ. **2004:** *81,* 657.

We can rationalize the bonding in these three-center bonds with molecular orbital theory. *Six* atomic orbitals—an sp^3 and p orbital from each B atom and an s orbital from each H atom—are combined into *six* molecular orbitals in these two bridge bonds. Of these six molecular orbitals, *two* are bonding orbitals, and these are the orbitals into which the four electrons are placed. The concept of bridge bonds can be extended to B—B—B bonds to describe the structure of higher boranes, such as B_5H_9 (Fig. 21-12).

Boron hydrides are widely used in reactions for synthesizing organic compounds. They continue to provide new and exciting developments in chemistry.

Other Boron Compounds.   Boron compounds are widely distributed in Earth's crust, but concentrated ores are found in only a few locations—in Italy, Russia, Tibet, Turkey, and the desert regions of California. Typical of these ores is the hydrated borate *borax,* $Na_2B_4O_7 \cdot 10\,H_2O$. Figure 21-13 suggests how borax can be converted to a variety of boron compounds.

One useful compound that can be obtained by crystallization from a solution of borax and hydrogen peroxide is *sodium perborate,* $NaBO_3 \cdot 4\,H_2O$. This formula is deceptively simple; a more precise formula is $Na_2[B_2(O_2)_2(OH)_4] \cdot 6\,H_2O$. Sodium perborate is the bleach alternative used in many color-safe bleaches. The key to the bleaching action is the presence of the two peroxo groups (—O—O—) bridging the boron atoms in the $[B_2(O_2)_2(OH)_4]^{2-}$ ion.

One of the key compounds from which other boron compounds can be synthesized is *boric acid,* $B(OH)_3$. The weakly acidic nature of boric acid comes about in a rather unusual way: The electron-deficient $B(OH)_3$ accepts a OH^- ion from the self-ionization of water, forming the complex ion $[B(OH)_4]^-$. Thus, the source of the H_3O^+ in $B(OH)_3(aq)$ is the water itself. This ionization scheme, together with the fact that $B(OH)_3$ is a *mono*protic, not *tri*protic, acid suggests that the best formula of boric acid is $B(OH)_3$, not H_3BO_3.

$$B(OH)_3(aq) + 2\,H_2O(l) \longrightarrow H_3O^+(aq) + B(OH)_4^-(aq) \qquad K_a = 5.6 \times 10^{+10}$$

Borate salts, as expected of the salts of a weak acid, produce basic solutions by hydrolysis, which accounts for their use in cleaning agents. Boric acid also acts as an insecticide, particularly to kill roaches, and as an antiseptic in eyewash solutions. Boron compounds are used in products as varied as adhesives, cement, disinfectants, fertilizers, fire retardants, glass, herbicides, metallurgical fluxes, and textile bleaches and dyes.

CONCEPT ASSESSMENT ✓

Boron forms a compound with the formula $B_2H_2(CH_3)_4$. Suggest a probable structure for this compound.

▶ **FIGURE 21-13**
Preparation of some boron compounds
$Na_2B_4O_7 \cdot 10\,H_2O$ (borax) is converted to
$B(OH)_3$ by reaction with H_2SO_4. When heated
strongly, $B(OH)_3$ is converted to B_2O_3. A
variety of boron-containing compounds and
boron itself can be prepared from B_2O_3.

EXAMPLE 21-3

Writing Chemical Equations from a Summary Diagram of Reaction Chemistry. Using Figure 21-13, write chemical equations for the successive conversions of borax to **(a)** boric acid, **(b)** B_2O_3, and **(c)** impure boron metal.

Solution

Figure 21-13 lists the key substances involved in each reaction. We must identify other plausible reactants and products.

(a) Conversion of a salt to the corresponding acid is an acid–base reaction and does not involve changes in oxidation states. Balancing should be possible by inspection. The additional substances required in the equation are Na_2SO_4 and H_2O.

$$Na_2B_4O_7 \cdot 10\,H_2O + H_2SO_4 \longrightarrow 4\,B(OH)_3 + Na_2SO_4 + 5\,H_2O$$

(b) Conversion of a hydroxo compound to an oxide requires that H_2O be driven off.

$$2\,B(OH)_3 \xrightarrow{\Delta} B_2O_3 + 3\,H_2O$$

(c) The direct reduction of B_2O_3 with Mg produces impure boron.

$$3\,Mg + B_2O_3 \xrightarrow{\Delta} 2\,B + 3\,MgO$$

Practice Example A: Using Figure 21-13, write chemical equations for the sequence of reactions by which borax is converted to diborane.

Practice Example B: Using Figure 21-13 write chemical equations for the sequence of reactions by which borax is converted to BF_3.

PROPERTIES AND USES OF GROUP 13 METALS

In their appearance and physical properties and in most of their chemical behaviors, aluminum, gallium, indium, and thallium are metallic. Some properties of the group 13 metals are listed in Table 21.5.

Formation of Aluminum Bromide movie

The most important of the group 13 metals is aluminum, which is used mainly in lightweight alloys. Aluminum, like most of the other main-group metals, is an active metal. Because it is easily oxidized to the 3+ ion, aluminum is an excellent reducing agent—for example, reacting with acids to reduce $H^+(aq)$ to $H_2(g)$.

$$2\,Al(s) + 6\,H^+(aq) \longrightarrow 2\,Al^{3+}(aq) + 3\,H_2(g) \tag{21.19}$$

TABLE 21.5   Some Properties of the Group 13 Metals

	Al	Ga	In	Tl
Atomic number	13	31	49	81
Atomic (metallic) radius, pm	143	122	163	170
Ionic (M^{3+}) radius, pm	53	62	79	88
Electronegativity	1.5	1.6	1.7	1.8
First ionization energy, kJ mol^{-1}	577.6	578.8	558.3	589.3
Electrode potential $E°$, V[a]	−1.676	−0.56	−0.34	+0.72
Melting point, °C	660.37	29.78	156.17	303.55
Boiling point, °C	2467	2403	2080	1457
Density, g/cm^3 at 20 °C	2.698	5.907	7.310	11.85
Hardness[b]	2.75	1.5	1.2	1.25
Electrical conductivity[b]	59.7	9.1	19.0	8.82

[a]For the reduction $M^{3+}(aq) + 3\,e^- \longrightarrow M(s)$.
[b]See footnotes b and c of Table 21.2.

Koubek, E. "Acid-Base Chemistry of the Aluminum Ion in Aqueous Solution." *J. Chem. Educ.* **1998**: *75*, 60.

Laing, Michael. "A WARNING: Explosion Hazards of Reacting Magnesium and Aluminum with Powdered Silver Nitrate (LTE)." *J. Chem. Educ.* **1994**: *71*, 270.

Arnáiz, F. J., et al. "Microscale Thermite Reactions." *J. Chem. Educ.* **1998**: *75*, 1630.

▶ Certain drain cleaners are a mixture of NaOH and Al(s). When they are added to water, reaction (21.20) occurs. The evolved $H_2(g)$ helps unplug a stopped-up drain. The heat of reaction melts fats and grease, and the NaOH(aq) solubilizes them.

▲ Thermite reaction.

Thermite movie

▶ As discussed on page 991, a superconducting material loses its electrical resistance below a certain temperature. Metals typically become superconducting only a few degrees above 0 K.

Are You Wondering . . .

If aluminum reacts with and dissolves in both acidic and basic solutions, why does it not also dissolve in pH-neutral water?

Metallic aluminum reacts rapidly with the oxygen in air to give a thin, tough, water-insoluble coating of Al_2O_3. This oxide layer protects the metal beneath it from further reaction. In either acidic or basic solution, but not in pH-neutral water, the Al_2O_3 layer reacts and dissolves.

$$Al_2O_3(s) + 6\,H^+(aq) \longrightarrow 2\,Al^{3+}(aq) + 3\,H_2O(l)$$

$$Al_2O_3(s) + 2\,OH^-(aq) + 3\,H_2O(l) \longrightarrow 2[Al(OH)_4]^-(aq)$$

Once the Al_2O_3 layer has been removed, the underlying metal displays its true reactivity: Aluminum is a sufficiently active metal to displace $H_2(g)$ from pure water. We could never use aluminum metal in aircraft and building construction were it not for the protection of the Al_2O_3 surface coating.

Aluminum is unusual in that it also reacts with basic solutions. This behavior is due to the acid properties of $Al(OH)_3$, a topic discussed further on page 894.

$$2\,Al(s) + 2\,OH^-(aq) + 6\,H_2O(l) \longrightarrow 2[Al(OH)_4]^-(aq) + 3\,H_2(g) \quad (21.20)$$

Air or other oxidants easily oxidize powdered aluminum in highly exothermic reactions that are used in some rocket fuels and explosives.

$$2\,Al(s) + \tfrac{3}{2}O_2(g) \longrightarrow Al_2O_3(s) \qquad \Delta H = -1676\text{ kJ} \quad (21.21)$$

Aluminum is such a good reducing agent that it will extract oxygen from metal oxides, producing aluminum oxide while liberating the other metal in its free state. This reaction, known as the **thermite reaction**, is used in the on-site welding of large metal objects.

$$Fe_2O_3(s) + 2\,Al(s) \longrightarrow Al_2O_3(s) + 2\,Fe(l) \quad (21.22)$$

Gallium metal is of great importance in the electronics industry. It is used to make gallium arsenide (GaAs), a compound that can convert light directly into electricity (photoconduction). This semiconducting material is also used in light-emitting diodes (LEDs; page 908) and in solid-state devices such as transistors.

Indium is a soft silvery metal used to make low-melting alloys. Like GaAs, InAs also finds use in low-temperature transistors and as a photoconductor in optical devices.

Thallium and its compounds are extremely toxic; as a result, they have few industrial uses. One possible use, however, is in high-temperature superconductors. For example, a thallium-based ceramic with the approximate formula $Tl_2Ba_2Ca_2Cu_3O_{8+x}$ exhibits superconductivity at temperatures as high as 125 K.

OXIDATION STATES OF GROUP 13 METALS

Aluminum, at the top of the group of four metals in group 13, occurs almost exclusively in the +3 oxidation state in its compounds. Gallium also favors the +3 oxidation state. Indium compounds can be found with +3 and +1 oxidation states, though the +3 is more common. In thallium, this preference is reversed. For example, thallium forms the oxide Tl_2O, the hydroxide TlOH, and the carbonate Tl_2CO_3. These compounds are ionic and in some respects resemble group 1 compounds. Thus, TlOH is both very soluble and a strong base in aqueous solution. The higher stability of the +1 over the +3 oxidation state of thallium is often described as the **inert pair effect**. Thallium has the electron configuration $[Xe]4f^{14}5d^{10}6s^26p^1$. In forming the Tl^+ ion, a Tl atom loses the $6p$ electron and retains two electrons in its $6s$ subshell. It is this pair of electrons—$6s^2$—that is called the inert pair. The electron configuration $(n-1)s^2(n-1)p^6(n-1)d^{10}ns^2$ is commonly encountered in ions of the post-transition elements. One explanation of the inert pair effect is that the small bond energies and lattice energies associated with the large atoms and ions at the bottom of a group are not sufficiently great to offset the ionization energies of the ns^2 electrons.

ALUMINUM

Aluminum is the third most abundant element and comprises 8.3% by mass of Earth's solid crust. On average, more than 5 million tons of aluminum are produced per year in the United States.

Production of Aluminum.   When an aluminum cap was placed atop the Washington Monument in 1884, aluminum was still a semiprecious metal. At that time it cost $1 per ounce to produce, equivalent to the daily wage of a skilled laborer working a 10-hr day. As a result, aluminum was used mainly in jewelry and artwork. But just two years later, all this changed. In 1886, Charles Martin Hall in the United States and Paul Héroult in France independently discovered an economically feasible method of producing aluminum from Al_2O_3 by electrolysis.

The manufacture of Al involves several interesting principles. The chief ore, *bauxite*, contains Fe_2O_3 as an impurity that must be removed. The principle used in the separation is that Al_2O_3 is an *amphoteric* oxide and dissolves in NaOH(aq), whereas the iron oxide is a *basic* oxide and does not (Fig. 21-14).

$$Al_2O_3(s) + 2\,OH^-(aq) + 3\,H_2O(l) \longrightarrow 2[Al(OH)_4]^-(aq)$$

When the solution containing $[Al(OH)_4]^-$ is slightly acidified, $Al(OH)_3(s)$ precipitates. Pure Al_2O_3 is obtained by heating the $Al(OH)_3$.

$$[Al(OH)_4]^-(aq) + H_3O^+(aq) \longrightarrow Al(OH)_3(s) + 2\,H_2O$$

$$2\,Al(OH)_3(s) \xrightarrow{\Delta} Al_2O_3(s) + 3\,H_2O(g)$$

◀ Stimulated by a remark by one of his professors, Charles Martin Hall invented the electrolytic process for the production of aluminum at the age of 23, eight months after his graduation from Oberlin College. Paul Héroult, a student of Le Châtelier, and also at the age of 23, invented the identical process in the same year.

(a)

(b)

(c)

▲ **FIGURE 21-14**
Purifying bauxite
(a) When an excess of $OH^-(aq)$ is added to a solution containing $Al^{3+}(aq)$ and $Fe^{3+}(aq)$, the Fe^{3+} precipitates as $Fe(OH)_3(s)$ and the $Al(OH)_3(s)$ first formed redissolves to produce $[Al(OH)_4]^-(aq)$. **(b)** The $Fe(OH)_3(s)$ is filtered off, and the $[Al(OH)_4]^-(aq)$ is made slightly acidic through the action of CO_2, here added as dry ice. **(c)** The precipitated $Al(OH)_3(s)$ collects at the bottom of a clear, colorless solution.

Aluminum production website: http://www.tms.org/pubs/journals/JOM/9905/Welch-9905. html (non-commercial)

Aluminum production consumes a significant proportion of the electricity that is produced. It is economical to locate the smelters close to a source of inexpensive hydroelectricity, like at Kitimat, B.C. (near the Alaska Panhandle) even though these are often remote locations.

▲ FIGURE 21-15
Electrolysis cell for aluminum production
The cathode is a carbon lining in a steel tank. The anodes are also made of carbon. Liquid aluminum is denser than the electrolyte medium and collects at the bottom of the tank.

Al_2O_3 has a very high melting point (2020 °C) and produces a liquid that is a poor electrical conductor. Thus, its electrolysis is not feasible without a better conducting solvent. That was the crux of the discovery by Hall and Héroult. They found, independently, that up to 15% Al_2O_3, by mass, can be dissolved in the molten mineral *cryolite*, Na_3AlF_6, at about 1000 °C. The liquid is a good electrical conductor, so the electrolysis of Al_2O_3 is accomplished in molten cryolite. A typical electrolysis cell, pictured in Figure 21-15, produces aluminum of 99.6–99.8% purity.

The electrode reactions are not known with certainty, but the overall electrolysis reaction is

Oxidation:	$3\{C(s) + 2O^{2-} \longrightarrow CO_2(g) + 4e^-\}$	
Reduction:	$4\{Al^{3+} + 3e^- \longrightarrow Al(l)\}$	
Overall:	$3C(s) + 4Al^{3+} + 6O^{2-} \longrightarrow 4Al(l) + 3CO_2(g)$	(21.23)

The energy consumed to produce aluminum by electrolysis is very high, about 15,000 kWh/ton Al [compared, for example, with 3000 kWh per ton of Cl_2 in the electrolysis of NaCl(aq)]. This means that aluminum production facilities are generally located near low-cost power sources, typically hydroelectric power. The energy required to recycle Al is only about 5% of that to produce the metal from bauxite, and currently about 45% of the Al produced in the United States is by the recycling of scrap aluminum.

Aluminum Halides. Aluminum fluoride, AlF_3, has considerable ionic character. It has a high melting point (1040 °C) and when molten is a conductor of electric current. In contrast, the other aluminum halides exist as *molecular* species with the formula Al_2X_6 (for which X = Cl, Br, or I). We can think of this molecule as comprising two AlX_3 units. When two identical units combine, the resulting molecule is called a **dimer**. The dimeric structure of Al_2Cl_6 consists of two Cl atoms bonded exclusively to each Al atom and two Cl atoms bridging the two metal atoms (Fig. 21-16). Bonding in this molecule can be described by sp^3 hybridization of the two Al atoms. Each bridging Cl atom appears to bond

Are You Wondering . . .

Why so much energy is consumed in the electrolytic production of aluminum?

Any process that must be carried out at a high temperature requires large amounts of energy for heating. In the electrolytic production of Al, the electrolysis bath must be kept at about 1000 °C, which is done by means of electric heating. Two other factors, however, are also involved in the large energy consumption. First, to produce one mole of Al, *three* moles of electrons must be transferred: $Al^{3+} + 3\,e^- \longrightarrow Al(l)$. Additionally, the molar mass of Al is relatively low, 27 g mol^{-1}. The electric current equivalent to the passage of one mole of electrons produces only 9 g Al. In contrast, one mole of electrons produces 12 g Mg, 20 g Ca, or 108 g Ag. Yet the same factors that make Al production a significant energy consumer make Al an outstanding energy producer when it is used in a battery. (Recall the aluminum–air battery described on page 846.)

to two Al atoms in two ways. The bond to one Al atom is a conventional covalent bond: Each atom contributes one electron to the bond. The bond to a second Al atom is a coordinate covalent bond, where the chlorine atom provides the pair of electrons for the bond, noted by arrows in Figure 21-16.

The aluminum halides are very reactive Lewis acids. They easily accept a pair of electrons, forming an acid–base compound called an **adduct**. Adduct formation results in the formation of a covalent bond between the Lewis acid and Lewis base. In the following reaction, $AlCl_3$ is the Lewis acid and diethyl ether, $(C_2H_5)_2O$, is the Lewis base.

Aluminum halides are used in a number of organic reactions in which, by means of adduct formation, they act as catalysts.

The hydride ion, H^-, can be thought of as similar to a halide ion, and the AlH_4^- ion as an adduct of AlH_3 and H^-. Lithium aluminum hydride, $LiAlH_4$, is an important reducing agent in organic chemistry.

Another important halide *complex* of aluminum is *cryolite*, Na_3AlF_6. Cryolite exists as $3\,Na^+ + AlF_6^{3-}$. In the molten state, it is the solvent and electrolyte in the Hall–Héroult process for producing aluminum metal. For aluminum manufacturing, natural cryolite has largely been displaced by cryolite synthesized in lead-clad vessels by the reaction

$$6\,HF + Al(OH)_3 + 3\,NaOH \longrightarrow Na_3AlF_6 + 6\,H_2O \qquad (21.24)$$

Bonding scheme   Electrostatic potential map

▲ **FIGURE 21-16**
Bonding in Al$_2$Cl$_6$
Two Cl atoms bridge the $AlCl_3$ units and produce the dimer Al_2Cl_6. Electrons donated by these Cl atoms to Al atoms are indicated by arrows.

Aluminum Oxide and Hydroxide. Aluminum oxide has several common names. It is often referred to as *alumina*; when in crystalline form, it is called *corundum*. Corundum, when pure, is also known as the gemstone *white sapphire*. Certain other gemstones consist of corundum with small amounts of transition metal ions as impurities: Cr^{3+} in ruby and Fe^{3+} and Ti^{4+} in blue sapphire, for example. Artificial gemstones are made by fusing corundum with carefully controlled amounts of other oxides.

▶ The origin of colors in gemstones is discussed on page 1032.

The bonding and crystal structure of alumina account for its physical properties. The small Al^{3+} ion and small O^{2-} ion make a strong ionic bond. The crystal has a cubic closest packed structure of O^{2-} ions, with Al^{3+} ions filling the octahedral holes. Because of this structure, alumina is a very hard material and is often used as an abrasive. It is also resistant to heat (mp 2020 °C) and is used in linings for high-temperature furnaces and as catalyst supports in industrial chemical processes. Aluminum oxide is relatively unreactive except at very high temperatures. Its stability at high temperatures classifies it as a *refractory* material.

As mentioned previously, aluminum is protected against reaction with water in the pH range 4.5–8.5 by a thin, impervious coating of Al_2O_3. This coating can be purposely thickened to enhance the corrosion resistance of the metal by a process known as *anodizing*. An aluminum object is used for the anode and a graphite electrode is used for the cathode in an electrolyte bath of $H_2SO_4(aq)$. The half-reaction occurring at the anode during electrolysis is

$$2\,Al(s) + 3\,H_2O(l) \longrightarrow Al_2O_3(s) + 6\,H^+(aq) + 6\,e^-$$

Al_2O_3 coatings of varying porosity and thickness can be obtained. Also, the oxide can be made to absorb pigments or other additives. Anodized aluminum is commonly used in architectural components of buildings, such as bronze or black window frames.

▲ Drinking cups made of anodized aluminum.

Aluminum hydroxide is *amphoteric*. It reacts with acids in a manner typical of metal hydroxides.

$$Al(OH)_3(s) + 3\,H_3O^+(aq) \longrightarrow [Al(H_2O)_6]^{3+}(aq) \tag{21.25}$$

Also, it reacts with bases in a reaction best represented as the formation of a hydroxo complex ion.

$$Al(OH)_3(s) + OH^-(aq) \longrightarrow [Al(OH)_4]^-(aq) \tag{21.26}$$

Poskozim, Paul S. "Multiply Bonded Main Group Metals and Metalloids (edited by Robert West and F. Gordon A. Stone)." *J. Chem. Educ.* **1998:** *75,* 698 (June 1998).

▶ A disadvantage of the use of aluminum sulfate in sizing paper is that its acidic character contributes to deterioration of the paper. In contrast, calcium carbonate maintains an alkaline medium in paper (page 883).

Aluminum Sulfate and Alums. Aluminum sulfate is the most important commercial aluminum compound. It is prepared by the reaction of hot concentrated $H_2SO_4(aq)$ on $Al_2O_3(s)$. The product that crystallizes from solution is $Al_2(SO_4)_3 \cdot 18\,H_2O$. Over 1 million tons of aluminum sulfate are produced annually in the United States, about half of which is used in water purification. In this application, the pH of the water is adjusted so that $Al(OH)_3(s)$ precipitates when aluminum sulfate is added. As the $Al(OH)_3(s)$ settles, it removes suspended solids in the water. Another important use is in the sizing of paper. *Sizing* refers to incorporating materials such as waxes, glues, or synthetic resins into paper to make the paper more water resistant. $Al(OH)_3$ precipitated from $Al_2(SO_4)_3(aq)$ helps deposit the sizing agent in the paper.

▶ Alum crystals.

When an aqueous solution of equimolar amounts of $Al_2(SO_4)_3$ and K_2SO_4 is allowed to crystallize, the crystals obtained are of potassium aluminum sulfate, $KAl(SO_4)_2 \cdot 12 H_2O$. This is just one of a large class of double salts called alums. **Alums** have the formula $M(I)M(III)(SO_4)_2 \cdot 12 H_2O$, where M(I) is a unipositive cation (other than Li^+) and M(III) is a tripositive cation—$Al^{3+}, Ga^{3+}, In^{3+}, Ti^{3+}, V^{3+}, Cr^{3+}, Mn^{3+}, Fe^{3+}, Co^{3+}, Re^{3+}$, or Ir^{3+}. The actual ions present in the alums are $[M(H_2O)_6]^+$, $[M(H_2O)_6]^{3+}$, and SO_4^{2-}. The most common alums have $M(I) = K^+, Na^+$, or NH_4^+ and $M(III) = Al^{3+}$. Li^+ does not form alums because the ion is too small to meet the crystal structure requirements. Sodium aluminum sulfate is the leavening acid in baking powders, and potassium aluminum sulfate is used in dyeing. The fabric to be dyed is dipped into a solution of the alum and heated in steam. Hydrolysis of $[Al(H_2O)_6]^{3+}$ deposits $Al(OH)_3$ into the fibers of the material, and the dye is adsorbed on the $Al(OH)_3$.

◀ In the industrial world, *alum* usually refers to simple aluminum sulfate; terms such as *potash* (potassium) *alum* and *ammonium alum* designate the double salts.

CONCEPT ASSESSMENT ✓

AlF_3 is almost insoluble in anhydrous HF, but it dissolves if KF is present. Passage of BF_3 through the resulting solution causes AlF_3 to precipitate. How can you explain these observations?

21-5   GROUP 14: THE CARBON FAMILY

The properties of the group 14 elements vary dramatically within the group. Tin and lead, at the bottom of the group, have mainly metallic properties. Germanium, sometimes referred to as a *metalloid* (or *semi-metal*), exhibits semiconductor behavior. Silicon, although also exhibiting semiconductor properties, is mostly nonmetallic in its chemical behavior but is sometimes classified as a metalloid. Carbon, the first member of group 14, is a nonmetal. We will first discuss carbon and silicon and then tin and lead; germanium is mentioned only briefly.

The essential differences between carbon and silicon, as outlined in Table 21.6, are perhaps the most striking between any second- and third-period elements within a group in the periodic table. As suggested by the approximate

TABLE 21.6   Comparison of Carbon and Silicon

Carbon	Silicon
Two principal allotropes: graphite and diamond	One stable, diamond-type crystalline modification
Forms two stable *gaseous* oxides, CO and CO_2, and several less stable ones, such as C_3O_2	Forms only one *solid* oxide (SiO_2) that is stable at room temperature; a second oxide (SiO) is stable only in the temperature range 1180–2480 °C
Insoluble in alkaline media	Reacts in alkaline media, forming $H_2(g)$ and $SiO_4^{4-}(aq)$
Principal oxoanion is CO_3^{2-}, which has a trigonal-planar shape	Principal oxoanion is SiO_4^{2-}, which has a tetrahedral shape
Strong tendency for catenation,[a] with straight and branched chains and rings containing up to hundreds of C atoms	Less tendency for catenation,[a] with silicon atom chains limited to about six Si atoms
Readily forms multiple bonds through use of the orbital sets $sp^2 + p$ and $sp + p^2$	Multiple bond formation much less common than with carbon
Approximate single-bond energies, kJ mol^{-1}: C—C, 347 C—H, 414 C—O, 360	Approximate single-bond energies, kJ mol^{-1}: Si—Si, 226 Si—H, 318 Si—O, 464

[a]Catenation is the joining together of like atoms into chains.

▲ Fabric for use in composite materials woven from carbon fibers.

 Pisanty, Alejandro. "The electronic structure of graphite: A chemist's introduction to band theory." *J. Chem. Educ.* **1991:** *68,* 804.

Website on allotropes of carbon: http://cnst.rice.edu/pics.html (non-commercial)

 Allotropes of Carbon: Graphite, Diamond and Fullerene models

▶ Because of their expected future importance, diamond films were named "Molecule of the Year" by the journal *Science* in 1990. In 1991, the fullerenes earned that honor.

bond energies, strong C—C and C—H bonds account for the central role of carbon-atom chains and rings in establishing the chemical behavior of carbon. A study of these chains and rings and their attached atoms is the focus of organic chemistry (Chapter 26) and biochemistry (Chapter 27). The weaker Si—Si and Si—H bonds imply a less important "organic chemistry" of silicon, and the strength of the Si—O bond accounts for the predominance of the silicates and related compounds among silicon compounds.

CARBON

Carbon is so much the central element to the study of organic and biochemistry that the rich and important inorganic chemistry of carbon is sometimes overlooked. It is the "inorganic" aspects of the chemistry of carbon that we emphasize in this section.

Production and Uses of Carbon. Graphite is a form of carbon that is widely distributed in Earth's crust, some of it in deposits rich enough for commercial exploitation. The bulk of industrial graphite, however, is synthesized from carbon-containing materials, such as coke. The key requirement is to heat the high-carbon-content material to a temperature of about 3000 °C in an electric furnace. In this process, the carbon atoms fuse into larger and larger ring systems, leading ultimately to the graphite structure that we studied in Chapter 12 (Fig. 12-33).

Graphite has excellent lubricating properties, even when dry. That is because the planes of carbon atoms are held together by relatively weak forces and can easily slip past one another. This property is handy in pencil "lead," actually a thin rod made from a mixture of graphite and clay that glides easily on paper. Graphite's principal use is based on its ability to conduct electric current; it is used for electrodes in batteries and industrial electrolysis. Graphite's use in foundry molds, furnaces, and other high-temperature environments is based on its ability to withstand high temperatures.

A newly developed use of graphite is in the manufacture of strong, lightweight composites consisting of graphite fibers and various plastics. These composites are used in products ranging from tennis rackets to lightweight aircraft. When carbon-based fibers, such as rayon, are carefully heated to a very high temperature, all volatile matter is driven off, leaving a carbon residue with the graphite structure.

As indicated in the phase diagram for carbon in Figure 21-17, graphite is the more stable form of carbon, not only at room temperature and pressure but at temperatures up to 3000 °C and pressures of 10^4 atm and higher. Diamond is the more stable form of carbon at very high pressures. Diamonds can be synthesized from graphite by heating the graphite to temperatures of 1000–2000 °C and subjecting it to pressures of 10^5 atm or more. Usually the graphite is mixed with a metal such as iron. The metal melts, and the graphite is converted to diamond within the liquid metal. Diamonds can then be picked out of the solidified metal.

According to Figure 21-17, we might expect diamond to revert to graphite at room temperature and pressure. Fortunately for the jewelry industry and for those who treasure diamonds as gems, many phase changes that require a rearrangement in bond type and crystal structure occur extremely slowly. That is very much the case with the diamond–graphite transition.

Most diamonds that are used as gemstones are natural diamonds. For industrial purposes, inferior specimens of natural diamonds or, increasingly, synthetic diamonds are used. The industrial use depends on two key properties. Diamonds are used as abrasives because they are extremely hard (10 on the Mohs hardness scale). No harder substance is known. Diamonds also have a high thermal conductivity (they dissipate heat quickly), so they are used in

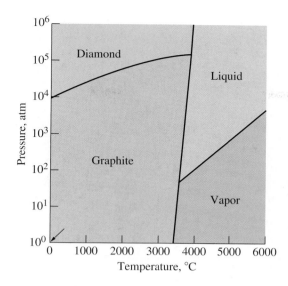

◀ **FIGURE 21-17**
Simplified phase diagram for carbon
So that the vast range of pressures
required (from 1 to 1,000,000 atm) can
be indicated, pressure is plotted on a
logarithmic scale. The arrow marks the
point 1 atm, 25 °C.

drill bits for cutting steel and other hard materials. The rapid dissipation of heat makes the drilling process faster and increases the lifetime of the bit. A recent development has been the creation of diamond films, that can be deposited directly onto metals, which imparts some of the properties of diamond to the metal, for example, high thermal conductivity for use in heat sinks for computer chips.

Carbon can be obtained in several other forms of mixed crystalline or amorphous structure. Incomplete combustion of natural gas, such as in an improperly adjusted Bunsen burner in the laboratory, produces a smoky flame. This smoke can be deposited as finely divided soot called **carbon black**. Carbon black is used as filler in rubber tires (several kilograms per tire), as a pigment in printing inks, and as the transfer material in carbon paper, typewriter ribbons, laser printers, and photocopying machines. Recently, new allotropes of carbon have been isolated from the decomposition of graphite. These allotropes, known as fullerenes and nanotubes, were presented in Chapter 12 (page 499). Recall that the molecule C_{60} is remarkably stable and has a shape resembling a soccer ball (12 pentagonal faces, 20 hexagonal faces, and 60 vertices). Other fullerenes include C_{70}, C_{74}, and C_{82}. Fullerenes are typically produced by laser decomposition of graphite under a helium atmosphere. Because nitrogen and oxygen interfere with the process of forming fullerenes, soot (by the combustion of hydrocarbons in air) does not contain fullerenes.

Two other noteworthy carbon-containing materials are coke and charcoal. When coal is heated in the absence of air, volatile substances are driven off, leaving a high-carbon residue called *coke*. This same type of destructive distillation of wood produces *charcoal*. Currently, coke is the principal metallurgical reducing agent. It is used in blast furnaces, for instance, to reduce iron oxide to iron metal.

Carbon Dioxide. The chief oxides of carbon are carbon monoxide, CO, and carbon dioxide, CO_2. There are about 380 ppm of CO_2 in air (0.038% by volume). CO occurs to a much lesser extent. Although they are only minor constituents of air, these two oxides are important in many ways.

Carbon dioxide is the only oxide of carbon formed when carbon or carbon-containing compounds are burned in an *excess* of air (providing an abundance of O_2). This condition exists when a fuel-lean mixture is burned in an automobile engine. Thus, for the combustion of the gasoline component octane,

$$C_8H_{18}(l) + \frac{25}{2}O_2(g) \longrightarrow 8\,CO_2(g) + 9\,H_2O(l) \qquad (21.27)$$

▲ **Synthetic diamonds**

King, A. G. "Research Advances: Designing Dendrimers To Offer Micelle-type Nanocontainers; Optical Biosensor for Glucose Possible through Biocatalytic Nanoparticle Growth; Carbon Nanotubes and Human Cells?" *J. Chem. Educ.* 2005: *82*, 666.

Nakamoto, K., McKinney, M. A. "Application of the Correlation Method to Vibrational Spectra of C60 and Other Fullerenes: Predicting the Number of IR- and Raman-Active Bands." *J. Chem. Educ.* 2000: *77*, 775 (June 2000).

Oxides of Carbon: You can purchase from hardware stores propane welding kits having two nozzles: one for propane and one for oxygen. Fill balloons with different ratios of the two gases and ignite the balloon with a candle at the end of a stick. Intensities of the explosions depend on the composition of the mixture.

Carvalho, A. P., et al. "Acid-Base Reactions with Carbon Dioxide." *J. Chem. Educ.* 2002: *79*, 1464A.

▶ **FIGURE 21-18**
CO bound to hemoglobin
Carbon monoxide binds to the iron atoms in hemoglobin more strongly than does oxygen. Thus, toxic amounts of carbon monoxide can cause death by oxygen deprivation. The portion of the hemoglobin molecule shown here is called a *heme* group. An iron atom (yellow) is at the center of the group and is surrounded by four nitrogen atoms. In hemoglobin, an O_2 molecule projects above the plane of the iron and nitrogen atoms, but here it has been replaced by a CO molecule (black and red).

Huddle, B. P., et al. "Analysis of Carbon Monoxide in Blood." *J. Chem. Educ.* **2003**: 80, 441.

Jaffe, D., et al. "Measuring Carbon Monoxide in Auto Exhaust by Gas Chromatography." *J. Chem. Educ.* **1995**: 72, 364.

If the combustion occurs in a *limited* quantity of air, carbon monoxide is also produced. This condition prevails when a fuel-rich mixture is burned in an automobile engine. One possibility for the incomplete combustion of octane is

$$C_8H_{18}(l) + 12\,O_2(g) \longrightarrow 7\,CO_2(g) + CO(g) + 9\,H_2O(l) \qquad (21.28)$$

CO as an air pollutant comes chiefly from the incomplete combustion of fossil fuels in automobile engines. CO is an inhalation poison because CO molecules bond irreversibly to Fe atoms in hemoglobin in blood and displace the O_2 molecules that the hemoglobin normally carries (Fig. 21-18).

Not only does incomplete combustion of gasoline contribute to air pollution, but also it represents a loss of efficiency. A given quantity of gasoline evolves less heat if CO(g) is formed as a combustion product rather than $CO_2(g)$.

CONCEPT ASSESSMENT ✓

With a minimum of calculation, determine how much less heat is produced per mol of $C_8H_{18}(l)$ burned in reaction (21.28) than in reaction (21.27).

Dry ice in hot water produces stage fog. It is not the CO_2 that is released that causes the fog, but the moisture in the air that condenses out.

Although carbon dioxide can be obtained directly from the atmosphere as a by-product of the liquefaction of air, this is not an important source. Some of the principal commercial sources of CO_2 are summarized in Table 21.7.

The major use of carbon dioxide (about 50%) is as a refrigerant in the form of dry ice for freezing, preserving, and transporting food. Carbonated beverages account for about 20% of CO_2 consumption. Other important uses are in oil recovery in oil fields and in fire-extinguishing systems. Of course, the major use is not by humans but by algae and plants.

TABLE 21.7   Some Industrial Methods of Preparing CO₂

Method	Chemical Reaction
Recovery from exhaust stack gases in the combustion of carbonaceous fuels, such as the combustion of coke	$C(s) + O_2(g) \longrightarrow CO_2(g)$
Recovery in ammonia plants from steam–reforming reactions used to produce hydrogen	$CH_4(g) + 2\,H_2O(g) \longrightarrow CO_2(g) + 4\,H_2(g)$
Decomposition (calcination) of limestone at about 900 °C	$CaCO_3(s) \longrightarrow CaO(s) + CO_2(g)$
Fermentation by-product in the production of ethanol	$C_6H_{12}O_6(aq) \longrightarrow 2\,C_2H_5OH(aq) + 2\,CO_2(g)$
	a sugar

→ Main cycle
→ Fossilization tributary
→ Disruption by human activities

◄ **FIGURE 21-19**
The carbon cycle

Atmospheric CO_2 is the source of all the carbon-containing compounds (organic compounds) synthesized by green plants. Here we briefly consider the *carbon cycle*—the major exchanges that occur between the atmosphere and the surface of Earth. A portion of the carbon cycle is represented in Figure 21-19. Atmospheric CO_2 is the only source of carbon available to plants for making organic compounds by the process of *photosynthesis*. The process is extremely complicated, and its details have been known for only a few decades (Melvin Calvin, Nobel Prize, 1961). It involves up to 100 sequential steps for the conversion of 6 mol CO_2 to 1 mol $C_6H_{12}O_6$ (glucose). The overall change is

$$6\,CO_2 + 6\,H_2O \xrightarrow[\text{sunlight}]{\text{chlorophyll}} C_6H_{12}O_6 + 6\,O_2 \qquad \Delta H = +2.8 \times 10^3 \text{ kJ}$$

The overall reaction is highly endothermic. The required energy comes from sunlight. Chlorophyll, a green pigment in plants, is crucial to the process. Atmospheric oxygen is a by-product of the reaction.

Here are some of the ideas illustrated in the diagram. When animals consume plants, carbon atoms pass to the animals. Some carbon is returned to the atmosphere as CO_2 when the animals breathe and when they expel gas (methane). Additional CO_2 returns to the atmosphere as plants and animals die and their remains are broken down by bacteria. Some carbon in decaying organic matter is converted to coal, petroleum, and natural gas. This carbon is unavailable for photosynthesis.

Not represented in the drawing is the cycle of CO_2 through the oceans of the world. Phytoplankton (small, floating green organisms) also carry on photosynthesis, converting CO_2 to organic compounds. The plankton are the base of the ocean food chain, directly and indirectly supporting all the animals in the oceans.

Huge quantities of carbon have accumulated in the form of carbonate rocks (mostly $CaCO_3$). These come from the shells of decayed mollusks in ancient seas.

Human activities now play a far more significant role in the carbon cycle than in preindustrial times. Slash-and-burn agricultural methods—particularly in rain forests—are returning CO_2 to the atmosphere more rapidly than naturally occurring fires do. The combustion of fossil fuels is replacing stored carbon by carbon dioxide to an even greater extent. We have already seen the possible consequences of this distortion of the carbon cycle: an increased level of atmospheric CO_2 and a future global warming (page 259). Human disruption of the natural carbon cycle has become a widely debated issue.

Carbon Monoxide. A modern method of making carbon monoxide is the steam reforming of natural gas, represented as

$$CH_4(g) + H_2O(g) \longrightarrow CO(g) + 3 H_2(g) \tag{21.29}$$

The term *steam* refers to gaseous water. *Reforming* refers to the restructuring of a carbon compound, such as CH_4 to CO. The reforming of natural gas (mostly CH_4) is an important source of $H_2(g)$ for use in the synthesis of NH_3 (page 941).

There are three main uses of carbon monoxide. One is in synthesizing other compounds. For example, a mixture of CO and H_2 produced by reforming methane or some other hydrocarbon and known as *synthesis gas* can be converted to a new organic chemical product, such as methanol.

$$CO(g) + 2 H_2(g) \longrightarrow CH_3OH(l)$$

Another use of CO is as a reducing agent. In a blast furnace, for instance, **coke**, a rather pure form of carbon produced by heating coal in the absence of air, is converted to CO. The CO then reduces iron oxide to iron.

$$Fe_2O_3(s) + 3 CO(g) \longrightarrow 2 Fe(l) + 3 CO_2(g)$$

A third use of CO is as a fuel, usually mixed with CH_4, H_2, and other combustible gases (recall Section 7-9).

OTHER INORGANIC CARBON COMPOUNDS

Carbon combines with metals to form *carbides*. In many cases, the carbon atoms occupy the holes or voids in metal structures, forming *interstitial carbides*. With active metals, the carbides are ionic. *Calcium carbide* forms in the high-temperature reaction of lime and coke:

$$CaO(s) + 3 C(s) \xrightarrow{2000\,°C} CaC_2(s) + CO(g) \tag{21.30}$$

Calcium carbide is important because acetylene ($HC{\equiv}CH$) can easily be made from it, and acetylene can be used to synthesize many chemical compounds.

$$CaC_2(s) + 2 H_2O(l) \longrightarrow Ca(OH)_2(s) + C_2H_2(g) \tag{21.31}$$

The solid CaC_2 can be regarded as a face-centered cubic array of Ca^{2+} ions with the C_2^{2-} ions in the octahedral holes.

Carbon disulfide, CS_2, can be synthesized by the reaction of methane and sulfur vapor in the presence of a catalyst.

$$CH_4(g) + 4 S(g) \longrightarrow CS_2(l) + 2 H_2S(g) \tag{21.32}$$

Carbon disulfide is a highly flammable, volatile liquid that acts as a solvent for sulfur, phosphorus, bromine, iodine, fats, and oils. Its uses as a solvent are decreasing, however, because it is poisonous. Other important uses are in the manufacture of rayon and cellophane.

Carbon tetrachloride, CCl_4, can be prepared by the direct chlorination of methane.

$$CH_4(g) + 4 Cl_2(g) \longrightarrow CCl_4(l) + 4 HCl(g) \tag{21.33}$$

Carbonates. Show the difference between baking soda ($NaHCO_3$) and baking powder ($NaHCO_3$ and citric acid). The powder fizzes in water but the baking soda does not fizz until citric acid is added.

Lagier, Claudia, Olivieri, Alejandro. "Calculation of solubilities of carbonates and phosphates in water as influenced by competitive acid-base reactions." *J. Chem. Educ.* **1990:** *67*, 934.

Fenster, A. A., et al. "A versatile demonstration with calcium carbide." *J. Chem. Educ.* **1987:** *64*, 444.

$\mathbf{\bullet}$ $= C_2^{2-}$ ions

$\bullet$ $= Ca^{2+}$ ions

▲ **Structure of calcium carbide**

Although CCl_4 has been extensively used as a solvent, dry-cleaning agent, and fire extinguisher, these uses have been steadily declining because CCl_4 causes liver and kidney damage and is a known carcinogen.

Certain groupings of atoms, several containing C atoms, have some of the characteristics of a halogen atom. They are called *pseudohalogens* and include

—CN (cyanide)   —OCN (cyanate)   —SCN (thiocyanate)   —N$_3$ (azide)

The *cyanide* ion, CN^-, is similar to the halide ions, X^-, in that it forms an insoluble silver salt, AgCN, and an acid HCN. Hydrocyanic acid, a liquid that boils at about room temperature, is a very weak acid, unlike HCl. Another important difference is that CN^- is poisonous. Despite its extreme toxicity, HCN has important uses in the manufacture of plastics. The combination of two cyanide groups produces *cyanogen*, $(CN)_2$. This gas resembles chlorine gas in undergoing a disproportionation reaction in basic solution.

$$(CN)_2 + 2\,OH^-(aq) \longrightarrow CN^-(aq) + OCN^-(aq) + H_2O(l) \qquad (21.34)$$

Cyanogen is used in organic synthesis, as a fumigant, and as a rocket propellant.

SILICON

Among the elements, silicon is second only to oxygen in its abundance in Earth's crust. Compared to its fellow group-14 member carbon, silicon is to the mineral world what carbon is to the living world—the backbone element.

Production and Uses of Silicon.   Elemental silicon is produced when quartz or sand (SiO_2) is reduced by reaction with coke in an electric arc furnace.

$$SiO_2 + 2\,C \xrightarrow{\Delta} Si + 2\,CO(g) \qquad (21.35)$$

Very high purity Si for solar cells can be made by reducing Na_2SiF_6 with metallic Na. In turn, Na_2SiF_6 is a by-product of the formation of phosphate fertilizers (page 948). High-purity silicon is required in the manufacture of transistors and other semiconductor devices.

Oxides of Silicon; Silicates.   Silicon forms only one stable oxide with the empirical formula SiO_2, silica. In silica, each Si atom is bonded to *four* O atoms and each O atom to *two* Si atoms. The structure is that of a network covalent solid, as suggested by Figure 21-20(a). This structure is reminiscent of the

Bell, Jerry A. "The Journal's 75th Anniversary: Diamond or Fullerene?" *J. Chem. Educ.* **1998:** *75,* 22 (January 1998).

Hildebrand, A., Hilgers, U., Blume, R., Wiechoczek, D. "Playing with the Soccer Ball-an Experimental Introduction to Fullerene Chemistry." *J. Chem. Educ.* **1996:** *73,* 1066 (November 1996).

Beaton, J. M. "Paper Models for Fullerenes C60-C84" *J. Chem. Educ.* **1995:** 72, 863.

Acetylene, produced from CaO(s) by way of CaC$_2$(s), can be used to make gasoline. This is one route to making gasoline from coal.

Silicates website: http://mineral. galleries.com/minerals/ silicate/class.htm (commercial)

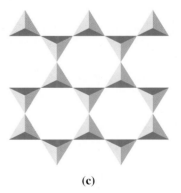

= Silicon   = Oxygen

(a)   (b)   (c)

▲ **FIGURE 21-20**
Structures of silica and silicates
(a) A three-dimensional network of bonds in silica, SiO_2. **(b)** The silicate anion, SiO_4^{4-}, commonly found in silicate materials. The Si atom is in the center of the tetrahedron and is surrounded by four O atoms. **(c)** A depiction of the structure of a mica, using tetrahedra to represent the SiO_4 units. The cations K^+ and Al^{3+} are also present but are not shown. This is the usual way that materials scientists represent silicates and similar materials.

diamond structure, and silica has certain properties that resemble those of diamond. For example, quartz, a form of silica, is fairly hard (with a Mohs hardness of 7, compared with 10 for diamond), has a high melting point (about 1700 °C), and is a nonconductor of electricity. Silica is the basic raw material of the glass and ceramics industries.

The central feature of all *silicates* is the SiO_4^{4-} tetrahedron depicted in Figure 21-20(b). These tetrahedra may be arranged in a wide variety of ways.

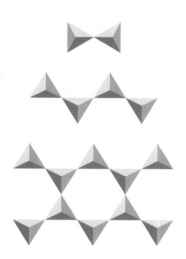

- *Simple SiO_4 tetrahedra.* Typical minerals in which the anions are simple SiO_4^{4-} tetrahedra are *thorite* ($ThSiO_4$) and *zircon* ($ZrSiO_4$).

- *Two SiO_4 tetrahedra joined end-to-end.* The silicon atoms in the two tetrahedra share an O atom between them in the anion $Si_2O_7^{6-}$, found in the mineral *thortveitite* ($Sc_2Si_2O_7$).

- *SiO_4 tetrahedra joined into long chains.* Each Si atom shares an O atom with the Si atom in an adjacent tetrahedron on either side. An example is *spodumene*, the principal source of lithium and lithium compounds. Its empirical formula is $LiAl(SiO_3)_2$.

- *SiO_4 tetrahedra joined into a double chain.* Half the Si atoms share three of their four O atoms with Si atoms in adjacent tetrahedra, and half share only two. In *chrysotile asbestos*, double chains are held together by cations (chiefly Mg^{2+}); this mineral has a fibrous appearance. The empirical formula is $Mg_3(Si_2O_5)(OH)_4$.

- *SiO_4 tetrahedra are bonded together in two-dimensional sheets.* Each Si atom shares O atoms with the Si atoms in three adjacent tetrahedra. This structure is depicted in Figure 21-20(c). In *muscovite mica*, with the empirical formula, $KAl_2(AlSi_3O_{10})(OH)_2$, the counterions that bond sheets together in layers are mostly K^+ and Al^{3+}. Bonding within the sheets is stronger than that between sheets, so muscovite mica flakes easily.

- *SiO_4 tetrahedra are bonded together in three-dimensional structures.* Three-dimensional arrays of tetrahedra result when each Si atom shares all four O atoms with the Si atoms in four adjoining tetrahedra (as in Figure 21-20a). This is the most common arrangement, occurring in silica (quartz) and in the majority of silicate minerals.

In contrast to carbon, the $3p$ orbitals of silicon do not protrude out far from the $3s$ orbital. As such, the bonding properties of silicon and carbon are quite different due to the inability of silicon to effectively delocalize electrons. Science fiction sometimes uses life forms based on silicon rather than carbon. This is unlikely. Sometimes people say: "Carbon is to life what silicon is to geology".

Are You Wondering . . .

Why silica (SiO_2) does not exist as simple molecules as CO_2 does?

Because both silicon and carbon are in group 14 of the periodic table and have four valence electrons, we might expect them to form oxides with similar properties. In CO_2, the side-to-side overlap of $2p$ orbitals of the C and O atoms is extensive (see page 435). The carbon-to-oxygen double bond in CO_2 proves to be stronger (799 kJ mol^{-1}) than two single bonds (2 $\times$ 360 kJ mol^{-1}). This results in the familiar Lewis structure of CO_2.

$$:\ddot{O}=C=\ddot{O}:$$

Silicon, being in the third period, would have to use $3p$ orbitals to form double bonds with oxygen. The side-to-side overlap of these orbitals with the $2p$ orbitals of oxygen is quite limited. In terms of energy, a stronger bonding arrangement results if the Si atoms form *four* single bonds with O atoms (bond energy: 4 $\times$ 464 kJ mol^{-1} = 1856 kJ total) rather than *two* double bonds (bond energy: 2 $\times$ 640 kJ mol^{-1} = 1280 kJ total). Because each O atom must simultaneously bond to two Si atoms, the result is a network of —Si—O—Si— bonds (see Figure 21-20a).

On page 880 we contrasted Be and Mg, the second- and third-period members of group 2. Here is another example of how the second-period member of a group (that is, carbon) differs from the higher period members.

The empirical formula of the mineral *beryl* is $Be_3Al_2Si_6O_{18}$. Using the several descriptions of silicate minerals just given as a guide, describe the structure of the silicate anion in beryl.

SiO$_2$ is a weakly acidic oxide and slowly dissolves in strong bases. It forms a series of silicates, such as Na$_2$SiO$_4$ (sodium orthosilicate) and Na$_2$SiO$_3$ (sodium metasilicate). These compounds are somewhat soluble in water and, as a result, are sometimes referred to as "water glass."

Silicate anions are bases; when acidified, they produce silicic acids which are unstable and decompose to silica. The silica obtained, however, is not a crystalline solid or powder. Depending on the acidity of the solution, the silica is obtained as a colloidal dispersion, a gelatinous precipitate, or a solid-like gel in which all the water is entrapped. These hydrated silicates are polymers of silica formed by the elimination of water molecules between neighboring molecules of silicic acid. The process begins with the reaction

$$SiO_4{}^{4-}(aq) + 4\,H^+(aq) \longrightarrow Si(OH)_4$$

It is followed by

where —H and —OH combine to form water (HOH), and Si—O—Si bridges are produced.

Silicates in Ceramics and Glass.   Hydrated silicate polymers are important in the ceramics industry. A colloidal dispersion of particles in a liquid is called a *sol*. The sol can be poured into a mold and, following removal of some of the liquid, is converted to a *gel*. The gel is then processed into the final ceramic product. This sol–gel process can produce exceptionally lightweight ceramic materials.

Uses of these advanced ceramics fall into two general categories: (1) electrical, magnetic, or optical applications (as in the manufacture of integrated circuit components) and (2) applications that take advantage of the ceramic's mechanical and structural properties at high temperatures. These latter properties have been explored in developing ceramic components for gas turbines and automotive engines. Quite possibly the automobile engine of the future will be a ceramic engine—lightweight and more fuel-efficient because higher operating temperatures are possible. Some engines already have several ceramic components, such as engine valves and valve seats. There is some truth to the vision of this ceramic future as the new stone age.

If sodium and calcium carbonates are mixed with sand and fused at about 1500 °C, the result is a liquid mixture of sodium and calcium silicates. When cooled, the liquid becomes more viscous and eventually becomes a solid that is transparent to light; this solid is called a **glass**. Crystalline solids have a long-range order, whereas glasses are *amorphous solids* in which order is found over relatively short distances only. Think of the structural units in glass (silicate anions) as being in a jumbled rather than a regular arrangement. A glass and a crystalline solid also differ in their melting behavior. A glass softens and melts over a broad temperature range, whereas a crystalline solid has a definite, sharp melting point. Different types of glass and methods of making them are described later in this section.

◄ H$_4$SiO$_4$ is called *ortho*silicic acid. When a combination of one H atom and one OH group (equivalent to a molecule of H$_2$O) are eliminated from the *ortho* acid, the resulting acid, H$_2$SiO$_3$, is called *meta*silicic acid.

▲ Ceramic components of an automobile engine. (Photo courtesy of Kyocera Industrial Ceramics Corp./Vancouver, WA)

Hawkes, Stephen J. "Glass Doesn't Flow and Doesn't Crystallize and It Isn't a Liquid." *J. Chem. Educ.* **2000:** 77, 846 (July 2000).

Burke, B. A. "Silicate-PVA polymers." *J. Chem. Educ.* **1988:** 65, 895.

Silanes and Silicones.

Several silicon–hydrogen compounds are known, but because Si—Si single bonds are not particularly strong, the chain length in these compounds, called *silanes*, is limited to six.

$$H-\underset{\overset{|}{H}}{\overset{\overset{\displaystyle H}{|}}{Si}}-H \qquad H-\underset{\overset{|}{H}}{\overset{\overset{\displaystyle H}{|}}{Si}}-\underset{\overset{|}{H}}{\overset{\overset{\displaystyle H}{|}}{Si}}-H \qquad H-\underset{\overset{|}{H}}{\overset{\overset{\displaystyle H}{|}}{Si}}-\underset{\overset{|}{H}}{\overset{\overset{\displaystyle H}{|}}{Si}}-\underset{\overset{|}{H}}{\overset{\overset{\displaystyle H}{|}}{Si}}-H \cdots \quad S_6H_{14}$$

Monosilane Disilane Trisilane Hexasilane

Smith, D. W. "The thermo-chemistry of catenation in silanes versus alkanes." *J. Chem. Educ.* **1988:** *65*, 414.

Other atoms or groups of atoms can be substituted for H atoms in silanes to produce compounds called *organosilanes*. Typical is the direct reaction of Si and methyl chloride, CH_3Cl.

$$2\,CH_3Cl + Si \longrightarrow (CH_3)_2SiCl_2$$

The reaction of $(CH_3)_2SiCl_2$, dichlorodimethylsilane, with water produces an interesting compound, *dimethylsilanol*, $(CH_3)_2Si(OH)_2$. Dimethylsilanol undergoes a polymerization reaction in which H_2O molecules are eliminated from among large numbers of silanol molecules. The result of this polymerization is a material consisting of molecules with long silicon–oxygen chains: **silicones**.

a silicone

Silicones are important polymers because they are versatile. They can be obtained either as oils or as rubber-like materials. Silicone oils are not volatile and do not decompose when heated. Also, they can be cooled to low temperatures without solidifying or becoming viscous. Silicone oils are excellent high-temperature lubricants. In contrast, hydrocarbon oils break down at high temperatures, become very viscous, and then solidify at low temperatures. Silicone rubbers retain their elasticity at low temperatures and are chemically resistant and thermally stable. This makes them useful in caulking around windows, for instance.

▲ Some common applications of silicones.

Silicone uses website: http://www.dynamixcosmo.com/silicone.htm (commercial)

Silicon Halides.

Silicon reacts readily with the halogens to form the products SiX_4. As we might expect from their molecular structures and molar masses, at room temperature SiF_4 is a gas, $SiCl_4$ and $SiBr_4$ are liquids and SiI_4 is a solid. Both SiF_4 and $SiCl_4$ are readily hydrolyzed with water, but the former is only partially hydrolyzed.

$$2\,SiF_4(g) + 4\,H_2O(l) \rightleftharpoons SiO_2(s) + 2\,H_3O^+(aq) + [SiF_6]^{2-}(aq) + 2\,HF(aq) \qquad (21.36)$$

$$SiCl_4(l) + 2\,H_2O(l) \longrightarrow SiO_2(s) + 4\,HCl(aq) \qquad (21.37)$$

The ability of the Si atom to expand its valence shell is illustrated by the formation of the ion $[SiF_6]^{2-}$. For example, $K_2[SiF_6]$ can be prepared by the reaction of SiF_4 with metal fluorides in aqueous HF; the K^+ salt is sparingly soluble. The corresponding $[SiCl_6]^{2-}$ has not yet been prepared, probably because the chloride ion is too big for six of them to fit around the Si atom.

$SiCl_4$ is manufactured on a large scale to produce finely divided silica (reaction 21.37), used as a reinforcing filler in silicone rubber, and very pure silicon for transistors used in computer chips.

Glass Making.

Glass and the art of glassmaking have been known for centuries. Beautiful stained-glass windows can be seen in medieval and modern churches; ancient glass containers for perfume and oil are displayed in many museums. Today, glass is indispensable in almost every facet of life.

◀ Stained-glass windows of the Spiral Church in Dallas, Texas.

Soda–lime glass is the oldest form of glass. The starting material in its manufacture is a mixture of sodium carbonate (*soda* ash), calcium carbonate (which decomposes to form quick*lime* when heated), and silicon dioxide. The mixture can be fused at a relatively low temperature (1300 °C) compared with the melting point of pure silica (1710 °C), and it is easy to form into the shapes needed. The effect of the sodium ions is to break up the crystalline lattice of the SiO_2; the calcium ions render the glass insoluble in water, so it can be used for such items as drinking glasses and windows. At the high temperatures employed, chemical reactions occur that produce a mixture of sodium and calcium silicates as the ultimate glass product.

Glass containing even small amounts of Fe_2O_3 has a distinctive green color (bottle glass). Glass can be made colorless by incorporating MnO_2 into the glassmaking process. The MnO_2 oxidizes green $FeSiO_3$ to yellow $Fe_2(SiO_3)_3$ and is itself reduced to Mn_2O_3, which imparts a violet color. The yellow and violet are complementary colors, so the glass appears colorless. Where desired, color can be imparted by means of appropriate additives, such as CoO for cobalt blue glass. To produce an opaque glass, additives such as calcium phosphate are used. In Bohemian crystal, most of the Na^+ is replaced by K^+; a glass with exceptional transparency and brightness can be made by incorporating lead oxides (as in Waterford crystal).

A problem with soda–lime glass is its high coefficient of thermal expansion—its dimensions change significantly with temperature. The glass cannot withstand thermal shock. This limitation posed a particular problem for the lanterns used in the early days of railroads. In the rain, the hot glass in these lanterns would easily shatter. Adding B_2O_3 to the glass solved the problem. A *borosilicate* glass has a low coefficient of thermal expansion and is thus resistant to thermal shock. This is the glass commonly known by its trade name, Pyrex. It is widely used in chemical laboratories and for cookware in the home.

Most glass has small bubbles or impurities in it that decrease its ability to transmit light without scattering—a phenomenon observed in the distorted images produced by the thick bottoms of drinking glasses. In modern *fiber-optic* cables, sound waves are converted to electrical impulses, which are transmitted as laser light beams. The light must be transmitted over long distances without distortion or loss of signal. For this purpose, a special glass made of pure silica is required. The key to making this glass is in purifying silica, which can be done by a series of chemical reactions. First, impure quartz or sand is reduced to silicon by using coke as a reducing agent. The silicon is then allowed to react with $Cl_2(g)$ to form $SiCl_4(g)$.

$$SiO_2(s) + 2\,C(s) \longrightarrow Si(s) + 2\,CO(g)$$

$$Si(s) + 2\,Cl_2(g) \longrightarrow SiCl_4(g)$$

Brown, William Hamilton. "A simple method of distinguishing borosilicate and soda lime glass." *J. Chem. Educ.* 1979: *56*, 692.

Soda lime glass website: http://www.sylvania.com/beyond/glass/soda.htm (Commercial)

Finally, the SiCl$_4$ is burned in a methane–oxygen flame. SiO$_2$ deposits as a fine ash, and chlorocarbon compounds escape as gaseous products. The SiO$_2$, with impurity levels reduced to parts per billion, can then be melted and drawn into the fine filaments required in fiber-optic cable. Tens of millions of miles of fiber-optic cable are currently produced annually in the United States.

PROPERTIES AND USES OF TIN AND LEAD

The data in Table 21.8 suggest that tin and lead are rather similar to each other. Both are soft and malleable and melt at low temperatures. The ionization energies and standard electrode potentials of the two metals are also about the same. This means that their tendencies to be oxidized to the +2 oxidation state are comparable.

The fact that both tin and lead can exist in two oxidation states, +2 and +4, is an example of the inert pair effect (page 890). In the +2 oxidation state, the inert pair ns^2 is not involved in bond formation, whereas in the +4 oxidation state, the pair does participate. Tin displays a stronger tendency to exist in the +4 oxidation state than does lead. That tendency is consistent with the trend observed in group 13, in which the lower oxidation state is favored farther down a group.

Another difference between tin and lead is that tin exists in two common crystalline forms (α and β), whereas lead has but a single solid form. The α (gray), or nonmetallic, form of tin is stable below 13 °C; the β (white), or metallic, form of tin is stable above 13 °C. Ordinarily, when a sample of β tin is cooled, it must be kept below 13 °C for a long time before the transition to α tin occurs. Once it does begin, however, the transformation takes place rather rapidly and with dramatic results. Because α tin is less dense than the β variety, the tin expands and crumbles to a powder. This transformation leads to the disintegration of objects made of tin. It has been a particular problem in churches in colder climates because some organ pipes are made of tin or tin alloys. The transformation is known in northern Europe as *tin disease*, *tin pest*, or *tin plague*. It added to the troubles of Napoleon's army in the siege of Moscow because the soldiers' buttons were made of tin—as the cold winter wore on, the buttons disintegrated.

The chief tin ore is tin(IV) oxide, SnO$_2$, known as *cassiterite*. After initial purification, the tin(IV) oxide is reduced with carbon (coke) to produce tin metal.

$$\text{SnO}_2(s) + \text{C}(s) \xrightarrow{\Delta} \text{Sn}(l) + \text{CO}_2(g) \tag{21.38}$$

Nearly 50% of the tin metal produced is used in tinplate, especially in plating iron for use in cans for storing foods. The next most important use (about 25% of the total produced) is in the manufacture of **solders**—low-melting

Arniz, F. J., Pedrosa, M. R. "Microscale Transformations of Some Lead Compounds. A Cycle for Lead Minimizing the Production of Wastes." *J. Chem. Educ.* **1999**: *76*, 1687 (December 1999)

TABLE 21.8 Some Properties of Tin and Lead		
	Sn	**Pb**
Atomic number	50	82
Atomic (metallic) radius, pm	141	175
Ionic (M^{2+}) radius, pm	93	118
First ionization energy, kJ mol^{-1}	709	716
Electrode potential $E°$, V		
[M^{2+}(aq) + 2 e$^-$ ⟶ M(s)]	-0.137	-0.125
[M^{4+}(aq) + 2 e$^-$ ⟶ M^{2+}(aq)]	$+0.154$	$+1.5$
Melting point, °C	232	327
Boiling point, °C	2623	1751
Density, g/cm^3 at 20 °C	5.77 (α, gray)	11.34
	7.29 (β, white)	
Hardness[a]	1.6	1.5
Electrical conductivity[a]	14.4	7.68

[a]See footnotes b and c of Table 21.2.

alloys used to join wires or pieces of metal. Other important alloys of tin are *bronze* (90% Cu, 10% Sn) and *pewter* (85% Sn, 7% Cu, 6% Bi, 2% Sb). Alloys of Sn and Pb are used to make organ pipes.

Lead is found chiefly as lead(II) sulfide, PbS, an ore known as *galena*. The lead(II) sulfide is first converted to lead(II) oxide by strongly heating it in air, a process called **roasting**. The oxide is then reduced with coke to produce the metal.

$$2\,PbS(s) + 3\,O_2(g) \xrightarrow{\Delta} 2\,PbO(s) + 2\,SO_2(g) \qquad (21.39)$$

$$2\,PbO(s) + C(s) \xrightarrow{\Delta} 2\,Pb(l) + CO_2(g) \qquad (21.40)$$

Over half the lead produced is used in lead–acid (storage) batteries. Other uses include the manufacture of solder and other alloys, ammunition, and radiation shields (to protect against X rays).

COMPOUNDS OF GROUP 14 METALS

Oxides.   Tin forms two primary oxides, SnO and SnO_2. By heating SnO in air, it can be converted to SnO_2. One use of SnO_2 is as a jewelry abrasive.

Lead forms a number of oxides, and the chemistry of some of these oxides is not completely understood. The best known oxides of lead are yellow PbO, *litharge*; red-brown lead dioxide, PbO_2; and a mixed-valence oxide known as *red lead*, Pb_3O_4. Lead oxides are used in the manufacture of lead–acid (storage) batteries, glass, ceramic glazes, cements (PbO), metal-protecting paints (Pb_3O_4), and matches (PbO_2). Other lead compounds are generally made from the oxides.

Because lead tends to be in the +2 oxidation state, lead(IV) compounds tend to undergo reduction to compounds of lead(II) and are therefore good oxidizing agents. A case in point is PbO_2. In Chapter 20, we noted its use as the cathode in lead–acid storage cells. The reduction of PbO_2(s) can be represented by the half-equation

$$PbO_2(s) + 4\,H^+(aq) + 2\,e^- \longrightarrow Pb^{2+}(aq) + 2\,H_2O(l) \qquad E^\circ = +1.455\,V$$

PbO_2(s) is a better oxidizing agent than $Cl_2(g)$ and nearly as good as MnO_4^-(aq). For example, PbO_2(s) can oxidize HCl(aq) to $Cl_2(g)$.

$$PbO_2(s) + 4\,HCl(aq) \longrightarrow PbCl_2(aq) + 2\,H_2O(l) + Cl_2(g) \qquad E^\circ_{cell} = 0.097\,g$$

Halides.   Both chlorides of tin—$SnCl_2$ and $SnCl_4$—have important uses. Tin(II) chloride, $SnCl_2$, is a good reducing agent and is used in the quantitative analysis of iron ores to reduce iron(III) to iron(II) in aqueous solution. Tin(IV) chloride, $SnCl_4$, is formed by the direct reaction of tin and $Cl_2(g)$; it is the form in which tin is recovered from scrap tinplate. Tin(II) fluoride, SnF_2 (stannous fluoride), was used as an anticavity additive to toothpaste, but has largely been replaced by NaF in gel toothpastes.

The increasing preference for the +2 over the +4 oxidation state down group 14 due to the inert pair effect is readily evident in the halides. Thus GeX_4 compounds are more stable than GeX_2, whereas PbX_2 compounds are more stable than PbX_4.

Other Compounds.   As we should expect from the solubility guidelines (Table 5.1), one of the few soluble lead compounds is lead(II) nitrate, $Pb(NO_3)_2$. It is formed in the reaction of PbO_2 with nitric acid.

$$2\,PbO_2(s) + 4\,HNO_3(aq) \longrightarrow 2\,Pb(NO_3)_2(aq) + 2\,H_2O(l) + O_2(g)$$

Addition of a soluble chromate salt to $Pb(NO_3)_2$(aq) produces the pigment lead(II) chromate (*chrome yellow*), $PbCrO_4$. Another lead-based pigment used in ceramic glazes and once extensively used in the manufacture of paint is *white lead*, a basic lead carbonate, $2\,PbCO_3 \cdot Pb(OH)_2$.

◄ Another mixed-valence oxide that we have encountered on several occasions in this text is Fe_3O_4 (see, for example, page 83).

◀ Solar cells employing gallium arsenide (gold and red) placed on a silicon-based solar cell. The cells containing gallium arsenide are more efficient and can be made smaller than a comparable silicon cell.

Until the 1980s, the principal application of gallium metal was in high-temperature thermometers. Now an unlikely compound—gallium arsenide, (GaAs)—has become one of the most versatile high-technology materials of our time. Among the properties of gallium arsenide is the ability to convert electric energy into light. A crystal of GaAs can serve as the light-generating component of a light-emitting diode (LED), a device employed in indicator lights on stereo equipment and calculator displays. GaAs can also be fabricated into diode lasers, very small lasers used in compact-disc systems, and for transmitting infrared light through fiber-optic cables.

LEAD POISONING

Schneider, Maxyne, S. S. J. "Lead poisoning danger in pencils (L)." *J. Chem. Educ.* **1972:** *49,* 379.

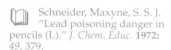

Lead poisoning website: http://www.aeclp.org/ (non-commercial)

Brouwer, H. "Screening Technique for Lead and Cadmium in Toys and Other Materials Using Atomic Absorption Spectroscopy." *J. Chem. Educ.* **2005:** *82,* 611.

Beginning with the ancient Romans and continuing to fairly recent times, lead has been used in plumbing systems, including those designed to transport water. Exposure to lead has also occurred through cooking and eating utensils and pottery glazes. In colonial times, lead poisoning was clearly diagnosed as the cause of "dry bellyache" suffered by some North Carolinians who consumed rum made in New England. The distilling equipment used in the manufacture of the rum had components made of lead.

Mild forms of lead poisoning produce nervousness and mental depression. More severe cases can lead to permanent nerve, brain, and kidney damage. Lead interferes with the biochemical reactions that produce the iron-containing heme group in hemoglobin. As little as $10-15\ \mu g$ Pb/dL in blood seems to produce physiological effects, especially in small children. The phaseout out of leaded gasoline has resulted in a dramatic drop in average lead levels in blood (Fig. 21-21). The principal sources of lead contamination now seem to be lead-based painted surfaces found in old buildings and soldered joints in plumbing systems. Lead has been eliminated from modern plumbing solder, which is now a mixture of 95% Sn and 5% Sb. Because lead is toxic, its disposal is closely monitored. Recycling provides about three-quarters of the current lead metal production.

CONCEPT ASSESSMENT ✓

To prevent the air oxidation of aqueous solutions of Sn^{2+} to Sn^{4+}, metallic tin is sometimes kept in contact with the $Sn^{2+}(aq)$. Suggest how this contact helps prevent the oxidation.

Recall the discussion of the band theory and semiconductors on pages 453–456. Gallium arsenide is an intrinsic semiconductor. This compound, with eight valence electrons per formula unit (three from Ga and five from As), has a filled valence band. If sufficient electric energy is supplied, however, electrons are promoted to the conduction band. When the excited electrons return to the ground state (valence band), they emit photons of light with a wavelength proportional to the energy associated with the band gap (ΔE in Figure 11-35).

What is special about GaAs semiconductors is that the band gap can be "tuned" by adding controlled amounts of another semiconductor—gallium phosphide. GaAs and GaP form solid solutions whose compositions can be varied in all proportions. GaP has a band-gap energy corresponding to that of green light (540 nm), whereas the band-gap energy in GaAs corresponds to infrared light (890 nm).* A series of solid solutions of GaAs and GaP can be represented by the general formula GaP_xAs_{1-x}. The band gap increases with increased amounts of phosphorus, so the emitted light increases in energy. Ga–P–As semiconductors whose compositions fall between those of GaP and GaAs emit light of wavelength between 540 and 890 nm. For example, the most common LED, with the formula $GaP_{0.40}As_{0.60}$, emits 660 nm red light.

The effect of the composition of Ga–P–As semiconductors on the color of the emitted light is due in part to electronegativity differences (ΔEN) and in part to differences in atomic sizes. In GaP, ΔEN is slightly greater, and the length of the unit cell in the crystal lattice is smaller than in GaAs. These factors lead to more ionic character in the bonds and a larger band-gap energy in GaP than in GaAs. Thus the emitted light from GaP should be of a shorter wavelength than that from GaAs.

An interesting effect is noted when the temperature of an LED is changed. When an LED with the composition $GaP_{0.40}As_{0.60}$ is cooled to the boiling point of liquid nitrogen (77 K), the color shifts from that of the 660 nm red light observed at room temperature to a 639 nm *orange* light. This effect is attributed to a slight contraction of the crystal lattice of the semiconductor, which brings the atoms into closer contact and increases the band-gap energy.

These new semiconductor materials require new methods for their synthesis. Instead of precipitation from solution, the technique used is *chemical vapor deposition* (CVD). A chemical reaction is carried out between trimethylgallium, $Ga(CH_3)_3(g)$, and highly toxic arsine, $AsH_3(g)$; GaAs is deposited from the vapor phase as a thin film. If an appropriate amount of phosphine, $PH_3(g)$, is included in the reaction mixture, the film produced is GaP_xAs_{1-x}.

The application of gallium arsenide described here and its use in high-speed computers have changed the demand for GaAs from practically none in the early 1980s to a current worldwide market measured in the hundreds of millions of dollars.

*Lisensky, G., R. Penn, M. Geselbracht, and A. Ellis, *J. Chem. Educ.* **1992**: *69*, 151.

 ▲ FIGURE 21-21
Lead in gasoline and in blood
The level of lead in the blood of a representative human population showed a dramatic decline that paralleled the decline in the use of lead additives in gasoline in the 1970s. (Data source: E. P. A. Office of Policy Analysis, 1984.)

Summary

21-1 Group 1: The Alkali Metals—The **alkali metals** (group 1) are the most active of the metals, as indicated by their low ionization energies and large negative electrode potentials. Lithium exhibits some properties similar to magnesium in group 2. The similar properties exhibited by the pairs of elements (Li, Mg), (Be, Al), and (B, Si) are known as **diagonal relationships**. Most of the alkali metals are prepared by the electrolysis of their molten salts. Electrolysis of NaCl(aq) produces NaOH(aq), from which many other sodium compounds can then be prepared (Fig. 21-2). Na_2CO_3 can be produced from NaCl, NH_3, and $CaCO_3$ by the Solvay process (Fig. 21-4). A **detergent** is a cleansing agent, often sodium salts with long-chain hydrocarbon anions terminating in a sulfate group. A **soap** is also a detergent, but soaps are the sodium salts of long-chain fatty acids terminating in the carboxylate group.

21-2 Group 2: Alkaline Earth Metals—The **alkaline earth metals** (group 2), like group 1 metals, are also very active. Some group 2 metals are prepared by the electrolysis of a molten salt (Fig. 21-8), and some by chemical reduction. Among the most important of the alkaline earth compounds are the carbonates, especially $CaCO_3$. The oxide of calcium, CaO, called **quicklime**, is formed by the high-temperature decomposition (**calcination**) of limestone. The hydroxide of calcium, $Ca(OH)_2$, called **slaked lime**, is formed in the reaction of quicklime and water. Reversible reactions involving CO_3^{2-}, HCO_3^{-}, $CO_2(g)$, and H_2O account for the formation of limestone caves and interior features such as **stalactites** and **stalagmites** (Fig. 21-9). **Plaster of Paris** is the hemihydrate of calcium sulfate, $CaSO_4 \cdot \frac{1}{2}H_2O$, formed by heating the mineral gypsum, $CaSO_4 \cdot 2H_2O$.

21-3 Ions in Natural Waters: Hard Water—**Temporary hard water** contains the bicarbonate ion, HCO_3^{-} and can be softened by boiling the water. Water may also have noncarbonate anions that lead to **permanent hard water**. Water can be softened either through chemical reactions or by **ion exchange** (Fig. 21-10).

21-4 Group 13: The Boron Family—Group 13 contains one nonmetal, B, and the metals Al, Ga, In, and Tl. Boron compounds are often electron deficient (less than an octet of electrons around the B atoms). Three-center, two-electron bonds are used in describing the bonding in diborane (Fig. 21-11). Aluminum occurs almost exclusively in the +3 oxidation state whereas thallium is mostly in the +1 oxidation state. This is a manifestation of the presence of a pair of s electrons in the valence shells of certain post-transition elements. These electrons do not participate in chemical bonding, a consequence referred to as the **inert pair effect**. The principal metal of group 13 is aluminum, whose large-scale use is made possible by an effective method of production (Fig. 21-15). The amphoterism of Al_2O_3 is the basis for separating Al_2O_3 from impurities, mostly Fe_2O_3. Electrolysis is carried out in molten Na_3AlF_6 with Al_2O_3 as a solute. Aluminum is a powerful reducing agent in the **thermite reaction**, in which Fe_2O_3 is reduced to the metal. Aluminum chloride forms a **dimer**, in which two bridging chlorine atoms join together two $AlCl_3$ units (Fig. 21-16). $AlCl_3$ is very reactive. For example, a molecule of $AlCl_3$, a Lewis acid, attaches itself to a Lewis base to form an addition compound called an **adduct**. **Alums** are a class of double salts with the formula $M(I)M(III)(SO_4)_2 \cdot 12H_2O$. Gallium has gained importance in the electronics industry because of the desirable semiconductor properties of gallium arsenide (GaAs).

21-5 Group 14: The Carbon Family—Group 14 contains one nonmetal (C), two metalloids (Si and Ge), and the metals Sn, and Pb. Group 14 is notable for the significant differences between the first two members (Table 21.6). Carbon is found in several different physical forms in addition to its allotropes, one of these is **carbon black**. Carbon monoxide and carbon dioxide are both formed in the combustion of fossil fuels. Carbon monoxide is a poison (Fig. 21-18) and carbon dioxide plays a key role in the carbon cycle (Fig. 21-19). All of the elements of group 14 form halides of the type MX_4. All but carbon can employ expanded valence shells to form compounds of the form species such as the anion $[MX_6]^{2-}$. Progressing down group 14, the halide MX_2 becomes more stable than MX_4 because of the inert pair effect. Silica (SiO_2) and various silicate anions are ubiquitous components of the mineral world. They are also constituents of ceramic materials and **glass**. Organosilanes, compounds in which the hydrogen atoms of silanes are replaced by organic groups, can be polymerized to form **silicones**. Tin and lead in group 14 have some similarities (Table 21.8): They are both soft metals with low melting points. They also have some differences, including the fact that tin acquires the oxidation state +4 rather easily, whereas the +2 oxidation state is favored by lead. One of the most important uses of tin is in low-melting-point alloys known as **solders**. Both elements are obtained by the reduction of their oxides. The metallurgical method of converting a sulfide ore to an oxide, typified by the conversion of PbS to PbO upon strong heating, is called **roasting**.

Integrative Example

Without performing detailed calculations, demonstrate that reaction (21.15) correctly describes the dissolving action of rainwater on limestone (for $CaCO_3$, $K_{sp} = 2.8 \times 10^{-9}$).

Strategy

Write the equations that, when combined, yield equation (21.15) for the overall reaction occurring when rainwater

acts on limestone. Evaluate the sources and relative importance of the different species involved in the dissolution of the limestone. Describe the overall result.

Solution

The relevant equations to describe the dissolution of calcium carbonate in rainwater are the solubility product expression for $CaCO_3$ and two equations describing the ionization of CO_2 in water (that is, carbonic acid). The three equations are

$$CaCO_3(s) \rightleftharpoons Ca^{2+}(aq) + CO_3^{2-}(aq)$$
$$K_{sp} = 2.8 \times 10^{-9}$$

$$CO_2 + 2\,H_2O \rightleftharpoons H_3O^+ + HCO_3^-$$
$$K_{a_1} = 4.4 \times 10^{-7} \quad (21.13)$$

$$HCO_3^- + H_2O \rightleftharpoons H_3O^+ + CO_3^{2-}$$
$$K_{a_2} = 4.7 \times 10^{-11} \quad (21.14)$$

Equation (21.15) is related to these three equations in this way:

K_{sp} expression + equation (21.13) − equation (21.14)

This equation leads to

$$CaCO_3(s) + H_2O + CO_2 \rightleftharpoons Ca^{2+}(aq) + 2\,HCO_3^-(aq)$$
$$K = (K_{sp} \times K_{a_1})/K_{a_2} = 2.6 \times 10^{-5} \quad (21.15)$$

Next, consider which is the greater source of CO_3^{2-} ions in solution: a saturated aqueous solution of $CaCO_3$ or an aqueous carbonic acid solution. In saturated $CaCO_3$(aq),

$$[Ca^{2+}] = [CO_3^{2-}]; \; K_{sp} = [Ca^{2+}][CO_3^{2-}] = [CO_3^{2-}]^2$$
$$= 2.8 \times 10^{-9}.$$

$$[CO_3^{2-}] = (2.8 \times 10^{-9})^{\frac{1}{2}} = 5.3 \times 10^{-5}\,M.$$

In a carbonic acid solution, H_2CO_3 is a weak *diprotic* acid with $K_{a_2} \ll K_{a_1}$. Thus,

$$[H_3O^+] = [HCO_3^-], \text{ and } [CO_3^{2-}] = K_{a_2} = 4.7 \times 10^{-11}\,M$$

Note that the carbonate ion concentration in a saturated $CaCO_3$ solution is much greater than the carbonate ion concentration observed in a carbonic acid solution. This means that when the two processes occur simultaneously, carbonate ion from the dissolution of $CaCO_3$ acts as a common ion in the carbonic acid equilibrium. This displaces reaction (21.14) *to the left*, converting CO_3^{2-} to HCO_3^- while consuming H_3O^+. Removal of H_3O^+ in reaction (21.14) stimulates reaction (21.13) to shift *to the right*, producing more H_3O^+ and, simultaneously, more HCO_3^-. The overall effect is that H_2O, CO_2, and CO_3^{2-} (from $CaCO_3$) are consumed and HCO_3^- is produced, just as suggested by equation (21.15).

Assessment

We have assessed the qualitative correctness of reaction (21.15). To calculate the quantitative extent of the dissolution of $CaCO_3$(s) in rainwater is somewhat more difficult. The calculation centers on the combined equilibrium constant expression for reaction (21.15), $K = 2.6 \times 10^{-5}$, and is affected by the partial pressure of atmospheric CO_2 in equilibrium with rainwater. Typical data are given in Chapter 16, Exercise 86.

Exercises

Group 1: (Alkali) Metals

1. Use information from the chapter to write chemical equations to represent each of the following:
   (a) reaction of cesium metal with chlorine gas
   (b) formation of sodium peroxide (Na_2O_2)
   (c) thermal decomposition of lithium carbonate
   (d) reduction of sodium sulfate to sodium sulfide
   (e) combustion of potassium to form potassium superoxide
2. Use information from the chapter to write chemical equations to represent each of the following:
   (a) reaction of rubidium metal with water
   (b) thermal decomposition of aqueous $KHCO_3$
   (c) combustion of lithium metal in oxygen gas
   (d) action of concentrated aqueous H_2SO_4 on KCl(s)
   (e) reaction of lithium hydride with water
3. Describe a simple test for determining whether a pure white solid is LiCl or KCl.
4. Describe two methods for determining the identity of an unknown compound that is either Li_2CO_3 or K_2CO_3.
5. Arrange the following compounds in the expected order of increasing solubility in water, and give the basis for your arrangement: Li_2CO_3, Na_2CO_3, $MgCO_3$.
6. The first electrolytic process to produce sodium metal used molten NaOH as the electrolyte. Write probable half-equations and an overall equation for this electrolysis.

7. A 0.872-L NaCl(aq) solution is electrolyzed for 2.50 min with a current of 0.810 A.
   (a) Calculate the pH of the solution after electrolysis.
   (b) Why doesn't the result depend on the initial concentration of the NaCl(aq)?
8. A lithium battery used in a cardiac pacemaker has a voltage of 3.0 V and a capacity of 0.50 A h (ampere hour). Assume that 5.0 μW of power is needed to regulate the heartbeat.
   [*Hint:* See Appendix B.]
   (a) How long will the implanted battery last?
   (b) How many grams of lithium must be present in the battery for the lifetime calculated in part (a)?
9. An analysis of a Solvay-process plant shows that for every 1.00 ton of NaCl consumed, 1.03 tons of $NaHCO_3$ are obtained. The quantity of NH_3 consumed in the overall process is 1.5 lb.
   (a) What is the percent efficiency of this process for converting NaCl to $NaHCO_3$?
   (b) Why is so little NH_3 required?
10. Consider the reaction $Ca(OH)_2(s) + Na_2SO_4(aq) \rightleftharpoons CaSO_4(s) + 2\,NaOH(aq)$.
    (a) Write a net ionic equation for this reaction.
    (b) Will the reaction essentially go to completion?
    (c) What will be $[SO_4^{2-}]$ and $[OH^-]$ *at equilibrium* if a slurry of $Ca(OH)_2(s)$ is mixed with 1.00 M Na_2SO_4(aq)?

Group 2: (Alkaline Earth) Metals

11. In the manner used to construct Figure 21-2, complete the diagram outlined. Specifically, indicate the reactants (and conditions) you would use to produce the indicated substances from $Ca(OH)_2$.

12. Replace the calcium-containing substances shown in the diagram accompanying Exercise 11 by their magnesium-containing equivalents. Then describe the reactants (and conditions) you would use to produce the indicated substances from $MgSO_4$.

13. In the Dow process (Fig. 21-7), the starting material is Mg^{2+} in seawater and the final product is Mg metal. This process seems to violate the principle of conservation of charge. Does it? Explain.

14. Which has the (a) higher melting point, MgO or BaO; (b) greater solubility in water, MgF_2 or $MgCl_2$? Explain.

15. Write chemical equations to represent the following:
    (a) reduction of BeF_2 to Be metal with Mg as a reducing agent
    (b) reaction of barium metal with $Br_2(l)$
    (c) reduction of uranium(IV) oxide to uranium metal with calcium as the reducing agent
    (d) calcination of dolomite, a mixed calcium magnesium carbonate ($MgCO_3 \cdot CaCO_3$)
    (e) complete neutralization of phosphoric acid with quicklime

16. Write chemical equations for the reactions you would expect to occur when:
    (a) $Mg(HCO_3)_2(s)$ is heated to a high temperature
    (b) $BaCl_2(l)$ is electrolyzed
    (c) $Sr(s)$ is added to cold dilute $HBr(aq)$
    (d) $Ca(OH)_2(aq)$ is added to $H_2SO_4(aq)$
    (e) $CaSO_4 \cdot 2\,H_2O(s)$ is heated

17. *Without performing detailed calculations*, indicate whether equilibrium is displaced either far to the left or far to the right for each of the following reactions. Use data from Appendix D as necessary.
    (a) $BaSO_4(s) + CO_3^{2-}(aq) \rightleftharpoons BaCO_3(s) + SO_4^{2-}(aq)$
    (b) $Mg_3(PO_4)_2(s) + 3\,CO_3^{2-}(aq) \rightleftharpoons$
    $$3\,MgCO_3(s) + 2\,PO_4^{3-}(aq)$$
    (c) $Ca(OH)_2(s) + 2\,F^-(aq) \rightleftharpoons CaF_2(s) + 2\,OH^-(aq)$

18. *Without performing detailed calculations*, indicate why you would expect each of the following reactions to occur to a significant extent as written. Use data from Appendix D as necessary.
    (a) $BaCO_3(s) + 2\,CH_3CO_2H(aq) \longrightarrow$
    $$Ba^{2+}(aq) + 2\,CH_3CO_2^-(aq) + H_2O(l) + CO_2(g)$$
    (b) $Ca(OH)_2(s) + 2\,NH_4^+(aq) \longrightarrow$
    $$Ca^{2+}(aq) + 2\,NH_3(aq) + 2\,H_2O(l)$$
    (c) $BaF_2(s) + 2\,H_3O^+(aq) \longrightarrow$
    $$Ba^{2+}(aq) + 2\,HF(aq) + 2\,H_2O(l)$$

Hard Water

19. Write an equation to show the softening of temporary hard water with quicklime.

20. Write an equation to show the softening of temporary hard water with ammonia.

21. A certain hard water contains 185.0 ppm HCO_3^-, and all the cations associated with the HCO_3^- are Ca^{2+}.
    (a) What is $[Ca^{2+}]$, expressed in parts per million?
    (b) What is $[Ca^{2+}]$, expressed in milligrams per liter?
    (c) How many grams of $Ca(OH)_2$ are required to soften 1.00×10^6 g of this water?

22. For the hard water described in Exercise 21,
    (a) how many grams of $CaCO_3$ would be precipitated in softening 1.00×10^6 g of this water with $Ca(OH)_2$?
    (b) Show that in the $CaCO_3$, half the Ca^{2+} is derived from the $Ca(OH)_2$ used in the water softening and half from the water itself.

23. A sample of hard water is passed through a cation-exchange resin in which cations are exchanged for H_3O^+. The water coming off the resin has a pH = 2.37. Assume that the cations in the water are Ca^{2+}, and determine the hardness expressed as ppm Ca^{2+}.

24. The hardness of a sample of water is due only to $CaSO_4$. When this water is passed through an anion-exchange resin, SO_4^{2-} ions are replaced by OH^-. A 25.00-mL sample of the water so treated requires 22.42 mL of 1.00×10^{-3} M H_2SO_4 for its titration. What is the hardness of the water expressed in ppm $CaSO_4$? Assume that the density of the water is 1.00 g/mL.

25. What mass of bathtub ring will form if 32.1 L of water having 82.6 ppm Ca^{2+} is treated with an excess of the soap potassium stearate, $CH_3(CH_2)_{16}COO^-K^+$?

26. One of the components of bathtub ring is magnesium palmitate, $Mg(CH_3(CH_2)_{14}CO_2)_2$. A saturated solution of magnesium palmitate is found to contain 80 ppm $Mg^{2+}(aq)$. What is the K_{sp} of magnesium palmitate?

Group 13: The Boron Family

27. The molecule tetraborane has the formula B_4H_{10}.
    (a) Show that this is an electron-deficient molecule.
    (b) How many bridge bonds must occur in the molecule?
    (c) Show that butane, C_4H_{10}, is not electron-deficient.

28. Write Lewis structures for the following species, both of which involve coordinate covalent bonding:
    (a) tetrafluoroborate ion, BF_4^-, used in metal cleaning and in electroplating baths
    (b) boron trifluoride ethylamine, used in curing epoxy resins (ethylamine is $C_2H_5NH_2$)

29. Write chemical equations to represent:
    (a) the preparation of boron from BBr_3
    (b) the formation of BF_3 from B_2O_3
    (c) the combustion of boron in hot $N_2O(g)$

30. Assign oxidation states to all the atoms in a perborate ion based on the structure on page 888.

31. Write chemical equations to represent the
    (a) reaction of $Al(s)$ with $HCl(aq)$;
    (b) reaction of $Al(s)$ with $NaOH(aq)$;
    (c) oxidation of $Al(s)$ to $Al^{3+}(aq)$ by an aqueous solution of sulfuric acid; the reduction product is $SO_2(g)$.

32. Write plausible equations for the
    (a) reaction of $Al(s)$ with $Br_2(l)$;
    (b) production of Cr from $Cr_2O_3(s)$ by the thermite reaction, with Al as the reducing agent;
    (c) separation of Fe_2O_3 impurity from bauxite ore.

33. In some foam-type fire extinguishers, the reactants are $Al_2(SO_4)_3(aq)$ and $NaHCO_3(aq)$. When the extinguisher is activated, these reactants mix, producing $Al(OH)_3(s)$ and $CO_2(g)$. The $Al(OH)_3-CO_2$ foam extinguishes the fire. Write a net ionic equation to represent this reaction.

34. Some baking powders contain the solids $NaHCO_3$ and $NaAl(SO_4)_2$. When water is added to this mixture of compounds, $CO_2(g)$ and $Al(OH)_3(s)$ are two of the products. Write plausible net ionic equations for the formation of these two products.

35. The maximum resistance to corrosion of aluminum is between pH 4.5 and 8.5. Explain how this observation is consistent with other facts about the behavior of aluminum presented in this text.

36. Describe a series of *simple* chemical reactions that you could use to determine whether a particular metal sample is "aluminum 2S" (99.2% Al) or "magnalium" (70% Al, 30% Mg). You are permitted to destroy the metal sample in the testing.

37. In the purification of bauxite ore, a preliminary step in the production of aluminum, $[Al(OH)_4]^-(aq)$ can be converted to $Al(OH)_3(s)$ by passing $CO_2(g)$ through the solution. Write an equation for the reaction that occurs. Could $HCl(aq)$ be used instead of $CO_2(g)$? Explain.

38. In 1825, Hans Oersted produced aluminum chloride by passing chlorine over a heated mixture of carbon and aluminum oxide. In 1827, Friedrich Wöhler obtained aluminum by heating aluminum chloride with potassium. Write plausible equations for these reactions.

39. A description for preparing potassium aluminum alum calls for dissolving aluminum foil in $KOH(aq)$. The solution obtained is treated with $H_2SO_4(aq)$, and the alum is crystallized from the resulting solution. Write plausible equations for these reactions.

40. Handbooks and lists of chemicals do not contain entries under the formulas $Al(HCO_3)_3$ and $Al_2(CO_3)_2$. Explain why these compounds do not exist.

Group 14: The Carbon Family

41. Comment on the accuracy of a jeweler's advertising that "diamonds last forever." In what sense is the statement true, and in what ways is it false?

42. A temporary fix for a "sticky" lock is to scrape a pencil point across the notches on the key and to work the key in and out of the lock a few times. What is the basis of this fix?

43. Write a chemical equation to represent:
    (a) the reduction of silica to elemental silicon by aluminum
    (b) the preparation of potassium metasilicate by the high-temperature fusion of silica and potassium carbonate
    (c) the reaction of Al_4C_3 with water to produce methane

44. Write a chemical equation to represent:
    (a) the reaction of potassium cyanide solution with silver nitrate solution
    (b) the combustion of Si_3H_8 in an excess of oxygen
    (c) the reaction of dinitrogen with calcium carbide to give calcium cyanamide (CaNCN)

45. Describe what is meant by the terms *silane* and *silanol*. What is their role in the preparation of silicones?

46. Describe and explain the similarities and differences between the reaction of a silicate with an acid and that of a carbonate with an acid.

47. Methane and sulfur vapor react to form carbon disulfide and hydrogen sulfide. Carbon disulfide reacts with $Cl_2(g)$ to form carbon tetrachloride and S_2Cl_2. Further reaction of carbon disulfide and S_2Cl_2 produces additional carbon tetrachloride and sulfur. Write a series of equations for the reactions described here.

48. In a manner similar to that outlined on page 904.
    (a) write equations to represent the reaction of $(CH_3)_3SiCl$ with water, followed by the elimination of H_2O from the resulting silanol molecules.
    (b) Does a silicone polymer form from part (a)?
    (c) What would be the corresponding product obtained from CH_3SiCl_3?

49. Show that the empirical formula given for muscovite mica is consistent with the expected oxidation states of the elements present.

50. Show that the empirical formula given for crysotile asbestos is consistent with the expected oxidation states of the elements present.

51. Write plausible chemical equations for the (a) dissolving of lead(II) oxide in nitric acid; (b) heating of $SnCO_3(s)$; (c) reduction of lead(II) oxide by carbon; (d) reduction of $Fe^{3+}(aq)$ to $Fe^{2+}(aq)$ by $Sn^{2+}(aq)$; (e) formation of lead(II) sulfate during high-temperature roasting of lead(II) sulfide.

52. Write plausible chemical equations for preparing each compound from the indicated starting material: (a) $SnCl_2$ from SnO; (b) $SnCl_4$ from Sn; (c) $PbCrO_4$ from PbO_2. What reagents (acids, bases, salts) and equipment commonly available in the laboratory are needed for each reaction?

53. Lead(IV) oxide, PbO_2, is a good oxidizing agent. Use appropriate data from Appendix D to determine whether $PbO_2(s)$ in a solution with $[H_3O^+] = 1$ M is a sufficiently good oxidizing agent to carry the following oxidations to the point at which the concentration of the species being oxidized decreases to one-thousandth of its initial value.
(a) $Fe^{2+}(1$ M$)$ to Fe^{3+}
(b) $SO_4^{2-}(1$ M$)$ to $S_2O_8^{2-}$
(c) $Mn^{2+}(1 \times 10^{-4}$ M$)$ to MnO_4^-

54. Tin(II) ion, Sn^{2+}, is a good reducing agent. Use data from Appendix D to determine whether Sn^{2+} is a sufficiently good reducing agent to reduce (a) I_2 to I^-; (b) Fe^{2+} to $Fe(s)$; (c) Cu^{2+} to $Cu(s)$; (d) $Fe^{3+}(aq)$ to $Fe^{2+}(aq)$. Assume that all reactants and products are in their standard states.

Integrative and Advanced Exercises

55. A chemical that should exist as a crystalline solid is seen to be a mixture of a solid and liquid in a container on a storeroom shelf. Give a plausible reason for that observation. Should the chemical be discarded or is it still useful for some purposes?

56. The following series of observations is made: (1) a small piece of Dry Ice [$CO_2(s)$] is added to 0.005 M $Ca(OH)_2(aq)$. (2) Initially, a white precipitate forms. (3) After a short time the precipitate dissolves.
(a) Write chemical equations to explain these observations.
(b) If the 0.005 M $Ca(OH)_2(aq)$ is replaced by 0.005 M $CaCl_2(aq)$, would a precipitate form? Explain.
(c) If the 0.005 M $Ca(OH)_2(aq)$ is replaced by 0.010 M $Ca(OH)_2(aq)$, a precipitate forms but does not re-dissolve. Explain why.

57. The melting point of NaCl(s) is 801 °C, much higher than that of NaOH (322 °C). More energy is consumed to melt and maintain molten NaCl than NaOH. Yet the preferred commercial process for the production of sodium is electrolysis of NaCl(l) rather than NaOH(l). Give a reason or reasons for this discrepancy.

58. When a 0.200-g sample of Mg is heated in air, 0.315 g of product is obtained. Assume that all the Mg appears in the product.
(a) If the product were pure MgO, what mass should have been obtained?
(b) Show that the 0.315 g product could be a mixture of MgO and Mg_3N_2.
(c) What is the mass percent of MgO in the $MgO–Mg_3N_2$ mixed product?

59. Comment on the feasibility of using a reaction similar to (21.3) to produce (a) lithium metal from LiCl; (b) cesium metal from CsCl, with Na(l) as the reducing agent in each case.
[Hint: Consider data from Table 21.2.]

60. Concerning the thermite reaction,
(a) use data from Appendix D to calculate $\Delta H°$ at 298 K for the reaction.

$$2\ Al(s) + Fe_2O_3(s) \longrightarrow 2\ Fe(s) + Al_2O_3(s)$$

(b) Write an equation for the reaction when $MnO_2(s)$ is substituted for $Fe_2O_3(s)$, and calculate $\Delta H°$ for this reaction.

(c) Show that if MgO were substituted for Fe_2O_3, the reaction would be *endothermic*.

61. Use data from Appendix D (Table D-2) to calculate a value of $E°$ for the reduction of $Li^+(aq)$ to Li(s), and compare your result with the value listed in Table 21.2.

62. The electrolysis of 0.250 L of 0.220 M $MgCl_2$ is conducted until 104 mL of gas (a mixture of H_2 and water vapor) is collected at 23 °C and 748 mmHg. Will $Mg(OH)_2(s)$ precipitate if electrolysis is carried to this point? (Use 21 mmHg as the vapor pressure of the solution.)

63. A particular water sample contains 56.9 ppm SO_4^{2-} and 176 ppm HCO_3^-, with Ca^{2+} as the only cation.
(a) How many parts per million of Ca^{2+} does the water contain?
(b) How many grams of CaO are consumed in removing HCO_3^-, from 602 kg of the water?
(c) Show that the Ca^{2+} remaining in the water after the treatment described in part (b) can be removed by adding Na_2CO_3.
(d) How many grams of Na_2CO_3 are required for the precipitation referred to in part (c)?

64. An Al production cell of the type pictured in Figure 21-15 operates at a current of 1.00×10^5 A and a voltage of 4.5 V. The cell is 38% efficient in using electrical energy to produce chemical change. (The rest of the electrical energy is dissipated as thermal energy in the cell.)
(a) What mass of Al can be produced by this cell in 8.00 h?
(b) If the electrical energy required to power this cell is produced by burning coal (85% C; heat of combustion of C = 32.8 kJ/g) in a power plant with 35% efficiency, what mass of coal must be burned to produce the mass of Al determined in part (a)?

65. Use data from Appendix D (Table D-2) to estimate the minimum voltage required to electrolyze Al_2O_3 in the Hall–Héroult process, reaction (21.23). Use $\Delta G_f°[Al_2O_3(l)] = -1520$ kJ mol^{-1}. Show that the oxidation of the graphite anode to $CO_2(g)$ permits the electrolysis to occur at a lower voltage than if the electrolysis reaction were $Al_2O_3(l) \longrightarrow 2\ Al(l) + \frac{3}{2}O_2(g)$.

66. At 20 °C, a saturated aqueous solution of $Pb(NO_3)_2$ maintains a relative humidity of 97%. What must be the composition of this solution, expressed as g $Pb(NO_3)_2/100.0$ g H_2O?

67. Use information from this chapter and elsewhere in this text to explain why the compounds $PbBr_4$ and PbI_4 do *not* exist.

68. The reaction of borax, calcium fluoride, and concentrated sulfuric acid yields sodium hydrogen sulfate, calcium sulfate, water, and boron trifluoride as products. Write a balanced equation for this reaction.

69. The dissolution of $MgCO_3(s)$ in $NH_4^+(aq)$ can be represented as

$$MgCO_3(s) + NH_4^+(aq) \rightleftharpoons$$

$$Mg^{2+}(aq) + HCO_3^-(aq) + NH_3(aq)$$

Calculate the molar solubility of $MgCO_3$ in each of the following solutions: **(a)** 1.00 M $NH_4Cl(aq)$; **(b)** a buffer that is 1.00 M NH_3 and 1.00 M NH_4Cl; **(c)** a buffer that is 0.100 M NH_3 and 1.00 M NH_4Cl.

70. Show that, in principle, $Na_2CO_3(aq)$ can be converted almost completely to $NaOH(aq)$ by the reaction

$$Ca(OH)_2(s) + Na_2CO_3(aq) \longrightarrow$$

$$CaCO_3(s) + 2\,NaOH(aq)$$

71. Assume that the packing of spherical atoms in crystalline metals is the same for Li, Na, and K, and explain why Na has a higher density than *both* Li and K. [*Hint:* Use data from Table 21.2.]

72. Would you expect the lattice energy of $MgS(s)$ to be less than, greater than, or about the same as that of $MgO(s)$? Use appropriate data from various locations in this text to obtain the values of the two lattice energies. Use a value of 456 kJ for the process $S^-(g) + e^- \longrightarrow S^{2-}(g)$.

Feature Problems

73. In Chapter 20, we examined the relationship of electrode potentials to thermodynamic data. In fact, electrode potentials can be calculated from tabulated thermodynamic data (many of which, in turn, were established from electrochemical measurements). To demonstrate this fact and to pursue further the discussion in the Are You Wondering feature on page 873, combine the three steps for the oxidation of Li(s) with a corresponding set of three steps for the reduction of H^+ (1 M) to $H_2(g)$. Obtain $\Delta H°$ for the overall reaction.
    (a) Neglect entropy changes that occur (that is, assume that $\Delta G° \approx \Delta H°$), and estimate the value of $E°_{Li^+/Li}$.
    (b) Combine the calculated $\Delta H°$ value with a value of $\Delta S°$ to obtain another estimate of $E°_{Li^+/Li}$.
    [*Hint:* Hydration energies for $Li^+(g)$ and $H^+(g)$ to form 1 M solutions are -506 and -1079 kJ/mol, respectively. Also, use data from various locations in this text.]

74. Mono Lake in eastern California is a rather unusual salt lake. The lake has no outlets; water leaves only by evaporation. The rate of evaporation is great enough that the lake level would be lowered by four feet per year if not for fresh water entering through underwater springs and streams originating in the nearby Sierra Nevada mountains. The principal salts in the lake are the chlorides, bicarbonates, and sulfates of sodium. An approximate "recipe" for simulating the lake water is to dissolve 18 tablespoons of sodium bicarbonate, 10 tablespoons of sodium chloride, and 8 teaspoons of Epsom salt (magnesium sulfate heptahydrate) in 1 gallon of water (although the lake water actually contains only trace amounts of magnesium ion). Assume that 1 tablespoon of any of the salts weighs about 10 g. (1 tablespoon = 3 teaspoons.)
    (a) Expressed as grams of salt per liter, what is the approximate salinity of Mono Lake? How does this salinity compare with seawater, which is approximately 0.438 M NaCl and 0.0512 M $MgCl_2$?
    (b) Estimate an approximate pH for Mono Lake water. How does your estimate compare to the observed pH of about 9.8? Actually, the recipe for the lake water also calls for a pinch of borax. How would its presence affect the pH? [Borax is a sodium salt, $Na_2B_4O_7 \cdot 10\,H_2O$, related to the weak monoprotic boric acid ($pK_a = 9.25$).]
    (c) Mono Lake has some unusual limestone formations called *tufa*. They form at the site of underwater springs and grow only underwater, although some project above water, having formed at a time when the lake level was higher. Explain how the tufa form. [*Hint:* What chemical reaction(s) is(are) involved?]

Self-Assessment Exercises

75. In your own words, define the following terms: **(a)** dimer; **(b)** adduct; **(c)** calcination; **(d)** amphoteric oxide; **(e)** three-center bond.

76. Briefly describe each of the following ideas, methods, or phenomena: **(a)** diagonal relationship; **(b)** preparation of deionized water by ion exchange; **(c)** thermite reaction; **(d)** inert pair effect.

77. Explain the important distinction between each pair of terms: **(a)** peroxide and superoxide; **(b)** quicklime and slaked lime; **(c)** temporary and permanent hard water; **(d)** soap and detergent; **(e)** silicate and silicone; **(f)** sol and gel.

78. Of the following oxides, the one with the highest melting point is **(a)** Li_2O; **(b)** BaO; **(c)** MgO; **(d)** SiO_2.

79. The best oxidizing agent of the following oxides is **(a)** Li_2O; **(b)** MgO; **(c)** Al_2O_3; **(d)** CO_2; **(e)** SnO_2; **(f)** PbO_2.

80. Of the following substances, the one that cannot be used to soften temporary hard water is **(a)** NH_3; **(b)** Na_2CO_3; **(c)** $Ca(OH)_2$; **(d)** NH_4Cl; **(e)** CaO.

81. Listed are several pairs of substances. For some pairs, one or both members of the pair react individually with water to produce a gas. For others, neither member of the pair reacts with water. The pair for which *each* member reacts with water and yields the *same* gaseous product is **(a)** $Al(s)$ and $Ba(s)$; **(b)** $Ca(s)$ and $CaH_2(s)$; **(c)** $Na(s)$ and $Na_2O_2(s)$; **(d)** $K(s)$ and $KO_2(s)$; **(e)** $NaHCO_3(s)$ and $HCl(aq)$.

82. Complete and balance the following. Write the simplest equation possible. If no reaction occurs, so state.

    (a) $Li_2CO_3(s) \xrightarrow{\Delta}$

    (b) $CaCO_3(s) + HCl(aq) \longrightarrow$

    (c) $Al(s) + NaOH(aq) \longrightarrow$

    (d) $BaO(s) + H_2O(l) \longrightarrow$

    (e) $Na_2O_2(s) + CO_2(g) \longrightarrow$

83. Assuming that water, common reagents (acids, bases, salts), and simple laboratory equipment are available, give a practical method to prepare **(a)** $MgCl_2$ from $MgCO_3(s)$; **(b)** $NaAl(OH)_4$ from $Na(s)$ and $Al(s)$; and **(c)** Na_2SO_4 from $NaCl(s)$.

84. Write the simplest chemical equation to represent the reaction of **(a)** $K_2CO_3(aq)$ and $Ba(OH)_2(aq)$; **(b)** $Mg(HCO_3)_2(aq)$ on heating; **(c)** tin(II) oxide when heated with carbon; **(d)** $CaF_2(s)$ and H_2SO_4 (concd aq); **(e)** $NaHCO_3(s)$ and $HCl(aq)$; **(f)** $PbO_2(s)$ and $HBr(aq)$; and **(g)** the reduction of SiF_4 to pure Si, using Na as the reducing agent.

85. Write an equation to represent the reaction of gypsum, $CaSO_4 \cdot 2\,H_2O$, with ammonium carbonate to produce ammonium sulfate (a fertilizer), calcium carbonate, and water.

86. Write chemical equations to represent the most probable outcome in each of the following. If no reaction is likely to occur, so state.

    (a) $B(OH)_3 \xrightarrow{\Delta}$

    (b) $Al_2O_3(s) \xrightarrow{\Delta}$

    (c) $CaSO_4 \cdot 2\,H_2O(s) \xrightarrow{\Delta}$

87. A chemical dictionary gives the following descriptions of the production of some compounds. Write plausible chemical equations based on these descriptions.

    (a) lead(II) carbonate: adding a solution of sodium bicarbonate to a solution of lead nitrate

    (b) lithium carbonate: reaction of lithium oxide with ammonium carbonate solution

    (c) hydrogen peroxide: by the action of dilute sulfuric acid on barium peroxide

    (d) lead(IV) oxide: action of an alkaline solution of calcium hypochlorite on lead(II) oxide

88. Name the chemical compound(s) you would expect to be the *primary* constituent(s) of **(a)** stalactites; **(b)** gypsum; **(c)** bathtub ring; **(d)** "barium milkshake"; **(e)** blue sapphires.

89. How many cubic meters of $CO_2(g)$ at 102 kPa and 288 K are produced in the calcination of 5.00×10^3 kg of the mineral dolomite, $CaMg(CO_3)_2$?

90. A sample of water has a hardness expressed as 77.5 ppm Ca^{2+}. The sample is passed through an ion exchange column and the Ca^{2+} is replaced by H_3O^+. What is the pH of the water as it leaves the column?

 eMedia Exercises

91. The alkali metals are described as being the most chemically reactive elements. The **Sodium and Potassium in Water** movie (*Activebook 21-1*) shows examples of vigorous reactions. Based upon the principles described in this section, as well as those of atomic properties and thermodynamics, account for the differences in the observed reactivity between sodium and potassium.

92. Use the **Solubility Products of Ionic Compounds** activity (*Activebook 21-2*) to compare the solubilities of group 1 and 2 metal compounds. **(a)** What general observations can you make about the differences in the solubilities of the two different groups of metals? **(b)** What atomic properties are related to these differences?

93. The **Thermite** movie (*Activebook 21-4*) illustrates the energetics involved in the oxidation of metallic aluminum. What do your observations of the thermite reaction indicate about the requirements for the production of metallic aluminum from ore?

94. **(a)** View the **Allotropes of Carbon** models (*Activebook 21-5*), and describe the hybridization of carbon in each form. **(b)** Suggest reasons for the differences in the mechanical properties of the different forms of carbon. **(c)** Which of the structures of carbon is also characteristic of other elements in group 14?

CHEMISTRY OF THE MAIN-GROUP ELEMENTS II: GROUPS 18, 17, 16, 15, AND HYDROGEN

CONTENTS

Bromine, a nonmetal, is a reactant in the synthesis of flame retardants for use in plastics.

We begin this chapter with a brief survey of the noble gases, a special group of unreactive nonmetals. We next examine the halogens, the most active group of nonmetals, and then proceed through the periodic table from right to left, moving from active nonmetals to the elements with increasing metallic character. This approach is opposite that of Chapter 21, where we progressed from the most metallic elements (group 1) to the elements having more nonmetallic character. Finally, in this chapter we shall consider hydrogen. Hydrogen has unique chemistry and is not easily placed in any group of the periodic table. Among the fundamental concepts emphasized in this chapter are atomic, physical, and thermodynamic properties; bonding and structure; acid–base chemistry; and oxidation states, redox reactions, and electrochemistry.

▲ Gaseous atoms in the region of an electric discharge emit light. The light emitted by neon atoms is red-orange in color. Neon lights of other colors use other noble gases or mixtures of gases.

▲ **William Ramsay (1852–1916)** This distinguished Scottish chemist received the 1904 Nobel Prize in Chemistry for his work on the noble gases.

▶ As we learned in Chapter 13 (page 543), using helium–oxygen mixtures instead of air for deep-sea diving eliminates nitrogen and prevents nitrogen narcosis ("rapture of the deep"). Also, because helium is more rapidly and smoothly expelled from the blood than is nitrogen, helium–oxygen mixtures prevent the condition known as the *bends*.

Welch, Lawrence E., Mossman, Daniel M. "An Environmental Chemistry Experiment: The Determination of Radon Levels in Water." *J. Chem. Educ.* **1994:** 71, 521.

22-1 GROUP 18: THE NOBLE GASES

In 1785, Henry Cavendish, the discoverer of hydrogen, passed electric discharges through air to form oxides of nitrogen. (A similar process occurs during lightning storms.) He then dissolved these oxides in water to form nitric acid. Even by using excess oxygen, Cavendish was unable to get all the air to react. He suggested that air contained an unreactive gas making up "not more than 1/120 of the whole." John Rayleigh and William Ramsay isolated this gas one century later (1894) and named it argon. The name is derived from the Greek *argos*, "lazy one," meaning "inert." Its *inability* to form chemical compounds with any of the other elements—its chemical inertness—was found to be argon's most notable feature. Because argon resembled no other known element, Ramsay placed it in a separate group of the periodic table and reasoned that there should be other members of this group.

Ramsay then began a systematic search for other inert gases. In 1895, he extracted helium from a uranium mineral. A few years later, by very carefully distilling liquid argon, he was able to extract three additional inert gases: neon, krypton, and xenon. The final member of the group of inert gases, a radioactive element called radon, was discovered in 1900. In 1962, compounds of Xe were first prepared, and so the inert gases proved not to be completely inert after all. Since that time, this group of gases has been called the **noble gases**. They are found in group 18 of the periodic table shown on the inside front cover.

OCCURRENCE

Air contains 0.000524% He, 0.001818% Ne, and 0.934% Ar, by volume. The proportion of Kr is about 1 ppm by volume, and that of Xe, 0.05 ppm. The atmosphere is the only source of all these gases except helium. The main source of helium is certain natural gas wells in the western United States that produce natural gas containing up to 8% He by volume. It is cost-effective to extract helium from natural gas even down to levels of about 0.3%. Underground helium accumulates as a result of α-particle emission by radioactive elements in Earth's crust. Whereas the abundance of He on Earth is very limited, it is second only to hydrogen in the universe as a whole.

PROPERTIES AND USES

The lighter noble gases are commercially important, in part because they are chemically inert. The efficiency and life of electric lightbulbs are increased when they are filled with an argon–nitrogen mixture. Electric discharge through neon-filled glass or plastic tubes produces a distinctive red light (neon light). Krypton and xenon are used in lasers and in flashlamps in photography. Helium has several unique physical properties. Best known of these is that it exists as a liquid at temperatures approaching 0 K. All other substances freeze to solids at temperatures well above 0 K. (The melting point of solid H_2, for example, is 14 K.) Because of their inertness, both He and Ar are

Are You Wondering . . .

Why argon is so much more abundant in the atmosphere than all the other noble gases?

Most of the noble gases have escaped from the atmosphere since Earth was formed, but Ar is an exception. The concentration of Ar remains quite high because it is constantly being formed by the radioactive decay of potassium-40, a reasonably abundant, naturally occurring radioactive isotope. Helium is also constantly produced through α-particle emissions by radioactive decay processes, but because the molar mass of He is 10 times less than that of Ar, it escapes from the atmosphere into outer space at a higher rate.

used to blanket materials that need to be protected from nitrogen and oxygen in the air, as in certain types of welding, in metallurgical processes, and in the preparation of ultrapure Si and Ge and other semiconductor materials. Helium mixed with oxygen is used as a breathing mixture for deep-sea diving and in certain medical applications. Large quantities of liquid helium are used to maintain low temperatures (cryogenics). Metals essentially lose their electrical resistivity at liquid He temperatures and become *superconductors*. Powerful magnets can be made by immersing the coils of electromagnets in liquid helium. Such magnets are used in particle accelerators and in nuclear fusion research. More familiar uses of large electromagnets cooled by liquid helium are nuclear magnetic resonance (NMR) instruments in research laboratories and magnetic resonance imaging (MRI) devices in hospitals. Helium is also used to fill lighter-than-air airships (blimps).

▲ An MRI image of a head.

XENON COMPOUNDS

Initially, the noble gases were found to be chemically inert. This apparent inertness helped provide a theoretical framework for the Lewis theory of bonding. Subsequently it was found that compounds of xenon can be made fairly easily, and these compounds have added significantly to our knowledge of chemical bonding.

In the 1930s, Linus Pauling did theoretical calculations suggesting that xenon should form oxide and fluoride compounds, but attempts to make them failed at that time. In 1962, N. Bartlett and D. H. Lohmann discovered that O_2 and PtF_6 would join in a 1:1 mole ratio to form the compound O_2PtF_6. Properties of this compound suggest it to be ionic: $[O_2]^+[PtF_6]^-$. The energy required to extract an electron from O_2 is 1177 kJ mol^{-1}, almost identical to the first ionization energy of Xe, 1170 kJ mol^{-1}. The size of the Xe atom is also roughly the same as that of the dioxygen molecule. Thus, it was reasoned that the compound $XePtF_6$ might exist. Bartlett and Lohmann were able to prepare a yellow crystalline solid with that composition.*

Soon thereafter, chemists around the world synthesized several additional noble gas compounds. In general, the conditions necessary to form noble gas compounds are as Pauling predicted:

▲ Because of the explosive nature of hydrogen, helium is now used in airships.

Luckenbaugh, Raymond W. "Radon's Link to Lung Cancer (L)." *J. Chem. Educ.* **1994:** *71*, 902.

- a readily ionizable (therefore, high atomic number) noble gas atom
- highly electronegative atoms (such as F or O) to bond to it

Xenon compounds have been synthesized that have Xe in four possible oxidation states.

XeF$_2$ and XeF$_4$ models

	+2	**+4**	**+6**	**+8**
Examples:	XeF$_2$	XeF$_4$, XeOF$_2$	XeF$_6$, XeO$_3$	XeO$_4$, H$_4$XeO$_6$

Fill a balloon or two with helium to show that it is a very low density gas.

Because it is difficult to oxidize Xe to these positive oxidation states, we would expect Xe compounds to be easily reduced, making them very strong oxidizing agents. For example, in aqueous acidic solution

$$XeF_2(aq) + 2\,H^+(aq) + 2\,e^- \longrightarrow Xe(g) + 2\,HF(aq) \qquad E^\circ = +2.64\,V$$

The significance of this large E° value is that XeF_2 is not very stable in aqueous solution; XeF_2 oxidizes the water, producing $O_2(g)$.

Reduction:	$2\{XeF_2(aq) + 2\,H^+(aq) + 2\,e^- \longrightarrow Xe(g) + 2\,HF(aq)\}$
Oxidation:	$2\,H_2O(l) \longrightarrow 4\,H^+(aq) + O_2(g) + 4\,e^-$
Overall:	$2\,XeF_2(aq) + 2\,H_2O(l) \longrightarrow 2\,Xe(g) + 4\,HF(aq) + O_2(g)$

$$\begin{aligned} E^\circ_{cell} &= E^\circ(\text{reduction}) - E^\circ(\text{oxidation}) \\ &= E^\circ_{XeF_2/Xe} - E^\circ_{O_2/H_2O} \\ &= 2.64\,V - (1.229\,V) = 1.41\,V \end{aligned}$$

▲ Crystals of xenon tetrafluoride under magnification.

*It has since been established that this solid is more complicated than first thought. It has the formula Xe(PtF$_6$)$_n$, where *n* is between 1 and 2.

Use two balloons, one filled with hydrogen and one with helium. Using a long stick with a lighted match at the end, show that the hydrogen explodes while the helium does not.

Meek, Terry L. "Electronegativities of the Noble Gases." *J. Chem. Educ.* **1995:** 72, 17.

Hyman, Herbert H. "The chemistry of the noble gases." *J. Chem. Educ.* **1964:** 41, 174.

▶ For XeF_6, seven orbitals are needed to accommodate the seven pairs of electrons; hence sp^3d^3 hybrid orbitals are used as a basis for a description of the bonding according to the valence-bond model.

(a)

(b)

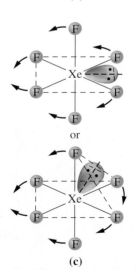

(c)

▲ **FIGURE 22-1**
Molecular shapes of the fluorides of xenon as predicted by VSEPR theory **(a)** XeF_2; **(b)** XeF_4; **(c)** XeF_6.

Xenon reacts directly only with F_2. When the gases are heated together at 400 °C in a sealed nickel vessel, the products depend on the Xe/F_2 mole ratio.

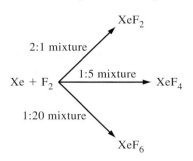

The fluorides XeF_2, XeF_4, and XeF_6 are colorless crystalline solids and are stable if kept from contact with water. The oxides of Xe are obtained from the fluorides. XeO_3 is an explosive white solid, and XeO_4 is an explosive colorless gas. The shapes of the three fluorides of xenon can be interpreted using VSEPR theory, the results of which are summarized in Figure 22-1. The structure of XeF_6 is depicted with the possible distortion of an octahedron because of the presence of the lone pair of electrons. The prediction of the nonoctahedral shape for XeF_6 was an important success for VSEPR theory.

To conform to the shapes indicated by VSEPR theory (or experiment, when the structure is known), bonding theory based on hybridization of orbitals requires the hybrid orbitals sp^3d for XeF_2, sp^3d^2 for XeF_4, and sp^3d^3 for XeF_6. However, in light of the observed bond lengths and bond energies in these fluorides and the high energy (estimated to be 1000 kJ mol^{-1}) required to promote an electron from a $5p$ to a $5d$ orbital, there is doubt as to whether d orbitals are involved in the bond formation. A molecular orbital description can be constructed that does not involve the participation of the xenon $5d$ orbitals, but in its simplest form this description cannot explain the nonoctahedral shape of XF_6. The situation described here reinforces the caveat that approximate theories of chemical bonding must be viewed critically.

CONCEPT ASSESSMENT ✓

Which is likely to be the more stable, XeF_2 or $XeCl_2$? Explain

22-2 GROUP 17: THE HALOGENS

The word *halogen* was introduced (1811) to describe the ability of chlorine to form ionic compounds with metals—salts. The name is based on Greek words meaning "salt former." The name was later extended to include fluorine, bromine, and iodine as well. Mendeleev placed the halogens in Group VII of his periodic table (page 341), which is now group 17 in the IUPAC table (page 51). Current interest in the halogens extends far beyond their ability to form metallic salts.

PROPERTIES

The **halogens** exist as diatomic molecules, symbolized by X_2, where X is a generic symbol for a halogen atom. That these elements occur as nonpolar diatomic molecules accounts for their relatively low melting and boiling points (Table 22.1). As expected, melting and boiling points increase from the smallest and lightest member of the group, fluorine, to the largest and heaviest, iodine. Conversely, chemical reactivity toward other elements and compounds progresses in the *opposite* order, with fluorine being the most reactive and iodine the least reactive.

TABLE 22.1   Group 17 Elements: The Halogens

	Fluorine (F)	Chlorine (Cl)	Bromine (Br)	Iodine (I)
Physical form at room temperature	Pale yellow gas	Yellow-green gas	Dark red liquid	Violet-black solid
Melting point, °C	−220	−101	−7.2	114
Boiling point, °C	−188	−35	58.8	184
Electron configuration	$[He]2s^22p^5$	$[Ne]3s^23p^5$	$[Ar]3d^{10}4s^24p^5$	$[Kr]4d^{10}5s^25p^5$
Covalent radius, pm	71	99	114	133
Ionic (X^-) radius, pm	133	181	196	220
First ionization energy, kJ mol^{-1}	1681	1251	1140	1008
Electron affinity, kJ mol^{-1}	−328.0	−349.0	−324.6	−295.2
Electronegativity	4.0	3.0	2.8	2.5
Standard electrode potential, V $(X_2 + 2\,e^- \longrightarrow 2\,X^-)$	2.866	1.358	1.065	0.535

Fluorine has the highest electronegativity of all the elements and a small atomic radius. Ionic bonds between fluoride and metal ions are strong, as are most covalent bonds between fluorine and other nonmetal atoms.* This tendency to form strong bonds with other atoms makes F_2 a reactive substance. Iodine atoms, because they are larger in size and have lower electronegativity, form weaker ionic and covalent bonds than do the other halogens. We would expect astatine ($Z = 85$) also to be a halogen. Because it is radioactive and has only short-lived isotopes, only about 0.05 μg astatine has ever been prepared. Nevertheless, its chemical behavior appears to be similar to that of iodine.

Much of the reaction chemistry of the halogens involves oxidation–reduction reactions in aqueous solutions. For these reactions, standard electrode potentials are the best guides to the reactivity of the halogens. Among the properties of the halogens listed in Table 22.1 are potentials for the half-reaction

$$X_2 + 2\,e^- \longrightarrow 2\,X^-(aq)$$

By this measure, fluorine is clearly the most reactive element of the group ($E° = 2.866$ V). Of all the elements, it shows the greatest tendency to gain electrons and is therefore the most easily reduced. Given this fact, it is not surprising that fluorine occurs naturally only in combination with other elements, and only as the fluoride ion, F^-. Although both chlorine and bromine can exist in a variety of positive oxidation states, they are found in their naturally occurring compounds only as chloride and bromide ions. There are, however, naturally occurring compounds in which iodine is in a positive oxidation state (such as the iodate ion, IO_3^-, in $NaIO_3$). In the case of iodine, the tendency for I_2 to be reduced to I^- is not particularly great ($E° = 0.535$ V).

ELECTRODE POTENTIAL DIAGRAMS

When we summarize the reduction tendencies of main-group metals and their ions, generally one or, at most, a few $E°$ values tell the story, and these values are easily incorporated into tables such as that in Appendix D. However, the oxidation–reduction chemistry of some of the nonmetals is much richer and involves a larger number of relevant $E°$ values. In these cases, *electrode potential diagrams* are particularly useful for summarizing $E°$ data. Partial diagrams for chlorine are shown in Figure 22-2. In these diagrams, a number written above a line segment is the $E°$ value for reduction of the species on the left (higher

 Liprandi, D. A., Reinheimer, O. R., Paredes, J. F., L'Argentière, P. C. "A Simple, Safe Way To Prepare Halogens and Study Their Visual Properties at a Technical Secondary School." *J. Chem. Educ.* **1999**: 76, 532 (April 1999).

 Recall that the halogens are extremely toxic.

Physical Properties of the Halogens movie

---

*The weaker-than-expected fluorine-to-fluorine bond in F_2 (159 kJ mol^{-1}) is probably the result of repulsions between the fluorine nuclei and between lone-pair $2p$ electrons. Both repulsions are rather strong because the atomic radius of fluorine is small. The weakness of the fluorine-to-fluorine bond contributes to the reactivity of F_2.

Acidic solution ($[H^+] = 1$ M):

$$
\begin{array}{cccccc}
+7 & +5 & +3 & +1 & 0 & -1
\end{array}
$$

$$
ClO_4^- \xrightarrow{1.189\ V} ClO_3^- \xrightarrow{1.181\ V} HClO_2 \xrightarrow{1.645\ V} HOCl \xrightarrow{1.611\ V} Cl_2 \xrightarrow{1.358\ V} Cl^-
$$

(?)

1.450 V

▶ **FIGURE 22-2**
Standard electrode potential diagrams for chlorine
The numbers in color are the oxidation states of the Cl atom. $E°$ values are written above the line segments for the reduction of the species on the left to the species on the right. All reactants and products are at unit activity. Because of the basic properties of the ClO_2^- and OCl^- ions, the weak acids $HClO_2$ and $HOCl$ form in acidic solution.

Basic solution ($[OH^-] = 1$ M):

$$
\begin{array}{cccccc}
+7 & +5 & +3 & +1 & 0 & -1
\end{array}
$$

$$
ClO_4^- \xrightarrow{0.374\ V} ClO_3^- \xrightarrow{(?)} ClO_2^- \xrightarrow{0.681\ V} OCl^- \xrightarrow{0.421\ V} Cl_2 \xrightarrow{1.358\ V} Cl^-
$$

0.488 V   0.890 V

(?)

Borrell, P., Dixon, D. T."Electrode potential diagrams and their use in the Hill-Bendall or Z-scheme for photosynthesis." *J. Chem. Educ.* 1984: *61*, 83.

oxidation state) to the one on the right (lower oxidation state). For a reduction involving species not joined by a line segment, we generally can calculate the appropriate value of $E°$ by the method illustrated in Example 22-1.

EXAMPLE 22-1

Using an Electrode Potential Diagram to Determine $E°$ for a Half-Reaction. Determine $E°$ for the reduction of ClO_3^- to ClO_2^- in a basic solution [marked (?) in Figure 22-2].

Solution

We are seeking $E°$ for the reduction half-reaction $ClO_3^- + H_2O + 2\,e^- \longrightarrow ClO_2^- + 2\,OH^-$. Two half-reactions and their corresponding $E°$ values from Figure 22-2 are represented next, along with the $\Delta G°$ values (that is, $-nFE°$).

$$ClO_3^- + 2\,H_2O + 4\,e^- \longrightarrow OCl^- + 4\,OH^-$$

$$E° = 0.488\ V; \quad \Delta G° = -4F \times 0.488\ V$$

$$ClO_2^- + H_2O + 2\,e^- \longrightarrow OCl^- + 2\,OH^-$$

$$E° = 0.681\ V; \quad \Delta G° = -2F \times 0.681\ V$$

KEEP IN MIND ▶
that when combining an oxidation and a reduction half-equation, electrons must cancel in the overall redox equation. However, when combining only reduction half-equations, electrons must *not* cancel out. The resultant half-equation must still be balanced for numbers of atoms and for charge.

Recall that we cannot simply add or subtract $E°$ values when we combine two or more half-reactions to obtain yet another *half-reaction*, but we can add $\Delta G°$ values (page 833). To get the desired half-equation, we must write the reverse of the second of the two-half equations above and change the sign of its $\Delta G°$.

$$
\begin{array}{ll}
ClO_3^- + 2\,H_2O + 4\,e^- \longrightarrow OCl^- + 4\,OH^- & \Delta G° = -4F \times 0.488\ V \\
OCl^- + 2\,OH^- \longrightarrow ClO_2^- + H_2O + 2\,e^- & \Delta G° = +2F \times 0.681\ V \\
\hline
ClO_3^- + H_2O + 2\,e^- \longrightarrow ClO_2^- + 2\,OH^- & \\
\end{array}
$$

$$\Delta G° = F(2 \times 0.681 - 4 \times 0.488)\ V$$

For the desired half-reaction, we can also write that $\Delta G° = -nFE°$, leading to the expression

$$\Delta G° = -2FE° = F[(2 \times 0.681) - (4 \times 0.488)]\ V$$

$$E° = \frac{F[(2 \times 0.681) - (4 \times 0.488)]\ V}{-2F} = 0.295\ V$$

Practice Example A: Determine the missing $E°$ value for the dashed line that joins ClO_3^- and Cl^- in basic solutions in Figure 22-2.

Practice Example B: Determine the missing $E°$ value for the dashed line that joins ClO_3^- and Cl_2 in acidic solutions in Figure 22-2.

PRODUCTION AND USES

Although the existence of fluorine had been known since early in the nineteenth century, no one was able to devise a chemical reaction to extract the free element from its compounds. Finally, in 1886, H. Moissan succeeded in preparing $F_2(g)$ by an electrolysis reaction. Moissan's method, which is still the only important commercial method for fluorine extraction, involves the electrolysis of HF dissolved in molten KHF_2,

$$2\,HF \xrightarrow[\text{KF}\cdot 2\,\text{HF(l)}]{\text{electrolysis}} H_2(g) + F_2(g) \tag{22.1}$$

consisting of the following electrode reactions:

$$\textit{Anode:} \qquad 2\,F^- \longrightarrow F_2(g) + 2\,e^-$$

$$\textit{Cathode:} \quad 2\,H^+ + 2\,e^- \longrightarrow H_2(g)$$

Moissan also developed the electric furnace and was honored for both these achievements with the Nobel Prize in chemistry in 1906. Nevertheless, the challenge of producing fluorine by means of a chemical reaction remained. In 1986, one century after Moissan isolated fluorine, the chemical synthesis of fluorine was announced (see Exercise 8).

Although chlorine can be prepared by several chemical reactions, electrolysis of NaCl(aq) is the usual industrial method, as we have mentioned previously (see page 855). The electrolysis reaction is

$$2\,Cl^-(aq) + 2\,H_2O(l) \xrightarrow{\text{electrolysis}} 2\,OH^-(aq) + H_2(g) + Cl_2(g) \tag{22.2}$$

Bromine can be extracted from seawater, where it occurs in concentrations of about 70 ppm as Br^-, or from inland brine solutions. The seawater or brine solution is adjusted to pH 3.5 and treated with $Cl_2(g)$, which oxidizes Br^- to Br_2 in this displacement reaction.

$$Cl_2(g) + 2\,Br^-(aq) \longrightarrow Br_2(l) + 2\,Cl^-(aq) \qquad E^{\circ}_{\text{cell}} = 0.293\text{ V} \tag{22.3}$$

The liberated Br_2 is swept from seawater with a current of air or from brine with steam. A dilute bromine vapor forms and can be concentrated by various methods.

Certain marine plants, such as seaweed, absorb and concentrate I^- selectively in the presence of Cl^- and Br^-. Iodine is obtained in small quantities from such plants. In the United States, I_2 is obtained from inland brines by a process similar to that for the production of Br_2. Another abundant natural source of iodine is $NaIO_3$, found in large deposits in Chile. Because the oxidation state of iodine must be reduced from +5 in IO_3^- to 0 in I_2, the conversion of IO_3^- to I_2 requires the use of a reducing agent. Aqueous sodium hydrogen sulfite (bisulfite) is used as the reducing agent in the first part of a two-step procedure, followed by the reaction of I^- with additional IO_3^- to produce I_2.

$$IO_3^-(aq) + 3\,HSO_3^-(aq) \longrightarrow I^-(aq) + 3\,SO_4^{2-}(aq) + 3\,H^+(aq) \tag{22.4}$$

$$5\,I^-(aq) + IO_3^-(aq) + 6\,H^+(aq) \longrightarrow 3\,I_2(s) + 3\,H_2O(l) \tag{22.5}$$

The halogen elements form a variety of useful compounds, and the elements themselves are largely used to produce these compounds. All of the halogens are used to make halogenated organic compounds. For example, elemental fluorine is used to produce compounds such as polytetrafluoroethylene, the plastic Teflon. In the past, fluorine was used to make chlorofluorocarbons (CFCs), which were used as refrigerants, but international treaties have banned the production of CFCs in most countries because they damage the stratospheric ozone layer (see page 954). Now fluorine is used to make hydrochlorofluorocarbons (HCFCs), which are more environmentally benign alternatives to CFCs. Fluorinated organic compounds tend to be chemically inert, and it is this inertness that makes them useful as components in harsh chemical environments. Fluorine is a key element in a variety of useful inorganic compounds. Some of these compounds and their uses are listed in Table 22.2.

◀ The hydrogen difluoride ion in KHF_2 features a strong hydrogen bond, with a H^+ midway between two F^- ions: $[F—H—F]^-$.

▲ **Salt formations in the Dead Sea**
The high concentrations of salts in the Dead Sea make it a good source of bromine and a number of other chemicals.

▲ **A test for Br^-(aq)**
Reaction (22.3) is used as a qualitative test in the laboratory. The liberated Br_2 is extracted from the top aqueous layer into the bottom layer, here the organic solvent chloroform, $CHCl_3$.

Choi, M. M. F. "Microscale Chemistry in a Plastic Petri Dish: Preparation and Chemical Properties of Chlorine Gas." *J. Chem. Educ.* **2002**: *79*, 992.

Williams, H. P., et al. "Aqueous Bromine Solutions from HBr by 3% Hydrogen Peroxide." *J. Chem. Educ.* 1990: 67, 525.

This article describes the construction and use of an iodine thermometer: Ramette, R. W. *J. Chem. Educ.* 2003: 80, 878.

TABLE 22.2   Important Inorganic Compounds of Fluorine

Compound	Uses
Na_3AlF_6	Manufacture of aluminum
BF_3	Catalyst
CaF_2	Optical components, manufacture of HF, metallurgical flux
ClF_3	Fluorinating agent, reprocessing nuclear fuels
HF	Manufacture of F_2, AlF_3, Na_3AlF_6, and fluorocarbons
LiF	Ceramics manufacture, welding, and soldering
NaF	Fluoridating water, dental prophylaxis, insecticide
SF_6	Insulating gas for high-voltage electrical equipment
SnF_2	Manufacture of toothpaste
UF_6	Manufacture of uranium fuel for nuclear reactors

With an annual production of over 13 million tons, elemental chlorine ranks about eighth in quantity among manufactured chemicals in the United States. It has three main commercial uses: (1) production of chlorinated organic compounds (about 70%), chiefly ethylene dichloride, CH_2ClCH_2Cl, and vinyl chloride, $CH_2{=}CHCl$ (the monomer of polyvinyl chloride, PVC); (2) as a bleach in the paper and textile industries and for the treatment of swimming pools, municipal water, and sewage (about 20%); and (3) production of dozens of chlorine-containing inorganic chemicals (about 10%).

▶ The major industrial source of HCl is the chlorination of organic compounds; for example,

$CH_4 + Cl_2 \longrightarrow$
$\qquad\qquad CH_3Cl + HCl$

Bromine is used to make brominated organic compounds. Some of these are used as fire retardants and pesticides. Others are used extensively as dyes and pharmaceuticals. An important inorganic bromine compound is AgBr, the primary light-sensitive agent used in photographic film.

Iodine is of much less commercial importance than chlorine. Iodine and its compounds, however, do have applications as catalysts, antiseptics, and germicides and in the preparation of pharmaceuticals and photographic emulsions (as AgI).

Holbrook, J. B., Sabry-Grant, R., Smith, B. C., Tandel, T. V. "Lattice enthalpies of ionic halides, hydrides, oxides, and sulfides: Second-electron affinities of atomic oxygen and sulfur." *J. Chem. Educ.* 1990: 67, 304.

HYDROGEN HALIDES

We have encountered the hydrogen halides from time to time throughout this text. In aqueous solution, they are called the *hydrohalic acids*. Except for HF, hydrohalic acids are strong acids in water. The unexpected weak acid nature of HF(aq) is discussed on page 691.

One well-known property of HF is its ability to etch (and ultimately to dissolve) glass. The reaction is similar to one between HF and silica, SiO_2.

▲ Glass etched with hydrofluoric acid.

$$SiO_2(s) + 4\,HF(aq) \longrightarrow 2\,H_2O(l) + SiF_4(g) \qquad (22.6)$$

As a result of reaction (22.6), HF must be stored in special containers coated with a lining of Teflon or polyethylene.

Hydrogen fluoride is commonly produced by a method discussed in Section 21-1. When a halide salt (such as fluorite, CaF_2) is heated with a *nonvolatile* acid, such as concentrated H_2SO_4(aq), a sulfate salt and the volatile hydrogen halide are produced.

$$CaF_2(s) + H_2SO_4(\text{concd aq}) \xrightarrow{\Delta} CaSO_4(s) + 2\,HF(g) \qquad (22.7)$$

This method also works for preparing HCl(g) but not for HBr(g) or HI(g). That is because concentrated H_2SO_4(aq) is a sufficiently strong oxidizing agent to oxidize Br^- to Br_2 and I^- to I_2.

$$2\,NaBr(s) + 2\,H_2SO_4(\text{concd aq}) \xrightarrow{\Delta} Na_2SO_4(s) + 2\,H_2O(l) + Br_2(g) + SO_2(g) \qquad (22.8)$$

We can get around this difficulty by using a *nonoxidizing* nonvolatile acid, such as phosphoric acid. Also, all the hydrogen halides can be formed by the direct combination of the elements.

$$H_2(g) + X_2(g) \longrightarrow 2\,HX(g) \qquad (22.9)$$

The reaction of $H_2(g)$ and $F_2(g)$ is very fast, however, occurring with explosive violence under some conditions. With $H_2(g)$ and $Cl_2(g)$, the reaction also proceeds rapidly (explosively) in the presence of light (photochemically initiated), although some HCl is made this way commercially. With Br_2 and I_2, the reaction occurs more slowly and a catalyst is required.

The data in Table 22.3 show that the standard free energies of formation of $HF(g)$, $HCl(g)$, and $HBr(g)$ are large and negative, suggesting that for them reaction (22.9) goes to completion. For $HI(g)$, conversely, ΔG_f° is small and positive. This suggests that even at room temperature $HI(g)$ should dissociate to some extent into its elements. Because the dissociation of $HI(g)$ has a high activation energy, however, the reaction occurs only very slowly in the absence of a catalyst. As a result, $HI(g)$ is stable at room temperature.

TABLE 22.3 Free Energy of Formation of Hydrogen Halides at 298 K

	ΔG_f°, kJ mol^{-1}
HF(g)	−273.2
HCl(g)	−95.30
HBr(g)	−53.45
HI(g)	+1.70

EXAMPLE 22-2

Determining K_p for a Dissociation Reaction from Free Energies of Formation. What is the value of K_p for the dissociation of $HI(g)$ into its elements at 298 K?

Solution

Dissociation of $HI(g)$ into its elements is the reverse of the formation reaction, and ΔG° for the dissociation is the *negative* of ΔG_f° for $HI(g)$ listed in Table 22.3.

$$HI(g) \longrightarrow \frac{1}{2}H_2(g) + \frac{1}{2}I_2(s) \qquad \Delta G^\circ = -1.70 \text{ kJ} \qquad (22.10)$$

Now we can use the relationship $\Delta G^\circ = -RT \ln K$.

$$\ln K_p = \frac{-\Delta G^\circ}{RT} = \frac{-(-1.70 \times 10^3 \text{ J mol}^{-1})}{8.3145 \text{ J mol}^{-1} \text{ K}^{-1} \times 298 \text{ K}} = 0.686$$

$$K_p = e^{0.686} = 1.99$$

Practice Example A: What is the value of K_p for the dissociation of $HF(g)$ into its elements at 298 K?

Practice Example B: Use data from Table 22.3 to determine K_p and the percent dissociation of $HCl(g)$ into its elements at 298 K.

OXOACIDS AND OXOANIONS

Fluorine, the most electronegative element, adopts the −1 oxidation state in its compounds. The other halogens, when bonded to a more electronegative element such as oxygen, can have any one of several positive oxidation states: +1, +3, +5, or +7. This variability of oxidation states, which was illustrated through electrode potential diagrams for chlorine (Fig. 22-2), is emphasized again by the oxoacids listed in Table 22.4. Chlorine forms a complete set of oxoacids in all these oxidation states, but bromine and iodine do not. Only a few of the oxoacids can be isolated in pure form ($HClO_4$, HIO_3, HIO_4, H_5IO_6); the rest are stable only in aqueous solution.

Meek, Terry L. "Acidities of oxoacids: Correlation with charge distribution." *J. Chem. Educ.* **1992:** *69*, 270.

Kildahl, Nicholas K. "A procedure for determining formulas for the simple p-block oxoacids." *J. Chem. Educ.* **1991:** *68*, 1001.

TABLE 22.4 Oxoacids of the Halogens[a]

Oxidation State of Halogen	Chlorine	Bromine	Iodine
+1	HOCl	HOBr	HOI
+3	$HClO_2$	—	—
+5	$HClO_3$	$HBrO_3$	HIO_3
+7	$HClO_4$	$HBrO_4$	HIO_4; H_5IO_6

[a]In all these acids, H atoms are bonded to O atoms—as shown for HOCl, HOBr, and HOI—not to the central halogen atom. More accurate representations of the other acids would be $HOClO$ (instead of $HClO_2$), $HOClO_2$ (instead of $HClO_3$), and so on.

Hypochlorite, OCl⁻
(linear)

Chlorite, ClO_2^-
(angular)

Chlorate, ClO_3^-
(trigonal pyramidal)

Perchlorate, ClO_4^-
(tetrahedral)

▶ Oxoanions of chlorine.

✓ Remind students to never mix bleach with ammonia. The formation of toxic chlorine gas can result.

An easily prepared oxidizing agent for laboratory use is an aqueous solution of chlorine ("chlorine water"). The solution is not just one of Cl_2, however. The $Cl_2(aq)$ disproportionates into $HOCl(aq)$ and $HCl(aq)$. Although the disproportionation of Cl_2 in water is nonspontaneous when all reactants and products are in their standard states, the reaction does occur to a limited extent in solutions that are not strongly acidic, as the $E°$ and $\Delta G°$ values indicate.

Reduction:	$Cl_2(g) + 2\,e^- \longrightarrow 2\,Cl^-(aq)$	
Oxidation:	$Cl_2(g) + 2\,H_2O(l) \longrightarrow 2\,HOCl(aq) + 2\,H^+(aq) + 2\,e^-$	
Overall:	$Cl_2(g) + H_2O(l) \longrightarrow HOCl(aq) + H^+(aq) + Cl^-(aq)$	(22.11)

$$E°_{cell} = E°_{Cl_2/Cl^-} - E°_{HOCl/Cl_2} = 1.358\,V - 1.611\,V = -0.253\,V$$

$$\Delta G° = -nFE° = 48.8\,kJ$$

KEEP IN MIND ▶

that $E°_{Cl_2/Cl^-}$ is independent of pH, but both $E°_{HOCl/Cl_2}$ and $E°_{OCl^-/Cl_2}$ are pH dependent. They become smaller as the pH increases, increasing E_{cell} and making ΔG less positive and eventually negative. In terms of Le Châtelier's principle, the smaller $[H^+]$ (greater $[OH^-]$), the more the disproportionation reaction is favored.

In contrast, the disproportionation is spontaneous for standard-state conditions in basic solution.

Reduction:	$Cl_2(g) + 2\,e^- \longrightarrow 2\,Cl^-(aq)$	
Oxidation:	$Cl_2(g) + 4\,OH^-(aq) \longrightarrow 2\,OCl^-(aq) + 2\,H_2O(l) + 2\,e^-$	
Overall:	$Cl_2(g) + 2\,OH^-(aq) \longrightarrow OCl^-(aq) + Cl^-(aq) + H_2O(l)$	(22.12)

$$E°_{cell} = E°_{Cl_2/Cl^-} - E°_{OCl/Cl_2} = 1.358\,V - 0.421\,V = 0.937\,V$$

$$\Delta G° = -nFE° = -181\,kJ$$

$HOCl(aq)$ is an effective germicide used, for example, in water purification and the treatment of swimming pools. Aqueous solutions of *hypochlorite* salts, notably $NaOCl(aq)$, are used as common household bleaches.

Are You Wondering . . .

If there are oxoacids of fluorine?

The hypothetical oxoacid of fluorine, $HFO_2(HOFO)$, would have a *positive* formal charge on the central F atom.

$$:\ddot{O}-\overset{+1}{\underset{}{\ddot{F}}}-\ddot{O}-H$$

This is not something that we would expect of fluorine, the most electronegative of all the elements. Hypothetical oxoacids with more O atoms would have the F atom with even higher positive formal charges. Fluorine does form HOF, an oxoacid with no formal charges $H:\ddot{O}-\ddot{F}:$, but HOF exists only in the solid and liquid states. In water, HOF decomposes to HF, H_2O_2, and $O_2(g)$.

Chlorine dioxide is an important bleach for paper and fibers. Its reduction with peroxide ion in aqueous solution produces *chlorite* salts:

$$2 \, ClO_2(g) + O_2^{2-}(aq) \longrightarrow 2 \, ClO_2^-(aq) + O_2(g) \qquad (22.13)$$

Sodium chlorite is used as a bleaching agent for textiles.

Chlorate salts form when $Cl_2(g)$ disproportionates in hot alkaline solutions. (Hypochlorites form in cold alkaline solutions; recall reaction 22.12.)

$$3 \, Cl_2(g) + 6 \, OH^-(aq) \longrightarrow 5 \, Cl^-(aq) + ClO_3^-(aq) + 3 \, H_2O(l) \qquad (22.14)$$

Chlorates are good oxidizing agents. Also, solid chlorates produce oxygen gas when they decompose, which makes them useful in matches and fireworks. A simple laboratory method of producing $O_2(g)$ involves heating $KClO_3(s)$ in the presence of $MnO_2(s)$, a catalyst.

$$2 \, KClO_3(s) \xrightarrow[MnO_2]{\Delta} 2 \, KCl(s) + 3 \, O_2(g) \qquad (22.15)$$

A similar reaction is used as a source of emergency oxygen in aircraft and submarines.

Perchlorate salts are prepared mainly by electrolyzing chlorate solutions. Oxidation of ClO_3^- occurs at a Pt anode through the half-reaction

$$ClO_3^-(aq) + H_2O(l) \longrightarrow ClO_4^-(aq) + 2 \, H^+(aq) + 2 \, e^- \qquad E^\circ = -1.189 \text{ V} \qquad (22.16)$$

An interesting laboratory use of perchlorates is in aqueous solution studies in which complex-ion formation is to be avoided. ClO_4^- has one of the lowest tendencies of any anion to act as a ligand in complex-ion formation in water. Compared with the other oxoacid salts, perchlorates are relatively stable. For example, they do not disproportionate, because no oxidation state higher than +7 is available to chlorine. At elevated temperatures or in the presence of a readily oxidizable compound, however, perchlorate salts may react explosively, so caution is advised when using them. Mixtures of ammonium perchlorate and powdered aluminum are used as the propellant in some solid-fuel rockets, such as those used on the space shuttle. Ammonium perchlorate is especially dangerous to handle, because an explosive reaction may occur when the oxidizing agent ClO_4^- acts on the reducing agent NH_4^+.

INTERHALOGEN COMPOUNDS

Not only does each halogen element form diatomic molecules X_2 but each can form the molecules XY. In such **interhalogen** compounds, the X and Y represent two different halogens, as in ClF, BrCl, or IBr. Other interhalogen compounds consist of polyatomic molecules, such as XY_3, XY_5, or XY_7. Some of the more common ones are listed in Table 22.5. The molecular structures of the interhalogen compounds feature the large, less electronegative halogen as the central atom and the smaller halogen atoms as terminal atoms. Molecular shapes of the interhalogen compounds agree quite well with VSEPR theory predictions. Structures for IF_x ($x = 1, 3, 5, 7$) are shown in Figure 22-3, including one type that we have not seen previously: In IF_7, *seven* electron pairs are distributed around the central I atom in the form of a pentagonal-bipyramid.

► Solid household bleach normally contains $Ca(OCl)Cl$, which is obtained by the reaction of Cl_2 and $Ca(OH)_2$:

$$Ca(OH)_2 + Cl_2 \longrightarrow$$
$$Ca(OCl)Cl + H_2O$$

▲ **Bleaching with hypochlorite ion**
Both strips of cloth are heavily stained with tomato sauce. Pure water (left) has little ability to remove the stain. NaOCl (right) rapidly bleaches (oxidizes) the colored components of the sauce to colorless products.

◄ A particularly destructive explosion of ammonium perchlorate occurred at a rocket fuel plant in Henderson, Nevada, in 1988.

Johnson, Garrett K. "Preparation and analysis of solid solutions in the potassium perchlorate-permanganate system." *J. Chem. Educ.* **1979:** 56, 618.

Fessenden, Elizabeth. "Structural chemistry of the interhalogen compounds." *J. Chem. Educ.* **1951:** 28, 619.

Robinson, W. R. "Perchlorate Salts of Metal Ion Complexes: Potential Explosives." *J. Chem. Educ.* **1985:** 62, 1001.

TABLE 22.5	**Some Interhalogen Compounds**		
XY	**XY₃**	**XY₅**	**XY₇**
$ClF(g)^a$	$ClF_3(g)$	$ClF_5(g)$	
$BrF(g)$	$BrF_3(l)$	$BrF_5(l)$	
$BrCl(g)$	$IF_3(s)$	$IF_5(l)$	$IF_7(g)$
$ICl(s)$	$ICl_3(s)$		
$IBr(s)$			

[a]The states of matter are given for 25 °C and 1 atm, except IF_3 which decomposes above −28°.

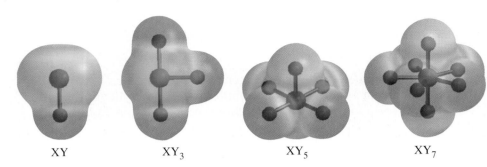

XY   XY$_3$ XY$_5$ XY$_7$

▲ **FIGURE 22-3**
Structures and electrostatic potential maps of the interhalogen compounds of iodine and fluorine

▲ **FIGURE 22-4**
Structure of the I$_3^-$ ion
Notice that in the electrostatic potential map for I$_3^-$, the three lone pairs around the central iodine atom lead to a neutral charge distribution at this atom, not the negative charge suggested by formal charge arguments.

Most interhalogen compounds are very reactive. ClF$_3$ and BrF$_3$, for example, react with explosive violence with water, organic materials, and some inorganic materials. These two fluorides are used to fluorinate compounds, as in the preparation of UF$_6$ for the separation of uranium isotopes by gaseous diffusion. ICl is used as an iodination reagent in organic chemistry.

POLYHALIDE IONS

The triiodide ion, I$_3^-$, is one of a group of species called **polyhalide ions** that are produced by the reaction of a halide ion with a halogen molecule. In this reaction, the halide ion acts as a *Lewis base* (an electron-pair donor) and the halogen molecule as a *Lewis acid* (an electron-pair acceptor).

$$:\!\ddot{I}\!-\!\ddot{I}\!: \;+\; :\!\ddot{I}\!:^- \;\longrightarrow\; \left[:\!\ddot{I}\!-\!\ddot{I}\!-\!\ddot{I}\!:\right]^- \tag{22.17}$$

The structure of the I$_3^-$ ion is shown in Figure 22-4. The familiar iodine solutions used as antiseptics typically contain triiodide ion, and triiodide ion solutions are widely used in analytical chemistry.

CONCEPT ASSESSMENT ✔

Do you expect the ions ICl$_2^+$ and ICl$_2^-$ to have the same shape? Explain.

22-3 GROUP 16: THE OXYGEN FAMILY

Of the group 16 elements, oxygen and sulfur are clearly nonmetallic in their behavior, but some metallic properties begin to appear toward the bottom of the group with tellurium and polonium.

PROPERTIES

On the basis of electron configurations alone, we expect oxygen and sulfur to be similar. Both elements form ionic compounds with active metals, and both form similar covalent compounds, such as H$_2$S and H$_2$O, CS$_2$ and CO$_2$, SCl$_2$ and Cl$_2$O.

Even so, there are important differences between oxygen and sulfur compounds. For example, H$_2$O has a very high boiling point (100 °C) for a compound of such low molecular mass (18 u), whereas the boiling point of H$_2$S (molecular mass, 34 u) is more normal (−61 °C). This difference in behavior can be explained in terms of the extensive hydrogen bonding that occurs in H$_2$O but not in H$_2$S (see page 494). Table 22.6 is a comparison of some properties of sulfur and oxygen. In general, the differences can be attributed to the following characteristics of the oxygen atom: (1) small size, (2) high electronegativity, and (3) its inability to employ an expanded valence shell in Lewis structures.

TABLE 22.6 Comparisons of Oxygen and Sulfur	
Oxygen	**Sulfur**
$O_2(g)$ at 298 K and 1 atm	$S_8(s)$ at 298 K and 1 atm
Two allotropes: $O_2(g)$ and $O_3(g)$	Two solid crystalline forms and many different molecular species in liquid and gaseous states
Principal oxidation states: $-2, -1, 0 \left(-\frac{1}{2} \text{ in } O_2^-\right)$	Possible oxidation states: all values from -2 to $+6$
$O_2(g)$ and $O_3(g)$ are very good oxidizing agents	$S_8(s)$ is a poor oxidizing agent
Forms, with metals, oxides that are mostly ionic in character	Forms ionic sulfides with the most active metals, but many metal sulfides have partial covalent character
O^{2-} completely hydrolyzes in water, producing OH^-	S^{2-} strongly hydrolyzes in water to HS^- (and OH^-)
O is not often the central atom in a structure and can never have more than four atoms bonded to it; more commonly it has two (as in H_2O) or three (as in H_3O^+)	S is the central atom in many structures; can easily accommodate up to six atoms around itself (e.g., SO_3, SO_4^{2-}, SF_6)
Can form only two-atom and three-atom chains, as in H_2O_2 and O_3; compounds with O—O bonds decompose readily	Can form molecules with up to six S atoms per chain in compounds such as H_2S_n, Na_2S_n, $H_2S_nO_6$
Forms the oxide CO_2, which reacts with NaOH(aq) to produce Na_2CO_3(aq)	Forms the sulfide CS_2, which reacts with NaOH(aq), producing Na_2CS_3(aq) and Na_2CO_3(aq)
Forms, with hydrogen, the compound H_2O, which is a liquid at 298 K and 1 atm; is extensively hydrogen-bonded; has a large dipole moment; is an excellent solvent for ionic solids; forms hydrates and aqua complexes; is oxidized with difficulty	Forms, with hydrogen, the compound H_2S, which is a (poisonous) gas at 298 K and 1 atm; is not hydrogen-bonded; has a small dipole moment; is a poor solvent; forms no complexes; is easily oxidized

As indicated in Table 22.6, the principal oxidation states of oxygen are -2, -1, and 0. Sulfur, conversely, can exhibit all oxidation states from -2 to $+6$, including several "mixed" oxidation states, such as $+2.5$ in the tetrathionate ion, $S_4O_6^{2-}$.

OCCURRENCE, PRODUCTION, AND USES

Oxygen.   Oxygen is the most abundant element in Earth's crust, making up 45.5% by mass. It is also the most abundant element in seawater, accounting for nearly 90% of the mass. In the atmosphere, it is second only to nitrogen in abundance, accounting for 23.15% by mass and 21.04% by volume. Although it is obtained to a limited extent by the decomposition of oxygen-containing compounds and the electrolysis of water, the principal commercial source of oxygen is the fractional distillation of liquid air, which also produces nitrogen, argon, and other noble gases. This process involves only physical changes and is described in Figure 22-5.

Gordon, J., et al. "The Determination of the Percent of Oxygen in Air Using a Gas Pressure Sensor." *J. Chem. Educ.* **2005**: *82*, 286.

You can do the standard demo of filling balloons with nitrogen, oxygen, and helium, and then bursting them with a match at the end of a long rod.

Braathen, Per Christian. "Determination of the Oxygen Content of Air." *J. Chem. Educ.* **2000**: *77*, 1410 (November 2000).

◀ FIGURE 22-5
The fractional distillation of liquid air— a simplified representation
Clean air is fed into a compressor and cooled by refrigeration. The cold air then expands through a nozzle and is cooled still further—enough to cause it to liquefy. The liquid air is filtered to remove solid CO_2 and hydrocarbons and then distilled. Liquid air enters the top of the column where nitrogen, the most volatile component (lowest boiling point), passes off as a gas. In the middle of the column, gaseous argon is removed. Liquid oxygen, the least volatile component, collects at the bottom. The normal boiling points of nitrogen, argon, and oxygen are 77.4, 87.5, and 90.2 K, respectively.

Najdoski, Metodija, Petrusevski, Vladimir M. "A Novel Experiment for Fast and Simple Determination of the Oxygen Content in the Air." *J. Chem. Educ.* **2000:** *77*, 1447 (November 2000).

Demonstrate the paramagnetic property of liquid oxygen by pouring it onto the poles of a permanent bar magnet.

Generate oxygen by mixing MnO_2 in a flask with a 30% solution of H_2O_2. The manganese is reduced in a exothermic reaction and a plume of steam exits the flask.

TABLE 22.7	Uses of Oxygen Gas

Manufacture of iron and steel
Manufacture and fabrication of other metals (cutting and welding)
Chemicals manufacture and other oxidation processes
Water treatment
Oxidizer of rocket fuels
Medicinal uses
Petroleum refining

Annually, oxygen is one of the principal manufactured chemicals in the United States, used in the several ways outlined in Table 22.7. With its ready commercial availability, O_2 is not commonly prepared in the laboratory. In a submarine, in spacecraft, and in an emergency breathing apparatus, however, it is necessary to generate small quantities of oxygen from solids. The reaction of potassium *superoxide* with CO_2 works well for this purpose; it removes CO_2 while O_2 is being formed.

$$4\,KO_2(s) + 2\,CO_2(g) \longrightarrow 2\,K_2CO_3(s) + 3\,O_2(g)$$

CONCEPT ASSESSMENT ✓

Which of the following dilute aqueous solutions can be used to obtain oxygen and hydrogen gases simultaneously through electrolysis using platinum electrodes: $H_2SO_4(aq)$, $CuSO_4(aq)$, $NaOH(aq)$, $KNO_3(aq)$, $NaI(aq)$? Explain.

▲ These vast formations of solid sulfur were formed by the solidification of liquid sulfur obtained by the Frasch process.

Nagel, Miriam C. "Herman Frasch, sulfur king (PROFILES)." *J. Chem. Educ.* **1981:** *58*, 60.

Lebowitz, Samuel H. "A demonstration working model of the Frasch process for mining sulfur." *J. Chem. Educ.* **1931:** *8*, 1630.

Sulfur. Sulfur is the sixteenth most abundant element in Earth's crust, accounting for 0.0384% by mass. Sulfur occurs as elemental sulfur, as mineral sulfides and sulfates, as $H_2S(g)$ in natural gas, and as organosulfur compounds in oil and coal. Extensive deposits of elemental sulfur are found in Texas and Louisiana, some of them in offshore sites. This sulfur is mined in an unusual way known as the **Frasch process** (Fig. 22-6). Superheated water (at about 160 °C and 16 atm) is forced down the outermost of three concentric pipes into an underground bed of sulfur-containing rock. The sulfur melts and forms a liquid pool. Compressed air (at 20–25 atm) is pumped down the innermost pipe and forces the liquid sulfur–water mixture up the remaining pipe.

▶ **FIGURE 22-6**
The Frasch process
Sulfur is melted by using superheated water, and liquid sulfur is forced to the surface.

◄ FIGURE 22-7
Sources and uses of sulfur and its oxides

Although the Frasch process was once the principal source of elemental sulfur, that is no longer the case. This change has been brought about by the need to control sulfur emissions from industrial operations. H_2S is a common impurity in oil and natural gas. After being removed from the fuel, H_2S is reduced to elemental sulfur in a two-step process. A stream of H_2S gas is split into two parts. One part (about one-third of the stream) is burned to convert H_2S to SO_2. The streams are rejoined in a catalytic converter at 200–300 °C, where the following reaction occurs:

$$2\,H_2S(g) + SO_2(g) \longrightarrow 3\,S(g) + 2\,H_2O(g) \qquad (22.18)$$

About 90% of all the sulfur produced is burned to form $SO_2(g)$ (Fig. 22-7), and in turn, most $SO_2(g)$ is converted to sulfuric acid, H_2SO_4. Elemental sulfur does have a few uses of its own, however. One of these is in vulcanizing rubber (page 1117); another is as a fungicide used for dusting grapevines.

Sheffield, M. C. et al. "Analysis of Selenium in Brazil Nuts by Microwave Digestion and Fluorescence Detection." *J. Chem. Educ.* **2002**: *79*, 1345.

Selenium and Tellurium.   Selenium and tellurium have properties similar to those of sulfur, but they are more metallic. For example, sulfur is an electrical insulator, whereas selenium and tellurium are semiconductors. Selenium and tellurium are obtained mostly as by-products of metallurgical processes, such as in the anode mud deposited in the electrolytic refining of copper (page 854). Although there is not much use for tellurium compounds, selenium is used in the manufacture of rectifiers (devices that convert alternating to direct electric current). Both Se and Te are employed in the preparation of alloys, and their compounds are used as additives to control the color of glass.

Selenium also displays the property of *photoconductivity*: The electrical conductivity of selenium increases in the presence of light. This property is used, for example, in photocells in cameras. In some modern photocopying machines, the light-sensitive element is a thin film of Se deposited on aluminum. The light and dark areas of the image being copied are converted into a distribution of charge on the light-sensitive element. A dry black powder (toner) coats the charged portions of the light-sensitive element, and this image is transferred to a sheet of paper. Next, the dry powder is fused to the paper. In the final step, the electrostatic charge on the light-sensitive element is neutralized to prepare it for the next cycle.

▲ A selenium-coated light-sensitive element from a photocopier.

Polonium.   Polonium is a very rare, radioactive metal. Because it is extremely low in abundance, it has not found much practical use. Polonium was the first new radioactive element isolated from uranium ore by Marie and Pierre Curie in 1898. Madame Curie named it after her native Poland.

ALLOTROPY OF OXYGEN: OZONE

As we first learned in Chapter 10, allotropy refers to the existence of an element in two or more different molecular forms, and we were introduced to the allotrope of ordinary dioxygen, O_2; it is ozone, O_3. Normally, the quantity of O_3

▲ **FIGURE 22-8**
Some molecular forms of sulfur

in the atmosphere is quite limited at low altitudes, about 0.04 part per million (ppm). However, its level increases (perhaps severalfold) in smog situations (see page 601). Ozone levels exceeding 0.12 ppm are considered unhealthful.

The reaction producing $O_3(g)$ directly from $O_2(g)$ is highly endothermic and occurs only rarely in the lower atmosphere.

$$3\,O_2(g) \longrightarrow 2\,O_3(g) \qquad \Delta H° = +285\;kJ$$

Seeley, J. V., et al. "A Simple Method for Measuring Ground-Level Ozone in the Atmosphere." *J. Chem. Educ.* 2005: 82, 282.

This reaction does occur in high-energy environments such as electrical storms. The pungent odor you may at times smell around heavy-duty electrical equipment or xerographic office copiers is probably O_3. The chief method of producing ozone in the laboratory, in fact, is to pass an electric discharge (high-energy electrons) through $O_2(g)$. Because ozone is unstable and decomposes back to $O_2(g)$, it is always generated at the point of use.

Ozone is an excellent oxidizing agent. Its oxidizing ability is surpassed by few other substances (two are F_2 and OF_2). Its most important use is as a substitute for chlorine in purifying drinking water. Its advantages are that it does not impart a taste to the water and it does not form the potentially carcinogenic chlorination products that chlorine can. Its main disadvantage is that O_3 is unstable and quickly disappears from the water after it is treated. Thus, after leaving the waterworks the water is not as well protected against bacterial contamination as is water treated with chlorine.

An important environmental problem centered on atmospheric ozone is discussed in the Focus On feature for this chapter (page 954).

ALLOTROPY AND POLYMORPHISM OF SULFUR

Sharma, B. D. "Allotropes and polymorphs." *J. Chem. Educ.* 1987: 64, 404.

Sulfur has more allotropes than any other element (Fig. 22-8). The most common allotrope in the solid state is the S_8 ring, although an additional half-dozen cyclic structures are known with up to 20 S atoms per ring. In sulfur vapor, S, S_2, S_4, S_6, and S_8 can all exist under the appropriate conditions. Long-chain molecules of sulfur atoms are found in liquid sulfur. *Rhombic sulfur* (S_α), the stable solid at room temperature, is made up of cyclic S_8 molecules. At 95.5 °C, it converts to a different polymorphic form *monoclinic sulfur* (S_β), which is also made up of S_8 molecules but has a different crystal structure than S_α. At 119 °C, S_β melts, yielding *liquid sulfur* (S_λ), a straw-colored, mobile liquid comprised mostly of S_8 molecules but with other cyclic molecules containing from 6 to 20 atoms. At 160 °C, the cyclic molecules open up and recombine into long spiral-chain molecules, producing *liquid sulfur* (S_μ), a dark, viscous liquid. The chain length and viscosity reach a maximum at about 180 °C. At higher temperatures, the chains break up and the viscosity decreases. At 445 °C, the liquid boils, producing *sulfur vapor*. S_8 molecules predominate in the vapor at the boiling point but break down into smaller molecules at higher temperatures. *Plastic sulfur* forms if liquid S_μ is poured into cold water. Plastic sulfur consists of long, spiral-chain molecules and has rubberlike properties. On standing, it becomes brittle and reverts to rhombic sulfur.

To summarize,

$$S_\alpha \xrightarrow{95.5\,°C} S_\beta \xrightarrow{119} S_\lambda \xrightarrow{160} S_\mu \xrightarrow{445} S_8(g) \xrightarrow{} S_6 \xrightarrow{1000} S_4 \xrightarrow{2000} S_2 \longrightarrow S$$

Birdwhistell, K. R., Long, J. W. "The Phases of Sulfur (TD)." *J. Chem. Educ.* 1995: 72, 56.

Some of these forms of sulfur are shown in Figure 22-9.

| (a) | (b) | (c) | (d) |

▲ **FIGURE 22-9**
Several macroscopic forms of sulfur
(a) Rhombic sulfur. **(b)** Monoclinic sulfur. **(c)** On the left, monoclinic sulfur has just melted to form an orange liquid. On the right, after continued heating, the liquid becomes red and more viscous. **(d)** Liquid sulfur is poured into water to produce plastic sulfur.

Because some of these transitions, especially those in the solid state, are sluggish, additional phenomena are occasionally seen. For example, if rhombic sulfur is heated rapidly, it may melt at 113 °C and fail to convert to monoclinic sulfur. However, monoclinic sulfur may then freeze from this liquid, only to melt again at 119 °C.

McNaught, Ian J. "A Modified Hydrogen/Oxygen Balloon Demonstration." *J. Chem. Educ.* **1998**: *75*, 52 (January 1998).

OXYGEN COMPOUNDS

Oxygen is so central to the study of chemistry that we constantly refer to its physical and chemical properties in developing a framework of chemical principles. For instance, our discussion of stoichiometry began with combustion reactions—reactions of substances with $O_2(g)$ to form products such as $CO_2(g)$, $H_2O(l)$, and $SO_2(g)$. Combustion reactions also figured prominently in the presentation of thermochemistry. Many of the molecules and polyatomic anions described in the chapters on chemical bonding were oxygen-containing species. Water was a primary subject in the discussion of liquids, solids, and intermolecular forces as well as in the study of acid–base and other solution equilibria. The dual roles of hydrogen peroxide as an oxidizing agent and a reducing agent were described in Section 5-6; and the kinetics of the decomposition of H_2O_2 was examined in detail in Chapter 14. The acidic, basic, and amphoteric properties of element oxides were outlined in Chapter 9.

A systematic study of oxygen compounds is generally done in conjunction with the study of the other elements. Thus, the oxides of boron were considered in the discussion of boron chemistry in Chapter 21; the oxides of carbon were also considered there. The survey of the chemistry of the alkali and alkaline earth metals in Chapter 21 provided an opportunity to describe normal oxides, peroxides, and superoxides; and the important oxides of sulfur, nitrogen, and phosphorus are discussed in this chapter.

Reactions with Oxygen movie

SULFUR COMPOUNDS

As in the corresponding discussion for the halogens (Section 22-2), oxidation–reduction chemistry is a primary concern here. To assist in this discussion, we provide electrode potential diagrams for some important sulfur-containing species in Figure 22-10.

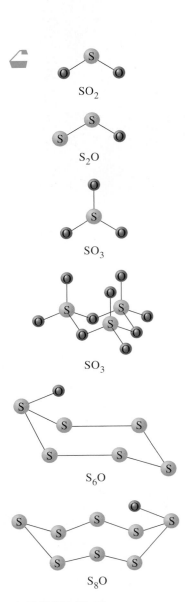

Acidic solution ($[H^+] = 1\ M$):

$$\underset{+6}{SO_4^{2-}} \overset{-0.22\ V}{\underline{\quad\quad}} \underset{+5}{S_2O_6^{2-}} \overset{0.564\ V}{\underline{\quad\quad}} \underset{+4}{SO_2(aq)} \overset{0.507\ V}{\underline{\quad\quad}} \underset{+2.5}{S_4O_6^{2-}} \overset{0.080\ V}{\underline{\quad\quad}} \underset{+2}{S_2O_3^{2-}} \overset{0.465\ V}{\underline{\quad\quad}} \underset{0}{S} \overset{0.144\ V}{\underline{\quad\quad}} \underset{-2}{H_2S(aq)}$$

0.158 V   0.449 V

Basic solution ($[OH^-] = 1\ M$):

$$\underset{+6}{SO_4^{2-}} \overset{-0.936\ V}{\underline{\quad\quad}} \underset{+4}{SO_3^{2-}} \overset{-0.576\ V}{\underline{\quad\quad}} \underset{+2}{S_2O_3^{2-}} \overset{-0.74\ V}{\underline{\quad\quad}} \underset{0}{S} \overset{-0.476\ V}{\underline{\quad\quad}} \underset{-2}{S^{2-}}$$

−0.66 V

▲ **FIGURE 22-10**
Electrode potential diagrams for sulfur

Structures of some sulfur oxides

FIGURE 22-11
Structures of some sulfur oxides
To conform to the observed structures of SO_2, S_2O, and SO_3, the hybridization scheme proposed for the central S atom is sp^2. S_2O has a similar structure to SO_2 but with a S atom substituted for one O atom. The SO_3 exists in equilibrium with the trimer $(SO_3)_3$, in which the O—S—O angle is approximately tetrahedral and the hybridization of the S should be sp^3. The oxides S_6O and S_8O illustrate sulfur's ability to form ring compounds.

Sulfur Dioxide and Sulfur Trioxide.   More than a dozen oxides of sulfur have been reported, but only sulfur dioxide, SO_2, and sulfur trioxide, SO_3, are commonly encountered. Typical structures are shown in Figure 22-11. The main commercial methods of producing $SO_2(g)$ are the direct combustion of sulfur and the "roasting" of metal sulfides.

$$S(s) + O_2(g) \overset{\Delta}{\longrightarrow} SO_2(g) \tag{22.19}$$

$$2\ ZnS(s) + 3\ O_2(g) \overset{\Delta}{\longrightarrow} 2\ ZnO(s) + 2\ SO_2(g) \tag{22.20}$$

The main use of SO_2 is in the synthesis of SO_3 to make sulfuric acid, H_2SO_4. In the modern process, the *contact process*, $SO_2(g)$ is formed by reaction (22.19) or (22.20). Then sulfur trioxide is produced by oxidizing $SO_2(g)$ in an exothermic, reversible reaction.

$$2\ SO_2(g) + O_2(g) \rightleftharpoons 2\ SO_3(g) \tag{22.21}$$

Reaction (22.21) is the key step in the process, but it occurs very slowly unless catalyzed. The principal catalyst is V_2O_5 mixed with alkali metal sulfates. The catalysis involves adsorption of the $SO_2(g)$ and $O_2(g)$ on the catalyst, followed by reaction at active sites and desorption of SO_3 (recall Figure 14-19).

Sulfuric Acid. SO_3 reacts with water to form H_2SO_4, but the direct reaction of $SO_3(g)$ and water produces a fine mist of $H_2SO_4(aq)$ droplets with unreacted $SO_3(g)$ trapped inside the droplets. This misting would result in a great loss of product and a tremendous pollution problem. To avoid these outcomes, $SO_3(g)$ is instead bubbled through 98% H_2SO_4 in towers packed with a ceramic material. The $SO_3(g)$ readily dissolves in the sulfuric acid and reacts with the small amount of water present to increase the concentration of the sulfuric acid. The result is a form of sulfuric acid sometimes called *oleum* but more commonly called *fuming sulfuric acid*. In a sense, the product is greater than 100% H_2SO_4. Sufficient water is added to the circulating acid in the tower to maintain the required concentration. Later, sulfuric acid of the strength desired is produced by dilution with water. If we use the formula $H_2S_2O_7$ (disulfuric acid) as an example of a particular oleum, the reactions are

$$SO_3(g) + H_2SO_4(l) \longrightarrow H_2S_2O_7(l) \tag{22.22}$$

$$H_2S_2O_7(l) + H_2O(l) \longrightarrow 2\ H_2SO_4(l) \tag{22.23}$$

$$H_2SO_4(l) \overset{H_2O}{\longrightarrow} H_2SO_4(aq) \tag{22.24}$$

(a)   (b)

Duffy, J. A. "Optical Basicity: A Practical Acid-Base Theory for Oxides and Oxyanions." *J. Chem. Educ.* **1996**: 73, 1138 (December 1996).

Sulfuric acid extracts water from objects, which is one reason that it burns the skin so badly. Pour some conc. sulfuric acid onto sugar and watch the water being removed leaving black carbon. Again, wear proper protection.

◀ **(a)** Concentrated sulfuric acid is added to cane sugar. **(b)** Carbon is produced in the reaction.

Dilute sulfuric acid, $H_2SO_4(aq)$, enters into all the common reactions of a strong acid, such as neutralizing bases. It reacts with metals to produce $H_2(g)$ and dissolves carbonates to liberate $CO_2(g)$.

Concentrated sulfuric acid has some distinctive properties. It has a very strong affinity for water, strong enough that it will even remove H and O atoms (in the proportion H_2O) from some compounds. In the reaction of concentrated sulfuric acid with a carbohydrate like sucrose, all the H and O atoms are removed and a residue of pure carbon is left.

Silverstein, T. P., Zhang, Yi. "Sugar Dehydration without Sulfuric Acid: No More Choking Fumes in the Classroom!" *J. Chem. Educ.* **1998**: 75, 748 (June 1998).

$$C_{12}H_{22}O_{11}(s) \xrightarrow{H_2SO_4(\text{concd})} 12\ C(s) + 11\ H_2O(l) \qquad (22.25)$$

The concentrated acid is a moderately good oxidizing agent and is able, for example, to react with copper.

$$Cu(s) + 2\ H_2SO_4(\text{concd}) \longrightarrow Cu^{2+}(aq) + SO_4^{2-}(aq) + 2\ H_2O(l) + SO_2(g) \qquad (22.26)$$

For a very long time, sulfuric acid has ranked among the top manufactured chemicals, with annual production in the United States of about 45 million tons. Sulfuric acid continues to have many uses, but the bulk of H_2SO_4 is used in the manufacture of fertilizers. Other uses are found in various metallurgical processes, oil refining, and the manufacture of the white pigment titanium dioxide. Also familiar is its use as the electrolyte in storage batteries for automobiles and emergency power supplies. We might say that sulfuric acid was the workhorse of the "old economy" but that it has a lesser role in the "new economy."

Riethmiller, Steven. "Charles H. Winston and Confederate Sulfuric Acid." *J. Chem. Educ.* **1995**: 72, 575 (July 1995).

When $SO_2(g)$ reacts with water, it produces $H_2SO_3(aq)$, but this acid, *sulfurous acid*, has never been isolated in pure form. Salts of sulfurous acid, *sulfites*, are good reducing agents and are easily oxidized by $O_2(g)$. For example,

$$O_2(g) + 2\ SO_3^{2-}(aq) \longrightarrow 2\ SO_4^{2-}(aq) \qquad (22.27)$$

But sulfite ion can also act as an oxidizing agent, as in this reaction with H_2S.

$$2\ H_2S(g) + 2\ H^+(aq) + SO_3^{2-}(aq) \longrightarrow 3\ H_2O(l) + 3\ S(s) \qquad (22.28)$$

Both H_2SO_3 and H_2SO_4 are diprotic acids. They ionize in two steps and produce two types of salts, one in each ionization step. The term **acid salt** is sometimes used for salts such as $NaHSO_3$ and $NaHSO_4$ because their anions undergo a further *acid* ionization. H_2SO_3 is a weak acid in both ionization steps, whereas H_2SO_4 is strong in the first step and somewhat weak in the second. If a solution of H_2SO_4 is sufficiently dilute, however (less than about 0.001 M), we can treat the acid as if both ionization steps go to completion.

Show the effect of heats of dilution by having two beakers of conc. sulfuric acid and one of water. Add acid slowly to one beaker (this is the correct procedure). Use a thermometer to show that the temperature does increase quite dramatically. Then, using a shield, use an eye-dropper and add a few drops of water to acid (this is the incorrect procedure). You should be able to make the water splatter. For this, use proper protection, eye glasses, and proper shields. Discuss the seriousness of acid burns.

Sulfates and Sulfites. Sulfate and sulfite salts have a number of important uses. Calcium sulfate dihydrate (gypsum) is used to make the hemihydrate (plaster of Paris) for the building industry (page 884). Aluminum sulfate is

◀ Actually, $NaHSO_3$ cannot be isolated as a solid. When we attempt to crystallize this salt from an aqueous solution containing HSO_3^-, the reaction $2\ HSO_3^- \longrightarrow S_2O_5^{2-} + H_2O$ occurs. The product obtained is sodium *metabisulfite*, $Na_2S_2O_5$.

SO_3^{2-}, sulfite

SO_4^{2-}, sulfate

$S_2O_3^{2-}$, thiosulfate

$S_2O_6^{2-}$, dithionate

$S_3O_6^{2-}$, trithionate

$S_4O_6^{2-}$, tetrathionate

▲ **FIGURE 22-12**
Structures of some oxoanions of sulfur

Atterholt, C., Butcher, D. J., Bacon, J. R., Kwochka, W. R., Woosley, R. "Implementation of an Environmental Focus in an Undergraduate Chemistry Curriculum by the Addition of Gas Chromatography-Mass Spectrometry." *J. Chem. Educ.* 2000: 77, 1550 (December 2000).

Johns, N., Longstaff, S. J. "A convenient, low-cost method for determining sulfate in acid rain (F&R)." *J. Chem. Educ.* 1987: 64, 449, 35.

used in water treatment and in sizing paper (page 894). Copper(II) sulfate is employed as a fungicide and algicide and in electroplating. The chief application of sulfites is in the pulp and paper industry. Sulfites solubilize *lignin*, a polymeric substance that coats the cellulose fibers in wood. This treatment frees the fibers for processing into wood pulp and then paper. Sulfites are also used as reducing agents in photography and as scavengers of $O_2(aq)$ in treating boiler water (reaction 22.27). Compounds of sulfur(IV) have long been used as food preservatives and antioxidants. For example, exposure to $SO_2(g)$ prevents the discoloration of dried fruits, and soluble sulfites act as antimicrobial agents in winemaking.

Thiosulfates. In addition to sulfite and sulfate ions, another important sulfur–oxygen ion is thiosulfate ion, $S_2O_3^{2-}$. The prefix *thio* signifies that a S atom replaces an O atom in a compound. Thus, the thiosulfate ion can be viewed as a sulfate ion, SO_4^{2-}, in which a S atom replaces one of the O atoms. The formal oxidation state of S in $S_2O_3^{2-}$ is +2, but as Figure 22-12 indicates, the two S atoms are not equivalent: The central S atom is in the oxidation state +6, and the terminal S atom, −2. The structures of several other thio anions are also shown in Figure 22-12.

Thiosulfates can be prepared by boiling elemental sulfur in an alkaline solution of sodium sulfite. The sulfur is oxidized and the sulfite ion is reduced, both to thiosulfate ion.

$$SO_3^{2-}(aq) + S(s) \longrightarrow S_2O_3^{2-}(aq) \qquad (22.29)$$

Thiosulfate solutions are important in photographic processing (see page 1027). They are also common analytical reagents, often used in conjunction with iodine. For example, in one method of analysis for copper, an excess of iodide ion is added to $Cu^{2+}(aq)$, producing $CuI(s)$ and triiodide ion, I_3^-.

$$2\,Cu^{2+}(aq) + 5\,I^-(aq) \longrightarrow 2\,CuI(s) + I_3^-(aq) \qquad (22.30)$$

The excess triiodide ion is then titrated with a standard solution of $Na_2S_2O_3(aq)$, forming I^- and $S_4O_6^{2-}$, the *tetrathionate* ion.

$$I_3^-(aq) + 2\,S_2O_3^{2-}(aq) \longrightarrow 3\,I^-(aq) + S_4O_6^{2-}(aq) \qquad (22.31)$$

OXYGEN AND SULFUR HALIDES

Both oxygen and sulfur form a number of interesting compounds with the halogens. Oxygen, for example, forms the fluorides OF_2 and O_2F_2, which have structures similar to those of water and hydrogen peroxide but which are much more reactive. Sulfur also forms compounds with the halogens; the analogous compounds SF_2 and S_2F_2 are known, as are the compounds SF_4 and SF_6. The reactivities of SF_4 and SF_6 are quite different. SF_6 is a colorless, odorless inert (unreactive) gas, whereas SF_4 is a powerful fluorinating agent.

$$3\,SF_4 + 4\,BCl_3 \longrightarrow 4\,BF_3 + 3\,SCl_2 + 3\,Cl_2$$

Sulfur and chlorine also form the compounds S_2Cl_2 and SCl_4, but the best-known dihalide is SCl_2. It is a foul-smelling, red liquid (melting point, −122 °C; boiling point, 59 °C) that has been used in the production of the notorious, and highly poisonous, mustard gas.

$$SCl_2 + 2\,CH_2CH_2 \longrightarrow S(CH_2CH_2Cl)_2$$

Mustard gas is not a gas, but a volatile liquid (melting point, 13 °C; boiling point, 235 °C). During World War I it was sprayed as a mist that stayed close to the ground and was blown by wind onto the enemy. Exposure to mustard gas causes blistering of the skin, internal and external bleeding, blindness, and, after four or five weeks, death.

Pressurized fluidized-bed boiler

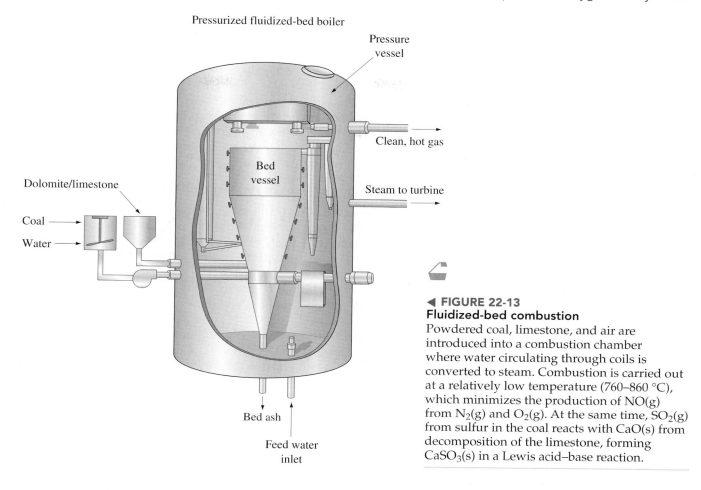

FIGURE 22-13

▲ **FIGURE 22-13**
Fluidized-bed combustion
Powdered coal, limestone, and air are
introduced into a combustion chamber
where water circulating through coils is
converted to steam. Combustion is carried out
at a relatively low temperature (760–860 °C),
which minimizes the production of NO(g)
from N_2(g) and O_2(g). At the same time, SO_2(g)
from sulfur in the coal reacts with CaO(s) from
decomposition of the limestone, forming
$CaSO_3$(s) in a Lewis acid–base reaction.

SO_2 EMISSIONS AND THE ENVIRONMENT

Industrial smog consists primarily of particles (ash and smoke), SO_2(g), and
H_2SO_4 mist. A variety of industrial operations produce significant quantities
of SO_2(g), but the main contributors to atmospheric releases of SO_2(g) are
power plants burning coal or high-sulfur fuel oils. SO_2 can oxidize to SO_3, especially when the reaction is catalyzed on the surfaces of airborne particles or
through reaction with NO_2.

$$SO_2(g) + NO_2(g) \longrightarrow SO_3(g) + NO(g) \qquad (22.32)$$

In turn, SO_3 can react with water vapor in the atmosphere to produce
H_2SO_4 mist, a component of acid rain. Also, the reaction of H_2SO_4 with airborne NH_3 produces particles of $(NH_4)_2SO_4$. The details of the effect of low
concentrations of SO_2 and H_2SO_4 on the body are not well understood, but it
is clear that these substances are respiratory irritants. Levels above 0.10 ppm
are considered potentially harmful.

The control of industrial smog and acid rain hinges on the removal of sulfur
from fuels and the control of SO_2(g) emissions. Dozens of processes have been
proposed for removing SO_2 from smokestack gases, one of which is illustrated
in Figure 22-13.

(a)

(b)

▲ Electrostatic potential
maps of **(a)** OF_2 and **(b)** OCl_2.

CONCEPT ASSESSMENT ✓

Explain the difference between the electrostatic potential maps for OF_2 and OCl_2.

Coppola, B. D., Hovick, J. W., Daniels, D. S. "I Scream, You Scream...: A New Twist on the Liquid Nitrogen Demonstrations." *J. Chem. Educ.* **1994;** *71,* 1080.

Use liquid nitrogen to freeze objects. Fill a balloon with nitrogen and show that it does not burn like the hydrogen-filled balloon.

Pure oxygen can lead to sustained combustion. Since the air is about 20% oxygen and 80% nitrogen, the nitrogen dilutes the oxygen so that sustained combustion is not possible.

22-4 GROUP 15: THE NITROGEN FAMILY

The chemistry of the group 15 elements is an extensive subject, especially that of the first two members of the series—nitrogen and phosphorus. We will discuss the special significance of these two elements to living matter later in the text, but even here you should get a sense of the richness of their chemistry. For example, nitrogen atoms can exist in many oxidation states (Fig. 22-14).

Moving farther to the left in the periodic table, we expect the appearance of metallic behavior to become more significant among the heavier elements in the group. We begin by examining this feature.

METALLIC–NONMETALLIC CHARACTER IN GROUP 15

All the elements in group 15 have the valence-shell electron configuration ns^2np^3. This configuration suggests nonmetallic behavior and doesn't give any clues as to metallic character that might exist. Table 22.8, however, indicates the usual decrease of ionization energy with increasing atomic number. These values, taken together with physical properties from the table, do suggest the order of metallic character within the group. Nitrogen and phosphorus are nonmetallic, arsenic and antimony are metalloids, and bismuth is metallic. The first ionization energy of bismuth is actually somewhat less than that of magnesium, and its third ionization energy (2466 kJ mol^{-1}) is less than the third ionization energy of aluminum (2745 kJ mol^{-1}). The electronegativities indicate a high degree of nonmetallic character for nitrogen and less so for the remaining members of the group.

Acidic solution ($[H^+] = 1 \text{ M}$):

+5	+4	+3	+2	+1	0	−1	−2	−3
	0.803 V	1.065 V	0.996 V	1.591 V	1.766 V	−1.87 V	1.42 V	1.275 V

$$NO_3^- \text{—} N_2O_4 \text{—} HNO_2 \text{—} NO \text{—} N_2O \text{—} N_2 \text{—} NH_3OH^+ \text{—} N_2H_5^+ \text{—} NH_4^+$$

FIGURE 22-14
Electrode potential diagrams for nitrogen

Basic solution ($[OH^-] = 1 \text{ M}$):

+5	+4	+3	+2	+1	0	−1	−2	−3
	−0.86 V	0.867 V	−0.46 V	0.76 V	0.94 V	−3.04 V	0.73 V	0.10 V

$$NO_3^- \text{—} N_2O_4 \text{—} NO_2^- \text{—} NO \text{—} N_2O \text{—} N_2 \text{—} NH_2OH \text{—} N_2H_4 \text{—} NH_3$$

TABLE 22.8 Selected Properties of Group 15 Elements

Element	Covalent Radius, pm	Electronegativity	First Ionization Energy, kJ mol⁻¹	Common Physical Form(s)	Density of Solid, g cm⁻³	Comparative Electrical Conductivity[a]
N	75	3.0	1402	Gas	1.03 (−252 °C)	—
P	110	2.1	1012	Wax-like white solid;	1.82	—
				Red solid	2.20	10^{-17}
As	121	2.0	947	Yellow solid;	2.03	—
				Gray solid with metallic luster	5.78	6.1
Sb	140	1.9	834	Yellow solid;	5.3	—
				Silvery white metallic solid	6.69	4.0
Bi	155	1.9	703	Pinkish white metallic solid	9.75	1.5

[a]These values are relative to an assigned value of 100 for silver.

Three group 15 elements—phosphorus, arsenic, and antimony—exhibit allotropy. The common forms of phosphorus at room temperature, both non-metallic, are white and red phosphorus. For arsenic and antimony, the more stable allotropic forms are the metallic ones. These forms have high densities, moderate thermal conductivities, and limited abilities to conduct electricity. Bismuth is a metal despite its low electrical conductivity, which, nevertheless, is better than that of manganese and almost as good as that of mercury. The nonmetals and metals in group 15 are also distinguishable by their oxides. The oxides of nitrogen and phosphorus (for example, N_2O_3 and P_4O_6) are acidic when they react with water. As with the nonmetals in groups 16 and 17, this is typical for nonmetal oxides. Arsenic(III) oxide and antimony(III) oxide are amphoteric, whereas bismuth(III) oxide acts only as a base, a property typical of metal oxides.

OCCURRENCE, PRODUCTION, AND USES

Nitrogen. Nitrogen occurs mainly in the atmosphere. Its abundance in Earth's solid crust is only 0.002% by mass. The only important nitrogen-containing minerals are KNO_3 (niter, or saltpeter) and $NaNO_3$ (soda niter, or Chile saltpeter), found in a few desert regions. Other natural sources of nitrogen-containing compounds are plant and animal protein and the fossilized remains of ancient plant life, such as coal.

Until about 100 years ago, sources of pure nitrogen and its compounds were quite limited. This all changed with invention of a process for the liquefaction of air in 1895 (see Figure 22-5) and development of the Haber–Bosch process for converting nitrogen to ammonia in 1908 (page 941). A host of nitrogen compounds can be made from ammonia. Nitrogen gas has many important uses of its own in addition to being a precursor of manufactured nitrogen compounds. Some of these uses are listed in Table 22.9.

Phosphorus.   Although phosphorus is the eleventh most abundant element and makes up about 0.11% of Earth's crust by mass, it was not discovered until 1669. It was originally isolated from putrefied urine—an effective if not particularly pleasant source. Today the principal source of phosphorus compounds is phosphate rock, a class of minerals known as *apatites*, such as fluorapatite $[Ca_5(PO_4)_3F$ or $3 Ca_3(PO_4)_2 \cdot CaF_2]$. Elemental phosphorus is prepared by heating phosphate rock, silica (SiO_2), and coke (C) in an electric furnace. The overall change that occurs is

$$2\, Ca_3(PO_4)_2(s) + 10\, C(s) + 6\, SiO_2(s) \xrightarrow{\Delta} 6\, CaSiO_3(l) + 10\, CO(g) + P_4(g) \quad (22.33)$$

The $P_4(g)$ is condensed, collected, and stored under water as white phosphorus.

Although compounds of phosphorus are vitally important to living organisms (DNA and phosphates in bones and teeth, for example), the element itself is not widely used. Almost all the elemental phosphorus produced is reoxidized to give P_4O_{10} for the manufacture of high-purity phosphoric acid. The rest is used to make organophosphorus compounds and phosphorus sulfides (P_4S_3) in match heads.

McRae, R., et al. "The Liquid Nitrogen Fountain." *J. Chem. Educ.* **2002:** *79*, 1220.

Nolan, William T., Gish, Thaddeus J. "The Joys of Liquid Nitrogen." *J. Chem. Educ.* **1996:** *73*, 651 (July 1996).

Nolan, William R., Gish, Thaddeus J. 'The authors reply to "The Joys of Liquid Nitrogen".' *J. Chem. Educ.* **1997:** *74*, 617 (June 1997).

Blatchley, Ronald C. "The Joys of Liquid Nitrogen." *J. Chem. Educ.* **1997:** *74*, 616 (June 1997).

▲ Viruses for use in medical research are frozen in liquid nitrogen.

Hughes, Elvin, Jr. "A demonstration of the molar volume of nitrogen gas (TD)." *J. Chem. Educ.* **1992:** *69*, 763.

TABLE 22.9   Uses of Nitrogen Gas
Provide a blanketing (inert) atmosphere for the production of chemicals and electronic components
Pressurized gas for enhanced oil recovery
Metals treatment
Refrigerant (e.g., fast freezing of foods)

Arsenic and Antimony. Arsenic is obtained by heating arsenic-containing metal sulfides. For example, FeAsS yields FeS and As(g). The As(g) deposits as As(s), which can be used to make other compounds. Some arsenic is also obtained by the reduction of arsenic(III) oxide with CO(g). Antimony is obtained mainly from its sulfide ores. Bismuth is obtained as a by-product of the refining of other metals.

Both As and Sb are used in making alloys of other metals. For example, the addition of As and Sb to Pb produces an alloy that has desirable properties for use as electrodes in lead–acid batteries. Arsenic and antimony are used to produce semiconductor materials, such as GaAs, GaSb, and InSb, in electronic devices. (Recall the discussion of GaAs photocells on page 908.)

NITROGEN COMPOUNDS

The substance from which all nitrogen compounds are ultimately derived, $N_2(g)$, is unusually stable. One explanation of the limited reactivity of the N_2 molecule is based on its electronic structure. As discussed in Chapter 10, the bond between the two N atoms in N_2 is a *triple* covalent bond, which is unusually strong and difficult to break. In thermochemical terms, the enthalpy change associated with breaking the bonds in one mole of N_2 molecules is very high—the dissociation reaction is highly endothermic.

$$N{\equiv}N(g) \longrightarrow 2\,N(g) \quad \Delta H° = +945.4\ kJ$$

Also, the Gibbs energies of formation of many nitrogen compounds are positive, which means that their formation reactions are not spontaneous. For NO(g),

$$\frac{1}{2}N_2(g) + \frac{1}{2}O_2 \longrightarrow NO(g) \quad \Delta G_f° = 86.55\ kJ$$

Reactions with a positive Gibbs energy of formation, such as the formation of NO(g) from its elements, do not occur to any significant extent at normal temperatures and atmospheric conditions. Just imagine the situation if $\Delta G_f°[NO(g)] = -86.55\ kJ\ mol^{-1}$ instead of $+86.55\ kJ\ mol^{-1}$. The reaction of $N_2(g)$ and $O_2(g)$ to form NO(g) would likely proceed to a far greater extent. With an atmosphere depleted in $O_2(g)$ and rich in noxious NO(g), life as we know it would not be possible on Earth.

Nitrides. Nitrogen forms binary compounds with most other elements, and these compounds can be grouped into four categories. In ionic (salt-like) nitrides, the nitrogen is present as the N^{3-} ion. These compounds form with lithium and the group 2 metals. Thus, when magnesium is burned in air (see Figure 2-1), a small quantity of magnesium nitride forms, together with the principal product, magnesium oxide.

$$3\,Mg(s) + N_2(g) \xrightarrow{\Delta} Mg_3N_2(s) \tag{22.34}$$

The nitride ion is a very strong base. In aqueous solution, it accepts protons from water molecules to form ammonia molecules and hydroxide ions.

$$N^{3-}(aq) + 3\,H_2O(l) \longrightarrow NH_3(aq) + 3\,OH^-(aq)$$

In the reaction of magnesium nitride with water, magnesium and hydroxide ions combine to form insoluble $Mg(OH)_2$, and the ammonia is released as a gas, which is easily detectable by its odor.

$$Mg_3N_2(s) + 6\,H_2O(l) \longrightarrow 3\,Mg(OH)_2(s) + 2\,NH_3(g)$$

When nitrogen combines with other typical nonmetals, it does so by forming covalent bonds, yielding covalent nitrides. Bonding in these nitrides can be described in terms of the general principles presented in Chapters 10 and 11. Some binary covalent nitrides are $(CN)_2$, P_3N_5, As_4N_4, S_2N_2, and S_4N_4. Nitrogen combines with elements of group 13, producing compounds of the form MN (where M = B, Al, Ga, In, or Tl). The products are isoelectronic with graphite and diamond and resemble them structurally. A fourth type of binary nitrides are the metallic nitrides with formulas such as MN, M_3N, and M_4N. These are *interstitial compounds*, in which N atoms occupy some or all of the interstices (voids) in the structure of the metal. They are hard, chemically inert, high-melting-point solids with important uses as refractory materials and catalysts. Typical examples are TiN, VN, and UN (with melting points 2950 °C, 2050 °C, and 2800 °C, respectively).

Ammonia and Related Compounds.   The Haber–Bosch process for the synthesis of ammonia involves the reaction

$$N_2(g) + 3 H_2(g) \rightleftharpoons 2 NH_3(g) \qquad (22.35)$$

As we noted in an earlier encounter with this reaction (page 653), a high yield of ammonia requires (1) a high temperature (400 °C), (2) a catalyst to speed up the reaction, and (3) a high pressure (about 200 atm). The key to achieving essentially 100% yield is continuous removal of NH_3 and recycling of the unreacted $N_2(g)$ and $H_2(g)$. The NH_3 is removed by liquefaction. The Haber–Bosch process is outlined in Figure 22-15. A critical aspect of the process is having a source of $H_2(g)$. Mostly, this is made by the re-forming of natural gas (see page 900).

Ammonia is the starting material in the manufacture of most other nitrogen compounds, but it has some direct uses of its own. Its most important use is as a fertilizer. The highest concentration in which nitrogen fertilizer can be applied to fields is as pure liquid NH_3, known as "anhydrous ammonia." $NH_3(aq)$ is also applied in a variety of household cleaning products, such as commercial glass cleaners. In these products, the ammonia acts as an inexpensive base to produce $OH^-(aq)$. The $OH^-(aq)$ reacts with grease and oil molecules to convert them into compounds that are more soluble in water. In addition, the aqueous ammonia solution dries quickly, leaving few streaks on glass.

Because ammonia is a base, a simple approach to producing certain nitrogen compounds is to neutralize ammonia with an appropriate acid. The acid–base reaction that forms ammonium sulfate, an important solid fertilizer, is

$$2 NH_3(aq) + H_2SO_4(aq) \longrightarrow (NH_4)_2SO_4(aq) \qquad (22.36)$$

▲ **Fritz Haber (1868–1934)**
Haber's perfection of the ammonia synthesis reaction, which made the manufacture of inexpensive explosives possible, was of critical importance to Germany during World War I. After the war, Haber again applied his chemical knowledge for his country's benefit by attempting, unsuccessfully, to extract gold from seawater for use in paying war reparations. Despite his past services, this Jewish scientist was driven from his academic post by the Nazi regime in 1933.

Vitz, Ed. "Ammonia Can Crush." *J. Chem. Educ.* **1999:** *76,* 932 (July 1999) (Demonstration)

Feldman, M. R., et al. "Fritz Haber (PROFILES)." *J. Chem. Educ.* **1983:** *60,* 463.

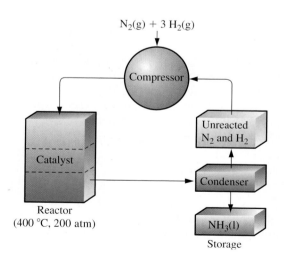

▲ **FIGURE 22-15**
Ammonia synthesis reaction—the Haber–Bosch process
The gaseous N_2–H_2 mixture is introduced into a reactor at high temperature and pressure in the presence of a catalyst. The gaseous N_2–H_2–NH_3 mixture leaves the reactor and is cooled as it passes through a condenser. Liquefied NH_3 is removed, and the remaining N_2–H_2 mixture is compressed and returned to the reactor. The yield is essentially 100%.

▲ Anhydrous liquid ammonia being applied directly to the soil.

Stage Smoke: Place two beakers next to each other. One contains concentrated NH_3 and the other concentrated HCl. The fumes mix and produce "smoke" of NH_4Cl. This is one way smoke is made on stage. NH_4Cl is non-toxic, but be careful with the concentrated components. It is not necessary to mix the liquids, although that is more dramatic.

▲ Urea.

Driscoll, Jerry A. "Acid Rain Demonstration: The Formation of Nitrogen Oxides as a By-Product of High-Temperature Flames in Connection with Internal Combustion Engines." *J. Chem. Educ.* 1997: 74, 1424 (December 1997).

▲ The lifting thrusters of a space shuttle, shown here in an in-flight test, use methylhydrazine, CH_3NHNH_2, as a fuel.

Ammonium chloride, made by the reaction of $NH_3(aq)$ and $HCl(aq)$, is used in the manufacture of dry-cell batteries, in cleaning metals, and as an agent to help solder flow smoothly when soldering metals. Ammonium nitrate, made by the reaction of $NH_3(aq)$ and $HNO_3(aq)$, is used both as a fertilizer and as an explosive. The explosive power of ammonium nitrate was not fully appreciated until a shipload of this material exploded in Texas City, Texas, in 1947, killing many people. More recently, mixtures of ammonium nitrate and fuel oil were used as explosives in the terrorist attacks on the World Trade Center in New York City in 1993 and the Murrah Federal Building in Oklahoma City in 1995. The reaction of $NH_3(aq)$ and $H_3PO_4(aq)$ yields ammonium phosphates [such as $NH_4H_2PO_4$ and $(NH_4)_2HPO_4$]. These compounds are good fertilizers because they supply two vital plant nutrients, N and P; they are also used as fire retardants.

Urea, which contains 46% nitrogen by mass, is often manufactured at ammonia synthesis plants by a simple reaction.

$$2\,NH_3 + CO_2 \longrightarrow \underset{\text{urea}}{CO(NH_2)_2} + H_2O \qquad (22.37)$$

Urea is an excellent fertilizer, either as a pure solid, as a solid mixed with ammonium salts, or in a very concentrated aqueous solution mixed with NH_4NO_3 or NH_3 (or both). Urea is also used as a feed supplement for cattle and in the production of polymers and pesticides.

Other Hydrides of Nitrogen.   A great deal has been said in this text about the principal hydride of nitrogen: ammonia, NH_3. Here we describe some lesser-known hydrides. If a H atom in NH_3 is replaced by the group $-NH_2$, the resulting molecule is H_2N-NH_2 or N_2H_4, *hydrazine* ($pK_{b_1} = 6.07$; $pK_{b_2} = 15.05$). Replacement of a H atom in NH_3 by $-OH$ produces NH_2OH, *hydroxylamine* ($pK_b = 8.04$). Hydrazine and hydroxylamine are weak bases. Because it has two N atoms, N_2H_4 ionizes in two steps. Hydrazine and hydroxylamine form salts analogous to ammonium salts, such as $N_2H_5{}^+NO_3{}^-$, $N_2H_6{}^{2+}SO_4{}^{2-}$, and $NH_3OH^+Cl^-$. As expected, these salts hydrolyze in water to yield acidic solutions.

Hydrazine and some of its derivatives burn in air with the evolution of large quantities of heat; they are used as rocket fuels. For the combustion of hydrazine,

$$N_2H_4(l) + O_2(g) \longrightarrow N_2(g) + 2\,H_2O(l) \qquad \Delta H° = -622.2\,\text{kJ} \qquad (22.38)$$

Reaction (22.38) can also be used to remove dissolved $O_2(g)$ from boiler water. Hydrazine is particularly valued for this purpose because no salts (ionic compounds) form that would be objectionable in the water. The industrial preparation of hydrazine was described in Chapter 4 (page 130).

Both hydrazine and hydroxylamine can act as either oxidizing or reducing agents (usually the latter), depending on the pH and the substances with which they react. The oxidation of hydrazine in acidic solution by nitrite ion produces *hydrazoic acid*, $HN_3(aq)$.

$$N_2H_5{}^+(aq) + NO_2{}^-(aq) \longrightarrow HN_3(aq) + 2\,H_2O(l) \qquad (22.39)$$

Pure HN_3 is a colorless liquid that boils at 37 °C. It is very unstable and will detonate when subjected to shock. In aqueous solution, HN_3 is a weak acid; its salts are called *azides*. Azides resemble chlorides in some properties (for instance, AgN_3 is insoluble in water), but they are unstable. Some azides (such as lead azide) are used to make detonators. The release of $N_2(g)$ by the decomposition of sodium azide, NaN_3, is the basis of the air-bag safety system in automobiles (page 196).

$$\ddot{:}\!N\!=\!N\!=\!\ddot{N}\diagdown_H \longleftrightarrow :N\!\equiv\!N\!-\!\ddot{\ddot{N}}\diagdown_H$$

OXIDES OF NITROGEN

Nitrogen forms a series of oxides in which the oxidation state of N can have every value ranging from +1 to +5 (Table 22.10). All these oxides are gases at 25 °C, except N_2O_5, which is a solid with a sublimation pressure of 1 atm at 32.5 °C. It is impossible to obtain either brown $NO_2(g)$ or its colorless dimer, $N_2O_4(g)$, as a pure gas at temperatures between about −10 °C and 140 °C because of the equilibrium between them (review Example 15-9). At lower temperatures, N_2O_4 can be obtained as a pure solid, and above 140 °C, the gas-phase equilibrium strongly favors $NO_2(g)$. In the solid state, N_2O_3 is pale blue; in the liquid state, it is bright blue.

All nitrates decompose on heating, but only NH_4NO_3 yields $N_2O(g)$. Nitrates of active metals, such as $NaNO_3$, yield the corresponding nitrite and $O_2(g)$. Nitrates of less active metals, such as $Pb(NO_3)_2$, yield the metal oxide, $NO(g)$ and $O_2(g)$. These methods of preparing oxides of nitrogen are outlined in Table 22.11.

As mentioned in our assessment of the metallic–nonmetallic character of the group 15 elements, the oxides of nitrogen are acidic. N_2O_3 and N_2O_5 react with water to give acidic solutions. The acid anhydride of nitric acid is N_2O_5.

$$N_2O_5(s) + H_2O(l) \longrightarrow 2\, HNO_3(aq)$$

The acid anhydride of nitrous acid, HNO_2, is N_2O_3. Nitrogen dioxide, NO_2, produces both HNO_3 and NO when it reacts with water. But N_2O is not an acid anhydride in the usual sense; it is related to *hyponitrous* acid, $H_2N_2O_2$ ($HON{=}NOH$), which yields N_2O and H_2O on decomposition.

$$H_2N_2O_2 \longrightarrow N_2O + H_2O$$

Among the oxides of nitrogen, N_2O has anesthetic properties and finds some use in dentistry (laughing gas). NO_2 is employed in the manufacture of nitric acid. N_2O_4 is used extensively as an oxidizer in rocket fuels. NO is the most important oxide of nitrogen from a biological standpoint. In humans, it plays a role in maintaining blood pressure, aids in the immune response in killing foreign organisms, and is essential to the establishment of long-term memory. In 1996, scientists discovered that hemoglobin carries NO as well as O_2. The NO causes the walls of blood vessels to thin, making it easier for oxygen to be transported to the surrounding tissues. This discovery has resulted in the development of several new medications.

One of the interesting features of the oxides of nitrogen is that their free energies of formation are all *positive* quantities. This feature suggests that the oxides are thermodynamically unstable, for example,

$$2\, N_2O(g) \longrightarrow 2\, N_2(g) + O_2(g) \qquad \Delta G° = -208\ \text{kJ (at 298 K)} \qquad (22.40)$$

Actually, $N_2O(g)$ is quite stable at room temperature because the activation energy for its decomposition is very high—about 250 kJ mol⁻¹. At higher temperatures (about 600 °C), its rate of decomposition becomes appreciable.

TABLE 22.10   Oxides of Nitrogen

O.S. of N	Formula
+1	N_2O
+2	NO
+3	N_2O_3
+4	NO_2
+4	N_2O_4
+5	N_2O_5

Nitrogen Dioxide and Dinitrogen Tetroxide movie

Volkovich, V. A., Griffiths, T. R. "Catalytic Oxidation of Ammonia: A Sparkling Experiment." *J. Chem. Educ.* **2000:** *77,* 177 (February 2000).

NH_4NO_3 is a strong oxidizing agent. Sprinkle Zn dust on solid NH_4NO_3 and moisten. An exothermic reaction produces ZnO "smoke."

Foster, Natalie I., Heindel, Ned D. "The discovery of nitroglycerine: Its preparation and therapeutic utility (SBS)." *J. Chem. Educ.* **1981:** *58,* 364.

Clyde, Dale D. "Dynamite Demo?" *J. Chem. Educ.* **1995:** *72,* 1130 (December 1995).

Carr, James D. "Stoichiometry for copper dissolution in nitric acid: A comment (LTE)." *J. Chem. Educ.* **1990:** *67,* 183.

Solomon, Sally, Hur, Chinhyu, Lee, Alan, Smith, Kurt. "Quick Method for Making Colored-Flame Flash Paper." *J. Chem. Educ.* **1995:** *72,* 1133 (December 1995).

TABLE 22.11   Preparation of Oxides of Nitrogen

Oxide	A Method of Preparation
N_2O	$NH_4NO_3(s) \xrightarrow{\Delta} N_2O(g) + 2\,H_2O(g)$
NO	$3\,Cu(s) + 8\,H^+(aq) + 2\,NO_3^-(aq) \longrightarrow 3\,Cu^{2+}(aq) + 2\,NO(g) + 4\,H_2O(l)$
N_2O_3	$2\,NO(g) + N_2O_4(g) \xrightarrow{-20\,°C} 2\,N_2O_3(l)$
NO_2	$2\,Pb(NO_3)_2(s) \xrightarrow{\Delta} 2\,PbO(s) + 4\,NO_2(g) + O_2(g)$
	$2\,NO(g) + O_2(g) \rightleftharpoons 2\,NO_2(g) \qquad K_p = 1.6 \times 10^{12}$ (at 298 K)
N_2O_4	$2\,NO_2(g) \rightleftharpoons N_2O_4(g) \qquad K_p = 8.84$ (at 298 K)
N_2O_5	$4\,HNO_3(l) + P_4O_{10}(s) \xrightarrow{-10\,°C} 4\,HPO_3(s) + 2\,N_2O_5(s)$

▲ The combustion of copper gauze in $N_2O(g)$.

Bretherick, Leslie. "Nitric acid, nitrates, and nitro compounds: Energetic servants, but overwhelming masters (SAFETY)." *J. Chem. Educ.* **1989**: *66*, A220.

▶ Nitroglycerin is used to dilate coronary arteries in the treatment of angina. It exerts its effect by virtue of its metabolic conversion to nitric oxide.

▲ A copper penny reacting with nitric acid. The reaction is that given by equation (22.43). The blue-green color of the solution is due to Cu^{2+}(aq), and the reddish brown color is that of nitrogen dioxide, NO_2(g).

▲ Flash paper is used by magicians for dramatic effect. It can be made by treating paper with nitric and sulfuric acids. This process converts the cellulose fibers into nitrocellulose, which burns cleanly and rapidly.

Reaction (22.40) accounts for the ability of N_2O to support combustion because the O_2(g) necessary for the combustion is produced by the decomposition of N_2O. Overall reactions of the following sort occur.

$$H_2(g) + N_2O(g) \longrightarrow H_2O(l) + N_2(g)$$
$$Cu(s) + N_2O(g) \longrightarrow CuO(s) + N_2(g)$$

Nitrogen monoxide (nitric oxide), NO(g), is produced commercially by the oxidation of NH_3(g) in the presence of a catalyst (the Ostwald process). This oxidation is the first step in converting NH_3 to a number of other nitrogen compounds.

$$4\,NH_3(g) + 5\,O_2(g) \xrightarrow[850\,°C]{Pt} 4\,NO(g) + 6\,H_2O(g) \tag{22.41}$$

Another source of NO, usually unwanted, is in high-temperature combustion processes, such as those that occur in automobile engines and in electric power plants. At the same time that the fuel combines with oxygen from air to produce a high temperature, N_2(g) and O_2(g) in the hot air combine to a limited extent to form NO(g).

$$N_2(g) + O_2(g) \xrightarrow{\Delta} 2\,NO(g) \tag{22.42}$$

Brown nitrogen dioxide, NO_2(g), is often seen in reactions involving nitric acid. An example is the reaction of Cu(s) with warm concentrated HNO_3(aq).

$$Cu(s) + 4\,H^+(aq) + 2\,NO_3^-(aq) \longrightarrow Cu^{2+}(aq) + 2\,H_2O(l) + 2\,NO_2(g) \tag{22.43}$$

Of particular interest to atmospheric chemists is the key role of NO_2(g) in the formation of photochemical smog (page 602).

Nitric Acid and Nitrates.   The commercial synthesis of nitric acid does not use N_2O_5, as might be expected. It involves the following three reactions, the first of which—the Ostwald process—was described previously. NO(g) from reaction (22.45) is recycled into reaction (22.44).

$$4\,NH_3(g) + 5\,O_2(g) \xrightarrow[850\,°C]{Pt} 4\,NO(g) + 6\,H_2O(g) \tag{22.41}$$

$$2\,NO(g) + O_2(g) \longrightarrow 2\,NO_2(g) \tag{22.44}$$

$$3\,NO_2(g) + H_2O(l) \longrightarrow 2\,HNO_3(aq) + NO(g) \tag{22.45}$$

Nitric acid is used in the preparation of various dyes; drugs; fertilizers (ammonium nitrate); and explosives, such as nitroglycerin, nitrocellulose, and trinitrotoluene (TNT). It is also used in metallurgy and in reprocessing spent nuclear fuels. Nitric acid is about twelfth, by mass, among the top chemicals produced in the United States.

Nitric acid is also a good oxidizing agent. For example, copper reacts with dilute HNO_3(aq), producing primarily NO or, with concentrated HNO_3(aq), NO_2 (reaction 22.43). With a more active metal such as Zn, the reduction product has N in one of its lower oxidation states, for example, NH_4^+. Nitrates can be made by neutralizing nitric acid with appropriate bases.

(a) White phosphorus   **(b)** Red phosphorus

▲ **FIGURE 22-16**
Two forms of phosphorus
(a) Structure of white phosphorus: the P_4 molecule. **(b)** Structure of red phosphorus.

ALLOTROPES OF PHOSPHORUS

White phosphorus is a white, waxy, phosphorescent solid that can be cut with a knife. (A phosphorescent material glows in the dark.) It is a nonconductor of electricity, can ignite spontaneously in air (hence it is stored under water), and is insoluble in water but soluble in some nonpolar solvents, such as CS_2. The solid has P_4 molecules as its basic structural units (Fig. 22-16a). The P_4 molecule is tetrahedral, with a P atom at each corner. The phosphorus-to-phosphorus bonds in P_4 appear to involve the overlap of $3p$ orbitals almost exclusively. Such overlap normally produces 90° bond angles, but in P_4 the P—P—P bond angles are 60°. The bonds are strained, and as might be expected, species with strained bonds are reactive.

When white phosphorus is heated to about 300 °C out of contact with air, it transforms to *red phosphorus*. What appears to happen is that one P—P bond per P_4 molecule breaks, and the resulting fragments join together into long chains (Fig. 22-16b). Red P is less reactive than white P. Because they have a different atomic arrangement in their basic structural units, red and white phosphorus are allotropic forms of phosphorus rather than just different solid phases. The triple point of red phosphorus is 590 °C and 43 atm. Thus, red phosphorus sublimes without melting (at about 420 °C).

Despite the fact that white P is the form obtained by condensing $P_4(g)$ and that the conversion of white P to red P is a very slow process at ambient temperatures, red P is actually the more thermodynamically stable of the two forms at 298.15 K. Nevertheless, white P is assigned values of 0 for ΔH_f° and ΔG_f°, and for red P, these values are negative.

PHOSPHORUS COMPOUNDS

In Chapter 27 we will discover that compounds of phosphorus are essential to all living organisms. However, there is also a significant "inorganic" chemistry of phosphorus, as we will see in this section.

Phosphine.   The most important compound of phosphorus and hydrogen is phosphine, PH_3. This compound is analogous to ammonia in that it acts as a base and forms phosphonium (PH_4^+) compounds. Unlike ammonia, PH_3 is

Nitroglycerin explodes easily when jarred. Nobel made his fortune by inventing dynamite (sawdust soaked with nitroglycerin), which does not explode when jarred.

Obtain or make a small amount of nitroglycerin, put a few drops from an eyedropper on a metal plate and hit it with a hammer.

▲ The glow of white phosphorus gave the element its name—*phos*, light, and *phorus*, bringing. The solid has a relatively high vapor pressure, and the glow results from the slow reaction between phosphorus vapor and oxygen in air.

◄ Phosphine is extremely poisonous and has been used as a fumigant against rodents and insects.

◄ The white and red allotropes of phosphorus.

thermally unstable. Phosphine is produced by the disproportionation of P_4 in aqueous base.

$$P_4(s) + 3\,OH^-(aq) + 3\,H_2O(l) \longrightarrow 3\,H_2PO_2^-(aq) + PH_3(g)$$

Phosphorus Trichloride. Another phosphorus(III) molecule is phosphorus trichloride, PCl_3. One typical reaction of PCl_3 is its hydrolysis, which produces hydrochloric and phosphorous acids.

$$PCl_3(l) + 6\,H_2O(l) \longrightarrow H_3PO_3(aq) + 3\,H_3O^+(aq) + 3\,Cl^-(aq)$$

PCl_3 is the most important phosphorus halide, and a variety of phosphorus(III) compounds are made from it. It is produced by the direct action of $Cl_2(g)$ on elemental phosphorus. Although you may never see PCl_3, chemicals made from it are everywhere—soaps and detergents, plastics and synthetic rubber, nylon, motor oils, and insecticides and herbicides. A variety of organic groups can replace one or more chlorine atoms of PCl_3 to give a family of phosphine-like compounds. These are good Lewis bases and can act as ligands in complex-ion formation.

The halide PCl_5 is obtained by the reaction of Cl_2 with PCl_3 in tetrachloromethane (CCl_4). In the gas phase, PCl_5 exists as discrete trigonal bipyramidal molecules. In the solid state, it exists as $[PCl_4]^+[PCl_6]^-$, in which the ions are tetrahedral and octahedral, respectively.

CONCEPT ASSESSMENT ✓

In the solid phase, PCl_5 forms PCl_4^+ and PCl_6^+. However, PBr_5 forms $PBr_4^+Br^-$. Suggest a reason for this difference in structure.

Oxides of Phosphorus. The simplest formulas we can write for the oxides that have phosphorus in the oxidation states +3 and +5 are P_2O_3 and P_2O_5, respectively. The corresponding names are "phosphorus trioxide" and "phosphorus pentoxide." P_2O_3 and P_2O_5 are only empirical formulas, however. The true molecular formulas of the oxides are double those—that is, P_4O_6 and P_4O_{10}.

The structure of each oxide molecule is based on the P_4 tetrahedron and so must have *four* P atoms, not two. As shown in Figure 22-17(a), in P_4O_6 one O atom bridges each pair of P atoms in the P_4 tetrahedron, which means that there are *six* O atoms per P_4 tetrahedron. In P_4O_{10}, in addition to the six bridging O atoms, one O atom is bonded to each corner P atom (Fig. 22-17b). This means that there are a total of *ten* O atoms per P_4 tetrahedron.

The reaction of P_4 with a limited quantity of $O_2(g)$ produces P_4O_6. If an excess of $O_2(g)$ is used, P_4O_{10} is obtained. Both oxides react with water to form oxoacids—both are *acid anhydrides*.

$$P_4O_6(l) + 6\,H_2O(l) \longrightarrow 4\,H_3PO_3(aq)$$
phosphorous acid

$$P_4O_{10}(s) + 6\,H_2O(l) \longrightarrow 4\,H_3PO_4(aq) \tag{22.46}$$
phosphoric acid

Phosphoric Acid. Phosphoric acid $OP(OH)_3$ has an approximately tetrahedral arrangement of oxygen atoms around the phosphorus atom and is triprotic. Phosphorous acid on the other hand has an approximately tetrahedral arrangement of atoms around the phosphorus atom but the acid is only diprotic. The reason for this is that one of the hydrogen atoms is directly attached to the phosphorus atom. Ionizable hydrogen atoms in oxyacids are associated with the linkage E—OH (see page 691).

Phosphoric acid ranks about seventh among the chemicals manufactured in the United States, with an annual production of over 13 million tons. It is used mainly to make fertilizers, but also it is used to treat metals to make them more corrosion-resistant. Phosphoric acid has many uses in the food industry:

(a) P_4O_6

(b) P_4O_{10}

● = P   ● = O

▲ **FIGURE 22-17**
Molecular structures of P_4O_6 and P_4O_{10}

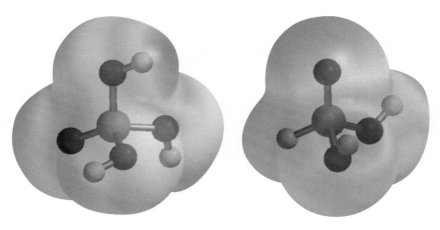

◀ Phosphoric and phosphorous acids.

Lozano-Calero, D., et al. "Determination of Phosphorus in Cola Drinks." *J. Chem. Educ.* **1996:** *73*, 1173.

It is used to make baking powders and instant cereals, in cheese making, in curing hams, and in soft drinks to impart tartness.

If P_4O_{10} and H_2O are combined in a 1 : 6 mole ratio in reaction (22.46), the liquid product should be pure H_3PO_4, that is, 100% H_3PO_4, a compound called *orthophosphoric* acid. An analysis of the liquid, however, shows it to be only about 87.3% H_3PO_4. The "missing" phosphorus is still present in the liquid, but as $H_4P_2O_7$, a compound called either *diphosphoric acid* or *pyrophosphoric acid*. A molecule of diphosphoric acid forms when a molecule of H_2O is eliminated from between two molecules of orthophosphoric acid (Fig. 22-18). If a third molecule of orthophosphoric acid joins in by the elimination of another H_2O molecule, the product is $H_5P_3O_{10}$, triphosphoric acid, and so on. As a class, the chain-like phosphoric acid structures are called *polyphosphoric* acids, and their salts are called *polyphosphates* (see Figure 22-18). Two especially important derivatives of the polyphosphoric acids present in living organisms are the substances known as ADP and ATP. The "A" portion of the acronym stands for adenosine, a combination of an organic base called adenine and a five-carbon sugar called ribose. If this adenosine combination is linked to a diphosphate ion, the product is ADP, adenosine diphosphate. Addition of a phosphate ion to ADP yields ATP; adenosine triphosphate. These polyphosphates are described in more detail in Chapter 27.

Most phosphoric acid is made by the action of sulfuric acid on phosphate rock.

$$3\ Ca_3(PO_4)_2 \cdot CaF_2(s)\ +\ 10\ H_2SO_4(\text{concd aq})\ +\ 20\ H_2O(l)\ \longrightarrow$$

fluorapatite

$$6\ H_3PO_4(aq)\ +\ 10\ CaSO_4 \cdot 2\ H_2O(s)\ +\ 2\ HF(aq) \quad (22.47)$$

gypsum

▲ **FIGURE 22-18**
Formation of polyphosphoric acids
Removal of H_2O molecules results in P—O—P bridges.

orthophosphoric acid
H_3PO_4

diphosphoric acid
(pyrophosphoric acid)
$H_4P_2O_7$

triphosphoric acid
$H_5P_3O_{10}$

The HF is converted to insoluble Na_2SiF_6, and the gypsum is filtered off along with other insoluble impurities. The phosphoric acid is concentrated by evaporation. Phosphoric acid obtained by this "wet process" contains a variety of metal ions as impurities and is dark green or brown. Nevertheless, it is satisfactory for the manufacture of fertilizers and for metallurgical operations.

If H_3PO_4 from reaction (22.47) is used in place of H_2SO_4 to treat phosphate rock, the principal product is calcium dihydrogen phosphate. This compound, a fertilizer containing 20–21% P, is marketed under the name *triple superphosphate*.

$$3 \, Ca_3(PO_4)_2 \cdot CaF_2(s) + 14 \, H_3PO_4(\text{concd aq}) + 10 \, H_2O(l) \longrightarrow$$
$$10 \, Ca(H_2PO_4)_2 \cdot H_2O(s) + 2 \, HF(aq) \qquad (22.48)$$
$$\text{triple superphosphate}$$

PHOSPHORUS AND THE ENVIRONMENT

Phosphates are widely used as fertilizers because phosphorus is an essential nutrient for plant growth. However, heavy fertilizer use may lead to phosphate pollution of lakes, ponds, and streams, causing an explosion of plant growth, particularly algae. The algae deplete the oxygen content of the water, eventually killing fish. This type of change, occurring in freshwater bodies as a result of their enrichment by nutrients, is called **eutrophication**. Eutrophication is a natural process that occurs over geological time periods, but it can be greatly accelerated by human activities.

Natural sources of plant nutrients include animal wastes, decomposition of dead organic matter, and natural nitrogen fixation. Human sources include industrial wastes and municipal sewage plant effluents, in addition to fertilizer runoff. One way to reduce phosphate discharges into the environment is to remove them from the wastewater in sewage treatment plants. In the processing of sewage, polyphosphates are degraded to orthophosphates by bacterial action. The orthophosphates can then be precipitated, either as iron(III) phosphates, aluminum phosphates, or as calcium phosphate or hydroxyapatite $[Ca_5(OH)(PO_4)_3]$. The precipitating agents are generally aluminum sulfate, iron(III) chloride, or calcium hydroxide (slaked lime). In a fully equipped modern sewage treatment plant, up to 98% of the phosphates in sewage can be removed.

▲ The natural eutrophication of a lake is greatly accelerated by phosphates in wastewater and the agricultural runoff of fertilizers.

Cronyn, M. W. "The Proper Place for Hydrogen in the Periodic Table." *J. Chem. Educ.* **2003:** *80*, 947.

22-5 HYDROGEN: A UNIQUE ELEMENT

There are only two elements in the first period, hydrogen and helium. Hydrogen is quite reactive, but helium is inert. In the case of helium there is no difficulty relating its electronic structure and chemical properties to those of the other noble gases in group 18. On the other hand the chemical and physical properties of hydrogen cannot be correlated with any of the main groups in the periodic table. Hydrogen is truly unique and is best considered on its own.

The electron configuration of hydrogen is $1s^1$, and like the alkali metals, this s electron is in the s orbital of the valence shell. Alkali metal atoms tend to lose one electron to form M^+ ions. Although H^+ is known in acid–base chemistry, a hydrogen atom has a much greater tendency to form a covalent bond through the sharing of a pair of electrons. Hydrogen's electron configuration resembles that of the halogens in being just one electron short of that of a noble gas. But unlike the halogens hydrogen rarely form H^- ions, except with the most active metals.

In still other ways hydrogen is like the group 14 elements—both have half-filled valence shells and similar electronegativity values. Thus, the groups $H—$ and $CH_3—$ have one unpaired electron and can form compounds such as LiH and LiCH$_3$. In spite of all of this, hydrogen is best treated as a group on its own.

Think how important hydrogen has been in the study of chemistry. John Dalton based atomic masses on a value of 1 for the H atom. Humphry Davy (1810) proposed that hydrogen is the key element in acids. We saw in Chapter 8 that theoretical studies of the H atom provided us with our modern view of atomic structure. In Chapter 11 we found that the H_2 molecule was the starting point for modern theories of chemical bonding. For all of its theoretical significance, though, hydrogen is also of great practical importance, as we will emphasize in this section.

OCCURRENCE AND PREPARATION

Hydrogen is a very minor component of the atmosphere, about 0.5 ppm at Earth's surface. At altitudes above 2500 km, the atmosphere is mostly atomic hydrogen at extremely low pressures. In the universe as a whole, hydrogen accounts for about 90% of the atoms and 75% of the mass. On Earth, *hydrogen occurs in more compounds than does any other element.*

Electrolysis of Water animation

The free element can easily be produced, but from only a few of its compounds. Our first choice might be H_2O—the most abundant hydrogen compound. To extract hydrogen from water means reducing the oxidation state of H from +1 in H_2O to 0 in H_2. This requires an appropriate *reducing* agent, such as carbon (coal or coke), carbon monoxide, or a hydrocarbon—particularly methane (natural gas). The first pair of reactions that follow are called the **water gas** reactions; they represent a way of making combustible gases—CO and H_2—from steam.

Water gas reactions:

$$C(s) + H_2O(g) \longrightarrow CO(g) + H_2(g) \qquad (22.49)$$

$$CO(g) + H_2O(g) \longrightarrow CO_2(g) + H_2(g) \qquad (22.50)$$

Re-forming of methane: $CH_4(g) + H_2O(g) \longrightarrow CO(g) + 3 H_2(g)$

Make hydrogen gas by mixing zinc metal with HCl. Hydrogen in a balloon makes a nice bang.

Another source of $H_2(g)$ is as a by-product in petroleum refining.

Often we use methods in the chemical laboratory that are not commercially feasible. Electrolysis of water is one useful laboratory method; another involves the reaction of active metals (recall the list in Table 5.3) in acidic solutions, such as

$$Zn(s) + 2 H^+(aq) \longrightarrow Zn^{2+}(aq) + H_2(g)$$

HYDROGEN COMPOUNDS

Hydrogen forms binary compounds, called **hydrides**, with most of the other elements. Binary hydrides are usually grouped into three broad categories: covalent, ionic, and metallic. *Covalent hydrides* are those formed between hydrogen and nonmetals. Some of these hydrides are simple molecules that can be formed by the direct union of hydrogen and the second element, such as

$$H_2(g) + Cl_2(g) \longrightarrow 2 HCl(g)$$

$$3 H_2(g) + N_2(g) \longrightarrow 2 NH_3(g)$$

Ionic hydrides form between hydrogen and the most active metals, particularly those of groups 1 and 2. In these compounds hydrogen exists as the hydride *ion*, H^-.

$$2 M(s) + H_2(g) \longrightarrow 2 MH(s) \qquad M(s) + H_2(g) \longrightarrow MH_2(s)$$

(M is any group 1 metal)   (M is Ca, Sr, or Ba)

Ionic hydrides react vigorously with water to produce $H_2(g)$. CaH_2, a gray solid, has been used as a portable source of $H_2(g)$ for filling weather observation balloons.

$$CaH_2(s) + 2 H_2O(l) \longrightarrow Ca(OH)_2(s) + 2 H_2(g) \qquad (22.51)$$

▲ **Reaction of CaH_2 with water**
The pink color of phenolphthalein indicator added to the water signals the production of $Ca(OH)_2$ in reaction (22.51).

▲ Liquid vegetable oils contain long molecules with some carbon-to-carbon double bonds. When some of these double bonds in the molecules are hydrogenated to give carbon-to-carbon single bonds, the result is conversion of the liquid to a solid "partially hydrogenated vegetable oil."

Metallic hydrides are commonly formed with the transition elements—groups 3 to 12. A distinctive feature of these hydrides is that in many cases they are *nonstoichiometric*—the ratio of H atoms to metal atoms is variable, not fixed. This is because H atoms can enter the voids or holes among the metal atoms in a crystalline lattice and fill some but not others.

USES OF HYDROGEN

Hydrogen is not listed among the top chemicals produced, because only a small percentage is ever sold to customers. Most hydrogen is produced and used on the spot. In these terms, its most important use (about 42%) is in the manufacture of NH_3 (reaction 22.35). The next most important use of H_2 (about 38%) is in petroleum refining, where it is produced in some operations and consumed in others, such as in the production of the high-octane gasoline component, isooctane, from diisobutylene.

In similar reactions, called **hydrogenation reactions**, hydrogen atoms, in the presence of a catalyst, can be added to double or triple bonds in other molecules. This type of reaction, for example, converts liquid oleic acid, $C_{17}H_{33}COOH$, to solid stearic acid, $C_{17}H_{35}COOH$.

$$CH_3(CH_2)_7CH{=}CH(CH_2)_7COOH + H_2(g) \xrightarrow{\text{Ni}} CH_3(CH_2)_{16}COOH \qquad (22.52)$$

oleic acid   stearic acid

Similar reactions serve as the basis for converting oils that contain carbon–carbon double bonds, such as vegetable oils, into solid or semisolid fats, such as shortening.

Another important chemical manufacturing process that uses hydrogen is the synthesis of methyl alcohol (methanol), an alternative fuel.

$$CO(g) + 2\,H_2(g) \xrightarrow{\text{catalyst}} CH_3OH(g)$$

Hydrogen gas is an excellent reducing agent and in some cases is used to produce metals from their oxide ores. For example, at 850 °C

$$WO_3(s) + 3\,H_2(g) \longrightarrow W(s) + 3\,H_2O(g)$$

The uses of hydrogen described here, together with several others, are listed in Table 22.12.

Surface Reaction— Hydrogenation animation

TABLE 22.12 Some Uses of Hydrogen

Synthesis of:
  ammonia, NH_3
  hydrogen chloride, HCl
  methanol, CH_3OH

Hydrogenation reactions in:
  petroleum refining
  converting oils to fats

Reduction of metal oxides, such as those of iron, cobalt, nickel, copper, tungsten, molybdenum

Metal cutting and welding with atomic and oxyhydrogen torches

Rocket fuel, usually $H_2(l)$ in combination with $O_2(l)$

Fuel cells for generating electricity, in combination with $O_2(g)$

HYDROGEN AND THE ENVIRONMENT—A HYDROGEN ECONOMY

As we contemplate the eventual decline of the world's supplies of fossil fuels, hydrogen emerges as an attractive means of storing, transporting, and using energy. For example, when an automobile engine burns hydrogen rather than gasoline, its exhaust is essentially pollution-free. The range of supersonic aircraft could be increased if they used liquid hydrogen as a fuel. A hypersonic airplane (the space plane) might also become possible. As we learned in Chapter 20, one method of using hydrogen that is already available combines H_2 and O_2 to form H_2O in an electrochemical fuel cell, which converts chemical energy directly to electricity. The subsequent conversion of electrical energy to mechanical energy (work) can be carried out much more efficiently than can the conversion of heat to mechanical energy.

Information about the use of hydrogen as an alternative fuel can be found at http://www.eere.energy.gov/afdc/

The basic problems are in finding a cheap source of hydrogen and an effective means of storing it. One possibility is to use hydrogen made by the electrolysis of seawater. This possibility requires an abundant energy source, however—perhaps nuclear fusion energy if it can be developed. Another alternative is the thermal decomposition of water. The problem here is that even at 2000 °C, water is only about 1% decomposed. What is needed is a thermochemical cycle, a series of reactions that have as their overall reaction: $2\,H_2O(l) \longrightarrow 2\,H_2(g) + O_2(g)$. Ideally, no single reaction in the cycle would require a very high temperature. Still another alternative being studied involves the use of solar energy to decompose water—photodecomposition.

Storage of gaseous hydrogen is difficult because of the bulk of the gas. When liquefied, hydrogen occupies a much smaller volume, but because of its very low boiling point (-253 °C), the $H_2(l)$ must be stored at very low temperatures. Also, hydrogen must be maintained out of contact with oxygen or air, with which it forms explosive mixtures. One approach may be to dissolve $H_2(g)$ in a metal or metal alloy, such as an iron–titanium alloy. The gas can be released by mild heating. In an automobile, this storage system would replace the gasoline tank. The heat required to release hydrogen from the metal would come from the engine exhaust.

If the problems described here can be solved, not only could hydrogen be used to supplant gasoline as a fuel for transportation but it could also replace natural gas for space heating. Because H_2 is a good reducing agent, it could replace carbon (as coal or coke) in metallurgical processes and, of course, it would be abundantly available for reaction with N_2 to produce NH_3 for the manufacture of fertilizers. The combination of all these potential uses of hydrogen could lead to a fundamental change in our way of life and give rise to what is called a **hydrogen economy**.

TRIATOMIC HYDRIDES: REVISITING MOLECULAR ORBITAL THEORY

Triatomic hydrides are exemplified by molecules such as methylene, CH_2. Methylene is a stable but very reactive molecule and, consequently, exists only under special experimental circumstances and in interstellar clouds.

We know that a triatomic molecule can be linear or bent and for methylene it is not immediately obvious which is the more stable. Let us construct the molecular orbitals of CH_2 first assuming it is linear and then bent. Once we have done that we may be able to answer the question.

Carbon has four valence-shell atomic orbitals: $2s$, $2p_x$, $2p_y$ and $2p_z$; the two hydrogen atoms each have a $1s$ orbital. From these four orbitals we can construct four sigma orbitals as shown in Figure 22-19.

The orbital energy-level diagram for *linear* CH_2 is shown in Figure 22-20. The total of six valence electrons fill the two σ-bonding orbitals, and half fill each of the two nonbonding carbon orbitals, that is, $2p_x$ and $2p_y$. The carbon $2p_x$ and $2p_y$ are the highest occupied molecular orbitals (abbreviated HOMO). The antibonding σ_s^* is the lowest unoccupied molecular orbital (abbreviated LUMO).

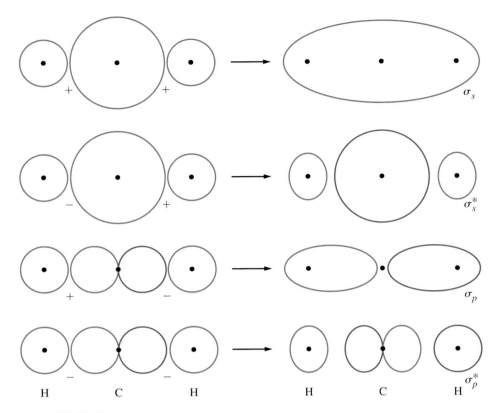

▲ FIGURE 22-19
An outline of the formation of the σ and σ^* orbitals of linear CH_2
The z-axis is assumed to be the internuclear axis.

We conclude that linear CH_2 is held together by two three-center σ-bonds. This molecular orbital picture also suggests that CH_2 is paramagnetic (two unpaired electrons), which is observed experimentally.

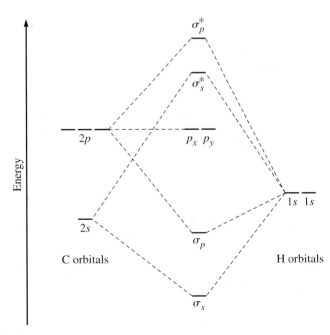

▲ FIGURE 22-20
Molecular orbital energy level diagram for linear CH_2

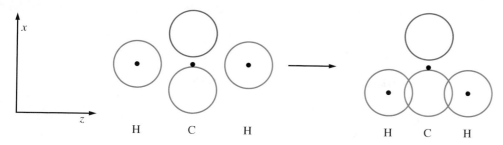

▲ **FIGURE 22-21**
The interaction of the hydrogen 1s orbitals with the carbon 2px orbital as the CH2 molecule is bent

▲ **FIGURE 22-22**
Molecular orbital energy level diagram for bent CH2
The σ designation of the orbitals is not absolutely accurate because cylindrical symmetry is lost in a bent molecule. The subscript on the σ symbol designates the major atomic orbital contributing to the molecular orbital.

▲ Molecular orbitals of bent CH_2.

Now let us consider what happens if we bend the CH_2 molecule. As we move the hydrogen 1s orbitals off the z-axis, the σ_s bonding orbital undergoes only a slight energy change, but the σ_z orbital becomes progressively less bonding (destabilized), and its energy rises compared to the linear structure. Figure 22-21 shows what happens to the $2p_x$ orbital as the hydrogen 1s orbitals are moved off the z-axis: The carbon $2p_x$ orbital begins to overlap with the hydrogen 1s orbitals. This overlap lowers the energy of the $2p_x$ orbital, since the orbital becomes bonding rather than nonbonding. Figure 22-22 gives the resulting orbital energy diagram for the bent CH_2 molecule.

Which structure is favored for CH_2? Bent CH_2 could gain additional stability by having an additional bonding pair in the σ_{p_x} orbital, which has some bonding character. On the other hand, while linear CH_2 has only two pairs of bonding electrons, it avoids some electron repulsion by having only one electron in each of the $2p_x$ and $2p_y$ orbitals. The actual experimental situation is somewhere between these two extremes, as the molecule is bent at a 140° bond angle, and has a single electron in each of the HOMO orbitals.

In the stratosphere, at altitudes between 25 and 35 km, the concentration of O_3 (expressed in molecules per cubic centimeter) is several times higher than at ground level. When expressed in proportion to the other gases present, the O_3 content of this part of the stratosphere— as much as 8 ppm—is considerably greater than at ground level (0.04 ppm). This belt of the stratosphere is called the *ozone layer*.

Stratospheric ozone plays a vital role in protecting life on Earth. First, ozone absorbs certain ultraviolet (UV) radiation that at Earth's surface causes skin cancer and eye damage in humans and is harmful to other biological organisms as well. Second, in absorbing UV radiation, O_3 molecules dissociate, evolving heat, and thus help to maintain a heat balance in the atmosphere.

The chemical reactions that produce $O_3(g)$ in the upper atmosphere are

$$O_2 + \text{UV radiation} \longrightarrow O + O \qquad (22.53)$$

$$O_2 + O + M \longrightarrow O_3 + M \qquad (22.54)$$

Equation (22.53) describes how an O_2 molecule absorbs UV and dissociates. Atomic and molecular oxygen then react to form ozone (22.54). The "third body," M [for example, $N_2(g)$], carries off excess energy; otherwise, the O_3 formed would be too energetic and simply decompose.

Equation (22.55) illustrates the first of the two important functions of ozone: absorbing UV radiation. The second function, that of releasing heat into the atmosphere, is illustrated by equation (22.56).

$$O_3 + \text{UV radiation} \longrightarrow O_2 + O \qquad (22.55)$$

$$O_3 + O \longrightarrow 2\,O_2 \qquad (22.56)$$

$$\Delta H = -389.8 \text{ kJ}$$

Reaction (22.56) is an ozone-destroying reaction that occurs naturally. There are other natural ozone-destroying processes that have (22.56) as their overall reaction, such as

$$NO + O_3 \longrightarrow NO_2 + O_2$$

$$\underline{NO_2 + O \longrightarrow NO + O_2}$$

Overall reaction: $\quad O_3 + O \longrightarrow 2\,O_2$

What is interesting about this pair of reactions is that NO consumed in the first reaction is replenished in the second. A little NO goes a long way. Atmospheric NO is produced mainly from N_2O released by soil bacteria. Thus, natural events account for the continuous formation and destruction of stratospheric ozone and the maintenance of a steady-state concentration of about 8 ppm.

It has recently become apparent that certain gases produced by human activities are contributing to ozone depletion and threatening the integrity of the ozone layer. For example, NO produced by combustion in supersonic jets operating in the stratosphere may contribute to ozone destruction. Most worrisome, though, are gaseous chlorofluorocarbons (CFCs). These molecules have a very long lifetime in the atmosphere and eventually rise to the stratosphere in low concentrations. In the stratosphere, they can absorb ultraviolet radiation and dissociate. For example,

$$CCl_2F_2 + \text{UV radiation} \longrightarrow CClF_2 + Cl$$

Figure 22-23 shows the qualitative dependence of orbital energies as a function of bond angle. This diagram can be used to rationalize the geometries of triatomic hydrides. The transient molecule BeH_2 has four valence electrons, just enough to occupy the two low-energy σ-bonding orbitals. As Figure 22-23

▶ **FIGURE 22-23**
The qualitative variation of molecular orbital energies as a function of bond angle in triatomic hydrides

(a)   (b)

▲ **FIGURE 22-24**
Ozone levels over Antarctica in the year 2000
(a) The light blue and dark blue regions at the center constitute the ozone hole, with the concentration of ozone being lowest in the dark blue region. Higher concentrations of ozone are found in the yellow and green regions. **(b)** Growth of the ozone hole since it was first detected. The ozone hole now extends into populated regions of Chile. In October 2000, the citizens of southern Chile were warned to stay indoors due to possible burns from UV radiation.

📖 Williams, Kathryn R. "Refrigeration—From Ice Man to Ozone Hole." *J. Chem. Educ.* **2000:** 77, 1540 (December 2000). Pirjola, Lisa. "Local Atmospheric Chemistry and Ozone Model (LACOM)." *J. Chem. Educ.* **2000:** 77, 1650 (December 2000). Harvey, Erica, Sweeney, Robert. "Modeling Stratospheric Ozone Kinetics, Part I: The Chapman Cycle: OzoneModelingPartI.mcd." *J. Chem. Educ.* **1999:** 76, 1309 (September 1999). Harvey, Erica, Sweeney, Robert. "Modeling Stratospheric Ozone Kinetics, Part II: Addition of Hydrogen, Nitrogen and Chlorine: OzoneModelingPartII.mcd." *J. Chem. Educ.* **1999:** 76, 1310 (September 1999).

Cl atoms from this reaction can then set up an ozone-destroying cycle.

$$Cl + O_3 \longrightarrow ClO + O_2$$
$$ClO + O \longrightarrow Cl + O_2$$

Overall reaction: $$O_3 + O \longrightarrow 2\,O_2 \qquad (22.56)$$

Currently, the most convincing evidence that depletion of stratospheric ozone is indeed occurring comes from studies in Antarctica. With the coming of spring (October) a large depletion of O_3 occurs over a period of several weeks, before more normal levels return (Fig. 22-24). The chemical reactions postulated to account for this are much more complex than the simplified scheme outlined here. In addition, meteorological conditions play an important role. Evidence is mounting that ozone destruction also occurs in Arctic regions and perhaps worldwide. The most significant measures taken to date to rectify the problem of ozone depletion in the stratosphere are international agreements on chlorofluorocarbons that have led to significant reductions in their production and use.

shows, these orbitals have their lowest energy in the linear configuration, and hence we expect BeH_2 to be a linear molecule. If we consider the water molecule, the eight valence electrons occupy the two σ-bonding orbitals, the in-plane σ orbital, which is at low energy in the bent molecule, and the nonbonding p_y orbital of the oxygen atom. Thus water should be, and is found to be, a bent molecule.

CONCEPT ASSESSMENT ✔

Based on molecular orbital theory, would you expect $NH_2{}^-$ to be linear or bent? How does this compare to VSEPR and valence-bond theory?

Summary

22-1 Group 18: The Noble Gases—The **noble gases** (group 18) form very few compounds. The chemistry of this group is concerned mainly with compounds of xenon and the two most electronegative elements, F and O.

22-2 Group 17: The Halogens—The **halogens** (group 17) are among the most reactive elements, forming compounds with all elements in the periodic table. Electrode potential diagrams are a way to summarize the oxidation–reduction chemistry of an element, and are introduced for the oxidation states of chlorine. Often electrode potentials for reduction processes not specifically represented in a diagram can be obtained by means of calculations based on the relationship $\Delta G^\circ = -nFE^\circ$. The oxoacids and oxoanions of chlorine are described in terms of the methods required to prepare them, their acid–base properties, their strengths as oxidizing or reducing agents, and their structures. In this group we observe several differences between the first and higher members of a group of the periodic table. Thus, for example, we note the failure of fluorine to form stable oxoacids. The later members of the group form **interhalogens**, such as ICl, and **polyhalide ions**, such as I_3^-.

22-3 Group 16: The Oxygen Family

The oxygen family (group 16) includes two reactive nonmetals (O and S), two metalloids (Se and Te), and a metal (Po). Again note the difference in properties between the first and second member of this group. The ability to form strong π bonds with $2p$ orbitals by oxygen contrasts with the single bond chain-like structures favored by sulfur. Sulfur is extracted from underground sources by the **Frasch process**. Sulfur forms the important acids H_2SO_4 and H_2SO_3. The salt $NaHSO_4$ is an example of an **acid salt** since the anion HSO_4^- possesses an ionizable proton.

22-4 Group 15: The Nitrogen Family

The nitrogen family (group 15) shows the progression of properties from nonmetallic to metallic within a group. The chemistry of nitrogen and phosphorus is wide and diverse. The ammonium salts of nitric acid are used in fertilizers. Phosphate ions are also important in fertilizers and in living systems as ADP or ATP. Also, phosphates are implicated in the pollution process of **eutrophication**.

22-5 Hydrogen: A Unique Element

Hydrogen is a unique element that does not fit into any group. Hydrogen can occur as $H^+(aq)$ in aqueous solutions and as H^- in **hydrides**, for example, $NaH(s)$. Hydrogen is a good reducing agent and can be used in **hydrogenation reactions** (equation 22.52). Hydrogen can be obtained from water by electrolysis and also by the **water gas** reaction (equation 22.49). Hydrogen gas is potentially a very promising nonpolluting source of energy and could lead to the so-called **hydrogen economy**.

Integrative Example

For use in analytical chemistry, sodium thiosulfate solutions must be carefully prepared. In particular, the solutions must be kept from becoming acidic. In strongly acidic solutions, thiosulfate ion disproportionates into $SO_2(g)$ and $S_8(s)$.

▲ **Decomposition of thiosulfate ion**
When an aqueous solution of $Na_2S_2O_3$ is acidified, the sulfur is in the colloidal state when first formed (right).

Show that the disproportionation of $S_2O_3^{2-}(aq)$ is spontaneous for standard-state conditions in acidic solution, but not in basic solution.

Strategy

Begin by writing the half-equations and an overall equation for the disproportionation reaction. Determine $E°_{cell}$ for the reaction and thus whether the reaction is spontaneous for standard-state conditions in acidic solution. Then make a qualitative assessment of whether the reaction is likely to be more spontaneous or less spontaneous in basic solution.

Solution

Base the overall equation on the verbal description of the reaction.

Reduction:
$$4 S_2O_3^{2-}(aq) + 24 H^+(aq) + 16 e^- \longrightarrow S_8(s) + 12 H_2O(l)$$

Oxidation:
$$4\{S_2O_3^{2-}(aq) + H_2O(l) \longrightarrow 2 SO_2(g) + 2 H^+(aq) + 4 e^-\}$$

Overall:
$$8 S_2O_3^{2-}(aq) + 16 H^+(aq) \longrightarrow$$
$$S_8(s) + 8 SO_2(g) + 8 H_2O(l) \quad (22.57)$$

To determine $E°_{cell}$ for the reaction (22.57), use data from Figure 22-10. That figure gives an $E°$ value for the reduction half-reaction (0.465 V) but no value for the oxidation. To obtain this missing $E°$, use additional data from Figure 22-10 together with the method of Example 22-1. That is, the sum of the half-equation

$$4 SO_2(g) + 4 H^+(aq) + 6 e^- \longrightarrow S_4O_6^{2-}(aq) + 2 H_2O(l)$$
$$\Delta G° = -6FE° = -6F \times 0.507 \text{ V}$$

and the half-equation

$$S_4O_6^{2-}(aq) + 2 e^- \longrightarrow 2 S_2O_3^{2-}(aq)$$
$$\Delta G° = -2FE° = -2F \times 0.080 \text{ V}$$

yields the desired new half-equation and its $E°$ value.

$$4 SO_2(g) + 4 H^+(aq) + 8 e^- \longrightarrow 2 S_2O_3^{2-}(aq) + 2 H_2O(l)$$
$$\Delta G° = -F[(6 \times 0.507) + (2 \times 0.080)] \text{ V}$$
$$\Delta G° = -8FE° = -F(3.202) \text{ V}$$
$$E° = (3.202/8) \text{ V} = 0.400 \text{ V}$$

Now we can calculate $E°_{cell}$ for reaction (22.57).

$$E°_{cell} = E°(\text{reduction}) - E°(\text{oxidation})$$
$$= 0.465 \text{ V} - 0.400 \text{ V} = 0.065 \text{ V}$$

The disproportionation is spontaneous for standard-state conditions in acidic solution.

Increasing $[OH^-]$, as would be the case in making the solution basic, means decreasing $[H^+]$. In fact, $[OH^-] = 1$ M corresponds to $[H^+] = 1 \times 10^{-14}$ M. Because equation (22.57) has $H^+(aq)$ on the *left* side of the equation, a decrease in $[H^+]$ favors the *reverse* reaction (by Le Châtelier's principle). At some point before the solution becomes basic, the forward reaction is no longer spontaneous.

Assessment

This calculation demonstrated in a qualitative way that $S_2O_3{}^{2-}(aq)$ is stable in basic solutions and spontaneously disproportionates in acidic solutions. To determine the pH at which the disproportionation becomes spontaneous, one can use the Nernst equation, as seen in Exercise 84.

Exercises

The Noble Gases

1. A 55-L cylinder contains Ar at 145 atm and 26 °C. What minimum volume of air at STP must have been liquefied and distilled to produce this Ar? Air contains 0.934% Ar, by volume.

2. Some sources of natural gas contain 8% He by volume. How many liters of such a natural gas must be processed at STP to produce 5.00 g of He?
   [*Hint:* What are the apparent molar masses of air and of the He–O_2 mixture?]

3. Use VSEPR theory to predict the probable geometric structures of (a) XeO_3; (b) XeO_4; (c) $XeF_5{}^+$.

4. Use VSEPR theory to predict the probable geometric structures of the molecules (a) O_2XeF_2; (b) O_3XeF_2; (c) $OXeF_4$.

5. Write a chemical equation for the hydrolysis of XeF_4 that yields XeO_3, Xe, O_2, and HF as products.

6. Write a chemical equation for the hydrolysis in alkaline solution of XeF_6 that yields $XeO_6{}^{4-}$, Xe, O_2, F^-, and H_2O as products.

The Halogens

7. Freshly prepared solutions containing iodide ion are colorless, but over time they usually turn yellow. Describe a plausible chemical reaction (or reactions) to account for this observation.

8. Fluorine can be prepared by the reaction of hexafluoromanganate(IV) ion, $MnF_6{}^{2-}$, with antimony pentafluoride to produce manganese(IV) fluoride and $SbF_6{}^-$, followed by the disproportionation of manganese(IV) fluoride to manganese(III) fluoride and $F_2(g)$. Write chemical equations for these two reactions.

9. Make a general prediction about which of the halogen elements, F_2, Cl_2, Br_2, or I_2, displaces other halogens from a solution of halide ions. Which of the halogens is able to displace $O_2(g)$ from water? Which is able to displace $H_2(g)$ from water?

10. The following properties of astatine have been measured or estimated: (a) covalent radius; (b) ionic radius (At^-); (c) first ionization energy; (d) electron affinity; (e) electronegativity; (f) standard reduction potential. Based on periodic relationships and data in Table 22.1, what values would you expect for these properties?

11. The abundance of F^- in seawater is 1 g F^- per ton of seawater. Suppose that a commercially feasible method could be found to extract fluorine from seawater.

(a) What mass of F_2 could be obtained from 1 km^3 of seawater ($d = 1.03$ g cm^{-3})?
(b) Would the process resemble that for extracting bromine from seawater? Explain.

12. Fluorine is produced chiefly from fluorite, CaF_2. Fluorine can also be obtained as a by-product of the production of phosphate fertilizers, derived from phosphate rock [3 $Ca_3(PO_4)_2 \cdot CaF_2$]. What is the maximum mass of fluorine that could be extracted as a by-product from 1.00×10^3 kg of phosphate rock?

13. Show by calculation whether the disproportionation of chlorine gas to chlorate and chloride ions will occur under standard-state conditions in an acidic solution.

14. Show by calculation whether the reaction
   $$2\,HOCl(aq) \longrightarrow HClO_2(aq) + H^+(aq) + Cl^-(aq)$$
   will go essentially to completion as written for standard-state conditions.

15. Predict the geometric structures of (a) $\underline{Br}F_3$; (b) $\underline{I}F_5$; (c) $Cl_3\underline{I}F^-$. (Central atom underlined.)

16. Which of the following species has a linear structure: $\underline{Cl}F_2{}^+$, $I\underline{Br}F^-$, $O\underline{Cl}_2$, $\underline{Cl}F_3$, or $\underline{S}F_4$? (Central atom underlined.) Do any two of these species have the same structure?

Oxygen

17. Each of the following compounds decomposes to produce $O_2(g)$ when heated: (a) HgO(s); (b) $KClO_4$(s). Write plausible equations for these reactions.

18. $O_3(g)$ is a powerful oxidizing agent. Write equations to represent oxidation of (a) I^- to I_2 in acidic solution; (b) sulfur in the presence of moisture to sulfuric acid;

(c) $[Fe(CN)_6]^{4-}$ to $[Fe(CN)_6]^{3-}$ in basic solution. In each case $O_3(g)$ is reduced to $O_2(g)$.

19. *Without performing detailed calculations*, determine which of the following compounds has the greatest percent oxygen by mass: dinitrogen tetroxide, aluminum oxide, tetraphosphorus hexoxide, or carbon dioxide.

20. *Without performing detailed calculations,* determine which decomposition yields the most $O_2(g)$ **(a)** per mole and **(b)** per gram of substance.
    (1) ammonium nitrate $\longrightarrow$
    $\qquad\qquad$ nitrogen + oxygen + water
    (2) hydrogen peroxide $\longrightarrow$ oxygen + water
    (3) potassium chlorate $\longrightarrow$
    $\qquad\qquad$ potassium chloride + oxygen

21. The natural abundance of O_3 in unpolluted air at ground level is about 0.04 parts per million (ppm) by volume. What is the approximate partial pressure of O_3 under these conditions, expressed in millimeters of mercury?

22. A typical concentration of O_3 in the ozone layer is 5×10^{12} O_3 molecules cm^{-3}. What is the partial pressure of O_3, expressed in millimeters of mercury, in that layer? Assume a temperature of 220 K.

23. Explain why the volumes of $H_2(g)$ and $O_2(g)$ obtained in the electrolysis of water are not the same.

24. In the electrolysis of a sample of water 22.83 mL of $O_2(g)$ was collected at 25.0 °C at an oxygen partial pressure of 736.7 mmHg. Determine the mass of water that was decomposed.

25. Hydrogen peroxide is a somewhat stronger acid than water. For the ionization

    $$H_2O_2(aq) + H_2O(l) \longrightarrow H_3O^+(aq) + HO_2^-(aq)$$

    $pK_a = 11.75$. Calculate the expected pH of a typical antiseptic solution that is 3.0% H_2O_2 by mass.

26. In water, O^{2-} is a strong base. If 50.0 mg of Li_2O is dissolved in 750.0 mL of aqueous solution, what will be the pH of the solution?

27. The conversion of $O_2(g)$ to $O_3(g)$ can be accomplished in an electric discharge, $3\,O_2(g) \longrightarrow 2\,O_3(g)$. Use a bond dissociation energy of 498 kJ mol^{-1} for $O_2(g)$ and data from Appendix D to calculate an average oxygen-to-oxygen bond energy in $O_3(g)$.

28. Estimate the average bond energy in $O_3(g)$ from the structure on page 391 and data in Table 11.3. Compare this result with that of Exercise 27.

29. Use Lewis structures and other information to explain the observation that
    (a) H_2S is a gas at room temperature, whereas H_2O is a liquid.
    (b) O_3 is diamagnetic.

30. Use Lewis structures and other information to explain the observation that
    (a) The oxygen-to-oxygen bond lengths in O_2, O_3, and H_2O_2 are 121, 128, and 148 pm, respectively.
    (b) The oxygen-to-oxygen bond length of O_2 is 121 pm and for O_2^+ is 112 pm. Why is the bond length for O_2^+ so much shorter than for O_2?

31. Which of the following reactions are likely to go to completion or very nearly so?
    (a) $H_2O_2(aq) + 2\,I^-(aq) + 2\,H^+(aq) \longrightarrow$
    $\qquad\qquad I_2(s) + 2\,H_2O(l)$
    (b) $O_2(g) + 2\,H_2O(l) + 4\,Cl^-(aq) \longrightarrow$
    $\qquad\qquad 2\,Cl_2(g) + 4\,OH^-(aq)$
    (c) $O_3(g) + Pb^{2+}(aq) + H_2O(l) \longrightarrow$
    $\qquad\qquad PbO_2(s) + 2\,H^+(aq) + O_2(g)$
    (d) $HO_2^-(aq) + 2\,Br^-(aq) + H_2O(l) \longrightarrow$
    $\qquad\qquad 3\,OH^-(aq) + Br_2(l)$

32. Each of the following compounds produces $O_2(g)$ when strongly heated: **(a)** $HgO(s)$; **(b)** $KClO_4(s)$; **(c)** $Hg(NO_3)_2(s)$; **(d)** $H_2O_2(aq)$. Write a plausible equation for the reaction that occurs in each instance.

Sulfur

33. Give an appropriate name to each of the following compounds: **(a)** ZnS; **(b)** $KHSO_3$; **(c)** $K_2S_2O_3$; **(d)** SF_4.

34. Give an appropriate formula for each of the following compounds: **(a)** calcium sulfate dihydrate; **(b)** hydrosulfuric acid; **(c)** sodium hydrogen sulfate; **(d)** disulfuric acid.

35. Give a specific example of a chemical equation that illustrates the
    (a) reaction of a metal sulfide with $HCl(aq)$;
    (b) action of a *nonoxidizing* acid on a metal sulfite;
    (c) oxidation of $SO_2(aq)$ to $SO_4^{2-}(aq)$ by $MnO_2(s)$ in acidic solution;
    (d) disproportionation of $S_2O_3^{2-}$ in acidic solution.

36. Show how you would use elemental sulfur, chlorine gas, metallic sodium, water, and air to produce aqueous solutions containing **(a)** Na_2SO_3; **(b)** Na_2SO_4; **(c)** $Na_2S_2O_3$.
    [*Hint:* You will have to use information from other chapters as well as this one.]

37. Describe a chemical test you could use to determine whether a white solid is Na_2SO_4 or $Na_2S_2O_3$. Explain the basis of this test using a chemical equation or equations.

38. Explain why sulfur can occur naturally as sulfates, but not as sulfites.

39. Salts like $NaHSO_4$ are called *acid* salts because their anions undergo further ionization. What is the pH of 250 mL of water solution containing 12.5 g $NaHSO_4$? [*Hint:* Use data from Chapter 16, as necessary.]

40. What mass of Na_2SO_3 was present in a sample that required 26.50 mL of 0.0510 M $KMnO_4$ for its oxidation to Na_2SO_4 in an acidic solution? MnO_4^- is reduced to Mn^{2+}.

41. A 1.100-g sample of copper ore is dissolved, and the $Cu^{2+}(aq)$ is treated with excess KI. The liberated I_3^- requires 12.12 mL of 0.1000 M $Na_2S_2O_3$ for its titration. What is the mass percent copper in the ore?

42. A 25.0-L sample of a natural gas, measured at 25 °C and 740.0 Torr, is bubbled through $Pb^{2+}(aq)$, yielding 0.535 g of $PbS(s)$. What mass of sulfur can be recovered per cubic meter of this natural gas?

Nitrogen Family

43. Write balanced equations for the following important commercial reactions involving nitrogen and its compounds.
(a) the principal artificial method of fixing atmospheric N_2
(b) oxidation of ammonia to NO
(c) preparation of nitric acid from NO

44. When heated, each of the following substances decomposes to the products indicated. Write balanced equations for these reactions.
(a) $NH_4NO_3(s)$ to $N_2(g)$, $O_2(g)$, and $H_2O(g)$
(b) $NaNO_3(s)$ to sodium nitrite and oxygen gas
(c) $Pb(NO_3)_2(s)$ to lead(II) oxide, nitrogen dioxide, and oxygen

45. Sodium nitrite can be made by passing oxygen and nitrogen monoxide gases into an aqueous solution of sodium carbonate. Write a balanced equation for this reaction.

46. Concentrated $HNO_3(aq)$ used in laboratories is usually 15 M HNO_3 and has a density of 1.41 g mL^{-1}. What is the percent by mass of HNO_3 in this concentrated acid?

47. In 1968, before pollution controls were introduced, over 75 billion gallons of gasoline were used in the United States as a motor fuel. Assume an emission of oxides of nitrogen of 5 grams per vehicle mile and an average mileage of 15 miles per gallon of gasoline. How many kilograms of nitrogen oxides were released into the atmosphere in the United States in 1968?

48. One reaction that competes with reaction (22.41), the Ostwald process, is the reaction of gaseous ammonia and nitrogen monoxide to produce gaseous nitrogen and gaseous water. Use data from Appendix D to determine $\Delta H°$ for this reaction, per mole of ammonia consumed.

49. Use information from this chapter and previous chapters to write chemical equations to represent the following:
(a) equilibrium between nitrogen dioxide and dinitrogen tetroxide in the gaseous state
(b) the reduction of nitrous acid by $N_2H_5^+$ forming hydrazoic acid, followed by the reduction of additional nitrous acid by the hydrazoic acid, yielding nitrogen and dinitrogen monoxide
(c) the neutralization of $H_3PO_4(aq)$ to the second equivalence point by $NH_3(aq)$

50. Use information from this chapter and previous chapters to write plausible chemical equations to represent the following:
(a) the reaction of silver metal with $HNO_3(aq)$
(b) the complete combustion of the rocket fuel, unsymmetrical dimethylhydrazine, $(CH_3)_2NNH_2$
(c) the preparation of sodium triphosphate by heating a mixture of sodium dihydrogen phosphate and sodium hydrogen phosphate.

51. Draw plausible Lewis structures for
(a) dimethylhydrazine, $(CH_3)_2NNH_2$
(b) nitryl chloride, $ClNO_2$ (Central atom is N)
(c) phosphorous acid, a *diprotic* acid with the empirical formula H_3PO_3

52. Both nitramide and hyponitrous acid have the formula $H_2N_2O_2$. Hyponitrous acid is a weak diprotic acid; nitramide contains the amide group ($—NH_2$). Draw plausible Lewis structures for these two substances.

53. Supply an appropriate name for each of the following: **(a)** $HPO_4{}^{2-}$; **(b)** $Ca_2P_2O_7$; **(c)** $H_6P_4O_{13}$.

54. Write an appropriate formula for each of the following: **(a)** hydroxylamine; **(b)** calcium hydrogen phosphate; **(c)** lithium nitride.

55. Use Figure 22-14 to establish $E°$ for the reduction of N_2O_4 to NO in an acidic solution.

56. Use Figure 22-14 to establish $E°$ for the reduction of $NO_3{}^-$ to $NO_2{}^-$ in a basic solution.

Hydrogen

57. Use data from Table 7.2 (page 252) to calculate the standard enthalpies of combustion of the four alkane hydrocarbons listed there.

58. Based on the results of Exercise 57, which alkane evolves the greatest amount of heat upon combustion on **(a)** a *per mole* basis and **(b)** a *per gram* basis? Which is the most desirable alkane from the standpoint of reducing the emission of carbon dioxide to the atmosphere? Explain.

59. Write chemical equations for the following reactions:
(a) the displacement of $H_2(g)$ from $HCl(aq)$ by $Al(s)$
(b) the re-forming of propane gas (C_3H_8) with steam
(c) the reduction of $MnO_2(s)$ to $Mn(s)$ with $H_2(g)$

60. Write equations to show how to prepare $H_2(g)$ from each of the following substances: **(a)** H_2O; **(b)** $HI(aq)$; **(c)** $Mg(s)$; **(d)** $CO(g)$. Use other common laboratory reactants as necessary, that is, water, acids or bases, metals, and so on.

61. $CaH_2(s)$ reacts with water to produce $Ca(OH)_2$ and $H_2(g)$. $Ca(s)$ reacts with water to produce the same products. $Na(s)$ reacts with water to form $NaOH$ and $H_2(g)$. *Without doing detailed calculations*, determine **(a)** which of these reactions produces the most H_2 per liter of water used, and **(b)** which solid—CaH_2, Ca, or Na—produces the most $H_2(g)$ *per gram* of the solid.

62. What volume of $H_2(g)$ at 25 °C and 752 mmHg is required to hydrogenate oleic acid, $C_{17}H_{33}COOH(l)$, to produce one mole of stearic acid, $C_{17}H_{35}COOH(s)$? Assume reaction (22.52) proceeds with a 95% yield.

63. *Without doing detailed calculations*, explain in which of the following materials you would expect to find the greatest mass percent of hydrogen: seawater, the atmosphere, natural gas (CH_4), ammonia.

64. How many grams of $CaH_2(s)$ are required to generate sufficient $H_2(g)$ to fill a 235-L weather observation balloon at 722 mmHg and 19.7 °C?

$$CaH_2(s) + 2 H_2O(l) \longrightarrow Ca(OH)_2(aq) + 2 H_2(g)$$

Integrative and Advanced Exercises

65. Explain why, expressed as a *mass percent*, the % N_2 in air is less than the 78.084% listed in Table 6.3 whereas the % O_2 is greater than the 20.946%.

66. A 0.25-mL sample of $H_2O(l)$ at 20 °C ($d = 0.998$ g mL^{-1}) is allowed to vaporize into a closed 18.5-L container of dry air at 20 °C. What is the relative humidity of this sample of air? The vapor pressure of water at 20 °C = 17.5 mmHg.

67. Suppose that no attempt is made to separate the $H_2(g)$ and $O_2(g)$ produced by the electrolysis of water. What volume of a H_2–O_2 mixture, saturated with $H_2O(g)$ and collected at 23 °C and 755 mmHg, would be produced by electrolyzing 17.3 g water? Assume that the water vapor pressure of the dilute electrolyte solution is 20.5 mmHg.

68. The photograph was taken after a few drops of a deep-purple acidic solution of $KMnO_4(aq)$ were added to $NaNO_3(aq)$ (left) and to $NaNO_2(aq)$ (right). Explain the difference in the results shown.

69. Zn can reduce NO_3^- to $NH_3(g)$ in basic solution. (The following equation is *not* balanced.)

$$NO_3^-(aq) + Zn(s) + OH^-(aq) + H_2O(l) \longrightarrow$$
$$[Zn(OH)_4]^{2-}(aq) + NH_3(g)$$

The NH_3 can be neutralized with an excess of HCl(aq). Then, the unreacted HCl can be titrated with NaOH. In this way a quantitative determination of NO_3^- can be achieved. A 25.00-mL sample of nitrate solution was treated with zinc in basic solution. The $NH_3(g)$ was passed into 50.00 mL of 0.1500 M HCl. The excess HCl required 32.10 mL of 0.1000 M NaOH for its titration. What was the $[NO_3^-]$ in the original sample?

70. Oxygen atoms are an important constituent of the thermosphere, a layer of the atmosphere with temperatures up to 1500 K. Calculate the average translational kinetic energy of O atoms at 1500 K.

71. One reaction for the production of adipic acid, $HOOC(CH_2)_4COOH$, used in the manufacture of nylon, involves the oxidation of cyclohexanone, $C_6H_{10}O$, in a nitric acid solution. Assume that dinitrogen monoxide is also formed, and write a balanced equation for this reaction.

72. Despite the fact that it has the higher molecular mass, XeO_4 exists as a gas at 298 K, whereas XeO_3 is a solid. Give a plausible explanation for this observation.

73. The text mentions that ammonium perchlorate is an explosion hazard. Assuming that NH_4ClO_4 is the sole reactant in the explosion, write a plausible equation(s) to represent the reaction that occurs.

74. The following bond energies are given for 298 K: O_2, 498; N_2, 946; F_2, 159; Cl_2, 243; ClF, 251; OF (in OF_2), 213; ClO (in Cl_2O), 205; and NF (in NF_3), 280 kJ mol^{-1}. Calculate ΔH_f° at 298 K for 1 mol of **(a)** ClF(g); **(b)** OF_2(g); **(c)** Cl_2O(g); **(d)** NF_3(g).

75. The standard electrode potential of fluorine cannot be measured directly because F_2 reacts with water, displacing O_2. Using thermodynamic data from Appendix D, obtain a value of E_{F_2/F^-}°.

76. Polonium is the only element known to crystallize in the simple cubic form. In this structure, the interatomic distance between a Po atom and each of its six nearest neighbors is 335 pm. Use this description of the crystal structure to estimate the density of polonium.

77. Refer to Figure 11-25 to arrange the following species in the expected order of increasing **(a)** bond length and **(b)** bond strength (energy): O_2, O_2^+, O_2^-, O_2^{2-}. State the basis of your expectation.

78. One reaction of a chlorofluorocarbon implicated in the destruction of stratospheric ozone is $CFCl_3 + h\nu \longrightarrow CFCl_2 + Cl$.
(a) What is the energy of the photons ($h\nu$) required to bring about this reaction, expressed in kilojoules per mole?
(b) What is the frequency and wavelength of the light necessary to produce the reaction? In what portion of the electromagnetic spectrum is this light found?

79. The composition of a phosphate mineral can be expressed as % P, % P_4O_{10}, or % BPL [bone phosphate of lime, $Ca_3(PO_4)_2$].
(a) Show that % P = 0.436 × (% P_4O_{10}) and % BPL = 2.185 × (% P_4O_{10}).
(b) What is the significance of a % BPL greater than 100?
(c) What is the % BPL of a typical phosphate rock?

80. Estimate the percent dissociation of $Cl_2(g)$ into Cl(g) at 1 atm total pressure and 1000 K. Use data from Appendix D and equations found elsewhere in this text, as necessary.

81. *Peroxonitrous acid* is an unstable intermediate formed in the oxidation of HNO_2 by H_2O_2. It has the same formula as *nitric acid*, HNO_3. Show how you would expect peroxonitrous and nitric acids to differ in structure.

82. The structure of $N(SiH_3)_3$ involves a planar arrangement of N and Si atoms, whereas that of the related compound $N(CH_3)_3$ has a pyramidal arrangement of N and C atoms. Propose bonding schemes for these molecules that are consistent with this observation.

83. In the extraction of bromine from seawater (reaction 22.3), seawater is first brought to a pH of 3.5 and then treated with $Cl_2(g)$. In practice, the pH of the seawater is adjusted with H_2SO_4, and the mass of chlorine used is 15% in excess of the theoretical. Assuming a seawater sample with an initial pH of 7.0, a density of 1.03 g cm^{-3}, and a bromine content of 70 ppm by mass, what masses of H_2SO_4 and Cl_2 would be used in the extraction of bromine from 1.00×10^3 L of seawater?

84. Refer to the Integrative Example on page 956. Assume that the disproportionation of $S_2O_3^{2-}$ is no longer spontaneous when the partial pressure of $SO_2(g)$ above a solution with $[S_2O_3^{2-}] = 1$ M has dropped to 1×10^{-6} atm. Show that this condition is reached while the solution is still acidic.

85. The bond energies of Cl_2 and F_2 are 243 and 155 kJ mol^{-1}, respectively. Use these data to explain why XeF_2 is a much more stable compound than $XeCl_2$. [*Hint:* Recall that Xe exists as a monatomic gas.]

86. Write plausible half-equations and a balanced oxidation–reduction equation for the disproportionation of XeF_4 to Xe and XeO_3 in aqueous acidic solution. Xe and XeO_3 are produced in a $2:1$ mol ratio, and $O_2(g)$ is also produced.

87. A handbook gives the value $E° = 0.174$ V for the reduction half-reaction $S + 2H^+ + 2e^- \longrightarrow H_2S(g)$. In Figure 22-10, the value given for the segment S—$H_2S(aq)$ is 0.144 V. Why are these $E°$ values different? Can both be correct?

88. The solubility of $Cl_2(g)$ in water is 6.4 g L^{-1} at 25 °C. Some of this chlorine is present as Cl_2, and some is found as HOCl or Cl^-. For the hydrolysis reaction

$$Cl_2(aq) + 2H_2O(l) \longrightarrow$$
$$HOCl(aq) + H_3O^+(aq) + Cl^-(aq)$$
$$K_c = 4.4 \times 10^{-4}$$

For a saturated solution of Cl_2 in water, calculate $[Cl_2]$, $[HOCl]$, $[H_3O^+]$, and $[Cl^-]$.

89. Not shown in Figure 22-14 are electrode potential data involving hydrazoic acid. Given that $E° = -3.09$ V for the reduction of HN_3 to N_2 in acidic solution, what is $E°$ for the reduction of HN_3 to NH_4^+ in acidic solution?

Feature Problems

90. Various thermochemical cycles are being explored as possible sources of $H_2(g)$. The object is to find a series of reactions that can be conducted at moderate temperatures (about 500 °C) and that results in the decomposition of water into H_2 and O_2. Show that the following series of reactions meets this requirement.

$$FeCl_2 + H_2O \longrightarrow Fe_3O_4 + HCl + H_2$$
$$Fe_3O_4 + HCl + Cl_2 \longrightarrow FeCl_3 + H_2O + O_2$$
$$FeCl_3 \longrightarrow FeCl_2 + Cl_2$$

91. The decomposition of aqueous hydrogen peroxide is catalyzed by $Fe^{3+}(aq)$. A proposed mechanism for this catalysis involves two reactions. In the first reaction, Fe^{3+} is reduced by H_2O_2. In the second, the iron is oxidized back to its original form, while hydrogen peroxide is reduced. Write an equation for the overall reaction and show that the overall reaction is indeed spontaneous. What are the minimum and maximum values of $E°$ for a catalyst to function in this way? Which of the following should be able to catalyze the decomposition of hydrogen peroxide by the mechanism outlined here: **(a)** Cu^{2+}, **(b)** Br_2, **(c)** Al^{3+}, **(d)** Au^{3+}? In the reaction between iodic acid and hydrogen peroxide in the presence of starch indicator, the color of the reaction mixture oscillates between deep blue and colorless. What is the basis of these changes in color? Will this oscillation of color continue indefinitely? Explain. [*Hint:* Refer to Problem 96 in Chapter 14, particularly to equation (c).]

92. Both in this chapter and in Chapter 20, we have stressed the relationship between $E°$ values and thermodynamic properties. We can use this relationship to add some missing features to an electrode potential diagram. For example, note that $ClO_2(g)$, which has Cl in the oxidation state $+4$, is not included in Figure 22-2. Using data from Figure 22-2 and Appendix D, add $ClO_2(g)$ to the electrode potential diagram for acidic solutions, and indicate the $E°$ values that link $ClO_2(g)$ to $ClO_3^-(aq)$ and to $HClO_2(aq)$.

93. Figure 15-1 (page 623) shows that I_2 is considerably more soluble in $CCl_4(l)$ than it is in $H_2O(l)$. The concentration of I_2 in its saturated aqueous solution is 1.33×10^{-3} M, and the equilibrium achieved when I_2 distributes itself between H_2O and CCl_4 is

$$I_2(aq) \rightleftharpoons I_2(CCl_4) \qquad K_c = 85.5$$

(a) A 10.0-mL sample of saturated $I_2(aq)$ is shaken with 10.0 mL CCl_4. After equilibrium is established, the two liquid layers are separated. How many milligrams of I_2 will be in the aqueous layer?
(b) If the 10.0 mL of aqueous layer from part (a) is extracted with a second 10.0-mL portion of CCl_4, how many milligrams of I_2 will remain in the aqueous layer when equilibrium is reestablished?
(c) If the 10.0-mL sample of saturated $I_2(aq)$ in part (a) had originally been extracted with 20.0 mL CCl_4, would the mass of I_2 remaining in the aqueous layer have been less than, equal to, or greater than that in part (b)? Explain.

94. The so-called pyroanions, $X_2O_7^{n-}$, form a series of structurally similar polyatomic anions for the elements Si, P, and S.
(a) Draw the Lewis structures of these anions, and predict the geometry of the anions. What is the maximum number of atoms that can lie in a plane?
(b) Each pyroanion in part (a) corresponds to a pyroacid, $X_2O_7H_n$. Compare each pyroacid to the acid containing only one atom of the element in its maximum oxidation state. From this comparison, suggest a strategy for the preparation of these pyroacids.
(c) What is the chlorine analogue of the pyroanions? For which acid is this species the anhydride?

95. A description of bonding in XeF_2 based on the valence bond model requires the $5d$ orbitals of Xe. A more satisfactory description uses a molecular orbital approach involving three-center bonds. Assume that bonding involves the $5p_z$ orbital of Xe and the $2p_z$ orbitals of the two F atoms. These three atomic orbitals combine to give three molecular orbitals: one bonding, one nonbonding, and one antibonding. Recall that for bonding to occur, atomic orbitals with the same phase must overlap to form bonding molecular orbitals (see Chapter 11).
    (a) Construct diagrams similar to Figure 11-31 to indicate the overlap of the three atomic orbitals in forming the three molecular orbitals. Assume that the order of energy of the molecular orbitals is bonding MO < nonbonding MO < antibonding MO.
    (b) Sketch a molecular orbital energy-level diagram, and assign the appropriate number of electrons from fluorine and xenon to the molecular orbitals. What is the bond order?
    (c) With the aid of VSEPR theory, show that this molecular orbital description based on three-center bonds works well for XeF_4 but not for XeF_6.

96. The sketch is a portion of the phase diagram for the element sulfur. The transition between solid orthorhombic (S_α) and solid monoclinic (S_β) sulfur, in the presence of sulfur vapor, is at 95.3 °C. The triple point involving monoclinic sulfur, liquid sulfur, and sulfur vapor is at 119 °C.

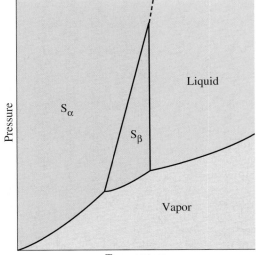

(a) How would you modify the phase diagram to represent the melting of orthorhombic sulfur that is sometimes observed at 113 °C?
[*Hint:* What would the phase diagram look like if the monoclinic sulfur did not form?]
(b) Account for the observation that if a sample of rhombic sulfur is melted at 113 °C and then heated, the liquid sulfur freezes at 119 °C upon cooling.

Self-Assessment Exercises

97. In your own words, define the following terms: **(a)** polyhalide ion; **(b)** polyphosphate; **(c)** interhalogen; **(d)** disproportionation.
98. Briefly describe each of the following terms: **(a)** Frasch process; **(b)** water gas reactions; **(c)** eutrophication; **(d)** electrode potential diagram.
99. Explain the important distinctions between each pair of terms: **(a)** acid salt and acid anhydride; **(b)** azide and nitride; **(c)** white phosphorus and red phosphorus; **(d)** ionic hydride and metallic hydride.
100. To displace Br_2 from an aqueous solution of Br^-, add **(a)** $I_2(aq)$; **(b)** $Cl_2(aq)$; **(c)** $H_2(g)$; **(d)** $Cl^-(aq)$; **(e)** $I_3^-(aq)$.
101. All of the following compounds yield $O_2(g)$ when heated to about 1000 K except **(a)** $KClO_3$; **(b)** $KClO_4$; **(c)** N_2O; **(d)** $CaCO_3$; **(e)** $Pb(NO_3)_2$.
102. All of the following substances are bases except for **(a)** H_2NNH_2; **(b)** NH_3; **(c)** HN_3; **(d)** NH_2OH; **(e)** CH_3NH_2.
103. The best reducing agent of the following substances is **(a)** H_2S; **(b)** O_3; **(c)** H_2SO_4; **(d)** NaF; **(e)** H_2O.
104. Of the following substances the one that is unimportant is the production of fertilizers is **(a)** NH_3; **(b)** phosphate rock; **(c)** HNO_3; **(d)** Na_2CO_3; **(e)** H_2SO_4.
105. All of the following have a tetrahedral shape except **(a)** SO_4^{2-}; **(b)** XeF_4; **(c)** CCl_4; **(d)** XeO_4; **(e)** NH_4^+.
106. Two of the following, through a reaction occurring in a weakly acidic solution, produce the same gaseous product. They are **(a)** $CaH_2(s)$; **(b)** $Na_2O_2(s)$; **(c)** $NaOH(s)$; **(d)** $Al(s)$; **(e)** $NaHCO_3(s)$; **(f)** $N_2H_4(l)$.
107. Write a plausible chemical equation to represent the reaction of **(a)** $Cl_2(g)$ with cold $NaOH(aq)$; **(b)** $NaI(s)$ with hot H_2SO_4(concd aq); **(c)** $Cl_2(g)$ with $KI_3(aq)$; **(d)** $NaBr(s)$ with hot H_3PO_4(concd aq); **(e)** $NaHSO_3(aq)$ with $MnO_4^-(aq)$ in dilute $H_2SO_4(aq)$.
108. Give a practical laboratory method that you might use to produce small quantities of the following gases and comment on any difficulties that might arise: **(a)** O_2; **(b)** NO; **(c)** H_2; **(d)** NH_3; **(e)** CO_2.
109. Complete and balance equations for these reactions.
    (a) $LiH(s) + H_2O(l) \longrightarrow$
    (b) $C(s) + H_2O(g) \xrightarrow{\Delta}$
    (c) $NO_2(g) + H_2O(l) \longrightarrow$
110. If Br^- and I^- occur together in an aqueous solution, I^- can be oxidized to IO_3^- with an excess of $Cl_2(aq)$. Simultaneously, Br^- is oxidized to Br_2, which is extracted with $CS_2(l)$. Write chemical equations for the reactions that occur.
111. Suppose that the sulfur present in seawater as SO_4^{2-} (2650 mg L^{-1}) could be recovered as elemental sulfur. If this sulfur were then converted to H_2SO_4, how many cubic kilometers of seawater would have to be processed to yield the average U.S. annual consumption of about 45 million tons of H_2SO_4?

112. Although relatively rare, all of the following compounds exist. Based on what you know about related compounds (for example, from the periodic table), propose a plausible name or formula for each compound: **(a)** silver(I) astatide; **(b)** Na_4XeO_6; **(c)** magnesium polonide; **(d)** H_2TeO_3; **(e)** potassium thioselenate; **(f)** $KAtO_4$.

113. A portion of the standard electrode potential diagram of selenium is given below. What is the $E°$ value for the reduction of H_2SeO_3 to H_2Se?

$$SeO_4{}^{2-} \xrightarrow{\text{1.15 V}} H_2SeO_3 \xrightarrow{\text{0.74 V}} Se \xrightarrow{\text{−0.35 V}} H_2Se$$

(?)

114. Construct a diagram in the manner of Figure 22-2 for the reactions of the elements **(a)** Xe, **(b)** I_2, **(c)** S, **(d)** P_4, **(e)** H_2, with O_2, strong acid, strong base, F_2 and Cl_2. You may *not* be able to find all the conditions for these reactions in this book; simply give the likely product.

eMedia Exercises

115. Observe the three-dimensional structures of the **XeF₂** and **XeF₄** models (*Activebook 22-1*). **(a)** Using the principles of VSPER theory, suggest a plausible structure for the molecule in this series, formed through the reaction with additional fluorines. **(b)** Will similar molecules form with other halogens? Why or why not?

116. The **Physical Properties of Halogens** movie (*Activebook 22-2*) illustrates the properties of three halogens. **(a)** What evidence of a periodic trend do you find in this illustration? What is the basis of this trend? **(b)** Based upon these observations, predict the physical state of fluorine.

117. In the **Reactions with Oxygen** movie (*Activebook 22-3*), the oxidizing power of oxygen is illustrated. **(a)** Describe the change in oxidation state for each of the elements undergoing a reaction. **(b)** In which cases is more than one oxide compound possible? **(c)** What are the oxidation states of the elements in the other possible compounds?

118. Two common oxides of nitrogen are seen in the **Nitrogen Dioxide and Dinitrogen Tetroxide** movie (*Activebook 22-4*.) These oxides exist in equilibrium. **(a)** From the procedure carried out in the movie, predict whether the conversion from NO_2 to N_2O_4 is an endothermic or exothermic reaction. **(b)** Does your prediction agree with thermodynamic data for this reaction?

119. A common method of producing gaseous hydrogen and oxygen is seen in the **Electrolysis of Water** animation (*Activebook 22-5*). **(a)** What is the volume (in mL) of water that must undergo electrolysis in order to produce 0.50 L of a mixture of hydrogen and oxygen gas under STP conditions? **(b)** What is the volume of oxygen produced in this procedure?

120. The process shown in the **Electrolysis of Water** animation (*Activebook 22-5*) typically is not an economically favorable process. **(a)** Calculate the enthalpy of the electrolysis reaction for one mole of water. **(b)** What is the enthalpy change associated with the formation of a total volume of 0.50 L of gas under STP conditions?

121. About 40% of hydrogen used in industrial processes comes from petroleum refining. An example of a refining step is shown in the **Surface Reaction—Hydrogenation** animation (*Activebook 22-5*). **(a)** What role does the metal surface play in this reaction? **(b)** In some experimental studies, deuterium (D_2) is used in place of hydrogen. What would be the product of a reaction of ethylene with deuterium?

23

THE TRANSITION ELEMENTS

CONTENTS

📖 Beattie, James K. "A New Perspective on Rutile." *J. Chem. Educ.* **1998:** *75*, 641 (May 1998).

☑ Rutile website: http://mineral.galleries.com/ minerals/oxides/rutile/ rutile.htm (commercial)
Transition metal website: http://www.chemicalelements.com/ groups/transition.html (commercial)

Whiskers of rutile, TiO_2, in quartz (left) and titanium ore (right), a source of rutile. Titanium metal, obtained from rutile, is used in industry because it has low density and high strength. Pure TiO_2 is a bright white pigment used in paints and specialty papers.

There are more transition elements—members of the *d* and *f* blocks—than main-group elements. Although some of the transition elements are rare and of limited use, others play crucial roles in many aspects of modern life. All the transition elements are metals; among them are both the chief structural metal, iron (Fe), and important alloying metals in the manufacture of steel (V, Cr, Mn, Co, Ni, Mo, W). The best electrical conductors (Ag, Cu) are transition metals. The compounds of several transition metals (Ti, Fe, Cr) are the primary constituents of paint pigments. Compounds of silver (Ag) provide the essential material for photography. Specialized materials for modern applications, such as color television screens, use compounds of the *f*-block elements (lanthanide oxides). Nine of the transition metals are essential elements for living organisms.

The chemistry of the *d*-block and *f*-block elements has both theoretical and practical significance. These elements and their compounds provide insight into fundamental aspects of bonding, magnetism, and reaction chemistry.

23-1   GENERAL PROPERTIES

The high melting points, good electrical conductivity, and moderate-to-extreme hardness of the transition elements result from the ready availability of electrons and orbitals for metallic bonding (see Section 11-7). Some similarities are found among the transition elements, but each element also has some unique properties that make it and its compounds useful in particular ways. Table 23.1 lists properties of the fourth-period transition elements—the first transition series.

 Periodic Table activity

TABLE 23.1   Selected Properties of Elements of the First Transition Series

	Sc	Ti	V	Cr	Mn	Fe	Co	Ni	Cu	Zn
Atomic number	21	22	23	24	25	26	27	28	29	30
Electron config.[a]	$3d^14s^2$	$3d^24s^2$	$3d^34s^2$	$3d^54s^1$	$3d^54s^2$	$3d^64s^2$	$3d^74s^2$	$3d^84s^2$	$3d^{10}4s^1$	$3d^{10}4s^2$
Metallic radius, pm	161	145	132	125	124	124	125	125	128	133
Ioniz. energy, kJ mol^{-1}										
First	631	658	650	653	717	759	758	737	745	906
Second	1235	1310	1414	1592	1509	1561	1646	1753	1958	1733
Third	2389	2653	2828	2987	3248	2957	3232	3393	3554	3833
$E°$, V[b]	−2.03	−1.63	−1.13	−0.90	−1.18	−0.440	−0.277	−0.257	+0.340	−0.763
Common positive oxidation states[c]	3	2, 3, 4	2, 3, 4, 5	2, 3, 6	2, 3, 4, 7	2, 3, 6	2, 3	2, 3	1, 2	2
mp, °C	1397	1672	1710	1900	1244	1530	1495	1455	1083	420
Density, g cm^{-3}	3.00	4.50	6.11	7.14	7.43	7.87	8.90	8.91	8.95	7.14
Hardness[d]	—	—	—	9.0	5.0	4.5	—	—	2.8	2.5
Electrical conductivity[e]	3	4	6	12	1	16	25	23	93	27

[a]Each atom has an argon inner-core configuration.
[b]For the reduction process, $M^{2+}(aq) + 2 e^- \longrightarrow M(s)$ [except for scandium, where the ion is $Sc^{3+}(aq)$].
[c]The most important oxidation states are printed in red.
[d]Hardness values are on the Mohs scale (see Table 22.2).
[e]Electrical conductivity compared with an arbitrarily assigned value of 100 for silver.

ATOMIC (METALLIC) RADII

In Table 23.1, with the exception of Sc and Ti, we find little variation among the atomic radii across the first transition series. The chief difference in atomic structure between successive elements involves one unit of positive charge on the nucleus and one electron in an orbital of an *inner* electron shell. This is not a major difference and does not cause much of a change in atomic radius, especially in the middle of the series.

When an element of the first transition series is compared with elements of the second and third series within the same group, important differences appear. Consider the members of group 6—Cr, Mo, and W. As we might expect, the atomic radius of Mo is larger than that of Cr; but contrary to our expectation, the atomic radius of W is the same as that of Mo, not larger. In the aufbau process, 18 electrons are added in progressing from Cr to Mo, and all of them enter *s*, *p*, and *d* subshells. Between Mo and W, however, 32 electrons must be added, and 14 of them enter the $4f$ subshell. Electrons in an *f* subshell are not very effective in screening outer-shell electrons from the nucleus. As a result, the outer-shell electrons are held more tightly by the nucleus than we would otherwise expect. Atomic radii do not increase. In fact, in the series of elements in which the $4f$ subshell is filled, atomic radii decrease somewhat. This phenomenon occurs in the lanthanide series (Z = 58 to 71) and is called the **lanthanide contraction**. The lanthanide contraction is made more apparent in the graphs in Figure 23-1.

Strauss, S. H. "In Search of a Deep Understanding of the Relative Stabilities of Transition Metal Halides." *J. Chem. Educ.* 2001: *78*, 1635.

Ping, M., et al. "A formula for calculating atomic radii of metals." *J. Chem. Educ.* 1990: *67*, 218.

Lloyd, D. R. "On the lanthanide and 'scandinide' contractions." *J. Chem. Educ.* 1986: *63*, 502.

▶ **FIGURE 23-1**
Atomic radii of the *d*-block elements
The radii of the fourth-period transition elements (blue) are smaller than those of the corresponding group members in the succeeding periods. This trend is not seen between the fifth-period (black) and sixth-period (red) members, illustrating the contraction in atomic radii associated with the lanthanide series.

Munoz-Paez, Adela. "Transition Metal Oxides: Geometric and Electronic Stuctures: Introducing Solid-State Topics in Inorganic Cheminstry Courses." *J. Chem. Educ.* **1994:** *71*, 381.

Vanquickenborne, L. G., Pierloot, K., Devoghel, D. "Transition Metals and the Aufbau Principle." *J. Chem. Educ.* **1994:** *71*, 469.

ELECTRON CONFIGURATIONS AND OXIDATION STATES

The elements of the first transition series have electron configurations with the following characteristics:

- an inner core of electrons in the argon configuration
- two electrons in the $4s$ orbital for eight members and one $4s$ electron for the remaining two (Cr and Cu)
- a number of $3d$ electrons, ranging from one in Sc to ten in Cu and Zn

As we have seen for some of the main-group elements in Chapters 21 and 22, an element may display several oxidation states. Often, however, one particular oxidation state is the most common for an element. Ti atoms, with the electron configuration $[Ar]3d^2 4s^2$, tend to use all four electrons beyond the argon core in compound formation and display the oxidation state +4. It is also possible, however, for Ti atoms to use fewer electrons, as through the loss of the $4s^2$ electrons to form the ion Ti^{2+}. With Ti, then, we note two features: (1) several possible oxidation states, as shown in Figure 23-2, and (2) a maximum oxidation state corresponding to the group number, 4. These two features continue with V, Cr, and Mn, for which the maximum oxidation states are +5, +6 and +7, respectively. A shift in behavior occurs in groups 8–12, however. Thus, although Fe, Co, and Ni can all exist in more than one oxidation state, they do not display the wide variety found in the earlier members of the first transition series. Nor do they exhibit a maximum oxidation state corresponding to their group number. In crossing the first transition series, the nuclear charge, number of d electrons, and energy requirement for the successive ionization of d electrons increase. Involvement of a large number of d electrons in bond formation becomes increasingly unfavorable energetically, and only the lower oxidation states are commonly encountered for these later elements of the first transition series.

Although the transition elements display a variety of oxidation states, they differ in the ease with which these oxidation states can be attained and in their stabilities. The stability of an oxidation state for a given transition metal depends on a number of factors—other atoms to which the transition metal atom is bonded; whether the compound is in solid form or in solution; and the pH of the solution. For example, $TiCl_2$ is a well-characterized compound as a solid, but the Ti^{2+} ion is oxidized to Ti^{3+} by dissolved oxygen in aqueous solutions and even by the water itself. Conversely, $Co^{3+}(aq)$ readily oxidizes water to $O_2(g)$ and is itself reduced to $Co^{2+}(aq)$. $Co^{3+}(aq)$ can be stabilized, however, in certain complex ions. Generally speaking, higher oxidation states in transition

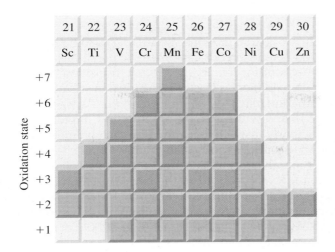

◀ **FIGURE 23-2**
Positive oxidation states of the elements of the first transition series
Common oxidation states are shown in red and less common ones in gray. Some oxidation states are rather rare, and a zero or negative oxidation state is occasionally found, chiefly in transition metal complexes. For example, the oxidation state of Cr is -2 in $Na_2[Cr(CO)_5]$, -1 in $Na_2[Cr_2(CO)_{10}]$, and 0 in $Cr(CO)_6$.

metals are stabilized when oxide or fluoride ions are bound to the metal. In Figure 23-2 and elsewhere, the term *common* oxidation state refers to an oxidation state often found in aqueous solution.

Another feature of the transition metals is the progressively increasing stability of higher oxidation states in descending a group of the periodic table, the reverse of the trend often seen for main-group elements. Consider Cr, Mo, and W in group 6, all of which can exhibit oxidation states ranging from $+6$ to -2. The number of compounds with Cr in the $+6$ oxidation state is rather limited, whereas those of Mo and W abound. Chromium is encountered in the oxidation states $+5$ and $+4$ mostly in unstable intermediates, whereas Mo and W exhibit a rich chemistry in these states. The most stable oxidation state of chromium is $+3$. Although it is a strong reducing agent, $Cr^{2+}(aq)$ nevertheless is readily obtainable, whereas Mo and W are not obtainable as the simple $+2$ cation. This trend favoring lower oxidation states for the first group member and higher oxidation states for the later members is also found in other groups of transition metals. For instance, although Fe does not exhibit an oxidation state corresponding to the group number, Os does form the stable oxide OsO_4 with Os in the $+8$ oxidation state.

> ✓ Moving across the transition elements in a period, atomic radii decrease and then rise (Figure 23-1). As the atomic number Z increases, electrons enter different d orbitals and shielding is not great as the d electrons are added. Hence, the outer-shell electrons feel an increase in Z_{eff} and they are more tightly held.

IONIZATION ENERGIES AND ELECTRODE POTENTIALS

Ionization energies are fairly constant across the first transition series. Values of the first ionization energies are about the same as for the group 2 metals. Standard electrode potentials gradually increase in value across the series. With the exception of the oxidation of Cu to Cu^{2+}, however, all these elements are more readily oxidized than hydrogen. This means that the metals displace $H_2(g)$ from $H^+(aq)$. Additional comments on electrode potentials, some supported by electrode potential diagrams, are found throughout the chapter.

IONIC AND COVALENT COMPOUNDS

We tend to think of metals as forming ionic compounds with nonmetals. This is certainly the case with group 1 and most group 2 metal compounds. However, some metal compounds have significant covalent character; $BeCl_2$ and $AlCl_3$ (Al_2Cl_6), for example, are molecular compounds. Transition metal compounds display both ionic and covalent character. In general, compounds with the transition metal in lower oxidation states are essentially ionic, while those in higher oxidation states have covalent character. As an example, MnO is a green ionic solid with a melting point of 1785 °C, whereas Mn_2O_7 is a dark red, oily, molecular liquid that boils at room temperature and is highly explosive. Another feature of ionic compounds of the transition metals is that the metal atoms often occur in polyatomic cations or anions rather than as the simple, monatomic ion. Some common examples are VO_2^+, MnO_4^-, and $Cr_2O_7^{2-}$.

*Surface Reaction—
Hydrogenation
animation*

Mattson, B., et al.
"Demonstrating
Heterogeneous Gas-Phase
Catalysis with the Gas
Reaction Catalyst Tube."
J. Chem. Educ. **2003:** *80, 768.*

▲ Color-enhanced image
of magnetic domains in a
ferromagnetic garnet film.

Rodgers, G. E. "Student-
presented demonstrations
on the colors of transition metal
complexes." *J. Chem. Educ.* **1988:**
65, 543.

Cortel, A. "Demonstrations
on Paramagnetism with an
Electronic Balance." *J. Chem. Educ.*
1998: *75,* 61.

CATALYTIC ACTIVITY

An unusual ability to adsorb gaseous species makes some transition metals, such as Ni and Pt, good heterogeneous catalysts. The possibility of multiple oxidation states seems to account for the ability of some transition metal ions to serve as catalysts in certain oxidation–reduction reactions. In still other types of catalysis, complex-ion formation may play an important role. As we have seen in a limited way in Chapter 18 and will explore more fully in Chapter 24, complex-ion formation is a particularly distinctive feature of transition metal chemistry.

Catalysis is an essential aspect of about 90% of all chemical manufacturing processes, and the transition metals are often the key elements in the catalysts used. To name a few—Ni is used in the hydrogenation of oils (page 950); Pt, Pd, and Rh are used in catalytic converters in automobiles (page 602); Fe_3O_4 is the main component of the catalyst used in the synthesis of ammonia (page 653); and V_2O_5 is used in the conversion of $SO_2(g)$ to $SO_3(g)$ in the manufacture of sulfuric acid (page 934).

COLOR AND MAGNETISM

As we will explain more fully in Section 24-6, electronic transitions that occur within partially filled *d* subshells impart color to solid transition metal compounds and their solutions. Absence of these transitions, in turn, accounts for the fact that so many main-group metal compounds are colorless.

Because most transition elements have partially filled *d* subshells, many transition metals and their compounds are paramagnetic—that is, they have unpaired electrons. This description certainly fits Fe, Co, and Ni, but these three metals are unique among the elements in displaying a special magnetic property: the ability to be made into permanent magnets, a property known as **ferromagnetism**. A key feature of ferromagnetism is that in the solid state, the metal atoms are thought to be grouped together into small regions—called *domains*—containing rather large numbers of atoms. Instead of the individual magnetic moments of the atoms within a domain being randomly oriented, all the magnetic moments are directed in the same way. In an unmagnetized piece of iron, the domains are oriented in several directions and their magnetic effects cancel. When the metal is placed in a magnetic field, however, the domains line up and a strong resultant magnetic effect is produced. This alignment of domains may actually involve the growth of domains with favorable orientations at the expense of those with unfavorable orientations (rather like a recrystallization of the material). The ordering of domains can persist when the object is removed from the magnetic field, and thus permanent magnetism results. Paramagnetism and ferromagnetism are compared in Figure 23-3.

The key factors in ferromagnetism: (1) The atoms involved have unpaired electrons (a property possessed by many atoms), and (2) interatomic distances are of just the right magnitude to make possible the ordering of atoms into domains. If atoms are too large, interactions among them are too weak to produce this ordering. With small atoms, the tendency is for atoms to pair and their magnetic moments to cancel. This critical factor of atomic size is just met in Fe, Co, and Ni. It is possible, however, to prepare *alloys* of other metals in which this condition is also met. Some examples are Al–Cu–Mn, Ag–Al–Mn, and Bi–Mn.

COMPARISON OF TRANSITION AND MAIN-GROUP ELEMENTS

With the main-group elements, the *s* and *p* orbitals of the outermost electron shell are the most important in determining the nature of the chemical bonding that occurs. Participation in bonding by *d* orbitals is essentially nonexistent for second-period elements and for group 1 and 2 metals. With the transition elements, *d* orbitals are as important as *s* and *p* orbitals. Most of the observed behavioral differences between the transition and main-group elements—multiple versus single oxidation states, complex-ion formation, color, magnetic properties, and catalytic activity—can be traced to the orbitals that are most involved in bond formation.

Magnetic field absent   In presence of magnetic field

Paramagnetism

Ferromagnetism

◀ **FIGURE 23-3**
Ferromagnetism and paramagnetism compared
In a paramagnetic material, the effect of a magnetic field is to align the magnetic moments of the individual atoms. In a ferromagnetic material, the magnetic moments are aligned within domains even in the absence of a magnetic field, but the direction of the alignment varies from one domain to another. The effect of the magnetic field is to change the orientation of these varied alignments into a single direction—the direction of the magnetic field.

CONCEPT ASSESSMENT ✓

Why is +3 the most stable oxidation state for Fe, while it is +2 for Co and Ni?

23-2 PRINCIPLES OF EXTRACTIVE METALLURGY

Many of the transition elements have important uses related to their metallic properties—iron for its structural strength and copper for its excellent electrical conductivity, for example. Unlike the more chemically reactive metals of groups 1 and 2 and aluminum in group 3, which are produced mainly by modern methods of electrolysis, the transition metals are obtained by procedures developed over many centuries.

The term *metallurgy* describes the general study of metals. **Extractive metallurgy** describes the winning of metals from their ores. There is no single method of extractive metallurgy, but a few basic operations generally apply. Let us illustrate them with the extractive metallurgy of zinc.

Concentration. In mining operations, the desired mineral from which a metal is to be extracted often constitutes only a small percent (or occasionally just a fraction of a percent) of the material mined. It is necessary to separate the desired ore from waste rock before proceeding with other metallurgical operations. One useful method, *flotation*, is described in Figure 23-4.

O'Klatner, B. L., et al. "Metallurgy in the Laboratory: Preparation of Pure Antimony." *J. Chem. Educ.* **2000:** *77*, 251.

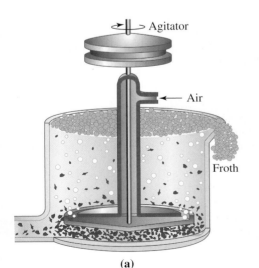

→ Agitator

← Air

Froth

(a)

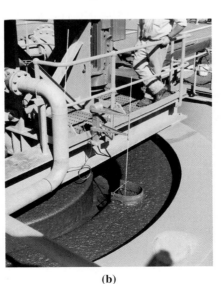

(b)

◀ **FIGURE 23-4**
Concentration of an ore by flotation
(a) Powdered ore is suspended in water in a large vat, together with suitable additives, and the mixture is agitated with air. Particles of ore become attached to air bubbles, rise to the top of the vat, and are collected in the overflow froth. Particles of undesired waste rock (gangue) fall to the bottom. **(b)** The froth formed in the flotation process.

Roasting. An ore is roasted (heated to a high temperature) to convert a metal compound to its oxide, which can then be reduced. For zinc, the commercially important ores are $ZnCO_3$ (smithsonite) and ZnS (sphalerite). $ZnCO_3(s)$, like the carbonates of the group 2 metals, decomposes to $ZnO(s)$ and $CO_2(g)$ when it is strongly heated. When strongly heated in air, $ZnS(s)$ reacts with $O_2(g)$, producing $ZnO(s)$ and $SO_2(g)$. In modern smelting operations, $SO_2(g)$ is converted to sulfuric acid rather than being vented to the atmosphere.

$$ZnCO_3(s) \xrightarrow{\Delta} ZnO(s) + CO_2(g) \tag{23.1}$$

$$2\,ZnS(s) + 3\,O_2(g) \xrightarrow{\Delta} 2\,ZnO(s) + 2\,SO_2(g) \tag{23.2}$$

 Reduction of CuO movie

Reduction. Because it is inexpensive and easy to handle, carbon, in the form of coke or powdered coal, is used as the reducing agent whenever possible. Several reactions occur simultaneously in which both $C(s)$ and $CO(g)$ act as reducing agents. The reduction of ZnO is carried out at about 1100 °C, a temperature above the boiling point of zinc. The zinc is obtained as a vapor and condensed to the liquid.

$$ZnO(s) + C(s) \xrightarrow{\Delta} Zn(g) + CO(g) \tag{23.3}$$

$$ZnO(s) + CO(g) \xrightarrow{\Delta} Zn(g) + CO_2(g) \tag{23.4}$$

Refining. The metal produced by chemical reduction is usually not pure enough for its intended uses. Impurities must be removed; that is, the metal must be refined. The refining process chosen depends on the nature of the impurities. The impurities in zinc are mostly Cd and Pb, which can be removed by the fractional distillation of liquid zinc.

Most of the zinc produced worldwide, however, is refined electrolytically, usually in a process that combines reduction and refining. ZnO from the roasting step is dissolved in $H_2SO_4(aq)$. This is represented by the ionic equation

$$ZnO(s) + 2\,H^+(aq) + SO_4{}^{2-}(aq) \longrightarrow Zn^{2+}(aq) + SO_4{}^{2-}(aq) + H_2O(l) \tag{23.5}$$

Powdered Zn is added to the solution to displace less active metals, such as Cd. Then the solution is electrolyzed. The electrode reactions are

▶ The sulfate anion is a spectator ion in this reaction and could be cancelled.

Cathode: $Zn^{2+}(aq) + 2\,e^- \longrightarrow Zn(s)$

Anode: $H_2O \longrightarrow \frac{1}{2}O_2(g) + 2\,H^+(aq) + 2\,e^-$

Unchanged: $SO_4{}^{2-}(aq) \longrightarrow SO_4{}^{2-}(aq)$

Overall: $Zn^{2+}(aq) + SO_4{}^{2-}(aq) + H_2O(l) \longrightarrow$

$$Zn(s) + 2\,H^+(aq) + SO_4{}^{2-}(aq) + \tfrac{1}{2}O_2(g) \tag{23.6}$$

Note that in the overall electrolysis reaction, Zn^{2+} is reduced to pure metallic zinc and sulfuric acid is regenerated. The acid is recycled in reaction (23.5).

EXAMPLE 23-1

Writing Chemical Equations for Metallurgical Processes. Write chemical equations to represent the **(a)** roasting of galena, PbS; **(b)** reduction of $Cu_2O(s)$ with charcoal as a reducing agent; **(c)** deposition of pure silver from an aqueous solution of Ag^+.

Solution

(a) We expect this process to be essentially the same as reaction (23.2).

$$2\,PbS(s) + 3\,O_2(g) \xrightarrow{\Delta} 2\,PbO(s) + 2\,SO_2(g)$$

(b) The simplest possible equation is

$$Cu_2O(s) + C(s) \xrightarrow{\Delta} 2\,Cu(l) + CO(g)$$

(c) This process involves a reduction half-reaction. The accompanying oxidation half-reaction is not specified. Nor is it specified whether this is an electrolysis process or whether silver is displaced by a more active metal. In either case, the reduction half-reaction is

$$Ag^+(aq) + e^- \longrightarrow Ag(s)$$

Practice Example A: Write plausible chemical equations to represent the **(a)** roasting of Cu_2S; **(b)** reduction of WO_3 with $H_2(g)$; **(c)** thermal decomposition of HgO to its elements.

Practice Example B: Write chemical equations to represent the **(a)** reduction of Cr_2O_3 to chromium with silicon as the reducing agent; **(b)** conversion of $Co(OH)_3(s)$ to $Co_2O_3(s)$ by roasting; **(c)** production of pure $MnO_2(s)$ from $MnSO_4(aq)$ at the anode in an electrolysis cell.

[*Hint:* A few simple products are not specifically mentioned; propose plausible ones.]

Zone Refining. In discussing freezing-point depression (Section 13-8), we assumed that a solute is *soluble* in a liquid solvent and *insoluble* in the solid solvent that freezes from solution. This behavior suggests a particularly simple way to purify a solid: Melt the solid and then refreeze a portion of it. Impurities remain in the liquid phase, and the solid that freezes is pure. In practice, the method is not quite so simple because the solid that freezes is wet with unfrozen liquid and thereby retains some impurities. Also, one or more solutes (impurities) might be slightly soluble in the solid solvent. In any case, the impurities do distribute themselves between the solid and liquid, concentrating in the liquid phase. If the solid that freezes from a liquid is remelted and the molten material refrozen, the solid obtained in the second freezing is purer than that in the first. Repeating the melting and refreezing procedure hundreds of times produces a very pure solid product.

The purification procedure just described implies that the melting and refreezing is done in batches, but in practice it is done *continuously*. In the method known as **zone refining**, a cylindrical rod of material is alternately melted and refrozen as a series of heating coils passes along the rod (Fig. 23-5). Impurities concentrate in the molten zones, and the portions of the rod behind these zones are somewhat purer than the portions in front of the zones. Eventually, impurities are swept to the end of the rod, which is cut off. The principle of zone

White, A. D. "A simple illustration of zone refining." *J. Chem. Educ.* **1986:** *63*, 514.

Zone Refining activity

◄ **FIGURE 23-5**
Zone refining
As a heating coil moves up the rod of material, melting occurs. Impurities concentrate in the molten zone. The portion of the rod below the molten zone is purer than the portion in or above the molten zone. With each successive passage of the heating coil, the rod becomes purer.

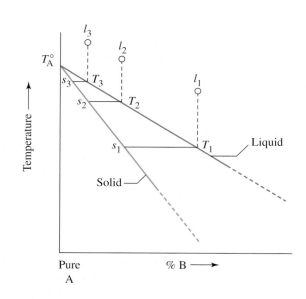

▲ FIGURE 23-6
The principle of zone refining
The red line shows the freezing points of solutions of impurity B in substance A. The blue line gives the composition of the solid that freezes from these solutions. In some cases, the blue line is nearly coincident with the temperature axis. When a solution of composition l_1 is cooled to temperature T_1, it freezes to produce a solid of composition s_1. If a small quantity of this solid is removed from the solution and melted, it produces a new liquid, l_2. The freezing point of l_2 is T_2, and the composition of the solid freezing from the solution is s_2. When removed from the solution, a small portion of this solid produces liquid l_3 and so on. With each melting/freezing cycle, the melting point increases and the point representing the composition of the solid moves closer to pure A. In zone refining the melting/freezing cycles are conducted continuously, not in batches as described here.

refining is shown graphically in Figure 23-6. This process is capable of producing materials in which the impurity levels are as low as 10 parts per billion (ppb), a common requirement of substances used in semiconductors.

THERMODYNAMICS OF EXTRACTIVE METALLURGY

It is interesting to think of the reduction of zinc oxide by carbon, as shown in reaction (23.3), as a competition between zinc and carbon for O atoms. Zinc has them initially in ZnO, and carbon acquires them in forming CO. To establish the conditions under which carbon will reduce zinc oxide to zinc, we start by comparing the relative tendencies for zinc and carbon to undergo oxidation. We can assess these tendencies through free energy changes.

$$(a) \quad 2\,C(s) + O_2(g) \longrightarrow 2\,CO(g) \qquad \Delta G^\circ_{(a)}$$
$$(b) \quad 2\,Zn(g) + O_2(g) \longrightarrow 2\,ZnO(s) \qquad \Delta G^\circ_{(b)}$$

To determine if the reduction of zinc oxide to zinc by carbon is a spontaneous reaction, we need the value of ΔG° for the overall reaction, represented below by reversing equation (b) and adding it to equation (a).

$$(a) \qquad 2\,C(s) + O_2(g) \longrightarrow 2\,CO(g) \qquad\qquad \Delta G^\circ_{(a)}$$
$$-\,(b) \qquad 2\,ZnO(s) \longrightarrow 2\,Zn(s) + O_2(g) \qquad -\,\Delta G^\circ_{(b)}$$

Overall: $\quad 2\,ZnO(s) + 2\,C(s) \longrightarrow 2\,Zn(s) + 2\,CO(g) \qquad \Delta G^\circ = \Delta G^\circ_{(a)} - \Delta G^\circ_{(b)}$

We still need some numerical data to complete our assessment. In Figure 23-7, the blue line gives $\Delta G^\circ_{(a)}$ as a function of temperature, and the top red line gives $\Delta G^\circ_{(b)}$.

KEEP IN MIND ▶
that a nonspontaneous process can sometimes be achieved by *coupling* with a spontaneous process. In the reduction of ZnO with C, the nonspontaneous
$2\,ZnO \longrightarrow 2\,Zn + O_2$
is coupled with the spontaneous
$2\,C + O_2 \longrightarrow 2\,CO$.

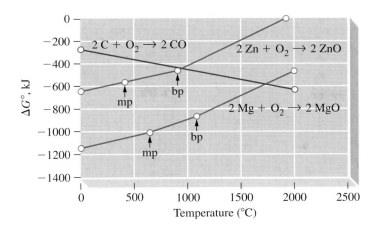

◀ FIGURE 23-7
$\Delta G°$ as a function of temperature for some reactions of extractive metallurgy
The points on the lines marked by arrows indicate the melting points and boiling points of Zn and Mg. At these points, the states of matter in which the metal exists change from (s) to (l) and from (l) to (g), respectively.

Figure 23-7 shows that at low temperatures, $\Delta G_{(b)}^{\circ}$ is much more negative than $\Delta G_{(a)}^{\circ}$. This makes $\Delta G°$ for the overall reaction positive and the reaction *nonspontaneous*. At high temperatures, the situation is reversed: $\Delta G_{(a)}^{\circ}$ is more negative than $\Delta G_{(b)}^{\circ}$, and the overall reaction is *spontaneous*. The switchover from nonspontaneous to spontaneous occurs at the point of intersection of the blue line and the red line—about 950 °C. There, $\Delta G°$ for the overall reaction is *zero*.

When we make a similar assessment for the reduction $2\,MgO(s) + 2\,C(s) \longrightarrow 2\,Mg(g) + 2\,CO(g)$, we conclude that the reaction does not become spontaneous until a temperature in excess of 1700 °C is reached. This is an exceedingly high temperature at which to carry out a chemical reaction, and it is not used in the metallurgy of magnesium.

Alternative Methods in Extractive Metallurgy.   Some common variations of the methods previously discussed are worth mentioning. First, many ores contain several metals, and it is not always necessary to separate them. For example, a major use of vanadium, chromium, and manganese is in making alloys with iron. Obtaining each metal by itself is not commercially important. Thus, the principal chromium ore *chromite*, $Fe(CrO_2)_2$, can be reduced to give an alloy of Fe and Cr called *ferrochrome*. Ferrochrome may be added directly to iron, together with other metals, to produce one type of steel. Vanadium and manganese can be isolated as the oxides V_2O_5 and MnO_2, respectively. When iron-containing compounds are added to these oxides and the mixtures are reduced, ferrovanadium and ferromanganese alloys form.

Extensive production of titanium was an important development of the latter half of the twentieth century, spurred first by the needs of the military and then by the aircraft industry. Steel is unsuitable as the structural metal for aircraft because it has a high density ($d = 7.8\ g/cm^3$). Aluminum has the

Are You Wondering . . .

Why the slope of the blue line in Figure 23-7 is negative, whereas the other slopes are positive?

Recall from Chapter 19 that $\Delta G° = \Delta H° - T\,\Delta S°$ and that $\Delta H°$ does not change appreciably with temperature. Thus, the temperature variation of $\Delta G°$ is determined primarily by the $-T\,\Delta S°$ term. We expect $\Delta S°$ to be negative for the reaction $2\,Zn(s) + O_2(g) \longrightarrow 2\,ZnO(s)$, because a mole of gas is lost. The term $-T\,\Delta S°$ is *positive*, and $\Delta G°$ *increases* with temperature. Conversely, in the reaction $2\,C(s) + O_2(g) \longrightarrow 2\,CO(g)$, an additional mole of gas forms, resulting in a positive value of $\Delta S°$. As a consequence, $-T\,\Delta S°$ is *negative* and $\Delta G°$ *decreases* with temperature.

▲ Vacuum-distilled metallic titanium sponge produced by the Kroll process.

advantage of a low density ($d = 2.70 \text{ g/cm}^3$), but it loses strength at high temperatures. For certain aircraft components, titanium is a good alternative to aluminum and steel because its density is moderately low ($d = 4.50 \text{ g/cm}^3$) and it does not lose strength at high temperatures.

Titanium metal cannot be produced by reduction of TiO_2 with carbon because the metal and carbon react to form titanium carbides. Also, at high temperatures the metal reacts with air to form TiO_2 and TiN. The metallurgy of titanium, then, must be conducted out of contact with air and with an active metal rather than with carbon as a reducing agent.

The first step in the production of Ti is the conversion of *rutile* ore (TiO_2) to $TiCl_4$ by reaction with carbon and $Cl_2(g)$.

$$TiO_2(s) + 2\,C(s) + 2\,Cl_2(g) \xrightarrow{800\ °C} TiCl_4(g) + 2\,CO(g) \qquad (23.7)$$

The purified $TiCl_4$ is next reduced to Ti with a good reducing agent. The *Kroll process* uses Mg.

$$TiCl_4(g) + 2\,Mg(l) \xrightarrow{1000\ °C} Ti(s) + 2\,MgCl_2(l) \qquad (23.8)$$

The $MgCl_2(l)$ is removed and electrolyzed to produce Cl_2 and Mg, which are recycled in reactions (23.7) and (23.8), respectively. The Ti is obtained as a sintered (fused) mass called *titanium sponge*. This sponge must be subjected to further treatment and alloying with other metals before it can be used.

The Kroll process is slow; it takes a week to produce a few tons of Ti. It is also demanding in health and safety terms because it requires high-temperature vacuum distillation to remove the Mg and $MgCl_2$ from the titanium. Recently, an electrolytic process has been suggested for the production of Ti from rutile. Porous pellets of TiO_2 are placed at the cathode of an electrolytic cell containing molten calcium chloride. The pellets dissolve in the electrolyte and oxide ions (O^{2-}) are discharged as oxygen at a graphite anode. The Ti(IV) is reduced at the cathode, which is the vessel containing the electrolytic cell and is made of either graphite or titanium. The titanium metal is obtained as sponge. This method, devised by Derek Fray, George Chen, and Tom Farthing in the United Kingdom, is being developed as a commercial process for the production of Ti(s) at a substantially lower cost than the Kroll process.

▲ Electrolytic production of Ti(s) from $TiO_2(s)$.

Metallurgy of Copper.   The extraction of copper from its ores (generally sulfides) is rather complicated, chiefly because the copper ores usually contain iron sulfides. The scheme of extractive metallurgy previously discussed produces copper contaminated with iron. For some metals, such as V, Cr, and Mn, contamination with iron is not a problem because the metals are mostly used in the manufacture of steel. Copper, however, is prized commercially for the properties of the pure metal. To avoid contamination with iron, several changes to the usual metallurgical methods are necessary.

Concentration of copper is done by flotation, and roasting converts iron sulfides to iron oxides. The copper remains as the sulfide if the temperature is kept below 800 °C. Smelting of the roasted ore in a furnace at 1400 °C causes the material to melt and separate into two layers. The bottom layer, called *copper matte*, consists chiefly of the molten sulfides of copper and iron. The top layer is a silicate slag formed by the reaction of oxides of Fe, Ca, and Al with SiO_2 (which typically is present in the ore or can be added). For example,

$$FeO(s) + SiO_2(s) \xrightarrow{\Delta} FeSiO_3(l) \qquad (23.9)$$

▲ Slag formed during the smelting of copper ore.

A process called *conversion* is carried out in another furnace, where air is blown through the molten copper matte. First, the remaining iron sulfide is converted to the oxide, followed by formation of slag [$FeSiO_3(l)$]. The slag is poured off, and air is again blown through the furnace. The following reactions occur and yield a product that is about 98–99% Cu.

$$2\,Cu_2S(l) + 3\,O_2(g) \xrightarrow{\Delta} 2\,Cu_2O(l) + 2\,SO_2(g) \qquad (23.10)$$

$$2\,Cu_2O(l) + Cu_2S(l) \xrightarrow{\Delta} 6\,Cu(l) + SO_2(g) \qquad (23.11)$$

The product of reaction (23.11) is called *blister copper* because frozen bubbles of $SO_2(g)$ are present. Blister copper can be used where high purity is not required (as in plumbing).

Refining blister copper to obtain high-purity copper is done electrolytically by the method outlined on page 853. High-purity copper is essential in electrical applications.

Pyrometallurgical Processes. The metallurgical method based on roasting an ore, followed by reduction of the oxide to the metal, is called **pyrometallurgy**, the prefix *pyro-* suggesting that high temperatures are involved. Some of the characteristics of pyrometallurgy are as follows:

- large quantities of waste materials produced in concentrating low-grade ores
- high energy consumption to maintain high temperatures necessary for roasting and reduction of ores
- gaseous emissions that must be controlled, such as $SO_2(g)$ in roasting

Many of the metallurgical processes described earlier fall into this category.

Hydrometallurgical Processes. In **hydrometallurgy**, the materials handled are water and aqueous solutions at moderate temperatures rather than dry solids at high temperatures. Generally, three steps are involved in hydrometallurgy.

1. *Leaching:* Metal ions are extracted (leached) from the ore by a liquid. Leaching agents include water, acids, bases, and salt solutions. Oxidation–reduction reactions may also be involved.

2. *Purification and concentration:* Impurities are separated, and the solution produced by leaching may be made more concentrated. Methods include the adsorption of impurities on the surface of activated charcoal, ion exchange, and the evaporation of water.

3. *Precipitation:* The desired metal ions are either precipitated in an ionic solid or reduced to the free metal, often electrolytically.

Hydrometallurgy has long been used in obtaining silver and gold from natural sources. A typical gold ore currently being processed in the United States has only about 10 g Au per ton of ore. The leaching step in gold processing is known as *cyanidation*. In this process, $O_2(g)$ oxidizes the free metal to Au^+, which complexes with CN^-.

$$4\,Au(s) + 8\,CN^-(aq) + O_2(g) + 2\,H_2O(l) \longrightarrow 4[Au(CN)_2]^-(aq) + 4\,OH^-(aq)$$

$$(23.12)$$

The $[Au(CN)_2]^-(aq)$ is then filtered and concentrated. This is followed by displacement of Au(s) from solution by an active metal such as zinc.

$$2[Au(CN)_2]^-(aq) + Zn(s) \longrightarrow 2\,Au(s) + [Zn(CN)_4]^{2-}(aq) \qquad (23.13)$$

In one hydrometallurgical process for zinc, a zinc sulfide ore is leached with a sulfuric acid solution at 150 °C and an oxygen pressure of about 7 atm. The overall reaction is

$$ZnS(s) + H_2SO_4(aq) + \tfrac{1}{2}O_2(g) \longrightarrow ZnSO_4(aq) + S(s) + H_2O(l) \qquad (23.14)$$

▶ Waste solution from the leaching operation at a gold-mining facility in the Mojave Desert of California.

▲ **FIGURE 23-8**
Typical blast furnace
Iron ore, coke, and limestone are added at the top of the furnace, and hot air is introduced through the bottom. Maximum temperatures are attained near the bottom of the furnace where molten iron and slag are drained off. The principal reactions occurring in the blast furnace are outlined in Table 23.2.

▶ In the United States, slightly over half of all iron and steel production comes from recycled iron and steel.

In this process, there is no $SO_2(g)$ emission. Also, mercury impurities in the ZnS ore are retained in the leaching solution rather than being emitted with $SO_2(g)$ as in the traditional roasting process. Following the leaching process, $ZnSO_4(aq)$ is electrolyzed to produce pure Zn at the cathode, and $H_2SO_4(aq)$ is regenerated; see reaction (23.6). The $H_2SO_4(aq)$ is recycled into the leaching operation.

CONCEPT ASSESSMENT ✓

The text describes the production of pure zinc from zinc sulfide ore both by a pyrometallurgical and a hydrometallurgical process. Which aspects of the two processes are different and which are similar?

23-3 METALLURGY OF IRON AND STEEL

Iron is the most widely used metal from Earth's crust, and for this reason, we use this section to explore the metallurgy of iron and its principal alloy—steel—somewhat more fully. A type of steel called *wootz steel* was first produced in India about 3000 years ago; that same steel became famous in ancient times as Damascus steel, prized for making swords because of its suppleness and ability to hold a cutting edge. Many technological advances have been made since ancient times. These include introduction of the blast furnace around AD 1300, the Bessemer converter in 1856, the open-hearth furnace in the 1860s, and the basic oxygen furnace in the 1950s. A true understanding of the iron- and steelmaking processes has developed only within the past few decades, however. This understanding is based on concepts of thermodynamics, equilibrium, and kinetics.

PIG IRON

The reactions that occur in a blast furnace are complex. A highly simplified representation of the reduction of iron ore to impure iron is

$$Fe_2O_3(s) + 3\,CO(g) \longrightarrow 2\,Fe(l) + 3\,CO_2(g) \qquad (23.15)$$

A more complete description of the blast furnace reactions, including the removal of impurities as slag, is given in Table 23.2. Approximate temperatures are given for these reactions so that you can key them to regions of the blast furnace pictured in Figure 23-8.

TABLE 23.2 Some Blast Furnace Reactions

Formation of gaseous reducing agents $CO(g)$ and $H_2(g)$:

$C + H_2O \longrightarrow CO + H_2$ (>600 °C)

$C + CO_2 \longrightarrow 2\,CO$ (1700 °C)

$2\,C + O_2 \longrightarrow 2\,CO$ (1700 °C)

Reduction of iron oxide:

$3\,CO + Fe_2O_3 \longrightarrow 2\,Fe + 3\,CO_2$ (900 °C)

$3\,H_2 + Fe_2O_3 \longrightarrow 2\,Fe + 3\,H_2O$ (900 °C)

Slag formation to remove impurities from ore:

$CaCO_3 \longrightarrow CaO + CO_2$ (800–900 °C)

$CaO + SiO_2 \longrightarrow CaSiO_3(l)$ (1200 °C)

$6\,CaO + P_4O_{10} \longrightarrow 2\,Ca_3(PO_4)_2(l)$ (1200 °C)

Impurity formation in the iron:

$MnO + C \longrightarrow Mn + CO$ (1400 °C)

$SiO_2 + 2\,C \longrightarrow Si + 2\,CO$ (1400 °C)

$P_4O_{10} + 10\,C \longrightarrow 4\,P + 10\,CO$ (1400 °C)

 How a blast furnace works website: http://www.steel.org/learning/howmade/blast_furnace.htm (commercial)

Iron slag website: http://www.taraonline.com/nationalslagassoc/ (commercial)

Geselbracht, M. J., Ellis, A. B., Penn, R. L., Lisensky, G. C., Stone, D. S. "Mechanical Properties of Metals: Experiments with Steel, Copper, Tin, Zinc, and Soap Bubbles." *J. Chem. Educ.* **1994**: *71*, 254.

The blast furnace charge—that is, the solid reactants—consists of iron ore, coke, a slag-forming flux, and perhaps some scrap iron. The exact proportions depend on the composition of the iron ore and its impurities. The common ores of iron are the oxides and carbonate: hematite (Fe_2O_3), magnetite (Fe_3O_4), limonite ($2\,Fe_2O_3 \cdot 3\,H_2O$), and siderite ($FeCO_3$). The purpose of the flux is to maintain the proper ratio of acidic oxides (SiO_2, Al_2O_3, and P_4O_{10}) to basic oxides (CaO, MgO, and MnO) to obtain an easily liquefied silicate, aluminate, or phosphate slag. Because acidic oxides predominate in most ores, the flux generally employed is limestone, $CaCO_3$, or dolomite, $CaCO_3 \cdot MgCO_3$.

The iron obtained from a blast furnace is called **pig iron**. It contains about 95% Fe, 3–4% C, and varying quantities of other impurities. *Cast iron* can be obtained by pouring pig iron directly into molds of the desired shape. Cast iron is very hard and brittle and is used only where it is not subjected to mechanical or thermal shock, such as in engine blocks, brake drums, and transmission housings in automobiles.

▲ Pouring pig iron.

◀ Thermal shock occurs when an object undergoes a rapid change of temperature. Engine blocks get quite hot, but because they cool slowly, they are not usually subject to thermal shock.

◀ Steel made with 18% Cr and 8% Ni resists corrosion and is commonly known as *stainless steel*.

STEEL

The three fundamental changes that must be made to convert pig iron to **steel** are

1. reduction of the carbon content from 3–4% in pig iron to 0–1.5% in steel

2. removal, through slag formation, of Si, Mn, and P (each present in pig iron to the extent of 1% or so), together with other minor impurities

3. addition of alloying elements (such as Cr, Ni, Mn, V, Mo, and W) to give the steel its desired end properties

The most important method of steelmaking today is the **basic oxygen process**. Oxygen gas at about 10 atm pressure and a stream of powdered limestone are fed through a water-cooled tube (called a *lance*) and discharged above the molten pig iron (Fig. 23-9). The reactions that occur (Table 23.3) accomplish the first two objectives. A typical reaction time is 22 minutes. The reaction vessel is tilted to pour off the liquid slag floating on top of the iron, and then the desired alloying elements are added.

Steelmaking has been undergoing rapid technological changes. It is now possible to make iron and steel directly from iron ore in a single-step, continuous process at temperatures below the melting point of any of the materials used in the process. In the *direct reduction of iron* (DRI), $CO(g)$ and $H_2(g)$, obtained in the reaction of steam with natural gas, are used as reducing agents. The economic viability of the DRI process depends on an abundant supply of natural gas. Currently, only a small percentage of the world's iron production is by direct reduction, but this is a fast-growing component of the iron and steel industry, particularly in the Middle East and South America.

Cooling water   Oxygen

Exhaust gases

Molten iron

▲ **FIGURE 23-9**
A basic oxygen furnace

Oxygen blast furnace website: http://www.schoolscience.co.uk/content/4/chemistry/steel/msch4pg1.html (non-commercial)

Gisser, K. R. C., Geselbracht, M., Cappellari, A., Hunsberger, L., Ellis, A. B., Perepezko, J., Lisensky, G. C. "Nickel-Titanium Memory Metal: A 'Smart' Material Exhibiting a Solid-State Phase Change and Superelasticity." *J. Chem. Educ.* **1994:** *71,* 334.

Titanium bikes website: http://www.titaniumsports.com/ (commercial).

TABLE 23.3 Some Reactions Occurring in Steelmaking Processes

$$2\,C + O_2 \longrightarrow 2\,CO$$
$$2\,FeO + Si \longrightarrow 2\,Fe + SiO_2$$
$$FeO + Mn \longrightarrow Fe + MnO$$
$$FeO + SiO_2 \longrightarrow FeSiO_3$$
slag
$$MnO + SiO_2 \longrightarrow MnSiO_3$$
slag
$$4\,P + 5\,O_2 \longrightarrow P_4O_{10}$$
$$6\,CaO + P_4O_{10} \longrightarrow 2\,Ca_3(PO_4)_2$$
slag

▲ A computer-generated representation of titanium joint implants at the shoulders, elbows, hips, and knees.

▲ White TiO_2(s), mixed with other components to produce the desired color, is the leading pigment used in paints.

CONCEPT ASSESSMENT ✓

Write a balanced chemical equation for the direct reduction of iron(III) oxide by hydrogen gas.

23-4 FIRST-ROW TRANSITION METAL ELEMENTS: SCANDIUM TO MANGANESE

The properties and uses of the first-row transition metals span a wide range, strikingly illustrating periodic behavior despite the small variation in some of the atomic properties listed in Table 23.1. The preparation, uses, and reactions of the compounds of these metals illustrate concepts we have previously discussed, including the variability of oxidation states.

SCANDIUM

Scandium is a rather obscure metal, though not especially rare. It constitutes about 0.0025% of Earth's crust, which makes it more abundant than many better-known metals, including lead, uranium, molybdenum, tungsten, antimony, silver, mercury, and gold. Its principal mineral form is *thortveitite,* $Sc_2Si_2O_7$. Most scandium is obtained from uranium ores, however, in which it occurs only to the extent of about 0.01% Sc by mass. The commercial uses of scandium are limited, and its production is measured in gram or kilogram quantities, not in tons. One application is in high-intensity lamps. The pure metal is usually prepared by the electrolysis of a fused mixture of $ScCl_3$ with other chlorides.

Because of its noble-gas electron configuration, the Sc^{3+} ion lacks some of the characteristic properties of transition metal ions. For instance, the ion is colorless and diamagnetic, as are most of its salts. In its chemical behavior, Sc^{3+} most closely resembles Al^{3+}, as in the hydrolysis of $[Sc(H_2O)_6]^{3+}$(aq) to yield acidic solutions and in the formation of an amphoteric gelatinous hydroxide, $Sc(OH)_3$.

TITANIUM

Titanium is the ninth most abundant element, constituting 0.6% of Earth's solid crust. The metal is greatly valued for its low density, high structural strength, and corrosion resistance. The first two properties account for its extensive use in the aircraft industry, and the third for its uses in the chemical industry: in pipes, component parts of pumps, and reaction vessels. Titanium is also used in dental and other bone implants. The metal provides a strong support and bone bonds directly to a titanium implant, making it a part of the body.

Several compounds of titanium are of particular commercial importance. *Titanium tetrachloride*, $TiCl_4$, is the starting material for preparing other Ti compounds and plays a central role in the metallurgy of titanium. $TiCl_4$ is also used to formulate catalysts for the production of plastics. The usual method of preparing $TiCl_4$ involves the reaction of naturally occurring rutile (TiO_2) with carbon and $Cl_2(g)$ [reaction (23.7)].

$TiCl_4$ is a colorless liquid (mp -24 °C; bp 136 °C). In the $+4$ oxidation state, all the valence-shell electrons of Ti atoms are employed in bond formation. In this oxidation state, Ti bears a strong resemblance to the group 14 elements, with some properties and a molecular shape (tetrahedral) similar to those of CCl_4 and $SiCl_4$. The hydrolysis of $TiCl_4$, when carried out in moist air, is the basis for a type of smoke grenade in which $TiO_2(s)$ is the smoke.

$$TiCl_4(l) + 2\,H_2O(l) \longrightarrow TiO_2(s) + 4\,HCl(g)$$

$SiCl_4$ also fumes in moist air in a similar reaction.

Titanium dioxide, TiO_2, is bright white, opaque, inert, and nontoxic. Because of these properties and its relative low cost, it is now the most widely used white pigment for paints. In this application, TiO_2 has displaced toxic basic lead carbonate—so-called white lead. TiO_2 is also used as a paper whitener and in glass, ceramics, floor coverings, and cosmetics.

To produce pure TiO_2 for these and other uses, a gaseous mixture of $TiCl_4$ and O_2 is passed through a silica tube at about 700 °C.

$$TiCl_4(g) + O_2(g) \xrightarrow{\Delta} TiO_2(s) + 2\,Cl_2(g)$$

A list of minerals containing the first-row transition metals is in House, J. E., House, K. A., *Descriptive Inorganic Chemistry*, Harcourt Academic Press, (2001), p. 376.

Bare, W. D., Resto, W. "Vanadium Ions as Visible Electron Carriers in a Redox System (TD)." *J. Chem. Educ.* **1994:** *71*, 692.

Vanadium

Vanadium is a fairly abundant element (0.02% of Earth's crust) found in several dozen ores. Its principal ores are rather complex, such as *vanadinite*, $3\,Pb_3(VO_4)_2 \cdot PbCl_2$. The metallurgy of vanadium is not simple, but vanadium of high purity (99.99%) is obtainable. For most of its applications, though, vanadium is prepared as an iron–vanadium alloy, *ferrovanadium*, containing from 35 to 95% V. About 80% of the vanadium produced is for the manufacture of steel. Vanadium-containing steels are used in applications requiring strength and toughness, such as in springs and high-speed machine tools.

The most important compound of vanadium is the pentoxide, V_2O_5, used mainly as a catalyst, as in the conversion of $SO_2(g)$ to $SO_3(g)$ in the contact method for the manufacture of sulfuric acid. The activity of V_2O_5 as an oxidation catalyst may be linked to its reversible loss of oxygen occurring from 700 to 1100 °C.

In its compounds, vanadium can exist in a variety of oxidation states. In each of these oxidation states, vanadium forms an oxide or ion. The ions display distinctive colors in aqueous solution (Fig. 23-10). The acid–base properties of vanadium oxides are in accord with factors established earlier in the text: If the central metal atom is in a low oxidation state, the oxide acts as a base; in higher oxidation states for the central atom, acidic properties become important. Vanadium oxides with V in the $+2$ and $+3$ oxidation states are basic, whereas those in the $+4$ and $+5$ oxidation states are amphoteric.

Most compounds with vanadium in its highest oxidation state ($+5$) are good oxidizing agents. In its $+2$ oxidation state, vanadium (as V^{2+}) is a good reducing agent. The oxidation–reduction relationships between the ionic species pictured in Figure 23-10 are summarized in Table 23.4.

▲ **FIGURE 23-10**
Some vanadium species in solution
The yellow solution has vanadium in the $+5$ oxidation state, as VO_2^+. In the blue solution, the oxidation state is $+4$, in VO^{2+}. The green solution contains V^{3+}, and the violet solution contains V^{2+}.

TABLE 23.4	Oxidation States of Vanadium Species in Acidic Solution	
O.S. Change	Reduction Half-Reaction	$E°$
$+5 \longrightarrow +4$:	$VO_2^+(aq) + 2\,H^+(aq) + e^- \longrightarrow VO^{2+}(aq) + H_2O(l)$ (yellow) (blue)	1.000 V
$+4 \longrightarrow +3$:	$VO^{2+}(aq) + 2\,H^+(aq) + e^- \longrightarrow V^{3+}(aq) + H_2O(l)$ (green)	0.337 V
$+3 \longrightarrow +2$:	$V^{3+}(aq) + e^- \longrightarrow V^{2+}(aq)$ (violet)	−0.255 V
$+2 \longrightarrow 0$:	$V^{2+}(aq) + 2\,e^- \longrightarrow V(s)$	−1.13 V

EXAMPLE 23-2

Using Electrode Potential Data to Predict an Oxidation–Reduction Reaction. Can $MnO_4^-(aq)$ be used to oxidize $VO^{2+}(aq)$ to $VO_2^+(aq)$ for standard-state conditions in an acidic solution? If so, write a balanced equation for the redox reaction.

Solution

We start by writing two half-equations, one for the reduction of MnO_4^- to Mn^{2+}; the other, for the oxidation of VO^{2+} to VO_2^+. Both are in acidic solution. We find one $E°$ value in Table 23.4 and the other in Table 20.1. We then combine the $E°$ values into $E°_{cell}$.

Reduction: $MnO_4^- + 8\,H^+ + 5\,e^- \longrightarrow Mn^{2+} + 4\,H_2O$

Oxidation: $5(VO^{2+} + H_2O \longrightarrow VO_2^+ + 2\,H^+ + e^-)$

Overall: $5\,VO^{2+}(aq) + MnO_4^-(aq) + H_2O(l) \longrightarrow$
$$5\,VO_2^+(aq) + Mn^{2+}(aq) + 2\,H^+(aq)$$

$$E°_{cell} = E°_{MnO_4^-/Mn^{2+}} - E°_{VO_2^+/VO^{2+}} = 1.51\text{ V} - 1.000\text{ V} = 0.51\text{ V}$$

Because $E°_{cell}$ is positive, we predict that MnO_4^- should oxidize VO^{2+} to VO_2^+ for standard-state conditions in acidic solution.

Practice Example A: Use data from Tables 20.1 and 23.4 to determine whether nitric acid can be used to oxidize $V^{3+}(aq)$ to $VO^{2+}(aq)$ for standard-state conditions. If so, write a balanced equation for the reaction.

Practice Example B: Select a *reducing* agent from Table 20.1 that can be used to reduce VO^{2+} to V^{2+} for standard-state conditions in acidic solution. Consider that the reduction occurs in two stages: $VO^{2+} \longrightarrow V^{3+} \longrightarrow V^{2+}$, but note that the V^{2+} must not be reduced to $V(s)$.

CHROMIUM

▶ The word *chromium* is derived from the Greek *chroma*, meaning color—an apt name, given the range of colors found in chromium compounds.

Although it is found only to the extent of 122 parts per million (0.0122%) in Earth's crust, chromium is one of the most important industrial metals. The production of ferrochrome from *chromite*, $Fe(CrO_2)_2$, was discussed in Section 23-2. Chromium metal is hard and maintains a bright surface through the protective action of an invisible oxide coating. Because it is resistant to corrosion, chromium is extensively used in plating other metals.

Steel is chrome-plated from an aqueous solution containing CrO_3 and H_2SO_4. The plating obtained is thin and porous. It tends to develop cracks unless the steel is first plated with copper or nickel, which provides the true protective coating. Then chromium is plated over this layer for decorative purposes. The efficiency of chrome-plating is limited by the fact that reduction of Cr(VI) to Cr(0) produces only $\frac{1}{6}$ mol Cr per mole of electrons. In other words, large quantities of electric energy are required for chrome-plating relative to other types of metal plating.

◀ Chrome-plating shown on the engine of a motorcycle.

Chromium, like vanadium, has a variety of oxidation states in aqueous solution, each having a different color.

O.S. + 2: $[Cr(H_2O)_6]^{2+}$, blue

O.S. + 3:   (acidic) $[Cr(H_2O)_6]^{3+}$, violet   (basic) $[Cr(OH)_4]^-$, green

O.S. + 6:   (acidic) $Cr_2O_7^{2-}$, orange   (basic) CrO_4^{2-}, yellow

The oxides and hydroxides of chromium conform to the general principles of acid–base behavior: CrO is basic, Cr_2O_3 is amphoteric, and CrO_3 is acidic.

Pure chromium reacts with dilute $HCl(aq)$ or $H_2SO_4(aq)$ to produce $Cr^{2+}(aq)$. Nitric acid and other oxidizing agents alter the surface of the metal (perhaps by formation of an oxide coating). They render the metal resistant to further attack—it becomes *passive*. A better source of chromium compounds than the pure metal is the alkali metal chromates, which contain Cr(VI) and can be obtained directly from chromite ore by reactions such as

$$4\,Fe(CrO_2)_2 + 8\,Na_2CO_3 + 7\,O_2 \xrightarrow{\Delta} 2\,Fe_2O_3 + 8\,Na_2CrO_4 + 8\,CO_2 \quad (23.16)$$

The *sodium chromate*, Na_2CrO_4, produced by this reaction is the source of many industrially important chromium compounds.

The Cr(VI) oxidation state is also observed in the red oxide, CrO_3. As expected, this oxide dissolves in water to produce a strongly acidic solution. The product of the reaction is not the expected chromic acid, H_2CrO_4, however, which has never been isolated in the pure state. Instead, the observed reaction is

$$2\,CrO_3(s) + H_2O(l) \longrightarrow 2\,H^+(aq) + Cr_2O_7^{2-}(aq) \quad (23.17)$$

It is possible to crystallize a *dichromate* salt from an aqueous solution of CrO_3. If the solution is made basic, the color turns from orange to yellow. From basic solutions, only *chromate* salts can be crystallized. Thus, whether a solution contains Cr(VI) as $Cr_2O_7^{2-}$ or CrO_4^{2-} or a mixture of the two depends on the pH. The relevant equations follow.

$$2\,CrO_4^{2-}(aq) + 2\,H^+(aq) \rightleftharpoons Cr_2O_7^{2-}(aq) + H_2O(l) \quad (23.18)$$

$$K_c = \frac{[Cr_2O_7^{2-}]}{[CrO_4^{2-}]^2[H^+]^2} = 3.2 \times 10^{14} \quad (23.19)$$

Le Châtelier's principle predicts that the forward reaction of (23.18) is favored in acidic solutions and that the predominant Cr(VI) species is $Cr_2O_7^{2-}$. In basic solution, H^+ ions are removed and the reverse reaction is favored, forming CrO_4^{2-} as the principal species. Careful control of the pH is necessary when $Cr_2O_7^{2-}$ is used as an oxidizing agent or CrO_4^{2-} as a precipitating agent. In addition, equation (23.19) can be used to calculate the relative amounts of the two ions as a function of $[H^+]$.

Chromate ion in basic solution can be used to precipitate metal chromates such as $BaCrO_4(s)$ and $PbCrO_4(s)$. It is not a good oxidizing agent, however; it is not readily reduced.

$$CrO_4^{2-}(aq) + 4\,H_2O(l) + 3\,e^- \longrightarrow [Cr(OH)_4]^-(aq) + 4\,OH^-(aq) \quad E° = -0.13\,V$$

◀ The colors may also depend on other species present in solution. For example, if $[Cl^-]$ is high, $[Cr(H_2O)_6]^{3+}$ is converted to $[CrCl_2(H_2O)_4]^+$ and the violet color changes to green.

Jones, R. B., Dreisbach, J. H. "Classroom Demonstration of Chromium(VI)/Chromium(III) in the Breathalyzer Test Reaction (TD)." *J. Chem. Educ.* **1994:** 71, 158.

Seymour, P. "Chromium Pollution: An Experiment Adapted for Freshman Engineering Students." *J. Chem. Educ.* **1999:** 76, 927.

Kalbus, L. H., Petrucci, R. H., Forman, J. E., Kalbus, G. E. "Titration of Chromate–Dichromate Mixtures." *J. Chem. Educ.* **1991:** 68, 677.

Chromate ion (CrO_4^{2-})

Dichromate ion ($Cr_2O_7^{2-}$)

▲ FIGURE 23-11
Decomposition of
$(NH_4)_2Cr_2O_7$
Ammonium dichromate (left) contains both an oxidizing agent, $Cr_2O_7^{2-}$, and a reducing agent, NH_4^+. The products of the reaction between these two ions are $Cr_2O_3(s)$ (right), $N_2(g)$, and $H_2O(g)$. Considerable heat and light are also evolved (center).

Dichromates are poor precipitating agents but excellent oxidizing agents, which are used in a variety of industrial processes. In the chrome leather tanning process, for example, animal hides are immersed in $Na_2Cr_2O_7(aq)$, which is then reduced by $SO_2(g)$ to soluble basic chromic sulfate, $Cr(OH)SO_4$. Collagen, a protein in hides, reacts to form an insoluble chromium complex. The hides become *leather*, a tough, pliable material resistant to biological attack.

Dichromates are easily reduced to Cr_2O_3. In the case of ammonium dichromate, simply heating the compound produces Cr_2O_3 in a dramatic reaction (Fig. 23-11).

Chromium(II) compounds can be prepared by the reduction of Cr(III) compounds with zinc in acidic solution or electrolytically at a lead cathode. The most distinctive feature of Cr(II) compounds is their reducing power.

$$Cr^{3+}(aq) + e^- \longrightarrow Cr^{2+}(aq) \qquad E° = -0.424 \text{ V}$$

That is, the oxidation of $Cr^{2+}(aq)$ occurs readily. In fact, Cr(II) solutions can be used to purge gases of trace amounts of $O_2(g)$, through the following reaction, illustrated in Figure 23-12.

$$4\,Cr^{2+}(aq) + O_2(g) + 4\,H^+(aq) \longrightarrow 4\,Cr^{3+}(aq) + 2\,H_2O(l) \qquad E°_{cell} = +1.653 \text{ V}$$

Pure Cr can be obtained in small amounts by reducing Cr_2O_3 with Al in a reaction similar to the thermite reaction.

$$Cr_2O_3(s) + 2\,Al(s) \longrightarrow Al_2O_3(s) + 2\,Cr(l) \qquad (23.20)$$

▶ FIGURE 23-12
Relationship between Cr^{2+} and Cr^{3+}
The solution on the left, containing blue $Cr^{2+}(aq)$, is prepared by dissolving chromium metal in HCl(aq). Within minutes, the $Cr^{2+}(aq)$ is oxidized to green $Cr^{3+}(aq)$ by atmospheric oxygen (right). The green color is that of the complex ion $[CrCl_2(H_2O)_4]^+(aq)$.

MANGANESE

Manganese is a fairly abundant element, constituting about 1% of Earth's crust. Its principal ore is *pyrolusite*, MnO_2. Like V and Cr, Mn is most important in steel production, generally as the iron–manganese alloy, *ferromanganese*. Ferromanganese can be obtained by the reduction of a mixture of pyrolusite and hematite iron ores with carbon.

$$MnO_2 + Fe_2O_3 + 5\,C \xrightarrow{\Delta} Mn + 2\,Fe + 5\,CO$$
ferromanganese

Mn participates in the purification of iron by reacting with sulfur and oxygen and removing them through slag formation. In addition, Mn increases the hardness of steel. Steel containing high proportions of Mn is extremely tough and wear-resistant in such applications as railroad rails, bulldozers, and road scrapers.

The electron configuration of Mn is $[Ar]3d^54s^2$. By employing first the two $4s$ electrons and then, consecutively, up to all five of its unpaired $3d$ electrons, manganese exhibits all oxidation states from +2 to +7. The most important reactions of manganese compounds are oxidation–reduction reactions. Standard electrode potential diagrams are given in Figure 23-13. These diagrams help explain the following observations:

- Mn^{3+}(aq) is unstable; that is, its disproportionation is spontaneous.

$$2\,Mn^{3+}(aq) + 2\,H_2O(l) \longrightarrow Mn^{2+}(aq) + MnO_2(s) + 4\,H^+(aq) \quad E^{\circ}_{cell} = 0.54\ V \qquad (23.21)$$

- Manganate ion, MnO_4^{2-}, is also unstable in acidic solution; its disproportionation is spontaneous.

$$3\,MnO_4^{2-}(aq) + 4\,H^+(aq) \longrightarrow MnO_2(s) + 2\,MnO_4^-(aq) + 2\,H_2O(l) \quad E^{\circ}_{cell} = 1.70\ V \qquad (23.22)$$

- If $[OH^-]$ is kept sufficiently high, the following reaction can be reversed; thus, manganate ion can be maintained as a stable species in a strongly basic medium.

$$3\,MnO_4^{2-}(aq) + 2\,H_2O(l) \longrightarrow MnO_2(s) + 2\,MnO_4^-(aq) + 4\,OH^-(aq) \quad E^{\circ}_{cell} = 0.04\ V \qquad (23.23)$$

Manganese dioxide is used in dry-cell batteries, in glass and ceramic glazes, and as a catalyst; it is also the principal source of manganese compounds. When MnO_2 is heated in the presence of an alkali and an oxidizing agent, a manganate salt is produced.

$$3\,MnO_2 + 6\,KOH + KClO_3 \xrightarrow{\Delta} 3\,K_2MnO_4 + KCl + 3\,H_2O$$

Puerta, M. C., Valerga, P. "Thermal Decomposition of a Natural Manganese Dioxide: A Laboratory Experiment for Undergraduate Students." *J. Chem. Educ.* **1990**: *67*, 344.

Steffel, Margaret J. "Reduction of permanganate: A kinetics demonstration for general chemistry." *J. Chem. Educ.* **1990**: *67*, 598.

Acidic solution ($[H^+] = 1\ M$):

+7	+6	+4	+3	+2	0

$$\underset{\text{(purple)}}{MnO_4^-} \xrightarrow{\ 0.56\ V\ } \underset{\text{(green)}}{MnO_4^{2-}} \xrightarrow{\ 2.27\ V\ } \underset{\text{(black)}}{MnO_2} \xrightarrow{\ 0.95\ V\ } \underset{\text{(red)}}{Mn^{3+}} \xrightarrow{\ 1.49\ V\ } \underset{\text{(pale pink)}}{Mn^{2+}} \xrightarrow{\ -1.18\ V\ } Mn$$

1.70 V   1.23 V

Basic solution ($[OH^-] = 1\ M$):

+7	+6	+5	+4	+3	+2	0

$$\underset{\text{(purple)}}{MnO_4^-} \xrightarrow{\ 0.56\ V\ } \underset{\text{(green)}}{MnO_4^{2-}} \xrightarrow{\ 0.27\ V\ } \underset{\text{(blue)}}{MnO_4^{3-}} \xrightarrow{\ 0.96\ V\ } \underset{\text{(black)}}{MnO_2} \xrightarrow{\ -0.2\ V\ } \underset{\text{(brown)}}{Mn(OH)_3} \xrightarrow{\ 0.15\ V\ } \underset{\text{(pink)}}{Mn(OH)_2} \xrightarrow{\ -1.55\ V\ } Mn$$

0.62 V   −0.04 V

◀ **FIGURE 23-13**
Electrode potential diagrams for manganese

K_2MnO_4 is extracted from the fused mass with water and can then be oxidized to $KMnO_4$, *potassium permanganate* (with Cl_2 as an oxidizing agent, for instance). Potassium permanganate, $KMnO_4$, is an important laboratory oxidizing agent. For chemical analyses, it is generally used in acidic solutions in which it is reduced to $Mn^{2+}(aq)$. In the analysis of iron by MnO_4^-, a sample of Fe^{2+} is prepared by dissolving iron in an acid and reducing any Fe^{3+} back to Fe^{2+}. Then the sample is titrated with $MnO_4^-(aq)$.

$$5\,Fe^{2+}(aq) + MnO_4^-(aq) + 8\,H^+(aq) \longrightarrow 5\,Fe^{3+}(aq) + Mn^{2+}(aq) + 4\,H_2O(l) \quad (23.24)$$

$Mn^{2+}(aq)$ has a barely discernible pale pink color. $MnO_4^-(aq)$ is an intense purple color. At the end point of the titration reaction (23.24), the solution acquires a lasting light purple color with just one drop of excess $MnO_4^-(aq)$ (recall Figure 5-11). $MnO_4^-(aq)$ is less satisfactory for titrations in alkaline solutions because the insoluble reduction product, brown $MnO_2(s)$, obscures the end point.

CONCEPT ASSESSMENT ✔

The dichromate ion is formed by the condensation of chromate ion in an acidic solution. Further condensation occurs at low pH to form $[Cr_3O_{10}]^{2-}$. Suggest the structures for these anions. What other elements form similar anions?

23-5   THE IRON TRIAD: IRON, COBALT, AND NICKEL

The transition elements iron, cobalt, and nickel comprise the *iron triad*. Iron, with an annual worldwide production of over 500 million tons, is the most important metal in modern civilization. It is widely distributed in Earth's crust at an abundance of 4.7%. The major commercial use of iron is to make steel (see Section 23-3).

Cobalt is among the rarer elements. It comprises only about 0.0020% of Earth's crust, but it occurs in sufficiently concentrated deposits (ores) so that its annual production runs into the millions of pounds. Cobalt is used primarily in alloys with other metals. Like iron, cobalt is ferromagnetic. One alloy of cobalt, Co_5Sm, makes a particularly strong and lightweight permanent magnet. Because of the strength of its magnetic field, magnets of this alloy are used in the manufacture of miniature electronic devices.

Nickel ranks twenty-fourth in abundance among the elements in Earth's crust. Its ores are mainly the sulfides, oxides, silicates, and arsenides. Particularly large deposits are found in Canada. Of the 300 million pounds of nickel consumed annually in the United States, about 80% goes to the production of alloys. Another 15% is used in electroplating, and the remainder for miscellaneous purposes (for example, as catalysts).

OXIDATION STATES

Variability of oxidation state is seen in the iron triad, even if not to the same degree as with vanadium, chromium, and manganese. The +2 oxidation state is commonly encountered in all three metals.

▲ Cobalt–samarium magnets are used in high-efficiency motors.

Samarium magnet website: http://www.newi.ac.uk/buckleyc/magnet.htm (non-commercial)

Senozan, N. M., et al. "Iron as Nutrient and Poison." *J. Chem. Educ.* **1997:** *74*, 1060.

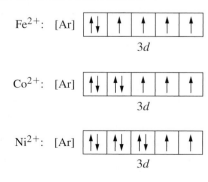

For cobalt and nickel, the +2 oxidation state is the most stable, but for iron, the most stable is +3.

The electron configuration of Fe^{3+} has a half-filled d subshell with all the d electrons unpaired. This type of electron configuration has a special stability. As we can see from the orbital diagrams of Co^{2+} and Ni^{2+}, neither would have a half-filled $3d$ subshell following the loss of one additional electron. Co^{3+} and Ni^{3+} are not readily formed. To illustrate the contrast between Fe^{3+}, on the one hand, and Co^{3+} and Ni^{3+}, on the other, consider the following observations.

- $Fe^{2+}(aq)$ is spontaneously oxidized to $Fe^{3+}(aq)$ by $O_2(g)$ at 1 atm in a solution with $[H^+] = 1$ M.

$$4\,Fe^{2+}(aq) + O_2(g) + 4\,H^+(aq) \longrightarrow 4\,Fe^{3+}(aq) + 2\,H_2O(l) \qquad E^\circ_{cell} = 0.44\ V \qquad (23.25)$$

  This reaction is still spontaneous with lower O_2 partial pressures and less acidic solutions.

- For the half-reaction $Co^{3+}(aq) + e^- \longrightarrow Co^{2+}(aq)$, $E^\circ = 1.82$ V. The reduction of $Co^{3+}(aq)$ to $Co^{2+}(aq)$ occurs readily; conversely, the oxidation of $Co^{2+}(aq)$ to Co^{3+} occurs only with difficulty. As will be noted in Chapter 24, however, the oxidation state +3 can be attained when Co^{3+} is the central metal ion in very stable complex ions.

- Nickel(III) compounds are used in batteries. For example, in the nickel–cadmium (Nicad) cell, the cathode half-reaction is $NiO(OH) + H^+ + e^- \longrightarrow Ni(OH)_2$. It is the ease of this reduction, when combined with the oxidation half-reaction, $Cd(s) + 2\,OH^-(aq) \longrightarrow Cd(OH)_2(s) + 2\,e^-$, that produces a cell with a voltage of about 1.5 V.

SOME REACTIONS OF THE IRON TRIAD ELEMENTS

The reactions of the iron triad elements are many and varied. The metals are more active than hydrogen and liberate $H_2(g)$ from an acidic solution. Hydrated colored ions are characteristic: Co^{2+} and Ni^{2+} are red and green, respectively. In aqueous solution, Fe^{2+} is pale green and fully hydrated Fe^{3+} is purple. Generally, however, solutions of $Fe^{2+}(aq)$ are yellow to brown, but this color is probably due to the presence of species formed in the hydrolysis of $Fe^{3+}(aq)$. Like the hydrolysis of $Al^{3+}(aq)$, described on page 696, that of $Fe^{3+}(aq)$ produces an acidic solution.

$$[Fe(H_2O)_6]^{3+}(aq) + H_2O(l) \rightleftharpoons [FeOH(H_2O)_5]^{2+}(aq) + H_3O^+(aq) \quad K_a = 8.9 \times 10^{-4} \qquad (23.26)$$

Some reactions that can be used to identify and distinguish between $Fe^{2+}(aq)$ and $Fe^{3+}(aq)$ are summarized in Table 23.5.

An interesting set of reactions involves the complex ions $[Fe(CN)_6]^{4-}$ and $[Fe(CN)_6]^{3-}$. These ions are commonly called *ferrocyanide* and *ferricyanide*, respectively. $Fe^{3+}(aq)$ yields a dark blue precipitate called *Prussian blue* when treated with potassium ferrocyanide, $K_4[Fe(CN)_6](aq)$, whereas $Fe^{2+}(aq)$ yields a similar blue precipitate, called *Turnbull's blue*, when treated with potassium

◀ The blue precipitate that establishes the presence of $Fe^{2+}(aq)$ from the corroding nails in Figure 20-19 is Turnbull's blue.

◀ In Chapter 24, we will learn to write the systematic names for ferrocyanide and ferricyanide ions; they are hexacyanoferrate(II) and hexacyanoferrate(III), respectively.

TABLE 23.5 Some Qualitative Tests for $Fe^{2+}(aq)$ and $Fe^{3+}(aq)$		
Reagent	**$Fe^{2+}(aq)$**	**$Fe^{3+}(aq)$**
NaOH(aq)	Green precipitate	Red-brown precipitate
$K_4[Fe(CN)_6]$	White precipitate, turning blue rapidly	Prussian blue precipitate
$K_3[Fe(CN)_6]$	Turnbull's blue precipitate	Red-brown (no precipitate)
KSCN(aq)	No color	Deep red

$Cr(CO)_6$

$Fe(CO)_5$

$Ni(CO)_4$

▲ **FIGURE 23-14**
Structures of some simple carbonyls

▶ In the metallurgy of nickel (the Mond process), CO(g) is passed over a mixture of metal oxides. Nickel is carried off as $Ni(CO)_4(g)$, while the other oxides are reduced to the metals.

 Carbonyl website: http://www.ilpi.com/organomet/carbonyl.html (non-commercial)

📖 Carriedo, Gabino A. "The Use of Cyclic Voltammetry in the Study of the Chemistry of Metal Carbonyls: An Introductory Experiment." *J. Chem. Educ.* **1988:** 65, 1020.

📖 Kebbekus, Barbara B. "A Chemical-Medical Mystery: Gold Jewelry and Black Marks on Skin." *J. Chem. Educ.* **2000:** 77, 1298 (October 2000).

📖 Sogo, S. G. "Isolation of Copper from a 5-Cent Coin. An Example of Electrorefining." *J. Chem. Educ.* **2004:** 81, 530.

TABLE 23.6	Three Metal Carbonyls		
	Number of e⁻		
	From Metal	From CO	Total
$Cr(CO)_6$	24	12	36
$Fe(CO)_5$	26	10	36
$Ni(CO)_4$	28	8	36

ferricyanide, $K_3[Fe(CN)_6](aq)$. Together, these two and similar related precipitates are known commercially as *iron blue*. Iron blue is used as a pigment for paints, printing inks, laundry bluing, art colors, cosmetics (eye shadow), and blueprinting. An additional sensitive test for $Fe^{3+}(aq)$ is the formation of a blood-red complex ion with thiocyanate ion, $SCN^-(aq)$.

$$[Fe(H_2O)_6]^{3+} + SCN^-(aq) \longrightarrow [FeSCN(H_2O)_5]^{2+} + H_2O(l)$$

With only a few exceptions, the transition metals form compounds with carbon monoxide (CO), called **metal carbonyls**. In the simple metal carbonyls listed in Table 23.6,

- Each CO molecule contributes an electron pair to an empty orbital of the metal atom.
- All electrons are paired (most metal carbonyls are diamagnetic).
- The metal atom acquires the electron configuration of the noble gas Kr.

The structures of the simple carbonyls in Figure 23-14 are those that we would predict from VSEPR theory (based on a number of electron pairs around the central atom equal to the number of CO molecules).

Metal carbonyls are produced in several ways. Nickel combines with CO(g) at ordinary temperatures and pressures in a reversible reaction.

$$Ni(s) + 4\,CO(g) \rightleftharpoons Ni(CO)_4(l)$$

With iron, it is necessary to use higher temperatures (200 °C) and CO(g) pressures (100 atm).

$$Fe(s) + 5\,CO(g) \rightleftharpoons Fe(CO)_5(g)$$

In other cases, the carbonyl is obtained by reducing a metal compound in the presence of CO(g).

Carbon monoxide poisoning results from a reaction similar to carbonyl formation. CO molecules coordinate with Fe atoms in hemoglobin in the blood, displacing the O_2 molecules normally carried by hemoglobin. The metal carbonyls themselves are also very poisonous.

CONCEPT ASSESSMENT ✓

What is the oxidation state of iron in the compound $Fe(CO)_5$?

23-6 GROUP 11: COPPER, SILVER, AND GOLD

Throughout the ages, Cu, Ag, and Au have been the preferred metals for coins because they are so durable and resistant to corrosion. The data in Table 23.7 help us understand why this is so. The metal ions are easy to reduce to the free metals, which means that the metals are difficult to oxidize.

In Mendeleev's periodic table, the alkali metals (group 1) and the coinage metals (group 11) appear together as group I. The only similarity between the two subgroups, however, is that both have a single *s* electron in the valence

TABLE 23.7	Some Properties of Copper, Silver, and Gold		
	Cu	**Ag**	**Au**
Electron configuration	$[Ar]3d^{10}4s^1$	$[Kr]4d^{10}5s^1$	$[Xe]4f^{14}5d^{10}6s^1$
Metallic radius, pm	128	144	144
First ioniz. energy, kJ mol^{-1}	745	731	890
Electrode potential, V			
$M^+(aq) + e^- \longrightarrow M(s)$	+0.520	+0.800	+1.83
$M^{2+}(aq) + 2 e^- \longrightarrow M(s)$	+0.340	+1.39	—
$M^{3+}(aq) + 3 e^- \longrightarrow M(s)$	—	—	+1.52
Oxidation states[a]	+1, +2	+1, +2	+1, +3

[a]The most common oxidation states are shown in red.

Epp, D. N. "Small Scale One-Pot Reactions of Copper, Iron, and Silver." *J. Chem. Educ.* **1995**: *72*, 545.

shells of their atoms. More significant are the differences between the group 1 and group 11 metals. For example, the first ionization energies for the group 11 metals are much larger than for the group 1 metals, and the standard electrode potentials, $E°$, are positive for the group 11 metals and negative for the group 1 metals.

Like the other transition elements that precede them in the periodic table, the group 11 metals can use d electrons in chemical bonding. Thus they can exist in different oxidation states, exhibit paramagnetism and color in some of their compounds, and form complex ions. They also possess to a high degree some of the distinctive physical properties of metals—malleability, ductility, and excellent electrical and thermal conductivity.

Copper, silver, and gold—the coinage metals—are used in jewelry making and the decorative arts. Gold, for instance, is extraordinarily malleable and can be pounded into thin translucent sheets known as gold leaf. The coinage metals are valued by the electronics industry for their ability to conduct electricity. Silver has the highest electrical conductivity of any pure element, but both copper and gold are more often used as electrical conductors because copper is inexpensive and gold does not readily corrode. The most important use of gold is as the monetary reserve of nations throughout the world.

Blyth, K. M., et al. "Analysis of Gold Ores by Fire Assay." *J. Chem. Educ.* **2004**: *81*, 1780.

Generally, the coinage metals are resistant to air oxidation, although silver will tarnish through reactions with sulfur compounds in air to produce black Ag_2S. In moist air, copper corrodes to produce green basic copper carbonate. This is the green color associated with copper roofing and gutters and bronze statues. (Bronze is an alloy of Cu and Sn.) Fortunately, this corrosion product forms a tough adherent coating that protects the underlying metal. The corrosion reaction is complex but may be summarized as

$$2\,Cu(s) + H_2O(g) + CO_2(g) + O_2(g) \longrightarrow Cu_2(OH)_2CO_3(s) \qquad (23.27)$$
$$\text{basic copper carbonate}$$

▲ **Copper wire and gold leaf**

The group 11 metals do not react with HCl(aq), but both Cu and Ag react with concentrated $H_2SO_4(aq)$ or $HNO_3(aq)$. The metals are oxidized to Cu^{2+} and Ag^+, respectively, and the reduction products are $SO_2(g)$ in $H_2SO_4(aq)$ and either $NO(g)$ or $NO_2(g)$ in $HNO_3(aq)$.

Au does not react with either acid, but it will react with "royal water"—*aqua regia* (1 part HNO_3 and 3 parts HCl). The $HNO_3(aq)$ oxidizes the metal and Cl^- from the HCl(aq) promotes the formation of the stable complex ion $[AuCl_4]^-$.

$$Au(s) + 4\,H^+(aq) + NO_3^-(aq) + 4\,Cl^-(aq) \longrightarrow [AuCl_4]^-(aq) + 2\,H_2O(l) + NO(g) \quad (23.28)$$

Trace amounts of Cu are essential to life, but larger quantities are toxic, especially to bacteria, algae, and fungi. Among the many copper compounds used as pesticides are the basic acetate, carbonate, chloride, hydroxide, and sulfate. Commercially, the most important copper compound is $CuSO_4 \cdot 5\,H_2O$.

In addition to its agricultural applications, $CuSO_4$ is employed in batteries and electroplating, in the preparation of other copper salts, and in a variety of industrial processes.

Silver(I) nitrate is the principal silver compound of commerce and is also an important laboratory reagent for the precipitation of anions, most of which form insoluble silver salts. These precipitation reactions can be used for the quantitative determination of anions, either gravimetrically (by weighing precipitates) or volumetrically (by titration). Most other Ag compounds are derived from $AgNO_3$. Ag compounds are used in electroplating, in the manufacture of batteries, in medicinal chemistry, as catalysts, and in cloud seeding (AgI). Their most important use by far (mostly as silver halides) is in photography (see Section 24-10), although this is dimishing now due to the advent of digital cameras.

Gold compounds are used in electroplating, photography, medicinal chemistry (as anti-inflammatory agents for severe rheumatoid arthritis, for example), and the manufacture of special glasses and ceramics (such as ruby glass).

▲ Gold plating on a space antenna.

CONCEPT ASSESSMENT ✓

What is the electron configuration of gold(III) ion?

Jensen, W. B. "The Place of Zinc, Cadmium, and Mercury in the Periodic Table." *J. Chem. Educ.* **2003:** *80*, 952.

23-7 GROUP 12: ZINC, CADMIUM, AND MERCURY

The properties of the group 12 elements are consistent with elements having full subshells, $(n-1)d^{10}ns^2$; some of those properties are summarized in Table 23.8. The low melting and boiling points of the group 12 metals can probably be attributed to the fact that, with only the ns^2 electrons participating, metallic bonding is weak. Mercury is the only metal that exists as a liquid at room temperature and below (although liquid gallium can easily be supercooled to room temperature). Mercury differs from Zn and Cd in a number of ways in addition to physical appearance.

- Mercury has little tendency to combine with oxygen. Its oxide, HgO, is thermally unstable.
- Very few mercury compounds are water soluble, and most are not hydrated.
- Many mercury compounds are covalent. Except for HgF_2, mercury halides are only slightly ionized in aqueous solution.
- Mercury(I) forms a common diatomic ion with a metal–metal covalent bond, Hg_2^{2+}.
- Mercury will not displace $H_2(g)$ from $H^+(aq)$.

TABLE 23.8 Some Properties of the Group 12 Metals

	Zn	Cd	Hg
Density, g cm^{-3}	7.14	8.64	13.59 (liquid)
Melting point, °C	419.6	320.9	−38.87
Boiling point, °C	907	765	357
Electron configuration	[Ar]$3d^{10}4s^2$	[Kr]$4d^{10}5s^2$	[Xe]$4f^{14}5d^{10}6s^2$
Atomic radius, pm	133	149	160
Ionization energy, kJ mol^{-1}			
First	906	867	1006
Second	1733	1631	1809
Principal oxidation state(s)	+2	+2	+1, +2
Electrode potential $E°$, V			
[$M^{2+}(aq) + 2\,e^- \longrightarrow M$]	−0.763	−0.403	+0.854
[$M_2^{2+}(aq) + 2\,e^- \longrightarrow 2\,M$]	—	—	+0.796

Some of these differences exhibited by mercury can probably be attributed to the *relativistic effect* discussed in Chapter 9 (page 365). Because the speed of the 6s electrons reaches a significant fraction of the speed of light, as they approach the high positive charge of the mercury nucleus, their masses increase (as predicted by Einstein's theory of relativity) and the 6s orbital shrinks in size. The closer approach of the 6s electrons to the nucleus subjects them to a greater attractive force than that experienced by the ns^2 electrons in Zn and Cd. As a result, for example, the first ionization energy of Hg is greater than that of Zn or Cd.

USES OF THE GROUP 12 METALS AND THEIR COMPOUNDS

About one-third of the zinc produced is used in coating iron to give it corrosion protection (Section 20-6). The product is called *galvanized iron*. Large quantities of Zn are consumed in the manufacture of alloys. For example, about 20% of the production of Zn is used in *brass*, a copper alloy having 20–45% Zn and small quantities of Sn, Pb, and Fe. Brass is a good electrical conductor and is corrosion resistant. Zinc is also employed in the manufacture of dry-cell batteries, in printing (lithography), in the construction industry (roofing materials), and as sacrificial anodes in corrosion protection (Section 20-6).

Although poisonous, cadmium is substituted for zinc as a shiny and protective plating on iron in special applications. It is used in bearing alloys, in low-melting solders, in aluminum solders, and as an additive to impart strength to copper. Another application, based on its neutron-absorbing capacity, is in control rods and shielding for nuclear reactors.

The principal uses of mercury take advantage of its metallic and liquid properties and its high density. It is used in thermometers, barometers, gas-pressure regulators, and electrical relays and switches, and as electrodes, as in the chlor–alkali process (Section 20-8). Mercury vapor is used in fluorescent tubes and street lamps. Mercury alloys, called **amalgams**, can be made with most metals, and some of these amalgams are of commercial importance. A silver dental filling is an amalgam of mercury with an alloy containing about 70% Ag, 26% Sn, 3% Cu, and 1% Zn.

Table 23.9 lists a few important compounds of the group 12 metals and some of their uses. Some of the most interesting compounds are the semiconductors ZnO, CdS, and HgS, which are also the artist's pigments zinc white, cadmium yellow, and vermilion (red), respectively. Like all semiconductor materials, these compounds have an electronic structure consisting of a valence band and a conduction band (see Section 11-7). When light interacts with these compounds, electrons from the valence band may absorb photons and be excited into the conduction band. The energy of the light absorbed must equal or exceed the energy difference between the bands, called the *band gap*. The characteristic colors of these materials depend on the widths of the band gaps, as described on page 909.

▲ A brass seagoing chronometer made by John Harrison in the eighteenth century.

Brass chronometers are featured in the interesting book, *Greenwich Time and the Longitude*, by Derek House. See also the website: http://www.rog.nmm.ac.uk/museum/harrison/ (non-commercial)

◀ Iron is one of the few metals that does not form an amalgam. Mercury is generally stored and shipped in iron containers.

TABLE 23.9	Some Important Compounds of the Group 12 Metals
Compound	Uses
ZnO	Reinforcing agent in rubber; pigment; cosmetics; dietary supplement; photoconductors in copying machines
ZnS	Phosphors in X-ray and television screens; pigment; luminous paints
$ZnSO_4$	Rayon manufacture; animal feeds; wood preservative
CdO	Electroplating; batteries; catalyst
CdS	Solar cells; photoconductor in xerography; phosphors; pigment
$CdSO_4$	Electroplating; standard voltaic cells (Weston cell)
HgO	Polishing compounds; dry cells; antifouling paints; fungicide; pigment
$HgCl_2$	Manufacture of Hg compounds; disinfectant; fungicide; insecticide; wood preservative
Hg_2Cl_2	Electrodes; pharmaceuticals; fungicide

Wu, R. S. S. "Change of Forms of Cadmium in the Aquatic Environment." *J. Chem. Educ.* 1995: 72, 264.

Rice, J. K., et al. "Rapid Determination of Mercury in Seafood in an Introductory Environmental Science Class." *J. Chem. Educ.* 2005: 82, 265.

Information about the effects of environmental mercury can be found at http://www.epa.gov/mercury/.

The area with outbreak of patients

▲ The area of contamination in Japan where mercury poisoning was observed.

MERCURY AND CADMIUM POISONING

Accumulations of mercury in the body affect the nervous system and cause brain damage. One form of chronic mercury poisoning, "hatter's disease," afflicted the Mad Hatter in *Alice's Adventures in Wonderland*. The disease was fairly common in the nineteenth century. Mercury compounds were used to convert fur to felt for making hats. Many hat makers of the time worked in hot, cramped spaces and used these compounds without special precautions. The hatters inadvertently ingested or inhaled the toxic mercury compounds while they worked.

One proposed mechanism of mercury poisoning, based on the fact that Hg has a high affinity for sulfur, involves interference with the functioning of sulfur-containing enzymes. Organic mercury compounds are generally more poisonous than inorganic ones and much more toxic than the element itself. An insidious aspect of mercury poisoning is that certain microorganisms have the ability to convert mercury(II) compounds to methylmercury (CH_3Hg^+) compounds, which then concentrate in the food chains of fish and other aquatic life. An early discovery of the environmental hazard of mercury was in Japan in the 1950s. Dozens of cases of mercury poisoning, including over 40 deaths, occurred among residents of the shores of Minamata Bay. Local seafood with up to 20 ppm of mercury was a major component of the victims' diet. The source of contamination was traced to a chemical plant discharging mercury waste into the bay.

In the free state, mercury is most poisonous as a vapor. Levels of mercury that exceed 0.05 mg Hg/m^3 air are considered unsafe. Although we think of mercury as having a low vapor pressure, the concentration of Hg in its saturated vapor far exceeds this limit, and mercury vapor levels sometimes exceed safe limits where mercury is used—as in chlor–alkali plants, thermometer factories, and smelters.

Although zinc is an essential element in trace amounts, cadmium, which so closely resembles zinc, is a poison. One effect of cadmium poisoning is an extremely painful skeletal disorder known as "itai-itai kyo" (Japanese for "ouch-ouch" disease). This disorder was discovered in an area of Japan where effluents from a zinc mine became mixed with irrigation water used in rice fields, and cadmium poisoning was discovered in people who ate the rice. Cadmium poisoning can also cause liver damage, kidney failure, and pulmonary disease. The mechanism of cadmium poisoning may involve substitution in certain enzymes of Cd (a poison) for Zn (an essential element). Concern over cadmium poisoning has increased with an awareness that some cadmium is almost always found in zinc and zinc compounds, materials that have many commercial applications.

CONCEPT ASSESSMENT ✔

Suggest the geometry of the cadmium anion $[CdCl_5]^{3-}$.

23-8 LANTHANIDES

The elements from cerium ($Z = 58$) through lutetium ($Z = 71$) are inner transition elements; their electron configurations feature the filling of $4f$ orbitals. These elements, together with lanthanum ($Z = 57$), which closely resembles them, are variously called the *lanthanide*, *lanthanoid*, or *rare earth elements*. The rare earth elements are "rare" only relative to the alkaline earth metals (group 2). Otherwise, they are not particularly rare. Ce, Nd, and La, for example, are more abundant than lead, and Tm is about as abundant as iodine. The lanthanides occur primarily as oxides, and mineral deposits containing them are found in various locations. Large deposits near the California-Nevada border are being developed to provide oxides of the lanthanides for use as phosphors in color monitors and television sets. Cobalt–samarium (Co_5Sm) magnets are used in high-efficiency motors.

▲ The individual elements of a CRT computer screen are phosphors that contain the lanthanide elements. The phosphors glow red, blue, or green depending on their composition. (™ Netscape ®)

Because the differences in electron configuration among the lanthanides are mainly in $4f$ orbitals, and because $4f$ electrons play a minor role in chemical bonding, strong similarities are found among these elements. For example, $E°$ values for the reduction process $M^{3+}(aq) + 3\,e^- \longrightarrow M(s)$ do not show much variation. All fall between -2.38 V (La) and -1.99 V (Eu). The differences in properties that do exist among the lanthanides arise mostly from the lanthanide contraction discussed in Section 23-1. This contraction is best illustrated in the radii of the ions M^{3+}. These radii decrease regularly by about 1–2 pm for each unit increase in atomic number, from a radius of 106 pm for La^{3+} to 85 pm for Lu^{3+}.

The lanthanides, which we can represent by the general symbol Ln, are reactive metals that liberate $H_2(g)$ from hot water and from dilute acids by undergoing oxidation to $Ln^{3+}(aq)$. The lanthanides combine with $O_2(g)$, sulfur, the halogens, $N_2(g)$, $H_2(g)$, and carbon in much the same way as expected for metals about as active as the alkaline earths. The pure metals can be prepared by electrolytic reduction of Ln^{3+} in a molten salt.

The most common oxidation state for the lanthanides is $+3$. About half the lanthanides can also be obtained in the oxidation state $+2$; the other half, $+4$. The special stability associated with an electron configuration involving half-filled f orbitals (f^7) may account for some of the observed oxidation states, but the reason for the predominance of the $+3$ oxidation state is less clear. Most of the lanthanide ions are paramagnetic and colored in aqueous solution.

The lanthanide elements are extremely difficult to extract from their natural sources and to separate from one another. All the methods for doing so are based on this principle: Species that are strongly dissimilar can often be completely separated in a one-step process, such as separating $Ag^+(aq)$ and $Cu^{2+}(aq)$ by adding $Cl^-(aq)$; AgCl is insoluble. At best, species that are very similar can only be fractionated in a one-step process. That is, the ratio of the concentration of one species to that of another is altered slightly. To achieve a complete separation means repeating the same basic step hundreds or even thousands of times. To achieve the separation of the lanthanides, the methods of fractional crystallization, fractional precipitation, solvent extraction, and ion exchange were brought to their highest level of performance.

Moeller, Therald. "Periodicity and the Lanthanides and Actinides." *J. Chem. Educ.* **1970**: *47*, 417.

Lanthanides website: http://www.molycorp.com/lanthanides.html (commercial)

23-9   HIGH-TEMPERATURE SUPERCONDUCTORS

Magnetically levitated trains, magnetic resonance imaging (MRI) for medical diagnoses, and particle accelerators used in high-energy physics all require high magnetic fields generated by superconducting electromagnets. Superconductors offer no resistance to an electric current, so electricity is conducted with no loss of energy (Fig. 23-15).

◀ **FIGURE 23-15**
The small magnet induces an electric current in the superconductor below it. Associated with this current is another magnetic field that opposes the field of the small magnet, causing it to be repelled. The magnet remains suspended above the superconductor as long as the superconducting current is present, and the current persists as long as the temperature of the superconductor is maintained at the boiling point of liquid nitrogen (77 K).

▲ In vivo fluorescence imaging using quantum dots injected into the tail vein of nude mice and then imaged using a small animal scanner. The white outline in the figure is the mouse.

Nanotechnology is a field of science based on the behavior of matter on the nano (10^{-9} m) scale. In the macroscopic world physical and chemical properties do not depend on sample size, but if the sample is subdivided into microscopic, nanometer sized units the physical and chemical properties do change. That is what makes nanoscale studies so interesting. Consider silver; its color, melting point, malleability, and chemical properties on the nanoscale are all different from what we observe at the macroscopic level.

Figure 23-16 illustrates through the different colors in each of the vials how the shape and size of a microscopic material affect the emission of light. The change in properties with particle size is due to the differing interactions among the atoms. On the macroscopic level, the interatomic and intermolecular interactions between the atoms or molecules are averaged over the entire sample, while at the nanoscale level the interactions are not averaged. One type of new material produced by nanotechnology is known as quantum dots.

▲ **FIGURE 23-16**
Nanocrystals in suspension
Each vial contains either silver or gold, and the color difference is influenced by particle sizes and shapes as seen in the structures above and below the vials.

QUANTUM DOTS

A quantum dot is a cluster of atoms with a diameter of the order of tens of nanometers as illustrated in the following figure.

These small clusters have unusual shapes and sizes that lead to different physical and chemical characteristics such as the absorbance and emission of light. Semiconduc-

If cooled to near absolute zero, all metals become superconducting. Several metals and alloys superconduct even at marginally higher temperatures of 10–15 K. To maintain a superconductor at these extremely low temperatures requires liquid helium (bp, 4 K) as a coolant.

In the mid-1980s, materials made of lanthanum, strontium, copper, and oxygen were found to become superconducting at 30 K. This was a much higher temperature for superconductivity than had been previously achieved. More surprising, the new materials were not metals but *ceramics*! In short order, other types of ceramic superconductors were discovered.

One of these new types was particularly easy to make. When a stoichiometric mixture of yttrium oxide (Y_2O_3), barium carbonate ($BaCO_3$), and copper(II) oxide (CuO) is heated in a stream of $O_2(g)$, a ceramic is produced with the approximate formula $YBa_2Cu_3O_x$ (where x is slightly less than 7). This so-called YBCO ceramic becomes superconducting at the remarkably high temperature of 92 K. Although a temperature of 92 K is still quite low, it is far above the boiling point of helium. In fact, it is above the boiling point of nitrogen (77 K). Thus, inexpensive liquid nitrogen can be used as the coolant.

Many variations of the basic YBCO formula are possible. Almost any lanthanide element can be substituted for yttrium, and combinations of group 2 elements can be substituted for barium. All these variations yield materials that are superconducting at relatively high temperatures, but of the group, the yttrium compound is superconducting at the highest temperature.

The May 2005 issue of *J. Chem. Educ.* contains several articles about advances in nanotechnology.

A procedure for making high-temperature ceramic superconductors is at http://www.futurescience.com/scpart1.html.

the ultraviolet and visible region of the electromagnetic spectrum. One way to determine the size of a quantum dot is to measure the absorbance wavelength and calculate the dot's diameter using an equation derived using a "particle-in-a-sphere model," similar to the particle-in-a-box model discussed in Chapter 8.

Quantum dots have many possible uses, such as

- Fixed cell imaging of cells, tissue sections using fluorescence and TEM* detection
- Ex vivo cell imaging of membrane surface receptors and intracellular organelles and molecules using fluorescence detection
- In vivo animal targeting of cell, tissues, organs, and tumors using fluorescence, PET[†] and MRI[‡] detection

Other areas of application include neuroelectronic interfaces, new drug-delivery systems, biosensors, optoelectronics, communications, DNA computing, and even consumer products such as suntan lotion, to name just a few.

* transmission electron microscopy

[†] positron emission tomography

[‡] magnetic resonance imaging.

tor quantum dots are composed of a transition metal and a nonmetal. For example, a group 12 metal such as cadmium or zinc and a group 16 nonmetal such as sulfur, selenium, or tellurium can combine to form II–VI quantum dots. (The II and VI refer to those groups in Mendeleev's periodic table on page 341.) This type of metal–nonmetal combination is typically found in semiconductor materials. One of the characteristics of semiconductors we learned about in Chapter 11 is the existence of a band gap between the valence and conduction bands. The band gap of II–VI quantum dots can be tuned, by their size and shape, to range from 2.5 to 4.5 eV, which means they will absorb in

The record high temperature for superconductivity set by the YBCO ceramics was soon eclipsed by another group of ceramics containing bismuth and copper, such as $Bi_2Sr_2CaCu_2O_8$. One of these is superconducting at 110 K, but this record was also short-lived. A ceramic containing thallium and copper, with the approximate formula $TlBa_2Ca_3Cu_4O_y$ (where y is slightly larger than 10), was found to become superconducting at 125 K. Now, the search continues for materials that might become superconducting at room temperature (about 293 K).

Structurally, ceramic superconductors have a feature in common. Copper and oxygen atoms are bonded together in planar sheets. In YBCO superconductors, the Cu–O planes are widely separated. In bismuth superconductors, the Cu–O planes occur in "sandwiches" consisting of two closely spaced sheets separated by a layer of group 2 ions. These sandwiches are separated from one another by several layers of bismuth oxide. In the thallium superconductors, the Cu–O planes are stacked in groups of three—triple-decker sandwiches.

The current theory of superconductivity, developed in the 1950s, explains the superconducting behavior of metals at very low temperatures but not the higher-temperature superconductivity of ceramics. It seems that the electrons in all known superconductors move through the material in pairs—a sort of buddy system that allows the electrons to move without resistance. The mechanism by which electron pairs form in high-temperature superconductors, however, is clearly different from that in low-temperature superconductors.

Lack of a suitable theory complicates the search for higher-temperature superconductors. When the mechanism for high-temperature superconductors is better understood, new breakthroughs might be easier to accomplish. Perhaps a room-temperature superconducting material will be possible.

Despite this less-than-complete understanding of high-temperature superconductors, engineers are already building devices that use the new materials. Wires have been made that are superconducting at liquid nitrogen temperatures, and new devices for precise magnetic field measurements using ceramic superconductors are now being produced. Ultimately, ceramic superconductors may find application in low-cost, energy-efficient electric power transmission.

Summary

23-1 General Properties—More than half the elements are the metals known as transition elements. Most are more reactive than hydrogen. Transition metals tend to exist in several different oxidation states in their compounds (see Table 23.1), and they readily form complex ions (discussed in Chapter 24). Many transition metals and their compounds are paramagnetic, and certain of the metals (Fe, Co, and Ni) and their alloys exhibit **ferromagnetism**. Within a group of *d*-block elements, the members of the second and third transition series resemble one another more than they do the group member in the first transition series. This is a consequence of the phenomenon known as the **lanthanide contraction** occurring in the sixth period.

23-2 Principles of Extractive Metallurgy—The extraction of metals from their ores is called **extractive metallurgy**. **Pyrometallurgy** relies on roasting an ore with subsequent reduction of the oxide to the metal. In **hydrometallurgy** metal ions are leached from ores using aqueous solutions of acid or bases. Various methods can be used to refine impure metals. One technique for producing an ultrapure metal is **zone refining**, which involves the continuous melting and refreezing of the metal to concentrate the impurities in one region of the sample, which is then discarded (Fig. 23-5). The thermodynamics of metallurgy can be viewed as the appropriate coupling of reactions into a spontaneous process (Fig. 23-7).

23-3 Metallurgy of Iron and Steel—The conversion of iron(III) oxide into iron by reduction with carbon monoxide in a blast furnace (Fig. 23-8) leads to the formation of **pig iron**. Pig iron is converted to **steel** through the **basic oxygen process** (Fig. 23-9).

23-4 First-Row Transition Elements: Scandium to Manganese—Oxidation–reduction reactions are commonly encountered with transition metal compounds of Sc, Ti, V, Cr, and Mn. Two common types of oxidizing agents are the dichromates and permanganates. In aqueous solution, dichromate ion is in equilibrium with chromate ion, which is a good precipitating agent for a number of metal ions. Most oxides and hydroxides of the transition metals are basic if the metal is in one of its lower oxidation states. In higher oxidation states, some transition metal oxides and hydroxy compounds are amphoteric, and in the highest oxidation states, a few are acidic (as is CrO_3, for example).

23-5 The Iron Triad: Iron, Cobalt, and Nickel—The iron triad elements (Fe, Co, and Ni) exhibit a variability in oxidation state with +2 the most common. Like other transition elements these metals form compounds with carbon monoxide called **metal carbonyls**.

23-6 Group 11: Copper, Silver, and Gold—The metals Cu, Ag, and Au are resistant to corrosion and are widely used in coins and jewelry. These so-called coinage metals are excellent conductors of heat and electricity and are highly malleable. They also find many uses in the electronics industry.

23-7 Group 12: Zinc, Cadmium, and Mercury—These group 12 elements have chemical properties consistent with a filled *d* subshell. Zn is used in an alloy with copper to produce brass, which is a good electrical conductor and is resistant to corrosion. Most metals form alloys with mercury called **amalgams**.

23-8 Lanthanides—This first series of *f*-block elements have long been known as the rare earth elements, not because of their scarcity but because they are difficult to separate from one another. Their chemical behavior is strongly influenced by the lanthanide contraction, which produces similarities in their atomic and ionic sizes.

23-9 High-Temperature Superconductors—High-temperature superconducting materials have been made using some of the transition elements. In particular, a ceramic material that is superconducting at 92 K is made from yttrium, barium, copper, and oxygen. These ceramic materials have the potential for many applications, for example, more efficient electric power transmission.

Integrative Example

Although a number of slightly soluble copper(I) compounds (such as CuCN) can exist in contact with water, it is not possible to prepare a solution with a high concentration of Cu^+ ion.

Show that $Cu^+(aq)$ disproportionates to $Cu^{2+}(aq)$ and $Cu(s)$, and explain why a high $[Cu^+]$ cannot be maintained in aqueous solution.

Strategy

Write a plausible equation describing the disproportionation reaction. Then determine E°_{cell} for the reaction, followed by the equilibrium constant K, and see what conclusions can be drawn from the numerical value of K.

Solution

The half-equations and overall equation for the disproportionation are

Reduction: $Cu^+(aq) + e^- \longrightarrow Cu(s)$

Oxidation: $Cu^+(aq) \longrightarrow Cu^{2+}(aq) + e^-$

Overall: $2\,Cu^+(aq) \longrightarrow Cu^{2+}(aq) + Cu(s)$

Find E° values for the couples $Cu^+/Cu(s)$ and Cu^{2+}/Cu^+ in Appendix D and combine them to obtain E°_{cell}.

$E^\circ_{cell} = E^\circ(\text{reduction}) - E^\circ(\text{oxidation})$

$= E^\circ_{Cu^+/Cu(s)} - E^\circ_{Cu^{2+}/Cu^+} = 0.520\ V - 0.159\ V = 0.361\ V$

Use equation (20.17) to obtain the value of K. In the equation $n = 1$,

$E^\circ_{cell} = \dfrac{0.025693\ V}{n} \ln K$

$\ln K = \dfrac{n \times E^\circ_{cell}}{0.025693\ V} = \dfrac{1 \times 0.361\ V}{0.025693\ V} = 14.1$

$K = e^{14.1} = 1.3 \times 10^6$

Thus, for the disproportionation reaction,

$K = \dfrac{[Cu^{2+}]}{[Cu^+]^2} = 1.3 \times 10^6$

and

$[Cu^{2+}] = 1.3 \times 10^6 \times [Cu^+]^2$

To maintain $[Cu^+] = 1\ M$ in solution, $[Cu^{2+}]$ would have to be more than $1 \times 10^6\ M$—a clear impossibility.

Assessment

As a practical matter, we could not maintain $[Cu^+]$ at much more than $0.002\ M$, for even this would require that $[Cu^{2+}] \approx 5\ M$.

Exercises

Properties of the Transition Elements

1. By means of orbital diagrams, write electron configurations for the following transition element atom and ions: **(a)** Ti; **(b)** V^{3+}; **(c)** Cr^{2+}; **(d)** Mn^{4+}; **(e)** Mn^{2+}; **(f)** Fe^{3+}.

2. Arrange the following species according to the number of unpaired electrons they contain, starting with the one that has the greatest number: Fe, Sc^{3+}, Ti^{2+}, Mn^{4+}, Cr, Cu^{2+}.

3. Describe how the transition elements compare with main-group metals (such as group 2) with respect to oxidation states, formation of complexes, colors of compounds, and magnetic properties.

4. With only minor irregularities, the melting points of the first series of transition metals rise from that of Sc to that of Cr and then fall to that of Zn. Give a plausible explanation for this phenomenon based on atomic structure.

5. Why do the atomic radii vary so much more for two main-group elements that differ by one unit in atomic number than they do for two transition elements that differ by one unit?

6. The metallic radii of Ni, Pd, and Pt are 125, 138, and 139 pm, respectively. Why is the difference in radius between Pt and Pd so much less than between Pd and Ni?

7. Which of the first transition series elements exhibits the greatest number of different oxidation states in its compounds? Explain.

8. Why is the number of common oxidation states for the elements at the beginning and those at the end of the first transition series less than for elements in the middle of the series?

9. As a group, the lanthanides are more reactive metals than are those in the first transition series. How do you account for this difference?

10. The maximum difference in standard reduction potential, $E^\circ_{M^{2+}/M(s)}$, among members of the first transition series is about 2.4 V. For the lanthanides, the maximum difference in $E^\circ_{M^{3+}/M(s)}$ is only about 0.4 V. How do you account for this fact?

Reactions of Transition Metals and Their Compounds

11. Complete and balance the following equations. If no reaction occurs, so state.

    (a) $TiCl_4(g) + Na(l) \xrightarrow{\Delta}$

    (b) $Cr_2O_3(s) + Al(s) \xrightarrow{\Delta}$

    (c) $Ag(s) + HCl(aq) \longrightarrow$

    (d) $K_2Cr_2O_7(aq) + KOH(aq) \longrightarrow$

    (e) $MnO_2(s) + C(s) \xrightarrow{\Delta}$

12. By means of a chemical equation, give an example to represent the reaction of (a) a transition metal with a nonoxidizing acid; (b) a transition metal oxide with NaOH(aq); (c) an inner transition metal with HCl(aq).

13. Write balanced chemical equations for the following reactions described in the chapter.
    (a) the reaction of $Sc(OH)_3(s)$ with HCl(aq)
    (b) oxidation of $Fe^{2+}(aq)$ by $MnO_4^-(aq)$ in basic solution to give $Fe^{3+}(aq)$ and $MnO_2(s)$
    (c) the reaction of $TiO_2(s)$ with molten KOH to form K_2TiO_3

(d) oxidation of Cu(s) to $Cu^{2+}(aq)$ with H_2SO_4 (concd aq) to form $SO_2(g)$

14. Write balanced equations for the following reactions described in the chapter.
    (a) Sc(l) is produced by the electrolysis of Sc_2O_3 dissolved in $Na_3ScF_6(l)$.
    (b) Cr(s) reacts with HCl(aq) to produce a blue solution containing $Cr^{2+}(aq)$.
    (c) $Cr^{2+}(aq)$ is readily oxidized by $O_2(g)$ to $Cr^{3+}(aq)$.
    (d) Ag(s) reacts with concentrated $HNO_3(aq)$, and $NO_2(g)$ is evolved.

15. Suggest a series of reactions, using common chemicals, by which each of the following syntheses can be performed.
    (a) $Fe(OH)_3(s)$ from FeS(s)
    (b) $BaCrO_4(s)$ from $BaCO_3(s)$ and $K_2Cr_2O_7(aq)$

16. Suggest a series of reactions, using common chemicals, by which each of the following syntheses can be performed.
    (a) $Cu(OH)_2(s)$ from CuO(s)
    (b) $CrCl_3(aq)$ from $(NH_4)_2Cr_2O_7(s)$

Extractive Metallurgy

17. One of the simplest metals to extract from its ores is mercury. Mercury vapor is produced by roasting cinnabar ore (HgS) in air. Alternatives to this simple roasting, designed to reduce or eliminate SO_2 emissions, is to roast the ore in the presence of a second substance. For example, when cinnabar is roasted with quicklime, the products are mercury vapor and calcium sulfide and calcium sulfate. Write equations for the two reactions described here.

18. According to Figure 23-7, $\Delta G°$ decreases with temperature for the reaction $2 C(s) + O_2(g) \longrightarrow 2 CO(g)$. How would you expect $\Delta G°$ to vary with temperature for the following reactions?
    (a) $C(s) + O_2(g) \longrightarrow CO_2(g)$
    (b) $2 CO(g) + O_2(g) \longrightarrow 2 CO_2(g)$

19. Calcium will reduce MgO(s) to Mg(s) at all temperatures from 0 to 2000 °C. Use this fact, together with the melting point (839 °C) and boiling point (1484 °C) of calcium, to sketch a plausible graph of $\Delta G°$ as a function of temperature for the reaction $2 Ca(s) + O_2(g) \longrightarrow 2 CaO(s)$.

20. One method of obtaining chromium metal from chromite ore is as follows. After reaction (23.16), sodium chromate is reduced to chromium(III) oxide by carbon. Then the chromium(III) oxide is reduced to chromium metal by silicon. Write plausible equations to describe these two reactions.

Oxidation–Reduction

21. Write plausible half-equations to represent each of the following in acidic solution.
    (a) $VO^{2+}(aq)$ as an oxidizing agent
    (b) $Cr^{2+}(aq)$ as a reducing agent

22. Write plausible half-equations to represent each of the following in basic solution.
    (a) oxidation of $Fe(OH)_3(s)$ to FeO_4^{2-}
    (b) reduction of $[Ag(CN)_2]^-$ to silver metal

23. Use electrode potential data from this chapter or Appendix D to predict whether each of the following reactions will occur to any significant extent under standard-state conditions.
    (a) $2 VO_2^+ + 6 Br^- + 8 H^+ \longrightarrow$
    $$2 V^{2+} + 3 Br_2(l) + 4 H_2O$$
    (b) $VO_2^+ + Fe^{2+} + 2 H^+ \longrightarrow VO^{2+} + Fe^{3+} + H_2O$
    (c) $MnO_2(s) + H_2O_2 + 2 H^+ \longrightarrow$
    $$Mn^{2+} + 2 H_2O + O_2(g)$$

24. You are given these three reducing agents: Zn(s), $Sn^{2+}(aq)$, and $I^-(aq)$. Use data from Appendix D to determine which of them can, under standard-state conditions in acidic solution, reduce
    (a) $Cr_2O_7^{2-}(aq)$ to $Cr^{3+}(aq)$
    (b) $Cr^{3+}(aq)$ to $Cr^{2+}(aq)$
    (c) $SO_4^{2-}(aq)$ to $SO_2(g)$

25. Refer to Example 23-2. Select a reducing agent (from Table 20.1 or Appendix D) that will reduce VO^{2+} to V^{3+} and no further in acidic solution.

26. The electrode potential diagram for manganese in acidic solutions in Figure 23-13 does not include a value of $E°$ for the reduction of MnO_4^- to Mn^{2+}. Use other data in the figure to establish this $E°$, and compare your result with the value found in Table 20.1.

27. Use data from the text to construct a standard electrode potential diagram relating the following chromium species in acidic solution.

28. Use data from the text to construct a standard electrode potential diagram relating the following vanadium species in acidic solution.

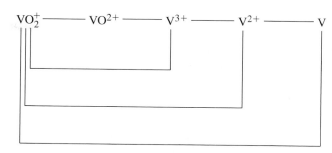

Chromium and Chromium Compounds

29. When a soluble lead compound is added to a solution containing primarily *orange* dichromate ion, *yellow* lead chromate precipitates. Describe the equilibria involved.

30. When *yellow* $BaCrO_4$ is dissolved in HCl(aq), a *green* solution is obtained. Write a chemical equation to account for the color change.

31. When Zn(s) is added to $K_2Cr_2O_7$ dissolved in HCl(aq), the color of the solution changes from orange to green, then to blue, and, over a period of time, back to green. Write equations for this series of reactions.

32. If CO_2(g) under pressure is passed into Na_2CrO_4(aq), $Na_2Cr_2O_7$(aq) is formed. What is the function of the CO_2(g)? Write a plausible equation for the net reaction.

33. Use equation (23.19) to determine $[Cr_2O_7^{2-}]$ in a solution that has $[CrO_4^{2-}] = 0.20$ M and a pH of **(a)** 6.62 and **(b)** 8.85.

34. If a solution is prepared by dissolving 1.505 g Na_2CrO_4 in 345 mL of a buffer solution with pH = 7.55, what will be $[CrO_4^{2-}]$ and $[Cr_2O_7^{2-}]$?

35. How many grams of chromium would be deposited on an object in a chrome-plating bath (see page 980) after 1.00 h at a current of 3.4 A?

36. How long would an electric current of 3.5 A have to pass through a chrome-plating bath (see page 980) to produce a chromium deposit 0.0010 mm thick on an object with a surface area of 0.375 m^2? (The density of Cr is 7.14 g cm^{-3}.)

37. Why is it reasonable to expect the chemistry of dichromate ion to involve mainly oxidation–reduction reactions and that of chromate ion to involve mainly precipitation reactions?

38. What products are obtained when Mg^{2+}(aq) and Cr^{3+}(aq) are each treated with a limited amount of NaOH(aq)? With an excess of NaOH(aq)? Why are the results different in these two cases?

The Iron Triad

39. Will reaction (23.25) still be spontaneous in the forward direction in a solution containing equal concentrations of Fe^{2+} and Fe^{3+}, a pH of 3.25, and under an O_2(g) partial pressure of 0.20 atm?

40. Based on the description of the nickel–cadmium cell on page 985, and with appropriate data from Appendix D, estimate $E°$ for the reduction of NiO(OH) to $Ni(OH)_2$.

41. Write a net ionic equation to represent the precipitation of Prussian blue, described on page 985.

42. The reaction to form Turnbull's blue (page 985) appears to occur in two stages. First, Fe^{2+}(aq) is oxidized to Fe^{3+}(aq) and ferricyanide ion is reduced to ferrocyanide ion. Then, the Fe^{3+}(aq) and ferrocyanide ion combine. Write equations for these reactions.

Group 11 Metals

43. Write plausible equations for the following reactions occurring in the hydrometallurgy of the coinage metals.
   (a) Copper is precipitated from a solution of copper(II) sulfate by treatment with H_2(g).
   (b) Gold is precipitated from a solution of Au^+ by adding iron(II) sulfate.
   (c) Copper(II) chloride solution is reduced to copper(I) chloride when treated with SO_2(g) in acidic solution.

44. In the metallurgical extraction of silver and gold, an alloy of the two metals is often obtained. The alloy can be separated into Ag and Au either with concentrated HNO_3 or boiling concentrated H_2SO_4, in a process called *parting*. Write chemical equations to show how these separations work.

45. Use the result of the Integrative Example to determine whether a solution can be prepared with $[Cu^+]$ equal to **(a)** 0.20 M; **(b)** 1.0×10^{-10} M.

46. Show that the corrosion reaction in which Cu is converted to its basic carbonate (reaction 23.27) can be thought of in terms of a combination of oxidation–reduction, acid–base, and precipitation reactions.

Group 12 Metals

47. Use data from Table 23.8 to determine $E°$ for the reduction of Hg^{2+} to Hg_2^{2+} in aqueous solution.
48. At 400 °C, $\Delta G° = -25$ kJ for the reaction $2\,Hg(l) + O_2(g) \longrightarrow 2\,HgO(s)$. If a sample of $HgO(s)$ is heated to 400 °C, what will be the equilibrium partial pressure of $O_2(g)$?
49. Use Figure 23-7 to estimate for the reaction $ZnO(s) + C(s) \rightleftharpoons Zn(l) + CO(g)$, at about 800 °C, **(a)** a value of K_p and **(b)** the equilibrium pressure of $CO(g)$.
50. The vapor pressure of $Hg(l)$ as a function of temperature is $\log P(mmHg) = (-0.05223a/T) + b$, where $a = 61,960$ and $b = 8.118$; T is the Kelvin temperature. Show that at 25 °C, the concentration of $Hg(g)$ in equilibrium with $Hg(l)$ greatly exceeds the maximum permissible level of 0.05 mg Hg/m^3 air.
51. In ZnO, the band gap between the valence and conduction bands is 290 kJ mol^{-1}, and in CdS it is 250 kJ mol^{-1}. Show that CdS absorbs some visible light but ZnO does not. Explain the observed colors: ZnO is white and CdS is yellow.
52. CdS is yellow, HgS is red, and CdSe is black. Which of these materials has the largest band gap? the smallest? How does the band gap relate to the observed color?

Integrative and Advanced Exercises

53. Although Au reacts with and dissolves in aqua regia (3 parts HCl + 1 part HNO_3), Ag does not dissolve. What is (are) the likely reason(s) for this difference?
54. The text mentions that scandium metal is obtained from its molten chloride by electrolysis, and that titanium is obtained from its chloride by reduction with magnesium. Why are these metals not obtained by the reduction of their oxides with carbon (coke), as are metals such as zinc and iron?
55. The text notes that in small quantities, zinc is an essential element (though it is toxic in higher concentrations). Tin is considered to be a toxic metal. Can you think of reasons why, for food storage, tinplate instead of galvanized iron is used in cans?
56. In an atmosphere polluted with industrial smog, Cu corrodes to a basic sulfate, $Cu_2(OH)_2SO_4$. Propose a series of chemical reactions to describe this corrosion.
57. What formulas would you expect for the metal carbonyls of **(a)** molybdenum, **(b)** osmium; **(c)** rhenium? Note that the simple carbonyls shown in Figure 23-14 have one metal atom per molecule. Some metal carbonyls are *binuclear*; that is, they have two metal atoms bonded together in the carbonyl structure. Also, **(d)** explain why iron and nickel carbonyls are liquids at room temperature, whereas that of cobalt is a solid, and **(e)** describe the probable nature of the bonding in the compound $Na[V(CO)_6]$.
58. For the straight-line graphs in Figure 23-7, explain why **(a)** breaks occur at the melting points and boiling points of the metals; **(b)** the slopes of the lines become more positive at these breaks; **(c)** the break at the boiling point is sharper than at the melting point.
59. Attempts to make CuI_2 by the reaction of $Cu^{2+}(aq)$ and $I^-(aq)$ produce $CuI(s)$ and $I_3^-(aq)$ instead. Without performing detailed calculations, show why this reaction should occur.

$$2\,Cu^{2+}(aq) + 5\,I^-(aq) \longrightarrow 2\,CuI(s) + I_3^-(aq)$$

60. Without performing detailed calculations, show that significant disproportionation of AuCl occurs if you attempt to make a saturated aqueous solution. Use data from Table 23.7 and K_{sp} $(AuCl) = 2.0 \times 10^{-13}$.
61. In acidic solution, silver(II) oxide first dissolves to produce $Ag^{2+}(aq)$. This is followed by the oxidation of $H_2O(l)$ to $O_2(g)$ and the reduction of Ag^{2+} to Ag^+.

(a) Write equations for the dissolution and oxidation–reduction reactions.
(b) Show that the oxidation–reduction reaction is indeed spontaneous.

62. Equation (23.18), which represents the chromate–dichromate equilibrium, is actually the sum of two equilibrium expressions. The first is an acid–base reaction, $H^+ + CrO_4^{2-} \rightleftharpoons HCrO_4^-$. The second reaction involves elimination of a water molecule between two $HCrO_4^-$ ions (a dehydration reaction), $2\,HCrO_4^- \rightleftharpoons Cr_2O_7^{2-} + H_2O$. If the ionization constant, K_a, for $HCrO_4^-$ is 3.2×10^{-7}, what is the value of K for the dehydration reaction?
63. Show that under the following conditions, $Ba^{2+}(aq)$ can be separated from $Sr^{2+}(aq)$ and $Ca^{2+}(aq)$ by precipitating $BaCrO_4(s)$ with the other ions remaining in solution:

$$[Ba^{2+}] = [Sr^{2+}] = [Ca^{2+}] = 0.10\ M$$
$$[HC_2H_3O_2] = [C_2H_3O_2^-] = 1.0\ M$$
$$[Cr_2O_7^{2-}] = 0.0010\ M$$
$$K_{sp}(BaCrO_4) = 1.2 \times 10^{-10}$$
$$K_{sp}(SrCrO_4) = 2.2 \cdot 10^{-5}$$

Use data from this and previous chapters, as necessary.

64. A 0.589-g sample of pyrolusite ore (impure MnO_2) is treated with 1.651 g of oxalic acid ($H_2C_2O_4 \cdot 2\,H_2O$) in an acidic medium (reaction 1). Following this, the excess oxalic acid is titrated with 30.06 mL of 0.1000 M $KMnO_4$ (reaction 2). What is the mass percent of MnO_2 in the pyrolusite? The following equations are neither complete nor balanced.

(1) $\quad H_2C_2O_4(aq) + MnO_2(s) \longrightarrow Mn^{2+}(aq) + CO_2(g)$
(2) $\quad H_2C_2O_4(aq) + MnO_4^-(aq) \longrightarrow Mn^{2+}(aq) + CO_2(g)$

65. Both $Cr_2O_7^{2-}(aq)$ and $MnO_4^-(aq)$ can be used to titrate $Fe^{2+}(aq)$ to $Fe^{3+}(aq)$. Suppose you have available as titrants two solutions: 0.1000 M $Cr_2O_7^{2-}(aq)$ and 0.1000 M $MnO_4^-(aq)$.

(a) For which solution would the greater volume of titrant be required for the titration of a particular sample of $Fe^{2+}(aq)$? Explain.
(b) How many mL of 0.1000 M $MnO_4^-(aq)$ would be required for a titration if the same titration requires 24.50 mL of 0.1000 M $Cr_2O_7^{2-}(aq)$?

66. The only important compounds of Ag(II) are AgF_2 and AgO. Why would you expect these two compounds to be stable, but not other silver(II) compounds such as $AgCl_2$, $AgBr_2$, and AgS?

67. A certain steel is to be analyzed for Cr and Mn. By suitable treatment, the Cr in the steel is oxidized to $Cr_2O_7^{2-}$(aq) and the Mn to MnO_4^-(aq). A 10.000-g sample of steel is used to produce 250.0 mL of a solution containing $Cr_2O_7^{2-}$(aq) and MnO_4^-(aq). A 10.00-mL portion of this solution is added to $BaCl_2$(aq), and by proper adjustment of the pH, the chromium is completely precipitated as $BaCrO_4$(s); 0.549 g is obtained. A second 10.00-mL portion of the solution requires exactly 15.95 mL of 0.0750 M Fe^{2+}(aq) for its titration in acidic solution. Calculate the % Cr and % Mn in the steel sample.
[*Hint:* In the titration MnO_4^-(aq) is reduced to Mn^{2+}(aq) and $Cr_2O_7^{2-}$(aq) is reduced to Cr^{3+}(aq); the Fe^{2+}(aq) is oxidized to Fe^{3+}(aq).]

68. Nickel can be determined as nickel dimethylglyoximate, a brilliant scarlet precipitate that has the composition 20.31% Ni, 33.26% C, 4.88% H, 22.15% O, and 19.39% N. A 15.020-g steel sample is dissolved in concentrated HCl(aq). The solution obtained is suitably treated to remove interfering ions, to establish the proper pH, and to obtain a final solution volume of 250.0 mL. A 10.00-mL sample of this solution is then treated with dimethylglyoxime. The mass of purified, dry nickel dimethylglyoximate obtained is 0.104 g.
(a) What is the empirical formula of nickel dimethylglyoximate?
(b) What is the mass percent nickel in the steel sample?

69. A solution is believed to contain one or more of the following ions: Cr^{3+}, Zn^{2+}, Fe^{3+}, Ni^{2+}. When the solution is treated with excess NaOH(aq), a precipitate forms. The solution in contact with the precipitate is colorless. The precipitate is dissolved in HCl(aq), and the resulting solution is treated with NH_3(aq). No precipitation occurs. Based solely on these observations, what conclusions can you draw about the ions present in the original solution? That is, which ion(s) are likely present, which are most likely not present, and about which can we not be certain?
[*Hint:* Refer to Appendix D for solubility product and complex-ion formation data.]

Feature Problems

70. As a continuation of Problem 89 of Chapter 19 and the discussion on page 972, consider the three graphs of $\Delta G°$ as a function of temperature shown in the following figure.

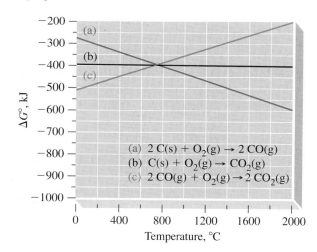

(a) Explain the shapes of the three graphs. Specifically, why is one line essentially parallel to the temperature axis, why does one have a positive slope, and why does one have a negative slope?
(b) Table 23.2 lists as an additional blast furnace reaction, $C(s) + CO_2(g) \longrightarrow 2\,CO(g)$. Determine how $\Delta G°$ for this reaction is related to the three reactions shown in the figure, and plot $\Delta G°$ for this reaction as a function of temperature. If an equilibrium is established in this reaction at 1000 °C and the partial pressure of CO_2(g) is 0.25 atm, what should be the equilibrium partial pressure of CO(g)?

71. Several transition metal ions are found in cation group 3 of the qualitative analysis scheme outlined in

Figure 18-7. At one point in the separation and testing of this group, a solution containing Fe^{3+}, Co^{2+}, Ni^{2+}, Al^{3+}, Cr^{3+}, and Zn^{2+} is treated with an excess of NaOH(aq), together with H_2O_2(aq).
(1) The excess NaOH(aq) causes *three* of the cations to precipitate as hydroxides and *three* to form hydroxo complex ions.
(2) In the presence of H_2O_2(aq), the cation in one of the insoluble hydroxides is oxidized from the +2 to the +3 oxidation state, and one of the hydroxo complex ions is also oxidized.
(3) The three insoluble hydroxides are found as a dark precipitate.
(4) The solution above the precipitate has a yellow color.
(5) The dark precipitate from (3) reacts with HCl(aq), and all the cations return to solution; one of the cations is reduced from the +3 to the +2 oxidation state.
(6) The solution from (5) is treated with 6 M NH_3(aq), and a precipitate containing one of the cations forms.
(a) Write equations for the reactions referred to in item (1).
(b) Write an equation for the most likely reaction in which a hydroxide precipitate is oxidized in item (2).
(c) What is the ion responsible for the yellow color of the solution in item (4)? Write an equation for its formation.
(d) Write equations for the dissolution of the precipitate and the reduction of the cation in item (5).
(e) Write an equation for the precipitate formation in item (6).
[*Hint:* You may need solubility product and complex-ion formation data from Appendix D, together with descriptive information from this chapter and from elsewhere in the text.]

Self-Assessment Exercises

72. In your own words, define the following terms: **(a)** domain; **(b)** flotation; **(c)** leaching; **(d)** amalgam.

73. Briefly describe each of the following ideas, phenomena, or methods: **(a)** lanthanide contraction; **(b)** zone refining; **(c)** basic oxygen process; **(d)** slag formation.

74. Explain the important distinctions between each pair of terms: **(a)** ferromagnetism and paramagnetism; **(b)** roasting and reduction; **(c)** hydrometallurgy and pyrometallurgy; **(d)** chromate and dichromate.

75. Describe the chemical composition of the material called **(a)** pig iron; **(b)** ferromanganese alloy; **(c)** chromite ore; **(d)** brass; **(e)** aqua regia; **(f)** blister copper; **(g)** stainless steel.

76. Three properties expected for transition elements are **(a)** low melting points; **(b)** high ionization energies; **(c)** colored ions in solution; **(d)** positive standard electrode (reduction) potentials; **(e)** diamagnetism; **(f)** complex ion formation; **(g)** catalytic activity.

77. The only diamagnetic ion of the following group is **(a)** Cr^{2+}; **(b)** Zn^{2+}; **(c)** Fe^{3+}; **(d)** Ag^{2+}; **(e)** Ti^{3+}.

78. All of the following elements have an ion displaying the +6 oxidation state *except* **(a)** Mo; **(b)** Cr; **(c)** Mn; **(d)** V; **(e)** S.

79. The best oxidizing agent of the following group of ions is **(a)** $Ag^{+}(aq)$; **(b)** $Cl^{-}(aq)$; **(c)** $H^{+}(aq)$; **(d)** $Na^{+}(aq)$; **(e)** $OH^{-}(aq)$.

80. To separate Fe^{3+} and Ni^{2+} from an aqueous solution containing both ions, with one cation forming a precipitate and the other remaining in solution, add to the solution **(a)** $NaOH(aq)$; **(b)** $H_2S(g)$; **(c)** $HCl(aq)$; **(d)** $NH_3(aq)$.

81. Of the following, the two solids that will liberate $Cl_2(g)$ when heated with $HCl(aq)$ are **(a)** $NaCl(s)$; **(b)** $ZnCl_2(s)$; **(c)** $MnO_2(s)$; **(d)** $CuO(s)$; **(e)** $K_2Cr_2O_7(s)$; **(f)** $NaOH(s)$.

82. Provide the missing name or formula for the following:

(a) chromium(VI) oxide   _____

(b) _____ K_2MnO_4

(c) _____ $Cr(CO)_6$

(d) barium dichromate   _____

(e) _____ $La_2(SO_4)_3 \cdot 9\,H_2O$

(f) gold(III) cyanide trihydrate   _____

83. Balance the following oxidation–reduction equations.

(a) $Fe_2S_3(s) + H_2O + O_2(g) \longrightarrow Fe(OH)_3(s) + S(s)$

(b) $Mn^{2+}(aq) + S_2O_8^{2-}(aq) + H_2O \longrightarrow$
$$MnO_4^{-}(aq) + SO_4^{2-}(aq) + H^{+}(aq)$$

(c) $Ag(s) + CN^{-}(aq) + O_2(g) + H_2O \longrightarrow$
$$[Ag(CN)_2]^{-}(aq) + OH^{-}(aq)$$

 # eMedia Exercises

84. Many transition metals exhibit catalytic properties. The activity of a transition metal as a catalyst is illustrated in the **Surface Reaction—Hydrogenation** animation (*Activebook 23-1*). **(a)** What role does the metal play in the depicted reaction? **(b)** In what sense is the metal acting as a catalyst? **(c)** Why might transition metals exhibit greater catalytic activity than other elements?

85. A method of purifying metals is shown in the **Zone Refining** activity (*Activebook 23-2*). **(a)** What type of impurities could be removed by this process? **(b)** Would this process be useful in the separation of metals making up an alloy? Why or why not?

24

COMPLEX IONS AND COORDINATION COMPOUNDS

CONTENTS

Obtain an array of coordination compounds (anhydrous and hydrated) to show the colors. Dissolve the compounds in water. Add various ligands: KCN, NH_3, EDTA, $NaCl$, KI, etc. to show the range of colors. Note how quickly the complexes form.

Turquoise is a mineral of copper, $CuAl_6(PO_4)_4(OH)_8 \cdot 4\ H_2O$. The distinctive color of this gemstone and many others is a consequence of the nature of metal–ligand bonding in complex ions, a central topic of this chapter.

Chapter 23 included discussions of several situations involving a succession of color changes that were attributed to changes in oxidation state. The color changes discussed in this chapter are not generally caused by oxidation–reduction reactions. Instead, they are observed with changes in the groups (ligands) bound to a metal center, even though the oxidation state of the metal remains unchanged. Explanation of this observation requires a fuller exploration of the nature of complex ions and coordination compounds, a subject that was briefly introduced in Chapter 18. One topic we will consider is the geometric structure of complex ions, which reveals new possibilities for isomerism: the existence of compounds having identical compositions but different structures and properties. We will also examine the nature of the bonding between ligands and the metal centers to which they are attached. It is through an understanding of bonding in complex ions that we can gain some insight into the origin of their colors.

24-1   WERNER'S THEORY OF COORDINATION COMPOUNDS: AN OVERVIEW

▲ **Alfred Werner (1866–1919)**
Werner's success in explaining coordination compounds came in large part through his application of new ideas: the theory of electrolytic dissociation and principles of structural chemistry.

Prussian blue (page 985), accidentally discovered early in the eighteenth century, was perhaps the first known coordination compound—the type explored in this chapter. However, nearly a century passed before the uniqueness of these compounds came to be appreciated. In 1798, B. M. Tassaert obtained yellow crystals of a compound having the formula $CoCl_3 \cdot 6\,NH_3$ from a mixture of $CoCl_3$ and $NH_3(aq)$. What seemed unusual was that both $CoCl_3$ and NH_3 are stable compounds capable of independent existence, yet they combine to form still another stable compound. Such compounds made up of two simpler compounds came to be called **coordination compounds**.

In 1851, another coordination compound of $CoCl_3$ and NH_3 was discovered. This one had the formula $CoCl_3 \cdot 5\,NH_3$ and formed purple crystals. The two compounds are shown in Figure 24-1. Their formulas follow.

$$CoCl_3 \cdot 6\,NH_3 \qquad CoCl_3 \cdot 5\,NH_3$$
$$\text{(yellow)} \qquad\qquad \text{(purple)}$$
$$\text{(a)} \qquad\qquad\qquad \text{(b)}$$

The mystery of coordination compounds deepened as more were discovered and studied. For example, when treated with $AgNO_3(aq)$, compound (a) formed *three* moles of $AgCl(s)$, as expected, but compound (b) formed only *two* moles of $AgCl(s)$.

Inorganic coordination chemistry was a hot field of research in the second half of the nineteenth century, and all the pieces started to fall into place with the work of the Swiss chemist Alfred Werner. Werner's theory of coordination compounds explained the reactions of compounds (a) and (b) with $AgNO_3(aq)$ by considering that, in aqueous solutions, these two compounds ionize in the following way:

(a) $[Co(NH_3)_6]Cl_3(s) \xrightarrow{\;H_2O\;} [Co(NH_3)_6]^{3+}(aq) + 3\,Cl^-(aq)$

(b) $[CoCl(NH_3)_5]Cl_2(s) \xrightarrow{\;H_2O\;} [CoCl(NH_3)_5]^{2+}(aq) + 2\,Cl^-(aq)$

Thus, compound (a) produces the three moles of Cl^- per mole of compound necessary to precipitate three moles of $AgCl(s)$, while compound (b) produces only two moles of Cl^-. Werner's proposal of this ionization scheme was based on extensive studies of the electrical conductivity of coordination compounds. Compound (a) is a better conductor than compound (b), consistent with producing four ions per formula unit compared to three for compound (b). $CoCl_3 \cdot 4\,NH_3$ is a still poorer conductor, corresponding to the formula $[CoCl_2(NH_3)_4]Cl$. $CoCl_3 \cdot 3\,NH_3$ is a *nonelectrolyte*, corresponding to the formula $[CoCl_3(NH_3)_3]$.

Stress the difference between the covalent ligand-central atom bond with the ionic complex-counter ion bond.

Greenaway, A. M., et al. "Cobalt(III) ammines-'Werner' complexes: An undergraduate experiment." *J. Chem. Educ.* **1982:** *59,* 419.

▲ **FIGURE 24-1**
Two coordination compounds
The compound on the left is $[Co(NH_3)_6]Cl_3$. The compound on the right is $[CoCl(NH_3)_5]Cl_2$.

The heart of Werner's theory, proposed in 1893, was that certain metal atoms, primarily those of transition metals, have two types of valence or bonding capacity. One, the *primary* valence, is based on the number of electrons the atom loses in forming the metal ion. A *secondary* valence is responsible for the bonding of other groups, called **ligands**, to the central metal ion.

In modern usage, a **complex** is any species involving coordination of ligands to a metal center. The metal center can be an atom or an ion, and the complex can be a cation, an anion, or a neutral molecule. In a chemical formula, a complex—a metal center and attached ligands—is set off by square brackets, [ ]. Compounds that are complexes or contain complex ions are known as **coordination compounds**.

Syamal, A. "Some improper terms in coordination chemistry." *J. Chem. Educ.* **1985:** *62,* 143.

Myers, Thomas R. "Rules for coordination number of metal ions (CEC)." *J. Chem. Educ.* **1981:** *58,* 681.

Woolf, A. A. "Coordination and radius ratio: A graphical representation." *J. Chem. Educ.* **1989:** *66,* 509.

$$[Co(NH_3)_6]^{3+} \qquad [CoCl_4(NH_3)_2]^- \qquad [CoCl_3(NH_3)_3] \qquad K_4[Fe(CN)_6]$$

complex cation   complex anion   neutral complex   coordination compound

The **coordination number** of a complex is the number of points around the metal center at which bonds to ligands can form. Coordination numbers ranging from 2 to 12 have been observed, although 6 is by far the most common number, followed by 4. Coordination number 2 is limited mostly to complexes of Cu(I), Ag(I), and Au(I). Coordination numbers greater than 6 are not often found in members of the first transition series, but are more common in those of the second and third series. Stable complexes with coordination numbers 3 and 5 are rare. The coordination number observed in a complex depends on a number of factors, such as the ratio of the radius of the central metal atom or ion to the radii of the attached ligands.

Coordination numbers of some common ions are listed in Table 24.1. The four most commonly observed geometric shapes of complex ions are shown in Figure 24-2. One practical use of the coordination number is to assist in writing and interpreting formulas of complexes, as illustrated in Example 24-1.

TABLE 24.1 Some Common Coordination Numbers of Metal Ions			
Cu^+	2, 4		
Ag^+	2		
Au^+	2, 4	Al^{3+}	4, 6
		Sc^{3+}	6
		Cr^{3+}	6
Fe^{2+}	6	Fe^{3+}	6
Co^{2+}	4, 6	Co^{3+}	6
Ni^{2+}	4, 6	Au^{3+}	4
Cu^{2+}	4, 6	Pt^{4+}	6
Zn^{2+}	4		
Pt^{2+}	4		

Linear

Square planar

Tetrahedral

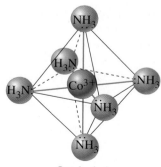

Octahedral

Toofan, Jahansooz. "A Simple Expression between Critical Radius Ratio and Coordination Number." *J. Chem. Educ.* **1994:** *71,* 147.

King, R. B. "The Shapes of Coordination Polyhedra." *J. Chem. Educ.* **1996:** *73,* 993 (October 1996).

Note that in Figure 24-2 all the ligands are the same and hence no distortions of these shapes are observed.

Coordination Number activity

▲ **FIGURE 24-2**
Structures of some complex ions
Attachment of the NH_3 molecules occurs through the lone-pair electrons on the N atoms.

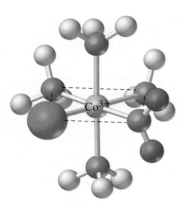

▲ The complex ion
[CoCl(NO₂)(NH₃)₄]⁺

📖 Williams, G. M., Olmstead,
     J., III, Breksa, A. P., III.
"Coordination complexes of cobalt:
Inorganic synthesis in the general
chemistry laboratory." *J. Chem.
Educ.* **1989:** 66, 1043.

📖 Thomas, N. C., Pringle,
     K., Deacon, G. B. "Cobalt(II)
and cobalt(III) coordination
compounds." *J. Chem. Educ.* **1989:**
66, 516.

EXAMPLE 24-1

Relating the Formula of a Complex to the Coordination Number and Oxidation State of the Central Metal. What are the coordination number and oxidation state of Co in the complex ion $[CoCl(NO_2)(NH_3)_4]^+$?

Solution

The complex ion has as ligands *one* Cl^- ion, *one* NO_2^- ion, and *four* NH_3 molecules. The coordination number is 6. Of these six ligands, *two* carry a charge of 1− each (the Cl^- and NO_2^- ions) and four are *neutral* (the NH_3 molecules). The total contribution of the anions to the net charge on the complex ion is 2−. Because the net charge on the complex ion is 1+, the oxidation state of the central cobalt ion is +3. Diagrammatically, we can write

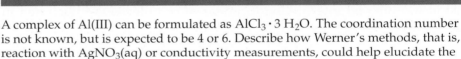

Oxidation state = x Charge of 1− on Cl^- } Total negative charge: 2−
                         Charge of 1− on NO_2^-

$[CoCl(NO_2)(NH_3)_4]^+$

Coordination number = 6   Net charge on complex ion
                           $x - 2 = +1$
                           $x = +3$

Practice Example A: What are the coordination number and oxidation state of nickel in the ion $[Ni(CN)_4I]^{3-}$?

Practice Example B: Write the formula of a complex with cyanide ion ligands, an iron ion with an oxidation state of +3, and a coordination number of 6.

CONCEPT ASSESSMENT ✓

A complex of Al(III) can be formulated as $AlCl_3 \cdot 3\,H_2O$. The coordination number is not known, but is expected to be 4 or 6. Describe how Werner's methods, that is, reaction with $AgNO_3(aq)$ or conductivity measurements, could help elucidate the actual coordination number.

24-2   LIGANDS

KEEP IN MIND ▶

that the covalent bond formed in the Lewis acid–base reaction is a *coordinate* covalent bond. Thus we can think of the coordination number of a transition metal ion in a complex as the number of coordinate covalent bonds in the complex.

A common feature shared by the ligands in coordination complexes is the ability to donate electron pairs to central metal atoms or ions. Ligands are *Lewis bases*. In accepting electron pairs, central metal atoms or ions act as *Lewis acids*. A ligand that uses one pair of electrons to form one point of attachment to the central metal atom or ion is called a **monodentate** ligand. Some examples of monodentate ligands are monatomic anions such as the halide ions, polyatomic anions such as hydroxide ion, simple molecules such as ammonia (called *ammine* when it is a ligand), and more complex molecules such as methylamine, CH_3NH_2 (Table 24.2).

$$\left[:\overset{..}{\underset{..}{Cl}}: \right]^- \qquad \left[:\overset{..}{\underset{..}{O}}-H \right]^- \qquad H-\overset{H}{\underset{H}{N}}: \qquad H-\overset{H}{\underset{H}{C}}-\overset{H}{\underset{H}{N}}:$$

Ligand name: Chloro   Hydroxo   Ammine   Methylamine

TABLE 24.2 Some Common Monodentate Ligands

Formula	Name as Ligand	Formula	Name as Ligand	Formula	Name as Ligand
Neutral molecules		**Anions**		**Anions**	
H_2O	Aqua	F^-	Fluoro	SO_4^{2-}	Sulfato
NH_3	Ammine	Cl^-	Chloro	$S_2O_3^{2-}$	Thiosulfato
CO	Carbonyl	Br^-	Bromo	NO_2^-	Nitrito-N-[a]
NO	Nitrosyl	I^-	Iodo	ONO^-	Nitrito-O-[a]
CH_3NH_2	Methylamine	O^{2-}	Oxo	SCN^-	Thiocyanato-S-[b]
C_5H_5N	Pyridine	OH^-	Hydroxo	NCS^-	Thiocyanato-N-[b]
		CN^-	Cyano		

[a] If the nitrite ion is attached through the N atom (—NO_2), the designation *nitrito-N-* is used; if attached through an O atom (—ONO), *nitrito-O-*.
[b] If the thiocyanate ion is attached through the S atom (—SCN), the name *thiocyanato-S-* is used; if attachment is through the N atom (—NCS), *thiocyanato-N-*.

◄ KEEP IN MIND
that the lone pairs of electrons of a polydentate ligand must be far enough apart to attach to the metal center at two or more points; the donated pairs of electrons must be on different atoms.

Motivate students by pointing out that ligand complexes with many transition elements, such as iron and zinc, play important roles in biochemistry.

Some ligands are capable of donating more than a single electron pair from *different* atoms in the ligand and to *different* sites in the geometric structure of a complex. These are called **polydentate** ligands. The molecule *ethylenediamine* (en) can donate two electron pairs, one from each N atom. Since en attaches to the metal center at two points, it is called a **bidentate** ligand.

$$H—\overset{..}{N}—CH_2CH_2—\overset{..}{N}—H$$
$$\quad\ \ |\qquad\qquad\qquad\ \ |$$
$$\quad\ \ H\qquad\qquad\qquad\ H$$

Three common polydentate ligands are shown in Table 24.3.

◄ KEEP IN MIND
that the $EDTA^{4-}$ ligand is not planar as suggested in Table 24.3. Use VSEPR theory to gain an insight into the shape of this polyatomic anion. Also, refer to Figure 24-23.

TABLE 24.3 Some Common Polydentate Ligands (Chelating Agents)

Abbreviation	Name	Formula
en	Ethylenediamine	H_2N—CH_2—CH_2—NH_2
ox^{2-} [a]	Oxalato	oxalate structure with two C bonded, each to two O
$EDTA^{4-}$ [b]	Ethylenediaminetetraacetato	EDTA structure

[a] Oxalic acid is a diprotic acid denoted H_2ox. It is the ox^{2-} anion that binds as a bidentate ligand.
[b] Ethylenediaminetetraacetic acid, a tetraprotic acid, is denoted H_4EDTA.

(a)

▶ **FIGURE 24-3**

Three representations of the chelate [Pt(en)$_2$]$^{2+}$

(a) Overall structure. **(b)** The ligands attach at adjacent corners along an edge of the square. They do *not* bridge the square by attaching to opposite corners. Bonds are shown in red, and the square-planar shape is indicated by the black parallelogram.

(b)

Figure 24-3 represents the attachment of two ethylenediamine (en) ligands to a Pt^{2+} ion. Here is how we can establish that each ligand is attached to two positions in the coordination sphere around the Pt^{2+} ion.

- Because Pt^{2+} ion exhibits a coordination number of 4 with monodentate ligands, and because [Pt(en)$_2$]$^{2+}$ is unable to attach additional ligands such as NH$_3$, H$_2$O, or Cl$^-$, we conclude that each en group must be attached at two points.

- The en ligands in the complex ion exhibit no further basic properties. They cannot accept protons from water to produce OH$^-$, as they would if they had an available lone pair of electrons. Both —NH$_2$ groups of each en molecule must be tied up in the complex ion.

Note the two five-member rings (pentagons) outlined in Figure 24-3(b). They consist of Pt, N, and C atoms. When the bonding of a polydentate ligand to a metal ion produces a ring (normally with five or six members), we refer to the complex as a **chelate** (pronounced KEY-late). The polydentate ligand is called a **chelating agent**, and the process of chelate formation is called *chelation*.

Smith, D. W. "Valence, Covalence, Hypervalence, Oxidation State, and Coordination Number." *J. Chem. Educ.* **2005:** 82, 1202.

CONCEPT ASSESSMENT ✔

The ligand diethylenetriamine (abbreviated det), H$_2$NCH$_2$CH$_2$NHCH$_2$CH$_2$NH$_2$, can form complexes. Classify this ligand as mono-, bi-, tri- or quadridentate.

Are You Wondering . . .

How such strange terms as ligand, monodentate, and chelate got into the vocabulary of chemistry?

Ligand comes from the Latin word *ligare*, which means to bind. It is quite appropriate to describe groups that are bound to a metal center as ligands. Dentate is also derived from a Latin word, *dens*, meaning tooth. Figuratively speaking, a monodentate ligand has one tooth; a bidentate ligand has two teeth; and a polydentate ligand has several. A ligand attaches itself to the metal center in accordance with the number of "teeth" it possesses. This is an easily remembered and colorful metaphor. Chelate is derived from the Greek word *chela*, which means a crab's claw. The way in which a chelating agent attaches itself to a metal ion resembles a crab's claw—another colorful metaphor.

24-3   NOMENCLATURE

The system of naming complexes originated with Werner, but it has been modified several times over the years. Even today, usage varies somewhat. Our approach will be to consider a few general rules that permit us to relate names and formulas of simple complexes. We will not consider any of the complicated cases for which writing names and formulas is more challenging.

1. *Anions as ligands are named by using the ending* -o. As implied by Table 24.2, normally *-ide* endings change to *-o*, *-ite* to *-ito*, and *-ate* to *-ato*.

2. *Neutral molecules as ligands generally carry the unmodified name.* For example, the name ethylenediamine is used both for the free molecule and for the molecule as a ligand. Aqua, ammine, carbonyl, and nitrosyl are important exceptions (see Table 24.2).

3. *The number of ligands of a given type is denoted by a prefix.* The usual prefixes are *mono* = 1, *di* = 2, *tri* = 3, *tetra* = 4, *penta* = 5, and *hexa* = 6. As in many other cases, the prefix *mono*- is often not used. If the ligand name is a composite name that itself contains a numerical prefix, such as ethylene*di*amine, place parentheses around the name and precede it with *bis* = 2, *tris* = 3, *tetrakis* = 4, and so on. Thus, dichloro signifies *two* Cl^- ions as ligands, and *penta*aqua signifies *five* H_2O molecules. To indicate the presence of *two* ethylenediamine (en) ligands, we write *bis*(ethylenediamine).

4. *When we name a complex, ligands are named first, in alphabetical order, followed by the name of the metal center. The oxidation state of the metal center is denoted by a Roman numeral. If the complex is an anion, the ending* -ate *is attached to the name of the metal.* Prefixes (*di, tri, bis, tris,* . . .) are ignored in establishing the alphabetical order. Thus, $[CrCl_2(H_2O)_4]^+$ is called tetraaquadichlorochromium(III) ion; $[CoCl_2(en)_2]^+$ is dichlorobis(ethylenediamine)cobalt(III) ion; and $[Cr(OH)_4]^-$ is tetrahydroxochromate(III) ion. For complex anions of a few of the metals, the English name is replaced by the Latin name given in Table 24.4. Thus, $[CuCl_4]^{2-}$ is the tetrachlorocuprate(II) ion.

5. *When we write the formula of a complex, the chemical symbol of the metal center is written first, followed by the formulas of anions and then neutral molecules.* If there are two or more different anions or neutral molecules as ligands, they are written in alphabetical order according to the first chemical symbols of their formulas. Thus, in the formula of the tetraaminechloronitrito-*N*-cobalt(III) ion, Cl^- precedes NO_2^-, and both are placed ahead of the neutral NH_3 molecules: $[CoCl(NO_2)(NH_3)_4]^+$.

6. *In names and formulas of coordination compounds, cations come first followed by anions.* This is the same order as in simple ionic compounds like NaCl for sodium chloride. For example, the formula $[Pt(NH_3)_4][PtCl_4]$ represents the coordination compound tetraammineplatinum(II) tetrachloroplatinate(II).

◄ Occasionally, the metal center will be in the oxidation state 0, as in $[W(CO)_6]$ hexacarbonyltungsten(0).

TABLE 24.4   Names for Some Metals in Complex Anions

Iron	⟶	**Ferrate**
Copper	⟶	**Cuprate**
Tin	⟶	**Stannate**
Silver	⟶	**Argentate**
Lead	⟶	**Plumbate**
Gold	⟶	**Aurate**

EXAMPLE 24-2

Relating Names and Formulas of Complexes. **(a)** What is the name of the complex $[CoCl_3(NH_3)_3]$? **(b)** What is the formula of the compound pentaaquachlorochromium(III) chloride? **(c)** What is the name of the compound $K_3[Fe(CN)_6]$?

Solution

(a) $[CoCl_3(NH_3)_3]$ consists of *three* ammonia molecules and *three* chloride ions attached to a central Co^{3+} ion; it is electrically neutral. The name of this neutral complex is triamminetrichlorocobalt(III).

(b) The central metal ion is Cr^{3+}. There are five H_2O molecules and one Cl^- ion as ligands. The complex ion carries a net charge of 2+. Two Cl^- ions are required to neutralize the charge on this complex cation. The formula of the coordination compound is $[CrCl(H_2O)_5]Cl_2$.

(c) This compound consists of K^+ cations and complex anions having the formula $[Fe(CN)_6]^{3-}$. Each cyanide ion carries a charge of $1-$, so the oxidation state of the iron must be $+3$. The Latin-based name "ferrate" is used because the complex ion is an anion. The name of the anion is hexacyanoferrate(III) ion. The coordination compound is potassium hexacyanoferrate(III).

Practice Example A: What is the formula of the compound potassium hexachloroplatinate(IV)?

Practice Example B: What is the name of the compound $[Co(SCN)(NH_3)_5]Cl_2$?

Although most complexes are named in the manner just outlined, some common, or trivial, names are still in use. Two such trivial names are ferrocyanide for $[Fe(CN)_6]^{4-}$ and ferricyanide for $[Fe(CN)_6]^{3-}$. These common names suggest the oxidation state of the central metal ions through the o and i designations (o for the ferrous ion, Fe^{2+}, in $[Fe(CN)_6]^{4-}$ and i for the ferric ion, Fe^{3+}, in $[Fe(CN)_6]^{3-}$). These trivial names do not indicate that the metal ions have a coordination number of 6, however. The systematic names—hexacyanoferrate(II) and hexacyanoferrate(III)—are more informative.

CONCEPT ASSESSMENT ✓

A student named a coordination complex tripotassium dichlorodibromodihydroxoiron. The student's instructor pointed out that although the correct formula for the compound could be deduced, this name violates the IUPAC convention. How does this name violate IUPAC rules, and what is the correct name?

24-4 ISOMERISM

As previously noted (page 93), *isomers* are substances that have the same formulas but differ in their structures and properties. Several kinds of isomerism are found among complex ions and coordination compounds. These can be lumped into two broad categories: **Structural isomers** differ in basic structure or bond type—what ligands are bonded to the metal center and through which atoms. **Stereoisomers** have the same number and types of ligands and the same mode of attachment, but they differ in the way in which the ligands occupy the space around the metal center. Of the following five examples, the first three are types of structural isomerism (ionization, coordination, and linkage isomerism), and the remaining two are types of stereoisomerism (geometric and optical isomerism).

IONIZATION ISOMERISM

The two coordination compounds whose formulas are shown here have the same central ion (Cr^{3+}), and five of the six ligands (NH_3 molecules) are the same. The compounds differ in that one has SO_4^{2-} ion as the sixth ligand, with a Cl^- ion to neutralize the charge of the complex ion, whereas the other has Cl^- as the sixth ligand and SO_4^{2-} to neutralize the charge of the complex ion.

$[CrSO_4(NH_3)_5]Cl$	$[CrCl(NH_3)_5]SO_4$
pentaamminesulfatochromium(III) chloride	pentaamminechlorochromium(III) sulfate
(a)	(b)

Chung, C. "Computation of the number of isomers of coordination compounds containing different monodentate ligands." *J. Chem. Educ.* **1979:** *56*, 398.

▶ Structural isomers are also known as constitutional isomers.

Some students have a more difficult time than others in visualizing three-dimensional structures. Make sure that all rules on these matters are clear and do not rely on visualization alone.

Gargallo, M. F., Lechuga, L., Puerta, M. C., Gonzalez-Vilchez, F., Vilaplana, R. "Stereoisomerism in coordination chemistry: A laboratory experiment for undergraduate students." *J. Chem. Educ.* **1988:** *65*, 1018.

COORDINATION ISOMERISM

A situation somewhat similar to that just described can arise when a coordination compound is composed of both complex cations and complex anions. The ligands can be distributed differently between the two complex ions, as are $NH_3(aq)$ and CN^- in these two compounds.

$[Co(NH_3)_6][Cr(CN)_6]$

hexaamminecobalt(III) hexacyanochromate(III)

(a)

$[Cr(NH_3)_6][Co(CN)_6]$

hexaamminechromium(III) hexacyanocobaltate(III)

(b)

LINKAGE ISOMERISM

Some ligands may attach to the central metal ion of a complex ion in different ways. For example, the nitrite ion, a monodentate ligand, has electron pairs available for coordination both on the N and O atoms.

Whether attachment of this ligand is through the N or an O atom, the formula of the complex ion is unaffected. The properties of the complex ion, however, may be affected. When attachment occurs through the N atom, the ligand can be referred to as nitro or, more properly, nitrito-*N*- when naming the complex. Coordination through an O atom can be referred to as nitrito or, more properly, nitrito-*O*- when naming the complex.

Bose, R. N., et al. "Linkage Isomerization by Two-Dimensional ^{31}P Nuclear Magnetic Resonance Spectroscopy. An Undergraduate Inorganic Laboratory Experiment." *J. Chem. Educ.* **2001:** *78,* 83.

$[Co(NO_2)(NH_3)_5]^{2+}$

pentaamminenitrito-*N*-cobalt(III) ion

(a)

$[Co(ONO)(NH_3)_5]^{2+}$

pentaamminenitrito-*O*-cobalt(III) ion

(b)

The structures of these compounds are illustrated in Figure 24-4.

Lyon, John M. "A Way To Predict the Relative Stabilities of Structural Isomers." *J. Chem. Educ.* **1999:** *76,* 364 (March 1999).

(a) $[Co(NO_2)(NH_3)_5]^{2+}$

(b) $[Co(ONO)(NH_3)_5]^{2+}$

◀ **FIGURE 24-4**
Linkage isomerism—illustrated
(a) Pentaamminenitrito-*N*-cobalt(III) cation.
(b) Pentaamminenitrito-*O*-cobalt(III) cation.

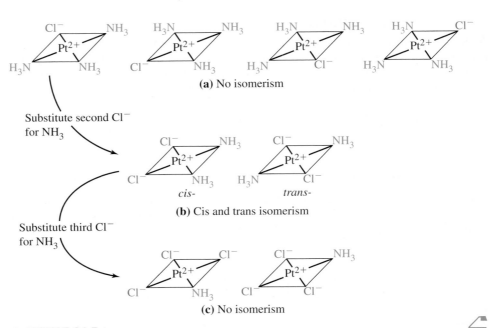

(a) No isomerism

Substitute second Cl⁻ for NH₃

cis-   *trans-*

(b) Cis and trans isomerism

Substitute third Cl⁻ for NH₃

(c) No isomerism

▲ **FIGURE 24-5**
Geometric isomerism—illustrated
For the square-planar complexes shown here, isomerism exists only when two Cl⁻ ions have replaced NH_3 molecules.

 Use sCISsors and TRANSverse as mnemonics.

Baker, R. W., George, A. V., Harding, M. M. "Models and Molecules—A Workshop on Stereoisomers." *J. Chem. Educ.* **1998:** *75,* 853.

Haudrechy, Arnaud. "A Simple Method of Drawing Stereoisomers from Complicated Symmetrical Structures." *J. Chem. Educ.* **2000:** *77,* 864.

Krishnan, C. V. "Cis, trans isomerism and polarity of molecules (F&R)." *J. Chem. Educ.* **1986:** *63,* 601.

cis-[PtCl₂(NH₃)₂]

trans-[PtCl₂(NH₃)₂]

▲ The geometric isomers of [PtCl₂(NH₃)₂]

▶ The term *cis* means "on this side" in Latin, and *trans* means "across." Domestic airline flights in the United States are *cis*atlantic, whereas flights to Europe are *trans*atlantic.

GEOMETRIC ISOMERISM

If a single Cl⁻ ion is substituted for an NH_3 molecule in the square-planar complex ion $[Pt(NH_3)_4]^{2+}$ in Figure 24-2, it does not matter at which corner of the square this substitution is made. As shown in Figure 24-5(a), all four possibilities are alike. If a *second* Cl⁻ is substituted for an NH_3, there are two distinct possibilities (Fig. 24-5b). The two Cl⁻ ions can either be along the same edge of the square (***cis***) or on opposite corners, across from each other (***trans***). To distinguish clearly between these two possibilities, we must either draw a structure or refer to the appropriate name. The formula alone will not distinguish between them. (Note that this complex is a neutral species, not an ion.)

$$[PtCl_2(NH_3)_2]$$
*cis-*diamminedichloroplatinum(II)
or
*trans-*diamminedichloroplatinum(II)

The type of isomerism described here in which the positions of the ligands produce distinct isomers is called **geometric isomerism**. Interestingly, if a *third* Cl⁻ ion is substituted, isomerism disappears (Fig. 24-5c). There is only one complex ion with the formula $[PtCl_3(NH_3)]^-$.

With an octahedral complex, the situation is a bit more complicated. Take the complex ion $[Co(NH_3)_6]^{3+}$ of Figure 24-2 as an example. If one Cl⁻ is substituted for an NH_3, a single structure results. With the substitution of *two* Cl⁻ ions for NH_3 molecules, *cis* and *trans* isomers result. The *cis* isomer has two Cl⁻ ions along the same edge of the octahedron (Fig. 24-6a). The *trans* isomer has two Cl⁻ ions on opposite corners, that is, at opposite ends of a line drawn through the central metal ion (Fig. 24-6b). One difference between the two is that the *cis* isomer has a purple color and the *trans* has a bright green color.

If a *third* Cl⁻ is substituted for an NH_3 in Figure 24-6(a), two possibilities exist. If this third substitution is at either the top or bottom of the structure, the result is that three Cl⁻ ions appear on the same face of the octahedron. This is called a *fac* (facial) isomer. If the third substitution is at either of the other two positions, the result is three Cl⁻ ions around a perimeter or meridian of the octahedron. This is a *mer* (meridional) isomer.

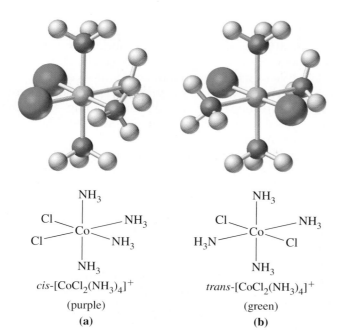

cis-[CoCl$_2$(NH$_3$)$_4$]$^+$

(purple)

(a)

$trans$-[CoCl$_2$(NH$_3$)$_4$]$^+$

(green)

(b)

fac-[CoCl$_3$(NH$_3$)$_3$]

▲ **FIGURE 24-6**
Cis and *trans* isomers of an octahedral complex
The Co^{3+} ion is at the center of the octahedron, and NH$_3$ and Cl$^-$ ligands are at the vertices.

mer-[CoCl$_3$(NH$_3$)$_3$]

▲ **The geometric isomers of [CoCl$_3$(NH$_3$)$_3$]**

CONCEPT ASSESSMENT ✓

Explain why the substitution of a *fourth* Cl$^-$ for an NH$_3$ in *mer*-[CoCl$_3$(NH$_3$)$_3$] may produce some of the same product as the substitution of a fourth Cl$^-$ for an NH$_3$ in *fac*-[CoCl$_3$(NH$_3$)$_3$], but it may also produce a different product.

EXAMPLE 24-3

Identifying Geometric Isomers. Sketch structures of all the possible isomers of [CoCl(ox)(NH$_3$)$_3$].

Solution

The Co^{3+} ion exhibits a coordination number of 6. The structure is octahedral. Recall that ox (oxalate ion) is a bidentate ligand carrying a double-negative charge (see Table 24.3). Also, as shown in Figure 24-3, a bidentate ligand must be attached in *cis* positions, not *trans*. Once the ox ligand is placed, any position is available to the Cl$^-$. This leaves two possibilities for the three NH$_3$ molecules. They can be situated (1) on the same face of the octahedron (*fac* isomer) or (2) around a perimeter of the octahedron (*mer* isomer).

Gawley, R. E. "Chirality Made Simple: A 1- and 2-Dimensional Introduction to Stereochemistry." *J. Chem. Educ.* **2005:** *82,* 1009.

Collins, M. J. "Demonstrating Chirality: Using a Mirror with Physical Models to Show Non-superimposability of Chiral Molecules with Their Mirror Images." *J. Chem. Educ.* **2001:** *78,* 1484.

fac isomer

mer isomer

Practice Example A: Sketch the geometric isomers of [CoCl$_2$(ox)(NH$_3$)$_2$]$^-$.

Practice Example B: Sketch the geometric isomers of [MoCl$_2$(C$_5$H$_5$N)$_2$(CO)$_2$]$^+$.

▲ FIGURE 24-7
Superimposable and nonsuperimposable objects—a cubical, open-top box
(a) You can place the box into its mirror image (hypothetically) in several ways. The box and its mirror image are superimposable.
(b) No matter how you place the box in its mirror image, the stickers will not appear in the same position. This box and its mirror image are nonsuperimposable.

▶ A process based on chirality would be creating the maximum number of matched pairs of gloves from a bin of gloves of identical sizes of which 90 are for the right hand, but only 10 are for the left hand.

▶ The prefixes *dextro* and *levo* are derived from the Latin words *dexter*, right, and *levo*, left.

Chirality animation

Herrero, S., Uson, M. A. "A Straightforward Method for Assigning Stereochemical Lambda/Delta Descriptors to Octahedral Coordination Compounds." *J. Chem. Educ.* **1995**: 72, 1065 (December 1995).

▶ FIGURE 24-8
Optical isomers
The two structures are nonsuperimposable mirror images. Like a right hand and a left hand, one structure cannot be superimposed onto the other.

OPTICAL ISOMERISM

To understand optical isomerism, we need to understand the relationship between an object and its mirror image. Features on the right side of the object appear on the left side of its image in a mirror, and vice versa. Certain objects can be rotated in such a way as to be *superimposable* on their mirror images, but other objects are *nonsuperimposable* on their mirror images. An unmarked tennis ball is superimposable on its mirror image, but a left hand is nonsuperimposable on its mirror image (a right hand).

Consider the open-top cubical cardboard box pictured in Figure 24-7(a). There are a number of hypothetical ways in which the box can be superimposed on its mirror image. Now imagine that a distinctive sticker is placed at a corner of one side of the box (Fig. 24-7b). In this case, there is no way that the box and its mirror image can be superimposed; they are clearly different. This is equivalent to saying that there is no way that a formfitting left glove can be worn on a right hand (turning it inside out is not allowed).

The two structures of $[Co(en)_3]^{3+}$ depicted in Figure 24-8 are related to each other as are an object and its image in a mirror. Furthermore, the two structures are *nonsuperimposable*, like a left and a right hand. The two structures represent two different complex ions; they are isomers.

Structures that are nonsuperimposable mirror images of each other are called **enantiomers** and are said to be **chiral** (pronounced KYE-rull). (Structures that are superimposable are *achiral*.) Whereas other types of isomers may differ significantly in their physical and chemical properties, enantiomers have identical properties except in a few specialized situations. These exceptions involve phenomena that are directly linked to chirality, or handedness, at the molecular level. An example is *optical activity*, pictured in Figure 24-9.

Interactions between a beam of polarized light and the electrons in an enantiomer cause the plane of the polarized light to rotate. One enantiomer rotates the plane of polarized light to the right (clockwise) and is said to be *dextrorotatory* (designated + or *d*). The other enantiomer rotates the plane of polarized light to the same extent, but to the left (counterclockwise). It is said to be *levorotatory* (− or *l*). Because they can rotate the plane of polarized light, the enantiomers are said to be *optically active* and are referred to as **optical isomers**.

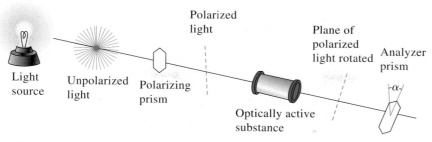

▲ **FIGURE 24-9**
Optical activity
Light from an ordinary source consists of electromagnetic waves vibrating in all planes; it is unpolarized. This light is passed through a polarizer, a material that screens out all waves except those vibrating in a particular plane. The plane of polarization of transmitted polarized light is then changed by passage through an optically active substance. The angle through which the plane of polarization has been rotated is determined by rotating an analyzer (a second polarizer) to the extent that all the polarized light is absorbed.

When an optically active complex is synthesized, a mixture of the two optical isomers (enantiomers) is obtained, such as the two $[Co(en)_3]^{3+}$ isomers in Figure 24-8. The optical rotation of one isomer just cancels that of the other. The mixture, called a *racemic mixture*, produces no net rotation of the plane of polarized light. Separating the *d* and *l* isomers of a racemic mixture is called *resolution*. This separation can sometimes be achieved through chemical reactions controlled by chirality, with the two enantiomers behaving differently. Many phenomena of the living state, such as the effectiveness of a drug, the activity of an enzyme, and the ability of a microorganism to promote a reaction, involve chirality. We will return to a discussion of chirality in Chapters 26 and 27.

Optical Activity animation

Lu, Gentu. "Successive determination of charge numbers of complex cations and of ionic chloride in the hydrate isomers of chromium(III) chloride." *J. Chem. Educ.* **1989**: *66*, 856.

Optical isomerism can confuse students who wonder why plane polarized light and chemical reactivity are related. In fact they are not. Rotation of plane polarized light is a physical property. Chemical activity, or lack of it, is not a physical property. The physical and chemical properties, however, both depend upon the existence of a center of asymmetry.

Griffin, Susan F. "Chiral crackers: A palatable approach to optical isomerism." *J. Chem. Educ.* **1991**: *68*, 1029.

Are You Wondering . . .

How to tell if its mirror image is superimposable on a molecule?

The complex ion $[CrBr_2(H_2O)_2(NH_3)_2]^+$ has five isomers; one is shown below with its mirror image. To test if the mirror image is superimposable on the original, imagine rotating the mirror image about the vertical axis (H_2O—Cr—NH_3) by 180° so that the two Br^- ligands are in the same position as in the original molecule. We see that the NH_3 and H_2O ligands that are in the same plane as the two Br^- ligands are in reversed positions when compared with the original molecule. Thus the molecule and its mirror image are not superimposable. The molecule is potentially optically active.

▲ **FIGURE 24-10**
Hypothetical structures for $[CoCl_2(NH_3)_4]^+$
If the complex ion had this hexagonal structure, there should be *three* distinct isomers, but only two isomers exist—cis and trans.

ISOMERISM AND WERNER'S THEORY

The study of isomerism played a crucial role in the development of Werner's theory of coordination chemistry. Werner proposed that complexes with coordination number 6 have an octahedral structure, but other possibilities were also proposed. For example, Figure 24-10 shows a hypothetical hexagonal structure for $[CoCl_2(NH_3)_4]^+$, similar to that of benzene. However, this hexagonal structure would require the existence of *three* isomers, but a third isomer was never found; the only two isomers are those pictured in Figure 24-6. Additional direct evidence came with the discovery of optical isomerism in the tris(ethylenediamine)cobalt(III) ion (Fig. 24-8). Neither the hexagonal structure nor alternative structures can account for this isomerism—but, as we have seen, the octahedral structure does. Werner even succeeded in preparing an optically active octahedral complex with only inorganic ligands, to overcome objections that the optical activity of tris(ethylenediamine)cobalt(III) ion owed its optical activity to its carbon atoms and not to its geometric structure.

CONCEPT ASSESSMENT ✔

Of the following complex cations, which are identical, which are geometrical isomers, which are enantiomers?

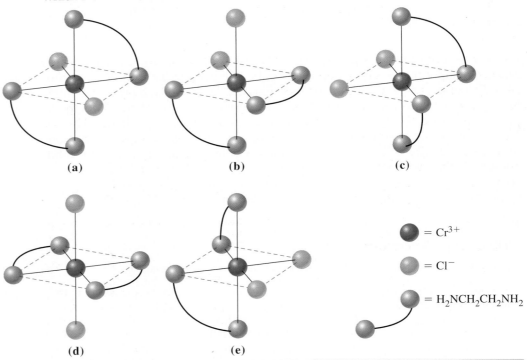

(a)   (b)   (c)

(d)   (e)

= Cr^{3+}

= Cl^-

= $H_2NCH_2CH_2NH_2$

Venkataraman, D., Du, Y., Wilson, S. R., Hirsch, K. A., Zhang, P., Moore, J. S. "A Coordination Geometry Table of the *d*-Block Elements and Their Ions." *J. Chem. Educ.* **1997:** *74,* 915 (August 1997).

▶ Modifications of the simple crystal field theory that take into account such factors as the partial covalency of the metal–ligand bond are called *ligand field theory*. This term is often used to signify both the purely electrostatic crystal field theory and its modifications.

24-5   BONDING IN COMPLEX IONS: CRYSTAL FIELD THEORY

The theories of chemical bonding that were so useful in earlier chapters do not help much in explaining the characteristic colors and magnetic properties of complex ions. In transition metal ions, we need to focus on how the electrons in the *d* orbitals of a metal ion are affected when they are in a complex. A theory that provides that focus and an explanation of these properties is crystal field theory.

In the **crystal field theory**, bonding in a complex ion is considered to be an electrostatic attraction between the positively charged nucleus of the central metal ion and electrons in the ligands. Repulsions also occur between the ligand electrons and electrons in the central ion. In particular, the crystal field theory focuses on the repulsions between ligand electrons and *d* electrons of the central ion.

First, a reminder about the *d* orbitals introduced in Figure 8-30: All five of the orbitals are alike in energy when in an isolated atom or ion, but they are *unlike* in their spatial orientations. One of them, d_{z^2}, is directed along the *z* axis, and another, $d_{x^2-y^2}$, has lobes along the *x* and *y* axes. The remaining three have lobes extending into regions between the perpendicular *x*, *y*, and *z* axes. In the

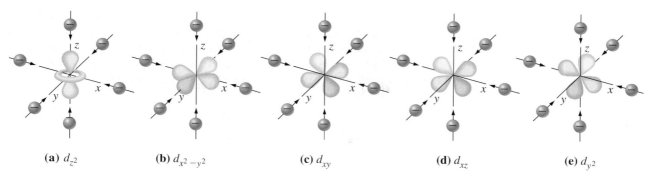

(a) d_{z^2} **(b)** $d_{x^2-y^2}$ **(c)** d_{xy} **(d)** d_{xz} **(e)** d_{y^2}

▲ **FIGURE 24-11**
Approach of six anions to a metal ion to form a complex ion with octahedral structure
The ligands (anions, in this case) approach the central metal ion along the x, y, and z axes. Maximum repulsion occurs with the d_{z^2} and $d_{x^2-y^2}$ orbitals, and their energies are raised. Repulsions with the other d orbitals are not as great. A difference in energy results between the two sets of d orbitals.

presence of ligands, because repulsions exist between ligand electrons and d electrons, the d-orbital energy levels of the central metal ion are raised. As we will soon see, however, they are not all raised to the same extent.

    Figure 24-11 depicts six anions (ligands) approaching a central metal ion along the x, y, and z axes. This direction of approach leads to an octahedral complex. Repulsions between ligand electrons and d-orbital electrons are strengthened in the direct, head-to-head approach of ligands to the d_{z^2} orbitals (Fig. 24-11a) and $d_{x^2-y^2}$ orbitals (Fig. 24-11b). These two orbitals have their energy raised with respect to an average d-orbital energy for a central metal ion in the field of the ligands. For the other three orbitals (d_{xy}, d_{xz}, and d_{yz}, Figure 24-11c–e), ligands approach between the lobes of the orbitals and there is a gain in stability over the head-to-head approach; these orbital energies are lowered with respect to the average d-orbital energy. The difference in energy between the two groups of d orbitals is called *crystal field splitting* and is represented by the symbol Δ (Fig. 24-12).

Tudela, David A. "Common Inorganic Chemistry Textbook Mistake: Incorrect Use of Pairing Energy in Crystal Field Stabilization Energy Expressions." *J. Chem. Educ.* **1999**: 76, 134 (January 1999).

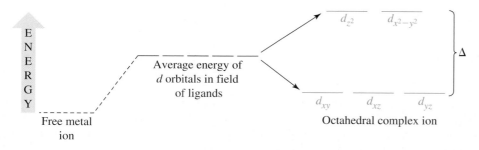

◀ **FIGURE 24-12**
Splitting of d energy levels in the formation of an octahedral complex ion
The d-orbital energy levels of the free central ion are raised in the presence of ligands to the average level shown, but the five levels are split into two groups.

    The removal of the degeneracy of the d orbitals by the crystal field has important consequences for the electron configurations of transition metal ions having between 4 and 7 d electrons. Consider the transition metal ion Cr^{2+} with a d^4 configuration. If the four d electrons are assigned to the orbitals of lowest energy first, the first three electrons go into the d_{xy}, d_{xz}, and d_{yz} orbitals according to Hund's rule (page 317)—but what about the fourth electron? The aufbau process (page 318) suggests that the electron should pair up with one of the three electrons already in the d_{xy}, d_{xz}, and d_{yz} orbitals.

Placing the fourth electron in the lower level confers extra stability (lower energy) on the complex, but some of this stability is offset because it requires energy, called the **pairing energy** (P), to force an electron into an orbital that is already occupied by an electron. Alternatively, the electron could be assigned to either the $d_{x^2-y^2}$ or d_{z^2} orbital, avoiding the pairing energy.

$$\begin{array}{cc} \uparrow & \underline{} \\ \underline{d_{x^2-y^2}} & d_{z^2} \end{array}$$

$$\begin{array}{ccc} \uparrow & \uparrow & \uparrow \\ \underline{d_{xy}} & \underline{d_{xz}} & \underline{d_{yz}} \end{array}$$

Parmer, Swarn Singh. "The crystal field stabilization energy (CFSE) (TF)." *J. Chem. Educ.* **1981**: *58*, 1035.

Placing the fourth electron in the upper level requires energy and offsets the extra stability acquired by placing the first three electrons in the lower level. To pair or not to pair, that is the question.

Whether the fourth electron enters the lowest level and becomes paired or, instead, enters the upper level with the same spin as the first three electrons depends on the magnitude of Δ. If Δ is greater than the pairing energy, P, greater stability is obtained if the fourth electron is paired with one in the lower level. If Δ is less than the pairing energy, greater stability is obtained by keeping the electrons unpaired. Thus, for octahedral chromium(II) complexes, there are two possibilities for the number of unpaired electrons. In one case, there are four unpaired electrons when $\Delta < P$; this situation corresponds to the maximum number of unpaired electrons and is referred to as **high spin**. Ligands such as H_2O and F^- produce only a small crystal field splitting, leading to high-spin complexes; such ligands are said to be *weak-field ligands*. As an example, $[Cr(H_2O)_6]^{2+}$ is a weak-field complex. In the other case, when $\Delta > P$, there are two unpaired electrons; this corresponds to the minimum number of unpaired electrons and is referred to as **low spin**. Ligands such as NH_3 and CN^- produce large crystal field splitting, leading to low-spin complexes; such ligands are said to be *strong-field ligands*. $[Cr(CN)_6]^{4-}$ is a strong-field complex.

▶ These two possibilities exist for complex ions because the crystal field splitting and pairing energies are small and of comparable value. In considering the electron configurations in atoms, the spacing between energy levels is much greater than the pairing energy.

Different ligands can be arranged in order of their abilities to produce a splitting of the d energy levels. This arrangement is known as the **spectrochemical series**.

Strong field

(large Δ)

▶ The spectrochemical series.

$CN^- > \underline{N}O_2^- > en > py \approx \underline{N}H_3 > EDTA^{4-} > \underline{S}CN^- > H_2O >$

$\underline{O}NO^- > ox^{2-} > \underline{O}H^- > F^- > \underline{S}CN^- > Cl^- > Br^- > I^-$

(small Δ)

Weak field

Underlining indicates the donor atom.

▶ If we call the energy separation for the octahedral complex Δ_o, the comparative value for the tetrahedral complex is 0.44 Δ_o and for the square-planar complex, 1.74 Δ_o. The splitting between the d_{xy} and $d_{x^2-y^2}$ orbitals in a square-planar complex is Δ_o, just as in an octahedral complex, because these orbitals are equally affected by ligand repulsions in both complexes.

To summarize, consider these two complexes of Co(III): $[CoF_6]^{3-}$ and $[Co(NH_3)_6]^{3+}$. The F^- ion is a weak-field ligand, whereas NH_3 is a strong-field ligand. Because the crystal field splitting for NH_3 is greater than the pairing energy for Co^{3+}, we have the following situations.

Strong field

$$\begin{array}{cc} \underline{} & \underline{} \\ d_{x^2-y^2} & d_{z^2} \end{array}$$

Weak field

$$\begin{array}{cc} \uparrow & \uparrow \\ \underline{d_{x^2-y^2}} & \underline{d_{z^2}} \end{array}$$

$$\begin{array}{ccc} \uparrow\downarrow & \uparrow & \uparrow \\ \underline{d_{xy}} & \underline{d_{xz}} & \underline{d_{yz}} \end{array} \qquad \begin{array}{ccc} \uparrow\downarrow & \uparrow\downarrow & \uparrow\downarrow \\ \underline{d_{xy}} & \underline{d_{xz}} & \underline{d_{yz}} \end{array}$$

High-spin complex $\qquad\qquad$ Low-spin complex

$[CoF_6]^{3-}$ $\qquad\qquad\qquad$ $[Co(NH_3)_6]^{3+}$

$\Delta < P$ $\qquad\qquad\qquad\qquad$ $\Delta > P$

So far, we have considered just octahedral complexes. In the formation of complex ions of other geometric structures, ligands approach from different directions and produce different patterns of splitting of the *d* energy level. Figure 24-13 shows the pattern for tetrahedral complexes, and Figure 24-14 shows the pattern for square-planar complexes. In comparisons of hypothetical complexes of different structures having the same combinations of ligands, metal ions, and metal–ligand distances, we find the greatest energy separation of the *d* levels for the square-planar complex and the smallest energy separation for the tetrahedral complex. Because the tetrahedral splitting is small, almost all tetrahedral complexes are high spin.

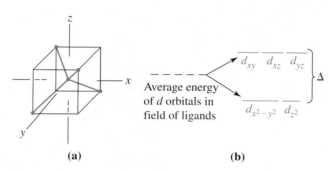

(a)   (b)

▲ **FIGURE 24-13**
Crystal field splitting in a tetrahedral complex ion
(a) The positions of attachment of ligands to a metal ion leading to the formation of a tetrahedral complex ion. (b) Interference with the *d* orbitals directed along the *x*, *y*, and *z* axes is not as great as with those that lie between the axes (see Figure 24-11). As a result, the pattern of crystal field splitting is reversed from that of an octahedral complex.

Uffelman, E. S., et al. "Microscale Syntheses, Reactions, and ^{1}H NMR Spectroscopic Investigations of Square Planar Macrolyclic Tetraamido-*N* Co(III) Complexes Relevant to Green Chemistry." *J. Chem. Educ.* **2004**: *81*, 325.

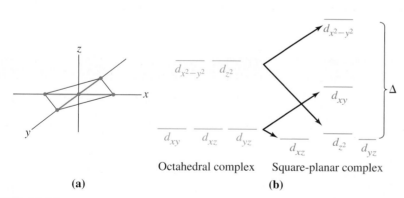

Octahedral complex   Square-planar complex

(a)   (b)

▲ **FIGURE 24-14**
Comparison of crystal field splitting in a square-planar and an octahedral complex
(a) The positions of attachment of ligands to a metal ion leading to the formation of a square-planar complex. (b) Splitting of the *d* energy level in a square-planar complex can be related to that of the octahedral complex. There are no ligands along the *z* axis in a square-planar complex, so we expect the repulsion between ligands and d_{z^2} electrons to be much less than in an octahedral complex. The d_{z^2} energy level is lowered considerably from that in an octahedral complex. Similarly, the energy levels of the d_{xz} and d_{yz} orbitals are lowered slightly because the electrons in these orbitals are concentrated in planes perpendicular to that of the square-planar complex. The energy of the $d_{x^2-y^2}$ orbital is raised because the *x* and *y* axes represent the direction of approach of four ligands to the central ion. The energy of the d_{xy} orbital is also raised because this orbital lies in the plane of the ligands in the square-planar complex.

Uffelman, E. S., et al. "Microscale Syntheses, Reactions, and ^{1}H NMR Spectroscopic Investigations of Square Planar Macrocyclic Tetraamido-*N* Cu(III) Complexes Relevant to Green Chemistry." *J. Chem. Educ.* **2004**: *81*, 182.

Are You Wondering . . .

If the two groups of orbitals split equally with respect to the average energy of the *d* orbitals?

The answer is no. The reason is that the total energy must be constant. If we consider a d^{10} ion such as Zn^{2+} in an octahedral field, the destabilization due to the four electrons in the $d_{x^2-y^2}$ and d_{z^2} orbitals must be offset by the stabilization gained by the six electrons in the d_{xy}, d_{xz}, and d_{yz}, orbitals. This requires that

$$(6 \times \text{the energy of } d_{xy}, d_{xy}, d_{yz} \text{ orbitals}) + (4 \times \text{the energy of } d_{x^2-y^2}, d_{z^2}) = 0$$

That is, the energy gained equals the energy lost. Also, the energy difference between the orbitals is

$$(\text{the energy of } d_{x^2-y^2}, d_{z^2}) - (\text{the energy of } d_{xy}, d_{xy}, d_{yz} \text{ orbitals}) = \Delta$$

To satisfy these two relationships, it is necessary that

$$\text{the energy of } d_{xy}, d_{xz}, d_{yz} \text{ orbitals} = -0.4 \, \Delta$$
$$\text{the energy of } d_{x^2-y^2}, d_{z^2} = 0.6 \, \Delta$$

The splitting is as shown.

The splitting of the two groups of orbitals is not equal with respect to the average energy of the *d* orbitals.

CONCEPT ASSESSMENT ✓

From the following crystal field splitting diagrams identify: **(i)** a tetrahedral Mn^{2+} complex, **(ii)** a strong-field octahedral complex of Co^{3+}, **(iii)** a weak-field octahedral complex of Fe^{2+}, **(iv)** a tetrahedral Ni^{2+} complex, **(v)** a high-spin octahedral complex of Fe^{3+}.

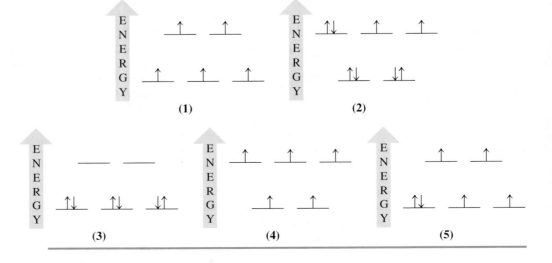

24-6   MAGNETIC PROPERTIES OF COORDINATION COMPOUNDS AND CRYSTAL FIELD THEORY

The paramagnetism of the dioxygen molecule was dramatically illustrated in Chapter 10 (page 378) by the interaction of liquid oxygen with the pole tips of a strong magnet. The origin of the paramagnetism is the existence of unpaired electrons in the molecule. Transition metal coordination compounds exhibit varying degrees of paramagnetism and can also be diamagnetic. A paramagnetic substance is pulled into, and a diamagnetic substance is pushed out of, a magnetic field. A straightforward way to measure magnetic properties is to weigh a substance "in" and "out" of a magnetic field, as illustrated in Figure 24-15. The mass of the substance is the same whatever magnetic property the substance possesses. However, if the substance is diamagnetic, it is slightly repelled by a magnetic field and *weighs* less within the field. If the substance is paramagnetic, it *weighs* more within the field.

The degree to which a substance weighs more in the magnetic field depends on the number of unpaired electrons. In the previous section, we saw that a high-spin d^n complex has more unpaired electrons than a low-spin d^n complex. Thus, measuring the change in weight of the complex in a magnetic field allows us to determine whether a complex is high or low spin. The magnetic properties of a complex depend on the magnitude of the crystal field splitting. Strong-field ligands tend to form low-spin, weakly paramagnetic, or even diamagnetic, complexes. Weak-field ligands tend to form high-spin, strongly paramagnetic complexes. The results of measuring the magnetic properties of coordination compounds can therefore be interpreted from crystal field theory, as demonstrated in Examples 24-4 and 24-5.

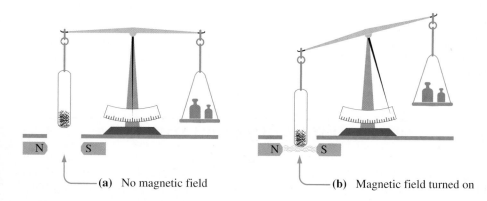

(a) No magnetic field

(b) Magnetic field turned on

◀ **FIGURE 24-15**
Paramagnetism—illustrated
(a) A sample is weighed in the absence of a magnetic field.
(b) When the field is turned on, the balanced condition is upset. The sample gains weight because it is now subjected to two attractive forces: the force of gravity *and* the force of interaction of the external magnetic field and the unpaired electrons.

EXAMPLE 24-4

Using the Spectrochemical Series to Predict Magnetic Properties. How many unpaired electrons would you expect to find in the octahedral complex $[Fe(CN)_6]^{3-}$?

Solution

The Fe atom has the electron configuration $[Ar]3d^64s^2$. The Fe^{3+} ion has the configuration $[Ar]3d^5$. CN^- is a strong-field ligand. Because of the large energy separation in the d levels of the metal ion produced by this ligand, we expect all the electrons to be in the lowest energy level. There should be only one unpaired electron.

Practice Example A: How many unpaired electrons would you expect to find in the octahedral complex $[MnF_6]^{2-}$?

Practice Example B: How many unpaired electrons would you expect to find in the tetrahedral complex $[CoCl_4]^{2-}$? Would you expect more, fewer, or the same number of unpaired electrons as in the octahedral complex $[Co(H_2O)_6]^{2+}$?

EXAMPLE 24-5

Using the Crystal Field Theory to Predict the Structure of a Complex from Its Magnetic Properties. The complex ion $[Ni(CN)_4]^{2-}$ is diamagnetic. Use ideas from the crystal field theory to speculate on its probable structure.

Solution

We can eliminate an octahedral structure because the coordination number is 4 (not 6). Our choice is between tetrahedral and square-planar.

The electron configuration of Ni is $[Ar]3d^84s^2$, and that of Ni(II) is $[Ar]3d^8$. Because the complex ion is diamagnetic, all $3d$ electrons must be paired. Let us see how we would distribute these $3d$ electrons if the structure were tetrahedral (recall Figure 24-13). We would place four electrons (all paired) into the two lowest d levels. We would then distribute the remaining four electrons among the three higher-level d orbitals. Two of the electrons would be unpaired, and the complex ion would be paramagnetic.

Because the tetrahedral structure would be paramagnetic, we can conclude that the structure of the diamagnetic $[Ni(CN)_4]^{2-}$ ion must be square-planar. Let's also demonstrate that this is a reasonable conclusion based on the d-orbital energy-level diagram for a square-planar complex (recall Figure 24-14). First, the three lowest-energy orbitals are filled with electrons (six), and then we assume that the energy separation between the d_{xy} and $d_{x^2-y^2}$ orbitals is large enough that the final two electrons remain paired in the d_{xy} orbital. This corresponds to a diamagnetic complex ion.

Practice Example A: The complex ion $[Co(CN)_4]^{2-}$ is paramagnetic with three unpaired electrons. Use ideas from the crystal field theory to speculate on its probable structure.

Practice Example B: Would you expect $[Cu(NH_3)_4]^{2+}$ to be diamagnetic or paramagnetic? Can you use this information about the magnetic properties of $[Cu(NH_3)_4]^{2+}$ to help you determine whether the structure of $[Cu(NH_3)_4]^{2+}$ is tetrahedral or square-planar? Explain.

24-7 COLOR AND THE COLORS OF COMPLEXES

Poncini, L., Wimmer, F. L. "Color classification of coordination compounds." *J. Chem. Educ.* 1987: 64, 1001.

Rodger, G. E. "Student-presented demonstrations on the colors of transition metal complexes." *J. Chem. Educ.* 1988: 65, 543.

Figure 24-16 uses two situations for mixing color to help clarify the nature of colors. Figure 24-16(a) represents *additive mixing*, the type of color mixing that occurs when colored spotlights are superimposed. Figure 24-16(b), conversely, represents *subtractive mixing*, the type of color mixing that occurs when paint pigments or colored solutions are mixed.

PRIMARY, SECONDARY, AND COMPLEMENTARY COLORS

For the additive mixing of light beams in Figure 24-16(a), the **primary colors** are defined as any three colors that, when combined, yield white light (W). The colors used in the figure are *red* (R), *green* (G), and *blue* (B); their sum can be represented as R + G + B = W. The **secondary colors** are those produced by combining two primary colors. Figure 24-16(a) indicates that the secondary colors are *yellow* (Y = R + G), *cyan* (C = G + B), and *magenta* (M = B + R).

Each secondary color is a **complementary color** of one of the primary colors. Again, from Figure 24-16(a), cyan (C) is the complementary color of red (R); magenta (M), of green (G); and yellow (Y), of blue (B). Figure 24-16(a) shows that when a primary color and its complementary color are mixed, the result is white light. This must be the case: Because cyan, for example, is itself the

▶ Additive color mixing is used in color monitors and color television screens. Subtractive color mixing is used for all the photographs and art in this text.

(a) Additive color mixing

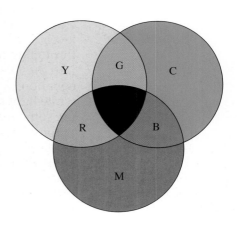

(b) Subtractive color mixing

▲ **FIGURE 24-16**
The mixing of colors
(a) The additive mixing of three beams of colored light: red (R), green (G), and blue (B). The secondary colors—yellow (Y), cyan (C), and magenta (M)—are produced in regions where two of the beams overlap. The overlap of all three beams produces white light (W). (b) The subtractive mixing of three pigments with the primary colors magenta (M), yellow (Y), and cyan (C). Here, the secondary colors—red (R), green (G), and blue (B)—form when two of the primary colors are mixed. A mixture of all three primary colors produces a very dark brown to black color.

In four-color printing, such as in this book and in color printers in computer systems, the basic inks used are magenta, yellow, cyan, and black. In photographs and drawings in this book, very small dots of these four basic colors, printed singly and in various combinations, produce the colored images you see. (With a magnifying glass, you can see individual dots of color.)

 Recall that about 10% of the male population is color blind. Many do not know it.

 Shakhashiri, B. Z., Dirreen, G. E., Juergens, F. "Color, solubility, and complex ion equilibria of nickel(II) species in aqueous solution (TD)." *J. Chem. Educ.* **1980:** *57,* 900.

combination of two of the primary colors—green and blue (C = G + B)—the combination of cyan and red (C + R) is the same as the combination of the three primary colors: G + B + R = W.

In subtractive color mixing, some of the wavelength components of white light are removed by absorption, and the reflected light (for example, from a painted surface or colored fabric) or transmitted light (as seen through glass or a solution) is deficient in some wavelength components. The reflected or transmitted light is colored. In subtractive color mixing (Fig. 24-16b), there are also primary, secondary, and complementary colors. In this case, *magenta* (M), *yellow* (Y), and *cyan* (C) are the primary colors and *green* (G), *blue* (B), and *red* (R) are the secondary colors. If a material absorbs all three primary colors, there is essentially no light left to be reflected or transmitted; the material appears black, or nearly so. If a material absorbs one color, primary or secondary, the reflected or transmitted light is the complementary color. Thus, a magenta sweater has that color because the dye it contains strongly absorbs green light and reflects magenta, the complement of green. A solution of red food dye has that color because the dye absorbs cyan light and transmits red.

Color Wheel activity

COLORED SOLUTIONS

Now let's direct our attention specifically to colored solutions. Colored solutions contain species that can absorb photons of visible light and use the energy of those photons to promote electrons in the species to higher energy levels. The energies of the photons must just match the energy differences through which the electrons are to be promoted. Because the energies of photons are related to the frequencies (and wavelengths) of light (recall Planck's equation, $E = hv$), only certain wavelength components are absorbed as white light passes through the solution. The emerging light, because it is lacking some wavelength components, is no longer white; it is colored.

Ions having (1) a noble-gas electron configuration, (2) an outer shell of 18 electrons, or (3) the "18 + 2" configuration (18 electrons in the $n - 1$ shell and two in the n, or outermost, shell) do not have electron transitions in the energy range corresponding to visible light. White light passes through these solutions without being absorbed; these ions are colorless in solution. Examples are the alkali and alkaline earth metal ions, the halide ions, Zn^{2+}, Al^{3+}, and Bi^{3+}.

Crystal field splitting of the d energy levels produces the energy difference, Δ, that accounts for the colors of complex ions. Promotion of an electron from a lower to a higher d level results from the absorption of the appropriate components of white light; the transmitted light is colored. Subtracting one color from white light leaves the complementary color. A solution containing $[Cu(H_2O)_4]^{2+}$ absorbs most strongly in the yellow region of the spectrum (about 580 nm). The wavelength components of the light transmitted combine to produce the color *blue*. Thus, aqueous solutions of copper(II) compounds usually have a characteristic blue color. In the presence of high concentrations of Cl^-, copper(II) forms the complex ion $[CuCl_4]^{2-}$. This species absorbs strongly in the blue region of the spectrum. The transmitted light is *yellow*, as is the color of the solution. Figure 24-17 suggests light absorption by these solutions. The colors of some complex ions of chromium are given in Table 24.5. The colors of six related coordination compounds of cobalt(III) are shown in Figure 24-18.

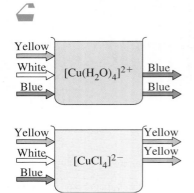

▲ FIGURE 24-17
Light absorption and transmission
$[Cu(H_2O)_4]^{2+}$ absorbs in the yellow region of the spectrum and transmits blue light. $[CuCl_4]^{2-}$ absorbs in the blue region of the spectrum and transmits yellow light.

 The demonstration on page 1001 can be done here too.

 Crystal Field Theory: Chromium Complexes activity

TABLE 24.5 Some Coordination Compounds of Cr^{3+} and Their Colors	
Isomer	Color
$[Cr(H_2O)_6]Cl_3$	Violet
$[CrCl(H_2O)_5]Cl_2$	Blue-green
$[Cr(NH_3)_6]Cl_3$	Yellow
$[CrCl(NH_3)_5]Cl_2$	Purple

▶ FIGURE 24-18
Effect of ligands on the colors of coordination compounds
These compounds all consist of a six-coordinate cobalt complex ion in combination with nitrate ions. In each case, the complex ion has five NH_3 molecules and one other group as ligands.

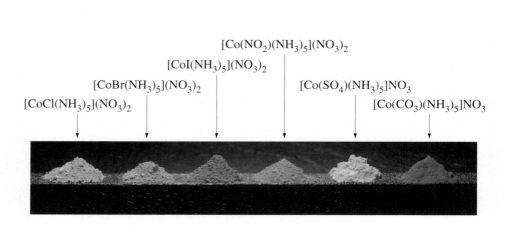

EXAMPLE 24-6

Relating the Colors of Complexes to the Spectrochemical Series. Table 24.5 lists the color of $[Cr(H_2O)_6]Cl_3$ as violet, whereas that of $[Cr(NH_3)_6]Cl_3$ is yellow. Explain this difference in color.

Solution

Here are the basic facts that we must use: Both chromium(III) complexes are octahedral, and the electron configuration of Cr^{3+} is $[Ar]3d^3$. From these facts, we can construct the energy-level diagram shown here. The three unpaired electrons go into the three lower-energy d orbitals. When a photon of light is absorbed, an electron is promoted from the lower to an upper energy level. The quantity of energy required for this promotion depends on the energy level separation, Δ.

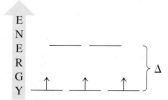

According to the spectrochemical series, NH_3 produces a greater splitting of the d energy level than does H_2O. We should expect $[Cr(NH_3)_6]^{3+}$ to absorb light of a *shorter* wavelength (higher energy) than does $[Cr(H_2O)_6]^{3+}$. Thus, $[Cr(NH_3)_6]^{3+}$ absorbs in the violet region of the spectrum, and the transmitted light is *yellow*. $[Cr(H_2O)_6]^{3+}$ absorbs in the yellow region of the spectrum, and the transmitted light is *violet*.

Practice Example A: The color of $[Co(H_2O)_6]^{2+}$ is pink, whereas that of tetrahedral $[CoCl_4]^{2-}$ is blue. Explain this difference in color.

Practice Example B: One of the following solids is yellow, and the other is green: $Fe(NO_3)_2 \cdot 6\,H_2O$; $K_4[Fe(CN)_6] \cdot 3\,H_2O$. Indicate which is which, and explain your reasoning.

Earl, B. L. "The colorful complexes of copper(II)." *J. Chem. Educ.* 1985: *62*, 798.

Johnson, A. R., et al. "Species Distribution Diagrams in the Copper-Ammonia System: An Updated and Expanded Demonstration Illustrating Complex Equilibria." *J. Chem. Educ.* 2005: *82*, 408.

Zingales, R. "Chemical Equilibria Involving Copper(II) Ethylenediamine Complexes." *J. Chem. Educ.* 2003: *80*, 535.

Thompson, M. L., Kateley, L. J. "The Nernst Equation: Determination of Equilibrium Constants for Complex Ions of Silver." *J. Chem. Educ.* 1999: *76*, 95 (January 1999).

Toma, H. E., Araki, K., Dovidauskas, S. "A Cyclic Voltammetry Experiment Illustrating Redox Potentials, Equilibrium Constants, and Substitution Reactions in Coordination Chemistry." *J. Chem. Educ.* 2000: *77*, 1351 (October 2000).

24-8   ASPECTS OF COMPLEX-ION EQUILIBRIA

In Chapter 18, we learned that complex-ion formation can have a great effect on the solubilities of substances, as in the ability of $NH_3(aq)$ to dissolve rather large quantities of $AgCl(s)$. To calculate the solubility of $AgCl(s)$ in $NH_3(aq)$, we had to use the formation constant, K_f, of $[Ag(NH_3)_2]^+$. Equations 24.1 and 24.2 illustrate how we dealt with formation constants in Chapter 18, with $[Zn(NH_3)_4]^{2+}$ as an example.

$$Zn^{2+}(aq) + 4\,NH_3(aq) \rightleftharpoons [Zn(NH_3)_4]^{2+}(aq) \tag{24.1}$$

$$K_f = \frac{[[Zn(NH_3)_4]^{2+}]}{[Zn^{2+}][NH_3]^4} = 4.1 \times 10^8 \tag{24.2}$$

In fact, cations in aqueous solution exist mostly in *hydrated* form. That is, $Zn^{2+}(aq)$ is actually $[Zn(H_2O)_4]^{2+}$. As a result, when NH_3 molecules bond to Zn^{2+} and form an ammine complex ion, they do not enter an empty coordination sphere. They must displace H_2O molecules. This displacement occurs in a stepwise fashion. The reaction

$$[Zn(H_2O)_4]^{2+} + NH_3 \rightleftharpoons [Zn(H_2O)_3NH_3]^{2+} + H_2O \tag{24.3}$$

for which

$$K_1 = \frac{[[Zn(H_2O)_3NH_3]^{2+}]}{[[Zn(H_2O)_4]^{2+}][NH_3]} = 3.9 \times 10^2 \tag{24.4}$$

is followed by

$$[Zn(H_2O)_3NH_3]^{2+} + NH_3 \rightleftharpoons [Zn(H_2O)_2(NH_3)_2]^{2+} + H_2O \qquad (24.5)$$

for which

$$K_2 = \frac{[[Zn(H_2O)_2(NH_3)_2]^{2+}]}{[[Zn(H_2O)_3NH_3]^{2+}][NH_3]} = 2.1 \times 10^2 \qquad (24.6)$$

and so on.

The value of K_1 in equation (24.4) is often designated as β_1 and called the formation constant for the complex ion $[Zn(H_2O)_3NH_3]^{2+}$. The formation of $[Zn(H_2O)_2(NH_3)_2]^{2+}$ is represented by the *sum* of equations (24.3) and (24.5),

$$[Zn(H_2O)_4]^{2+} + 2\,NH_3 \rightleftharpoons [Zn(H_2O)_2(NH_3)_2]^{2+} + 2\,H_2O \qquad (24.7)$$

The formation constant β_2, in turn, is given by the *product* of equations (24.4) and (24.6).

$$\beta_2 = \frac{[[Zn(H_2O)_2(NH_3)_2]^{2+}]}{[[Zn(H_2O)_4]^{2+}][NH_3]^2} = K_1 \times K_2 = 8.2 \times 10^4 \qquad (24.8)$$

For the next ion in the series, $[Zn(H_2O)(NH_3)_3]^{2+}$, $\beta_3 = K_1 \times K_2 \times K_3$. For the final member, $[Zn(NH_3)_4]^{2+}$, $\beta_4 = K_1 \times K_2 \times K_3 \times K_4$, and it is this product of terms that we called the formation constant in Section 18-8 and listed as K_f in Table 18.2. Additional stepwise formation constants are presented in Table 24.6.

The large numerical value of K_1 for reaction (24.3) indicates that Zn^{2+} has a greater affinity for NH_3 (a stronger Lewis base) than it does for H_2O. Displacement of ligand H_2O molecules by NH_3 occurs even if the number of NH_3 molecules present in aqueous solution is much smaller than the number of H_2O molecules, as in dilute $NH_3(aq)$. The fact that the successive K values decrease regularly in the displacement process, at least for displacements involving neutral molecules as ligands, is due in part to statistical factors: An NH_3 molecule has a better chance of replacing a H_2O molecule in $[Zn(H_2O)_4]^{2+}$, in which each coordination position is occupied by H_2O, than in $[Zn(H_2O)_3NH_3]^{2+}$, in which one of the positions is already occupied by NH_3. Also, once the degree of substitution of NH_3 for H_2O has become large, the chances improve for H_2O molecules to replace NH_3 molecules in a reverse reaction. Again, this tends to reduce the value of K. If irregularities arise in the succession of K values, it is often because of a change in structure of the complex ion at some point in the series of displacement reactions.

KEEP IN MIND ▶

that the product relationship between equilibrium constants is equivalent to a summation of $\Delta G°$ values. Hence, when an overall $\Delta G°$ is used to evaluate K_n

$\Delta G°$ (overall) =
$\quad \Delta G_1° + \Delta G_2° + \Delta G_3° + \cdots$
$\quad = -RT \ln K_1 - RT \ln K_2 -$
$\qquad\qquad RT \ln K_3 - \cdots$
$\quad = -RT \ln(K_1 \times K_2 \times K_3 \cdots)$
$\quad = -RT \ln \beta_n = -RT \ln K_f$

TABLE 24.6 Stepwise and Overall Formation (Stability) Constants for Several Complex Ions

Metal[a] Ion	Ligand	K_1	K_2	K_3	K_4	K_5	K_6	β_n (or K_f)[b]
Ag^+	NH_3	2.0×10^3	7.9×10^3					1.6×10^7
Zn^{2+}	NH_3	3.9×10^2	2.1×10^2	1.0×10^2	5.0×10^1			4.1×10^8
Cu^{2+}	NH_3	1.9×10^4	3.9×10^3	1.0×10^3	1.5×10^2			1.1×10^{13}
Ni^{2+}	NH_3	6.3×10^2	1.7×10^2	5.4×10^1	1.5×10^1	5.6	1.1	5.3×10^8
Cu^{2+}	en	5.2×10^{10}	2.0×10^9					1.0×10^{20}
Ni^{2+}	en	3.3×10^7	1.9×10^6	1.8×10^4				1.1×10^{18}
Ni^{2+}	EDTA	4.2×10^{18}						4.2×10^{18}

[a]In many tabulations in the chemical literature, formation-constant data are presented as logarithms: that is, $\log K_1$, $\log K_2, \ldots,$ and $\log \beta_n$.
[b]The β_n listed is for the number of steps shown: e.g., for $[Ag(NH_3)_2]^+$, $\beta_2 = K_f = K_1 \times K_2$; for $[Ni(en)_3]^{2+}$, $\beta_3 = K_f = K_1 \times K_2 \times K_3$; and for $[Ni(EDTA)]^{2-}$, $\beta_1 = K_f = K_1$.

If the ligand in a substitution process is polydentate, it displaces as many H_2O molecules as there are points of attachment. Thus, ethylenediamine (en) displaces H_2O molecules in $[Ni(H_2O)_6]^{2+}$ two at a time, in three steps. The first step is

$$[Ni(H_2O)_6]^{2+} + en \rightleftharpoons [Ni(en)(H_2O)_4]^{2+} + 2\,H_2O \qquad K_1(\beta_1) = 3.3 \times 10^7 \quad (24.9)$$

Note from Table 24.6 that the complex ions with polydentate ligands have much larger formation constants than do those with monodentate ligands. For example, K_f (that is, β_3) for $[Ni(en)_3]^{2+}$ is 1.1×10^{18}, whereas K_f (that is, β_6) for $[Ni(NH_3)_6]^{2+}$ is 5.3×10^8. The additional stability of chelates over complexes with monodentate ligands is known as the **chelation (or chelate) effect**. This effect can be partly attributed to the increase in entropy associated with chelation. In the displacement of H_2O by NH_3, the entropy change is small [two particles on each side of an equation such as (24.3)]. An ethylenediamine molecule, conversely, displaces *two* H_2O molecules [two particles on the left and three on the right of equation (24.9)]. The larger, positive value of $\Delta S°$ for the displacement by ethylenediamine means a more negative $\Delta G°$ and a larger K.

Chung, C. "Entropy effects in chelation reactions." *J. Chem. Educ.* **1984**: 61, 1062.

CONCEPT ASSESSMENT ✔

The Cr(III) cation in aqueous solution can form 6-coordinate complexes with ethylenediamine and $EDTA^{4-}$. Which complex do you expect to be the most stable if all water molecules in the six-coordinate Cr^{3+}(aq) ion are replaced?

24-9   ACID–BASE REACTIONS OF COMPLEX IONS

We have described complex-ion formation in terms of Lewis acids and bases. Complex ions may also exhibit acid–base properties in the Brønsted–Lowry sense; that is, they may act as proton donors or acceptors. Figure 24-19 represents the ionization of $[Fe(H_2O)_6]^{3+}$ as an acid. A proton from a *ligand* water molecule in hexaaquairon(III) ion is transferred to a *solvent* water molecule. The H_2O ligand is converted to OH^-.

$$[Fe(H_2O)_6]^{3+} + H_2O \rightleftharpoons [FeOH(H_2O)_5]^{2+} + H_3O^+ \qquad K_{a_1} = 9 \times 10^{-4} \quad (24.10)$$

The second ionization step is

$$[FeOH(H_2O)_5]^{2+} + H_2O \rightleftharpoons [Fe(OH)_2(H_2O)_4]^+ + H_3O^+ \quad K_{a_2} = 5 \times 10^{-4} \quad (24.11)$$

From these K_a values, we see that Fe^{3+}(aq) is fairly acidic (compared, for example, with acetic acid, with $K_a = 1.8 \times 10^{-5}$). To suppress ionization (hydrolysis) of $[Fe(H_2O)_6]^{3+}$, we need to maintain a low pH by the addition of acids such as HNO_3 or $HClO_4$. The ion $[Fe(H_2O)_6]^{3+}$ is violet in color, but aqueous solutions of Fe^{3+}(aq) are generally yellow because of the presence of hydroxo complex ions.

Soukup, R. W., et al. "Metal complexes as color indicators for solvent parameters." *J. Chem. Educ.* **1985**: 62, 459.

▲ **FIGURE 24-19**
Ionization of $[Fe(H_2O)_6]^{3+}$

The ions Cr^{3+} and Al^{3+} behave in a manner similar to Fe^{3+} except that, with them, hydroxo complex-ion formation can continue until complex anions are produced. $Cr(OH)_3$ and $Al(OH)_3$, as we previously noted, are soluble in alkaline as well as acidic solutions; they are amphoteric.

Regarding the acid strengths of aqua complex ions, a critical factor is the charge-to-radius ratio of the central metal ion. Thus, the small, highly charged Fe^{3+} attracts electrons away from an O—H bond in a ligand water molecule more strongly than does Fe^{2+}. Hence, $[Fe(H_2O)_6]^{3+}$ is a stronger acid ($K_{a_1} = 9 \times 10^{-4}$) than is $[Fe(H_2O)_6]^{2+}$ ($K_{a_1} = 1 \times 10^{-7}$).

24-10 SOME KINETIC CONSIDERATIONS

> The demonstration on page 1001 can be done here too.

When $NH_3(aq)$ is added to an aqueous solution containing Cu^{2+}, there is a change in color from pale blue to very deep blue. The reaction involves NH_3 molecules displacing H_2O molecules as ligands.

$$[Cu(H_2O)_4]^{2+} + 4\,NH_3 \longrightarrow [Cu(NH_3)_4]^{2+} + 4\,H_2O$$
$$\text{(pale blue)} \qquad\qquad \text{(very deep blue)}$$

This reaction occurs very rapidly—as rapidly as the two reactants can be brought together. The addition of $HCl(aq)$ to an aqueous solution of Cu^{2+} produces an immediate color change from pale blue to green, or even yellow if the $HCl(aq)$ is sufficiently concentrated.

$$[Cu(H_2O)_4]^{2+} + 4\,Cl^- \longrightarrow [CuCl_4]^{2-} + 4\,H_2O$$
$$\text{(pale blue)} \qquad\qquad \text{(yellow)}$$

▶ The terms *labile* and *inert* are not related to the thermodynamic stabilities of complex ions or to the equilibrium constants for ligand-substitution reactions. The terms are *kinetic* terms, referring to the rates at which ligands are exchanged.

Complex ions in which ligands can be interchanged rapidly are said to be **labile**. $[Cu(H_2O)_4]^{2+}$, $[Cu(NH_3)_4]^{2+}$, and $[CuCl_4]^{2-}$ are all labile (Fig. 24-20).

In freshly prepared $CrCl_3(aq)$, the ion *trans*-$[CrCl_2(H_2O)_4]^+$ produces a green color, but the color gradually turns to violet (Fig. 24-21). This color change results from the very slow exchange of H_2O for Cl^- ligands. A complex ion that exchanges ligands slowly is said to be *nonlabile*, or **inert**. In general, complex ions of the first transition series, except for those of Cr(III) and Co(III), are kinetically labile. Those of the second and third transition series are generally kinetically inert. Whether a complex ion is labile or inert affects the ease with which it can be studied. The inert ones are easiest to obtain and characterize, which may explain why so many of the early studies of complex ions were based on Cr(III) and Co(III).

▲ **FIGURE 24-20**
Labile complex ions
The exchange of ligands in the coordination sphere of Cu^{2+} occurs very rapidly. The solution at the extreme left is formed by dissolving $CuSO_4$ in concentrated $HCl(aq)$. Its yellow color is due to $[CuCl_4]^{2-}$. When a small amount of water is added, the mixture of $[Cu(H_2O)_4]^{2+}$ and $[CuCl_4]^{2-}$ ions produces a yellow-green color. When $CuSO_4$ is dissolved in water, a light blue solution of $[Cu(H_2O)_4]^{2+}$ forms. NH_3 molecules readily displace H_2O molecules as ligands and produce deep blue $[Cu(NH_3)_4]^{2+}$ (extreme right).

24-11 APPLICATIONS OF COORDINATION CHEMISTRY

The applications of coordination chemistry are numerous and varied. They range from analytical chemistry to biochemistry. The several brief examples in this section give some idea of this diversity.

HYDRATES

When a compound is crystallized from an aqueous solution of its ions, the crystals obtained are often hydrated. As originally described in Chapter 3 a hydrate is a substance that has a fixed number of water molecules associated with each formula unit. In some cases, the water molecules are ligands bonded directly to a metal ion. The coordination compound $[Co(H_2O)_6](ClO_4)_2$ may be represented as the hexahydrate, $Co(ClO_4)_2 \cdot 6\,H_2O$. In the hydrate $CuSO_4 \cdot 5\,H_2O$, four H_2O molecules are associated with copper in the complex ion $[Cu(H_2O)_4]^{2+}$, and the fifth with the SO_4^{2-} anion by hydrogen bonding. Another possibility for hydrate formation is that the water molecules may be incorporated into definite positions in the solid crystal but not associated with any particular cations or anions, as in $BaCl_2 \cdot 2\,H_2O$. This is called *lattice water*. Finally, part of the water may be coordinated to an ion and part of it may be lattice water, as appears to be the case with alums, such as $KAl(SO_4)_2 \cdot 12\,H_2O$.

▲ **FIGURE 24-21**
Inert complex ions
The green solid $CrCl_3 \cdot 6\,H_2O$ produces the green aqueous solution on the left. The color is due to *trans*-$[CrCl_2(H_2O)_4]^+$. A slow exchange of H_2O for Cl^- ligands leads to a violet solution of $[Cr(H_2O)_6]^{3+}$ in one or two days (right).

STABILIZATION OF OXIDATION STATES

The standard electrode potential for the reduction of Co(III) to Co(II) is

$$Co^{3+}(aq) + e^- \longrightarrow Co^{2+}(aq) \quad E° = +1.82\ V$$

This large positive value suggests that $Co^{3+}(aq)$ is a strong oxidizing agent, strong enough to oxidize water to $O_2(g)$.

$$4\,Co^{3+}(aq) + 2\,H_2O(l) \longrightarrow 4\,Co^{2+}(aq) + 4\,H^+(aq) + O_2(g) \quad E°_{cell} = +0.59\ V \quad (24.12)$$

Yet one of the complex ions featured in this chapter has been $[Co(NH_3)_6]^{3+}$. This ion is stable in water solution, even though it contains cobalt in the +3 oxidation state. Reaction (24.12) will not occur if the concentration of Co^{3+} is sufficiently low and $[Co^{3+}]$ is kept very low because of the great stability of the complex ion.

$$Co^{3+}(aq) + 6\,NH_3(aq) \rightleftharpoons [Co(NH_3)_6]^{3+}(aq) \quad \beta_6 = K_f = 4.5 \times 10^{33}$$

In fact, the concentration of free Co^{3+} is so low that for the half-reaction

$$[Co(NH_3)_6]^{3+} + e^- \longrightarrow [Co(NH_3)_6]^{2+}$$

$E°$ is only $+0.10\ V$. As a consequence, not only is $[Co(NH_3)_6]^{3+}$ stable but also $[Co(NH_3)_6]^{2+}$ is rather easily oxidized to the Co(III) complex.

The ability of strong electron-pair donors (strong Lewis bases) to stabilize high oxidation states in the way that NH_3 does in Co(III) complexes and O^{2-} in Mn(VII) complexes (such as MnO_4^-) affords a means of attaining certain oxidation states that might otherwise be difficult or impossible to attain.

PHOTOGRAPHY: FIXING A PHOTOGRAPHIC FILM

A black-and-white photographic film is an emulsion of a finely divided silver halide (typically AgBr) coated on a strip of polymer, such as a modified cellulose. In the *exposure* step, the film is exposed to light and some of the tiny granules of AgBr(s) absorb photons. The photons promote the oxidation of Br^- to Br and the reduction of Ag^+ to Ag. The Ag and Br atoms remain in the crystalline lattice of AgBr(s) as "defects," in numbers that depend on the intensity of the light absorbed: The brighter the light, the more Ag atoms. Because the actual number of Ag atoms produced in the exposure is not large, the silver is invisible to the eye. The pattern of distribution of the Ag atoms, however, creates a *latent* image of the object photographed. To obtain a visible image, the film is developed.

Schaeffer, R. W., Chan, B., Marshall, S. R., Blasiole, B., Khan, N., Yoder, K. L., Trainer, M. E., Yoder, C. H. "Preparation and Analysis of Multiple Hydrates of Simple Salts." *J. Chem. Educ.* **2000:** *77,* 509 (April 2000).

Houk, C., Hart, C. "Hazards in a photography lab: A cyanide incident case study (SAFETY)." *J. Chem. Educ.* **1987:** *64,* A234.

In the *developing* step, the exposed film is placed in a solution of a mild reducing agent such as hydroquinone, $C_6H_4(OH)_2$. An oxidation–reduction reaction occurs in which Ag^+ ions are reduced to Ag and the hydroquinone is oxidized. The action of the developer is such that reduction of Ag^+ to Ag occurs just in those granules of AgBr(s) that contain Ag atoms of the latent image. As a result, the number of Ag atoms in the film is greatly increased, and the latent image becomes visible. Bright regions of the photographed object appear as dark regions in the photographic image. At this stage, the film is a photographic *negative*. This negative cannot be exposed to light, however, because reduction of Ag^+ to Ag could still occur in the previously unexposed granules of AgBr(s). The negative must be fixed.

The *fixing* step requires that the black metallic silver of the negative remain on the film and the unexposed AgBr(s) be removed. A common fixer is an aqueous solution of sodium thiosulfate (also known as sodium hyposulfite or hypo). Because the complex ion $[Ag(S_2O_3)_2]^{3-}$ has a large formation constant, the following reaction is driven to completion—the AgBr(s) dissolves.

$$AgBr(s) + 2\,S_2O_3{}^{2-}(aq) \longrightarrow [Ag(S_2O_3)_2]^{3-}(aq) + Br^-(aq) \qquad (24.13)$$

Once the negative has been fixed, it is used to produce a *positive* image, the final photograph. This is done by projecting light through the negative onto a piece of photographic paper. Regions of the negative that are dark transmit little light to the photographic paper and will appear light when the photographic paper is subsequently developed and fixed. Conversely, light areas of the negative will appear dark in the final print. In this way, the areas of light and dark in the final print are the same as in the photographed object.

QUALITATIVE ANALYSIS

In discussing qualitative cation analysis in Section 18-9 (page 767), we showed how the group 1 precipitate—AgCl(s), $PbCl_2(s)$, or $Hg_2Cl_2(s)$—is separated by taking advantage of the stable complex ion formed by $Ag^+(aq)$ and $NH_3(aq)$.

$$AgCl(s) + 2\,NH_3(aq) \longrightarrow [Ag(NH_3)_2]^+(aq) + Cl^-(aq)$$

The qualitative analysis scheme abounds in other examples of complex-ion formation. For example, at a point in the procedure for cation group 3, a test is needed for Co^{2+}. In the presence of SCN^- ion, Co^{2+} forms a blue thiocyanato complex ion, $[Co(SCN)_4]^{2-}$ (Fig. 24-22a). A problem develops, however, if even a trace amount of Fe^{3+} is present in the solution. Fe^{3+} reacts with SCN^- to produce $[FeSCN(H_2O)_5]^{2+}$, a strongly colored, blood-red complex ion (Fig. 24-22b). Fortunately, this complication can be resolved by treating a solution containing both Co^{2+} and Fe^{3+} with an excess of F^-. The Fe^{3+} is converted to the extremely stable, pale yellow $[FeF_6]^{3-}$. The complex ion $[CoF_4]^{2-}$, being much less stable than $[Co(SCN)_4]^{2-}$, does not form. As a result, the $[Co(SCN)_4]^{2-}(aq)$ can be detected via the blue-green solution color (Fig. 24-22c).

▶ **FIGURE 24-22**
Qualitative tests for Co^{2+} and Fe^{3+}
(a) $[Co(SCN)_4]^{2-}$ complex ion.
(b) $[FeSCN(H_2O)_5]^{2+}$ complex ion.
(c) Mixture of $[FeF_6]^{3-}$ and $[Co(SCN)_4]^{2-}$.

(a)   (b)   (c)

SEQUESTERING METAL IONS

Metal ions can act as catalysts in promoting undesirable chemical reactions in a manufacturing process, or they may alter the properties of the material being manufactured. Thus, for many industrial purposes, it is imperative to remove mineral impurities from water. Often these impurities, such as Cu^{2+}, are present only in trace amounts, and precipitation of metal ions is feasible only if K_{sp} for the precipitate is very small. An alternative is to treat the water with a chelating agent. This reduces the free cation concentrations to the point at which the cations can no longer enter into objectionable reactions. The cations are said to be *sequestered*. Among the chelating agents widely employed are the salts of *ethylenediaminetetraacetic acid* (H_4EDTA), usually as the sodium salt.

$$4\ Na^{+} \begin{bmatrix} ^{-}OOCCH_2 \quad\quad\quad CH_2COO^{-} \\ \quad\quad NCH_2CH_2N \\ ^{-}OOCCH_2 \quad\quad\quad CH_2COO^{-} \end{bmatrix}$$

A representative complex ion formed by a metal ion, M^{n+}, with the hexadentate $EDTA^{4-}$ anion is depicted in Figure 24-23. The high stability of such complexes can be attributed to the presence of five, five-member chelate rings.

In the presence of $EDTA^{4-}(aq)$, Ca^{2+}, Mg^{2+}, and Fe^{3+} in hard water are unable to form boiler scale or to precipitate as insoluble soaps. The cations are sequestered in the complex ions: $[Ca(EDTA)]^{2-}$, $[Mg(EDTA)]^{2-}$, and $[Fe(EDTA)]^{-}$, having K_f values of 4.0×10^{10}, 4.0×10^{8}, and 1.7×10^{24}, respectively.

Chelation with EDTA can be used in treating some cases of metal poisoning. If a person with lead poisoning is fed $[Ca(EDTA)]^{2-}$, the following exchange occurs because $[Pb(EDTA)]^{2-}$ ($K_f = 2 \times 10^{18}$) is even more stable than $[Ca(EDTA)]^{2-}$ ($K_f = 4 \times 10^{10}$).

$$Pb^{2+} + [Ca(EDTA)]^{2-} \longrightarrow [Pb(EDTA)]^{2-} + Ca^{2+}$$

The body excretes the lead complex, and the Ca^{2+} remains as a nutrient. A similar method can be used to rid the body of radioactive isotopes, as in the treatment of plutonium poisoning.

Some plant fertilizers contain EDTA chelates of metals such as Cu^{2+} as a soluble form of the metal ion for the plant to use. Metal ions can catalyze reactions that cause mayonnaise and salad dressings to spoil, and the addition of EDTA reduces the concentration of metal ions by chelation.

Hart, J. R. "EDTA-type chelating agents in everyday consumer products: Some food, cleaning, and photographic applications." *J. Chem. Educ.* **1985:** *62, 75.*

▲ Some products containing EDTA.

◄ **FIGURE 24-23**
Structure of a metal–EDTA complex
The central metal ion M^{n+} (pale green) can be Ca^{2+}, Mg^{2+}, Fe^{2+}, Fe^{3+}, and so on. The ligand is $EDTA^{4-}$, and the net charge on the complex is $+n - 4$. Structural diagrams and ball-and-stick models are shown for the two optical isomers of an $[MEDTA]^{n-4}$ complex.

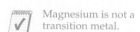

▲ **FIGURE 24-24**
The porphyrin structure

Smith, Richard A.
"The Colors of Life:
An Introduction to the Chemistry
of Porphyrins and Related
Compounds (by Lionel R.
Milgrom)." *J. Chem. Educ.* **1998**: *75,*
420 (April 1998).

Magnesium is not a
transition metal.

BIOLOGICAL APPLICATIONS: PORPHYRINS

The structure in Figure 24-24 is commonly found in both plant and animal matter. If the eight R groups are all H atoms, the molecule is called *porphin*. The central N atoms can give up their H atoms, and a metal atom can coordinate simultaneously with all four N atoms. The porphin is a tetradentate ligand for the central metal, and the metal–porphin complex is called a *porphyrin*. Specific porphyrins differ in their central metals and in the R groups on the porphin rings.

In *photosynthesis*, carbon dioxide and water, in the presence of inorganic salts, a catalytic agent called *chlorophyll*, and sunlight, combine to form carbohydrates.

$$n\,CO_2 + n\,H_2O \xrightarrow[\text{chlorophyll}]{\text{sunlight}} (CH_2O)_n + n\,O_2 \qquad (24.14)$$

$$\text{carbohydrates}$$

Carbohydrates are the main structural materials of plants. Chlorophyll is a green pigment that absorbs sunlight and directs the storage of this energy into the chemical bonds of the carbohydrates. The structure of one type of chlorophyll is shown in Figure 24-25; it is a porphyrin. The central metal ion is Mg^{2+}.

Green is the complementary color of magenta—a purplish red—so we should expect chlorophyll to absorb light in the red region of the spectrum (about 670–680 nm). This suggests that green plants should grow more readily in red light than in light of other colors, and some experimental evidence indicates that this is the case. For example, the maximum rate of formation of $O_2(g)$ by reaction (24.14) occurs with red light.

In Chapter 27, we will consider another porphyrin structure that is essential to life—hemoglobin.

▶ **FIGURE 24-25**
Structure of chlorophyll *a*

Summary

24-1 Werner's Theory of Coordination Compounds: An Overview—Many metal atoms or ions, particularly among the transition elements, have the ability to bond with **ligands** (electron-pair donors) to form a **complex**, a species in which there are coordinate covalent bonds between ligands and metal centers. The number of electron pairs donated to the central metal atom or ion by the ligands is the **coordination number**. A compound having one or more complexes as a constitutent is called a **coordination compound**.

24-2 Ligands—A ligand that attaches to a central metal atom or ion by donating a single electron pair is said to be **monodentate**. A **bidentate** ligand binds to the central metal atom or ion with two pairs of electrons (Fig. 24-3). **Polydentate** ligands are able to attach simultaneously to

two or more positions at the metal center. This multiple attachment produces complexes with five- or six-member rings of atoms—**chelates**. A polydentate ligand is also referred to as a **chelating agent**.

24-3 Nomenclature—The name of a complex conveys information about the number and kinds of ligands; the oxidation state of the metal center; and whether the complex is a neutral species, a cation, or an anion.

24-4 Isomerism—The positions at which ligands are attached to the metal center are not always equivalent, and as a consequence isomerism occurs in coordination complexes. **Structural isomers** differ in what ligands are attached to the metal ion and through which atoms, one example being linkage isomerism (Fig. 24-4). In **geometric**

isomerism, different structures with different properties result, depending on where the attachment of ligands occurs. In coordination complexes in which there are two ligands of one type and the remainder of another type, the *cis* isomer has the two identical ligands on the same side of a square in a planar structure (Fig. 24-5) or the same edge of an octahedral structure (Fig. 24-6). The *trans* isomer has the two ligands on opposite corners of a square (Fig. 24-5) or diametrically opposed in an octahedral structure (Fig. 24-6). **Optical isomers** differ by being nonsuperimposable mirror images of each other (Fig. 24-8). The two isomers so related are called **enantiomers** and they are said to be **chiral**. Optical isomerism and geometrical isomerism are forms of **stereoisomerism**, that is, isomerism based on the way ligands occupy the three-dimensional space around the metal center.

24-5 Bonding in Complex Ions: Crystal Field Theory— **Crystal field theory** is a bonding theory useful in explaining the magnetic properties and characteristic colors of complex ions (Fig. 24-11). This theory emphasizes the splitting of the *d* energy level of the central metal ion as a result of repulsions between *d*-orbital electrons of the central ion and electrons of the ligands (Fig. 24-12). Whether or not electrons are accommodated in the upper *d* orbitals depends on whether the crystal field splitting, Δ, is greater than the **pairing energy** (P). In d^n complexes, where $4 \leq n \leq 7$, **low spin** complexes occur when $P > \Delta$, and **high spin** complexes occur when $P < \Delta$. A prediction of the magnitude of *d*-level splitting produced by a ligand can be made via the ranking known as the **spectrochemical series**.

24-6 Magnetic Properties of Coordination Compounds and Crystal Field Theory—The magnetic properties of coordination compounds—whether diamagnetic or paramagnetic, and to what degree—can be assessed by measuring the change in weight of the substance when placed in a magnetic field (Fig. 24-15).

24-7 Color and the Colors of Complexes—The colors displayed by coordination complexes (Fig. 24-18) arise from the absorption of certain wavelength components of white light as an electron is excited from a lower energy *d* orbital to a higher enery *d* orbital in a crystal field. The transmitted light is deficient in the absorbed wavelengths and hence of a different color. The relationship of **primary**, **secondary**, and **complementary colors** is described and presented visually in Figure 24-16.

24-8 Aspects of Complex-Ion Equilibria—Formation of a coordination complex can be viewed as a stepwise equilibrium process in which other ligands displace H_2O molecules from aqua complex ions. The stepwise constants can be combined into an overall formation constant for the complex ion, K_f. When a chelating agent binds to a metal ion, an increased stability is observed due to the entropy changes produced when the chelating agent displaces water molecules from binding sites in the coordination sphere. This greater stability achieved is called the **chelation (chelate) effect**.

24-9 Acid–Base Reactions of Complex Ions—The ability of ligand water molecules to ionize causes some aqua complexes to exhibit acidic properties and helps explain amphoterism.

24-10 Some Kinetic Considerations—Also important in determining properties of a complex ion is the rate at which the ion exchanges ligands between its coordination sphere and the solution. Exchange is rapid in a **labile** complex and slow in an **inert** complex.

24-11 Applications of Coordination Chemistry—Complex-ion formation can be used to stabilize certain oxidation states, such as Co(III). Other applications include dissolving precipitates, such as AgCl by $NH_3(aq)$ in the qualitative analysis scheme and AgBr by $Na_2S_2O_3(aq)$ in the photographic process, and sequestering ions by chelation, as with EDTA.

Integrative Example

Absorbance is a measure of the proportion of monochromatic (single-color) light that is absorbed as the light passes through a solution. An *absorption spectrum* is a graph of absorbance as a function of wavelength. High absorbances correspond to large proportions of the light entering a solution being absorbed. Low absorbances signify that large proportions of the light are transmitted. The absorption spectrum of $[Ti(H_2O)_6]^{3+}(aq)$ is shown in Figure 24-26(a).

◀ **FIGURE 24-26**
The color of $[Ti(H_2O)_6]^{3+}(aq)$
(a) The absorption spectrum of $[Ti(H_2O)_6]^{3+}(aq)$.
(b) A solution containing $[Ti(H_2O)_6]^{3+}(aq)$.

(a) Describe the color of light that $[Ti(H_2O)_6]^{3+}(aq)$ absorbs most strongly, and the color of the solution. **(b)** Describe the electron transition responsible for the absorption peak, and determine the energy associated with this absorption.

◀ Emeralds in a matrix

Many of the beautifully colored stones that we consider precious or semiprecious are chemically impure. It is the impurities—transition metal ions—that are responsible for the brilliant colors. Consider ruby and emerald. Both of these gems contain small amounts of Cr^{3+} ion as the color-causing impurity. Rubies, however, have a deep red color, whereas emeralds have a distinctive blue-green color. Let us see why.

In a ruby crystal, the principal constituent is aluminum oxide (Al_2O_3), or *corundum*, with a structural pattern in which each Al^{3+} ion is surrounded by six O^{2-} ions.

Although the radius of the Cr^{3+} ion is somewhat larger (62 pm) than that of Al^{3+} (53 pm), these values match well enough that Cr^{3+} is able to replace Al^{3+} in the crystal lattice. In ruby, about 1% of the Al^{3+} ions are replaced by Cr^{3+} ions.

Because Al^{3+} has no valence electrons and no readily available electron transitions for its core electrons, a pure crystal of corundum is colorless. The color of ruby is the result of electron transitions between d orbitals of Cr^{3+} ions. Cr^{3+} has the ground-state electron configuration: $[Ar]3d^3$. The six O^{2-} ions create an octahedral crystal field about the Cr^{3+} ion and split the energy levels of the d orbitals into two groups (recall Figure 24-12). In the ground state, the three valence electrons occupy the three lower-energy d orbitals, and the two higher-energy d orbitals are vacant. Two excited states of the Cr^{3+} ion can be reached by absorption of two different frequencies (colors) of visible light. One transition, a low-energy transition, requires absorption of a yellow-green light; and the other, a high-energy transition, the absorption of violet light. As a consequence of these absorptions, the light that is transmitted by a ruby is *red* with a light purple tint.

The basic structure of an emerald is that of a crystal of *beryl*, $3\,BeO \cdot Al_2O_3 \cdot 6\,SiO_2$. Here, Cr^{3+} replaces Al^{3+} in the same type of octahedral field as in ruby but with

Strategy

The highest absorbances in the spectrum shown in Figure 24-26(a) come at about 500 nm. We use the electromagnetic spectrum in Figure 8-3 to determine the color of the absorbed light. We determine that the electron configuration of Ti^{3+}, the central ion in the complex ion, is $[Ar]3d^1$. In the ground state, the $3d$ electron is in one of the three degenerate lower levels in the d-orbital splitting diagram for an octahedral complex (Fig. 24-12).

Solution

(a) The electromagnetic spectrum in Figure 8-3 indicates that the absorbed light should be dark green. Figure 24-16(b) indicates that, in subtractive color mixing, the complementary color of green is magenta. Thus the color of the transmitted light (and hence the observed color of the solution) is a blend of red and blue.

(b) The quantity of energy we seek is that corresponding to electromagnetic radiation at the peak of the absorption spectrum: 500 nm. First we can establish the frequency of this light from $c = \nu \times \lambda$.

$$\nu = \frac{c}{\lambda} = \frac{2.998 \times 10^8 \text{ m s}^{-1}}{500 \times 10^{-9} \text{ m}} = 6.00 \times 10^{14} \text{ s}^{-1}$$

Then, we use Planck's equation to determine E:

$$E = h\nu = (6.626 \times 10^{-34} \text{ J s}) \times (6.00 \times 10^{14} \text{ s}^{-1}) = 3.98 \times 10^{-19} \text{ J}$$

dramatically different results. The presence of BeO and SiO_2 in the beryl crystal weakens the crystal field. The effect of the weaker field is a smaller energy separation (Δ) between the two groups of d orbitals in Cr^{3+} than is found in ruby. The energy per photon required to produce electron transitions between the d orbitals is less for Cr^{3+} in emerald than in ruby. The low-energy transition shifts from yellow-green to yellow-red, and the higher-energy transition is also lowered slightly in energy. As a result, when light passes through an emerald, most of the red and violet colors are absorbed and the blue and green are transmitted; the emerald takes on a blue-green color.

For rubies and emeralds to exhibit their colors continuously, there must be a mechanism by which electrons in Cr^{3+} can revert from their excited states back to the ground state. This occurs in two stages. First, electrons drop from the higher-energy states to a lower, intermediate state somewhat above the ground state. The energies of these transitions are in the infrared region of the spectrum; the emissions are invisible and appear as heat, which stimulates the vibrations of the ions in the crystal. The final transition to the ground state produces a red light. This type of light emission, in which a lower energy light is emitted following the absorption of higher energy light, is called *fluorescence*. Interestingly, both ruby and emerald display a red fluorescence emission. (When rubies and emeralds are observed in ultraviolet, or "black," light, *both* give off a red light.) In ruby, this red emission adds to the red color of the transmitted light, and in emerald, it is of just the right wavelength to enhance the character of the green color. The transitions referred to in this discussion are suggested in the diagram.

◀ **Light absorption and emission in a ruby**
The absorption of violet and yellow-green light from an incident white light beam causes the transmitted light to be red in color. In addition, the ruby emits red light by fluorescence.

This is the energy per photon. If we want the energy on a per-mole basis, we can write

$$E = (3.98 \times 10^{-19} \text{ J photon}^{-1}) \times (6.022 \times 10^{23} \text{ photon mol}^{-1}) \times \frac{1 \text{ kJ}}{1000 \text{ J}}$$

$$= 240 \text{ kJ mol}^{-1}$$

Assessment
Using ideas of subtractive color mixing, we ascertained the wavelength components of white light that the complex cation absorbs. The broadness of the absorption band is due to vibrations in the metal to oxygen bonds. By using the maximum of the absorption curve, we calculated the most probable energy of the absorbed photons.

Exercises

Nomenclature

1. Write the formula and name of
   (a) a complex ion having Cr^{3+} as the central ion and two NH_3 molecules and four Cl^- ions as ligands
   (b) a complex ion of iron(III) having a coordination number of 6 and CN^- as ligands
   (c) a coordination compound comprising two types of complex ions: one a complex of Cr(III) with ethylenediamine (en), having a coordination number of 6; the other, a complex of Ni(II) with CN^-, having a coordination number of 4

2. What are the coordination number and the oxidation state of the central metal ion in each of the following complexes? Name each complex.
   (a) $[Co(NH_3)_6]^{2+}$
   (b) $[AlF_6]^{3-}$
   (c) $[Cu(CN)_4]^{2-}$
   (d) $[CrBr_2(NH_3)_4]^+$
   (e) $[Co(ox)_3]^{4-}$
   (f) $[Ag(S_2O_3)_2]^{3-}$

3. Supply acceptable names for the following.
   (a) $[Co(OH)(H_2O)_4(NH_3)]^{2+}$
   (b) $[Co(ONO)_3(NH_3)_3]$
   (c) $[Pt(H_2O)_4][PtCl_6]$
   (d) $[Fe(ox)_2(H_2O)_2]^-$
   (e) $Ag_2[HgI_4]$

4. Write appropriate formulas for the following.
   (a) potassium hexacyanoferrate(III)
   (b) bis(ethylenediamine)copper(II) ion
   (c) pentaaquahydroxoaluminum(III) chloride
   (d) amminechlorobis(ethylenediamine) chromium(III) sulfate
   (e) tris(ethylenediamine)iron(III) hexacyanoferrate(II)

Bonding and Structure in Complex Ions

5. Draw Lewis structures for the following ligands:
   (a) H_2O; (b) CH_3NH_2; (c) ONO^-; (d) SCN^-.
6. Draw Lewis structures for the following ligands:
   (a) hydroxo; (b) sulfato; (c) oxalato; (d) thiocyanato-N-.
7. Draw a plausible structure to represent:
   (a) $[PtCl_4]^{2-}$
   (b) fac-$[Co(H_2O)_3(NH_3)_3]^{2+}$
   (c) $[CrCl(H_2O)_5]^{2+}$
8. Draw plausible structures of the following chelate complexes.
   (a) $[Pt(ox)_2]^{2-}$
   (b) $[Cr(ox)_3]^{3-}$

(c) $[Fe(EDTA)]^{2-}$

9. Draw plausible structures corresponding to each of the following names.
   (a) pentamminesulfatochromium(III) ion
   (b) trioxalatocobaltate(III) ion
   (c) triamminedichloronitrito-O-cobalt(III)
10. Draw plausible structures corresponding to each of the following names.
    (a) pentamminenitrito-N-cobalt(III) ion
    (b) ethylenediaminedithiocyanato-S-copper(II)
    (c) hexaaquanickel(II) ion

Isomerism

11. Which of these general structures for a complex ion would you expect to exhibit *cis* and *trans* isomerism? Explain.
    (a) tetrahedral
    (b) square-planar
    (c) linear
12. Which of these octahedral complexes would you expect to exhibit *geometric* isomerism? Explain.
    (a) $[CrOH(NH_3)_5]^{2+}$
    (b) $[CrCl_2(H_2O)(NH_3)_3]^+$
    (c) $[CrCl_2(en)_2]^+$
    (d) $[CrCl_4(en)]^-$
    (e) $[Cr(en)_3]^{3+}$
13. If A, B, C, and D are four different ligands,
    (a) how many geometric isomers will be found for square-planar $[PtABCD]^{2+}$?
    (b) Will tetrahedral $[ZnABCD]^{2+}$ display optical isomerism?
14. Write the names and formulas of three coordination isomers of $[Co(en)_3][Cr(ox)_3]$.
15. Draw a structure for *cis*-dichlorobis(ethylenediamine)cobalt(III) ion. Is this ion chiral? Is the *trans* isomer chiral? Explain.
16. The structures of four complex ions are given. Each has Co^{3+} as the central ion. The ligands are H_2O, NH_3, and oxalate ion, $C_2O_4{}^{2-}$. Determine which, *if any*, of these complex ions are isomers (geometric or optical); which,

if any, are identical (that is, have identical structures); and which, *if any*, are distinctly different.

(a)   (b)

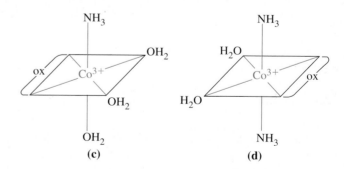

(c)   (d)

Crystal Field Theory

17. Describe how the crystal field theory explains the fact that so many transition metal compounds are colored.
18. Cyano complexes of transition metal ions (such as Fe^{2+} and Cu^{2+}) are often yellow, whereas aqua complexes are often green or blue. Explain the basis for this difference in color.

19. If the ion Co^{2+} is linked with strong-field ligands to produce an octahedral complex, the complex has *one* unpaired electron. If Co^{2+} is linked with weak-field ligands, the complex has *three* unpaired electrons. How do you account for this difference?

20. In contrast to the case of Co^{2+} considered in Exercise 19, no matter what ligand is linked to Ni^{2+} to form an octahedral complex, the complex always has *two* unpaired electrons. Explain this fact.

21. Predict:
   (a) which of the complex ions, $[MoCl_6]^{3-}$ and $[Co(en)_3]^{3+}$, is diamagnetic and which is paramagnetic
   (b) the number of unpaired electrons expected for the tetrahedral complex ion $[CoCl_4]^{2-}$.

22. Predict:
   (a) whether the square-planar complex ion $[Cu(py)_4]^{2+}$ is diamagnetic or paramagnetic

(b) whether octahedral $[Mn(CN)_6]^{3-}$ or tetrahedral $[FeCl_4]^-$ has the greater number of unpaired electrons.

23. In Example 24-5, we chose between a tetrahedral and a square-planar structure for $[Ni(CN)_4]^{2-}$ based on magnetic properties. Could we similarly use magnetic properties to establish whether the ammine complex of Ni(II) is octahedral $[Ni(NH_3)_6]^{2+}$ or tetrahedral $[Ni(NH_3)_4]^{2+}$? Explain.

24. In both $[Fe(H_2O)_6]^{2+}$ and $[Fe(CN)_6]^{4-}$ ions, the iron is present as Fe(II); however, $[Fe(H_2O)_6]^{2+}$ is paramagnetic, whereas $[Fe(CN)_6]^{4-}$ is diamagnetic. Explain this difference.

Complex-Ion Equilibria

25. Write equations to represent the following observations.
   (a) A mixture of $Mg(OH)_2(s)$ and $Zn(OH)_2(s)$ is treated with $NH_3(aq)$. The $Zn(OH)_2$ dissolves, but the $Mg(OH)_2(s)$ is left behind.
   (b) When $NaOH(aq)$ is added to $CuSO_4(aq)$, a pale blue precipitate forms. If $NH_3(aq)$ is added, the precipitate redissolves, producing a solution with an intense deep blue color. If this deep blue solution is made acidic with $HNO_3(aq)$, the color is converted back to pale blue.

26. Write equations to represent the following observations.
   (a) A quantity of $CuCl_2(s)$ is dissolved in concentrated $HCl(aq)$ and produces a yellow solution. The solution is diluted to twice its volume with water and assumes a green color. On dilution to ten times its original volume, the solution becomes pale blue.
   (b) When chromium metal is dissolved in $HCl(aq)$, a blue solution is produced that quickly turns green. Later the green solution becomes blue-green and then violet.

27. Which of the following complex ions would you expect to have the largest overall K_f, and why? $[Co(NH_3)_6]^{3+}$, $[Co(en)_3]^{3+}$, $[Co(H_2O)_6]^{3+}$, $[Co(H_2O)_4(en)]^{3+}$.

28. Use data from Table 24.6 to determine values of **(a)** β_4 for the formation of $[Zn(NH_3)_4]^{2+}$; **(b)** β_4 for the formation of $[Ni(H_2O)_2(NH_3)_4]^{2+}$.

29. Write a series of equations to show the stepwise displacement of H_2O ligands in $[Fe(H_2O)_6]^{3+}$ by ethylenediamine, for which $\log K_1 = 4.34$, $\log K_2 = 3.31$, and $\log K_3 = 2.05$. What is the overall formation constant, $\beta_3 = K_f$, for $[Fe(en)_3]^{3+}$?

30. A tabulation of formation constant data lists the following $\log K$ values for the formation of $[CuCl_4]^{2-}$: $\log K_1 = 2.80$, $\log K_2 = 1.60$, $\log K_3 = 0.49$, and $\log K_4 = 0.73$. What is the overall formation constant $\beta_4 = K_f$ for $[CuCl_4]^{2-}$?

31. Explain the following observations in terms of complex-ion formation.
   (a) $Al(OH)_3(s)$ is soluble in $NaOH(aq)$ but insoluble in $NH_3(aq)$.
   (b) $ZnCO_3(s)$ is soluble in $NH_3(aq)$, but ZnS(s) is not.
   (c) The molar solubility of AgCl in pure water is about 1×10^{-5} M; in 0.04 M NaCl(aq), it is about 2×10^{-6} M; but in 1 M NaCl(aq), it is about 8×10^{-5} M.

32. Explain the following observations in terms of complex-ion formation.
   (a) $CoCl_3$ is unstable in aqueous solution, being reduced to $CoCl_2$ and liberating $O_2(g)$. Yet, $[Co(NH_3)_6]Cl_3$ can be easily maintained in aqueous solution.
   (b) AgI is insoluble in water and in dilute $NH_3(aq)$, but AgI will dissolve in an aqueous solution of sodium thiosulfate.

Acid–Base Properties

33. Which of the following would you expect to react as a Brønsted–Lowry acid: $[Cu(NH_3)_4]^{2+}$, $[FeCl_4]^-$, $[Al(H_2O)_6]^{3+}$, or $[Zn(OH)_4]^{2-}$? Why?

34. Write simple chemical equations to show how the complex ion $[CrOH(H_2O)_5]^{2+}$ acts as **(a)** an acid; **(b)** a base.

Applications

35. From data in Chapter 18,
   (a) Derive an equilibrium constant for reaction (24.13), and explain why this reaction (the fixing of photographic film) is expected to go essentially to completion.
   (b) Explain why $NH_3(aq)$ cannot be used in the fixing of photographic film.

36. Show that the oxidation of $[Co(NH_3)_6]^{2+}$ to $[Co(NH_3)_6]^{3+}$ referred to on page 1027 should occur spontaneously in alkaline solution with H_2O_2 as an oxidizing agent.

Integrative and Advanced Exercises

37. From each of the following names, you should be able to deduce the formula of the complex ion or coordination compound intended. Yet, these are not the best systematic names that can be written. Replace each name with one that is more acceptable: **(a)** cupric tetraammine ion; **(b)** dichlorotetraammine cobaltic chloride; **(c)** platinic(IV) hexachloride ion; **(d)** disodium copper tetrachloride; **(e)** dipotassium antimony(III) pentachloride.

38. Magnus's green salt has the empirical formula $PtCl_2 \cdot 2\,NH_3$. It is a coordination compound consisting of both complex cations and complex anions. Write the probable formula of this coordination compound according to Werner's theory, and assign it a systematic name.

39. How many isomers are there of the complex ion $[CoCl_2(en)(NH_3)_2]^+$? Sketch their structures.

40. Explain the following observations through a series of equations. The green solid $CrCl_3 \cdot 6\,H_2O$ dissolves in water to form a green solution. The solution slowly turns blue-green; after a day or two, the solution is violet. When the violet solution evaporates to dryness, a green solid remains.

41. The *cis* and *trans* isomers of $[CoCl_2(en)_2]^+$ can be distinguished via a displacement reaction with oxalate ion. What difference in reactivity toward oxalate ion would you expect between the *cis* and *trans* isomers? Explain.

42. Write half-equations and an overall equation to represent the oxidation of tetraammineplatinum(II) ion to *trans*-tetraamminedichloroplatinate(IV) ion by Cl_2. Then make sketches of the two complex ions.

43. We learned in Chapter 16 that for polyprotic acids, ionization constants for successive ionization steps decrease rapidly. That is, $K_{a_1} \gg K_{a_2} \gg K_{a_3}$. The ionization constants for the first two steps in the ionization of $[Fe(H_2O)_6]^{3+}$ (reactions 24.10 and 24.11) are more nearly equal in magnitude. Why does this multistep ionization seem not to follow the pattern for polyprotic acids?

44. Following are the names of five coordination compounds containing complexes with platinum(II) as the central metal ion and ammonia molecules and/or chloride ions as ligands: **(a)** potassium amminetrichloroplatinate(II), **(b)** diamminedichloroplatinum(II), **(c)** triamminechloroplatinum(II) chloride, **(d)** tetraammineplatinum(II) chloride, **(e)** potassium tetrachloroplatinate(II). Make a rough sketch of the expected graph when electric conductivity is plotted as a function of the chlorine content of the compounds. [*Hint:* Your graph should be based on five points, but no quantitative data are given.]

45. For a solution that is 0.100 M in $[Fe(H_2O)_6]^{3+}$,
    (a) assuming that ionization of the aqua complex ion proceeds only through the first step, equation (24.10), calculate the pH of the solution.
    (b) Calculate $[[FeOH(H_2O)_5]^{2+}]$ if the solution is also 0.100 M $HClO_4$. (ClO_4^- does not complex with Fe^{3+}.)
    (c) Can the pH of the solution be maintained so that $[[FeOH(H_2O)_5]^{2+}]$ does not exceed 1×10^{-6} M? Explain.

46. A solution that is 0.010 M in Pb^{2+} is also made to be 0.20 M in a salt of EDTA (that is, having a concentration of the $EDTA^{4-}$ ion of 0.20 M). If this solution is now made 0.10 M in H_2S and 0.10 M in H_3O^+, will PbS(s) precipitate?

47. Without performing detailed calculations, show why you would expect the concentrations of the various ammine–aqua complex ions to be negligible compared with that of $[Cu(NH_3)_4]^{2+}$ in a solution having a total Cu(II) concentration of 0.10 M and a total concentration of NH_3 of 1.0 M. Under what conditions would the concentrations of these ammine–aqua complex ions (such as $[Cu(H_2O)_3NH_3]^{2+}$) become more significant relative to the concentration of $[Cu(NH_3)_4]^{2+}$? Explain.

48. Verify the statement on page 1029 that neither Ca^{2+} nor Mg^{2+} found in natural waters is likely to precipitate from the water on the addition of other reagents if the ions are complexed with EDTA. Assume reasonable values for the total metal ion concentration and that of *free* EDTA, such as 0.10 M each.

49. Estimate the total $[Cl^-]$ required in a solution that is initially 0.10 M $CuSO_4$ to produce a visible yellow color.

$$[Cu(H_2O)_4]^{2+} + 4\,Cl^- \rightleftharpoons [CuCl_4]^- + 4\,H_2O$$
$$\text{(blue)} \qquad\qquad\qquad \text{(yellow)}$$
$$K_f = 4.2 \times 10^5$$

Assume that 99% conversion of $[Cu(H_2O)_4]^{2+}$ to $[CuCl_4]^{2-}$ is sufficient for this to happen, and ignore the presence of any mixed aqua–chloro complex ions.

50. Refer to the stability of $[Co(NH_3)_6]^{3+}(aq)$ on page 1027, and
    (a) verify that E°_{cell} reaction (24.12) is +0.59 V.
    (b) Calculate $[Co^{3+}]$ in a solution that has a total concentration of cobalt of 1.0 M and $[NH_3] = 0.10$ M.
    (c) Show that for the value of $[Co^{3+}]$ calculated in part (b), reaction (24.12) will not occur.
    [*Hint:* Assume a low, but reasonable, concentration of Co^{2+} (say, 1×10^{-4} M) and a partial pressure of $O_2(g)$ of 0.2 atm.]

51. A Cu electrode is immersed in a solution that is 1.00 M NH_3 and 1.00 M in $[Cu(NH_3)_4]^{2+}$. If a standard hydrogen electrode is the cathode, E_{cell} is +0.08 V. What is the value obtained by this method for the formation constant, K_f, of $[Cu(NH_3)_4]^{2+}$?

52. The following concentration cell is constructed.

$$Ag|Ag^+(0.10\ M[Ag(CN)_2]^-, 0.10\ M\ CN^-)\|Ag^+(0.10\ M)|Ag$$

If K_f for $[Ag(CN)_2]^-$ is 5.6×10^{18}, what value would you expect for E_{cell}?
[*Hint:* Recall that the anode is on the left.]

53. The compound $CoCl_2 \cdot 2\,H_2O \cdot 4\,NH_3$ may be one of the hydrate isomers $[CoCl(H_2O)(NH_3)_4]Cl \cdot H_2O$ or $[Co(H_2O)_2(NH_3)_4]Cl_2$. A 0.10 M aqueous solution of the compound is found to have a freezing point of $-0.56\,^\circ C$. Determine the correct formula of the compound. The freezing-point depression constant for water is 1.86 mol kg$^{-1}\,^\circ C$, and for aqueous solutions, molarity and molality can be taken as approximately equal.

54. A compound is analyzed and found to contain 46.2% Pt, 33.6% Cl, 16.6% N, and 3.6% H. The freezing point of a 0.1 M aqueous solution of the compound is −0.74 °C. What is the structural formula of the compound? What possible isomeric forms are there for this compound?

55. The compound $Co(en)_2(NO_2)_2Cl$ has been prepared in a number of isomeric forms. One form undergoes no reaction with either $AgNO_3$ or en and is optically inactive. A second form reacts with $AgNO_3$ to form a white precipitate, does not react readily with en, and is optically inactive. A third form is optically active and reacts both with en and $AgNO_3$. Assuming a coordination number of 6 for the cobalt ion, identify each of the three isomeric forms by name, and sketch each of the structures.

56. The formation constants of the ions hexammine-nickel(II), tris(ethylenediamine)nickel(II) and penta-ethylenehexaminenickel(II) are $\beta_6 = 3.2 \times 10^8$, $\beta_3 = 1.6 \times 10^{18}$, and $\beta_1 = 2.0 \times 10^{19}$, respectively. Make reasonable assumptions concerning the enthalpy changes, and show that the formation constants illustrate the chelate effect. Pentaethylenehexamine (penten) is the hexadentate ligand shown below.

$$\underset{\underset{\displaystyle NH}{\diagup}{}}{H_2NCH_2CH_2}\ \underset{\underset{\displaystyle NH}{\diagup}{}}{CH_2CH_2}\ \underset{\underset{\displaystyle NH}{\diagup}{}}{CH_2CH_2}\ \underset{\underset{\displaystyle NH}{\diagup}{}}{CH_2CH_2}\ CH_2CH_2NH_2$$

57. Acetyl acetone undergoes an isomerization to form a type of alcohol called an *enol*.

The enol, abbreviated acacH, can act as a bidentate ligand as the anion acac⁻. Which of the following compounds are optically active: $Co(acac)_3$; *trans*-$[Co(acac)_2(H_2O)_2]Cl_2$; *cis*-$[Co(acac)_2(H_2O)_2]Cl_2$?

58. We have seen that complex formation can stabilize oxidation states. An important illustration of this fact is the oxidation of water in acidic solutions by $Co^{3+}(aq)$ but not by $[Co(en)_3]^{3+}$. Use the following data.

$$[Co(H_2O)_6]^{3+} + e^- \longrightarrow [Co(H_2O)_6]^{2+}$$
$$E° = 1.82\ V$$

$$[Co(H_2O)_6]^{2+} + 3\ en \longrightarrow [Co(en)_3]^{2+} + 6\ H_2O(l)$$
$$\log \beta_3 = 12.18$$

$$[Co(H_2O)_6]^{3+} + 3\ en \longrightarrow [Co(en)_3]^{3+} + 6\ H_2O(l)$$
$$\log \beta_3 = 47.30$$

Calculate $E°$ for the reaction

$$[Co(en)_3]^{3+} + e^- \longrightarrow [Co(en)_3]^{2+}$$

Show that $[Co(en)_3]^{3+}$ is stable in water but $Co^{3+}(aq)$ is not.

59. The amino acid glycine ($NH_2CH_2CO_2H$, denoted Hgly) binds as an anion and is a bidentate ligand. Draw and name all possible isomers of $[Co(gly)_3]$. How many isomers are possible for the compound $[Co(gly)_2Cl(NH_3)]$?

60. The structure of $K_2[PtCl_6]$ in the solid state is shown here. Identify the type of cubic unit cell, and describe the structure in terms of the holes occupied by the various ions.

Feature Problems

61. A structure that Werner examined as a possible alternative to the octahedron is the trigonal prism.

(a) Does this structure predict the correct number of isomers for the complex ion $[CoCl_2(NH_3)_4]^+$? If not, why not?

(b) Does this structure account for optical isomerism in $[Co(en)_3]^{3+}$? Explain.

62. Werner demonstrated that octahedral complexes can exhibit optical isomerism, and to Werner's satisfaction, this confirmed the octahedral arrangement of ligands. However, skeptics of his theory said that because the ligands contained carbon atoms, he could not rule out carbon as the source of the optical activity. Werner devised and prepared the following compound in which the OH^- groups act as bridging groups.

$$\left[Co \left(\begin{array}{c} H \\ O \\ \diagup \quad \diagdown \\ \quad \quad Co(NH_3)_4 \\ \diagdown \quad \diagup \\ O \\ H \end{array} \right)_3 \right]^{6+}$$

Werner resolved this compound into its optical isomers, confirming his theory and confounding his critics. What are the oxidation states of the Co ions? If the complex is low spin, what is the number of unpaired electrons in the molecule? Draw the structures of the two optical isomers.

63. The crystal field model discussed in the text describes how the degeneracy of the d orbitals is removed by an octahedral field of ligands. We have seen that the d_{xy}, d_{xz}, and d_{yz} orbitals are stabilized (lower energy) with respect to the average energy of the d orbitals and that the $d_{x^2-y^2}$ and d_{z^2} orbitals are destabilized. As described in the Are You Wondering feature on page 1018, the stabilization is -0.4Δ and destabilization is 0.6Δ. The crystal field stabilization energy (CFSE) can be defined as CFSE = [(number of electrons in the d_{xy}, d_{xz}, and d_{yz} orbitals) $\times$ (-0.4Δ)] + [(number of electrons in the $d_{x^2-y^2}$ and d_{z^2} orbitals) $\times$ (0.6Δ)]. The following table contains the enthalpy of hydration for the reaction

$$M^{2+}(g) + 6 H_2O(l) \longrightarrow [M(H_2O)_6]^{2+}(aq)$$

Dipositive Metal Ion	Hydration Energy, kJ mol^{-1}
Ca	−2468
Sc	−2673
Ti	−2750
V	−2814
Cr	−2799
Mn	−2743
Fe	−2843
Co	−2904
Ni	−2986
Cu	−2989
Zn	−2936

(a) Plot the hydration energies as a function of the atomic number of the metals shown.
(b) Assuming that all the hexaaqua complexes are high spin, which ions have zero CFSE?
(c) If lines are drawn between those ions with CFSE = 0, a line of negative slope is obtained. Can you explain this finding?
(d) The ions that do not have CFSE = 0 have heats of hydration that are more negative than the lines drawn in part (c). What is the explanation for this?
(e) Estimate the value of Δ for the Fe(II) ion in an octahedral field of water molecules.
(f) What wavelength of light would the $[Fe(H_2O)_6]^{2+}$ ion absorb?

Self-Assessment Exercises

64. In your own words, describe the following terms or symbols: **(a)** coordination number; **(b)** Δ; **(c)** ammine complex; **(d)** enantiomer.

65. Briefly describe each of the following ideas, phenomena, or methods: **(a)** spectrochemical series; **(b)** crystal field theory; **(c)** optical isomer; **(d)** structural isomerism.

66. Explain the important distinction between each of the following pairs: **(a)** coordination number and oxidation number; **(b)** monodentate and polydentate ligands; **(c)** cis and *trans* isomers; **(d)** dextrorotatory and levorotatory compounds; **(e)** low-spin and high-spin complexes.

67. The oxidation state of Ni in the complex ion $[Ni(CN)_4I]^{3-}$ is **(a)** −3; **(b)** −2; **(c)** 0; **(d)** +2; **(e)** +3.

68. The coordination number of Pt in the complex ion $[PtCl_2(en)_2]^{2+}$ is **(a)** 2; **(b)** 3; **(c)** 4; **(d)** 5; **(e)** 6.

69. Of the following complex ions, the one that exhibits isomerism is **(a)** $[Ag(NH_3)_2]^+$; **(b)** $[CoNO_2(NH_3)_5]^{2+}$; **(c)** $[Pt(en)(NH_3)_2]^{2+}$; **(d)** $[CoCl(NH_3)_5]^{2+}$; **(e)** $[PtCl_6]^{2-}$.

70. Of the following complex ions, the one that is optically active is **(a)** *cis*-$[CoCl_2(en)_2]^+$; **(b)** $[CoCl_2(NH_3)_4]^+$; **(c)** $[CoCl_4(NH_3)_2]^-$; **(d)** $[CuCl_4]^-$.

71. The number of unpaired electrons in the complex ion $[Cr(NH_3)_6]^{2+}$ is **(a)** 5; **(b)** 4; **(c)** 3; **(d)** 2; **(e)** 1.

72. Of the following, the one that is a Brønsted–Lowry acid is **(a)** $[Cu(NH_3)_4]^{2+}$; **(b)** $[FeCl_4]^-$; **(c)** $[Fe(H_2O)_6]^{3+}$; **(d)** $[Zn(OH)_4]^-$.

73. The most soluble of the following solids in $NH_3(aq)$ is **(a)** $Ca(OH)_2$; **(b)** $Cu(OH)_2$; **(c)** $BaSO_4$; **(d)** $MgCO_3$; **(e)** Fe_2O_3.

74. Name the following coordination compounds. Which one(s) exhibit(s) isomerism? Explain.
(a) $[CoBr(NH_3)_5]SO_4$
(b) $[Cr(NH_3)_6][Co(CN)_6]$
(c) $Na_3[Co(NO_2)_6]$
(d) $[Co(en)_3]Cl_3$

75. Write appropriate formulas for the following species.
(a) dicyanoargentate(I) ion
(b) triamminenitrito-N-platinum(II) ion
(c) aquachlorobis(ethylenediamine)cobalt(III) ion
(d) potassium hexacyanochromate(II)

76. Draw structures to represent these four complex ions: **(a)** $[PtCl_4]^{2-}$; **(b)** $[FeCl_4(en)]^-$; **(c)** *cis*-$[FeCl_2(ox)(en)]^-$; **(d)** *trans*-$[CrCl(OH)(NH_3)_4]^+$.

77. How many different structures are possible for each of the following complex ions?
(a) $[Co(H_2O)(NH_3)_5]^{3+}$
(b) $[Co(H_2O)_2(NH_3)_4]^{3+}$
(c) $[Co(H_2O)_3(NH_3)_3]^{3+}$
(d) $[Co(H_2O)_4(NH_3)_2]^{3+}$

78. Indicate what type of isomerism may be found in each of the following cases. If no isomerism is possible, so indicate.
  (a) $[Zn(NH_3)_4][CuCl_4]$
  (b) $[Fe(CN)_5SCN]^{4-}$
  (c) $[NiCl(NH_3)_5]^+$
  (d) $[PtBrCl_2(py)]^-$
  (e) $[Cr(OH)_3(NH_3)_3]^-$

79. Indicate what type of isomerism may be found in each of the following cases. If no isomerism is possible, so indicate.
  (a) $[Cr(en)_2Br_2]^+$
  (b) $[Co(ox)_2Br(SCN)]^{3-}$
  (c) $[NiCl_4(en)]^{2-}$
  (d) $[PtBrCl(ox)]^-$
  (e) $[Cr(Cl)_3(det)]$, det is $H_2NCH_2CH_2NHCH_2CH_2NH_2$

80. Of the complex ions $[Co(H_2O)_6]^{3+}$ and $[Co(en)_3]^{3+}$, one has a yellow color in aqueous solution; the other, blue. Match each ion with its expected color, and state your reason for doing so.

81. Using the method presented in Appendix E, construct a concept map depicting the essential ideas of crystal field theory, and how the theory explains the colors and magnetic properties of transition metal complexes.

 eMedia Exercises

82. For each of the **Ligands** models presented in *Activebook 24-2*, **(a)** draw the Lewis structures and identify the points of interaction for each ligand. **(b)** Describe the bonding interaction between these ligands and metal atoms in terms of Lewis acid–base theory.

83. After viewing the **Chirality** animation (*Activebook 24-4*), describe why your two hands are not physically superimposible. Repeat this exercise for the coordination compound $[Co(en)_3]^{3+}$.

84. Suggest how the measurement procedures described in the **Optical Activity** animation (*Activebook 24-4*) could be used to follow the synthesis of enantiomers. How would this approach differ from other methods of characterization?

25

NUCLEAR CHEMISTRY

CONTENTS

📖 Atwood, Charles H. "Teaching Aids For Nuclear Chemistry (Nuclear Chemistry-SOA)." *J. Chem. Educ.* **1994:** *71*, 845.

☑ When radioactivity was first discovered, its dangers were not appreciated. The first workers in the area did not take the precautions that are routine today.

📖 Hughes, E. A., Zalts A., "Radioactivity in the Classroom." *J. Chem. Educ.* **2000:** *77*, 613 (May 2000).

☑ Web site on the history of radioactivity: http://www.accessexcellence.com/ (commercial).

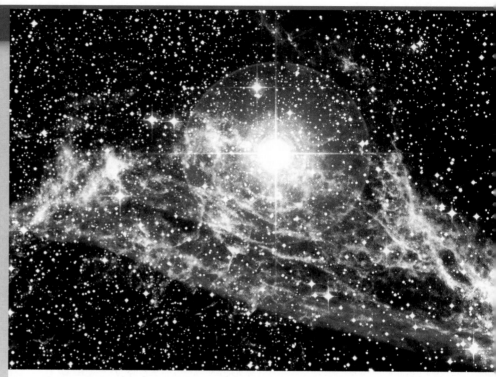

The thin strands of nebulosity are the remains of a star that ended its life in an enormous supernova explosion around 11,000 years ago. Near the center of this large shell of gas is a rapidly spinning neutron star believed to be the surviving core of the original star. Elementary particles, such as neutrons, and nuclear reactions, such as those occurring in stars, are discussed in this chapter.

The origin of all the elements is the stars, including our sun. Nuclear fusion in stars creates heavier elements from lighter ones. The heaviest elements, those with atomic numbers greater than 83, have unstable nuclei—that is, they are *radioactive*.

Certain isotopes of the lighter elements are also radioactive. The isotope carbon-14, for example, has chemical and physical properties that are essentially identical to those of the much more abundant isotopes carbon-12 and carbon-13. Carbon-14, however, is radioactive, and it is this property that is used in the technique known as radiocarbon dating.

In this chapter, we will consider a variety of phenomena that originate within the nuclei of atoms. Collectively, we refer to these phenomena as *nuclear chemistry*. While stars are the natural source of all the elements, we will discuss how new heavy elements and radioactive isotopes of existing lighter elements can be made artificially. We will also discuss the effects of ionizing radiation on matter. These effects can have both positive and negative outcomes and are a subject of society's continuing nuclear debate.

25-1   RADIOACTIVITY

The term *radioactivity* was proposed by Marie Curie to describe the emission of ionizing radiation by some of the heavier elements. Ionizing radiation, as the name implies, interacts with matter to produce ions. This means that the radiation is sufficiently energetic to break chemical bonds. Some ionizing radiation is particulate (consisting of particles), and some is nonparticulate. We introduced α, β, and γ radiation in Section 2-2. Let's describe them again in more detail, together with two other nuclear processes.

ALPHA PARTICLES

Alpha (α) particles are the nuclei of helium-4 atoms, $^4_2\text{He}^{2+}$, ejected spontaneously from the nuclei of certain radioactive atoms. We can think of α-particle emission as a process in which a bundle of two protons and two neutrons is emitted by a radioactive nucleus, resulting in a lighter nucleus. Alpha particles produce large numbers of ions via their collisions and near collisions with atoms as they travel through matter, but their penetrating power is low. (Generally, a few sheets of paper can stop them.) Because they have a positive charge, α particles are deflected by electric and magnetic fields (recall Figure 2-10).

We can represent the production of α particles by means of a nuclear equation. A **nuclear equation** is written to conform to two rules.

1. The sum of mass numbers must be the same on both sides.
2. The sum of atomic numbers must be the same on both sides.

In equation (25.1), the alpha particle is represented as ^4_2He.

$$^{238}_{92}\text{U} \longrightarrow {}^{234}_{90}\text{Th} + {}^4_2\text{He} \tag{25.1}$$

Mass numbers total 238, and atomic numbers total 92. The loss of an α particle results in a *decrease* of 2 in the atomic number and 4 in the mass number of the nucleus.

BETA PARTICLES

Beta (β^-) particles are deflected by electric and magnetic fields in the *opposite* direction from α particles. They are less massive than α particles, so they are deflected more strongly than α particles (recall Figure 2-10). Also, they have a greater penetrating power through matter than do α particles (a book rather than just a few sheets of paper may be required to stop them). Beta ($-$) particles are electrons, but they are electrons that originate from the nuclei of atoms in nuclear decay processes. Electrons that surround the nucleus are given the familiar symbol, e^-.

The simplest decay process producing a β^- particle is the decay of a free neutron, which is unstable outside the nucleus of an atom.

$$^1_0\text{n} \longrightarrow {}^1_1\text{p} + {}^0_{-1}\beta + \nu \tag{25.2}$$

A β^- particle does not have an atomic number, but its $1-$ charge is equivalent to an atomic number of -1. In nuclear equations, the β^- particle is represented as $^0_{-1}\beta$. Also, a β^- particle is small enough, compared to protons and neutrons, that its mass can be ignored in most calculations. Equation (25.2) introduces the symbol ν to represent an entity called a *neutrino*.

▲ Alpha particles leave a trail of liquid droplets, artificially colored green in this photograph, as they pass through a supersaturated vapor in a detector known as a cloud chamber. The chamber also contains He(g), and the trail of one α particle (yellow) is striking the nucleus of a He atom. Following the collision, the α particle and the He atom (red) move apart along lines at about a 90° angle.

◀ **KEEP IN MIND**

that in a *nuclear* equation we represent only the nuclei of atoms, not the atoms as a whole. Although, we do not keep track of electrons, electric charge is conserved by the requirement that the sums of the atomic numbers be the same on the two sides of the equation.

Separation of Alpha, Beta, and Gamma Rays animation

A neutrino has no charge and its detection was not easy. Theoretically, in order to balance nuclear equations, it was known that such a particle must exist. Many elementary particles have been found through experiments based on symmetry arguments.

▲ **A colorized cloud chamber photograph**
Point P marks an atomic nucleus that interacts with a γ-ray photon (not visible), producing a β⁻ particle and a positron (spiral green and red tracks, respectively). The photon also dislodges an orbital electron (vertical green track).

▲ **FIGURE 25-1**
Production of γ rays
The transition of a $^{230}_{90}$Th nucleus between the two energy states shown results in the emission of 0.05 MeV of energy in the form of γ rays.

An electronvolt (eV) is the energy acquired by an electron when it falls through an electric potential difference of 1 volt:

$$1 \text{ eV} = 1.6022 \times 10^{-19} \text{ J}$$
$$1 \text{ MeV} = 1 \times 10^{6} \text{ eV}$$

This particle was first postulated in the 1930s as necessary for the conservation of certain properties during the β⁻ decay process. Because they interact so weakly with matter, neutrinos were not detected until the 1950s. Even today, little is known of their properties, including their rest mass. (Rest mass is discussed on page 288).

For a typical β⁻ decay process, as represented by equation (25.3), we can think of a neutron *within* the nucleus of an atom spontaneously converting to a proton and an electron. This proton remains in the nucleus, whereas the electron is emitted as a β⁻ particle. Because of the extra proton, the atomic number *increases* by one unit, while the mass number is unchanged. The elusive neutrino is generally not included in the nuclear equation.

$$^{234}_{90}\text{Th} \longrightarrow ^{234}_{91}\text{Pa} + ^{0}_{-1}\beta \tag{25.3}$$

In a similar manner, in some decay processes a *proton* within the nucleus is converted to a neutron, and a β⁺ particle and a neutrino* are emitted.

$$^{1}_{1}\text{p} \longrightarrow ^{1}_{0}\text{n} + ^{0}_{+1}\beta + \nu \tag{25.4}$$

The β⁺ particle, also called a **positron**, has properties similar to the β⁻ particle, except that it carries a *positive* charge. (See the photograph in the margin.) This particle is also known as a *positive electron* and is designated $^{0}_{+1}\beta$ in nuclear equations. Positron emission is commonly encountered with artificially produced radioactive nuclei of the lighter elements. For example,

$$^{30}_{15}\text{P} \longrightarrow ^{30}_{14}\text{Si} + ^{0}_{+1}\beta \tag{25.5}$$

ELECTRON CAPTURE

Another process that achieves the same effect as positron emission is **electron capture (EC)**. In this case, an electron from an inner electron shell (usually the shell $n = 1$) is absorbed by the nucleus, where it converts a proton to a neutron. When an electron from a higher quantum level drops to the energy level vacated by the captured electron, X radiation is emitted. For example,

$$^{202}_{81}\text{Tl} + ^{0}_{-1}\text{e} \longrightarrow ^{202}_{80}\text{Hg} \text{ (followed by X radiation)} \tag{25.6}$$

GAMMA RAYS

Some radioactive decay processes that yield α or β⁻ particles leave the nucleus in an excited state. The nucleus then loses energy in the form of electromagnetic radiation called gamma rays. **Gamma (γ) rays** are a highly penetrating form of radiation that are *undeflected* by electric and magnetic fields (recall Figure 2-10). (Lead bricks more than several centimeters thick may be required to stop them.) In the radioactive decay of $^{234}_{92}$U, 77% of the nuclei emit α particles having an energy of 4.18 MeV. The remaining 23% of the $^{234}_{92}$U nuclei produce α particles with energies of 4.13 MeV. In the latter case, the $^{230}_{90}$Th nuclei are left with an excess energy of 0.05 MeV. This energy is released as γ rays. If the unstable excited Th nucleus is denoted as $^{230}_{90}\text{Th}^{\ddagger}$, we can write

$$^{234}_{92}\text{U} \longrightarrow ^{230}_{90}\text{Th}^{\ddagger} + ^{4}_{2}\text{He} \tag{25.7}$$

$$^{230}_{90}\text{Th}^{\ddagger} \longrightarrow ^{230}_{90}\text{Th} + \gamma \tag{25.8}$$

This γ-emission process is represented diagrammatically in Figure 25-1.

---

*There appear to be two related entities: the neutrino and antineutrino. Neutrinos accompany positron emission and electron capture; antineutrinos are associated with β⁻ emission.

Are You Wondering . . .

How an α particle gets out of a nucleus?

The answer has to do with quantum theory and the nature of the forces involved. Consider the potential energy diagram shown below. The blue line represents the potential energy, where we imagine an α particle as a separate particle within a nucleus such as $^{238}_{92}U$. Region A represents the potential energy of the α particle when it is held within the nucleus by the forces inside the uranium nucleus. Region C represents the potential energy of the α particle when it is free of the nucleus. The potential energy along the downward curving portion of the blue line represents the Coulomb (electrostatic) repulsion between the positively charged α particle and the nucleus remaining after the α particle has escaped ($^{234}_{90}Th$).

To get to region C, the α particle must get past the barrier in region B. The potential energy just beyond A, the radius of the nucleus, is greater than the energy of the α particle. (We know this from the measured energy of the α particle.) The α particle could not escape the nucleus if it were governed by classical physics because this would require an input of energy equal to the height of the barrier. Radioactive nuclei decay spontaneously, however, without an input of energy. How can the α particle get from region A to region C?

It passes through the barrier in a process known as *tunneling*. Classically, to go from A to C, the α particle would violate the principle of the conservation of energy. The α particle, however, possesses wave-like properties, as seen through the wave function at the bottom of the figure. Quantum mechanics predicts a finite probability of finding the α particle in a classically forbidden region. The wave function for the α particle trails off in the barrier region (B) and then reaches the outside, where it appears as a wave with much smaller amplitude. There is a finite probability (ψ^2) of finding the α particle outside the nucleus: The α particle has tunneled through the barrier.

Moreover, an alternative form of the uncertainty principle tells us that energy conservation can be violated by an amount ΔE for the length of time Δt given by

$$\Delta E \times \Delta t = \frac{h}{4\pi}$$

That is, the wave–particle duality of quantum theory allows the conservation of energy to be violated for brief periods—long enough for an α particle to tunnel through the barrier. ΔE corresponds to the energy difference between the barrier height and the α particle's energy, and Δt corresponds to the time required to pass through the barrier. The higher and wider the potential energy barrier, the less time the particle has to escape and the less likely it will do so. Thus, the height and width of the barrier control the rate of decay.

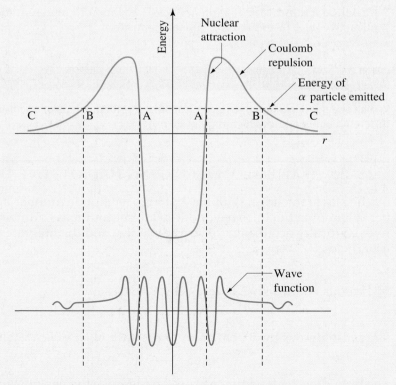

◀ Tunneling of an α particle out of the nucleus.

EXAMPLE 25-1

Writing Nuclear Equations for Radioactive Decay Processes. Write nuclear equations to represent **(a)** α-particle emission by ^{222}Rn and **(b)** radioactive decay of bismuth-215 to polonium-215.

Solution

(a) Two of the species involved in this process can be identified from the information given. The $^{222}_{86}$Rn nucleus ejects an α particle, $^{4}_{2}$He, as shown in the following incomplete nuclear equation.

$$^{222}_{86}\text{Rn} \longrightarrow \text{?} + {}^{4}_{2}\text{He}$$

Because the ejected α particle contains two protons, the unknown product must contain two fewer protons than $^{222}_{86}$Rn: $Z_{\text{unk}} = 86 - 2 = 84$. This atomic number identifies the element as polonium, $_{84}$Po. The mass number (A) of the product can be obtained by subtracting the mass number of the α particle from that of the radon isotope: $A = 222 - 4 = 218$. The completed nuclear equation is

$$^{222}_{86}\text{Rn} \longrightarrow {}^{218}_{84}\text{Po} + {}^{4}_{2}\text{He}$$

(b) The atomic number of bismuth is 83 and that of polonium is 84. We can approach this problem as we did part (a).

$$^{215}_{83}\text{Bi} \longrightarrow {}^{215}_{84}\text{Po} + \text{?}$$

There is no change in mass number, so the particle has a zero mass number. Its atomic number is $Z = 83 - 84 = -1$. Only a $^{0}_{-1}\beta$ particle fits these parameters: Beta ($-$) decay is the only type of emission leading to an increase of one unit in atomic number without a change in the mass number.

$$^{215}_{83}\text{Bi} \longrightarrow {}^{215}_{84}\text{Po} + {}^{0}_{-1}\beta$$

Practice Example A: Write a nuclear equation to represent β^--particle emission by $^{241}_{94}$Pu.

Practice Example B: Write a nuclear equation to represent the decay of a radioactive nucleus to produce ^{58}Ni and a positron.

Olbris, D. J., et al. *"Nucleogenesis! A Game with Natural Rules for Teaching Nuclear Synthesis and Decay." J. Chem. Educ.* **1999:** *76,* 349.

CONCEPT ASSESSMENT ✔

Which type(s) of radioactive decay transform(s) the nucleus of an atom to that of a different element, and which type(s) do not?

Hutchison, S. G., Hutchison F. I. "Radioactivity in Everyday Life." *J. Chem. Educ.* **1997:** *74,* 501 (May 1997).

KEEP IN MIND ▶

that *nuclide* is the general term for an atom with a particular atomic number and mass number. Different nuclides of an element are referred to as *isotopes*.

25-2   NATURALLY OCCURRING RADIOACTIVE ISOTOPES

Of the stable nuclides, $^{209}_{83}$Bi has the highest atomic number and mass number. All known nuclides beyond it in atomic and mass numbers are radioactive. Naturally occurring $^{238}_{92}$U is radioactive and disintegrates by the loss of α particles.

$$^{238}_{92}\text{U} \longrightarrow {}^{234}_{90}\text{Th} + {}^{4}_{2}\text{He}$$

$^{234}_{90}$Th is also radioactive; it decays by β^- emission.

$$^{234}_{90}\text{Th} \longrightarrow {}^{234}_{91}\text{Pa} + {}^{0}_{-1}\beta$$

$^{234}_{91}$Pa also decays by β^- emission to produce $^{234}_{92}$U, which is also radioactive.

$$^{234}_{91}\text{Pa} \longrightarrow {}^{234}_{92}\text{U} + {}^{0}_{-1}\beta$$

The term *daughter* is commonly used to describe the new nuclide produced in a radioactive decay. Thus, ^{234}Th is the daughter of ^{238}U, ^{234}Pa is the daughter of ^{234}Th, and so on.

Ronneau, C. "Radioactivity: A natural phenomenon." *J. Chem. Educ.* **1990:** *67,* 736.

*U-238 Decay Series
simulation*

◀ **FIGURE 25-2**
**The natural radioactive decay series
for $^{238}_{92}$U (uranium series)**
The long arrows pointing down and
to the left correspond to α-particle
emissions. The short horizontal
arrows represent β^- emissions. Other
natural decay series originate with
$^{232}_{90}$Th (thorium series) and $^{235}_{92}$U
(actinium series).

The chain of radioactive decay that begins with $^{238}_{92}$U continues through a number of steps of α and β^- emission until it eventually terminates with a stable isotope of lead—$^{206}_{82}$Pb. The entire scheme is outlined in Figure 25-2. All naturally occurring radioactive nuclides of high atomic number belong to one of three **radioactive decay series**: the *uranium* series just described, the *thorium* series, or the *actinium* series. (The actinium series actually begins with uranium-235, which was once called actino-uranium.)

Even though some of the daughters in natural radioactive decay schemes have very short half-lives, all are present because they are constantly forming as well as decaying. It is likely that only about one gram of radium-226 was present in several tons of uranium ore processed by Marie Curie in her discovery of radium in 1898. Nevertheless, she was successful in isolating it. The ore also contained only a fraction of a milligram of polonium, which she was able to detect but not isolate.

Radioactive decay schemes can be used to determine the ages of rocks and thereby the age of Earth (see Section 25-5). The appearance of certain radioactive substances in the environment can also be explained through radioactive decay series. The nuclides ^{210}Po and ^{210}Pb have been detected in cigarette smoke. These radioactive isotopes are derived from ^{238}U, found in trace amounts in the phosphate fertilizers used in tobacco fields. These α-emitting isotopes have been implicated in the link between cigarette smoking and cancer and heart disease.

Radioactivity, which is so common among isotopes of high atomic number, is a relatively rare phenomenon among the naturally occurring lighter isotopes. Even so, ^{40}K is a radioactive isotope, as are ^{50}V and ^{138}La. ^{40}K decays by β^- emission and by electron capture.

$$^{40}_{19}\text{K} \longrightarrow {}^{40}_{20}\text{Ca} + {}^{0}_{-1}\beta \qquad \text{and} \qquad {}^{40}_{19}\text{K} + {}^{0}_{-1}\text{e} \longrightarrow {}^{40}_{18}\text{Ar}$$

At the time Earth was formed ^{40}K was much more abundant than it is now. It is believed that the high argon content of the atmosphere (0.934% by volume and almost all of it as ^{40}Ar) is derived from the radioactive decay of ^{40}K. Aside from ^{40}K and ^{14}C (produced by cosmic radiation), the most important radioactive isotopes of the lighter elements are produced *artificially*.

Venable, Margaret H. "A Devotion to Their Science: Pioneer Women of Radioactivity." (Edited by Marlene F. Rayner-Canham and Geoffrey W. Rayner-Canham). *J. Chem. Educ.* **1998:** *75,* 151 (February 1998).

Web site on Marie Curie: http://www.aip.org/history/curie/ (non-commercial).

▲ **Marie Sklodowska Curie
(1867–1934)**
Marie Curie shared the 1903 Nobel Prize in physics for studies on radiation phenomena. In 1911, she won the Nobel Prize in chemistry for her discovery of polonium and radium.

▲ **Iréne Joliot-Curie (1897–1956)**

Iréne Joliot-Curie and her husband, Frédéric Joliot, shared the 1935 Nobel Prize in chemistry for the artificial production of radioactive nuclides.

Atwood, C. H., et al. "Simulating and Visualizing Nuclear Reactions." *J. Chem. Educ.* **1995**: 72, 515.

CONCEPT ASSESSMENT ✓

Explain why francium, the heaviest of the alkali metals (group 1), is not found in minerals containing the other alkali metals and is also one of the rarest elements.

25-3 NUCLEAR REACTIONS AND ARTIFICIALLY INDUCED RADIOACTIVITY

Ernest Rutherford discovered that atoms of one element can be transformed into atoms of another element. He did this in 1919 by bombarding $^{14}_{7}N$ nuclei with α particles, producing $^{17}_{8}O$ and protons. In this way, he was able to obtain protons outside atomic nuclei. The process can be represented as

$$^{14}_{7}N + ^{4}_{2}He \longrightarrow ^{17}_{8}O + ^{1}_{1}H \tag{25.9}$$

In reaction (25.9), instead of a nucleus disintegrating spontaneously, it must be struck by another small particle to induce a nuclear reaction. $^{17}_{8}O$ is a naturally occurring *nonradioactive* isotope of oxygen (0.037% natural abundance). The situation with $^{30}_{15}P$, which can also be produced by a nuclear reaction, is somewhat different.

In 1934, when bombarding aluminum with α particles, Iréne Joliot-Curie (daughter of Marie and Pierre Curie) and her husband, Frédéric Joliot, observed the emission of two types of particles: neutrons and positrons. The Joliots observed that when bombardment by α particles was stopped, the emission of neutrons also stopped; the emission of positrons continued, however. Their conclusion was that the nuclear bombardment produces $^{30}_{15}P$, which undergoes radioactive decay by the emission of positrons.

$$^{27}_{13}Al + ^{4}_{2}He \longrightarrow ^{30}_{15}P + ^{1}_{0}n$$

$$^{30}_{15}P \longrightarrow ^{30}_{14}Si + ^{0}_{+1}\beta$$

The first radioactive nuclide obtained by artificial means was $^{30}_{15}P$. Now, over 1000 artificially radioactive nuclides have been produced, and their number considerably exceeds the number of nonradioactive ones (about 280).

EXAMPLE 25-2

Writing Equations for Nuclear Bombardment Reactions. Write a nuclear equation for the production of ^{56}Mn by bombardment of ^{59}Co with neutrons.

Solution

First, we must realize that a particle is produced along with ^{56}Mn. To find the mass number (A) of the unknown particle, we must subtract the mass number of the Mn atom from that of the Co atom plus the neutron that initiates the reaction. Thus, for the unknown particle, $A = 59 + 1 - 56 = 4$. Subtracting the atomic number of Mn from that of Co provides the atomic number of the unknown particle: $Z = 27 - 25 = 2$. The unknown particle must have $A = 4$ and $Z = 2$; it is an α particle.

$$^{59}_{27}Co + ^{1}_{0}n \longrightarrow ^{56}_{25}Mn + ^{4}_{2}He$$

Practice Example A: Write a nuclear equation for the production of ^{147}Eu by bombardment of ^{139}La with ^{12}C.

Practice Example B: Write a nuclear equation for the production of ^{124}I by bombardment of ^{121}Sb with α particles. Also, write an equation for the subsequent decay of ^{124}I by positron emission.

25-4 TRANSURANIUM ELEMENTS

Until 1940, the only known elements were those that occur naturally. In 1940, bombardment of $^{238}_{92}U$ atoms with neutrons produced the first synthetic element. First, the unstable nucleus $^{239}_{92}U$ forms. This nucleus then undergoes β^- decay, yielding the element neptunium, with $Z = 93$.

$$^{234}_{92}U + {}^{1}_{0}n \longrightarrow {}^{239}_{92}U + \gamma$$

$$^{239}_{92}U \longrightarrow {}^{239}_{93}Np + {}^{0}_{-1}\beta$$

Bombardment by neutrons is an effective way to produce nuclear reactions because these heavy uncharged particles are not repelled as they approach a nucleus.

Since 1940, all the elements from $Z = 93$ to 112, as well as elements 114 and 116, have been synthesized. Many of the new elements of high atomic number have been formed by bombarding transuranium atoms with the nuclei of lighter elements. For example, an isotope of the element $Z = 105$ can be produced by bombarding atoms of $^{249}_{98}Cf$ with $^{15}_{7}N$ nuclei.

$$^{249}_{98}CF + {}^{15}_{7}N \longrightarrow {}^{260}_{105}Db + 4\,{}^{1}_{0}n \qquad (25.10)$$

To bring about nuclear reactions such as (25.10) requires bombarding atomic nuclei with energetic particles. Such energetic particles can be obtained in an accelerator. A type of accelerator known as a cyclotron is illustrated in Figure 25-3.

A *charged-particle accelerator*, as the name implies, can produce only beams of charged particles (such as $^{1}_{1}H^+$) as projectiles. In many cases, neutrons are most effective as projectiles for nuclear bombardment. The neutrons required can be generated through a nuclear reaction produced by a charged-particle beam. In the following reaction, $^{2}_{1}H$ represents a beam of deuterons (actually, $^{2}_{1}H^+$) from an accelerator.

$$^{9}_{4}Be + {}^{2}_{1}H \longrightarrow {}^{10}_{5}B + {}^{1}_{0}n$$

Another important source of neutrons for nuclear reactions is a nuclear reactor (as we will see in Section 25-8).

Seaborg, Glenn T. "Nuclear fission and transuranium elements: 50 years ago (SYMP)." *J. Chem. Educ.* **1989**: 66, 379.

▲ Standford Linear Accelerator Center (SLAC0 PEP-II collider). Electrons (blue) and positrons (pink) circulate in opposite directions along the two rings before being forced to collide. These collisions produce large quantities of B mesons and anti-B mesons.

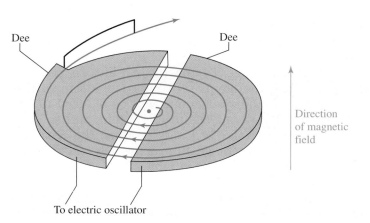

Direction of magnetic field

Dee   Dee

To electric oscillator

Web site on a cyclotron: http://www.nscl.msu.edu/ (non-commercial).

▲ **FIGURE 25-3**
The cyclotron
This type of accelerator consists of two hollow, flat, semicircular boxes, called *dees*, that are kept electrically charged. The entire assembly is maintained within a magnetic field. The particles to be accelerated, in the form of positive ions, are produced at the center of the opening between the dees. They are then attracted into the negatively charged dee and forced into a circular path by the magnetic field. When the particles leave the dee and enter the gap, the electric charges on the dees are reversed, so that the particles are attracted into the opposite dee. The particles are accelerated as they pass the gap and travel a wider circular path in the new dee. This process is repeated many times until the particles are brought to the required energy.

25-5   RATE OF RADIOACTIVE DECAY

In time, we can expect every atomic nucleus of a radioactive nuclide to disintegrate, but it is impossible to predict when any one nucleus will do so. Although we cannot make predictions for a particular atom, we can use statistical methods to make predictions for a collection of atoms. Based on experimental observations, a **radioactive decay law** has been established.

> *The rate of disintegration of a radioactive material—called the* activity, A, *or the* decay rate—*is directly proportional to the number of atoms present.*

In mathematical terms,

$$\text{rate of decay} \propto N \quad \text{and} \quad \text{rate of decay} = A = \lambda N \tag{25.11}$$

Schultz, E. "Dice Shaking as an Analogy for Radioactive Decay and First Order Kinetics." *J. Chem. Educ.* 1997: *74*, 505.

The activity is expressed in atoms per unit time, such as atoms per second. N is the number of atoms in the sample being observed; λ is the **decay constant**, which has units of time^{-1}. Consider the case of a 1,000,000-atom sample disintegrating at the rate of 100 atoms per second. In such a case, $N = 1.0 \times 10^6$ and

$$\lambda = A/N = 100 \text{ atom s}^{-1}/1.0 \times 10^6 \text{ atom} = 1.0 \times 10^{-4} \text{ s}^{-1}$$

First-Order Process animation

Radioactive decay is a *first-order* process. To relate it to the first-order kinetics that we studied in Chapter 14, think of the activity as corresponding to a rate of reaction; the number of atoms as corresponding to the concentration of a reactant; and the decay constant, λ, as corresponding to a rate constant, k. This correspondence can be carried further by writing an integrated radioactive decay law and a relationship between the decay constant and the **half-life** of the process—the length of time required for half of a radioactive sample to disintegrate.

$$\ln\left(\frac{N_t}{N_0}\right) = -\lambda t \tag{25.12}$$

$$t_{1/2} = \frac{0.693}{\lambda} \tag{25.13}$$

Ball, D. W. "How Radioactive Is Your Banana?" *J. Chem. Educ.* 2004: *81*, 1440.

Muse, L. A., et al. "A method for the determination of half-lives of long lived radioisotopes." *J. Chem. Educ.* 1982: *59*, 431.

In these equations, N_0 represents the number of atoms at some initial time ($t = 0$); N_t is the number of atoms at some later time, t; λ is the decay constant; and $t_{1/2}$ is the half-life.

Recall from Chapter 14 (page 584) that the half-life of a first-order process is a *constant*. Thus, if half the atoms of a radioactive sample disintegrate in 2.5 min, the number of atoms remaining will be reduced to one-fourth the original number in 5.0 min, one-eighth in 7.5 min, and so on. The shorter the half-life, the larger the value of λ and the faster the decay process. Half-lives of radioactive nuclides range from extremely short to very long, as suggested by the representative data in Table 25.1.

TABLE 25.1   Some Representative Half-Lives

Nuclide	Half-Life[a]	Nuclide	Half-Life[a]	Nuclide	Half-Life[a]
$^{3}_{1}\text{H}$	12.26 y	$^{40}_{19}\text{K}$	1.25×10^9 y	$^{214}_{84}\text{Po}$	1.64×10^{-4} s
$^{14}_{6}\text{C}$	5730 y	$^{80}_{35}\text{Br}$	17.6 min	$^{222}_{86}\text{Rn}$	3.823 d
$^{13}_{8}\text{O}$	8.7×10^{-3} s	$^{90}_{38}\text{Sr}$	27.7 y	$^{226}_{88}\text{Ra}$	1.60×10^3 y
$^{28}_{12}\text{Mg}$	21 h	$^{131}_{53}\text{I}$	8.040 d	$^{234}_{90}\text{Th}$	24.1 d
$^{32}_{15}\text{P}$	14.3 d	$^{137}_{55}\text{Cs}$	30.23 y	$^{238}_{92}\text{U}$	4.51×10^9 y
$^{35}_{16}\text{S}$	88 d				

[a]s, second; min, minute; h, hour; d, day; y, year.

EXAMPLE 25-3

Using the Half-Life Concept and the Radioactive Decay Law to Describe the Rate of Radioactive Decay. The phosphorus isotope ^{32}P is used in biochemical studies to determine the pathways of phosphorus atoms in living organisms. Its presence is detected through its emission of β^- particles. **(a)** What is the decay constant for ^{32}P, expressed in the unit s^{-1}? **(b)** What is the activity of a 1.00-mg sample of ^{32}P (that is, how many atoms disintegrate per second)? **(c)** Approximately what mass of ^{32}P will remain in the original 1.00-mg sample after 57 days? (See Table 25.1.) **(d)** What will be the rate of radioactive decay after 57 days?

Solution

(a) We can determine λ from $t_{1/2}$ with equation (25.13). The first result we get has the unit d^{-1}. We must convert this unit to h^{-1}, min^{-1}, and s^{-1}.

$$\lambda = \frac{0.693}{14.3\ d} \times \frac{1\ d}{24\ h} \times \frac{1\ h}{60\ min} \times \frac{1\ min}{60\ s} = 5.61 \times 10^{-7}\ s^{-1}$$

(b) First, let us find the number of atoms in 1.00 mg of ^{32}P.

$$\text{no. }^{32}\text{P atoms} = 0.00100\ g \times \frac{1\ mol\ ^{32}\text{P}}{32.0\ g} \times \frac{6.022 \times 10^{23}\ ^{32}\text{P atoms}}{1\ mol\ ^{32}\text{P}}$$

$$= 1.88 \times 10^{19}\ ^{32}\text{P atoms}$$

Then, we can multiply this number by the decay constant to get the activity or decay rate.

$$\text{activity} = \lambda N = 5.61 \times 10^{-7}\ s^{-1} \times 1.88 \times 10^{19}\ \text{atoms}$$

$$= 1.05 \times 10^{13}\ \text{atoms/s}$$

(c) A period of 57 days is $57/14.3 = 4.0$ half-lives. As shown in Figure 25-4, the quantity of radioactive material decreases by one-half for every half-life. The quantity remaining is $\left(\frac{1}{2}\right)^4$ of the original quantity.

$$?\ mg\ ^{32}\text{P} = 1.00\ mg \times \left(\frac{1}{2}\right)^4 = 1.00\ mg \times \frac{1}{16} = 0.063\ mg\ ^{32}\text{P}$$

(d) The activity is directly proportional to the number of radioactive atoms remaining (activity $= \lambda N$), and the number of atoms is directly proportional to the mass of ^{32}P. When the mass of ^{32}P has dropped to one-sixteenth its original mass, the number of ^{32}P atoms also falls to one-sixteenth the original number, and the rate of decay is one-sixteenth the original activity.

$$\text{rate of decay} = \frac{1}{16} \times 1.05 \times 10^{13}\ \text{atoms/s} = 6.56 \times 10^{11}\ \text{atoms/s}$$

 Radioactive Decay activity

Crippen, Kent J., Curtright Robert D. "Modeling Nuclear Decay: A Point of Integration between Chemistry and Mathematics." *J. Chem. Educ.* **1998:** *75,* 1434 (November 1998).

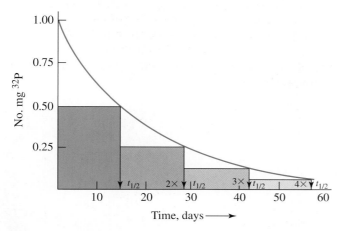

▲ **FIGURE 25-4**
Radioactive decay of a hypothetical ^{32}P sample—Example 25-3 illustrated

Practice Example A: ^{131}I is a β^- emitter used as a tracer for radioimmunoassays in biological systems. Use information in Table 25.1 to determine **(a)** the decay constant in s^{-1}; **(b)** the activity of a 2.05-mg sample of ^{131}I; **(c)** the percentage of ^{131}I remaining after 16 days; and **(d)** the rate of β^- emission after 16 days.

Practice Example B: ^{223}Ra has a half-life of 11.4 days. How long would it take for the activity associated with a sample of ^{223}Ra to decrease to 1.0% of its current value?

Are You Wondering . . .

Whether, like first-order chemical reactions, radioactive decay is temperature-dependent?

We learned in Chapter 14 that an important determinant of the rate of a chemical reaction is the height of the energy barrier between the reactants and products (the activation energy). The higher the temperature, the greater the number of molecules that can surmount the barrier as a result of collisions and the faster the reaction proceeds. Although there is also an energy barrier that confines nuclear particles to the nucleus, molecular collisions do not invest any energy in nuclear particles. Moreover, in radioactive decay, nuclear particles do not escape the nucleus by surmounting an energy barrier—they tunnel through it. Thus, the rates of radioactive decay processes are independent of temperature.

CONCEPT ASSESSMENT ✓

Why are radioactive nuclides with intermediate half-lives generally more hazardous than those with either extremely short or extremely long half-lives?

RADIOCARBON DATING

DeLorenzo, Ron. "California earthquakes: Predicting the next big one using radiocarbon dating (AA)." *J. Chem. Educ.* **1980:** *57*, 601.

Kulp, J. Laurence. "Dating with carbon 14." *J. Chem. Educ.* **1953:** *30*, 432.

Web site to calculate carbon dating: http://www.museum.mq.edu.au/eegypt2/carbdate.html (non-commercial).

In the upper atmosphere, $^{14}_{6}$C is formed at a constant rate by the bombardment of $^{14}_{7}$N with neutrons.

$$^{14}_{7}\text{N} + ^{1}_{0}\text{n} \longrightarrow ^{14}_{6}\text{C} + ^{1}_{1}\text{H}$$

The neutrons are produced by cosmic rays. $^{14}_{6}$C disintegrates by β^- emission.

Carbon-containing compounds in living organisms are in equilibrium with ^{14}C in the atmosphere—that is, these organisms replace ^{14}C atoms that have undergone radioactive decay with "fresh" ^{14}C atoms through interactions with their environment. The ^{14}C isotope is radioactive and has a half-life of 5730 years. The activity associated with ^{14}C that is in equilibrium with its environment is about 15 disintegrations per minute (dis min^{-1}) per gram of carbon. When an organism dies (for instance, when a tree is cut down), this equilibrium is destroyed and the disintegration rate falls off because the dead organism no longer absorbs new ^{14}C. From the measured disintegration rate at some later time, the age can be estimated (that is, the elapsed time since the ^{14}C equilibrium was disrupted).

▶ The remains of a man frozen in a glacier in the Austrian Alps have been dated by the radiocarbon method as 5300 years old.

EXAMPLE 25-4

Applying the Integrated Rate Law for Radioactive Decay: Radiocarbon Dating. A wooden object found in an Indian burial mound is subjected to radiocarbon dating. The activity associated with its ^{14}C content is 10 dis min^{-1} g^{-1}. What is the age of the object? In other words, how much time has elapsed since the tree was cut down?

Solution

The solution requires three equations: (25.11), (25.12), and (25.13). Equation (25.13) is used to determine the decay constant.

$$\lambda = \frac{0.693}{5730 \text{ y}} = 1.21 \times 10^{-4} \text{ y}^{-1}$$

Next, equation (25.11) relates to the actual number of atoms: N at $t = 0$ (the time when the ^{14}C equilibrium was destroyed) and N_t at time t (the present time). The activity just before the ^{14}C equilibrium was destroyed was 15 dis min^{-1} g^{-1}; at the time of the measurement, it is 10 dis min^{-1} g^{-1}. The corresponding numbers of atoms are equal to these activities divided by λ.

$$N_0 = A_0/\lambda = 15/\lambda \quad \text{and} \quad N_t = A_t/\lambda = 10/\lambda$$

Finally, we substitute into equation (25.12).

$$\ln\frac{N_t}{N_0} = \ln\frac{10/\lambda}{15/\lambda} = \ln\frac{10}{15} = -(1.21 \times 10^{-4} \text{ y}^{-1})t$$

$$-0.41 = -(1.21 \times 10^{-4} \text{ y}^{-1})t$$

$$t = \frac{0.41}{1.21 \times 10^{-4} \text{ y}^{-1}} = 3.4 \times 10^3 \text{ y}$$

Practice Example A: What is the age of a mummy, given a ^{14}C activity of 8.5 dis min^{-1} g^{-1}?

Practice Example B: What should be the current activity, in dis min^{-1} g^{-1}, of a wooden object believed to be 1100 years old?

Bindel, Thomas H. "The Tasmanian empire: A radioactive dating activity (INS)." *J. Chem. Educ.* **1988**: *65*, 47.

Rowe, M. W. "Radioactive dating: A method for geochronology (CP)." *J. Chem. Educ.* **1985**: *62*, 580.

THE AGE OF EARTH

The natural radioactive decay scheme of Figure 25-2 suggests the eventual fate of all $^{238}_{92}U$ in nature—conversion to lead. Naturally occurring uranium minerals always have associated with them some nonradioactive lead formed by radioactive decay. From the mass ratio of $^{206}_{82}Pb$ to $^{238}_{92}U$ in such a mineral, it is possible to estimate the age of the igneous rock containing the mineral. The age of the rock refers to the time elapsed since molten magma solidified to form the rock. One assumption of this method is that the initial radioactive nuclide, the final stable nuclides, and all the products of a decay series remain in the rock. Another assumption is that any lead present in the rock initially consisted of the several isotopes of lead in their present, naturally occurring abundances.

The half-life of $^{238}_{92}U$ is 4.5×10^9 years. According to the natural decay scheme of Figure 25-2, the basic change that occurs as atoms of $^{238}_{92}U$ and its daughters pass through the entire sequence of steps is

$$^{238}_{92}U \longrightarrow ^{206}_{82}Pb + 8\,^4_2He + 6\,^0_{-1}\beta$$

The decay sequence for $^{238}U \longrightarrow ^{206}Pb$ has 14 steps. The first step, however, has a much longer half-life than any of the other steps in the series and can thus be thought of as the rate-determining step, with the subsequent steps being "fast." As discussed in Chapter 14, we can ignore the effect on the overall rate of fast steps that occur after the slow, rate-determining step. Thus, the half-life for ^{238}U is essentially equal to the time it takes to convert half the initial ^{238}U to the ^{206}Pb isotope. Discounting the mass associated with the β^- particles, for every 238 g of uranium that undergoes complete decay, 206 g of lead and 32 g of helium are produced.

▲ A lunar rock that has been radiometrically dated to be about 4.6 billion years old.

Fairhall, A. W. "Dating of uranium minerals by the specific radioactivity of lead." *J. Chem. Educ.* **1963**: *40*, 626.

 Web site http://www.talkorigins.org/faqs/dating.html (commercial).

Suppose that in a hypothetical rock containing no lead initially, 1.000 g of $^{238}_{92}U$ had disintegrated through one half-life, 4.51×10^9 years. At the end of that time, 0.500 g $^{238}_{92}U$ would have disintegrated and another 0.500 g would remain. The quantity of $^{206}_{82}Pb$ now present in the rock would be

$$0.500 \text{ g } ^{238}_{92}U \times \frac{206 \text{ g } ^{206}_{82}Pb}{238 \text{ g } ^{238}_{92}U} = 0.433 \text{ g } ^{206}_{82}Pb$$

The ratio of lead-206 to uranium-238 in the rock would be

$$^{206}_{82}Pb/^{238}_{92}U = 0.433/0.500 = 0.866$$

If the $^{206}_{82}Pb/^{238}_{92}U$ mass ratio is less than 0.866, the age of the rock is less than one half-life of $^{238}_{92}U$. A higher ratio indicates a greater age for the rock. The best estimates of the age of the oldest rocks, and presumably of Earth itself, are about 4.5×10^9 years. These estimates are based on the $^{206}_{82}Pb/^{238}_{92}U$ ratio and on ratios for other pairs of isotopes from natural radioactive decay series.

25-6   ENERGETICS OF NUCLEAR REACTIONS

The energy change accompanying a nuclear reaction can be described using the mass–energy equivalence derived by Albert Einstein.

$$E = mc^2 \qquad (25.14)$$

KEEP IN MIND ▶
that the mass in equation (25.14) is the rest mass of the particle, as discussed on page 288.

An energy change in a process is always accompanied by a mass change, and the constant that relates them is the square of the speed of light. In chemical reactions, energy changes are so small that the equivalent mass changes are undetectable (though real nevertheless). In fact, we base the balancing of equations and stoichiometric calculations on the principle that mass is conserved (unchanged) in a chemical reaction. In nuclear reactions, energies are orders of magnitude greater than in chemical reactions. Perceptible changes in mass do occur.

📖 Treptow, Richard S. "E = mc² for the Chemist: When Is Mass Conserved?" *J. Chem. Educ.* **2005**: *82*, 1636.

If the exact masses of atoms are known, the energy of a nuclear reaction can be calculated with equation (25.14). The term m is the net change in mass, in kilograms, and c is expressed in meters per second. The resulting energy is in joules. Another common unit for expressing nuclear energy is the megaelectronvolt (MeV). (Recall from page 1042 that $1 \text{ eV} = 1.6022 \times 10^{-19}$ J.)

$$1 \text{ MeV} = 1.6022 \times 10^{-13} \text{ J} \qquad (25.15)$$

Equation (25.15) is a conversion factor between megaelectronvolts and joules. A conversion factor between atomic mass units (u) and joules (J) is also helpful. This relationship can be established by determining the energy associated with a mass of 1 u. This calculation is based on carbon-12, and note that 1 u is exactly $\frac{1}{12}$ of the mass of a carbon-12 atom. The mass, in grams, corresponding to 1 u can be calculated as follows:

$$1 \text{ u} \times \frac{1 \text{ } ^{12}C \text{ atom}}{12 \text{ u}} \times \frac{1 \text{ mol } ^{12}C}{6.0221 \times 10^{23} \text{ atoms } ^{12}C} \times \frac{12 \text{ g}}{1 \text{ mol } ^{12}C} = 1.6606 \times 10^{-24} \text{ g}$$

Converting this value of m to kilograms and using it in equation (25.14) gives

$$E = 1 \text{ u} \times \frac{1.6606 \times 10^{-24} \text{ g}}{u} \times \frac{1 \text{ kg}}{1000 \text{ g}} \times (2.9979 \times 10^8)^2 \frac{m^2}{s^2}$$

$$= 1.4924 \times 10^{-10} \text{ J}$$

Thus, the energy equivalent of 1 u is

$$1 \text{ atomic mass unit (u)} = 1.4924 \times 10^{-10} \text{ J} \qquad (25.16)$$

Finally, to express this energy in MeV,

$$1 \text{ atomic mass unit (u)} = 1.4924 \times 10^{-10} \text{ J} \times \frac{1 \text{ MeV}}{1.6022 \times 10^{-13} \text{ J}} = 931.5 \text{ MeV} \qquad (25.17)$$

These conversion factors are used in Example 25-5, together with the principle that the total mass–energy of the products of a nuclear reaction is equal to the total mass–energy of the reactants. The masses required in calculations based on nuclear reactions are *nuclear* masses. The relationship of a nuclear mass to a nuclidic (atomic) mass is

nuclear mass = nuclidic (atomic) mass − mass of extranuclear electrons

EXAMPLE 25-5

Calculating the Energy of a Nuclear Reaction with the Mass–Energy Relationship. What is the energy, in joules and in megaelectronvolts, associated with the α decay of ^{238}U?

$$^{238}_{92}U \longrightarrow {}^{234}_{90}Th + {}^{4}_{2}He$$

The nuclidic (atomic) masses in atomic mass units (u) are

$$^{238}_{92}U = 238.0508 \text{ u} \qquad {}^{234}_{90}Th = 234.0437 \text{ u} \qquad {}^{4}_{2}He = 4.0026 \text{ u}$$

Solution

The net change in mass that accompanies the decay of a single nucleus of ^{238}U is shown below. Note that the masses of the extranuclear electrons do not enter into the calculation of the net change in mass.

change in mass

= nuclear mass of $^{234}_{90}$Th + nuclear mass of $^{4}_{2}$He − nuclear mass of $^{238}_{92}$U

= [234.0437 u − (90 × mass e$^-$)] + [4.0026 u − (2 × mass e$^-$)]

$\qquad\qquad\qquad\qquad$ − [238.0508 u − (92 × mass e$^-$)]

= 234.0437 u + 4.0026 u − 238.0508 u − 92 × mass e$^-$ + 92 × mass e$^-$

= −0.0045 u

We can use this loss of mass and conversion factors (25.16) and (25.17) to write

$$E = -0.0045 \text{ u} \times \frac{1.49 \times 10^{-10} \text{ J}}{\text{u}} = -6.7 \times 10^{-13} \text{ J}$$

or

$$E = -0.0045 \text{ u} \times \left(\frac{931.5 \text{ MeV}}{\text{u}} \right) = -4.2 \times \text{MeV}$$

The negative sign denotes that energy is lost in the nuclear reaction. This is the kinetic energy of the departing α particle.

Practice Example A: What is the energy associated with the α decay of ^{146}Sm (145.913053 u) to ^{142}Nd (141.907719 u)? Use 4.002603 u as the mass of ^{4}He.

Practice Example B: The decay of ^{222}Rn by α-particle emission is accompanied by a loss of 5.590 MeV of energy. What quantity of mass, in atomic mass units (u), is converted to energy in this process?

◀ **KEEP IN MIND**
that you can use either nuclear or nuclidic (atomic) masses in calculations based on a nuclear equation. The change in mass will be the same in either case because the masses of the electrons will cancel out.

Figure 25-5 suggests formation of the nucleus of a $^{4}_{2}$He atom from two protons and two neutrons. In this process, there is a *mass defect* of 0.0305 u. That is, the experimentally determined mass of a $^{4}_{2}$He nucleus is 0.0305 u *less* than the combined mass of two protons and two neutrons. This "lost" mass is liberated as energy. With expression (25.17), we can show that 0.0305 u of mass is equivalent to an energy of 28.4 MeV. Because this is the energy released in forming a $^{4}_{2}$He nucleus, it is called the **nuclear binding energy**. Viewed another way, a $^{4}_{2}$He nucleus would have to absorb 28.4 MeV to cause its protons and neutrons to become separated. If the binding energy is considered to be apportioned equally among the two protons and two neutrons in $^{4}_{2}$He, the binding energy is 7.10 MeV per nucleon. Similar calculations for other nuclei yield the data used to plot the graph shown in Figure 25-6.

◀ Nucleons are nuclear particles: protons and neutrons.

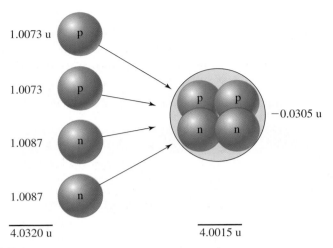

▲ **FIGURE 25-5**
Nuclear binding energy in $_2^4$He
The mass of a helium nucleus ($_2^4$He) is 0.0305 u (atomic mass unit) less than the combined masses of two protons and two neutrons. The energy equivalent to this loss of mass (called the mass defect) is the nuclear energy that binds the nuclear particles together.

Figure 25-6 indicates that the maximum binding energy per nucleon is found in a nucleus with a mass number of approximately 60. This finding leads to two interesting conclusions: (1) If small nuclei are combined into a heavier one (up to about $A = 60$), the binding energy per nucleon increases and a certain quantity of mass must be converted to energy. The nuclear reaction is highly exothermic. This *fusion* process serves as the basis of the hydrogen bomb. (2) For nuclei with mass numbers above 60, the addition of extra nucleons to the nucleus would require the expenditure of energy (since the binding energy per nucleon decreases). However, the *disintegration* of heavier nuclei into lighter ones is accompanied by the release of energy. This nuclear *fission* process serves as the basis of the atomic bomb and conventional nuclear power reactors. Nuclear fission and fusion will be discussed after we examine Figure 25-6 and consider the question of nuclear stability.

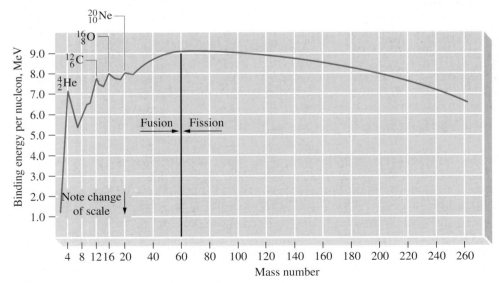

▲ **FIGURE 25-6**
Average binding energy per nucleon as a function of atomic number

25-7   NUCLEAR STABILITY

A number of basic questions have probably occurred to you as nuclear decay processes have been described: Why do some radioactive nuclei decay by α emission, some by β^- emission, and so on? Why do the lighter elements have so few naturally occurring radioactive nuclides, whereas all those of the heavier elements seem to be radioactive?

Our first clue to answers for such questions comes from Figure 25-6, in which several nuclides are specifically noted. These nuclides have higher binding energies per nucleon than those of their neighbors. Their nuclei are especially stable. This observation is consistent with a theory of nuclear structure known as the *shell theory*. In the formation of a nucleus, protons and neutrons are believed to occupy a series of nuclear shells. This process is analogous to building up the electronic structure of an atom by the successive addition of electrons to electronic shells. Just as the aufbau process periodically produces electron configurations of exceptional stability, so do certain nuclei acquire a special stability as nuclear shells are closed. This condition of special stability of an atomic nucleus occurs for certain numbers of protons or neutrons known as **magic numbers** (Table 25.2).

Another observation concerning nuclei is that among stable nuclei, the number of protons and the number of neutrons is most commonly *even*. There are fewer stable nuclei with odd numbers of protons and of neutrons. The relationship between numbers of protons (Z), numbers of neutrons (N), and the stability of isotopes is summarized in Table 25.3. Note particularly that stable atoms with the combination Z odd–N odd are very rare. This combination is found only in the nuclides ^2_1H, ^6_3Li, $^{10}_5B$, and $^{14}_7N$. Still another observation is that elements of *odd* atomic number generally have only one or two stable isotopes, whereas those of *even* atomic number have several. Thus, F ($Z = 9$) and I ($Z = 53$) each have only one stable nuclide, and Cl ($Z = 17$) and Cu ($Z = 29$) each have two. On the other hand, O ($Z = 8$) has three and Ca ($Z = 20$) has six.

Neutrons are thought to provide a nuclear force to bind protons and neutrons together into a stable unit. Without neutrons, the electrostatic forces of repulsion between positively charged protons would cause the nucleus to fly apart. For the elements of lower atomic numbers (up to about $Z = 20$), the required number of neutrons for a stable nucleus is about equal to the number of protons, for example, ^4_2He, $^{12}_6C$, $^{16}_8O$, $^{28}_{14}Si$, $^{40}_{20}Ca$. For higher atomic numbers, because of increasing repulsive forces between protons, larger numbers of neutrons are required and the neutron–proton (N/Z) ratio increases. For bismuth, the ratio is about $1.5 : 1$. Above atomic number 83, no matter how many neutrons are present, the nucleus is unstable. Thus, all isotopes of the known elements with $Z > 83$ are radioactive. Figure 25-7 indicates roughly the range of N/Z ratios as a function of atomic number for stable atoms.

Using the ideas outlined here, nuclear scientists have predicted the possible existence of atoms of high atomic number that should have very long half-lives, a belt of stability in Figure 25-7. After a search of many years, such atoms have been created. In 1999, the bombardment of a plutonium-242 target with calcium-48 ions produced the as-yet unnamed isotopes $^{287}114$ and $^{289}114$, with half-lives of 5 s and 30 s, respectively. Although these half-lives may appear short, they are practically an eternity compared to the half-lives of many other superheavy atoms, which are in the microsecond range.

TABLE 25.2   Magic Numbers for Nuclear Stability

Number of Protons	Number of Neutrons
2	2
8	8
20	20
28	28
50	50
82	82
114	126
	184

TABLE 25.3   Distribution of Naturally Occurring Stable Nuclides

Combination	Number of Nuclides
Z even–N even	163
Z even–N odd	55
Z odd–N even	50
Z odd–N odd	4

Campbell, Mark L. "Simple Rules for Determining Nuclear Stability and Type of Radioactive Decay." *J. Chem. Educ.* **1995:** *72*, 892 (October 1995).

Blanck, Harvey F. "Predicting nuclear stability using the periodic table." *J. Chem. Educ.* **1989:** *66*, 757.

CONCEPT ASSESSMENT

What proton number is found in a greater number of isotopes than any other proton number? What is the corresponding situation for neutron numbers?

Norman, Eric B. "Stellar Alchemy: The Origin of the Chemical Elements (Nuclear Chemistry-SOA)." *J. Chem. Educ.* **1994:** *71,* 813.

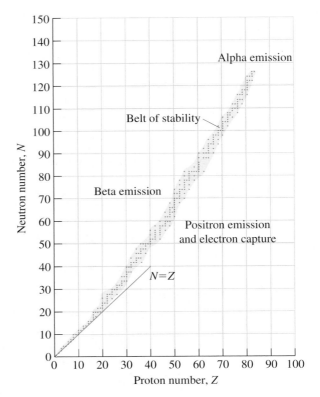

▲ **FIGURE 25-7**
Neutron-to-proton ratio and the stable nuclides up to Z = 83
The points within the belt of stability identify the stable nuclides. Some radioactive nuclides are also in this belt, but most lie outside, and the mode of their radioactive decay is indicated. The stable nuclides of low atomic numbers lie on or near the line $N = Z$; they have a neutron-to-proton ratio of one, or nearly so. At higher atomic numbers, the neutron-to-proton ratios increase to about 1.5.

EXAMPLE 25-6

Predicting Which Nuclei Are Radioactive. Which of the following nuclides would you expect to be stable, and which radioactive? **(a)** ^{82}As; **(b)** ^{118}Sn; **(c)** ^{214}Po.

Solution

(a) Arsenic-82 has $Z = 33$ and $N = 49$. This is an odd–odd combination that is found in only four of the lighter elements. ^{82}As is radioactive. (Note also that this nuclide is outside the belt of stability in Figure 25-7.)

(b) Tin has an atomic number of 50—a magic number. The neutron number is 68 in the nuclide ^{118}Sn. This is an even–even combination, and we should expect the nucleus to be stable. Moreover, Figure 25-7 shows that this nuclide is within the belt of stability. ^{118}Sn is a stable nuclide.

(c) ^{214}Po has an atomic number of 84. All known atoms with $Z > 83$ are radioactive. ^{214}Po is radioactive.

Practice Example A: Which of the following nuclides would you expect to be stable, and which radioactive? **(a)** ^{88}Sr; **(b)** ^{118}Cs; **(c)** ^{30}S.

Practice Example B: Write plausible nuclear equations to represent the radioactive decay of the fluorine isotopes ^{17}F and ^{22}F.

CONCEPT ASSESSMENT ✓

Of the radioactive nuclides among the following, which one is most likely to decay by β^- emission, and which one by β^+ emission: ^{44}Ca, ^{57}Cu, ^{100}Zr, ^{235}U? Explain.

25-8   NUCLEAR FISSION

In 1934, Enrico Fermi proposed that transuranium elements might be produced by bombarding uranium with neutrons. He reasoned that the successive loss of β^- particles would cause the atomic number to increase, perhaps to as high as 96. When such experiments were carried out, it was found that, in fact, the product did emit β^- particles. But in 1938, Otto Hahn, Lise Meitner, and Fritz Strassman found by chemical analysis that the products did not correspond to elements with $Z > 92$. Neither were they the neighboring elements of uranium—Ra, Ac, Th, and Pa. Instead, the products were radioisotopes of much lighter elements, such as Sr and Ba. Neutron bombardment of uranium nuclei causes certain of them to undergo **fission** into smaller fragments, as suggested by Figure 25-8.

The energy equivalent of the mass destroyed in a fission event is somewhat variable, but the average energy is approximately 3.20×10^{-11} J (200 MeV).

$$^{235}_{92}\text{U} + ^{1}_{0}\text{n} \longrightarrow ^{236}_{92}\text{U} \longrightarrow \text{fission fragments} + \text{neutrons} + 3.20 \times 10^{-11} \text{ J}$$

An energy of 3.20×10^{-11} J may seem small, but this energy is for the fission of a *single* $^{235}_{92}\text{U}$ nucleus. What if 1.00 g $^{235}_{92}\text{U}$ were to undergo fission?

$$? \text{ kJ} = 1.00 \text{ g } ^{235}\text{U} \times \frac{1 \text{ mol } ^{235}\text{U}}{235 \text{ g } ^{235}\text{U}} \times \frac{6.022 \times 10^{23} \text{ atoms } ^{235}\text{U}}{1 \text{ mol } ^{235}\text{U}} \times \frac{3.20 \times 10^{-11} \text{ J}}{1 \text{ atoms } ^{235}\text{U}}$$

$$= 8.20 \times 10^{10} \text{ J} = 8.20 \times 10^{7} \text{ kJ}$$

This is an enormous quantity of energy! To release that quantity of energy would require the complete combustion of nearly three tons of coal.

NUCLEAR REACTORS

In the fission of $^{235}_{92}\text{U}$, on average, 2.5 neutrons are released per fission event. These neutrons, on average, produce two or more fission events. The neutrons produced by the second round of fission produce another four or five events, and so on. The result is a *chain reaction*. If the reaction is uncontrolled, the released energy causes an explosion; this is the basis of the atomic bomb. Fission leading to an uncontrolled explosion occurs only if the quantity of ^{235}U exceeds the critical mass. The *critical mass* is the quantity of ^{235}U sufficiently large to retain enough neutrons to sustain a chain reaction. Quantities smaller than this are subcritical; neutrons escape at too great a rate to produce a chain reaction.

Reed, B. Cameron. "Estimating the Critical Mass of a Fissionable Isotope." *J. Chem. Educ.* **1996**: 73, 162 (February 1996).

◀ Ida Tacke Nodack, codiscoverer of the element rhenium, was the first person to suggest that Fermi's proposed experiments had produced fission. Her explanation was not generally accepted, however, until several years later.

Steinberg, Ellis P. "Radiochemistry of the fission products (SYMP)." *J. Chem. Educ.* **1989**: 66, 367.

Miller, Warren F., Jr. "Present and future nuclear reactor designs: Weighing the advantages and disadvantages of nuclear power with an eye on improving safety and meeting future needs." *J. Chem. Educ.* **1993**: 70, 109.

Settle, F. A., Jr., Erbschloe, D., Astore, W., Thomas, D. "The origins, production, and use of the atomic bomb: An interdisciplinary undergraduate seminar." *J. Chem. Educ.* **1993**: 70, 360.

Wiesner, E., et al. "Politics, Chemistry, and the Discovery of Nuclear Fission." *J. Chem. Educ.* **2001**: 78, 889.

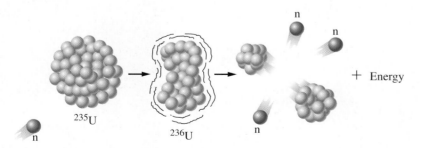

▲ **FIGURE 25-8**
Nuclear fission of $^{235}_{92}\text{U}$ with thermal neutrons
A neutron possessing ordinary thermal energy strikes a $^{235}_{92}\text{U}$ nucleus. First, the unstable nucleus $^{236}_{92}\text{U}$ is produced; this then breaks up into a light fragment, a heavy fragment, and several neutrons. Various nuclear fragments are possible, but the most probable mass numbers are 97 for the light fragment and 137 for the heavy one.

▶ **The core of a nuclear reactor**
The characteristic blue glow in the water surrounding the core is called *Cerenkov radiation*. It results when charged particles pass through a transparent medium faster than does light in the same medium. The charged particles are produced by nuclear fission. The radiation is analogous to the shock wave produced in a sonic boom.

Nuclear Reactors activity

Web site on nuclear reactors: http://www.nrc.gov/ NRC/reactors.html (non-commercial).

   In a nuclear reactor, the release of fission energy is controlled. One common design, called the *pressurized water reactor* (PWR), is pictured in Figure 25-9. In the core of the reactor, rods of uranium-rich fuel are suspended in water maintained under a pressure of 70 to 150 atm. The water serves a dual purpose. First, it slows down the neutrons from the fission process so that they possess only normal thermal energy. These thermal neutrons are better able to induce fission than highly energetic ones. In this capacity, the water acts as a **moderator**. Water also functions as a heat transfer medium. Fission energy maintains the water at a high temperature (about 300 °C). The high-temperature water is brought in contact with colder water in a heat exchanger. The colder water is converted to steam, which drives a turbine, which in turn drives an electric generator. A final component of the nuclear reactor is a set of **control rods**, usually cadmium metal, whose function is to absorb neutrons. When the rods are lowered into the reactor, the fission process is slowed down. When the rods are raised, the density of neutrons and the rate of fission increase.

 ▲ **FIGURE 25-9**
Pressurized water nuclear reactor
(a) Schematic of a nuclear power plant. (b) A nuclear power plant in New York State.

Are You Wondering . . .

About nuclear reactor safety?

There have been two notorious accidents at nuclear power stations. The first occurred at the Three Mile Island (TMI) generating plant near Middleton, Pennsylvania, in 1979. The TMI reactor is of the light-water type, in which water is used as the moderator and coolant. In this accident, some coolant (also the moderator) was lost; the chain reaction in the reactor stopped because there were too few slow neutrons. However, radioactive decay of the fission fragments continued, causing the fuel rods to get very hot. A partial meltdown resulted and, in turn, caused a fracture in one of the reactors. The fracture permitted the venting of a small amount of radioactive steam into the atmosphere. The reactor is now sealed, but electronic robots have discovered substantial damage to the fuel rods.

The second incident occurred at Chernobyl, in the Ukraine, in 1986. Graphite was used as the moderator there. When the coolant was turned off because of human error, the chain reaction went out of control. A tremendous rise in temperature followed, leading to a meltdown. During the meltdown, the graphite moderator surrounding the rods burned and radioactive smoke spewed out of the reactor. Radioactive materials were dispersed over much of Europe, Canada, and the United States. Although only a few dozen people were killed in the Chernobyl accident, many more will eventually die of cancer because of the related radiation. The type of accident observed at Chernobyl cannot happen in a light-water reactor, in which the coolant is the moderator.

Other nations have used nuclear power without experiencing accidents. In France and Japan, two-thirds of the electrical energy is produced by nuclear power stations. The safety record of nuclear reactors is particularly high, but the need for the storage of the nuclear waste produced is a vexing problem. Ways of dealing with these problems are discussed in the Focus On feature on page 1066.

(a)

(b)

(c)

▲ **(a)** The Three Mile Island nuclear reactor, site of a small nuclear accident in 1979. **(b)** A mutated pine tree in front of the Chernobyl nuclear reactor, site of a major nuclear accident in 1986. **(c)** A nuclear power plant in France that has operated for decades without mishap.

Mammano, Nicholas J. "A chemistry lesson at Three Mile Island." *J. Chem. Educ.* **1980:** *57*, 286.

Choppin, Gregory R. "Aspects of Nuclear Waste Disposal of Use in Teaching Basic Chemistry (Nuclear Chemistry-SOA)." *J. Chem. Educ.* **1994:** *71*, 826.

Web site on breeder reactors: http://www.inel.gov/resources/tours/ebr1.htm (non-commercial).

BREEDER REACTORS

All that is required to initiate the fission of $^{235}_{92}U$ are neutrons of ordinary thermal energies. Conversely, nuclei of $^{238}_{92}U$, the abundant nuclide of uranium (99.28%), undergo the following reactions only when struck by energetic neutrons.

$$^{238}_{92}U + {}^{1}_{0}n \longrightarrow {}^{239}_{92}U$$

$$^{238}_{92}U \longrightarrow {}^{239}_{93}Np + {}^{0}_{-1}\beta$$

$$^{239}_{93}Np \longrightarrow {}^{239}_{94}Pu + {}^{0}_{-1}\beta$$

A fissionable nuclide such as $^{235}_{92}U$ is called *fissile*; $^{239}_{94}Pu$ is also fissile. A nuclide such as $^{238}_{92}U$, which can be converted into a fissile nuclide, is said to be *fertile*. In a *breeder nuclear reactor*, a small quantity of fissile nuclide provides the neutrons that convert a large quantity of a fertile nuclide into a fissile one. (The newly formed fissile nuclide then participates in a self-sustaining chain reaction.)

An obvious advantage of the breeder reactor is that the amount of uranium fuel available immediately jumps by a factor of about 100. This is the ratio of naturally occurring $^{238}_{92}U$ to $^{235}_{92}U$. But the potential advantage is even greater than this. Breeder reactors might use as nuclear fuels materials that have even very low uranium contents, such as shale deposits with about 0.006% U by mass.

There are, however, important disadvantages to breeder reactors. This is especially true of the type known as the *liquid-metal-cooled fast breeder reactor* (LMFBR). Systems must be designed to handle a liquid metal, such as sodium, which becomes highly radioactive in the reactor. Also, both the rates of heat and neutron production are greater in the LMFBR than in the PWR, so materials deteriorate more rapidly. Perhaps the greatest unsolved problems are those of handling radioactive wastes and reprocessing plutonium fuel. Plutonium is

Clark, R. W. "What ever happened to cold fusion?" *J. Chem. Educ.* **1991:** *68*, 277.

one of the most toxic substances known. It can cause lung cancer when inhaled in even microgram (10^{-6} g) amounts. Furthermore, because plutonium has a long half-life (24,000 y), any accident involving it could leave an affected area almost permanently contaminated.

25-9   NUCLEAR FUSION

Jensen, Torkil H. "Fusion–A Potential Power Source (Nuclear Chemistry–SOA)." *J. Chem. Educ.* **1994:** *71*, 820.

Web site on nuclear fusion: http://fusedweb.pppl.gov/ (non-commercial).

▶ In the hydrogen bomb, these high temperatures are attained by exploding an atomic (fission) bomb, which triggers the fusion reaction.

The **fusion** of atomic nuclei is the process that produces energy in the sun. An uncontrolled fusion reaction is the basis of the hydrogen bomb. A controlled fusion reaction could provide an almost unlimited source of energy. The nuclear reaction that holds the most immediate promise is the deuterium–tritium reaction.

$$^2_1H + ^3_1H \longrightarrow ^4_2He + ^1_0n$$

The difficulties in developing a fusion energy source are probably without parallel in the history of technology. In fact, the feasibility of a controlled fusion reaction has yet to be fully demonstrated. There are a number of problems. To permit their fusion, the nuclei of deuterium and tritium must be forced into close proximity. Because atomic nuclei repel one another, this close approach requires the nuclei to have very high thermal energies. At the temperatures necessary to initiate a fusion reaction, gases are completely ionized into a mixture of atomic nuclei and electrons known as a *plasma*. Still higher plasma temperatures—over 40,000,000 K—are required to initiate a self-sustaining reaction (one that releases more energy than is required to get it started). A method must be devised to confine the plasma out of contact with other materials. The plasma loses thermal energy to any material it strikes. Also, a plasma must be at a sufficiently high density for a sufficient time to permit the fusion reaction to occur. The two methods receiving greatest attention are confinement in a magnetic field and heating of a frozen deuterium–tritium pellet with laser beams. Another series of technical problems involves the handling of liquid lithium, which is the anticipated heat-transfer medium and tritium (^3_1H) source.

$$^7_3Li + ^1_0n \longrightarrow ^4_2He + ^3_1H + ^1_0n$$
$$\text{(fast)} \qquad\qquad \text{(slow)}$$

▲ The plasma chamber of a fusion reactor of the magnetic confinement type (called a *tokamak*). The chamber walls are lined with carbon-fiber composite tiles to protect against the high-temperature plasma.

Finally, for the magnetic containment method, the magnetic field must be produced by superconducting magnets, which currently are very expensive to operate.

The advantages of fusion over fission could be enormous. Since deuterium constitutes about one in every 6500 H atoms, the oceans of the world can supply an almost limitless amount of nuclear fuel. It is estimated that there is sufficient lithium on Earth to provide a source of tritium for about 1 million years. Also, nuclear fusion would not pose the vexing problems of radioactive waste storage and disposal associated with nuclear fission.

25-10   EFFECT OF RADIATION ON MATTER

Use a Geiger counter to test various substances for radiation. Many rocks display some radiation. Contrast the background radiation with the radiation from common substances.

Although there are substantial differences in the way in which α particles, β^- and β^+ particles, and γ rays interact with matter, they share an important feature: They dislodge electrons from atoms and molecules to produce ions. The ionizing power of radiation may be described in terms of the number of ion pairs formed per centimeter of path through a material. An *ion pair* consists of an ionized electron and the resulting positive ion. Alpha particles have the greatest ionizing power, followed by β particles and then γ rays. The ionized electrons produced directly by the collisions of particles of radiation with atoms are called *primary* electrons. These electrons may themselves possess sufficient energies to cause *secondary* ionizations.

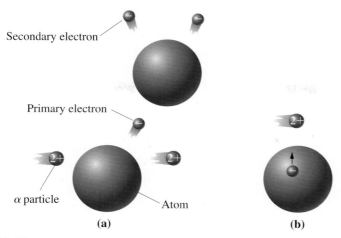

▲ FIGURE 25-10
Some interactions of radiation with matter
(a) The production of primary and secondary electrons by collisions. **(b)** The excitation of an atom by the passage of an α particle. An electron is raised to a higher energy level within the atom. The excited atom reverts to its normal state by emitting radiation.

Not all interactions between radiation and matter produce ion pairs. In some cases, electrons are simply raised to higher atomic or molecular energy levels. The return of these electrons to their normal states is then accompanied by radiation—X rays, ultraviolet light, or visible light, depending on the energies involved.

Some of the possibilities described here are depicted in Figure 25-10.

RADIATION DETECTORS

The interactions of radiation with matter can serve as bases for the detection of radiation and the measurement of its intensity. One of the simplest methods is that used by Henri Becquerel in his discovery of radioactivity—the exposure of a photographic film, as in film badge radiation detectors. The effect of α and β particles, and γ rays on a photographic emulsion is similar to that of X rays.

One type of detector used to study high-energy radiation such as γ rays is the *bubble chamber*. In this device, a liquid, usually hydrogen, is kept just at its boiling point. As ion pairs are produced by the transit of an ionizing ray, bubbles of vapor form around the ions. The tracks of bubbles can be photographed and analyzed, and different types of radiation produce different tracks. Charged particles, for example, can be detected by their deflection in a magnetic field.

The most common device for detecting and measuring ionizing radiation is the *Geiger–Müller (G–M) counter*, depicted in Figure 25-11. The G–M counter consists of a cylindrical cathode with a wire anode running along its axis. The anode and cathode are sealed in a gas-filled glass tube. Ionizing radiation passing through the tube produces primary ions, and this is followed by secondary ionization. The positive ions are attracted to the cathode and the electrons to the anode, leading to a pulse of electric current. The tube is quickly recharged in preparation of the next ionizing event. The pulses of electric current are counted.

A detector widely used in biological studies is the *scintillation counter*. It is especially useful in detecting radiation that is not energetic enough to cause ionization. The radiation excites certain atoms in the detecting medium; when these atoms revert to their ground state, they emit pulses of light that can be counted. The light emission is similar to that produced when phosphors in a television screen are struck by cathode rays.

▲ A film badge used for detecting radiation.

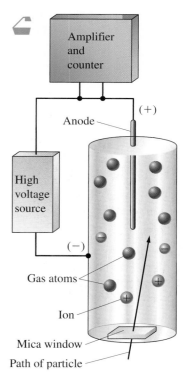

▲ FIGURE 25-11
A Geiger–Müller counter
Radiation enters the G–M tube through the mica window. The radiation ionizes some of the gas (usually argon) in the tube. A pulse of electric current passes through the electric circuit and is counted.

▲ Laboratory technician checking for radioactive isotopes.

Web site on radiation dosage: http://healthandenergy.com/rad_chart.html (commercial).

EFFECT OF IONIZING RADIATION ON LIVING MATTER

All life exists against a background of naturally occurring ionizing radiation—cosmic rays, ultraviolet light, and emanations from radioactive elements such as uranium in rocks. The level of this radiation varies from point to point on Earth, being greater, for instance, at higher elevations. Only in recent times have humans been able to create situations in which organisms might be exposed to radiation at levels significantly higher than natural background radiation.

The interactions of radiation with living matter are the same as with other forms of matter—ionization, excitation, and dissociation of molecules. There is no question of the effect of large doses of ionizing radiation on organisms—the organisms are killed. But even slight exposures to ionizing radiation can cause changes in cell chromosomes. Thus it is believed that, even at low dosage rates, ionizing radiation can result in birth defects, leukemia, bone cancer, and other forms of cancer. The nagging question that has eluded any definitive answers is how great an increase in the incidence of birth defects and cancers might be caused by certain levels of radiation.

RADIATION DOSAGE

One unit long used to describe exposure to radiation is the rad. One **rad** (*radiation absorbed dose*) corresponds to the absorption of 1×10^{-2} J of energy per kilogram of matter. The effect of a dose of one rad on living matter is variable, however, and a better unit is one that takes this variability into account. The **rem** (*radiation equivalent for man*) is the rad multiplied by the *relative biological effectiveness* (*Q*). The factor *Q* takes into account that equal doses of radiation of different types may have differing effects. Table 25.4 summarizes several radiation units.

It is thought that a dose of 1000 rem absorbed in a short time interval will kill 100% of the population. A short-term dose of 450 rem would probably result in death within 30 days of about 50% of the population. A single dose of 1 rem delivered to 1 million people would probably produce about 100 cases of

TABLE 25.4 Radiation Units[a]	
Unit	**Definition**
Radioactive decay:	
Becquerel, Bq	s^{-1} (disintegrations per second)
Curie, Ci	An amount of radioactive material decaying at the same rate as 1 g of radium (3.70×10^{10} dis s^{-1})
	$1 \text{ Ci} = 3.70 \times 10^{10}$ Bq
Adsorbed dose:	
Gray, Gy	One gray of radiation deposits one joule of energy per kilogram of matter
Rad	1 rad = 0.01 Gy
Equivalent dose:	
Sievert, Sv	1 Sv = 100 rem
Rem	1 rem = 1 rad × *Q*
	The quality factor, *Q*, is about 1 for X rays, γ rays, and β^- particles; 3 for slow neutrons; 10 for protons and fast neutrons; and 20 for α particles

[a]SI units are shown in blue. Sources of α radiation are relatively harmless when external to the body and extremely hazardous when taken internally, as in the lungs or stomach. Other forms of radiation (X rays, γ rays), because they are highly penetrating, are hazardous even when external to the body.

cancer within 20–30 years. The total body radiation received by most of the world's population from normal background sources is about 0.13 rem [130 millirem (mrem)] per year. The dose delivered in a chest X-ray examination is about 20 mrem.

Some of the foregoing statements about radiation dosages and their anticipated effects are based on (1) medical histories of the survivors of the Hiroshima and Nagasaki atomic blasts, (2) the incidence of leukemia and other cancers in children whose mothers received diagnostic radiation during pregnancy, and (3) the occurrence of lung cancers among uranium miners in the United States. What does all of this tell us about a safe level of radiation exposure? One approach has been to extrapolate from these high doses to the lower doses affecting the general population. This has led the U.S. National Council on Radiation Protection and Measurements to recommend that the dosage for the general population be limited to 0.17 rem (170 mrem) per year from all sources above background level. Experts disagree, however, on how the data observed for high dosages should be extrapolated to low doses. Some experts believe that the 0.17 rem/y figure is too high. If they are right, an additional dosage of 0.17 rem/y above normal background levels might cause statistically significant increases in the incidence of birth defects and cancers.

Yalow, R. S. "Development and Proliferation of Radioimmunoassay Technology." *J. Chem. Educ.* **1999:** 76, 767.

Web site on cancer therapy: http://ctep.info.nih.gov/ (non-commercial).

25-11 APPLICATIONS OF RADIOISOTOPES

We have described both the destructive capacity of nuclear reactions and the potential of these reactions to provide new sources of energy. Less heralded but equally important are a variety of practical applications of radioactivity. We close this chapter with a brief survey of some uses of radioisotopes.

CANCER THERAPY

Ionizing radiation in low doses can induce cancers, but this same radiation, particularly γ rays, is also used in the treatment of cancer. Although ionizing radiation tends to destroy all cells, cancerous cells are more easily destroyed than normal ones. Thus, a carefully directed beam of γ rays or high-energy X rays of the appropriate dosage may be used to arrest the growth of cancerous cells. Also coming into use for some forms of cancer is radiation therapy that employs beams of protons or neutrons.

RADIOACTIVE TRACERS

The small mass differences between the isotopes of an element may produce small differences in physical properties. The differing rates of diffusion of $^{238}UF_6(g)$ and $^{235}UF_6(g)$ result from such a mass difference (page 209). Generally speaking, though, the physical and chemical properties of the various isotopes of an element are practically identical. However, if one of the isotopes is radioactive, its actions can be easily followed with radiation detectors. This is the principle behind the use of *radioactive tracers*, or tagged atoms. For example, if a small quantity of radioactive ^{32}P (as a phosphate) is added to a nutrient solution fed to plants, the uptake of all the phosphorus atoms—radioactive and nonradioactive alike—can be followed by charting the regions of the plant that become radioactive. Similarly, the fate of iodine (as iodide ion) in the body can be determined by having a person drink a solution of dissolved iodides containing a small quantity of a radioactive iodide as a tracer. Abnormalities in the thyroid gland can be detected in this way. Because I^- concentrates in the thyroid, people can protect themselves by ingesting nonradioactive iodides before being exposed to a radioactive iodide. The thyroid becomes saturated with the nonradioactive iodide and rejects the radioactive iodide. Iodide tablets were distributed to the general population in some regions of Europe before the arrival of fallout from the Chernobyl nuclear accident in 1986.

(a)

(b)

▲ **Nuclear medicine provides methods for diagnosing life-threatening conditions**
In these thallium-201 scans of a heart, γ rays released in the radioactive decay of ^{201}Tl are detected and used to provide an image of the blood flow to the heart wall (heart muscle). **(a)** Normal heart wall; **(b)** heart with deficient blood flow.

▲ **FIGURE 25-12**
Structure of thiosulfate ion, $S_2O_3{}^{2-}$
The central S atom is in the +6 oxidation state. The terminal S atom is in the −2 oxidation state.

▲ Neutron activation was used to establish that this painting was not painted by Rembrandt, but by an artist in the school of Rembrandt.

Industrial applications of tracers are also numerous. The fate of a catalyst in a chemical plant can be followed by incorporating a radioactive tracer in the catalyst, such as ^{192}Ir in a Pt–Ir catalyst. Monitoring the activity of the ^{192}Ir makes it possible to determine the rate at which the catalyst is being carried away and to which parts of the plant it is being carried.

STRUCTURES AND MECHANISMS

Often the mechanism of a chemical reaction or the structure of a species can be inferred from experiments using radioisotopes as tracers. Consider the following experimental proof that the two S atoms in the thiosulfate ion, $S_2O_3{}^{2-}$, are not equivalent.

$S_2O_3{}^{2-}$ is prepared from radioactive sulfur (^{35}S) and sulfite ion containing the nonradioactive isotope ^{32}S.

$$^{35}S + {}^{32}SO_3{}^{2-} \longrightarrow {}^{35}S{}^{32}SO_3{}^{2-} \qquad (25.18)$$

When the thiosulfate ion is decomposed by acidification, all the radioactivity appears in the precipitated sulfur and none in the $SO_2(g)$. The bonds of the ^{35}S atoms must be different from those of the ^{32}S atoms (Fig. 25-12).

$$^{35}S{}^{32}SO_3{}^{2-} + 2\,H^+ \longrightarrow H_2O + {}^{32}SO_2(g) + {}^{35}S(s) \qquad (25.19)$$

In reaction (25.20), nonradioactive KIO_4 is added to a solution containing iodide ion labeled with the radioisotope ^{128}I. All the radioactivity appears in the I_2 and none in the $IO_3{}^-$. This proves that all the $IO_3{}^-$ is produced by reduction of $IO_4{}^-$ and none by oxidation of I^-.

$$IO_4{}^- + 2\,{}^{128}I^- + H_2O \longrightarrow {}^{128}I_2 + IO_3{}^- + 2\,OH^- \qquad (25.20)$$

ANALYTICAL CHEMISTRY

The usual procedure of analyzing a substance by precipitation involves filtering, washing, drying, and weighing a pure precipitate. An alternative is to incorporate a radioactive isotope in the precipitating reagent. By measuring the activity of the precipitate and comparing it with that of the original solution, the amount of precipitate can be calculated without having to purify, dry, and weigh it.

Another method of importance in analytical chemistry is *neutron activation analysis*. In this procedure, the sample to be analyzed, normally nonradioactive, is bombarded with neutrons; the element of interest is converted to a radioisotope. The conversion of a stable isotope (X) to an unstable isotope (X*) by neutron capture can be represented as

$$^AX + {}_0^1n \longrightarrow {}^{(A+1)}X* \longrightarrow {}^{(A+1)}X + \gamma$$

In this example, the excited nucleus that is formed decays with the emission of a γ ray with a distinctive energy. Neutron-activated nuclei may decay by other modes, however, such as β decay. The activity of the radioisotope formed is measured. This measurement, together with such factors as the rate of neutron bombardment, the half-life of the radioisotope, and the efficiency of the radiation detector, can be used to calculate the quantity of the element in the sample. The method is especially attractive because (1) trace quantities of elements can be determined (sometimes in parts per billion or less); (2) a sample can be tested without destroying it; and (3) the sample can be in any state of matter, including biological materials. Neutron activation analysis has been used, for instance, to determine the authenticity of old paintings. Old masters formulated their own paints. Differences between formulations are easily detected through the trace elements they contain.

RADIATION PROCESSING

Radiation processing describes industrial applications of ionizing radiation—γ rays from ^{60}Co or electron beams from electron accelerators. The ionizing radiation is used in the production of certain materials or to modify their prop-

▲ The strawberries on the right have been preserved by irradiation.

erties. Its most extensive current use is in breaking, re-forming, and cross-linking polymer chains to affect the physical and mechanical properties of plastics used in foamed products, electrical insulation, and packaging materials. Ionizing radiation is used to sterilize medical supplies such as sutures, syringes, and hospital garb. In sewage treatment plants, radiation processing has been used to decrease the settling time of sewage sludge and to kill pathogens. Radiation is now being used in some instances in the preservation of foods as an alternative to canning, freeze-drying, or refrigeration. In radiation processing, the irradiated material is *not* rendered radioactive, although the ionizing radiation may produce some chemical changes.

Hunter, J., Murphy, B., Nelson, J. "N-only bridging thiocyanate, homo- and heterobinuclear complexes: A laboratory project in macrocyclic coordination chemistry utilizing a range of physical techniques." *J. Chem. Educ.* 1991: *68*, 59.

Web site on radioactive waste: http://www.citizen.org/cmep/RAGE/radwaste/radwaste.html (commercial); http://starfire.ne.uiuc.edu/ne201/course/topics/nuclear_waste/ (non-commercial).

Summary

25-1 Radioactivity—All the heavier elements ($Z > 83$) and a few of the lighter ones have naturally occurring nuclides that produce ionizing radiation. **Alpha (α) particles** emanating from radioactive nuclei are identical to the nuclei of helium-4 atoms, $^4_2\text{He}^{2+}$. **Beta (β^-) particles** are electrons that originate from the conversion of a neutron to a proton in the radioactive nucleus; **positrons (β^+)** are positively charged particles otherwise identical to electrons that originate in the nucleus in the conversion of a proton to a neutron. Beta ($-$) particles and positrons have a greater penetrating power through matter than do α particles. **Electron capture** (EC) occurs when an electron from a low-lying energy level is absorbed by the nucleus. The electron and a proton combine to form a neutron and liberate X radiation. **Gamma (γ) rays** are a nonparticulate form of electromagnetic radiation released when a nucleus in an excited state returns to the ground state. **Nuclear equations** to represent nuclear processes must be balanced, which requires that (1) the sum of the mass numbers and (2) the sum of the atomic numbers must be the same on both sides of the nuclear equation (equation 25.1).

25-2 Naturally Occurring Radioactive Isotopes—All naturally occurring radioactive nuclides of high atomic number are members of a **radioactive decay series** that originates with a long-lived isotope of high atomic number and terminates with a stable isotope such as ^{206}Pb (Fig. 25-2).

25-3 Nuclear Reactions and Artificially Induced Radioactivity—Radioactive nuclides can be synthesized by nuclear reactions in which target nuclei are bombarded with energetic particles such as α particles or neutrons. Over 1000 radioactive nuclides have been produced in this way. Many of them have important practical applications.

25-4 Transuranium Elements—Elements beyond $Z = 92$, commonly referred to as the transuranium elements, have been synthesized by bombarding naturally occurring isotopes with charged particles produced in a charged-particle accelerator (Fig. 25-3).

25-5 Rate of Radioactive Decay—The **radioactive decay law**, based on experimental observations, states that the decay rate is directly proportional to the number of atoms present; hence it is a first-order process (equation 25.11). The proportionality constant between the decay rate and the number of atoms is the **decay constant, λ**. The **half-life, $t_{1/2}$**, is the time it takes for half of the radioactive atoms in a sample to decay. Important applications of the radioactive decay law are radiocarbon dating to determine the age of materials derived from once-living matter and determining the age of rocks and of Earth itself.

25-6 Energetics of Nuclear Reactions—The energy changes in nuclear reactions are a consequence of Einstein's discovery of a mass–energy equivalence (equation 25.14). **Nuclear binding energy** is the energy released when nucleons fuse together into a nucleus; the "lost" mass is known as the mass defect. A plot of binding energy per nucleon versus mass number passes through a maximum at about $A = 60$. Thus, the *fusion* of nucleons is favored at lower mass numbers, and the *fission* of nuclei into lighter fragments is favored at higher mass numbers (Fig. 25-6).

25-7 Nuclear Stability—The stability of a nuclide depends on the ratio N/Z, on whether the numbers of neutrons (N) and protons (Z) are odd or even, and whether either is a **magic number** arising from nuclear shell theory (Table 25.2). A plot of N versus Z shows that all stable nuclides lie within a belt of stability originating along the line $N = Z$, and expanding above the line at higher values of Z (Fig. 25-7). Most radioactive nuclides lie outside the belt and undergo radioactive decay of a type that moves daughter nuclides into the belt.

25-8 Nuclear Fission—In the process of **fission**, the nucleus of a heavy nuclide, such as ^{235}U, splits into two smaller fragments after being struck by a thermal neutron (Fig. 25-8). Also released are two or three neutrons that can trigger the fission of other nuclei in a chain reaction. Essential components of a nuclear power reactor (Fig. 25-9) are the fissionable (*fissile*) nuclide, a **moderator** (such as water) to slow down the neutrons released during fission, **control rods** (such as cadmium) to control the fission by absorbing neutrons, and a heat-transfer medium (such as water).

25-9 Nuclear Fusion—The **fusion** of lighter nuclei into heavier ones converts small quantities of mass into enormous amounts of energy. This process occurs continuously in stars and in the hydrogen bomb. A controlled fusion reaction has yet to be achieved, but fusion research is being actively pursued because of the enormous potential of fusion as an energy source.

25-10 Effect of Radiation on Matter—The ionizing power of radiation (Fig. 25-10) is the basis both of radiation's effects on matter and methods used to detect radiation. Radiation detectors include simple film badges, Geiger–Müller (G–M) counters for routine measurements (Fig. 25-11), and scintillation counters in biomedical

▲ Pouring molten nuclear waste glass to demonstrate methods of immobilizing nuclear waste.

A distinct advantage of nuclear power generation over the use of fossil fuels is that it does not produce oxides of sulfur and nitrogen as air pollutants. Nor does nuclear power generation produce $CO_2(g)$, so it does not contribute to the potential problem of global warming (page 259). However, nuclear power generation has its own waste problem. The disposal of nuclear wastes is one of the most difficult environmental problems.

Radioactive waste can be divided into two broad categories. Low-level waste consists of items used in handling radioactive materials (such as gloves and other protective clothing) and waste solutions from medical and laboratory use. The radioactive elements in these items have relatively short half-lives (30 years maximum) and low levels of activity. They can be stored in cement casks and buried. After about 300 years, these materials will no longer be radioactive.

The greater challenge is in handling spent fuel rods from nuclear reactors and other high-level radioactive wastes. In addition to significant quantities of uranium and plutonium, spent fuel rods contain a number of daughter isotopes with half-lives of hundreds of years. Plutonium, with a half-life of 24,000 years, is so toxic that any accidental release would contaminate an area for a very long time.

studies. Two units of measure are used to quantifiy exposure to radioactivity. One—the **rad** (radiation absorbed dose)—is related to the amount of radiation energy absorbed, while the other—the **rem** (radiation equivalent for man)—takes into account the differing effects of the various types of radiation (Table 25.4).

25-11 Applications of Radioisotopes—Radioactive nuclides have important uses in diagnostic medicine, in cancer therapy, in studying the mechanisms of chemical and biochemical reactions, and as tracers in various scientific and industrial settings. Additionally, radiation processing is used in processing and preserving food.

Integrative Example

On April 26, 1986, an explosion at the nuclear power plant at Chernobyl, Ukraine, released the greatest quantity of radioactive material ever associated with an industrial accident. (See the discussion and photo on page 1059.) One of the radioisotopes in this emission was ^{131}I, a β^- emitter with a half-life of 8.04 days.

Assume that the total quantity of ^{131}I released was 250 g, and determine the number of *curies* associated with this ^{131}I 30.0 days after the accident.

Strategy

From the initial mass of ^{131}I and the known half-life of ^{131}I determine how many grams of ^{131}I remain after 30 days. Convert this mass to a number of atoms using the molar mass of ^{131}I and Avogadro's number. Finally, the product of the number of atoms and the decay constant yields the activity in disintegrations per second, which can be converted to curies.

Solution

In equation (25.12), use $\lambda = 0.693/8.04$ d and $t = 30.0$ d. Because the mass of ^{131}I is directly proportional to the number of ^{131}I atoms, we can replace N_0 by $mass_0 = 250$ g, and N_t by $mass_t$, the mass we seek.

$$\ln \frac{mass_t}{mass_0} = \ln \frac{mass_t}{250 \text{ g}} = \frac{-0.693}{8.04 \text{ d}} \times 30.0 \text{ d} = -2.59$$

$$mass_t = 250 \text{ g} \times e^{-2.59} = 250 \text{ g} \times 0.0750 = 18.8 \text{ g}$$

To determine the number of iodine-131 atoms, use the molar mass, 131 g ^{131}I/mol ^{131}I, and the Avogadro constant.

$$N_t = 18.8 \text{ g } ^{131}I \times \frac{1 \text{ mol } ^{131}I}{131 \text{ g } ^{131}I} \times \frac{6.022 \times 10^{23} \text{ } ^{131}I \text{ atoms}}{1 \text{ mol } ^{131}I}$$

$$= 8.64 \times 10^{22} \text{ } ^{131}I \text{ atoms}$$

In the United States, high-level wastes are currently stored underwater at temporary sites at power plants and elsewhere while awaiting final storage at a permanent site. An appropriate site would have to be geologically stable for tens of thousands of years. One or two such sites are now under careful study, but agreement on a final site is still a strongly debated issue.

France, which has an extensive nuclear power program including one breeder reactor, has chosen a different route for handling nuclear reactor waste: *reprocessing*. The first step in nuclear fuel reprocessing is the removal of uranium and plutonium from spent fuel rods. These elements are formed into fuel pellets for loading new fuel rods. Low-level waste is dealt with in the manner already described. What remains at this point are isotopes with long half-lives (up to 100 years). These are stabilized by incorporating them into a borosilicate (Pyrex-like) glass. The boron in the glass is a good neutron absorber. The radioactive glass is placed in sealed containers, and the containers are stored in specially designed silos. The silos are intended to contain the waste for at least 1000 years, and consideration is also being given to storage in caves known to have been geologically stable since the last ice age.

Reprocessing uranium and plutonium is a hazardous operation that must be done with extreme care, mostly through the use of remote-control equipment. An attendant problem with reprocessing is that the plutonium recovered from spent fuel rods is of weapons grade. Strict safeguards are required to ensure that none of this material is diverted for weapons production.

Thus, while nuclear energy is clean in that it does not contribute to problems such as acid rain and global warming, it does present its own set of very difficult problems. In planning a future energy strategy, the issues are as much social and political as they are scientific. How much risk are we willing to accept in return for the perceived benefits of a given course of action? Should our efforts be directed to developing a new generation of safe nuclear reactors to reduce the effects of global warming associated with fossil fuels? Should greater emphasis be given to energy conservation and the more efficient use of energy than to increasing our reliance on nuclear energy? Should we largely forgo nuclear fission as an energy source while awaiting practical development of less risky fusion power, a technology that has not yet been demonstrated? Is an expanded development of solar energy and other unconventional energy sources a way around the dilemmas posed by fossil fuels and nuclear power? These are all questions that must be seriously debated as we make decisions affecting the energy needs and resources of our society.

To establish the decay constant in s^{-1} and to obtain λ from $t_{1/2}$, use the method outlined in Example 25-3a.

$$\lambda = 0.693/t_{1/2} = \frac{0.693}{8.04\ d} \times \frac{1\ d}{24\ h} \times \frac{1\ h}{60\ min} \times \frac{1\ min}{60\ s}$$

$$= 9.98 \times 10^{-7}\ s^{-1}$$

To determine the decay rate (activity) after 30.0 days, use the two previous results in equation (25.11).

$$A = \lambda N = 9.98 \times 10^{-7}\ s^{-1} \times 8.64 \times 10^{22}\ atoms$$

$$= 8.62 \times 10^{16}\ dis\ s^{-1}$$

Finally, to express the activity in curies use the definition of a curie given in Table 25.4.

$$A = 8.62 \times 10^{16}\ dis\ s^{-1} \times \frac{1\ Ci}{3.70 \times 10^{10}\ dis\ s^{-1}}$$

$$= 2.33 \times 10^{6}\ Ci$$

Assessment

In this calculation we could also have shown that in 30 days (about $4 \times t_{1/2}$) approximately 93% of the ^{131}I had disintegrated. In the process, approximately 2×10^{6} Ci of radiation was emitted. If we also knew the energy of the β^{-} particles and something about the exposed population, we could also have estimated radiation doses in rads.

Exercises

Radioactive Processes

1. What nucleus is obtained in each process?
    (a) $^{234}_{94}Pu$ decays by α emission.
    (b) $^{248}_{97}Bk$ decays by β^{-} emission.
    (c) $^{196}_{82}Pb$ goes through two successive EC processes.
2. What nucleus is obtained in each process?
    (a) $^{214}_{82}Pb$ decays through two successive β^{-} emissions.
    (b) $^{226}_{88}Ra$ decays through three successive α emissions.
    (c) $^{69}_{33}As$ decays by β^{+} emission.
3. Based on a favorable N/Z ratio for the product nucleus, write the most plausible equation for the decay of $^{14}_{6}C$.
4. Write a plausible equation for the decay of tritium, $^{3}_{1}H$, the radioactive isotope of hydrogen.

Radioactive Decay Series

5. The natural decay series starting with the radionuclide $^{232}_{90}$Th follows the sequence represented here. Construct a graph of this series, similar to Figure 25-2.

$$^{232}_{90}\text{Th}-\alpha-\beta-\beta-\alpha-\alpha-\alpha\overset{\alpha-\beta}{\underset{\beta-\alpha}{\rightleftharpoons}}\overset{\alpha-\beta}{\underset{\beta-\alpha}{\rightleftharpoons}}\nearrow^{208}_{82}\text{Pb}$$

6. The natural decay series starting with the radionuclide $^{235}_{92}$U follows the sequence represented here. Construct a graph of this series, similar to Figure 25-2.

$$^{235}_{92}\text{U}-\alpha-\beta-\alpha\overset{\alpha-\beta}{\underset{\beta-\alpha}{\rightleftharpoons}}-\alpha-\alpha-\alpha-\beta\overset{\alpha-\beta}{\underset{\beta-\alpha}{\rightleftharpoons}}\nearrow^{207}_{82}\text{Pb}$$

7. The uranium series described in Figure 25-2 is also known as the "4n + 2" series because the mass number of each nuclide in the series can be expressed by the equation $A = 4n + 2$, where n is an integer. Show that this equation is indeed applicable to the uranium series.

8. Just as the uranium series is called the "4n + 2" series, the thorium series can be called the "4n" series and the actinium series the "4n + 3" series. A "4n + 1" series has also been established, with $^{241}_{94}$Pu as the parent nuclide. To which series does each of the following belong: **(a)** $^{214}_{83}$Bi; **(b)** $^{216}_{84}$Po; **(c)** $^{215}_{85}$At; **(d)** $^{235}_{92}$U?

Nuclear Reactions

9. Supply the missing information in each of the following nuclear equations representing a radioactive decay process.
   (a) $^{160}_{?}\text{W} \longrightarrow {}^{?}_{?}\text{Hf} + ?$
   (b) $^{38}_{?}\text{Cl} \longrightarrow {}^{?}_{?}\text{Ar} + ?$
   (c) $^{214}_{?}? \longrightarrow {}^{?}_{?}\text{Po} + {}^{0}_{-1}\beta$
   (d) $^{32}_{17}\text{Cl} \longrightarrow {}^{?}_{16}? + ?$

10. Complete the following nuclear equations.
    (a) $^{23}_{11}\text{Na} + ? \longrightarrow {}^{24}_{11}\text{Na} + {}^{1}_{1}\text{H}$
    (b) $^{59}_{27}\text{Co} + {}^{1}_{0}\text{n} \longrightarrow {}^{56}_{25}\text{Mn} + ?$
    (c) $? + {}^{2}_{1}\text{H} \longrightarrow {}^{240}_{94}\text{Pu} + {}^{0}_{-1}\beta$
    (d) $^{246}_{96}\text{Cm} + ? \longrightarrow {}^{254}_{102}\text{No} + 5\,{}^{1}_{0}\text{n}$
    (e) $^{238}_{92}\text{U} + ? \longrightarrow {}^{246}_{99}\text{Es} + 6\,{}^{1}_{0}\text{n}$

11. Write equations for the following nuclear reactions.
    (a) bombardment of ^{7}Li with protons to produce ^{8}Be and γ rays

    (b) bombardment of ^{9}Be with $^{2}_{1}$H to produce ^{10}B
    (c) bombardment of ^{14}N with neutrons to produce ^{14}C

12. Write equations for the following nuclear reactions.
    (a) bombardment of ^{238}U with α particles to produce ^{239}Pu
    (b) bombardment of tritium ($^{3}_{1}$H) with $^{2}_{1}$H to produce ^{4}He
    (c) bombardment of ^{33}S with neutrons to produce ^{33}P

13. Write nuclear equations to represent the formation of an isotope of element 111 with a mass number of 272 by the bombardment of bismuth-209 by nickel-64 nuclei, followed by a succession of five α-particle emissions.

14. Write nuclear equations to represent the formation of a hypothetical isotope of element 118 with a mass number of 293 by the bombardment of lead-208 by krypton-86 nuclei, followed by a chain of α-particle emissions to the element seaborgium.

Rate of Radioactive Decay

15. Of the radioactive nuclides in Table 25.1,
    (a) which one has the largest value for the decay constant, λ?
    (b) Which one loses 75% of its radioactivity in approximately one month?
    (c) Which ones lose more than 99% of their radioactivity in one month?

16. In a comparison of two radioisotopes, isotope A requires 18.0 hours for its decay rate to fall to $\frac{1}{16}$ its initial value, while isotope B has a half-life that is 2.5 times that of A. How long does it take for the decay rate of isotope B to decrease to $\frac{1}{32}$ of its initial value?

17. The disintegration rate for a sample containing $^{60}_{27}$Co as the only radioactive nuclide is 6740 dis h^{-1}. The half-life of $^{60}_{27}$Co is 5.2 years. Estimate the number of atoms of $^{60}_{27}$Co in the sample.

18. How many years must the radioactive sample of Exercise 17 be maintained before the disintegration rate falls to 101 dis min^{-1}?

19. A sample containing $^{234}_{88}$Ra, which decays by α-particle emission, disintegrates at the following rate, expressed as disintegrations per minute or counts per minute (cpm): $t = 0$, 1000 cpm; $t = 1$ h, 992 cpm; $t = 10$ h, 924 cpm; $t = 100$ h, 452 cpm; $t = 250$ h, 138 cpm. What is the half-life of this nuclide?

20. Iodine-129 is a product of nuclear fission, whether from an atomic bomb or a nuclear power plant. It is a β^- emitter with a half-life of 1.7×10^7 years. How many disintegrations per second would occur in a sample containing 1.00 mg ^{129}I?

21. Suppose that a sample containing ^{32}P has an activity 1000 times the detectable limit. How long would an experiment have to be run with this sample before the radioactivity could no longer be detected?

22. What mass of carbon-14 must be present in a sample to have an activity of 1.00 mCi?

Age Determinations with Radioisotopes

23. A wooden object is claimed to have been found in an Egyptian pyramid and is offered for sale to an art museum. Radiocarbon dating of the object reveals a disintegration rate of 10.0 dis $min^{-1} g^{-1}$. Do you think the object is authentic? Explain.

24. The lowest level of ^{14}C activity that seems possible for experimental detection is 0.03 dis $min^{-1} g^{-1}$. What is the maximum age of an object that can be determined by the carbon-14 method?

25. What should be the mass ratio $^{208}Pb/^{232}Th$ in a meteorite that is approximately 2.7×10^9 years old? The half-life of ^{232}Th is 1.39×10^{10} years. [*Hint:* One ^{208}Pb atom is the final decay product of one ^{232}Th atom.]

26. Concerning the decay of ^{232}Th described in Exercise 25, a certain rock has a $^{208}Pb/^{232}Th$ mass ratio of 0.25/1.00. Estimate the age of the rock.

Energetics of Nuclear Reactions

27. Using appropriate equations in the text, determine
    (a) the energy in joules corresponding to the destruction of 6.02×10^{-23} g of matter;
    (b) the energy in megaelectronvolts that would be released if one α particle were completely destroyed.

28. The measured mass of the nucleus of an atom of silver-107 is 106.879289 u. For this atom, determine the binding energy per nucleon in megaelectronvolts.

29. Use the electron mass from Table 2.1 and the measured mass of the nuclide $^{19}_{9}F$, 18.998403 u, to determine the binding energy per nucleon (in megaelectronvolts) of this atom.

30. Use the electron mass from Table 2.1 and the measured mass of the nuclide $^{56}_{26}Fe$, 55.934939 u, to determine the binding energy per nucleon (in megaelectronvolts) of this atom.

31. Calculate the energy, in megaelectronvolts, released in the nuclear reaction

$$^{10}_{5}B + ^{4}_{2}He \longrightarrow ^{13}_{6}C + ^{1}_{1}H$$

The nuclidic masses are $^{10}_{5}B = 10.01294$ u; $^{4}_{2}He = 4.00260$ u; $^{13}_{6}C = 13.00335$ u; $^{1}_{1}H = 1.00783$ u.

32. You are given the following nuclidic masses: $^{6}_{3}Li = 6.01513$ u; $^{4}_{2}He = 4.00260$ u; $^{3}_{1}H = 3.01604$ u; $^{1}_{0}n = 1.008665$ u. How much energy, in megaelectronvolts, is released in the following nuclear reaction?

$$^{6}_{3}Li + ^{1}_{0}n \longrightarrow ^{4}_{2}He + ^{3}_{1}H$$

33. Calculate the number of neutrons that could be created with 6.75×10^6 MeV of energy.

34. When β^+ and β^- particles collide, they annihilate each other, producing two γ rays that move away from each other along a straight line. What is the approximate energies of these two γ rays, in MeV?

Nuclear Stability

35. Which member of the following pairs of nuclides would you expect to be most abundant in natural sources: **(a)** $^{20}_{10}Ne$ or $^{22}_{10}Ne$; **(b)** $^{17}_{8}O$ or $^{18}_{8}O$; **(c)** $^{6}_{3}Li$ or $^{7}_{3}Li$? Explain your reasoning.

36. Which member of the following pairs of nuclides would you expect to be most abundant in natural sources: **(a)** $^{40}_{20}Ca$ or $^{42}_{20}Ca$; **(b)** $^{31}_{15}P$ or $^{32}_{15}P$; **(c)** $^{63}_{30}Zn$ or $^{64}_{30}Zn$? Explain your reasoning.

37. One member each of the following pairs of radioisotopes decays by β^- emission, and the other by positron (β^+) emission: **(a)** $^{29}_{15}P$ and $^{33}_{15}P$; **(b)** $^{120}_{53}I$ and $^{134}_{53}I$. Which is which? Explain your reasoning.

38. Each of the following isotopes is radioactive: **(a)** $^{28}_{15}P$; **(b)** $^{45}_{19}K$; **(c)** $^{73}_{30}Zn$. Which would you expect to decay by β^+ emission?

39. Some nuclides are said to be doubly magic. What do you suppose this term means? Postulate some nuclides that might be doubly magic, and locate them in Figure 25-7.

40. Both β^- and β^+ emissions are observed for artificially produced radioisotopes of low atomic numbers, but only β^- emission is observed with naturally occurring radioisotopes of high atomic number. Why do you suppose this is so?

Fission and Fusion

41. Refer to the Integrative Example. In contrast to the Chernobyl accident, the 1979 nuclear accident at Three Mile Island released only 170 curies of ^{131}I. How many milligrams of ^{131}I does this represent?

42. Explain why more energy is released in a fusion process than in a fission process?

Effect of Radiation on Matter

43. Explain why the rem is more satisfactory than the rad as a unit for measuring radiation dosage.

44. Discuss briefly the basic difficulties in establishing the physiological effects of low-level radiation.

45. ^{90}Sr is both a product of radioactive fallout and a radioactive waste in a nuclear reactor. This radioisotope is

a β^- emitter with a half-life of 27.7 years. Suggest reasons why ^{90}Sr is such a potentially hazardous substance.

46. ^{222}Rn is an α-particle emitter with a half-life of 3.82 days. Is it hazardous to be near a flask containing this isotope? Under what conditions might ^{222}Rn be hazardous?

Applications of Radioisotopes

47. Describe how you might use radioactive materials to find a leak in the $H_2(g)$ supply line in an ammonia synthesis plant.

48. Explain why neutron activation analysis is so useful in identifying trace elements in a sample, in contrast to ordinary methods of quantitative analysis, such as precipitation or titration.

49. A small quantity of NaCl containing radioactive $^{24}_{11}Na$ is added to an aqueous solution of $NaNO_3$. The solution is cooled, and $NaNO_3$ is crystallized from the solution. Would you expect the $NaNO_3(s)$ to be radioactive? Explain.

50. The following reactions are carried out with HCl(aq) containing some tritium (^3_1H) as a tracer. Would you expect any of the tritium radioactivity to appear in the $NH_3(g)$? In the H_2O? Explain.

$$NH_3(aq) + HCl(aq) \longrightarrow NH_4Cl(aq)$$

$$NH_4Cl(aq) + NaOH(aq) \longrightarrow$$
$$NaCl(aq) + H_2O(l) + NH_3(g)$$

Integrative and Advanced Exercises

51. In some cases, the most abundant isotope of an element can be established by rounding off the atomic mass to the nearest whole number, as in ^{39}K, ^{85}Rb, and ^{88}Sr. But in other cases, the isotope corresponding to the rounded-off atomic mass does not even occur naturally, as in ^{64}Cu. Explain the basis of this observation.

52. The overall change in the radioactive decay of $^{238}_{92}U$ to $^{206}_{82}Pb$ is the emission of eight α particles. Show that if this loss of eight α particles were not also accompanied by six β^- emissions, the product nucleus would still be radioactive.

53. Use data from the text to determine how many metric tons (1 metric ton = 1000 kg) of bituminous coal (85% C) would have to be burned to release as much energy as is produced by the fission of 1.00 kg $^{235}_{92}U$.

54. One method of dating rocks is based on their $^{87}Sr/^{87}Rb$ ratio. ^{87}Rb is a β^- emitter with a half-life of 5×10^{11} years. A certain rock has a mass ratio $^{87}Sr/^{87}Rb$ of 0.004/1.00. What is the age of the rock?

55. How many millicuries of radioactivity are associated with a sample containing 5.10 mg ^{229}Th, which has a half-life of 7340 years?

56. What mass of ^{90}Sr, with a half-life of 27.7 years, is required to produce 1.00 millicurie of radioactivity?

57. Refer to the Integrative Example. Another radioisotope produced in the Chernobyl accident was ^{137}Cs. If a 1.00-mg sample of ^{137}Cs is equivalent to 89.8 millicuries, what must be the half-life (in years) of ^{137}Cs?

58. The percent natural abundance of ^{40}K is 0.0117%. The radioactive decay of ^{40}K atoms occurs 89% by β^- emission; the rest is by electron capture and β^+ emission. The half-life of ^{40}K is 1.25×10^9 years. Calculate the number of β^- particles produced per second by the ^{40}K present in a 1.00-g sample of the mineral *microcline*, $KAlSi_3O_8$.

59. The carbon-14 dating method is based on the assumption that the rate of production of ^{14}C by cosmic ray bombardment has remained constant for thousands of years and that the ratio of ^{14}C to ^{12}C has also remained constant. Can you think of any effects of human activities that could invalidate this assumption in the future?

60. Calculate the minimum kinetic energy (in megaelectronvolts) that α particles must possess to produce the nuclear reaction

$$^4_2He + ^{14}_7N \longrightarrow ^{17}_8O + ^1_1H$$

The nuclidic masses are $^4_2He = 4.00260$ u; $^{14}_7N = 14.00307$ u; $^1_1H = 1.00783$ u; $^{17}_8O = 16.99913$ u.

61. Hydrogen gas is spiked with tritium to the extent of 5.00% by mass. What is the activity in curies of a 4.65-L sample of this gas at 25.0 °C and 1.05 atm pressure? [*Hint:* Use data from the chapter and elsewhere in the text, as necessary.]

62. ^{40}K undergoes radioactive decay by electron capture to ^{40}Ar and by β^- emission to ^{40}Ca. The fraction of the decay that occurs by electron capture is 0.110. The half-life of ^{40}K is 1.25×10^9 years. Assuming that a rock in which ^{40}K has undergone decay retains all the ^{40}Ar produced, what would be the $^{40}Ar/^{40}K$ mass ratio in a rock that is 1.5×10^9 years old?

63. A certain shale deposit containing 0.006% U by mass is being considered for use as a potential fuel in a breeder reactor. Assuming a density of 2.5 g/cm³, how much energy could be released from 1.00×10^3 cm³ of this material? Assume a fission energy of 3.20×10^{-11} J per fission event (that is, per U atom).

64. An ester forms from a carboxylic acid and an alcohol.

$$RCO_2H + HOR' \longrightarrow RCO_2R' + H_2O$$

This reaction is superficially similar to the reaction of an acid with a base such as sodium hydroxide. The mechanism of the reaction can be followed by using the tracer ^{18}O. This isotope is not radioactive, but other physical measurements can be used to detect its presence. When the *esterification* reaction is carried out with the alcohol containing oxygen-18 atoms, no oxygen-18 beyond its naturally occurring abundance is found in the water produced. How does this result affect the perception that this reaction is like an acid–base reaction?

65. The conversion of CO_2 into carbohydrates by plants via photosynthesis can be represented by the reaction

$$6\ CO_2(g) + 6\ H_2O \xrightarrow{\text{light}} C_6H_{12}O_6 + 6\ O_2(g)$$

To study the mechanism of photosynthesis, algae were grown in water containing ^{18}O, that is, $H_2{}^{18}O$. The oxygen evolved contained oxygen-18 in the same ratio to the other oxygen isotopes as the water in which the reaction was carried out. In another experiment, algae were grown in water containing only ^{16}O, but with oxygen-18 present in the CO_2. The oxygen evolved in this experiment contained no oxygen-18. What conclusion can you draw about the mechanism of photosynthesis from these experiments?

66. Assume that when Earth formed, uranium-238 and uranium-235 were equally abundant. Their current percent natural abundances are 99.28% uranium-238 and 0.72% uranium-235. Given half-lives of 4.5×10^9 years for uranium-238 and 7.1×10^8 years for uranium-235, determine the age of Earth corresponding to this assumption.

Feature Problems

67. The *packing fraction* of a nuclide is related to the fraction of the total mass of a nuclide that is converted to nuclear binding energy. It is defined as the fraction $(M - A)/A$, where M is the actual nuclidic mass and A is the mass number. Use data from a handbook (such as the *Handbook of Chemistry and Physics*, published by the CRC Press) to determine the packing fractions of some representative nuclides. Plot a graph of packing fraction versus mass number, and compare it with Figure 25-6. Explain the relationship between the two.

68. For medical uses, radon-222 formed in the radioactive decay of radium-226 is allowed to collect over the radium metal for a period of time. Then, the gas is withdrawn and sealed into a glass vial. Following this, the radium is allowed to disintegrate for another period of time, when a new sample of radon-222 can be withdrawn. The procedure can be continued indefinitely. The process is somewhat complicated by the fact that radon-222 itself undergoes radioactive decay to polonium-218, and so on. The half-lives of radium-226 and radon-222 are 1.60×10^3 years and 3.82 days, respectively.
(a) Beginning with pure radium-226, the number of radon-222 atoms present starts at zero, increases for a time, and then falls off again. Explain this behavior. That is, because the half-life of radon-222 is so much shorter than that of radium-226, why doesn't the radon-222 simply decay as fast as it is produced, without ever building up to a maximum concentration?
(b) Write an expression for the rate of change (dD/dt) in the number of atoms (D) of the radon-222 daughter in terms of the number of radium-226 atoms present initially (P_0) and the decay constants of the parent (λ_p) and daughter (λ_d).
(c) Integration of the expression obtained in part (b) yields the following expression for the number of atoms of the radon-222 daughter (D) present at a time t.

$$D = \frac{P_0\lambda_p(e^{-\lambda_p \times t} - e^{-\lambda_d \times t})}{\lambda_d - \lambda_p}$$

Starting with 1.00 g of pure radium-226, approximately how long will it take for the amount of radon-222 to reach its maximum value: one day, one week, one year, one century, or one millenium?

69. Most nuclear power plants use zirconium in the fuel rods because zirconium maintains its structural integrity under exposure to the radiation in the nuclear reactor. The nuclear accidents at both Three Mile Island and Chernobyl involved the evolution of hydrogen gas from the reduction of water. The half-cell reduction potential for Zr is

$$ZrO_2(s) + 4\ H_3O^+(aq) + 4\ e^- \longrightarrow$$
$$Zr(s) + 6\ H_2O(l)\quad E° = -1.43\ V$$

(a) Can Zr reduce water under standard-state conditions?
(b) Calculate the equilibrium constant for the reduction of water by zirconium.
(c) Is the reaction spontaneous if the pH = 7 and Zr, ZrO_2, and water are in their standard states?
(d) Was the reduction of water by Zr the culprit in the reactor accidents mentioned above?

70. Radioactive decay and mass spectrometry are often used to date rocks after they have cooled from a magma. ^{87}Rb has a half-life of 4.8×10^{10} years and follows the radioactive decay

$$^{87}Rb \longrightarrow {}^{87}Sr + \beta^-$$

A rock was dated by assaying the product of this decay. The mass spectrum of a homogenized sample of rock showed the $^{87}Sr/^{86}Sr$ ratio to be 2.25. Assume that the original $^{87}Sr/^{86}Sr$ ratio was 0.700 when the rock cooled. Chemical analysis of the rock gave 15.5 ppm Sr and 265.4 ppm Rb, using the average atomic masses from a periodic table. The other isotope ratios were $^{86}Sr/^{88}Sr = 0.119$ and $^{84}Sr/^{88}Sr = 0.007$. The isotopic ratio for $^{87}Rb/^{85}Rb$ is 0.330. The isotopic masses are as follows:

Isotope	Atomic Mass/u
^{87}Rb	86.909
^{85}Rb	84.912
^{88}Sr	87.906
^{86}Sr	85.909
^{84}Sr	83.913
^{87}Sr	86.909

Calculate the following:
(a) the average atomic mass of Sr in the rock
(b) the original concentration of Rb in the rock in ppm
(c) the percentage of rubidium-87 decayed in the rock
(d) the time since the rock cooled

Self-Assessment Exercises

71. In your own words, define the following symbols: **(a)** α; **(b)** β^-; **(c)** β^+; **(d)** γ; **(e)** $t_{1/2}$.

72. Briefly describe each of the following ideas, phenomena, or methods: **(a)** radioactive decay series; **(b)** charged-particle accelerator; **(c)** neutron-to-proton ratio; **(d)** mass–energy relationship; **(e)** background radiation.

73. Explain the important distinctions between each pair of terms: **(a)** electron and positron; **(b)** half-life and decay constant; **(c)** mass defect and nuclear binding energy; **(d)** nuclear fission and nuclear fusion; **(e)** primary and secondary ionization.

74. Which of the following types of radiation is deflected in a magnetic field? **(a)** X ray; **(b)** γ ray; **(c)** β ray; **(d)** neutrons.

75. A process that produces a one-unit increase in atomic number is **(a)** electron capture; **(b)** β^- emission; **(c)** α emission; **(d)** γ-ray emission.

76. Of the following nuclides, the one most likely to be radioactive is **(a)** ^{31}P; **(b)** ^{66}Zn; **(c)** ^{35}Cl; **(d)** ^{108}Ag.

77. One of the following elements has eight naturally occurring *stable* isotopes. We should expect that one to be **(a)** Ra; **(b)** Au; **(c)** Cd; **(d)** Br.

78. Of the following nuclides, the highest nuclear binding energy per nucleon is found in **(a)** ^3_1H; **(b)** $^{16}_8O$; **(c)** $^{56}_{26}Fe$; **(d)** $^{235}_{92}U$.

79. The most radioactive of the isotopes of an element is the one with the largest value of its **(a)** half-life, $t_{1/2}$; **(b)** neutron number, N; **(c)** mass number, Z; **(d)** radioactive decay constant, λ.

80. Given a radioactive nuclide with $t_{1/2} = 1.00$ h and a current disintegration rate of 1000 atoms s^{-1}, three hours from now the disintegration rate will be **(a)** 1000 atoms s^{-1}; **(b)** 333 atoms s^{-1}; **(c)** 250 atoms s^{-1}; **(d)** 125 atoms s^{-1}.

81. Write nuclear equations to represent
    (a) the decay of ^{214}Ra by α-particle emission
    (b) the decay of ^{205}At by positron emission
    (c) the decay of ^{212}Fr by electron capture
    (d) the reaction of two deuterium nuclei (deuterons) to produce a nucleus of ^3_2He
    (e) the production of $^{243}_{97}Bk$ by the α-particle bombardment of $^{241}_{95}Am$
    (f) a nuclear reaction in which thorium-232 is bombarded with α particles, producing a new nuclide and four neutrons.

82. ^{232}Ra has a half-life of 11.4 d. How long would it take for the radioactivity associated with a sample of ^{232}Ra to decrease to 1% of its current value?

83. A sample of radioactive $^{35}_{16}S$ disintegrates at a rate of 1.00×10^3 atoms min^{-1}. The half-life of $^{35}_{16}S$ is 87.9 d. How long will it take for the activity of this sample to decrease to the point of producing **(a)** 253; **(b)** 104; and **(c)** 52 dis min^{-1}?

eMedia Exercises

84. Several types of radioactive emission are compared in the **Separation of Alpha, Beta, and Gamma Rays** animation (*Activebook 25-1*). **(a)** What are the ratios of the masses of the different particles described in the movie? What effect would a difference in mass have on a particle's interaction with other matter? **(b)** Positron emission is described in the text. Where would this particle impinge on the fluorescent screen in this animation?

85. The **U-238 Decay Series** simulation (*Activebook 25-2*) illustrates the natural decay of $^{238}_{92}U$. What is the total number and type of radioactive species produced by this series of reactions? What is the final product of the series?

86. The rate of radioactive decay is described in the **First-Order Process** animation (*Activebook 25-5*). On an atomic scale, describe why a radioactive decay process would be expected to exhibit first-order reaction kinetics as opposed to zero- or second-order kinetics.

87. Observe the operation of a nuclear reactor in the **Nuclear Reactors** activity (*Activebook 25-8*). In this application, what measures are taken to control the nuclear reaction? What are potential points of failure or points of release of radioactive material in this reactor design?

26

ORGANIC CHEMISTRY

CONTENTS

Hocking, Martin B. "Vanillin: Synthetic Flavoring from Spent Sulfite Liquor." *J. Chem. Educ.* **1997:** *74,* 1055 (September 1997).

✓ Web site with organic tutorials: http://www.mchmultimedia.com (commercial).

✓ Point out that, as with all chemicals, good safety precautions must always be practiced with organic solvents and compounds. Encourage students to look up the toxicities of solvents and compounds: e.g., Web site: http://www.atsdr.cdc.gov/ (noncommercial).

Kauffman, G. B., Chooljian, S. H. "Wohler's Urea Synthesis: Modern Version." *J. Chem. Educ.* **1997:** *74,* 1493 (December 1997).

Coffee beans contain an alkaloid compound commonly known as caffeine. Caffeine is a stimulant of the central nervous system producing alertness and heightened concentration. (Greg Vaughn/PacificStock.com)

To early nineteenth-century chemists, organic chemistry meant the study of compounds obtainable only from living matter, which was thought to have the "vital force" needed to make these compounds. In 1828, Friedrich Wöhler set out to synthesize ammonium cyanate, NH_4OCN, as in the reaction

$$AgOCN(s) + NH_4Cl(aq) \xrightarrow{\Delta} AgCl(s) + NH_4OCN(aq)$$

The white crystalline solid he obtained from the solution had none of the properties of ammonium cyanate, even though it had the same composition. The compound was not NH_4OCN but $(NH_2)_2CO$—*urea,* an organic compound. As Wöhler excitedly reported to J. J. Berzelius, "I must tell you that I can make urea without the use of kidneys, either man or dog. Ammonium cyanate is urea."

Since that time, chemists have synthesized millions of organic compounds, and today organic compounds number about 98% of all known chemical substances. In this chapter, we build on the introduction to organic compounds in Chapter 3 by exploring some of the principal types of organic compounds. In the next chapter, we will study the connection between organic compounds and living matter that once seemed so mysterious.

▲ FIGURE 26-1
Representation of the methane molecule
(a) Tetrahedral structure showing bond angle. **(b)** Dashed-wedged line structure convention used to suggest a three-dimensional structure through a structural formula. The solid lines represent bonds in the plane of the page. The dashed lines project *away* from the viewer (into the page), and the heavy wedge projects *toward* the viewer (out of the page). **(c)** Ball-and-stick model. **(d)** Space-filling model.

"Wöhler's Synthesis of Urea: How Do the Textbooks Report It?" *J. Chem. Educ.* **1996:** 73, 883 (September 1996).

Where possible, ball-and-stick and plastic space-filling models should be replaced with computer generated models. Rasmol, (PC, Mac) or Chime (Web) are useful. Thousands of molecular structures can be found on the internet with the extension .pdb (Protein Data Bank); e.g. Web site http://www.eou.edu/chemweb/ molmodel/mmp1.html (noncommercial).

▲ FIGURE 26-2
The ethane molecule, C_2H_6
(a) Structural formula.
(b) Dashed-wedged line structure. **(c)** Space-filling model.

KEEP IN MIND ▶
that the hybridization of the C atoms in ethane and propane is sp^3, as in methane. The tetrahedral geometry at the C atoms in alkanes means that the propane chain is not linear.

26-1   ORGANIC COMPOUNDS AND STRUCTURES: AN OVERVIEW

As we learned in Chapter 3, organic compounds contain carbon and hydrogen atoms or carbon and hydrogen in combination with a few other types of atoms, such as oxygen, nitrogen, and sulfur. Carbon is singled out for special study because the ability of C atoms to form strong covalent bonds with one another allows them to join together into straight chains, branched chains, and rings. The nearly infinite number of possible bonding arrangements of C atoms accounts for the vast number and variety of organic compounds.

The simplest organic compounds are those of carbon and hydrogen— **hydrocarbons**—and the simplest hydrocarbon is methane, CH_4, the chief constituent of natural gas.

From VSEPR theory we expect the electron group geometry around the central C atom in CH_4 to be tetrahedral (Fig. 26-1a). The four H atoms are equivalent: They are equidistant from the C atom and attached to it by covalent bonds of equal strength. The angle between any two C—H bonds is 109°28'. Figure 26-1(a) calls attention to a problem: How can we draw the three-dimensional structure of organic molecules in two dimensions? In a common method, often known as the **dashed-wedged line notation**, the following convention is adopted.

1. Ordinary lines are used to show bonds that lie in the plane of the paper.

2. Solid wedge lines are used to show bonds that stick out toward the viewer; that is, in front of the plane of the paper.

3. Dashed lines are used to show bonds directed away from the viewer; that is, behind the plane of the paper.

The dashed-wedged line notation is illustrated in Figure 26-1(b). Figure 26-1 also shows other commonly employed depictions of methane. As shown in Figure 11-6 (page 428), the chemical bonding in methane can be described by four σ bonds formed by the overlap of four hydrogen 1s orbitals with four equivalent sp^3 hybrid orbitals on the carbon atom.

The removal of one H atom from a CH_4 molecule leaves the —CH_3 group. Now imagine forming a covalent bond between two —CH_3 groups. The resulting molecule is *ethane*, C_2H_6 (Fig. 26-2). By increasing the number of C atoms in the chain, we can obtain still more hydrocarbons. The three-carbon molecule propane, C_3H_8, is pictured in Figure 26-3.

▲ **FIGURE 26-3**
The propane molecule, C_3H_8
(a) Structural formula. **(b)** Condensed structural formula. **(c)** Ball-and-stick model.
(d) Space-filling model. **(e)** Dashed-wedged line notation.

SKELETAL ISOMERISM

There are *two* ways of assembling a hydrocarbon molecule with four C and ten H atoms. There are *two* different compounds with the formula C_4H_{10}. One is butane and the other, isobutane (methylpropane in Figure 3-2 on page 70).

As we have previously learned, compounds that have the same molecular formula but different structural formulas are called *isomers*. In the case of butane, the isomers differ in their structural skeletons, or carbon-atom frameworks—one is a straight chain and the other, a branched chain. This type of isomerism is called **skeletal isomerism**.

> It is useful to show students that skeletal isomers have different physical properties such as melting points and boiling points. See Table 26.3.

EXAMPLE 26-1

Identifying Isomers. Write structural formulas for all the possible isomers with the molecular formula C_5H_{12}.

Isomerism animation

Solution

A general strategy is to first write the longest chain of C atoms from left to right. This gives the straight-chain structure labeled (1). To finish this structure, we add an appropriate number of H atoms (12, in this case) to give each C atom four bonds.

$$
\begin{array}{ccccccccc}
& \text{H} & \text{H} & \text{H} & \text{H} & \text{H} & \\
& | & | & | & | & | & \\
\text{H}- & \text{C} & - \text{C} & - \text{C} & - \text{C} & - \text{C} & -\text{H} \\
& | & | & | & | & | & \\
& \text{H} & \text{H} & \text{H} & \text{H} & \text{H} &
\end{array}
$$
(1)

Now, let's look for isomers with four C atoms in the longest chain and one C atom as a branch (five C atoms in all). There is only *one* possibility. Notice that if structure (2) is flipped from left to right, the identical structure (2') is obtained.

Again, we complete the structure of this isomer by adding H atoms

$$
\begin{array}{ccccccc}
& & \text{H} & & & & \\
& & | & & & & \\
& \text{H}- & \text{C} & -\text{H} & & & \\
& \text{H} & | & \text{H} & \text{H} & & \\
& | & | & | & | & & \\
\text{H}- & \text{C} & - \text{C} & - \text{C} & - \text{C} & -\text{H} \\
& | & | & | & | & & \\
& \text{H} & \text{H} & \text{H} & \text{H} & &
\end{array}
$$

Smith, Homer A., Jr. "The Centennial of Systematic Organic Nomenclature." *J. Chem. Educ.* **1992:** *69*, 863.

Traynham, James G. "The Official Rules for Organic Chemical Nomenclature: Emergence, Evolution, Emphasis, and Errors (TS)." *J. Chem. Educ.* **1987:** *64*, 325.

Hambly, Gordon F. "Organic Nomenclature: Making It a More Exciting Teaching and Learning Experience (CEC)." *J. Chem. Educ.* **1983:** *60*, 553.

▲ A Swiss stamp commemorating the 100th anniversary of an international congress in Geneva, at which a systematic nomenclature of organic compounds was adopted.

Finally, let's consider a three-carbon chain with two one-carbon branches. Again, there is only *one* possibility.

The number of isomers with the formula C_5H_{12} is three.

Practice Example A: Write condensed structural formulas for the five possible isomers with the formula C_6H_{14}.

Practice Example B: Write condensed structural formulas for the nine possible isomers with the formula C_7H_{16}.

In Chapter 3, we mentioned a way of greatly simplifying the writing of organic structures that we might consider again here. We draw lines to represent chemical bonds, and wherever a line ends or meets another line, there is a C atom. We then assume that enough H atoms are bonded to the C atoms to satisfy the need for each C atom to form *four* bonds. Such structural formulas are called *line-angle formulas*, or *line structures*. Notice that in the line-angle formulas written below for the three isomers in Example 26-1, we arrange the lines in a zigzag fashion, just as observed in the three-dimensional structures of these molecules.

(1)   (2)   (3)

CONCEPT ASSESSMENT ✓

In 1874, van't Hoff and Le Bel published separate papers advancing the hypothesis that the four bonds from a central carbon extend tetrahedrally. This marked the beginning of the field of stereochemistry. Part of their justification was that there was only one known compound with the formula CH_2X_2. Using the compound CH_2F_2 as an example, determine the expected number of isomers if the orientation of the bonds to a carbon atom is tetrahedral and the expected number if the orientation is square-planar.

NOMENCLATURE

Early organic chemists often assigned names related to the origin or properties of new compounds. Some of these names are still in common use. Citric acid is found in citrus fruit; uric acid is present in urine; formic acid is found in ants (from the Latin word for ant, *formica*); and morphine induces sleep (from *Morpheus*, the ancient Greek god of sleep). As thousands upon thousands of new compounds were synthesized, it became apparent that a system of common names was unworkable. Following several interim systems, one recommended by the International Union of Pure and Applied Chemistry (IUPAC) was adopted.

In this introduction to nomenclature, we will consider only hydrocarbons with all carbon-to-carbon bonds as single bonds. These are known as **saturated hydrocarbons**, or alkanes. We have no trouble naming the first few: CH_4, methane; C_2H_6, ethane; C_3H_8, propane. We encounter our first difficulty with C_4H_{10}, which has two isomers. This problem is resolved by assigning the name *butane* to the straight-chain isomer, $CH_3CH_2CH_2CH_3$, and *isobutane*

TABLE 26.1	Some Common Alkyl Groups
Name	**Structural Formula**
Methyl	$-CH_3$
Ethyl	$-CH_2CH_3$
Propyl[a]	$-CH_2CH_2CH_3$
Isopropyl	CH_3CHCH_3
Butyl[a]	$-CH_2CH_2CH_2CH_3$
	CH_3
Isobutyl	$-CH_2CHCH_3$
s-Butyl[b]	$CH_3CHCH_2CH_3$
	CH_3
t-Butyl[c]	CH_3CCH_3

[a] In the past, the prefix *normal* or *n-* was used for a straight-chain alkyl group, such as *n*-propyl or *n*-butyl.
[b] *s* = secondary.
[c] *t* = tertiary.

to the branched-chain isomer, $CH_3CH(CH_3)_2$. This method is inadequate for the C_5H_{12} alkanes, for which there are three structural isomers (Example 26-1), and it is even less satisfactory for alkanes with greater numbers of C atoms. We avoid ambiguous names, however, with the following rules.

1. Select the *longest* continuous carbon chain in the molecule, and use the hydrocarbon name of this chain as the base name. Except for the common names methane, ethane, propane, and butane, standard Greek prefixes relate the name to the number of C atoms in the chain, as in *pent*ane (C_5), *hex*ane (C_6), *hept*ane (C_7), *oct*ane (C_8), ...

2. Consider every branch of the main chain to be a substituent derived from another hydrocarbon. For each of these substituents, change the ending of its name from *ane* to *yl*. That is, the alkane substituent becomes an **alkyl group** (Table 26.1).

3. Number the C atoms of the continuous base chain so that the substituents appear *at the lowest numbers* possible.

4. Name each substituent according to its chemical identity and the number of the C atom to which it is attached. For identical substituents use *di, tri, tetra,* and so on, and write the appropriate carbon number for each substituent.

5. Separate numbers from one another by commas, and from letters by hyphens.

6. List the substituents *alphabetically* by name.

◄ Do not try to memorize these rules at the outset. Refer to them as you proceed through the examples, and they will become part of your vocabulary of organic chemistry.

Leung, Sam H. "Amino Acids, Aromatic Compounds, and Carboxylic Acids: How Did They Get Their Common Names?" *J. Chem. Educ.* **2000:** *77,* 48 (January 2000).

◄ **KEEP IN MIND**
that in using alphabetical order, we do not consider the prefixes *di, tri,* . . . or symbols such as *s* and *t*. Thus, *t*-butyl, precedes methyl in the name 4-*t*-butyl-2-methylheptane.

EXAMPLE 26-2

Naming an Alkane Hydrocarbon. Give an appropriate IUPAC name for the following compound, an important constituent of gasoline.

$$\underset{1}{CH_3}-\underset{2}{\overset{\overset{\displaystyle CH_3}{|}}{\underset{\underset{\displaystyle CH_3}{|}}{C}}}-\underset{3}{CH_2}-\underset{4}{\overset{\overset{\displaystyle CH_3}{|}}{CH}}-\underset{5}{CH_3}$$

Solution

The C atoms are numbered in red, and the side-chain substituents to be named are shown in blue. The longest chain of C atoms is five, and the carbons are numbered so that the one with two substituent groups is number 2, instead of number 4. Each substituent is a methyl group, $-CH_3$. Two methyl groups are on the second C atom, and one methyl group is on the fourth C atom. The correct name is 2,2,4-trimethylpentane.

If we had numbered the C atoms from right to left, we would have obtained the name 2,4,4-trimethylpentane. This is *not* an acceptable name because it does not use the *smallest* numbers possible.

Practice Example A: Give an appropriate IUPAC name for the hydrocarbon

$$
\begin{array}{ccc}
& CH_3 & CH_3 \\
& | & | \\
CH_3CH_2CHCH_2CH_2 & CCH_2CH_2CH_3 \\
& & | \\
& & CH_3
\end{array}
$$

Practice Example B: Give an appropriate IUPAC name for the hydrocarbon $CH_3CH_2CH(CH_3)CH_2CH_2CH(CH_3)CH_2CH_3$.

EXAMPLE 26-3

Writing the Formula to Correspond to the Name of an Alkane Hydrocarbon.
Write a condensed structural formula for 4-*t*-butyl-2-methylheptane.

Solution

Because the compound is a heptane, the longest chain of C atoms is seven.

$$C-C-C-C-C-C-C$$

Starting on the left, we attach a methyl group to the second C atom.

$$
\begin{array}{c}
CH_3 \\
| \\
C-C-C-C-C-C-C
\end{array}
$$

Next, we attach a *t*-butyl group to the fourth C atom.

$$
\begin{array}{c}
CH_3 \\
| \\
CH_3-C-CH_3 \\
CH_3 \quad\quad | \\
| \\
C-C-C-C-C-C-C
\end{array}
$$

Finally, we add the remaining hydrogen atoms to give each C atom four bonds.

$$
\begin{array}{c}
CH_3 \\
| \\
CH_3 \quad CH_3-C-CH_3 \\
| \quad\quad\quad | \\
CH_3-CH-CH_2-CH-CH_2-CH_2-CH_3
\end{array}
$$

Practice Example A: Write a condensed structural formula for 3-ethyl-2,6-dimethylheptane.

Practice Example B: Write a condensed structural formula for 3-isopropyl-2-methylpentane.

POSITIONAL ISOMERISM

A variety of atoms or groups of atoms can be substituents on carbon chains, for example, Br. The three monobromopentanes possess the same carbon skeleton. Because they differ in the position of the bromine atom on the carbon chain, these structural isomers are also called **positional isomers**.

$CH_3CH_2CH_2CH_2CH_2Br$ $CH_3CH_2CH_2CHCH_3$ $CH_3CH_2CHCH_2CH_3$
                                                            | |
                                                            Br   Br

    1-Bromopentane   2-Bromopentane   3-Bromopentane

FUNCTIONAL GROUPS

Organic compounds typically contain elements in addition to carbon and hydrogen. These elements occur as distinctive groupings of one or several atoms. In some cases, these groupings of atoms are substituted for H atoms in hydrocarbon chains or rings. In other cases, they may build from the C atom itself. For example, the carbonyl group consists of a C atom in the skeletal structure

to which an O atom is attached by a double bond $\left(\begin{array}{c}\diagdown\\ \diagup\end{array}C{=}O\right)$. These distinctive

groupings of atoms are called **functional groups**, and the remainder of the molecule is sometimes referred to by the symbol R. Usually, the R refers to an alkyl group. The physical and chemical properties of organic molecules generally depend on the particular functional groups present. The remainder of the molecule (R) often has little effect on these properties.

A convenient way to study organic chemistry, then, is to consider the properties associated with specific functional groups. We have already encountered a few functional groups in earlier chapters, such as the $-OH$ group in alcohols and the $-COOH$ group in carboxylic acids. Table 26.2 lists the major types of organic compounds, with their distinctive functional groups shown in blue. By combining information from Tables 26.1 and 26.2, for example, you should be able to identify $(CH_3)_2CHOCH_2CH_2CH_3$ as isopropyl propyl ether.

Byrd, S., et al. "Learning the Functional Groups: Keys to Success." *J. Chem. Educ.* **2001:** *78,* 1355.

Welsh, M. J. "Organic Functional Group Playing Card Deck." *J. Chem. Educ.* **2003:** *80,* 426.

26-2   ALKANES

In this section we will explore some properties of the alkanes. The essential characteristic of **alkane** hydrocarbon molecules is that they have only single covalent bonds. The bonds in these compounds are said to be *saturated*.

The alkanes range in complexity from methane, CH_4, to molecules containing 50 C atoms or more (found in petroleum). Most have the formula C_nH_{2n+2}, and each alkane differs from the preceding one in a sequence by a $-CH_2-$, or *methylene* group. Substances whose molecules differ only by a constant unit such as $-CH_2-$ are said to form a **homologous series**. Members of such a series usually have closely related chemical and physical properties. The data in Table 26.3 indicate that boiling points are related to molecular masses and shapes in the ways discussed in Section 12-5. For example, the straight-chain C_4, C_5, and C_6 alkane molecules are more easily polarized than their branched-chain isomers. Intermolecular attractions between the straight-chain molecules are strongest, and they have the highest boiling points. Isomers with more compact structures have lower boiling points (recall Figure 12-25).

✓ Point out that alkanes are nonpolar, water insoluble compounds with relatively low melting points and boiling points.

Boiling Points of Organic Molecules activity

TABLE 26.2   Some Classes of Organic Compounds and Their Functional Groups

Class	General Structural Formula[a]	Example	Name of Example
Alkane	R—H	$CH_3CH_2CH_2CH_2CH_2CH_3$	Hexane
Alkene	$\diagdown$C$=$C$\diagup$	$CH_2=CHCH_2CH_2CH_3$	1-Pentene
Alkyne	—C≡C—	$CH_3C≡CCH_2CH_2CH_2CH_2CH_3$	2-Octyne
Alcohol	R—OH	$CH_3CH_2CH_2CH_2OH$	1-Butanol
Alkyl halide	R—X[b]	$CH_3CH_2CH_2CH_2CH_2CH_2Br$	1-Bromohexane
Ether	R—O—R	CH_3—O—$CH_2CH_2CH_3$	1-Methoxypropane (methyl propyl ether)[c]
Amine	R—NH_2	$CH_3CH_2CH_2$—NH_2	1-Aminopropane (propylamine)[c]
Aldehyde	$\underset{\displaystyle \ }{R-\overset{\displaystyle O}{\overset{\displaystyle \|}{C}}-H}$	$CH_3CH_2CH_2\overset{\displaystyle O}{\overset{\displaystyle \|}{C}}-H$	Butanal (butyraldehyde)[c]
Ketone	$R-\overset{\displaystyle O}{\overset{\displaystyle \|}{C}}-R$	$CH_3CH_2\overset{\displaystyle O}{\overset{\displaystyle \|}{C}}CH_2CH_2CH_3$	3-Hexanone (ethyl propyl ketone)[c]
Carboxylic acid	$R-\overset{\displaystyle O}{\overset{\displaystyle \|}{C}}-OH$	$CH_3CH_2CH_2\overset{\displaystyle O}{\overset{\displaystyle \|}{C}}-OH$	Butanoic acid (butyric acid)[c]
Ester	$R-\overset{\displaystyle O}{\overset{\displaystyle \|}{C}}-OR$	$CH_3CH_2CH_2\overset{\displaystyle O}{\overset{\displaystyle \|}{C}}-OCH_3$	Methyl butanoate (methyl butyrate)[c]
Amide	$R-\overset{\displaystyle O}{\overset{\displaystyle \|}{C}}-NH_2$	$CH_3CH_2CH_2\overset{\displaystyle O}{\overset{\displaystyle \|}{C}}-NH_2$	Butanamide (butyramide)[c]
Arene	Ar—H[d]	⬡—CH_2CH_3	Ethylbenzene
Aryl halide	Ar—X[b]	⬡—Br	Bromobenzene
Phenol	Ar—OH	Cl—⬡—OH	4-Chlorophenol (p-chlorophenol)[c]

[a] The functional group is shown in red. R stands for an alkyl group.
[b] X stands for a halogen atom; F, Cl, Br, or I.
[c] Common name.
[d] Ar stands for an aromatic (*aryl*) group such as the benzene ring.

CONCEPT ASSESSMENT

Illustrate the meaning of homologous series by writing a homologous series for alkyl halides.

Formula	Isomer	Boiling Point, °C	Formula	Isomer	Boiling Point, °C
C_4H_{10}	Butane	−0.5	C_6H_{14}	Hexane	68.7
	Methylpropane	−11.7		3-Methylpentane	63.3
C_5H_{12}	Pentane	36.1		2-Methylpentane	60.3
	2-Methylbutane	27.9		2,3-Dimethylbutane	58.0
	2,2-Dimethylpropane	9.5		2,2-Dimethylbutane	49.7

TABLE 26.3   Boiling Points of Some Isomeric Alkanes

CONFORMATIONS

With ball-and-stick models, we can visualize an important type of motion in alkane molecules—rotation of groups with respect to one another about the σ bond connecting them. Figure 26-4 suggests two of the many possible orientations of the two —CH_3 groups in the ethane molecule. In one of these configurations, one set of C—H bonds is directly behind the other when the molecule is viewed head-on. This is called the *eclipsed* conformation. The distance between the H atoms on the adjacent C atoms is at a minimum, leading to the condition of maximum repulsion between the H atoms. In another configuration, called the *staggered* conformation, the H atoms are located a maximum distance apart. Although we expect the staggered conformation to be more stable than the eclipsed, at room temperature ethane molecules have sufficient thermal energy so that the —CH_3 groups can freely rotate about the C—C bond, making all conformations accessible to the molecule. At lower temperatures, however, ethane does occur mostly in the staggered conformation. Similar situations are encountered in the higher alkanes.

Pellegrinet, S. C., et al. "A Set of Hands-On Exercises on Conformational Analysis." *J. Chem. Educ.* **2005**: *82, 73.*

CONCEPT ASSESSMENT ✓

Use Figure 26-4 as a guide in drawing the different conformations of 1,2-dichloroethane. Although this compound has only a limited solubility in water, one conformation should have a greater solubility than any other. Which is it and why?

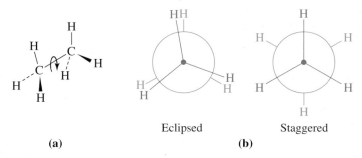

Eclipsed   Staggered

(a)   (b)

Kim, Jae Hyun. "Alkanes in Motion (Program for Mac OS-Compatible Computers: J. Chem. Educ. Software Vol. 9C, No. 1)." *J. Chem. Educ.* **1997**: *74,* 1015 (August 1997).

Kim, Jae Hyun. "Four Programs for Windows: Abstract of Volume 4D, Number 2: Alkanes in Motion." *J. Chem. Educ.* **1996**: *73,* 1079 (November 1996).

▲ **FIGURE 26-4**
Rotations about the C—C bond in ethane
(a) Side view of the molecule showing rotation about the C—C bond.
(b) Conformations of C_2H_6 in a representation known as a Newman projection. This is based on a head-on view of a ball-and-stick model of ethane. The small solid circle (red) represents the C atom in front, and the red H atoms are those bonded to this C atom. The large open circle (blue) represents the rear C atom, and the blue H atoms are those bonded to it.

RING STRUCTURES

Alkanes in chain structures have the formula C_nH_{2n+2} and are called **aliphatic**. Alkanes can also exist in ring, or cyclic, structures; such alkanes are called **alicyclic**. Think of these rings as having formed by the joining together of the two ends of an aliphatic chain after the elimination of a H atom from each end. Simple alicyclic compounds have the formula C_nH_{2n}.

Cyclopropane
C_3H_6

Cyclobutane
C_4H_8

Cyclopentane
C_5H_{10}

Cyclohexane
C_6H_{12}

The line-angle representations of the four alicyclic compounds above are an equilateral triangle, a square, a pentagon, and a hexagon, respectively. By the nomenclature rules on page 1077, we would name the following alicyclic compound 1,1,3-trimethylcyclopentane.

The bond angles in cyclopropane are 60°, compared with the normal 109.5°; the bonds are highly strained (Fig. 26-5). The inherent instability of cyclopropane is reflected in the value of ΔG_f°, which is 104 kJ mol^{-1}; this means that cyclopropane is unstable with respect to its elements. In contrast, ΔG_f°, for propane is -23 kJ mol^{-1}, and it is stable with respect to the elements carbon and hydrogen. As a result, numerous reactions occur in which the ring breaks open to yield a chain molecule—propane or a propane derivative. Cyclopropane is more reactive than the other alkanes and, in several ways, its reactivity resembles that of alkenes (discussed in Section 26-3).

The cyclobutane molecule buckles slightly, so the four C atoms are not all in the same plane. In the cyclopentane molecule, the most stable arrangement is for one of the C atoms to be buckled out of the plane of the other four.

For cyclohexane, there are a number of arrangements, or **conformations**, of the molecule. Two of these are shown as ball-and-stick models in Figure 26-6. These are the *boat* and the *chair conformations*. The cyclohexane molecule flips between these and other conformations fairly easily at room temperature.

PREPARATION OF ALKANES

The chief source of alkanes is petroleum, as we describe at the end of this section, but several laboratory methods are also available for their preparation. In the presence of a catalyst, unsaturated hydrocarbons, whether containing double or triple bonds, may be converted to alkanes by the addition of H atoms to the multiple bond systems (equation 26.1). In another type of reaction, halogenated hydrocarbons react with alkali metals to produce alkanes of double the carbon content (equation 26.2). Finally, alkali metal salts of carboxylic acids may be fused with alkali metal hydroxides. Sodium carbonate and an alkane with one carbon less than the metal carboxylate are formed (equation 26.3).

$$CH_2{=}CH_2 + H_2 \xrightarrow{\text{Pt or Pd}} CH_3{-}CH_3 \qquad (26.1)$$

$$2\,CH_3CH_2Br + 2\,Na \xrightarrow{\text{heat/pressure}} 2\,NaBr + CH_3CH_2CH_2CH_3 \qquad (26.2)$$

$$CH_3{-}\overset{\overset{\displaystyle O}{\|}}{C}{-}ONa + NaOH \xrightarrow{\Delta} Na_2CO_3 + CH_4 \qquad (26.3)$$

No "head-on" overlap of atomic orbitals

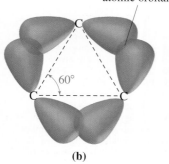

(b)

▲ **FIGURE 26-5**
Ring strain in cyclopropane
(a) Ball-and-stick model.
(b) Valence-bond picture of cyclopropane using sp^3 hybrids orbitals, which leads to poor overlap of the orbitals and hence weak bonds.

(a)

(b)

Leriverend, Pierre. "A Simple Way to Draw the Chair and Boat Conformations of Cyclohexane." *J. Chem. Educ.* **1991:** *68*, 957.

 FIGURE 26-6
Two important conformations of cyclohexane
(a) Boat form. **(b)** Chair form. The H atoms extending laterally from the ring—equatorial H atoms—are shown in red. The H atoms projecting above and below the ring—axial H atoms—are in blue.

REACTIONS OF THE ALKANES

Saturated hydrocarbons have little affinity for most chemical reactants. They are nonpolar substances that are insoluble in water and unreactive toward acids, bases, or oxidizing agents. Halogens react only slowly with alkanes at room temperature, but at higher temperatures, particularly in the presence of light, halogenation occurs. In such a reaction, called a **substitution reaction**, a halogen atom *substitutes* for a hydrogen atom. This substitution occurs by a *chain reaction*, written as follows for the chlorination of methane. (Only the electrons involved in bond breakage or formation are shown.)

Stevens, M. P. "A simple and colorful demonstration of light-catalyzed bromination of an alkane." *J. Chem. Educ.* **1992:** *69*, 1028.

Weiss, H. M., et al. "A Safe Simple Halogenation Experiment." *J. Chem. Educ.* **1999:** *76*, 534.

$$Initiation: \quad Cl{:}Cl \xrightarrow[\text{light}]{\text{heat or}} 2\,Cl\cdot$$

$$Propagation: \quad H_3C{:}H + Cl\cdot \longrightarrow H_3C\cdot + H{:}Cl$$

$$H_3C\cdot + Cl{:}Cl \longrightarrow H_3C{:}Cl + Cl\cdot$$

$$Termination: \quad Cl\cdot + Cl\cdot \longrightarrow Cl{:}Cl$$

$$H_3C\cdot + Cl\cdot \longrightarrow H_3C{:}Cl$$

$$H_3C\cdot + H_3C\cdot \longrightarrow H_3C{:}CH_3$$

The reaction is initiated when some Cl_2 molecules absorb sufficient energy to dissociate into Cl atoms (represented above as $Cl\cdot$). Cl atoms collide with CH_4 molecules to produce methyl *free radicals* ($H_3C\cdot$), which combine with Cl_2 molecules to form the product, CH_3Cl. When any or all of the last three reactions proceed to the extent of consuming the free radicals present, the reaction stops. The overall equation for the formation of chloromethane is

◀ The reaction of H_2 with Cl_2 to form HCl, discussed on page 924, proceeds by a similar mechanism.

$$CH_4 + Cl_2 \xrightarrow[\text{light}]{\text{heat or}} CH_3Cl + HCl \qquad (26.4)$$

This free-radical chain reaction usually yields a mixture of products, not just chloromethane. Polyhalogenation can also occur to form CH_2Cl_2, dichloromethane (methylene chloride, a solvent and paint remover); $CHCl_3$, trichloromethane (chloroform, a solvent and fumigant); and CCl_4, tetrachloromethane (carbon tetrachloride, a solvent).

The most commonly encountered reaction of alkanes is with oxygen. Alkanes burn; the *oxidation* of hydrocarbons underlies their important use as fuels. For example, octane reacts with oxygen as follows.

Bromination of an alkane (cyclohexane) can be readily shown. To a beaker of cyclohexane, add an eyedropper full of dilute bromine (bromine in water), which turns the solution brown. Put the beaker under an incandescent light and the color disappears as bromination takes place. The light is needed to initiate free-radical formation. Bromine is highly toxic and can cause severe burns. It also vaporizes easily and its fumes are toxic.

$$C_8H_{18}(l) + \frac{25}{2}O_2(g) \longrightarrow 8\,CO_2(g) + 9\,H_2O(l) \qquad \Delta H° = -5.48 \times 10^3 \text{ kJ} \quad (26.5)$$

TABLE 26.4   Principal Petroleum Fractions

Boiling Range, °C	Composition	Fraction	Uses
Below 0	C_1 to C_4	Gas	Gaseous fuel
0–50	C_5 to C_7	Petroleum ether	Solvents
50–100	C_6 to C_8	Ligroin	Solvents
70–150	C_6 to C_9	Gasoline	Motor fuel
150–300	C_{10} to C_{16}	Kerosene	Jet fuel, diesel oil
Over 300	C_{16} to C_{18}	Gas–oil	Diesel oil, cracking stock
—	C_{18} to C_{20}	Wax–oil	Lubricating oil, mineral oil, cracking stock
—	C_{21} to C_{40}	Paraffin wax	Candles, wax paper
—	above C_{40}	Residuum	Roofing tar, road materials, waterproofing

Chen, Chien T. "Understanding the Fate of Petroleum Hydrocarbons in the Subsurface Environment." *J. Chem. Educ.* **1992:** 69, 357.

ALKANES FROM PETROLEUM

The lower molecular mass alkanes, methane and ethane, are found principally in natural gas. Propane and butane are found dissolved in petroleum; they can be extracted as gases and sold as liquefied petroleum gas (LPG). Higher alkanes are obtained by the fractional distillation of petroleum, a complex mixture of at least 500 compounds. The main petroleum fractions are listed in Table 26.4. (The liquid–vapor equilibrium principles that underlie fractional distillation were discussed on page 546.)

Not all the gasoline components referred to in Table 26.4 are equally desirable in fuels. Some of them burn more smoothly than others. (Explosive burning results in engine knocking.) The hydrocarbon *2,2,4-trimethylpentane*, a structural isomer of octane, has excellent engine performance, and it is given an octane rating of 100. *Heptane* has poor engine performance; its octane rating is 0. These two hydrocarbons serve as a basis for establishing the quality of automotive fuels. A gasoline that gives the same performance as a mixture of 87% 2,2,4-trimethylpentane and 13% heptane is assigned an octane number of 87, for example. In general, branched-chain hydrocarbons have higher octane numbers (burn more smoothly) than their straight-chain counterparts.

$$CH_3-\underset{\underset{CH_3}{|}}{\overset{\overset{CH_3}{|}}{C}}-CH_2-\underset{\underset{H}{|}}{\overset{\overset{CH_3}{|}}{C}}-CH_3 \qquad CH_3-CH_2-CH_2-CH_2-CH_2-CH_2-CH_3$$

2,2,4-Trimethylpentane
Octane rating: 100

n-Heptane
Octane rating: 0

▲ A catalytic cracking unit (cat cracker) at a petroleum refinery.

▶ Not only do the processes of cracking, re-forming, and alkylation produce a higher grade of gasoline but they also increase the yield of gasoline obtained from crude oil.

Gasoline obtained by fractional distillation of petroleum has an octane number of 50–55 and is not acceptable for use in automobiles, which require fuels with octane numbers near 90. Extensive modifications of the gasoline fraction are required. In *thermal cracking*, large hydrocarbon molecules are broken down into molecules in the gasoline range, and the presence of special catalysts promotes the production of branched-chain hydrocarbons. For example, the molecule $C_{15}H_{32}$ might be broken down into C_8H_{18} and C_7H_{14}. The process of *re-forming*, or isomerization, converts straight-chain to branched-chain hydrocarbons and other types of hydrocarbons having higher octane numbers. In thermal and catalytic cracking, some low-molecular mass hydrocarbons are rejoined into higher molecular mass hydrocarbons by a process known as *alkylation*.

The octane rating of gasoline can be further improved by adding antiknock compounds to prevent premature combustion. At one time, the preferred additive was tetraethyllead, $(C_2H_5)_4Pb$. Lead additives have now been phased out of gasoline in the United States, and substitutes such as the oxygenated hydrocarbons methanol and ethanol are used instead.

26-3 ALKENES AND ALKYNES

A straight- or branched-chain alkane has the maximum number of H atoms possible for its number of C atoms. In other classes of hydrocarbons, compounds with the same number of C atoms but fewer H atoms, the C atoms must either join into rings, form carbon-to-carbon multiple bonds, or both. This is essential so that the C atoms can have valence-shell octets. Hydrocarbons whose molecules contain some double or triple bonds between C atoms are said to be **unsaturated**. If there is *one double bond* in the molecules, the hydrocarbons are the simple **alkenes**, or **olefins**; they have the general formula C_nH_{2n}. Simple **alkynes** have *one triple bond* in their molecules and have the general formula C_nH_{2n-2}.

In the examples that follow, systematic names are shown in blue. The names given in parentheses are also commonly used.

> The physical properties of alkenes and alkynes are similar to those of alkanes, but their chemical properties are very different.

$$CH_3CH_2CH_2C{=}CH_2$$
$$\overset{|}{CH_2CH_3}$$

$$CH_2{=}CH_2 \qquad CH_3CH_2CH{=}CH_2$$
Ethene   1-Butene   2-Ethyl-1-pentene
(ethylene)

$$HC{\equiv}CH \qquad CH_3CH_2C{\equiv}CH \qquad CH_3CHC{\equiv}CCH_3$$
$$\overset{|}{CH_3}$$
Ethyne   1-Butyne   4-Methyl-2-pentyne
(acetylene)   (ethylacetylene)   (isopropylmethylacetylene)

Following are the modifications of the rules on page 1077 required to name alkenes and alkynes.

1. Select as the base chain the longest chain containing the multiple bond.
2. Number the C atoms of the chain to place the multiple bond at the lowest possible number.
3. Use the ending *ene* for alkenes and *yne* for alkynes.

Thus, in the name 2-ethyl-1-pentene, the longest chain *containing the multiple bond* is a five-carbon chain (*pent-*). This is *not* a substituted hexane, and it is *not* a hexene. The double bond makes the molecule an alkene, and its location between the first and second carbon makes it a 1-pentene. The ethyl group is attached to the second C atom, and so the alkene is named 2-ethyl-1-pentene.

The alkenes are similar to the alkanes in physical properties. At room temperature, those containing two to four C atoms are gases; those with five to 18 are liquids; those with more than 18 are solids. In general, alkynes have higher boiling points than their alkane and alkene counterparts.

GEOMETRIC ISOMERISM

The molecules 2-butene, $CH_3CH{=}CHCH_3$, and 1-butene, $CH_2{=}CHCH_2CH_3$, differ in the position of the double bond and are *positional* isomers. But another kind of isomerism is possible in 2-butene, represented by these two structures.

(a) *cis*-2-Butene   (b) *trans*-2-Butene

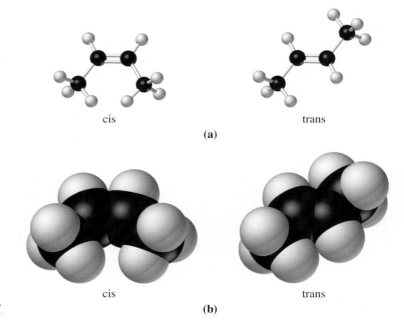

▶ **FIGURE 26-7**
Geometric isomerism in 2-butene
(a) Ball-and-stick models. (b) Space-filling models.

cis   trans
(a)

cis   trans
(b)

Molecular models are very helpful when explaining stereoisomerism to students.

As we learned in Section 11-4, a double bond between C atoms consists of the overlap of sp^2 hybrid orbitals to form a σ bond *and* the sideways overlap of p orbitals to form a π bond. Rotation about this double bond is severely restricted. Molecule (a) cannot be converted into molecule (b) simply by twisting one end of the molecule through 180°, so the two molecules are distinctly different (Fig. 26-7). To distinguish between these two molecules by name, we call molecule (a) *cis*-2-butene (*cis*, Latin, on the same side), and we call molecule (b) *trans*-2-butene (*trans*, Latin, across). This type of isomerism is called **geometric isomerism**.

As noted in Chapter 24, geometric isomerism is only one type of a more general kind of isomerism known as *stereoisomerism* (from the Greek word *stereos*, meaning solid, or three-dimensional, in nature). The number and types of atoms and bonds in stereoisomers are the same, but certain atoms are oriented differently in space. Another type of stereoisomerism, also introduced in Chapter 24, is *optical isomerism*. As we will see in the next chapter, stereoisomerism plays an important role in the unique chemical reactions found in living organisms.

PREPARATION AND USES

The general laboratory preparation of alkenes uses an **elimination reaction**, a reaction in which atoms are removed from adjacent positions on a carbon chain. A small molecule is produced, and an additional bond is formed between the C atoms. For example, H_2O is eliminated in the following reaction.

$$CH_3-\underset{\underset{HO}{|}}{\overset{\overset{H}{|}}{C}}-\underset{\underset{H}{|}}{\overset{\overset{H}{|}}{C}}-H \xrightarrow[\text{H}_2\text{SO}_4]{\Delta} CH_3CH{=}CH_2 + H_2O \qquad (26.6)$$

The principal alkene of the chemical industry is ethylene (ethene), the highest-volume organic chemical produced in the United States. Its chief use is in the manufacture of polymers, although it is also used to manufacture other organic chemicals. Reaction (26.6) is relatively unimportant in the commercial production of ethylene, which is obtained mainly by thermal cracking of other hydrocarbons.

The simplest alkyne is acetylene, which can be prepared from coal, water, and limestone in a three-step process.

$$CaCO_3 \xrightarrow{\Delta} CaO + CO_2$$

$$CaO + 3\,C \xrightarrow[2000\ °C]{\text{electric furnace}} \underset{\substack{\text{calcium acetylide} \\ \text{(calcium carbide)}}}{CaC_2} + CO$$

$$CaC_2 + 2\,H_2O \longrightarrow \underset{\text{acetylene}}{HC\equiv CH} + Ca(OH)_2 \qquad (26.7)$$

Most other alkynes are prepared from acetylene by taking advantage of the acidity of the C—H bond. In the presence of a very strong base, such as sodium amide, the amide anion removes the proton from the acetylene to form ammonia and the salt sodium acetylide. The acetylide can then react with an alkyl halide.

$$H—C\equiv C—H + Na^+NH_2^- \longrightarrow H—C\equiv C^-Na^+ + NH_3$$

$$H—C\equiv C^-Na^+ + CH_3Br \longrightarrow H—C\equiv C—CH_3 + Na^+Br^- \qquad (26.8)$$

By continuing this reaction, the triple bond can be positioned as desired in the chain, as in the synthesis of 2-pentyne.

$$H—C\equiv C—CH_3 + NaNH_2 \longrightarrow Na^{+\,-}C\equiv C—CH_3 + NH_3$$

$$Na^{+\,-}C\equiv C—CH_3 + CH_3CH_2Br \longrightarrow CH_3CH_2C\equiv CCH_3 + Na^+Br^- \quad (26.9)$$

At one time, acetylene was one of the most important organic raw materials in the chemical industry, but it is no longer among the top 50 industrial chemicals. At present, the chief use of acetylene is in the manufacture of other chemicals for polymer production, such as vinyl chloride, $H_2C\!=\!CHCl$, which is polymerized to polyvinyl chloride (PVC). Acetylene produces high-temperature flames when burned in excess oxygen, and this is the basis of oxyacetylene torches used for cutting and welding metals.

$$HC\equiv CH(g) + \frac{5}{2}O_2(g) \longrightarrow 2\,CO_2(g) + H_2O(l) \qquad \Delta H = -1300\ \text{kJ}$$

The large negative enthalpy of combustion of acetylene is due to acetylene's large *positive* enthalpy of formation: $\Delta H_f^\circ[C_2H_2(g)] = +226.7\ \text{kJ mol}^{-1}$.

ADDITION REACTIONS

Unlike alkanes, which react by *substitution*, alkenes react by *addition*. In an **addition reaction** of an alkene, two new groups become bonded to the C atoms at the site of the double bond, and the carbon-to-carbon double bond is converted to a single bond.

$$CH_2\!=\!CH_2 + Br_2 \longrightarrow \underset{\substack{| \quad | \\ Br \quad Br}}{CH_2—CH_2} \qquad (26.10)$$

In this reaction, the two Br atoms are identical, as are the two —CH_2 groups. Br_2 and $CH_2\!=\!CH_2$ are known as *symmetrical* reactants. HBr and $CH_3CH\!=\!CH_2$ are *unsymmetrical* reactants. When at least one reactant is symmetrical, it is a fairly straightforward matter to predict the reaction product. We have a problem, however, in predicting the products when both reactants are unsymmetrical. Let's consider, for example, the reaction of *unsymmetrical* HBr with *unsymmetrical* propene. Which of the two likely products should we expect?

$$CH_3CH\!=\!CH_2 + H—Br \longrightarrow \underset{\substack{| \quad | \\ Br \quad H}}{CH_3CH—CH_2} \text{ or } \underset{\substack{| \quad | \\ H \quad Br}}{CH_3CH—CH_2}$$

▲ Cutting steel with an oxyacetylene torch.

To demonstrate the formation of acetylene from CaC_2, add water to a vacuum flask, followed by a few pellets of CaC_2 which fizzes. Stopper the flask and hold a match over the side opening of the flask to show that the gas burns. From Fenster, A. E., Harpp, D. N., and Schwarcz, J. A. "A Versatile Demonstration with Calcium Carbide." *J. Chem. Educ.* **1987**: *64*, 444.

Testing for Unsaturated Hydrocarbons with Bromine movie

On page 1083, bromination of an alkane takes place in a light source. Repeat the demonstration to show the bromination of an alkene. Now, however, even in the absence of light, the color disappears as the bromination takes place, showing that bromination of alkenes does not require the formation of light-activated free radicals. Recall the safety precautions from page 1083.

Weiss, Hilton M. "The Addition of Hydrogen Bromide to Simple Alkenes." *J. Chem. Educ.* **1995:** *72,* 848 (September 1995).

▶ A quick way to remember this rule is "them that has, gets" (referring to H atoms).

Because HBr is a polar molecule with its positive end at the H atom and its negative end at the Br atom, 2-bromopropane is the sole product of this reaction. This result is consistent with an empirical rule proposed by Vladimir Markovnikov in 1871 (modified slightly to include reactants other than HBr).

> *When an unsymmetrical reactant (HX, HOH, HOSO₃H) is added to an unsymmetrical alkene or alkyne, the more positive fragment (usually H) adds to the carbon atom that has the greatest number of attached H atoms.*

The addition of H_2O to a double bond is the reverse of the reaction in which a double bond is formed by the elimination of H_2O (reaction 26.6). In this reversible reaction, the addition reaction is favored in dilute acid, and the elimination reaction is favored in *concentrated* $H_2SO_4(aq)$.

▶ Notice how the H and OH add to the double bond in accordance with Markovnikov's rule. H adds to the C atom with the greater number of attached H atoms—that is, to —CH_2.

$$CH_3 \overset{CH_3}{\underset{CH_3}{C}}{=}\overset{H}{\underset{H}{C}} + HOH \xrightarrow{10\% \; H_2SO_4} CH_3-\overset{CH_3}{\underset{OH}{C}}-\overset{H}{\underset{H}{C}}-H \qquad (26.11)$$

t-butyl alcohol

The addition reactions of alkynes also follow Markovnikov's rule, for example,

Brown, T. M., et al. "A quick and effective demonstration of anti-Markovnikov addition to alkenes." *J. Chem. Educ.* **1991:** *68,* 785.

$$CH_3C{\equiv}CH + HCl \longrightarrow CH_3\overset{Cl}{\underset{}{C}}{=}CH_2 + HCl \longrightarrow CH_3\overset{Cl}{\underset{Cl}{C}}-CH_3$$

The reaction stops at the addition of one mole of HCl unless an excess of the reagent is added. This is because the rate of addition of the hydrogen halide to the alkyne is greater than the rate of addition of the hydrogen halide to the halo-substituted alkene that is formed in the first addition reaction.

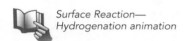 *Surface Reaction— Hydrogenation animation*

Hydrogen adds to both alkenes and alkynes in the presence of a metal catalyst such as palladium or platinum. This process is called *hydrogenation*. The hydrogenation of 1-butyne is as follows.

$$CH_3CH_2C{\equiv}CH + H_2 \xrightarrow{Pt} CH_3CH_2CH{=}CH_2 + H_2 \xrightarrow{Pt} CH_3CH_2CH_2CH_3$$

Since hydrogen rapidly adds to the double bond of alkenes, the reaction cannot be stopped at the alkene stage. If the alkene is the desired product, a different heterogeneous catalyst known as Lindlar's catalyst is employed. Using this catalyst, the addition of hydrogen to an alkyne in which the triple bond is not at the terminus of the chain leads to the formation of a cis alkene (see Chapter 14, Exercise 84).

▶ Lindlar's catalyst is a heterogeneous catalyst prepared by precipitating palladium on calcium carbonate and treating this mixture with lead acetate and quinoline.

$$CH_3CH_2C{\equiv}CCH_3 + H_2 \xrightarrow[\text{catalyst}]{\text{Lindlar's}} \overset{CH_3CH_2}{\underset{H}{}}{C}{=}C\overset{CH_3}{\underset{H}{}}$$

2-pentyne \qquad\qquad *cis*-2-pentene

In contrast, using sodium in liquid ammonia as a hydrogenation agent leads to the formation of the trans alkene.

✓ Point out that the hydrogenation of unsaturated vegetable oils is used to make margarine and Crisco.

$$CH_3CH_2C{\equiv}CCH_3 + H_2 \xrightarrow{\text{Na in NH}_3(l)} \overset{CH_3CH_2}{\underset{H}{}}{C}{=}C\overset{H}{\underset{CH_3}{}}$$

2-pentyne \qquad\qquad *trans*-2-pentene

The difference arises because of the different mechanisms involved. These two methods have important synthetic applications.

26-4 AROMATIC HYDROCARBONS

Aromatic hydrocarbons have ring structures with unsaturation (multiple-bond character) in the carbon-to-carbon bonds in the rings. Most aromatic hydrocarbons are based on the molecule benzene, C_6H_6. In Section 11-6, bonding in the benzene molecule was discussed in some detail. Several ways of representing the molecule were also shown, including

Kekulé structures   Simplified
molecular orbital
representation

Other examples of aromatic hydrocarbons include

Toluene   *o*-Xylene   Naphthalene   Anthracene

Toluene and *o*-xylene are *substituted benzenes*, and naphthalene and anthracene feature *fused benzene rings*. When rings are fused together, the resultant structure has two C and four H atoms fewer than the starting structures. Thus, the formula for naphthalene is $C_6H_6 + C_6H_6 - 2C - 4H = C_{10}H_8$; for anthracene: $C_{10}H_8 + C_6H_6 - 2C - 4H = C_{14}H_{10}$. In this text, we use the inscribed circle for the simple benzene ring and alternating single and double bonds for fused rings. For the fused-ring systems, the bond arrangement represents one of the possible resonance structures for the molecule.

CHARACTERISTICS OF AROMATIC HYDROCARBONS

Aromatic hydrocarbons are highly flammable and should always be handled with care. Prolonged inhalation of benzene vapor results in a decreased production of both red blood cells and white blood cells, which can be fatal. Also, benzene is a carcinogen. Benzene and some other toxic aromatic compounds have been isolated in the tar formed by burning cigarettes, in polluted air, and as a decomposition product of grease in the charcoal grilling of meat.

A close examination of the structures of aromatic molecules shows that they all share two common features.

- They are *planar* (flat), *cyclic* molecules.
- They have a *conjugated* bonding system—a bonding scheme among the ring atoms that consists of alternating single and double bonds. The system must extend throughout the ring, and the π electron clouds associated with the double bonds must involve $(4n + 2)$ electrons, where $n = 1, 2, \ldots$.

Thus, the benzene molecule has six electrons in the π electron clouds: $(4 \times 1) + 2 = 6$. The naphthalene molecule has 10: $(4 \times 2) + 2 = 10$. And the anthracene molecule has 14: $(4 \times 3) + 2 = 14$. Neither of the two molecules depicted below is aromatic; both are aliphatic.

$$CH_2{=}CH{-}CH{=}CH{-}CH{=}CH_2$$

1,3,5-Hexatriene   1,3-Cyclopentadiene

The 1,3,5-hexatriene molecule has six π electrons in its conjugated bonding system, but it is not cyclic. The 1,3-cyclopentadiene molecule is cyclic, but has only four π electrons in a conjugated bonding system that does not extend completely around the ring.

Murray, C. F. "Polycyclic Aromatic Hydrocarbons (by Ronald G. Harvey)." *J. Chem. Educ.* **1998:** *75*, 1392 (November 1998).

◀ As in the case of alicyclic compounds, neither the C atoms at the vertices nor the H atoms bonded to them are shown in these structures.

▲ August Kekulé (1829–1896), who proposed the hexagonal ring structure for benzene in 1865. His representation of this molecule is still widely used.

Anderson, H. J., Bauer, L. "Comments on the Treatment of Aromaticity and Acid-Base Character of Pyridine and Pyrrole in Contemporary Organic Chemistry Textbooks." *J. Chem. Educ.* **1999:** *76*, 1151 (August 1999).

Klein, D. J. "Aromaticity via Kekulé structures and conjugated circuits (SYM)." *J. Chem. Educ.* **1992:** *69*, 691.

Benzene and its homologues are similar to other hydrocarbons in being insoluble in water but soluble in organic solvents. The boiling points of the aromatic hydrocarbons are slightly higher than those of the alkanes of similar carbon content. For example, hexane, C_6H_{14}, boils at 69 °C, whereas benzene boils at 80 °C. This can be explained by the planar structure and delocalized electron charge density of benzene, which increases the attractive forces between molecules. The symmetrical structure of benzene permits closer packing of molecules in the crystalline state and results in a higher melting point than for hexane. Benzene melts at 5.5 °C and hexane melts at −95 °C.

When one of the six equivalent H atoms of a benzene molecule is removed, the resulting species is called a **phenyl** group. Two phenyl groups may bond together, as in biphenyl, or phenyl groups may be substituents in other molecules, as in phenylhydrazine, used in the detection of sugars.

Phenyl group   Biphenyl   Phenylhydrazine

NAMING AROMATIC HYDROCARBONS

Other atoms or groups may be substituted for H atoms on the benzene molecule, and to name these compounds, we use a numbering system for the C atoms in the ring. If the name of an aromatic compound is based on a common name other than benzene (such as toluene), the characteristic substituent group (for example, the —CH_3 in toluene) is assigned position "1" on the benzene ring. Otherwise, the substituents are listed alphabetically, as in 2-bromochlorobenzene shown below.

3-Bromotoluene
(*m*-bromotoluene)

2-Bromochlorobenzene
(*o*-bromochlorobenzene)

1,4-Dichlorobenzene
(*p*-dichlorobenzene)

2-Chlorotoluene
(*o*-chlorotoluene)

The terms *ortho*, *meta*, and *para* (*o*-, *m*-, *p*-) can be used when there are two substituents on the benzene ring. **Ortho** refers to substituents on adjacent carbon atoms, **meta** to substituents with one carbon atom between them, and **para** to substituents opposite one another on the ring.

USES OF AROMATIC HYDROCARBONS

Over 90% of the billions of pounds of benzene produced annually in the United States is derived from petroleum. The process involves dehydrogenation and cyclization of hexane to the aromatic hydrocarbon. The most important use of the petroleum-produced benzene is in manufacturing ethylbenzene for the production of styrene plastics. Other applications include the manufacture of phenol, the synthesis of dodecylbenzene (for detergents), and as an octane enhancer in gasoline. The production of aromatic compounds by dehydrogenation (removal of hydrogen) of alkanes yields large amounts of hydrogen gas, which is an important reactant in the synthesis of ammonia (page 941).

AROMATIC SUBSTITUTION REACTIONS

Unlike alkenes and alkynes, aromatic molecules react by *substitution*, not by addition of atoms across a double bond. This difference in reactivity is due to the special stability of the electrons in the aromatic ring. In aromatic rings,

Polyaromatic hydrocarbons are the featured molecules in the February 2004 issue of *J. Chem. Educ.*

p-Dichlorobenzene use in mothballs. Pass some mothballs containing *p*-dichlorobenzene around the class. Naphthalene is also used for mothballs but is being replaced by *p*-dichlorobenzene not because it is any safer, but because the smell is less intense.

certain electrons are delocalized into a π electron cloud. In alkene and alkyne molecules, the regions of high electron density associated with multiple bonds are localized between specific C atoms. These localized π bonds are much more reactive than the delocalized π bonds of the aromatic ring.

Jones-Wilson, T. M., et al. "A Green Starting Material for Electrophilic Aromatic Substitution for the Undergraduate Organic Laboratory." *J. Chem. Educ.* **2005:** *82,* 616.

Zanger, M.; "The aromatic substitution game." *J. Chem. Educ.* **1993:** *70,* 985.

The substitution of a single atom or group, X, for a H atom in C_6H_6 can occur at any one of the six positions of the benzene ring. We say that the six positions are equivalent. If a group Y is substituted for a H atom in C_6H_5X, this question arises: To which of the remaining five positions does the Y group go? If all the sites on the benzene ring were equally preferred, the distribution of the products would be a purely statistical one. That is, there are five possible positions where Y can be substituted, and we should get 20% of each one. Since there are two possibilities that lead to an *ortho* isomer and two that lead to a *meta* isomer, however, we should expect the distribution of products to be 40% ortho, 40% meta, and 20% para.

350% ortho $(\frac{2}{5})$ 40% meta $(\frac{2}{5})$ 20% para $(\frac{1}{5})$

The following scheme describes the products resulting from nitration followed by chlorination (reaction 26.12) and chlorination followed by nitration (reaction 26.13). It shows that the substitution is *not random*. The $-NO_2$ group directs Cl to a meta position. Almost no ortho or para isomer is formed in reaction (26.12). The Cl group, on the other hand, is an ortho, para director. Essentially no meta isomer is produced in reaction (26.13).

(26.12)

(26.13)

Whether a group is an ortho, para, or meta director depends on how the presence of one substituent alters the electron distribution in the benzene ring. As a result, attack by a second group is more likely at one type of position than another. Examination of many reactions leads to the following order.

Ortho, para directors: $-NH_2$, $-OR$, $-OH$, $-OCOR$, $-R$, $-X$ (X = halogen)
                 (from strongest to weakest)

Meta directors: $-NO_2$, $-CN$, $-SO_3H$, $-CHO$, $-COR$, $-COOH$, $-COOR$
                 (from strongest to weakest)

When two groups of the same type (both o-, p-directing or both m-directing) are present, the stronger director wins out. When two groups of different type (one o-, p-directing and one m-directing) are present, then it has been found that the o-, p-directing group guides the reaction.

EXAMPLE 26-4

Predicting the Products of an Aromatic Substitution Reaction. Predict the products of the mononitration of

Solution

—OH is an ortho, para director, and we should expect the products

2,6-Dinitrophenol   2,4-Dinitrophenol

Practice Example A: Predict the major product(s) of the mononitration of benzaldehyde, C_6H_5CHO.

Practice Example B: Predict the major product(s) of the mononitration of 1,3-dichlorobenzene.

CONCEPT ASSESSMENT ✔

The nitro group (—NO_2) is the strongest directing group of the functional groups listed on page 1091. Why wasn't its directing effect considered in Example 26-4?

26-5   ALCOHOLS, PHENOLS, AND ETHERS

Alcohols and **phenols** are characterized by the **hydroxyl** group, —OH. In alcohols, the hydroxyl group is bound to an sp^3 hybridized (aliphatic) carbon atom. If this C atom also has *one* R group (and two H atoms) bonded to it, the alcohol is a *primary* alcohol. If the C atom has *two* R groups (and one H atom), the alcohol is a *secondary* alcohol. Finally, if there are *three* R groups on the C atom (and no H atoms), the alcohol is a *tertiary* alcohol.

1-Butanol   2-Butanol   Methyl-2-propanol
(butyl alcohol)   (s-butyl alcohol)   (t-butyl alcohol)
(a *primary* alcohol)   (a *secondary* alcohol) (a *tertiary* alcohol)

The systematic naming of alcohols uses the suffix *-ol* and was discussed in Chapter 3.

In phenols, the hydroxyl group is attached to a benzene ring.

Phenol   2,4,6-Trinitrophenol
(carbolic acid)   (picric acid)

A molecule may have more than one —OH group. Those with two —OH groups are known as *diols* (or glycols), and those with more than two —OH groups are called *polyols*. Ethylene glycol, a diol, is used in automobile antifreeze solutions; glycerol, a polyol, is an important biological molecule used as part of the body's mechanism for fat storage.

$$
\begin{array}{cc}
\underset{\substack{| \quad\quad |\\ \text{OH} \quad \text{OH}}}{\text{CH}_2\text{—CH}_2} &
\underset{\substack{| \quad\quad | \quad\quad |\\ \text{OH} \quad \text{OH} \quad \text{OH}}}{\text{CH}_2\text{—CH—CH}_2} \\
\text{1,2-Ethanediol} & \text{1,2,3-Propanetriol} \\
\text{(ethylene glycol)} & \text{(glycerol)}
\end{array}
$$

Physical properties of aliphatic alcohols are strongly influenced by hydrogen bonding. As the chain length increases, however, the influence of the polar hydroxyl group on the properties of the molecule diminishes. The molecule becomes less like water and more like a hydrocarbon. As a consequence, low-molecular mass alcohols tend to be water soluble, while high-molecular mass alcohols are not. The boiling points and solubilities of the phenols vary widely, depending on the nature of the other substituents on the benzene ring.

CONCEPT ASSESSMENT ✓

Explain why the name *s*-pentyl alcohol does not unambiguously identify a compound while the name *s*-butyl alcohol does.

PREPARATION AND USES OF ALCOHOLS

Two methods by which alcohols can be synthesized are by the hydration of alkenes and the hydrolysis of alkyl halides.

$$
\text{CH}_3\text{CH}=\text{CH}_2 + \text{H}_2\text{O} \xrightarrow{\text{H}_2\text{SO}_4} \underset{\substack{|\\ \text{CH}_3\text{CHCH}_3}}{\overset{\text{OH}}{}} \tag{26.14}
$$
$$
\underset{\text{propene}}{} \quad\quad\quad\quad \underset{\substack{\text{2-propanol}\\ \text{(isopropyl alcohol)}}}{}
$$
$$
\text{(propylene)}
$$

$$
\underset{\text{1-bromopropane}}{\text{CH}_3\text{CH}_2\text{CH}_2\text{Br}} + \text{OH}^- \longrightarrow \underset{\text{1-propanol}}{\text{CH}_3\text{CH}_2\text{CH}_2\text{OH}} + \text{Br}^- \tag{26.15}
$$

Methanol (wood alcohol) is a highly toxic substance that can lead to blindness or death if ingested. Most methanol is manufactured from carbon monoxide and hydrogen.

$$
\text{CO(g)} + 2\,\text{H}_2\text{(g)} \xrightarrow[\substack{200\ \text{atm}\\ \text{ZnO, Cr}_2\text{O}_3}]{350\ °\text{C}} \text{CH}_3\text{OH(g)}
$$

Methanol is the most extensively produced alcohol. It ranks about twenty-first among all industrial chemicals. It is used in the synthesis of other organic chemicals and as a solvent, but potentially its most important use may be as a motor fuel (recall Section 7–9).

Ethanol, $\text{CH}_3\text{CH}_2\text{OH}$ is grain alcohol, which is found in alcoholic beverages. It is easily produced by the fermentation of sugarcane juice or from materials containing natural sugars. The industrial method involves the hydration of ethylene with sulfuric acid catalyst (similar to reaction 26.14).

Ethylene glycol, $\text{HOCH}_2\text{CH}_2\text{OH}$, is water soluble and has a higher boiling point (197 °C) than water. These properties make it an excellent permanent, nonvolatile antifreeze for automobile radiators. It is also used in the manufacture of solvents, paint removers, and plasticizers (softeners).

Glycerol (glycerin), $\text{HOCH}_2\text{CH(OH)CH}_2\text{OH}$, is obtained commercially as a by-product in the manufacture of soap. It is a sweet, syrupy liquid that is miscible with water in all proportions. Because it takes up moisture from the air, glycerol can be used to keep skin moist and soft and is found in lotions and cosmetics.

▲ **Giant soap bubble**
A soap bubble consists of an air pocket enclosed in a thin film of soap in water. As the water evaporates, the film breaks and the bubble bursts. Glycerol added to the soap–water mixture forms hydrogen bonds to both the soap and water molecules. This slows the rate of evaporation of the water and increases the strength of the film, allowing the production of very large bubbles.

📖 Jensen, W. B. "The Origin of Alcohol Proof." *J. Chem. Educ.* **2004:** *81*, 1258.

📖 Lee, D. W., Jensen, C. M. "Dry-Ice Bath Based on Ethylene Glycol Mixtures." *J. Chem. Educ.* **2000:** *77*, 629 (May 2000).

Demonstration: Combustion of alcohols and the making of "sterno." Sterno is a solid fuel used in camping equipment. **Chemicals & Apparatus:** (i) Calcium acetate, ethanol. (ii) two 600 mL beakers, beaker tongs, large watch glass. **Preparation:** Prepare a saturated solution of calcium acetate (300 g of salt in 1000 mL H_2O). **In class:** Add 40 mL of calcium acetate solution to one beaker and 300 mL of ethanol to the other. Transfer the solutions back and forth until they solidify. The solid can then be lighted, demonstrating the change to "fire water." Extinguish by placing the watch glass on top of the beaker. HOT! Handle with tongs.

☑ Diethyl ether was the first general anesthetic used in medicine. However, it has been replaced by other compounds because of its high flammability.

An interesting derivative of an alcohol is the alkoxide ion, formed by the reaction of sodium or potassium metal with the alcohol.

$$CH_3OH + Na \longrightarrow CH_3O^- + Na^+ + \frac{1}{2}H_2(g)$$

The alkoxide ion can react with a haloalkane as follows:

$$CH_3O^- + CH_3CH_2Cl \longrightarrow CH_3CH_2OCH_3 + Cl^-$$

The compound formed is an ether, which is described next.

ETHERS

An **ether** is a compound with the general formula R—O—R'. Structurally, ethers can be pure aliphatic, pure aromatic, or mixed.

$$CH_3-O-CH_3$$

Dimethyl ether   Diphenyl ether   Methyl phenyl ether (anisole)

KEEP IN MIND ▶
that although dimethyl ether has the same formula as ethanol (C_2H_6O), the two substances have quite different physical and chemical properties. This is because each has a different functional group (see Table 26.2). The two are skeletal isomers.

Symmetrical ethers, such as diethyl ether, can be prepared by the elimination of a water molecule from between two alcohol molecules with a strong dehydrating agent, such as concentrated H_2SO_4.

$$CH_3CH_2OH + HOCH_2CH_3 \xrightarrow[140\ °C]{\text{concd } H_2SO_4} CH_3CH_2OCH_2CH_3 + H_2O \quad (26.16)$$

Chemically, ethers are comparatively unreactive. The ether linkage is stable in the presence of most oxidizing and reducing agents, as well as dilute acids and alkalis.

Diethyl ether has been used extensively as a general anesthetic. It is easy to administer and produces excellent relaxation of the muscles. Also, it affects the pulse rate, rate of respiration, and blood pressure only slightly. However, it is somewhat irritating to the respiratory passages and produces nausea. Methyl propyl ether (neothyl) is also used as an anesthetic and is less irritating to the respiratory passages. Dimethyl ether, a gas at room temperatures, is used as a propellant for aerosol sprays. Higher molecular mass ethers are used as solvents for varnishes and lacquers. Methyl t-butyl ether, an unsymmetrical ether, marketed under the name MTBE, has been used as an octane enhancer in gasoline. However, because of its relatively high solubility in water (≈ 5 g/100 g H_2O), in some localities it has caused rather extensive groundwater pollution through leakage from underground storage tanks; it is currently being phased out of use.

▶ This molecule should be named t-butyl methyl ether (TBME), but has been referred to by industrial chemists as MTBE for so long that methyl t-butyl ether has become the commonly used name for this compound.

$$H_3C-\overset{\overset{\displaystyle CH_3}{|}}{\underset{\underset{\displaystyle CH_3}{|}}{C}}-O-CH_3$$

Methyl t-butyl ether (MTBE)

📖 Wong, J. W., Ngim, K. K., Eiserich, J. P., Yeo, H. C. H., Shibamoto, T., Mabury, S. "A. Determination of Formaldehyde in Cigarette Smoke." *J. Chem. Educ.* **1997**: *74*, 1100 (September 1997).

26-6 ALDEHYDES AND KETONES

Aldehydes and ketones contain the **carbonyl group**.

$$\overset{R}{\underset{R'}{\diagdown}}C=O$$

If either the R or R' group is a H atom, the compound is an **aldehyde**. If the R and R' groups are alkyl or aromatic (aryl) groups, the compound is a **ketone**.

Methanal (formaldehyde)   3-Chlorobutanal (β-chlorobutyraldehyde)   Benzaldehyde

Propanone
(acetone)

3-Pentanone
(diethyl ketone)

1-Phenylethanone
(acetophenone)

▲ False-color scanning electron micrograph of the sticky surface of a 3M Post-it note. The bubbles are 15–40 μm in diameter and consist of a urea–formaldehyde adhesive. Each time the note is pressed to a surface, fresh adhesive is released. The note can be reattached to a surface as long as some of the bubbles remain.

The IUPAC naming system for aldehydes uses the suffix -*al*. The parent chain is the longest chain containing the aldehyde group. Accordingly, the four-carbon aldehyde is called butanal because the name is derived from the alkane (butane) with the -*e* replaced by -*al*. The numbering of the chain starts at the carbon of the aldehyde group; it is always at position one and need not be specified. Thus 3-chloro-2-methylbutanal is

$$CH_3-\underset{\underset{Cl}{|}}{CH}-\underset{\underset{CH_3}{|}}{CH}-\underset{\overset{O}{||}}{C}-H$$

The IUPAC naming system for ketones uses the suffix -*one*. The parent chain must include the carbonyl group and be numbered from the end of the chain that reaches the carbonyl group first; this ensures, as required by IUPAC rules, that the number for the carbonyl group is as low as possible. For example, the molecule

$$CH_3-\underset{\underset{Cl}{|}}{CH}-\underset{\underset{CH_3}{|}}{CH}-\underset{\overset{O}{||}}{C}-CH_3$$

is 4-chloro-3-methyl-2-pentanone.

◀ **KEEP IN MIND**
that the CHO functional group can be only at the terminus of a carbon chain, whereas the CO functional group cannot be at the end of a carbon chain.

PREPARATION AND USES

Aldehydes can be produced by the oxidation of a *primary* alcohol with an oxidizing agent such as dichromate ion in acidic solution. However, the aldehyde so formed is readily oxidized further to a carboxylic acid (Section 26-7).

Hiegel, G. A., et al. "The TCICA Test for Distinguishing Aldehydes and Ketones." *J. Chem. Educ.* **2001**: 78, 1105.

$$CH_3CH_2OH \xrightarrow[H^+]{Cr_2O_7^{2-}} CH_3CHO \xrightarrow[H^+]{Cr_2O_7^{2-}} CH_3CO_2H \qquad (26.17)$$

ethanol
(a primary alcohol)

acetaldehyde
(an aldehyde)

acetic acid
(an acid)

A milder oxidizing agent in a nonaqueous medium is required to stop the oxidation at the aldehyde. This partial oxidation can be done with the reagent pyridinium chlorochromate (PCC) in an organic solvent such as dichloromethane. For example,

$$CH_3(CH_2)_8CH_2OH \xrightarrow{PCC, CH_2Cl_2} CH_3(CH_2)_8CHO$$

Oxidation of a *secondary* alcohol produces a ketone.

◀ PCC is formed as yellow-orange crystals by the reaction between CrO_3 and HCl in pyridine.

$ClCrO_3^-$

(26.18)

$$CH_3CH(OH)CH_3 \xrightarrow[H^+]{Cr_2O_7^{2-}} CH_3\overset{\overset{O}{||}}{C}CH_3$$

2-propanol
(a secondary alcohol)

acetone
(a ketone)

Formaldehyde ($H_2C{=}O$), a colorless gas that dissolves readily in water, is the simplest aldehyde. Formaldehyde is used in the manufacture of synthetic resins. A polymer of formaldehyde called paraformaldehyde is used as an antiseptic and an insecticide.

Some breathalyzers use potassium dichromate to oxidize ethanol, causing a color change from orange to green. If possible, ask your local police station to provide someone to demonstrate this in class.

Esteb, J. J., et al. "A Solvent-Free Oxidation of Alcohols in an Organic Laboratory." *J. Chem. Educ.* **2003**: *80*, 907.

Vanillin, the compound responsible for vanilla flavor, is an aldehyde. Alpha-demascone and 2-octanone are the two ketones responsible for berry and mushroom flavor, respectively.

Aldehydes and ketones occur widely in nature. Typical natural sources are

Benzaldehyde	Cinnamaldehyde	Camphor
(almonds)	(cinnamon)	(obtained from camphor tree)

Acetone is the most important of the ketones. It is a volatile liquid (boiling point, 56 °C) and highly flammable. Acetone is a good solvent for a variety of organic compounds and is widely used in solvents for varnishes, lacquers, and plastics. Unlike many common organic solvents, acetone is miscible with water in all proportions.

ADDITION REACTIONS OF THE CARBONYL GROUP IN KETONES AND ALDEHYDES

The double bond of the carbonyl group can undergo addition reactions like the double bond in alkenes. For example, a ketone can be reduced to a secondary alcohol using a reagent such as sodium borohydride, $NaBH_4$, in aqueous solution.

This reaction can be formally thought of as addition of a dihydrogen molecule across the carbonyl double bond, but the actual mechanism is the addition of H^- followed by the addition of a proton.

The difference between the double bond in an alkene and a carbonyl group is the polarity of the carbonyl group, so that when asymmetric reagents such as HCN are added, the negatively charged CN^- adds to the region of partial positive charge on the carbon atom; for example,

This molecule is called cyanohydrin, and it is the first member of a class of molecules called *cyanohydrins*. The important synthetic consequence of this reaction is that the carbon content of the molecule is increased by one carbon atom.

26-7   CARBOXYLIC ACIDS AND THEIR DERIVATIVES

▶ The carboxyl group is represented either as —COOH or —CO₂H.

As we learned in Chapter 3, **carboxylic acids** contain the **carboxyl group** (*carb*onyl and hydr*oxyl*).

These acids have the general formula R—COOH. In many compounds, R is an aliphatic residue. Such compounds are called fatty acids because high-molecular mass compounds of this type are readily available from naturally occurring fats and oils. If two carboxyl groups are found on the same molecule, the acid is called a dicarboxylic acid. The carboxyl group can also be found attached to the benzene ring.

Perez, G. V., Perez, A. L. "Organic Acids without a Carboxylic Acid Functional Group." *J. Chem. Educ.* **2000**: *77*, 910 (July 2000).

Acetic acid
(an aliphatic acid)

Benzoic acid
(an aromatic acid)

Oxalic acid
(an aliphatic
dicarboxylic acid)

o-Phthalic acid
(an aromatic
dicarboxylic acid)

Oxidation of a primary alcohol or an aldehyde can produce a carboxylic acid. For this purpose, the oxidizing agent is generally $KMnO_4$(aq) in an alkaline medium. Because the medium is alkaline, the product is the potassium salt, but the free carboxylic acid can be regenerated by making the medium acidic.

Take a piece of rusted iron or steel and show that oxalic acid is a good rust remover.

$$CH_3CH_2OH \xrightarrow[\text{OH}^-, \text{ heat}]{KMnO_4} CH_3COO^-K^+ \xrightarrow{H^+} CH_3COOH + K^+ \qquad (26.19)$$

$$CH_3CH_2CH_2OH \xrightarrow[\text{OH}^-, \text{ heat}]{KMnO_4} CH_3CH_2COO^-K^+ \xrightarrow{H^+} CH_3CH_2COOH + K^+ \quad (26.20)$$

Substituted aliphatic acids can be named either by their IUPAC names or by using Greek letters in conjunction with common names. Aromatic acids are named as derivatives of benzoic acid.

Similar to alcohols, low-molecular-weight carboxylic acids are soluble in water because of their ability to hydrogen bond with water. Carboxylic acids also have relatively high melting and boiling points because of hydrogen bonding.

Olmsted, J. A., III. "Synthesis of Aspirin: A General Chemistry Experiment." *J. Chem. Educ.* **1998:** 75, 1261.

3-Chlorobutanoic acid
β-chlorobutyric acid

3-Methylbenzoic acid
m-methylbenzoic acid
(also toluic acid)

2-Hydroxybenzoic acid
o-hydroxybenzoic acid
(also salicylic acid)

Because many derivatives of the carboxylic acids involve simple replacement of the hydroxyl groups, special names have been developed for the remaining portion of the molecule, that is,

For example, the group

is called the **acetyl group**. The acetyl derivative of o-hydroxybenzoic (salicylic) acid is ordinary aspirin.

Acetylsalicylic acid
(aspirin)

Carboxyl groups display the chemistry of both carbonyl and hydroxyl groups. Donation of a proton to a base leads to salt formation. The sodium and potassium salts of long-chain fatty acids are known as *soaps*. The structure of the soap sodium palmitate was presented on page 878, and soap formation (saponification) is discussed further in the next chapter. The reaction between an alcohol and a carboxylic acid leads, as we see next, to a different class of compounds.

McDonald, Chris E. "The Oxidation of Primary Alcohols to Esters: Three Related Investigative Experiments." *J. Chem. Educ.* **2000**: 77, 750 (June 2000).

▶ IUPAC names appear below the structural formulas with the more common names in parentheses.

ESTERS

The product of the reaction of a carboxylic acid and an alcohol is called an **ester**. Esters are formed by the elimination of H_2O (HOH) between the two molecules. The mechanism of this reaction is such that the —OH comes from the *acid* and the —H from the *alcohol*.

$$CH_3CH_2O—H + HO—\overset{\displaystyle O}{\overset{\displaystyle \|}{C}}CH_3 \xrightarrow[\text{heat}]{H^+} H_2O + CH_3CH_2O—\overset{\displaystyle O}{\overset{\displaystyle \|}{C}}CH_3 \qquad (26.21)$$

ethanol ethanoic acid   ethyl ethanoate
(ethyl alcohol) (acetic acid)   (ethyl acetate)

This type of reaction is a **condensation reaction**, a reaction in which two molecules are combined by the elimination of a small molecule such as water.

Are You Wondering . . .

If reaction (26.21) is reversible, how can we ensure a good yield of the ester?

In order to push the reaction toward the ester, we can apply Le Châtelier's principle and either add an excess of alcohol or remove the water as it is formed (there are experimental techniques to do this).

Esters have two-part names. The first part is the alkyl designation of the alcohol; the second part is the carboxylic acid name with the ending changed to *-oate*. For example, the combination of acetic acid and ethanol is *ethyl ethanoate*.

The reaction of a carboxylic acid and an alcohol is reversible. An ester is hydrolyzed by water in the presence of hydrogen ion to give the alcohol and the carboxylic acid. The hydrolysis goes to completion when it is carried out in the presence of the hydroxide ion; and in this case, the products are the alcohol and a salt of the carboxylic acid.

$$CH_3CH_2CO_2CH_2CH_3 \xrightarrow{OH^-} CH_3CH_2COO^- + CH_3CH_2OH$$

Unlike the pungent odors of the carboxylic acids from which they are derived, esters have very pleasant aromas. The characteristic fragrances of many flowers and fruits can be traced to the esters they contain. Esters are used in perfumes and in the manufacture of flavoring agents for the confectionery and soft drink industries. Most esters are colorless liquids that are insoluble in water. Their melting points and boiling points are generally lower than those of alcohols and acids of comparable carbon content. This is because of the absence of hydrogen bonding in esters.

▲ The distinctive aroma and flavor of oranges are due in part to the ester octyl acetate, $CH_3(CH_2)_6CH_2OOCCH_3$.

AMIDES

Heating the ammonium salt of a carboxylic acid results in the elimination of water and the formation of an **amide**. Further loss of water occurs if the amide is heated with a strong dehydrating agent such as P_4O_{10}. The final product, which contains the group —C≡N, is called a *nitrile*. These reactions can be reversed by stepwise treatment with water.

There are a number of medically important amides, including the penicillins and acetaminophen.

$$CH_3—\overset{\displaystyle O}{\overset{\displaystyle \|}{C}}—O^-NH_4^+ \xrightarrow{\text{heat}} CH_3—\overset{\displaystyle O}{\overset{\displaystyle \|}{C}}—NH_2 + H_2O \qquad (26.22)$$

ammonium acetate   acetamide

$$\text{heat} \downarrow P_4O_{10}$$

$$CH_3C≡N + H_2O \qquad (26.23)$$

Amides, like esters, can be hydrolyzed. When simple amides, such as acetamide, are heated with water in the presence of an acid catalyst, they form the parent carboxylic acid and ammonia.

Despite the presence of the NH_2 group in simple amides, they are not Brønsted bases like amines or ammonia because the carbonyl group promotes the resonance structures shown below.

$$CH_3-C{\overset{\displaystyle \ddot{O}:}{\underset{\ddot{N}H_2}{}}} \longleftrightarrow CH_3-C{\overset{\displaystyle :\ddot{O}:^-}{\underset{\overset{+}{N}H_2}{}}}$$ ◀ Resonance in an amide.

The lone pair of electrons on the nitrogen atom is delocalized over the carbonyl group toward the more electronegative oxygen atom. In fact, as seen from the resonance structures, it is the carbonyl group that is most likely to be protonated in acidic conditions. The protonation of the oxygen in a carbonyl group is often an important first step in reactions of esters and amides under acidic conditions.

REDUCTION OF CARBOXYLIC ACIDS, ESTERS, AND AMIDES

The reduction of carboxylic acids, esters, and amides requires the strong reducing agent lithium aluminum hydride, $LiAlH_4$. An example is the reduction of methyl propionate to give propanol and methanol.

Simek, J. W., et al. "Reduction of Carboxylic Acids with Sodium Borohydride and an Electrophile." *J. Chem. Educ.* **1997**; 74, 107.

$$CH_3-CH_2-\overset{\overset{\displaystyle O}{\|}}{C}-OCH_3 \xrightarrow{LiAlH_4} CH_3-CH_2-\overset{\overset{\displaystyle O-H}{|}}{CH_2} + HO-CH_3$$

The reduction of ethanamide with $LiAlH_4$ gives the primary amine ethanamine (ethyl amine).

$$CH_3-\overset{\overset{\displaystyle O}{\|}}{C}-NH_2 \xrightarrow{LiAlH_4} CH_3-CH_2-NH_2 + H_2O$$

This reaction provides an alternative synthesis of amines, the class of molecules we discuss next.

26-8   AMINES

Amines are organic derivatives of ammonia, NH_3, in which one or more organic groups (R) are substituted for H atoms. Their classification is based on the number of R groups bonded to the nitrogen atom—one for primary amines, two for secondary, and three for tertiary.

$CH_3CH_3NH_2$

Ethylamine
(a primary amine)

Diphenylamine
(a secondary amine)

$$CH_3\overset{\overset{\displaystyle CH_2CH_3}{|}}{N}CH_2CH_2CH_3$$

Ethylmethylpropylamine
(a tertiary amine)

One of the chief methods of preparing an amine is by the reduction of a nitro compound.

$$\text{⬡}-NO_2 \xrightarrow[HCl]{Fe} \text{⬡}-NH_3^+Cl^- \xrightarrow{NaOH} \text{⬡}-NH_2 \qquad (26.24)$$

An alternative method of preparing an amine involves the reaction of ammonia with an alkyl halide.

$$NH_3 + CH_3Br \longrightarrow CH_3NH_3^+Br^-$$

Many amines demonstrate biological activity, including cocaine, nicotine, morphine, quinine, and vitamin B$_6$, to name just a few.

The methylammonium bromide formed reacts with additional ammonia to give the amine.

$$CH_3NH_3{}^+Br^- + NH_3 \longrightarrow CH_3NH_2 + NH_4{}^+Br^-$$

The formation of pure primary amines is difficult by this method because when the primary amine is formed, it can take part in a further substitution reaction with the alkyl halide to form a secondary amine, for example,

$$CH_3NH_2 + CH_3Br \longrightarrow \overset{\displaystyle CH_3}{\overset{|}{CH_3NH}} + HBr \qquad (26.25)$$

The compound formed here is dimethylamine. Further reaction with bromomethane produces the tertiary amine, trimethylamine.

Amines of low molecular mass are gases that are readily soluble in water, yielding basic solutions. The volatile members have odors similar to ammonia, but more fish-like. Primary and secondary amines form hydrogen bonds, but these bonds are weaker than those in water because nitrogen is less electronegative than oxygen. Like ammonia, amines have trigonal pyramidal structures with a lone pair of electrons on the N atom. Also like ammonia, amines owe their basicity to these lone-pair electrons. In aromatic amines, because of unsaturation in the benzene ring, electrons are drawn into the ring, which reduces the electron charge density on the nitrogen atom. As a result, aromatic amines are *weaker* bases than ammonia. Aliphatic amines are somewhat stronger bases than ammonia.

$$NH_3 + H_2O \rightleftharpoons NH_4{}^+ + OH^- \qquad K_b = 1.8 \times 10^{-5}$$
$$\underset{\text{methylamine}}{CH_3NH_2} + H_2O \rightleftharpoons CH_3NH_3{}^+ + OH^- \qquad K_b = 42 \times 10^{-5}$$

$$\underset{\text{aniline}}{\bigcirc}-NH_2 + H_2O \rightleftharpoons \bigcirc-NH_3{}^+ + OH^- \qquad K_b = 7.4 \times 10^{-10}$$

Amines can also be used to make amides. This is done by reaction of an amine and a carboxylic acid. For example, the reaction between methylamine and acetic acid first gives the ammonium carboxylate salt, which on heating gives the N-substituted amide.

$$CH_3-\overset{\displaystyle O}{\overset{||}{C}}-OH + CH_3NH_2 \longrightarrow CH_3-\underset{\substack{\text{an ammonium}\\\text{carboxylate salt}}}{\overset{\displaystyle O}{\overset{||}{C}}-O^-NH_3CH_3{}^+} \xrightarrow{\text{heat}} CH_3-\underset{\substack{\text{N-methyl acetamide}\\\text{or N-methyl ethanamide}}}{\overset{\displaystyle O}{\overset{||}{C}}-NHCH_3} + H_2O$$

Tylenol

An example of a N-substituted amide is the pain reliever Tylenol.

Amides can be hydrolyzed under both acidic and basic conditions. Under acid conditions, the products are the carboxylic acid and the alkyl ammonium salt of the amine. Under basic conditions, the products are the salt of the carboxylic acid and the amine. The —CO—NH— linkage present in N-substituted amides is called a *peptide bond*, and it is a key bond type in proteins, as we will discover in Chapter 27.

Dimethylamine is an accelerator for the removal of hair from hides in the processing of leather. Butyl- and pentylamines are used as antioxidants, corrosion inhibitors, and in the manufacture of oil-soluble soaps. Dimethylamine and trimethylamine are used in the manufacture of ion-exchange resins. Additional applications are found in the manufacture of disinfectants, insecticides, herbicides, drugs, dyes, fungicides, soaps, cosmetics, and photographic developers.

Anthony-Cahill, Spencer. "Bioorganic Chemistry: Peptides and Proteins (edited by Sidney M. Hecht)." *J. Chem. Educ.* **1999:** *76*, 905 (July 1999).

Important derivatives of ammonia are the *tetraalkyl ammonium salts*. One such salt can be produced by the reaction of ammonia with an excess of iodomethane. The ammonium salt formed, known as a *quaternary ammonium salt*, has four organic groups attached to the nitrogen atom. Tetramethylammonium iodide can be viewed as forming in the reaction of one mole of trimethylamine with an additional mole of iodomethane.

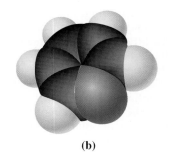

$$
\begin{array}{c}
\underset{\underset{CH_3}{|}}{\overset{\overset{CH_3}{|}}{CH_3-N:}} + CH_3I \longrightarrow \left[\underset{\underset{CH_3}{|}}{\overset{\overset{CH_3}{|}}{CH_3-N-CH_3}} \right]^+ + I^-
\end{array}
\qquad (26.26)
$$

The quaternary ammonium ion is often incorporated into systems involved in transmission of nerve impulses in the human body. One example is acetylcholine. Many poisons that affect the central nervous system also contain a quaternary ammonium functional group.

Amines have a characteristic fishy smell that can be removed by the application of citric acid, as in lemon juice.

$$CH_3-\overset{\overset{\displaystyle O}{\|}}{C}-OCH_2CH_2\overset{\overset{\displaystyle CH_3}{|}}{\underset{\underset{\displaystyle CH_3}{|}}{N^+}}-CH_3$$

Acetylcholine

▲ Acetylcholine transmits nerve impulses.

26-9   HETEROCYCLIC COMPOUNDS

In the ring structures considered to this point, all the ring atoms have been carbon; these structures are said to be carbocyclic. There are many compounds, however, both natural and synthetic, in which one or more of the atoms in a ring structure is not carbon. These ring structures are said to be **heterocyclic**. The heterocyclic systems most commonly encountered contain N, O, and S atoms, and the rings are of various sizes.

Pyridine is a nitrogen analogue of benzene (Fig. 26-8). Unlike benzene, it is water soluble and has basic properties (the unshared pair of electrons on the N atom is not part of the π electron cloud of the ring system). Pyridine, a liquid with a disagreeable odor, was once obtained exclusively from coal tar, but it is now used so extensively that several synthetic methods have been developed for its production. It is used in the production of pharmaceuticals such as sulfa drugs and antihistamines, as a denaturant for ethyl alcohol, as a solvent for organic chemicals, and in the preparation of waterproofing agents for textiles. A number of other examples of heterocyclic compounds are discussed in Chapter 27.

(a)

(b)

▲ **FIGURE 26-8**
Pyridine
In the pyridine molecule, a nitrogen atom replaces one of the CH units of benzene. Its formula is C_5H_5N.
(a) Structural formula.
(b) Space-filling model.

26-10   NOMENCLATURE OF STEREOISOMERS IN ORGANIC COMPOUNDS

We have already learned about one form of stereoisomerism in organic compounds, namely cis–trans isomerism. In this section we will look at another form of stereoisomerism, optical isomerism, as well as one of the modern systems of nomenclature used to name stereoisomers.

CHIRALITY

The phenomenon of **optical isomerism** was introduced in Chapter 24 in conjunction with transition metal complexes (coordination compounds). A solution of an optically active compound can rotate the plane of polarized light. The requirement for optical activity is that the molecule be asymmetric—that is, its mirror image cannot be superimposed on the original molecule. This situation can arise at a tetrahedral C atom when all four groups attached to the C atom are different. Consider the molecule 3-methylhexane shown in Figure 26-9. The illustration shows that there are two nonsuperimposable isomers of 3-methylhexane related as mirror images. The two isomers are said to be *enantiomers*, or optical isomers. A molecule that is not superimposable on its mirror image is said to be **chiral**.

Chirality animation

Collins, M. J. "Demonstrating Chirality: Using a Mirror with Physical Models to Show Non-superimposability of Chiral Molecules with Their Mirror Images." *J. Chem. Educ.* **2001**: *78*, 1484.

Gawley, R. E. "Chirality Made Simple: A 1- and 2-Dimensional Introduction to Stereochemistry." *J. Chem. Educ.* **2005**: *82*, 1009.

▶ FIGURE 26-9
Nonsuperimposable mirror images of 3-methylhexane
Notice in the diagram that we have adopted the convention used by organic chemists in drawing chiral centers: The groups attached to the central carbon in the plane of the paper are connected with solid lines, the group in front of the plane of the paper is attached by a wedge, and the group behind the plane of the paper is indicated by a dashed line.

Mirror

In contrast with chiral molecules, such as 3-methylhexane, compounds whose structures are superimposable on their mirror images are **achiral**. Examples of chiral and achiral molecules are shown here, using the dashed-wedged line notation.

Chiral   Chiral   Achiral   Chiral

KEEP IN MIND ▶
that a solution of one enantiomer rotates the plane of polarized light in one direction while a solution of the other enantiomer rotates the light in the opposite direction. With a 50:50 mixture of the two enantiomers—a racemic mixture—no rotation of the plane of polarized light is observed.

All the chiral molecules shown contain an atom that is connected to four different substituent groups. The C atom to which the four different groups are attached is said to be **asymmetric**, or a *stereocenter*. Centers of this type are often denoted by an asterisk. Molecules with one stereocenter are always chiral. As we will see in Chapter 27, molecules incorporating more than one stereocenter need not be chiral. As we will also see in Chapter 27, many chiral molecules occur in nature, and as described later in this chapter, the existence of chirality can also play an important role in establishing some reaction mechanisms.

📖 A striking way of demonstrating the difference between the *d* and *l* enantiomers is to obtain *d*-carvone and *l*-carvone. One smells like dill and the other like mint.

EXAMPLE 26-5

Identifying a Chiral Molecule. Predict whether either 2-chloropentane or 3-chloropentane is chiral.

Solution

To decide whether a molecule is chiral, we look for a C atom that has four different groups attached. The two compounds are depicted below.

We see that 2-chloropentane contains a C atom that has four different groups attached; hence, it is chiral. However, 3-chloropentane does not have such a C atom; its structure is identical to its mirror image and the molecule is therefore achiral.

Practice Example A: Which of the following chlorofluorohydrocarbons is chiral: (a) $CF_3CH_2CCl_3$; (b) $CF_2HCHFCCl_3$; (c) $CClFHCHHCCl_2F$?

Practice Example B: Which of the following chloroalcohols is chiral: (a) $CH_2ClCH_2CH_2OH$; (b) $CH_2ClCH(OH)CH_3$; (c) $CH(OH)ClCH_2CH_3$?

CONCEPT ASSESSMENT ✓

How many chiral centers are there in 2,3-bromopentane? How many different stereoisomers are there?

NAMING ENANTIOMERS: THE *R, S* SYSTEM OF NOMENCLATURE

The compound 2-chlorobutane has two enantiomers. We need a system of nomenclature that indicates the arrangement or configuration of the four groups about the chiral center so that we can distinguish between them. Such a system was developed by three chemists, R. S. Cahn, C. Ingold, and V. Prelog. The first step is to rank the four substituents in order of decreasing priority. The rules for assigning priorities will be described shortly.

Suppose that in the hypothetical compound *Cabcd* substituent *a* has the highest priority, *b* the second highest, *c* the third highest, and *d* the lowest. Now position the molecule (mentally, on paper, or with a model set) so that the lowest priority substituent is as far away from the viewer as possible (Fig. 26-10). This procedure results in two possible arrangements for the remaining substituents (one for each enantiomer). In the **R, S system**, if the sequence from *a* to *b* to *c*, as viewed toward the substituent of lowest priority, is clockwise, the configuration of the stereocenter is named *R* (*rectus*, Latin, meaning right). Conversely, if the sequence is counterclockwise, the stereocenter is named *S* (*sinister*, Latin, meaning left). The symbol (*R*) or (*S*) is added as a prefix to the name of the chiral compound, as in (*R*)-2-chlorobutane and (*S*)-2-chlorobutane. A racemic mixture of the enantiomers is designated (*R, S*) as in (*R, S*)-2-chlorobutane.

Rules for Assigning Priorities to Substituents. In order to apply the *R, S* nomenclature to a stereocenter, we must first describe how the priorities are assigned to substituents. When looking at the atoms attached directly to the stereocenter, the rules devised by Cahn, Ingold, and Prelog are as follows:

Rule 1. A substituent atom of higher atomic number takes precedence over one of lower atomic number. Consider the enantiomer of 1-chloro-1-iodoethane shown below.

Priority I > Priority Cl > Priority C
(*S*)-1-chloro-1-iodoethane

The order of priority as viewed toward the H atom (which has the lowest priority) is counterclockwise. Therefore the enantiomer is (*S*)-1-chloro-1-iodoethane.

Rule 2. If two substituent atoms attached to the stereocenter have the same priority, proceed along the two substituent chains until a point of difference is reached. The atom of higher atomic number at this point establishes the priority. Thus, an ethyl group takes priority over a methyl group for the following reason. Although at the point of attachment to the stereocenter each substituent has a C atom, equal in priority, beyond these C atoms the methyl group has a H atom and the ethyl group has a higher-priority C atom.

It is important to understand that the decision on priority is made at the *first* point of difference along otherwise similar substituent chains.

▲ **FIGURE 26-10**
Assignment of *R* and *S* configuration at a tetrahedral stereocenter
The group of lowest priority is placed as far away from the viewer as possible.

The enantiomers of 2-chlorobutane

Starkey, Ronald. "Determination of the *R* or *S* Configuration of Tetrahedral Stereocenters: A Graphical Flowchart Approach." *J. Chem. Educ.* **1995**: *72*, 315.

Mandal, Dipak Kumar. "The R/S System: A New and Simple Approach to Determining Ligand Priority and a Unified Method for the Assignment and Correlation of Stereogenic Center Configuration in Diverse Stereoformulas." *J. Chem. Educ.* **2000**: *77*, 866 (July 2000).

Wang, J., et al. "Determining a chiral molecule's R/S configuration using the rule of multiplication." *J. Chem. Educ.* **1992:** *69*, 373.

Aalund, M. P., et al "A simple hand method for Cahn-Ingold-Prelog assignment of R and S configuration to chiral carbons." *J. Chem. Educ.* **1986:** *63*, 600.

When that point has been reached, the constitution of the remainder of the chain is immaterial.

$$C^* \!-\! \underset{\underset{H}{|}}{\overset{\overset{H}{|}}{C}} \!-\! CH_2Cl \quad \text{ranks lower than} \quad C^* \!-\! \underset{\underset{H}{|}}{\overset{\overset{CH_3}{|}}{C}} \!-\! CH_3$$

First point of difference: H ← → CH₃

Rule 3. Double bonds and triple bonds are treated as if they were single, and the atoms in them are duplicated or triplicated at each end by the particular atoms at the *other end of the multiple bond.* For example,

$$\underset{H}{\overset{H}{>}}C\!=\!C\underset{R}{\overset{H}{<}} \quad \text{is treated as} \quad -\underset{\underset{C}{|}}{\overset{\overset{H}{|}}{C}}-\underset{\underset{C}{|}}{\overset{\overset{H}{|}}{C}}-R$$

$$-C\!\equiv\!C\!-\!R \quad \text{is treated as} \quad -\underset{\underset{C}{|}}{\overset{\overset{C}{|}}{C}}-\underset{\underset{C}{|}}{\overset{\overset{C}{|}}{C}}-R$$

$$-\underset{}{\overset{\overset{O}{\|}}{C}}-OH \quad \text{is treated as} \quad -\underset{\underset{OH}{|}}{\overset{\overset{O}{|}}{C}}-O$$

Note that the atoms shown in red are added simply for the purpose of assigning priority to the groups containing a multiple bond; they are *not* really there! To illustrate, the —CH₂OH group has lower priority than —CHO.

$$*C\!-\!\underset{\underset{H}{|}}{\overset{\overset{O}{\|}}{C}}\!=\!O \quad \text{treated as} \quad *C\!-\!\underset{\underset{H}{|}}{\overset{\overset{O}{|}}{C}}\!-\!O \quad \text{ranks higher than} \quad *C\!-\!\underset{\underset{H}{|}}{\overset{\overset{H}{|}}{C}}\!-\!OH$$

First point of difference

The assignment of priorities and configuration of a chiral center is illustrated in Example 26-6.

EXAMPLE 26-6

Assignment of Priorities and Configuration of a Chiral Center. Name each of the following compounds, including the assignment of configuration.

$$\text{(a)} \quad CH_3CH_2\!-\!\underset{\underset{I}{\big\downarrow}}{\overset{\overset{CH_2-CH_2-CH_3}{|}}{C}}\text{-}\text{-}\text{-}H \qquad \text{(b)} \quad H\text{-}\underset{\underset{CH_3}{\big\downarrow}}{\overset{\overset{OH}{|}}{C}}\text{-}\text{-}CH_2CH_2Br$$

Solution

To assign the configuration at the stereocenter, we must first assign the priorities of the substituents. Then we determine the *R* or *S* configuration by viewing the molecule toward the atom of lowest priority.

(a) This molecule is 3-iodohexane with C-3 as the chiral center. The order of priorities of atoms attached to C-3 is

$$I > C \text{ (ethyl)} = C \text{ (propyl)} > H$$

In order to decide the ranking of the ethyl group relative to the propyl group, we go to the first point of difference in the chains of these substituents.

We see that the propyl group ranks higher than the ethyl group, so the order of priorities is

$$I > C \text{ (propyl)} > C \text{ (ethyl)} > H$$

Viewing the molecule toward the lowest priority H atom

we see that the priorities decrease in a counterclockwise manner, so the configuration at the stereo center is S. The complete name of the molecule is (S)-3-iodohexane.

(b) This molecule is 4-bromo-2-butanol, with C-2 as the chiral center. The order of priorities of atoms attached to C-2 is

$$O > C \text{ (bromoethyl)} = C \text{ (methyl)} > H$$

In order to decide the ranking of the bromoethyl group relative to the methyl group, we go to the first point of difference in the chains of these substituents.

We see that the bromoethyl group ranks higher than the methyl group, so the order of priorities is

$$I > C \text{ (bromoethyl)} > C \text{ (methyl)} > H$$

Viewing the molecule toward the lowest priority H atom is not quite as straightforward as in part (a). This is because the H atom is in the plane of the paper and thus not as far away from the viewers as possible. We can tackle this problem in one of two ways. The first requires some three-dimensional "vision," or "stereoperception," in that we imagine picking up the molecule by the methyl group and bromoethyl group and reorienting the molecule so that the H atom points away from us, to give

where we can now discern the sequence of priorities as clockwise, so the compound is (R)-4-bromo-2-butanol.

Alternatively, we can switch a pair of groups so that the group of lowest priority is bonded by a dashed line.

Now draw the view of the molecule toward the group of lowest priority.

Here the sequence of priorities is counterclockwise. Because we switched two groups, we created the enantiomer of the molecule whose configuration we are actually seeking. Thus, although in the switched molecule the order of priorities corresponds to an S configuration, the *original* molecule corresponds to the R configuration. Therefore, as determined previously, the molecule is (R)-4-bromo-2-butanol.

Practice Example A: Indicate whether each of the following structures has the R configuration or the S configuration.

Practice Example B: Do the structures in each of the following pairs represent identical molecules or pairs of enantiomers?

NAMING THE STEREOISOMERS OF HIGHLY SUBSTITUTED ALKENES: THE *E, Z* SYSTEM OF NOMENCLATURE

As long as each of the sp^2 carbon atoms of an alkene is bonded to only one substituent, we can use the terms *cis* and *trans* to designate the geometric isomers of the alkene. But how can we decide which is the cis or trans isomers for a compound such as 1-chloro-1,2-difluoroethene, which has *three* substituents bonded to the sp^2 carbons?

Which is cis? Which is trans?

An alternative system for naming such alkenes has been adopted by IUPAC; the **E, Z system**. The Cahn-Ingold-Prelog rules, discussed previously, are used systematically to assign priorities to the substituents on the sp^2 carbon atoms of the double bond. The stereochemistry about the double bond is assigned Z (from the German word *zusammen*, meaning together) if the two groups of higher priority *at each end of the double bond* are on the same side of the molecule. If the two groups of higher priority are on opposite sides of the double bond, the configuration is denoted by an E (from the German word *entgegen*, meaning opposite).

The two stereoisomers of 1-chloro-1,2-difluoroethene are

Note that, as in *R, S* nomenclature, the E or Z is placed in parentheses. The E, Z system of nomenclature can be used for all alkene stereoisomers; consequently the IUPAC recommends that this system be used exclusively. However, many chemists continue to use the cis and trans designations for simple alkenes.

EXAMPLE 26-7

Assignment of Configurations of Alkenes. Name each of the following compounds, including the assignment of configuration.

Solution

To assign the configuration of the alkene, we must first assign the priorities to the substituents attached to each carbon in the double bond. Once this is done we can assign the E or Z designation.

(a) One of the sp^2 carbon atoms is bonded to a Cl atom and a C atom, thus the chlorine atom has highest priority. The other sp^2 carbon is bonded to an ethyl group and an isopropyl group. The carbon of the isopropyl group is bonded to C, C, and H, and the carbon of the ethyl group to C, H, and H. A carbon can be canceled in each group. Of the remaining atoms, the carbon has the highest priority. Thus, the isopropyl group has precedence. The groups of highest priority are on the same side of the double bond. The complete name of the molecule is (Z)-1,2-dichloro-3-ethyl-4-methyl-2-pentene.

(b) One of the sp^2 carbon atoms is bonded to a fluoromethyl group and an isopropyl group. The carbon of the fluoromethyl group is bonded to F, H, and H; the carbon of the isopropyl group to C, C, and H. Of these six atoms, the fluorine has the highest priority. Thus, the fluoromethyl group has precedence. The other sp^2 carbon atom is bonded to an ethyl group and a chloroethyl group. Because the first point of difference on these substituent chains is a Cl atom, the chloroethyl group has precedence. The groups of highest priority are on opposite sides of the double bond. The complete name of the molecule is (*E*)-2-chloro-3-ethyl-4-fluoromethyl-5-methyl-3-hexene.

Practice Example A: Assign a configuration to each of the following alkenes.

(a)
$$
\begin{array}{ccc}
CH_3CH_2 & & H \\
& C{=}C & \\
H & & CH_2CH_3
\end{array}
$$

(b)
$$
\begin{array}{ccc}
Br & & CH_2Br \\
& C{=}C & \\
Cl & & CH_3
\end{array}
$$

(c)
$$
\begin{array}{ccc}
ClCH_2CH_2 & & F \\
& C{=}C & \\
CH_3CH_2 & & H
\end{array}
$$

(d)
$$
\begin{array}{ccc}
CH_3 & & C{\equiv}C{-}H \\
& C{=}C & \\
H & & CH_2CH_3
\end{array}
$$

Practice Example B: Draw and label the *E* and *Z* isomers of the following compounds.

(a) $CH_3CH_2CH{=}CHCH_3$

(b)
$$
CH_3CH_2C{=}CHCH_2CH_3 \\
| \\
Cl
$$

(c)
$$
CH_3CH_2C{=}CHCH_3 \\
| \\
CH_3
$$

(d)
$$
\begin{array}{c}
Cl \\
| \\
CH_3CH{-}C{=}CClCH_3 \\
| \\
CH_3
\end{array}
$$

26-11 AN INTRODUCTION TO SUBSTITUTION REACTIONS AT sp^3 HYBRIDIZED CARBON ATOMS

We have seen that a H atom in an alkane can be replaced by a halogen. It is also possible to carry out a substitution reaction in which a different atom or group of atoms replaces the halogen. An example of such a reaction is the replacement of a Cl atom in chloromethane by a hydroxyl group to give methanol.

$$CH_3Cl + OH^- \longrightarrow CH_3OH + Cl^- \tag{26.27}$$

This type of chemical reaction is called a **nucleophilic substitution reaction** because the hydroxide ion is a **nucleophile**—a reactant that seeks centers of positive charge in a molecule. We learned in Chapter 11 that the carbon-to-chlorine bond is polar, so the C atom is a region of slight positive charge and is said to be **electrophilic** (electron attracting). In this substitution reaction, the hydroxide ion attacks at the slightly positive C atom, pushing out the chloride ion, which is called the **leaving group**.

Nucleophiles, often denoted by the abbreviation Nu, may be negatively charged or neutral, but every nucleophile contains at least one pair of unshared electrons. Nucleophiles are, in fact, Lewis bases. The nucleophilic substitution of a haloalkane is described by either of two general equations.

Silversmith, Ernest F. "Correction to Nucleophilic Addition vs. Substitution: A Puzzle for the Organic Laboratory by Ernest F. Silversmith" *J. Chem. Educ.* **1998**: 75, 1387 (November 1998) and *J. Chem. Educ.* **1998**: 75, 221 (February 1988).

$$
\underset{\text{Nucleophile}}{Nu\!:^-} + \underset{\underset{\text{Electrophile}}{\uparrow}}{R{-}\overset{\delta+\;\;\delta-}{\underset{\cdot\cdot}{\overset{\cdot\cdot}{X}}}\!:} \longrightarrow R{-}Nu + \underset{\text{Leaving group}}{:\overset{\cdot\cdot}{\underset{\cdot\cdot}{X}}\!:^-}
$$

$$\text{Nu:} + \overset{\delta+}{\text{R}}\!\!-\!\!\overset{\delta-}{\underset{..}{\overset{..}{\text{X}}}}\!\!: \longrightarrow [\text{R}\!-\!\text{Nu}]^+ + :\underset{..}{\overset{..}{\text{X}}}:^-$$

Nucleophile $\uparrow$ Leaving group

Electrophile

As examples, consider these reactions, which were encountered previously in this chapter. In the reaction between sodium methylacetylide and bromoethane

$$\text{Na}^+{}^-\text{C}\equiv\text{C}-\text{CH}_3 + \text{CH}_3\text{CH}_2\text{Br} \longrightarrow \text{CH}_3\text{CH}_2\text{C}\equiv\text{CCH}_3 + \text{Na}^+\text{Br}^- \quad (26.9)$$

the nucleophile is the methylacetylide anion, and the Br^- anion is the leaving group. Similarly, in the reaction between sodium ethoxide and iodomethane

$$\text{Na}^+{}^-\text{OCH}_2\text{CH}_3 + \text{CH}_3\text{I} \longrightarrow \text{CH}_3\text{CH}_2\text{OCH}_3 + \text{Na}^+\text{I}^- \quad (26.28)$$

the nucleophile is the ethoxide anion. Finally, in the formation of alkyl ammonium salts

$$\text{CH}_3\text{CH}_2\text{Br} + \text{NH}_3 \longrightarrow \text{CH}_3\text{CH}_2\overset{\displaystyle H}{\underset{\displaystyle H}{\overset{|}{\underset{|}{\text{N}^+}}}}\!\!-\!\!\text{H} + \text{Br}^- \quad (26.29)$$

the nucleophile is the ammonia molecule.

In studying these reactions, you may have noticed the similarity of the reaction

$$\text{Nu:}^- + \text{RX} \longrightarrow \text{RNu} + \text{X}^-$$

to the Brønsted–Lowry acid–base reaction

$$\text{B:}^- + \text{HX} \longrightarrow \text{HB} + \text{X}^-$$

In a Brønsted–Lowry acid–base reaction, the stronger base and the stronger acid react to form the weaker acid and the weaker base. Similarly, in a nucleophilic substitution reaction, a stronger base (conjugate base of a weak acid) displaces a weaker base (conjugate base of a strong acid). This idea enables us to decide on the likelihood of a reaction occurring. Thus, for example, we would not expect the reaction

$$\text{HO}^- + \text{H}_3\text{C} - \text{H} \longrightarrow\!\!\!\!\!/ \;\; \text{H}_3\text{COH} + \text{H}^-$$

to occur because the hydride ion is a much stronger base than the hydroxide ion. Recall that NaH reacts with water to produce hydrogen gas and aqueous sodium hydroxide.

In a nucleophilic substitution reaction, both the nucleophile and the leaving group are bases. If the difference in base strength between the two is not very large, the equilibrium constant for the resulting reaction will be close to unity. The substitution reaction will reach equilibrium rather than going to completion, as it would if the equilibrium constant were large. For example, the iodide and chloride ions are both weak bases (HI and HCl are both strong acids, but HI is stronger; see page 668) so that the reaction

$$\text{Cl}^- + \text{CH}_3\text{CH}_2\text{CH}_2-\text{I} \rightleftharpoons \text{I}^- + \text{CH}_3\text{CH}_2\text{CH}_2-\text{Cl} \quad (26.30)$$

is shifted toward the chloroalkane because I^- is a weaker base than Cl^-. Such equilibria can be shifted to the right or left by the removal of one of the products. For example, if the reaction is carried out in acetone, the product is iodopropane because sodium chloride is insoluble in acetone, whereas sodium iodide is soluble.

EXAMPLE 26-8

Identifying Electrophiles and Nucleophiles. Decide which of the following compounds and ions are electrophiles and which are nucleophiles: **(a)** CH_3O^-; **(b)** methanal; **(c)** CH_3CH_2Cl; **(d)** CH_3NH_2.

Solution

To decide whether a molecule is an electrophile or a nucleophile, it is helpful to write a Lewis structure.

(a) The Lewis structure of the methoxide ion is

The methoxide ion is seen to be a nucleophile because it has a pair of electrons to share.

(b) The Lewis structure of methanal is

The carbonyl group is polar since the more electronegative oxygen atom has a greater share of the electrons of the double bond. The C atom in the carbonyl group is electrophilic. Methanal is an electrophile.

(c) The Lewis structure of chloroethane is

The polar character of the carbon-to-chlorine bond renders this molecule an electrophile.

(d) The Lewis structure of methanamine is

The methanamine molecule is seen to be a nucleophile because it has a pair of electrons to share.

Practice Example A: Which of the following are electrophiles and which are nucleophiles?

$$H^- \qquad AlCl_3 \qquad \overset{H}{\underset{H}{>}}C=C\overset{H}{\underset{H}{<}} \qquad CH_3S^-$$

(a) **(b)** **(c)** **(d)**

Practice Example B: Identify the electrophiles and the nucleophiles and the likely products in the following reactions.

(a) $CH_3I + NH_3 \longrightarrow$

(b) $CH_3CH_2Cl + CH_3S^- \longrightarrow$

(c) $CN^- + CH_3CH_2CHClCH_3 \longrightarrow$

The S$_N$1 and S$_N$2 Mechanisms of Nucleophilic Substitution Reactions

Chemical research, starting in the 1890s, has shown that nucleophilic substitution reactions can involve two types of mechanisms. The reaction between chloromethane and the hydroxide ion (26.27) has a rate law that is first order in both the nucleophile and the electrophile (molecule containing the polar bond). That is,

$$\text{rate} = k[\text{OH}^-][\text{CH}_3\text{Cl}]$$

The mechanism for this reaction involves a bimolecular rate-determining step in which the nucleophilic group approaches the electrophilic carbon atom, and simultaneously, the leaving group departs. The entering and leaving groups act at the same time in what is known as a *concerted step*, as depicted in this schematic representation.

$$\text{HO}\!:^- \; + \; \text{CH}_3-\overset{..}{\underset{..}{\text{Cl}}}\!: \; \longrightarrow \; \text{CH}_3-\overset{..}{\underset{..}{\text{O}}}\text{H} \; + \; :\overset{..}{\underset{..}{\text{Cl}}}\!:^-$$

The pair of curved arrows summarizes our visualization of how electrons flow to form and break bonds. Thus, the arrow starts from an electron-rich center (the electrons on the hydroxyl group in this case) to an electron-poor region (the C atom in the polar carbon-to-chlorine bond).

This mechanism is designated **S$_N$2,** with the S indicating substitution, the N indicating nucleophilic, and the 2 indicating that the rate-determining step is bimolecular. The reaction profile for an S$_N$2 reaction is shown in Figure 26-11, in which the transition state formed by the HO$^-$ ion and the chloromethane is shown. The hydroxide attacks on the side opposite the Cl atom, and the C—Cl bond starts to break as the C—O simultaneously starts to form, producing the transition state shown. In the S$_N$2 mechanism, the nucleophile donates a pair of electrons to the electrophile to form a covalent bond.

Is there any experimental evidence to support this mechanism and postulated transition state? First, the rate law is suggestive of a bimolecular step; second, an observation by Paul Walden in 1893 confirmed the formation of the transition state as shown in Figure 26-12. Walden discovered that if the C atom bonded to the halogen is stereogenic, or chiral, the configuration at the chiral carbon is inverted—that is, the molecular structure is inverted and an enantiomer of the opposite configuration is formed. Thus, when (S)-2-iodobutane undergoes nucleophilic substitution by the hydroxide group, the compound (R)-2-butanol is formed (Fig. 26-12). This *inversion of configuration* is taken as confirmation of the proposed bimolecular mechanism and the five-coordinate transition state.

▲ **FIGURE 26-11**
Reaction profile for an S$_N$2 reaction
The bonds that are forming and breaking in the transition state are shown by dotted lines.

Bimolecular Reaction animation

◀ **KEEP IN MIND**
that the electrophile accepts the pair of electrons. Thus, the nucleophile acts as a Lewis base, and the electrophile as a Lewis acid.

▲ **FIGURE 26-12**
Inversion of configuration in the S$_N$2 mechanism

The other mechanism of nucleophilic substitution at haloalkanes has a rate law that is first order in the concentration of haloalkane only. The reaction between 2-bromo-2-methylpropane and water, in which H$_2$O acts as the nucleophile,

$$(\text{CH}_3)_3\text{CBr} + \text{H}_2\text{O} \longrightarrow (\text{CH}_3)_3\text{COH} + \text{HBr}$$

has the rate law

$$\text{rate} = k\,[(\text{CH}_3)_3\text{CBr}]$$

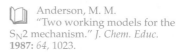
Wright, S. W. "A demonstration of the S$_N$2 reaction and the effects of structure, leaving group, and solvent." *J. Chem. Educ.* **1992:** *69,* 235.

Anderson, M. M. "Two working models for the S$_N$2 mechanism." *J. Chem. Educ.* **1987:** *64,* 1023.

This rate law suggests that the rate-determining step is unimolecular. The unimolecular step is the dissociation of the haloalkane into ions—a bromide ion and a *carbocation*.

The planar carbocation immediately reacts with the nucleophile, water in this case.

The conjugate acid of an alcohol is formed, which immediately dissociates in the presence of excess water, forming the neutral alcohol and a hydronium ion.

This mechanism is designated **S$_N$1.** Again, the S indicates substitution and the N nucleophilic; in this case, the 1 indicates that the rate-determining step is unimolecular. The reaction profile for an S$_N$1 reaction is shown in Figure 26-13, which includes three transition states and two intermediates.

Apart from the rate law, what other evidence is there for the planar carbocation? Again, we can use a chiral haloalkane and investigate the chirality of the product. When one of the enantiomers of 3-bromo-3-methylhexane reacts with water, the product is a racemic mixture of the enantiomers of 3-methyl-3-hexanol. The carbocation intermediate formed in the rate-determining step is planar. The water molecule (nucleophile) can form a new bond on either face of the carbocation intermediate. This results in a 50:50 mixture of the product enantiomers (Fig. 26-14). The formation of a racemic mixture provides confirmation of the unimolecular rate-determining step in the S$_N$1 mechanism.

When is a mechanism S$_N$1, and when is it S$_N$2? To answer this question, we need to briefly discuss some kinetic studies carried out by Christopher Ingold and Edward Hughes in 1937. Measurement of rates of reaction under different sets of experimental conditions can provide insight into reaction mechanisms.

▶ **FIGURE 26-13**
Reaction profile for the S$_N$1 reaction between *t*-butyl bromide and water
The carbocation formed in the rate-determining step is planar. The central C atom in the carbocation intermediate is *sp^2* hybridized. The remaining *p* orbital is used in the formation of the new chemical bond. The central C atom of the 2,2-dimethylethyloxonium ion (the second intermediate) becomes *sp^3* hybridized subsequently.

◄ FIGURE 26-14
Formation of a racemic mixture in an S_N1 reaction

Are You Wondering . . .

Why we did not use the hydroxide ion in the hydrolysis of 2-bromo-2-methylpropane?

It is important to recognize that the carbocation is also a Brønsted–Lowry acid, which can react with a strong base such as the hydroxide ion. Loss of a proton in an acid–base reaction results in the formation of an alkene. This type of reaction is called an *elimination reaction* and is illustrated below.

McClelland, B. W. "Chart for Deciding Mechanism for Reaction of Alkyl Halide with Nucleophile/Base." *J. Chem. Educ.* **1994:** *71,* 1047.

In organic reactions, it is quite common for more than one reaction to take place with the same starting materials. In fact, when 2-bromo-2-methylpropane reacts with hydroxide ion in an aqueous solution, both the alkene and the alcohol are formed. Organic chemists can manipulate the reaction conditions (for example, by changing the solvent) to make one product dominant over the other.

For example, consider the rate of the following second-order reaction between a bromoalkane and the nucleophile Cl^-.

$$R—Br + Cl^- \longrightarrow R—Cl + Br^-$$

The rate of reaction decreases with increasing length and branching of the R group, in the following order.

$$CH_3Br > CH_3CH_2Br > CH_3CH_2CH_2Br > CH_3CHBr > CH_3CBr$$

Relative rate   1200   40   16   1   Too slow to measure

In the S_N2 mechanism, the nucleophile attacks the electrophilic center on the side *opposite* the leaving group, often called *backside attack*. Because the nucleophile attacks the backside of the carbon that is bonded to the halogen, bulky substituents attached to this carbon will make it harder for the nucleophile to get to the backside and thus will slow down the reaction (Fig. 26-15). The S_N2 mechanism can therefore provide an explanation for the observed decrease in rate of reaction when bulky groups are substituted for hydrogen atoms attached to the electrophilic C atom. The obstruction of the nucleophile from interacting with the center of partial positive charge is called *steric hindrance*.

◄ In the same manner that alcohols are classified as primary, secondary, and tertiary, this principle is also used for haloalkanes. Thus, 2-bromopropane is a secondary haloalkane.

(a)

(b)

(c)

(d)

(e)

▲ **FIGURE 26-15**
Steric hindrance—illustrated
Space-filling views of the molecules **(a)** bromomethane, **(b)** bromoethane, **(c)** bromopropane, **(d)** 1-methylbromoethane, and **(e)** 1,1-dimethylbromoethane viewed from attacking nucleophile's vantage point. The bulk of the substituents decreases access to the center of partial positive charge on the C atom attached to the halogen and therefore decreases the rate of an S_N2 reaction.

With these ideas in mind, we can now appreciate why the reaction of 1,1-dimethyl-1-bromoethane (*t*-butyl bromide) with water proceeds by a different mechanism. The nucleophile (water) cannot attack the carbon in a concerted step (S_N2 mechanism) because of steric hindrance. The reaction does not proceed until the carbocation is formed by dissociation of the bromide ion in the rate-determining step. The water molecule then undergoes nucleophilic attack at the positively charged C atom, forming the protonated alcohol (Fig. 26-13), which subsequently deprotonates in the aqueous solvent. Thus, in conclusion, we expect haloalkanes that are highly substituted at the C atom to which the halogen is attached to undergo nucleophilic substitution by an S_N1 mechanism.

In this brief description of the mechanisms of nucleophilic substitution reactions, we have touched on only one of the factors involved in determining which mechanism prevails. There are a number of others, such as solvent effects and nucleophilicity (how good a nucleophile the nucleophile is), discussions of which are found in organic chemistry texts.

EXAMPLE 26-9

Recognizing S_N1 and S_N2 Reactions and Predicting the Products. Predict whether the following reactions will take place, and suggest the likely mechanism.

(a) $CN^- + CH_3CH_2CH_2Cl \longrightarrow$

(b) $Br^- + CH_3CH_2OH \longrightarrow$

(c) $CH_3OH + (CH_3)_3CCl$ (in methanol) $\longrightarrow$

Solution

To decide whether a reaction of this type will take place, first identify the electrophile, nucleophile, and leaving group.

(a) The nucleophile is the CN^- ion, the electrophile is the chloropropane, and the leaving group is the Cl^- ion. The CN^- is a much stronger base than the Cl^- ion, so the equilibrium constant for the reaction should be large. The chloropropane is a primary haloalkane, so the likely mechanism is S_N2 and the product will be butanonitrile (or 1-cyanopropane).

(b) The nucleophile is the Br^- ion, the electrophile is the ethanol, and the potential leaving group is the OH^- ion. The OH^- is a much stronger base than the Br^- ion, so the equilibrium constant for the reaction is much *less* than one. No reaction is expected.

(c) The nucleophile is the CH_3OH molecule, the electrophile is the *t*-butyl chloride, and the leaving group is the Cl^- ion. In this case we have to know the relative basicities of CH_3OH and Cl^- in order to decide in which direction the reaction will proceed. If we assume that the basicities of methanol and chloride ion are about the same (neither likes to accept a proton), we expect an equilibrium to be established. However, the fact that we are using a large excess of methanol (methanol is the solvent) would shift the equilibrium toward the product (Le Châtelier's principle). The product is *t*-butyl alcohol, and the likely mechanism is S_N1 since the electrophile is a tertiary haloalkane.

Practice Example A: Predict whether the following reactions will take place, and suggest the likely mechanism.

(a) $CH_3CC^- + CH_3Br \longrightarrow$

(b) $Cl^- + CH_3CH_2CN \longrightarrow$

(c) $CH_3NH_2 + (CH_3)_3CCl \longrightarrow$

Practice Example B: From the following information, identify and provide chemical equations for the mechanism of the reaction.

(a) The following reaction is carried out in acetone (propanone).

$$ \underset{Cl\ \ \ H}{\diagup\!\!\!\diagdown\!\!\!\bigwedge} + CN^- \longrightarrow \underset{H\ \ \ CN}{\diagup\!\!\!\diagdown\!\!\!\bigwedge} $$

(b) An optically pure sample of 2-iodobutane is dissolved in methanol. The resultant solution of *sec*-butyl methyl ether is optically inactive.

26-12 SYNTHESIS OF ORGANIC COMPOUNDS

Originally, all organic compounds were isolated from natural sources. However, as chemists developed an understanding of the chemical behavior of organic compounds, they began to devise methods of synthesizing compounds from simple starting materials. Moreover, some of the compounds synthesized by the newly developed methods had never been observed to occur naturally.

In organic synthesis, chemists attempt to transform simple, readily available compounds into more complex molecules with desirable physical and chemical properties. Some syntheses are designed to make biologically active compounds that are otherwise available only from natural sources, and in only small quantities at high cost. Other synthetic approaches are designed to make new compounds, similar to naturally occurring ones but even more powerful in biological activity, such as medications to fight disease.

The approach that a synthetic organic chemist takes is to apply a knowledge of a wide variety of reaction types and reaction mechanisms to devise a synthetic scheme for assembling simple molecules into more complex structures. Figure 26-16 summarizes the chemical transformations between functional groups considered in this chapter. This summary stresses that each type of reaction has three components—the starting materials, the products, and the required reagents. For any reaction, we can complete a chemical equation if we have information about two of the three components of the reaction and if we know the type of reaction that converts the starting materials to the products. For example, in the following nucleophilic substitution reaction,

$$CH_3Br + ? \longrightarrow CH_3CN + ?$$

we see that CN has been substituted for Br as a functional group. In order to achieve this transformation, the nucleophile CN^- is required and we complete the equation.

$$CH_3Br + CN^- \longrightarrow CH_3CN + Br^-$$

◀ FIGURE 26-16
Functional group transformations
A summary of functional group transformations, each of which requires a specific reagent as described in the text. When using this diagram, remember that changes in the R group are not indicated because this depends on the particular group involved. The symbols 1°, 2°, and 3° stand for primary, secondary, and tertiary, respectively.

A somewhat different, and more common, situation is that represented by

$$? + Br^- \longrightarrow CH_3Br + ?$$

where we need to work backward to decide on the electrophile in a nucleophilic substitution reaction to get the desired product, CH_3Br. The electrophile will need to be connected to the leaving group (for example, another halogen atom) in the same manner and place as the Br atom will be in the product. An appropriate complete equation is

$$CH_3I + Br^- \longrightarrow CH_3Br + I^-$$

Let's apply the approach outlined above to the synthesis of ethyl ethanoate, starting only from inorganic substances and carbon (coke). First, we break the desired compound down into its constituent molecules, namely ethanol and ethanoic acid, which can be combined to give the ester.

$$CH_3COOH + HOCH_2CH_3 \longrightarrow H_2O + CH_3COOCH_2CH_3$$

We therefore need to be able to produce ethanol, which can, in turn, be converted into ethanoic acid.

$$HOCH_2CH_3 \xrightarrow{?} H_3CCOOH$$

The reagent required to oxidize ethanol is $K_2Cr_2O_7$ in acidic solution. We now need a route to the synthesis of ethanol from carbon. One inorganic reagent that we have at our disposal that contains a OH group is water. We therefore write the equation

$$? + H_2O \longrightarrow HOCH_2CH_3$$

A consideration of the reactions that we have discussed in this chapter (Fig. 26-16) indicates that one possibility is the addition of water to the double bond in ethene in the presence of sulfuric acid as a catalyst. Thus, we write

$$H_2C{=}CH_2 + H_2O \xrightarrow{H_2SO_4} HOCH_2CH_3$$

To continue, the ethene molecule has to be generated. Ethene is related to ethyne by a hydrogenation reaction.

$$H-C{\equiv}C-H + H_2 \xrightarrow[\text{heat and pressure}]{Pt} H_2C{=}CH_2$$

Our source of carbon is the element carbon and we need a way of producing a molecule with a carbon-chain length of two. The production of calcium carbide (CaC_2) and its subsequent hydrolysis to give ethyne is described on page 1087.

We have now completed the description of the desired synthesis. The underlying strategy is to break the desired molecule down into its constituent molecules and work backward, using the chemical transformations available. This approach is known as *retrosynthesis* and is the method of choice in modern synthetic organic chemistry.

Are You Wondering . . .

Why we did not use the nucleophilic substitution by hydroxide ion in chloroethane to produce ethanol?

This is a perfectly acceptable approach to the synthesis of ethanol. It would require the substitution of a Cl atom for a H atom in ethane which, in turn, can be produced by the hydrogenation of ethyne, which is synthesized as described. Often, in the design of a synthetic pathway, one or more routes are possible. The one chosen is usually the one that produces the greatest yield of the desired product.

26-13 POLYMERS AND POLYMERIZATION REACTIONS

AN OVERVIEW

Polymers are made up of simple molecules with low molecular masses joined together into extremely large molecules. Polymers with molecular masses below about 20,000 u are called low polymers and those above 20,000 u, high polymers.

Garner, C. M., et al. "The Synthesis of a Superabsorbent Polymer." *J. Chem. Educ.* **1997**: *74*, 95.

One familiar polymer is *polyethylene*. As its name implies, its basic unit, or *monomer*, is the ethylene molecule, which has the Lewis structure

$$
\begin{array}{cc}
H & H \\
| & | \\
C & \!\!=\!\! C \\
| & | \\
H & H
\end{array}
$$

We can imagine that the polymerization of ethylene begins with the "opening up" of the double bonds in ethylene molecules.

$$
\begin{array}{cc}
H & H \\
| & | \\
\cdot C & \!\!-\!\! C \cdot \\
| & | \\
H & H
\end{array}
$$

Then each C atom in the resulting molecular fragment (radical) forms an additional single covalent bond with a C atom in another molecular fragment, and so on, producing the structure shown below.

$$
\cdots - \begin{array}{c} H \\ | \\ C \\ | \\ H \end{array} - \begin{array}{c} H \\ | \\ C \\ | \\ H \end{array} - \begin{array}{c} H \\ | \\ C \\ | \\ H \end{array} - \begin{array}{c} H \\ | \\ C \\ | \\ H \end{array} - \begin{array}{c} H \\ | \\ C \\ | \\ H \end{array} - \begin{array}{c} H \\ | \\ C \\ | \\ H \end{array} - \cdots
$$

In the following notation, the monomer unit is enclosed in square brackets and the subscript n signifies the number of monomers present in the final *macromolecule*. Typically, n might range from several hundred to several thousand.

$$
\left[\begin{array}{cc}
H & H \\
| & | \\
C & \!\!-\!\! C \\
| & | \\
H & H
\end{array} \right]_n
$$

Another polymer in which monomer units join end to end is *latex*—natural rubber.

Rubber

Early rubber products were of limited use because they were sticky in hot weather and stiff in cold weather. In 1839, Charles Goodyear accidentally discovered that by heating a sulfur–rubber mixture, a product could be made that was stronger, more elastic, and more resistant to heat and cold than natural rubber. This process is now called vulcanization (after *Vulcan*, the Roman god of fire). The purpose of vulcanization is to form *cross-links* between long polymer chains. An example of a cross-link through two sulfur atoms is shown on the next page.

$$\cdots CH_2-\underset{\underset{S}{|}}{\underset{\underset{\underset{}{|}}{CH_3}}{C}}=CH-CH-CH_2-\underset{|}{\underset{CH_3}{C}}=CH-CH_2\cdots$$

$$\cdots CH_2-\underset{\underset{CH_3}{|}}{\underset{\underset{}{S}}{C}}=CH-CH-CH_2-\underset{|}{\underset{CH_3}{C}}=CH-CH_2\cdots$$

Synthesis of Nylon 610 movie

Point out that polysaccharides and proteins are naturally occurring polymers.

▶ Molecules of a *poly*mer are formed by the joining together of many simple molecules called *mono*mers.

▲ Extruding polyethylene film.

Hodgson, S. C., Orbell, J. D., Bigger, S. W., Scheirs, J. "Studying Thermally Induced Chemical and Physical Transformations in Common Synthetic Polymers: A Laboratory Project." *J. Chem. Educ.* **2000**: 77, 745 (June 2000).

Polymers are familiar products in the modern world. Nylon, one of the first polymers developed, is like an artificial silk and is used in making clothing, ropes, and sails. The fluorine-containing polymer Teflon (polytetrafluoroethylene) is used in nonstick frying and baking pans. Polyvinyl chloride (PVC) is used in food wrap, hoses, pipes, and floor tile. In all, the polymer industry is a very large one. It has been estimated, for example, that about half of all chemists work with polymers. Of particular interest to them are the reactions that can be used to make polymers. We will briefly survey the main types of polymerization reactions in this final section of the chapter.

CHAIN-REACTION POLYMERIZATION

Monomers with carbon-to-carbon double bonds typically undergo **chain-reaction polymerization**. The net result is that the double bonds open up and monomer units add to growing chains. As with other chain reactions, the mechanism involves three characteristic steps: initiation, propagation, and termination. Let us illustrate this mechanism for the formation of the polymer polyethylene from the monomer ethylene (ethene).

The key to the polymerization reaction is the free-radical initiator. In reaction (26.31), an organic peroxide dissociates into two peroxy radicals. The radicals add to the C=C double bonds of ethylene molecules to form radical intermediates that attack more ethylene molecules and form new intermediates of longer and longer length (26.32). The chains terminate as a result of reactions such as (26.33).

Initiation: $R-O:O-R \longrightarrow 2\ R-O\cdot$ (26.31)
an organic peroxide

followed by

$$CH_2=CH_2 + RO\cdot \longrightarrow R-O-CH_2-CH_2\cdot$$

Propagation: $ROCH_2CH_2\cdot + CH_2=CH_2 \longrightarrow ROCH_2CH_2CH_2CH_2\cdot$ (26.32)

$$RO(CH_2)_3CH_2\cdot + CH_2=H_2 \longrightarrow RO\cdot(CH_2)_5CH_2\cdot$$

Termination: $RO(CH_2)_xCH_2\cdot + RO\cdot \longrightarrow RO(CH_2)_xCH_2OR$ (26.33)

or

$$RO(CH_2)_xCH_2\cdot + RO(CH_2)_yCH_2\cdot \longrightarrow RO(CH_2)_xCH_2CH_2(CH_2)_yOR$$

Several polymers formed by chain-reaction polymerization are listed in Table 26.5.

Are You Wondering . . .

What effect the —OR groups have on polymers such as polyethylene?

Essentially, they have no effect on the properties of the polymer. This is because there are hundreds, possibly thousands, of monomer units in the polymer, and the —OR groups are only at the ends of each polymer strand. The long chain of monomer units gives the polymer its particular properties, and the —OR group serves only to initiate the reaction and to terminate the polymer chains.

TABLE 26.5	Some Polymers Produced by Chain-Reaction Polymerization		
Name	Monomer	Polymer	Uses
Polyethylene	$CH_2{=}CH_2$	${-}(CH_2{-}CH_2)_n{-}$	Bags, bottles, tubing, packaging film
Polypropylene	$CH_2{=}CHCH_3$	$\left(CH_2{-}\underset{\underset{CH_3}{\mid}}{CH}\right)_n$	Laboratory and household ware, artificial turf, surgical casts, toys
Poly(vinyl chloride) PVC	$CH_2{=}CHCl$	$\left(CH_2{-}\underset{\underset{Cl}{\mid}}{CH}\right)_n$	Bottles, floor tile, food wrap, piping, hoses
Poly(tetrafluoroethylene), Teflon	$CF_2{=}CF_2$	${-}(CF_2{-}CF_2)_n{-}$	Bearings, insulation, nonstick surfaces, gaskets, industrial ware
Polystyrene	$CH_2{=}CH$	$\left(CH_2{-}CH\right)_n$	Packaging, refrigerator doors, cups, ice buckets, and coolers (as foam)

STEP-REACTION POLYMERIZATION

In **step-reaction polymerization**, also called *condensation polymerization*, the monomers typically have two or more functional groups that react to join the two molecules together. Usually, this involves the elimination of a small molecule, such as H_2O. In chain-reaction polymerization, the reaction of a monomer can occur only at the end of a growing polymer chain, but in step-reaction polymerization, any pair of monomers is free to join into a *dimer*; the dimer can join with a monomer to form a *trimer*; two dimers can join to form a *tetramer*; and so on. Step-reaction polymerization tends to occur slowly and produces polymers of only moderately high molecular masses (less than 10^5 u). The formation of polyethylene glycol terephthalate, Dacron, is illustrated in the following reaction, and several other polymers formed by this method are listed in Table 26.6.

terephthalic acid   ethylene glycol

poly(ethylene glycol terephthalate)
(Dacron)

STEREOSPECIFIC POLYMERS

The physical properties of a polymer are determined by a number of factors, such as the average length (average molecular mass) of the polymer chains and the strength of intermolecular forces between chains. Another important factor is whether the polymer chains display any crystallinity—that is, an ordered geometry and spacing of the atoms between polymer chains. In general, amorphous polymers are glass-like or rubbery. A high-strength fiber, on the other hand, must possess some crystallinity. Many polymers have both crystalline and amorphous regions. The relative amount of each type of region affects the physical properties of the polymer.

TABLE 26.6 Some Polymers Produced by Step-Reaction Polymerization

Name	Monomer	Polymer	Uses
Poly(ethylene glycol terephthalate) (Dacron)	HOCH₂CH₂OH and HOOC—⬡—COOH	[see structure]	Textile fabrics, twine and rope, fire hoses, plastic containers
Poly(hexamethyl-eneadipamide) nylon 66	H₂N(CH₂)₆NH₂ and HOOC(CH₂)₄COOH	[see structure]	Hosiery, rope, tire cord, parachutes, artificial blood vessels
Polyurethane	HO(CH₂)₄OH and OCN(CH₂)₆NCO	[see structure]	Spandex fibers, bristles for brushes, cushions and mattresses (as foam)

The usual designation of a polymer, as applied to polypropylene, for example, is not very revealing about the structure of the polymer.

$$\left[\begin{matrix} H & H \\ | & | \\ C & C \\ | & | \\ H & CH_3 \end{matrix}\right]_n$$

It does not indicate the orientation of the —CH₃ groups along the polymer chain.

If propylene (CH₃—CH=CH₂) is polymerized by the method shown for ethylene on page 1118, the orientation of the —CH₃ groups is random (Fig. 26-17). A polymer of this type is called *atactic*. Because there is no regularity

Produce "slime" by adding borax to polyvinylalcohol. The borax causes cross-linking to occur in the PVA. The slime is a polymer that can be pulled and stretched to the amusement of students. To make slime: Dissolve 40 grams of polyvinyl alcohol in a liter of water. Separately, dissolve 40 grams of borax in a liter of water. Combine about 75 mL of the PVA solution with 25 mL of borax to make slime. Free —OH groups become cross-linked through the borax.

▲ **FIGURE 26-17**
Three representations of a polypropylene chain
In the *atactic* polymer, the —CH₃ groups are randomly distributed on the chain. In the *isotactic* polymer, all —CH₃ groups are shown coming out of the plane of the page. In the *syndiotactic* polymer, —CH₃ groups alternate along the chain—one in front of the plane of the page, the next one behind the plane, and so on.

to the structure, atactic polymers are amorphous. In an *isotactic* polymer, all —CH$_3$ groups have the same orientation, and in a *syndiotactic* polymer, the —CH$_3$ groups have an orientation that alternates back and forth along the chain. Because of their structural regularity, isotactic and syndiotactic polymers possess crystallinity, which makes them stronger and more resistant to chemical attack than an atactic polymer.

In the 1950s, Karl Ziegler and Giulio Natta developed procedures for controlling the spatial orientation of substituent groups on a polymer chain by using special catalysts [such as $(CH_3CH_2)_3Al + TiCl_4$]. This discovery, recognized through the award of a Nobel Prize in 1963, revolutionized polymer chemistry. Through stereospecific polymerization, it is possible to literally tailor-make large molecules.

Summary

26-1 Organic Compounds and Structures: An Overview— Organic chemistry deals with compounds of carbon, the simplest of which, called **hydrocarbons**, contain only carbon and hydrogen atoms. The carbon atoms are bonded to one another in straight or branched chains or in rings. In **saturated hydrocarbons** all chemical bonds are single bonds. Isomers that differ in their structural skeletons are called **skeletal isomers**. Isomers in which the position(s) of a substituent(s) on the main chain differ are termed **positional isomers**. Alkane substituents, for example —CH$_3$, branching off a main hydrocarbon chain are referred to as **alkyl groups** (Table 26.1). Distinctive groups of atoms, for example, the —OH group and the —COOH group, are referred to as **functional groups** (Table 26.2). Organic compounds are typically classified according to their functional groups. A three-dimensional representation of hydrocarbons can be accomplished using the **dashed-wedged line notation**. In this notation, solid lines represent bonds in the plane of the paper, solid wedges show bonds sticking out toward the viewer, and dashed lines show bonds directed away from the viewer.

26-2 Alkanes— Among saturated hydrocarbons, also known as the **alkanes**, those based on a straight or branched chains of carbon atoms have the formula C$_n$H$_{2n+2}$ and are called **aliphatic** hydrocarbons. Aliphatic hydrocarbons that differ in sequence by a constant unit such as —CH$_2$— form a **homologous series**. Hydrocarbons that form ring structures are termed **alicyclic**. Hydrocarbons can adopt different **conformations**, or arrangements, of their atoms. Aliphatic hydrocarbons have eclipsed and staggered conformations, while alicyclic hydrocarbons have boat and chair conformations. Alkanes are relatively unreactive except with halogens, which can substitute for hydrogen atoms in a type of reaction called a **substitution reaction** (reaction 26.4). Hydrocarbons react with oxygen during combustion to form carbon dioxide and water. The principal natural sources of alkanes are natural gas and petroleum.

26-3 Alkenes and Alkynes— Hydrocarbons whose molecules contain fewer hydrogen atoms than found in the corresponding alkane are **unsaturated** hydrocarbons. The unsaturation is due to the presence of one or more carbon-to-carbon double or triple bonds. Hydrocarbons containing one or more double bonds are **alkenes**, or **olefins**, while those containing one or more triple bonds are **alkynes**. The placement of double or triple bonds in an unsaturated hydrocarbon can lead to positional isomers, as in 2-butene versus 1-butene, for example. In 2-butene the orientation of the two end methyl groups leads to cis and trans isomers, a type of isomerism called **geometric isomerism**. Alkenes can be prepared in the laboratory by the removal of atoms on adjacent carbon atoms. This type of reaction is known as an **elimination reaction.** In **addition reactions** of alkenes and alkynes new groups are added across adjacent carbon atoms at the multiple bond.

26-4 Aromatic Hydrocarbons— Many unsaturated hydrocarbons with ring structures are classified as **aromatic hydrocarbons**; most are based on the benzene molecule, C$_6$H$_6$. Two systems are commonly used to name substituents on a benzene ring. One uses a numbering system, such as 1,2-dichlorobenzene. The other uses the relative positions of substituents. Substituents on adjacent carbon atoms are referred to as **ortho** (*o*); substituents separated by one carbon are **meta** (*m*); and substituents opposite each other on the ring are **para** (*p*). A **phenyl** group is a benzene ring with one hydrogen atom removed. Reactions of aromatic molecules occur by substitution rather than addition. Substitution patterns on the ring are not random but occur based on the properties of the substituent group. Some functional groups are classified as *ortho, para directors* while others are classified as *meta directors*.

26-5 Alcohols, Phenols, and Ethers— Hydrocarbons that contain a —OH (**hydroxyl**) group are classified as **alcohols** in aliphatic compounds and **phenols** in aromatic compounds. Aliphatic alcohols are also classified as primary, secondary, or tertiary, depending on how many other substituents (excluding H atoms) are attached to the same carbon atom as the hydroxyl group—one for primary, two for secondary, and three for tertiary. Diols and polyols are molecules with two or more hydroxyl groups, respectively. Alcohols can be prepared by the hydrolysis of alkyl halides or the hydration of alkenes. **Ethers** are relatively unreactive hydrocarbons with the general formula R—O—R'.

◀ Green chemistry ideas are encouraging the development of products that reduce the use of hazardous substances such as in Raid® Earth Options which uses plant-based active ingredients instead of synthetic organic compounds.

(9) increase energy efficiency

(10) design chemicals and products that degrade after use

(11) analyze in real time to prevent pollution

(12) minimize the potential for accidents

Synthesis of organic molecules typically takes place in organic solvents because most organic molecules are not soluble in aqueous environments. Unfortunately, most organic solvents are flammable, carcinogenic, and environmentally unfriendly. Can some of the green chemistry principles be applied to the synthesis of organic compounds used in the manufacturing of everyday products? One possible answer to this question is to use ionic liquids in place of organic solvents.

In 1991, the Office of Pollution Prevention and Toxics of the U.S. Environmental Protection Agency started a grants program to encourage the development of chemical products and processes that reduce or eliminate the use and generation of hazardous substances. The theme of this program has become known as "green chemistry," which is now defined as an approach to pollution prevention by application of innovative scientific solutions to real-world environmental situations. Green chemistry is based on 12 principles:

(1) prevent waste

(2) design safer chemical products

(3) design less hazardous chemical syntheses

(4) use renewable feedstocks

(5) avoid excess reagents in chemical syntheses; use catalysts and stoichiometric amounts

(6) avoid multistep reactions

(7) maximize atom economy (see Feature Problem 109, page 140)

(8) use safe solvents and reaction conditions

IONIC LIQUIDS

Ionic liquids are organic salts with room temperature melting points and are thus easily obtained in the liquid state. Common ionic liquids are 1-ethyl-3-methylimidazolium chloride (EMIC), 1-butyl-4-methylpyridinium chloride (BMPC), and phosphonium or tetraalkyl ammonium compounds. Recently, environmental friendly halogen-free ionic liquids have been identified, such as 1-ethyl-3-methylimidazolium tosylate (EMIM-Ts). Properties that make these compounds attractive as solvents are their very good dissolution properties for most organic and inorganic compounds, high thermal stability, lack of a measurable vapor pressure, and nonflammability. The advantages of ionic liquids include optimization of properties through a broad choice of anion/cation combination (tailor-made solvents), reaction rate enhancement, and higher yields when used as replacements for Volatile Organic Compounds (VOC) in chemical processes or extraction procedures.

EMIC

26-6 Aldehydes and Ketones—The **carbonyl group** has a carbon atom attached by a double bond to an oxygen atom, $\overset{R}{\underset{R'}{\diagdown}}C{=}O$. If one of the two substituents attached to the carbonyl group is an H atom, the compound is an **aldehyde**, otherwise it is a **ketone**. In IUPAC nomenclature, the suffix *-al* is used for aldehydes and *-one* for ketones. Oxidation of a primary alcohol produces an aldehyde, while oxidation of a secondary alcohol yields a ketone. The polarity of the carbonyl group, together with asymmetric reagents, can be used to increase the carbon-chain length of a molecule.

26-7 Carboxylic Acids and Their Derivatives—The **carboxyl group** (—COOH) is a combination of the carbonyl and hydroxyl groups. **Carboxylic acids** contain the carboxyl group, and can be prepared by the oxidation of aldehydes. An **acetyl group** results when the —OH of a carboxyl group is replaced by a methyl group; an **amide** group results when it is replaced by —NH₂. An **ester** is formed when an alcohol and a carboxylic acid react by the elimination of water. A reaction in which two molecules combine by eliminating H_2O or some other small molecule is known as a **condensation reaction**.

26-8 Amines—**Amines** are organic derivatives of ammonia. They are classified according to the number of organic groups (R) substituted for hydrogen atoms in

As an example of the potential use of ionic liquids in organic synthesis, consider the effect of a chloroaluminate ionic liquid (AlCl₃:EMIC) on an important type of organic reaction known as the Diels–Alder reaction. The chloroaluminate ionic liquid at room temperature is polar, exhibits high solubility towards organic solutes, and has variable Lewis acidity. The diagram illustrates how the acidity of AlCl₃:EMIC changes as the mole fraction of AlCl₃ increases. Below an AlCl₃ mole fraction of 0.5, the ionic liquid is a basic melt with $AlCl_4^-$ and Cl^- dominating, while above AlCl₃ mole fraction 0.5, the ionic liquid is considered an acidic melt with $Al_2Cl_7^-$ and $AlCl_4^-$ dominating.

Thus, the reaction in the acidic melt form of the ionic liquid is 10 times faster than in water, and it is 175 times faster than in ethyl ammonium nitrate (EAN). On the other hand, for basic melt conditions, the reaction is only half as fast in water and seven times faster than in EAN. Additionally, the 2S isomer is favored over the 2R in the products.

Recovery of the reactants and products from the ionic liquid solvent is easy. They have high vapor pressures and can be separated by raising the temperature of the system. The ionic liquid can be reused. The EAN solvent is potentially explosive while AlCl₃:EMIC is not. Thus we see how several of the goals of green chemistry are achieved by replacing traditional organic solvents with ionic liquids in synthetic organic chemistry.

◀ Reprinted with permission from **MNDO calculations of ions in chloroaluminate molten salts** Larry P. Davis, Chester J. Dymek, Jr. James J. P. Stewart, Henry P. Clark, Walter J. Lauderdale; *J. Am. Chem. Soc.*; 1985; *107*(18); 5041–5046. Copyright 1985 American Chemical Society.

The Diels–Alder reaction, which occurs between a diene (for example, cyclopenta-1,3-diene) and a dienophile (for example, methyl acrylate) to form Diels–Alder adducts, is strongly affected by the acidity of the solvent

(2R)-methyl bicyclo[2.2.1]hept-5-ene-2-carboxylate

Cyclopenta-1,3-diene   Methyl acrylate

(2S)-methyl bicyclo[2.2.1]hept-5-ene-2-carboxylate

NH₃. A primary amine has one substituent; a secondary amine, two substituents; and a tertiary amine, three substituents. Amines are weak bases, with the aliphatic amines being stronger bases than ammonia and the aromatic amines being weaker.

26-9 Heterocyclic Compounds—Ring compounds in which one or more of the ring atoms is not a carbon atom are called **heterocyclic** compounds. The most common noncarbon ring members are N, O, and S. Heterocyclic compounds tend to be more soluble in water than the parent compound due to the polarity of the heterocycle.

26-10 Nomenclature of Stereoisomers in Organic Compounds—**Optical isomers** contain an **asymmetric** carbon atom, one attached to four different groups. As a result, an optical isomer and its mirror image are nonsuperimposable, which makes them optically active—they rotate the plane of polarized light. Molecules with nonsuperimposable mirror images are termed **chiral**, while molecules with superimposable mirror images are **achiral**. Molecules with sp^3 stereocenters are named using the **R, S system**. The rules for an R, S designation require assigning priorities to the substituents on a chiral C atom and "reading" the descending priority order of the substituents when the molecule is viewed in a particular orientation. If the descending priority order is clockwise, the molecule is R; if it is counterclockwise, the molecule is S. Stereoisomers of alkenes having sp^2 centers with more than one substituent are named by the **E, Z system**. Molecules are given the Z designation when higher priority substituents at each end of a double bond are on the same side of the double bond and the E designation when they are on opposite sides of the double bond.

26-11 An Introduction to Substitution Reactions at sp^3 Hybridized Carbon Atoms

The most common reaction involving sp^3 hybridized carbon atoms is a **nucleophilic substitution reaction**, in which a **nucleophile** attacks the **electrophilic** carbon atom yielding the product and a **leaving group**. The nucleophile contains a pair of electrons that seek the slightly positive carbon atom of the other reactant. The leaving group is the substituent that is pushed off the electrophilic carbon atom during the reaction. The two mechanisms for nucleophilic substitution reactions are S_N1 and S_N2. The S_N1 reaction mechanism is unimolecular, with the rate-determining step being the formation of a planar carbocation, and results in a racemic mixture of the product enantiomers. The S_N2 reaction mechanism includes a bimolecular rate-determining step and an inversion of the configuration at the chiral carbon of the product molecule.

26-12 Synthesis of Organic Compounds

The synthesis of larger and more complex organic compounds from simpler precursors can be achieved through a sequence of reactions of different types and varied mechanisms. Figure 26-16 summarizes a number of functional group transformations that can be used in designing synthetic strategies. One powerful strategy is to work backward from the desired product to the starting materials, a method known as retrosynthesis.

26-13 Polymers and Polymerization Reactions

Polymers are a very important class of substances in modern life. One method of polymerization, the joining of monomers to form polymers, is called **step-reaction polymerization**, or condensation polymerization. It produces polymers of moderate molecular mass. Another type of polymerization mechanism is **chain-reaction polymerization**, a three-step process involving initiation, propagation, and termination, producing polymers of high molecular mass.

Integrative Example

The female of a species of worm produces the sex attractant *spodoptol*, which has the following structure.

$$\text{HOCH}_2\text{CH}_2\text{CH}_2\text{CH}_2\text{CH}_2\text{CH}_2\text{CH}_2\text{CH}_2 \qquad \text{CH}_2\text{CH}_2\text{CH}_2\text{CH}_3$$
$$\text{C}=\text{C}$$
$$\text{H} \qquad\qquad \text{H}$$
$$\text{Spodoptol}$$

Spodoptol is a pheromone that attracts the male worms of the species. Putting synthetic spodoptol in traps can be used to control the population of worms. Devise a synthesis of spodoptol starting from the alcohol shown below.

$$\text{HOCH}_2\text{CH}_2\text{CH}_2\text{CH}_2\text{CH}_2\text{CH}_2\text{CH}_2\text{CH}_2\text{C}\equiv\text{CH}$$

Strategy
In designing the synthesis, we break down the spodoptol molecule into the starting material and the necessary alkyl group that has to be attached to a double bond, namely a *n*-butyl group. In order to produce the alkene skeleton structure, we will have to convert the triple bond in the starting material to a double bond with cis stereochemistry.

Solution
Thus, *working backward*, this cis isomer is obtained by using Lindlar's catalyst (recall page 1088).

$$\text{HOCH}_2(\text{CH}_2)_6\text{CH}_2\text{C}\equiv\text{C}(\text{CH}_2)_3\text{CH}_3 \xrightarrow[\substack{\text{Lindlar's} \\ \text{catalyst}}]{\text{H}_2}$$

$$\text{HO}(\text{CH}_2)_7\text{CH}_2 \qquad (\text{CH}_2)_3\text{CH}_3$$
$$\text{C}=\text{C}$$
$$\text{H} \qquad\qquad \text{H}$$

Now make the alkyne needed in the above hydrogenation. The starting material provided lacks the butyl group

at the triple bond. To attach the alkyl group, we can perform a nucleophilic substitution at 1-bromobutane with the acetylide ion generated from the starting material, by using sodium amide.

$$^-\text{O}(\text{CH}_2)_8\text{C}\equiv\text{C}{:}^- + \text{CH}_3(\text{CH}_2)_3\text{Br} \longrightarrow$$
$$^-\text{O}(\text{CH}_2)_8\text{C}\equiv\text{C}(\text{CH}_2)_3\text{CH}_3 + \text{Br}^-$$

Because the alcohol proton of the acetylide is also acidic, we need to add an *excess* of sodium amide to give the combined alkoxide and acetylide. (Ammonia is also produced in the reaction.)

$$\text{HO}(\text{CH}_2)_8\text{C}\equiv\text{CH} \xrightarrow[\text{NaNH}_2]{\text{excess}} {}^-\text{O}(\text{CH}_2)_8\text{C}\equiv\text{C}{:}^-$$

We can now combine these steps into a complete synthesis where we have converted the alkoxide to the alcohol in the next-to-last step by adding ethanol. The ethanol gives up a proton to the alkoxide we have synthesized (the ethoxide ion is the weaker base).

$$\text{HO}(\text{CH}_2)_8\text{C}\equiv\text{CH} \xrightarrow[\text{NaNH}_2]{\text{excess}} {}^-\text{O}(\text{CH}_2)_8\text{C}\equiv\text{C}{:}^- \xrightarrow{\text{CH}_3(\text{CH}_2)_3\text{Br}}$$

$$^-\text{O}(\text{CH}_2)_8\text{C}\equiv\text{C}(\text{CH}_2)_3\text{CH}_3 \xrightarrow{\text{C}_2\text{H}_5\text{OH}} \text{HO}(\text{CH}_2)_8\text{C}\equiv\text{C}(\text{CH}_2)_3\text{CH}_3$$

$$\downarrow \text{H}_2 \ \substack{\text{Lindlar's} \\ \text{catalyst}}$$

$$\text{HO}(\text{CH}_2)_8 \qquad (\text{CH}_2)_3\text{CH}_3$$
$$\text{C}=\text{C}$$
$$\text{H} \qquad\qquad \text{H}$$

Assessment
Using the backward synthetic approach—retrosynthesis—we have established a possible synthetic pathway for the synthesis of spodoptol from the starting material. This is a common approach in the development of a synthetic route to a target compound.

Exercises

Organic Structures

1. Write structural formulas corresponding to these condensed formulas.
   (a) $CH_3CH_2CHBrCHBrCH_3$
   (b) $(CH_3)_3CCH_2C(CH_3)_2CH_2CH_2CH_3$
   (c) $(C_2H_5)_2CHCH=CHCH_2CH_3$

2. Draw a structural formula for each of the following compounds.
   (a) 3-isopropyloctane
   (b) 2-chloro-3-methylpentane
   (c) 2-pentene
   (d) dipropyl ether

3. Supply a structural formula for each of the following compounds.
   (a) 1,3,5-trimethylbenzene
   (b) *p*-nitrophenol
   (c) 3-amino-2,5-dichlorobenzoic acid (a plant-growth regulator)

4. Write structural formulas corresponding to these condensed formulas.
   (a) $(CH_3)_3CCH_2CH(CH_3)CH_2CH_2CH_3$
   (b) $(CH_3)_2CHCH_2C(CH_3)_2CH_2Br$
   (c) $Cl_3CCH_2CH(CH_3)CH_2Cl$

5. Draw Lewis structures of the following simple organic molecules: (a) $CH_3CHClCH_3$; (b) $HOCH_2CH_2OH$; (c) CH_3CHO.

6. Draw Lewis structures of the following simple organic molecules: (a) CH_3CH_2COOH; (b) H_3CCN; (c) $CH_3CH_2NH_2$.

7. With appropriate sketches, represent chemical bonding in terms of the overlap of hybridized and unhybridized atomic orbitals in the following molecules.
   (a) C_4H_{10}
   (b) $H_2C=CHCl$
   (c) $CH_3C\equiv CH$

8. With appropriate sketches, represent chemical bonding in terms of the overlap of hybridized and unhybridized atomic orbitals in the following molecules.

   (a) $CH_3\overset{O}{\overset{\|}{C}}CH_3$ (b) $CH_3\overset{O}{\overset{\|}{C}}-OH$
   (c) $H_2C=C=CH_2$

Isomers

9. What are the differences between structural, positional, and geometric isomers. Which term best describes each of the following pairs of isomers?
   (a) $CH_3CH_2CH_2Cl$ and $CH_3CHClCH_3$
   (b) $CH_3CH(CH_3)CH_2CH_3$ and $CH_3(CH_2)_3CH_3$

10. Which term—structural, positional, or geometric—best describes each of the following pairs of isomers?
    (a) $CHCl=CHCl$ and $CH_2=CCl_2$
    (b) $CH_2=CHCH_2CH_3$ and $CH_2=C(CH_3)_2$

    (c) $\underset{H}{\overset{HOOC}{>}}C=C\underset{H}{\overset{COOH}{<}}$ and $\underset{H}{\overset{HOOC}{>}}C=C\underset{COOH}{\overset{H}{<}}$

11. Draw structural formulas for all the isomers of C_7H_{16}.

12. Draw and name all the isomers of (a) C_6H_{14}; (b) C_4H_8; (c) C_4H_6.
    [*Hint:* Do not forget double bonds, rings, and combinations of these.]

13. Identify the chiral carbon atoms, if any, in the following compounds.

    (a) [structure] (b) [structure]

    (c) [structure]

14. Identify the chiral carbon atoms, if any, in the following compounds.

    (a) [structure with OH] (b) [structure with Cl] (c) [structure]

15. Identify the chiral carbon atoms, if any, in the following compounds.

    (a) [structure with Cl, CO₂H] (b) [structure with NH₂, CO₂H] (c) [structure with NH₂, CO₂H]

16. Identify the chiral carbon atoms, if any, in the following compounds.

    (a) [structure with OH] (b) [structure with OH, Cl] (c) HO—[structure with CO₂H, CO₂H, CO₂H]

Functional Groups

17. Identify the functional group in each compound (i.e., alcohol, amine, etc.).
    (a) $CH_3CHBrCH_2CH_3$
    (b) $C_6H_5CH_2CHO$
    (c) $CH_3COCH_2CH_3$
    (d) $C_6H_4(OH)_2$

18. Identify the functional group in each compound (i.e., alcohol, amine, etc.).
    (a) CH_3CH_2COOH
    (b) $(CH_3)_2CHCH_2OCH_3$
    (c) $CH_3CH(NH_2)CH_2CH_3$
    (d) CH_3COOCH_3

19. The functional groups in each of the following pairs have certain features in common, but what is the essential difference between them?
    (a) carbonyl and carboxyl
    (b) aldehyde and ketone
    (c) acetic acid and acetyl group

20. By name or formula, give one example of each of the following types of compounds: (a) aromatic nitro compound; (b) aliphatic amine; (c) chlorophenol; (d) aliphatic diol; (e) unsaturated aliphatic alcohol; (f) alicyclic ketone; (g) halogenated alkane; (h) aromatic dicarboxylic acid.

21. Identify and name the functional groups in each of the following.

    (a) HO—C(=O)—⟨benzene⟩—OH

    (b) CH_3—C(=O)—OCH_2CH_3

    (c) CH_3—C(=O)—CH_2CH_2—CO_2H

    (d) ⟨benzene with CHO and OH⟩

22. Identify and name the functional groups in each of the following.

    (a) CH_3—C(=O)—CH_2—CH_2—C(=O)—CH_3

    (b) CH_3—CH_2—$CONHCH_3$

    (c) HO—⟨benzene with OCH₃⟩—CH(OH)—CH_2—N(H)—CH_3

    (d) H_2C(—C(=O)—OH)—HO—C(—C(=O)—OH)—H_2C—C(=O)—OH

23. Give the isomers of $C_4H_{10}O$ that are ethers.
24. Give the isomers of $C_5H_{12}O$ that are ethers.
25. Give the isomers of the carboxylic acid with molecular formula $C_5H_{10}O_2$.
26. Give the isomers of the carboxylic acid with the molecular formula $C_4H_8O_2$.
27. Give the isomers of the esters having the molecular formula $C_5H_{10}O_2$.
28. Give the isomers of the esters having the molecular formula $C_4H_8O_2$.
29. Give the noncyclic isomers with molecular formula $C_4H_8O_2$ that contain more than one functional group.
30. Give the isomers with molecular formula $C_5H_{10}O_2$ that contain more than one functional group.

Nomenclature and Formulas

31. Give an acceptable name for each of the following.
    (a) $CH_3CH_2CH_2CHCH_2CHCH_2CH_3$ (with two CH_3 substituents)
    (b) CH_3—C(CH_3)(CH_3)—CH_3
    (c) $CH_3CH_2CHCH_2$—C(Cl)(C_2H_5)—CH_2CH_3 (with Cl substituent)

32. Give an acceptable name for each of the following.
    (a) ⟨benzene with two Cl⟩
    (b) ⟨benzene with CH_3 and NO_2⟩
    (c) NH_2—⟨benzene⟩—COOH

33. Give an acceptable name for each of the following structures.
    (a) $CH_3CH_2C(CH_3)_3$
    (b) $(CH_3)_2C=CH_2$

(c) CH₃—CH—CH—CH₃
         |
         CH₂

(d) $CH_3C{\equiv}CCH(CH_3)_2$

(e) $CH_3CH(C_2H_5)CH(CH_3)CH_2CH_3$

(f) $CH_3CH(CH_3)CH(CH_3)C(C_3H_7){=}CH_2$

34. Draw a condensed structure to correspond to each of the following names.
(a) isopentane
(b) cyclohexene
(c) 2-methyl-3-hexyne
(d) 2-butanol
(e) isopropyl ethyl ether
(f) propionaldehyde

35. Does each of the following names convey sufficient information to suggest a specific structure? Explain.
(a) pentene
(b) butanone
(c) butyl alcohol
(d) methylaniline
(e) methylcyclopentane
(f) dibromobenzene

36. Indicate why each of these names is incorrect, and give a correct name.
(a) 3-pentene
(b) pentadiene
(c) 1-propanone
(d) bromopropane
(e) 2,6-dichlorobenzene
(f) 2-methyl-3-pentyne

37. Supply condensed structural formulas for the following substances.
(a) 2,4,6-trinitrotoluene (TNT—an explosive)
(b) methyl salicylate (oil of wintergreen)
[*Hint:* Salicylic acid is *o*-hydroxybenzoic acid.]
(c) 2-hydroxy-1,2,3-propanetricarboxylic acid (citric acid, $C_6H_8O_7$)

38. Supply condensed structural formulas for the following substances.
(a) *o-t*-butylphenol (an antioxidant in aviation gasoline)
(b) 1-phenyl-2-aminopropane (benzedrine—an amphetamine, ingredient in "pep pills")
(c) 2-methylheptadecane (a sex pheromone of tiger moths—a chemical used for communication among members of the species)
[*Hint:* Heptadeca means 17.]

39. Name the following amines.

(a)   CH₃—CH₂
              |
              NH
              |
           CH₃—CH₂

(b) H₂N—⟨benzene ring⟩—NO₂

(c) ⟨cyclopentane⟩—NH—CH₂CH₃

(d) CH₃—CH₂—N—CH₂—CH₃
                    |
                    CH₃

40. Name the following amines.
(a) CH₃—CH₂—NH₂

(b)

(c) ⟨cyclopropane⟩—N—⟨cyclopropane⟩ (with H above N)

(d) Cl—CH₂—CH₂—NH₂

Alkanes

41. Write the structure of each alkane.
(a) molecular mass = 72 u; forms four monochlorination products
(b) molecular mass = 72 u; forms a single monochlorination product

42. Write the structure of each alkane.
(a) molecular mass = 44 u; forms two different monochlorination products
(b) molecular mass = 58 u; forms two different monobromination products

Alkenes

43. Why is it not necessary to refer to ethene and propene as 1-ethene and 1-propene? Can the same be said for butene?

44. Alkenes (olefins) and cyclic alkanes (alicyclics) each have the generic formula C_nH_{2n}. In what important ways do these types of compounds differ structurally?

45. Draw the structures of the products of each of the following reactions.
(a) propene + hydrogen (Pt, heat)
(b) 2-butanol + heat (in the presence of sulfuric acid)

46. Use Markovnikov's rule to predict the product of the reaction of:

                    Cl
                    |
(a) HCl with CH₃C=CH₂

(b) HCN with $CH_3C{\equiv}CH$

(c) HCl with $CH_3CH{=}C(CH_3)_2$

Aromatic Compounds

47. Supply a name or structural formula for each of the following.
(a) phenylacetylene
(b) *m*-dichlorobenzene

(c)

48. Supply a name or structural formula for each of the following.
(a) *p*-phenylphenol
(b) 2-hydroxy-4-isopropyltoluene (thymol—flavor constituent of the herb thyme)

(c)

Organic Reactions

49. Identify the following compounds as electrophiles, nucleophiles, or neither:
(a) NH_3;
(b) CH_3Cl;
(c) Br^-;
(d) CH_3OH;
(e) $CH_3NH_3^+$.

50. Identify the following compounds as electrophiles, nucleophiles, or neither:
(a) N_3^-;
(b) NH_4^+;
(c) $CH_3CHClCH_3$;
(d) OH^-;
(e) $H_2C=O$.

51. Describe what is meant by each of the following reaction types, and illustrate with an example from the text: **(a)** aliphatic substitution reaction; **(b)** aromatic substitution reaction; **(c)** addition reaction; **(d)** elimination reaction.

52. Starting with acetylene as the only source of carbon, together with any inorganic reagents required, devise a method to synthesize **(a)** 1,1,2,2-tetrabromoethane; **(b)** acetaldehyde.

53. Draw a structure to represent the principal product of each of the following reactions.
(a) 1-pentanol + excess dichromate ion (acid solution)
(b) butyric acid + ethanol (acid solution)
(c) $CH_3CH_2C{=}CH_2 + H_2O$ (in the presence of H_2SO_4)
  with CH_3 substituent

54. Predict the products of the monobromination of **(a)** *m*-dinitrobenzene; **(b)** aniline; **(c)** *p*-bromoanisole.

55. Write the formulas of the products formed from the reaction of propene with each of the following substances:
(a) H_2;
(b) Cl_2;
(c) HCN;
(d) HCl;
(e) H_2O (in acid).

56. Write the formulas of the products formed from the reaction of 2-butene with each of the following substances:
(a) H_2;
(b) Cl_2;
(c) HCN;
(d) HCl;
(e) H_2O (in acid).

57. Identify the following types of reactions.

(a)

(b) (alkene) $\xrightarrow[Pt]{H_2}$ (alkane)

(c) (carboxylic acid with CO_2H) + (alcohol with OH) $\longrightarrow$ (ester with CO_2)

58. Identify the following types of reactions.

(a) (amine with NH_2) + (chloride with Cl) $\longrightarrow$ (amine with N–H)

(b) (alcohol with OH) + (chloride with Cl) $\longrightarrow$ (ether with O)

(c) (alcohol with OH) $\xrightarrow{[O]}$ (aldehyde with CHO)

Note: The symbol [O] is sometimes used to designate oxidation.

59. Write the formulas of the products formed in each of the following reactions. If no reaction occurs, write N.R.
(a) $CH_3CH_2CO_2^-(aq) + HCl(aq) \longrightarrow$
(b) $CH_3CH_2CO_2CH_3 + H_2O \xrightarrow{H^+}$
(c) $CH_3CH_2CO_2CH_2CH_3 + NaOH(aq) \longrightarrow$

60. Write the formulas of the products formed in each of the following reactions. If no reaction occurs, write N.R.
(a) $CH_3CH_2CO_2CH_3 \xrightarrow{LiAlH_4}$
(b) $CH_3CH_2CO_2CH_3 \xrightarrow{NaBH_4}$
(c) $HCO_2CH_2CH_3(aq) \xrightarrow{H^+}$

61. Write the formulas of the products formed in each of the following reactions. If no reaction occurs, write N.R.
(a) $CH_3CO_2H + NH_3 \xrightarrow{heat}$
(b) $CH_3CH_2CONH_2 \xrightarrow{heat}$
(c) $CH_3CH_2CONH_2(aq) + NaOH(aq) \longrightarrow$

62. Write the formulas of the products formed in each of the following reactions. If no reaction occurs, write N.R.

(a) $CH_3CO_2H + CH_3NH_2 \xrightarrow{heat}$

(b) $CH_3CH_2CONHCH_3 \xrightarrow{LiAlH_4}$

(c) $CH_3CH_2CONHCH_3 + HCl(aq) \longrightarrow$

63. Which of the following species gives the reaction indicated? Write the structures of the reaction products.

(1) $CH_3CH_2\overset{\overset{\displaystyle O}{\|}}{C}{-}OCH_3$ (2) $CH_3CH_2\overset{\overset{\displaystyle O}{\|}}{C}{-}OH$ (3) $CH_3\overset{\overset{\displaystyle O}{\|}}{C}{-}O^-$

(a) reacts with dilute HCl
(b) hydrolyzes
(c) neutralizes dilute NaOH

64. Which of the following species gives the reaction indicated? Write the structures of the reaction products.

(1) $CH_3CH_2\overset{\overset{\displaystyle O}{\|}}{C}{-}NH_2$

(2) $CH_3CH_2NH_2$

(3) $CH_3CH_2CH_2NH_3{}^+Cl^-$

(a) neutralizes dilute HCl
(b) hydrolyzes
(c) neutralizes dilute NaOH

65. Write the equilibrium constant expression for the equilibrium present when butanamine is dissolved in water.

66. Write the equilibrium constant expression for the equilibrium present when *N*-methylbutanamine (methylbutyl amine) is dissolved in water.

67. Write the formulas of the products expected to form in the following situations. If no reaction occurs, write N.R.

(a) $CH_3CH_2NH_2(aq) + HCl(aq) \longrightarrow$
(b) $(CH_3)_3N(aq) + HBr(aq) \longrightarrow$
(c) $CH_3CH_2NH_3{}^+(aq) + H_3O^+(aq) \longrightarrow$
(d) $CH_3CH_2NH_3{}^+(aq) + OH^-(aq) \longrightarrow$

68. Write the formulas of the products expected to form in the following situations. If no reaction occurs, write N.R.

(a) $NH(aq) + HCl(aq) \longrightarrow$

(b) $(CH_3)_4N^+(aq) + HCl(aq) \longrightarrow$
(c) $CH_3CH_2NH_2(aq) + OH^-(aq) \longrightarrow$
(d) $(CH_3)_3NH^+ + OH^- \longrightarrow$

69. To prepare methyl ethyl ketone, which of these compounds would you oxidize: 2-propanol, 1-butanol, 2-butanol, or *t*-butyl alcohol? Explain.

70. Indicate the principal product(s) you would expect in (a) treating $CH_3CH_2CH=CH_2$ with *dilute* $H_2SO_4(aq)$; (b) exposing a mixture of chlorine and propane gases to ultraviolet light; (c) heating a mixture of isopropyl alcohol and benzoic acid; (d) oxidizing *s*-butyl alcohol with $Cr_2O_7{}^{2-}$ in acidic solution.

71. Match the following compounds with the chemical properties given below. Write the structure of the products of the reactions described in (a)–(e).

(1) OH   (2)

(3)

(a) is easily oxidized
(b) neutralizes NaOH(aq)
(c) forms an ester with ethanol
(d) can be oxidized to a carboxylic acid
(e) can be dehydrated to an alcohol

72. Match the following compounds with the chemical properties given below. Write the structure of the products of the reactions described in (a)–(e).

(1) NH_2 (2) Cl (3)

(a) neutralizes HCl(aq)
(b) neutralizes NaOH(aq)
(c) forms an amide with ethanoic acid
(d) reacts with ammonia
(e) reacts with $CN^-(aq)$

Organic Stereochemistry

73. Draw suitable structural formulas to show that there are *four* structural isomers of $C_3H_6Cl_2$.

74. Which of the following pairs of molecules are isomers and which are not? Explain.

(a) $CH_3CH_2CH_2CH_3$ and $CH_3CH=CHCH_3$
(b) $CH_3(CH_2)_5CH(CH_3)_2$ and
$\qquad CH_3(CH_2)_4CH(CH_3)CH_2CH_3$
(c) $CH_3CHClCH_2CH_3$ and $CH_3CH_2CH_2CH_2CH_2Cl$

(d) and

(e) and

(f) and

75. For each pair of structures shown below, indicate whether the two species are identical molecules, enantiomers, or isomers of some other sort.

(a) and

(b) and

(c) and

(d) and

(e) and

(f) and

76. For each pair of structures shown below, indicate whether the two species are identical molecules, enantiomers, or isomers of some other sort.

(a)

(b)

(c)

(d)

(e)

(f)

77. Name the following molecules with the appropriate stereochemical designation.

(a)

(b)

(c)

(d)

78. Name the following molecules with the appropriate stereochemical designation.

(a)

(b)

(c)

(d)

79. Name the following molecules with the appropriate stereochemical designation.

(a)   (b)

(c)

(d)

80. Name the following molecules with the appropriate stereochemical designation.

(a)   (b)

(c)

(d)

81. Draw the structure for each of the following.
  (a) (Z)-1,3,5-tribromo-2-pentene
  (b) (E)-1,2-dibromo-3-methyl-2-hexene
  (c) (S)-1-bromo-1-chlorobutane
  (d) (R)-1,3-dibromohexane
  (e) (S)-1-chloro-2-propanol

82. Draw the structure for each of the following.
  (a) (R)-1-bromo-1-chloroethane
  (b) (E)-2-bromo-2-pentene
  (c) (Z)-1-chloro-3-ethyl-3-heptene
  (d) (R)-2-hydroxypropanoic acid
  (e) (S)-2-aminopropanoate anion

Nucleophilic Substitution Reactions

83. Answer the following questions for this S_N2 reaction.

$$CH_3CH_2CH_2CH_2Br + NaOH \longrightarrow$$
$$CH_3CH_2CH_2CH_2OH + NaBr$$

(a) What is the rate expression for the reaction?
(b) Draw the reaction profile for the reaction. Label all parts. Assume that the products are lower in energy than the reactants.
(c) What is the effect on the rate of the reaction of doubling the concentration of *n*-butyl bromide?
(d) What is the effect on the rate of the reaction of halving the concentration of sodium hydroxide?

84. Answer the following questions for this S_N1 reaction.

$$CH_3CH_2CH_2\underset{\underset{CH_3}{|}}{\overset{\overset{CH_3}{|}}{C}}Br + CH_3CH_2OH \longrightarrow$$

$$CH_3CH_2CH_2\underset{\underset{CH_3}{|}}{\overset{\overset{CH_3}{|}}{C}}OCH_2CH_3 + HBr$$

(a) What is the rate expression for the reaction?
(b) Draw the reaction profile for the reaction. Label all parts. Assume that the products are lower in energy than the reactants.
(c) What is the effect on the rate of the reaction of doubling the concentration of 1-bromo-1-methylpentane?
(d) The solvent for the reaction is ethanol. What is the effect on the rate of the reaction of adding more ethanol?

85. Write equations for the substitution reaction of *n*-bromobutane, a typical primary haloalkane, with the following reagents. **(a)** $NaOH$; **(b)** NH_3; **(c)** $NaCN$; **(d)** CH_3CH_2ONa.

86. Write equations for the substitution reaction of *n*-bromopentane, a typical primary haloalkane with the following reagents. **(a)** NaN_3; **(b)** $N(CH_3)_3$; **(c)** $CH_3CH_2C \equiv CNa$; **(d)** CH_3CH_2SNa.

87. An optically pure sample of $CH_3CH_2CH(CH_3)Cl$ is hydrolyzed by water, and the resulting solution is optically inactive. **(a)** Write the formula of the product. **(b)** By which nucleophilic substitution reaction mechanism does this reaction occur?

88. An optically pure sample of $CH_3CH_2CH(CH_3)Cl$ reacts with CH_3O^- in dimethyl sulfoxide [$(CH_3)_2SO$, a convenient solvent for organic reactions], and the resulting solution is optically active. **(a)** Write the formula of the product. **(b)** By which nucleophilic substitution reaction mechanism does this reaction occur?

89. An optically pure sample of $CH_3CH(Cl)CH_2CH_3$ is dissolved in ethanol, and the resulting solution is optically inactive. **(a)** Write the formula of the product. **(b)** By which nucleophilic substitution reaction mechanism does this reaction occur?

90. An optically pure sample of $CH_3CH(Cl)CH_2CH_3$ reacts with CH_3S^- in dimethyl sulfoxide, and the resulting solution is optically active. **(a)** Write the formula of the product. **(b)** By which nucleophilic substitution reaction mechanism does this reaction occur?

Polymerization Reactions

91. In referring to the molecular mass of a polymer, we can speak only of the average molecular mass. Explain why the molecular mass of a polymer is not a unique quantity, as it is for a substance like benzene.
92. Explain why Dacron is called a polyester. What is the percent oxygen, by mass, in Dacron?
93. Nylon 66 is produced by the reaction of 1,6-hexanediamine with adipic acid. A different nylon polymer is obtained if sebacyl chloride is substituted for the

adipic acid. What is the basic repeating unit of this nylon structure?

94. Would you expect a polymer to be formed by the reaction of terephthalic acid with ethyl alcohol in place of ethylene glycol? With glycerol in place of ethylene glycol? Explain.

Integrative and Advanced Exercises

95. In the chlorination of CH_4, some CH_3CH_2Cl is obtained as a product. Explain why this should be so.
96. Supply condensed or structural formulas for the following substances.
(a) 1,5-cyclooctadiene (an intermediate in the manufacture of resins)
(b) 3,7,11-trimethyl-2,6,10-dodecatriene-1-ol (farnesol—odor of lily of the valley)
[*Hint:* Dodeca means 12.]
(c) 2,6-dimethyl-5-hepten-1-al (used in the manufacture of perfume)
97. Draw structural formulas for all the isomers listed in Table 26.3, and show that, indeed, the substances with more compact structures have lower boiling points.

98. By drawing suitable structural formulas, establish that there are 17 isomers of $C_6H_{13}Cl$.
[*Hint:* Refer to Example 26-1.]
99. Write the structures of the isomers you would expect to obtain in the mononitration of *m*-methoxybenzaldehyde.

What does the fact that no 3-methoxy-5-nitrobenzaldehyde forms imply about the strength of meta and ortho, para directors?

100. The symbol:

is often used to represent benzene. It is also the structural formula of cyclohexatriene. Are benzene and cyclohexatriene the same substance? Explain.

101. Use the half-reaction method to balance the following redox equations.

(a) $C_6H_5NO_2 + Fe + H^+ \longrightarrow$
$$C_6H_5NH_3^+ + Fe^{3+} + H_2O$$

(b) $C_6H_5CH_2OH + Cr_2O_7^{2-} + H^+ \longrightarrow$
$$C_6H_5CO_2H + Cr^{3+} + H_2O$$

(c) $CH_3CH{=}CH_2 + MnO_4^- + H_2O \longrightarrow$
$$CH_3CHOHCH_2OH + MnO_2 + OH^-$$

102. A 10.6-g sample of benzaldehyde was allowed to react with 5.9 g $KMnO_4$ in an excess of KOH(aq). After filtration of the MnO_2(s) and acidification of the solution, 6.1 g of benzoic acid was isolated. What was the percent yield of the reaction?
[*Hint:* Write half-equations for the oxidation and reduction half-reactions.]

103. Combustion of a 0.1908-g sample of a compound gave 0.2895 g CO_2 and 0.1192 g H_2O. Combustion of a second sample weighing 0.1825 g yielded 40.2 mL of N_2(g), collected over 50% KOH(aq) (vapor pressure = 9 mmHg) at 25 °C and 735 mmHg barometric pressure. When 1.082 g of compound was dissolved in 26.00 g benzene (mp 5.50 °C, K_f = 5.12 °C m^{-1}), the solution had a freezing point of 3.66 °C. What is the molecular formula of this compound?

104. Explain why a polymer formed by chain-reaction polymerization generally has a higher molecular mass than a corresponding polymer formed by step-reaction polymerization.

105. The three isomeric tribromobenzenes, I, II, and III, when nitrated, form three, two, and one mononitrotribromobenzenes, respectively. Assign correct structures to I, II, and III.

106. Write the name and structure of each aromatic hydrocarbon.
(a) Formula: C_8H_{10}; forms three-ring monochlorination products
(b) Formula: C_9H_{12}; forms one-ring mononitration product
(c) Formula: C_9H_{12}; forms four-ring mononitration products

107. In the molecule 2-methylbutane, the organic chemist distinguishes the different types of H and C atoms as being primary (1°), secondary (2°), and tertiary (3°). For the monochlorination of hydrocarbons, the following ratio of reactivities has been found: 3°/2°/1°, 4.3:3:1. How many different monochloro derivatives of 2-methylbutane are possible, and what percent of each would you expect to find?

$$
\begin{array}{c}
\overset{1°}{H} \\
|\\
{}^{1°}H{-}\overset{1°}{C}{-}H^{1°} \\
{}^{1°}H \quad\quad H^{2°}\ H^{1°} \\
|\quad\quad\quad\ |\ \ |\\
{}^{1°}H{-}\overset{1°}{C}{-}\overset{3°}{C}{-}\overset{2°}{C}{-}\overset{1°}{C}{-}H^{1°}\\
|\quad\quad |\quad\ |\quad\ |\\
{}^{1°}H \quad H^{3°}\ H^{2°}\ H^{1°}
\end{array}
$$

108. A particular colorless organic liquid is known to be one of the following compounds: 1-butanol, diethyl ether, methyl propyl ether, butyraldehyde, or propionic acid. Can you identify which it is, based on the following tests? If not, what additional test would you perform? (1) A 2.50-g sample dissolved in 100.0 g water has a freezing point of −0.7 °C. (2) An aqueous solution of the liquid does not change the color of blue litmus paper. (3) When alkaline $KMnO_4$(aq) is added to the liquid and the mixture is heated, the purple color of the MnO_4^- disappears.

109. The azide anion N_3^- is a nucleophile and, when attached to a carbon atom, undergoes reduction to the amino group and free nitrogen. Suggest a method of preparation of the primary amine propanamine.

110. The cyanide anion is a nucleophile and, when attached to a carbon atom, is reduced to a primary amine. Suggest a method of preparing propanamine from chloroethane.

111. The cyanide anion is a nucleophile and, when attached to a carbon atom, undergoes hydrolysis under basic conditions to the carboxylate anion. Suggest a method of preparing sodium butanoate from chloropropane. How can sodium butanoate be converted into butanoic acid?

112. The iodide ion cannot displace the —OH group in ethanol, but excess HI will react to produce ethyl iodide. Suggest a reason why.

113. Starting with the compounds chloromethane, chloroethane, sodium azide, sodium cyanide, and a reducing agent, suggest how the following compounds could be synthesized.
(a) N-methylpropanamide
(b) ethylethanoate
(c) methylethylamine
(d) tetramethylammonium chloride

114. Write structural formulas for the following.
(a) 2,4-dimethyl-1,4-pentadiene
(b) 2,3-dimethylpentane
(c) 1,2,4-tribromobenzene
(d) methylethanoate
(e) 2-butanone

115. Give the systematic names, including any stereochemical designations, for each of the following.

(a)
$$
\begin{array}{c}
CH_3{-}CH{-}CH_2{-}CH{-}CH_3\\
\quad\ |\quad\quad\quad\quad\ |\\
\quad CH_2 \quad\quad\quad Cl\\
\quad\ |\\
\quad CH_2\\
\quad\ |\\
\quad CH_2\\
\quad\ |\\
\quad CH_3
\end{array}
$$

(b)
$$
\begin{array}{c}
CH_3{-}CH_2{-}CH{-}CH{-}CO_2H\\
\quad\quad\quad\quad\ |\quad\ |\\
\quad\quad\quad\quad Cl\ \ NH_2
\end{array}
$$

(c) $CH_3OCH_2CH_3$

(d)
$$
\begin{array}{c}
CH_2{-}CH_2{-}CH_2{-}NH_2\\
|\\
Cl
\end{array}
$$

(e)

$$CH_3 \quad CH_3$$
$$C=C$$
$$ClH_2C \quad Cl$$

116. Write structural formulas for all the isomers of C_4H_7Cl. Indicate any geometrical or optical isomers that occur.

117. Compound A is an alcohol of formula $C_5H_{12}O$ that can be resolved into optical isomers.
  (a) Draw *three* possible structures of compound A.
  (b) Treatment of A with CrO_3/pyridine gives compound B, which also exhibits optical activity. What are the structural formulas of A and of B? Name and draw the enantiomers of A and B.

118. Levomethadyl acetate (shown below) is used in the treatment of narcotic addiction.

  (a) Name the functional groups in levomethadyl acetate. **(b)** What is the hybridization of the numbered carbon atoms and the nitrogen atom? **(c)** Which, if any, of the numbered carbon atoms are chiral?

119. Thiamphenicol (shown below) is an antibacterial agent.

  (a) Name the functional groups of thiamphenicol.
  (b) What is the hybridization of the numbered carbon atoms and the nitrogen atom?
  (c) Which, if any, of the numbered carbon atoms are chiral?

120. Ephedrine (shown below) is used as a decongestant in cold remedies.

  (a) Name the functional groups of ephedrine. **(b)** What is the hybridization of the numbered carbon atoms and the nitrogen atom? **(c)** Which, if any, of the numbered carbon atoms are chiral? **(d)** The pH of a solution of 1 g of ephedrine in 200 g of water is 10.8. What is the pK_b of ephedrine?

121. How would you synthesize (E)- and (Z)-3-heptene from acetylene and any other chemicals?

122. How would you synthesize (R)-2-butanamine from (S)-2-butanol?

Feature Problem

123. The reduction of aldehydes and ketones with a suitable hydride-containing reducing agent is a good way of synthesizing alcohols. This approach would be even more effective if, instead of a hydride, we could use a source of nucleophilic carbon. Attack by a carbon atom on a carbonyl group would give an alcohol and simultaneously form a carbon-to-carbon bond. How can we make a C atom in an alkane nucleophilic? This was achieved by Victor Grignard, who created the organometallic reagent R—MgBr, with the following reaction in diethyl ether.

$$R-Br + Mg \longrightarrow R-MgBr$$

The Grignard reagent (R—MgBr) is rarely isolated. It is formed in solution and used immediately in the desired reaction. The alkylmetal bond is highly polar, with the partial negative charge on the C atom, which makes the C atom highly nucleophilic. The Grignard reagent can attack a carbonyl group in an aldehyde or ketone as follows.

metal alkoxide

Addition of dilute aqueous acid solution to the metal alkoxide furnishes the alcohol. The important synthetic consequence of this procedure is that we have prepared a product with more carbon atoms than present in the starting material. A simple starting material can be transformed into a more complex molecule.

(a) What is the product of the reaction between methanal and the Grignard reagent formed from 1-bromobutane after the addition of dilute acid?

(b) Using a Grignard reagent, devise a synthesis for 2-hexanol.

(c) Using a Grignard reagent, devise a synthesis for 2-methyl-2-hexanol.

(d) Grignard reagents can also be formed with aryl halides such as chlorobenzene. What would be the product of the reaction between the Grignard reagent of chlorobenzene and propanone? Can you think of an alternative synthesis of this product, again using a Grignard reagent?

(e) The basicity of the C atom bound to the magnesium in the Grignard reagent can be used to make Grignard reagents of terminal alkynes. Write the equation of the reaction between ethylmagnesium bromide and 1-hexyne. [*Hint:* Ethane is evolved.]

(f) Using a Grignard reagent, suggest a synthesis for 2-heptyn-1-ol.

Self-Assessment Exercises

124. In your own words, define the following terms or symbols:
(a) *t*   **(c)** ⬡   **(d)** carbonyl group
(b) R—   **(e)** primary amine

125. Briefly describe each of the following ideas, phenomena, or methods: **(a)** substitution reaction; **(b)** octane rating of gasoline; **(c)** stereoisomerism; **(d)** ortho, para director; **(e)** step-reaction (condensation) polymerization.

126. Explain the important distinctions between each pair of terms: **(a)** alkane and alkene; **(b)** aliphatic and aromatic compound; **(c)** alcohol and phenol; **(d)** ether and ester; **(e)** amine and ammonia.

127. Describe the characteristics of each of the following types of isomers: **(a)** structural; **(b)** positional; **(c)** cis; **(d)** ortho.

128. The compound isoheptane is best represented by the formula **(a)** C_7H_{14}; **(b)** $CH_3(CH_2)_5CH_3$; **(c)** $(CH_3)_2CH(CH_2)_3CH_3$; **(d)** $C_6H_{11}CH_3$.

129. A compound with the same hydrogen to carbon ratio as cyclobutane is **(a)** C_4H_{10}; **(b)** $CH_3CH=CHCH_3$; **(c)** $CH_3C \equiv CCH_3$; **(d)** C_6H_6.

130. Three isomers exist of the hydrocarbon **(a)** C_3H_8; **(b)** C_4H_8; **(c)** C_4H_{10}; **(d)** C_6H_6; **(e)** C_5H_{12}.

131. To prepare methyl ethyl ketone, one should oxidize **(a)** 2-propanol; **(a)** 1-butanol; **(c)** 2-butanol; **(d)** *t*-butyl alcohol.

132. The most acidic acid of the following substances is:

NH₂ ⬡   COOH ⬡   OH ⬡ CH_3CHO

(a)   **(b)**   **(c)**   **(d)**

133. Which hydrocarbon has the greater number of isomers, C_4H_8 or C_4H_{10}? Explain your choice.

134. Which isomer of pentane forms only primary alcohols and why?

135. For each of the following pairs, indicate which substance has
(a) the higher boiling point, C_6H_{12} or C_6H_6;
(b) the greater solubility in water, C_3H_7OH or $C_7H_{15}OH$;
(c) the greater acidity in aqueous solution, C_6H_5CHO or C_6H_5COOH.

136. Appendix E describes a useful study aid known as concept mapping. Using the method presented in Appendix E, construct a concept map illustrating the different concepts in Section 26-10.

eMedia Exercises

137. View the organic molecules models displayed in *Activebook 26-1*. By right-clicking (Windows) or click-holding (Macintosh) on each molecule, adjust the Display representation (wireframe, sticks, ball-and-stick, space-filling) of the different molecules. What information is emphasized by each of the different types of displays?

138. Compare the physical properties of the entire series of alkanes and alcohols found in the **Boiling Points of Organic Molecules** activity (*Activebook 26-2*). **(a)** How do the trends in boiling point vary between the two series of molecules? **(b)** What physical property is most closely correlated with the boiling points of alkanes? **(c)** What other physical property is also observed to influence the boiling point of alcohols?

139. The nature of the addition reactions of alkenes makes possible one method of detecting their presence shown in the **Testing for Unsaturated Hydrocarbons with Bromine** movie (*Activebook 26-3*). Predict the products of the illustrated reaction and explain the observed color difference between the two tests shown.

140. The **Synthesis of Nylon 610** movie (*Activebook 26-13*) illustrates a polymerization reaction. **(a)** Draw an extended structure of the polymer structure formed. **(b)** What properties of the polymer allow it to be removed continuously from the interface of the two reactants? **(c)** Suggest a chemical method of altering the physical properties of polymers formed through condensation reactions.

27

CHEMISTRY OF THE LIVING STATE

CONTENTS

Vestling, Martha M. "Insulin: HPLC mapping of protease digestion products: A biochemistry laboratory experiment." *J. Chem. Educ.* **1991**, *68*, 958.

Cox, James R. "Teaching Noncovalent Interactions in the Biochemistry Curriculum through Molecular Visualization: The Search for π Interactions." *J. Chem. Educ.* **2000**, *77*, 1424 (November 2000).

Transfer ribonucleic acid, tRNA, shown as a ribbon model. A wire frame model of tRNA is superimposed on the ribbon model. The red spheres represent magnesium ions, and the red and green spheres at the top highlight the anticodon triplet. As we learn in this chapter, nucleic acids are important components in the chemistry of life.

The planet Earth teems with life—from the tiny amoeba to the enormous whale. In spite of extraordinary differences in outward appearance, all living organisms share similar needs and chemical structures. Raw materials (food) are required for building cells and providing the energy of metabolism and the information of heredity. The cells of almost all forms of living things on Earth use the same types of complicated structures to perform specialized functions. In this chapter, we will stress the structures of the macromolecules common to all organisms. Our discussion will emphasize how fundamental principles of chemistry acquired throughout the text can contribute to a knowledge of the living state.

27-1 CHEMICAL STRUCTURE OF LIVING MATTER: AN OVERVIEW

From one-celled organisms to humans, the living state includes some highly complex forms of matter. About 50 of the known elements occur in measurable concentrations in living matter. Of these, about 25 have functions that are definitely known. Four elements together—oxygen, carbon, hydrogen, and nitrogen—account for 96% of human body mass. Figure 27-1 identifies the elements found in living matter. As shown in Figure 27-2, the complex structures of living matter are synthesized in several stages from a few simple environmental precursors—N_2, H_2O, and CO_2.

In addition to water, which is the most abundant compound in the majority of living organisms, other important constituents are lipids, carbohydrates, proteins, and nucleic acids. These four types of macromolecular substances are the principal topics of this chapter.

The **cell** is the fundamental unit of all life. Cells contain a variety of substructures, such as a nucleus, mitochondria, and chloroplasts (plant cells). Cells combine to form tissues; tissues may be grouped into organs; organs combine into organ systems, and organ systems together form organisms.

▲ **FIGURE 27-1**
Elements in living matter
For the most part, the elements essential to living matter are also among the more abundant elements in Earth's crust and in seawater. It is likely that lifeforms developed from the elements available to them.

▶ **FIGURE 27-2**
Cellular organization

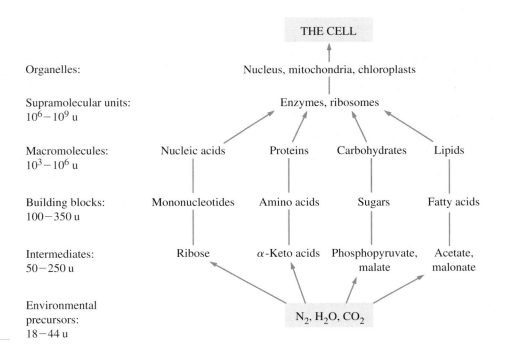

27-2   LIPIDS

Lipids are best described through their physical properties rather than in precise structural terms. **Lipids** are those constituents of plant and animal tissue that are soluble in low-polarity solvents, such as chloroform, carbon tetrachloride, diethyl ether, and benzene. Many compounds fit this description, but we will discuss only a few of them.

Triglycerides are esters of glycerol (1,2,3-propanetriol) and long-chain monocarboxylic acids (fatty acids). Some common fatty acids are listed in Table 27.1. *Triglyceride* is a common name; the systematic name of the triglycerides is triacylglycerols. *Glycerol* provides the three-carbon backbone, and the fatty acids provide *acyl* groups (in blue below).

Glycerol   Fatty acid

◀ **KEEP IN MIND**
that in forming an ester, a carboxylic acid loses its —OH group. The group that remains,

$$\overset{O}{\underset{}{\underset{\parallel}{RC}}}-$$

is the *acyl* group.

Barreto, M. C. "Lipid Extraction and Cholesterol Quantification: A Simple Protocol." *J. Chem. Educ.* **2005:** *82,* 103.

TABLE 27.1   Some Common Fatty Acids

Common Name	IUPAC Name	Formula
Saturated Acids		
Lauric acid	Dodecanoic acid	$C_{11}H_{23}CO_2H$
Myristic acid	Tetradecanoic acid	$C_{13}H_{27}CO_2H$
Palmitic acid	Hexadecanoic acid	$C_{15}H_{31}CO_2H$
Stearic acid	Octadecanoic acid	$C_{17}H_{35}CO_2H$
Unsaturated Acids		
Oleic acid	9-Octadecenoic acid	$C_{17}H_{33}CO_2H$
Linoleic acid	9,12-Octadecadienoic acid	$C_{17}H_{31}CO_2H$
Linolenic acid	9,12,15-Octadecatrienoic acid	$C_{17}H_{29}CO_2H$
Eleostearic acid	9,11,13-Octadecatrienoic acid	$C_{17}H_{29}CO_2H$

If all acyl groups are the same, the triglyceride is a *simple* triglyceride; otherwise it is a *mixed* triglyceride. In naming a triglyceride, the name *glyceryl* is written first, followed by a compound name for the three acyl groups. The acyl groups are named in the order in which they are attached to the glyceryl backbone. The first two names are given an *o* ending and the third, an *ate* ending. If all acyl groups are the same, only the ending *ate* is used, together with the prefix *tri*.

Bender, J. D., Catino, A. J., III., Hess, K. R., Lassman, M. E., Leber, P. A., Reinard, M. D., Strotman, N. A., Pike, C. S. "A Biochemical GC-MS Application for the Organic Chemistry Laboratory: Determination of Fatty Acid Composition of *Arabidopsis thaliana* Lipids." *J. Chem. Educ.* **2000:** *77,* 1466 (November 2000).

Glycerol   Glyceryl tripalmitate   Glyceryl trioleate   Glyceryl lauropalmitostearate
                Tripalmitin   Triolein   (a mixed glyceride)
                (a simple triglyceride; a fat) (a simple triglyceride; an oil)

Triglycerides can be *hydrolyzed* in alkaline solution to produce glycerol and salts of the fatty acids. The hydrolysis process is called **saponification**, and the salts are commonly known as **soaps**. For example, the hydrolysis of tristearin with aqueous KOH gives glycerol and the soap potassium stearate

$$
\begin{array}{l}
\underset{\text{tristearin}}{
\begin{array}{l}
CH_2OC(CH_2)_{16}CH_3 \\
CHOC(CH_2)_{16}CH_3 \\
CH_2OC(CH_2)_{16}CH_3
\end{array}} + 3\,KOH \longrightarrow
\underset{\text{glycerol}}{
\begin{array}{l}
CH_2OH \\
CHOH \\
CH_2OH
\end{array}} + 3\,CH_3(CH_2)_{16}CO^-K^+ \quad (27.1)
\end{array}
$$

potassium stearate (a soap)

The cleansing action of soaps was described in Section 21-1 (page 878).

Fats and oils are both triglycerides (*glyceryl esters*), but differ from each other by the nature of the acid components in the triglycerides. **Fats** are glyceryl esters in which *saturated* fatty acid components predominate; they are solids at room temperature. **Oils** have a predominance of *unsaturated* fatty acids and are liquids at room temperature. The compositions of fats and oils are variable and depend not only on the particular plant or animal species involved but also on dietary and climatic factors. Some common fats and oils are listed in Table 27.2.

When pure, fats and oils are colorless, odorless, and tasteless. The characteristic colors, odors, and flavors commonly associated with fats and oils come from other organic substances present as impurities. The yellow color of butter is that of β-carotene (a yellow pigment also found in carrots and marigolds). The taste of butter is attributed to 3-hydroxy-2-butanone and diacetyl.

Hanks, T. W. "Models of 2-Butanone: Using Graphics to Illustrate Complementary Approaches to Molecular Structure and Reactivity (CS)." *J. Chem. Educ.* **1994:** *71*, 62.

Stanish, I. et al. "Efficient Separation of Yolk from White in Boiled Chicken Eggs Leads to Convenient Extraction of Biologically Viable Phosphatidylcholine Lipids." *J. Chem. Educ.* **2002:** *79*, 481.

3-Hydroxy-2-butanone   Diacetyl

TABLE 27.2	Some Common Fats and Oils					
	Component Acids,[a] % by Mass					
	Saturated			Unsaturated		
Lipid	Myristic	Palmitic	Stearic	Oleic	Linoleic	Linolenic
Fats						
Butter	7–10	24–26	10–13	28–31	1–3	0.2–0.5
Lard	1–2	28–30	12–18	40–50	7–13	0–1
Edible Oils						
Corn	1–2	8–12	2–5	19–49	34–62	—
Safflower	—	6–7	2–3	12–14	75–80	0.5–1.5

[a]The formulas of the individual acids are listed in Table 27.1.

Are You Wondering . . .

What "calorie-free" fats are?

Doyle, Ellin. "Trans Fatty Acids." *J. Chem. Educ.* **1997**: *74*, 1030 (September 1997).

Doyle, Ellin. "Olestra? The Jury's Still Out." *J. Chem. Educ.* **1997**: *74*, 370 (April 1997).

In olestra, an ester of fatty acids and sucrose, the sucrose molecule takes the place of glycerol as the backbone of the ester. When olestra is burned in a bomb calorimeter, the liberated heat is comparable to that obtained in the combustion of other oils and fats. So, in this sense, olestra is *not* calorie free. However, the sucrose backbone of the olestra molecule can bond with six, seven, or eight acyl groups instead of the three acyl groups in a triglyceride, as shown below. Human enzymes cannot break down this bulky molecule, and so it is not digested. It is in this sense that it is calorie free.

Olestra

Triglyceride

Unsaturated fats and oils can be converted to saturated ones by the catalytic addition of hydrogen (hydrogenation). Thus, oils or low-melting fats are changed to higher-melting fats. These higher-melting fats, when mixed with skim milk, fortified with vitamin A, and artificially colored, are known as *margarines*. Unsaturation in a fat or oil is also removed when the fat or oil decomposes. Edible fats and oils both hydrolyze and cleave at the double bonds by oxidation on exposure to heat, air, and light. When this happens, the fat becomes rancid. The low-molecular-mass fatty acids produced by this cleavage have offensive odors, as exhibited by butyric acid in rancid butter. Antioxidants are commonly added to oils used in the high-temperature cooking of potato chips and other foods to retard this oxidative rancidity.

Medical evidence suggests a relationship between a high intake of saturated fats and the incidence of coronary heart disease. For this reason, many diets call for the substitution of unsaturated fatty acids for saturated fatty acids in foods. In general, most mammal fats are saturated, whereas those derived from vegetables and seafood are unsaturated.

▲ Corn oil has the approximate composition listed in Table 27.2. Hydrogenation converts some of the unsaturated to saturated fatty acid components—the primary change required in making margarine from vegetable oils.

CONCEPT ASSESSMENT ✔

What are the products of the saponification of one mole of glyceryl palmitooleolinolenate with three moles of sodium hydroxide?

Duffy, Lawrence K. "A Guide to Phospholipid Chemistry (by Donald J. Hanahan)." *J. Chem. Educ.* **1999:** *76*, 326 (March 1999).

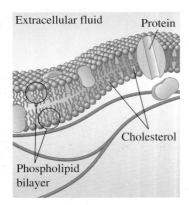

▲ A cell membrane is a bilayer (double layer) of phospholipid molecules with the polar head groups oriented toward the aqueous phase. Other lipid molecules, such as cholesterol, can be embedded in the bilayer. Some proteins are also found in the bilayer; membrane-bound proteins often act as ion pumps by providing a channel for the ions to pass through.

PHOSPHOLIPIDS

Phospholipids (phosphatides) occur in all animal cells and are especially prevalent in nerve tissue. They are derived from glycerol, fatty acids, phosphoric acid, and a nitrogen-containing base—ethanolamine in a class of phospholipids called *cephalins* and choline in class called *lecithins*. In the following structures, R and R' are long-chain alkyl groups.

Phosphatidylethanolamine (a cephalin)   Phosphatidylcholine (a lecithin)

Like soap molecules, the phospholipids have a hydrophilic head (the phosphate-ethanolamine or phosphate-choline portions shown in blue above) and hydrophobic tails (the two alkyl chains). This enables phospholipids to solubilize and transport fats and oils in aqueous medium, whether this occurs in transporting lipids in the bloodstream or in emulsifying fats and oils in salad dressings.

Cell membranes (the outer boundary of all living cells) consist of a bilayer of phospholipids having their hydrophilic heads in an aqueous medium and their hydrophobic portions turned inward into a medium of cholesterol and proteins.

27-3   CARBOHYDRATES

The literal meaning of "carbohydrate" is hydrate of carbon: $C_x(H_2O)_y$. Thus, sucrose, or cane sugar, $C_{12}H_{22}O_{11}$, is equivalent to $C_{12}(H_2O)_{11}$. A more useful definition is that **carbohydrates** are polyhydroxy aldehydes, polyhydroxy ketones, their derivatives, and substances that yield them on hydrolysis. Carbohydrates that are aldehydes are called aldoses; those that are ketones are called ketoses. A five-carbon carbohydrate is a pentose, a six-carbon one, a hexose, and so on. The structures in the margin are those of two familiar hexoses—glucose and fructose, an aldose and a ketose, respectively.

The simplest carbohydrates are collections of individual small molecules of the formula $C_x(H_2O)_y$ and are called **monosaccharides**. **Oligosaccharides** are larger molecules comprised of two to ten monosaccharide units bonded together. Names can be assigned to reflect the actual number of such units present, such as *di*saccharide and *tri*saccharide. Mono- and oligosaccharides are also called **sugars**. **Polysaccharides** contain more than ten monosaccharide units in their basic molecular structure, and many are in the *macromolecular* range. The general term for all carbohydrates is *glycoses*. In summary,

Cunha, A. C., Pereira, L. O. R., de Souza, M. C. B. V., Ferreira, V. F. "Use of Protecting Groups in Carbohydrate Chemistry: An Advanced Organic Synthesis Experiment." *J. Chem. Educ.* **1999:** *76*, 79 (January 1999).

	Monosaccharides
	aldoses (aldotriose, aldotetrose, …)
	ketoses (ketotriose, ketotetrose, …)
	Oligosaccharides (from two to ten monosaccharide units)
Glycoses	disaccharides (e.g., sucrose)
	trisaccharides (e.g., raffinose)
	and so on.
	Polysaccharides (more than ten monosaccharide units)
	(e.g., starch and cellulose)

Glucose — Fructose (margin structures)

◀ **FIGURE 27-3**
Optical isomers of glyceraldehyde
The structure in **(a)** is not superimposable on **(b)**, just as a right hand and a left hand are not superimposable.

    The simplest glycose is 2,3-dihydroxypropanal (glyceraldehyde), an *aldotriose*. As Figure 27-3 illustrates, the central C atom in glyceraldehyde has four different groups attached to it and is therefore chiral. As we have seen in Chapters 24 and 26, such molecules exhibit an interesting form of stereoisomerism—*optical isomerism*. There are *two* nonsuperimposable structures for glyceraldehyde. Such structures are related to each other like a right and a left hand, or like an object and its nonsuperimposable mirror image; they are *enantiomers* (see Section 24-4 and Section 26-11).

    Optically active molecules affect plane-polarized light (Fig. 27-4). Interactions between a beam of polarized light and the electrons in an enantiomer cause a rotation of the plane of the polarized light. One enantiomer rotates the plane of polarized light to the right (clockwise) and is said to be **dextrorotatory** (designated+). The other enantiomer rotates the plane of polarized light to the same extent, but to the left (counterclockwise). It is said to be **levorotatory** (designated−). Because of their ability to rotate the plane of polarized light, isomers of these types are said to be *optically active*, and they are called *optical isomers*. Almost all molecules exhibiting optical isomerism possess at least one asymmetric, or chiral, C atom.

◀ The prefixes *dextro* and *levo* are derived from the Latin words *dexter*, meaning right, and *laevus*, meaning left.

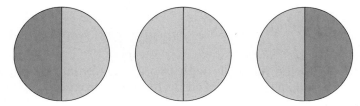

▲ **FIGURE 27-4**
View through the analyzer prism of a polarimeter (see also Figure 24-9)
The field of view of polarized light from a sodium vapor lamp is split in half. The analyzer prism in the eyepiece has been rotated in the correct direction—clockwise (to the right) or counterclockwise (to the left)—and through the appropriate angle, α, when the two halves transmit light of equal intensity (center). For incorrect angles of rotation, one semicircle is darker than the other.

    Use sheets of polarizing filters to show the effects of polarized light. Once the effect of placing two sheets of polarized filter at a right angle have been shown to reduce the transmitted light to zero, place a third sheet at 45° between the two that are at right angles. In this orientation, 25% of the light passes. When two sheets are at an angle ϕ to each other, $\cos^2 \phi$ of the light intensity passes through and $\sin^2 \phi$ does not.

The arrangement of groups at an asymmetric C atom is called the **absolute configuration**. We have already described the R, S system of nomenclature for describing the absolute configuration of chiral centers. The configuration of glyceraldehyde shown in Figure 27-3(a) is (R)-glyceraldehyde. The (S)-glyceraldehyde is shown in Figure 27-3(b). But which configuration rotates the plane of polarized light in a dextrorotatory (+) sense? Optical rotation studies alone cannot tell us which of the enantiomers rotates the plane of plane-polarized light in a positive sense or a negative sense, because there is no way to assign the R or S configuration to a particular one of a pair of enantiomers. That is, there is no relationship between the absolute configuration and the sign of the rotation; both must be determined experimentally by independent methods. The assignment of which configuration, R or S, is the dextrorotary (+) isomer has been achieved using X-ray studies. These methods show that the enantiomer that corresponds to the dextrorotatory (+) isomer has the R configuration and is named (R)-(+)-glyceraldehyde (Fig. 27-3a). Correspondingly, the levorotatory (−) isomer is found to correspond to the S configuration and is named (S)-(−)-glyceraldehydes (Fig. 27-3b). It is purely fortuitous that the positive rotation corresponds to the R configuration.

Emil Fischer studied carbohydrates in the late nineteenth century when techniques for determining the configuration of compounds were not available. Fischer arbitrarily assigned the configuration shown in Figure 27-3(a) to the dextrorotatory isomer of glyceraldehyde. Fischer designated this configuration D and named the isomer D-(+)-glyceraldehyde; D-(+)-glyceraldehyde is (R)-(+)-glyceraldehyde, and L-(−)-glyceraldehyde is (S)-(−)-glyceraldehyde. This system, extended to other chiral structures, is called the D, L convention.

We have already seen how to use a dashed-wedged line diagram to represent the three-dimensional structure of a molecule such as glyceraldehyde. Drawing these diagrams is not too difficult for compounds containing one or two stereocenters, but the process becomes increasingly cumbersome for compounds having several chiral centers, which carbohydrates often do. The German chemist Emil Fischer, in addition to assigning the configuration to (R)-(+)-glyceraldehyde, introduced a convention for representing three-dimensional structures in two-dimensional drawings, now called **Fischer projection formulas**.

The Fischer projections have two aspects to them: The first is how the stereochemistry at a chiral carbon atom is represented in two dimensions, and the second is how the carbon-chain backbone is arranged on the page. First, the bonds between each C atom and its four substituents are drawn in the form of a cross, the central carbon being at the point of intersection. The horizontal lines signify bonds directed toward the viewer; the vertical lines point away. Dashed-wedged line structures have to be arranged in this way to allow their conversion into Fischer projections. Consider (R)-(+)-glyceraldehyde.

$$
\underset{\text{HO}}{\overset{\text{CHO}}{\underset{}{\text{H}\cdots\text{C}}}}\overset{}{\underset{\text{CH}_2\text{OH}}{}} \;\xrightarrow{\;\;}\; \underset{\text{CH}_2\text{OH}}{\overset{\text{CHO}}{\text{H}\blacktriangleright\text{C}\blacktriangleleft\text{OH}}} \;\xrightarrow{\;\;}\; \underset{\text{CH}_2\text{OH}}{\overset{\text{CHO}}{\text{H}\!-\!\!-\!\!-\!\!-\!\text{OH}}}
$$

In order to view the molecule with two groups pointing toward us, we imagine the molecule as being picked up by the hydroxyl group and the hydrogen atom and then turned to bring these groups toward us, as shown. The CHO and CH$_2$OH groups naturally take up positions away from us. The Fischer projection is drawn with the H and OH groups connected by a horizontal line and the CHO and CH$_2$OH groups joined by a vertical line. Note that the central C atom is not drawn in, but is understood to be at the point of intersection of the lines; including this C atom would make the Fischer projection indistinguishable from a Lewis structure, which contains no stereochemical information.

Starkey, L. S. "The Use of Stick Figures to Visualize Fischer Projections." *J. Chem. Educ.* 2001: *78*, 1486.

Zhang, Q., Zhang, S. "A New Method to Convert the Fischer Projection of a Monosaccharide to the Haworth Projection." *J. Chem. Educ.* 1999: *76*, 799 (June 1999).

Siloac, Edward. "Bird-in-the-Hand Method for Determination of Absolute Configuration in Fischer Projections." *J. Chem. Educ.* 1999: *76*, 798 (June 1999).

Signorella, S., Sala, L. F. "An Easy Way to Convert a Fischer Projection into a Zigzag Representation." *J. Chem. Educ.* 1991: *68*, 105.

▲ **Emil Fischer (1852–1919)** Fischer was awarded the Nobel Prize in 1902 for his research on the structures of sugars. Later he also elucidated how amino acid molecules join to form proteins.

In the Fischer notation, the structural formula is drawn so that the backbone of the molecule is arranged from top to bottom, with the most oxidized portion of the molecule (—CHO) at the top and the least oxidized (—CH$_2$OH) at the bottom. Attached groups (—H and —OH) are written to the sides. The end groups of the backbone are considered to extend *behind* the plane of the page, *away* from the viewer. The glyceraldehyde enantiomers are written as

$$
\begin{array}{ccc}
& \text{CHO} & \\
\text{HO} & \!\!\!\!-\!\!\!\!\!-\!\!\!\! & \text{H} \\
& \text{CH}_2\text{OH} &
\end{array}
\qquad
\begin{array}{ccc}
& \text{CHO} & \\
\text{H} & \!\!\!\!-\!\!\!\!\!-\!\!\!\! & \text{OH} \\
& \text{CH}_2\text{OH} &
\end{array}
$$

(*S*)-(−) Glyceraldehyde   (*R*)-(+)-Glyceraldehyde
(L)-(−) Glyceraldehyde   (D)-(+)-Glyceraldehyde

and are used to establish the D, L configuration for other sugars.

The —H and —OH groups on the next-to-last (penultimate) C atom extend in *front* of the page, *toward* the viewer. If the —OH group on this penultimate C atom is to the *right*, the configuration is D. If the —OH is to the left, the configuration is L. This convention is applied below to the four-carbon aldoses, where the penultimate C atom and attached groups are shaded with blue. All D sugars have the same configuration at this penultimate carbon. Figure 27-5 may help you to picture the relationship between a three-dimensional structure and its two-dimensional representation.

$$
\begin{array}{ccc}
& \text{CHO} & \\
\text{H} & - & \text{OH} \\
\text{H} & - & \text{OH} \\
& \text{CH}_2\text{OH} &
\end{array}
\quad
\begin{array}{ccc}
& \text{CHO} & \\
\text{HO} & - & \text{H} \\
\text{HO} & - & \text{H} \\
& \text{CH}_2\text{OH} &
\end{array}
\qquad
\begin{array}{ccc}
& \text{CHO} & \\
\text{HO} & - & \text{H} \\
\text{H} & - & \text{OH} \\
& \text{CH}_2\text{OH} &
\end{array}
\quad
\begin{array}{ccc}
& \text{CHO} & \\
\text{H} & - & \text{OH} \\
\text{HO} & - & \text{H} \\
& \text{CH}_2\text{OH} &
\end{array}
$$

Mirror   Mirror
D-(−)-Erythrose   L-(+)-Erythrose   D-(−)-Threose   L-(+)-Threose

D-Erythrose and L-erythrose are enantiomers, as are D-threose and L-threose. If we compare the configurations of D-erythrose and D-threose, we note that these two molecules are *not* mirror images. On the other hand, they are isomers of each other and both are optically active. Optical isomers that are *not* mirror images of each other are called **diastereomers**.

$$
\begin{array}{ccc}
& \text{CHO} & \\
\text{H} & - & \text{OH} \\
\text{H} & - & \text{OH} \\
& \text{CH}_2\text{OH} &
\end{array}
\qquad
\begin{array}{ccc}
& \text{CHO} & \\
\text{HO} & - & \text{H} \\
\text{H} & - & \text{OH} \\
& \text{CH}_2\text{OH} &
\end{array}
$$

Mirror
D-Erythrose   D-Threose
Not mirror images

Enantiomers differ only in the *direction*, not the extent of their rotation of plane-polarized light. Diastereomers do differ in the extent to which they rotate plane-polarized light. They also differ in physical and chemical properties; for example, they have different solubilities in a particular solvent and react with chemical reagents at different rates.

A mixture of equal amounts of the D and L configurations of a particular substance, called a **racemic mixture**, does not rotate the plane of polarized light either to the left or to the right. The designation DL-erythrose, for example, signifies a racemic mixture. Often, when molecules with chiral centers are

◀ **KEEP IN MIND**
that D and L are like *R* and *S* in that they indicate the configuration of a chiral carbon atom, but they do not indicate whether the compound rotates plane-polarized light to the right (+) or to the left (−).

(a)

$$
\begin{array}{ccc}
& \text{CHO} & \\
\text{H} & -\text{C}- & \text{OH} \\
\text{H} & -\text{C}- & \text{OH} \\
& \text{CH}_2\text{OH} &
\end{array}
$$

(b)

▲ **FIGURE 27-5**
The structure of D-(−)-erythrose
The three-dimensional structure **(a)** is represented in two dimensions by **(b)**.

Are You Wondering . . .

How the *R, S* nomenclature is used in compounds with more than one chiral center?

Each chiral center in the carbon chain is numbered according to the IUPAC convention, and the name is constructed with the prefix *R* or *S*, together with the position in the chain. To illustrate this, consider L-threose with two chiral centers, at positions 2 and 3 (numbering starts from the aldehyde group). Remembering that the groups attached to the horizontal lines point toward the viewer, we see that, considering each center in turn, both chiral centers are *S*. The chiral centers are designated (2*S*,3*S*), and the complete systematic name is (2*S*,3*S*)-2,3,4-trihydoxy-1-butanal.

synthesized, the product is a racemic mixture. This is because the creation of these centers is a random process, like flipping a coin (an equal probability for heads or tails). If optically pure isomers are desired, the racemic mixture must be separated into the component enantiomers by a process called *resolution*. Sometimes this is carried out using an enzyme that reacts with one enantiomer but not the other.

MONOSACCHARIDES

Starkey, Ronald. "SOS: A Mnemonic for the Stereochemistry of Glucose." *J. Chem. Educ.* **2000**: *77*, 734 (June 2000).

Vasilarou, A-M. G., Georgiou, C. A. "Enzymatic Spectrophotometric Reaction Rate Determination of Glucose in Fruit Drinks and Carbonated Beverages. An Analytical Chemistry Laboratory Experiment for Food Science-Oriented Students." *J. Chem. Educ.* **2000**: *77*, 1327 (October 2000).

Of the 16 possible aldohexoses, only three occur widely in nature: D-glucose, D-mannose, and D-galactose. These three sugar molecules exist in a straight-chain form only to a very small extent (less than 0.5% for glucose). The predominant form for each is *cyclic*. In this ring formation, the —OH group of the fifth C atom (C-5) adds to the carbonyl of the C-1 atom and produces a ring composed of five C atoms and one O atom, as illustrated in Figure 27-6. The conformation of the six-member ring is of the chair type (recall Figure 26-3).

D-(+)-Glucose

α-D-(+)-Glucose

▶ **FIGURE 27-6**
Representation of ring closure in glucose molecule
The straight chain D-(+)-glucose molecule folds back on itself to bring the —OH group on the C-5 atom close to the aldehyde group of the C-1 atom. A proton is transferred, and this is followed by the formation of a six-member ring with an O atom joining the C-1 and C-5 atoms.

Extended   Folded   Cyclic

When the chain form of a sugar is converted to the ring form, a new chiral (asymmetrical) center is produced at the C-1 atom. There are two possible orientations at this center. In the α form, the —OH at C-1 is *axial* (directed down); in the β form, it is *equatorial* (extends out from the ring). The α and β forms of glucose are pictured in Figure 27-7.

α-D-(+)-Glucose β-D-(+)-Glucose

▲ **FIGURE 27-7**
α and β forms of D-glucose
In the α form, the —OH group at C-1 (in red) is axial, extending below the chair-like ring. In the β form, the —OH group is equatorial and extends out from the ring.

Sandell, A. "A Handy Reagent for Testing the Reducing Power of Sugars." *J. Chem. Educ.* **1994:** *71*, 346.

The naming of monosaccharides in the ring form is complicated, but each item in a name conveys precise information. Thus, D-(+)-glucose refers to the straight-chain form of glucose in the D configuration; the (+) indicates this form is dextrorotatory. The name α-D-(+)-glucose denotes the ring form derived from D-glucose with the α configuration at the C-1 atom.

Monosaccharides such as glucose are known as **reducing sugars**, which means that a sufficient amount of the straight-chain form is in equilibrium with the cyclic form that the sugar engages in an oxidation–reduction reaction with $Cu^{2+}(aq)$. The $Cu^{2+}(aq)$ is reduced to insoluble red Cu_2O, and the aldehyde portion of the sugar is oxidized (to an acid). The test for a reducing sugar is conducted with alkaline copper ion complexed with tartrate (Fehling's solution) or citrate ion (Benedict's solution).

▲ A test for a reducing sugar, producing a silver mirror from an ammoniacal solution containing silver ion.

$$\text{Certain cyclic sugars} \rightleftharpoons \underset{\text{straight-chain form}}{\begin{array}{c} \text{CHO} \\ | \\ \text{CHOH} \\ | \end{array}} \xrightarrow{Cu^{2+}} \underset{}{\begin{array}{c} \text{COOH} \\ | \\ \text{CHOH} \\ | \end{array}} + \underset{\text{red ppt}}{Cu_2O(s)} \qquad (27.2)$$

CONCEPT ASSESSMENT ✓

Can a Fischer projection formula be used to represent D-(−)-glucose? Explain.

DISACCHARIDES

Two monosaccharides can join together by eliminating a H_2O molecule between them—a condensation reaction. This combination of monosaccharides is called a *disaccharide*. In describing a disaccharide, we must consider the identity of the component monosaccharides and whether the configuration of the linkage between the monosaccharides is α or β. The important, naturally occurring disaccharides—maltose, cellobiose, lactose, and sucrose—are presented in Figure 27-8.

In *maltose*, a H atom on the C-1 hydroxyl group of one glucose unit reacts with the hydroxyl group on the C-4 atom of a second glucose unit. The two units are linked in the α manner. Equilibrium is possible between the cyclic and straight-chain forms of maltose, so it is a reducing sugar. Maltose is produced by the action of malt enzyme on starch. In the presence of yeast, maltose undergoes fermentation—first to glucose and then to ethanol and $CO_2(g)$.

Deal, S. T., et al. "Carbohydrate Analysis: Can We Control the Ripening of Bananas?" *J. Chem. Educ.* **2002:** *79*, 479.

Maltose (α form)

Lactose (β form)

Cellobiose

Sucrose

■ Glucose　■ Galactose　■ Fructose

▲ **FIGURE 27-8**
Some common disaccharides

▲ **Sucrose**

Robyt, John F. "Graphic Representation of Oligosaccharide and Polysaccharide Structures Containing Hexopyranose Units." *J. Chem. Educ.* **1986**: *63*, 560.

Mathews, K. R., et al. "Quantitative Assay for Starch by Colorimetry Using a Desktop Scanner." *J. Chem. Educ.* **2004**: *81*, 702.

MacDonald, J. J. "Photosynthesis: Why Does It Occur?" *J. Chem. Educ.* **1995**: *72*, 1113 (December 1995).

Cellobiose can be obtained by the careful hydrolysis of cellulose. It is a glucose–glucose disaccharide with β linkages. *Lactose*, or milk sugar, is naturally present in milk, where its concentration may range from 0 to 7%. It is a galactose–glucose disaccharide with β linkages. *Sucrose* is ordinary table sugar (cane or beet sugar). It is a glucose–fructose disaccharide linked 1α, 2β. Neither of the two cyclic sugar units can open up into a chain form, and so sucrose is *not* a reducing sugar.

POLYSACCHARIDES

Polysaccharides are composed of monosaccharide units joined into long chains by oxygen linkages. *Starch*, with a molecular mass between 20,000 and 1,000,000 u, is the reserve carbohydrate of many plants and is the bulk constituent of cereals, rice, corn, and potatoes. Its structural features are brought out in Figure 27-9. *Glycogen* is the reserve carbohydrate of animals; it is stored in the liver and in muscle tissue. It has a higher molecular mass than starch, and the polysaccharide chains are more branched. *Cellulose* is the main structural material of plants. It is the chief component of wood pulp, cotton, and straw. Complete hydrolysis of cellulose produces glucose. Cellulose has a molecular mass between 300,000 and 500,000 u, corresponding to 1800–3000 glucose units. Most animals, including human beings, do not possess the necessary enzymes to hydrolyze β linkages. As a result, they cannot digest cellulose. Certain bacteria in ruminants (cows, deer, camels) and termites can hydrolyze cellulose, allowing them to use it as a food. Termites, as we know, subsist on a diet of wood.

PHOTOSYNTHESIS

As we have noted in Sections 7-9 and 24-11, the process of photosynthesis involves the conversion by plants of carbon dioxide and water into carbohydrates. Photosynthesis requires the catalyst chlorophyll (see Figure 24-23) and sunlight.

$$n\,CO_2 + n\,H_2O \xrightarrow[\text{chlorophyll}]{\text{sunlight}} C_n(H_2O)_n + n\,O_2 \qquad (27.3)$$

Maltose unit

Starch

Cellobiose unit

Cellulose

▲ **FIGURE 27-9**
Two common polysaccharides

Equation (27.3) is greatly oversimplified. The currently accepted mechanism, proposed by Melvin Calvin (Nobel Prize, 1961), involves as many as 100 sequential steps for the conversion of six moles of carbon dioxide to one mole of glucose. The elucidation of this mechanism was greatly aided by the use of carbon-14 as a radioactive tracer. For simplicity, the overall photosynthetic process is divided into two phases: (1) the conversion of solar energy to chemical energy—the light reactions; and (2) the synthesis, promoted by enzymes, of carbohydrates. This latter phase, called the dark reactions, can occur in the absence of light.

Choi, M. M. F., et al. "Application of Datalogger in Observing Photosynthesis." *J. Chem. Educ.* **2002**: 79, 980.

BIOMASS

Biomass is any living matter. An important component of biomass is the organic material produced by photosynthesis, that is, plants or their principal constituents—cellulose, starch, sugars. Plant biomass can be used directly as a fuel, or it may be converted to other gaseous, liquid, or solid materials, which can be used as fuels or chemical raw materials.

Perhaps the best known and most widely used conversion method is the fermentation of sugars to ethanol. Fermentation involves the decomposition of organic matter in the absence of air and through the action of a microorganism.

Dehydration of Sugar movie

$$\text{hexose sugar} \xrightarrow{\text{yeast}} 2\,CH_3CH_2OH + 2\,CO_2$$

In the United States, the main raw material for the production of ethanol by fermentation is corn.

The conversion of plant material to fossil fuels requires geologic processes and geologic time scales, thereby limiting the future availability of these fuels as energy sources and as raw materials. In principle, most of the compounds now being produced from fossil fuels could be made directly from cellulose. Methanol (wood alcohol) is formed by the destructive distillation (pyrolysis) of wood. Cellulose can be hydrolyzed to glucose and then converted to ethanol by fermentation. Fermentation processes can also be used to produce a series of oxygenated compounds—alcohols and ketones—which can be converted to hydrocarbons. Thus, the entire spectrum of organic chemicals could be produced from the simple molecules CO_2 and H_2O. The required energy would be mostly solar.

▲ A converter for the pyrolysis of biomass.

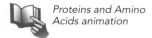 Bowen, R., Hartung, R., Gindt, Y. M. "A Simple Protein Purification and Folding Experiment for General Chemistry Laboratory." *J. Chem. Educ.* **2000:** *77,* 1456 (November 2000).

Proteins and Amino Acids animation

Anderson, G. L. "Demonstration of Enantiomer Specificity of Proteins and Drugs." *J. Chem. Educ.* **2004:** *81,* 971.

Vitz, E. "Amino Acid Complementarity: A Biochemical Exemplar of Stoichiometry for General and Health Sciences Chemistry." *J. Chem. Educ.* **2005:** *82,* 1013.

27-4 PROTEINS

When a protein is hydrolyzed by dilute acids, bases, or hydrolytic enzymes, the result is a mixture of α-amino acids. An *amino acid* is a carboxylic acid that also contains an amine group, $—NH_2$; an **α-amino acid** has the amino group on the α carbon atom—the C atom next to the carboxyl group. Thus, proteins are high-molecular-mass polymers composed of α-amino acids. Of the known α-amino acids, about 20 have been identified as the building blocks of plant and animal proteins. Some of these amino acids are listed in Table 27.3.

TABLE 27.3 Some Common Amino Acids

Name	Symbol	Formula	pI[a]
Neutral Amino Acids			
Glycine	Gly	$HCH(NH_2)CO_2H$	6.03
Alanine	Ala	$CH_3CH(NH_2)CO_2H$	6.10
Valine[b]	Val	$(CH_3)_2CHCH(NH_2)CO_2H$	6.04
Leucine[b]	Leu	$(CH_3)_2CHCH_2CH(NH_2)CO_2H$	6.04
Isoleucine[b]	Ileu or Ile	$CH_3CH_2CH(CH_3)CH(NH_2)CO_2H$	6.04
Serine	Ser	$HOCH_2CH(NH_2)CO_2H$	5.70
Threonine[b]	Thr	$CH_3CHOHCH(NH_2)CO_2H$	5.6
Phenylalanine[b]	Phe	$C_6H_5CH_2CH(NH_2)CO_2H$	5.74
Methionine[b]	Met	$CH_3SCH_2CH_2CH(NH_2)CO_2H$	5.71
Cysteine	Cys	$HSCH_2CH(NH_2)CO_2H$	5.05
Cystine	$(Cys)_2$	$[SCH_2CH(NH_2)CO_2H]_2$	5.1
Tyrosine	Tyr	$4–HOC_6H_4CH_2CH(NH_2)CO_2H$	5.70
Tryptophan[b]	Trp	(structure) $CH_2CH(NH_2)CO_2H$	5.89
Proline[c]	Pro	(structure) CO_2H	6.21
Acidic Amino Acids			
Aspartic acid	Asp	$HO_2CCH_2CH(NH_2)CO_2H$	2.96
Glutamic acid	Glu	$HO_2CCH_2CH_2CH(NH_2)CO_2H$	3.22
Basic Amino Acids			
Lysine[b]	Lys	$H_2N(CH_2)_4CH(NH_2)CO_2H$	9.74
Arginine	Arg	$H_2NC(=NH)NH(CH_2)_3CH(NH_2)CO_2H$	10.73
Histidine	His	(structure) $CH_2CH(NH_2)CO_2H$	7.58

[a]pH of *isoelectric point*.
[b]Essential amino acids. In addition, arginine and glycine are required by the chick, arginine by the rat, and histidine by human infants.
[c]The secondary amino group makes proline an *α-imino* acid. Nevertheless, it is commonly listed with amino acids.

Proteins are the basis of protoplasm and are found in all living organisms. In animals, proteins—as muscle, skin, hair, and other tissue—make up the bulk of the body's nonskeletal structure. As enzymes, proteins catalyze biochemical reactions; as hormones, they regulate metabolic processes; and as antibodies, they counteract the effect of invading organisms.

◀ The word "protein" is derived from the Greek word *proteios*, meaning "of first importance" (similar to the derivation of "proton").

Amino Acids.   Other than glycine ($H_2NCH_2CO_2H$), naturally occurring amino acids are optically active, mostly with an L configuration.

An L-amino acid

The reference structure for establishing the absolute configurations of amino acids is again glyceraldehyde, with the $—NH_2$ group substituting for $—OH$ and $—CO_2H$, for $—CHO$. The molecule shown above has an L configuration because the $—NH_2$ group appears on the *left*.

Certain amino acids that are required for proper health and growth in human beings cannot be synthesized by the body. These amino acids, which are called the *essential amino acids*, must be ingested as food. Eight amino acids are known to be essential; the case of three others is less certain (see Table 27.3).

Amino acids are colorless, crystalline, high-melting-point solids that are moderately soluble in water. In a strongly acidic solution (low pH), the amino acid exists as a cation: A proton from solution attaches itself to the unshared pair of electrons on the nitrogen atom in the $—NH_2$ group. In a strongly basic solution (high pH), an anion forms through the loss of protons by the $—CO_2H$ and $—NH_3^+$ groups. At an intermediate point, a proton is lost from the $—CO_2H$ but retained by the $—NH_3^+$ group. The product is a dipolar ion, or a **zwitterion**.

Barrelle, M., Gaude, D., Salon, M. C. "A Study on Amino Acids: Synthesis of Alpha-Aminophenylacetic Acid (Phenylglycine) and Determination of Its Isoelectric Point." *J. Chem. Educ.* **1983**: *60*, 676.

Hermann, C. K. F. "Using Copper sulfate as a Classification Test for Amino Acids and Amines." *J. Chem. Educ.* **1995**: *72*, 940.

Helser, T. L. "Amino acid chromatography: The "best" technique for student labs." *J. Chem. Educ.* **1990**: *67*, 964.

Amino acids are amphoteric. In most amino acids, the acidity of the $—NH_3^+$ group is slightly greater than the basicity of the $—CO_2^-$ group. The largest group of amino acids are close to pH neutral. The pH at which the dipolar structure predominates is called the **isoelectric point**, or p*I*. At this pH, the molecule does not migrate in an electric field. At a pH above the p*I*, the molecule migrates to the anode (positive electrode); and below the p*I*, to the cathode (negative electrode). Most basic amino acids have a p*I* well above 7, acidic ones well below 7, and most neutral ones slightly less than 7 (5.7–6.1).

Peptides.   Two amino acid molecules can be joined by the elimination of a water molecule between them. The amino acids thus joined form a dipeptide. The bond between the two amino acid units is called a **peptide bond**.

a dipeptide

Anthony-Cahill, Spencer.
"Bioorganic Chemistry:
Peptides and Proteins (edited by
Sidney M. Hecht)." *J. Chem. Educ.*
1999: *76*, 905 (July 1999).

A tripeptide has three amino acid residues and two peptide linkages. A large number of amino acid units may join to form a **polypeptide**.

The amino acid unit present at one end of a polypeptide chain has a free $-NH_2$ group; this is the N-terminal end. The other end of the chain has a free $-CO_2H$ group; this is the C-terminal end. The polypeptide structure is written with the N-terminal end to the left and the C-terminal end to the right. The base name of the polypeptide is that of the C-terminal amino acid. The other amino acid units in the chain are named as substituents of this acid. Their names change from an *ine* to the *yl* ending. Abbreviations are also commonly used in writing polypeptide names, as illustrated in Example 27-1.

EXAMPLE 27-1

Naming a Polypeptide. What is the name of the polypeptide whose structure is shown below?

$$H_2N-CH_2-\overset{\overset{\displaystyle O}{\|}}{C}-NH-\underset{\underset{\displaystyle CH_3}{|}}{CH}-\overset{\overset{\displaystyle O}{\|}}{C}-NH-\underset{\underset{\displaystyle CH_2OH}{|}}{CH}-\overset{\overset{\displaystyle O}{\|}}{C}-OH$$

(a)   (b)   (c)

Solution

We can identify the three amino acids in this tripeptide using Table 27.3. (a) = glycine; (b) = alanine; (c) = serine. The C-terminal amino acid is serine. The name is glycylalanylserine (Gly-Ala-Ser).

Practice Example A: What is the name of the polypeptide shown below?

$$H_2N-\underset{\underset{\displaystyle CH_3CHOH}{|}}{CH}-\overset{\overset{\displaystyle O}{\|}}{C}-NH-\underset{\underset{\displaystyle CH_3CHOH}{|}}{CH}-\overset{\overset{\displaystyle O}{\|}}{C}-NH-\underset{\underset{\displaystyle CH_2CH_2SCH_3}{|}}{CH}-\overset{\overset{\displaystyle O}{\|}}{C}-OH$$

Practice Example B: Write the structural formula of the polypeptide serylglycylvaline.

CONCEPT ASSESSMENT ✓

At pH = 7, what is the most probable charge on the tripeptide molecule, Gly-Ala-Ser, described in Example 27-1?

Amino Acid Sequencing. Suppose that a tripeptide is known to consist of the three amino acids: A, B, and C. What is the correct structure: ABC, BAC, ...? Can you see that there are six possibilities? For longer chains, of course, the number of possibilities is enormous. Determining the sequence of amino acids in a polypeptide chain is one of the most significant problems in all of biochemistry. The method employed is outlined in Figure 27-10, and the structure of a typical polypeptide, beef insulin, is shown in Figure 27-11.

▲ **FIGURE 27-10**
Experimental determination of amino acid sequence
In the reaction between DNFB and a polypeptide, the N-terminal amino acid
ends up with the yellow marker (a dinitrophenyl group, DNP) attached to it.
By gentle hydrolysis and repeated use of the marker, a polypeptide chain
can be broken down and the sequence of the individual units determined.

▲ **FIGURE 27-11**
Amino acid sequence in beef insulin—primary structure of a protein
There are two polypeptide chains joined by disulfide (—S—S—) linkages. One chain
has 21 amino acids, and the other 30. In chain A, the Gly at the left end is N-terminal
and the Asp is C-terminal. In chain B, Phe is N-terminal and Ala is C-terminal.

EXAMPLE 27-2

Determining the Sequence of Amino Acids in a Polypeptide. A polypeptide, on
complete hydrolysis, yielded the amino acids A, B, C, D, and E. Partial hydrolysis
and sequence proof gave single amino acids, together with the following larger
fragments: AD, CD, DCB, BE, and BC. What must be the sequence of amino acids in
the polypeptide?

Solution

By arranging the fragments in the following manner,

        AD
         DC
         DCB
            BE
         CB

we see that the sequence ADCBE is consistent with the fragments observed. However, the sequence EBCDA is also possible because we do not know whether A or E
is the N-terminal end of the polypeptide.

Practice Example A: On complete hydrolysis, a pentapeptide yields the amino
acids Val, Phe, Gly, Cys, and Tyr. Partial hydrolysis yields the fragments Val-Phe,
Gly-Cys, Cys-Val-Phe, and Phe-Tyr. Glycine (Gly) is the N-terminal acid. What is
the sequence of amino acids in the polypeptide?

Practice Example B: On complete hydrolysis, a hexapeptide yields the amino
acids Ala, Gly, Ser, Trp, and Val. Partial hydrolysis yields the fragments Val-Trp,
Gly-Gly-Ala, Ser-Gly-Gly, and Ala-Val-Trp. Serine (Ser) is the N-terminal acid.
What is the sequence of amino acids in the polypeptide?

The distinction between large polypeptides and proteins is arbitrary. It is generally accepted that if the molecular mass is over 10,000 u (roughly 50–75 amino acid units), the substance is a **protein**. Proteins possess characteristic isoelectric points, and their acidity or basicity depends on their amino acid composition. When proteins are heated, treated with salts, or exposed to UV light, profound and complex changes called **denaturation** occur. Denaturation usually brings about a lowering of solubility and loss of biological activity. The frying or boiling of an egg involves the denaturation (coagulation) of the egg albumin, a protein. The beauty shop permanent wave takes advantage of a denaturation process that is reversible. The proteins found in hair (e.g., keratin) contain disulfide linkages (—S—S—). When hair is treated with a reducing agent, these linkages break—a denaturation process. Following this step, the hair is set into the desired style. Next, the hair is treated with a mild oxidizing agent. The disulfide linkages are reestablished, and the hair remains in the style in which it was set.

THE STRUCTURE OF PROTEINS

Ault, A. "A 'Polypeptide Demonstrator'".
J. Chem. Educ. **2004:** *81*, 196.

The **primary structure** of a protein refers to the exact sequence of amino acids in the polypeptide chains that make up the protein. But what are the shapes of the long polymeric chains themselves? Are they simply limp and entangled like a plate of spaghetti or is there some order within chains and among chains? The structure or shape of an entire protein chain is referred to as **secondary structure**. In 1951, based on X-ray diffraction studies on polylysine, a synthetic polypeptide, Linus Pauling and R. B. Corey proposed that the orientation of this polypeptide and thus of the protein chain is *helical*. A spiral, helical, or spring-like shape can be either left- or right-handed, but because proteins are composed of L amino acids, their helical structure is right-handed (Fig. 27-12).

Other types of orientations are also possible. For example, β-keratin and silk fibroin are arranged in pleated sheets. In these proteins, the side chains extend above and below the pleated sheets, and there is hydrogen bonding

▶ **FIGURE 27-12**
Secondary structure of a protein—an α helix
The helical structure is stabilized by hydrogen bonds between

$$\begin{matrix} O \\ \| \\ —C— \end{matrix}$$ groups in one turn and $$\begin{matrix} H \\ | \\ —N--- \end{matrix}$$ groups in the next turn above. The bulky R groups are directed outward from the atoms in the spiral.

Yamana, Shukichi. "An Easily Constructed Helix Model."
J. Chem. Educ. **1992:** *69*, 275.

Van Woert, Howard C., Jr. "Using the Protein Alpha-Helix in Teaching (LTE)."
J. Chem. Educ. **1984:** *61*, 565.

Jeffreys, J. A. D. "Drawing a Protein Alpha-Helix."
J. Chem. Educ. **1983:** *60*, 549.

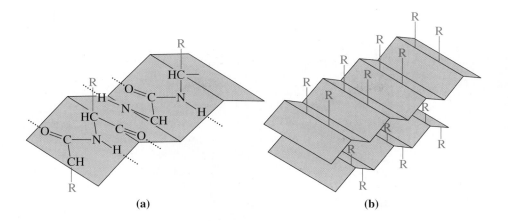

◀ **FIGURE 27-13**
Pleated-sheet model of β-keratin
(a) A polypeptide chain showing the direction of interpolypeptide hydrogen bonds (other polypeptide chains lie to the left and to the right of the chain shown). Bulky R groups extend above and below the pleated sheet. **(b)** The stacking of pleated sheets.

between *different* molecules (interpeptide bonding) lying next to each other and about 0.47 nm apart in the same sheet. These sheets are stacked on top of one another about 1.0 nm apart, rather like a pile of sheets of corrugated roofing (Fig. 27-13). Some proteins, such as gamma globulin, are amorphous: They do not have a definite secondary structure.

Many proteins possess additional structural features. For example, rather than being elongated, the coils may be twisted, knotted, and so forth. The final statement regarding the shape of a protein molecule lies in a description of its **tertiary structure.** Because the internal hydrogen bonding between atoms in successive turns of a protein helix is weak, these hydrogen bonds ought to be easily broken. In particular, we should expect them to be replaced by hydrogen bonds to water molecules when the protein is placed in water. That is, the α helix should open up and become a randomized structure when placed in water. But experimental evidence indicates that this does not happen, which leads to the conclusion that other forces must be involved in entwining the long α-helical chains into definite geometric shapes. Three types of linkages involved in tertiary structures are described in Figure 27-14. The tertiary structure of myoglobin is shown in Figure 27-15.

Barton, J. S. "Protein denaturation and tertiary structure." *J. Chem. Educ.* **1986:** *63,* 367.

FIGURE 27-14
Linkages contributing to the tertiary structure of proteins
(a) *Salt linkages.* Acid–base interactions between different coils. Here, the carboxyl group of an aspartic acid unit on one coil donates a proton to the free amine group of a lysine unit on another. **(b)** *Hydrogen bonding.* Interactions between side chains of certain amino acids, for example, aspartic acid and serine. **(c)** *Disulfide linkages.* Oxidation of the highly reactive thioalcohol group (—SH) of cysteine to a disulfide (—S—S—) can occur (as in beef insulin).

The folding of a polypeptide chain into a tertiary structure is influenced by an additional factor. The hydrophobic hydrocarbon portions of the chains (R groups) tend to pull away from the aqueous medium and retreat to the interior of the structure, leaving ionic groups at the exterior.

▲ **FIGURE 27-15**
Representation of the tertiary structure of myoglobin
The primary structure is that of a peptide of 153 units in a single chain. Secondary structure involves coiling of 70% of the chain into an α helix.

▶ **FIGURE 27-16**
The four levels of protein structure
Hemoglobin is the oxygen-carrying protein in red blood cells. The iron-containing heme units are shown as red discs. The primary structure of the protein is determined by its amino acid sequence. The secondary structure (α helix) is stabilized through formation of hydrogen bonds, as illustrated in Figure 27-12. The tertiary structure is determined by interactions between the R groups and their surroundings, causing the polypeptide chains to fold in a particular manner. Finally, the quaternary structure is an aggregation of two or more folded chains—four chains in the case of hemoglobin. Not all proteins have a quaternary structure.

Marino, Francis. "Use of Tangle Links to Show Globular Protein Structure." *J. Chem. Educ.* **1994:** *71, 741.*

Hemoglobin model

Smith, J. M. A., et al. "A molecular model for the quaternary structure of ferritin." *J. Chem. Educ.* **1988:** *65, 1083.*

The hemoglobin molecule consists of four separate polypeptide chains or subunits. The arrangement of these four subunits constitutes a still higher order of structure referred to as the **quaternary structure.** The levels of protein structure in hemoglobin, from primary to quaternary, are depicted in Figure 27-16.

Even minor changes in the structure of a protein can have profound effects. Hemoglobin contains four polypeptide chains, each with 146 amino acid units. The substitution of valine for glutamic acid at one site in two of these chains gives rise to the sometimes fatal blood disease known as sickle-cell anemia. Apparently, the altered hemoglobin has a reduced ability to transport oxygen through the blood, although it does seem to provide some defense against malaria.

CONCEPT ASSESSMENT ✓

Polypeptides can fold into helical coils. Would you also expect polysaccharides to form helical coils? Explain.

▶ A computer image of the three-dimensional structure of ribulose-1,5-biphosphate carboxylase-oxygenase (RuBisCo), which consists of 37,792 atoms. This structure was elucidated in 1988, after an 18-year effort. RuBisCo is the most abundant protein on Earth. Its estimated annual worldwide production by plants is 4×10^{13} g (40 million tons). RuBisCo is the enzyme that initiates the process of photosynthesis.

27-5   ASPECTS OF METABOLISM

Although living organisms differ markedly in appearance, there is a striking similarity in the chemical reactions of their life processes. We refer to the totality of these reactions as **metabolism.** Metabolic reactions in which substances are broken down are referred to as *catabolism.* Metabolic reactions in which more complex substances are synthesized from simpler ones are called *anabolism.* Reactions having $\Delta G > 0$ are said to be *endergonic,* and those with $\Delta G < 0$ are *exergonic.* The substances involved in metabolism are called *metabolites.* Metabolism is a complex subject that we can outline only briefly. The discussion that follows centers on the summary of metabolism given in Figure 27-17.

Starch can be detected by the use of iodine, with which if forms a purple complex (see page 619). Potatoes are a good source of starch. A more interesting demonstration uses a semipermeable membrane. The starch does not pass through, so one side tests positive to starch and the other side does not. Starch decomposes into glucose that does pass through: (ChemMatters April 2001 issue)

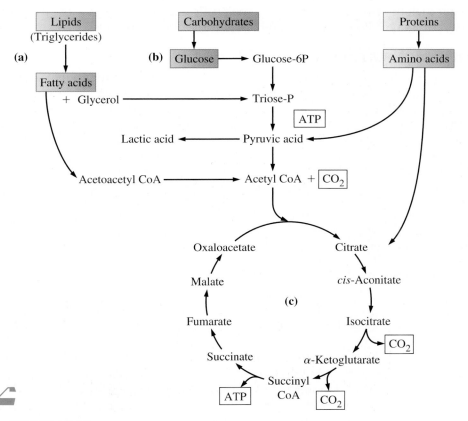

▲ **FIGURE 27-17**
Metabolism outline
(a) *Fatty acid section.* Fatty acids are degraded two C atoms at a time. Acetyl units enter into the citric acid cycle (c) as acetyl CoA. **(b)** *Glycolysis section (Embden–Meyerhof pathway).* These reactions are anaerobic (no oxygen required). Carbohydrates are degraded to the six-carbon sugar glucose, and then to the three-carbon triose-P (glyceraldehyde-3-phosphate). Next, the three-carbon acid pyruvic acid is formed from triose-P. Pyruvic acid loses a molecule of CO_2, yielding the two-carbon acetyl unit, which combines with coenzyme A (CoA) to form acetyl CoA. **(c)** *Citric acid cycle (Krebs cycle).* A two-carbon acetyl unit from acetyl CoA joins with the four-carbon oxaloacetate unit to produce the six-carbon tricarboxylic acid citric acid (designated here as citrate). A two-step conversion to isocitrate occurs, followed by the loss of a molecule of CO_2 and formation of the five-carbon α-ketoglutarate. Another CO_2 molecule is lost in the formation of succinyl CoA. The remainder of the cycle involves a succession of four-carbon acids leading to oxaloacetate. The oxaloacetate regenerated at the end of the cycle now joins with another acetyl unit, and the cycle is repeated. The overall change occurring in the cycle is that a two-carbon acetyl unit enters the cycle and two molecules of CO_2 leave.

▶ In glucose-6-phosphate, a phosphate group replaces the —OH group on the C-6 atom of the cyclic glucose molecule (see Figure 27-7).

$$H_2C-O-\overset{\overset{\displaystyle O^-}{|}}{\underset{\underset{\displaystyle O}{|}}{P}}-OH$$

▶ The structure of glyceraldehyde-3-phosphate is

$$\begin{array}{c} \overset{\displaystyle O}{\underset{\displaystyle \parallel}{C}}-H \\ | \\ H-\overset{|}{C}-OH \quad O^- \\ | \qquad | \\ H-\overset{|}{C}-O-\overset{|}{P}-OH \\ | \qquad \parallel \\ H \qquad O \end{array}$$

CARBOHYDRATE METABOLISM

Starch is the principal source of energy for humans and other animals. Digestion of starch begins in the mouth with the action of salivary enzymes, the amylases. Starch is converted to maltose and polysaccharides known as dextrins. This process continues briefly in the stomach (until the enzymes are denatured by the acid present), and the maltose and polysaccharides pass into the small intestine. Here, amylase from the pancreas completes the conversion of polysaccharides to maltose, and the enzyme *maltase* converts the maltose to glucose. Glucose is absorbed through the wall of the small intestine into the bloodstream and distributed to other organs.

Glucose is ultimately oxidized to carbon dioxide and water, with the liberation of energy. The principal intermediate in this process is glucose-6-phosphate (glucose-6P). Once formed, glucose-6P may be converted to glycogen (a polysaccharide stored in the liver), revert back to glucose, or be metabolized. The major metabolic route (Fig. 27-17) involves the anaerobic (absence of air) glycolysis pathway, followed by an aerobic cycle, the citric acid cycle.

LIPID METABOLISM

The digestion of fats and oils occurs in the small intestine through the action of a combination of lipase enzymes. The products of this enzyme hydrolysis are glycerol, mixtures of mono- and diglycerides, and fatty acids. These are absorbed into the bloodstream through the wall of the intestine. Glycerol is converted to glyceraldehyde-3-phosphate (triose phosphate) and joins into the glucose metabolic route previously described. Fatty acids are oxidized to carbon dioxide and water, with the release of energy, in a series of reactions known as β oxidation. In this process, oxidation occurs at the β carbon atom of a fatty acid, followed by cleavage. Thus, two-carbon pieces (acetic acid) are split off. The process also requires coenzyme A (CoA). For example, with palmitic acid, $C_{15}H_{31}COOH$, the process is repeated seven times, with the formation of eight molecules of acetyl CoA, which enter the Krebs cycle (Fig. 27-17).

PROTEIN METABOLISM

In the stomach, HCl(aq) and the enzyme *pepsin* hydrolyze about 10% of the amide linkages in proteins and produce polypeptides in the molecular mass range of 500 to several thousand atomic mass units. In the small intestine, peptidases such as trypsin and chymotrypsin (from the pancreas) cleave the polypeptides into very small fragments. These fragments are then acted on by aminopeptidase and carboxypeptidase. The resulting free amino acids pass through the wall of the intestine, into the bloodstream, and to all the cells of the body, where they are the building blocks of proteins. Protein synthesis is directed by the nucleic acids DNA and RNA (page 1161).

ENERGY RELATIONSHIPS IN METABOLISM

Selig, T. C., et al. "Detection of ATP and NADH: A bioluminescent experience." *J. Chem. Educ.* 1984: 61, 918.

The fundamental agents involved in energy transfers from exergonic to endergonic reactions are **adenosine *di*phosphate (ADP)** and **adenosine *tri*phosphate (ATP)**. The following equation represents the conversion of one mole of ATP to one mole of ADP.

$$ATP^{4-} + H_2O \longrightarrow ADP^{3-} + HPO_4^{2-} + H^+ \qquad \Delta G^{\circ\prime} = -32.4 \text{ kJ} \qquad (27.6)$$

▶ Additional thermodynamic aspects of ADP/ATP conversions were presented in Chapter 19 (page 810).

Figure 27-18 represents the reverse of reaction (27.6).

The energy released in the oxidation of foods is picked up by ADP, which is converted to ATP. Enzymes catalyze each step in the overall conversion. The oxidation of one mole of glucose to CO_2 and H_2O is accompanied by the conversion of 38 mol ADP to 38 mol ATP. These two processes are represented below.

$$C_6H_{12}O_6 + 6\,O_2 \longrightarrow 6\,CO_2 + 6\,H_2O \quad \Delta G^{\circ} = -2880 \text{ kJ}$$

$$38 \times \{ADP^{3-} + HPO_4^{2-} + H^+ \longrightarrow ATP^{4-} + H_2O\} \quad \Delta G^{\circ\prime} = 38 \times 32.4 \text{ kJ} = 1230 \text{ kJ}$$

▲ **FIGURE 27-18**
Conversion of ADP to ATP
The H^+ ion entering into the reaction and the H_2O molecule produced are shown beside the main reaction arrow.

◀ Based on the discussion of the expanded valence shell (page 394), we represent all the P-to-O bonds in Figure 27-18 as single bonds. Sometimes these structures are written with one P-to-O double bond in each phosphate unit.

Thus, of the 2880 kJ of energy released in the oxidation of one mole of glucose, 1230 kJ of energy is stored in the high-energy bonds of ATP. The efficiency of this energy storage is $(1230/2880) \times 100\% = 43\%$. That is, nearly half of the energy released in carbohydrate metabolism is stored in the human body for later use. This is a much more efficient use of energy than in an internal combustion engine, for example. If the metabolism of glucose occurred in a single step, with just one mole of ADP converted to one mole of ATP, the efficiency would drop to $(32.4/2880) \times 100\% = 1.1\%$. So we can see why the metabolism of sucrose is such a complex, multistep process.

ENZYMES

An **enzyme** is a biological catalyst that contains protein. Enzymes are specific for each biological transformation and catalyze a reaction without requiring a change in temperature or pH. Originally, enzymes were assigned common or trivial names, such as pepsin and catalase. Present practice, however, is to name them after the processes they catalyze, usually employing an *ase* ending.

A model for enzyme action was introduced in the discussion of enzyme kinetics in Section 14-11. According to this model, an enzyme can exert its catalytic activity only after combining with the reacting substance, the *substrate*, to form a complex. The site on the enzyme where the substrate bonds is called the *active site*; some enzymes have more than one active site. Reaction of the substrate (S) with the enzyme (E) to form a complex (ES) permits the reaction to proceed via a path of lower activation energy than the noncatalyzed path. When the complex decomposes, products (P) are formed and the enzyme is regenerated.

Johnson, A. Kristin. "A Simple Method for Demonstrating Enzyme Kinetics Using Catalase from Beef Liver Extract." *J. Chem. Educ.* **2000:** *77,* 1451 (November 2000).

Ochs, Raymond S. "Understanding Enzyme Inhibition." *J. Chem. Educ.* **2000:** *77,* 1453 (November 2000).

Hardee, J. R., Montgomery, T. M., Jones, W. H. "Chemistry and Flatulence: An Introductory Enzyme Experiment." *J. Chem. Educ.* **2000:** *77,* 498 (April 2000).

$$E + S \rightleftharpoons ES \longrightarrow E + P$$

One example is the hydrolysis of sucrose. Recall from Figure 27-8 that sucrose is a disaccharide of glucose and fructose.

Patterson, J., et al. "Use of Enzymes in Organic Synthesis: Reduction of Ketones by Baker's Yeast Revisited." *J. Chem. Educ.* **2005:** *82,* 1049.

sucrose
$C_{12}H_{22}O_{11}$

glucose
$C_6H_{12}O_6$

fructose
$C_6H_{12}O_6$

Fenster, A. E., et al. "A useful model for the "lock and key" analogy." *J. Chem. Educ.* **1984:** *61,* 967.

The first step is the binding of sucrose to the active site of the enzyme sucrase, as illustrated in Figure 27-19. When the sucrose is in the active site of the enzyme, a number of chemical processes can take place. For example, a proton can be transferred from the sucrase to the glucose, which causes the active site of the sucrase to open up, causing the C—O bond joining fructose and glucose to weaken. The transfer of a proton from an amino acid side chain of the sucrase molecule may destroy hydrogen bonding within the enzyme and cause it to open up; this process stretches the sucrose molecule by pulling at each end, as suggested in Figure 27-20. In this distorted form, the C—O of the disaccharide is highly susceptible to attack by a water molecule. Figure 27-21 shows that after this reaction, glucose and fructose are formed and the proton transferred back to the sucrase, which causes the active site to return to its original state. The smaller fructose and glucose molecules leave the active site, and the enzyme is ready to go again.

▶ **FIGURE 27-19**
Sucrase binding a sucrose molecule
The figure illustrates the "pocket" in the enzyme sucrase that the sucrose fits into. The globular protein sucrase (in blue) is much larger than sucrose.

Sucrase

▶ **FIGURE 27-20**
Change in enzyme conformation after binding of substrate
The transfer of a proton (in orange) from the catalase to the sucrose is thought to open up the enzyme structure, leading to a weakening of the C—O bond in sucrose.

Sucrase

▲ FIGURE 27-21
Completion of the enzyme-catalyzed reaction
The weakened C—O bond in sucrose is susceptible to nucleophilic attack by a
water molecule (in red) to produce glucose and fructose. These smaller molecules
escape the pocket designed to fit sucrose. And the sucrase returns to its original state
with the proton (orange) returned to the hydoxyl group.

Enzyme Catalysis animation

Enzymes such as sucrase do not contain metal ions, but almost a third of
known enzymes do. An enzyme with a metal ion in the active site is carboxypeptidase, a metalloenzyme active in the digestion of proteins into individual amino acids. In the process, each peptide bond between amino acids is
cleaved. A water molecule is broken apart, the H and OH are added to the
ends of the polypeptide chain, and an amino acid is released. Hydrolysis reactions of this type are the reverse of condensation reactions.

Carboxypeptidase cleaves amino acids one at a time, starting from the carboxyl end of the substrate protein. The enzyme consists of a single polypeptide chain containing 307 amino acids and a single Zn(II) ion. As shown in
Figure 27-22, the metal ion is located in a cleft in the molecule, held in place by
coordination to three amino acids—two histidines and one glutamic acid. The
Zn(II) ion adopts an approximate tetrahedral geometry with the fourth coordination site occupied by a water molecule.

▶ **FIGURE 27-22**
Structure of carboxypeptidase
(a) In this illustration, the secondary structure of the helices (blue), pleated sheets (purple), and nonspecific secondary structure (yellow) combine to give a visualization of the overall tertiary structure of carboxypeptidase. **(b)** Coordination of the Zn(II) ion in the active site.

(a)   (b)

During the hydrolysis of a protein by carboxypeptidase, the protein substrate binds in the active site of the enzyme, as suggested by Figure 27-23. The substrate is held near the zinc center by hydrogen bonding to several amino acids in the cleft. The details of the mechanism have not been conclusively determined, except that it is known that it is the water coordinated to the Zn(II) that is used in the cleavage of the peptide bond. The proximity of the peptide linkage to the highly polarized water molecule coordinated to the Zn(II) ion permits the cleavage of the peptide bond and release of an amino acid.

The optimum temperature for enzyme activity is about 37 °C (98 °F) for enzymes present in warm-blooded animals. Above this temperature, enzyme activity declines as the secondary and tertiary structures are disrupted and the active site is distorted.

The two enzymes described here provide only a glimpse of the fascinating chemistry involved in the action of enzymes, which is currently a very active area of research.

▶ **FIGURE 27-23**
Binding of protein to the active site of carboxypeptidase
A schematic of the C-terminus of a protein bound at the active site of carboxypeptidase. Hydrogen bonding to enzyme side chains holds the protein in place to facilitate nucleophilic attack by the water molecule.

27-6   NUCLEIC ACIDS

Lipids, carbohydrates, and proteins together with water constitute about 99% of most living organisms. The remaining 1% includes compounds of vital importance to the existence of life. Among these are the **nucleic acids**, which carry the information that directs the metabolic activity of cells. The two nucleic acids are **DNA**, or **deoxyribonucleic acid**, and **RNA**, or **ribonucleic acid**.

DNA is found in the cell nucleus on rodlike structures called chromosomes, which also contain protein. DNA contains the hereditary information that is passed from generation to generation. At specific locations along the chromosomes are *genes*, which are DNA sequences that control particular traits.

Figure 27-24 shows the chemical constituents of DNA and RNA. DNA is made up of the pentose sugar 2-deoxyribose, the purine bases adenine and

Benedetti, G., Morosetti, S. "A Method for Building Simple Physical Models: Representing the Structures of Nucleic Acids." *J. Chem. Educ.* **1992:** *69*, 569.

Howard, Kathleen P. "Thermodynamics of DNA Duplex Formation: A Biophysical Chemistry Laboratory Experiment." *J. Chem. Educ.* **2000:** *77*, 1469 (November 2000).

Fancy, N., Mehl, A. F. "Examining the Rate of Renaturation for Genomic DNA Isolated from *E. coli*: An Integrated Physical Biochemistry Laboratory." *J. Chem. Educ.* **1999:** *76*, 646 (May 1999).

▲ FIGURE 27-24
Constituents of nucleic acids
Tracing the hydrolysis reactions in the reverse direction, the combination of a pentose sugar and a purine or a pyrimidine base yields a nucleoside. A nucleoside in combination with phosphoric acid yields a nucleotide. A nucleic acid is a polymer of nucleotides. If the sugar is 2-deoxyribose and the bases are A, G, T, and C, the nucleic acid is DNA. If the sugar is ribose and the bases are A, G, U, and C, the nucleic acid is RNA. (The term "2-deoxy" means without an O atom on the second C atom.)

Cady, S. G. "A 3D Model of Double-Helical DNA Showing Variable Chemical Details." *J. Chem. Educ.* **2005:** *82, 79.*

Nordell, K. J., et al. "Liver and Onions: DNA Extraction from Animal and Plant Tissues." *J. Chem. Educ.* **1999:** *76,* 400A.

McCorkle, G. M., et al. "RNA's as catalysts: A new class on enzymes." *J. Chem. Educ.* **1987:** *64,* 221.

guanine, and the pyrimidine bases cytosine and thymine. RNA differs in that it contains ribose instead of deoxyribose, and the base uracil instead of thymine. Both DNA and RNA contain phosphate groups. The combination of a pentose sugar and a purine or pyrimidine base is called a *nucleoside*. The combination of a nucleoside and a phosphate group is called a *nucleotide*. A DNA molecule is made up of two strands of nucleotides held together by hydrogen bonds and twisted into a helix. RNA is generally single stranded. Figure 27-25 represents a portion of a nucleic acid chain and shows how the constituents are joined by phosphate groups. If the sugar is 2-deoxyribose and the bases are adenine (A), guanine (G), thymine (T), and cytosine (C), the nucleic acid is DNA. If the sugar is ribose and the bases are adenine (A), guanine (G), uracil (U), and cytosine (C), the nucleic acid is RNA.

▲ **FIGURE 27-25**
A portion of a nucleic acid chain

The usual *double helix* form of DNA is shown in Figure 27-26. The postulation of this structure by Francis Crick and James Watson in 1953 was one of the great scientific breakthroughs of modern times. Their work was critically dependent on precise X-ray diffraction studies of DNA done by Maurice Wilkins and Rosalind Franklin and on a set of regularities regarding the purine and pyrimidine bases in nucleic acids discovered by Erwin Chargaff. These regularities, known as the *base-pairing rules*, require the following:

1. The amount of adenine is equal to the amount of thymine (A = T).
2. The amount of guanine is equal to the amount of cytosine (G = C).
3. The total amount of purine bases is equal to the total amount of pyrimidine bases (G + A = C + T).

To maintain the structure of a double helix, hydrogen bonding must occur between the two single strands. The necessary conditions for hydrogen bonding exist only if an A on one strand appears opposite a T on the other, or if a G is opposite a C. C cannot be paired with T because the relatively small molecules

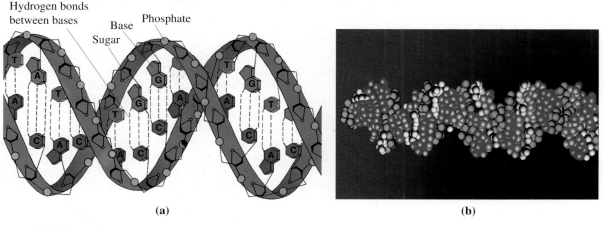

Hydrogen bonds between bases · Base · Phosphate · Sugar

(a) **(b)**

▲ **FIGURE 27-26**
DNA model
(a) Schematic representation. **(b)** Space-filling model.

Deoxyribonucleic Acid (DNA) model

(single ring) would not approach each other closely enough. The combination of G and A cannot occur because the molecules are too large (double rings).

DNA molecules have a unique ability to replicate—that is, to make exact copies of themselves. The critical step in DNA replication requires the molecule to unwind into single strands. As the unwinding occurs, free nucleotides present in the nucleus become attached to the exposed portions of the two single strands, converting each to a new double helix of DNA consisting of one old strand and one new strand (Fig. 27-27).

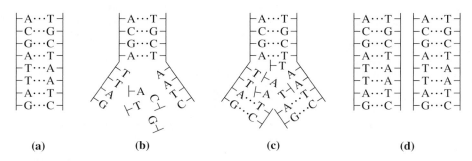

(a) **(b)** **(c)** **(d)**

Serra, Martin J. "Genomics: The Science and Technology Behind the Human Genome Project (by Charles R. Cantor and Cassandra L. Smith)." *J. Chem. Educ.* **2000:** *77*, 33 (January 2000).

▲ **FIGURE 27-27**
Replication of a DNA molecule
(a) A DNA double helix. **(b)** The two strands begin to "unzip". **(c)** Nucleotides from the cellular fluid crowd into the region between the two strands and attach to the exposed strands through hydrogen bonds. **(d)** Two DNA double helices identical to the original one.

There are two pieces of evidence, each very convincing, that the process just outlined does indeed occur. First, electron micrographs of the DNA molecule have been obtained that capture DNA in the act of replication. Another elegant experiment involves growing bacteria in a medium containing ^{15}N atoms so that all the N atoms of the bases of the DNA molecules are ^{15}N. The bacteria are then transferred to a nutrient with nucleotides containing normal ^{14}N. Here, the bacteria are allowed to divide and reproduce. The DNA of the offspring cells are then analyzed. Those of the first generation, for example, consist of DNA molecules with one strand having ^{15}N and the other ^{14}N atoms. This is exactly the result to be expected if replication occurs by the unzipping process described in Figure 27-27. The central importance of the base sequences in DNA is that they act as a chemical template for the formation of an organism's proteins; that is, they act as a gene. This, together with a discussion of RNA, is outlined in the Focus On feature of this chapter.

The Genetic Code

		Second base		
	U	C	A	G

First base

U:
- UUU, UUC } Phe
- UUA, UUG } Leu
- UCU, UCC, UCA, UCG } Ser
- UAU, UAC } Tyr
- UAA Stop, UAG Stop
- UGU, UGC } Cys
- UGA Stop
- UGG Trp

C:
- CUU, CUC, CUA, CUG } Leu
- CCU, CCC, CCA, CCG } Pro
- CAU, CAC } His
- CAA, CAG } Gln
- CGU, CGC, CGA, CGG } Arg

A:
- AUU, AUC, AUA } Ile
- AUG Met
- ACU, ACC, ACA, ACG } Thr
- AAU, AAC } Asn
- AAA, AAG } Lys
- AGU, AGC } Ser
- AGA, AGG } Arg

G:
- GUU, GUC, GUA, GUG } Val
- GCU, GCC, GCA, GCG } Ala
- GAU, GAC } Asp
- GAA, GAG } Glu
- GGU, GGC, GGA, GGG } Gly

▲ **The genetic code**

Trinucleotide sequences (*codons*) are used by ribosomes to identify the amino acids needed in protein synthesis. Note that the codons UAA, UAG, and UGA are signal codons. They signal the ribosome to stop protein synthesis.

The puzzle of protein synthesis is that it occurs outside the nucleus of the cell but is directed by DNA, which is found only inside the nucleus. How is the necessary information transmitted? Here is where RNA plays a key role. The following discussion relates to the process outlined in Figure 27-28.

In addition to unwinding for its own replication, DNA unwinds for the synthesis of a kind of RNA molecule called *messenger* RNA, or mRNA. The new strand of mRNA carries the genetic information from DNA coded in the sequence of its nucleotides. The mRNA migrates out of the nucleus into the cell cytoplasm, where it binds to cell components called ribosomes. The combination of the mRNA and its ribosomes is called a polysome.

Another type of RNA called *transfer* RNA, or tRNA, comes in 20 different forms, each of which can bond with only one specific kind of amino acid. The function of tRNA is to bring a specific amino acid to a site on the ribosome where the amino acid can form a polypeptide bond and become part of a growing polypeptide chain. The ribosome moves along the mRNA chain, picking up different tRNA molecules and incorporating their amino acids into the polypeptide chain. When the ribosome reaches the end of the mRNA chain, it separates from the chain and releases the protein molecule that has been synthesized. The entire process is like the stringing of beads.

The code (set of directions) that determines the exact sequence of amino acids in the synthesis of a protein is incorporated in the chromosomal DNA. It is found in the particular pattern of base molecules on the double helix. Since there are only four different bases possible in an mRNA molecule—U, A, G, and C—but 20 different amino acids, it is clear that the code cannot correspond to individual base molecules. There are $4^2 = 16$ combinations of base molecules taken two at a time (i.e., UU, UA, UG, UC, etc.). But these could account for only 16 amino acids. When the base molecules are taken three at a time, there are $4^3 = 64$ possible combinations. A group of three base molecules in a DNA strand, called a triplet, causes a complementary set of base molecules to appear in the mRNA formed on it. In turn, this triplet, or *codon*, on the mRNA must be matched by a complementary triplet, called an *anticodon*, in a tRNA molecule. The particular tRNA with this anticodon carries a specific amino acid to the site of protein synthesis.

Following are the significant features of the genetic code shown in the table.

Summary

27-1 Chemical Structure of Living Matter: An Overview— Four general categories of substances found in living organisms are lipids, carbohydrates, proteins, and nucleic acids. **Cells**, which are the fundamental structural units of living things, contain macromolecules from each of these categories (Fig. 27-2).

27-2 Lipids— A range of substances of biological origin that are soluble in nonpolar or low-polarity solvents are classified as **lipids**. One familiar group of lipids is the **triglycerides**, esters of glycerol with long-chain monocarboxylic (fatty) acids. If saturated fatty acids predominate, the triglyceride is a **fat**. If unsaturation (in the form of double bonds) occurs in some of the fatty acid components, the triglyceride is an **oil**. **Saponification**, the hydrolysis of a triglyceride with a strong base, yields glycerol and salts of the fatty acid components (equation 27.1). The salt of a fatty acid is called a **soap**.

27-3 Carbohydrates— The most common among simple **carbohydrate** molecules are five- and six-carbon-chain polyhydroxy aldehydes and ketones. These molecules can be represented by **Fischer projection formulas**, which project the three-dimensional structures in two dimensions (Fig. 27-5). Carbohydrates contain chiral carbon atoms, existing therefore as optical isomers. One isomer, designated *d* or (+), rotates the plane of polarized light "to the right" (clockwise) and is said to be **dextrorotatory**. Its enantiomer, designated *l* or (−), rotates polarized light "to the left" (counterclockwise) and is **levorotatory** (Fig. 27-4). Commonly encountered for carbohydrates with more than one chiral center are **diastereomers**, optical isomers that are not mirror images and hence not enantiomers. The arrangement of groups at an asymmetric carbon atom is called the **absolute configuration** and is designated by the *R*, *S* system of nomenclature. Syntheses of carbohydrates generally lead to equal amounts of enantiomers in mixtures referred to as **racemic mixtures**.

- There is more than one triplet code for most amino acids.
- The first two letters of the codon are most significant. There is considerable variation in the third.

- There are three "stop" codons that do not correspond to any amino acids; they end the synthesis of a polypeptide chain. There is also an "initiation" codon that begins the synthesis of a polypeptide chain.
- The various codons direct the incorporation of the same amino acids, whether in bacteria, plants, lower animals, or humans.

▲ **FIGURE 27-28**
Protein synthesis
(a) Through the action of an enzyme, a tRNA molecule brings a single amino acid to a site on a ribosome. The anticodon of the tRNA (AAA for the example shown) must be complementary to the codon of the mRNA (UUU). (The amino acid carried by this tRNA is phenylalanine.) The amino acid is added to the chain in the manner shown; the chain moves from the tRNA on the left to the one on the right. **(b)** As the ribosome moves along the mRNA strand, more and more amino acid units are added through the proper matching of tRNA molecules with the code on the mRNA. **(c)** When the ribosome reaches the end of the mRNA strand, it and the completed protein are released. The ribosome is free to repeat the process.

Monosaccharides are the simplest carbohydrate structures (Fig. 27-7). Two to ten monosaccharide units can join to form an **oligosaccharide**, for example, two monosaccharide units join to form a disaccharide (Fig. 27-8). Together, monosaccharides and oligosaccharides are also known as **sugars**. **Polysaccharides** contain from a few to a few thousand monosaccharide units. The most common of these are starch, glycogen, and cellulose (Fig. 27-9). A **reducing sugar** is one that can reduce Cu^{2+} to copper(II) oxide.

27-4 Proteins—Some 20 different **α-amino acids** (Table 27.3) are the basic building blocks of **proteins**, which consist of a long chain of amino acids. An α-amino acid has an amino group and a carboxyl group connected to the rest of the molecule at the α carbon atom. The pH at which the amino acid exists predominantly as a dipolar ion, a **zwitterion**, is the **isoelectric point**. Two amino acid molecules may join by eliminating a H_2O molecule between them to form a **peptide bond** (equation 27.5). When several peptides are linked together, the chain is referred to as a **polypeptide** chain. The linear sequence of amino acids of a

protein is known as its **primary structure** (Fig. 27-11). The structure or shape of the entire amino acid chain in a protein is referred to as its **secondary structure**. Types of secondary structure include helical coils (Fig. 27-12) and pleated sheets (Fig. 27-13). **Tertiary structure** is the three-dimensional arrangement of the amino acid chains with respect to each other (Fig. 27-15), while **quaternary structure** is the arrangement of different polypeptide chains to form a larger biomolecule, such as hemoglobin (Fig. 27-16). **Denaturation** occurs when a protein loses it biological activity due to the unfolding of its tertiary structure.

27-5 Aspects of Metabolism—Lipids, carbohydrates, and proteins are complex molecules that are broken down into their simplest units as part of the process of **metabolism** (Fig. 27-17). Carbohydrates are degraded into monosaccharides, proteins into amino acids, and lipids into glycerol and fatty acids. Ultimately, these degradation products are decomposed into still smaller molecules, such as CO_2, H_2O, NH_3, and urea. **Enzymes** are proteins that catalyze metabolic reactions. Energy released in catabolic processes is used to convert **adenosine diphosphate (ADP)** to **adenosine triphosphate (ATP)**, which can then supply the energy needs of other processes.

27-6 Nucleic Acids—Nucleic acids are made up of pentose sugars, purine and pyrimidine bases, and phosphate groups (Fig. 27-24). Two classes of nucleic acids are **ribonucleic acid (RNA)** and **deoxyribonucleic acid (DNA)** (Figs. 27-25 and 27-26). RNA contains the sugar ribose, while DNA contains the sugar 2-deoxyribose. Nucleic acids carry the information that directs the metabolic activity of cells and the hereditary information that is passed from one generation to the next.

Integrative Example

L-Threonine is one of the essential amino acids. It is found in animal protein (for example, eggs and milk) but is missing in some grains, such as rice. It is now common practice to fortify grains with the essential amino acids that they lack. The structure of L-threonine is shown below.

$$CH_3—CH—CH—C—OH$$

with OH, O, and NH$_2$ groups shown

$$pK_{a_1} = 2.15 \quad pK_{a_2} = 9.12$$

Use the above data to determine the principal form of L-threonine and the direction that it will migrate under the influence of an electric field in a gel that is 0.25 M in NaH_2PO_4 and 0.50 M in Na_2HPO_4.

Strategy

The key to this problem is to recognize that the NaH_2PO_4/Na_2HPO_4 mixture is a buffer that controls the pH of the gel. Once the pH of the gel is established we can identify the ionization state for the bulk of the L-threonine and hence the direction it will migrate.

Solution

Use pK_{a_2} from Table 16.4 and the Henderson–Hasselbalch equation to calculate the pH of the gel.

$$pH = pK_{a_2} + \log([HPO_4^{2-}]/[H_2PO_4^-])$$

and

$$pH = 7.20 + \log(0.50/0.25) = 7.50$$

The structures of the three ionic forms in which L-threonine can appear are

Acidic solution:

$$CH_3CH(OH)CHCOOH$$
$$NH_3^+$$

Isoelectric point:

$$CH_3CH(OH)CHCOO^-$$
$$NH_3^+$$

Basic solution:

$$CH_3CH(OH)CHCOO^-$$
$$NH_2$$

The pH at the first equivalence point in the titration of a weak diprotic acid is given by equation (17.5). Applied to L-threonine, the result is

$$pH = \frac{pK_{a_1} + pK_{a_2}}{2} = \frac{2.15 + 9.12}{2} = 5.64$$

The predominant species at this first equivalence point of pH = 5.64 is the dipolar zwitterion, which would not migrate at all in an electric field. However, in the gel medium of pH = 7.50 the hydroxide ion concentration is 100 times greater. The predominant species is the anion with charge −1. This form of the L-threonine migrates toward the positive electrode, the anode.

Assessment

This problem suggests two ways to establish the isoelectric point of an amino acid. The first, used here, is to calculate p*I* by combining pK_a values of a polyprotic amino acid. Another way is to find the pH of a gel medium in which the amino acid does not migrate in the presence of an applied electric field, hence pH = p*I*. Additionally, migration through an electric field in a gel (gel electrophoresis) can be used to separate amino acid mixtures.

Exercises

Structure and Composition of the Cell

Exercises 1 to 4 refer to a typical Escherichia coli *bacterium. This is a cylindrical cell about 2 μm long and 1 μm in diameter, weighing about 2 × 10⁻¹² g and containing about 80% water by volume.*

1. The intracellular pH is 6.4 and $[K^+] = 1.5 \times 10^{-4}$ M. Determine the number of **(a)** H_3O^+ ions and **(b)** K^+ ions in a typical cell.

2. Calculate the number of lipid molecules present, assuming their average molecular mass to be 700 u and the lipid content to be 2% by mass.

3. The cell is about 15% protein by mass with 90% of the protein in the cytoplasm. Assuming an average molecular mass of 3×10^4 u, how many protein molecules are present in the cytoplasm?

4. A single chromosomal DNA molecule contains about 4.5 million nucleotide units. If this molecule were extended so that the nucleotide units were 450 pm apart, what would be the length of the molecule? How does this compare with the length of the cell itself? What does this result suggest about the shape of the DNA molecule?

Lipids

5. Name the following compounds.

(a) H$_2$CO—C(=O)—C$_{15}$H$_{31}$
    HCO—C(=O)—C$_{17}$H$_{29}$
    H$_2$CO—C(=O)—C$_{11}$H$_{23}$

(b) H$_2$CO—C(=O)—C$_{17}$H$_{33}$
    HCO—C(=O)—C$_{17}$H$_{33}$
    H$_2$CO—C(=O)—C$_{17}$H$_{33}$

(c) C$_{13}$H$_{27}$CO$_2^-$Na$^+$

6. Write structural formulas for the following.
   (a) glyceryl palmitolauroeleostearate
   (b) tripalmitin
   (c) potassium myristate
   (d) butyl oleate

7. Describe the similarities and differences between (a) trilaurin and trilinolein, (b) a soap and a phospholipid such as a lecithin.
8. Write a structural formula for a generic phosphatidic acid—an acid that produces a cephalin when esterified with ethanolamine and a lecithin when esterified with choline. Mono- and diglycerides are found in many processed foods. Write structural formulas for a generic monoglyceride and a generic diglyceride.
9. Oleic acid is a moderately unsaturated fatty acid. Linoleic acid is *polyunsaturated*. What structural feature characterizes polyunsaturated fatty acids? Is stearic acid polyunsaturated? Is eleostearic acid? Why do you suppose safflower oil is so highly recommended in dietary programs?
10. Corn oil and safflower oil are popular cooking oils (Table 27.2). They can be converted to solid fats by hydrogenation. Which would consume the greater amount of H$_2$(g) in its hydrogenation to a solid fat, 1 kg of corn oil or 1 kg of safflower oil? Explain.
11. Write structural formulas to represent the products of the saponification of tripalmitin with NaOH(aq).
12. Calculate the maximum mass of the sodium soap that can be prepared from 105 g of glyceryl trimyristate.

Carbohydrates

13. Characterize the two sugars represented below using the terminology from page 1142. Further indicate whether the sugar has a D or L configuration.

14. Write the structure for the straight-chain form of L-glucose. Does the structure determine if this isomer is levorotatory? Explain.
15. From the given structure of L-(+)-arabinose, derive the structure of (a) D-(−)-arabinose; (b) a diastereomer of L-(+)-arabinose.

CHO
H——OH
HO——H
HO——H
CH$_2$OH

L-(+)-Arabinose

16. Describe the similarities and differences in the structures of the following three compounds. (a) β-D-(+)-glucose, (b) D-(−)-arabinose, (c) D-(+)-glucose.
17. The following terms are all related to stereoisomers and their optical activity. Explain the meaning of each: (a) dextrorotatory; (b) levorotatory; (c) racemic mixture; (d) (R).
18. The following terms are all related to optical isomers. Explain the meaning of each: (a) diastereomers; (b) enantiomers; (c) (−); (d) D configuration.
19. Explain the meaning of the term *reducing sugar*. What structural feature characterizes a reducing sugar, and what is the test for a reducing sugar? What mass of Cu$_2$O(s) should be produced when 0.500 g glucose is subjected to this test?
20. There are eight aldopentoses. Draw their structures, and indicate which are enantiomers.
21. The pure α and β forms of D-glucose rotate the plane of polarized light to the right by 112° and 18.7°, respectively (denoted as +112 and +18.7). Are these two forms of glucose enantiomers or diastereomers?
22. When a mixture of the pure α and β forms of D-glucose is allowed to reach equilibrium in solution, the rotation changes to +52.7 (a phenomenon known as mutarotation). What are the percentages of the α and β forms in the equilibrium mixture? [*Hint:* Refer to Exercise 21.]

Fischer Projections and R, S Nomenclature

23. For each pair of Fischer projections, decide whether they represent the same compound, enantiomers, or diastereomers. Check your conclusion by designating the configuration at each stereocenter as R or S.

(a)

(b)

(c)

(d)

24. For each pair of Fischer projections, decide whether they represent the same compound, enantiomers, or diastereomers. Check your conclusion by designating the configuration at each stereocenter as R or S.

(a)

(b)

(c)

(d)

25. Redraw each of the following molecules as a Fischer projection; then assign R or S to each stereocenter.

(a)

(b)

(c)

(d)

26. Redraw each of the following molecules as a Fischer projection; then assign R or S to each stereocenter.

(a)

(b)

(c)

(d)

(e)

Amino Acids, Polypeptides, and Proteins

27. Describe what is meant by each of the following terms, using specific examples where appropriate: **(a)** α-amino acid; **(b)** zwitterion; **(c)** isoelectric point; **(d)** peptide bond; **(e)** tertiary structure.
28. Describe what is meant by each of the following terms, using specific examples where appropriate: **(a)** polypeptide; **(b)** protein; **(c)** N-terminal amino acid; **(d)** α helix; **(e)** denaturation.
29. Write the formulas of the species expected if the amino acid phenylalanine is maintained in **(a)** 1.0 M HCl; **(b)** 1.0 M NaOH; **(c)** a buffer solution with pH = 5.7.
30. Draw plausible structures for the amino acid histidine at **(a)** pH = 3.0; **(b)** pH = 7.6; **(c)** pH = 12.0.
31. Write the structures of **(a)** alanylcysteine; **(b)** threonylvalylglycine.
32. For the polypeptide Met-Val-Thr-Cys, **(a)** write the structural formula; **(b)** name the polypeptide. [*Hint:* Which is the N-terminal, and which is the C-terminal amino acid?]
33. A mixture of the amino acids lysine, proline, and aspartic acid is placed in a gel buffered at pH 6.3. An electric current is applied between an anode and a cathode immersed in the gel. Toward which electrode will each amino acid migrate?
34. A mixture of the amino acids histidine, glutamic acid, and phenylalanine is placed in a gel buffered at pH 5.7. An electric current is applied between an anode and a cathode immersed in the gel. Toward which electrode will each amino acid migrate?
35. Draw condensed structural formulas showing what form you would expect for the essential amino acid threonine **(a)** in strongly acidic solutions, **(b)** at the isoelectric point, and **(c)** in strongly basic solutions.
36. Draw condensed structural formulas for the following amino acids buffered at pH 6.0: **(a)** aspartic acid; **(b)** lysine; and **(c)** alanine.
37. Write the structures of **(a)** the different tripeptides that can be obtained from a combination of alanine, serine, and lysine; **(b)** the tetrapeptides containing two serine and two alanine amino acid units.

38. Write the structures of the different tetrapeptides that can be obtained from a combination of alanine, lysine, serine, and phenylalanine. Give the abbreviated formula of each (such as Ala-Lys-Ser-Phe), starting at the N-terminal end.
39. After undergoing complete hydrolysis, a polypeptide yields the following amino acids: Gly, Leu, Ala, Val, Ser, Thr. Partial hydrolysis yields the following fragments: Ser-Gly-Val, Thr-Val, Ala-Ser, Leu-Thr-Val, Gly-Val-Thr. An experiment using a marker establishes that Ala is the N-terminal amino acid.
    (a) Establish the amino acid sequence in this polypeptide.
    (b) What is the name of the polypeptide?
40. After undergoing complete hydrolysis, a polypeptide yields the following amino acids: Ala, Gly, Lys, Ser, Phe. Partial hydrolysis yields the following fragments: Ala-Lys-Ser, Gly-Phe-Gly, Ser-Gly, Gly-Phe, Lys-Ser-Gly. An experiment using a marker establishes that Ala is the N-terminal amino acid.
    (a) Establish the amino acid sequence in this polypeptide.
    (b) What is the name of the polypeptide?
41. Describe what is meant by the primary, secondary, and tertiary structure of a protein. What is the quaternary structure? Do all proteins have a quaternary structure? Explain.
42. Sickle-cell anemia is sometimes referred to as a "molecular" disease. Comment on the appropriateness of this term.
43. The amino acid (*R*)-alanine is found in insect larvae. Draw the Fischer projection of this amino acid.
44. The amino acid (*R*)-serine is found in earthworms. Draw the Fischer projection of this amino acid.
45. Draw the dashed-wedged line structure for (*S*)-alanine and (*S*)-phenylalanine.
46. Draw the dashed-wedged line structure for (*R*)-proline and (*S*)-valine.

Nucleic Acids

47. What are the two major types of nucleic acids? List their principal components.
48. DNA has been called the "thread of life." Comment on the appropriateness of this expression.
49. If one strand of a DNA molecule has the base sequence of AGC, what must be the sequence on the opposite strand? Draw a structure of this portion of the double helix, showing all hydrogen bonds.
50. If one strand of a DNA molecule has the base sequence TCT, what must be the sequence on the opposite strand? Draw a structure of this portion of the double helix, showing all hydrogen bonds.

Integrative and Advanced Exercises

51. The protein molecule hemoglobin contains four iron atoms. The mass percent iron in hemoglobin is 0.34%. What is the molecular mass of hemoglobin?
52. A 1.00-mL solution containing 1.00 mg of an enzyme was deactivated by the addition of 0.346 μmol AgNO$_3$. What is the *minimum* molecular mass of the enzyme? Why does this calculation yield only a minimum value?

53. What minimum volume of natural gas is needed to produce the hydrogen consumed in converting 15.5 kg of the oil glyceryl trioleate (triolein) to the fat glyceryl tristearate (tristearin)? The natural gas is 92.0% CH_4 and 8.0% C_2H_6 by volume and is measured at 25.5 °C and 756 mmHg pressure. The hydrogen is produced by steam re-forming the natural gas. Assume that natural gas and steam are the only reactants and that carbon dioxide is the only product other than hydrogen.

54. The text states that there are 16 possible aldohexoses. Draw their structures, and indicate which are enantiomers.

55. The term "epimer" is used to describe diastereomers that differ in the configuration about a *single* carbon atom. Which pairs of the eight possible aldopentoses are epimers?

56. The amino acid ornithine, not normally found in proteins, has the following structure at a pH of 1.0.

$$\overset{+}{H_3N}-CH_2-CH_2-CH_2-\underset{\underset{+NH_3}{|}}{CH}-\overset{\overset{O}{\|}}{C}-OH$$

$$pK_{a_1} = 1.94; \quad pK_{a_2} = 8.65; \quad pK_{a_3} = 10.76$$

What is the pI value of this amino acid?

57. In the experiment described on page 1163, the first-generation offspring of DNA molecules each contained one strand with ^{15}N atoms and one with ^{14}N. If the experiment were carried through a second, third, and fourth generation, what fractions of the DNA molecules would still have strands with ^{15}N atoms?

58. Bradykinin is a nonapeptide obtained by the partial hydrolysis of blood serum protein. It causes a lowering of blood pressure and an increase in capillary permeability. Complete hydrolysis of bradykinin yields three proline (Pro), two arginine (Arg), two phenylalanine (Phe), one glycine (Gly), and one serine (Ser) amino acid units. The N-terminal and C-terminal units are both arginine (Arg). In a hypothetical experiment, partial hydrolysis and sequence proof reveals the following fragments: Gly-Phe-Ser-Pro; Pro-Phe-Arg; Ser-Pro-Phe; Pro-Pro-Gly; Pro-Gly-Phe; Arg-Pro-Pro; Phe-Arg. Deduce the sequence of amino acid units in bradykinin.

59. With the aid of the table on page 1164, propose a plausible sequence on a DNA strand that would code for the synthesis of the polypeptide Ser-Gly-Val-Ala. Why is there more than one possible sequence for the DNA strand?

60. Refer to the Integrative Example. A 1.00-g sample of threonine is dissolved in 10.0 mL of 1.00 M HCl, and the solution is titrated with 1.00 M NaOH. Sketch a titration curve for the titration, indicating the approximate pH at representative points on the curve [such as the initial pH, the half-neutralization point(s) and the equivalence point(s)].

61. Projection formulas impose certain limitations and care must be taken in drawing and manipulating them. Use (R)-(+)-glyceraldehyde as an example and show that:
    (a) Rotating the Fischer projection by 90° in the plane of the paper produces the opposite absolute configuration. What is the effect of rotation by 180° and 270° in the plane of the paper?
    (b) Interchanging two substituents converts one enantiomer into the other. What is the effect of two such interchanges?

62. A pentapeptide was isolated from a cell extract and purified. A portion of the compound was treated with 2,4-dinitrofluorobenzene (DNFB), and the resulting material hydrolyzed (recall Figure 27-10). Analysis of the hydrolysis products revealed one mole of DNP-methionine, two moles of methionine, and one mole each of serine and glycine. A second portion of the original compound was partially hydrolyzed and separated into four products. Separately, the four products were hydrolyzed further, giving the following four sets of compounds: (1) one mole of DNP-methionine, one mole of methionine, and one mole of glycine; (2) one mole of DNP-methionine and one mole of methionine; (3) one mole of DNP-serine and one mole of methionine; (4) one mole of DNP-methionine, one mole of methionine, and one mole of serine. What is the amino acid sequence of the pentapeptide?

63. Eighteen of the nineteen 1-amino acids have the *S* configuration at the α carbon (the first carbon after the carboxyl carbon). Cysteine is the only 1-amino acid that has an *R* configuration. Explain.

64. The amino acid threonine, (2S,3R)-2-amino-3-hydroxybutanoic acid, has two stereocenters. Draw the Fischer projection of threonine. How many other possible stereoisomers are there of threonine?

65. Coupling ATP hydrolysis to a thermodynamically unfavorable reaction can shift the equilibrium of a reaction (see Chapter 19).
    (a) Calculate K for the hypothetical reaction A $\longrightarrow$ B when $\Delta G^{\circ\prime}$ is 23 kJ mol^{-1} at 25 °C.
    (b) Calculate K for the same reaction when it is coupled to the hydrolysis of ATP ($\Delta G^{\circ\prime} = -30$ kJ mol^{-1}). Compare with the value obtained in part (a).
    (c) Many cells maintain [ATP] to [ADP] ratios of 400 or more. Calculate the ratio of [B] to [A] when [ATP]/[ADP] = 400 and [P_i] = 5 mM. Compare this ratio to that for the uncoupled reaction.

Feature Problems

66. Useful information about the structures of triglycerides can be obtained through saponification reactions. *The saponification value of a triglyceride is the number of milligrams of KOH required to saponify 1.00 g of the triglyceride.* Unsaturation in the fatty acids in triglycerides can be discovered by studying reactions in which I_2 is added across double bonds. *The iodine number is the number of grams of I_2 that reacts with 100 g of a triglyceride.*
    (a) Determine the saponification value of glyceryl tristearate and the iodine number of glyceryl trioleate.
    (b) Castor oil is a mixture of triglycerides with about 90% of its fatty acid content in ricinoleic acid,

$CH_3(CH_2)_5CHOHCH_2$=$CH(CH_2)_7COOH$. Estimate the saponification value and the iodine number of castor oil.

(c) Based on the composition given in Table 27.2, estimate the range of values for the saponification value and iodine number of safflower oil.

67. The so-called Ruff degradation is a chain-shortening reaction in which an aldose chain is shortened by one C atom, hexoses, for example, being converted into pentoses. In the Ruff degradation, the calcium salt of an aldonic acid (the corresponding carboxylic acid of an aldose) is oxidized with hydrogen peroxide. Ferric ion catalyzes the reaction. The calcium salt of the aldonic acid necessary for the Ruff degradation is obtained by oxidizing an aldose with an aqueous solution of bromine and then adding calcium hydroxide. The reaction scheme is as follows

$$RCHOHCHO \xrightarrow[\text{2. Ca (OH)}_2]{\text{1. Br}_2, \text{H}_2\text{O}} RCHOHCO_2^- (Ca^{2+})_{1/2}$$

$$\downarrow \begin{smallmatrix} H_2O_2 \\ Fe^{3+}(aq) \end{smallmatrix}$$

$$RCHO + CO_2$$

where R represents the rest of the chain of the aldose.
(a) Show that D-glucose can be degraded into D-arabinose. Which other aldose can be degraded into D-arabinose?
(b) Which two monosaccharides can be degraded into D-glyceraldehyde by employing the Ruff degradation only once?

68. If D-(+)-glyceraldehyde is treated with HCN in aqueous solution under basic conditions for three days at room temperature, cyanohydrins are formed (see Chapter 26). The cyanohydrins are not isolated, but are hydrolyzed to hydroxyacids in the same reaction mixture using dilute sulfuric acid. In this process, a new stereocenter is formed in the molecule. The products are diastereomers, formed in unequal amounts, and separable from each other by recrystallization because of their different physical properties, including solubilities. The trihydroxybutanoic acids are separated and then oxidized to tartaric acid with dilute nitric acid, which oxidizes only the primary alcohol group.
(a) Ignoring stereochemistry, draw the reaction sequence for the transformations described above and hence deduce the structure of tartaric acid.
(b) Starting from the Fischer projection of D-(+)-glyceraldehyde and using the reaction scheme from part (a), draw Fischer projections of the two trihydroxybutanoic acids formed and designate the chiral centers as R or S.
(c) Starting from the Fischer projection of D-(+)-glyceraldehyde and using the reaction scheme from part (a), draw Fischer projections of the two forms of tartaric formed and designate the chiral centers as R or S.
(d) One form of tartaric acid obtained is optically active, rotating the plane of polarized light in a negative sense (−). The other isomer formed, called *meso*-tartaric acid, is not optically active. Explain why the other isomer is not optically active. Draw the dashed-wedged line structure that corresponds to the Fischer projection of *meso*-tartaric acid, Can you describe how the two halves of the molecule are related? Using Fischer projections, write equations for the conversion of L-(−)-glyceraldehyde to tartaric acid. Show clearly the stereochemistry of the tartaric acids that are formed, and indicate whether you expect them to be optically active.

Self-Assessment Exercises

69. In your own words, define the following terms or symbols: **(a)** (+); **(b)** L; **(c)** sugar; **(d)** α-amino acid; **(e)** isoelectric point.

70. Briefly describe each of the following ideas, phenomena, or methods: **(a)** saponification; **(b)** chiral carbon atom; **(c)** racemic mixture; **(d)** denaturation of a protein.

71. Explain the important distinctions between each pair of terms: **(a)** fat and oil; **(b)** enantiomer and diastereomer; **(c)** primary and secondary structure of a protein; **(d)** DNA and RNA; **(e)** ADP and ATP.

72. The substance *glyceryl trilinoleate* (linoleic acid: $C_{17}H_{31}COOH$) is best described as a **(a)** fat; **(b)** oil; **(c)** wax; **(d)** fatty acid; **(e)** phospholipid.

73. The best description of the observed rotation of plane polarized light by a sugar sample labeled DL-erythrose is **(a)** to the left; **(b)** to the right; **(c)** alternately to the right and then to the left; **(d)** neither to the left nor the right; **(e)** clockwise.

74. Of the following names, the one that refers to a simple sugar in its cyclic (ring) form is **(a)** β-galactose; **(b)** L-(−)-glyceraldehyde; **(c)** D-(+)-glucose; **(d)** DL-erythrose; **(e)** (R)-(+)-glyceraldehyde.

75. The coagulation of egg whites by boiling is an example of **(a)** saponification; **(b)** inversion of a sugar; **(c)** hydrolysis of a protein; **(d)** denaturation of a protein; **(e)** condensation of amino acids.

76. A molecule in which the energy of metabolism is stored is **(a)** glucose; **(b)** DNA; **(c)** RNA; **(d)** glycerol; **(e)** ATP.

77. Of the following, the one that is not a constituent of a nucleic acid chain is **(a)** purine base; **(b)** phosphate group; **(c)** glycerol; **(d)** pentose sugar; **(e)** pyrimidine base.

78. The structure of the DNA molecule is best described as **(a)** a random coil; **(b)** a double helix; **(c)** a pleated sheet; **(d)** partly coiled; **(e)** a branched chain.

79. What is the maximum mass of a sodium soap that can be prepared from 125 g of glyceryl tripalmitate?

80. With reference to Figure 27-25, identify the purine bases, the pyrimidine bases, the pentose sugars, and the phosphate groups. Is this a chain of DNA or RNA? Explain.

81. Upon complete hydrolysis of a pentapeptide the following amino acids are obtained: valine, phenylalanine, glycine, cysteine, and tyrosine. Partial hydrolysis yields the following fragments: Val-Phe; Cys-Gly; Cys-Val-Phe; Tyr-Phe. If glycine is the N-terminal acid, what is the sequence of amino acids in the polypeptide?

82. Appendix E describes a useful study aid known as concept mapping. Using the method presented in Appendix E, construct a concept map illustrating the concepts in Section 27-4.

 eMedia Exercises

83. The characteristic structure of polypeptides is illustrated in the **Proteins and Amino Acids** animation (*Activebook 27-4*). **(a)** Write out the entire molecular structure for the tripeptide Lys-Ala-Phe. **(b)** What aspects of polypeptide structures allow them to be abbreviated in the form Lys-Ala-Phe? **(c)** How many different tripeptides could be formed from these three amino acids?

84. **(a)** From the **Enzyme Catalysis** animation (*Activebook 27-5*), describe the role of primary and secondary structure in the selectivity of the catalyst. **(b)** In this animation, in what sense is the reaction catalytic?

85. View the **Deoxyribonucleic Acid (DNA)** model found in *Activebook 27-6*. There are a number of options for adjusting the image of this segment under the "Display" menu (backbone, ribbon, strands, cartoon). You can also modify the representation of only a portion of the molecule by first using the Select > Nucleic submenu to pick out a particular structure. **(a)** Why are multiple depictions of the DNA structure useful? **(b)** Adjust the display to show the backbone of the segment in ball-and-stick view, and the bases in wireframe view, and adjust the Options to display the hydrogen bonds. What do you learn about the tertiary structure of DNA from this view?

MATHEMATICAL OPERATIONS

A-1 EXPONENTIAL ARITHMETIC

Measured quantities in this text range from very small to very large. For example, the mass of an individual hydrogen atom is 0.00000000000000000000000167 g, and the number of molecules in 18.0153 g of the substance water is 602,214,000,000,000,000,000,000. These numbers are difficult to write in conventional form and are even more cumbersome to handle in numerical calculations. We can greatly simplify them by expressing them in exponential form. The *exponential form* of a number consists of a coefficient (a number with value between 1 and 10) multiplied by a power of 10.

The number 10^n is the *nth power* of 10. If n is a *positive* quantity, 10^n is *greater than 1*. If n is a *negative* quantity, 10^n is *between 0 and 1*. The value of $10^0 = 1$.

Positive powers

$10^0 = 1$

$10^1 = 10$

$10^2 = 10 \times 10 = 100$

$10^3 = 10 \times 10 \times 10 = 1000$

Negative powers

$10^0 = 1$

$10^{-1} = \dfrac{1}{10} = 0.1$

$10^{-2} = \dfrac{1}{10 \times 10} = \dfrac{1}{10^2} = 0.01$

$10^{-3} = \dfrac{1}{10 \times 10 \times 10} = \dfrac{1}{10^3} = 0.001$

To express the number 3170 in exponential form, we write

$$3170 = 3.17 \times 1000 = 3.17 \times 10^3$$

For the number 0.00046 we write

$$0.00046 = 4.6 \times 0.0001 = 4.6 \times 10^{-4}$$

A simpler method of converting a number to exponential form that avoids intermediate steps is illustrated below.

$$3\underset{3\ 2\ 1}{\underbrace{1\ 7\ 0}} = 3.17 \times 10^3$$

$$0.0\underset{1\ 2\ 3\ 4}{\underbrace{0\ 0\ 4}}6 = 4.6 \times 10^{-4}$$

That is, to convert a number to exponential form,

- Move the decimal point to obtain a coefficient with value between 1 and 10.
- The exponent (power) of 10 is equal to the number of places the decimal point is moved.
- If the decimal point is moved *to the left*, the exponent of 10 is *positive*.
- If the decimal point is moved *to the right*, the exponent of 10 is *negative*.

To convert a number from exponential form to conventional form, move the decimal point the number of places indicated by the power of 10. That is,

$$6.1 \times 10^6 = 6.\underset{1\,2\,3\,4\,5\,6}{\underbrace{100000}} = 6{,}100{,}000$$

$$8.2 \times 10^{-5} = \underset{5\,4\,3\,2\,1}{\underbrace{0.00008}}2 = 0.000082$$

Electronic calculators designed for scientific and engineering work easily accommodate exponential numbers. A typical procedure is to key in the number, followed by the key "EXP" or "EE." Thus, the keystrokes required for the number 6.57×10^3 are

$$\boxed{6}\;\boxed{.}\;\boxed{5}\;\boxed{7}\;\boxed{\text{EXP}}\;\boxed{3}$$

and the result displayed is $\boxed{6.57^{03}}$

For the number 6.25×10^{-4}, the keystrokes are

$$\boxed{6}\;\boxed{.}\;\boxed{2}\;\boxed{5}\;\boxed{\text{EXP}}\;\boxed{4}\;\boxed{\pm}$$

and the result displayed is $\boxed{6.25^{-04}}$

Some calculators have a mode setting that automatically converts all numbers and calculated results to the exponential form, regardless of the form in which numbers are entered. In this mode setting you can generally also set the number of significant figures to be carried in displayed results.

▶ The instructions given here are for a typical electronic calculator. The keystrokes required with your calculator may be somewhat different. Look for specific instructions in the instruction manual supplied with the calculator.

ADDITION AND SUBTRACTION. To add or subtract numbers written in exponential form, first express each quantity as *the same power of 10*. Then add and/or subtract the coefficients as indicated. That is, treat the power of 10 as you would a unit common to the terms being added and/or subtracted. In the example that follows, convert 3.8×10^{-3} to 0.38×10^{-2} and use 10^{-2} as the common power of 10.

$$(5.60 \times 10^{-2}) + (3.8 \times 10^{-3}) - (1.52 \times 10^{-2}) = (5.60 + 0.38 - 1.52) \times 10^{-2}$$

$$= 4.46 \times 10^{-2}$$

MULTIPLICATION. Consider the numbers $a \times 10^y$ and $b \times 10^z$. Their product is $a \times b \times 10^{(y+z)}$. *Coefficients are multiplied, and exponents are added.*

$$0.0220 \times 0.0040 \times 750 = (2.20 \times 10^{-2})(4.0 \times 10^{-3})(7.5 \times 10^2)$$

$$= (2.20 \times 4.0 \times 7.5) \times 10^{(-2-3+2)} = 66 \times 10^{-3}$$

$$= 6.6 \times 10^1 \times 10^{-3} = 6.6 \times 10^{-2}$$

DIVISION. Consider the numbers $a \times 10^y$ and $b \times 10^z$. Their quotient is

$$\frac{a \times 10^y}{b \times 10^z} = (a/b) \times 10^{(y-z)}$$

Coefficients are divided, and the exponent of the denominator is subtracted from the exponent of the numerator.

$$\frac{20.0 \times 636 \times 0.150}{0.0400 \times 1.80} = \frac{(2.00 \times 10^1)(6.36 \times 10^2)(1.50 \times 10^{-1})}{(4.00 \times 10^{-2}) \times 1.80}$$

$$= \frac{2.00 \times 6.36 \times 1.50 \times 10^{(1+2-1)}}{(4.00 \times 1.80) \times 10^{-2}} = \frac{19.1 \times 10^2}{7.20 \times 10^{-2}}$$

$$= 2.65 \times 10^{(2-(-2))} = 2.65 \times 10^4$$

RAISING A NUMBER TO A POWER.   To "square" the number $a \times 10^y$ means to determine the value $(a \times 10^y)^2$, or the product $(a \times 10^y)(a \times 10^y)$. According to the rule for multiplication, this product is $(a \times a) \times 10^{(y+y)} = a^2 \times 10^{2y}$. When an exponential number is raised to a power, *the coefficient is raised to that power and the exponent is multiplied by the power*. For example,

$$(0.0034)^3 = (3.4 \times 10^{-3})^3 = (3.4)^3 \times 10^{(3)(-3)} = 39 \times 10^{-9} = 3.9 \times 10^{-8}$$

EXTRACTING THE ROOT OF AN EXPONENTIAL NUMBER.   To extract the root of a number is the same as raising the number to a fractional power. This means that the square root of a number is the number to the one-half power; the cube root is the number to the one-third power; and so on. Thus,

$$\sqrt{a \times 10^y} = (a \times 10^y)^{1/2} = a^{1/2} \times 10^{y/2}$$

$$\sqrt{156} = \sqrt{1.56 \times 10^2} = (1.56)^{1/2} \times 10^{2/2} = 1.25 \times 10^1 = 12.5$$

In the following example, where the cube root is sought, the exponent (-5) is not divisible by 3; the number is rewritten with an exponent (-6) that is divisible by 3.

$$(3.52 \times 10^{-5})^{1/3} = (35.2 \times 10^{-6})^{1/3} = (35.2)^{1/3} \times 10^{-6/3} = 3.28 \times 10^{-2}$$

A-2   LOGARITHMS

The *common* logarithm (log) of a number (N) is the exponent (x) to which the base 10 must be raised to yield the number N. That is, $\log N = x$ means that $N = 10^x = 10^{\log N}$. For simple powers of ten, for example,

$$\log 1 = \log 10^0 = 0$$

$$\log 10 = \log 10^1 = 1 \qquad \log 0.10 = \log 10^{-1} = -1$$

$$\log 100 = \log 10^2 = 2 \qquad \log 0.01 = \log 10^{-2} = -2$$

Most of the numbers that result from measurements and appear in calculations are not simple powers of 10, but it is not difficult to obtain logarithms of these numbers with an electronic calculator. To find the logarithm of a number, enter the number, followed by the "LOG" key.

$$\log 734 = 2.866$$

$$\log 0.0150 = -1.824$$

Another common example requires us to find the number having a certain logarithm. This number is often called the *antilogarithm* or the *inverse* logarithm. For example, if $\log N = 4.350$, what is N? N, the antilogarithm, is simply $10^{4.350}$, and to find its value we enter 4.350, followed by the key "10^x". Depending on the calculator used, it is usually necessary to press the key "INV" or "2nd F" before the log key.

$$\log N = 4.350$$

$$N = 10^{4.350}$$

$$N = 2.24 \times 10^4$$

If the task is to find the antilogarithm of -4.350, we again note that $N = 10^{-4.350}$, and $N = 4.47 \times 10^{-5}$. The required keystrokes on a typical electronic calculator are

$$\boxed{4}\,\boxed{.}\,\boxed{3}\,\boxed{5}\,\boxed{0}\,\boxed{\pm}\,\boxed{\text{INV}}\,\boxed{\text{log}}$$

and the display, to three significant figures, is

$$\boxed{4.47^{-05}}$$

SOME USEFUL RELATIONSHIPS. From the definition of a logarithm we can write $M = 10^{\log M}$, $N = 10^{\log N}$, and $M \times N = 10^{\log(M \times N)}$. This means that

$$\log(M \times N) = \log M + \log N$$

Similarly, it is not difficult to show that

$$\log \frac{M}{N} = \log M - \log N$$

Finally, because $N^2 = N \times N$, $10^{\log N^2} = 10^{\log N} \times 10^{\log N}$, and

$$\log N^2 = \log N + \log N = 2 \log N$$

Or, in more general terms,

$$\log N^a = a \log N$$

This expression is especially useful for extracting the roots of numbers. Thus, to determine $(2.5 \times 10^{-8})^{1/5}$, we write

$$\log(2.5 \times 10^{-8})^{1/5} = \tfrac{1}{5} \log(2.5 \times 10^{-8}) = \tfrac{1}{5}(-7.60) = -1.52$$

$$(2.5 \times 10^{-8})^{1/5} = 10^{-1.52} = 0.030$$

SIGNIFICANT FIGURES IN LOGARITHMS. To establish the number of significant figures to use in a logarithm or antilogarithm, use this fundamental rule: All digits to the *right* of the decimal point in a logarithm are significant. Digits to the *left* are used to establish the power of 10. Thus, the logarithm -2.08 is expressed to *two* significant figures. The antilogarithm of -2.08 should also be expressed to *two* significant figures; it is 8.3×10^{-3}. To help settle this point, take the antilogarithms of -2.07, -2.08, and -2.09. You will find these antilogs to be 8.5×10^{-3}, 8.3×10^{-3}, and 8.1×10^{-3}, respectively. Only *two* significant figures are justified.

NATURAL LOGARITHMS. Logarithms can be expressed to a base other than 10. For instance, because $2^3 = 8$, $\log_2 8 = 3$ (read as, "the logarithm of 8 to the base 2 is equal to 3"). Similarly, $\log_2 10 = 3.322$. Several equations in this text are derived by the methods of calculus and involve logarithms. These equations require that the logarithm be a "natural" one. A *natural* logarithm has the base $e = 2.71828\ldots$. A logarithm to the base "e" is usually denoted as *ln*.

The relationship between a "natural" and "common" logarithm simply involves the factor $\log_e 10 = 2.303$. That is, for the number N, $\ln N = 2.303 \log N$. The methods and relationships described for logarithms and antilogarithms to the base 10 all apply to the base e as well, except that the relevant keys on an electronic calculator are "ln" and "e^x" rather than "LOG" and "10^x".

A-3 ALGEBRAIC OPERATIONS

An algebraic equation is solved when one of the quantities, the unknown, is expressed in terms of all the other quantities in the equation. This effect is achieved when the unknown is present, *alone*, on one side of the equation, and the rest of the terms are on the other side. To solve an equation, a rearrangement of terms may be necessary. The basic principle governing these rearrangements is quite simple. *Whatever is done to one side of the equation must be done to the other as well.*

$$3x^2 + 6 = 33 \qquad \textit{Solve for x.}$$

$$3x^2 + 6 - 6 = 33 - 6 \qquad \text{(1) Subtract 6 from each side.}$$

$$3x^2 = 27$$

$$\frac{3x^2}{3} = \frac{27}{3} \qquad \text{(2) Divide each side by 3.}$$

$$x^2 = 9$$

$$\sqrt{x^2} = \sqrt{9} \qquad \text{(3) Extract the square root of each side.}$$

$$x = 3 \qquad \text{(4) Simplify. The square root of 9 is 3.}$$

QUADRATIC EQUATIONS.   A quadratic equation has the form $ax^2 + bx + c = 0$, where a, b, and c are constants (a cannot be equal to 0). A number of calculations in the text require us to solve a quadratic equation. At times, quadratic equations are of the form

$$(x + n)^2 = m^2$$

Such equations can be solved by extracting the square root of each side.

$$x + n = \pm m \quad \text{and} \quad x = m - n \quad \text{or} \quad x = -m - n$$

More likely, however, the *quadratic formula* will be needed.

$$x = \frac{-b \pm \sqrt{b^2 - 4ac}}{2a}$$

In Example 15-13 on page 649, the following equation must be solved.

$$\frac{(0.300 - x)}{(0.200 + x)(0.100 + x)} = 2.98$$

This is a quadratic equation, but before the quadratic formula can be applied, the equation must be rearranged to the standard form: $ax^2 + bx + c = 0$. This is accomplished in the steps that follow.

$$(0.300 - x) = 2.98(0.200 + x)(0.100 + x)$$

$$0.300 - x = 2.98(0.0200 + 0.300x + x^2)$$

$$0.300 - x = 0.0596 + 0.894x + 2.98x^2$$

$$2.98x^2 + 1.894x - 0.240 = 0 \tag{A.1}$$

Now we can apply the quadratic formula.

$$x = \frac{-1.894 \pm \sqrt{(1.894)^2 + (4 \times 2.98 \times 0.240)}}{2 \times 2.98}$$

$$= \frac{-1.894 \pm \sqrt{3.587 + 2.86}}{2 \times 2.98}$$

$$= \frac{-1.894 \pm \sqrt{6.45}}{2 \times 2.98} = \frac{-1.894 \pm 2.54}{2 \times 2.98}$$

$$= \frac{-1.894 + 2.54}{2 \times 2.98} = \frac{0.65}{5.96} = 0.11$$

Note that only the $(+)$ value of the $(\pm)$ sign was used in solving for x. If the $(-)$ value had been used, a negative value of x would have resulted. However, for the given situation a negative value of x is meaningless.

The Method of Successive Approximations. The quadratic equation that was just solved using the quadratic formula can be solved by an alternative method that can be extended to equations of higher order, such as the cubic, quartic, and quintic equations often encountered in solving equilibrium problems. To illustrate the method suppose we wish to solve expression (A.1) without recourse to the quadratic formula. We can rewrite the equation as follows

$$x = \frac{2.98x^2 - 0.240}{-1.894}$$

and make a guess at the value of x, which we substitute into the right hand side of the equation to calculate a new value of x. If we guess 0.15, which is reasonable given the starting concentrations involved in Example 15-13, we calculate

$$x = \frac{2.98 \times (0.15)^2 - 0.240}{-1.894} = 0.091$$

We can now use this value of x to calculate a new one.

$$x = \frac{2.98 \times (0.091)^2 - 0.240}{-1.894} = 0.114$$

Repeating this procedure one more time, we get

$$x = \frac{2.98 \times (0.114)^2 - 0.240}{-1.894} = 0.106$$

One more attempt gives a value of 0.11, which is in agreement with the answer previously obtained. The method that we have just used is called the method of successive approximations.

Let us now apply the method of successive approximations to the equation obtained in the Integrative Example of Chapter 15, namely

$$256x^5 - 0.74[(1.00 - x)(1.00 - 2x)^2] = 0 \tag{A.2}$$

The approach we can take here is to guess a value of x; evaluate the expression to see how close to zero it comes; and then adjust the value of x accordingly. Let us start with a guess of 0.40. The result is

$$256(0.40)^5 - 0.74[(1.00 - 0.40)(1.00 - 2 \times 0.40)^2] = 2.60$$

Clearly the value of 0.40 is too large. If we now try 0.10 we obtain a value of -0.42. We have overshot the value of x. We can now try a value of 0.25 (halfway between our two previous guesses) and obtain 0.11. We realize now that we have to reduce the guessed value of x slightly to get closer to zero. If we try 0.20 we obtain -0.13, and if we next try the value $x = 0.225$ we obtain -0.03. We are now very close to our goal of finding the value of x that satisfies the expression. One final guess of 0.23 gives a value of -0.001, a very satisfactory result.

An alternative approach is to rewrite expression (A.2) as

$$x^5 = \frac{0.74[(1.00 - x)(1.00 - 2x)^2]}{256}$$

and evaluate x as the fifth root of this new expression. If we substitute a value of $x = 0.40$ on the right side, we obtain $x = 0.15$ on the left side. Now using this value on the right we calculate a new value of $x = 0.26$ on the left. Using this value we obtain $x = 0.22$ on the left, and finally with this last value we obtain $x = 0.23$, in agreement with our previous procedure. Which method we use is a matter of convenience, but the second method provides a new value of x whereas the first method may require more trial and error. When using the method of successive approximations, it is often a useful strategy to take the average of two results in order to speed up the convergence. The method of successive approximations can be very useful, but sometimes, depending how the equation is set up, the convergence to the correct answer may be slow or the process may even diverge. In such circumstances, the expression can be graphed as a function of x to ascertain where the solutions occur. In any event, we must always make sure that any answer obtained is reasonable from a chemical or physical point of view.

A-4   GRAPHS

Suppose the following sets of numbers are obtained for two quantities x and y by laboratory measurement.

$$x = 0, 1, 2, 3, 4, \ldots$$

$$y = 2, 4, 6, 8, 10, \ldots$$

The relationship between these sets of numbers is not difficult to establish.

$$y = 2x + 2$$

Ideally, the results of experimental measurements are best expressed through a mathematical equation. Sometimes, however, an exact equation cannot be written, or its form is not clear from the experimental data. The graphing of data is very useful in such cases. In Figure A-1 the points listed above are located on a coordinate grid in which x values are placed along the horizontal axis (abscissa) and y values along the vertical axis (ordinate). For each point the x and y values are indicated in parentheses.

The data points are seen to define a straight line. A mathematical equation of a straight line has the form

$$y = mx + b$$

Values of m, the *slope* of the line, and b, the *intercept*, can be obtained from the straight-line graph.

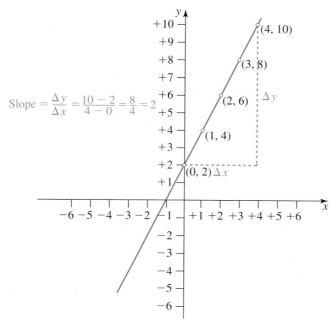

$$\text{Slope} = \frac{\Delta y}{\Delta x} = \frac{10 - 2}{4 - 0} = \frac{8}{4} = 2$$

▲ FIGURE A-1
A straight-line graph: $y = mx + b$

When $x = 0$, $y = b$. The intercept is the point where the straight line intersects the y-axis. The slope can be obtained from two points on the graph.

$$y_2 = mx_2 + b \quad \text{and} \quad y_1 = mx_1 + b$$

$$y_2 - y_1 = m(x_2 - x_1) + b - b$$

$$m = \frac{y_2 - y_1}{x_2 - x_1}$$

From the straight line in Figure A-1, can you establish that $m = b = 2$?

The technique used above to eliminate the constant b is applied to logarithmic functions in several places in the text. For example, the expression written below is from page 481. In this expression P is a pressure, T is a Kelvin temperature, and A and B are constants. The equation is that of a straight line.

$$\ln P = -A\left(\frac{1}{T}\right) + B$$

equation of straight line: $\qquad y \;=\; m \cdot x \;+\; b$

We can write this equation twice, for the point (P_1, T_1) and the point (P_2, T_2).

$$\ln P_1 = -A\left(\frac{1}{T_1}\right) + B \quad \text{and} \quad \ln P_2 = -A\left(\frac{1}{T_2}\right) + B$$

The difference between these equations is

$$\ln P_2 - \ln P_1 = -A\left(\frac{1}{T_2}\right) + B + A\left(\frac{1}{T_1}\right) - B$$

$$\ln\frac{P_2}{P_1} = A\left(\frac{1}{T_1} - \frac{1}{T_2}\right)$$

A-5 USING CONVERSION FACTORS (DIMENSIONAL ANALYSIS)

Some calculations in general chemistry require that a quantity measured in one set of units be converted to another set of units. Consider this fact.

$$1 \text{ m} = 100 \text{ cm}$$

Divide each side of the equation by 1 m.

$$\frac{1 \text{ m}}{1 \text{ m}} = \frac{100 \text{ cm}}{1 \text{ m}}$$

On the left side of the equation, the numerator and denominator are identical; they cancel.

$$1 = \frac{100 \text{ cm}}{1 \text{ m}} \tag{A.3}$$

On the right side they are not identical, but they are equal because they do represent the *same length*. The ratio 100 cm/1 m, when multiplied by a length in meters, converts that length to centimeters. The ratio is called a *conversion factor*.

Consider the question, "how many centimeters are there in 6.22 m?" The measured quantity is 6.22 m, and multiplying this quantity by 1 does not change its value.

$$6.22 \text{ m} \times 1 = 6.22 \text{ m}$$

Now replace the factor "1" by its equivalent—the conversion factor (A.3). Cancel the unit, m, and carry out the multiplication.

$$6.22 \ \cancel{m} \times \underbrace{\frac{100 \text{ cm}}{1 \ \cancel{m}}}_{\substack{\text{this factor} \\ \text{converts} \\ \text{m to cm}}} = 622 \text{ cm}$$

Next consider the question, "how many meters are there in 576 cm?" If we use the same factor (A.3) as before, the result is nonsensical.

$$576 \text{ cm} \times \frac{100 \text{ cm}}{1 \text{ m}} = 5.76 \times 10^4 \text{ cm}^2/\text{m}$$

Factor (A.3) must be rearranged to 1 m/100 cm.

$$576 \ \cancel{cm} \times \underbrace{\frac{1 \text{ m}}{100 \ \cancel{cm}}}_{\substack{\text{this factor} \\ \text{converts} \\ \text{cm to m}}} = 5.76 \text{ m}$$

This second example emphasizes two points.

1. There are two ways to write a conversion factor—in one form or its reciprocal (inverse). Because a conversion factor is equal to 1, its value is not changed by the inversion, but:

2. A conversion factor must be used in such a way as to produce the necessary cancellaton of units.

Calculations based on conversion factors are always of the form

> *information sought = information given × conversion factor(s)*   (A.4)

Often several conversions must be made in sequence in order to get to the desired result. For example, if we want to know how many yards (yd) there are in 576 cm, we find that there is no direct cm → yd conversion factor available. From the inside back cover of the text, however, we do find a conversion factor for cm → in. Thus, we can develop a *conversion pathway*, that is, a series of conversion factors that will take us from centimeters to yards:

$$\text{cm} \quad \rightarrow \quad \text{in} \quad \rightarrow \quad \text{ft} \quad \rightarrow \quad \text{yd}$$

$$? \text{ yards} = 576 \ \cancel{cm} \times \frac{1 \ \cancel{in}}{2.54 \ \cancel{cm}} \times \frac{1 \ \cancel{ft}}{12 \ \cancel{in}} \times \frac{1 \text{ yd}}{3 \ \cancel{ft}}$$

$$= 6.30 \text{ yd}$$

We can use the same idea of a conversion pathway to deal with the somewhat more challenging situation faced when the units are squared (or cubed). Consider the question, "how many square feet (ft²) correspond to an area of 1.00 square meter (m²), given that 1 m = 39.37 in and 12 in = 1 ft?" Here, it may be helpful to begin by drawing a sketch or outline of the situation. Figure A-2 represents an area of 1.00 m². Think of it as a square with sides 1 m long. Figure A-2 also represents the length 1 ft and an area of 1.00 ft². Do you see that there is somewhat more than 9 ft² in 1 m²?

◀ Because of the importance of the cancellation of units, this problem-solving method is often called *unit analysis* or *dimensional analysis*.

▲ **FIGURE A-2**
Comparison of one square foot and one square meter
One meter is slightly longer than 3 ft; 1 m² is somewhat larger than 9 ft².

We can write expression (A.4) as follows:

$$? \text{ ft}^2 = 1.00 \text{ m}^2 \times \underbrace{\left(\frac{39.37 \text{ in}}{1 \text{ m}}\right)\left(\frac{39.37 \text{ in}}{1 \text{ m}}\right)}_{\substack{\text{to convert} \\ \text{m}^2 \text{ to in}^2}} \times \underbrace{\left(\frac{1 \text{ ft}}{12 \text{ in}}\right)\left(\frac{1 \text{ ft}}{12 \text{ in}}\right)}_{\substack{\text{to convert} \\ \text{in}^2 \text{ to ft}^2}}$$

This is the same as writing

$$? \text{ ft}^2 = 1.00 \text{ m}^2 \times \frac{(39.37)^2 \text{ in}^2}{1 \text{ m}^2} \times \frac{1 \text{ ft}^2}{(12)^2 \text{ in}^2} = 10.8 \text{ ft}^2$$

Another way to look at the problem is to convert the length 1.00 m to feet,

$$? \text{ ft} = 1.00 \text{ m} \times \frac{39.37 \text{ in}}{1 \text{ m}} \times \frac{1 \text{ ft}}{12 \text{ in}} = 3.28 \text{ ft}$$

and square the result

$$? \text{ ft}^2 = 3.28 \text{ ft} \times 3.28 \text{ ft} = 10.8 \text{ ft}^2$$

Our last example incorporates several ideas discussed above. Here we will examine the situation in which the units in both the numerator and denominator must be converted. Consider the question, "how many meters per second (m/s) correspond to a speed of 63 mph, given that 1 mi = 5280 ft?"

We need to convert from miles to meters in the numerator and from hours to seconds in the denominator. We will need to use conversion factors from elsewhere in Appendix A-5 in addition to the given value. Also, we must be careful that our conversion factors produce the correct cancellation of units.

$$? \frac{\text{m}}{\text{s}} = \frac{63 \text{ mi}}{1 \text{ h}} \times \frac{1 \text{ h}}{60 \text{ min}} \times \frac{1 \text{ min}}{60 \text{ s}} \times \frac{5280 \text{ ft}}{1 \text{ mi}} \times \frac{12 \text{ in}}{1 \text{ ft}} \times \frac{1 \text{ m}}{39.37 \text{ in}}$$

$$= 28 \frac{\text{m}}{\text{s}}$$

In an alternative approach we break down the problem into three steps: (1) Convert 63 miles to a distance in meters; (2) convert 1 hour to a time in seconds; and (3) express the speed as a ratio of distance over time.

Step 1.

$$\text{distance} = 63 \text{ mi} \times \frac{5280 \text{ ft}}{1 \text{ mi}} \times \frac{12 \text{ in}}{1 \text{ ft}} \times \frac{1 \text{ m}}{39.37 \text{ in}} = 1.0 \times 10^5 \text{ m}$$

Step 2.

$$\text{time} = 1 \text{ h} \times \frac{60 \text{ min}}{1 \text{ h}} \times \frac{60 \text{ s}}{1 \text{ min}} = 3.6 \times 10^3 \text{ s}$$

Step 3.

$$\text{speed} = \frac{\text{distance}}{\text{time}} = \frac{1.0 \times 10^5 \text{ m}}{3.6 \times 10^3 \text{ s}} = 28 \frac{\text{m}}{\text{s}}$$

In conclusion, we have shown (1) how to make a conversion factor; (2) that a conversion factor may be inverted; (3) that a series of conversion factors may be used to make a conversion pathway; (4) that conversion factors may be raised to powers, if necessary; and (5) that conversions of values with units in both the numerator and the denominator (such as miles per hour or pounds per square inch) can be performed in one step or in several steps.

SOME BASIC PHYSICAL CONCEPTS

APPENDIX

B-1   VELOCITY AND ACCELERATION

Time elapses as an object moves from one point to another. The *velocity* of the object is defined as the distance traveled per unit of time. An automobile that travels a distance of 60.0 km in exactly one hour has a velocity of 60.0 km/h (or 16.7 m/s).

Table B.1 contains data on the velocity of a free-falling object. For this motion, velocity is not constant—it increases with time. The falling object "speeds up" continuously. The rate of change of velocity with time is called *acceleration*. Acceleration has the units of distance per unit time per unit time. With the methods of calculus, mathematical equations can be derived for the velocity (u) and distance (d) traveled in a time (t) by an object that has a constant acceleration (a).

$$u = at \tag{B.1}$$

$$d = \tfrac{1}{2}at^2 \tag{B.2}$$

For a free-falling object, the constant acceleration, called the *acceleration due to gravity*, is $a = g = 9.8 \text{ m/s}^2$. Equations (B.1) and (B.2) can be used to calculate the velocity and distance traveled by a free-falling object.

TABLE B.1	Velocity and Acceleration of a Free-Falling Body		
Time Elapsed, s	Total Distance, m	Velocity, m/s	Acceleration, m/s²
0	0		
		4.9	
1	4.9		9.8
		14.7	
2	19.6		9.8
		24.5	
3	44.1		9.8
		34.3	
4	78.4		

B-2   FORCE AND WORK

Newton's *first law* of motion states that an object at rest remains at rest, and that an object in motion remains in uniform motion unless acted upon by an external force. The tendency for an object to remain at rest or in uniform motion is called *inertia*; a *force* is what is required to overcome inertia. Since the application of a force either gives an object motion or changes its motion, the actual effect of a force is to change the velocity of an object. Change in velocity is an *acceleration*, so force is what provides an object with acceleration.

Newton's *second law* of motion describes the force F required to produce an acceleration a in an object of mass m.

$$F = ma \tag{B.3}$$

The basic unit of force in the SI system is the *newton* (N). It is the force required to provide a one-kilogram mass with an acceleration of one meter per second per second.

$$1\,N = 1\,kg \times 1\,m\,s^{-2} \tag{B.4}$$

The force of gravity on an object (its weight) is the product of the mass of the object and the acceleration due to gravity, g.

$$F = mg \tag{B.5}$$

Work (w) is performed when a force acts through a distance.

$$\text{work }(w) = \text{force }(F) \times \text{distance }(d) \tag{B.6}$$

The *joule* (J) is the amount of work associated with a force of one newton (N) acting through a distance of one meter.

$$1\,J = 1\,N \times 1\,m \tag{B.7}$$

From the definition of the newton in expression (B.4), we can also write

$$1\,J = 1\,kg \times 1\,m\,s^{-2} \times 1\,m = 1\,kg\,m^2\,s^{-2} \tag{B.8}$$

B-3 ENERGY

Energy is defined as the capacity to do work, but there are other useful descriptions of energy as well. For example, a moving object possesses a kind of energy known as *kinetic energy*. We can obtain a useful equation for kinetic energy by combining some of the other simple equations in this appendix. Thus, because work is the product of a force and distance (equation B.6), and force is the product of a mass and acceleration (equation B.3), we can write

$$w \text{ (work)} = m \times a \times d \tag{B.9}$$

Now, if we substitute equation (B.2) relating acceleration (a), distance (d), and time (t), into equation (B.9), we obtain

$$w \text{ (work)} = m \times a \times \frac{1}{2}at^2 \tag{B.10}$$

Finally, let's substitute expression (B.1) relating acceleration (a) and velocity (u) into (B.10). That is, because $a = u/t$,

$$w \text{ (work)} = \frac{1}{2}m\left(\frac{u}{t}\right)^2 t^2 \tag{B.11}$$

Think of the work in (B.11) as the amount of work necessary to produce a velocity of u in an object of mass m. This amount of work is the energy that appears in the object as kinetic energy (e_k).

$$e_k \text{ (kinetic energy)} = \frac{1}{2}mu^2 \tag{B.12}$$

An object at rest may also have the capacity to do work by changing its position. The energy it possesses, which can be transformed into actual work, is called *potential energy*. Think of potential energy as energy "stored" within an object. Equations can be written for potential energy, but the exact forms of these equations depend on the manner in which the energy is "stored."

B-4   Magnetism

Attractive and repulsive forces associated with a magnet are centered at regions called *poles*. A magnet has a north and a south pole. If two magnets are aligned such that the north pole of one is directed toward the south pole of the second, an attractive force develops. If the alignment brings like poles into proximity, either both north or both south, a repulsive force develops. *Unlike poles attract; like poles repel.*

A *magnetic field* exists in that region surrounding a magnet in which the influence of the magnet can be felt. Internal changes produced within an iron object by a magnetic field, not produced in a field-free region, are responsible for the attractive force that the object experiences.

B-5   Static Electricity

Another property with which certain objects may be endowed is *electric charge*. Analogous to the case of magnetism, *unlike charges attract, and like charges repel* (recall Figure 2-4). In Coulomb's law, stated below, a *positive* force between electrically charged objects is *repulsive*; a *negative* force is *attractive*.

$$F = \frac{Q_1 Q_2}{\varepsilon r^2} \tag{B.13}$$

where Q_1 is the magnitude of the charge on object 1,

Q_2 is the magnitude of the charge on object 2,

r is the distance between the objects, and

ε is a proportionality constant called the *dielectric constant*, whose numerical value reflects the effect that the medium separating two charged objects has on the force existing between them. For vacuum, $\varepsilon = 1$; for other media, ε is greater than 1 (for example, for water $\varepsilon = 78.5$).

An *electric field* exists in that region surrounding an electrically charged object in which the influence of the electric charge is felt. If an uncharged object is brought into the field of a charged object, the uncharged object may undergo internal changes that it would not experience in a field-free region. These changes may lead to the production of electric charges in the formerly uncharged object, a phenomenon called *induction* (illustrated in Figure B-1).

Glass rod

Metal rod

Gold leaf

◀ **FIGURE B-1**
Production of electric charges by induction in a gold-leaf electroscope
The glass rod acquires a positive electric charge by being rubbed with a silk cloth. As the rod is brought near the electroscope, a separation of charge occurs in the electroscope. The leaves become positively charged and repel one another. Negative charge is attracted to the spherical terminal at the end of the metal rod. If the glass rod is removed, the charges on the electroscope redistribute themselves, and the leaves collapse. If the spherical ball is touched by an electric conductor before the glass rod is removed, negative charge is removed from the ball. The electroscope retains a net positive charge, and the leaves remain outstretched.

B-6   CURRENT ELECTRICITY

Current electricity is a flow of electrically charged particles. In electric currents in metallic conductors, the charged particles are electrons; in molten salts or in aqueous solutions, the particles are both negatively and positively charged ions.

The unit of electric charge is called a *coulomb* (C). The unit of electric current known as the *ampere* (A) is defined as a flow of one coulomb per second through an electrical conductor. Two variables determine the magnitude of the electric current I flowing through a conductor. These are the potential difference, or voltage drop, E, along the conductor, and the electrical resistance of the conductor, R. The units of voltage and resistance are the *volt* (V) and *ohm*, respectively. The relationship of electric current, voltage, and resistance is given by Ohm's law.

$$I = \frac{E}{R} \tag{B.14}$$

One joule of energy is associated with the passage of one coulomb of electric charge through a potential difference (voltage) of one volt. That is, one joule = one volt-coulomb. Electric *power* refers to the rate of production (or consumption) of electric energy. It has the unit *watt* (W).

$$1\,W = 1\,J\,s^{-1} = 1\,V\,C\,s^{-1}$$

Since one coulomb per second is a current of one ampere,

$$1\,W = 1\,V \times 1\,A \tag{B.15}$$

Thus, a 100-watt light bulb operating at 110 V draws a current of 100 W/110 V = 0.91 A.

B-7   ELECTROMAGNETISM

The relationship between electricity and magnetism is an intimate one. Interactions of electric and magnetic fields result in (1) magnetic fields associated with the flow of electric current (as in electromagnets), (2) forces experienced by current-carrying conductors when placed in a magnetic field (as in electric motors), and (3) electric current being induced when an electric conductor is moved through a magnetic field (as in electric generators). Several observations described in this text can be understood in terms of electromagnetic phenomena.

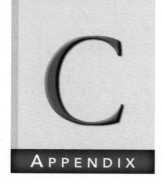

APPENDIX

SI UNITS

The system of units that will in time be used universally for expressing all measured quantities is Le Système International d'Unités (The International System of Units), adopted in 1960 by the Conference Générale des Poids et Measures (General Conference of Weights and Measures). A summary of some of the provisions of the SI convention is provided here.

C-1 SI BASE UNITS

A single unit has been established for each of the basic quantities involved in measurement. These are as follows:

Physical Quantity	Unit	Abbreviation
Length	Meter	m
Mass	Kilogram	kg
Time	Second	s
Electric current	Ampere	A
Temperature	Kelvin	K
Luminous intensity	Candela	cd
Amount of substance	Mole	mol
Plane angle	Radian	rad
Solid angle	Steradian	sr

C-2 SI PREFIXES

Distinctive prefixes are attached to the base unit to express quantities that are *multiples* (greater than) or *submultiples* (less than) of the base unit. The multiples and submultiples are obtained by multiplying the base unit by powers of ten.

Multiple	Prefix	Abbreviation	Submultiple	Prefix	Abbreviation
10^{12}	tera	T	10^{-1}	deci	d
10^{9}	giga	G	10^{-2}	centi	c
10^{6}	mega	M	10^{-3}	milli	m
10^{3}	kilo	k	10^{-6}	micro	μ
10^{2}	hecto	h	10^{-9}	nano	n
10^{1}	deka	da	10^{-12}	pico	p
			10^{-15}	femto	f
			10^{-18}	atto	a

C-3   DERIVED SI UNITS

A number of quantities must be derived from measured values of the SI base quantities [for example, volume has the unit (length)^3]. Two sets of derived units are given, those whose names follow directly from the base units and those that are given special names. Notice that the units used in the text differ in some respects from those in the table. For example, the text expresses density as $g\,cm^{-3}$, molar mass as $g\,mol^{-1}$, molar volume as $mL\,mol^{-1}$ or $L\,mol^{-1}$, and molar concentration (molarity) as $mol\,L^{-1}$, or M.

▶ Two other SI conventions are illustrated through this table: (a) Units are written in singular form—meter or m, *not* meters or ms; (b) negative exponents are preferred to the shilling bar or solidus (/), that is, $m\,s^{-1}$ and $m\,s^{-2}$, *not* m/s and m/s/s.

Physical Quantity	Unit	Abbreviation
Area	Square meter	m^2
Volume	Cubic meter	m^3
Velocity	Meter per second	$m\,s^{-1}$
Acceleration	Meter per second squared	$m\,s^{-2}$
Density	Kilogram per cubic meter	$kg\,m^{-3}$
Molar mass	Kilogram per mole	$kg\,mol^{-1}$
Molar volume	Cubic meter per mole	$m^3\,mol^{-1}$
Molar concentration	Mole per cubic meter	$mol\,m^{-3}$

Physical Quantity	Unit	Abbreviation	In Terms of SI Units
Frequency	hertz	Hz	s^{-1}
Force	newton	N	$kg\,m\,s^{-2}$
Pressure	pascal	Pa	$N\,m^{-2}$
Energy	joule	J	$kg\,m^2\,s^{-2}$
Power	watt	W	$J\,s^{-1}$
Electric charge	coulomb	C	$A\,s$
Electric potential difference	volt	V	$J\,A^{-1}\,s^{-1}$
Electric resistance	ohm	Ω	$V\,A^{-1}$

C-4   UNITS TO BE DISCOURAGED OR ABANDONED

There are several commonly used units whose use is to be discouraged and ultimately abandoned. Their gradual disappearance is to be expected, though each is used in this text. A few such units are listed.

▶ Another SI convention is implied here. No commas are used in expressing large numbers. Instead, spaces are left between groupings of three digits, that is, 101 325 rather than 101,325. Decimal points are written either as periods or commas.

Physical Quantity	Unit	Abbreviation	Definition of SI Units
Length	ångstrom	Å	1×10^{-10} m
Force	dyne	dyn	1×10^{-5} N
Energy	erg	erg	1×10^{-7} J
Energy	calorie	cal	4.184 J
Pressure	atmosphere	atm	101 325 Pa
Pressure	millimeter of mercury	mmHg	133.322 Pa
Pressure	torr	Torr	133.322 Pa

DATA TABLES

TABLE D.1 Ground-State Electron Configurations

Z	Element	Configuration	Z	Element	Configuration	Z	Element	Configuration
1	H	$1s^1$	37	Rb	$[Kr]\,5s^1$	72	Hf	$[Xe]\,4f^{14}5d^26s^2$
2	He	$1s^2$	38	Sr	$[Kr]\,5s^2$	73	Ta	$[Xe]\,4f^{14}5d^36s^2$
3	Li	$[He]\,2s^1$	39	Y	$[Kr]\,4d^15s^2$	74	W	$[Xe]\,4f^{14}5d^46s^2$
4	Be	$[He]\,2s^2$	40	Zr	$[Kr]\,4d^25s^2$	75	Re	$[Xe]\,4f^{14}5d^56s^2$
5	B	$[He]\,2s^22p^1$	41	Nb	$[Kr]\,4d^45s^1$	76	Os	$[Xe]\,4f^{14}5d^66s^2$
6	C	$[He]\,2s^22p^2$	42	Mo	$[Kr]\,4d^55s^1$	77	Ir	$[Xe]\,4f^{14}5d^76s^2$
7	N	$[He]\,2s^22p^3$	43	Tc	$[Kr]\,4d^55s^2$	78	Pt	$[Xe]\,4f^{14}5d^96s^1$
8	O	$[He]\,2s^22p^4$	44	Ru	$[Kr]\,4d^75s^1$	79	Au	$[Xe]\,4f^{14}5d^{10}6s^1$
9	F	$[He]\,2s^22p^5$	45	Rh	$[Kr]\,4d^85s^1$	80	Hg	$[Xe]\,4f^{14}5d^{10}6s^2$
10	Ne	$[He]\,2s^22p^6$	46	Pd	$[Kr]\,4d^{10}$	81	Tl	$[Xe]\,4f^{14}5d^{10}6s^26p^1$
11	Na	$[Ne]\,3s^1$	47	Ag	$[Kr]\,4d^{10}5s^1$	82	Pb	$[Xe]\,4f^{14}5d^{10}6s^26p^2$
12	Mg	$[Ne]\,3s^2$	48	Cd	$[Kr]\,4d^{10}5s^2$	83	Bi	$[Xe]\,4f^{14}5d^{10}6s^26p^3$
13	Al	$[Ne]\,3s^23p^1$	49	In	$[Kr]\,4d^{10}5s^25p^1$	84	Po	$[Xe]\,4f^{14}5d^{10}6s^26p^4$
14	Si	$[Ne]\,3s^23p^2$	50	Sn	$[Kr]\,4d^{10}5s^25p^2$	85	At	$[Xe]\,4f^{14}5d^{10}6s^26p^5$
15	P	$[Ne]\,3s^23p^3$	51	Sb	$[Kr]\,4d^{10}5s^25p^3$	86	Rn	$[Xe]\,4f^{14}5d^{10}6s^26p^6$
16	S	$[Ne]\,3s^23p^4$	52	Te	$[Kr]\,4d^{10}5s^25p^4$	87	Fr	$[Rn]\,7s^1$
17	Cl	$[Ne]\,3s^23p^5$	53	I	$[Kr]\,4d^{10}5s^25p^5$	88	Ra	$[Rn]\,7s^2$
18	Ar	$[Ne]\,3s^23p^6$	54	Xe	$[Kr]\,4d^{10}5s^25p^6$	89	Ac	$[Rn]\,6d^17s^2$
19	K	$[Ar]\,4s^1$	55	Cs	$[Xe]\,6s^1$	90	Th	$[Rn]\,6d^27s^2$
20	Ca	$[Ar]\,4s^2$	56	Ba	$[Xe]\,6s^2$	91	Pa	$[Rn]\,5f^26d^17s^2$
21	Sc	$[Ar]\,3d^14s^2$	57	La	$[Xe]\,5d^16s^2$	92	U	$[Rn]\,5f^36d^17s^2$
22	Ti	$[Ar]\,3d^24s^2$	58	Ce	$[Xe]\,4f^26s^2$	93	Np	$[Rn]\,5f^46d^17s^2$
23	V	$[Ar]\,3d^34s^2$	59	Pr	$[Xe]\,4f^36s^2$	94	Pu	$[Rn]\,5f^67s^2$
24	Cr	$[Ar]\,3d^54s^1$	60	Nd	$[Xe]\,4f^46s^2$	95	Am	$[Rn]\,5f^77s^2$
25	Mn	$[Ar]\,3d^54s^2$	61	Pm	$[Xe]\,4f^56s^2$	96	Cm	$[Rn]\,5f^76d^17s^2$
26	Fe	$[Ar]\,3d^64s^2$	62	Sm	$[Xe]\,4f^66s^2$	97	Bk	$[Rn]\,5f^97s^2$
27	Co	$[Ar]\,3d^74s^2$	63	Eu	$[Xe]\,4f^76s^2$	98	Cf	$[Rn]\,5f^{10}7s^2$
28	Ni	$[Ar]\,3d^84s^2$	64	Gd	$[Xe]\,4f^75d^16s^2$	99	Es	$[Rn]\,5f^{11}7s^2$
29	Cu	$[Ar]\,3d^{10}4s^1$	65	Tb	$[Xe]\,4f^96s^2$	100	Fm	$[Rn]\,5f^{12}7s^2$
30	Zn	$[Ar]\,3d^{10}4s^2$	66	Dy	$[Xe]\,4f^{10}6s^2$	101	Md	$[Rn]\,5f^{13}7s^2$
31	Ga	$[Ar]\,3d^{10}4s^24p^1$	67	Ho	$[Xe]\,4f^{11}6s^2$	102	No	$[Rn]\,5f^{14}7s^2$
32	Ge	$[Ar]\,3d^{10}4s^24p^2$	68	Er	$[Xe]\,4f^{12}6s^2$	103	Lr	$[Rn]\,5f^{14}6d^17s^2$
33	As	$[Ar]\,3d^{10}4s^24p^3$	69	Tm	$[Xe]\,4f^{13}6s^2$	104	Rf	$[Rn]\,5f^{14}6d^27s^2$
34	Se	$[Ar]\,3d^{10}4s^24p^4$	70	Yb	$[Xe]\,4f^{14}6s^2$	105	Db	$[Rn]\,5f^{14}6d^37s^2$
35	Br	$[Ar]\,3d^{10}4s^24p^5$	71	Lu	$[Xe]\,4f^{14}5d^16s^2$	106	Sg	$[Rn]\,5f^{14}6d^47s^2$
36	Kr	$[Ar]\,3d^{10}4s^24p^6$						

The electron configurations printed in blue are those of the noble gases. Each noble gas configuration serves as the core of the electron configurations of the elements that follow it, until the next noble gas is reached. Thus, [He] represents the core configuration of the second period elements; [Ne], the third period; [Ar], the fourth period; [Kr], the fifth period; [Xe], the sixth period; and [Rn], the seventh period.

**TABLE D.2 Thermodynamic Properties of Substances at 298.15 K*.
Substances are at 1 bar pressure. For aqueous solutions, solutes are
at unit activity (roughly 1 M). Data for ions in aqueous solution are relative
to values of *zero* for ΔH_f°, ΔG_f°, and S° for H^+**

Inorganic Substances

	ΔH_f°, kJ mol^{-1}	ΔG_f°, kJ mol^{-1}	S°, J mol^{-1} K^{-1}
Aluminum			
$Al(s)$	0	0	28.33
$Al^{3+}(aq)$	−531	−485	−321.7
$AlCl_3(s)$	−704.2	−628.8	110.7
$Al_2Cl_6(g)$	−1291	−1220.	490.
$AlF_3(s)$	−1504	−1425	66.44
$Al_2O_3(\alpha\ solid)$	−1676	−1582	50.92
$Al(OH)_3(s)$	−1276	—	—
$Al_2(SO_4)_3(s)$	−3441	−3100.	239
Barium			
$Ba(s)$	0	0	62.8
$Ba^{2+}(aq)$	−537.6	−560.8	9.6
$BaCO_3(s)$	−1216	−1138	112.1
$BaCl_2(s)$	−858.6	−810.4	123.7
$BaF_2(s)$	−1207	−1157	96.36
$BaO(s)$	−553.5	−525.1	70.42
$Ba(OH)_2(s)$	−944.7	—	—
$Ba(OH)_2 \cdot 8\ H_2O(s)$	−3342	−2793	427
$BaSO_4(s)$	−1473	−1362	132.2
Beryllium			
$Be(s)$	0	0	9.50
$BeCl_2(\alpha\ solid)$	−490.4	−445.6	82.68
$BeF_2(\alpha\ solid)$	−1027	−979.4	53.35
$BeO(s)$	−609.6	−580.3	14.14
Bismuth			
$Bi(s)$	0	0	56.74
$BiCl_3(s)$	−379.1	−315.0	177.0
$Bi_2O_3(s)$	−573.9	−493.7	151.5
Boron			
$B(s)$	0	0	5.86
$BCl_3(l)$	−427.2	−387.4	206.3
$BF_3(g)$	−1137	−1120.	254.1
$B_2H_6(g)$	35.6	86.7	232.1
$B_2O_3(s)$	−1273	−1194	53.97
Bromine			
$Br(g)$	111.9	82.40	175.0
$Br^-(aq)$	−121.6	−104.0	82.4
$Br_2(g)$	30.91	3.11	245.5
$Br_2(l)$	0	0	152.2
$BrCl(g)$	14.64	−0.98	240.1
$BrF_3(g)$	−255.6	−229.4	292.5
$BrF_3(l)$	−300.8	−240.5	178.2

*Data for inorganic substances and for organic compounds with up to two carbon atoms
per molecule are adapted from D. D. Wagman, et al., "The NBS Tables of Chemical
Thermodynamic Properties: Selected Values for Inorganic and C_1 and C_2 Organic Substances
in SI Units" *Journal of Physical and Chemical Reference Data* 11 (1982) Supplement 2. Data for
other organic compounds are from J. A. Dean, *Lange's Handbook of Chemistry*. 15th ed.,
McGraw-Hill, 1999 and other sources.

Inorganic Substances

	ΔH_f°, kJ mol^{-1}	ΔG_f°, kJ mol^{-1}	S°, J mol^{-1} K^{-1}
Cadmium			
Cd(s)	0	0	51.76
Cd^{2+}(aq)	-75.90	-77.61	-73.2
CdCl$_2$(s)	-391.5	-343.9	115.3
CdO(s)	-258.2	-228.4	54.8
Calcium			
Ca(s)	0	0	41.42
Ca^{2+}(aq)	-542.8	-553.6	-53.1
CaCO$_3$(s)	-1207	-1129	92.9
CaCl$_2$(s)	-795.8	-748.1	104.6
CaF$_2$(s)	$-1220.$	-1167	68.87
CaH$_2$(s)	-186.2	-147.2	42
Ca(NO$_3$)$_2$(s)	-938.4	-743.1	193.3
CaO(s)	-635.1	-604.0	39.75
Ca(OH)$_2$(s)	-986.1	-898.5	83.39
Ca$_3$(PO$_4$)$_2$(s)	-4121	-3885	236.0
CaSO$_4$(s)	-1434	-1322	106.7
Carbon (See also the table of organic substances.)			
C(g)	716.7	671.3	158.0
C(diamond)	1.90	2.90	2.38
C(graphite)	0	0	5.74
CCl$_4$(g)	-102.9	-60.59	309.9
CCl$_4$(l)	-135.4	-65.21	216.4
C$_2$N$_2$(g)	309.0	297.4	241.9
CO(g)	-110.5	-137.2	197.7
CO$_2$(g)	-393.5	-394.4	213.7
CO$_3{}^{2-}$(aq)	-677.1	-527.8	-56.9
C$_3$O$_2$(g)	-93.72	-109.8	276.5
C$_3$O$_2$(l)	-117.3	-105.0	181.1
COCl$_2$(g)	-218.8	-204.6	283.5
COS(g)	-142.1	-169.3	231.6
CS$_2$(l)	89.70	65.27	151.3
Chlorine			
Cl(g)	121.7	105.7	165.2
Cl$^-$(aq)	-167.2	-131.2	56.5
Cl$_2$(g)	0	0	223.1
ClF$_3$(g)	-163.2	-123.0	281.6
ClO$_2$(g)	102.5	120.5	256.8
Cl$_2$O(g)	80.3	97.9	266.2
Chromium			
Cr(s)	0	0	23.77
[Cr(H$_2$O)$_6$]$^{3+}$(aq)	-1999	—	—
Cr$_2$O$_3$(s)	$-1140.$	-1058	81.2
CrO$_4{}^{2-}$(aq)	-881.2	-727.8	50.21
Cr$_2$O$_7{}^{2-}$(aq)	$-1490.$	-1301	261.9
Cobalt			
Co(s)	0	0	30.04
CoO(s)	-237.9	-214.2	52.97
Co(OH)$_2$(pink solid)	-539.7	-454.3	79
Copper			
Cu(s)	0	0	33.15
Cu^{2+}(aq)	64.77	65.49	-99.6
CuCO$_3 \cdot$ Cu(OH)$_2$(s)	-1051	-893.6	186.2

Inorganic Substances

	ΔH_f°, kJ mol^{-1}	ΔG_f°, kJ mol^{-1}	S°, J mol^{-1} K^{-1}
Copper			
CuO(s)	−157.3	−129.7	42.63
Cu(OH)$_2$(s)	−449.8	—	—
CuSO$_4 \cdot 5$ H$_2$O(s)	−2280.	−1880.	300.4
Fluorine			
F(g)	78.99	61.91	158.8
F$^-$(aq)	−332.6	−278.8	−13.8
F$_2$(g)	0	0	202.8
Helium			
He(g)	0	0	126.2
Hydrogen			
H(g)	218.0	203.2	114.7
H$^+$(aq)	0	0	0
H$_2$(g)	0	0	130.7
HBr(g)	−36.40	−53.45	198.7
HCl(g)	−92.31	−95.30	186.9
HCl(aq)	−167.2	−131.2	56.5
HClO$_2$(aq)	−51.9	5.9	188.3
HCN(g)	135.1	124.7	201.8
HF(g)	−271.1	−273.2	173.8
HI(g)	26.48	1.70	206.6
HNO$_3$(l)	−174.1	−80.71	155.6
HNO$_3$(aq)	−207.4	−111.3	146.4
H$_2$O(g)	−241.8	−228.6	188.8
H$_2$O(l)	−285.8	−237.1	69.91
H$_2$O$_2$(g)	−136.3	−105.6	232.7
H$_2$O$_2$(l)	−187.8	−120.4	109.6
H$_2$S(g)	−20.63	−33.56	205.8
H$_2$SO$_4$(l)	−814.0	−690.0	156.9
H$_2$SO$_4$(aq)	−909.3	−744.5	20.1
Iodine			
I(g)	106.8	70.25	180.8
I$^-$(aq)	−55.19	−51.57	111.3
I$_2$(g)	62.44	19.33	260.7
I$_2$(s)	0	0	116.1
IBr(g)	40.84	3.69	258.8
ICl(g)	17.78	−5.46	247.6
ICl(l)	−23.89	−13.58	135.1
Iron			
Fe(s)	0	0	27.28
Fe^{2+}(aq)	−89.1	−78.90	−137.7
Fe^{3+}(aq)	−48.5	−4.7	−315.9
FeCO$_3$(s)	−740.6	−666.7	92.9
FeCl$_3$(s)	−399.5	−334.0	−142.3
FeO(s)	−272.0	—	—
Fe$_2$O$_3$(s)	−824.2	−742.2	87.40
Fe$_3$O$_4$(s)	−1118	−1015	146.4
Fe(OH)$_3$(s)	−823.0	−696.5	106.7
Lead			
Pb(s)	0	0	64.81
Pb^{2+}(aq)	−1.7	−24.43	10.5
PbI$_2$(s)	−175.5	−173.6	174.9

Inorganic Substances

	ΔH_f°, kJ mol^{-1}	ΔG_f°, kJ mol^{-1}	S°, J mol^{-1} K^{-1}
$PbO_2(s)$	−277.4	−217.3	68.6
$PbSO_4(s)$	−919.9	−813.1	148.6
Lithium			
$Li(g)$	159.4	126.7	138.8
$Li(s)$	0	0	29.12
$Li^+(aq)$	−278.5	−293.3	13.4
$LiCl(s)$	−408.6	−384.4	59.33
$LiOH(s)$	−484.9	−439.0	42.80
$LiNO_3(s)$	−483.1	−381.1	90.0
Magnesium			
$Mg(s)$	0	0	32.68
$Mg^{2+}(aq)$	−466.9	−454.8	−138.1
$MgCl_2(s)$	−641.3	−591.8	89.62
$MgCO_3(s)$	−1096	−1012	65.7
$MgF_2(s)$	−1123	−1070	57.24
$MgO(s)$	−601.7	−569.4	26.94
$Mg(OH)_2(s)$	−924.5	−833.5	63.18
$MgS(s)$	−346.0	−341.8	50.33
$MgSO_4(s)$	−1285	−1171	91.6
Manganese			
$Mn(s)$	0	0	32.01
$Mn^{2+}(aq)$	−220.8	−228.1	−73.6
$MnO_2(s)$	−520.0	−465.1	53.05
$MnO_4^-(aq)$	−541.4	−447.2	191.2
Mercury			
$Hg(g)$	61.32	31.82	175.0
$Hg(l)$	0	0	76.02
$HgO(s)$	−90.83	−58.54	70.29
Nitrogen			
$N(g)$	472.7	455.6	153.3
$N_2(g)$	0	0	191.6
$NF_3(g)$	−124.7	−83.2	260.7
$NH_3(g)$	−46.11	−16.45	192.5
$NH_3(aq)$	−80.29	−26.50	111.3
$NH_4^+(aq)$	−132.5	−79.31	113.4
$NH_4Br(s)$	−270.8	−175.2	113
$NH_4Cl(s)$	−314.4	−202.9	94.6
$NH_4F(s)$	−464.0	−348.7	71.96
$NH_4HCO_3(s)$	−849.4	−665.9	120.9
$NH_4I(s)$	−201.4	−112.5	117
$NH_4NO_3(s)$	−365.6	−183.9	151.1
$NH_4NO_3(aq)$	−339.9	−190.6	259.8
$(NH_4)_2SO_4(s)$	−1181	−901.7	220.1
$N_2H_4(g)$	95.40	159.4	238.5
$N_2H_4(l)$	50.63	149.3	121.2
$NO(g)$	90.25	86.55	210.8
$N_2O(g)$	82.05	104.2	219.9
$NO_2(g)$	33.18	51.31	240.1
$N_2O_4(g)$	9.16	97.89	304.3
$N_2O_4(l)$	−19.50	97.54	209.2
$N_2O_5(g)$	11.3	115.1	355.7
$NO_3^-(aq)$	−205.0	−108.7	146.4
$NOBr(g)$	82.17	82.42	273.7
$NOCl(g)$	51.71	66.08	261.7

Inorganic Substances

	ΔH_f°, kJ mol^{-1}	ΔG_f°, kJ mol^{-1}	S°, J mol^{-1} K^{-1}
Oxygen			
O(g)	249.2	231.7	161.1
O$_2$(g)	0	0	205.1
O$_3$(g)	142.7	163.2	238.9
OH$^-$(aq)	−230.0	−157.2	−10.75
OF$_2$(g)	24.7	41.9	247.4
Phosphorus			
P(α white)	0	0	41.09
P(red)	−17.6	−12.1	22.80
P$_4$(g)	58.91	24.44	280.0
PCl$_3$(g)	−287.0	−267.8	311.8
PCl$_5$(g)	−374.9	−305.0	364.6
PH$_3$(g)	5.4	13.4	210.2
P$_4$O$_{10}$(s)	−2984	−2698	228.9
PO$_4^{3-}$(aq)	−1277	−1019	−222
Potassium			
K(g)	89.24	60.59	160.3
K(s)	0	0	64.18
K$^+$(aq)	−252.4	−283.3	102.5
KBr(s)	−393.8	−380.7	95.90
KCN(s)	−113.0	−101.9	128.5
KCl(s)	−436.7	−409.1	82.59
KClO$_3$(s)	−397.7	−296.3	143.1
KClO$_4$(s)	−432.8	−303.1	151.0
KF(s)	−567.3	−537.8	66.57
KI(s)	−327.9	−324.9	106.3
KNO$_3$(s)	−494.6	−394.9	133.1
KOH(s)	−424.8	−379.1	78.9
KOH(aq)	−482.4	−440.5	91.6
K$_2$SO$_4$(s)	−1438	−1321	175.6
Silicon			
Si(s)	0	0	18.83
SiH$_4$(g)	34.3	56.9	204.6
Si$_2$H$_6$(g)	80.3	127.3	272.7
SiO$_2$(quartz)	−910.9	−856.6	41.84
Silver			
Ag(s)	0	0	42.55
Ag$^+$(aq)	105.6	77.11	72.68
AgBr(s)	−100.4	−96.90	107.1
AgCl(s)	−127.1	−109.8	96.2
AgI(s)	−61.84	−66.19	115.5
AgNO$_3$(s)	−124.4	−33.41	140.9
Ag$_2$O(s)	−31.05	−11.20	121.3
Ag$_2$SO$_4$(s)	−715.9	−618.4	200.4
Sodium			
Na(g)	107.3	76.76	153.7
Na(s)	0	0	51.21
Na$^+$(aq)	−240.1	−261.9	59.0
Na$_2$(g)	142.1	103.9	230.2
NaBr(s)	−361.1	−349.0	86.82
Na$_2$CO$_3$(s)	−1131	−1044	135.0
NaHCO$_3$(s)	−950.8	−851.0	101.7

Inorganic Substances

	ΔH_f°, kJ mol^{-1}	ΔG_f°, kJ mol^{-1}	S°, J mol^{-1} K^{-1}
NaCl(s)	−411.2	−384.1	72.13
NaCl(aq)	−407.3	−393.1	115.5
NaClO$_3$(s)	−365.8	−262.3	123.4
NaClO$_4$(s)	−383.3	−254.9	142.3
NaF(s)	−573.6	−543.5	51.46
NaH(s)	−56.28	−33.46	40.02
NaI(s)	−287.8	−286.1	98.53
NaNO$_3$(s)	−467.9	−367.0	116.5
NaNO$_3$(aq)	−447.5	−373.2	205.4
Na$_2$O$_2$(s)	−510.9	−447.7	95.0
NaOH(s)	−425.6	−379.5	64.46
NaOH(aq)	−470.1	−419.2	48.1
NaH$_2$PO$_4$(s)	−1537	−1386	127.5
Na$_2$HPO$_4$(s)	−1748	−1608	150.5
Na$_3$PO$_4$(s)	−1917	−1789	173.8
NaHSO$_4$(s)	−1126	−992.8	113.0
Na$_2$SO$_4$(s)	−1387	−1270	149.6
Na$_2$SO$_4$(aq)	−1390.	−1268	138.1
Na$_2$SO$_4 \cdot$ 10 H$_2$O(s)	−4327	−3647	592.0
Na$_2$S$_2$O$_3$(s)	−1123	−1028	155

Sulfur

S(g)	278.8	238.3	167.8
S(rhombic)	0	0	31.80
S$_8$(g)	102.3	49.63	431.0
S$_2$Cl$_2$(g)	−18.4	−31.8	331.5
SF$_6$(g)	−1209	−1105	291.8
SO$_2$(g)	−296.8	−300.2	248.2
SO$_3$(g)	−395.7	−371.1	256.8
SO$_4^{2-}$(aq)	−909.3	−744.5	20.1
S$_2$O$_3^{2-}$(aq)	−648.5	−522.5	67
SO$_2$Cl$_2$(g)	−364.0	−320.0	311.9
SO$_2$Cl$_2$(l)	−394.1	—	—

Tin

Sn(white)	0	0	51.55
Sn(gray)	−2.09	0.13	44.14
SnCl$_4$(l)	−511.3	−440.1	258.6
SnO(s)	−285.8	−256.9	56.5
SnO$_2$(s)	−580.7	−519.6	52.3

Titanium

Ti(s)	0	0	30.63
TiCl$_4$(g)	−763.2	−726.7	354.9
TiCl$_4$(l)	−804.2	−737.2	252.3
TiO$_2$(s)	−944.7	−889.5	50.33

Uranium

U(s)	0	0	50.21
UF$_6$(g)	−2147	−2064	377.9
UF$_6$(s)	−2197	−2069	227.6
UO$_2$(s)	−1085	−1032	77.03

Zinc

Zn(s)	0	0	41.63
Zn^{2+}(aq)	−153.9	−147.1	112.1
ZnO(s)	−348.3	−318.3	43.64

Organic Substances

	Name	ΔH_f°, kJ mol^{-1}	ΔG_f°, kJ mol^{-1}	S°, J mol^{-1} K^{-1}
$CH_4(g)$	Methane(g)	−74.81	−50.72	186.3
$C_2H_2(g)$	Acetylene(g)	226.7	209.2	200.9
$C_2H_4(g)$	Ethylene(g)	52.26	68.15	219.6
$C_2H_6(g)$	Ethane(g)	−84.68	−32.82	229.6
$C_3H_8(g)$	Propane(g)	−103.8	−23.3	270.3
$C_4H_{10}(g)$	Butane(g)	−125.6	−17.1	310.2
$C_6H_6(g)$	Benzene(g)	82.6	129.8	269.3
$C_6H_6(l)$	Benzene(l)	49.0	124.5	173.4
$C_6H_{12}(g)$	Cyclohexane(g)	−123.4	32.0	298.4
$C_6H_{12}(l)$	Cyclohexane(l)	−156.4	26.9	204.4
$C_{10}H_8(g)$	Naphthalene(g)	150.6	224.2	333.2
$C_{10}H_8(s)$	Naphthalene(s)	77.9	201.7	167.5
$CH_2O(g)$	Formaldehyde(g)	−108.6	−102.5	218.8
$CH_3CHO(g)$	Acetaldehyde(g)	−166.2	−128.9	250.3
$CH_3CHO(l)$	Acetaldehyde(l)	−192.3	−128.1	160.2
$CH_3OH(g)$	Methanol(g)	−200.7	−162.0	239.8
$CH_3OH(l)$	Methanol(l)	−238.7	−166.3	126.8
$CH_3CH_2OH(g)$	Ethanol(g)	−235.1	−168.5	282.7
$CH_3CH_2OH(l)$	Ethanol(l)	−277.7	−174.8	160.7
$C_6H_5OH(s)$	Phenol(s)	−165.1	−50.4	144.0
$(CH_3)_2CO(g)$	Acetone(g)	−216.6	−153.0	295.0
$(CH_3)_2CO(l)$	Acetone(l)	−247.6	−155.6	200.5
$CH_3COOH(g)$	Acetic acid(g)	−432.3	−374.0	282.5
$CH_3COOH(l)$	Acetic acid(l)	−484.5	−389.9	159.8
$CH_3COOH(aq)$	Acetic acid(aq)	−485.8	−396.5	178.7
$C_6H_5COOH(s)$	Benzoic acid(s)	−385.2	−245.3	167.6
$CH_3NH_2(g)$	Methylamine(g)	−22.97	32.16	243.4
$C_6H_5NH_2(g)$	Aniline(g)	86.86	166.8	319.3
$C_6H_5NH_2(l)$	Aniline(l)	31.6	149.2	191.3

TABLE D.3 Equilibrium Constants

A. Ionization Constants of Weak Acids at 25 °C

Name of acid	Formula	K_a	Name of acid	Formula	K_a
Acetic	$HC_2H_3O_2$	1.8×10^{-5}	Hyponitrous	$HON{=}NOH$	8.9×10^{-8}
Acrylic	$HC_3H_3O_2$	5.5×10^{-5}		$HON{=}NO^-$	4×10^{-12}
Arsenic	H_3AsO_4	6.0×10^{-3}	Iodic	HIO_3	1.6×10^{-1}
	$H_2AsO_4^-$	1.0×10^{-7}	Iodoacetic	$HC_2H_2IO_2$	6.7×10^{-4}
	$HAsO_4^{2-}$	3.2×10^{-12}	Malonic	$H_2C_3H_2O_4$	1.5×10^{-3}
Arsenous	H_3AsO_3	6.6×10^{-10}		$HC_3H_2O_4^-$	2.0×10^{-6}
Benzoic	$HC_7H_5O_2$	6.3×10^{-5}	Nitrous	HNO_2	7.2×10^{-4}
Bromoacetic	$HC_2H_2BrO_2$	1.3×10^{-3}	Oxalic	$H_2C_2O_4$	5.4×10^{-2}
Butyric	$HC_4H_7O_2$	1.5×10^{-5}		$HC_2O_4^-$	5.3×10^{-5}
Carbonic	H_2CO_3	4.4×10^{-7}	Phenol	HOC_6H_5	1.0×10^{-10}
	HCO_3^-	4.7×10^{-11}	Phenylacetic	$HC_8H_7O_2$	4.9×10^{-5}
Chloroacetic	$HC_2H_2ClO_2$	1.4×10^{-3}	Phosphoric	H_3PO_4	7.1×10^{-3}
Chlorous	$HClO_2$	1.1×10^{-2}		$H_2PO_4^-$	6.3×10^{-8}
Citric	$H_3C_6H_5O_7$	7.4×10^{-4}		HPO_4^{2-}	4.2×10^{-13}
	$H_2C_6H_5O_7^-$	1.7×10^{-5}	Phosphorous	H_3PO_3	3.7×10^{-2}
	$HC_6H_5O_7^{2-}$	4.0×10^{-7}		$H_2PO_3^-$	2.1×10^{-7}
Cyanic	$HOCN$	3.5×10^{-4}	Propionic	$HC_3H_5O_2$	1.3×10^{-5}
Dichloroacetic	$HC_2HCl_2O_2$	5.5×10^{-2}	Pyrophosphoric	$H_4P_2O_7$	3.0×10^{-2}
Fluoroacetic	$HC_2H_2FO_2$	2.6×10^{-3}		$H_3P_2O_7^-$	4.4×10^{-3}
Formic	$HCHO_2$	1.8×10^{-4}		$H_2P_2O_7^{2-}$	2.5×10^{-7}
Hydrazoic	HN_3	1.9×10^{-5}		$HP_2O_7^{3-}$	5.6×10^{-10}
Hydrocyanic	HCN	6.2×10^{-10}	Selenic	H_2SeO_4	strong acid
Hydrofluoric	HF	6.6×10^{-4}		$HSeO_4^-$	2.2×10^{-2}
Hydrogen peroxide	H_2O_2	2.2×10^{-12}	Selenous	H_2SeO_3	2.3×10^{-3}
Hydroselenic	H_2Se	1.3×10^{-4}		$HSeO_3^-$	5.4×10^{-9}
	HSe^-	1×10^{-11}	Succinic	$H_2C_4H_4O_4$	6.2×10^{-5}
Hydrosulfuric	H_2S	1.0×10^{-7}		$HC_4H_4O_4^-$	2.3×10^{-6}
	HS^-	1×10^{-19}	Sulfuric	H_2SO_4	strong acid
Hydrotelluric	H_2Te	2.3×10^{-3}		HSO_4^-	1.1×10^{-2}
	HTe^-	1.6×10^{-11}	Sulfurous	H_2SO_3	1.3×10^{-2}
Hypobromous	$HOBr$	2.5×10^{-9}		HSO_3^-	6.2×10^{-8}
Hypochlorous	$HOCl$	2.9×10^{-8}	Thiophenol	HSC_6H_5	3.2×10^{-7}
Hypoiodous	HOI	2.3×10^{-11}	Trichloroacetic	$HC_2Cl_3O_2$	3.0×10^{-1}

B. Ionization Constants of Weak Bases at 25 °C

Name of base	Formula	K_b	Name of base	Formula	K_b
Ammonia	NH_3	1.8×10^{-5}	Isoquinoline	C_9H_7N	2.5×10^{-9}
Aniline	$C_6H_5NH_2$	7.4×10^{-10}	Methylamine	CH_3NH_2	4.2×10^{-4}
Codeine	$C_{18}H_{21}O_3N$	8.9×10^{-7}	Morphine	$C_{17}H_{19}O_3N$	7.4×10^{-7}
Diethylamine	$(C_2H_5)_2NH$	6.9×10^{-4}	Piperdine	$C_5H_{11}N$	1.3×10^{-3}
Dimethylamine	$(CH_3)_2NH$	5.9×10^{-4}	Pyridine	C_5H_5N	1.5×10^{-9}
Ethylamine	$C_2H_5NH_2$	4.3×10^{-4}	Quinoline	C_9H_7N	6.3×10^{-10}
Hydrazine	NH_2NH_2	8.5×10^{-7}	Triethanolamine	$C_6H_{15}O_3N$	5.8×10^{-7}
	$NH_2NH_3^+$	8.9×10^{-16}	Triethylamine	$(C_2H_5)_3N$	5.2×10^{-4}
Hydroxylamine	NH_2OH	9.1×10^{-9}	Trimethylamine	$(CH_3)_3N$	6.3×10^{-5}

C. Solubility Product Constants[a]

Name of solute	Formula	K_{sp}	Name of solute	Formula	K_{sp}
Aluminum hydroxide	$Al(OH)_3$	1.3×10^{-33}	Lead(II) hydroxide	$Pb(OH)_2$	1.2×10^{-15}
Aluminum phosphate	$AlPO_4$	6.3×10^{-19}	Lead(II) iodide	PbI_2	7.1×10^{-9}
Barium carbonate	$BaCO_3$	5.1×10^{-9}	Lead(II) sulfate	$PbSO_4$	1.6×10^{-8}
Barium chromate	$BaCrO_4$	1.2×10^{-10}	Lead(II) sulfide[b]	PbS	3×10^{-28}
Barium fluoride	BaF_2	1.0×10^{-6}	Lithium carbonate	Li_2CO_3	2.5×10^{-2}
Barium hydroxide	$Ba(OH)_2$	5×10^{-3}	Lithium fluoride	LiF	3.8×10^{-3}
Barium sulfate	$BaSO_4$	1.1×10^{-10}	Lithium phosphate	Li_3PO_4	3.2×10^{-9}
Barium sulfite	$BaSO_3$	8×10^{-7}	Magnesium	$MgNH_4PO_4$	2.5×10^{-13}
Barium thiosulfate	BaS_2O_3	1.6×10^{-5}	ammonium phosphate		
Bismuthyl chloride	$BiOCl$	1.8×10^{-31}	Magnesium carbonate	$MgCO_3$	3.5×10^{-8}
Bismuthyl hydroxide	$BiOOH$	4×10^{-10}	Magnesium fluoride	MgF_2	3.7×10^{-8}
Cadmium carbonate	$CdCO_3$	5.2×10^{-12}	Magnesium hydroxide	$Mg(OH)_2$	1.8×10^{-11}
Cadmium hydroxide	$Cd(OH)_2$	2.5×10^{-14}	Magnesium phosphate	$Mg_3(PO_4)_2$	1×10^{-25}
Cadmium sulfide[b]	CdS	8×10^{-28}	Manganese(II) carbonate	$MnCO_3$	1.8×10^{-11}
Calcium carbonate	$CaCO_3$	2.8×10^{-9}	Manganese(II) hydroxide	$Mn(OH)_2$	1.9×10^{-13}
Calcium chromate	$CaCrO_4$	7.1×10^{-4}	Manganese(II) sulfide[b]	MnS	3×10^{-14}
Calcium fluoride	CaF_2	5.3×10^{-9}	Mercury(I) bromide	Hg_2Br_2	5.6×10^{-23}
Calcium hydroxide	$Ca(OH)_2$	5.5×10^{-6}	Mercury(I) chloride	Hg_2Cl_2	1.3×10^{-18}
Calcium hydrogen	$CaHPO_4$	1×10^{-7}	Mercury(I) iodide	Hg_2I_2	4.5×10^{-29}
phosphate			Mercury(II) sulfide[b]	HgS	2×10^{-53}
Calcium oxalate	CaC_2O_4	4×10^{-9}	Nickel(II) carbonate	$NiCO_3$	6.6×10^{-9}
Calcium phosphate	$Ca_3(PO_4)_2$	2.0×10^{-29}	Nickel(II) hydroxide	$Ni(OH)_2$	2.0×10^{-15}
Calcium sulfate	$CaSO_4$	9.1×10^{-6}	Scandium fluoride	ScF_3	4.2×10^{-18}
Calcium sulfite	$CaSO_3$	6.8×10^{-8}	Scandium hydroxide	$Sc(OH)_3$	8.0×10^{-31}
Chromium(II) hydroxide	$Cr(OH)_2$	2×10^{-16}	Silver arsenate	Ag_3AsO_4	1.0×10^{-22}
Chromium(III) hydroxide	$Cr(OH)_3$	6.3×10^{-31}	Silver azide	AgN_3	2.8×10^{-9}
Cobalt(II) carbonate	$CoCO_3$	1.4×10^{-13}	Silver bromide	$AgBr$	5.0×10^{-13}
Cobalt(II) hydroxide	$Co(OH)_2$	1.6×10^{-15}	Silver carbonate	Ag_2CO_3	8.5×10^{-12}
Cobalt(III) hydroxide	$Co(OH)_3$	1.6×10^{-44}	Silver chloride	$AgCl$	1.8×10^{-10}
Copper(I) chloride	$CuCl$	1.2×10^{-6}	Silver chromate	Ag_2CrO_4	1.1×10^{-12}
Copper(I) cyanide	$CuCN$	3.2×10^{-20}	Silver cyanide	$AgCN$	1.2×10^{-16}
Copper(I) iodide	CuI	1.1×10^{-12}	Silver iodate	$AgIO_3$	3.0×10^{-8}
Copper(II) arsenate	$Cu_3(AsO_4)_2$	7.6×10^{-36}	Silver iodide	AgI	8.5×10^{-17}
Copper(II) carbonate	$CuCO_3$	1.4×10^{-10}	Silver nitrite	$AgNO_2$	6.0×10^{-4}
Copper(II) chromate	$CuCrO_4$	3.6×10^{-6}	Silver sulfate	Ag_2SO_4	1.4×10^{-5}
Copper(II) ferrocyanide	$Cu_2[Fe(CN)_6]$	1.3×10^{-16}	Silver sulfide[b]	Ag_2S	6×10^{-51}
Copper(II) hydroxide	$Cu(OH)_2$	2.2×10^{-20}	Silver sulfite	Ag_2SO_3	1.5×10^{-14}
Copper(II) sulfide[b]	CuS	6×10^{-37}	Silver thiocyanate	$AgSCN$	1.0×10^{-12}
Iron(II) carbonate	$FeCO_3$	3.2×10^{-11}	Strontium carbonate	$SrCO_3$	1.1×10^{-10}
Iron(II) hydroxide	$Fe(OH)_2$	8.0×10^{-16}	Strontium chromate	$SrCrO_4$	2.2×10^{-5}
Iron(II) sulfide[b]	FeS	6×10^{-19}	Strontium fluoride	SrF_2	2.5×10^{-9}
Iron(III) arsenate	$FeAsO_4$	5.7×10^{-21}	Strontium sulfate	$SrSO_4$	3.2×10^{-7}
Iron(III) ferrocyanide	$Fe_4[Fe(CN)_6]_3$	3.3×10^{-41}	Thallium(I) bromide	$TlBr$	3.4×10^{-6}
Iron(III) hydroxide	$Fe(OH)_3$	4×10^{-38}	Thallium(I) chloride	$TlCl$	1.7×10^{-4}
Iron(III) phosphate	$FePO_4$	1.3×10^{-22}	Thallium(I) iodide	TlI	6.5×10^{-8}
Lead(II) arsenate	$Pb_3(AsO_4)_2$	4.0×10^{-36}	Thallium(III) hydroxide	$Tl(OH)_3$	6.3×10^{-46}
Lead(II) azide	$Pb(N_3)_2$	2.5×10^{-9}	Tin(II) hydroxide	$Sn(OH)_2$	1.4×10^{-28}
Lead(II) bromide	$PbBr_2$	4.0×10^{-5}	Tin(II) sulfide[b]	SnS	1×10^{-26}
Lead(II) carbonate	$PbCO_3$	7.4×10^{-14}	Zinc carbonate	$ZnCO_3$	1.4×10^{-11}
Lead(II) chloride	$PbCl_2$	1.6×10^{-5}	Zinc hydroxide	$Zn(OH)_2$	1.2×10^{-17}
Lead(II) chromate	$PbCrO_4$	2.8×10^{-13}	Zinc oxalate	ZnC_2O_4	2.7×10^{-8}
Lead(II) fluoride	PbF_2	2.7×10^{-8}	Zinc phosphate	$Zn_3(PO_4)_2$	9.0×10^{-33}
			Zinc sulfide[b]	ZnS	2×10^{-25}

[a]Data are at various temperatures around "room" temperature, from 18 to 25 °C.
[b]For a solubility equilibrium of the type $MS(s) + H_2O \rightleftharpoons M^{2+}(aq) + HS^-(aq) + OH^-(aq)$.

D. Complex-Ion Formation Constants[c, d]

Formula	K_f	Formula	K_f	Formula	K_f
$[Ag(CN)_2]^-$	5.6×10^{18}	$[Co(ox)_3]^{3-}$	10^{20}	$[HgI_4]^{2-}$	6.8×10^{29}
$[Ag(EDTA)]^{3-}$	2.1×10^7	$[Cr(EDTA)]^-$	10^{23}	$[Hg(ox)_2]^{2-}$	9.5×10^6
$[Ag(en)_2]^+$	5.0×10^7	$[Cr(OH)_4]^-$	8×10^{29}	$[Ni(CN)_4]^{2-}$	2×10^{31}
$[Ag(NH_3)_2]^+$	1.6×10^7	$[CuCl_3]^{2-}$	5×10^5	$[Ni(EDTA)]^{2-}$	3.6×10^{18}
$[Ag(SCN)_4]^{3-}$	1.2×10^{10}	$[Cu(CN)_4]^{3-}$	2.0×10^{30}	$[Ni(en)_3]^{2+}$	2.1×10^{18}
$[Ag(S_2O_3)_2]^{3-}$	1.7×10^{13}	$[Cu(EDTA)]^{2-}$	5×10^{18}	$[Ni(NH_3)_6]^{2+}$	5.5×10^8
$[Al(EDTA)]^-$	1.3×10^{16}	$[Cu(en)_2]^{2+}$	1×10^{20}	$[Ni(ox)_3]^{4-}$	3×10^8
$[Al(OH)_4]^-$	1.1×10^{33}	$[Cu(NH_3)_4]^{2+}$	1.1×10^{13}	$[PbCl_3]^-$	2.4×10^1
$[Al(ox)_3]^{3-}$	2×10^{16}	$[Cu(ox)_2]^{2-}$	3×10^8	$[Pb(EDTA)]^{2-}$	2×10^{18}
$[CdCl_4]^{2-}$	6.3×10^2	$[Fe(CN)_6]^{4-}$	10^{37}	$[PbI_4]^{2-}$	3.0×10^4
$[Cd(CN)_4]^{2-}$	6.0×10^{18}	$[Fe(EDTA)]^{2-}$	2.1×10^{14}	$[Pb(OH)_3]^-$	3.8×10^{14}
$[Cd(en)_3]^{2+}$	1.2×10^{12}	$[Fe(en)_3]^{2+}$	5.0×10^9	$[Pb(ox)_2]^{2-}$	3.5×10^6
$[Cd(NH_3)_4]^{2+}$	1.3×10^7	$[Fe(ox)_3]^{4-}$	1.7×10^5	$[Pb(S_2O_3)_3]^{4-}$	2.2×10^6
$[Co(EDTA)]^{2-}$	2.0×10^{16}	$[Fe(CN)_6]^{3-}$	10^{42}	$[PtCl_4]^{2-}$	1×10^{16}
$[Co(en)_3]^{2+}$	8.7×10^{13}	$[Fe(EDTA)]^-$	1.7×10^{24}	$[Pt(NH_3)_6]^{2+}$	2×10^{35}
$[Co(NH_3)_6]^{2+}$	1.3×10^5	$[Fe(ox)_3]^{3-}$	2×10^{20}	$[Zn(CN)_4]^{2-}$	1×10^{18}
$[Co(ox)_3]^{4-}$	5×10^9	$[Fe(SCN)]^{2+}$	8.9×10^2	$[Zn(EDTA)]^{2-}$	3×10^{16}
$[Co(SCN)_4]^{2-}$	1.0×10^3	$[HgCl_4]^{2-}$	1.2×10^{15}	$[Zn(en)_3]^{2+}$	1.3×10^{14}
$[Co(EDTA)]^-$	10^{36}	$[Hg(CN)_4]^{2-}$	3×10^{41}	$[Zn(NH_3)_4]^{2+}$	4.1×10^8
$[Co(en)_3]^{3+}$	4.9×10^{48}	$[Hg(EDTA)]^{2-}$	6.3×10^{21}	$[Zn(OH)_4]^{2-}$	4.6×10^{17}
$[Co(NH_3)_6]^{3+}$	4.5×10^{33}	$[Hg(en)_2]^{2+}$	2×10^{23}	$[Zn(ox)_3]^{4-}$	1.4×10^8

[c]The ligands referred to in this table are monodentate: Cl^-, CN^-, I^-, NH_3, OH^-, SCN^-, $S_2O_3^{2-}$; bidentate: ethylenediamine (en), oxalate ion (ox); tetradentate: ethylenediaminetetraacetato ion, $EDTA^{4-}$.
[d]The K_f values are cumulative or overall formation constants (see page 1024).

TABLE D.4 Standard Electrode (Reduction) Potentials at 25 °C

Reduction half-reaction	$E°$, V
$F_2(g) + 2\,e^- \longrightarrow 2\,F^-(aq)$	+2.866
$OF_2(g) + 2\,H^+(aq) + 4\,e^- \longrightarrow H_2O(l) + 2\,F^-(aq)$	+2.1
$O_3(g) + 2\,H^+(aq) + 2\,e^- \longrightarrow O_2(g) + H_2O(l)$	+2.075
$S_2O_8{}^{2-}(aq) + 2\,e^- \longrightarrow 2\,SO_4{}^{2-}(aq)$	+2.01
$Ag^{2+}(aq) + e^- \longrightarrow Ag^+(aq)$	+1.98
$H_2O_2(aq) + 2\,H^+(aq) + 2\,e^- \longrightarrow 2\,H_2O(l)$	+1.763
$MnO_4{}^-(aq) + 4\,H^+(aq) + 3\,e^- \longrightarrow MnO_2(s) + 2\,H_2O(l)$	+1.70
$PbO_2(s) + SO_4{}^{2-}(aq) + 4\,H^+(aq) + 2\,e^- \longrightarrow PbSO_4(s) + 2\,H_2O(l)$	+1.69
$Au^{3+}(aq) + 3\,e^- \longrightarrow Au(s)$	+1.52
$MnO_4{}^-(aq) + 8\,H^+(aq) + 5\,e^- \longrightarrow Mn^{2+}(aq) + 4\,H_2O(l)$	+1.51
$2\,BrO_3{}^-(aq) + 12\,H^+(aq) + 10\,e^- \longrightarrow Br_2(l) + 6\,H_2O(l)$	+1.478
$PbO_2(s) + 4\,H^+(aq) + 2\,e^- \longrightarrow Pb^{2+}(aq) + 2\,H_2O(l)$	+1.455
$ClO_3{}^-(aq) + 6\,H^+(aq) + 6\,e^- \longrightarrow Cl^-(aq) + 3\,H_2O(l)$	+1.450
$Au^{3+}(aq) + 2\,e^- \longrightarrow Au^+(aq)$	+1.36
$Cl_2(g) + 2\,e^- \longrightarrow 2\,Cl^-(aq)$	+1.358
$Cr_2O_7{}^{2-}(aq) + 14\,H^+(aq) + 6\,e^- \longrightarrow 2\,Cr^{3+}(aq) + 7\,H_2O(l)$	+1.33
$MnO_2(s) + 4\,H^+(aq) + 2\,e^- \longrightarrow Mn^{2+}(aq) + 2\,H_2O(l)$	+1.23
$O_2(g) + 4\,H^+(aq) + 4\,e^- \longrightarrow 2\,H_2O(l)$	+1.229
$2\,IO_3{}^-(aq) + 12\,H^+(aq) + 10\,e^- \longrightarrow I_2(s) + 6\,H_2O(l)$	+1.20
$ClO_4{}^-(aq) + 2\,H^+(aq) + 2\,e^- \longrightarrow ClO_3{}^-(aq) + H_2O(l)$	+1.189
$ClO_3{}^-(aq) + 2\,H^+(aq) + e^- \longrightarrow ClO_2(g) + H_2O(l)$	+1.175
$NO_2(g) + H^+(aq) + e^- \longrightarrow HNO_2(aq)$	+1.07
$Br_2(l) + 2\,e^- \longrightarrow 2\,Br^-(aq)$	+1.065
$NO_2(g) + 2\,H^+(aq) + 2\,e^- \longrightarrow NO(g) + H_2O(l)$	+1.03
$[AuCl_4]^-(aq) + 3\,e^- \longrightarrow Au(s) + 4\,Cl^-(aq)$	+1.002
$VO_2{}^+(aq) + 2\,H^+(aq) + e^- \longrightarrow VO^{2+}(aq) + H_2O(l)$	+1.000
$NO_3{}^-(aq) + 4\,H^+(aq) + 3\,e^- \longrightarrow NO(g) + 2\,H_2O(l)$	+0.956
$Cu^{2+}(aq) + I^-(aq) + e^- \longrightarrow CuI(s)$	+0.86
$Hg^{2+}(aq) + 2\,e^- \longrightarrow Hg(l)$	+0.854
$Ag^+(aq) + e^- \longrightarrow Ag(s)$	+0.800
$Fe^{3+}(aq) + e^- \longrightarrow Fe^{2+}(aq)$	+0.771
$O_2(g) + 2\,H^+(aq) + 2\,e^- \longrightarrow H_2O_2(aq)$	+0.695
$2\,HgCl_2(aq) + 2\,e^- \longrightarrow Hg_2Cl_2(s) + 2\,Cl^-(aq)$	+0.63
$MnO_4{}^-(aq) + e^- \longrightarrow MnO_4{}^{2-}(aq)$	+0.56
$I_2(s) + 2\,e^- \longrightarrow 2\,I^-(aq)$	+0.535
$Cu^+(aq) + e^- \longrightarrow Cu(s)$	+0.520
$H_2SO_3(aq) + 4\,H^+(aq) + 4\,e^- \longrightarrow S(s) + 3\,H_2O(l)$	+0.449
$C_2N_2(g) + 2\,H^+(aq) + 2\,e^- \longrightarrow 2\,HCN(aq)$	+0.37
$[Fe(CN)_6]^{3-}(aq) + e^- \longrightarrow [Fe(CN)_6]^{4-}(aq)$	+0.361
$VO^{2+}(aq) + 2\,H^+(aq) + e^- \longrightarrow V^{3+}(aq) + H_2O(l)$	+0.337
$Cu^{2+}(aq) + 2\,e^- \longrightarrow Cu(s)$	+0.340
$PbO_2(s) + 2\,H^+(aq) + 2\,e^- \longrightarrow PbO(s) + H_2O(l)$	+0.28
$Hg_2Cl_2(s) + 2\,e^- \longrightarrow 2\,Hg(l) + 2\,Cl^-(aq)$	+0.2676
$HAsO_2(aq) + 3\,H^+(aq) + 3\,e^- \longrightarrow As(s) + 2\,H_2O(l)$	+0.240
$AgCl(s) + e^- \longrightarrow Ag(s) + Cl^-(aq)$	+0.2223
$SO_4{}^{2-}(aq) + 4\,H^+(aq) + 2\,e^- \longrightarrow 2\,H_2O(l) + SO_2(g)$	+0.17
$Cu^{2+}(aq) + e^- \longrightarrow Cu^+(aq)$	+0.159
$Sn^{4+}(aq) + 2\,e^- \longrightarrow Sn^{2+}(aq)$	+0.154
$S(s) + 2\,H^+(aq) + 2\,e^- \longrightarrow H_2S(g)$	+0.144
$AgBr(s) + e^- \longrightarrow Ag(s) + Br^-(aq)$	+0.071
$2\,H^+(aq) + 2\,e^- \longrightarrow H_2(g)$	0
$Pb^{2+}(aq) + 2\,e^- \longrightarrow Pb(s)$	−0.125
$Sn^{2+}(aq) + 2\,e^- \longrightarrow Sn(s)$	−0.137
$AgI(s) + e^- \longrightarrow Ag(s) + I^-(aq)$	−0.152

Reduction half-reaction	$E°$, V
$V^{3+}(aq) + e^- \longrightarrow V^{2+}(aq)$	-0.255
$Ni^{2+}(aq) + 2\,e^- \longrightarrow Ni(s)$	-0.257
$H_3PO_4(aq) + 2\,H^+(aq) + 2\,e^- \longrightarrow H_3PO_3(aq) + H_2O(l)$	-0.276
$Co^{2+}(aq) + 2\,e^- \longrightarrow Co(s)$	-0.277
$In^{3+}(aq) + 3\,e^- \longrightarrow In(s)$	-0.338
$PbSO_4(s) + 2\,e^- \longrightarrow Pb(s) + SO_4^{2-}(aq)$	-0.356
$Cd^{2+}(aq) + 2\,e^- \longrightarrow Cd(s)$	-0.403
$Cr^{3+}(aq) + e^- \longrightarrow Cr^{2+}(aq)$	-0.424
$Fe^{2+}(aq) + 2\,e^- \longrightarrow Fe(s)$	-0.440
$2\,CO_2(g) + 2\,H^+(aq) + 2\,e^- \longrightarrow H_2C_2O_4(aq)$	-0.49
$Zn^{2+}(aq) + 2\,e^- \longrightarrow Zn(s)$	-0.763
$Cr^{2+}(aq) + 2\,e^- \longrightarrow Cr(s)$	-0.90
$Mn^{2+}(aq) + 2\,e^- \longrightarrow Mn(s)$	-1.18
$Ti^{2+}(aq) + 2\,e^- \longrightarrow Ti(s)$	-1.63
$U^{3+}(aq) + 3\,e^- \longrightarrow U(s)$	-1.66
$Al^{3+}(aq) + 3\,e^- \longrightarrow Al(s)$	-1.676
$Mg^{2+}(aq) + 2\,e^- \longrightarrow Mg(s)$	-2.356
$La^{3+}(aq) + 3\,e^- \longrightarrow La(s)$	-2.38
$Na^+(aq) + e^- \longrightarrow Na(s)$	-2.713
$Ca^{2+}(aq) + 2\,e^- \longrightarrow Ca(s)$	-2.84
$Sr^{2+}(aq) + 2\,e^- \longrightarrow Sr(s)$	-2.89
$Ba^{2+}(aq) + 2\,e^- \longrightarrow Ba(s)$	-2.92
$Cs^+(aq) + e^- \longrightarrow Cs(s)$	-2.923
$K^+(aq) + e^- \longrightarrow K(s)$	-2.924
$Rb^+(aq) + e^- \longrightarrow Rb(s)$	-2.924
$Li^+(aq) + e^- \longrightarrow Li(s)$	-3.040

Basic Solution

$O_3(g) + H_2O(l) + 2\,e^- \longrightarrow O_2(g) + 2\,OH^-(aq)$	$+1.246$
$ClO^-(aq) + H_2O(l) + 2\,e^- \longrightarrow Cl^-(aq) + 2\,OH^-(aq)$	$+0.890$
$H_2O_2(aq) + 2\,e^- \longrightarrow 2\,OH^-(aq)$	$+0.88$
$BrO^-(aq) + H_2O(l) + 2\,e^- \longrightarrow Br^-(aq) + 2\,OH^-(aq)$	$+0.766$
$ClO_3^-(aq) + 3\,H_2O(l) + 6\,e^- \longrightarrow Cl^-(aq) + 6\,OH^-(aq)$	$+0.622$
$2\,AgO(s) + H_2O(l) + 2\,e^- \longrightarrow Ag_2O(s) + 2\,OH^-(aq)$	$+0.604$
$MnO_4^-(aq) + 2\,H_2O(l) + 3\,e^- \longrightarrow MnO_2(s) + 4\,OH^-(aq)$	$+0.60$
$BrO_3^-(aq) + 3\,H_2O(l) + 6\,e^- \longrightarrow Br^-(aq) + 6\,OH^-(aq)$	$+0.584$
$2\,BrO^-(aq) + 2\,H_2O(l) + 2\,e^- \longrightarrow Br_2(l) + 4\,OH^-(aq)$	$+0.455$
$2\,IO^-(aq) + 2\,H_2O(l) + 2\,e^- \longrightarrow I_2(s) + 4\,OH^-(aq)$	$+0.42$
$O_2(g) + 2\,H_2O(l) + 4\,e^- \longrightarrow 4\,OH^-(aq)$	$+0.401$
$Ag_2O(s) + H_2O(l) + 2\,e^- \longrightarrow 2\,Ag(s) + 2\,OH^-(aq)$	$+0.342$
$Co(OH)_3(s) + e^- \longrightarrow Co(OH)_2(s) + OH^-(aq)$	$+0.17$
$2\,MnO_2(s) + H_2O(l) + 2\,e^- \longrightarrow Mn_2O_3(s) + 2\,OH^-(aq)$	$+0.118$
$NO_3^-(aq) + H_2O(l) + 2\,e^- \longrightarrow NO_2^-(aq) + 2\,OH^-(aq)$	$+0.01$
$CrO_4^{2-}(aq) + 4\,H_2O(l) + 3\,e^- \longrightarrow Cr(OH)_3(s) + 5\,OH^-(aq)$	-0.11
$S(s) + 2\,e^- \longrightarrow S^{2-}(aq)$	-0.48
$HPbO_2^-(aq) + H_2O(l) + 2\,e^- \longrightarrow Pb(s) + 3\,OH^-(aq)$	-0.54
$HCHO(aq) + 2\,H_2O(l) + 2\,e^- \longrightarrow CH_3OH(aq) + 2\,OH^-(aq)$	-0.59
$SO_3^{2-}(aq) + 3\,H_2O(l) + 4\,e^- \longrightarrow S(s) + 6\,OH^-(aq)$	-0.66
$AsO_4^{3-}(aq) + 2\,H_2O(l) + 2\,e^- \longrightarrow AsO_2^-(aq) + 4\,OH^-(aq)$	-0.67
$AsO_2^-(aq) + 2\,H_2O(l) + 3\,e^- \longrightarrow As(s) + 4\,OH^-(aq)$	-0.68
$Cd(OH)_2(s) + 2\,e^- \longrightarrow Cd(s) + 2\,OH^-(aq)$	-0.824
$2\,H_2O(l) + 2\,e^- \longrightarrow H_2(g) + 2\,OH^-(aq)$	-0.828
$OCN^-(aq) + H_2O(l) + 2\,e^- \longrightarrow CN^-(aq) + 2\,OH^-(aq)$	-0.97
$As(s) + 3\,H_2O(l) + 3\,e^- \longrightarrow AsH_3(g) + 3\,OH^-(aq)$	-1.21
$Zn(OH)_2(s) + 2\,e^- \longrightarrow Zn(s) + 2\,OH^-(aq)$	-1.246
$Sb(s) + 3\,H_2O(l) + 3\,e^- \longrightarrow SbH_3(g) + 3\,OH^-(aq)$	-1.338
$Al(OH)_4^-(aq) + 3\,e^- \longrightarrow Al(s) + 4\,OH^-(aq)$	-2.310
$Mg(OH)_2(s) + 2\,e^- \longrightarrow Mg(s) + 2\,OH^-(aq)$	-2.687

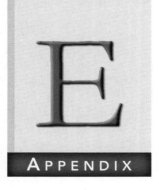

CONCEPT MAPS

As you study chemistry by reading this book and attending class, you will encounter many ideas and concepts. The task of linking them together can be quite daunting. An effective way to accomplish this task is through "concept mapping." A concept map is a visual map presenting the relationships among a set of connected concepts and ideas. It is a tangible way to display how your mind "perceives" a particular topic. By constructing a concept map, you reflect on what you understand and what you do not understand. In a concept map, each concept, usually represented by a word or two in a box, is connected to other concept boxes by lines or arrows. A word or brief phrase adjacent to the line or arrow defines the relationship between the connected concepts. Each major concept box has lines to and from several other concept boxes, thereby generating a network, or "map."

E-1   HOW TO CONSTRUCT A CONCEPT MAP

1. To create a concept map, construct a list of facts, terms, and ideas that you think are in any way associated with the topic, based on your reading and class attendance. Start by asking yourself, "What was the class or reading assignment about?" The answer to this question will provide the initial (most general) concepts. The list of concepts will grow as you think further about the answer to this question. You can review the chapter summaries, which emphasize the important points of the chapters, as well as the key terms of that chapter.

2. Review the concepts in your list, and categorize them from most general to most specific. Keep in mind that several of the concepts may have the same level of generality. At other times, it may be difficult to determine the relative importance of two related concepts; to get around this dilemma, try posing the following question: "Which concept can be understood without reference to the other?" The answer is likely the more general concept.

3. Once the categories have been decided, center the most general concept at the top of the page, and draw a box around it.

4. Arrange the next-most-general rank of concepts below the most general concept. Draw boxes around these concepts, and draw lines linking them to the most general concept. The links should have arrowheads to show the directions in which they should be read.

5. The next step is to label the linkages with short phrases, or even single words, which properly relate the linked concepts. When you place concept 1, a linkage phrase, and concept 2 in sequence, a sensible phrase should result. For example, measurements (concept 1) generate (linkage phrase) numbers (concept 2) which have (linkage phrase) uncertainty (concept 3). The inclusion of linkage labels is important. The appropriate linkage phrase shows that you understand the relationship between the concepts.

6. Proceed down the page, adding rows of ever-more-specific concepts. The most specific concepts should end up at the bottom of your map.

7. Throughout the map, search for cross-links between closely related concepts appearing on the same line. Use dashed lines with double arrowheads to indicate the cross-links.

8. As a last step, assess the map and redraw it if necessary to produce a more logical and neat map.

Once you have constructed the map, check that a concept appears only once and that you have labeled all linkages. Finally, remember that there is no one *correct* concept map for a collection of concepts. However, some concept maps are much more effective than others at displaying the relationships among a given set of concepts.

The diagram in this appendix represents a concept map for the scientific method and measurements. Notice that the concept of SI units could be further connected to such concepts as fundamental units and derived units.

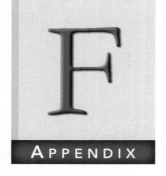

GLOSSARY

Absolute configuration refers to the spatial arrangement of the groups attached to a chiral carbon atom. The two possibilities are D and L.

The **absolute zero of temperature** is the temperature at which molecular motion is hypothesized to cease: $0 \text{ K} = -273.15 \text{ °C}$.

Accuracy is the "closeness" of a measured value to the true or accepted value of a quantity.

Acetyl (See **acyl**.)

An **achiral** molecule has a structure that is superimposable on its mirror image. (See also **chiral**.)

An **acid** is (1) a hydrogen-containing compound that can produce hydrogen ions, H^+ (Arrhenius theory); (2) a proton donor (Brønsted–Lowry theory); (3) an atom, ion, or molecule that can accept a pair of electrons to form a covalent bond (Lewis theory).

An **acid anhydride** is an oxide that reacts with water to form a ternary acid as the sole product.

An **acid–base indicator** is a substance used to measure the pH of a solution or to signal the equivalence point in an acid–base titration. The nonionized weak acid form has one color and the anionic form, a different color.

An **acid ionization constant**, K_a, is the equilibrium constant for the ionization reaction of a weak acid.

An **acid salt** contains an anion that can act as an acid (proton donor); examples are $NaHSO_4$ and NaH_2PO_4.

The **actinides** are a series of radioactive elements ($Z = 90 - 103$) characterized by partially filled $5f$ orbitals in their atoms.

An **activated complex** is an intermediate in a chemical reaction formed through collisions between energetic molecules. Once formed, it dissociates either into the products or back to the reactants.

Activation energy is the minimum total kinetic energy that molecules must bring to their collisions for a chemical reaction to occur.

Active sites are the locations at which catalysis occurs, whether on the surface of a heterogeneous catalyst or an enzyme.

Activity is the effective concentration of a species. It is obtained as the product of an activity coefficient and the ratio of the stoichiometic concentration or pressure to that of a reference state.

The **actual yield** is the *measured* quantity of a product obtained in a chemical reaction. (See also **theoretical yield** and **percent yield**.)

The **acyl group** is $-\overset{\displaystyle O}{\overset{\|}{C}}-R$. If $R = H$, this is called the **formyl** group; $R = CH_3$, **acetyl**; and $R = C_6H_5$, **benzoyl**.

In an **addition reaction**, functional group atoms are joined to the carbon atoms at points of unsaturation in alkene and alkyne hydrocarbon molecules.

An **adduct** is a compound formed by joining together two simpler molecules through a coordinate covalent bond, such as the adduct of $AlCl_3$ and $(C_2H_5)_2O$ pictured on page 893.

Adenosine diphosphate (ADP) and **adenosine triphosphate (ATP)** are agents involved in energy transfers during metabolism. The hydrolysis of ATP produces ADP, the ion HPO_4^{2-}, and a release of energy.

Adhesive forces are intermolecular forces between unlike molecules, such as molecules of a liquid and of a surface with which it is in contact.

Adsorption refers to the attachment of ions or molecules to the surface of a material.

ADP (See **adenosine diphosphate**.)

Alcohols contain the functional group $-OH$ and have the general formula ROH.

Aldehydes have the general formula $R-\overset{\displaystyle O}{\overset{\|}{C}}-H$.

Alicyclic hydrocarbon molecules have their carbon atom skeletons arranged in rings and resemble aliphatic (rather than aromatic) hydrocarbons.

Aliphatic hydrocarbon molecules have their carbon atom skeletons arranged in straight or branched chains.

Alkali metals is the family name for the group 1 elements of the periodic table.

Alkaline earth metals is the family name for the group 2 elements of the periodic table.

Alkane hydrocarbon molecules have only single covalent bonds between carbon atoms. In their chain structures alkanes have the general formula C_nH_{2n+2}.

Alkene hydrocarbons have one or more carbon-to-carbon double bonds in their molecules. The simple alkenes have the general formula C_nH_{2n}.

Alkyl groups are alkane hydrocarbon molecules from which one hydrogen atom has been extracted. For example, the group $-CH_3$ is the **methyl** group; $-CH_2CH_3$ is the **ethyl** group. (See also Table 26.1.)

Alkyne hydrocarbons have one or more carbon-to-carbon triple bonds in their molecules. The simple alkynes have the general formula C_nH_{2n-2}.

Allotropy refers to the existence of an *element* in two or more different *molecular* forms, such as O_2 and O_3 or red and white phosphorus.

An **alloy** is a mixture of two or more metals. Some alloys are solid solutions, some are heterogeneous mixtures, and some are intermetallic compounds.

An **alpha (α) particle** is a combination of two protons and two neutrons identical to the helium ion, that is, $^4He^{2+}$. Alpha particles are emitted in some radioactive decay processes.

Alums are sulfates of the general formula, $M(I)M(III)(SO_4)_2 \cdot 12 H_2O$. M(I) is most commonly an alkali metal or ammonium ion, and M(III) is most commonly Al^{3+}, Fe^{3+}, or Cr^{3+}.

Amalgams are metal alloys containing mercury. Depending on their compositions, some are liquid and some are solid.

An **amide** is derived from the ammonium salt of a carboxylic acid and has

the general formula R—C(=O)—NH$_2$.

An **amine** is an organic base having the formula RNH$_2$ (primary), R$_2$NH (secondary), or R$_3$N (tertiary), depending on the number of hydrogen atoms of an NH$_3$ molecule that are replaced by R groups.

An **α-amino acid** is a carboxylic acid that has an amino group (—NH$_2$) attached to the carbon atom adjacent to the **carboxyl group** (—COOH).

Amplitude is the height of the crest of a wave above the center line of the wave.

Ampoteric is the term used to describe the ability of certain oxides and hydroxo compounds to act as either acids or bases.

An **angular wave function**, $Y(\theta, \phi)$, is the part of a wave function that depends on the angles θ and ϕ when the Schrödinger wave equation is expressed in spherical polar coordinates. (See also **radial wave function**.)

Anhydride is a term meaning "without water." An acid anhydride is an element oxide that reacts with water to form an acid, and a base anhydride, to form a base.

An **anion** is a negatively charged ion. An anion migrates toward the anode in an electrochemical cell.

The **anode** is the electrode in an electrochemical cell at which an oxidation half-reaction occurs.

An **antibonding molecular orbital** describes regions in a molecule in which there is a low electron probability or charge density between two bonded atoms.

Aromatic hydrocarbons are organic substances whose carbon atom skeletons are arranged in hexagonal rings, based on benzene, C$_6$H$_6$.

In the **Arrhenius acid–base theory** an acid produces H$^+$ and a base produces OH$^-$ in aqueous solutions.

The **Arrhenius equation** relates the rate constant of a reaction to the temperature and activation energy.

Asymmetric is the term used to describe a C atom with four different substituent groups. A molecule with such a C atom is chiral.

One **atmosphere** (standard atmosphere) is the pressure exerted, under carefully specified conditions, by a column of mercury 760 mm high.

The **atmosphere** is the mixture of gases (nitrogen, oxygen, argon, and traces of others) that lies above the solid crust and oceans of Earth.

The **atom** is the basic building block of matter. The number of different atoms currently known is 114. A chemical element consists of a single type of atom, and a chemical compound consists of two or more different kinds of atoms.

The **atomic mass (weight)** of an element is the average of the isotopic masses weighted according to the naturally occurring abundances of the isotopes of the element and relative to the value of exactly 12 u for a carbon-12 atom.

An **atomic mass unit, u**, is used to express the masses of individual atoms. One u is 1/12 the mass of a carbon-12 atom.

The **atomic number, Z**, is the number of protons in the nucleus of an atom. It is also the number of electrons outside the nucleus of an electrically neutral atom.

Atomic (line) spectra are produced by dispersing light emitted by excited gaseous atoms. Only a discrete set of wavelength components (seen as colored lines) is present in a line spectrum.

ATP (See **adenosine triphosphate**.)

The **aufbau process** is a method of writing electron configurations. Each element is described as differing from the preceding one in terms of the orbital to which the one additional electron is assigned.

An **average bond energy** is the average of bond-dissociation energies for a number of different species containing a particular covalent bond. (See also **bond dissociation energy**.)

The **Avogadro constant, N$_A$**, has a value of 6.02214×10^{23} mol^{-1}. It is the number of elementary units in one mole.

Avogadro's law (hypothesis) states that at a fixed temperature and pressure, the volume of a gas is directly proportional to the amount of gas and that equal volumes of different gases, compared under identical conditions of temperature and pressure, contain equal numbers of molecules.

An **azeotrope** is a solution that boils at a constant temperature, producing vapor of the same composition as the liquid. In some cases, the azeotrope boils at a lower temperature than the solution components, in other cases, at a higher temperature.

A **balanced equation** has the same number of atoms of each type on both sides. (See also **chemical equation**.)

Band theory is a form of molecular orbital theory to describe bonding in metals and semiconductors.

A **barometer** is a device used to measure the pressure of the atmosphere.

Barometric pressure is the prevailing pressure of the atmosphere as indicated by a barometer.

A **base** is (1) a compound that produces hydroxide ions, OH$^-$, in water solution (Arrhenius theory); (2) a proton acceptor (Brønsted–Lowry theory); (3) an atom, ion, or molecule that can donate a pair of electrons to form a covalent bond (Lewis theory).

A **base anhydride** is an oxide that reacts with water to form a base.

A **base ionization constant, K$_b$**, is the equilibrium constant for the ionization reaction of a weak base.

The **basic oxygen process** is the principal process used to convert impure iron (pig iron) into steel.

A **battery** is a voltaic cell [or a group of voltaic cells connected in series (+ to −)] used to produce electricity from chemical change.

bcc (See **body-centered cubic**.)

A **beta (β^-) particle** is an electron emitted as a result of the conversion of a neutron to a proton in certain atomic nuclei undergoing radioactive decay.

A **bidentate** ligand attaches itself to the central atom of a complex at two points in the coordination sphere.

A **bimolecular process** is an elementary process involving the collision of two molecules.

Binary compounds are compounds composed of *two* elements.

A **body-centered cubic (bcc)** crystal structure is one in which the unit cell has structural units at each corner and one in the center of the cube.

Boiling is a process in which vaporization occurs throughout a liquid. It occurs when the vapor pressure of a liquid is equal to barometric pressure.

A **bomb calorimeter** is a device used to measure the heat of a combustion reaction. The quantity measured is the heat of reaction at constant volume, $q_V = \Delta U$.

A **bond angle** is the angle between two covalent bonds. It is the angle between hypothetical lines joining the nuclei of two atoms to the nucleus of a third atom to which they are covalently bonded.

Bond dissociation energy, D, is the quantity of energy required to break one mole of covalent bonds in a gaseous species, usually expressed in kJ mol^{-1}. (See also **average bond energy**.)

Bond length (bond distance) is the distance between the centers of two atoms joined by a covalent bond.

Bond order is one-half the difference between the numbers of electrons in bonding and in antibonding molecular orbitals in a covalent bond. A single bond has a bond order of 1; a double bond, 2; and a triple bond, 3.

A **bond pair** is a pair of electrons involved in covalent bond formation.

A **bonding molecular orbital** describes regions of high electron probability or charge density in the internuclear region between two bonded atoms.

The **Born–Fajans–Haber cycle** relates lattice energies of crystalline ionic solids to ionization energies, electron affinities, and enthalpies of sublimation, dissociation, and formation.

Boyle's law states that the volume of a fixed amount of gas at a constant temperature is inversely proportional to the gas pressure.

A **breeder reactor** is a nuclear reactor that creates more nuclear fuel than it consumes, for example, by converting ^{238}U to ^{239}Pu.

The **Brønsted–Lowry theory** describes acids as proton donors and bases as proton acceptors. An acid–base reaction involves the transfer of protons from an acid to a base.

Buffer capacity refers to the amount of acid and/or base that a buffer solution can neutralize while maintaining an essentially constant pH.

Buffer range is the range of pH values over which a buffer solution can maintain a fairly constant pH.

A **buffer solution** resists a change in its pH. It contains components capable of neutralizing small added amounts of acids and base.

By-products are substances produced along with the principal product in a chemical process, either through the main reaction or a side reaction.

Calcination refers to the decomposition of a solid by heating at temperatures below its melting point, such as the decomposition of calcium carbonate to calcium oxide and $CO_2(g)$.

The **calorie (cal)** is the quantity of heat required to change the temperature of one gram of water by one degree Celsius.

A **calorimeter** is a device (of which there are numerous types) used to measure a quantity of heat.

A **carbohydrate** is a polyhydroxy aldehyde, a polyhydroxy ketone, a derivative of these, or a substance that yields them upon hydrolysis. Carbohydrates can be viewed as "hydrates" of carbon, in the sense that their general formulas are $C_x(H_2O)_y$.

Carbon black is a finely divided amorphous form of carbon prepared by the incomplete combustion of hydrocarbons.

The **carbonyl group** is found in aldehydes, ketones, and carboxylic acids $\overset{\diagdown}{\diagup}C{=}O$.

The **carboxyl group** is $-\overset{\overset{O}{\|}}{C}-OH$.

A **carboxylic acid** has one or more carboxyl groups attached to a hydrocarbon chain or ring structure.

A **catalyst** provides an alternative mechanism of lower activation energy for a chemical reaction. The reaction is speeded up, and the catalyst is regenerated.

The **cathode** is the electrode of an electrochemical cell where a reduction half-reaction occurs.

Cathode rays are negatively charged particles (electrons) emitted at the negative electrode (cathode) in the passage of electricity through gases at very low pressures.

Cathodic protection is a method of corrosion control in which the metal to be protected is joined to a more active metal that corrodes instead. The protected metal acts as the cathode of a voltaic cell.

A **cation** is a positively charged ion. A cation migrates toward the cathode in an electrochemical cell.

The **cell** is the fundamental unit of living organisms.

A **cell diagram** is a symbolic representation of an electrochemical cell that indicates the substances entering into the cell reaction, electrode materials, solution concentrations, etc.

The **cell voltage (potential)**, E_{cell}, is the potential difference (voltage) between the two electrodes of an electrochemical cell.

A **central atom** in a structure is an atom that is bonded to two or more other atoms.

The **Celsius** temperature scale is based on a value of 0 °C for the normal melting point of ice and 100 °C for the normal boiling point of water.

In **chain reaction polymerization**, a reaction is initiated by "opening up" a carbon-to-carbon double bond. Monomer units add to free-radical intermediates to produce a long-chain polymer.

Charles's law states that the volume of a fixed amount of gas at a constant pressure is directly proportional to the Kelvin (absolute) temperature.

A **chelate** results from the attachment of polydentate ligands to the central atom of a complex ion. Chelates are five- or six-membered rings that include the central atom and atoms of the ligands.

A **chelating agent** is a polydentate ligand. It simultaneously attaches to two or more positions in the coordination sphere of the central atom of a complex ion.

The **chelation effect** refers to an exceptional stability conferred to a complex ion when polydentate ligands are present.

Chemical change (See **chemical reaction**.)

Chemical energy is the energy associated with chemical bonds and intermolecular forces.

A **chemical equation** is a symbolic representation of a chemical reaction. Symbols and formulas are used to represent reactants and products, and stoichiometric coefficients are used to balance the equation. (See also **balanced equation**.)

A **chemical formula** represents the relative numbers of atoms of each kind in a substance through symbols and numerical subscripts.

A **chemical property** is the ability (or inability) of a sample of matter to undergo a particular chemical reaction.

A **chemical reaction** is a process in which one set of substances (reactants) is transformed into a new set of substances (products).

Chemical symbols are abbreviations of the names of the elements consisting of one or two letters (e.g., N = nitrogen and Ne = neon).

Chiral refers to a molecule with a structure that is not superimposable on its mirror image. (See also **enantiomers**.)

A **chlor-alkali process** involves the electrolysis of NaCl(aq) to produce NaOH(aq), $Cl_2(g)$, and $H_2(g)$.

Chromatography is a separation technique in which the components in one phase (gas or liquid) are separated from one another as they pass over or through another phase (solid or liquid).

The term **cis** describes geometric isomers in which two groups are attached on the same side of a double bond in an organic molecule, or along the same edge of a square in a square-planar complex, or at two adjacent vertices of an octahedral complex. (See also **geometric isomerism**.)

A **closed system** is one that can exchange energy but not matter with its surroundings.

Cohesive forces are intermolecular forces between like molecules, such as within a drop of liquid.

Coke is a relatively pure form of carbon produced by heating coal out of contact with air (destructive distillation).

Colligative properties—vapor pressure lowering, freezing point depression, boiling point elevation, osmotic pressure—have values that depend on the number of solute particles in a solution but not on their identity.

Collision frequency is the number of collisions occurring between molecules in a unit of time.

Collision theory describes reactions in terms of molecular collisions—the frequency of collisions, the fraction of activated molecules, and the probability that collisions will be effective.

A **colloidal mixture** contains particles that are intermediate in size to those of a true solution and an ordinary heterogeneous mixture.

The **common ion effect** describes the effect on an equilibrium by a substance that furnishes ions that can participate in the equilibrium.

A **complementary color** is a secondary color that mixes with the opposite primary color on the color wheel (Fig. 24-16) to produce white light in additive color mixing or black in subtractive color mixing.

A **complex** is a polyatomic cation, anion, or neutral molecule in which groups (molecules or ions) called ligands are bonded to a central metal atom or ion.

A **complex ion** is a complex having a net electrical charge.

Composition refers to the components and their relative proportions in a sample of matter.

A **compound** is a substance made up of two or more elements. It does not change its identity in physical changes, but it can be broken down into its constituent elements by chemical changes.

Concentration (1) refers to the composition of a solution. (2) See **extractive metallurgy**.

In a **concentration cell** identical electrodes are immersed in solutions of different concentrations. The voltage (emf) of the cell is a function simply of the concentrations of the two solutions.

Condensation is the passage of molecules from the gaseous state to the liquid state.

A **condensation reaction** is one in which two molecules are combined by eliminating a small molecule (such as H_2O) between them.

A **condensed structural formula** is a simplified representation of a structural formula.

Conformations refer to the different spatial arrangements possible in a molecule. Examples are the "boat" and "chair" forms of cyclohexane.

A **conjugate acid** is formed when a Brønsted–Lowry base gains a proton. Every base has a conjugate acid.

A **conjugate base** remains after a Brønsted–Lowry acid has lost a proton. Every acid has a conjugate base.

Consecutive reactions are two or more reactions carried out in sequence. A product of each reaction becomes a reactant in a following reaction until a final product is formed.

A **continuous spectrum** is one in which all wavelength components of the visible portion of the electromagnetic spectrum are present.

The **contact process** is a process for the manufacture of sulfuric acid having as its key reaction the oxidation of $SO_2(g)$ to $SO_3(g)$ in contact with a catalyst.

Control rods are neutron-absorbing metal rods (e.g., Cd) that are used to control the neutron flux in a nuclear reactor and thereby control the rate of the fission reaction.

A **conversion factor** is a relationship between quantities expressed in different units. It is written as a *ratio* of two quantities that are either equal or otherwise equivalent to one another.

In a **coordinate covalent bond**, electrons shared between two atoms are contributed by just one of the atoms. As a result, the bonded atoms exhibit formal charges.

Coordination compounds are neutral complexes or compounds containing complex ions.

Coordination number is the number of positions around a central atom where ligands can be attached in the formation of a complex. Applied to a crystalline solid, coordination number signifies the number of nearest neighboring atoms (or ions of opposite charge) to any given atom (or ion) in a crystal.

Corrosion is the oxidation of a metal through the action of water, air, and/or salt solutions. A corrosion reaction consists of an oxidation and a reduction half-reaction.

Coupled reactions are sets of chemical reactions that occur together. One (or more) of the reactions taken alone is (are) *nonspontaneous* and other(s), *spontaneous*. The overall reaction is *spontaneous*.

A **covalent bond** is formed when electrons are shared between a pair of atoms. In valence bond theory, the sharing of the electrons is said to occur in the region in which atomic orbitals overlap.

Covalent radius is one-half the distance between the centers of two atoms that are bonded covalently. It is the atomic radius associated with an element in its covalent compounds.

The **critical point** refers to the temperature and pressure at which a liquid and its vapor become identical. It is the highest temperature point on the vapor pressure curve.

Crystal field theory describes bonding in complexes in terms of electrostatic attractions between ligands and the nucleus of the central metal. Particular attention is focused on the splitting of the *d* energy level of the central metal.

Cubic closest packed is one of the two ways in which spheres can be packed to minimize the amount of free space or voids among them. (See Figures 12-39 and 12-40.)

Dalton's law of partial pressures states that in a mixture of gases, the total pressure is the sum of the partial pressures of the gases present. (See also **partial pressure**.)

The **dashed-wedged line notation** is a method of conveying a three-dimensional perspective to a structure plotted in a plane. (See Figure 26-1.)

The *d* **block** refers to that section of the periodic table in which the process of orbital filling (aufbau process) involves a *d* subshell.

A **decay constant** is a first-order rate constant describing radioactive decay.

Degree of ionization refers to the extent to which molecules of a weak acid or weak base ionize. The degree of ionization increases as the weak electrolyte solution is diluted. (See also **percent ionization**.)

Deionized water is water that has been freed of most of its impurity ions by being passed first through a cation and then an anion exchange resin.

Degenerate orbitals are orbitals that are at the same energy level.

Deliquescence is a process in which atmospheric water vapor condenses on a highly soluble solid and the solid dissolves in the water to produce an aqueous solution.

A **delocalized molecular orbital** describes a region of high electron probability or charge density that extends over three or more atoms.

Denaturation refers to the loss of biological activity of a protein brought about by changes in its secondary and tertiary structures.

Density is a physical property obtained by dividing the mass of a material or object by its volume (i.e., mass per unit volume).

Deposition is the passage of molecules from the gaseous to the solid state.

Deoxyribonucleic acid (DNA) is the substance that makes up the genes of the chromosomes in the nuclei of cells.

Detergents are cleansing agents that act by emulsifying oils. Most common among synthetic detergents are the salts of organic sulfonic acids, $RSO_3^-Na^+$.

Dextrorotatory means the ability to rotate the plane of polarized light to the *right*, designated $(+)$.

Diagonal relationships refer to similarities that exist between certain pairs of elements in different groups and periods of the periodic table, such as Li and Mg, Be and Al, and B and Si.

Dialysis is a process, similar to osmosis, in which ions or molecules in solution pass through a semipermeable membrane but colloidal particles do not.

A **diamagnetic** substance has all its electrons paired and is slightly repelled by a magnetic field.

Diastereomers are optically active isomers of a compound, but their structures are *not* mirror images (as are enantiomers).

Diborane is the first in a series of electron-deficient boron hydrides. Its formula is B_2H_6.

Diffraction is the dispersion of light into its different components as a result of the interference produced by the reflection of light from a grooved surface.

Diffusion refers to the spreading of a substance (usually a gas or liquid) into a region where it is not originally present as a result of random molecular motion.

Dilution is the process of reducing the concentration of a solution by adding more solvent.

A **dimer** is a molecule comprised of two simpler formula units, such as Al_2Cl_6, which is a dimer of $AlCl_3$.

Dipole moment, μ, is a measure of the extent to which a separation exists between the centers of positive and negative charge within a molecule. The unit used to measure dipole moment is the **debye**, 3.34×10^{-30} C m.

A **disaccharide** is a sugar molecule formed when two monosaccharide molecules join together by eliminating a H_2O molecule between them.

Dispersion (London) forces are intermolecular forces associated with instantaneous and induced dipoles.

In a **disproportionation reaction**, the same substance is both oxidized and reduced.

Distillation is a procedure for separating a liquid from a mixture by vaporizing the liquid and condensing the vapor. In **simple** distillation a volatile liquid is separated from nonvolatile solutes. In **fractional** distillation volatile components of a solution are separated based on their different volatilities.

In a **double covalent bond**, *two pairs* of electrons are shared between bonded atoms. The bond is represented by a double-dash sign ($=$).

Effective nuclear charge, Z_{eff}, is the positive charge acting on a particular electron in an atom. Its value is the charge on the nucleus, reduced to the extent that other electrons screen the particular electron from the nucleus.

Effusion is the escape of a gas through a tiny hole in its container.

An **electrochemical cell** is a device in which the electrons transferred in an oxidation–reduction reaction are made to pass through an electrical circuit. (See also **electrolytic cell** and **voltaic cell**.)

An **electrode** is a metal surface on which an oxidation–reduction equilibrium is established between the metal and substances in solution.

An **electrode potential** is the electric potential developed on a metal electrode when an oxidation and a reduction half-reaction have reached equilibrium on the surface of the electrode.

Electrolysis is the decomposition of a substance, either in the molten state or in an electrolyte solution, by means of electric current.

An **electrolytic cell** is an electrochemical cell in which a nonspontaneous reaction is carried out by electrolysis.

Electromagnetic radiation is a form of energy propagated as mutually perpendicular electric and magnetic fields. It includes visible light, infrared, ultraviolet, X ray, and radio waves.

Electromotive force (emf) is the potential difference between two electrodes in a voltaic cell, expressed in volts.

Electron affinity is the energy change associated with the gain of an electron by a neutral gaseous atom.

Electron capture (E.C.) is a form of radioactive decay in which an electron from an inner electronic shell is absorbed by a nucleus. In the nucleus the electron is used to convert a proton to a neutron.

An **electron configuration** is a designation of how electrons are distributed among various orbitals in an atom.

Electronegativity is a measure of the electron-attracting power of a bonded atom; metals have low electronegativities, and nonmetals have high electronegativities.

The **electronegativity difference** between two atoms that are bonded together is used to assess the degree of polarity in the bond.

Electron group geometry refers to the geometrical distribution about a central atom of the electron pairs in its valence shell.

Electron spin is a characteristic of electrons giving rise to the magnetic properties of atoms. The two possibilities for electron spin are $+\frac{1}{2}$ and $-\frac{1}{2}$.

Electrons are particles carrying the fundamental unit of negative electric charge. They are found outside the nuclei of all atoms.

An **electrophilic** center in a molecule is an electron-attracting region of positive charge.

An **electrostatic potential map** depicts the electron charge distribution in a molecule. The color red is used to represent the region with the most negative charge, and blue represents the most positive charge.

An **element** is a substance composed of a single type of atom. It cannot be broken down into simpler substances by chemical reactions.

An **elementary process** is an event that significantly alters a molecule's energy or geometry or produces a new molecule(s). It represents a single step in a reaction mechanism.

An **elimination reaction** is one in which atoms are removed from adjacent positions on a hydrocarbon chain to produce a small molecule (e.g., H_2O) and an additional bond between carbon atoms.

An **empirical formula** is the simplest chemical formula that can be written for a compound, that is, having the smallest integral subscripts possible.

Enantiomers (optical isomers) are molecules whose structures are non-superimposable mirror images. The molecules are optically active, that is, able to rotate the plane of polarized light.

An **endothermic** process results in a lowering of the temperature of an isolated system or the absorption of heat by a system that interacts with its surroundings.

The **end point** is the point in a titration where the indicator used changes color. A properly chosen indicator has

A37 Appendix F Glossary

its end point coming as closely as possible to the equivalence point of the titration.

Energy is the capacity to do work. (See also **work**.)

An **energy-level diagram** is a representation of the allowed energy states for the electrons in atoms. The simplest energy-level diagram—that of the hydrogen atom—is shown in Figure 8-14.

The **English system** of measurement has the yard as its unit of length, the pound as its unit of mass, and the second as its unit of time.

Enthalpy, H, is a thermodynamic function used to describe constant-pressure processes: $H = U + PV$, and at constant pressure, $\Delta H = \Delta U + P\,\Delta V$.

Enthalpy change, ΔH, is the difference in enthalpy between two states of a system. For a chemical reaction carried out at constant temperature and pressure and with work limited to pressure–volume work, the enthalpy change is called the *heat of reaction at constant pressure*.

An **enthalpy diagram** is a diagrammatic representation of the enthalpy changes in a process.

Enthalpy (heat) of formation (See **standard enthalpy of formation**.)

Entropy, S, is a thermodynamic property related to the number of energy levels among which the energy of a system is spread. The greater the number of energy levels for a given total energy, the greater the entropy.

Entropy change, ΔS, is the difference in entropy between two states of a system.

An **enzyme** is a high molar mass protein that catalyzes biological reactions.

An **equation of state** is a mathematical expression relating the amount, volume, temperature, and pressure of a substance (usually applied to gases).

Equilibrium refers to a condition where forward and reverse processes proceed at equal rates and no further net change occurs. For example, amounts of reactants and products in a reversible reaction remain constant over time.

An **equilibrium constant expression** describes the relationship among the concentrations (or partial pressures) of the substances present in a system at equilibrium.

The **equivalence point** of a titration is the condition in which the reactants are in stoichiometric proportions. They consume each other, and neither reactant is in excess.

An **ester** is the product of the elimination of H_2O from between an acid and an alcohol molecule. Esters have the general formula
$$R-\overset{\displaystyle O}{\overset{\|}{C}}-O-R'\,.$$

An **ether** has the general formula $R-O-R'$.

Eutrophication is the deterioration of a freshwater body caused by nutrients such as nitrates and phosphates, which stimulate the growth of algae, oxygen depletion, and fish kills.

Evaporation is the physical process of a liquid changing to a vapor. (See also **vaporization**.)

In an **excited state** of an atom, one or more electrons are promoted to a higher energy level than in the ground state. (See also **ground state**.)

An **exothermic** process produces an increase in temperature in an isolated system or, for a system that interacts with its surroundings, the evolution of heat.

Expanded valence shell is a term used to describe Lewis structures in which certain atoms in the third or higher period of the periodic table appear to require 10 or 12 electrons in their valence shells.

An **extensive property** is one, like mass or volume, whose value depends on the quantity of matter observed.

Extractive metallurgy refers to the process of extracting a metal from its ores. Generally this occurs in four steps. **Concentration** separates the ore from waste rock (gangue). **Roasting** converts the ore to the metal oxide. **Reduction** (usually with carbon) converts the oxide to the metal. **Refining** removes impurities from the metal.

The **E, Z system** is a system of nomenclature used to describe the manner in which substituent groups are attached at a carbon-to-carbon double bond.

A **face-centered cubic (fcc)** crystal structure is one in which the unit cell has structural units at the eight corners and in the center of each face of the unit cell. It is derived from the cubic closest packed arrangement of spheres. (See Figure 12-40.)

The **Fahrenheit** temperature scale is based on a value of 32 °F as the melting point of ice and 212 °F as the boiling point of water.

A **family** of elements is a numbered group from the periodic table, sometimes carrying a distinctive name. For example, group 17 is the halogen family.

The **Faraday constant**, F, is the charge associated with one mole of electrons, $96{,}485\ \text{C/mol e}^-$.

Fats are triglycerides in which saturated fatty acid components predominate.

The f **block** is that portion of the periodic table where the process of filling of electron orbitals (aufbau process) involves f subshells. These are the lanthanide and actinide elements.

fcc (See **face-centered cubic**.)

Ferromagnetism is a property that permits certain materials (notably Fe, Co, and Ni) to be made into permanent magnets. The magnetic moments of individual atoms are aligned into domains. In the presence of a magnetic field, these domains orient themselves to produce a permanent magnetic moment.

In **filtration**, a solid–liquid mixture is passed through a filtering device that retains the solid as the liquid passes through.

A **Fischer projection formula** is a two-dimensional representation of a three-dimensional structural formula. It shows how the stereochemistry at a chiral carbon atom is represented in two dimensions, and how the carbon-chain backbone is arranged on the page.

The **first law of thermodynamics**, expressed as $\Delta U = q + w$, is an alternative statement of the law of conservation of energy. (See also **law of conservation of energy**.)

A **first-order reaction** is one for which the sum of the concentration-term exponents in the rate equation is 1.

Fission (See **nuclear fission**.)

A **flow battery** is a battery in which materials (reactants, products, electrolytes) pass continuously through the battery. The battery is simply a converter of chemical to electrical energy.

Formal charge is the number of outer-shell (valence) electrons in an isolated atom minus the number of electrons assigned to that atom in a Lewis structure.

The **formation constant**, K_f, describes equilibrium among a complex ion, the free metal ion, and ligands.

Formula mass is the mass of a formula unit of a compound, relative to a mass of exactly 12 u for carbon-12.

A **formula unit** is the smallest collection of atoms or ions from which the empirical formula of a compound can be established.

Fractional crystallization (recrystallization) is a method of purifying a substance by crystallizing the pure solid from a saturated solution while impurities remain in solution.

Fractional distillation (See **distillation**.)

Fractional precipitation is a technique in which two or more ions in solution, each capable of being precipitated by the same reagent, are separated by the use of that reagent.

The **Frasch process** is a method of extracting sulfur from underwater deposits. It is based on the use of superheated water to melt the sulfur.

Free energy, G, is a thermodynamic function designed to produce a criterion for spontaneous change. It is defined through the equation $G = H - TS$.

Free energy change, ΔG, is the change in free energy that accompanies a process and can be used to indicate the direction of spontaneous change. For a spontaneous process at constant temperature and pressure, $\Delta G < 0$. (See also **standard free energy change**.)

Free radicals are highly reactive molecular fragments containing unpaired electrons.

Freezing is the conversion of a liquid to a solid that occurs at a fixed temperature known as the **freezing point**.

The **frequency** of a wave motion is the number of wave crests or troughs that pass through a given point in a unit of time. It is expressed by the unit time^{-1} (e.g., s^{-1}, also called a hertz, Hz).

A **fuel cell** is a voltaic cell in which the cell reaction is the equivalent of the combustion of a fuel. Chemical energy of the fuel is converted to electricity.

A **function of state (state function)** is a property that assumes a unique value when the state or present condition of a system is defined. This value is *independent* of how the state is attained.

A **functional group** is an atom or grouping of atoms attached to a hydrocarbon residue, R. The functional group often confers specific properties to an organic molecule.

Fusion (See **nuclear fusion**.)

Galvanic cell (See **voltaic cell**.)

Galvanizing is the name given to any process in which an iron surface is coated with zinc to give it corrosion protection.

Gamma (γ) rays are a form of electromagnetic radiation of high penetrating power emitted by certain radioactive nuclei.

In a **gas**, atoms or molecules are generally much more widely separated than in liquids and solids. A gas assumes the shape of its container and expands to fill the container, thus having neither definite shape nor volume.

The **gas constant, R,** is the numerical constant appearing in the ideal gas equation ($PV = nRT$) and in several other equations as well.

The **general gas equation** is an expression based on the ideal gas equation and written in the form $P_1V_1/n_1T_1 = P_2V_2/n_2T_2$.

The **genetic code** relates to the sequences of bases in DNA molecules that determine complementary sequences in mRNA and, ultimately, sequences of amino acids in proteins.

Geometric isomerism in organic compounds refers to the existence of nonequivalent structures (cis and trans) that differ in the positioning of substituent groups relative to a double bond. In complexes, the nonequivalent structures are based on the positions at which ligands are attached to the metal center.

Glass is a transparent, amorphous solid consisting of Na^+ and Ca^{2+} ions in a network of SiO_4^{4-} anions. It is made by fusing together a mixture of sodium and calcium carbonates with sand.

Global warming refers to the warming of Earth that results from an accumulation in the atmosphere of gases such as CO_2 that absorb infrared radiation radiated from Earth's surface.

Graham's law states that the rates of effusion or diffusion of two different gases are inversely proportional to the square roots of their molar masses.

The **ground state** is the lowest energy state for the electrons in an atom or molecule.

A **group** is a vertical column of elements in the periodic table. Members of a group have similar properties.

A **half-cell** is a combination of an electrode and a solution. An oxidation–reduction equilibrium is established on the electrode. An electrochemical cell is a combination of two half-cells.

The **half-life** of a reaction is the time required for one-half of a reactant to be consumed. In a nuclear decay process, it is the time required for one-half of the atoms present in a sample to undergo radioactive decay.

A **half-reaction** describes one portion of an overall oxidation–reduction reaction, either the oxidation or the reduction.

Halogens (group 17) are the most reactive nonmetals, having the electron configuration ns^2np^5 in the electronic shell of highest principal quantum number.

Hard water contains dissolved minerals in significant concentrations. If the hardness is primarily due to HCO_3^- and associated cations, the water has **temporary hardness**. If the hardness is due to anions other than HCO_3^-

(e.g., SO_4^{2-}), the water has **permanent hardness**.

hcp (See **hexagonal closest packed**.)

Heat is a transfer of thermal energy as a result of a temperature difference.

Heat capacity is the quantity of heat required to change the temperature of an object or substance by one degree, usually expressed as J °C^{-1} or cal °C^{-1}. **Specific heat capacity** is the heat capacity per gram of substance, i.e., J °C^{-1} g^{-1}, and **molar heat capacity** is the heat capacity per mole, i.e., J °C^{-1} mol^{-1}.

A **heat of reaction** is energy converted from chemical to thermal (or vice versa) in a reaction. In an isolated system, this energy conversion causes a temperature change, and in a system that interacts with its surroundings, heat (q) is either evolved to or absorbed from the surroundings.

The **Heisenberg uncertainty principle** states that, when measuring the position and momentum of fundamental particles of matter, uncertainties in measurement are inevitable.

The **Henderson–Hasselbalch equation** has the form, pH = pK_a + log [conjugate base]/[acid], in which stoichiometric concentrations of the weak acid and its conjugate base are used in place of the equilibrium concentrations. There are limitations on its validity.

Henry's law relates the solubility of a gas to the gas pressure maintained above a solution of the gaseous solute. The solubility is directly proportional to the pressure of the gas above the solution.

The **hertz (Hz)** is the SI unit of frequency, equal to s^{-1}.

Hess's law states that the enthalpy change for an overall or net process is the sum of enthalpy changes for individual steps in the process.

Heterocyclic compounds are based on hydrocarbon ring structures in which one or more C atoms are replaced by atoms such as N, O, or S.

Heterogeneous catalysis is catalytic action that takes place on a surface separating two phases.

In a **heterogeneous mixture**, components separate into physically distinct regions of differing properties and often differing composition.

Hexagonal closest packed is one of the two ways in which spheres can be packed to minimize the amount of free space or voids among them. (See Figures 12-39 and 12-41.) The crystal structure based on this type of packing is referred to as **hcp**.

In a **high-spin complex**, weak crystal field splitting leads to a maximum number of unpaired electrons in the d subshell of the central metal atom or ion.

Homogeneous catalysis refers to a catalytic reaction taking place in a single phase.

A **homogeneous mixture (solution)** is a mixture of elements and/or compounds that has a uniform composition and properties within a given sample. However, the composition and properties may vary from one sample to another.

A **homologous series** is a group of compounds that differ in composition by some constant unit ($—CH_2$ in the case of alkanes).

Hund's rule (rule of maximum multiplicity) states that whenever orbitals of equal energy are available, electrons occupy these orbitals singly before any pairing of electrons occurs.

A **hybrid orbital** is one of a set of identical orbitals reformulated from pure atomic orbitals and used to describe certain covalent bonds.

Hybridization refers to combining pure atomic orbitals to generate hybrid orbitals in the valence bond approach to covalent bonding.

A **hydrate** is a compound in which a fixed number of water molecules is associated with each formula unit, such as $CuSO_4 \cdot 5\,H_2O$.

Hydration energy is the energy associated with dissolving gaseous ions in water, usually expressed per mole of ions.

Hydrides are compounds of hydrogen, usually divided into the categories of covalent (e.g., H_2O and HCl), ionic (e.g., LiH and CaH_2), and metallic (mostly nonstoichiometric compounds with the transition metals).

A **hydrocarbon** is a compound containing the two elements carbon and hydrogen. The C atoms are arranged in straight or branched chains or ring structures.

A **hydrogen bond** is an intermolecular force of attraction in which an H atom covalently bonded to one atom is attracted simultaneously to another highly nonmetallic atom of the same or a nearby molecule.

The **hydrogen economy** refers to a possible future in which hydrogen may become the principal fuel and metallurgical reducing agent, supplanting fossil fuels.

In a **hydrogenation reaction**, H atoms are added to multiple bonds between carbon atoms, converting carbon-to-carbon double bonds to single bonds and carbon-to-carbon triple bonds to double or single bonds. It is a reaction, for example, that converts an unsaturated to a saturated fatty acid.

Hydrolysis is a special name given to acid–base reactions in which ions act as acids or bases. As a result of hydrolysis, many salt solutions are not pH neutral, that is, pH $\neq$ 7.

Hydrometallurgy refers to metallurgical procedures where water and aqueous solutions are used to extract metals from their ores. In the first step, **leaching**, the target metal is obtained in soluble form in aqueous solution. Other steps include purifying the leached solution and depositing the metal from solution.

Hydronium ion, H_3O^+, is the form in which protons are found in aqueous solution. The terms "hydrogen ion" and "hydronium ion" are often used synonymously.

The **hydroxyl** group is $—OH$ and is usually found attached to a straight or branched hydrocarbon chain (an alcohol) or a ring structure (a phenol).

A **hypothesis** is a tentative explanation of a series of observations or of a natural law.

An **ICE table** is a format for organizing the data in an equilibrium calculation. It is based on the **i**nitial concentrations of reactants and products, **c**hanges in concentrations to attain equilibrium, and **e**quilibrium concentrations.

An **ideal (perfect) gas** is one whose behavior can be predicted by the ideal gas equation.

Ideal gas constant (See **gas constant**.)

The **ideal gas equation** relates the pressure, volume, temperature, and number of moles of ideal gas (n) through the expression $PV = nRT$.

An **ideal solution** has $\Delta H_{soln} = 0$ and certain properties (notably vapor pressure) that are predictable from the properties of the solution components.

Incomplete octet is a term used to describe situations in which an atom fails to acquire eight outer-shell electrons in a Lewis structure.

An **indicator** is an added substance that changes color at the equivalence point in a titration.

An **induced dipole** is an atom or molecule in which a separation of charge is produced by a neighboring dipole.

Industrial smog is air pollution in which the chief pollutants are $SO_2(g)$, $SO_3(g)$, H_2SO_4 mist, and smoke.

Inert complex is the term used to describe a complex ion in which the exchange of ligands occurs very slowly.

The **inert-pair effect** refers to the effects on the properties of certain post-transition elements that result from the presence of a pair of electrons in the s orbital of the valence shells of their atoms.

The **initial rate of a reaction** is the rate of a reaction immediately after the reactants are brought together.

Inner-transition elements are those of the f-block series, that is, the lanthanide and actinide elements.

An **inorganic compound** is any combination of elements that does not fit the category of organic compound. (See also **organic compound**.)

An **instantaneous dipole** is an atom or molecule with a separation of charge produced by a momentary displacement of electrons from their normal distribution.

An **instantaneous rate of reaction** is the exact rate of a reaction at some precise point in the reaction. It is obtained from the slope of a tangent line to a concentration–time graph.

An **integrated rate law (equation)** is derived from a rate law (equation) by the calculus technique of integration. It relates the concentration of a reactant (or product) to elapsed time from the start of a reaction. The equation has different forms depending on the order of the reaction.

An **intensive property** is *independent* of the quantity of matter involved in the observation. Density and temperature are examples of intensive properties.

An **interhalogen compound** is a covalent compound between two or more halogen elements, such as ICl and BrF_3.

An **intermediate** is the product of one reaction that is consumed in a following reaction in a process that proceeds through several steps.

An **intermolecular force** is an attraction *between* molecules.

The **internal energy, U**, of a system is the total energy attributed to the particles of matter and their interactions within a system.

An **ion** is a charged species consisting of a single atom or a group of atoms. It is formed when a neutral atom or a covalently bonded group of atoms either gains or loses electrons.

Ion exchange is a process in which ions held to the surface of an ion exchange material are exchanged for other ions in solution. For example, Na^+ may be exchanged for Ca^{2+} and Mg^{2+}, or OH^- may be exchanged for SO_4^{2-}.

An **ion pair** is an association of a cation and an anion in solution. Such combinations, when they occur, can have a significant effect on solution equilibria.

An **ion product,** Q_{sp}, is formulated in the same manner as a solubility product constant, K_{sp}, but with *nonequilibrium* concentration terms. A comparison of Q_{sp} and K_{sp} provides a criterion for precipitation from solution.

The **ion product of water,** K_w, is the product of $[H_3O^+]$ and $[OH^-]$ in pure water or in an aqueous solution. This product has a unique value that depends only on temperature. At 25 °C, $K_w = 1.0 \times 10^{-14}$.

An **ionic bond** results from the transfer of electrons between metal and nonmetal atoms. Positive and negative ions are formed and held together by electrostatic attractions.

An **ionic compound** is a compound consisting of positive and negative ions that are held together by electrostatic forces of attraction.

Ionic radius is the radius of a spherical ion. It is the atomic radius associated with an element in its ionic compounds.

The first **ionization energy,** I_1, is the energy required to remove the most loosely held electron from a *gaseous* atom. The second ionization energy, I_2, is the energy required to remove an electron from a gaseous unipositive ion, and so on.

An **irreversible** process takes place in one or several finite steps such that the system is not in equilibrium with its surroundings.

The **isoelectric point,** pI, of an amino acid is the pH at which the dipolar structure or **zwitterion** predominates.

Isoelectric species have the same number of electrons (usually in the same configuration). Na^+ and Ne are isoelectronic, as are CO and N_2.

An **isolated system** is one that exchanges neither energy nor matter with its surroundings.

Isomers are two or more compounds having the same formula but different structures and therefore different properties.

Isotopes of an element are atoms with different numbers of neutrons in their nuclei. That is, isotopes of an element have the same atomic numbers but different mass numbers.

Isotopic mass (See **nuclidic mass.**)

IUPAC (or **IUC**) refers to the International Union of Pure and Applied Chemistry.

The **joule,** J, is the basic SI unit of energy. It is the quantity of work done when a force of one newton acts through a distance of one meter

K_c is the relationship among the *concentrations* of the reactants and products in a reversible reaction at equilibrium. Concentrations are expressed as molarities.

K_p, the partial pressure equilibrium constant, is the relationship that exists among the partial pressures of gaseous reactants and products in a reversible reaction at equilibrium. Partial pressures are expressed in atm.

The **Kelvin** temperature is an *absolute* temperature. That is, the lowest attainable temperature is 0 K = −273.15 °C (the temperature at which molecular motion ceases). Kelvin and Celsius temperatures are related through the expression T (K) = t(°C) + 273.15.

A **ketone** has the general formula

$$R-\overset{\displaystyle O}{\overset{\displaystyle \|}{C}}-R'.$$

A **kilopascal (kPa)** is a unit of pressure equal to 1000 pascals (Pa) or 1000 N/m^{-2}. The standard atmosphere of pressure is 101.325 kPa.

Kinetic energy is energy of motion. The kinetic energy of an object with mass m and velocity u is K.E. = $\frac{1}{2}mu^2$.

The **kinetic molecular theory of gases** is a model for describing gas behavior. It is based on a set of assumptions and yields equations from which various properties of gases can be deduced.

The **Kroll process** is an industrial process for the manufacture of titanium metal from TiO_2. Key steps involve conversion of TiO_2 to $TiCl_4$ and reduction of $TiCl_4$ to Ti with Mg as the reducing agent.

Labile complex is the term used to describe a complex ion in which a rapid exchange of ligands occurs.

The **lanthanide contraction** refers to the decrease in atomic size in a series of elements in which an f subshell fills with electrons (an inner transition series). It results from the ineffectiveness of f electrons in shielding outer-shell electrons from the nuclear charge of an atom.

The **lanthanides** are the elements ($Z = 58 - 71$) characterized by a partially filled $4f$ subshell in their atoms. Because lanthanum resembles them, La ($Z = 57$) is generally considered together with them.

Lattice energy is the quantity of energy released in the formation of one mole of a crystalline ionic solid from its separated gaseous ions.

Gay-Lussac's **law of combining volumes** states that, when compared at the same temperature and pressure, the volumes of *gases* involved in a

reaction are in the ratio of small whole numbers.

The **law of conservation of energy** states that energy can neither be created nor destroyed in ordinary processes.

The **law of conservation of mass** states that the total mass of the products of a chemical reaction is the same as the total mass of the reactants entering into the reaction.

The **law of constant composition (definite proportions)** states that all samples of a compound have the same composition, that is, the same proportions by mass of the constituent elements.

The **law of multiple proportions** states that if two elements form two or more compounds, the masses of one element combined with a fixed mass of the second are in the ratio of small whole numbers when the different compounds are compared.

The **leaving group** is the species expelled from an electrophilic molecule following attack by a nucleophile.

Le Châtelier's principle states that an action that tends to change the temperature, pressure, or concentrations of reactants in a system at equilibrium stimulates a response that partially offsets the change while a new equilibrium condition is established.

Levorotatory means the ability to rotate the plane of polarized light to the *left*, designated (−).

Lewis acid (See **acid.**)

Lewis base (See **base.**)

A **Lewis structure** is a combination of Lewis symbols that depicts the transfer or sharing of electrons in a chemical bond.

In the **Lewis symbol** of an element, valence electrons are represented by dots placed around the chemical symbol of the element.

The **Lewis theory** refers to a description of chemical bonding through Lewis symbols and Lewis structures in accordance with a particular set of rules.

Ligands are the groups that are coordinated (bonded) to the central atom in a complex.

The **limiting reactant (reagent)** in a reaction is the reactant that is consumed completely. The quantity of product(s) formed depends on the quantity of the limiting reactant.

Line-angle formulas are shorthand representations of organic molecules in which bond lines are drawn, but chemical symbols are written only for elements other than carbon and hydrogen.

A **line spectrum** is produced from the emission of light produced from excited atom or ions. The spectrum contains lines at discrete wavelengths which arise from the transition of an electron from one energy level to another.

Lipids include a variety of naturally occurring substances (e.g., fats and oils) sharing the property of solubility in solvents of low polarity [such as in $CHCl_3$, CCl_4, C_6H_6, and $(C_2H_5)_2O$].

In a **liquid**, atoms or molecules are in close proximity (although generally not as close as in a solid). A liquid occupies a definite volume, but has the ability to flow and assume the shape of its container.

Liquid crystals are a form of matter with some, of the properties of a liquid and some, of a crystalline solid.

London forces (See **dispersion forces**.)

A **lone pair** is a pair of electrons found in the valence shell of an atom and *not* involved in bond formation.

In a **low-spin complex**, strong crystal field splitting leads to a minimum number of unpaired electrons in the *d* subshell of the central metal atom or ion.

Magic numbers is a term used to describe numbers of protons and neutrons that confer a special stability to an atomic nucleus.

The **main-group elements** are those in which *s* or *p* subshells are being filled in the aufbau process. They are also referred to as the *s*-block and *p*-block elements. They are found in groups 1, 2, and 13–18 in the periodic table (the A groups).

A **manometer** is a device used to measure the pressure of a gas, usually by comparing the gas pressure with barometric pressure.

Mass describes the quantity of matter in an object.

The **mass number,** *A*, is the total of the number of protons and neutrons in the nucleus of an atom.

A **mass spectrometer (mass spectrograph)** is a device used to separate and to measure the quantities and masses of different ions in a beam of positively charged gaseous ions.

Matter is anything that occupies space, has the property known as mass, and displays inertia.

Melting is the transition of a solid to a liquid and occurs at the **melting point**. The melting point and freezing point of a substance are identical.

A **meta (*m*-) isomer** has two substituents on a benzene ring separated by one C atom.

Metabolism refers to the totality of the chemical reactions occurring in living organisms.

A **metal** is an element whose atoms have small numbers of electrons in the outermost electronic shell. Removal of an electron(s) from a metal atom occurs without great difficulty, producing a positive ion (cation). Metals generally have a lustrous appearance, are malleable and ductile, and are able to conduct heat and electricity.

Metal carbonyls are complexes with *d*-block metals as central atoms and CO molecules as ligands, e.g., $Ni(CO)_4$.

Metallic radius is one-half the distance between the centers of adjacent atoms in a solid metal.

A **metalloid** is an element that may display both metallic and nonmetallic properties under the appropriate conditions.

The **method of initial rates** can be used to establish the order of a reaction from a series of measurements of the initial rate of the reaction. The initial concentration of one reactant is varied while the initial concentrations of all the other reactants are held constant.

The **metric system** is a system of measurement in which the unit of length is the meter, the unit of mass is the kilogram (1 kg = 1000 g), and the unit of time is the second.

A **millimeter of mercury (mmHg)** is a unit of pressure, usually applied to gases. For example, standard atmospheric pressure is equal to the pressure exerted by a 760-mm column of mercury.

A **millimole (mmol)** is one-thousandth of a mole (0.001 mol). It is especially useful in titration calculations.

A **mixture** is any sample of matter that is not pure, that is, not an element or compound. The composition of a mixture, unlike that of a substance, can be varied. Mixtures are either *homogeneous* or *heterogeneous.*

A **moderator** slows down energetic neutrons from a fission process so that they are able to induce additional fission.

Molality, *m*, is a solution concentration expressed as the amount of solute, in moles, divided by the mass of solvent, in kg.

Molar mass, *M*, is the mass of one mole of atoms, formula units, or molecules of a substance.

Molar solubility is the molarity of solute $(mol\ L^{-1})$ in a saturated solution.

Molarity, M, is the concentration of a solution expressed as the number of moles of solute per liter of solution.

A **mole** is an amount of substance containing Avogadro's number (6.02214×10^{23}) of atoms, formula units, or molecules.

Mole fraction describes a mixture in terms of the fraction of all the molecules that are of a particular type. It is the amount of one component, in moles, divided by the total amount of all the substances in the mixture.

A **mole percent** is a mole fraction expressed on a percentage basis, that is, mole fraction × 100%.

A **molecular compound** is a compound comprised of discrete molecules.

A **molecular formula** denotes the numbers of the different atoms present in a molecule. In some cases the molecular formula is the same as the empirical formula; in others it is an integral multiple of that formula.

Molecular geometry refers to the geometric shape of a molecule or polyatomic ion. In a species in which all electron pairs are bond pairs, the molecular geometry is the same as the electron-group geometry. In other cases, the two properties are related but not the same.

Molecular mass is the mass of a molecule relative to a mass of exactly 12 u for carbon-12.

Molecular orbital theory describes the covalent bonds in a molecule by replacing atomic orbitals of the component atoms by molecular orbitals belonging to the molecule as a whole. A set of rules is used to assign electrons to these molecular orbitals, thereby yielding the electronic structure of the molecule.

A **molecule** is a group of bonded atoms held together by covalent bonds and existing as a separate entity. A molecule is the smallest entity having the characteristic proportions of the constituent atoms present in a substance.

A **monodentate ligand** is a ligand that is able to attach to a metal center in a complex at only one position and using just one lone pair of electrons.

A **monomer** is a simple molecule that is capable of joining with others to form a complex long-chain molecule called a **polymer**.

A **monosaccharide** is a single, simple molecule having the structural features of a carbohydrate. It can also be called a simple sugar.

A **multiple covalent bond** is a bond in which more than two electrons are shared between the bonded atoms.

A **natural law** is a concise statement, often in mathematical terms, that summarizes observations of certain natural phenomena.

The **Nernst equation** is used to relate E_{cell}, E_{cell}° and the activites of the reactants and products in a cell reaction.

A **net ionic equation** represents a reaction between ions in solution in such a way that all nonparticipant (spectator) ions are eliminated from the equation. The equation must be balanced both atomically and for net electric charge.

A **network covalent solid** is a substance in which covalent bonds extend throughout the crystal, making the covalent bond both an *intra*molecular and an *inter*molecular force.

In a **neutralization** reaction, an acid and a base react in stoichiometric proportions, so that there is no excess of either acid or base in the final solution. The products are water and a salt.

Neutrons are electrically neutral fundamental particles of matter found in all atomic nuclei except that of the simple hydrogen atom, protium, ^{1}H.

The **neutron number** is the number of neutrons in the nucleus of an atom. It is equal to the mass number (A) minus the atomic number (Z).

The **nitrogen cycle** is a series of processes by which atmospheric N_2 is fixed, enters into the food chain of animals, and eventually is returned to the atmosphere by bacteria.

The **nitrogen family** comprises the elements in group 15. These elements display a progression of properties from nonmetallic to metallic within the group. Group 15 elements have the electron configuration ns^2np^3 in the electronic shell of highest principal quantum number.

Noble gases are elements whose atoms have the electron configuration ns^2np^6 in the electronic shell of highest principal quantum number. (The noble gas helium has the configuration $1s^2$.)

A **nonbonding molecular orbital** is a molecular orbital that neither contributes to nor detracts from bond formation in a molecule. (It does not affect the bond order.)

A **nonelectrolyte** is a substance that is essentially non-ionized, both in the pure state and in solution.

A **nonideal gas** departs from the behavior predicted by the ideal gas equation. Its behavior can only be predicted by other equations of state (e.g., the van der Waals equation).

A **nonmetal** is an element whose atoms tend to gain small numbers of electrons to form negative ions (anions) with the electron configuration of

a noble gas. Nonmetal atoms may also alter their electron configurations by sharing electrons. Nonmetals are mostly gases, liquid (bromine), or low melting point solids and are very poor conductors of heat and electricity.

In a **nonpolar molecule** the centers of positive and negative charge coincide. That is, there is no net separation of charge within the molecule.

A **nonspontaneous** process is one that will not occur naturally. A nonspontaneous process can be brought about only by intervention from outside the system, as in the use of electricity to decompose a chemical compound (electrolysis).

The **normal boiling point** is the temperature at which the vapor pressure of a liquid is 1 atm. It is the temperature at which the liquid boils in a container open to the atmosphere at a pressure of 1 atm.

The **normal melting point** is the temperature at which the melting of a solid occurs at 1 atm pressure. This is the same temperature as the **normal freezing point**.

Nuclear binding energy is the energy released when nucleons (protons and neutrons) are fused into an atomic nucleus. This energy replaces an equivalent quantity of matter.

A **nuclear equation** represents the changes that occur during a nuclear process. The target nucleus and bombarding particle are represented on the left side of the equation, and the product nucleus and ejected particle on the right side.

Nuclear fission is a radioactive decay process in which a heavy nucleus breaks up into two lighter nuclei and several neutrons, accompanied by the release of energy.

In **nuclear fusion** small atomic nuclei are fused into larger ones, with some of their mass being converted to energy.

A **nuclear reactor** is a device in which nuclear fission is carried out as a controlled chain reaction. That is, neutrons produced in one fission event trigger the fission of other nuclei, and so on.

Nucleic acids are cell components comprised of purine and pyrimidine bases, pentose sugars, and phosphoric acid.

A **nucleophile** is a reactant that seeks out a center of positive charge as a point of attack in a chemical reaction.

A **nucleophilic substitution reaction** is a reaction between a nucleophile and an electrophile. The nucleophile attacks at a positive center on the elec-

trophile, and the leaving group is ejected from another point.

Nuclide is a term used to designate an atom with a specific atomic number and mass number. It is represented by the symbolism $_Z^A E$.

Nuclidic mass is the mass, in atomic mass units, of an individual atom, relative to an arbitrarily assigned value of exactly 12 u as the nuclidic mass of carbon-12.

An **octet** refers to *eight* electrons in the outermost (valence) electronic shell of an atom in a Lewis structure.

The **octet rule** states that the number of electrons associated with bond pairs and lone pairs of electrons for each of the Lewis symbols (except H) in a Lewis structure will be eight (an **octet**).

An **odd-electron species** is one in which the total number of valence electrons is an *odd* number. At least one *unpaired* electron is present in such a species.

Oils are triglycerides in which unsaturated fatty acid components predominate.

Olefins are organic compounds that contain one or more carbon-to-carbon double bonds.

Oligosaccharides are carbohydrates consisting of two to ten monosaccharide units. (See also **sugar**.)

An **open system** is one that can exchange both matter and energy with its surroundings.

Optical isomerism results from the presence of a chiral atom in a structure, leading to a pair of optical isomers that differ only in the direction that they rotate the plane of polarized light. (See also **enantiomers**.)

Optical isomers, also called enantiomers (nonsuperimposable mirror images), are isomers that differ only in the direction they rotate the plane of polarized light.

An **orbital** is a mathematical function used to describe regions in an atom where the electron charge density or the probability of finding an electron is high. The several kinds of orbitals (s, p, d, f, . . .) differ from one another in the shapes of the regions of high electron charge density they describe.

An **orbital diagram** is a representation of an electron configuration in which the most probable orbital designation and spin of each electron in the atom are indicated.

The **order of a reaction** relates to the exponents of the concentration terms in the rate law for a chemical reaction. The order can be stated with respect to a particular reactant (first order in A, second order in B, . . .) or, more commonly, as the overall order. The overall order is the sum of the concentration-term exponents.

An **organic compound** is made up of carbon and hydrogen or carbon, hydrogen and a small number of other elements, such as oxygen, nitrogen, and sulfur.

An **ortho (o-) isomer** has two substituents attached to adjacent C atoms in a benzene ring.

Osmosis is the net flow of solvent molecules through a semipermeable membrane, from a more dilute solution (or from the pure solvent) into a more concentrated solution.

Osmotic pressure is the pressure that would have to be applied to a solution to stop the passage through a semipermeable membrane of solvent molecules from the pure solvent.

An **overall reaction** is the overall or net change that occurs when a process is carried out in more than one step.

An **overpotential** is the voltage in excess of the theoretical value required to produce a particular electrode reaction in electrolysis.

Oxidation is a process in which electrons are "lost" and the oxidation state of some atom increases. (Oxidation can occur only in combination with reduction.)

In an **oxidation–reduction (redox)** reaction certain atoms undergo changes in oxidation state. The substance containing atoms whose oxidation states *increase* is **oxidized**. The substance containing atoms whose oxidation states *decrease* is **reduced**.

An **oxidation state** relates to the number of electrons an atom loses, gains, or shares in combining with other atoms to form molecules or polyatomic ions.

An **oxidizing agent (oxidant)** makes possible an oxidation process by itself being *reduced*.

An **oxoacid** is an acid in which an ionizable hydrogen atom(s) is bonded through an oxygen atom to a central atom, that is, $E—O—H$. Other groups bonded to the central atom are either additional $—OH$ groups or O atoms (or in a few cases H atoms).

An **oxoanion** is a polyatomic anion containing a nonmetal, such as Cl, N, P, or S, in combination with some number of oxygen atoms.

The **oxygen family** comprises the elements in group 16. These elements display a progression of properties from nonmetallic to metallic within a group. All have the electron configuration ns^2np^4 in the electronic shell of highest principal quantum number.

The **ozone layer** refers to a region of the stratosphere from about 25 to 35 km above Earth's surface having a concentration of ozone, O_3, considerably greater than that at Earth's surface.

Pairing energy is the energy requirement to force an electron into an orbital that is already occupied by one electron.

A **para (p-) isomer** has two substituents located opposite to one another on a benzene ring.

A **paramagnetic** substance has one or more unpaired electrons in its atoms or molecules. It is attracted into a magnetic field.

A **partial pressure** is the pressure exerted by an individual gas in a mixture, independently of other gases. Each gas in the mixture expands to fill the container and exerts its own partial pressure.

A **pascal** (pa) is a pressure of one N/m^2.

The **Pauli exclusion principle** states that no two electrons may have all four quantum numbers alike. This limits occupancy of an orbital to two electrons with opposing spins.

The *p* **block** is that portion of the periodic table in which the filling of electron orbitals (aufbau process) involves *p* subshells.

A **peptide bond** is formed by the elimination of a water molecule from between two amino acid molecules. The H atom comes from the $—NH_2$ group of one amino acid and the $—OH$ group, from the $—COOH$ group of the other acid.

Percent is the number of parts of a constituent in 100 parts of the whole.

The **percent ionization** of a weak acid or a weak base is the percent of its molecules that ionize in an aqueous solution.

Percent natural abundances refer to the relative proportions, expressed as percentages by number, in which the isotopes of an element are found in natural sources.

Percent yield is the percent of the theoretical yield of product that is actually obtained in a chemical reaction. (See also **actual yield** and **theoretical yield**.)

A **perfect gas** is one whose behavior can be predicted by the ideal gas equation. It is also used to describe a gas whose molecules are "point masses" that do not interact with one another. (See also **ideal gas**.)

A **period** is a horizontal row of the periodic table. All members of a period

have atoms with the same highest principal quantum number.

The **periodic law** refers to the periodic recurrence of certain physical and chemical properties when the elements are considered in terms of increasing atomic number.

The **periodic table** is an arrangement of the elements, by atomic number, in which elements with similar physical and chemical properties are grouped together in vertical columns.

Permanent hard water (See **hard water**.)

The **peroxide** ion has the structure

$$\left[:\overset{..}{\underset{..}{O}}—\overset{..}{\underset{..}{O}}: \right]^{2-}.$$

pH is a shorthand designation for $[H_3O^+]$ in a solution. It is defined as $pH = -\log[H_3O^+]$.

A **phase diagram** is a graphical representation of the conditions of temperature and pressure at which solids, liquids, and gases (vapors) exist, either as single phases or states of matter or as two or more phases in equilibrium.

A **phenol** has the functional group $—OH$ as part of an aromatic hydrocarbon structure.

A **phenyl group** is a benzene ring from which one H atom has been removed: $—C_6H_5$.

Photochemical smog is air pollution resulting from reactions involving sunlight, oxides of nitrogen, ozone, and hydrocarbons.

The **photoelectric effect** is the emission of electrons by certain materials when their surfaces are struck by electromagnetic radiation of the appropriate frequency.

A **photon** is a "particle" of light. The energy of a beam of light is concentrated into these photons.

In a **physical change**, one or more physical properties of a sample of matter change, but the composition remains unchanged.

A **physical property** is a characteristic that a substance can display without undergoing a change in its composition.

A **pi (π) bond** results from the side-to-side overlap of *p* orbitals, producing a high electron charge density above and below the line joining the bonded atoms.

Pig iron is an impure form of iron (about 95% Fe and 3–4% C, together with small quantities of Mn, Si, and P) produced in a blast furnace.

p*K* is a shorthand designation for an ionization constant: $pK = -\log K$. p*K* values are useful when comparing the relative strengths of acids or bases.

Planck's constant, h, is the proportionality constant that relates the energy of a photon of light to its frequency. Its value is 6.626×10^{-34} J s.

Plaster of paris, $CaSO_4 \cdot \frac{1}{2}H_2O$, is a hemihydrate of calcium sulfate obtained by heating gypsum, $CaSO_4 \cdot 2 H_2O$. It is a widely used material in the construction industry.

pOH is a shorthand designation for $[OH^-]$ in a solution: $pOH = -\log[OH^-]$.

In a **polar covalent bond** a separation exists between the centers of positive and negative charge in the bond.

In a **polar molecule,** the presence of one or more polar covalent bonds leads to a separation of the positive and negative charge centers for the molecule as a whole. A polar molecule has a resultant dipole moment.

Polarizability describes the ease with which the electron cloud in an atom or molecule can be distorted in an electric field, that is, the ease with which a dipole can be induced.

A **polyatomic ion** is a combination of two or more covalently bonded atoms that exists as an ion.

A **polydentate ligand** is capable of donating more than a single electron pair to the metal center of a complex, from different atoms in the ligand and to different sites in the geometric structure.

In a **polyhalide ion** two or more halogen atoms are covalently bonded into a polyatomic anion, e.g., I_3^-.

A **polymer** is a complex, long-chain molecule made up of many (hundreds, thousands) smaller units called monomers.

Polymerization is the process of producing a giant molecule (polymer) from simpler molecular units (monomers).

Polymorphism refers to the existence of a solid substance in more than one crystalline form.

In a **polypeptide,** a large number of amino acid units join together through peptide bonds.

A **polyprotic acid** is capable of losing more than a single proton per molecule in acid–base reactions. Protons are lost in a stepwise fashion, with the first proton being the most readily lost.

A **polysaccharide** is a carbohydrate (such as starch or cellulose) consisting of more than ten monosaccharide units.

Positional isomers differ in the position on a hydrocarbon chain or ring where a functional group(s) is attached.

A **positron (β^+)** is a *positive* electron emitted as a result of the conversion of a proton to a neutron in a radioactive nucleus.

Potential energy is energy due to position or arrangement. It is the energy associated with forces of attraction and repulsion between objects.

The term **ppb** (parts per billion) refers to the number of parts of a component to one billion parts of the medium in which it is found.

The term **ppm** (parts per million) refers to the number of parts of a component to one million parts of the medium in which it is found.

The term **ppt** (parts per trillion) refers to the number of parts of a component to one trillion parts of the medium in which it is found.

A **precipitate** is an insoluble solid that deposits from a solution as a result of a chemical reaction.

Precision is the degree of reproducibility of a measured quantity—the closeness of agreement among repeated measurements.

Pressure is a force per unit area. Applied to gases, pressure is most easily understood in terms of the height of a liquid column that can be maintained by the gas.

Pressure–volume work is work associated with the expansion or compression of gases.

A **primary battery** produces electricity from a chemical reaction that cannot be reversed. As a result the battery cannot be recharged.

A **primary color** is one of a set of colors that when added together as light produce white light. Subtractive mixing leads to an absence of color (black). Red, yellow, and blue are a set of primary colors.

Primary structure refers to the sequence of amino acids in the polypeptide chains that make up a protein.

A **principal electronic shell (level)** refers to the collection of all orbitals having the same value of the principal quantum number, n. For example, the $3s$, $3p$, and $3d$ orbitals comprise the third principal shell ($n = 3$).

The **products** are the substances formed in a chemical reaction.

Properties are qualities or attributes that can be used to distinguish one sample of matter from others.

A **protein** is a large polypeptide, that is, having a molecular mass of 10,000 u or more.

A **proton acceptor** is a base in the Brønsted–Lowry acid–base theory.

A **proton donor** is an acid in the Brønsted–Lowry acid–base theory.

Protons are fundamental particles carrying the basic unit of positive electric charge and found in the nuclei of all atoms.

Proton number (See **atomic number.**)

A **pseudo-first-order** reaction is a reaction of higher order (e.g., second-order) that is made to behave like a first-order reaction by using large initial concentrations of all the reactants save one.

Pyrometallurgy is the traditional approach to extractive metallurgy that uses dry solid materials heated to high temperatures. (See also **extractive metallurgy** and **hydrometallurgy.**)

Qualitative cation analysis is a laboratory method, based on a variety of solution equilibrium concepts, for determining the presence or absence of certain cations in a sample.

Quantitative analysis refers to the analysis of substances or mixtures to determine the *quantities* of the various components rather than their mere presence or absence.

A **quantum** refers to a discrete unit of energy that is the smallest quantity by which the energy of a system can change.

Quantum numbers are integral numbers whose values must be specified in order to solve the equations of wave mechanics. Three different quantum numbers are required: the *principal quantum number*, n; the *orbital angular momentum quantum number*, l; and the *magnetic quantum number*, m_l. The permitted values of these numbers are interrelated.

The **quantum theory** is based on the proposition that energy transfers occur in the form of tiny, discrete units called quanta. Whenever an energy transfer occurs, it must involve an entire **quantum.**

Quaternary structure is the highest order structure that is found in some proteins. It describes how separate polypeptide chains may be assembled into a larger, more complex structure.

Quicklime is a common name for calcium oxide, CaO.

A **racemic mixture** is a mixture containing equal amounts of the enantiomers of an optically active substance.

A **rad** is a quantity of radiation able to deposit 1×10^{-2} J of energy per kilogram of matter.

A **radial wave function,** $R(r)$, is the part of a wave function that depends only on the distance r when the Schrödinger wave equation is expressed in spherical polar coordinates. (See also **angular wave function**.)

Radical (See **free radical**.)

The **radioactive decay law** states that the rate of decay of a radioactive material—the activity, A—is directly proportional to the number of atoms present.

A **radioactive decay series** is a succession of individual steps whereby an initial radioactive isotope (e.g., ^{238}U) is ultimately converted to a stable isotope (e.g., ^{206}Pb).

Radioactivity is a phenomenon in which small particles of matter (α or β particles) and/or electromagnetic radiation (γ rays) are emitted by unstable atomic nuclei.

Radiocarbon dating is a method of determining the age of a carbon-containing material based on the rate of decay of radioactive carbon-14.

A **random error** is an error made by the experimenter in performing an experimental technique or measurement, such as the error in estimating a temperature reading on a thermometer.

Raoult's law states that the vapor pressure of a solution component is equal to the product of the vapor pressure of the pure liquid and its mole fraction in solution: $P_A = x_A P_A^o$.

The **rate constant, k,** is the proportionality constant in a rate law that permits the rate of a reaction to be related to the concentrations of the reactants.

A **rate-determining step** in a reaction mechanism is an elementary process that is instrumental in establishing the rate of the overall reaction, usually because it is the slowest step in the mechanism.

The **rate law (rate equation)** for a reaction relates the reaction rate to the concentrations of the reactants. It has the form: rate $= k[A]^m[B]^n \ldots$.

The **rate of a chemical reaction** describes how fast reactants are consumed and products are formed, usually expressed as change of concentration per unit time.

Reactants are the substances that enter into a chemical reaction. This term is often applied to *all* the substances involved in a reversible reaction, but it can also be limited to the substances that appear on the *left* side of a chemical equation—the starting substances. (Substances on the *right* side of the equation are usually called products.)

A **reaction intermediate** is a species formed in one elementary reaction in a reaction mechanism and consumed in a subsequent one. As a result, the

species does not appear in the equation for the overall reaction.

A **reaction mechanism** is a set of elementary steps or processes by which a reaction is proposed to occur. The mechanism must be consistent with the stoichiometry and rate law of the overall reaction.

A **reaction profile** is a graphical representation of a chemical reaction in terms of the energies of the reactants, activated complex(es), and products.

The **reaction quotient, Q,** is a ratio of concentration terms (or partial pressures) having the same form as an equilibrium constant expression, but usually applied to *nonequilibrium* conditions.

A **reducing agent (reductant)** makes possible a reduction process by itself becoming *oxidized*.

A **reducing sugar** is one that is able to reduce $Cu^{2+}(aq)$ to red, insoluble Cu_2O. The sugar must have available an aldehyde group, which is oxidized to an acid.

A **reduction** process is one in which electrons are "gained" and the oxidation state of some atom decreases. (Reduction can only occur in combination with oxidation.) (See also **extractive metallurgy**.)

Refining (See **extractive metallurgy**.)

The **relative humidity** is the ratio of the partial pressure of water vapor in air to the vapor pressure of water at the same temperature, expressed on a percent basis.

A **rem** is a unit of radiation related to the rad, but taking into account the varying effects on biological matter of different types of radiation of the same energy.

Representative elements (See **main-group elements**.)

Resonance occurs when two or more plausible Lewis structures can be written for a species. The true structure is a composite or *hybrid* of these different contributing structures.

Rest mass is the mass of a particle (e.g., an electron) when it is essentially at rest. As its velocity approaches the speed of light, the mass of a particle increases.

Reverse osmosis is the passage through a semipermeable membrane of solvent molecules *from a solution into a pure solvent*. It can be achieved by applying to the solution a pressure in excess of its osmotic pressure.

A **reversible process** is one that can be made to reverse direction by just an infinitesimal change in a system property.

Ribonucleic acid (RNA), through its **messenger RNA (mRNA)** and **transfer**

RNA (tRNA) forms, is involved in the synthesis of proteins.

Roasting (See **extractive metallurgy**.)

The **root-mean-square speed** is the square root of the average of the squares of the speeds of all the gas molecules in a gaseous sample.

The **R, S system** is used to indicate the arrangement of the four groups bonded to a chiral center and to provide names that distinguish between optical isomers.

A **salt bridge** is a device (a U-tube filled with a salt solution) used to join two half-cells in an electrochemical cell. The salt bridge permits the flow of ions between the two half-cells.

The **salt effect** is that of ions *different* from those directly involved in a solution equilibrium. The salt effect is also known as the diverse or "uncommon" ion effect.

Salts are ionic compounds in which hydrogen atoms of acids are replaced by metal ions. Salts are produced by the neutralization of acids with bases.

Saponification is the hydrolysis of a triglyceride by a strong base. The products are glycerol and a soap.

Saturated hydrocarbon molecules contain only single bonds between carbon atoms.

A **saturated solution** is one that contains the maximum quantity of solute that is normally possible at the given temperature.

The **s block** refers to the portion of the periodic table in which the filling of electron orbitals (aufbau process) involves the s subshell of the electronic shell of highest principal quantum number.

The **Schrödinger equation** describes the electron in a hydrogen atom as a matter wave. Solutions to the Schrödinger equation are called wave functions.

The **scientific method** refers to the general sequence of activities—observation, experimentation, and the formulation of hypotheses, laws, and theories—that lead to the advancement of scientific knowledge.

The **second law of thermodynamics** relates to the direction of spontaneous change. One statement of the law is that all spontaneous processes produce an increase in the entropy of the universe.

A **secondary battery** produces electricity from a reversible chemical reaction. When electricity is passed through the battery in the reverse direction the battery is recharged.

A **secondary color** is the complement of a **primary color**. When light of a primary color and its complement (secondary) color are added, the result is white light. When they are subtracted, the result is an absence of color (black).

The **secondary structure** of a protein describes the structure or shape of a polypeptide chain, for example, a coiled helix.

A **second-order** reaction is one for which the sum of the concentration-term exponents in the rate equation is 2.

Self-ionization is an acid–base reaction in which one molecule acts as an acid and donates a proton to another molecule of the same kind acting as a base.

A **semiconductor** is characterized by a small energy gap between a filled valence band and an empty conduction band.

A **semipermeable membrane** permits the passage of some solution species but restricts the flow of others. It is a film of material containing submicroscopic holes.

The **shielding effect** refers to the effect of inner-shell electrons in shielding or screening outer-shell electrons from the full effects of the nuclear charge. In effect the inner electrons partially reduce the nuclear charge. (See also **effective nuclear charge.**)

SI units are the units of expressing measured quantities preferred by various international scientific agencies. (See Appendix C.)

A **side reaction** is a reaction that produces an undesired or unexpected product and accompanies a reaction intended to produce something else.

A **sigma (σ) bond** results from the end-to-end overlap of simple or hybridized atomic orbitals along the straight line joining the nuclei of the bonded atoms.

Significant figures are those digits in an experimentally measured quantity that establish the precision with which the quantity is known.

Silica is a term used to describe various solid forms of silicon dioxide, SiO_2.

A **silicone** is an organosilicon polymer containing O—Si—O bonds.

Simultaneous reactions are two or more reactions that occur at the same time.

A **single covalent bond** results from the sharing of *one pair* of electrons between bonded atoms. It is represented by a single dash sign (—).

Skeletal isomerism results from differences in the skeletal structures of molecules having the same composition.

A **skeletal structure** is an arrangement of atoms in a Lewis structure to correspond to the actual arrangement found by experiment.

Slaked lime is a common name for calcium hydroxide, $Ca(OH)_2$.

Smog is the general term used to refer to a condition in which polluted air reduces visibility, causes stinging eyes and breathing difficulties, and produces additional minor and major health problems. (See also **industrial smog** and **photochemical smog.**)

S_N1 is the designation for a nucleophilic substitution reaction in which the rate-determining step is unimolecular.

S_N2 is the designation for a nucleophilic substitution reaction in which the rate-determining step is bimolecular.

Soaps are the salts of fatty acids, e.g., $RCOO^-Na^+$, where the R group is a hydrocarbon chain containing from 3 to 21 C atoms. Sodium and potassium soaps are the common soaps used as cleansing agents.

Solders are low-melting alloys used for joining wires or pieces of metal. They usually contain metals such as Sn, Pb, Bi, and Cd.

In a **solid**, atoms or molecules are in close contact, often in a highly organized arrangement. A solid has a definite shape and occupies a definite volume. (See also **crystal.**)

The **solubility** of a substance is the concentration of its saturated solution.

The **solubility product constant, K_{sp},** is the equilibrium constant that describes the formation of a saturated solution of a slightly soluble ionic compound. It is the product of ionic concentration terms, with each term raised to an appropriate power.

A **solute** is a solution component that is dissolved in a solvent. A solution may have several solutes, with the solutes generally present in lesser amounts than is the solvent.

Solution (See **homogeneous mixture.**)

The **solvent** is the solution component in which one or more solutes are dissolved. Usually the solvent is present in greater amount than are the solutes and determines the state of matter in which the solution exists.

An *sp* **hybrid orbital** is one of the pair of orbitals formed by the hybridization of one *s* and one *p* orbital. The angle between the two orbitals is 180°.

An sp^2 **hybrid orbital** is one of the three orbitals formed by the hybridization of one *s* and two *p* orbitals. The angle between any two of the orbitals is 120°.

An sp^3 **hybrid orbital** is one of the four orbitals formed by the hybridization of one *s* and three *p* orbitals. The angle between any two of the orbitals is the tetrahedral angle—109.5°.

An sp^3d **hybrid orbital** is one of the five orbitals formed by the hybridization of one *s*, three *p*, and one *d* orbital. The five orbitals are directed to the corners of a trigonal bipyramid.

An sp^3d^2 **hybrid orbital** is one of the six orbitals formed by the hybridization of one *s*, three *p*, and two *d* orbitals. The six orbitals are directed to the corners of a regular octahedron.

spdf **notation** is a method of describing electron configurations in which the numbers of electrons assigned to each orbital are denoted as superscripts. For example, the electron configuration of Cl is $1s^2 2s^2 2p^6 3s^2 3p^5$.

The **specific heat** of a substance is the quantity of heat required to change the temperature of one gram of the substance by one degree Celsius.

Spectator ions are ionic species that are present in a reaction mixture but do not take part in the reaction. They are usually eliminated from a chemical equation.

The **spectrochemical series** is a ranking of ligand abilities to produce a splitting of the *d* energy level of a central metal ion in a complex ion.

Speed of light, *c*, has a value of 2.99792458×10^8 m s^{-1}.

A **spontaneous (natural) process** is one that is able to take place in a system left to itself. No external action is required to make the process go, although in some cases the process may take a very long time.

Stalactites and **stalagmites** are limestone ($CaCO_3$) formations in limestone caves produced by the slow decomposition of $Ca(HCO_3)_2(aq)$.

The **standard atmosphere (atm)** is the pressure exerted by a column of mercury exactly 760 mm high when the density of mercury is 13.5951 g cm^{-3} and the acceleration due to gravity is $g = 9.80665$ m s^{-2}.

A **standard cell potential, $E°$,** is the voltage of an electrochemical cell in which all species are in their standard states. (See also **cell potential.**)

Standard conditions of temperature and pressure (STP) refers to a gas maintained at a temperature of exactly 0 °C (273.15 K) and 760 mmHg (1 atm).

A **standard electrode potential, E°**, is the electric potential that develops on an electrode when the oxidized and reduced forms of some substance are in their *standard* states. Tabulated data are expressed in terms of the reduction process, that is, standard electrode potentials are standard reduction potentials.

The **standard enthalpy of formation**, ΔH_f°, of a substance is the enthalpy change that occurs in the formation of 1 mol of the substance in its standard state from the reference forms of its elements in their standard states. The reference forms of the elements are their most stable forms at the given temperature and 1 bar pressure.

The **standard enthalpy of reaction**, ΔH°, is the enthalpy change of a reaction in which all reactants and products are in their standard states.

Standard free energy change, ΔG°, is the free energy change of a process when the reactants and products are all in their standard states. The equation relating standard free energy change to the equilibrium constant is $\Delta G^\circ = -RT \ln K$.

The **standard free energy of formation**, ΔG_f°, is the standard free energy change associated with the formation of 1 mol of compound from its elements in their most stable forms at 1 bar pressure.

The **standard hydrogen electrode (SHE)** is an electrode at which equilibrium is established between H_3O^+ (a = 1) and H_2 (g, 1 bar) on an inert (Pt) surface. The standard hydrogen electrode is *arbitrarily* assigned an electrode potential of exactly 0 V.

The **standard molar entropy** is the absolute entropy evaluated when one mole of a substance is in its standard state at a particular temperature.

The **standard state** of a substance refers to that substance when it is maintained at 1 bar pressure and at the temperature of interest. For a gas it is the (hypothetical) pure gas behaving as an ideal gas at 1 bar pressure and the temperature of interest.

Standardization of a solution refers to establishing the exact concentration of the solution, usually through a titration.

A **standing wave** is a wave motion that reflects back on itself in such a way that the wave contains a certain number of points (nodes) that undergo no motion. A common example is the vibration of a plucked guitar string, and a related example is the description of electrons as matter waves.

Steel is a term used to describe iron alloys containing from 0 to 1.5% C together with other key elements, such as V, Cr, Mn, Ni, W, and Mo.

Step-reaction polymerization is a type of polymerization reaction in which monomers are joined together by the elimination of small molecules between them. For example, a H_2O molecule might be eliminated by the reaction of a H atom from one monomer with an —OH group from another.

In **stereoisomers**, the number and types of atoms and bonds in molecules are the same, but certain atoms are oriented differently in space. Cis and trans isomerism is one type of stereoisomerism; optical isomerism is another.

Stoichiometric coefficients are the coefficients used to balance an equation.

A **stoichiometric factor** is a conversion factor relating molar amounts of two species in a chemical reaction (i.e., a reactant to a product, one reactant to another, etc.). The numbers used in formulating the factor are stoichiometric coefficients.

Stoichiometric proportions refer to relative amounts of reactants that are in the same mole ratio as implied by the balanced equation for a chemical reaction. For example, a mixture of 2 mol H_2 and 1 mol O_2 is in stoichiometric proportions, and a mixture of 1 mol H_2 and 1 mol O_2 is not, for the reaction $2 H_2 + O_2 \longrightarrow 2 H_2O$.

Stoichiometry refers to quantitative measurements and relationships involving substances and mixtures of chemical interest.

The **stratosphere** is the region of the atmosphere that extends from approximately 12 to 55 km above Earth's surface.

A **strong acid** is an acid that is completely ionized in aqueous solution.

A **strong base** is a base that is completely ionized in aqueous solution.

A **strong electrolyte** is a substance that is completely ionized in solution.

A **structural formula** for a compound indicates which atoms in a molecule are bonded together, and whether by single, double, or triple bonds.

Structural isomers have the same number and kinds of atoms, but they differ in their structural formulas.

Sublimation is the passage of molecules from the solid to the gaseous state.

A **subshell** refers to a collection of orbitals of the same type. For example, the three $2p$ orbitals constitute the $2p$ subshell.

A **substance** has a constant composition and properties throughout a given sample and from one sample to another. All substances are either elements or compounds.

Substitution reactions are typical of those involving alkane and aromatic hydrocarbons. In such a reaction a functional group replaces an H atom on a chain or ring.

A **substrate** is the substance that is acted upon by an enzyme in an enzyme-catalyzed reaction. The substrate is converted to products, and the enzyme is regenerated.

A **sugar** is a monosaccharide (simple sugar), a disaccharide, or an oligosaccharide containing up to ten monosaccharide units.

The **superoxide** ion has the structure $\left[:\ddot{\text{O}} - \ddot{\text{O}}: \right]^{-}$.

Superphosphate is a mixture of $Ca(H_2PO_4)_2$ and $CaSO_4$ produced by the action of H_2SO_4 on phosphate rock.

A **supersaturated solution** contains more solute than normally expected for a saturated solution, usually prepared from a solution that is saturated at one temperature by changing its temperature to one where supersaturation can occur.

Surface tension is the energy or work required to extend the surface of a liquid.

The **surroundings** represent that portion of the universe with which a system interacts.

Synthesis gas is a mixture of CO(g) and H_2(g), generally made from coal or natural gas, that can be used as a fuel or in the synthesis of organic compounds.

A **system** is the portion of the universe selected for a thermodynamic study. (See also **open, closed**, and **isolated** systems.)

A **systematic error** is one that recurs regularly in a series of measurements because of an inherent error in the measuring system (e.g., through faulty calibration of a measuring device).

Temperature is a measure of the average molecular kinetic energy of a substance (translational kinetic energy for gases and liquids, and vibrational kinetic energy for solids).

Temporary hard water (See **hard water**.)

A **terminal atom** is any atom that is bonded to only one other atom in a molecule or polyatomic ion.

A **termolecular process** is an elementary process in a reaction mechanism in which three atoms or molecules must collide simultaneously.

A **ternary compound** is comprised of *three* elements.

The **tertiary structure** of a protein refers to its three-dimensional structure—for example, the twisting and folding of coils.

The **theoretical yield** is the quantity of product *calculated* to result from a chemical reaction. (See also **actual yield** and **percent yield**.)

A **theory** is a model or conceptual framework with which one is able to explain and make further predictions about natural phenomena.

Thermal energy is energy associated with random molecular motion.

The **thermite reaction** is an oxidation–reduction reaction that uses powdered aluminum metal as a reducing agent to reduce a metal oxide, such as Fe_2O_3, to the free metal.

The **thermodynamic equilibrium constant**, K, is an equilibrium constant expression based on activities. In dilute solutions activities can be replaced by molarities and in ideal gases, by partial pressures in atm. The activities of pure solids and liquids are 1.

A **thio** compound is one in which an S atom replaces an O atom. For example, replacement of an O by S converts SO_4^{2-} to $S_2O_3^{2-}$ (thiosulfate ion).

The **third law of thermodynamics** states that the entropy of a pure perfect crystal is *zero* at the absolute zero of temperature, 0 K.

The **titrant** is the solution that is added in a controlled fashion through a buret in a titration reaction. (See also **titration**.)

Titration is a procedure for carrying out a chemical reaction between two solutions by the controlled addition (from a buret) of one solution to the other. In a titration a means must be found, as by the use of an indicator, to locate the equivalence point.

A **titration curve** is a graph of solution pH versus volume of titrant. It outlines how pH changes during an acid–base titration, and it can be used to establish such features as the equivalence point of the titration.

A **torr** is a unit of pressure equal to the unit millimeter of mercury.

The term **trans** is used to describe geometric isomers in which two groups are attached on opposite sides of a double bond in an organic molecule, or at opposite corners of a square in a square-planar complex, or at positions above and below the central plane of an octahedral complex. (See also **geometric isomerism**.)

Transition elements are those elements whose atoms feature the filling of a *d* or *f* subshell of an inner electronic shell. If the filling of an *f* subshell occurs, the elements are sometimes referred to as *inner* transition elements.

The **transition state** in a chemical reaction is an intermediate state between the reactants and products. (See also **activated complex** and **reaction profile**.)

Transmutation is the process in which one element is converted to another as a result of a change affecting the nuclei of atoms (such as in radioactive decay).

A **transuranium element** is one with an atomic number $Z > 92$.

Triglycerides are esters of glycerol (1,2,3-propanetriol) with long-chain monocarboxylic (fatty) acids.

In a **triple covalent bond**, *three pairs* of electrons are shared between the bonded atoms. It is represented by a triple-dash sign ($\equiv$).

A **triple point** is a condition of temperature and pressure at which three phases of a substance (usually solid, liquid, and vapor) coexist at equilibrium.

The **troposphere** is the region of the atmosphere that extends from Earth's surface to a height of about 12 km.

Trouton's rule states that at their normal boiling points the entropies of vaporization of many liquids have about the same value: 87 J mol^{-1} K^{-1}.

A **unimolecular process** is an elementary process in a reaction mechanism in which a single molecule, when sufficiently energetic, dissociates.

A **unit cell** is a small collection of atoms, ions, or molecules occupying positions in a crystalline lattice. An entire crystal can be generated by straight-line displacements of the unit cell in the three perpendicular directions.

Unsaturated hydrocarbon molecules contain one or more carbon-to-carbon multiple bonds.

An **unsaturated solution** contains less solute than the solvent is capable of dissolving under the given conditions.

The **valence bond method** treats a covalent bond in terms of the overlap of pure or hybridized atomic orbitals. Electron probability (or electron charge density) is concentrated in the region of overlap.

Valence electrons are electrons in the electronic shell of highest principal quantum number, that is, electrons in the outermost shell.

The **valence-shell electron-pair repulsion (VSEPR) theory** is a theory used to predict probable shapes of molecules and polyatomic ions based on the mutual repulsions of electron pairs found in the valence shell of the central atom in the structure.

The **van der Waals equation** is an equation of state for nonideal gases. It includes correction terms to account for intermolecular forces of attraction and for the volume occupied by the gas molecules themselves.

The term **van der Waals forces** is used to describe, collectively, intermolecular forces of the London type and interactions between permanent dipoles.

One type of measure of an atomic size are **van der Waals radii**. van der Waals radii are strictly hard sphere radii measured using atomic distances in closest packed crystals.

Vaporization is the passage of molecules from the liquid to the gaseous state.

Vapor pressure is the pressure exerted by a vapor when it is in dynamic equilibrium with its liquid at a fixed temperature.

A **vapor-pressure curve** is a graph of vapor pressure as a function of temperature.

Viscosity refers to a liquid's resistance to flow. Its magnitude depends on intermolecular forces of attraction and in some cases, on molecular sizes and shapes.

A **volt** is the SI unit for cell voltage. It is defined as 1 joule per coulomb.

A **voltaic (galvanic) cell** is an electrochemical cell in which a *spontaneous* chemical reaction produces electricity.

Water gas is a mixture of $CO(g)$ and $H_2(g)$, together with some of the non-combustible gases CO_2 and N_2, produced by passing steam [$H_2O(g)$] over heated coke.

A **wave** is a disturbance that transmits energy through a medium.

The **wavelength** is the distance between successive crests or troughs of a wave motion.

Wave mechanics is a form of quantum theory based on the concepts of wave–particle duality, the Heisenberg uncertainty principle, and the treatment of electrons as matter waves. Mathematical solutions of the equations of wave mechanics are known as **wave functions** (ψ).

Wave-particle duality was postulated by de Broglie and states that at times particles of matter have wave-like properties and vice versa. This was demonstrated in the diffraction pattern observed when electrons were directed at a nickel crystal.

A **weak acid** is an acid that is only partially ionized in aqueous solution in a reversible reaction.

A **weak base** is a base that it only partially ionized in aqueous solution in a reversible reaction.

A **weak electrolyte** is a substance that is only partially ionized in solution in a reversible reaction.

Weight refers to the force exerted on an object when it is placed in a gravitational field (the "force of gravity"). The terms *weight* and *mass* are often used interchangeably.

Work is a form of energy transfer between a system and its surroundings that can be expressed as a force acting through a distance.

X-ray diffraction is a method of crystal structure determination based on the interaction of a crystal with X rays.

A **zero-order** reaction proceeds at a rate that is *independent* of reactant concentrations. The sum of the concentration-term exponent(s) in the rate equation is equal to *zero*.

The **zero-point energy** is the lowest possible energy in a quantum mechanical system, such as the "particle-in-a-box" energy corresponding to $n = 1$ (page 301).

Zone refining is a purification process in which a rod of material is subjected to successive melting and freezing cycles. Impurities are swept by a moving molten zone to the end of the rod, which is cut off.

A **zwitterion** is a compound (for example, an amino acid or polypeptide) containing both acid and base groups. Zwitterions, at neutral pH, typically have simultaneously positively charged groups (cations) and negatively charge groups (anions).

Note: Your answers may differ slightly from those given here, depending on the number of steps used to solve a problem and whether any intermediate results were rounded off.

CHAPTER 1

Practice Examples 1A. 177 °C **1B.** no; -15 °F $= -26.1$ °C **2A.** 1.46 g/mL **2B.** 2.987 cm **3A.** 2.76 g/cm^3 **3B.** The water level remains unchanged. The ice cube displaces its own mass of liquid and floats on the liquid water with about 90% of its volume submerged. The entire mass of the ice cube is accommodated in the 90% submerged volume when the ice is transformed into liquid water. **4A.** 1.8 kg **4B.** 0.857 g/mL **5A.** 21.3 **5B.** 1.1×10^6 **6A.** 26.7 **6B.** 15.6
Exercises 1. The theory with fewer assumptions and more accurate predictions is preferred. **3.** Cause-and-effect relationships may be difficult to establish ("God is subtle"); they do exist ("he is not malicious"). **5.** Controlled situations and careful observations are needed, and the results must be reproducible and consistent with predictions from the theory. **7.** Physical: (a) and (d); chemical: (b) and (c) **9.** Substance: (d); homogeneous mixture: (a); heterogeneous mixture: (b), (c) **11. (a)** Remove iron filings by attraction to a magnet. **(b)** Dissolve the sugar in water, glass is left behind; evaporate water from the sugar solution to recover solid sugar. **(c)** Carefully pour off the oil, which floats on the water. **(d)** Carefully pour off the water, leaving the very dense gold flakes behind. **13. (a)** 8.950×10^3 **(b)** 1.0700×10^4 **(c)** 2.40×10^{-2} **(d)** 4.7×10^{-3} **(e)** 9.383×10^2 **(f)** 2.75482×10^5 **15. (a)** 3.4×10^4 cm/s **(b)** 6.378×10^3 km **(c)** 7.4×10^{-11} m **(d)** 4.6×10^5 **17.** Exact: (a); measured: (b), (c), (d) **19. (a)** 3985 **(b)** 422.0 **(c)** 1.860×10^5 **(d)** 3.390×10^4 **(e)** 6.321×10^4 **(f)** 5.047×10^{-4} **21. (a)** 9.3×10^{-4} **(b)** 2.2×10^{-1} **(c)** 5.4×10^{-1} **(d)** 3.058×10^1 **23. (a)** 2.44×10^4 **(b)** 1.5×10^3 **(c)** 40.0 **(d)** 2.131×10^3 **(e)** 4.8×10^{-3} **25. (a)** 186.30 km/h **(b)** ≈ 10 km/kg **27. (a)** 127 mL **(b)** 0.0158 L **(c)** 0.981 L **(d)** 2.65×10^6 cm^3 **29. (a)** 174 cm **(b)** 29 m **(c)** 644 g **(d)** 112 kg **(e)** 7.00 dm^3 **(f)** 3.52×10^3 mL **31.** 3245 μg, which is equal to 3.245 mg and is much larger than 0.00515 mg **33.** 1.5 m **35. (a)** 10. s **(b)** 9.8 m/s **(c)** 2.5 min **37.** 2.47 acres **39.** 2.2×10^3 g/cm^2 = 2.2×10^4 kg/m^2 **41.** Low, 14 °F; high, 122 °F **43.** No,

-465 °F $= -276$ °C, which would be below 0 K, an impossibility **45.** bp of water, 35.1 °M; absolute zero, -59.2 °M **47.** 0.958 g/mL **49.** 0.790 g/mL **51.** 0.629 kg **53.** 1.1 kg **55.** 1.04×10^4 g **57.** Iron bar < aluminum foil < water **59.** 1.82×10^{-2} mm **61.** 0.9 L **63.** 9% A, 29% B, 49% C, 11% D, 3% F **65.** 1.10×10^3 g
Integrative and Advanced Exercises
71. 5.5×10^{16} tons **72.** 38.8 m **74. (a)** 4.9 mg m^{-2} h^{-1} **(b)** 5×10^1 y (1 sig. fig.) **76. (a)** -101 °C **(b)** 160.°C **(c)** -19.1 °C **(d)** 335°C **80.** 11 g/mL **81.** 2.0×10^4 kg
Feature Problem 88. Sketch (a) tells only that the mass of plastic is 50.0 g. Sketch (b) shows that the plastic is more dense than ethanol, $d > 0.789$ g/mL. Sketch (c) shows that the plastic is less dense than bromoform, i.e., $d < 2.89$ g/mL. Because the plastic is about 40% submerged, its density is about 0.40×2.89 g/mL ≈ 1.2 g/mL. Sketch (d) shows that the mass of displaced water is 44.4 g = 44.4 mL and the density of the plastic is 50.0 g/44.4 mL = 1.13 g/mL.

CHAPTER 2

Practice Examples 1A. 0.529 g **1B.** 6.85 g **2A.** To three significant figures, 1.21 g magnesium oxide and 0.79 g oxygen. Carrying a fourth significant figure (see margin note on page 19), 1.205 g magnesium and 0.795 g oxygen. **2B.** After the reaction: 16.59 g magnesium oxide, 3.41 g oxygen, no magnesium **3A.** $Z = 47$, $A = 47 + 62 = 109$; the isotope is $^{109}_{47}$Ag. **3B.** $^{112}_{48}$Cd has 48 p, 48 e, and 64 n. $^{A}_{50}$Sn^{2+} has 50 p and 48 e. The value of A depends on the number of neutrons and has a different value for each isotope of tin. **4A.** ^{202}Hg/^{12}C = 201.97062 u/12.000000 u = 16.830885. **4B.** $Z = 64$, $A = 158$ for $^{158}_{64}$Gd. The atomic mass of $^{158}_{64}$Gd = 12.00000 u $\times$ 13.16034 = 157.9241 u. The ratio ^{158}Gd/^{16}O = 157.9241 u/15.9949 u = 9.87340. **5A.** boron-11 **5B.** The second isotope must have a mass greater than the weighted average atomic mass of 114.82 u. It must be ^{115}In and much more abundant than ^{113}In, the other isotope. **6A.** $(0.9223 \times 27.97693$ u) + $(0.0467 \times 28.97649$ u) + $(0.0310 \times 29.97376$ u) = 28.09 u. **6B.** 7.5% lithium-6 and 92.5% lithium-7 **7A.** Li$^+$, S^{2-}, Ra^{2+}, F$^-$, I$^-$, and Al^{3+} **7B.** main-group metals: Na, Mg, Al; main-group nonmetals: S, Kr (noble gas), B, I, H; main-group metalloids: As, Si; transition metals: U,

Re **8A.** 248 g Cu. **8B.** 1.58×10^{22} lead-206 atoms. **9A.** 3.46×10^{21} **9B.** 62.5%
Exercises 1. No. Iron and oxygen from air form solid iron oxide, whereas carbon dioxide gas escapes from burning match. **3.** 0.268 g oxygen **5.** 21.625 g before and after reaction **7. (a)** 0.397 **(b)** 0.658 **(c)** 60.30% **9.** Both samples have 39.4% sodium $\pm$0.1% **11.** 0.422 g **13.** O-to-S mass ratios in the compounds are 3:2. **15. (a)** 3 H (compd. A): 1 H (compd. B): 2 H (compd. C) **(b)** Compd. B is N$_2$H$_2$ (given). Compd. A might be N$_2$H$_6$ (or NH$_3$) and compd. C might be N$_2$H$_4$ (or NH$_2$). **17.** 11% O **19.** All the charges are multiples of e. Millikan could have inferred the charge on the electron from these data. **21. (a)** Ratio of mass of electron to that of a H atom is 1: $1.8 \times 10^3 \approx 1/2000$ **(b)** for proton: 1.044×10^{-5} g/C, about 2000 times greater than for an electron: 5.686×10^{-9} g/C **23. (a)** $^{60}_{27}$Co **(b)** $^{32}_{15}$P **(c)** $^{59}_{26}$Fe **(d)** $^{226}_{88}$Ra **25.** The table has eight rows. The 1st row has no missing data. In the 2nd row fill in the blank spaces with $^{28}_{14}$Si, 14, 14, and 28; in the 3rd row with rubidium, $^{85}_{37}$Rb, 37, and 48; in 4th row, with potassium, 19, 19, 21, and 40; in the 5th row with arsenic, $^{75}_{33}$As, 33, and 75; and in the 6th row with neon ion, 10, 8, 10, and 20. The minimum information required is the atomic number or some way to determine it. This information is lacking for the 7th and 8th rows; there are several possibilities but no unique answer. **27. (a)** 46p, 46e, 62n **(b)** 8.9919908 **29.** 106.906 u **31. (a)** 2.914071 **(b)** 2.165216 **(c)** 18.50146 **33. (a)** $^{35}_{17}$Cl$^-$ **(b)** $^{60}_{27}$Co^{3+} **(c)** $^{124}_{50}$Sn^{2+} **35.** Calcium **37.** None. Masses of single atoms must be nearly integral (that of carbon-12 is an exact integral). Atomic masses that fail to meet this requirement must be weighted averages for two or more isotopes. **39.** 24.31 u **41.** 108.9 u **43.** 40.962 u **45. (a)** There are five peaks in the mass spectrum. **(b)** 73 u **47. (a)** Ge **(b)** similar: other group 14 elements, different: most of the elements (the farther removed from group 14, the more dissimilar) **(c)** Rb **(d)** At **49. (a)** $Z = 118$ **(b)** $Z = 119$ **51. (a)** 9.51×10^{24} **(b)** 2.81×10^{20} **(c)** 5.1×10^{13} **53. (a)** 6.347 mol Zn **(b)** 1.707×10^{27} Cr atoms **(c)** 3.3×10^{-10} g Au **(d)** 3.15476×10^{-23} g **55.** 2.4×10^{22} Cu atoms **57.** 8.7×10^{18} ^{204}Pb atoms **59. (a)** 1.4×10^{-6} mol Pb/L **(b)** 8.7×10^{14} Pb atoms/mL **61.** Sample (b)
Integrative and Advanced Exercises
66. 3×10^{15} g/cm^3 **68. (a)** ^{234}Th **(b)** Ti^{2+}

(c) $^{110}Sn^{2+}$ **70.** ^{210}Po **72.** 0.36% ^{15}N **73.** 200.6 u **78.** 7.1×10^{19} atoms ^{30}Si **82.** 50.1% Sn, 32.0% Pb, 17.9% Cd

Feature Problems 83. Within 1 mg (similar to a good laboratory balance) **86.** 2.43×10^5 km^3 **87.** 159 ppm Rb

CHAPTER 3

Practice Examples 1A. 4.0×10^1 g MgCl$_2$ **1B.** 8.12×10^{15} NO$_3^-$ ions; 2.44×10^{16} O atoms **2A.** 3.69×10^{21} Au atoms **2B.** Yes, $1.6 \times 10^{-2}\ \mu mol/m^3 > 9 \times 10^{-4}\ \mu mol/m^3$ **3A.** 18.9 g Br **3B.** 175 mL **4A.** 23.681% C; 3.180% H; 13.81% N; 18.32% P; 41.008% O **4B.** (b) and (e); they have the same empirical formula: CH$_2$O **5A.** empirical, C$_3$H$_7$O$_3$; molecular, C$_6$H$_{14}$O$_6$ **5B.** empirical and molecular formulas: C$_{13}$H$_{16}$Cl$_{12}$O$_8$ **6A.** C$_7$H$_{14}$O$_2$ **6B.** C$_4$H$_4$S **7A.** 0 for S; +6 for Cr; +1 for Cl; $-1/2$ for O **7B.** +2 for S; +1 for Hg; +7 for Mn; 0 for C **8A.** Li$_2$O; SnF$_2$; Li$_3$N **8B.** Al$_2$S$_3$; Mg$_3$N$_2$; V$_2$O$_3$ **9A.** cesium iodide; calcium fluoride; iron(II) oxide; chromium(III) chloride **9B.** calcium hydride; copper(I) chloride; silver sulfide; mercury(I) chloride **10A.** sulfur hexafluoride; nitrous acid; calcium hydrogen carbonate; iron(II) sulfate **10B.** ammonium nitrate; phosphorus trichloride; hypobromous acid; silver perchlorate; iron(III) sulfate **11A.** BF$_3$; K$_2$Cr$_2$O$_7$; H$_2$SO$_4$; CaCl$_2$ **11B.** Al(NO$_3$)$_3$; P$_4$O$_{10}$; Cr(OH)$_3$; HIO$_3$ **12A.** (a) not isomers (b) isomers **12B.** (a) isomers (b) not isomers **13A.** (a) alkane (b) chloroalkane (c) carboxylic acid (d) alkene **13B.** (a) alcohol (b) carboxylic acid and an alcohol (c) chlorocarboxylic acid (d) bromoalkene **14A.** (a) 2-propanol (b) 1-iodopropane (c) 3-methylbutanoic acid (d) propene **14B.** (a) 2-chloropropane (b) 1,4-dichlorobutane (c) 2-methyl propanoic acid **15A.** (a) CH$_3$(CH$_2$)$_3$CH$_3$; (b) CH$_3$CO$_2$H (c) ICH$_2$(CH$_2$)$_6$CH$_3$ (d) CH$_2$(OH)(CH$_2$)$_3$CH$_3$ **15B.** (a) CH$_3$CHCH$_2$ (b) CH$_2$(OH)(CH$_2$)$_5$CH$_3$ (c) CH$_2$ClCO$_2$H (d) CH$_3$(CH$_2$)$_4$CO$_2$H

Exercises 1. (a) H$_2$O$_2$ (b) CH$_3$CH$_2$Cl (c) P$_4$O$_{10}$ (d) CH$_3$CH(OH)CH$_3$ (e) HCO$_2$H **3.** (b) CH$_3$CH$_2$Cl (d) CH$_3$CH(OH)CH$_3$ (e) HCO$_2$H **5.** (a) 21 atoms (b) 1.29×10^{22} atoms (c) 2.195×10^{25} F atoms **7.** (a) 149.2 u (b) 11 mol H atoms (c) 60.055 g C (d) 2.73×10^{25} C atoms **9.** Response (a); it is the only choice that represents more than 2 mol N atoms. **11.** (a) 1.25 mol N$_2$O$_4$ (b) 1.43 mol N (c) 0.206 mol N **13.** 3×10^{22} Fe atoms **15.** Only response (b) is true. **17.** (a) 41 atoms (b) 4 H atoms:5 O atoms (c) 1.026 g C:1.000 g P (d) U (e) 15.1 g **19.** 15.59% H **21.** 15.88% H **23.** 74.05% C, 7.457% H, 8.635% N, 9.863% O **25.** (a) 64.07% Pb (b) 45.50% Fe (c) 2.72% Mg **27.** In order of increasing %Cr: CrO$_3$ < CrO$_2$ < Cr$_2$O$_3$ < CrO **29.** SO$_3$ and S$_2$O **31.** C$_4$H$_{10}$O$_3$ **33.** (a) C$_{19}$H$_{16}$O$_4$ (b) C$_9$H$_{10}$N$_4$O$_2$S$_2$ **35.** C$_{14}$H$_{10}$ **37.** C$_{16}$H$_{10}$N$_2$O$_2$ **39.** Titanium **41.** 894 u **43.** (a) 90.49% C, 9.495% H (b) C$_4$H$_5$ (c) C$_8$H$_{10}$ **45.** CH$_4$N **47.** C$_{10}$H$_8$ **49.** 3.710 g CO$_2$, 1.898 g H$_2$O **51.** (a) C = -4 (b) S = $+4$ (c) O = -1

(d) C = 0 (e) Fe = $+6$ **53.** Cr$_2$O$_3$, CrO$_2$ and CrO$_3$ **55.** (a) strontium oxide (b) zinc sulfide (c) potassium chromate (d) cesium sulfate (e) chromium(III) oxide (f) iron(III) sulfate (g) magnesium hydrogen carbonate (h) ammonium hydrogen phosphate (i) calcium hydrogen sulfite (j) copper(II) hydroxide (k) nitric acid (l) potassium perchlorate (m) bromic acid (n) phosphorous acid **57.** (a) carbon disulfide (b) silicon tetrafluoride (c) chlorine pentafluoride (d) dinitrogen pentoxide (e) sulfur hexafluoride (f) diiodine hexachloride **59.** (a) Al$_2$(SO$_4$)$_3$ (b) (NH$_4$)$_2$Cr$_2$O$_7$ (c) SiF$_4$; (d) Fe$_2$O$_3$ (e) C$_3$S$_2$ (f) Co(NO$_3$)$_2$ (g) Sr(NO$_2$)$_2$ (h) HBr(aq) (i) HIO$_3$ (j) PCl$_2$F$_3$ **61.** (a) TiCl$_4$ (b) Fe$_2$(SO$_4$)$_3$ (c) Cl$_2$O$_7$ (d) S$_2$O$_8^{2-}$ **63.** (a) chlorous acid (b) sulfurous acid (c) hydroselenic acid (d) nitrous acid **65.** MgCl$_2$·6 H$_2$O **67.** 22.3 g **69.** CuSiF$_6$·6 H$_2$O **71.** The correct name is (b), 2-butanol. **73.** Structures (a) and (c) are identical; (b) and (d) are isomers of either (a) or (c). **75.** (a) CH$_3$(CH$_2$)$_5$CH$_3$ (b) CH$_3$CH$_2$CO$_2$H (c) CH$_3$CH$_2$CH$_2$CH(CH$_3$)CH$_2$OH (d) CH$_3$CH$_2$F **77.** (a) methanol; CH$_3$OH; 32.04 u (b) 2-chlorohexane; CH$_3$(CH$_2$)$_3$CHClCH$_3$; 120.6 u (c) pentanoic acid; CH$_3$(CH$_2$)$_3$CO$_2$H; 102.1 u (d) 2-methyl-1-propanol; CH$_3$CH(CH$_3$)CH$_2$OH; 74.12 u

Integrative and Advanced Exercises 79. 1.24×10^{23} atoms ^{6}Li **82.** 2.50 kg **85.** CH$_4$ **89.** 26.9 u **93.** ZnSO$_4$·7 H$_2$O **96.** C$_{12}$H$_8$Cl$_6$O **Feature Problems 99.** (a) 5.00% N, 4.37% P, 4.15% K (b) (1) 60.6% P$_2$O$_5$; (2) 53.7% P$_2$O$_5$ (c) a "17.7-44.6-10.5" fertilizer (d) A "5-10-5" fertilizer cannot be prepared from (NH$_4$)$_2$HPO$_4$ and KCl alone. **101.** (a) 4.7×10^3 m^2 (b) 2.5 nm (c) $N_A \approx 5.8 \times 10^{23}$ mol^{-1}

CHAPTER 4

Practice Examples
1A. (a) 2 H$_3$PO$_4$ + 3 CaO $\longrightarrow$
$$Ca_3(PO_4)_2 + 3 H_2O$$
(b) C$_3$H$_8$ + 5 O$_2$ $\longrightarrow$ 3 CO$_2$ + 4 H$_2$O
1B. (a) 4 NH$_3$ + 7 O$_2$ $\longrightarrow$ 4 NO$_2$ + 6 H$_2$O
(b) 6 NO$_2$ + 8 NH$_3$ $\longrightarrow$ 7 N$_2$ + 12 H$_2$O
2A. 4 HgS + 4 CaO $\longrightarrow$
$$3 CaS + CaSO_4 + 4 Hg$$
2B. 2 C$_7$H$_6$O$_2$S + 17 O$_2$ $\longrightarrow$
$$14 CO_2 + 6 H_2O + 2 SO_2$$
3A. 2.64 mol O$_2$ **3B.** 8.63 mol Ag **4A.** 5.29 g Mg$_3$N$_2$ **4B.** 126 g H$_2$ **5A.** 0.710 g NH$_3$ **5B.** 3.50 g O$_2$ **6A.** 3.34 cm^3 alloy **6B.** 0.79 g Cu **7A.** (a) 0.4 mg H$_2$ (b) 0.15 g CO$_2$ **8A.** (a) 0.307 M (b) 0.524 M **9A.** 115 g **9B.** 50.9 g **10A.** 0.0675 M **10B.** 0.122 M **11A.** 18.1 mL **11B.** 2.00×10^2 mL, 4.96 g **12A.** 936 g PCl$_3$ **12B.** 1.86 kg POCl$_3$ **13A.** 3.8 g P$_4$ **13B.** 57 g O$_2$ **14A.** (a) 30.0 g (b) 25.7 g (c) 85.6% **14B.** 93.7% **15A.** 41.8 g CO$_2$ **15B.** 69.0 g **16A.** 2.47×10^3 g HNO$_3$ **16B.** 0.0734 g H$_2$

Exercises 1. (a) 2 SO$_3$ $\longrightarrow$ 2 SO$_2$ + O$_2$ (b) Cl$_2$O$_7$ + H$_2$O $\longrightarrow$ 2 HClO$_4$ (c) 3 NO$_2$ + H$_2$O $\longrightarrow$ 2 HNO$_3$ + NO (d) PCl$_3$ + 3 H$_2$O $\longrightarrow$ H$_3$PO$_3$ + 3 HCl

3. (a) 3 PbO + 2 NH$_3$ $\longrightarrow$
$$3 Pb + N_2 + 3 H_2O$$
(b) 4 FeSO$_4$ $\longrightarrow$ 2 Fe$_2$O$_3$ + 4 SO$_2$ + O$_2$
(c) 6 S$_2$Cl$_2$ + 16 NH$_3$ $\longrightarrow$
$$N_4S_4 + 12 NH_4Cl + S_8$$
(d) 2 C$_3$H$_7$CHOHCH(C$_2$H$_5$)CH$_2$OH +
$$23 O_2 \longrightarrow 16 CO_2 + 18 H_2O$$
5. (a) 2 Mg(s) + O$_2$(g) $\longrightarrow$ 2 MgO(s)
(b) 2 NO(g) + O$_2$(g) $\longrightarrow$ 2 NO$_2$(g)
(c) 2 C$_2$H$_6$(g) + 7 O$_2$(g) $\longrightarrow$
$$4 CO_2(g) + 6 H_2O(l)$$
(d) Ag$_2$SO$_4$(aq) + BaI$_2$(aq) $\longrightarrow$
$$BaSO_4(s) + 2 AgI(s)$$
7. (a) 2 C$_4$H$_{10}$(g) + 13 O$_2$(g) $\longrightarrow$
$$8 CO_2(g) + 10 H_2O(l)$$
(b) 2 CH$_3$CH(OH)CH$_3$(l) + 9 O$_2$(g) $\longrightarrow$
$$6 CO_2(g) + 8 H_2O(l)$$
(c) CH$_3$CH(OH)COOH(s) + 3 O$_2$(g) $\longrightarrow$
$$3 CO_2(g) + 3 H_2O(l)$$
9. (a) NH$_4$NO$_3$(s) $\overset{\Delta}{\longrightarrow}$ N$_2$O(g) + 2 H$_2$O(g)
(b) Na$_2$CO$_3$(aq) + 2 HCl(aq) $\longrightarrow$
2 NaCl(aq) + H$_2$O(l) + CO$_2$(g)
(c) 2 CH$_4$(g) + 2 NH$_3$(g) + 3 O$_2$(g) $\longrightarrow$
2 HCN(g) + 6 H$_2$O(g)
11. 2 N$_2$H$_4$ + N$_2$O$_4$ $\longrightarrow$ 4 H$_2$O + 3 N$_2$ **13.** 4.84 mol FeCl$_3$ **15.** (a) 0.401 mol O$_2$ (b) 128 g KClO$_3$ (c) 44.0 g KCl **17.** 96.0 g Ag$_2$CO$_3$ **19.** (a) 6.03 mol H$_2$ (b) 48.1 g H$_2$O (c) 284 g CaH$_2$ **21.** 79.7% Fe$_2$O$_3$ **23.** 1.03 g H$_2$ **25.** Al **27.** (a) 0.408 M CH$_3$OH (b) 0.154 M C$_2$H$_5$OH (c) 1.53 M CO(NH$_2$)$_2$ **29.** (a) 1.753 M (b) 0.320 M (c) 0.206 M **31.** (a) 4.73 g (b) 44.1 mL **33.** solution (d) **35.** the 46% sucrose solution **37.** 0.0820 M **39.** 0.236 M K$_2$SO$_4$ **41.** The ratio of the volume of the volumetric flask to that of the pipet must be 20:1, such as 100-mL flask and 5-mL pipet, 500-mL flask and 25-mL pipet, and so on. **43.** (a) 0.177 g Na$_2$S (b) 0.562 g Ag$_2$S **45.** 59.4 mL **47.** (a) 0.0693 mol (b) 2.91 M **49.** 12.8 g Ag$_2$CrO$_4$ **51.** 0.624 g Na **53.** 0.2649 M **55.** 3.00 mol NO(g) **57.** No, there is excess Cu(s). **59.** 143 g **61.** (a) 10.5 g NH$_3$ forms, and 10.1 g excess Ca(OH)$_2$ **63.** (a) 1.80 mol CCl$_2$F$_2$ (b) 1.55 mol CCl$_2$F$_2$ (c) 86.1% yield **65.** (a) 27.7 g (b) 17.1 g (c) 61.7% yield **67.** 76 g **69.** In synthesis, yield may be sacrificed for cost. In an analysis, it is essential that no product is lost (100% yield). **71.** 474 g HCl **73.** 74.4 mol Cl$_2$ **75.** 1.34×10^3 g NaNO$_3$

Integrative and Advanced Exercises 81. 3 FeS(s) + 5 O$_2$(g) $\longrightarrow$
Fe$_3$O$_4$(s) + 3 SO$_2$(g) **84.** 0.2 cm^2 **86.** 118 mL **87.** 9.1×10^5 L **89.** 7.25 M HCl **91.** 24% Mg **93.** 90.8% C$_2$H$_5$OH, 9.2% (C$_2$H$_5$)$_2$O **96.** (a) H$_2$(g) + $\frac{1}{2}$O$_2$(g) $\longrightarrow$ H$_2$O(g) (b) (100% reaction, O$_2$ limiting) yields 0.20 g H$_2$, 41.00 g H$_2$O. (c) 41.20 grams initial and final mass **98.** both (a) and (b) **100.** Add to the 345 mL of 1.29 M solution 29 mL of 0.775 M solution to yield 374 mL as the final solution volume. **105.** (a) 2 C$_3$H$_6$(g) + 2 NH$_3$(g) + 3 O$_2$(g) $\longrightarrow$ 2 C$_3$H$_3$N(l) + 6 H$_2$O(l) (b) 1.1×10^3 lb NH$_3$

Feature Problem 106. 360 fish $\cong 4 \times 10^2$ fish

CHAPTER 5

Practice Examples 1A. 0.540 M Cl⁻
1B. (a) 7.9×10^{-5} M F⁻ **(b)** 3.1 kg CaF_2
2A. (a) $Al^{3+}(aq) + 3\,OH^-(aq) \longrightarrow Al(OH)_3(s)$
(b) no reaction
(c) $Pb^{2+}(aq) + 2\,I^-(aq) \longrightarrow PbI_2(s)$
2B. (a) $Al^{3+}(aq) + PO_4^{3-}(aq) \longrightarrow AlPO_4(s)$
(b) $Ba^{2+}(aq) + SO_4^{2-}(aq) \longrightarrow BaSO_4(s)$
(c) $Pb^{2+}(aq) + CO_3^{2-}(aq) \longrightarrow PbCO_3(s)$
3A. $NH_3(aq) + HC_3H_5O_2(aq) \longrightarrow$
$\qquad\qquad\qquad NH_4^+(aq) + C_3H_5O_2^-(aq);$
the salt $NH_4C_3H_5O_2$ is ammonium propionate
3B. $CaCO_3(s) + 2\,HC_2H_3O_2(aq) \longrightarrow$
$CO_2(g) + H_2O(l) +$
$Ca^{2+}(aq) + 2\,C_2H_3O_2^-(aq)$ **4A. (a)** no **(b)** yes
4B. VO^{2+} oxidized, MnO_4^- reduced
5A. ox: $Al \longrightarrow Al^{3+} + 3\,e^-$; red:
$2\,H^+ + 2\,e^- \longrightarrow H_2(g)$; overall:
$2\,Al(s) + 6\,H^+(aq) \longrightarrow 2\,Al^{3+}(aq) + 3\,H_2(g)$
5B. oxid. $2\,Br^-(aq) \longrightarrow Br_2(l) + 2\,e^-$ red:
$Cl_2(g) + 2\,e^- \longrightarrow 2\,Cl^-(aq)$ overall:
$2\,Br^-(aq) + Cl_2(g) \longrightarrow Br_2(l) + 2\,Cl^-(aq)$
6A. $MnO_4^-(aq) + 8\,H^+(aq) + 5\,Fe^{2+}(aq) \longrightarrow$
$Mn^{2+}(aq) + 4\,H_2O(l) + 5\,Fe^{3+}(aq)$
6B. $3\,UO^{2+}(aq) + Cr_2O_7^{2-}(aq) +$
$8\,H^+(aq) \longrightarrow 3\,UO_2^{2+}(aq) + 2\,Cr^{3+}(aq) +$
$4\,H_2O(l)$ **7A.** $S(s) + 2\,OH^-(aq) +$
$2\,OCl^-(aq) \longrightarrow$
$SO_3^{2-}(aq) + H_2O(l) + 2\,Cl^-(aq)$
7B. $2\,MnO_4^-(aq) + 3\,SO_3^{2-}(aq) +$
$H_2O(l) \longrightarrow$
$2\,MnO_2(s) + 3\,SO_4^{2-}(aq) + 2\,OH^-(aq)$ **8A.** a
reducing agent **8B.** Au is a reducing agent;
$O_2(g)$ is an oxidizing agent. **9A.** 0.1019 M
9B. 0.130 M HCl **10A.** 65.4% Fe
10B. 0.03129 M $KMnO_4$
Exercises 1. (a) weak electrolyte **(b)** strong
electrolyte **(c)** strong electrolyte
(d) nonelectrolyte **(e)** strong electrolyte
3. The light would shine brightly in 1.0 M
HCl(aq), the strong electrolyte. The response
would be about the same in the
HCl(aq)-$HC_2H_3O_2$(aq) mixture because
$HC_2H_3O_2$, a weak electrolyte, would contribute little to the electric conductance.
5. Use colors and relative numbers of atoms
and the presence of distinctive groups as a
guide in identifying: **(a)** barium
bromide-strong electrolyte **(b)** propionic acid-
weak electrolyte **(c)** ammonia-weak electrolyte
7. (a) 0.238 M K⁺ **(b)** 0.334 M NO_3^-
(c) 0.17 M Al^{3+} **(d)** 0.627 M Na⁺
9. 3.04×10^{-3} M OH⁻
11. (a) 3.54×10^{-4} M Ca^{2+}
(b) 8.39×10^{-3} M K⁺ **(c)** 3.44×10^{-3} M Zn^{2+}
13. Solution (c) has the highest [K⁺].
15. 4.3×10^{-2} mg MgI_2 **17.** [Cl⁻] = 0.732 M
19. (a) $Pb^{2+}(aq) + 2\,Br^-(aq) \longrightarrow PbBr_2(s)$
(b) No reaction
(c) $Fe^{3+}(aq) + 3\,OH^-(aq) \longrightarrow Fe(OH)_3(s)$
21. (a) no reaction
(b) $Cu^{2+}(aq) + CO_3^{2-}(aq) \longrightarrow CuCO_3(s)$
(c) $3\,Cu^{2+}(aq) + 2\,PO_4^{3-}(aq) \longrightarrow$
$Cu_3(PO_4)_2(s)$ **23. (a)** $K_2SO_4(aq)$ **(b)** $H_2O(l)$
(c) KCl(aq) **25. (a)** mix $Sr(NO_3)_2$(aq) and
K_2SO_4(aq): $Sr^{2+}(aq) + SO_4^{2-}(aq) \longrightarrow$
$SrSO_4(s)$ **(b)** mix $Mg(NO_3)_2$(aq) and
NaOH(aq): $Mg^{2+}(aq) + 2\,OH^-(aq) \longrightarrow$
$Mg(OH)_2(s)$ **(c)** mix $BaCl_2$(aq) and
K_2SO_4(aq): $Ba^{2+}(aq) + SO_4^{2-}(aq) \longrightarrow$

$BaSO_4(s)$; remove $BaSO_4(s)$ by filtration, and
the filtrate is KCl(aq).
27. (a) $OH^-(aq) + HC_2H_3O_2(aq) \longrightarrow$
$H_2O(l) + C_2H_3O_2^-(aq)$ **(b)** no reaction
(c) $FeS(s) + 2\,H^+(aq) \longrightarrow H_2S(g) + Fe^{2+}(aq)$
(d) $HCO_3^-(aq) + H^+(aq) \longrightarrow$
$H_2O(l) + CO_2(g)$
(e) $Mg(s) + 2\,H^+(aq) \longrightarrow Mg^{2+}(aq) + H_2(g)$
29. As a salt: $NaHSO_4$(aq) $\longrightarrow$
$Na^+(aq) + HSO_4^-(aq)$; As an acid:
$HSO_4^-(aq) + OH^-(aq) \longrightarrow$
$H_2O(l) + SO_4^{2-}(aq)$ **31.** Only NH_3(aq) yields
a precipitate;
$2\,NH_3(aq) + 2\,H_2O(l) + Mg^{2+}(aq) \longrightarrow$
$2\,NH_4^+(aq) + Mg(OH)_2(s)$ **33. (a)** not redox
equation; no changes in O.S. **(b)** redox equation; O.S. for Cl decreases from 0 to −1, and
for Br, increases from −1 to 0 **(c)** redox equation; O.S. for Ag increases from 0 to +1, and
for N, decreases from +5 to +4 **(d)** not redox
equation, no changes in O.S. **35. (a)** reduction:
$2\,SO_3^{2-}(aq) + 6\,H^+(aq) + 4\,e^- \longrightarrow$
$S_2O_3^{2-}(aq) + 3\,H_2O(l)$ **(b)** reduction:
$2\,NO_3^-(aq) + 10\,H^+(aq) + 8\,e^- \longrightarrow$
$N_2O(g) + 5\,H_2O(l)$ **(c)** oxidation:
$Al(s) + 4\,OH^-(aq) \longrightarrow Al(OH)_4^-(aq) + 3\,e^-$
37. (a) $10\,I^-(aq) + + 2\,MnO_4^-(aq) +$
$16\,H^+(aq) \longrightarrow 5\,I_2(s) + 2\,Mn^{2+}(aq) +$
$8\,H_2O(l)$ **(b)** $3\,N_2H_4(l) + 2\,BrO_3^-(aq) \longrightarrow$
$3\,N_2(g) + 2\,Br^-(aq) + 6\,H_2O(l)$
(c) $Fe^{2+}(aq) + VO_4^{3-}(aq) + 6\,H^+(aq) \longrightarrow$
$Fe^{3+}(aq) + VO^{2+}(aq) + 3\,H_2O(l)$
(d) $3\,UO^{2+}(aq) + 2\,NO_3^-(aq) +$
$2\,H^+(aq) \longrightarrow$
$3\,UO_2^{2+}(aq) + 2\,NO(g) + H_2O(l)$
39. (a) $2\,MnO_2(s) + ClO_3^-(aq) +$
$2\,OH^-(aq) \longrightarrow$
$2\,MnO_4^-(aq) + Cl^-(aq) + H_2O(l)$
(b) $2\,Fe(OH)_3(s) + 3\,OCl^-(aq) +$
$4\,OH^-(aq) \longrightarrow$
$2\,FeO_4^{2-}(aq) + 3\,Cl^-(aq) + 5\,H_2O(l)$
(c) $6\,ClO_2(aq) + 6\,OH^-(aq) \longrightarrow$
$\qquad\qquad 5\,ClO_3^-(aq) + Cl^-(aq) + 3\,H_2O(l)$
41. (a) $3\,Cl_2(g) + 6\,OH^-(aq) \longrightarrow$
$\qquad\qquad 5\,Cl^-(aq) + ClO_3^-(aq) + 3\,H_2O(l)$
(b) $2\,S_2O_4^{2-}(aq) + H_2O(l) \longrightarrow$
$\qquad\qquad 2\,HSO_3^-(aq) + S_2O_3^{2-}(aq)$
43. (a) $5\,NO_2^-(aq) + 2\,MnO_4^-(aq) +$
$6\,H^+(aq) \longrightarrow$
$5\,NO_3^-(aq) + 2\,Mn^{2+}(aq) + 3\,H_2O(l)$
(b) $3\,Mn^{2+}(aq) + 2\,MnO_4^-(aq) +$
$4\,OH^-(aq) \longrightarrow 5\,MnO_2(s) + 2\,H_2O(l)$
(c) $Cr_2O_7^{2-}(aq) + 8\,H^+(aq) +$
$3\,C_2H_5OH \longrightarrow$
$2\,Cr^{3+}(aq) + 7\,H_2O(l) + 3\,CH_3CHO$
45. (a) $CH_4(g) + 4\,NO(g) \longrightarrow$
$\qquad\qquad 2\,N_2(g) + CO_2(g) + 2\,H_2O(g)$
(b) $16\,H_2S(g) + 8\,SO_2(g) \longrightarrow$
$\qquad\qquad 3\,S_8(s) + 16\,H_2O(g)$
(c) $10\,NH_3(g) + 3\,Cl_2O(g) \longrightarrow$
$6\,NH_4Cl(s) + 2\,N_2(g) + 3\,H_2O(l)$
47. (a) oxidizing agent: MnO_4^-; reducing
agent: SO_3^{2-} **(b)** oxidizing agent: NO_2;
reducing agent: H_2 **(c)** oxidizing agent: H_2O_2;
reducing agent: $[Fe(CN)_6]^{4-}$ **49.** 13.3 mL
NaOH(aq) **51.** 3.546 mL KOH **53.** 0.123 M
NaOH **55.** 0.077 M NaOH **57.** More acid
present than base, therefore acidic **59.** 34 mL
0.1000 M NaOH **61. (d) 63.** 0.01968 M $KMnO_4$
65. 53.23% Fe **67.** 37.0 g $Na_2C_2O_4$

Integrative and Advanced Exercises
71. $3\,Ca^{2+}(aq) + 2\,HPO_4^{2-}(aq) \longrightarrow$
$Ca_3(PO_4)_2(s) + 2\,H^+(aq)$ **74.** 108 ppm Mg
75. 0.0874 L
80. (a) $2\,FeS_2(s) + 2\,H_2O(l) + 7\,O_2(g) \longrightarrow$
$\qquad 2\,Fe^{2+}(aq) + 4\,SO_4^{2-}(aq) + 4\,H^+(aq)$
(b) $14\,Fe^{3+}(aq) + FeS_2(s) + 8\,H_2O(l) \longrightarrow$
$\qquad 15\,Fe^{2+}(aq) + 2\,SO_4^{2-}(aq) + 16\,H^+(aq)$
83. 44.6 g $Cl_2(g)$ **85.** 5.0×10^2 g ClO_2
88. Step 1: 45.9 g $NaHSO_3$; step 2: 1.0 L solution
Feature Problems 89. $x = 1.02 \approx 1$ **90.** 91.0%
MnO_2

CHAPTER 6

Practice Examples 1A. 7.60×10^2 mmHg
1B. 1.13 g/cm³ **2A.** 756.0 mmHg **2B.** 93 mm
3A. 139 torr **3B.** 3.5×10^2 g; cross-sectional
area of the added weight is immaterial
4A. 4.40 L **4B.** 317 mmHg **5A.** 1.69×10^3 °C
5B. 79°C **6A.** 59.0 g C_3H_8 **6B.** 65.2 L
7A. 24.4 L **7B.** 464 K **8A.** 2.11 mol He
8B. 5.59×10^{14} N_2 molecules **9A.** 2.11 mL
9B. 0.383 g O_2 **10A.** 86.5 g/mol **10B.** NO
11A. 0.162 g/L **11B.** 382 K **12A.** 35.6 g Na_3N
12B. 0.619 g Na(l) **13A.** 1.25 L **13B.** 150. L
14A. 13 atm **14B.** 5.5 atm **15A.** 0.0348 atm
$H_2O(g)$, 2.47 atm $CO_2(g)$ **15B.** 584 mmHg N_2,
157 mmHg O_2, 0.27 mmHg CO_2, 7.0 mmHg
Ar **16A.** 0.00278 mol HCl(aq) **16B.** 0.395 L gas
17A. NH_3(g): 661 m/s **17B.** 76.75 K
18A. 2.1×10^{-4} mol O_2 **18B.** 28.2 s
19A. 1.90×10^2 g/mol **19B.** 52.3 s **20A.** $Cl_2(g)$
20B. $Cl_2(g)$
Exercises 1. (a) 0.968 atm **(b)** 0.766 atm
(c) 1.17 atm **(d)** 2.22 atm **3.** 11.4 m **5.** 753
mmHg **7.** 1.03 kg cm⁻² **9. (a)** 52.8 L **(b)** 7.27 L
11. 576°C **13.** 50.6 atm **15.** 1 °C $\longrightarrow$ 2 °C
(0.37 %); 10 °C $\longrightarrow$ 20 °C (3.5 %) **17.** 0.134 g
Ar **19. (a)** 41.8 mg PH_3 **(b)** 7.41×10^{20} molecules **21.** Air in the bag expands under the
lower pressures at higher altitudes. **23.** 4.30 L
25. 4.89 g **27.** 5.32×10^4 mL **29.** 702 g Kr
31. 2.1×10^{-11} Pa **33.** 103 g/mol **35.** SF_4
37. 55.8 g mol⁻¹; the molecular formula must
have four C atoms and the rest H atoms,
leading to C_4H_8. **39.** 1.22×10^3 mmHg
41. (a) 1.18 g L⁻¹ **(b)** 1.80 g L⁻¹; balloon filled
with CO_2 has greater density than balloon
filled with air at 25°C and will not rise in air
at 25°C and 1 atm. **43.** P_4 **45.** 378 L
47. 3.3×10^7 L SO_2 **49.** 10.9% $KClO_3$
51. 73.6 L H_2 **53.** 5.59 L **55.** 2.06×10^3 g Ne
57. Action (d): add 0.60 g He **59. (a)** 842 mmHg
(b) $P_{benzene}$ = 89.5 mmHg; P_{Ar} = 752 mmHg
61. Sketch **(b) 63.** 2.37 L **65.** 751 mmHg
67. 326 m/s **69.** 7.83 u **71.** 1.51×10^3 K
73. 0.00473 mol $NO_2(g)$ **75. (a)** 1.07; **(b)** 1.05;
(c) 0.978; **(d)** 1.004
77. (a) P_{ideal} = 15.3 atm, P_{vdw} = 14.1 atm
(b) P_{ideal} = 19.4 atm, P_{vdw} = 18.3 atm
(c) P_{ideal} = 27.6 atm, P_{vdw} = 26.9 atm (the difference between P_{ideal} and P_{vdw} becomes progressively smaller at higher temperatures)
Integrative and Advanced Exercises 82. C_4H_6
83. 0.364 atm **86.** 2.24 atm **87. (a)** 12.5 atm
(b) 0.373 atm **89.** 153 mmHg **90.** 19.9% He
92. 23 L **95.** 31 mmHg **96. (a)** 3.42% $H_2O(g)$,
by volume **(b)** 3.42% H_2O by number of molecules **(c)** 1.95% H_2O by mass **97.** 34.6 L air
98. (a) 0.40 g/L **(b)** 2.9 atm **100.** 19°C
103(b). 7.37 L

Feature Problems 107. X = oxygen (16 u); nitryl fluoride has 2 atoms of O per molecule, nitrosyl fluoride, 1 atom of O; thionyl fluoride, 1 atom of O; and sulfuryl fluoride, 2 atoms of O. **108. (a)** N_2 from liquid air contains some Ar. **(b)** N_2 from liquid air has the greater density because the molecular mass of Ar is greater than that of N_2. **(c)** Mg reacts with N_2 but not with Ar, thus leaving pure residual Ar(g). **(d)** 0.50%

CHAPTER 7

Practice Examples 1A. 32.7 kJ **1B.** 4.89 kJ
2A. 3.0×10^2 g **2B.** 37.9°C
3A. -3.83×10^3 kJ/mol **3B.** 6.26 kJ/°C
4A. $q_{rxn} = -65.2$ kJ/mol **4B.** 33.4°C
5A. −114 J (work is done by the system)
5B. +14.6 kJ (work is done on the system)
6A. $+1.70 \times 10^2$ J **6B.** 179 J of work done by system. **7A.** 60.6 g **7B.** 0.15 kJ of heat evolved
8A. 3.31 kJ absorbed **8B.** 1.72 kg H_2O(s)
9A. $\Delta H° = -124$ kJ
9B. $\Delta H° = -2006$ kJ/mol $CH_3CHOHCH_3$(l)
10A. 6 C(graphite) + 13/2 H_2(g) + O_2(g) + 1/2 N_2(g) $\longrightarrow$ $C_6H_{13}O_2N$(s) **10B.** twice the negative of the value in Table 7.2: $\Delta H° = +92.22$ kJ
11A. $\Delta H° = -1367$ kJ/mol C_2H_5OH(l)
11B. $\Delta H° = -2.5 \times 10^3$ kJ/mol fuel
12A. −1273 kJ/mol $C_6H_{12}O_6$(s)
12B. −184 kJ/mol CH_3OCH_3(g)
13A. $\Delta H° = -112.3$ kJ/mol AgI(s)
13B. $\Delta H_f° = -505.8$ kJ/mol Ag_2CO_3(s)
Exercises 1. (a) $+2.9 \times 10^2$ kJ **(b)** −177 kJ
3. (a) Zn: 0.385 J g^{-1} $°C^{-1}$ **(b)** Pt: 0.13 J g^{-1} $°C^{-1}$
(c) Al: 0.905 J $g^{-1}$$°C^{-1}$ **5.** 5.4×10^2 °C
7. 24.0°C **9.** 2.3×10^2 J mol^{-1} $°C^{-1}$
11. -2.49×10^5 kJ **13. (a)** 65.59 kJ
(b) 3.65×10^3 kJ; **(c)** 1.45×10^3 kJ **15.**
(a) 504 kg **(b)** -6.20×10^5 kJ **(c)** 2.90×10^3 L
17. 1.36×10^3 kJ **19. (a)** -5×10^1 kJ/mol KOH
(b) Use more solute and less water to increase ΔT to three significant figures. **21.** 4.2×10^2 g
23. −56 kJ/mol H_2O **25.** 39.6 g ice
27. 2 g H_2O(g) **29.** 4.98 kJ/°C
31. (a) $q_{combustion} = -2.34 \times 10^3$ kJ/mol $C_5H_{10}O_5$
(b) $C_5H_{10}O_5$(g) + 5 O_2(g) $\longrightarrow$
5 CO_2(g) + 5 H_2O(l) $\Delta H = -2.34 \times 10^3$ kJ
33. (a) endothermic **(b)** +18 kJ/mol KCl
35. 7.72 kJ/°C **37.** 5.23°C **39. (a)** −3.4 L atm
(b) -3.5×10^2 J **(c)** −83 cal **41.** No work is done; nothing has been moved. **43. (a)** No pressure-volume work done.
(b) $\Delta n_{gas} = -1$ mol: work is done on system by the surroundings. **(c)** $\Delta n_{gas} = +1$ mol: work is done on the surroundings by the system. **45. (a)** 0 J **(b)** −562 J **(c)** 0.08 kJ
47. (a) yes, gas does work (w = negative).
(b) yes, gas absorbs heat energy so that $q = -w$ **(c)** temperature of the gas stays the same **(d)** $\Delta U = 0$ (temperature is constant).
49. impossible: The isothermal expansion of an ideal gas has $\Delta U = 0$ **51. (c)**
53. (a) ΔU − 2008 kJ/mol
(b) $\Delta H = -2012$ kJ/mol **55.** $\Delta H° = 30.74$ kJ
57. $\Delta H° = 290.$ KJ **59.** $\Delta H° = -217.5$ kJ
61. $\Delta H° = -747.5$ kJ **63.** $\Delta H° = -35.8$ kJ
65. (a) $\Delta H° = -55.7$ kJ **(b)** $\Delta H° = -1124$ kJ
67. $\Delta H_f° = -206.0$ kJ/mol ZnS(s)
69. $\Delta H° = +202.4$ kJ **71.** $\Delta H° = -1367$ kJ

73. $\Delta H_f° = -102.9$ kJ/mol CCl_4(g)
75. $\Delta H° = -55$ kJ **77.** 2.40×10^6 kJ
Integrative and Advanced Exercises 80. 3.5°C
81. -1.95×10^3 kJ/mol $C_6H_8O_7$ **87.** Sewage gas produces more heat per liter at STP than coal gas **90.** 69.1% efficient **91.** 303 g $C_6H_{12}O_6$
93. 87.0% CH_4, 13.0% C_2H_6 (by volume)
96. C_2H_6O(g) + 3 O_2(g) $\longrightarrow$
2 CO_2(g) + 3 H_2O(l), $\Delta H° = -1.45 \times 10^3$ kJ
97. 69 s **98.** −12 J
Feature Problems 105. (a) 45.0 mL of 1.00 M NaOH(aq) and 15.0 mL of 1.00 M citric acid
(b) An excess reactant in a constant reaction volume would mean that less than the maximum amount of heat would be released, leading to a lower temperature attained.
(c) $H_3C_6H_5O_7$(aq) + 3 OH^-(aq) $\longrightarrow$
3 H_2O(l) + $C_6H_5O_7^{3-}$(aq) **108. (a)** about −147 J **(b)** total work done is the sum of the areas of the 11 rectangles under the P-V curve
(c) maximum work = −152 J **(d)** maximum work of compression is for a one-step compression at 2.40 atm, i.e., 209 J; minimum work is the negative of (c), +152 J **(e)** $\Delta U = 0$; value of q is the negative of the work found in (d)
(f) The value of q/T for the process in (c) is ΔS, the change in the state function, entropy (S), introduced in Chapter 19.

CHAPTER 8

Practice Examples 1A. 4.34×10^{14} Hz
1B. 3.28 m **2A.** 410 to 520 kJ/mol
2B. 4.612×10^{14} Hz (orange), 6.662×10^{14} Hz (indigo). We see the reflected color, principally green. **3A.** Yes, it is for $n = 9$, that is, $E_9 = -2.69 \times 10^{-20}$ J **3B.** no **4A.** 486.2 nm
4B. 121.6 nm or 1216 Å **5A.** 80.13 nm **5B.** Be^{3+}
6A. 1.21×10^{-43} m **6B.** 3.96×10^4 km/s
7A. 6.4×10^{-43} m **7B.** 1.3 m/s **8A.** yes
8B. $\ell = 2$ or 1 **9A.** 3p
9B. $n = 3$; $\ell = 2$, 1, or 0; $m_\ell = 2$, 1, 0, −1, or −2
10A. Ti
10B. $1s^2 2s^2 2p^6 3s^2 3p^6 3d^{10} 4s^2 4p^6 4d^{10} 5s^2 5p^5$; ten 3d electrons; one unpaired electron.

11A. Fe: [Ar]

11B.

Bi: [Xe]

12A. (a) 5 **(b)** 6 **(c)** 0 **(d)** 2 **12B. (a)** 10 **(b)** 2 **(c)** 1
Exercises 1. 4.48 nm **3. (a)** and **(d)** are true
5. (c) **7.** 8.3 min **9. (a)** 6.9050×10^{14} s^{-1};
(b) 397.11 nm; **(c)** $n = 10$
11. (a) 5.71×10^{-18} J/photon; **(b)** 61.1 kJ/mol
13. $\Delta E = -1.550 \times 10^{-19}$ J; 2.339×10^{14} s^{-1}
15. 656.46 nm, 486.26 nm, 434.16 nm, 410.28 nm
17. $n = 8$ **19. (a)** 4.19×10^{-19} J/photon;
(b) 252 kJ/mol **21. (b)** has the greatest energy and **(d)** has the least energy **23.** The radiation has $\nu = 3.03 \times 10^{16}$ s^{-1} and is in the ultraviolet region. **25. (a)** 6.60×10^{-19} J/photon;
(b) ultraviolet yes, not infrared **27. (a)** 1.9 nm;
(b) -6.053×10^{-20} J **29. (a)** 1.384×10^{14} s^{-1};
(b) 2166 nm; **(c)** infrared **31. (a)** 8.5×10^{-10} m

(b) no orbit at 4.00 Å; **(c)** $n = 8$, energy is -3.405×10^{-20} J (relative to $E_\infty = 0$ J); **(d)** No 2.50×10^{-17} J is not an allowed energy level.
33. $n = 7$ to $n = 4$ **35. (a)** Line A: $n = 3$ to $n = 1$, Line B: $n = 4$ to $n = 1$ **(b)** H atom
37. (a) Line A: $n = 5$ to $n = 2$, Line B: $n = 6$ to $n = 2$ **(b)** Be^{3+} ion **39.** Electrons
41. 9.79×10^{-35} m **43.** The electron's position and velocity are both exactly known in the Bohr theory. This is not allowed by the Heisenberg uncertainty principle **45.** 1×10^{-13} m
47. 1.4×10^7 m s^{-1} **49.** 17 cm **51.** 16 inches
53. Discrete orbits in the Bohr atom versus regions of high electron probability in the wave mechanical atom. Both theories give the same value of the most probable distance of the electron from the nucleus. **55. (c)** **57. (a)** 5p;
(b) 4d; **(c)** 2s **59. (a)** one; **(b)** two; **(c)** ten;
(d) eighteen; **(e)** five **61.** 106 pm
63. For $2p_y$ wavefunction is $Y(\theta, \phi)_{py} = (0.75\pi)^{1/2} \sin \theta \sin \phi$, for all points in the xz plane, $\mu = 0$, and since $\sin 0° = 0$, entire xy plane is a node (zero probability of finding the p_y electron in xz plane).
65.

67.

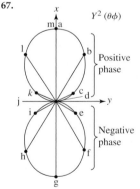

69. A plot of radial probability distribution vs r/a_0 for a 1s orbital gives a curve with a maximum at 1.0 ($r = a_0$), hence the maximum probability of finding an electron in hydrogen atom is at 0.53 pm. **71. (a)** 3p **(b)** 3d **(c)** 4f
73. $5d_{xy}$ **75.** Configuration (b) is correct, (a) violates the Pauli exclusion principle and (c) and (d) violate Hund's rule **77. (a)** 3; **(b)** 10;
(c) 2; **(d)** 2; **(e)** 14 **79. (a)** three; **(b)** two; **(c)** zero;
(d) fourteen; **(e)** two; **(f)** five (six with Z = 114);
(g) thirty-two **81. (a)** Pb: $[Xe]4f^{14}5d^{10}6s^2 6p^2$;
(b) 114:$[Rn]5f^{14}6d^{10}7s^2 7p^2$ **83.** Only (c) is a ground-state electron configuration (for nitrogen). **85. (a)** Au: $[Xe]4f^{14}5d^{10}6s^1$
(b) Mg: $[Ne]3s^2$ **(c)** Bi: $[Xe]4f^{14}5d^{10}6s^2 6p^3$
(d) In: $[Kr]4d^{10}5s^2 5p^1$ **(e)** Mo: $[Kr]4d^5 5s^1$

(f) Br: $[Ar]3d^{10}4s^2 4p^5$ **87. (a)** Ac **(b)** N **(c)** Ti **(d)** I **(e)** Ce

Integrative and Advanced Exercises
91. (a) The longest wavelength light for the photoelectric effect is 275 nm. This is UV light, not visible. **(b)** 2.02×10^{-19} J **(c)** 6.66×10^5 m/s **92.** 1.0×10^{20} photons/s **93.** $\lambda = 525$ nm, green **96.** From $n = 4$ to $n = 3$ **101.** 4.8 mJ **102.** 7×10^2 photon/s **105. (a)** 7.29×10^5 m/s **(b)** 2.43×10^{14} s^{-1}
Feature Problems 114. A plot of frequency versus n^{-2} gives a straight line plot with a slope $(-3.291 \times 10^{15}$ Hz) and y-intercept $(8.224 \times 10^{14}$ Hz), virtually identical to that predicted by the Balmer equation. **116. (a)** Two lines would be observed in the absorption spectrum ($n = 1 \longrightarrow n = 2$ at 121.5 nm and $n = 1 \longrightarrow n = 3$ at 102.6 nm) **(b)** Six emission lines should be seen for the transitions $n = 4$ to $n = 3$ (1875 nm), $n = 4$ to $n = 2$ (486.1 nm), $n = 4$ to $n = 1$ (97.2 nm); from $n = 3$ to $n = 2$ (656.3 nm), $n = 3$ to $n = 1$ (102.5 nm); and from $n = 2$ to $n = 1$ (121.5 nm). **(c)** Two lines are common to the absorption and emission spectra.

CHAPTER 9

Practice Examples 1A. S **1B.** Ca
2A. $V^{3+} < Ti^{2+} < Ca^{2+} < Sr^{2+} < Br^-$ **2B.** As
3A. K < Mg < S < Cl **3B.** Sb **4A.** Cl and Al are paramagnetic; the others are diamagnetic.
4B. Cr^{2+} **5A.** 280 K **5B.** 570 K
Exercises 1. 14 to 16 g/cm^3 **3.** Plot of density vs. atomic number has similar shape for both periods. **5.** Moseley discovered the link between atomic number and the periodic table. Thus, when all the elements with integral values in a certain range have been discovered, no new elements are possible in that range. **7. (a)** 118 **(b)** 119 **(c)** about 295 u and 298 u, respectively **9. (a)** Te **(b)** K **(c)** Cs **(d)** N **(e)** P **(f)** Au **11.** Electrons are being added to the same subshell in some instances but to a new subshell in others. **13. (a)** B **(b)** Te **15.** $Li^+ < Br < Se < I^-$ **17.** Fe^{2+} and Co^{3+}; Sc^{3+} and Ca^{2+}; F^- and Al^{3+}; Zn^{2+} and Cu^+ **19.** Yes, for example Cu^+ and Zn^{2+}
21. $Cs < Sr < As < S < F$ **23.** An electron may be attracted into a neutral atom in some cases and repelled in others, making EA a negative quantity in some cases and positive in others. The ejection of an electron from a neutral atom always requires an absorption of energy; I is always positive. **25.** 9952 kJ **27.** -456 kJ, exothermic **29.** The electron being removed from Na$^+$ must be removed from a positive ion, requiring a greater energy absorption than the removal of an electron from the neutral Ne atom. **31.** Only Fe^{2+}; the other ions all have noble-gas electron configurations. **33.** Diamagnetic: (a), (c), (d), (f); paramagnetic: (b), (e), (g) **35.** All atoms with odd Z must be paramagnetic, but some with even Z are also paramagnetic, for example, C. **37. (a)** Metals that should exhibit the photoelectric effect: Cs, Rb, and K (small first ionization energy); Zn, Cd, Hg should not (relatively large first ionization energies) **(b)** Rn **(c)** $+600$ kJ/mol **(d)** 5.7 g/cm^3 **39. (a)** 5.4 g/cm^3 **(b)** Ga$_2$O$_3$, 74% Ga **41.** 210 K **43. (a)** 1 **(b)** 1 **(c)** 3 **(d)** 4 **(e)** 2 **(f)** 2

Integrative and Advanced Exercises 47. Use data from Figure 9-8 and estimate the few missing data. Look for a group of four species in which two are of nearly equal radii, a third of twice the radius of the first two, and a fourth that is slightly larger than the third; (b) and (e) are best choices. **50.** Data yield an atomic mass of 75.7 u, indicating Gruppe V or Gruppe VI. **52.** Al: atomic radius about the same or larger, I_1 about the same or smaller; In: atomic radius larger, I_1 smaller; Se: atomic radius smaller, I_1 larger **54.** BrCl: mp $\approx$ 226 K, bp $\approx$ 286 K; ICl: mp $\approx$ 280 K, bp $\approx$ 348 K **57.** Yes, the data yield an atomic mass of 230 u, within about 4% of Mendeleev's assigned value. **60.** Value obtained, 5249 kJ/mol, in excellent agreement with the given 5251 kJ/mol **61.** Predicted: I_2 for Ba $< I_1$ for F $< I_3$ for Sc $< I_2$ for Na $< I_3$ for Mg [actual values: 965, 1681, 2389, 4562, and 7733 kJ/mol, respectively].
Feature Problems 66. A plot of $\nu^{1/2}$ versus Z provides $A = 2.30 \times 10^{15}$ Hz and $b = 0.969$.
67. (a) For $[Ne]3p^1$, $I_1 = 293$ kJ/mol; for $[Ne]4s^1$, $I_1 = 188$ kJ/mol; for $[Ne]3d^1$, $I_1 = 147$ kJ/mol; for $[Ne]4p^1$, $I_1 = 134$ kJ/mol. **(b)** For $[Ne]3p^1$, $Z_{eff} = 1.42$, for $[Ne]4s^1$, $Z_{eff} = 1.51$, for $[Ne]4p^1$, $Z_{eff} = 1.28$, for $[Ne]3d^1$, $Z_{eff} = 1.00$ **(c)** For $[Ne]3p^1$, $\bar{r}_{3p} = 4.7 \times 10^2$ pm, for $[Ne]4s^1$, $\bar{r}_{4s} = 8.4 \times 10^2$ pm, for $[Ne]4p^1$, $\bar{r}_{4p} = 9.5 \times 10^2$ pm, for $[Ne]3d^1$, $\bar{r}_{3d} = 5.6 \times 10^2$ pm. **(d)** The more deeply the orbital penetrates, the greater is its Z_{eff} and hence, the closer it is to the nucleus on average.

CHAPTER 10

Practice Examples

1A. $\cdot Mg \cdot$ $\cdot \ddot{G}e \cdot$ $K \cdot$ $\cdot \ddot{Ne} \colon$

1B. $\cdot \ddot{Sn} \cdot$ $[\colon \ddot{Br} \colon]^-$ $[\cdot Tl \cdot]^+$ $[\colon \ddot{S} \colon]^{2-}$

2A. (a) $[Na]^+\ [\colon \ddot{S} \colon]^{2-}\ [Na]^+$

(b) $[Mg]^{2+}[\colon \ddot{N} \colon]^{3-}[Mg]^{2+}[\colon \ddot{N} \colon]^{3-}[Mg]^{2+}$

2B. (a) $[\colon \ddot{I} \colon]^-[Ca]^{2+}[\colon \ddot{I} \colon]^-$

(b) $[Ba]^{2+}[\colon \ddot{S} \colon]^{2-}$

(c) $[Li]^+[\colon \ddot{O} \colon]^{2-}[Li]^+$

3A.

H—C—H (central C; bonded to two H, and to groups below); :Br—Br: H—Ö—Cl:

3B.

$\colon \ddot{I} - \ddot{N} - \ddot{I} \colon$ (with $\colon \ddot{I} \colon$ below N)   H—N—N—H (each N with H above and below)   H—C—C—H (each C with two H)

4A. P—Cl and N—H **4B.** P—O **5A.** The map with the most extensive red region is HF, signifying a high negative charge density associated with the high EN of F. **5B.** As in 5A, the most extensive red region is associated with an atom of high EN; in this case that is the O atom in CH$_3$OH.

6A. (a) $\ddot{S}=C=\ddot{S}$

(b) H—C≡N:

(c) $\colon \ddot{Cl} - C - \ddot{Cl} \colon$ (with a $\colon O \colon$ double-bonded above C)

6B. (a) H—C—Ö—H (with $\colon O \colon$ double-bonded above C)

(b) H—C—C—H (left C with H above and below; right C double-bonded to $\colon O \colon$ above and with H; H below)

7A. (a) $[\colon N≡O \colon]^+$

(b) $\left[\begin{array}{c} H\ \ H \\ H—N—N \colon \\ H\ \ H \end{array} \right]^+$

(c) $[\colon \ddot{O} \colon]^{2-}$

7B. (a) $\left[\begin{array}{c} \colon \ddot{F} \colon \\ \colon \ddot{F} - B - \ddot{F} \colon \\ \colon \ddot{F} \colon \end{array} \right]^-$

(b) $\left[\begin{array}{c} H \\ H—N—\ddot{O}—H \\ H \end{array} \right]^+$

(c) $[\colon N≡C—\ddot{O} \colon]^-$ or $[\colon \ddot{N}=C=\ddot{O} \colon]^-$

8A. $\colon \ddot{N}=\overset{\oplus}{O}—\overset{\ominus}{\ddot{Cl}} \colon$

Structure is less plausible because it has a positive formal charge on oxygen, the most electronegative atom in the molecule.

8B. H—$\overset{|}{\underset{H}{N}}$—C≡N: H—$\overset{|}{\underset{H}{N}}$=C=$\ddot{N} \colon$

The structure with no formal charges is the more plausible.

9A. $\overset{\ominus}{\ddot{O}}—\overset{\oplus}{S}=\ddot{O} \longleftrightarrow \ddot{O}=\overset{\oplus}{S}—\overset{\ominus}{\ddot{O}}$

9B.

$\overset{\colon O \colon}{\underset{\ominus}{\ddot{O}}—\overset{\oplus}{N}—\overset{\ominus}{\ddot{O}}} \longleftrightarrow \ddot{O}=\overset{\oplus}{N}—\overset{\ominus}{\ddot{O}}$

$\longleftrightarrow \ddot{O}—\overset{\oplus}{N}=\ddot{O}$ (with $\overset{\ominus}{\colon O \colon}$ above)

10A. trigonal-pyramidal **10B.** tetrahedral
11A. linear **11B.** linear
12A.

H—C—H (with H and H, and O below)

The H—C—H and H—C—O bond angles are ~109.5°; C—O—H bond angle is slightly less than 109.5°.

12B.

(structure of N bonded to two H, bonded to C, which is bonded to Ö and O—H)

The H—C—N, H—C—H and H—C—C angles are ~109.5°. C—O—H bond angle is slightly less than 109.5° The O—C—O and O—C—C bond angles are ~120°.

13A. H$_2$O$_2$: the individual bond moments do not cancel out. **13B.** PCl$_5$: the individual bond moments cancel out. **14A.** C—H bond: ~110 pm, C—Br bond: ~191 pm **14B.** This linear anion has the skeletal structure S-C-N, with a C-to-N triple bond and a formal charge of −1 on the S atom. **15A.** $\Delta H = -486$ kJ **15B.** $\Delta H_f = -4 \times 10^1$ kJ/mol NH_3 **16A.** exothermic **16B.** endothermic **Exercises 1. (a)** :K̈r: **(b)** ·G̈e· **(c)** ·N̈: **(d)** ·G̈a **(e)** ·Äs: **(f)** Rb·

3. (a) :Ï—C̈l: **(b)** :B̈r—B̈r: **(c)** :F̈—Ö—F̈:

(d) :Ï—N̈—Ï: **(e)** H—S̈e—H
        |
       :Ï:

5. (a) Cs^+[:B̈r:]⁻ **(b)** H—S̈b—H
                                    |
                                    H

(c) :C̈l—B—C̈l: **(d)** Cs^+[:C̈l:]⁻
        |
       :C̈l:

(e) Li^+[:Ö:]²⁻Li^+ **(f)** :Ï—C̈l:

7. H_2, ICl_3, and BF_3 are just three examples in which one or more atoms do not conform to the octet rule. **9. (a)** The deficiencies are one H atom as a central atom and lack of an octet for the N atom. **(b)** CaO is an ionic compound, and the Lewis structure should reflect the transfer of two electrons from the Ca to the O atom. **11.** (c) is correct. Structure (a) lacks an octet for the C atom; (b) is lacking two electrons with one C atom lacking an octet; (d) has one extra electron; it should be an odd-electron species.

13. (a) [:C̈l:]⁻ $[Ca]^{2+}$ [:C̈l:]⁻ **(b)** $[Ba]^{2+}$ [:S̈:]²⁻

(c) $[Li]^+$[:Ö:]²⁻$[Li]^+$ **(d)** $[Na]^+$[:F̈:]⁻

(e) $[Mg]^{2+}$[:N̈:]³⁻$[Mg]^{2+}$[:N̈:]³⁻$[Mg]^{2+}$

15. (a) Li^+[:S̈:]²⁻Li^+ **(b)** Na^+[:F̈:]⁻

(c) [:Ï:]⁻Ca^{2+}[:Ï:]⁻

(d) [:C̈l:]⁻Sc^{3+}[:C̈l:]⁻
          [:C̈l:]⁻

17. (a) formal charge H—   —C≡   ≡C
                           0   0   −1

(b) formal charge =O   —O   central C
                        0   −1   0

(c) formal charge —H   side C   central C
                        0   0   +1

19. Oxidation state is fixed, while formal charge is variable. Formal charges are used to decide between alternative Lewis structures, while oxidation state is used in balancing equations and naming compounds. The oxidation state of an element in its compounds is usually not zero, while its formal charge often is. **21. (a)** +1; **(b)** −1; **(c)** +1; **(d)** 0; **(e)** −1 **23.** The skeletal structure is O—C—O—H. Because of the 1+ charge on the ion, one of the atoms in the Lewis structure must have a formal charge of +1. Two different structures can be written with a +1 formal charge on the O atom, the terminal O in one case and the cen-

tral O in another. There is no basis to select one over the other.

25. (a) H—N̈—Ö—H **(b)** :Ö—C̈l—Ö—H
             | |
             H   :Ö:

(c) H—Ö—N̈=Ö **(d)**   :Ö:
                            ‖
                       :C̈l—S—C̈l:
                            ‖
                           :Ö:

27. (a) [:Ö—S—Ö:]²⁻
                  |
                 :Ö:

(b) [:Ö—N̈=Ö]⁻ ⟷ [:Ö=N̈—Ö:]⁻

(c) [:Ö—C=Ö]²⁻ ⟷ [Ö=C—Ö:]²⁻
            | |
           :Ö: :Ö:

   ⟷ [:Ö—C—Ö:]²⁻
               ‖
              :Ö:

(d) [H—Ö—Ö:]⁻

29. H H H :O:
         | | | ‖
       H—C—C=C—C—H
         |
         H

31. (a)   :O:
              ‖
           H—C—H

(b)   H :C̈l: H
           | | |
         H—C—C—C—Ö—H
           | | |
           H   H   H

33. (a)   H   :O:
               | ‖
           :C̈l—C—C—Ö—H
               |
               H

(b)   H H :O:
           | | ‖
         H—Ö—C—C—C—Ö—H
              | |
              H H

35. C—H < Br—H < F—H < Na—Cl < K—F **37. (a)** ≈4%; **(b)** ≈5%; **(c)** ≈60%; **(d)** ≈33% **39.** $F_2C=O$ is on the left and $H_2C=O$ is on the right. **41.** SF_4 is on the left and SiF_4 on the right.

43. [:Ö—N̈=Ö]⁻ ⟷ [:Ö=N̈—Ö:]⁻

45. The molecule seems best represented as a resonance hybrid of (1) and (2); (3) contains a very long N—N bond, while (4) contains no N—N bonds.

47. (a) H—C̈—H **(b)** :Ö—C̈l—Ö:
               |
               H

(c) ·Ö—N̈=Ö
            |
           :Ö:

49. (a) OH^-, diamagnetic **(b)** OH, paramagnetic **(c)** NO_3, paramagnetic **(d)** SO_3, diamagnetic **(e)** SO_3^{2-}, diamagnetic **(f)** HO_2, paramagnetic

51. (b) ICl_3 and SF_4 **53. (a)** linear **(b)** linear **(c)** tetrahedral **(d)** trigonal planar **(e)** bent **55. (a)** bent **(b)** planar **(c)** linear **(d)** octahedral **(e)** tetrahedral **57.** CO_3^{2-}: VSEPR notation: AX_3

59. (a) Ö=C=Ö **(b)** Ö=C—C̈l:
         Linear |
                           :C̈l:
                       Trigonal planar

(c) :C̈l—N̈=Ö
             |
            :Ö:
      Trigonal planar

61. (a) tetrahedral **(b)** tetrahedral **(c)** octahedral **(d)** linear **63.** tetrahedral

65.

A maximum of 5 atoms can be in the same plane.

67.

All angles ~109° except:
H—O_1—C <109°
H—O_3—C <109°   A maximum of
O_2—C—C ~120°   7 atoms can be
O_3—C—C ~120°   in the same plane.
O_2—C—O_3 ~120°

69. (a) bent, polar; **(b)** trigonal pyramidal, polar; **(c)** bent, polar; **(d)** planar, nonpolar; **(e)** octahedral, nonpolar; **(f)** tetrahedral, polar **71.** H_2O cannot be linear (dipole moments cancel in a linear structure). A structure with the O atoms along a straight line and the H atoms in different planes would produce a non-zero molecular dipole moment. **73.** (c) **75. (a)** I—Cl bond: 233 pm; **(b)** O—Cl bond: 172 pm; **(c)** C—F bond: 149 pm; **(d)** C—Br bond: 191 pm **77.** 144 pm **79.** endothermic **81.** $\Delta H = -113$ kJ **83. (a)** $\Delta H_f^\circ = 3$ kJ/mol or 39 kJ/mol depending on value used for O—H bond energy **(b)** $\Delta H_f^\circ = 99$ kJ/mol **83.** $\Delta H_{rxn}^\circ = -166$ kJ

Integrative and Advanced Exercises
87. $\Delta H = -744$ kJ **90.** molar mass = 42.0 g/mol, $H_3CHC=CH_2$ **92.** $H_2C=C=CH_2$ and $H_3C—C≡CH$; neither molecule is linear **95.** structure: H—N=N=N, shape has 3 Ns in a line, with 120° H—N—N bond angle. **96.** bent **99.** ΔH **(1)** = +717 kJ, ΔH **(2)** = −614 kJ, ΔH(net) = +103 kJ **102.** 307 kJ/mol **106.** $k = 0.0019$; $EA \approx -260$ kJ/mol **Feature Problems 112. (a)** 91 kJ/mol; **(b)** 0.97; **(c)** ~23% ionic **113. (a)** 1.49 D; **(b)** 92°; **(c)** 97.6°

CHAPTER 11

Practice Examples 1A. trigonal-pyramidal **1B.** trigonal-pyramidal. VSEPR has 109.5° bond angles, valence bond has 90° angles.

2A. Bent molecular geometry; sp^3-hybridized central Cl atom **2B.** See-saw molecular geometry; dsp^3-hybridized Br atom **3A.** All central atoms have sp^3 hybridization, approximately 109.5° bond angles. **3B.** The $C{=}O$ carbon is sp^2-hybridized with 120° bond angles; all other central atoms are sp^3-hybridized with 109.5° bond angles. **4A.** The triple-bonded C is sp-hybridized with 180° bond angles; the other C is sp^3-hybridized with 109.5° bond angles.

4B. :N≡N—Ö: ⟷ :N̈=N=Ö:

the central N is sp-hybridized, with 180° bond angles. **5A.** 53 kJ/mol. **5B.** yes, bond order = 0.5. **6A.** bond orders: **(a)** 2.5; **(b)** 0.5; **(c)** 3.0. **6B.** bond orders: **(a)** 2.5; **(b)** 2.0; **(c)** 1.5; **(d)** 1.0. Bond length increases with decreasing bond order.

7A. CN⁺

7B. BN

8A.

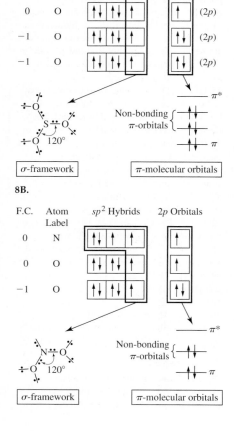

8B.

Exercises 1. VB method distinguishes between σ and π bonds, predicts molecular shape, explains hindered rotation around double bonds. **3. (a)** no prediction possible **(b)** 90° bond angles **(c)** and **(d)** 109.5° bond angles **5.** $CO_3{}^{2-}$, SO_2, and $NO_2{}^-$ **7. (a)** sp on C; **(b)** sp^2 on N, sp^3 on O; **(c)** sp^3 on Cl; **(d)** sp^3 on B **9.** sp^3d hybridization of Cl accounts for two lone pairs of electrons and allows for the overlap with $2p$ orbitals of three F atoms. **11. (a)** sp^3d^2 **(b)** sp **(c)** sp^3 **(d)** sp^2 **(e)** sp^3d **13. (a)** planar, sp^2 on each C **(b)** linear, sp on each C and N **(c)** sp^3 on C attached to three F, sp on other C and N **(d)** linear, sp on C and N **15. (a)** In HCN: 5 valence-shell electrons pairs, 4 bond pairs and one lone pair on N. A plausible Lewis structure has an H—C σ bond and a C≡N bond comprising 1 σ and 2 π bonds. **(b)** In C_2N_2: 9 electron pairs, 7 bond pairs and two lone pairs (one pair on each N atom). A plausible Lewis structure has a C—C σ bond and two N—C triple bonds, with each triple bond consisting of 1 σ and 2 π bonds. **(c)** In $CH_3CHCHCCl_3$: 21 electron pairs, with 12 bond pairs and 9 lone pairs (3 pairs on each Cl atom). A plausible Lewis structure has at the #1 C atom: three C—H and one C—C σ bonds; at the #2 and #3 C atoms: two C—C σ bonds to other C atoms, one σ bond to an H atom, and π bond between them; at the #4 C atom: one C—C σ bond and three C—Cl σ bonds. **(d)** In HONO: 9 electron pairs as 4 bond pairs and 5 lone pairs. A plausible Lewis structure has one N and one O atom as central atoms, joined by a σ bond; the central O atom is also linked to the H atom by a σ bond. The N atom and a terminal O atom are joined by a double bond—one σ and one π. **17.** The types of bonds are **(a)** four σ bonds: $C(sp^3)$—$Cl(3p)$ **(b)** σ: $O(2p)$—$N(sp^2)$, σ: $N(sp^2)$—$Cl(3p)$, π: $O(2p)$—$N(2p)$ **(c)** σ: $H(1s)$—$O_a(sp^3)$, σ: $O(sp^3)$—$N(sp^2)$, σ: $N(sp^2)$—$O_b(2p)$, π: $N(2p)$—$O_b(2p)$ **(d)** two σ: Cl$(3p)$—C(sp^2), σ: $O(2p)$—$C(sp^2)$, π: $O(2p)$—$C(2p)$ **19.** The structure has the following types of bonds and orbital overlaps producing them: (1) *four* C—H single bonds, σ: $C(sp^3)$—$H(1s)$; (2) *four* O—H single bonds, σ: $O(sp^3)$—$H(1s)$; (3) *two* C—C single bonds, σ: $C(sp^3)$—$C(sp^3)$; (4) *three* C—C single bonds, σ: $C(sp^3)$—$C(sp^2)$; (5) *one* C—O single bond, σ: $C(sp^3)$—$O(sp^3)$; (6) *three* C—O single bonds, σ: $C(sp^2)$—$O(sp^3)$; (7) *three* C—O double bonds, consisting of $\sigma[C(sp^2)$—$O(sp^2)]$ and $\pi[C(2p)$—$O(2p)]$. **21. (a)** Central S atom is sp^2 hybridized; the S—O bond is σ: $S(sp^2)$—$O(2p)$, and the S—S bond is a double bond comprising σ: $S(sp^2)$—$S(3p)$ and π: $S(3p)$—$S(3p)$. **(b)** Central Br atom is sp^3d hybridized and the three bonds are σ: $Br(sp^3d)$—$F(2p)$. **23.** In terms of the chain of C and H atoms (designated H_a—C_a—C_b—C_c—H_b), the bonds are H_a—C_a, single; C_a—C_b, triple; C_b—C_c, single; C_c—H_b, single; the C_c—O bond is double. The orbital overlaps are $\sigma[H_a(1s)$—$C_a(sp)]$; $\sigma[C_a(sp)$—$C_b(sp)]$; $\sigma[C_b(sp)$—$C_c(sp^2)]$; $\sigma[C_c(sp^2)$—$H_b(1s)]$; $\sigma[C_c(sp^2)$—$O(2p)]$; two $\pi[C_a(2p)$—$C_b(2p)]$, $\pi[C_c(2p)$—$O(2p)]$.

25. Valence bond theory describes bonds through orbital overlap of atomic orbitals on separated atoms. Molecular orbital theory describes bonds through the electron occupancies of orbitals belonging to a molecule as a whole. **27.** $N_2{}^-$, stable: bond order = 2.5, $N_2{}^{2-}$ stable: bond order = 2. **29.** Four consecutive bonding molecular orbitals with increasing energies and no intervening antibonding orbitals would be required, and this does not occur. **31. (a)** σ_{1s}: bonding MO always lower in energy than the associated antibonding MO; **(b)** σ_{2s}: 2s atomic orbital is lower in energy than the $2p$ atomic orbital; **(c)** σ_{1s}^*: 1s atomic orbital is lower in energy than the 2s atomic orbital; **(d)** σ_{2p}: a bonding orbital is expected to be more stable than an antibonding orbital.

33. (a) $\sigma_{2s}^2\sigma_{2s}^{*2}\sigma_{2p}^2\pi_{2p}^4\pi_{2p}^{*1}\sigma_{2p}^*$
(b) $\sigma_{2s}^2\sigma_{2s}^{*2}\sigma_{2p}^2\pi_{2p}^4\pi_{2p}^{*2}\sigma_{2p}^*$
(c) $\sigma_{2s}^2\sigma_{2s}^{*2}\sigma_{2p}^2\pi_{2p}^4\pi_{2p}^{*2}\sigma_{2p}^*$
(d) $\sigma_{2s}^2\sigma_{2s}^{*2}\pi_{2p}^4\sigma_{2p}^1\pi_{2p}^{*2}\sigma_{2p}^*$
(e) $\sigma_{2s}^2\sigma_{2s}^{*2}\pi_{2p}^4\sigma_{2p}^2\pi_{2p}^{*2}\sigma_{2p}^*$ **(f)** and
(g) $\sigma_{2s}^2\sigma_{2s}^{*2}\pi_{2p}^4\sigma_{2p}^2\pi_{2p}^{*2}\sigma_{2p}^*$

35. (a) bond order: NO^+, 3; $N_2{}^+$, 2.5 **(b)** NO^+, diamagnetic; $N_2{}^+$, paramagnetic **(c)** $N_2{}^+$ should have the greater bond length. **37.** To account for the resonance hybrid required by valence bond theory **39.** SO_2 is the only one with resonance forms and thus delocalized orbitals. **41.** The number of valence electrons (c) and the number of vacant atomic orbitals (d) are the most important factors. **43.** 7.02×10^{20} energy levels and electrons present **45. (a)** electrical conductor **(b)** insulator **(c)** insulator **(d)** semiconductor **(e)** electrical conductor **(f)** insulator **47.** Only **(d)** and **(f)** will produce an electron-poor, p-type semiconductor (Ga and B have fewer electrons than Si). **49.** Silicon contaminated with As has extra electrons that can be promoted into the conduction band by thermal excitation; these additional electrons can carry a current. Ultrapure silicon has no extra electrons in the lattice that can be used to carry a current. **51.** The minimum wavelength of light required is 1090 nm (IR radiation).

Integrative and Advanced Exercises 54. MO theory: First and second shells filled followed by σ_{3s}(↑↓); VB theory: overlap of two 3s orbitals; Lewis theory would not predict the molecule Na_2 because the Na atoms would have incomplete octets. **56. (a)** By MO theory, KO_2 is an ionic compound between K^+ cations and $O_2{}^-$ anions, with a bond order of 1.5 and the MO diagram: $\sigma_{2s}^2\sigma_{2s}^{*2}\sigma_{2p}^2\pi_{2p}^4\pi_{2p}^{*3}\sigma_{2p}^*$; K_2O_2 is an ionic compound between K^+ cations and $O_2{}^{2-}$ anions, with a bond order of 1 and the MO diagram: $\sigma_{2s}^2\sigma_{2s}^{*2}\sigma_{2p}^2\pi_{2p}^4\pi_{2p}^{*4}\sigma_{2p}^*$ **(b)** The Lewis structure for $O_2{}^{2-}$ has an O—O single bond and each O is surrounded with three lone pairs of electrons; in the $O_2{}^-$ ion, one of the lone pairs of electrons is replaced by a single unpaired electron. **60.** Bond angles about N are 125°, so N is sp^2-hybridized; N—O—F bond is 105°, meaning sp^3 hybridization for central O atom; orbital overlaps are σ: $F(2p)$—$O_a(sp^3)$, σ: $O(sp^3)$—$N(sp^2)$, σ: $N(sp^2)$—$O(2p)$, π: $N(2p)$—$O(2p)$.

62. (a) ClF_3 is T-shaped, AsF_5 is triangular bipyramidal, ClF_2^+ is bent, and AsF_6^- is octahedral. **(b)** The hybridization schemes are sp^3d for Cl in ClF_3 and for As in AsF_5, sp^3 for Cl in ClF_2^+, and sp^3d^2 for As in AsF_6^-. **64.** A possible electron configuration for an electronically excited He_2 molecule is $\sigma_{1s}^2 \sigma_{1s}^{*1} \sigma_{2s}^1$ with a bond order of 1. **66.** The sp^2 electrons are involved in σ bonding. For N the lone pair is in one sp^2 orbital; the remaining two half-filled sp^2 orbitals overlap with orbitals on adjacent C atoms. The $2p$ electrons are involved in π bonding. **70.** The composition data yield the formula $C_5H_7NO_2$, which from the names of the functional groups suggests a derivative of acetic acid and ethanol having also the cyano functional group (CN), leading to the plausible structural formula:
$N\equiv C-CH_2(C=O)-O-CH_2-CH_3$. The rest of the problem involves writing overlap schemes for a C-to-N triple bond, a C-to-O double bond, three C-to-C single bonds, two C-to-O single bonds, and seven C-to-H bonds. **72.** $C_4H_8N_2O_2$, $H_3C-C(=NOH)-C(=NOH)-CH_3$; C—H: $\sigma H(1s)-C(sp^3)$; C≡N: $\sigma C(sp^2)-N(sp^2)$, π: $C(2p)-N(2p)$; N—O: $\sigma N(sp^2)-O(sp^3)$; C—C: $\sigma C(sp^2)-C(sp^3)$; C—C: $\sigma C(sp^2)-C(sp^3)$; O—H: $\sigma H(1s)-O(sp^3)$ **73. (a)** 4.00 W **(b)** 8.9 A
Feature Problem 76. (a) -205.4 kJ/mol benzene **(b)** -117.9 kJ/mol cyclohexene **(c)** Resonance energy for benzene is ~148 kJ **(d)** ~168 kJ

CHAPTER 12
Practice Examples 1A. 0.923 kJ **1B.** -1.025 kJ **2A.** 151 torr **2B.** 1.70 g L^{-1} **3A.** vapor only **3B.** 0.0435 g H_2O vapor, 0.089 g liquid water **4A.** 121 mmHg **4B.** 42.9 mmHg **5A. (a)** R $\longrightarrow$ P, $H_2O(g)$ liquefies, then solidifies as the temperature is lowered at constant pressure. Then from P $\longrightarrow$ Q, H_2O is converted from solid to liquid when crossing the fusion curve OD by increasing the pressure at constant temperature. **5B.** No, the volume is 15.3 L for half-vaporization of the 1.00-mol sample at 100 °C and 53.1 L at point R. **6A.** CH_3CN (polar) **6B.** $(CH_3)_3CH < CH_2CH_2CH_2CH_3 < SO_3 < C_8H_{18} < C_6H_5CHO$ **7A.** $He < Ne < O_2 < O_3 < Cl_2 < (CH_3)_2CO$ **7B.** Higher molar masses produce larger London forces; polar CH_3NO_2 has additional intermolecular forces. **8A.** lower: RbI or CsI; higher: MgO **8B.** NaI **9A.** 524 pm **9B.** 6.628×10^7 pm^3 **10A.** 0.903 g/cm^3 **10B.** 6.035×10^{23} mol^{-1} **11A.** 402 pm **11B.** 2.21 g/cm^3 **12A.** -669.2 kJ/mol **12B.** -764 kJ/mol
Exercises 1. Nonpolar silicone adheres to cloth or leather and repels polar, hydrogen-bonded water. **3.** Yes, molasses is a viscous liquid, and its viscosity increases as the temperature is lowered (and in the northern hemisphere, January is about the coldest month of the year). **5.** Evaporation, an endothermic process, involves removal of energy from the surroundings; in an insulated container this

energy comes from within the liquid and its temperature falls. **7.** 8.88 L **9.** 40.5 kJ **11.** 221 L **13. (a)** 45 mmHg **(b)** 110 °C **15.** 226 mmHg **17. (a)** exothermic condensation **(b)** 100 °C if barometric pressure is 1 atm. **19.** 120.7 °C **21.** 0.907 mmHg **23.** 6.5 atm **25.** 49.7 kJ/mol **27.** 33 °C **29.** 0.099 atm **31.** CO_2, HCl, NH_3, SO_2, and H_2O **33. (a)** 776 kJ **(b)** 2.5×10^4 kJ **35.** liquid and vapor [assuming that for CO_2(l), $d > 0.16$ g/mL] **37. (a)** melts at 0 °C, vaporizes at 93.5 °C **(b)** liquefies at slightly above 91 mmHg and probably solidifies by 50 atm **(c)** liquefies at about 20 °C, solidifies at about -56 °C **39. (a)** 31.8 mmHg **(b)** 83.8 mmHg **(c)** 88.9 mmHg **41.** SO_2(g) only **43. (a)** 0.22 kg ice **(b)** 27 g of steam **45.** Initially, the soda is supercooled below the freezing point of water. The rapid escape of CO_2(g) initiates freezing of the water when the can is opened. **47. (a)** weak London forces and strong dipole—dipole forces; **(b)** moderate London forces; **(c)** moderate London forces, and moderate dipole—dipole forces; **(d)** strong hydrogen bonding and weak London forces; **(e)** weak London forces
49. (c) < (b) < (d) < (a) **51.** CH_3OH, due to hydrogen bonding **53.** Diamond, because all interactions are C—C single bonds. In graphite the distance between planes of C atoms is much greater than the C—C bond length. **55. (a)** diamond structure with alternating silicon and carbon atoms; **(b)** A σ-bond framework based on sp^2 hybridization for B and N and a π bond involving overlap of a filled $2p$ orbital on N and an empty $2p$ orbital on B. **57.** Yes, smaller ions produce larger interionic forces. **59.** There are two different ways of placing the third layer in the packing-of-spheres arrangement of Figure 12-39. **61. (a)** A diamond-shaped cell consisting of nine symbols, with a colored diamond at each corner and a gray square at the center; other unit cells are possible **(b)** 1 gray square, 2 open circles, 1 colored diamond **(c)** A square with circles at the four corners is not a unit cell. If the cell has a red diamond at its center, all the adjacent cells have a gray square; and vice versa. **63.** 18.5 g/cm^3 **65. (a)** 335 pm; **(b)** 9.23 g/cm^3 **(c)** 15.5° **67.** $\left(8 \times \frac{1}{8}\right) + \left(6 \times \frac{1}{2}\right)$ = four Ca^{2+} ions and eight F$^-$ ions;
$\left(8 \times \frac{1}{8}\right) + 1$ = two Ti^{4+} ions and $\left(4 \times \frac{1}{2}\right) + 2$ = four O^{2-} ions. **69. (a)** 6 for each **(b)** 4 **(c)** 7.62×10^{-23} cm^3 **(d)** 3.51 g/cm^3 **71.** All have a fcc array of anions with cations occupying octahedral holes. **73.** Compared to the lattice energy of NaCl(s), that of LiCl(s) is more negative, and those of KCl(s), RbCl(s), and CsCl(s) are progressively less negative. **75.** -645 kJ/mol; $MgCl_2$(s) is more stable than MgCl(s) because Mg^{2+} attracts anions more strongly than Mg^+.
Integrative and Advanced Exercises
79. Because isooctane has a smaller ΔH_{vap} than water, its v.p. should not decrease with temperature as steeply as that of water. With equation (12.2), calculate the v.p. of isooctane at 25 °C; it is 43 mmHg. For water at 25 °C,

v.p. = 23.8 mmHg. **82.** As expected, ΔH_{vap} decreases as temperature increases. **85.** The point is on the vapor pressure curve at 30.0 °C. **88. (a)** 31 atm; **(b)** -0.25 °C **89.** 87 °C **92.** 54.3% dimer, decreasing with increasing temperature **93.** 1.84 kg N_2 **98.** $\theta = 16.2°$ **104. (b)** $EA_2 = +881$ kJ/mol **105.** formula is Na_3ClO; coordination numbers of O^{2-} and Cl^- are both 6; shortest distance from Na^+ to O^{2-} is $\sqrt{2} \times (a/2)$; shortest distance from Cl^- to O^{2-} is $\sqrt{3} \times (a/2)$.
Feature Problems 108. 2.1×10^{-2} J m^{-2}
109. (a) $\ln\left(\dfrac{P_2}{P_1}\right) = \dfrac{-15,971}{R}\left(\dfrac{1}{T_1} - \dfrac{1}{T_2}\right) + \dfrac{14.55}{R}\ln\dfrac{T_2}{T_1} - \dfrac{0.160}{R}(T_2 - T_1)$ **(b)** 169 K

CHAPTER 13
Practice Examples 1A. 16.2%
1B. (a) $x_{H_2O} = 0.927$ **(b)** 3.73 M **(c)** 4.34 m
2A. $x_{glyc} = 0.03593$ **2B. (a)** 0.3038 M **(b)** 0.3426 m **(c)** $x_{sucr} = 0.005815$ **3A.** oxalic acid
3B. CCl_4 **4A.** (1) 31 g NH_4Cl; (2) 46 g NH_4Cl crystallized if both suggestions (1) and (2) are followed. **4B.** $KNO_3 > KClO_4 > K_2SO_4$
5A. 0.717 atm **5B.** 6.33 atm **6A.** 112 mmHg hexane, 127 mmHg pentane, and 239 mmHg total **6B.** 13.0 mmHg toluene, 51.5 mmHg benzene, and 64.5 mmHg total
7A. $x_{hex} = 0.469$, $x_{pent} = 0.531$
7B. $x_{tol} = 0.202$, $x_{benz} = 0.798$ **8A.** 0.857 atm
8B. 8.24 mg **9A.** 8.60×10^4 g/mol **9B.** 0.0105 atm **10A. (a)** 0.122 m; **(b)** 377 g/mol; **(c)** $C_{17}H_{20}O_6N_4$ **10B.** lower than 760.0 mmHg **11A.** 3.9 atm **11B.** 0.56 mL
Exercises 1. NH_2OH(s), because of hydrogen bonding. The hydrocarbons are insoluble in water and strong interionic forces render $CaCO_3$(s) insoluble in water. **3.** salicyl alcohol, an organic substance able to hydrogen bond to water molecules. **5.** Formic acid and propylene glycol are soluble in water; benzoic acid and butyl alcohol are only slightly soluble; iodoform and chlorobenzene are insoluble. **7.** KF and NaF should be water soluble, with KF the more soluble because K^+ is larger than Na^+. MgF_2 and CaF_2 should be much less soluble (or insoluble) because of the 2+ charge on the cations. **9.** 53.7% NaBr by mass **11.** 1.83×10^4 L **13.** True for all aqueous solutions of ethanol because ethanol is less dense than water; true for other ethanol solutions only if the second component is more dense than ethanol. **15.** 21.6 g **17.** $[SO_4^{2-}] = 4.80 \times 10^{-4}$ M **19.** 1.85 M CH_3OH **21.** 113 mL **23.** 0.410 m **25.** 54.8 g I_2 **27.** 4.19 M, 5.26 m **29. (a)** For C_7H_{16}, $x = 0.187$; for C_8H_{18}, $x = 0.427$; for C_9H_{20}, $x = 0.386$ **(b)** 18.7 mol % C_7H_{16}, 42.7 mol % C_8H_{18}, 38.6 mol % C_9H_{20} **31. (a)** $x_{solute} = 0.00204$ **(b)** $x_{solute} = 0.0101$ **33.** 207 mL glycerol **35.** 8.66 m **37. (a)** unsaturated **(b)** about 3 g **39.** 4.48×10^{-3} M **41.** 4×10^2 g **43.** 1.40×10^{-5} M **45.** Because of the low density of molecules in the gaseous state, the solution volume remains essentially constant as a gas dissolves in a liquid. Changes in concentration in the solution result from changes in

the number of dissolved gas molecules (recall Figure 13-11). This number is directly proportional to the mass of dissolved gas. **47.** 40.6 mmHg benzene, 16.3 mmHg toluene, 56.9 mmHg total **49.** 23.2 mmHg **51.** $x_{styrene} = 0.32$, $x_{ethylbenzene} = 0.68$ **53.** 1.29×10^3 mmHg **55.** 3.2×10^4 g/mol **57.** Concentrated NaCl(aq) is hypertonic and draws water into itself by osmosis. **59.** 22.4 L of solvent; the osmotic pressure equation resembles the ideal gas equation, and in this specific instance, Avogadro's law and the molar volume at STP. **61.** 2.8×10^5 g/mol **63.** 21 atm **65.** 1.2×10^2 g/mol **67. (a)** 20. °C/m; **(b)** cyclohexane, because of larger K_f **69.** $C_6H_4N_2O_4$ **71.** C_4H_4S **73.** 1.2×10^2 g NaCl **75. (a)** −0.19 °C **(b)** −0.37 °C **(c)** −0.37 °C **(d)** −0.56 °C **(e)** −0.37 °C **(f)** −0.19 °C **(g)** <−0.19 °C **77.** The weak acid and weak base neutralize each other, yielding an aqueous solution of a salt ($NH_4C_2H_3O_2$), which is a strong electrolyte.

Integrative and Advanced Exercises 80. At 29.6 °C, the water-saturated phenol phase is 29.3% H_2O; above 66.8 °C, the mol fraction of phenol is $x = 0.161$. **81.** 682 g H_2O **85.** add 4.5 kg H_2O **88.** ~10% palmitic acid **91.** In each solution, mole fraction solute = 0.0016 **94.** total surface area = 1.56×10^{-3} m² **(b)** surface area of a 1.00-mg cube of gold = 8.34×10^{-7} m² **99.** 34.62% O_2 and 65.38% N_2, by volume **101.** 1.3×10^2 g

Feature Problems 103. (a) Vapor has $x_{HCl} > 0.50$ **(b)** Because the vapor composition is different from that of the solution, the composition and boiling point of the remaining solution must change as vapor escapes **(c)** $x_{HCl} = 0.12$ and 110 °C **(d)** $x_{HCl} = 0.112$ **104. (a)** ≈90% **(b)** yes **(c)** high water solubility; this will produce a solution with a low x_{H_2O} **105. (a)** 0.92% mass/volume has $t_f = -0.60$ °C, reasonably close to the expected −0.52 C **(b)** calculated $t_f = -0.60$ °C

CHAPTER 14

Practice Examples 1A. 4.46×10^{-5} M s^{-1} **1B.** 1.62×10^{-4} M s^{-1} **2A. (a)** 3.3×10^{-4} M s^{-1}; **(b)** 0.37 M **2B.** 2.17 M; the results differ because slightly different rates of reaction were used. **3A.** first-order in N_2O_5 **3B.** 3.9×10^{-7} M min^{-1} **4A.** 4.4×10^{-2} M^{-2} s^{-1} **4B.** 2.4×10^{-7} min^{-1} **5A.** 1.0 M **5B.** first-order, with $k = 7.3 \times 10^{-4}$ s^{-1} **6A.** 64.2% **6B.** 25.2 min **7A.** 272 mmHg **7B. (a)** 1.9×10^{-7} mmHg; **(b)** 1.56×10^3 mmHg **8A.** first-order (constant half-life) with $k = 6.93 \times 10^{-3}$ s^{-1} **8B.** zero-order from a plot of [A] vs. t, with $k = 9.28 \times 10^{-3}$ M/min **9A.** 43 s. at 75 °C **9B.** $T_2 = 311$ K **10A.** $2 NO_2 \longrightarrow NO + NO_3$; Rate = $k_1[NO_2]^2$ **10B.** Rate = $(k_1 \times k_3 \times k_2^{-1})[NO_2][F_2]$, derived rate law agrees with the experimental rate law.

Exercises 1. (a) 3.1×10^{-4} M s^{-1} **(b)** -3.1×10^{-4} M s^{-1} **(c)** 9.3×10^{-4} M s^{-1} **3.** 1.0×10^{-3} M s^{-1} **5. (a)** 0.575 M; **(b)** 5.4 min **7. (a)** 3.52×10^{-5} M s^{-1} **(b)** 0.357 M **(c)** 4.5×10^2 s **9. (a)** 3000 mmHg **(b)** 1400 mmHg

11. (a) first order in A, second order in B **(b)** third order overall **(c)** 0.102 M^{-2} s^{-1} **13.** Rate = $k[NO]^2[Cl_2]$ **15. (a)** true **(b)** false, half-life is independent of [A] **17. (a)** 3.13% **(b)** 0.00193 M s^{-1} **19. (a)** 19 min **(b)** 0.18 g **21.** 20.6 min **23. (a)** 218 min **(b)** 2.3 L CO_2 **25. (a)** first order, constant value for k; **(b)** 1.86×10^{-3} s^{-1}; **(c)** 0.148 M **27. (a)** II **(b)** I **(c)** III **29.** slightly less than 75 s **31. (a)** 0.010 M s^{-1} **(b)** 0.0048 M s^{-1} **(c)** 0.0034 M s^{-1} **33.** 1.39×10^{-4} M min^{-1} **35.** Rate = $k[HI]^2$, second order in HI and overall with $k = 0.00118$ M^{-1} s^{-1} **37. (a)** zero order in A **(b)** half-life = 72 s **39. (a)** First experiment initial rate = 0.022 M min^{-1}; second experiment: initial rate = 0.089 M min^{-1} **(b)** reaction is second order in A **41.** rate = $k[A]^2$; $k = 0.020$ M^{-1} min^{-1} **43.** Half-life for zeroth order increases with increasing [A] while half-life for a second-order reaction decreases with increasing [A]. **45. (a)** also need fraction of successful collisions **(b)** fraction with sufficient energy to react increases dramatically, whereas average kinetic energy increases more gradually **(c)** catalyst provides an alternate pathway, with a lower E_a and often a different value for A **47. (a)** 63 kJ/mol **(b)** plot of potential energy versus progress of reaction shows $E_{products} > E_{reactants}$ by 21 kJ/mol and $E_{activated\ complex} - E_{reactants} = 84$ kJ/mol **49. (a)** two intermediates (B and C) **(b)** three transition states **(c)** fastest step has the lowest activation energy; step 3 is the fastest step with step 2 a close second **(d)** reactant A(step 1) is the reactant in the rate-limiting step **(e)** endothermic, need energy to go from A to B **(f)** exothermic, energy released when going from A to D **51.** 1.60×10^2 kJ/mol **53. (b)** 112 kJ/mol **(c)** 2.3×10^2 s **55. (a)** 34.8 kJ/mol **(b)** 61 °C **57. (a)** 51 kJ/mol **(b)** The rule is not expected to apply; E_a in Fig. 14-10 is four times as large the value calculated in part (a). **59. (a)** A catalyst reacts but is recovered unchanged. **(b)** A catalyst functions by *changing* the mechanism of the reaction to one having a lower E_a. **61.** The similarity between platinum and enzymes as catalysts is in the important role of active sites. The major difference is that platinum is rather nonspecific in the reactions it catalyzes, while an enzyme is for a specific reaction only. **63.** There must be an excess of substrate. **65.** Molecularity and reaction order correspond only for elementary processes. When the exponents in an overall rate law happen to correspond to the coefficients in an overall chemical equation, it is purely by chance. **67.** first step(fast) $N_2O_2 \rightleftharpoons 2 NO$, second step(slow) $H_2 + N_2O_2 \longrightarrow H_2O + N_2O$ third step(fast) $N_2 + H_2O \longrightarrow N_2O + H_2$ overall: $2 NO + 2 H_2 \longrightarrow N_2 + 2 H_2O$ **69.** First step: $Cl_2(g) \rightleftharpoons 2 Cl(g)$, second step: $2 Cl(g) + 2 NO(g) \longrightarrow 2 NOCl(g)$, overall: $Cl_2(g) + 2 NO(g) \longrightarrow 2 NOCl(g)$

Integrative and Advanced Exercises 72. (a) first-order **(b)** $k = 0.29$ min^{-1} **(c)** 0.10 M/min **(d)** 0.064 M/min **(e)** 0.29 M/min **73.** 1.86 M **76.** M^{1-o} s^{-1} **81.** 1.9×10^2 min

86. overall rate = $(k_1[Cl_2]/k_{-1})^{1/2} \times k_2 \times [CHCl_3]$; $k = 0.015$ **89.** $k = 1.0 \times 10^{-6}$ M^{-1} s^{-1} **90.** $k = 0.027$ s^{-1} **94.** Mechanism is not consistent with reaction stoichiometry; sum of elementary steps indicates HOBr is a product and this was not observed.

Feature Problems 95. (d) 1.1×10^{-3} M min^{-1}; **(e)** 5.5×10^{-3} M min^{-1}; **(f)** $k_{avg} = 0.071$ min^{-1} and reaction rate = $k[C_6H_5N_2Cl]$; **(g)** 9.8 min **(h)** about 21 min **(j)** 0.0661 min^{-1} **96. (a)** first-order in each reactant, second-order overall **(b)** 3.7×10^{-5} M s^{-1}; **(c)** 6.2×10^{-3} M^{-1} s^{-1}; **(d)** $k_3 = 0.0014$ M^{-1} s^{-1}, $k_{13} = 0.0030$ M^{-1} s^{-1}, $k_{24} = 0.0062$ M^{-1} s^{-1}, $k_{33} = 0.025$ M^{-1} s^{-1}; **(e)** 51 kJ/mol; **(f)** First step is slowest because it involves two anions which will repel one another.

CHAPTER 15

Practice Examples 1A. 0.263 M **1B.** 0.25 M **2A.** $K = 7.1 \times 10^2$ **2B.** $K = 1.7 \times 10^{-6}$ **3A.** $K_p = 1.7 \times 10^{-6}$ **3B.** $K_c = 95$ **4A.** $K_c = [Ca^{2+}]^5[HPO_4^{2-}]^3/[H^+]^4$ **4B.** $K_c = [H_2]^4/[H_2O]^4$; $K_p = (P_{H_2})^4/(P_{H_2O})^4$; $K_p = K_c$ **5A.** greater quantities of CO and H_2O; lesser quantities of CO_2 and H_2 **5B.** A net change occurs to the right. **6A.** Equilibrium shifts to the right, producing more CO_2. **6B. (a)** no effect; **(b)** more CO_2 and $CaCO_3$; less CaO **(c)** no effect **7A.** Both concentrations will increase because of doubling of the pressure, however, because equilibrium shifts to the left [N_2O_4] will more than double while that of [NO_2] will increase, but not to twice its original value. **7B.** no effect **8A.** greater at higher temperatures **8B.** [$NH_3(g)$] will be greater at 100 °C **9A.** $K_c = 2.3 \times 10^{-4}$ **9B.** 25.2 g N_2O_4 **10A.** $K_c = 1.5 \times 10^{-4}$, $K_p = 3.7 \times 10^{-3}$ **10B.** $K_p = 0.022$ **11A.** 0.481 atm **11B.** 0.716 atm **12A.** 0.262 mol HI **12B. (a)** decrease; equilibrium shifts to the right when reaction volume increases **(b)** 0.0118 mol N_2O_4 **13A.** [Ag^+] = [Fe^{2+}] = 0.489 M; [Fe^{3+}] = 0.71 M **13B.** [V^{3+}] = [Cr^{2+}] = 0.0057 M; [V^{2+}] = [Cr^{3+}] = 0.154 M

Exercises

1. (a) $2 COF_2(g) \rightleftharpoons CO_2(g) + CF_4(g)$;
$$K_c = \frac{[CO_2][CF_4]}{[COF_2]^2}$$

(b) $Cu(s) + 2 Ag^+(aq) \rightleftharpoons$
$$Cu^{2+}(aq) + 2 Ag(s); K_c = \frac{[Cu^{2+}]}{[Ag^+]^2}$$

(c) $S_2O_8^{2-}(aq) + 2 Fe^{2+}(aq) \rightleftharpoons$
$$2 SO_4^{2-}(aq) + 2 Fe^{3+}(aq)$$
$$K_c = \frac{[SO_4^{2-}]^2[Fe^{3+}]^2}{[S_2O_8^{2-}][Fe^{2+}]^2}$$

3. (a) $K_c = [NO_2]^2/[NO]^2[O_2]$ **(b)** $K_c = [Zn^{2+}]/[Ag^+]^2$ **(c)** $K_c = [OH^-]^2/[CO_3^{2-}]$ **5. (a)** $K_c = [HF]/[H_2]^{1/2}[F_2]^{1/2}$ **(b)** $K_c = [NH_3]^2/[N_2][H_2]^3$ **(c)** $K_c = [N_2O]^2/[N_2]^2[O_2]$ **(d)** $K_c = [ClF_3]/[Cl_2]^{1/2}[F_2]^{3/2}$ **7. (a)** $K_c = 0.0012$ **(b)** $K_c = 5.55 \times 10^5$

(c) $K_c = 0.429$ **9.** $K_p = P_{H_2O} =$ $(23.8/760) = 0.0313$; $K_c = 1.28 \times 10^{-3}$ **11.** $K_c = 9.7 \times 10^{-16}$ **13.** $K_p = 5 \times 10^{14}$ **15.** $K_c = 0.106$ **17. (a)** $K_c = 26.3$ **(b)** $K_p = 0.613$ **19.** 0.516 **21. (a)** $NH_3 + 7/4 O_2 \rightleftharpoons$ $NO_2 + 3/2 H_2O$; $K_p = 4.03 \times 10^{19}$ **23. (a)** When substituting n/V terms into the K_c expression, V appears the same number of times in the numerator and denominator and cancels out. **(b)** $K_c = K_p = 0.659$ **25.** No, Q_c does not equal K_c. **27. (a)** No, Q_c does not equal K_c. **(b)** A net change proceeds to the right. **29.** 0.033 mol H_2, 0.033 mol I_2, 0.234 mol HI **31.** 4.0×10^{-4} mol Cl_2 **33. (a)** 0.478 mol PCl_5, 0.623 mol PCl_3, 0.0725 mol Cl_2 **(b)** 0.41 mol PCl_5, 0.20 mol PCl_3, 0.20 mol Cl_2 **35. (a)** to the left **(b)** 26 g C_2H_5OH, 35 g CH_3COOH, 32 g $CH_3COOC_2H_5$, 68 g H_2O **37.** 5.58 atm **39.** $[Cd^{2+}] = 0.257$ M, $[Cr^{2+}] =$ 0.514 M, $[Cr^{3+}] = 0.486$ M; minimum mass of Cd = 10.1 g **41.** Sketch **(b)** is best because the proportions of the molecules represented correspond to the K_c value of 4.0. **43.** $P_{tot} = 749.0$ mmHg **45.** partial pressure of $O_2 = 0.529$ atm; total pressure = 0.601 atm **47. (a)** 30.1 atm **(b)** 32.4 atm **49.** Continuous removal of product(s) makes $Q < K$ and the reaction shifts to the right as a result. **51. (a)** decrease **(b)** increase **(c)** no effect **(d)** no effect **53. (a)** increased [NO] **(b)** increases rate of reaction **55.** The pressure of $N_2(g)$ will have increased when equilibrium is re-established, but not to twice its original pressure because equilibrium will have shifted to the right, consuming some of the N_2 and producing more NH_3. **57. (a)** shift to the right producing more CO and H_2 **(b)** no effect because number of moles of gases is unchanged in the reaction **(c)** shift to the right because 9 mol gaseous reactants yield 10 mol gaseous products

Integrative and Advanced Exercises
61. $[Fe^{2+}] = 0.111$ M, $[Fe^{3+}] =$ 0.049 M, $[Ag^+] = 0.15$ M **62.** 2.79 atm **64.** $K_p = 2.1 \times 10^{-3}$ **66.** $K_p = 12.0$ **69.** 0.177 **70.** 87.1 g/mol **73.** $K_p = 3.34 \times 10^{-4}$ **75.** 0.085 mol CH_4, 0.070 mol H_2O, 0.12 mol CO_2, 0.16 mol H_2 **79.** 24.6 atm

Feature Problems 80. $K_c = 4.0$ **82.** $K_p = 4.8 \times 10^{-8}$

CHAPTER 16

Practice Examples 1A. (a) acids: HF and H_3O^+; bases: H_2O and F^- **(b)** acids: HSO_4^- and NH_4^+; bases: NH_3 and SO_4^{2-} **(c)** acids: HCl and $HC_2H_3O_2$; bases: $C_2H_3O_2^-$ and Cl^- **1B.** HNO_2. is an acid $(HNO_2 + H_2O \rightleftharpoons H_3O^+ + NO_2^-)$. PO_4^{3-} is a base $(PO_4^{3-} + H_2O \rightleftharpoons HPO_4^{2-} + OH^-)$. HCO_3^- is amphiprotic $(HCO_3^- + H_2O \rightleftharpoons H_3O^+ + CO_3^{2-}$ and $HCO_3^- + H_2O \rightleftharpoons H_2CO_3$ and $OH^-)$. **2A.** $[H_3O^+] = 1.4 \times 10^{-3}$ M, $[OH^-] = 7.1 \times 10^{-12}$ M **2B.** 3.1 L **3A.** $[I^-] = 0.0025$ M, $[OH^-] = 4.0 \times 10^{-12}$ M, pH = 2.60 **3B.** pH = 1.466 **4A.** pH = 11.52 **4B.** pH = 13.74 **5A.** $K_a = 2.9 \times 10^{-8}$ **5B.** $K_b =$ 2.6×10^{-6} **6A.** pH = 1.80 **6B.** pH = 2.66

7A. pH = 2.29 **7B.** pH = 11.28 **8A.** 5.5% in 0.20 M, 17% in 0.020 M **8B.** $K_a = 1.4 \times 10^{-4}$ **9A.** $[H_3O^+] = [HOOCCH_2COO^-] =$ 0.0372 M, $[^-OOCCH_2COO^-] = 2.0 \times 10^{-6}$ M **9B.** $K_{a_2} = 5.3 \times 10^{-5}$, $K_{a_1} = 5.3 \times 10^{-2}$ **10A.** $[H_3O^+] = 0.21$ M, $[HSO_4^-] =$ 0.19 M, $[SO_4^{2-}] = 0.010$ M **10B.** $[HSO_4^-] =$ 0.014 M, $[H_3O^+] = 0.026$ M, $[SO_4^{2-}] =$ 0.0060 M **11A. (a)** acidic **(b)** neutral **(c)** basic **11B.** $H_2PO_4^- + H_2O \rightleftharpoons H_3O^+ + HPO_4^{2-}$ and $H_2PO_4^- + H_2O \rightleftharpoons H_3PO_4 + OH^-$; because of its larger K value, the first reaction occurs to the greater extent. **12A.** codeine hydrochloride **12B.** basic **13A.** pH = 8.08 **13B.** $[CN^-] = 3.6 \times 10^{-3}$ M **14A.** $HClO_4$, CH_2FCOOH **14B.** H_2SO_3, CCl_2FCH_2COOH **15A. (a)** BF_3 is a Lewis acid, NH_3 is a Lewis base. **(b)** H_2O is a Lewis base, Cr^{3+} is a Lewis acid. **15B.** Hydroxide ion and chloride ion are the Lewis bases; $Al(OH)_3$ and $SnCl_4$ are the Lewis acids.

Exercises 1. (a) acid **(b)** base **(c)** base **(d)** acid **(e)** acid **3.** Acids are **(a)** HOBr, H_3O^+ **(b)** HSO_4^-, H_3O^+ **(c)** H_2O, H_2S **(d)** $C_6H_5NH_3^+$, H_2O; bases are: **(a)** H_2O, OBr^- **(b)** H_2O, SO_4^{2-} **(c)** HS^-, OH^- **(d)** OH^-, $C_6H_5NH_2$ **5.** NH_3 **7. (a)** forward; **(b)** reverse; **(c)** reverse **9.** $[H_3O^+] =$ **(a)** 0.00165 M **(b)** 1.1×10^{-12} M **(c)** 2.3×10^{-12} M **(d)** 5.8×10^{-4} M; $[OH^-] =$ **(a)** 6.1×10^{-12} M **(b)** 0.0087 M **(c)** 0.00426 M **(d)** 1.7×10^{-11} M **11.** $[H_3O^+] =$ 4.0×10^{-14} M, pH = 13.40 **13.** $[H_3O^+] =$ 1.96×10^{-3} M **15.** 8.5 mL **17.** 53.9 mL **19.** pH = 10.20 **21.** $[H_3O^+] = 9.8 \times 10^{-3}$ M, pH = 2.01 **23. (a)** $[C_8H_7O_2^-] = 0.0030$ M **(b)** pH = 2.62 **25.** $K_a = 2.7 \times 10^{-3}$ **27.** 1.4 g **29.** $[H_3O^+] =$ 0.073 M, pH = 1.14, $[OH^-] =$ 1.4×10^{-13} M, pOH = 12.86 **31.** pH = 11.0 **33.** 0.063 g **35. (a)** pH = 11.23 **(b)** 34 mg NaOH **37.** sketch **(b)** **39. (a)** 0.0053 **(b)** 0.53% **41.** 0.0098 M NH_3 **43.** No, the degree of ionization is based on the assumption that $[HC_2H_3O_2]_{initial} \approx$ $[HC_2H_3O_2]_{initial} - [HC_2H_3O_2]_{equilibrium}$, which is invalid at 13% ionization. **45.** Very, very little ionization proceeds to the third step, which is the only step in which PO_4^{3-} is formed. **47.** $[S^{2-}] = K_2 = 1 \times 10^{-19}$ M in all cases. **(a)** $[H_3O^+] = [HS^-] = 8.7 \times 10^{-5}$ M **(b)** $[H_3O^+]$ $= [HS^-] = 2.2 \times 10^{-5}$ M **(c)** $[H_3O^+] = [HS^-] =$ 9.57×10^{-7} M **49. (a)** $[H_3O^+] =$ 0.76 M, $[HSO_4^-] = 0.74$ M, $[SO_4^{2-}] = 0.011$ M **(b)** $[H_3O^+] = 0.084$ M, $[HSO_4^-] =$ 0.066 M, $[SO_4^{2-}] = 0.0087$ M **(c)** $[H_3O^+] =$ 1.41×10^{-3} M, $[HSO_4^-] = 9 \times 10^{-5}$ M, $[SO_4^{2-}]$ $= 6.6 \times 10^{-4}$ M **51. (a)** From $C_{20}H_{24}O_2N_2 + H_2O$, $C_{20}H_{24}O_2N_2H^+$ is formed in the first ionzation and $C_{20}H_{24}O_2N_2H_2^{2+}$ in the second. **(b)** pH = 9.6 **53.** Products only are written: **(a)** $NH_3(aq) + NO_3^-(aq) + H_3O^+(aq)$ **(b)** $Na^+(aq) + HNO_2(aq) + OH^-(aq)$ **(c)** $K^+(aq) + HC_7H_5O_2(aq) + OH^-(aq)$ **(d)** no reaction **(e)** $C_6H_5NH_2(aq) + Cl^-(aq) + H_3O^+(aq)$ **55. (a)** neutral **(b)** basic **(c)** neutral **(d)** basic **(e)** acidic **57.** pH = 10.23 **59.** pH = 9.18

61. (a) $K_a > K_b$ and $HSO_3^-(aq)$ is acidic. **(b)** $K_a < K_b$ and $HS^-(aq)$ is basic **(c)** $K_a < K_b$ and $HPO_4^-(aq)$ is basic **63. (a)** $HClO_3$ **(b)** HNO_2 **(c)** H_3PO_4 **65. (a)** HI **(b)** HOClO **(c)** $CH_3CH_2CCl_2COOH$ **67.** Largest K_b: **(c)**, propylamine (hydrocarbon chains have low electronegativity); smallest K_b: **(a)**, ortho-chloroaniline (aromatic amines have lower basicity than aliphatic amines, and electron-withdrawing Cl atom decreases the basicity still more) **69. (a)** base **(b)** acid **(c)** base **71.** Lewis acids **(a)** $B(OH)_3$, **(b)** N_2H_4, **(c)** BF_3; Lewis bases **(a)** OH^- **(b)** H_3O^+ **(c)** $(C_2H_5)_2O$ **73.** $I_2(aq)$(Lewis acid) + $I^-(aq)$(Lewis base) $\longrightarrow$ $I_3^-(aq)$

75.

Integrative and Advanced Exercises
77. (a) base **(b)** base **(c)** acid or base **(d)** acid **78.** 2.1×10^{-3} M **79. (a)** no match (pH would be less than 2) **(b)** match at pH $\approx$ 5 **(c)** no match (pH would be about 7) **(d)** match at pH $\approx$ 11 **(e)** match at pH $\approx$ 11 **(f)** no match (pH would be greater than 5) **(g)** no match (pH would be 4.3, whereas the mark on the chart is closer to 5) **(h)** match at pH $\approx$ 2 **(i)** no match (pH would be closer to 2.5) **83.** $K_a = 5 \times 10^{-5}$ **84.** Choices **(a)**, **(b)**, and **(d)** are all impractical for various reasons; choose **(c)**, with 0.096 g NH_4Cl **92.** 9.73 g **93.** pH = 0.16 **96.** In H_3PO_3, one of the H atoms is bonded directly to the central P atom; the other two are bonded to O atoms, and those are the two that are ionizable.

Feature Problem 99. (a) pH 2.15 **(b)** pH = 11.95 **(c)** pH = 9.23

CHAPTER 17

Practice Examples 1A. In 0.500 M HF: $[H_3O^+] =$ 0.018 M, $[HF] = 0.482$ M; in 0.500 M HF/0.100 M HCl: $[H_3O^+] = 0.103$ M; $[HF] = 0.497$ M **1B.** 30 drops **2A.** $[H_3O^+] = 1.2 \times 10^{-4}$ M, $[CHO_2^-] =$ 0.150 M **2B.** 15 g **3A.** A reaction between acetic acid and an excess of sodium acetate forms an acetic acid–acetate ion buffer. **3B.** A reaction between HCl and excess NH_3 forms an ammonia–ammonium chloride buffer. **4A.** pH = 3.96 **4B.** pH = 4.51 **5A.** 21 g **5B.** The calculated pH is 5.09. **6A. (a)** pH = 3.54 **(b)** pH = 3.53 **(c)** pH = 3.55 **6B.** 1.3 mL **7A. (a)** pH = 0.824 **(b)** pH = 1.238 **(c)** pH = 7.00 **(d)** pH = 11.785 **7B. (a)** pH = 12.21 **(b)** pH = 11.79 **(c)** pH = 7.00 **8A. (a)** pH = 2.02 **(b)** pH = 2.70 **(c)** pH = 3.18 **(d)** pH = 8.08 **8B. (a)** pH = 11.15 **(b)** pH = 9.74 **(c)** pH = 9.26 **(d)** pH = 5.20 **9A.** pH = 12.18 **9B.** pH = 10.45

Exercises 1. (a) $[H_3O^+] = 0.0892$ M **(b)** $[OH^-] =$ 1.1×10^{-3} M **(c)** $[C_3H_5O_2^-] = 4.0 \times 10^{-5}$ M **(d)** $[I^-] = 0.0892$ M **3. (a)** pH increases by 1.05 units. **(b)** pH is unaffected. The common ion affects the degree of ionization of a weak acid in **(a)** but not of a strong acid in **(b)**. **5.** $[H_3O^+] =$ **(a)** 0.035 M **(b)** 4.0×10^{-4} M **(c)** 3.9×10^{-5} M **7.** $[CHO_2^-] = 0.77$ M **9. (a)** pH = 4.64 **(b)** pH = 9.68 **11.** Buffer solutions are: **(c)** , **(e)** , and **(f)** . After consideration of any reaction that might occur the buffer solution must contain a weak

acid or base and a conjugate weak acid or weak base. **13.** pH = 8.88 **15. (a)** 4.8 g $(NH_4)_2SO_4$ **(b)** 0.41 g $(NH_4)_2SO_4$ **17.** pH = 9.16 **19.** Mix 100. mL 0.100 M $HCHO_2$ and 58 mL 0.100 M $NaCHO_2$ **21. (a)** pH range is 3.89 to 5.89 **(b)** buffer capacity is 0.100 mol of acid or base per liter. **23. (a)** pH = 3.48 **(b)** pH = 3.52 **(c)** pH = 1.23 **25. (a)** calculated pH = 9.01 **(b)** Yes for dilution to 1.00 L but not to 1000 L, because the buffer components are too dilute; **(c)** pH = 8.99 **(d)** 1.1 mL **27. (a)** neutral: bromothymol blue, basic: thymolphthalein, remainder in acidic solution; **(b)** pH ≈ 4.7, pH ≈ 6.0 **29. (a)** Each indicator changes color in a rather narrow pH range, and this is known for a titration; it is not known when determining the pH of an "unknown" solution. **(b)** An indicator is a weak acid and consumes some base in an acid–base titration. **31. (a)** red **(b)** yellow **(c)** yellow **(d)** yellow **(e)** red **(f)** yellow **33.** pK_{HIn} = 3.84; 2,4-dinitrophenol is a relatively good indicator (within 1% of equivalence point volume). For more accurate work, a better indicator is needed. **35.** 0.1508 M H_3PO_4 **37.** pH = 11.63 **39. (a)** pH = 1.346 **(b)** pH = 2.034 **41. (a)** pH = 2.87 **(b)** pH = 3.51 **43.** In each case, the number of moles of acid, of titrant, and the endpoint volume are all the same. At the equivalence point, pH values differ due to the differences in the strength of the conjugate bases formed. **45. (a)** initial pH = 13.00, equivalence point pH = 7.00, 12.5 mL HI soln, phenolphthalein **(b)** initial pH = 11.62, equivalence point pH = 4.96, 40.0 mL HCl solution, methyl red **47. (a)** 11.9 mL; **(b)** 17.4 mL; **(c)** 17.5 mL **49. (a)** initial pH = 1.63, eqv.pt. pH = 7.43, bromothymol blue **(b)** initial pH = 2.28, eqv.pt. pH = 8.11, thymol blue **(c)** initial pH = 4.35, eqv.pt. pH = 10.20, alizarin yellow R **51.** Initial pOH = 1.00; after 24.00 mL of HCl, pOH = 2.69; at the equivalence point (25.00 mL HCl added), pOH = 7.00; after addition of 33.00 mL HCl, pOH = 12.14. **53.** Na_2S(aq) is basic because of the very small value of the second ionization constant of H_2S. **55. (a)** In the first reaction, H_3PO_4 is converted to $H_2PO_4^-$ and in the second, $H_2PO_4^-$ is converted to HPO_4^{2-}; in both of these CO_3^{2-} is converted to HCO_3^-. In the third reaction, HPO_4^{2-} is converted to PO_4^{3-} as OH^- combines with the final ionizable proton to form H_2O. **(b)** Na_2CO_3 is not a strong enough base to remove the third proton of H_3PO_4. **57.** K_{a_1} = 1.6 × 10⁻³, K_{a_2} = 1.6 × 10⁻⁸ **59. (a)** 0.0038 M; **(b)** 0.49 M **61. (a)** not possible; the concentrations do not conform to K_b for NH_3 **(b)** not possible; an appreciable amount of $HC_2H_3O_2$ forms **(c)** yes **(d)** not possible; NH_4^+ combines with OH^- to form free NH_3 and H_2O. **(e)** yes; a buffer solution **(f)** not possible; solution would be basic.
Integrative and Advanced Exercises
63. (a) HSO_4^-(aq) + OH^-(aq) ⟶ SO_4^{2-}(aq) + H_2O(l) **(b)** 2.8% NaCl, **(c)** bromthymol blue or phenol red **64. (a)** 27.8 mL **(b)** 3.3 mL **(c)** 2.1 × 10² mL **66. (a)** no sharp color change **(b)** approximately 18% **69. (a)** pH = pK_a + log[f/(1 − f)] **(b)** pH = 9.57 **70. (a)** pH = 7.40; [HPO_4^{2-}]/[HPO_4^-] =

1.6 **(b)** 26 g $Na_2HPO_4 \cdot 12 H_2O$ **71.** 3 drops of 10.0 M NH_3 **73. (a)** reaction 1: K = 1.0 × 10¹⁴, reaction 2: K = 1.8 × 10⁹ **(b)** reactions go to completion because of large values of K **87. (a)** initial pH = 8.34; final pH = 3.33 **(b)** initial pH = 12.15; 90% titrated, pH = 9.38 **(c)** 119 mL **(d)** 189 mL **(e)** 8.3% Na_2CO_3 **81. (a)** no significant change **(b)** pH = 4.40 **(c)** pH = 3.82 **82. (a)** pH at equivalence point = 7.93; indicator, bromthymol blue or phenol red **(b)** phosphate buffer **(c)** required ratio: [HPO_4^{2-}]/[$H_2PO_4^-$] = 5 **83.** pK_a = 12.2 **84.** 8.23

Feature Problem 88. (a) The curves cross at the half-equivalence point in the titration, where pH = pK_a = 4.74. **(b)** There are three carbonate containing species: H_2CO_3, HCO_3^- and CO_3^{2-}. Intersections occur at the half-equivalence points in each stepwise titration at pH = pK_{a_1} = 6.36 and pH = pK_{a_2} = 10.33; **(c)** There are four phosphate containing species: H_3PO_4, $H_2PO_4^-$, HPO_4^{2-}, and PO_4^{3-}. Points of intersection should occur at pH = pK_{a_1} = 2.15, pH = pK_{a_2} = 7.20 and pH = pK_{a_3} = 12.38

CHAPTER 18
Practice Examples
1A. K_{sp} = [Mg^{2+}][CO_3^{2-}]; K_{sp} = [Ag^+]³[PO_4^{3-}] **1B. (a)** $CaHPO_4$(s) ⇌
$$Ca^{2+}(aq) + HPO_4^{2-}(aq)$$
(b) K_{sp} = [Ca^{2+}][HPO_4^{2-}] **2A.** K_{sp} = 3 × 10⁻⁷ **2B.** K_{sp} = 1.9 × 10⁻⁹ **3A.** 3.7 × 10⁻⁸ M **3B.** 0.55 mg $BaSO_4$ **4A.** 1.3 × 10⁻⁴ M **4B.** 1 × 10⁻²⁰ M **5A.** yes **5B.** 9 drops **6A.** incomplete precipitation **6B.** [OH^-] = 0.02 M **7A.** 0.12% **7B.** Na_2CrO_4(aq) is best; [Ba^{2+}] = 5.5 × 10⁻⁷ M **8A.** no **8B.** yes **9A.** 0.074 M **9B.** 8.7 × 10⁻³ M **10A. (a)** Cu^{2+}(aq) + 2 OH^-(aq) ⟶
$$Cu(OH)_2(s)$$
(b) $Cu(OH)_2$(s) + 4 NH_3(aq) ⇌
$$[Cu(NH_3)_4]^{2+}(aq) + 2 OH^-(aq)$$
(c) [$Cu(NH_3)_4$]²⁺(aq) + 4 H_3O^+(aq) ⇌
$$[Cu(H_2O)_4]^{2+}(aq) + 4 NH_4^+(aq)$$
10B. (a) Zn^{2+}(aq) + 4 NH_3(aq) ⇌
$$[Zn(NH_3)_4]^{2+}(aq)$$
(b) [$Zn(NH_3)_4$]²⁺(aq) + 4 H_3O^+(aq) ⇌
$$[Zn(H_2O)_4]^{2+}(aq) + 4 NH_4^+(aq)$$
(c) [$Zn(H_2O)_4$]²⁺(aq) + 2 OH^-(aq) ⇌
$$Zn(OH)_2(s) + 4 H_2O(l)$$
(d) $Zn(OH)_2$(s) + 2 OH^-(aq) ⇌
$$[Zn(OH)_4]^{2-}(aq)$$
11A. precipitation occurs **11B.** no precipitation **12A.** [NH_3]$_{total}$ = 0.84 M **12B.** [$S_2O_3^{2-}$] = 0.20 M **13A.** 4 × 10⁻⁶ M **13B.** For this series of solutes, solubility decreases as K_{sp} decreases. **14A.** For FeS, Q_{spa} < K_{spa} and it does not precipitate; for Ag_2S, Q_{spa} > K_{spa} and it does precipitate. **14B.** pH = 2.7
Exercises 1. (a) [Ag^+]²[SO_4^{2-}]
(b) [Ra^{2+}][IO_3^-]² **(c)** [Ni^{2+}]³[PO_4^{3-}]²
(d) [PuO_2^{2+}][CO_3^{2-}] **3. (a)** [Cr^{3+}][F^-]³ = 6.6 × 10⁻¹¹ **(b)** [Au^{3+}]²[$C_2O_4^{2-}$]³ = 1 × 10⁻¹⁰
(c) [Cd^{2+}]³[PO_4^{3-}]² = 2.1 × 10⁻³³
(d) [Sr^{2+}][F^-]² = 2.5 × 10⁻⁹
5. AgI < AgCN < $AgIO_3$ < Ag_2SO_4 < $AgNO_2$; All but Ag_2SO_4 can be arranged in terms of increasing K_{sp} because [Ag^+] = $\sqrt{K_{sp}}$.

For Ag_2SO_4, calculate [Ag^+] and fit it in. **7.** yes **9.** 11 mg **11.** 4.5 × 10⁻³ M **13.** K_{sp} = 5.30 × 10⁻⁵ **15. (a)** s = 1.7 × 10⁻⁴ M **(b)** s = 7.3 × 10⁻⁶ M **(c)** s = 1.4 × 10⁻⁸ M **17.** Both reduce the solubility through the common ion effect. **19.** K_{sp} = 1.5 × 10⁻⁵ **21.** 0.079 M **23.** Yes if Ag^+ is used; no if CrO_4^{2-} is used. **25.** 27 ppm **27.** yes **29.** pH > 8.32 **31. (a)** yes **(b)** yes **(c)** no **33.** No, CaC_2O_4(s) should precipitate. **35.** 0.052% **37.** 2.5%; [Cl^-] = 0.16 M **39. (a)** no **(b)** yes **41. (a)** AgI(s) **(b)** [I^-] = 2.7 × 10⁻⁴ M **(c)** [Ag^+] = 3.1 × 10⁻¹³ M **(d)** yes **43. (a)** I^- precipitates first **(b)** [I^-] = 4.7 × 10⁻⁹ M **(c)** yes **45.** $MgCO_3$, FeS, $Ca(OH)_2$ **47.** pH = 9.60 **49. (a)** pH = 3.41 **(b)** 0.96 g **51.** [$PbCl_3$]⁻ forms in HCl(aq) because of the high [Cl^-]; Pb^{2+} does not form a complex ion with NO_3^- ions. **53.** K_f = 2.0 × 10³⁰ **55.** No, AgI(s) should form because Q_{sp} > K_{sp}. **57.** 1.4 × 10⁻⁶ g KI **59.** Yes, and the precipitation will be essentially complete. **61. (a)** Q_{spa}(1.7 × 10⁷) < K_{spa} and MnS(s) will not precipitate. **(b)** raise [$C_2H_3O_2^-$] to 0.21 M **63.** The tests for Hg_2^{2+} and Ag^+ could still yield valid conclusions, but the possible presence of Pb^{2+} would be missed. **65.** The valid conclusions are (a) and (c).
Integrative and Advanced Exercises 67. 68% **69.** 38% **71.** 0.012 M **74.** 2 g MnS/L **77. (a)** yes **(b)** no **(c)** yes **80.** K_{sp} = 1.2 × 10⁻¹⁶ **82.** 1.6 × 10⁻³ M **83.** [Pb^{2+}] = 6.5 × 10⁻⁴ M **85. (a)** Ag_2SO_4(s) + Ba^{2+}(aq) + 2 Cl^-(aq)
$$⟶ BaSO_4(s) + 2 AgCl(s)$$ **(b)** 0.63 g Ag_2SO_4
Feature Problems 86. K_{sp} = 3.0 × 10⁻⁴ **88. (a)** 1.7 × 10⁻⁴ M **(b)** 1.7 × 10⁻⁴ M **(c)** 2.8 × 10⁻⁵ M **(d)** 0.059 M (pptn. barely occurs) **(e)** 1.4 × 10⁻⁹ M (pptn. occurs)

CHAPTER 19
Practice Examples 1A. (a) decreases **(b)** increases **1B. (a)** uncertain **(b)** increases **2A.** 83.0 J mol⁻¹ K⁻¹ **2B.** 402 J mol⁻¹ **3A.** per mol NH_3(g): −99.4 J K⁻¹ **3B.** 312.4 J mol⁻¹ K⁻¹ **4A. (a)** case 2 **(b)** case 4 **4B. (a)** high temperatures **(b)** low temperatures **5A.** −1484 kJ **5B.** −70.48 kJ **6A. (a)** K = K_P = $P_{SiCl_4}/(P_{Cl_2})^2$ **(b)** K = [HOCl][H^+][Cl^-]/P_{Cl_2} **6B.** K = [Pb^{2+}]³(P_{NO})²/[H^+]⁸[NO_3^-]² **7A.** nonspontaneous, $\Delta G°$ = +4.73 kJ **7B.** NO_2 will spontaneously convert to N_2O_4. **8A.** K_{sp} = 8.5 × 10⁻¹⁷ **8B.** no appreciable reaction; K = 4 × 10⁻⁵ **9A.** 607 K **9B. (a)** K = 1.5 × 10⁷ **(b)** K = 1.7 × 10⁵ **10A.** 1240 K **10B.** K = 5 × 10⁹
Exercises 1. (a) decrease **(b)** increase **(c)** increase **3.** First law states energy is neither created nor destroyed; second law states that total entropy increases in all spontaneous processes. **5. (a)** increase **(b)** decrease **(c)** uncertain **(d)** decrease **7. (a)** negative **(b)** positive **(c)** positive **(d)** uncertain **(e)** negative **9. (a)** $\Delta H°_{vap}$ = +44.0 kJ/mol, $\Delta S°_{vap}$ = 118.9 J mol⁻¹ K⁻¹ **(b)** Hydrogen bonding in the liquid weakens as the temperature is raised, causing ΔS_{vap} to decrease and ΔH_{vap} to decrease. **11.** $C_6H_5CH_3$ **13.** The temperature at which the vapor pressure of water is 0.50 bar (about 380 Torr): about 81 °C. **15. (b)** is correct **17. (a)** case 2

(b) unable to predict **(c)** case 3
19. $\Delta G < 0$, $\Delta H = 0$, $\Delta S > 0$ (for nonreacting gases) **21. (a)** it may be that $\Delta S < 0$ **(b)** the reaction is endothermic **23.** $\Delta S° = -285$ J mol^{-1} K^{-1} **25. (a)** -506 kJ **(b)** forward **27. (a)** $\Delta G° = -1.6$ kJ; proceeds to equilibrium **(b)** $\Delta G° = -474.3$ kJ; goes to completion **(c)** $\Delta G° = -574.2$ kJ; goes to completion **29.** $C_6H_6(g) + 15/2\,O_2(g) \longrightarrow$
$6\,CO_2(g) + 3\,H_2O(l\ or\ g)$ **(a)** -3202 kJ **(b)** -3177 kJ **(c)** 25.5 kJ **31. (a)** $\Delta S° = -54.5$ J K^{-1} **(b)** $\Delta H° = -616$ kJ (actual value is -636.6 kJ) **(c)** $\Delta G° = -600.$ kJ (reaction is feasible and is favored at low temperatures) **33. (a)** $K = K_P = K_c(RT)^{-1}$ **(b)** $K = K_P = K_c$ **(c)** $K = K_p = K_c(RT)^2$ **35.** $K_p = 8.4 \times 10^{-13}$ **37. (a)** $\Delta G° = -76.0$ kJ, $K = 2.2 \times 10^{13}$ **(b)** $\Delta G° = -32$ kJ, $K = 4 \times 10^5$ **(c)** $\Delta G° = -28.1$ kJ, $K = 8.1 \times 10^4$ **39.** spontaneous in forward direction **41.** spontaneous in forward direction **43. (b)** is incorrect **45. (a)** $K_p = 0.659$ **(b)** $\Delta G° = 3.47$ kJ **(c)** net reaction to the right **47. (a)** $\Delta G° = -23.4$ kJ **(b)** $\Delta G° = +68.9$ kJ **(c)** $\Delta G° = +5.40$ kJ **(d)** $\Delta G° = +28.7$ kJ **49.** 204.6 kJ mol^{-1} (calculated value in excellent agreement with value in appendix D) **51. (a)** $P_{O_2} = 3.0 \times 10^{-21}$ atm **(b)** high temperature and continuous removal of oxygen **53. (a)** $\Delta S° = 215.2$ J K^{-1} **(b)** $\Delta H° = 91$ kJ **(c)** $\Delta G° = 27$ kJ **(d)** $K = 2 \times 10^{-5}$ **55.** 1.36×10^3 K **57.** $K_P = 6.0 \times 10^{-4}$ **59.** $T \approx 650$ K **61. (a)** $K_P = 0.014$ **(b)** 329 K **63.** -2.1×10^2 kJ and -206.1 kJ; assumption is reasonably good **65. (a)** $\Delta G° = 152.1$ kJ **(b)** $\Delta G° = -362.3$ kJ; coupled reaction is spontaneous

Integrative and Advanced Exercises
69. (a) and **(d)** are true **70.** 0.210 mol Br$_2$, 0.210 mol Cl$_2$, 0.580 mol BrCl **74.** 2.01×10^3 K **76.** $S° = 167$ J mol^{-1} K^{-1} **79.** 3.70 atm **81.** 297 K **84.** 647 K **85.** 4.2 mg AgBr/L

Feature Problems 88. (a) $\Delta G° = 8.557$ kJ/mol (using tabulated $\Delta G°$ values) or $\Delta G° = 8.556$ kJ/mol (using $\Delta H° = 44.012$ kJ/mol and $\Delta S° = 118.92$ J mol^{-1} K^{-1}) **(b)** 0.0317 bar; **(c)** 23.8 Torr; **(d)** 23.8 Torr **89. (a)** The graph for the formation of MgO(s) is below that of ZnO(s) at all temperatures. **(b)** The graph for CO(g) must be below that for ZnO(s), that is, at temperatures above 1000 °C. **(c)** Yes, but only above 1850 °C. **(d)** No, $\Delta G° > 0$ at all temperatures for this reaction. **(e)** $\Delta S° > 0$ for one reaction, $\Delta S° < 0$ for another, and $\Delta S° \approx 0$ for a third; **(f)** The C-CO line has a negative slope and, at some temperature, intersects all the metal-metal oxide lines, which have positive slopes.

CHAPTER 20

Practice Examples
1A. $Sc(s) + 3\,Ag^+(aq) \longrightarrow Sc^{3+}(aq) + 3\,Ag(s)$
1B. $Al(s) + 3\,Ag^+(aq) \longrightarrow$
$Al^{3+}(aq) + 3\,Ag(s)$,
$Al(s)|Al^{3+}(aq)\|Ag^+(aq)|Ag(s)$
2A. $E°_{cell} = 0.587$ V **2B.** $E°_{cell} = 0.74$ V **3A.** $E° = -0.48$ V **3B.** $E° = -0.424$ V **4A.** $\Delta G° = -1587$ kJ **4B.** $E°_{cell} = 1.229$ V **5A.** Copper will displace metals less active than itself, such as Ag$^+$(aq); $E°_{cell} = +0.460$ V **5B.** Na(s) reacts with H$_2$O to produce H$_2$(g)($E°_{cell} = +1.885$ V) rather than Mg(s) ($E°_{cell} = +0.357$ V).

6A. $E°_{cell} = -0.78$ V, not a feasible method
6B. (1) Oxidation of Sn^{2+} to Sn^{4+} by O$_2$(g)($E°_{cell} = +1.075$ V); **(2)** Reaction of Sn(s) with Sn^{4+}(aq) to form Sn^{2+}(aq)($E°_{cell} = +0.291$ V).
7A. $K = 10^{204}$; reaction goes to completion
7B. $K = 2.5$; reaction incomplete **8A.** $E_{cell} = 1.815$ V **8B.** $E_{cell} = 0.017$ V **9A.** $E_{cell} = 0.467$ V, spontaneous as written **9B.** $[Sn^{2+}]/[Pb^{2+}] = 2.6$ **10A.** $E_{cell} = 0.23$ V **10B.** $K_{sp} = 6.9 \times 10^{-9}$
11A. I$_2$(s) at the anode and H$_2$(g) and KOH(aq) at the cathode **11B.** Ag(s) plates out at the cathode while Ag(s) is oxidized to Ag$^+$(aq) at the anode. **12A.** 1.89 A **12B.** 5.23 h
Exercises 1. (a) 0.340 V $< E° < 0.800$ V **(b)** -0.440 V $< E° < 0.000$ V **2. (a)** $E° = 0.755$ V **3.** $E° = 0.755$ V **5.** $E° = -2.31$ V **7. (a)** $E° = -1.180$ V **(b)** $E° = 0.37$ V **(c)** $E° = -1.63$ V **(d)** $E° = -1.13$ V
9. Sodium reacts with water, producing H$_2$(g) instead of displacing Zn(s); aluminum is not as active a metal as sodium and does displace Zn(s). **11. (a)** spontaneous **(b)** nonspontaneous **(c)** nonspontaneous **(d)** spontaneous
13. (a) significant **(b)** significant **(c)** only to a limited extent **(d)** significant **(e)** will not occur
15. reactions **(a)** and **(b)** occur
17. (a) $3\,Ag(s) + NO_3^-(aq) + 4\,H^+(aq) \longrightarrow$
$3\,Ag^+(aq) + NO(g) + 2\,H_2O(l)$, $E°_{cell} = 0.156$ V
(b) $Zn(s) + 2\,H^+(aq) \longrightarrow$
$Zn^{2+}(aq) + H_2(g)$, $E°_{cell} = 0.763$ V
(c) Au(s) does not react with 1.00 M HNO$_3$(aq). **19. (a)** $2\,Al(s) + 3\,Sn^{2+}(aq) \longrightarrow$
$2\,Al^{3+}(aq) + 3\,Sn(s)$; $E°_{cell} = 1.539$ V
(b) $Fe^{2+}(aq) + Ag^+(aq) \longrightarrow$
$Fe^{3+}(aq) + Ag(s)$; $E°_{cell} = 0.029$ V
21. (a) $Cu(s) + 2\,Fe^{3+}(aq) \longrightarrow$
$Cu^{2+}(aq) + 2\,Fe^{2+}(aq)$, $E°_{cell} = 0.431$ V
(b) $2\,Al(s) + 3\,Pb^{2+}(aq) \longrightarrow$
$2\,Al^{3+}(aq) + 3\,Pb(s)$, $E°_{cell} = 1.551$ V
(c) $2\,H_2O(l) + 2\,Cl_2(g) \longrightarrow$
$O_2(g) + 4\,H^+(aq) + 4\,Cl^-(aq)$, $E°_{cell} = 0.129$ V
(d) $3\,Zn(s) + 2\,NO_3^-(aq) + 8\,H^+(aq) \longrightarrow$
$3\,Zn^{2+}(aq) + 2\,NO(g) + 4\,H_2O(l)$,
$E°_{cell} = 1.719$ V **23. (a)** $\Delta G° = -1.165 \times 10^3$ kJ **(b)** $\Delta G° = -268$ kJ **(c)** $\Delta G° = -3.1 \times 10^2$ kJ **25. (a)** $E°_{cell} = 0.25$ V **(b)** $\Delta G° = -2.4 \times 10^2$ kJ **(c)** $K = 1 \times 10^{42}$ **(d)** very large K; goes to completion **27. (a)** not possible **(b)** net reaction to the left **29.** $E°_{cell} = 1.591$ V **31.** $E° = 0.923$ V **33.** $[Ag^+] = 5.0 \times 10^{-6}$ M **35. (a)** $E_{cell} = 1.249$ V **(b)** $E_{cell} = 0.638$ V **37. (a)** E depends on pH only if the reduction half-reaction involves either H$^+$(aq) or OH$^-$(aq). **(b)** Reduction of oxoanions is accompanied by the loss of oxygen atoms, requiring H$^+$ ions on the left. **(c)** Switch from acidic to basic solution by adding OH$^-$ to both sides. On the left side H$^+$ and OH$^-$ combine to form H$_2$O; OH$^-$ remains on the right. **39. (a)** $[Cu^{2+}] = 6 \times 10^{-38}$ M **(b)** Since Zn(s) is able to reduce $[Cu^{2+}]$ to the extent given in **(a)**, the displacement reaction goes to completion. **41. (a)** $E_{cell} = 0.818$ V **(b)** $E° = -0.828$ V; difference due to reaction reversal and standard (1 M) rather than nonstandard concentration (0.65 M) **43.** $E_{cell} = 0.177$ V **45. (a)** $E_{cell} = 0.039$ V **(b)** decrease **(c)** $E_{cell} = 0.025$ V **(d)** $[Sn^{2+}] = 0.237$ M **(e)** $[Sn^{2+}] = 0.50$ M, $[Pb^{2+}] = 0.18$ M **47. (a)** $14\,H^+(aq) + Cr_2O_7^{2-}(aq) + 6\,Cl^-(aq) \longrightarrow 2\,Cr^{3+}(aq) + 7\,H_2O(l) + 3\,Cl_2(g)$,

$E°_{cell} = -0.03$ V; since cell voltage is negative, oxidation of Cl$^-$(aq) to Cl$_2$(g) by Cr$_2$O$_7^{2-}$(aq) under standard-state conditions won't occur spontaneously. We can drive the reaction in the forward direction by using high $[H^+]$ and $[Cl^-]$ and removing the Cl$_2$(g) as it is produced.
49. (a) $Cr(s)|Cr^{2+}(aq),\ Cr^{3+}(aq)\|Fe^{2+}(aq)$, $Fe^{3+}(aq)|Fe(s)$; **(b)** $E°_{cell} = 1.195$ V **51. (a)** $E°_{cell} = 1.229$ V **(b)** $E°_{cell} = 1.992$ V **(c)** $E°_{cell} = 2.891$ V
53. The Al-air battery has the greatest quantity of charge transferred per unit mass of metal oxidized because Al has the smallest molar mass of the three metals and forms the most highly charged cation of the three metals.
55. (a) Oxidation of iron metal enhanced in the body of the nail **(b)** blue precipitate in the vicinity of the scratch **(c)** a faint white, but no blue precipitate **57.** Hooking up an inert electrode to the metal pipe, along with the application of a small voltage across the two metals, converts the metal pipe into a cathode, thereby making it resistant to oxidation.
59. (a) 3.3 g **(b)** 0.90 g **(c)** 11 g **(d)** 2.9 g
61. (a) electrolysis, at >1.229 V
(b) spontaneous **(c)** electrolysis, at >0.236 V **(d)** electrolysis, at >0.183 V **63. (a)** H$_2$(g) and O$_2$(g) **(b)** $2\,H_2O(l) \longrightarrow 2\,H_2(g) + O_2(g)$, $E°_{cell} = -1.229$ V **65. (a)** 1.62 g Zn(s) **(b)** 20.2 min **67. (a)** 1079 C **(b)** 0.7642 A
Integrative and Advanced Exercises
69. $E° = -0.255$ V **71. (a)** 9.38×10^6 kJ **(b)** 2.61×10^3 kWh **74.** $[Cl^-] = 6.9 \times 10^{-4}$ M **76.** $\Delta G°_f = 127.3$ kJ **79. (a)** $E°_{cell} = 1.1501$ V **(b)** $E° = 0.079$ V **81.** $E_{cell} = 1.146$ V
84. 0.051% Ag **86.** $E_{cell} = 0.223$ V, $[Ag^+] = 1.8 \times 10^{-10}$ M; SHE is anode **90. (1)** metal must have reduction potential < -0.691 V, be readily available; **(2)** net: $2\,Al(s) + 3\,Ag_2S(s) \longrightarrow 6\,Ag(s) + 3\,S^{2-}(aq) + 2\,Al^{3+}(aq)$; **(3)** NaHCO$_3$ serves as an electrolyte; **(4)** chemicals are used, Al is consumed.
Feature Problems 93. (a) (1) Na(s) $\longrightarrow$
Na(amalg, 0.206%),
(2) Na(amalg, 0.206%) + $2\,H^+$(1 M) $\longrightarrow$
$2\,Na^+$(1 M) + H$_2$(g, 1 atm)
(b) (1) $\Delta G = -81.56$ kJ, **(2)** $\Delta G = -360.33$ kJ **(c)** $2\,Na(s) + 2\,H^+(aq,\ 1\ M) \longrightarrow$
$2\,Na^+$(1 M) + H$_2$(g, 1 atm) $\Delta G° = -523.45$ kJ; **(d)** $E°_{cell} = -2.713$ V, so $E°_{Na^+/Na} = -2.713$ V
95. (a) 2.66×10^{-13} F **(b)** 2.26×10^{-14} C **(c)** 1.41×10^5 K$^+$ ions **(d)** 0.93×10^{12} K$^+$ ions **(e)** Only about 1.5×10^{-5}% of the K$^+$ ions are transferred.

CHAPTER 21

Practice Examples 1A. electrolysis of NaCl(aq) to form NaOH(aq), followed by addition of NO$_2$(g) to NaOH(aq) **1B.** electrolysis of NaCl(aq) to produce NaOH(aq), the reaction of SO$_2$(g) with NaOH(aq), and the addition of S to the boiling solution **2A.** pH = 2.394
2B. $[Na^+] = 9.23 \times 10^{-3}$ M **3A.** The first two reactions, are those from Example 21-3, used to produce B$_2$O$_3$: $Na_2B_4O_7 \cdot 10\,H_2O + H_2SO_4 \longrightarrow 4\,B(OH)_3 + Na_2SO_4 + 5\,H_2O$;

$2\,B(OH)_3 \xrightarrow{\Delta} B_2O_3 + 3\,H_2O$ The next reaction is the high-temperature conversion of B$_2$O$_3$ to BCl$_3$ using carbon and chlorine:

$2 B_2O_3 + 3 C + 6 Cl_2 \xrightarrow{\Delta} 4 BCl_3 + 3 CO_2$
$LiAlH_4$ is used as a reducing agent to produce
diborane: $4 BCl_3 + 3 LiAlH_4 \longrightarrow$
$2 B_2H_6 + 3 LiCl + 3 AlCl_3$ **3B.** Obtain B_2O_3
by the reactions used in Example 21-3,
followed by the reaction
$3 CaF_2 + B_2O_3 + 3 H_2SO_4 \xrightarrow{heat}$
$\qquad 3 CaSO_4 + 3 H_2O + 2 BF_3(g)$
Exercises 1. (a) $2 Cs(s) + Cl_2(g) \longrightarrow$
$2 CsCl(s);$ **(b)** $2 Na(s) + O_2(g) \longrightarrow Na_2O_2(s);$
(c) $Li_2CO_3(s) \xrightarrow{heat} Li_2O(s) + CO_2(g);$
(d) $Na_2SO_4(s) + 4 C(s) \longrightarrow$
$Na_2S(s) + 4 CO(g);$ **(e)** $K(s) + O_2(g) \longrightarrow$
$KO_2(s)$ **3.** flame test: LiCl (red), KCl (violet)
5. $MgCO_3$ is least soluble because of high
charge and small radius of Mg^{2+}. Na_2CO_3 is
most soluble because of lower charge and
larger radius of Na^+. Li_2CO_3 falls in between:
$MgCO_3 < Li_2CO_3 < Na_2CO_3$
7. (a) pH = 11.161 **(b)** Increase in pH during
electrolysis depends only on amount of OH^-
produced and not on initial concentration because NaCl(aq) itself is neither acidic or basic.
9. (a) 71.5% **(b)** NH_3 in intermediate steps is
recycled.
11. $Ca(OH)_2(s) + 2 HCl(aq) \longrightarrow$
$\qquad CaCl_2(aq) + 2 H_2O(l);$
$CaCl_2(l) \xrightarrow{molten\ salt\ electrolysis} Ca(l) + Cl_2(g);$
$Ca(OH)_2(aq) + CO_2(g) \longrightarrow$
$\qquad CaCO_3(s) + H_2O(l);$
$CaCO_3(s) \xrightarrow{heat} CaO(s) + CO_2(g);$
$Ca(OH)_2(s) + H_2SO_4(aq) \longrightarrow$
$\qquad CaSO_4(s) + 2 H_2O(l);$
$Ca(OH)_2(s) + H_3PO_4(aq) \longrightarrow$
$\qquad CaHPO_4(aq) + 2 H_2O(l)$
13. The *overall* process is $Mg^{2+}(aq) + 2 Cl^-(aq)$
$\longrightarrow Mg(s) + Cl_2(g)$ and so electric charge is
conserved. **15. (a)** $BeF_2(s) + Mg(s) \xrightarrow{heat}$
$Be(s) + MgF_2(s)$ **(b)** $Ba(s) + Br_2(l) \longrightarrow$
$BaBr_2(s)$ **(c)** $UO_2(s) + 2 Ca(s) \xrightarrow{heat}$
$U(s) + 2 CaO(s)$ **(d)** $CaCO_3 \cdot MgCO_3(s)$
$\xrightarrow{heat} CaO(s) + MgO(s) + 2 CO_2(g)$
(e) $2 H_3PO_4(aq) + 3 CaO(s) \longrightarrow$
$Ca_3(PO_4)_2(s) + 3 H_2O(l)$ **17. (a)** slightly to the
left **(b)** to the left **(c)** to the right
19. $2 HCO_3^-(aq) + CaO(s) \longrightarrow$
$\qquad CaCO_3(s) + CO_2(g) + 2 OH^-(aq)$
21. (a) 60.76 ppm Ca^{2+} **(b)** 60.76 mg Ca^{2+}/L
(c) 112.3 g $Ca(OH)_2$ **23.** 85 ppm Ca^{2+} **25.** 40.2 g
27. (a) Ten B—H bonds require 20 of the 22
valence electrons, leaving just two electrons to
bond four B atoms together **(b)** four **(c)** C_4H_{10}
has normal Lewis structure
29. (a) $2 BBr_3 + 3 H_2 \longrightarrow 2 B + 6 HBr$
(b) (i) $B_2O_3(s) + 3 C(s) \xrightarrow{heat}$
$3 CO(g) + 2 B(s)$ **(ii)** $2 B_2O_3 + 3 F_2(g) \xrightarrow{heat}$
$2 BF_3(g)$ **(c)** $2 B(s) + 3 N_2O(g) \xrightarrow{heat}$
$3 N_2(g) + B_2O_3(s)$ **31. (a)** $2 Al(s) + 6 HCl(aq)$
$\longrightarrow 2 AlCl_3(aq) + 3 H_2(g);$
(b) $2 NaOH(aq) + 2 Al(s) + 6 H_2O(l) \longrightarrow$
$\qquad 2 Na^+(aq) + 2[Al(OH)_4]^-(aq) + 3 H_2(g);$
(c) $2 Al(s) + 3 SO_4^{2-}(aq) + 12 H^+(aq) \longrightarrow$
$\qquad 2 Al^{3+}(aq) + 3 SO_2(g) + 6 H_2O(l)$
33. $Al^{3+}(aq) + 3 HCO_3^-(aq) \longrightarrow$
$Al(OH)_3(s) + 3 CO_2(g)$ **35.** Either acid or base
can attack aluminum by dissolving the
$Al_2O_3(s)$ protective coating, but in more nearly

neutral solutions the metal is protected.
37. $[Al(OH)_4]^-(aq) + CO_2(aq) \longrightarrow$
$\qquad Al(OH)_3(s) + HCO_3^-(aq)$
39. $2 KOH(aq) + 2 Al(s) + 6 H_2O(l) \longrightarrow$
$\qquad 2 K[Al(OH)_4](aq) + 3 H_2(g);$
$2 K[Al(OH)_4](aq) + 4 H_2SO_4(aq) \longrightarrow$
$K_2SO_4(aq) + Al_2(SO_4)_3(aq) + 8 H_2O(l)$
$\xrightarrow{crystallize} 2 KAl(SO_4)_2$ **41.** Graphite is the
most stable form of carbon at room
temperature and room pressure, but diamonds
convert to graphite imperceptibly slowly
under these conditions.
43. (a) $3 SiO_2(s) + 4 Al(s) \xrightarrow{heat}$
$\qquad 2 Al_2O_3(s) + 3 Si(s);$
(b) $K_2CO_3(s) + SiO_2(s) \xrightarrow{heat}$
$\qquad CO_2(g) + K_2SiO_3(s);$
(c) $Al_4C_3(s) + 12 H_2O(l) \longrightarrow$
$\qquad 3 CH_4(g) + 4 Al(OH)_3(s)$
45. Silanes have the general formula Si_nH_{2n+2};
silanols substitute O—H for one or more of
the H atoms (used to produce silicones).
47. $2 CH_4(g) + S_8(s) \longrightarrow 2 CS_2(g) + 4 H_2S(g);$
$CS_2(g) + 3 Cl_2(g) \longrightarrow CCl_4(l) + S_2Cl_2(l);$
$4 CS_2(g) + 8 S_2Cl_2(g) \longrightarrow 4 CCl_4(l) + 3 S_8(s)$
49. $KAl_3(Si_3O_{10})(OH)_2$; oxidation states are:
K and H = +1, O = -2, Si = +4, Al = +3;
overall charge on compound = 0 = sum of
the oxidation states.
51. (a) $PbO(s) + 2 HNO_3(aq) \longrightarrow$
$\qquad Pb(NO_3)_2(aq) + H_2O(l);$
(b) $SnCO_3(s) \xrightarrow{heat} SnO(s) + CO_2(g);$
(c) $PbO(s) + C(s) \xrightarrow{heat} Pb(l) + CO(g);$
(d) $2 Fe^{3+}(aq) + Sn^{2+}(aq) \longrightarrow$
$\qquad 2 Fe^{2+}(aq) + Sn^{4+}(aq);$
(e) $2 PbS(s) + 3 O_2(g) \xrightarrow{heat}$
$\qquad 2 PbO(s) + 2 SO_2(g);$
$2 SO_2(g) + O_2(g) \longrightarrow 2 SO_3(g);$
$SO_3(g) + PbO(s) \longrightarrow PbSO_4(s)$
53. (a) yes; **(b)** no; **(c)** no
Integrative and Advanced Exercises
58. (a) 0.332 g **(c)** 69% **62.** $Mg(OH)_2(s)$ should
precipitate **63. (a)** 81.4 ppm Ca^{2+} **(b)** 48.7 g
CaO(s) **(c)** $CaCO_3(s)$ can be precipitated if
$[CO_3^{2-}] > 0.0014$ M **(d)** 2.2×10^2 g Na_2CO_3
64. (a) 268 kg Al **(b)** 1.3 metric tons of coal
66. 19 g $Pb(NO_3)_2/100.0$ g H_2O
69. (a) 7.4×10^{-3} M **(b)** 6.4×10^{-4} M
(c) 2.0×10^{-3} M **72.** We expect lattice energy
of MgO(s) to be more negative than that of
MgS(s) because of the smaller size of O^{2-}
compared to S^{2-} ion; lattice energies are:
MgO(s), -3789 kJ/mol; MgS(s), -3215 kJ/mol
Feature Problem 73. (a) $E° = -2.87$ V
(b) $E° = -3.03$ V $(-3.040$ V in Appendix D)

CHAPTER 22
Practice Examples 1A. $E° = 0.622$ V
1B. $E° = 1.453$ V **2A.** $K_p = 2 \times 10^{-48}$
2B. $K_p = 4 \times 10^{-34}; 4 \times 10^{-15}$% decomposed.
Exercises 1. 7.8×10^5 L air **3. (a)** trigonal-
pyramidal **(b)** tetrahedral **(c)** square-pyramidal
5. $3 XeF_4(s) + 6 H_2O(l) \longrightarrow$
$2 Xe(g) + 3/2 O_2(g) + 12 HF(g) + XeO_3(s)$
7. I^- ion is slowly oxidized to I_2 by O_2 in air:
$4 I^-(aq) + O_2(g) + 4 H^+(aq) \longrightarrow$
$2 I_2(aq) + 2 H_2O(l)$ possibly followed by
$I_2(aq) + I^-(aq) \longrightarrow I_3^-(aq)$ **9.** Each halogen
is able to displace the group 17 members
below it, but not those above it; only F_2 can

displace O_2 from water; none of the halogens
can displace H_2 from water.
11. (a) 1×10^6 kg F_2 **(b)** No, because no
common oxidizing agent can oxidize $F^-(aq)$
to $F_2(g)$. **13.** $6 Cl_2(aq) + 6 H_2O(l) \longrightarrow$
$2 ClO_3^-(aq) + 12 H^+ + 10 Cl^-(aq); E°_{cell} =$
-0.095 V; since the cell voltage is negative,
the disproportionation reaction will not
occur under standard state conditions.
15. (a) T-shaped **(b)** square-pyramidal
(c) square-planar
17. (a) $2 HgO(s) \xrightarrow{heat} 2 Hg(l) + O_2(g)$
(b) $2 KClO_4(s) \xrightarrow{heat} 2 KClO_3(s) + O_2(g)$.
19. The atom ratios $O/2^{nd}$ element are 2 O/
1 N in N_2O_4, 1.5 O/Al in Al_2O_3, 1.5 O/P in
P_4O_6, and 2O/1 C in CO_2. Because the atom
ratio of $O/2^{nd}$ element is no greater in any
of the compounds than in CO_2, and because
C has the smallest atomic mass of the elements in question, the mass %O is greatest
in CO_2. **21.** $P_{O_3} \approx 3 \times 10^{-5}$ mmHg
23. In the reaction
$2 H_2O(l) \xrightarrow{electrolysis} 2 H_2(g) + O_2(g)$ the
volume ratio of H_2/O_2 is the same as the mole
ratio: 2:1. **25.** pH = 5.89 **27.** 302 kJ/mol
29. (a) H_2S forms very weak hydrogen bonds
and is a gas; H_2O forms much stronger
hydrogen bonds and is a liquid. **(b)** all
electrons paired **31. (a)** $K = 3.2 \times 10^{41}$;
reaction goes essentially to completion
(b) $K = 2.1 \times 10^{-65}$; essentially no reaction
in the forward direction **(c)** $K = 9.0 \times 10^{20}$;
reaction goes essentially to completion
(d) $K = 4.8 \times 10^{-7}$; only slight reaction in the
forward direction **33. (a)** zinc sulfide
(b) potassium hydrogen sulfite **(c)** potassium
thiosulfate **(d)** sulfur tetrafluoride
35. (a) $FeS(s) + 2 HCl(aq) \longrightarrow$
$\qquad FeCl_2(aq) + H_2S(g);$
(b) $CaSO_3(s) + 2 HCl(aq) \longrightarrow$
$\qquad CaCl_2(aq) + H_2O(l) + SO_2(g)$
(c) $SO_2(aq) + MnO_2(s) \longrightarrow$
$\qquad Mn^{2+}(aq) + SO_4^{2-}(aq);$
(d) $S_2O_3^{-2}(aq) + 2 H^+(aq) \longrightarrow$
$\qquad S(s) + SO_2(g) + H_2O(l)$
37. $S_2O_3^{2-}(aq) + 2 H^+(aq) \longrightarrow$
$S(s) + SO_2(g) + H_2O(l)$; no reaction with
SO_4^{2-} **39.** pH = 1.21 **41.** 7.002% Cu, by mass
43. (a) $N_2(g) + 3 H_2(g) \rightleftharpoons 2 NH_3(g)$
(b) $4 NH_3(g) + 5 O_2(g) \longrightarrow$
$\qquad 4 NO(g) + 6 H_2O(g)$
(c) $2 NO(g) + O_2(g) \longrightarrow 2 NO_2(g)$ followed
by $3 NO_2(g) + H_2O(l) \longrightarrow$
$\qquad 2 HNO_3(aq) + NO(g)$
45. $2 Na_2CO_3(aq) + 4 NO(g) + O_2(g) \longrightarrow$
$\qquad 4 NaNO_2(aq) + 2 CO_2(g)$
47. 6×10^9 kg NO_x released.
49. (a) $2 NO_2(g) \rightleftharpoons N_2O_4(g)$
(b) $HNO_2(aq) + N_2H_5^+(aq) \longrightarrow$
$\qquad HN_3(aq) + 2 H_2O(l) + H^+(aq);$
$HN_3(aq) + HNO_2(aq) \longrightarrow$
$\qquad N_2(g) + H_2O(l) + N_2O(g)$
(c) $H_3PO_4(aq) + 2 NH_3(aq) \longrightarrow$
$\qquad (NH_4)_2HPO_4(aq)$

51.

(a)

(b)

(c)

53. (a) hydrogen phosphate ion **(b)** calcium pyrophosphate **(c)** tetraphosphoric acid
55. $E° = 1.031$ V **57.** $\Delta H°$ for the combustion of: $CH_4(g) = -890.3$ kJ/mol; $C_2H_6(g) = -1559.7$ kJ/mol; $C_3H_8(g) = -2219.9$ kJ/mol; $C_4H_{10}(g) = -2877.4$ kJ/mol
59. (a) $2 Al(s) + 6 HCl(aq) \longrightarrow$
$$2 AlCl_3(aq) + 3 H_2(g);$$
(b) $C_3H_8(g) + 3 H_2O(g) \longrightarrow$
$$3 CO(g) + 7 H_2(g);$$
(c) $MnO_2(s) + 2 H_2(g) \xrightarrow{heat}$
$$Mn(s) + 2 H_2O(g)$$
61. (a) $CaH_2(s) + H_2O(l)$ **(b)** $CaH_2(s)$
63. natural gas; 4 g H/16 g CH_4 exceeds 3 g H/17 g NH_3 and 2 g H/18 g H_2O(seawater)
Integrative and Advanced Exercises 68. No reaction on the left and the solution acquires the pink color of MnO_4^-(aq). On the right, MnO_4^-(aq) is consumed in oxidizing NO_2^-(aq) to NO_3^-(aq) and is converted to essentially colorless Mn^{2+}(aq). **69.** $[NO_3^-] = 0.1716$ M **70.** 3.0×10^{-20} J/atom
73. $2 NH_4ClO_4(s) \longrightarrow$
$$N_2(g) + 4 H_2O(g) + Cl_2(g) + 2 O_2(g)$$
76. 9.23 g/cm³ **78. (a)** 339 kJ/mol **(b)** 353 nm (near UV) **79. (a)** 2.185 g $Ca_3(PO_4)_2$
(b) larger %P than $Ca_3(PO_4)_2$ **(c)** 92.4% BPL
83. 15 g H_2SO_4 and 37 g Cl_2
84. nonspontaneous at pH 4.1 and above
86. $3 XeF_4(g) + 6 H_2O(l) \longrightarrow$
$$2 Xe(g) + XeO_3(g) + 12 HF(aq) + 3/2 O_2(g)$$
88. $[Cl_2] = 0.060$ M; $[HOCl] = [H_3O^+] = [Cl^-] = 0.030$ M **89.** Based on $E° = -3.09$ V for the reduction of N_2 to HN_3, and with data from Figure 22-14, $E°$ for the reduction of HN_3 to NH_4^+ is 0.696 V.
Feature Problems 90. First balance each equation. Double the first equation and add the result to the second equation and three times the third equation to give the net equation: $2 H_2O(g) \longrightarrow 2 H_2(g) + O_2(g)$
92. $E°(ClO_2/HClO_2) = 1.188$ V, $E°(ClO_3^-/ClO_2) = 1.174$ V

CHAPTER 23
Practice Examples
1A. (a) $2 Cu_2S(s) + 3 O_2(g) \xrightarrow{heat}$
$$2 Cu_2O(s) + 2 SO_2(g);$$
(b) $WO_3(s) + 3 H_2(g) \xrightarrow{heat}$
$W(s) + 3 H_2O(g);$
(c) $2 HgO(s) \xrightarrow{heat} 2 Hg(l) + O_2(g)$
1B. (a) $3 Si(s) + 2 Cr_2O_3(s) \xrightarrow{heat}$
$$3 SiO_2(s) + 4 Cr(s)$$
(b) $2 Co(OH)_3(s) \xrightarrow{heat}$
$$Co_2O_3(s) + 3 H_2O(g);$$

(c) $Mn^{2+}(aq) + 2 H_2O(l) \longrightarrow$
$$MnO_2(s) + 4 H^+(aq) + 2 e^-$$
2A. HNO_3(aq) is a suitable oxidizing agent, as seen from the standard cell voltage in the reaction: NO_3^-(aq) $+ 3 V^{3+}$(aq) $+ H_2O(l) \longrightarrow$
$$NO(g) + 3 VO^{2+}(aq) + 2 H^+(aq),$$
$E°_{cell} = +0.619$ V **2B.** standard electrode potential required to meet requirements of the reducing agent: 0.255 V $< -E° < 1.18$ V; some possibilities: $-E°[Cr^{2+}(aq)|Cr^{3+}(aq)] = +0.424$ V, $-E°[Fe(s)|Fe^{2+}(aq)] = +0.440$ V, $-E°[Zn(s)|Zn^{2+}(aq)] = +0.763$ V.

Exercises 1. (a) [Ar] $3d^24s^2$; **(b)** [Ar] $3d^2$; **(c)** [Ar] $3d^4$; **(d)** [Ar] $3d^3$; **(e)** [Ar] $3d^5$; **(f)** [Ar] $3d^5$ **3.** Unlike the main-group metals, transition metals usually display several oxidation states, readily form complexes and colored compounds, are mostly paramagnetic, and some are ferromagnetic. **5.** Main-group elements have electrons added to a valence-shell subshell whereas transition elements have electrons added to an inner-shell subshell.
7. manganese **9.** Ln atoms are larger, similar to each other, and more easily ionized than members of the first transition series.
11. (a) $TiCl_4(g) + 4 Na(l) \xrightarrow{heat}$
$$Ti(s) + 4 NaCl(l);$$
(b) $Cr_2O_3(s) + 2 Al(s) \xrightarrow{heat}$
$$2 Cr(l) + Al_2O_3(s);$$
(c) no reaction;
(d) $K_2Cr_2O_7(aq) + 2 KOH(aq) \longrightarrow$
$$2 K_2CrO_4(aq) + H_2O(l);$$
(e) $MnO_2(s) + 2 C(s) \xrightarrow{heat} Mn(l) + 2 CO(g)$
13. (a) $Sc(OH)_3(s) + 3 H^+(aq) \longrightarrow$
$$Sc^{3+}(aq) + 3 H_2O(l);$$
(b) $3 Fe^{2+}(aq) + MnO_4^-(aq) + 2 H_2O(l) \longrightarrow$
$$3 Fe^{3+}(aq) + MnO_2(s) + 4 OH^-(aq);$$
(c) $2 KOH(l) + TiO_2(s) \xrightarrow{heat}$
$$K_2TiO_3(s) + H_2O(g);$$
(d) $Cu(s) + 2 H_2SO_4(\text{concd aq}) \longrightarrow$
$$CuSO_4(aq) + SO_2(g) + 2 H_2O(l)$$
15. (a) $FeS(s) + 2 HCl(aq) \longrightarrow$
$$FeCl_2(aq) + H_2S(g),$$
$4 Fe^{2+}(aq) + O_2(g) + 4 H^+(aq) \longrightarrow$
$$4 Fe^{3+}(aq) + 2 H_2O(l),$$
$Fe^{3+}(aq) + 3 OH^-(aq) \longrightarrow Fe(OH)_3(s);$
(b) $BaCO_3(s) + 2 HCl(aq) \longrightarrow$
$$BaCl_2(aq) + H_2O(l) + CO_2(g),$$
$2 BaCl_2(aq) + K_2Cr_2O_7(aq) + 2 NaOH(aq)$
$\longrightarrow 2 BaCrO_4(s) + 2 KCl(aq) +$
$$2 NaCl(aq) + H_2O(l)$$
17. $HgS(s) + O_2(g) \xrightarrow{heat} Hg(l) + SO_2(g),$
$4 HgS(s) + 4 CaO(s) \xrightarrow{heat}$
$$4 Hg(l) + 3 CaS(s) + CaSO_4(s)$$
19. For the reaction $2 Ca(s) + O_2(g) \longrightarrow$
$2 CaO(s)$, $\Delta S° = -208.4$ J K^{-1} and $\Delta H° = -1270$ kJ. A plot of $\Delta G°$ versus temperature will consist of three linear segments of increasing positive slope, the first line is joined to the second at the melting point for Ca(s), while the second is joined to the third at the boiling point for Ca(l).
21. (a) $VO^{2+}(aq) + 2 H^+(aq) + e^- \longrightarrow$
$$V^{3+}(aq) + H_2O(l);$$
(b) $Cr^{2+}(aq) \longrightarrow Cr^{3+}(aq) + e^-$
23. (a) no **(b)** yes **(c)** yes **25.** possible reducing agents: $H_2(g)$, $Sn(s)$, $H_2S(g)$, $PbS(s)$

27. $E°[Cr_2O_7^{2-}/Cr^{3+}] = 1.33$ V, $E°[Cr_2O_7^{2-}/Cr^{2+}] = 0.892$ V, $E°[Cr^{3+}/Cr^{2+}] = -0.424$ V, $E°[Cr^{3+}/Cr] = -0.74$ V, $E°[Cr^{2+}/Cr] = -0.90$ V
29. $Cr_2O_7^{2-}(aq) + H_2O(l) \rightleftharpoons$
$$2 CrO_4^{2-}(aq) + 2 H^+(aq) \text{ and }$$
$Pb^{2+}(aq) + CrO_4^{2-}(aq) \rightleftharpoons PbCrO_4(s)$
31. $3 Zn(s) + Cr_2O_7^{2-}(aq, \text{orange}) + 14 H^+(aq)$
$\longrightarrow 3 Zn^{2+}(aq) + 2 Cr^{3+}(aq, \text{green}) +$
$$7 H_2O(l),$$
$Zn(s) + 2 Cr^{3+}(aq) \longrightarrow$
$$Zn^{2+}(aq) + 2 Cr^{2+}(aq, \text{blue});$$
$4 Cr^{2+}(\text{blue, aq}) + O_2(g) + 4 H^+(aq) \longrightarrow$
$$4 Cr^{3+}(\text{green, aq}) + 2 H_2O(l)$$
33. (a) $[Cr_2O_7^{2-}] = 0.74$ M **(b)** $[Cr_2O_7^{2-}] = 2.6 \times 10^{-5}$ M **35.** 1.10 g Cr(s)
37. $E°[Cr_2O_7^{2-}/Cr^{3+}] = 1.33$ V, making $Cr_2O_7^{2-}$ a good oxidizing agent; $E°[CrO_4^{2-}/Cr(OH)_3] = -0.11$ V, making CrO_4^- a poor oxidizing agent. However, many metal chromates are insoluble and can be precipitated from aqueous solution.
39. $E = 0.24$ V under these conditions and hence reaction is spontaneous.
41. $Fe^{3+}(aq) + K_4[Fe^{(II)}(CN)_6](aq) \longrightarrow$
$KFe^{(III)}[Fe^{(II)}(CN)_6](s) + 3 K^+(aq);$
alternate formulation:
$4 Fe^{3+}(aq) + 3[Fe(CN)_6]^{4-}(aq) \longrightarrow$
$$Fe_4[Fe(CN)_6]_3(s);$$
43. (a) $Cu^{2+}(aq) + H_2(g) \longrightarrow$
$$Cu(s) + 2 H^+(aq);$$
(b) $Au^+(aq) + Fe^{2+}(aq) \longrightarrow$
$$Au(s) + Fe^{3+}(aq);$$
(c) $2 Cu^{2+}(aq) + SO_2(g) + 2 H_2O(l) \longrightarrow$
$$2 Cu^+(aq) + SO_4^{2-}(aq) + 4 H^+(aq)$$
45. (a) an impossibly high concentration for Cu^+(aq) **(b)** an entirely reasonable concentration for Cu^+(aq) **47.** $E° = 0.912$ V
49. (a) $K_P = 0.02$ **(b)** $P_{CO} = 0.02$ atm **51.** ZnO, $\lambda = 413$ nm (near UV light); CdS, $\lambda = 479$ nm (blue light); near UV light subtracted from reflected white light still appears white (ZnO) whereas blue subtracted from reflected white light appears yellow (CdS).
Integrative and Advanced Exercises 53. Ag^+ forms an insoluble chloride, protecting the underlying metal; gold forms a stable soluble chloro complex while silver does not.
57. (a) $Mo(CO)_6$ **(b)** $Os(CO)_5$ **(c)** $Re_2(CO)_{10}$
(d) Weak intermolecular attractions in the low molecular mass, symmetrical nickel and iron carbonyls result in the liquid state at room temperature. Because of the two metal atoms in the higher molecular mass, less symmetrical cobalt carbonyl molecules, stronger intermolecular attractions lead to the solid state **(e)** ionic salt containing Na^+ and $V(CO)_6^-$ ions
61. (a) Net: $2 H_2O(l) + 4 Ag^{2+}(aq) \longrightarrow$
$$O_2(g) + 4 H^+(aq) + 4 Ag^+(aq)$$
(b) $E°_{cell} = 0.75$ V, indicating a spontaneous reaction **64.** 82.3% MnO_2 **65. (a)** more of the 0.1000 M MnO_4^-(aq) required because 1 mol MnO_4^-(aq) gains only 5 mol e^- while 1 mol $Cr_2O_7^{2-}$ gains 6 mol e^- **(b)** 29.40 mL
67. 28.2% Cr, 3.286% Mn **68.** $NiC_8H_{14}O_4N_4$, empirical molar mass: 288.91 g/mol; 3.52% Ni
Feature Problem 70. (a) If $\Delta_{n_{gas}} = 0$, then $\Delta S° \sim 0$ and $\Delta G°$ is essentially independent of

temperature (reaction b). If $\Delta_{n_{gas}} > 0$, then $\Delta S° > 0$, and $\Delta G°$ decreases with temperature (reaction a). If $\Delta_{n_{gas}} < 0$, then $\Delta S° < 0$, and $\Delta G°$ increases with temperature (reaction c); **(b)** $P_{co} = 3$ atm

CHAPTER 24

Practice Examples 1A. coordination number, 5; oxidation state, +2 **1B.** $[Fe(CN)_6]^{3-}$ **2A.** $K_2[PtCl_6]$ **2B.** pentaamminethiocyanato-S-cobalt(III) chloride **3A.** The oxalate ion occupies *cis* positions. One isomer has *trans* NH_3 ligands, one has *cis* NH_3 ligands, and one has an NH_3 and a Cl^- in *cis* positions **3B.** There are five: three with the two pyridines *cis*, and two with them *trans*. **4A.** three **4B.** three in each case **5A.** tetrahedral **5B.** Paramagnetic, but the structure cannot be determined from the magnetic properties. **6A.** greater *d* orbital energy splitting for $[Co(H_2O)_6]^{2+}$ than for $[CoCl_4]^{2-}$ **6B.** $[Fe(CN)_6]^{4-}$ absorbs light of *shorter* wavelength than does $[Fe(H_2O)_6]^{2+}$; $K_4[Fe(CN)_6]$ is yellow and $Fe(NO_3)_2 \cdot 6 H_2O$ is green.

Exercises 1. (a) $[CrCl_4(NH_3)_2]^-$, diamminetetrachlorochromate(III) ion **(b)** $[Fe(CN)_6]^{3-}$, hexacyanoferrate(III) ion **(c)** $[Cr(en)_3]_2[Ni(CN)_4]_3$, tris(ethylenediamine)chromium(III) tetracyanonickelate(II) **3. (a)** amminetetraaquahydroxocobalt(III) ion; **(b)** triamminetrinitrito-O-cobalt(III); **(c)** tetraaquaplatinum(II) hexachloroplatinate(IV); **(d)** diaquadioxalatoferrate(III) ion; **(e)** silver(I) tetraiodomercurate(II)

5.

(a) H—Ö—H   **(b)** H—C—N—H (with H H on top, H on bottom)

(c) $[\ddot{O}=\ddot{N}—\ddot{O}:]^-$ **(d)** $[\ddot{S}=C=\ddot{N}]^-$

7. (a) square-planar **(b)** octahedral; *fac* isomer has three NH_3 ligands on the same face **(c)** octahedral **9. (a)** octahedral **(b)** octahedral, three bidentate ligands **(c)** octahedral, three isomers **11. (a)** not possible; all positions in coordination sphere equivalent **(b)** possible **(c)** not possible [same reason as in (a)] **13. (a)** three isomers **(b)** yes **15.** The cis-isomer of the ion is chiral and optically active; the trans-isomer is achiral and not optically active. **17.** Energy differences between the *d* orbitals of the central metal in the field of the ligands correspond to different light frequencies and hence different colors. **19.** Because of the larger Δ in the strong-field complex, an additional two *d* electrons pair, leaving only one *d* electron unpaired. **21. (a)** $[Co(en)_3]^{3+}$ is diamagnetic **(b)** three unpaired electrons **23.** no, can only confirm or eliminate square-planar geometry **25. (a)** $Zn(OH)_2(s) + 4 NH_3(aq) \rightleftharpoons$
$[Zn(NH_3)_4]^{2+}(aq) + 2 OH^-(aq)$
(b) $Cu^{2+}(aq) + 2 OH^-(aq) \rightleftharpoons$
$Cu(OH)_2$ (s, pale, blue)
$Cu(OH)_2$(s, pale blue) $+ 4 NH_3(aq) \rightleftharpoons$

$[Cu(NH_3)_4]^{2+}$(aq, dark blue) $+ 2 OH^-$(aq)
$[Cu(NH_3)_4]^{2+}$(aq, dark blue) $+ 4 H_3O^+$(aq)
$\rightleftharpoons [Cu(H_2O)_4]^{2+}$(aq, pale blue) $+$
$4 NH_4^+$(aq)
27. $[Co(en)_3]^{3+}$, chelate effect **29.** $K_f = K_1 \times K_2 \times K_3 = 5.0 \times 10^9$ **31. (a)** Al^{3+} forms a hydroxo complex but not an ammine complex. **(b)** $ZnCO_3(s)$ produces a high enough $[Zn^{2+}]$ to form $[Zn(NH_3)_4]^{2+}$, but $ZnS(s)$ is too insoluble. **(c)** At low $[Cl^-]$ the solubility of $AgCl$ is suppressed by the common ion effect, but at higher $[Cl^-]$ the solubility increases due to the formation of $[AgCl_2]^-$.
33. $[Al(H_2O)_6]^{3+}$(aq); H^+ is released by one of the ligand molecules to an H_2O molecule in the solution to form H_3O^+(aq). **35. (a)** $K = 8.5$ **(b)** K for the dissolution of $AgBr(s)$ in $NH_3(aq)$ is only 8.0×10^{-6}.

Integrative and Advanced Exercises
37. (a) tetraamminecopper(II) ion; **(b)** tetraamminedichlorocobalt(III) chloride; **(c)** hexachloroplatinate(IV) ion; **(d)** sodium tetrachlorocuprate(II); **(e)** potassium pentachloroantimonate(III) **38.** $[Pt(NH_3)_4][PtCl_4]$, tetraammineplatinum(II) tetrachloroplatinate(II) **43.** It is easier for a solvent water molecule to extract a proton from a ligand water molecule when the remaining complex is positively charged. **45. (a)** pH = 2.04; **(b)** $[[FeOH(H_2O)_5]^{2+}] = 9 \times 10^{-4}$ M **(c)** No, this would require $[H_3O]^+ = 90$ M, which is not possible. **49.** $[Cl^-]_{total} = 0.52$ M **50. (b)** $[Co^{3+}] = 2.2 \times 10^{-28}$ M **(c)** for the given conditions $E_{cell} = -0.142$ V and the reaction is nonspontaneous **52.** $E_{cell} = 0.99$ V **54.** $[PtCl(NH_3)_5]Cl_3$; no isomerism **55.** I. *trans*-chlorobis(ethylenediamine) nitrito-N-cobalt(III) nitrite; II. *trans*-bis (ethylenediamine)dinitrito-N-cobalt(III) chloride; III. *cis*-bis(ethylenediamine) dinitrito-N-cobalt(III) chloride **60.** face-centered cubic structure; K^+ ions occupy tetrahedral holes and $[PtCl_6]^{2-}$ ions, octahedral holes.

Feature Problem 61. (a) No, this structure predicts three isomers, which is one more than the actual number of isomers for this complex ion. **(b)** No, the only possible structure with optical activity requires one of the en ligands to span the diagonal distance across the face of the prism, which is not possible.

CHAPTER 25

Practice Examples 1A. $^{241}_{94}Pu \longrightarrow$
$^{241}_{95}Am + ^{0}_{-1}\beta$ **1B.** $^{58}_{29}Cu \longrightarrow ^{58}_{28}Ni + ^{0}_{+1}\beta$
2A. $^{139}_{57}La + ^{12}_{6}C \longrightarrow ^{147}_{63}Eu + 4^{1}_{0}n$
2B. $^{121}_{51}Sb + ^{4}_{2}He \longrightarrow ^{124}_{53}I + ^{1}_{0}n$, $^{124}_{53}I \longrightarrow$
$^{0}_{+1}\beta + ^{124}_{52}Te$ **3A. (a)** 9.98×10^{-7} s^{-1}
(b) 9.40×10^{12} dis s^{-1} **(c)** 25% **(d)** 2.36×10^{12}
dis s^{-1} **3B.** 75.8 d **4A.** 4.7×10^3 y **4B.** 13 dis
min^{-1} (g C)$^{-1}$ **5A.** 2.544 MeV **5B.** 0.006001 u
6A. (a) ^{88}Sr stable **(b)** ^{118}Cs radioactive
(c) ^{30}S radioactive **6B.** positron emission by
^{17}F; β-emission by ^{22}F
Exercises 1. (a) $^{230}_{92}U$ **(b)** $^{248}_{98}Cf$ **(c)** $^{196}_{80}Hg$ **3.** $^{14}_{6}C$
$\longrightarrow ^{14}_{7}N + ^{0}_{-1}\beta$ **5.** $^{232}_{90}Th \longrightarrow ^{228}_{88}Ra \longrightarrow$

$^{228}_{89}Ac \longrightarrow ^{228}_{90}Th \longrightarrow ^{224}_{88}Ra \longrightarrow ^{220}_{86}Rn$
$\longrightarrow ^{216}_{84}Po$; first branch, first fork $[^{216}_{84}Po$
$\longrightarrow ^{212}_{82}Pb \longrightarrow ^{212}_{83}Bi]$; second fork $[^{216}_{84}Po$
$\longrightarrow ^{216}_{85}At \longrightarrow ^{212}_{83}Bi]$; second branch, first
fork $[^{212}_{83}Bi \longrightarrow ^{208}_{81}Tl \longrightarrow ^{208}_{82}Pb]$, 2nd fork
$[^{212}_{83}Bi \longrightarrow ^{212}_{84}Po \longrightarrow ^{208}_{82}Pb]$ **7.** "4n + 2" is
only consistent with the mass numbers: 206,
210, 214, 218, 222, 226, 230, 234, and 238, as
seen in Figure 25-2. **9. (a)** $^{160}_{74}W \longrightarrow$
$^{156}_{72}Hf + ^{4}_{2}He$; **(b)** $^{38}_{17}Cl \longrightarrow ^{38}_{18}Ar + ^{0}_{-1}\beta$;
(c) $^{214}_{83}Bi \longrightarrow ^{214}_{84}Po + ^{0}_{-1}\beta$; **(d)** $^{32}_{17}Cl \longrightarrow$
$^{32}_{16}S + ^{0}_{+1}\beta$ **11. (a)** $^{7}_{3}Li + ^{1}_{1}H \longrightarrow ^{8}_{4}Be + \gamma$;
(b) $^{9}_{4}Be + ^{2}_{1}H \longrightarrow ^{10}_{5}B + ^{1}_{0}n$; **(c)** $^{14}_{7}N + ^{1}_{0}n$
$\longrightarrow ^{14}_{6}C + ^{1}_{1}H$ **13.** $^{209}_{83}Bi + ^{64}_{28}Ni \longrightarrow$
$^{272}_{111}Rg + ^{1}_{0}n$, $^{272}_{111}Rg \longrightarrow ^{4}_{2}He + ^{252}_{101}Md$
15. (a) $^{214}_{84}Po$ with a half-life of 1.64×10^{-4} s
(b) $^{32}_{15}P$, with a half-life of 14.3 days **(c)** all with
half-lives less than about 4 days, that is,
$^{222}_{86}Rn, ^{24}_{12}Mg, ^{80}_{35}Br, ^{13}_{8}O,$ and $^{214}_{84}Po$ **17.** 4.4×10^8
cobalt-60 atoms **19.** 87.5 h **21.** 142 d **23.** Object
is about 3.35×10^3 years ago, which is more
recent than the era of pyramid construction.
25. 0.12 g $^{208}_{82}Pb$/1 g $^{232}_{90}Th$ **27. (a)** 5.42×10^{-9} J
(b) 3727 MeV **29.** 7.805 MeV per nucleon
31. 4.06 MeV **33.** 7.26×10^3 neutrons
35. (a) $^{20}_{10}Ne$ **(b)** $^{18}_{8}O$ **(c)** $^{7}_{3}Li$ **37.** β-emission: $^{33}_{15}P$,
$^{134}_{53}I$; β + emission: $^{29}_{15}P$, $^{120}_{53}I$ **39.** Doubly magic
nuclei have magical atomic numbers and
atomic masses: $^{4}_{2}He, ^{16}_{8}O, ^{40}_{20}Ca, ^{56}_{28}Ni, ^{208}_{82}Pb$
41. 1.37 mg of iodine-131 **43.** Takes into
account the extent of biological damage.
45. $^{90}_{38}Sr$ is in the same group of the periodic
table as Ca, and thus can become concentrated
in bones. **47.** Mix in a small amount of tritium
with the $H_2(g)$ and detect where its radioactivity appears. **49.** Yes, a small amount of
radioactive sodium ion will end up in the
crystallized $NaNO_3$.

Integrative and Advanced Exercises
53. 2.9×10^3 metric tons **56.** 7.0μg ^{90}Sr
57. 29 years **61.** 2.00×10^2 Ci **62.** 0.147
63. 1.2×10^7 kJ

Feature Problems 67. The plot of packing
fraction versus mass number and the plot in
Fig. 26-6 are essentially mirror images of one
another (maximum of one is the minimum of
the other). Packing fraction is proportional to
the negative of the mass defect per nucleon.
68. (a) Early in the decay process, the very
large number of radium-226 atoms multiplied
by a very small decay constant still exceeds the
product of the very small number of radon-222
atoms and its much larger decay constant. As a
result the amount of radon-222 increases with
time. Only after the amount of radon-222 has
reached a maximum does it begin to fall off.
(b) $dD/dt = \lambda_p(P) - \lambda_d(D) =$
$\lambda_p(P_oe^{\lambda_p(t)}) - \lambda_d(D)$; **(c)** 1 year (actually, the
maximum comes after ~2 months, however,
the difference between 1 year and 2 months is
negligible). **70. (a)** average atomic mass of Sr:
87.5 u **(b)** 267.4 ppm **(c)** 2.95% **(d)** 2.1×10^9 y

CHAPTER 26

Practice Examples
1A. $CH_3CH_2CH_2CH_2CH_2CH_3$,
$(CH_3)_2CHCH_2CH_2CH_3$,

$CH_3CH_2CH(CH_3)CH_2CH_3$,
$(CH_3)_2CHCH(CH_3)_2$, $(CH_3)_3CCH_2CH_3$
1B. $CH_3CH_2CH_2CH_2CH_2CH_2CH_3$,
$(CH_3)_2CHCH_2CH_2CH_2CH_3$,
$CH_3CH_2CH(CH_3)CH_2CH_2CH_3$,
$(CH_3)_2CHCH_2CH(CH_3)_2$,
$(CH_3)_2CHCH(CH_3)CH_2CH_3$,
$(CH_3)_3CCH_2CH_2CH_3$, $CH(CH_2CH_3)_3$,
$(CH_3)_3CCH(CH_3)_2$, $CH_3CH_2C(CH_3)_2CH_2CH_3$
2A. 3,6,6-trimethylnonane
2B. 3,6-dimethyloctane.
3A. $CH_3CH(CH_3)CH(CH_2CH_3)CH_2CH_2CH$
$(CH_3)_2$
3B. $CH_3CH(CH_3)CH[CH(CH_3)_2]CH_2CH_3$ **4A.** 3-
nitrobenzaldehyde **4B.** 1,3-dichloro-
2-nitrobenzene, 2,4-dichloro-1-nitrobenzene
5A. (b) and (c) are chiral **5B.** (b) and (c) are chiral. **6A.** All have R-configuration. **6B.** (a), (b)
and (c) are enantiomeric pairs. **7A.** (a) E; (b) Z;
(c) Z; (d) Z

7B.

(a) Z: [structure] E: [structure]

(b) Z: [structure] E: [structure]

(c) Z: [structure] E: [structure]

(d) Z: [structure] E: [structure]

8A. H^-: nucleophile, $AlCl_3$: electrophile, C_2H_4:
nucleophile, CH_3S^-: nucleophile
8B. (a) CH_3I(electrophile) +
  NH_3(nucleophile) $\longrightarrow$ $H_3CNH_3^+I^-$;
(b) CH_3CH_2Cl(electrophile) +
  CH_3S^-(nucleophile) $\longrightarrow$
  $H_3CCH_2SCH_3$ + Cl^-;
(c) $CH_3CH_2CHClCH_3$(electrophile) +
  CN^-(nucleophile) $\longrightarrow$
  $CH_3CH_2CH(CN)CH_3$ + Cl^-
9A. (a) $CH_3C{\equiv}C^-$ + CH_3Br—S_N2 $\longrightarrow$
  $CH_3C{\equiv}CCH_3$ + Br^-;
(b) No reaction;
(c) CH_3NH_2 + $(CH_3)_3CCl$—S_N1 $\longrightarrow$
  $[CH_3NH_2C(CH_3)_3]^+Cl^-$
9B. (a) S_N2 mechanism, organic product is
(S)-2-cyanobutane (b) S_N1 mechanism, product
is a racemic mixture [50% (R), 50% (S)] of s-butyl
methylether.

Exercises

1. (a) [structure: C—C—C—C—C with Br, Br]

(b) [structure]

3.

(a) [structure with CH_3, H_3C, CH_3]   (b) [structure O_2N—benzene—OH]

(c) [structure: Cl, COOH, Cl, NH_2 on benzene]

5. (a) [Lewis structure H—C—C—C—H with Cl]

(b) [Lewis structure H—O—C—C—O—H]

(c) [Lewis structure H—C—C=O]

(c) [structure C—C—C—C=C—C—C with C, C above]

7. (a) sp^3 hybridized carbon, all bonds are
σ-bonds; C—H bonds: $C(sp^3)$—$H(1s)$C—C
bonds: $C(sp^3)$—$C(sp^3)$ (b) sp^2 hybridized
carbon, one π-bond and 5 × σ-bonds; C—H
bonds: $C(sp^2)$—$H(1s)$, C—C σ-bond
$C(sp^2)$—$C(sp^2)$, C—Cl bond: $C(sp^2)$—$Cl(3p)$
and the C—C π-bond: $C(2p)$—$C(2p)$;
(c) sp and sp^3 hybridized carbon atoms,
two π-bond and 6 × σ-bonds; C—H bonds:
$C(sp^2)$—$H(1s)$ and $C(sp)$—$H(1s)$, C—Cσ-
bonds: $C(sp^3)$—$C(sp)$ and $C(sp)$—$C(sp)$, and the
two C—Cπ-bonds: $C(2p)$—$C(2p)$
9. (a) positional (b) structural (c) positional
11. nine possible structures **13.** (a) carbon 2
(b) no chiral carbon atoms (c) carbon 2
15. (a) carbon atom bonded to Cl, CH_3, H and
CO_2H (b) carbon atom bonded to NH_2, CH_3, H
and CO_2H (c) no chiral carbon atoms
17. (a) alkyl halide (b) aldehyde (c) ketone
(d) alcohol (polyol) **19.** (a) A carboxyl group
contains both a C=O and an OH group, while
a carbonyl is simply the C=O group. (b) An
aldehyde carbonyl group is bonded to an R
(or Ar) group and a H atom, while a ketone
carbonyl group is bonded to two R (or Ar)
groups. (c) The acetyl group, CH_3CO, results by
removing the OH group from the acetic acid
molecule. **21.** (a) carboxyl group and a
hydroxyl group attached to an aromatic ring
(b) ester group (c) ketone and carboxyl groups
(d) a hydroxyl and an aldehyde group attached
to an aromatic ring **23.** three isomers: diethyl
ether, 2-methoxypropane, and methyl propyl
ether **25.** four isomers: pentanoic acid,

3-methylbutanoic acid, 2-methylbutanoic acid,
2,2-dimethylpropanoic acid **27.** nine isomers:
n-propyl acetate, ethyl propanoate, isopropyl
acetate, n-butylformate, s-butylformate,
t-butylformate, isobutylformate, methyl-
n-butanoate, methyl 2-methylpropanoate
29. many isomers, including 1-hydroxy-
1-methoxy propene, 1-hydroxy-
2-ethoxyethene, 1-hydroxy-1-ethoxyethene,
2-hydroxy n-butanal, 3-hydroxy n-butanal,
4-hydroxy n-butanal, 4-hydroxy n-butanone,
1-hydroxy butanone, 3-hydroxy butanone,
vinyl oxyethanol, 1-methoxypropanone, etc.
31. (a) 3,5-dimethyloctane (b) 2,2-dimethyl-
propane (c) 3,3-dichloro-5-ethylheptane
33. (a) 2,2-dimethylbutane (b) 2-methyl-
propene (c) 1,2-dimethylcyclopropane
(d) 4-methyl-2-pentyne (e) 2-ethyl-
3-methylpentane (f) 3,4-dimethyl-2-propyl-
1-pentene **35.** (a) there can only be 1-pentene
or 2-pentene (b) sufficient (c) must specify as
1-butanol, 2-butanol, isobutanol, or t-butanol
(d) need position on ring (e) sufficient (f) need
positions on ring **37.** (a) $(NO_2)_3C_6H_2(CH_3)$
(b) $(CH_3COO)C_6H_4(OH)$
(c) $HOOCCH_2C(OH)(COOH)CH_2COOH$
39. (a) N,N-diethylamine (b) p-aminonitroben-
zene (c) N-ethyl-N-cyclopentylamine
(d) diethylmethylamine

41.

(a) [structure] 2-methylbutane   (b) [structure] 2,2-dimethylpropane

43. There is only one position for the double
bond in ethene and propene but two in butene.
45. (a) $CH_3CH_2CH_3$ (b) $CH_3CH{=}CHCH_3$
47. (a) C_6H_5—$C{\equiv}CH$;

(b) [structure benzene with Cl, Cl]

(c) 3,5-dihydroxyphenol **49.** (a) nucleophile;
(b) electrophile; (c) nucleophile;
(d) nucleophile; (e) neither **51.** (a) H on a
carbon chain is displaced by another group
(b) H on an aromatic ring is replaced by
another group (c) two fragments of a small
molecule add across a double bond (d) two
groups from within the same molecule join to
produce a small molecule, such as H and OH
to form H_2O **53.** (a) $CH_3CH_2CH_2COOH$
(b) $CH_3CH_2CH_2COOCH_2CH_3$
(c) $CH_3CH_2C(CH_3)_2OH$
55. (a) $H_3CCH_2CH_3$(sol.)
(b) $H_3CCHClCH_2Cl$(sol.)
(c) $H_3CCH(CN)CH_3$(aq) (d) $H_3CCHClCH_3$(aq)
(e) $H_3CCH(OH)CH_3$(aq) **57.** (a) S_N2
(b) hydrogenation (c) esterification
59. (a) $H_3CCH_2CO_2H$(aq) + Cl^-(aq);
(b) $H_3CCH_2CO_2H$(aq) + $HOCH_3$(aq)
(c) $H_3CCH_2CO_2Na$(aq) + $HOCH_2CH_3$(aq)
61. (a) $H_3CC(O)NH_2$(aq) + H_2O(l)
(b) CH_3CH_2CN(aq) + H_2O(l);
(c) $CH_3CH_2C(O)ONa$(aq) + NH_3(aq)

63. (a) (3): $CH_3COOH(aq) + Cl^-(aq)$
(b) (1): $CH_3CH_2C(O)OH(aq) + CH_3OH(aq)$;
(c) (2): $CH_3CH_2C(O)ONa(aq) + H_2O(l)$
65. $\dfrac{[CH_3CH_2CH_2NH_3^+][OH^-]}{[CH_3CH_2CH_2NH_2]} = K_b$
67. (a) $CH_3CH_2NH_3^+Cl^-$ (aq);
(b) $(CH_3)_3NH^+Br^-$; **(c)** no reaction;
(d) $CH_3CH_2NH_2(aq) + H_2O(l)$ **69.** 2-butanol
71. (a) (1) **(b)** (2) **(c)** (2) **(d)** (1) and (3) **(e)** none of the compounds

73.

75. (a) identical molecules, both achiral
(b) identical molecules, both R-enantiomer
(c) structural isomers **(d)** enantiomers,
R/S-optical isomers **(e)** identical molecules,
both R-enantiomer **(f)** identical molecules,
both R-enantiomer **77. (a)** (S)-3-bromo-
2-methylpentane **(b)** (S)-1,2-dibromopentane
(c) (R)-3-(bromomethyl)-5-chloropentan-
3-ol **(d)** (S)-1-bromopropan-2-ol
79. (a) (Z)-2-pentene **(b)** (E)-1-chloro-2-methyl-
1-butene **(c)** (E)-4-chloromethyl-3, 7-dimethyl-
3-octene **(d)** (Z)-5-bromo-3-bromomethyl-
2-methylpent-2-enal

81. (a)

(b)

(c)

(d)

(e)

83. (a) reaction
rate = $k_{obs}[CH_3CH_2CH_2CH_2Br][OH^-]$;
(b) A graph of potential energy versus the
progress of the reaction constitutes the reaction
profile; plot contains reactants on the left-hand
side and products on the right-hand side of an
arching line, whose peak is the transition state
for the reaction. The energy difference between
the reactants and the products is the ΔH_{rxn}
(which is negative in this case). The energy
difference between the reactants and the

transition state is the activation energy for the
reaction. **(c)** The reaction rate would increase
by a factor of two. **(d)** The reaction rate would
decrease by a factor of two.
85. (a) $CH_3CH_2CH_2CH_2Br(aq) + NaOH(aq)$
$\longrightarrow CH_3CH_2CH_2CH_2OH(aq) + NaBr(aq)$;
(b) $CH_3CH_2CH_2CH_2Br(aq) + NH_3(aq) \longrightarrow$
$CH_3CH_2CH_2CH_2NH_3^+(aq) + Br^-(aq)$;
(c) $CH_3CH_2CH_2CH_2Br(aq) + NaCN(aq)$
$\longrightarrow CH_3CH_2CH_2CH_2CN(aq) + NaBr(aq)$;
(d) $CH_3CH_2CH_2CH_2Br +$
$Na^+\,^-OCH_2CH_3(aq) \longrightarrow$
$NaBr(aq) + CH_3CH_2OCH_2CH_2CH_2CH_3$
87. (a) $CH_3CH_2CH(CH_3)OH$ (both R- and
S- forms); **(b)** S_N1
89. (a) $CH_3CH(OCH_2CH_3)CH_2CH_3$
(both R- and S- forms); **(b)** S_N1 **91.** Not all polymer chains have the same number of monomer
units, and thus individual polymer molecules
differ in mass. Hence we can only discuss an average molecular mass (weighted average of the
molecular masses). **93.** polymer repeating unit:
$-[-NH-(CH_2)_6-NH-C(O)-$
$(CH_2)_8-C(O)-]_n-$
Integrative and Advanced Exercises
95. Chlorination occurs by a free radical chain
reaction in which methyl radicals are formed.
Some of the methyl radicals can join to form
ethane molecules, which themselves can be
chlorinated to produce CH_3CH_2Cl.
101. (a) $C_6H_5NO_2 + 7 H^+ + 2 Fe \longrightarrow$
$C_6H_5NH_3^+ + 2 H_2O + 2 Fe^{3+}$;
(b) $3 C_6H_5CH_2OH + 2 Cr_2O_7^{2-} + 16 H^+$
$\longrightarrow 3 C_6H_5COOH + 4 Cr^{3+} + 11 H_2O$;
(c) $3 CH_3CH=CH_2 + 2 MnO_4^- + 4 H_2O$
$\longrightarrow 3 CH_2CHOHCH_2OH + 2 MnO_2 +$
$2 OH^-$
103. $C_4H_8N_2O_2$ **104.** In chain reaction
polymerization monomer units add to the end
of free radical chains, of which there are
relatively few; the molecular masses of these
chains can become very large. In step-reaction
polymerization many more polymer molecules
grow simultaneously and the average
molecular mass is much lower.
108. (1) Freezing point depression data are not
precise enough to distinguish between
compounds. (2) Propionic acid in aqueous
solution turns litmus red, so unknown is not
propionic acid. (3) Both alcohols and
aldehydes are oxidized by aqueous
permanganate, while ethers are unreactive.
The unknown must be 1-butanol or
butyraldehyde. Reaction of alcohol with
carboxylic acid would produce a pleasant
smelling ester; an aldehyde would not react.
109. First we replace the chloro group with an
azide group, then reduce the resulting azide
to the primary amine.
1) $n - C_3H_7Cl + N_3^- \longrightarrow$
$n - C_3H_7N_3 + Cl^-$
2) $n-C_3H_7N_3 \xrightarrow{[H]} n-C_3H_7NH_2 + N_2(g)$
112. OH is protonated by HI to form H_2O^+,
which is a better leaving group than
hydroxide. **118. (a)** ester, amine, arene
(b) (1) sp^2; (2) sp^3; (3) sp^3; (4) sp^3, N:sp^3
(c) carbons 2, 4 are chiral

CHAPTER 27
Practice Examples 1A. dithreonylmethionine
1B.

2A. pentapeptide sequence: Gly-Cys-Val-
Phe-Tyr **2B.** hexapeptide sequence: Ser-Gly-
Gly-Ala-Val-Trp
Exercises 1. (a) 3×10^2 H_3O^+ ions
(b) 1.2×10^5 K^+ ions **(c)** 5×10^6 protein
molecules **5. (a)** glyceryl palmitolinolenolaurate
or glyceryl palmitoeleosterolaurate **(b)** glyceryl
trioleate or triolein **(c)** sodium myristate
7. (a) Trilaurin is a saturated triglyceride (i.e. a
fat), while trilinolein is an unsaturated triglyceride (i.e. an oil). **(b)** Soaps are salts of fatty
acids (from saponification of triglycerides),
while phospholipids are derived from glycerols,
fatty acids, phosphoric acid, and a nitrogen-
containing base. Both have hydrophilic heads
and hydrophobic tails. **9.** Polyunsaturated fatty
acids have two or more carbon-to-carbon double bonds. Stearic is fully saturated, while
eleostearic acid has three $C=C$ bonds and
hence is unsaturated. Safflower oil has the
highest percentage of unsaturated fatty acids.
11. $CH_2OHCHOHCH_2OH$ (glycerol) and
$Na^+\,^-OOC(CH_2)_{14}CH_3$ (sodium palmitate)
13.

L-Glucose   D-Erythrulose
aldohexose   ketotetrose

15. (a) D-(−)-arabinose is the optical isomer of L-
(+)-arabinose [structure **(a)** below].
(b) A diastereomer of L-(+)-arabinose is a
molecule that is its optical isomer, but not its
mirror image. There are several such
diastereomers [e.g., structure **(b)** below].

17. (a) A dextrorotatory compound rotates the
plane of polarized light to the right (clockwise).
(b) A levorotatory compound rotates the plane
of polarized light to the left (counterclockwise).
(c) A mixture of equal parts of R- and
S-enantiomers **(d)** (R) is the designation given
to a chiral carbon atom when the group of lowest priority is directed away from the viewer

and the remaining groups are arranged such that they proceed from highest to lowest priority in a clockwise direction. **19.** A reducing sugar has enough of the straight-chain form present so that is will reduce Cu^{2+}(aq) to insoluble, red Cu_2O(s). **21.** They are not enantiomers because the rotational angles are different, and moreover they are of the same sign. **23. (a)** Enantiomers: *S*-config. (left structure), *R*-config. (right structure); **(b)** Different molecules: both *R*-configuration; **(c)** Diasteriomers: left structure *S,R*-configuration with *(S)* top and *(R)* bottom; right structure *S,S*-configuration; **(d)** Diasteriomers: left structure *R,R*-configuration; right structure *R,S*-configuration with *(R)* top and *(S)* bottom.

25. (a)

(b)

(c)

(d)

27. (a) An α-amino acid is a carboxylic acid that has an amine group and the carboxyl group attached to the same carbon atom. **(b)** A zwitterion is a form of an amino acid where the amine group is protonated and the carboxyl group is deprotonated. The zwitterionic form of glycine is $^+H_3NCH_2COO^-$. **(c)** The pH at which the zwitterionic form of an amino acid predominates in solution is known as the isoelectric point. The isoelectric point of glycine is $pI = 6.03$. **(d)** A peptide bond is the bond that forms between the carbonyl group of one amino acid and the amine group of another (with the elimination of H_2O). **(e)** Tertiary structure is the three-dimensional folding of the polypeptide chain in a protein.

29. (a)

(b)

(c)

31.

(a)

(b)

33. Proline will not migrate; lysine toward the cathode; aspartic acid toward the anode. **35. (a)** $^+H_3NCH(CHOHCH_3)COOH$ **(b)** $^+H_3NCH(CHOHCH_3)COO^-$ **(c)** $H_2NCH(CHOHCH_3)COO^-$ **37. (a)** Lys-Ser-Ala, Lys-Ala-Ser, Ser-Lys-Ala, Ser-Ala-Lys, Ala-Ser-Lys, Ala-Lys-Ser; **(b)** Ala-Ser-Ala-Ser, Ala-Ala-Ser-Ser, Ala-Ser-Ser-Ala, Ser-Ser-Ala-Ala, Ser-Ala-Ser-Ala, Ser-Ala-Ala-Ser **39. (a)** Ala-Ser-Gly-Val-Thr-Leu; **(b)** alanylserylglycylvalylthreonylleucine **41.** Primary structure: sequence of amino acids in the chain of the polypeptide. Secondary structure: folding, coiling, or convolutions of the protein chain. Tertiary structure: three-dimensional folding of the secondary structure of the

polypeptide chain in a protein. Quaternary structure: packing together of two or more protein molecules into a larger protein complex. Not all proteins have a quaternary structure since many proteins have but one polypeptide chain.

43.

45.

S-Alanine   *S*-Alanine

S-Phenylalanine   *S*-Phenylalanine

47. DNA and RNA: both contain sugars (deoxyribose and ribose), phosphate groups, and purine and pyrimidine bases. **49.** complementary sequence is TCG **Integrative and Advanced Exercises** **52.** 2.9×10^3 g/mol; more than one Ag^+ per protein might be needed **56.** $pI = 9.71$ **58.** nonapeptide: Arg Pro Pro Gly Phe Ser Pro Phe Arg **59.** AGA CCA CAA CGA **62.** Met is N-terminal. **(a)** Met Met Gly or Met Gly Met **(b)** Met Met **(c)** Ser Met **(d)** Met Met Ser or Met Ser Met **65. (a)** $K = 9.3 \times 10^{-5}$ **(b)** $K = 1.8 \times 10^5$ **(c)** $[B]/[A] = 2.5$; ratio: coupled/uncoupled $= 2.4 \times 10^4$. **Feature Problem 66. (a)** Saponification value = 189 for glyceryl tristearate, iodine number = 86.0 for glyceryl trioleate; **(b)** Castor oil: iodine number = 81.6, saponification value = 180; **(c)** For safflower oil: iodine number can range from 150 to 144 and saponification value from 211 to 179.

ANSWERS TO CONCEPT ASSESSMENT QUESTIONS AND SELF-ASSESSMENT EXERCISES

Note: Your answers may differ slightly from those given here, depending on the number of steps used to solve a problem and whether any intermediate results were rounded off.

CHAPTER 1

Concept Assessment Page 3. No, an experimental result contrary to that predicted by a hypothesis is reason to reject a hypothesis, not its proof. **Page 10.** The product (*mg*) is the same for the unknown and the "weights" of known mass, regardless of the value of *g*. The measured mass with a two-pan balance is the same on the moon as on Earth. The single pan electronic balance measures *weight*, which is converted to a "mass" reading. With such a balance calibrated on Earth, the "mass" will appear less when measured on the moon. **Page 11.** To find the *one* temperature, substitute $t(°C) = t(°F)$ into the equation $t(°F) = \frac{9}{5}t(°C) + 32$. Solve for $t(°F)$ to obtain the value -40 °F; thus -40 °F $= -40$ °C. **Page 14** The volume of wood is $1000\ g/(0.68\ g\ cm^{-3}) = 1470\ cm^3$. The wood displaces its own mass of water—1000 g, which has a volume of 1000 cm^3. The fraction of wood under water is $1000/1470 = 0.68$. **Page 18.** Yes to both questions. A measuring instrument might yield precise readings but be incorrectly calibrated—measurements might agree with one another but their average might not agree with the actual value. Measurements with an imprecise instrument might differ widely from the actual value, yet their average might, by chance, agree with the actual value. **Page 20.** The relationship 1 in = 2.54 cm is a definition—an *exact* quantity. A more precise relationship between meters and inches is 1 m = 100 cm × (1 in/2.54 cm) = 39.370079 in.

Self-Assessment Exercises 93. (e) 94. (a) 95. (c) 96. (d) and **(f) 97. (d) 98. (b) 99. (b) 100.** If no terminal zeros preceding the decimal point are significant, the order is **(e)** < **(a)** < **(c)** < **(b)** < **(d)**. Otherwise, uncertainties are in the placement of **(a)** and **(e)**, depending on whether any of their terminal zeros are significant. **101.** The correct response is **(d)**. Reason as follows: The mass of iron for **(a)** is 1000 g. By rough approximations see if any of the other choices is greater than 1000 g. Choices **(b)** and **(c)** are both less than 1000 g. In **(d)**, two fractions are required, the fractional mass of compound in the solution and the fractional

mass of iron in the compound: 10,000 mL × 1.3 g/mL × 0.30 × 0.344 ≈ 13,000 × 0.1 = 1300 g **102.** 0.114 mm **103.** When water exists as two or more states of matter in contact, the states are physically distinct regions with different properties; hence a heterogeneous mixture.

CHAPTER 2

Concept Assessment Page 36. Helmont assumed, incorrectly, that the tree interacted with its surroundings only through the soil, sunlight, and watering. The tree also interacted with the atmosphere, that is, with carbon dioxide gas (see photosynthesis, page 257). **Page 37.** The *final* mass, magnesium bromide plus unreacted bromine, equals the *initial* mass: 4.15 g + 82.6 g = 86.8 g, but without knowing the mass of unreacted bromine we cannot deduce the mass of magnesium bromide. **Page 43.** The discovery of cathode rays (electrons) refuted the idea that atoms are indivisible. The discovery of isotopes refuted the idea that all atoms of an element are alike in mass. The idea that atoms combine in simple numerical ratios remains valid. **Page 46.** The exception is the protium atom, ^1_1H, the most abundant isotope of hydrogen. It consists of a lone proton as the atomic nucleus. **Page 50.** The weighted average atomic mass of 51.9961 u, almost exactly 52 u, suggests that chromium might exist exclusively as $^{52}_{24}Cr$ atoms. Another possibility (which, in fact, is the case) is that chromium exists as a mixture of isotopes whose weighted average atomic mass is 51.9961 u. For zinc, we should conclude two or more isotopes. The weighted average atomic mass, 65.39 u, is too far from 65 u to suggest a single isotopic mass. **Page 55.** If all naturally occurring Au atoms have the mass 196.967g Au/N_A, they must all be $^{197}_{79}Au$, with no isotopes. If no Ag atom has the mass 107.868g Ag/N_A, there must be two or more naturally occurring isotopes. (In fact there are two: $^{107}_{47}Ag$ and $^{109}_{47}Ag$.)

Self-Assessment Exercises 91. (b) 92. (c) 93. (c) 94. (a) 95. (d) and **(f) 96. (c) 97. (d) 98. (b) 99.** FeO, with one Fe for every O atom, has the mass ratio 55.847 g Fe/15.9994 g O, or 3.491 g Fe/1.000 g O. The Fe/O mass ratio for the second compound is 2/3 of that for FeO, signifying two Fe for every three O atoms and the formula Fe_2O_3. For the third compound the Fe/O mass ratio is $^3/_4$ of that for FeO, signifying three Fe for every four O atoms and the

formula Fe_3O_4. **100.** Substitute $^{86}Sr = x$ and $^{87}Sr = 0.1686 - x$ as the fractional abundances of the two middle isotopes, together with the tabulated weighted-average atomic mass of Sr and other data into equation (2.3). Solve the equation to obtain $x = 0.09$, yielding the percent natural abundances of 9% for ^{86}Sr and 8% for ^{87}Sr. These results are only approximate because of the loss of significant figures in solving the equation. **101.** $1.3 × 10^{14}$ Au atoms. The successive conversions required are from mL seawater $\longrightarrow$ grams seawater $\longrightarrow$ kg seawater $\longrightarrow$ lb seawater $\longrightarrow$ ton seawater $\longrightarrow$ mg Au $\longrightarrow$ g Au $\longrightarrow$ mol Au $\longrightarrow$ Au atoms.

CHAPTER 3

Concept Assessment Page 70. For the *molecular* formula count the atoms in the condensed structural formula given: $C_4H_6O_2$. The *empirical* formula has the same ratio but with the smallest possible integers: $C_2H_3O_2$. Visualize the *structural* formula in terms of that of butane in Figure 3-2(a). Replace the—CH_3 groups at the two ends of the butane structure with —COOH groups (see structural formula of acetic acid in Figure 3-1). For the simplest *line-angle* formula, draw a line to represent H_2C—CH_2 and at an angle at each end of the line attach a —COOH group. **Page 74.** Compare the other four quantities to **(d)**—the 20.000-g brass weight. **(a)** 0.50 mol O_2 = 16.00 g; this might be the smallest mass but cannot be the largest. **(b)** $2.0 × 10^{23}$ Cu atoms = 1/3 mol Cu ≈ 21 g; this is now the largest mass. **(c)** $1.0 × 10^{24}$ H_2O molecules is more than 1.5 mol H_2O > 27 g; this is now the largest mass. **(e)** the mass of 1.0 mol Ne = 20. g. Conclusion: greatest mass, **(c)**; smallest mass, **(a)**. **Page 75.** C contributes the greatest number of atoms—13—and Cl contributes the greatest mass. A Cl atom, of which there are six, has nearly three times the mass of a C atom. **Page 79.** Obtain relative numbers of atoms in the formula by multiplying the molar mass by the mass fractions of the elements. In Example 3-5, for example, mol C = 0.6258 × 230 g × (1 mol C/12.011 g) = 11.98 mol C. Similarly, obtain 21.97 mol H and 3.995 mol H. Thus, the molecular formula is $C_{12}H_{22}O_4$ and the empirical formula is $C_6H_{11}O_2$. **Page 81.** In each combustion, 1 mol CO_2 forms for every mole C and 1 mol H_2O for every 2 mol H. Determine these amounts for each combustion: **(a)** 5 mol CO_2

and 2 mol H_2O; **(b)** 1.25 mol CO_2 and 2.5 mol H_2O; **(c)** 1 mol CO_2 and 1.5 mol H_2O; **(d)** 6 mol CO_2 and 3 mol H_2O. Thus, C_6H_5OH [response (d)] produces a greatest number of moles (and thus mass) of both CO_2 and H_2O. **Page 84.** The O.S. of N in NH_3 is -3. The O.S. of N is higher in H_2NNH_2; it is -2. Note also that the molar mass of N_2H_4 is 32 g/mol. **Page 94.** No. The greatest mass ratio of H_2O to CO_2 is found in CH_4, which has the highest percent H of all hydrocarbons; and its combustion produces only 2 mol H_2O (36 g) to 1 mol CO_2 (44 g). **Self-Assessment Exercises 106. (c) 107. (b) 108. (d) 109. (a) 110. (c) 111. (c) 112. (b) 113. (d) 114. (d) 115.** If the water of hydration constitutes about 50% of the mass of the hydrate, the mass of xH_2O must be about the same as the molar mass of Na_2SO_3. That is, $18.0x = 126$ and $x = 126/18 = 7$. The formula of the hydrate is $Na_2SO_3 \cdot 7 H_2O$. **116.** Molar mass of malachite = 221.12 g/mol $CuCO_3 \cdot Cu(OH)_2$. **(a)** % Cu = $[(2 \times 63.546)/221.12] \times 100\% = 57.48\%$ Cu **(b)** two mol CuO produced per mole of malachite; therefore, 1000 g malachite $\times (2 \times 79.545$ g CuO)/221.12 g malachite = 719.5 g CuO **117.** Use the method outlined in the Concept Assessment on page 79. The numbers of moles of the four elements per mole are 8 mol C, 9 mol H, 1 mol N, and 2 mol O. The molecular formula is $C_8H_9NO_2$. **118.** The 2.174-g sample contains 1.645 g C and 0.1912 g H. **(a)** percent composition: 75.67% C, 8.795% H, 15.45% O **(b)** empirical formula: $C_{13}H_{18}O_2$.

CHAPTER 4

Concept Assessment Page 114. (a) The product is $O_2(g)$, not $O(g)$. **(b)** The product is $O_2(g)$ exclusively, not a mixture of $O(g)$ and $O_2(g)$. **(c)** The product is KCl(s), not KClO(s). **Page 117. (a)** incorrect (3 mol S per *2 mol* H_2S) **(b)** incorrect (stoichiometric coefficients refer to moles, not grams) **(c)** correct (1 mol H_2O/1 mol H_2S is the same as 2 mol H_2O/2 mol H_2S) **(d)** correct (2 of every 3 mole of S on the left are in 2 mol H_2S, yielding 3 mol S on the right) **(e)** incorrect (3 moles of reactants yield 5 moles of product) **(f)** correct (no atoms can be created or destroyed in the reaction) **Page 119.** The reaction producing the greatest mass of $O_2(g)$ per gram of reactant is the one having the reactant of lowest molar mass. Clearly that reactant is $NH_4NO_3(s)$ in reaction **(a)**. **Page 124. (a)** Tripling the solution volume reduces the molarity to 1/3 of its initial value: 0.050 M NaCl. **(b)** Reducing the volume from 250.0 mL to 200.0 mL increases the molarity by 5/4, that is, to 1.000 M $C_{12}H_{22}O_{11}$. **(c)** The molarity of the first solution is reduced to 1/3, to 0.0900 M KCl; that of the second is reduced to 2/3, to 0.0900 M KCl. The total molarity of the final solution is 0.180 M KCl. **Page 127.** The balanced equation is $4 NH_3(g) + 5 O_2(g) \longrightarrow 4 NO(g) + 6 H_2O(l)$. Starting with 1.00 mol each of NH_3 and O_2, the limiting reactant is O_2. The amounts of

products are 0.80 mol NO and 1.20 mol H_2O. The only true statement is **(d)** all the $O_2(g)$ is consumed. **Page 130.** The answer must be consistent with the following facts. (1) The factor 0.90 must appear twice in the setup (which can include $0.90 \times 0.90 = 0.81$); (2) CH_3Cl is an intermediate and does not enter in; (3) the only molar masses needed are those of CH_4 (16 g/mol) and CH_2Cl_2 (85 g/mol). The correct response is **(a)**. **Self-Assessment Exercises 114. (d) 115. (d) 116. (a) 117. (c) 118. (d) 119. (d) 120. (a)** $2 C_8H_{18}(l) + 25 O_2(g) \longrightarrow 16 CO_2(g) + 18 H_2O(l)$ **(b)** $2 C_8H_{18}(l) + 23 O_2(g) \longrightarrow 12 CO_2(g) + 4 CO(g) + 18 H_2O(l)$, a reaction in which 25% of all C (4/16) end up as CO(g), as we were required to show. **121.** The ratio: molar mass CO_2/molar mass of calcite is 44.01 g CO_2/100.1 g $CaCO_3$ = 0.440 g CO_2/g $CaCO_3$. For magnesite the yield is 0.522 g CO_2/g $MgCO_3$, and for dolomite it is the average of the two: 0.481 g CO_2/g $CaCO_3 \cdot MgCO_3$. The observed value indicates that the sample was dolomite.

CHAPTER 5

Concept Assessment Page 146. (1). (e) 0.025 M $RbNO_3$(aq), the only strong electrolyte of the group. **(2). (a)** a strong electrolyte with a total ion concentration of 0.024 M. **Page 149.** Predicted as soluble based on guidelines in Table 5.1: **(a), (c), (g)**. Predicted as insoluble based on Table 5.1: **(b), (e), (h), (i)**. Inconclusive based on Table 5.1: **(d)** Li_2CO_3 might be soluble (Li^+ is a group 1 cation), but also might be one of the exceptions referred to in Table 5.1. **(f)** No data are available in Table 5.1 concerning permanagates, so the solubility of $Mg(MnO_4)_2$ is uncertain. **Page 153.** $H_2O(l)$ is suitable for K_2CO_3(s) and $ZnSO_4$(s), and HCl(aq) is suitable for CaO(s) and $BaCO_3$(s). H_2SO_4(aq) would not be suitable for CaO(s) and $BaCO_3$(s) because $CaSO_4$(s) and $BaSO_4$(s) might precipitate. **Page 157.** No reaction would occur in **(a)**. Two reduction half-reactions and no oxidation half-reaction. Reaction could occur under appropriate conditions in **(b)** because Cl_2(g) undergoes both oxidation and reduction. **Page 161.** This can occur as seen, for example, in the reverse of the disproportionation reaction directly above on this page. **Page 163.** An inaccurate statement. An oxidizing agent is necessary to oxidize Cl^-(aq) to Cl_2(g), but neither HCl(aq) or NaOH(aq) is an oxidizing agent. **Page 165.** An exactly neutral NaCl(aq) formed when 3.11×10^{-3} mol each of H^+ and OH^- ions neutralize one another. **Self-Assessment Exercises 96. (b) 97. (d) 98. (c) 99. (a) 100. (b) 101. (a) 102.** On average, the solution would have one H^+ ion and one Ac^- ion for every 19 HAc molecules.

CHAPTER 6

Concept Assessment Page 182. A water siphon passes over a "hump" from a pool of

water at a higher level to a receiver at a lower level. After the siphon is initially filled with water, the pressure of the atmosphere pushes water over the hump, beyond which the water flows freely. In a suction pump, air pressure pushes water up a partially evacuated pipe. **Page 188.** The direct proportionality of V and T must be based on an absolute temperature scale. While a change from 100 K to 200 K produces a doubling of V, a change from 100 °C to 200 °C produces only a 27% increase: $[(200 + 273)/(100 + 273)] = 1.27$. **Page 190.** Consider these facts. (1) V is directly proportional to the number of moles of O_2(g), and this must be 60.0 g O_2/32.00 g O_2 mol^{-1}. Only responses **(c)** and **(d)** meet this requirement. (2) The effect of changing P and T on the STP-volume must be expressed through the product $[(760 \text{ mmHg}/825 \text{ mmHg}) \times (303 \text{ K}/273 \text{ K})]$. The only correct response is **(d)**. **Page 198. (a)** 0.667 L SO_2(g)/1.00 L O_2(g), because the actual P and T are immaterial as long as the two gases are compared at the same t and P. **(b)** The 0.667-L SO_2(g) has to be adjusted for the an increase in T (by the factor 298 K/273 K) and a decrease in P (by the factor 760 mmHg/745 mmHg), leading to $V = 0.743$ L SO_2(g). **Page 200.** The correct responses— **(b)** and **(e)** —follow from basic ideas. Dalton's law of partial pressures dictates that P_{He} is not affected by any other gases present, and addition of 0.50 mol H_2 (1.0 g) will increase the total mass of gas by 1.0 g, independent of anything else that may happen. By simple estimates the other three statements can be shown to be false. **Page 204.** He(g) at 1000 K has twice the u_{rms} as at 250 K (change T to 4T in equation 6.20). At 250 K, u_{rms} of H_2(g) exceeds that of He(g) by the factor $\sqrt{2}$ (change M to $1/2$ M in equation 6.20). The two-fold increase in the first case exceeds the $\sqrt{2}$-fold increase in the second. He(g) at 1000 K has a greater u_{rms} than H_2(g) at 250 K. **Page 209.** The correct responses are **(a)** and **(c)**. The average kinetic energy of gas molecules depends only on T, and to two significant figures the mass of 0.50 mol He is the same as that of 1.0 mol H_2. **Page 211.** Rearrange equation (6.14) to the form $R = MP/dT$. Substitute molar masses, $P = 1$ atm (exactly), $T = 293.2$ K, and the density data. Solve for three values of R and see how closely they conform to the ideal gas constant $R = 0.08206$ L atm mol^{-1} K^{-1}. Increasing adherence to ideal gas behavior: $OF_2(R = 0.0724) < NO(R = 0.08194) < O_2(R = 0.08200)$. **Self-Assessment Exercises 114. (d) 115. (c) 116. (b) 117. (c) 118. (a) 119. (b) 120. (a) 121.** The best response is probably **(c)**. Ideal gas behavior is favored at high T and low P. Although T in **(d)** is higher than in **(c)** (400 °C compared to 200 °C), P is also much higher (10 atm compared to 0.50 atm); this pressure difference is probably more decisive than the temperature difference. **122.** Compare two columns with the radii r and $2r$, respectively.

The larger column has four times the cross-sectional area, volume, and mass of Hg(l) as the smaller column. But the force of gravity on this four-fold greater mass is distributed over a four-fold increase in area at the base of the column, yielding the same pressure as in the smaller column. **123.** Use the expression $M = dRT/P$ to determine the molar mass of the gas: $M = 58$ g/mol. In this gas there is 4.0 mol C and 10.0 mol H. The molecular formula is C_4H_{10}. **124.** Scale up the data in Table 6.3 by the factor $1/0.0379$, resulting in approximately 2060 squares for N_2, 550 circles for O_2, 25 marks for Ar(g), and one mark for CO_2(g).

CHAPTER 7

Concept Assessment Page 227. Dynamite exploding in an underground cavern is a close approximation to an isolated system. Titration of an acid with a base is an open system. A steam-filled cylinder in a steam engine with all valves closed constitutes a closed system. **Page 231 (1st).** Basic principle: law of conservation of energy. Assumptions: no heat loss to surroundings, d and *sp. ht.* of H_2O(l) independent of T. Because the mass of hot water is twice that of the colder water, the initial temperature difference of 60.00 °C is divided into a 40.00 °C warming of the cold water and a 20.00 °C cooling of the hot water; final $T = 50.00$ °C. **Page 231 (2nd).** The ΔT of a fixed mass of substance is inversely proportional to its specific heat; thus the object with the smaller ΔT has the greater specific heat. **Page 239.** The balloon feels warm because the dissolution of NH_3(g) in H_2O(l) is exothermic, $q < 0$. The balloon shrinks because the atmosphere (surroundings) does work on the system, $w > 0$. **Page 242.** In the bottom row T is uniform throughout the object while in the top row the object is hotter at the edges than in its interior. Heating in the top row is irreversible; the process is far from equilibrium. The bottom row represents reversible heating; removal of just a tiny amount of heat can change heating to cooling. **Page 243.** Enthalpy is a function of state. When a process returns a system to its initial state H returns to its initial value, meaning that $\Delta H = 0$. **Page 250.** The enthalpy change in forming 1 mol C_2H_2(g) from its elements is represented by the top line; that for forming 1 mol C_2H_4(g) is the next line down. Both of these lines are above the broken line representing $\Delta H = 0$. The formation of 1 mol C_2H_6 has $\Delta H < 0$ and is the first line below the broken line. $\Delta H°$ for the reaction of interest is represented by the distance between the first and third lines. **Page 257.** Yes, this can be done. The additional data needed are heat capacities as a function of T. The procedure is outlined in Figure 7-16. **Self-Assessment Exercises 112. (b) 113. (c) 114. (d) 115. (a) 116. (b) 117. (c) and (d) 118.** (1) Determine sp. ht. of Fe through the equation: $[1220 \text{ g} \times \text{sp. ht.} \times (34.4 - 126.5) °C] = -[981 \text{ g} \times 4.18 \text{ J g}^{-1} °C^{-1} \times (34.4 - 22.1) °C]$, yielding sp. ht. Fe = 0.449 J g^{-1} °C^{-1}. (2) Write a similar equation for the Fe/glycerol system. By introducing the appropriate factors and

canceling units, that equation reduces to $[1220 \times 0.449 \times (t - 99.8)] = -[325 \times 1.26 \times (219/92.1) \times (t - 26.2)]$, for which $t = 52.7$ °C. **119. (a)** N_2(g) + 1/2 O_2(g) $\longrightarrow$ N_2O(g) **(b)** S[s, rhombic] + O_2(g) + Cl_2(g) $\longrightarrow$ SO_2Cl_2(l) **(c)** CH_3CH_2COOH(l) + 7/2 O_2(g) $\longrightarrow$ 3 CO_2(g) + 3 H_2O(l) **120.** Write equations for (1) combustion of 1 mol C(graphite), (2) combustion of 1 mol CO(g), and (3) formation of 1 mol $COCl_2$(g) from CO(g) and Cl_2(g). Reverse equation (2) and add together the three equations and their ΔH values: -393.5 kJ + 283 kJ $-$ 108 kJ = $\Delta H_f° = -219$ kJ mol^{-1} $COCl_2$(g). **121.** $\Delta H_f° = 0$ for elements is arbitrarily set by convention. Enthalpies of formation of compounds must be determined by experiment. It is not impossible that a compound might have $\Delta H_f° = 0$, but it is highly improbable. **122.** In the relationship $\Delta H = \Delta U + \Delta(PV)$, because ΔH and ΔU are usually much larger than $\Delta(PV)$ they generally have the same sign. If ΔH and ΔU are close to zero, however, the sign and value of $\Delta(PV)$ may produce a situation in which ΔH and ΔU have different signs. **123.** In gas cooking, a vessel heats up quickly when in contact with the flame. The rate of combustion of the gas can be carefully controlled, and shutting off the gas quickly quenches the heat source. In typical electric cooking heat is transferred by conduction from a heated surface to the cooking vessel. Raising or lowering the temperature of the heated surface occurs more slowly; and because of its high heat capacity, the cooking surface remains hot for a rather long time after the current is turned off.

CHAPTER 8

Concept Assessment Page 282. The wavelength of red light is about 700 nm (see Fig. 8-3). Since frequency and wavelength are reciprocally related, doubling ν halves λ. The frequency-doubled light will have a wavelength about 350 nm—light in the near ultraviolet not visible to the human eye. **Page 285.** By studying emission spectra from the collision, scientists hope to identify the elements present in the comet and also on Jupiter's surface. **Page 289.** The threshold wavelength is 91.2 nm. Using 70.0 nm light as compared to 80.0 nm light produces more energetic electrons. Each photon produces one electron, and the number of electrons produced depends on the intensity (number of photons) of the light, provided its wavelength is less than the threshold wavelength. **Page 296.** The transition $n = 1$ to $n = 4$ corresponds to the greatest ΔE, but it involves *absorption* of a photon not emission. Photons are emitted in the other two transitions, with the transition $n = 4 \longrightarrow n = 2$ corresponding to the greater ΔE and hence shortest wavelength. **Page 299.** If the wavelengths are the same then the momenta are the same (equation 8.10). The speed of the proton will have to be $1/2000$th of the speed of the electron (that is, $m_p \times u_p = m_e \times u_e$, and $u_p = u_e \times m_e/m_p = u_e \times 1/2000$). **Page 302.** The state $n = 2$ has a peak $^1/_4$ of the

length from either end of the box, corresponding to the greatest probability of the particle being at those points. **Page 313.** An orbital with three angular nodes has $\ell = 3$; it is an f orbital. One radial node makes for a total of four nodes, and since the total number of nodes is $n - 1$, n must be 5. The orbital is a $5f$. **Page 323. 1.** (?) = Mn, and the leaders are **(i), (f), (l) 2.** [?] = Kr, and the leaders are **(j), (d)** or **(g) 3.** (?) = I, [?] = Kr, and the leaders are **(b), (c). 4.** (?) = U, [?] = Rn, and the leaders are **(a), (h), (k).**

Self-Assessment Exercises 122. Atomic orbitals of multielectron atoms resemble those of the H atom in having both angular and radial nodes. They differ in that subshell energy levels are not degenerate and their radial wave functions no longer conform to the expressions in Table 8.1. **123.** The effective nuclear charge is the positive charge at the nucleus that an electron experiences when shielding and penetration by other electrons are taken into account. **124.** The sketch should show that the basic difference is in the axis along which each p orbital is directed in the x, y, z axis system. **125.** The principal difference between a $2p_z$ and a $3p_z$ orbital is the presence of a radial node in the $3p_z$. Your sketch should convey information embodied in Figures 8-27b and 8-31. **126.** The correct response is **(a)**. Given that $\lambda = h/mu$, the larger the particle mass the smaller is the associated wavelength, which means that the shortest wavelength is associated with the α particle and the longest with the electron. **127. (a)** velocity (speed of light) is a fixed quantity in vacuum (2.998×10^8 m s^{-1}), independent of the frequency (color) of the light. **(b)** wavelength (λ) is inversely proportional to the frequency of light, as seen through equation (8.1), $c = \nu \cdot \lambda$, where c is a constant. **(c)** energy is directly proportional to frequency, as seen through Planck's equation (8.3), $E = h\nu$, whether expressed for a single photon or a mole of photons.

CHAPTER 9

Concept Assessment Page 346. (a) Ne **(b)** N^{3-} or P^{3-} **(c)** Zn^{2+}, Cd^{2+}, or Hg^{2+} **Page 350.** Z_{eff} increases and atomic radius decreases with increasing Z. The blue axis represents Z_{eff} and the blue line, Z_{eff} as a function of Z. The red axis represents atomic radius and the red line, atomic radius as a function of Z. **Page 352. (a)** B (at the top of group 13) **(b)** Cl (at the right end of the third period) **(c)** P^{3-} in period 3, group 15 (strong electron repulsions in an anion of high negative charge) **(d)** Tl (at the bottom of group 13) **Page 356. (a)** C (smallest group-14 atom, at the top of the group) **(b)** Kr (noble gas element in group 18) **(c)** Se (lower ionization energy than Br based on the expected trend; lower than As for the same reason as in the P/S comparison on page 355) **Page 357. (a)** group 17 (the smallest atoms in their periods) **(b)** group 2 (a filled ns subshell and essentially no affinity for an additional electron) **(c)** group 18 (noble gases have all shells and subshells closed) **Page 358. (a)** scandium (Sc^{3+} has noble gas electron configuration) **(b)** tellurium (Te^{2-} has a noble gas electron configuration) **(c)** manganese (Mn^{2+} has the electron configuration $[Ar]3d^5$) **Page 363. (a)** thallium **(b)** nitrogen **(c)** rubidium **(d)** iodine **(e)** aluminum **Self-Assessment Exercises 73. (b) 74. (a) 75. (d) 76. (b) 77. (a) 78. (d) 79.** The pairs Ar/K, Co/Ni, Te/I, and Th/Pa all have the first member with a lower atomic number and higher atomic mass than the second. The periodic table must be arranged by atomic number because only this order is consistent with the regularity in electron configurations that is the ultimate basis of the table. **80. (a)** 50 p **(b)** 69 n **(c)** 10 $4d$ electrons **(d)** two $3s$ electrons **(e)** two $5p$ electrons **(f)** four electrons in the valence shell ($5s^2 5p^2$) **81. (a)** F **(b)** Sc ($Z = 21$) **(c)** Te ($Z = 52$; which places it midway between Ar, $Z = 18$, and Rn, $Z = 86$) **82. (a)** C (top of the group) **(b)** Rb (first member of the period) **(c)** At (bottom of the group) **83. (a)** Ba **(b)** C **(c)** Bi (the order is Ba < Ca < Bi < As < S) **84.** Based on locations in the periodic table: Rb > Ca > Sc > Fe > Te > Br > O > F **85. (a)** A false statement; s orbitals have more electron density closer to the nucleus than do p orbitals. Therefore, s electrons shield other electrons from the nucleus more effectively than do p electrons. **(b)** True; because an s electron penetrates better than does a p electron it experiences a greater Z_{eff}. **(c)** This statement is true for all atoms except hydrogen, where $Z = Z_{eff} = 1$. **(d)** True, p electrons penetrate better than do d electrons. **(e)** The order given is the correct order. [To understand this order, recall the two exceptions to a regular increase in I with increasing Z in Table 9.4, and also the relationship between Z_{eff} and I in equation (9.6).] **86. (a)** This is not true; a $1s$ electron is closer to the nucleus than a $2s$ electron and experiences a Z_{eff} nearly equal to Z. **(b)** This is not true; the $2s$ electron penetrates closer to the nucleus and experiences a greater Z_{eff}. **(c)** This is true because Z_{eff} for a $2s$ electron is greater than for a $2p$ electron, making the $2s$ electron more difficult to ionize. **(d)** This is a true statement. Because of the greater penetration of a $2s$ electron, a $2p$ electron is more effectively shielded by a $2s$ electron than is a $2s$ electron shielded by a $2p$. **87.** These ionization energies are the reverse of electron affinities, for example, I for Li^- is minus EA for Li, that is, $+59.6$ kJ/mol. The variation of I with Z for these anions is the same as seen in Figure 9-10. **88.** I increases with Z but with small dips at C^+ and O^+ that can be related to the electron configurations of these unipositive ions (also refer to Table 9.4).

CHAPTER 10

Concept Assessment Page 375. The first and last symbols are acceptable; each has six dots with two unpaired. The unacceptable symbols have seven and five dots. **Page 378 (1st).** The bonds are all covalent, with one being coordinate covalent. **Page 378 (2nd).** groups 14, 15, and 16 (for example, the elements C, N, O, P, and S) **Page 381. (a)** Br **(b)** e **(c)** P **Page 390.** If covalent bonds between atoms involve equal contributions from all the bonded atoms, there are no formal charges. Where coordinate

covalent bonds are formed there will be formal charges. A polyatomic ion must have at least one atom with a formal charge, consistent with the charge on the ion. **Page 402.** ICl_2^- is a *linear* anion with five electrons pairs around the I atom (AX_2E_3). ICl_2^+ is a *bent* cation with four electron pairs around the I atom (AX_2E_2). The difference of one pair of electrons produces a completely different electron-group geometry and geometric shape. **Page 406.** In NH_3 the lone pair of electrons on the N atom pulls electron density away from the H atoms, creating a large resultant dipole moment. In NF_3 the highly electronegative F atoms pull electron density away from the N atom, producing highly polar N—F bonds that counteract the effect of the nitrogen lone pair and a greatly reduced resultant dipole moment. **Page 407.** Both the linear NO_2^+ cation and bent NO_2^- anion exhibit resonance that involves double bond character in the N—O bonds. However, electrons in the NO_2^+ cation will be more tightly held by the center of positive charge, leading to shorter N-to-O bond lengths in NO_2^+ than in NO_2^-. **Self-Assessment Exercises 118. (b) 119. (c) 120. (a) 121. (a) 122. (b) 123. (c) 124. (a)** The skeletal structure is Cl—O—Cl, with each atom surrounded by an octet of electrons. **(b)** Refer to the Lewis structure for PCl_3 on page 394 and replace the symbol Cl with F. **(c)** The Lewis structure should show three O atoms bonded to a central C atom, two of the C-to-O bonds as single and one as a double bond; two lone pairs of electrons on the doubly bonded O atom and three lone pairs of electrons on the singly bonded O atoms; three equivalent resonance structures. **(d)** Refer to the Lewis structure for PCl_5 on page 394 and replace P by Br and Cl by F. To accommodate 42 valence electrons add one lone pair of electrons to the central Br atom. **125. (a)** trigonal planar electron-group geometry (AXE_2) and a bent shape for SO_2 **(b)** tetrahedral electron-group geometry (AX_3E) and a trigonal-pyramidal shape for SO_3^{2-} **(c)** tetrahedral electron-group geometry (AX_4) and a tetrahedral shape for SO_4^{2-} **126.** Ba and Mg are active metals with a low EN, S is the most electronegative of the other three elements; Bi is more metallic than As, so Bi has the middle position in order of increasing EN: Ba < Mg < Bi < As < S. **127.** Three C—H bonds: 110 pm, 414 kJ/mol; one C—C bond: 154 pm, 347 kJ/mol; one C—Cl bond: 178 pm, 339 kJ/mol; one C-to-O double bond: 120 pm, 736 kJ/mol.

CHAPTER 11

Concept Assessment Page 430. The cation CH_3^+ is isoelectronic with BH_3 and has three pairs of electrons around the C atom; we expect sp^2 hybridization. In the anion CH_3^- there are four electron pairs suggesting sp^3 hybridization, as in CH_4. **Page 431.** The $sp^3 d^2$ hybridization scheme corresponds to six electron pairs around a central atom. Similar to PF_5 in the period above it, we expect the compound AsF_5. Now imagine adding F^- to AsF_5 to create $[AsF_6]^-$, which has 6 electron pairs

around the As atom and requires $sp^3 d^2$ hybridization. **Page 434.** Five bonding electron groups can be accommodated by $sp^3 d$ hybridization, but the distribution would be trigonal bipyramidal. What is needed is $sp^3 d^2$ hybridization in the species AX_5E. The lone-pair electrons are directed to a corner of an octahedron, and the remaining five positions determine the molecular geometry—square pyramidal. **Page 438.** To complete the octets of the N atoms, they must retain a lone pair of electrons, form a double bond between themselves, and a single bond to a H atom. The hybridization of the N atoms is sp^2. **Page 441.** The H_2^+ ion is formed by removal of one electron from H_2—a larger energy requirement than promoting a σ_{1s} electron to the σ_{1s}^* MO in the excited state of H_2. On the other hand, the bond order in H_2^+ is 0.5 and 0 in the excited state of H_2. H_2^+ is a stable species and the excited state of H_2 is not. **Page 445.** No. For example, the double bond in C_2 is made up of two π bonds and no σ bond (see Figure 11-25). **Page 447.** The molecule NeO is isoelectronic with F_2 and should have a bond order of 1. We expect it to be stable, but it has never been observed. **Page 452.** In HCO_2^- three atoms provide p orbitals for π bonding, just as in ozone. In the NO_3^- anion four atoms provide p orbitals. The delocalized π bonding in HCO_2^- is different than in NO_3^-. **Page 456.** GaN, a combination of group 13 and group 15 elements, is a semiconductor; this combination is equivalent to a group 14 semicondictor like Si or Ge. **Self-Assessment Exercises 86. (c) 87. (c) 88. (a) 89. (b) 90. (c) 91. (d) 92. (a) 93. (c) 94.** From VSEPR theory we conclude that BF_3 is a trigonal planar molecule (as seen in Table 11.1). The valence-bond method using pure s and p orbitals incorrectly predicts a trigonal pyramidal shape with 90° F-B-F bond angles. **95.** The Lewis structure of BrF_5 is based on 42 valence electrons; 40 are found in the octets around the five F atoms. The remaining two electrons are placed as a lone pair on the central Br atom (AX_5E). Six hybrid orbitals are required, and they must be $sp^3 d^2$. **96. (a)** 6 σ bonds **(b)** 2 π bonds **97.** The bond order in C_2 is two whereas that in Li_2 is one; C_2 has the greater bond energy.

CHAPTER 12

Concept Assessment Page 474. Because the ball drops faster through it, the 10W oil is less viscous than the 40W oil. Viscosity is inversely proportional to T, and the lower weight oil (10W) is preferred for low-temperature use (where higher weight oils might solidify). In hot desert regions higher weight oils (40W) are preferred because lightweight oils might become so mobile as to lose their lubricating properties. The strengths of intermolecular forces are directly related to viscosity, and hence the higher viscosity 40W oil has the stronger intermolecular forces. **Page 478.** Because of the different elevation (and barometric pressure) between land-locked, mountainous Switzerland and sea-level Manhattan Island, the lower boiling temperature results in a longer cooking time. **Page 479.** Hydrogen bonding occurs in NH_3 but not in N_2, resulting in stronger intermolecular attractions and consequently lower vapor pressures, a higher boiling point, and a higher critical temperature in NH_3 than in N_2. **Page 484.** Dew forms in the condensation of $H_2O(l)$ to $H_2O(l)$ and frost from the deposition of $H_2O(g)$ as $H_2O(s)$. Both processes are exothermic and give off heat to the surroundings—more heat in frost formation, because ΔH(deposition) = ΔH(condensation) + ΔH(freezing). **Page 489.** Wet books are placed in a cold, evacuated chamber. Moisture in the books freezes and the ice that is formed sublimes to $H_2O(g)$. This process avoids heating and involves a minimum of handling of the damaged books. **Page 493.** The greater number of electrons (much larger molar mass) in CCl_4 causes the intermolecular attractions (London dispersion forces) to outweigh the effect of the polar bonds in CH_3Cl. **Page 497.** The intermolecular interactions are both London dispersion forces and hydrogen bonds. In substances with small molecules, hydrogen bonding usually dominates. **Page 508.** According to the Bragg equation, $n\lambda = 2d \sin\theta$, if the extra distance traveled by the diffracted wave ($2d \sin\theta$) is to remain the same when n is doubled, the wavelength of the wave must be halved, so that $2n(\lambda/2) = n\lambda$. The required multiple is $^1/_2$. **Page 512.** The fcc unit cell contains four C_{60} molecules. The unit cell has four octahedral and eight tetrahedral holes occupied by 12 K atoms. The formula based on the unit cell is $K_{12}(C_{60})_4$, and the molecular formula is K_3C_{60}.

Self-Assessment Exercises 115. (c) 116. (c) 117. (b) 118. (a) 119. (d) and (f) 120. (a) $C_{10}H_{22}$; dispersion forces only and it has the higher molar mass **(b)** $(CH_3)_2O$; both compounds have about the same molar mass but $(CH_3)_2O$ is polar and C_3H_8 is not **(c)** CH_3CH_2OH; hydrogen bonding an important intermolecular force in CH_3CH_2OH but not in CH_3CH_2SH **121.** O_3 is the one that is out of place. The correct order of boiling points based on molar masses is $N_2 < F_2 < Ar < O_3 < Cl_2$ [O_3 is the only polar molecule in the group, but this is not important enough to put it after the more massive Cl_2 (bp: 162 K for O_3 and 239 K for Cl_2). **122.** The following listing reflects that organic compounds are lower melting than inorganic compounds, hydrogen bonding is an important intermolecular force for two of the compounds, and melting points of inorganic compounds are affected by ionic sizes and charges. $Ne < C_3H_8 < CH_3CH_2OH < CH_2OHCHOHCH_2OH < KI < K_2SO_4 < MgO$. **123.** Refer to the photograph on page 478 of water boiling under a reduced pressure. If the vapor is evacuated fast enough, to supply the required ΔH_{vap} the water may cool to $0°C$ and ice may begin to form. **124.** If there is too little $H_2O(l)$ in the sealed tube in Figure 12-11 initially, the liquid will all be converted to $H_2O(g)$ before T_c is reached. If too much

$H_2O(l)$ is present initially, the liquid will expand and cause the $H_2O(g)$ to condense. Only $H_2O(l)$ will be present at the time T_c is reached. **125. (a)** There is not enough $CCl_4(l)$ to produce $CCl_4(g)$ at the equilibrium vapor pressure of 110 Torr; only the vapor phase will be present. **(b)** Substitute vapor-pressure data at 25 °C and 77 °C into equation (12.2) and determine ΔH_{vap} (result: 32.2 kJ/mol). Determine number mol CCl_4 in 2.00 L $CCl_4(l)$ (result: 20.7 mol) and multiply by ΔH_{vap} (result: 667 kJ). **126. (a)** The diagonal of the face is 4r, where r is the atomic radius. It is also the diagonal of the red square pictured. The length of the unit cell l is the length of an edge of the red square. Use this information to determine that $l = 362$ pm. **(b)** $l^3 = 4.74 \times 10^7$ pm³ **(c)** 4 Cu atoms **(d)** Determine the total volume of 4 Cu atoms of radius r; express this as a percentage of the unit cell volume; the result is 74.1% **(e)** The mass of 4 Cu atoms is 4.221×10^{-22} g Cu **(f)** The mass of 4 Cu atoms divided by the volume of the unit cell is $d = 8.91$ g/cm³.

CHAPTER 13

Concept Assessment Page 532. Concentrations are independent of temperature if based solely on mass or temperature-independent properties related to mass, specifically, mass percent, molality, mole fraction, and mole percent. Concentrations based on volumes—volume percent and molarity—are temperature dependent. **Page 543.** HCl is undissociated in $C_6H_6(l)$, and the concentration of HCl in $C_6H_6(l)$ should closely follow $P_{HCl(g)}$ above the solution. On the other hand, HCl(g) reacts with $H_2O(l)$ to produce $H_3O^+(aq)$ and $Cl^-(aq)$. The relationship between $P_{HCl(g)}$ and the aqueous concentrations of ions is more complex. **Page 544.** Start with $(P_A° - P_A)/P_A° = x_B$. Note that $(P_A° - P_A)/P_A° = 1 - (P_A/P°_A)$. According to Raoult's law, $P_A = x_A P°_A$, which means that $P_A/P_A° = x_A$. Thus, we arrive at the true statement that $1 - x_A = x_B$. **Page 545.** This will happen if both components in an ideal solution have the same vapor pressure. The vapor pressure of the solution will be independent of the solution composition and the line will be parallel to the composition axis. The likelihood of this happening is not very great, although it might be found at one particular temperature where the vapor pressure curves of two liquids cross. **Page 549.** The similarities are that two different solutions are involved, water is transported from the more dilute to the more concentrated solution, and the process continues until the two solutions have the same concentration. The chief difference is that water is transported via the vapor phase in Figure 13-16a and through a semipermeable membrane in Figure 13-17. **Page 552.** If Figure 13-19 were based on water rather than some other solvent, the two fusion curves would have *negative* rather than positive slopes. However, there would still be a freezing-point depression and a boiling-point elevation. **Page 554.** When enough NaCl is present to depress the freezing point to

-21 °C, the NaCl(aq) is saturated. Any solute added beyond this point remains as undissolved NaCl(s) and can have no further effect on the freezing point of the solution.

Self-Assessment Exercises 109. (b) 110. (d) 111. (a) 112. (d) 113. (c) 114. Express concentration in g solute/100 g H_2O; the result obtained is 40 g $NH_4Cl/100$ g H_2O. From the graph, the solubility is seen to be about 42 g solute/100 g H_2O; the solution is unsaturated. **115. (a)** $[Na^+] = 0.16$ M **(b)** total ion concentration = 0.32 M **(c)** 8.1 atm **(d)** -0.60 °C **116. (a)** 7.80 M **(b)** 24.4 M **(c)** 34.0 m **(d)** $x_{glycerol} = 0.242$ **(e)** 75.8 mol % H_2O **117. 1.** lowest electrical conductivity: 0.15 m $C_{12}H_{22}O_{11}$(aq) (the only nonelectrolyte); **2.** lowest boiling point: 0.05 m NaCl (lowest total concenrtration of particles, 0.10 m) **3.** highest vapor presure: 0.05 m NaCl (lowest mole fraction of solute and highest mole fraction of water) **4.** lowest freezing point: 0.10 m KCl (highest total concentration of ions, 0.20 m).

CHAPTER 14

Concept Assessment Page 574. In the reaction $N_2(g) + 3 H_2(g) \longrightarrow 2 NH_3(g)$, compared to the rate of disappearance of N_2, the rate of disappearance of H_2 is three times as great and the rate of formation of NH_3 is twice as great. **Page 578.** If the initial and instantaneous rates of reaction are initially equal and remain so throughout a reaction, the concentration-time graph must be a straight line with negative slope, as seen in Figure 14-3. **Page 580.** If the reaction were first order the initial rate would double and if second order, quadruple, thus $1 < $ order (m) < 2. More precisely, $2^m = 2.83$ and $m = 1.50$ (solve this equation for m: $m \log 2 = \log 2.83$). **Page 587.** All four graphs can be plotted on the same sheet of paper. For example, take $[A]_0 = 3.0$ M and $k = 0.20$ s⁻¹ as the larger of two rate constants and $k = 0.10$ s⁻¹ as the smaller. Both concentration vs. time graphs will resemble Figure 14-5, but after starting at the same point, $[A]_0 = 3.0$ M, the one with the larger k has a shorter half-life and falls off more rapidly than the other. The two plots of $\ln k$ vs. t are straight lines, both starting at $\ln [A]_0 = \ln 3.0 = 1.10$, and having negative slopes, the steeper slope for the larger value of k. **Page 593. (a)** This condition can exist. The reaction is exothermic (similar to Figure 14-10). **(b)** This condition can exist, and the reaction is endothermic (imagine flipping the reaction profile in Figure 14-10 from left to right). **(c)** This condition cannot exist; E_a for an exothermic cannot be less than ΔH. **(d)** This condition can exist; its only distinction is that there is no heat of reaction. **(e)** This condition cannot exist; E_a cannot be negative. **Page 596.** Consider this equation from Figure 14-12: $E_a = R \times (-\text{slope of } \ln k$ vs. $1/T)$. The greater the value of E_a, the greater the slope of the graph and the more rapidly the rate of reaction changes with temperature.

Self-Assessment Exercises 100. (c) 101. (b) and (e) 102. (a) 103. (d) 104. (b) 105. (c) 106. In the first 100 s the concentration decreases to one-half its original value; $t_{1/2} = 100$ s and $k = 0.00693$ s⁻¹. The

instantaneous rate at 100 s is
$0.44 \text{ M} \times 0.00693 \text{ s}^{-1} = 3.0 \times 10^{-3} \text{ M s}^{-1}$.
107. (a) $t_{1/2} = 30.0$ min; after 60.0 min the concentration of reactant will be 25% of its initial value and the reaction will be 75% complete. **(b)** A zero-order reaction proceeds at a constant rate. If 50% of the reactant is consumed in 30.0 min, an additional 25% will be consumed in 15.0 min and the reaction will be 75% complete in 45.0 min. **108.** The reaction is second order because the half-life doubles in each successive half-life period (500 s in the 1st period, 1000s in the 2nd, and 2000s in the 3rd). Thus, the original 2.00 M has been reduced to 50% of its value (1.00M) in 500 s, 25% (0.50 M) in 1500 s and to 12.5% (0.25 M) in 3500 s. **109. (a)** $0.024 \text{ mol L}^{-1} \text{ min}^{-1}$ **(b)** [A] = 2.312 M (since the initial rate would be four times as great as in Experiment 1) **(c)** If the reaction is 1st order, $k = 0.693/35$ min $= 0.020 \text{ min}^{-1}$ and [A] = 1.3 M at $t = 30$ min in Experiment 2. **110. (a)** rate $= k_{\text{slow}}[A][B]$ (the same as the observed rate law) **(b)** rate $= (k_1 k_3/k_2)[A][B]^2$ (which is different than the observed rate law)

CHAPTER 15

Concept Assessment Page 628. Into the expression $K = [B]/[A]$, substitute [B] $= 54 - [A]$ and the given value of K; solve for [A] and [B]. If $K = 0.02$, [A] (open circles) $= 53$ and [B] (filled circles) $= 1$. If $K = 0.5$, [A] $= 36$ and [B] $= 18$. If $K = 1$, [A] $= [B] = 27$. **Page 630.** If $K > 1$ for the 2nd reaction, K for the 1st reaction will be the larger of the two, but if $K < 1$ for the 2nd reaction, K for the 1st reaction will be the smaller of the two. **Page 631.** Reverse given equation (invert its K value). To that equation add $CH_4(g) + H_2O(g) \rightleftharpoons CO(g) + 3 H_2(g)$; $CO(g)$ cancels and the overall equation is the one we seek; its K is the ratio of the other two K values. **Page 635.** The balanced equation is sufficient to determine the outcome of a reaction that goes to completion. If the reaction is reversible and reaches a state of equilibrium, the value of K is required as well. **Page 638. (a)** incorrect: would require that $CO(g)$ and $H_2O(g)$ be completely consumed—impossible with $K_p = 10.0$. **(b)** incorrect: would be violation of the law of conservation of mass. **(c)** incorrect; would require the consumption of some $CO_2(g)$, but the direction of net change must be in the forward reaction. **(d)** correct: an outcome that would result from a net change in the forward direction. **(e)** incorrect: sufficient data are given to calculate the composition of the equilibrium mixture. **Page 642. (a)** True—more $H_2(g)$ will form at the expense of the $H_2S(g)$ and $CH_4(g)$. **(b)** False—an inert gas has no effect on a constant-volume equilibrium condition. **(c)** True—K changes with T and so does the composition of the equilibrium mixture. **(d)** Uncertain—the partial pressures of $H_2S(g)$ and $CH_4(g)$ will rise because a net reaction occurs to the left, but the increase in partial pressures of $CS_2(g)$ and $H_2(g)$ caused by forcing these two gases into a smaller volume will be at least partly offset by the equilibrium shift to the left. **Page 643.** Equilibrium shifts in the

forward direction, the endothermic reaction. Student B, by holding the beaker, stimulates heat flow into the reaction mixture, probably achieving a higher yield of product.
Self-Assessment Exercises 87. (c) 88. (d) 89. (a) 90. (b) 91. (a) 92. (d) 93. Substitute the given data into $K_c = [C]^2/[B][A]^2$ to obtain $K_c = 1.9$. **94. (a)** increase (a net change to the right) **(b)** decrease (a net change to the left) **(c)** decrease (equilibrium favors the side with more moles of gas—the left) **(d)** no effect (catalyst only speeds the attainment of equilibrium) **(e)** decrease (raising T favors the endothermic reaction, the reverse reaction) **95. (a)** 0.0578 mol O_2 (the terms $[SO_3]^2$ and $[SO_2]^2$ cancel, leaving $[O_2] = 1/35.5$) **(b)** 0.231 mol O_2 (again, $[SO_3]^2$ and $[SO_2]^2$ cancel but "4" appears as an additional factor, leaving $[O_2] = 4/35.5$)

CHAPTER 16

Concept Assessment Page 668. (a) is a conjugate acid/base pair; HCO_3^- can transfer a proton to a base (e.g., OH^-) yielding CO_3^{2-}, and CO_3^{2-} can react with an acid (e.g., H_3O^+) to reform HCO_3^-. **(b)** is not a conjugate acid/base pair; SO_4^{2-} can be produced from HSO_3^- only through an oxidation process not in an acid–base reaction. **(c)** is not a conjugate acid/base pair; it is a pair of unrelated acids. **Page 671.** With pH $= \log[H_3O^+]$, the vast majority of solutions would have negative pH values. It is more convenient to incorporate the negative sign in the definition than to carry it in individual pH values. With pH $= -\ln[H_3O^+]$ the close relationship between pH and the powers of ten used in scientific notation would be completely lost. (The desire to establish this relationship was why the pH concept was devised in the first case.) **Page 680.** A concentrated solution of a weak acid may often have a lower pH than a dilute solution of a strong one. For example, the pH of 0.10 M $HC_2H_3O_2$—calculated as pH $= 2.89$ in Example 16-6—is lower than the pH of 0.0010 M HCl. **Page 687.** The relevant equations are $^+NH_3CH_2CH_2NH_3^+(aq) + H_2O(l) \rightleftharpoons H_3O^+(aq) + NH_2CH_2CH_2NH_3^+(aq)$ p$K_1 = 6.85$ and $NH_2CH_2CH_2NH_3^+(aq) + H_2O(l) \rightleftharpoons H_3O^+(aq) + NH_2CH_2CH_2NH_2(aq)$ p$K_2 = 9.92$. From equation (16.18), the values of the base ionization constants are p$K_{b_1} = 14.00 - 9.92 = 4.08$ and p$K_{b_2} = 14.00 - 6.85 = 7.15$. The base ionization reactions are $NH_2CH_2CH_2NH_2(aq) + H_2O(l) \rightleftharpoons NH_2CH_2CH_2NH_3^+(aq) + OH^-(aq)$ p$K_{b_1} = 4.08$ and $NH_2CH_2CH_2NH_3^+(aq) + H_2O(l) \rightleftharpoons {}^+NH_3CH_2CH_2NH_3^+(aq) + OH^-(aq)$ p$K_{b_2} = 7.15$ **Page 689.** Consider HPO_4^{2-}, which can act as an acid: $HPO_4^{2-}(aq) + H_2O(l) \rightleftharpoons H_3O^+(aq) + PO_4^{3-}(aq)$, $K_a = 4.2 \times 10^{-13}$ or as a base: $HPO_4^{2-}(aq) + H_2O(l) \rightleftharpoons H_2PO_4^-(aq) + OH^-(aq)$ $K_b = K_w/K_a = 1.00 \times 10^{-14}/4.2 \times 10^{-13} = 2.4 \times 10^{-2}$. Because K_b is much greater than K_a, $HPO_4^{2-}(aq)$ is basic. In a similar way, $H_2PO_4^-(aq)$ is seen to be acidic. Thus, depending on K values, ions in aqueous solutions may have pH values

ranging from acidic to neutral to basic.
Page 695. We should expect pK_a for ortho-chlorophenol to be smaller than for phenol because of the electron-withdrawing effect of the Cl atom. (Its pK_a is 8.55 compared to 10.00 for phenol.) **Page 697.** Picture three Br atoms joined by single bonds to a Fe(III) atom on which there is also a lone pair of electrons: Br_3Fe: Now imagine that a Br_2 molecule dissociates into Br^+ and Br^- ions. The electron-deficient Br^+, a Lewis acid, attaches to the lone-pair electrons of Fe(III), a Lewis base, forming $[FeBr_4]^+$. The final product is $[FeBr_4]^+Br^-$.
Self-Assessment Exercises 103. (a) 104. (c) 105. (d) 106. (e) 107. (c) 108. (b) 109. Determine the number of moles of H_3O^+ and OH^- that react to leave a slight excess of H_3O^+ in 40.20 mL solution, yielding a pH = 2.69. **110.** First determine the molarity of $HC_2H_3O_2(aq)$ that produces pH = 3.25. The product of this molarity and the 12.5 L of solution yields the number of moles of acetic acid required. The remainder of the problem involves the conversions: moles $\longrightarrow$ grams $HC_2H_3O_2 \longrightarrow$ grams $HC_2H_3O_2(aq) \longrightarrow$ mL $HC_2H_3O_2$ (answer: 37 mL). **111.** The salt is one of a strong base and weak acid and the anion hydrolyzes in water to produce a basic solution. The calculated pH = 8.58. **112.** The correct order by increasing pH is 0.10 M HI < 0.05 M H_2SO_4 < 0.05 M $HC_2H_2ClO_2$ < 0.50 M $HC_2H_3O_2$ < 0.50 M NH_4Cl < 1.0 M NaBr < 0.05 M $KC_2H_3O_2$ < 0.05 M NH_3 < 0.06 M NaOH < 0.05 M $Ba(OH)_2$. **113.** Solve the pair of equations pH $= 5 \times$ pOH and pH + pOH = 14.00 to obtain pH = 11.67. This is a rather strongly basic solution which can be obtained as 1.22 M $NH_3(aq)$.

CHAPTER 17

Concept Assessment Page 712. (a) no; NH_4Cl lowers the pH through the common-ion effect **(b)** yes, but only slightly. Diethylamine is a somewhat stronger base than NH_3, but only a rather small amount is being added. **(c)** no; HCl is a strong acid that will neutralize some of the NH_3, producing an aqueous solution of NH_3 and NH_4Cl. **(d)** no; since the added $NH_3(aq)$ is more dilute than the 0.10 M $NH_3(aq)$ the overall solution will be 0.075 M $NH_3(aq)$. **(e)** yes; $Ca(OH)_2(s)$ is a strong base. **Page 723. (a)** yellow; a low pH **(b)** yellow; a CH_3COOH/CH_3COO^- buffer solution is formed but its pH is about 5 **(c)** yellow; the buffer completely neutralizes the small amount of added OH^- **(d)** red; the buffer capacity is exceeded and the solution becomes basic. **Page 730.** Choice **(c)** is the correct one; 0.60 mol $NaC_2H_3O_2$, converts all the HCl to $HC_2H_3O_2$, producing a $HC_2H_3O_2/NaC_2H_3O_2$ buffer solution of pH ≈ 4. Choices **(a)** and **(b)** have essentially no effect on the pH, and while choice **(d)** would neutralize 80% of the acid, the amount of strong acid remaining would still produce a pH ≈ 1. **Page 731.** This is the titration of a weak base that ionizes in two stages (equations given in Concept Assessment answer for page 687). The titration curve would begin at a moderately high pH; the pH would drop during the titration, and there would be two equivalence points. In general, the curve would resemble that in Figure 17-13, but flipped from bottom to top. The two buffer regions and pH = pK_b values would be in segments of the curve between the two equivalence points. **Page 735.** (a) six species: K^+, H_3O^+, I^-, CH_3COO^-, OH^-, CH_3COOH (b) most abundant, K^+ (the spectator ion in highest concentration); 2nd most abundant, CH_3COO^- (produced in the neutralization of 3/4 of the CH_3COOH) (c) least abundant, OH^- (the final solution is acidic, so $[OH^-] < 10^{-7}$ M); 2nd least abundant, H_3O^+ (final solution a buffer with pH ≈ 5)

Self-Assessment Exercises

94. (a) $CHO_2^-(aq) + H_3O^+(aq) \rightleftharpoons$ $HCHO_2(aq) + H_2O(l)$; $HCHO_2(aq) + OH^-(aq)$ $\rightleftharpoons CHO_2^-(aq) + H_2O(l)$
(b) $C_6H_5NH_2(aq) + H_3O^+(aq) \rightleftharpoons$ $C_6H_5NH_3^+(aq) + H_2O(l)$; $C_6H_5NH_3^+(aq) + OH^-(aq) \rightleftharpoons$ $C_6H_5NH_2(aq) + H_2O(l)$
(c) $HPO_4^{2-}(aq) + H_3O^+(aq) \rightleftharpoons H_2PO_4^-(aq)$ $+ H_2O(l)$; $H_2PO_4^-(aq) + OH^-(aq) \rightleftharpoons$ $HPO_4^{2-}(aq) + H_2O(l)$ **95.** (a) equivalence point, pH = 7.00; bromothymol blue indicator (b) equivalence point, pH = 4.62; methyl red indicator (c) equivalence point, pH = 9.38; phenolphthalein indicator (d) equivalence point, pH = 10.6; alizarin yellow R indicator [neutralization to $PO_4^{3-}(aq)$ not possible]
96. (a) pH = 3.10 (b) pH = 4.20 (c) pH = 8.00 (d) pH = 11.08 **97.** (c) **98.** (d) **99.** (b)
100. (a) **101.** (b) **102.** (b) **103.** (a) above pH = 7; $Na_2CO_3(aq)$ at equivalence point strongly basic by hydrolysis of CO_3^{2-} (b) below pH = 7 because of hydrolysis of $NH_4^+(aq)$ at equivalence point (c) pH = 7; no hydrolysis of KI(aq) at the equivalence point.

CHAPTER 18

Concept Assessment Page 749. Because of the large excess of $MgF_2(s)$ the solution would remain saturated even when the volume of solution is doubled; $[Mg^{2+}]$ remains constant.
Page 759. It is largely immaterial. The only requirement is that the $AgNO_3(aq)$ be concentrated enough to bring about the precipitation without unduly diluting the solution from which the precipitation occurs. **Page 761.**
(a) At pH = 10.00, $[OH^-] = 1.0 \times 10^{-4}$ M and $[Mg^{2+}] = 1.8 \times 10^{-3}$ M, an entirely plausible result. (b) At pH = 5.00, $[OH^-] = 1 \times 10^{-9}$ M and $[Mg^{2+}] = 1.8 \times 10^7$ M, and impossible result. The situation here is that at pH = 5.00 the solution is not one of $Mg(OH)_2$. It is $MgCl_2(aq)$, and $[Mg^{2+}]$ in this solution depends on the solubility of $MgCl_2$.
Page 765. As expected, with $[Cl^-] = 0.0039$ M, the molar solubility of AgCl(s) is less than in pure water because of the common-ion effect. At higher concentrations of $Cl^-(aq)$, AgCl(s) becomes more soluble because of complex ion formation: AgCl(s) + $Cl^-(aq) \longrightarrow$ $[AgCl_2]^-(aq)$. **Page 768.** $Pb^{2+}(aq)$ is present because of the formation of the yellow $PbCrO_4(s)$; $Hg_2^{2+}(aq)$ is absent because of the negative test for that ion; the presence of

$Ag^+(aq)$ is uncertain because it really wasn't tested for. **Page 769.** Will not work because both ions would precipitate: $(NH_4)_2CO_3$, $H_2S(aq)$, and NaOH(aq); will not work because neither ion would precipitate: $HNO_3(aq)$ and $NH_3(aq)$. HCl(aq) will work because $CuCl_2$ is water soluble and AgCl is not.
Self-Assessment Exercises 92. The correct response is (d) because it is consistent with the formula PbI_2 and response (a) is incorrect because it is not consistent with the formula. Responses (b) and (c) are incorrect because the correct relationship between $[Pb^{2+}]$ and K_{sp} is $[Pb^+] = [1/4 \times K_{sp}]^{1/3}$. **93.** (a) **94.** (c) **95.** (b) **96.** (c) and (d) **97.** (a) **98.** (c)
99. (a) $H_2C_2O_4(s)$, an acid, more soluble in a basic solution (b) $MgCO_3(s)$ more soluble in acidic solution; CO_3^{2-} is a base. (c) CdS(s) is more soluble in acidic solution, but K_{sp} is so small that CdS is essentially insoluble even in strongly acidic solutions. (d) solubility of KCl(s) unaffected by solution pH. (e) solubility of $NaNO_3(s)$ also independent of pH (f) $Ca(OH)_2(s)$, a strong base, is more soluble in an acidic solution. **100.** NaOH(aq) precipitates both, and HCl(aq) and $NH_4Cl(aq)$ precipitate neither. $NH_3(aq)$ precipitates $Mg(OH)_2(s)$ from solution but forms the soluble complex $[Cu(NH_3)_4](OH)_2(aq)$. **101.** $Al(OH)_3(s)$ will precipitate. $[OH^-]$ in the acetic acid-acetate ion buffer is 4.3×10^{-10} M, but the ion product $[Al^{3+}][OH^-]^3$ exceeds K_{sp}. **102.** There is no precipitate because $[Ag^+]$ in equilibrium with $[Ag(CN)_2]^-$ is too low for K_{sp} of AgI to be exceeded. **103.** In both cases K for the dissolution reaction is similar to reaction (18.5), for which $K = K_{sp} \times K_f$. This K is an exceedingly small quantity for (a) but large for (b). $CuCO_3(s)$ is soluble in $NH_3(aq)$ and CuS(s) is not.

CHAPTER 19

Concept Assessment Page 782. No, spontaneous and non-spontaneous refer to the thermodynamics of a process, not the kinetics. A non-spontaneous process will not occur without external intervention, and a spontaneous reaction is not necessarily fast; it can occur very slowly. **Page 787.** Doubling the volume available to the gas in Figure 19-1 is equivalent to doubling the length of the box from L to $2L$ in Figure 19-3a. The expansion of the gas in Figure 19-1 seems driven by a tendency to fill all the available volume. The gas expansion can also be explained, however, as the tendency of the system energy to be distributed among the greater number of available energy levels in the $2L$ box compared to the L box. **Page 797.** ΔH as a function of T is a straight line with only a slight slope (positive or negative), in the negative energy region. The $T\Delta S$ line, in the same energy region, has a steep negative slope and intersects the ΔH line. The distance between the two lines ($\Delta H - T\Delta S$) represents ΔG. At the point of intersection, $\Delta G = 0$, at T below the intersection $\Delta G < 0$, and at T above the intersection $\Delta G > 0$.
Page 809. $H_2O(l, 1 \text{ atm}) \rightleftharpoons H_2O(g, 1 \text{ atm})$, is a process in which $\Delta H > 0$ and $\Delta S > 0$, as

represented by Figure 19-9. Below 100 °C, condensation of $H_2O(g, 1 \text{ atm})$ is favored and at 100 °C (the normal boiling point) condensation and vaporization are at equilibrium and $\Delta G = 0$. At 120 °C, vaporization predominates, $\Delta G < 0$, and $T\Delta S > \Delta H$.
Self-Assessment Exercises 95. (d) **96.** (c)
97. (a) **98.** (b) **99.** (a) and (d)
100. (a) 113.6 °C, the normal melting point of $I_2(s)$ (b) $\Delta G° = 0$, because solid and liquid are at equilibrium and also in their standard states **101.** (a) No reaction is expected because of the decrease in entropy and the expectation that the reaction is endothermic. As a check, with data from Appendix D, $\Delta G° = 326.4$ kJ for the reaction as written—a very large value.
(b) Based on the increase in entropy, the forward reaction should occur, at least to some extent. For this reaction, $\Delta G° = 75.21$ kJ.
(c) ΔS is probably small, and ΔH is probably also small (one Cl—Cl bond and one Br—Br bond are broken and two Br—Cl bonds are formed). $\Delta G°$ should be small and the forward reaction should occur to a significant extent. For this reaction $\Delta G° = -5.07$ kJ.
102. (a) Entropy change must be assessed for the system *and* its surroundings (S_{univ}), not just for the system alone. (b) An equilibrium constant can be calculated from $\Delta G°$ ($\Delta G° = -RT \ln K$), and K permits equilibrium calculations for nonstandard conditions. **103.** (a) Determine $\Delta H°_{vap}$ from $\Delta H°_f$ values. Use equation (19.4) to solve for $T_{bp} = 57$ °C (b) Assume that $\Delta H°_{vap}$ and $\Delta S°_{vap}$ are independent of T and $\Delta G°_{vap,298 \text{ K}} = 2.8$ kJ/mol (c) Because $\Delta G°_{vap,298 \text{ K}} > 0$, the vapor pressure is less than 1 atm at 298 K, consistent with $T_{bp} = 57$ °C
104. (a) exothermic, with $\Delta H = -124.0$ kJ
(b) $\Delta G° = -186.1$ kJ (c) $K = 4.1 \times 10^{32}$
(d) The reaction has $\Delta H < 0$, $\Delta S > 0$, and $\Delta G < 0$; it is spontaneous at all temperatures.

CHAPTER 20

Concept Assessment Page 827. At the anode, Zn(s) is oxidized to $Zn^{2+}(aq)$ and, to preserve charge balance, $NO_3^-(aq)$ migrates in from the salt bridge. At the cathode, $Cu^{2+}(aq)$ is reduced to Cu(s) and, to preserve charge balance, $K^+(aq)$ migrates in from the salt bridge.
Page 829. No changes in mass at the inert Pt(s) electrodes; a gain in mass at the Cu(s) electrode through the half reaction $Cu^{2+}(aq) + 2e^- \longrightarrow Cu(s)$; and a loss in mass at the Zn(s) electrode through the half reaction Zn(s) $\longrightarrow Zn^{2+}(aq) + 2e^-$.
Page 831. Standard-state conditions for $ClO_4^-(aq)$ and $H^+(aq)$ are $a \approx 1$ M; for $Cl_2(g)$, $a = 1$ bar ≈ 1 atm; for $H_2O(l)$, $a = 1$.
Page 836. The cell with $E° > 0$ proceeds toward the formation of more products. A net reaction also occurs in the case where $E° < 0$, but in the reverse direction; the concentrations on the left side of the equation increase and those on the right decrease, until equilibrium is reached. **Page 837.** $E_{cell} = E°_{cell}$ if all reactants and products are in their standard states, but also for any set of concentrations where $Q = 1$ in equation (20.18). **Page 839.** The precipitate is $PbSO_4(s)$, thereby reducing $[Pb^{2+}]$ in

the anode compartment and increasing the value of E_{cell}, so that $E_{cell} > E°_{cell}$. **Page 840.** The cell diagram $Pt(s)|Cl_2(g, 1\ atm)|Cl^-(0.50\ M)\|$ $Cl^-(0.10\ M)|Cl_2(g, 1\ atm)|Pt(s)$ has the net cell reaction: $0.50\ M\ Cl^-(aq) \longrightarrow 0.10\ M\ Cl^-(aq)$ and $E_{cell} = -0.0592\ V \times \log(0.10/0.50) = 0.041\ V$. **Page 846.** Dry cells and lead-acid cells "run down" as the concentrations of reactants and products eventually reach their equilibrium values, where ΔG and E_{cell} both become 0. This does not happen in a fuel cell because fuel is continuously added. **Page 848.** Both Al and Zn can be used because they are more active than Fe; Ni and Cu are less active and cannot be used.

Self-Assessment Exercises 99. (c), (e), and **(g) 100. (b) 101. (d) 102. (c) 103. (a) 104. (d) 105. (a) 106.** The reaction $3\ Zn(s) + 8\ H^+(aq) + 2\ NO_3^-(aq) \longrightarrow$ $3\ Zn^{2+}(aq) + 4\ H_2O(l) + 2\ NO(g)$ occurs in the cell: (anode) $Zn(s)|Zn^{2+}(1\ M)\|$ $H^+(1\ M), NO_3^-(1\ M)|NO(g, 1atm)|Pt(s)$ (cathode); $E°_{cell} = 1.719\ V$ **107.** pH = 1.82 **108. (a)** Use equation (20.16) to determine $K = 0.0223\ V$. Since for the given conditions $Q = 1.00$, the system is not at equilibrium. **(b)** Because $Q > K$, a net reaction occurs to the left. **109. (a)** $Fe(s) + Cu^{2+}(1\ M) \longrightarrow$ $Fe^{2+}(1\ M) + Cu(s)$; $E°_{cell} = -0.780\ V$ electrons flow from B to A. **(b)** $Sn^{2+}(1\ M) + 2\ Ag^+(1\ M) \longrightarrow Sn^{4+}(1\ M) + 2\ Ag(s)$; $E°_{cell} = 0.646\ V$; electrons flow from A to B. **(c)** $Zn(s) + Fe^{2+}(0.0010\ M) \longrightarrow$ $Zn^{2+}(0.10\ M) + Fe(s)$; $E_{cell} = 0.264\ V$ electrons flow from A to B. **110. (a)** $Cl_2(g)$ at anode and $Cu(s)$ at cathode **(b)** $O_2(g)$ at anode and $H_2(g)$ and $OH^-(aq)$ at cathode **(c)** $Cl_2(g)$ at anode and $Ba(l)$ at cathode **(d)** $O_2(g)$ at anode and $H_2(g)$ and $OH^-(aq)$ at cathode.

CHAPTER 21

Concept Assessment Page 879. By the diagonal relationship lithium and magnesium will be similar. Because $Mg(s)$ reacts with $N_2(g)$ we expect $Li(s)$ to do the same. The reactions are $3\ Mg(s) + N_2(g) \longrightarrow Mg_3N_2(s)$ and $6\ Li(s) + N_2(g) \longrightarrow 2\ Li_3N(s)$. **Page 882.** A plausible reaction is that $Mg(s)$ is oxidized to $MgO(s)$ and $CO_2(g)$ is reduced to $C(s)$, that is, $2\ Mg(s) + CO_2(g) \longrightarrow 2\ MgO(s) + C(s)$. **Page 884.** The small size of Be^{2+} precludes the possibility of six H_2O molecules coordinating to the central Be^{2+} ion, whereas this happens readily with the Mg^{2+} ion. **Page 888.** The structure of $B_2H_2(CH_3)_4$ is analogous to diborane (Fig. 21-11a) with two bridging H atoms and four methyl groups ($—CH_3$) in the terminal positions. **Page 895.** AlF_3 is an electron-deficient compound and forms $[AlF_4]^-$ in the presence of F^- from KF. BF_3 is a stronger Lewis acid than AlF_3 and abstracts a F^- ion from $[AlF_4]^-$. The result: $[AlF_4]^- + BF_3 \longrightarrow AlF_3(s) + [BF_4]^-$. **Page 898.** Determine $\Delta H°$ for each reaction using equation (7.21), the only difference is replacing 1 mol CO_2 in equation (21.27) by 1 mol CO in equation (21.28). The difference in the heat of reaction is $-110.5\ kJ/mol\ CO(g) -$ $[-393.5\ kJ/mol\ CO_2(g)] = 283\ kJ$. Reaction

(21.28) liberates 238 kJ less heat than reaction (21.27). **Page 903.** Refer to pages 901 and 902 and imagine a chain of tetrahedra starting with SiO_4^{4-} and increasing in increments of SiO_3^{2-}, yielding SiO_4^{4-}, $Si_2O_7^{6-}$, $Si_3O_{10}^{8-}$ $Si_4O_{13}^{10-}$, $Si_5O_{16}^{12-}$, $Si_6O_{19}^{14-}$. Now bend the six-unit silicate chain into a hexagonal ring (similar to that in the third structure on page 902) by eliminating one O^{2-} between the ends of the chain. The result is the anion $Si_6O_{18}^{12-}$. In beryl, $3\ Be^{2+}$ and $2\ Al^{3+}$ provide the necessary 12 units of positive charge.

Page 908. Dissolved $O_2(g)$ in $Sn^{2+}(aq)$ is able to oxidize Sn^{2+} to Sn^{4+}. The following spontaneous reaction reduces tin (IV) to tin (II): $Sn^{4+}(aq) + Sn(s) \longrightarrow 2\ Sn^{2+}(aq)$; $E°_{cell} = 0.154\ V - (-0.137\ V) = 0.017\ V$. Thus, as long as an excess of $Sn(s)$ is present, the $Sn^{2+}(aq)$ can be maintained with little or no $Sn^{4+}(aq)$ present.

Self-Assessment Exercises 78. (c) 79. (f) 80. (d) 81. (b) 82. (a) $Li_2CO_3(s) \xrightarrow{\Delta} Li_2O(s) + CO_2(g)$ **(b)** $CaCO_3(s) + 2\ HCl(aq) \longrightarrow$ $CaCl_2(aq) + H_2O(l) + CO_2(g)$ **(c)** $2\ Al(s) + 2\ NaOH(aq) + 6\ H_2O(l) \longrightarrow$ $2\ Na[Al(OH)_4](aq) + 3\ H_2(g)$ **(d)** $BaO(s) + H_2O(l) \longrightarrow Ba(OH)_2$ (aq, limited solubility) **(e)** $2\ Na_2O_2(s) + 2\ CO_2(g) \longrightarrow$ $2\ Na_2CO_3(s) + O_2(g)$ **83. (a)** $MgCO_3(s) + 2\ HCl(aq) \longrightarrow$ $MgCl_2(aq) + H_2O(l) + CO_2(g)$ **(b)** $2\ Na(s) + 2\ H_2O(l) \longrightarrow$ $2\ NaOH(aq) + H_2(g)$ followed by the reaction in Exercise 82(c) **(c)** $2\ NaCl(s) + H_2SO_4(concd.\ aq) \xrightarrow{\Delta}$ $Na_2SO_4(s) + 2\ HCl(g)$ **84. (a)** $K_2CO_3(aq) + Ba(OH)_2(aq) \longrightarrow$ $BaCO_3(s) + 2\ KOH(aq)$ **(b)** $Mg(HCO_3)_2(aq)$ $\xrightarrow{\Delta} MgCO_3(s) + H_2O(l) + CO_2(g)$ **(c)** $SnO(s) + C(s) \xrightarrow{\Delta} Sn(l) + CO(g)$ **(d)** $CaF_2(s) + H_2SO_4(concd.\ aq) \xrightarrow{\Delta}$ $CaSO_4(s) + 2\ HF(g)$ **(e)** $NaHCO_3(s) + HCl(aq) \longrightarrow$ $NaCl(aq) + H_2O(l) + CO_2(g)$ **(f)** $PbO_2(s) + 4\ HBr(aq) \longrightarrow$ $PbBr_2(s) + Br_2(l) + 2\ H_2O(l)$ **(g)** $SiF_4(g) + 4\ Na(l) \longrightarrow Si(s) + 4\ NaF(s)$ **85.** $CaSO_4 \cdot 2\ H_2O(s) + (NH_4)_2CO_3(aq) \longrightarrow$ $CaCO_3(s) + (NH_4)_2SO_4(aq) + 2\ H_2O(l)$ (reaction proceeds to the right because K_{sp} for $CaCO_3 < K_{sp}$ for $CaSO_4$) **86. (a)** $2\ B(OH)_3(s) \xrightarrow{\Delta} B_2O_3(s) + 3\ H_2O(g)$ **(b)** no reaction **(c)** $CaSO_4 \cdot 2\ H_2O(s)[gypsum] \xrightarrow{\Delta}$ $CaSO_4 \cdot \frac{1}{2}\ H_2O(s)[plaster\ of\ Paris] + 3/2\ H_2O(g)$ **87. (a)** $Pb(NO_3)_2(aq) + 2\ NaHCO_3(aq) \longrightarrow$ $PbCO_3(s) + 2\ NaNO_3(aq) + H_2O(l) + CO_2(g)$ [In $NaHCO_3(aq)$ the concentration of $CO_3^{2-}(aq)$ is high enough that K_{sp} of $PbCO_3$ is exceeded.] **(b)** $Li_2O(s) + (NH_4)_2CO_3(aq) \longrightarrow Li_2CO_3(s) + 2\ NH_3(g) + H_2O(l)$ [$Li_2O(s)$ is the anhydride of the strong base LiOH, which reacts with acidic $NH_4^+(aq)$ to liberate $NH_3(g)$; $Li_2CO_3(s)$ is only slightly sol-

uble, so most of it precipitates.] **(c)** $H_2SO_4(aq) + BaO_2(aq) \longrightarrow$ $H_2O_2(aq) + BaSO_4(s)$ [The forward reaction is favored by the formation of a precipitate, $BaSO_4(s)$.] **(d)** $2\ PbO(s) + Ca(OCl)_2(aq) \longrightarrow$ $CaCl_2(aq) + 2\ PbO_2(s)$ [Hypochlorite ion oxidizes lead(II) oxide to lead(IV) oxide.] **88. (a)** Stalactites are primarily $CaCO_3(s)$. **(b)** Gypsum is $CaSO_4 \cdot 2\ H_2O(s)$. **(c)** The bathtub ring is the insoluble calcium salts of long-chain carboxylic acids, such as calcium palmitate, $Ca[(CH_3)(CH_2)_{14}COO]_2(s)$. **(d)** a suspension of $BaSO_4(s)$ in water **(e)** $Al_2O_3(s)$ with Fe^{3+} and Ti^{4+} replacing some Al^{3+} in the crystal structure. **89.** Dolomite, molar mass of 184.4 g/mol, yields 2 mol $CO_2(g)$ per mol dolomite on decomposition. The 5.00×10^3 kg sample yields 5.42×10^4 mol CO_2 which, under the stated conditions, occupies a volume of 1.27×10^3 m^3. **90.** The 77.5 ppm $Ca^{2+}(aq)$ produces $[H_3O^+] = 3.87 \times 10^{-3}$ M or pH = 2.412.

CHAPTER 22

Concept Assessment Page 920. The larger EN difference and shorter bond length between Xe and F, compared to Xe and Cl, makes XeF_2 a more stable molecule than $XeCl_2$. **Page 928.** The ions do not have the same shape. ICl_2^+ (VSEPR notation, AX_2E_2) has a tetrahedral electron-group geometry and a bent molecular shape. ICl_2^- (VSEPR notation, AX_2E_3) has a trigonal-bipyramidal electron-group geometry, and a linear molecular shape. **Page 930.** $CuSO_4(aq)$ yields $Cu(s)$ at the Pt cathode and $O_2(g)$ at the Pt anode, and $NaI(aq)$ yields I_2 at the anode and $H_2(g)$ at the cathode. The other three solutions— $H_2SO_4(aq)$, $NaOH(aq)$, and $KNO_3(aq)$—all yield $H_2(g)$ at the cathode and $O_2(g)$ at the anode. **Page 937.** The Cl in OCl_2 shows more positive character (blue color) than does F in OF_2 because the electronegativity of Cl is considerably less than that of F. **Page 946.** The Br atom is larger than the Cl atom. A central P atom can accommodate only four Br atoms, as in the tetrahedral PBr_4^+ ion. But the central P atom can accommodate either four Cl atoms, as in the tetrahedral PCl_4^+ ion, or six, as in the octahedral PCl_6^- ion. **Page 955.** The ion NH_2^- is isoelectronic with H_2O. The bent shape is more stable than the linear shape because two σ molecular orbitals are occupied (see Figure 22-23). This observation is consistent with the VSEPR and valence-bond theories.

Self-Assessment Exercises 100. (b) 101. (d) 102. (c) 103. (a) 104. (d) 105. (b) 106. (a) and **(d) 107. (a)** $Cl_2(g) + 2\ NaOH(aq) \longrightarrow NaCl(aq) + NaOCl(aq) + H_2O(l)$ **(b)** $2\ NaI(s) + 2\ H_2SO_4(concd\ aq) \xrightarrow{\Delta}$ $Na_2SO_4(s) + 2\ H_2O(g) + SO_2(g) + I_2(g)$ **(c)** $Cl_2(g) + 2\ KI_3(aq) \longrightarrow 2\ KCl(aq) + 3\ I_2(s)$ **(d)** $3\ NaBr(s) + H_3PO_4(concd\ aq) \xrightarrow{\Delta}$ $Na_3PO_4(s) + 3\ HBr(g)$ **(e)** $5\ HSO_3^-(aq) + 2\ MnO_4^-(aq) + H^+(aq) \longrightarrow 5\ SO_4^{2-}(aq) + 2\ Mn^{2+}(aq) + 3\ H_2O(l)$ **108. (a)** $2\ KClO_3(s) \xrightarrow{\Delta} 2\ KCl(s) + 3\ O_2(g)$

[a catalyst such as MnO_2 is required; electrolysis of H_2O is an alternate method]
(b) $3 Cu(s) + 8 H^+(aq) + 2 NO_3^-(aq) \longrightarrow$ $3 Cu^{2+}(aq) + 4 H_2O(l) + 2 NO(g)$ [difficult to control reaction so that $NO(g)$ is the only reduction product] **(c)** $Zn(s) + 2 H^+(aq) \longrightarrow$ $Zn^{2+}(aq) + H_2(g)$ [a number of other metals can be used] **(d)** $NH_4Cl(aq) + NaOH(aq)$

$\xrightarrow{\Delta} NaCl(aq) + H_2O(l) + NH_3(g)$ [other ammonium salts and other bases work as well]
(e) $CaCO_3(s) + 2 HCl(aq) \longrightarrow$ $CaCl_2(aq) + H_2O(l) + CO_2(g)$ [other carbonates and acids can be used]
109. (a) $LiH(s) + H_2O(l) \longrightarrow$ $LiOH(aq) + H_2(g)$ **(b)** $C(s) + H_2O(g) \longrightarrow$ $CO(g) + H_2(g)$ **(c)** $3 NO_2(g) + H_2O(l) \longrightarrow$ $2 HNO_3(aq) + NO(g)$
110. $3 Cl_2(g) + I^-(aq) + 3 H_2O(l) \longrightarrow$ $6 Cl^-(aq) + IO_3^-(aq) + 6 H^+(aq)$; $Cl_2(g) +$ $2 Br^-(aq) \longrightarrow 2 Cl^-(aq) + Br_2(aq)$ **111.** One conversion pathway is ton $\longrightarrow$ lb $\longrightarrow$ kg $\longrightarrow$ g $H_2SO_4 \longrightarrow$ g S $\longrightarrow$ mg S $\longrightarrow$ L seawater $\longrightarrow$ $m^3 \longrightarrow km^3$ seawater, leading to about 5.0 km^3 seawater. **112. (a)** AgAt **(b)** sodium perxenate **(c)** MgPo **(d)** tellurous acid **(e)** K_2SeSO_3 **(f)** potassium perastatate **113.** Convert the $E°$ values to $\Delta G°$ values for the reduction of H_2SeO_3 to Se and from Se to H_2Se. Add those two $\Delta G°$ values to obtain $\Delta G°$ for the reduction of H_2SeO_3 to H_2Se. Convert this $\Delta G°$ value to $E°$, which proves to be 0.38 V.

CHAPTER 23

Concept Assessment Page 969. The electron configuration of Fe is $[Ar]3d^64s^2$ and for Fe^{3+}, $[Ar]3d^5$. The $3d^5$ subshell is half-filled and especially stable. Cobalt ($[Ar]3d^74s^2$) and nickel ($[Ar]3d^84s^2$) must lose four and five electrons, respectively, to achieve a half-filled $3d$ subshell. They simply lose the two $4s$ electrons instead. **Page 976.** Both involve reducing metallic compounds to the free metal, often from the same ores. Pyrometallurgy employs high temperatures, yields impure metals that must be refined, and generates gaseous emissions and solid wastes. Hydrometallurgy involves leaching desired metal ions into an aqueous solution, followed by chemical or electrolytic reduction to the metal. Lower temperatures are used, gaseous emissions are largely eliminated, but liquid waste solutions are generated. **Page 978.** $Fe_2O_3(s) + 3 H_2(g)$

$\xrightarrow{\Delta} 2 Fe(s) + 3 H_2O(g)$ **Page 984.** The $[Cr_3O_{10}]^{2-}$ anion consists of three tetrahedral structures arranged around the backbone $Cr—O—Cr—O—Cr$. The central Cr atom of the backbone is bonded to two additional O atoms and the Cr atoms at the ends to three other O atoms for a total of 10 O atoms. The O. S. of Cr is $+6$ and that of O is -2 (accounting for the $2-$ charge on the anion). Similar anions are polysilicate (Fig. 21-20) and polyphosphate (Fig. 22-18). **Page 986.** The CO groups in $Fe(CO)_5$ are neutral molecules; the sum of the O.S. of the C and O is 0, and the O.S. of Fe is also 0. **Page 988.** Au ($Z = 79$, group 11) has the electron configuration $[Xe]4f^{14}5d^{10}6s^1$; the electrons lost in forming Au^{3+} are the $6s$ and

two of the $5d$, resulting in $[Xe]4f^{14}5d^8$.
Page 990. The five pairs of electrons around the Cd^{2+} central ion in $[CdCl_5]^{3-}$ is consistent with trigonal bipyramidal molecular geometry (see Table 10-1).
Self-Assessment Exercises 75. (a) Pig iron is impure iron (95% Fe) formed in the reduction of iron ore in a blast furnace.
(b) Ferromanganese is an iron-manganese alloy formed by the reduction of a mixture of iron and manganese oxides. **(c)** Chromite ore, $Fe(CrO_2)_2$, is the principal chromium ore.
(d) Brass is an alloy of Zn and Cu with small amounts of Sn, Pb, and Fe. **(e)** Aqua regia is a mixture of $HCl(aq)$ and $HNO_3(aq)$ that dissolves inactive metals by a combination of oxidation and complex ion formation. **(f)** Blister copper, formed in the reduction of a mixture of $Cu_2O(s)$ and $Cu_2S(s)$, is impure $Cu(s)$ containing $SO_2(g)$. **(g)** Stainless steel is an iron alloy with varying quantities of other metals, such as Cr, Mn, and Ni, and a small and carefully controlled percentage of carbon. **76.** (c), **(f)**, and **(g) 77.** (b) **78.** (d) **79.** (a) **80.** (d) **81.** (c) and **(e) 82. (a)** CrO_3 **(b)** potassium manganate **(c)** chromium carbonyl **(d)** $BaCr_2O_7$ **(e)** lanthanum(III) sulfate nonahydrate **(f)** $Au(CN)_3 \cdot 3 H_2O$
83. (a) $2 Fe_2S_3(s) + 3 O_2(g) + 6 H_2O(l) \longrightarrow$ $4 Fe(OH)_3(s) + 6 S(s)$
(b) $2 Mn^{2+}(aq) + 8 H_2O(l) + 5 S_2O_8^{2-}(aq)$ $\longrightarrow 2 MnO_4^-(aq) + 16 H^+(aq) + 10 SO_4^{2-}(aq)$
(c) $4 Ag(s) + 8 CN^-(aq) + O_2(g) + 2 H_2O(l)$ $\longrightarrow 4 [Ag(CN)_2]^-(aq) + 4 OH^-(aq)$

CHAPTER 24

Concept Assessment Page 1004. Only one possibility for a six-coordinate complex— $[AlCl_3(H_2O)_3]$—a non-electrolyte that does not conduct electricity and yields no precipitate with $AgNO_3(aq)$. Three possible four-coordinate complexes: $[AlCl(H_2O)_3]Cl_2$, $[AlCl_2(H_2O)_2]Cl \cdot H_2O$, and $[AlCl_3(H_2O)] \cdot 2 H_2O$. The first two of these three can be differentiated by conductivity measurements; the first is the better conductor. The third cannot be distinguished from the six-coordinate complex by Werner's method.
Page 1006. Three N atoms can donate an electron pair, so the ligand is tridentate.
Page 1008. The formula of the coordination compound is $K_3[FeBr_2Cl_2(OH)_2]$ and the name is potassium dibromodichlorodihydroxoferrate(III). **Page 1011.** As seen from the models in the margin, substitution of a fourth Cl^- in the *mer*-isomer leads to all four Cl^- ligands in the same plane, but this same isomer cannot be obtained by substituting a fourth Cl^- in the *fac*-isomer. **Page 1014.** Structures (a) and (d) are identical and are geometric isomers of (b), (c), and (e). Structures (e) and (c) are enantiomers, and (b) and (e) are identical.
Page 1018. (i) 4 **(ii)** 3 **(iii)** 5 **(iv)** 2 **(v)** 1
Page 1025. Both ligands form chelates, but $[Cr(EDTA)]^-$ does so in a single step, while $[Cr(en)_3]^{3+}$ requires a succession of three steps. The β_1 for $[Cr(EDTA)]^-$ is much larger than β_1 or β_2 of $[Cr(en)_3]^{3+}$, but the cumulative formation constant, β_3 (or K_f), of $[Cr(en)_3]^{3+}$ should be similar to β_1 (or K_f) of $[Cr(EDTA)]^-$.

Self-Assessment Exercises 67. (d) 68. (e) 69. (b) 70. (a) 71. (d) 72. (c) 73. (b) 74. (a) pentaamminebromocobalt(III) sulfate **(b)** hexaamminechromium(III) hexacyanocobaltate(III) **(c)** sodium hexanitrito-*N*-cobaltate(III) **(d)** tris(ethylenediamine)cobalt(III) chloride **75. (a)** $[Ag(CN)_2]^-$ **(b)** $[Pt(NO_2)(NH_3)_3]^+$ **(c)** $[CoCl(en)_2(H_2O)]^{2+}$ **(d)** $K_4[Cr(CN)_6]$ **76. (a)** square-planar **(b)** octahedral **(c)** octahedral, Cl^- are *cis* **(d)** octahedral, Cl^- *trans* to OH^- **77. (a)** one structure only (all positions are equivalent for the H_2O ligand; NH_3 ligands attach at the remaining five) **(b)** two structures, *cis* and *trans* (based on the placement of H_2O) **(c)** two structures, *fac* and *mer* **(d)** two structures, *cis* and *trans* (based on the placement of NH_3) **78. (a)** coordination isomerism, based on the interchange of ligands between the complex cation and complex anion **(b)** linkage isomerism, based on the mode of attachment of the SCN^- ligand (either $—SCN^-$ or $—NCS^-$) **(c)** no isomerism **(d)** geometric isomerism, based on whether the Cl^- ligands are *cis* or *trans* **(e)** geometric isomerism, based on whether the NH_3 (or OH^-) ligands are *fac* or *mer*. **79. (a)** geometric isomerism (*cis* and *trans*) and optical isomerism in the *cis* isomer **(b)** geometric isomerism (*cis* and *trans*), optical isomerism in the *cis* isomer, and linkage isomerism in the thiocyanate ligand **(c)** no isomers **(d)** no isomers for this square-planar complex **(e)** two geometric isomers, one with the tridentate ligand occupying meridional positions and the other with the tridentate ligand occupying facial positions. **80.** Because en is a stronger field ligand than H_2O, more energy must be absorbed by $[Co(en)_3]^{3+}$ than by $[Co(H_2O)_6]^{3+}$ to stimulate an electronic transition. This means that $[Co(en)_3]^{3+}(aq)$ absorbs shorter wavelength light and transmits longer wavelength light than does $[Co(H_2O)_6]^{3+}(aq)$. Thus, $[Co(en)_3]^{3+}(aq)$ is yellow and $[Co(H_2O)_6]^{3+}(aq)$ is blue.

CHAPTER 25

Concept Assessment Page 1044. Radioactive decay that changes Z produces a different element. This includes α, β^-, β^+ emissions and electron capture. If there is no change in Z (emission of γ rays) the element remains the same. **Page 1046.** Francium, a radioactive element, is produced in the decay schemes of heavier elements and found only in conjunction with other decay products, not in natural sources of the alkali metals that Fr resembles. **Page 1050.** Radioactive nuclides with very long half-lives have a very low activity; those with very short half-lives have a high activity but they do not persist long. Those with intermediate half-lives may persist in the environment for a significant period of time at a high activity, making them potentially the most hazardous. **Page 1055.** Refer to Table 25.2 and Figure 25-7 and focus on magic numbers and the relative thickness and width of the belt of stability for a fixed proton number and a fixed neutron number. The greatest thickness comes at the magic number, $Z = 50$. (Tin has 10 stable isotopes.) The greatest width comes at the magic number, $N = 82$. (There are 7 stable nuclides with 82 n.) **Page 1056.** Refer to Figure 25-7. The point representing ^{44}Ca falls in the belt of stability; ^{44}Ca is a stable nuclide. ^{57}Cu falls below the $N = Z$ line and in the region of β^+ emission, while ^{100}Zr falls above the belt of stability and decays by β^- emission. ^{235}U falls above and beyond the belt of stability and decays by α-particle emission.

Self-Assessment Exercises 74. (c) 75. (b) 76. (d) 77. (c) 78. (c) 79. (d) 80. (d) 81. (a) $^{214}_{88}\text{Ra} \longrightarrow {}^{210}_{86}\text{Rn} + {}^{4}_{2}\text{He}$ **(b)** $^{205}_{85}\text{At} \longrightarrow {}^{205}_{84}\text{Po} + {}^{0}_{+1}\beta$ **(c)** $^{212}_{87}\text{Fr} + e^- \longrightarrow {}^{212}_{86}\text{Rn}$ **(d)** $^{2}_{1}\text{H} + {}^{2}_{1}\text{H} \longrightarrow {}^{3}_{2}\text{He} + {}^{1}_{0}\text{n}$ **(e)** $^{241}_{95}\text{Am} + {}^{4}_{2}\text{He} \longrightarrow {}^{243}_{97}\text{Bk} + 2\,{}^{1}_{0}\text{n}$ **(f)** $^{232}_{90}\text{Th} + {}^{4}_{2}\text{He} \longrightarrow {}^{232}_{92}\text{U} + 4\,{}^{1}_{0}\text{n}$ **82.** Use equation (25.13) to determine λ from $t_{1/2}(\lambda = 0.0608\text{ d}^{-1})$. Then use equation (25.12) with $N_t = 0.01N_0$ and solve for $t(t = 76\text{ d})$. **83.** Use equation (25.13) to determine λ from $t_{1/2}$ ($\lambda = 7.88 \times 10^{-3}\text{ d}^{-1}$). Then use equation (25.12) with $N_t/N_0 = 256/1000$ for (a), $104/1000$ for (b), and $52/1000$ for (c). The answers are **(a)** 173 d **(b)** 287 d **(c)** 375 d. Note that the activity in (c) is half of that in (b), and so the time for (c) is 88 days longer than for (b)—one half-life period.

CHAPTER 26

Concept Assessment Page 1076. All structures based on F atoms at two of the vertices of a tetrahedron and H atoms at the remaining two are superimposable. Only one molecule has the formula CH_2F_2. Two possibilities exist for four atoms at the corners of a square—two F atoms on one side (*cis*) or on opposite corners (*trans*). **Page 1080.** The generic formula of an alkane is C_nH_{2n+2}, and for an alkyl halide where an X atom replaces one H atom, $C_nH_{2n+1}X$. If we limit the series to straight-chain alkanes with X as a terminal atom, we have $H(CH_2)_nX$. That is, $n = 1$, HCH_2X or CH_3X; $n = 2$, HCH_2CH_2X or CH_3CH_2X; $n = 3$, $HCH_2CH_2CH_2X$ or $CH_3CH_2CH_2X$; and so on. **Page 1081.** The forces accounting for the solubility of 1,2-dichloroethane in water

are dipole-dipole forces. The polarity of $ClCH_2CH_2Cl$ stems from the negative charge density on the Cl atoms, and this density should be highest when the two Cl atoms are in closest proximity. This occurs in the eclipsed conformation with the two Cl atoms lined up (like the hour and minute hands at 12 o' clock), which should have the greatest solubility in water. **Page 1092.** Predicting the products based on the ortho,para director —OH gives the same results as when predicted based on the meta director —NO_2. **Page 1093.** In butyl acohol —OH attaches to either of the indicated C atoms in the skeleton C—C*—C*—C; in both cases the molecule is the same and there is only one *s*-butyl alcohol. In pentyl alcohol, —OH attaches to one of the indicated C atoms in C—C*—C#—C*—C. Here, the two structures are the same if attachment is at a C* atom, but a different molecule results if attachment is to the C# atom. The name "*s*-pentyl alcohol" is inadequate. **Page 1102.** There are two chiral centers, at the 2nd and 3rd C atoms (to which Br atoms are attached), and four stereoisomers. To show this, sketch a dashed line-wedge structure with the two Br atoms on the same side of the molecule; next to it sketch its nonsuperimposable mirror image. Sketch another structure with the two Br atoms on opposite sides of the molecule and its mirror image, making a total of four stereoisomers.

Self-Assessment Exercises 128. (c) 129. (b) 130. (e) 131. (c) 132. (b) 133. C_4H_8 has the greater number of isomers. C_4H_{10} is the saturated hydrocarbon butane and consists of only two skeletal isomers—normal butane and isobutane. C_4H_8, on the other hand, can be the saturated compounds, cyclobutane and methylcyclopropane, or the unsaturated 1-butene and 2-butene. **134.** A primary alcohol must have —OH on a terminal C atom. The pentane isomer with a central C and four terminal C atoms, $C(CH_3)_4$ [2,2-dimethylpropane], forms only primary alcohols. **135. (a)** C_6H_6 **(b)** C_3H_7OH **(c)** C_6H_5COOH

CHAPTER 27

Concept Assessment Page 1139. The products are 1 mol glycerol and 1 mol each of sodium palmitate, sodium oleate, and sodium linoleate. **Page 1145.** The mirror image of a (+) enantiomer is the (−) enantiomer, so the mirror image of D-(+)-glucose is L-(−)-glucose. There can be no D-(−)-glucose. **Page 1150.** This polypeptide structure is shown in Example 27-1. Ionization occurs only at the N-terminal and C-terminal ends of the chain and nowhere else along the chain. Since the N-terminal and C-terminal amino acids are at a pH more than one unit above their isoelectric points, the only significant ionization is at the C-terminal amino acid, which would be present as a 1− anion, making the net charge on the tripeptide also 1−. **Page 1154.** Helix formation in a protein (Fig. 27-12) requires close proximity of carbonyl and amide groups and formation of hydrogen bonds between them, occurring regularly over an entire macromolecule. In the polysaccharides (Fig. 27-9), O atoms and —OH groups could conceivably form hydrogen bonds between them, but more randomly and not in the very tight helical fashion seen in proteins.

Self-Assessment Exercises 72. (b) 73. (d) 74. (a) 75. (d) 76. (e) 77. (c) 78. (b) 79. Refer to page 1137 for the structure of tripalmitin; write an equation for the saponification reaction similar to (27.1); determine the molar masses of tripalmitin and sodium palmitate; calculate the theoretical yield of sodium palmitate; answer = 129 g. **80.** The bases attached to the sugars down the right side of the structure are adenine (purine), uracil (pyrimidine), guanine (purine), and cytosine (pyrimidine). The sugars have five-membered rings and are ribose, making this a RNA chain. The phosphate groups bind the sugars together down the left side of the structure **81.** Follow the method used in Example 27-2 to obtain Gly-Cys-Val-Phe-Tyr.

PHOTO CREDITS

p. vii (top), Mehau Kulyk/Photo Researchers, Inc.; p. vii (bottom), Dr. Jeremy Burgess/PhotoResearchers, Inc.; p. viii, Richard Megna/Fundamental Photographs, NYC; p. ix, (left) Clayton J. Price/Corbis/Stock Market, (right) George Hunter/GettyImages Inc. – Stone Allstock; p. x, Richard Megna/Fundamental Photographs, NYC; p. xi, Richard Megna/Fundamental Photographs, NYC; p. xii, Carey B. Van Loon/Carey B. Van Loon; p. xiii, Fritz Goro/Getty Images/Time Life Pictures

CHAPTER 1 p. 1, STSci/NASA/Photo Researchers, Inc.; p. 3, Stamp from the private collection of Professor C. M. Lang, photography by Gary J. Shulfer, University of Wisconsin, Stevens Point. "1973, France (Scott #B468)"; Scott Standard Postage Stamp Catalogue, Scott Pub. Co., Sidney, Ohio; 1-2, Paul Silverman/Fundamental Photographs, NYC; 1-3, Diane Schiumo/Fundamental Photographs, NYC; p. 6, Bruce Iverson/Bruce Iverson, Photomicrography; 1-5a-b, Carey B. Van Loon/Carey B. Van Loon; 1-5c-d, Richard Megna/Fundamental Photographs, NYC; 1-6, Carey B. Van Loon/Carey B. Van Loon; 1-7, Mehau Kulyk/Photo Researchers, Inc.; p. 10, Richard Megna/Fundamental Photographs, NYC; 1-10, Carey B. Van Loon/Carey B. Van Loon; 1-11 (left & right), Kristen Brochmann/Fundamental Photographs, NYC; p. 16, Richard Megna/Fundamental Photographs, NYC; p. 18 (left & right), Richard Megna/Fundamental Photographs, NYC; 1-13, Carey B. Van Loon/Carey B. Van Loon; p. 22, S.B. Brummer, Tyco Laboratories, Inc.; p. 27, Douglas C. Pizac/AP Wide World Photos; p. 30, AP Wide World Photos; p. 31 (86), Sargent-Welch/VWR International; p. 31 (87), Tom Leininger/University of Kansas School of Engineering; p. 32, Jet Propulsion Laboratory/NASA/Goddard Space Flight Center

CHAPTER 2 p. 34, AP Wide World Photos; 2-1, Carey B. Van Loon/Carey B. Van Loon; 2-2a-b, © 2005 Richard Megna, Fundamental Photographs, NYC; p. 36 (top), M. Claye/Jacana Scientific Control/Photo Researchers, Inc.; p. 36 (bottom), Dave Bartruff/Stock Boston; p. 37, The Granger Collection; 2-4a, Fundamental Photographs, NYC; 2-17, Carey B. Van Loon/Carey B. Van Loon; 2-18, Richard Megna/Fundamental Photographs, NYC; p. 56, Tom Bean/Corbis/Stock Market

CHAPTER 3 p. 67, Dr. Jeremy Burgess/Photo Researchers, Inc.; 3-1 (left), Carey B. Van Loon/Carey B. Van Loon; 3-6, Carey B. Van Loon/Carey B. Van Loon; 3-7, Tom Pantages/Tom Pantages; p. 96, Tom Pantages/Tom Pantages; p. 106, Carey B. Van Loon/Carey B. Van Loon

CHAPTER 4 p. 109, Roger Ressmeyer/Corbis/Bettmann; 4-1, Richard Megna/Fundamental Photographs, NYC; 4-2a, Richard Megna/Fundamental Photographs, NYC; 4-2b, Tom Bochsler/Pearson Education/PH College; 4-6a-c, Richard Megna/Fundamental Photographs, NYC; 4-8a-c, Richard Megna/Fundamental Photographs, NYC; p. 130, Martin Bond/Science Photo Library/Photo Researchers, Inc.; p. 140 (left), Ed Degginger/Color-Pic, Inc. p. 140 (right), Robert Mathena/Fundamental Photographs, NYC

CHAPTER 5 p. 142, Richard Megna/Fundamental Photographs, NYC; 5-1a, Tom Pantages/Tom Pantages; 5-1b, C Squared Studios/Getty Images, Inc.-Photodisc; 5-3a-c, Richard Megna/Fundamental Photographs, NYC; p. 146, Richard Megna/Fundamental Photographs, NYC; 5-4a-c, Richard Megna/Fundamental Photographs, NYC; 5-5, Carey B. Van Loon/Carey B. Van Loon; 5-6, Carey B. Van Loon/Carey B. Van Loon; p. 152, SuperStock, Inc.; p. 153, Tom Pantages/Tom Pantages; 5-7a-c, Joel Gordon/Joel Gordon Photography; 5-8, Carey B. Van Loon/Carey B. Van Loon; p. 160, © Phil Degginger/Color Pic, Inc.; p. 163, © 2005 Kristen Brochmann/Fundamental Photographs, NYC; 5-10a-c, Carey B. Van Loon/Carey B. Van Loon; p. 166, Runk/Schoenberger/Grant Heilman Photography, Inc.; 5-11a-c, Carey B. Van Loon/Carey B. Van Loon; p. 168, Carey B. Van Loon/Carey B. Van Loon; p. 173 (a&b), William H. Breazeale, Francis Marion University; p. 173 (c), Tom Pantages/Tom Pantages

CHAPTER 6 p. 178, Johner/Getty Images – Photonica Amana America, Inc.; 6-1, Carey B. Van Loon/Carey B. Van Loon; 6-2, Kristen Brochmann/Fundamental Photographs, NYC; 6-3, Richard Megna/Fundamental Photographs, NYC; p. 186, NASA/Science Source/Photo Researchers, Inc.; p. 188, Stamp from the private collection of Professor C.M. Lang, photography by Gary J. Shulfer, University of Wisconsin, Stevens Point. "1956, Italy (Scott #714);" Scott Standard Postage Stamp Catalogue, Scott Pub. Co., Sidney, Ohio; 6-10, Carey B. Van Loon/Carey B. Van Loon; 6-13, Carey B. Van Loon/Carey B. Van Loon; 6-20, Richard Megna/Fundamental Photographs, NYC; p. 212, Ken Graham/Getty Images Inc. – Stone Allstock; 6-24 (top), NASA Headquarters; 6-24 (center), Joyce Photographics/Photo Researchers, Inc.; 6-24 (bottom), Pete Seaward/Getty Images Inc. – Stone Allstock; p. 213 (top), Diane Hirsch/Fundamental Photographs, NYC; p. 213 (bottom), John Cancalosi/Stock Boston; p. 216 (left & right), Richard Megna/Fundamental Photographs, NYC; p. 219 (top & bottom), Michael Dalton/Fundamental Photographs, NYC

CHAPTER 7 p. 225, Richard Megna/Fundamental Photographs, NYC; 7-1, Kristen Brochmann/Fundamental Photographs, NYC; 7-2, Richard Megna/Fundamental Photographs, NYC; p. 228, Science Photo Library/Photo Researchers, Inc.; p. 231, Telebrands Corporation; p. 232 (a&b), Carey B. Van Loon/Carey B. Van Loon; p. 251 (top), Tom Pantages/Tom Pantages; p. 251 (bottom), Carey B. Van Loon/Carey B. Van Loon; p. 260, Simon Fraser/Science Photo Library/Photo Researchers, Inc.; p. 262, Bruce Ayres/Getty Images Inc. – Stone Allstock

CHAPTER 8 p. 277, Dennis Kunkel/Phototake NYC; 8-4a, Richard Megna/Fundamental Photographs, NYC; 8-4b, Rob Bartee/SuperStock, Inc.; 8-6, Richard Megna/Fundamental Photographs, NYC; 8-7a, Clayton J. Price/Corbis/Stock Market; 8-7b, George Hunter/Getty Images Inc. – Stone Allstock; 8-8a, Carey B. Van Loon/Carey B. Van Loon; 8-8b-e, Tom Pantages/Tom Pantages; 8-9 (left), Richard Megna/Fundamental Photographs, NYC; 8-9 (right), Wabash Instrument Corp./Fundamental Photographs, NYC; 8-10, Wabash Instrument Corp./Fundamental Photographs, NYC; p. 285, Robin Smith/Getty Images Inc. – Stone Allstock; p. 286, AIP Emilio Segre Visual Archives, gift of Jost Lemmerich; p. 287, Bettmann/Corbis/Bettmann; p. 290, Stamp from the private collection of Professor C. M. Lang, photography by Gary J. Shulfer, University of Wisconsin, Stevens Point. "1963, Denmark (Scott #409);" Scott Standard Postage Stamp Catalogue, Scott Pub. Co., Sidney, Ohio; p. 296, © The Nobel Foundation; 8-16a, Hank Morgan/Rainbow; 8-16b, Will & Deni McIntyre/Photo Researchers, Inc.; p. 298, Photo by Paul Ehrenfest, Jr., courtesy AIP Emilio Segre Visual Archives; p. 324, William Warren/Corbis/Bettmann

CHAPTER 9 p. 339, IBM Research, Almaden Research Center; p. 341, Stamp from the private collection of Professor C.M. Lang, photography by Gary J. Shulfer, University of Wisconsin, Stevens Point. "1957, Russia (Scott #1906) and 1969, Russia (Scott #3607);" Scott Standard Postage Stamp Catalogue, Scott Pub. Co., Sidney, Ohio; p. 342, Bettman/Corbis/Bettmann; 9-2b, British Department of the Environment, Transport, and the Regions; 9-12, Carey B. Van Loon/Carey B. Van Loon; 9-14a, Ed Degginger/Color-Pic, Inc.; 9-14b, Carey B. Van Loon/Carey B. Van Loon; 9-15, Carey B. Van Loon/Carey B. Van Loon; 9-16a-b, Carey B. Van Loon/Carey B. Van Loon; p. 364, Richard Megna/Fundamental Photographs, NYC

CHAPTER 10 p. 373, UPI/Corbis/Bettmann; 10-3, Richard Megna/Fundamental Photographs, NYC; 10-12, Carey B. Van

Loon/Carey B. Van Loon; **Table 10.1, p. 399,** Carey B. Van Loon/Carey B. Van Loon; **Table 10.1, p. 400** (top three photos), Tom Pantages/Phototake NYC; (bottom), Carey B. Van Loon/Carey B. Van Loon; **p. 410,** D. Nunuk/Photo Researchers, Inc.; **p. 411,** Anglo-Australian Observatory, photograph by David Malin

CHAPTER 11 11-4, Carey B. Van Loon/Carey B. Van Loon; **11-8,** Carey B. Van Loon/Carey B. Van Loon; **11-9,** Carey B. Van Loon/Carey B. Van Loon; **11-11a & b,** Carey B. Van Loon/Carey B. Van Loon; **11-14,** Carey B. Van Loon/Carey B. Van Loon; **p. 445,** Richard Megna/Fundamental Photographs, NYC; **p. 447,** UPI/Corbis/Bettmann; **11-29,** Clive Freeman, The Royal Institution/Science Photo Library/Photo Researchers, Inc.; **11-38,** Courtesy from: C F Matta and R J Gillespie; Journal of Chemical Education, Vol. 79, No. 9, Fig 1 (a) September 2002, pg 1142. jchemed.chem.wisc.edu; **11-39,** Courtesy from: C F Matta and R J Gillespie; Journal of Chemical Education, Vol. 79, No. 9, Fig 2a September 2002, pg 1142. jchemed.chem.wisc.edu; **p. 462,** Tom Pantages/Tom Pantages

CHAPTER 12 p. 471, Ben Osborne/Getty Images Inc. – Stone Allstock; **12-1,** Carey B. Van Loon/Carey B. Van Loon; **12-3,** Carey B. Van Loon/Carey B. Van Loon; **12-4,** Ed Degginger/Color-Pic, Inc.; **12-5,** Carey B. Van Loon/Carey B. Van Loon; **12-6,** Tom Pantages/Tom Pantages; **p. 474,** Tom Pantages/Tom Pantages; **12-10** (left & right), Carey B. Van Loon/Carey B. Van Loon; **p. 478,** Richard Megna/Fundamental Photographs, NYC; **12-11,** Images of critical points of benzene taken from the Chemistry Comes Alive! by Jerrold J. Jacobsen, John W. Moore, et al., published by Journal of Chemical Education Software; **12-16,** Carey B. Van Loon/Carey B. Van Loon; **p. 487,** Richard Megna/Fundamental Photographs, NYC; **12-23,** Tom Pantages/Tom Pantages; **12-25a & b,** Carey B. Van Loon/Carey B. Van Loon; **12-30,** Richard Megna/Fundamental Photographs, NYC; **p. 497,** Peter French/DRK Photo; **p. 498,** Tom Pantages/Tom Pantages; **12-34d,** Tom Pantages/Tom Pantages; **12-35b,** Boris I. Yakobson and Richard E. Smalley, Rice University; **12-38,** Richard Megna/Fundamental Photographs, NYC; **p. 502,** Adalberto Rios Szalay/Sexto Sol/Getty Images, Inc.—Photodisc; **12-39,** Carey B. Van Loon/Carey B. Van Loon; **12-40** (left & right), Carey B. Van Loon/Carey B. Van Loon; **p. 516,** Richard Megna/Fundamental Photographs, NYC

CHAPTER 13 p. 528, Richard Megna/Fundamental Photographs, NYC; **13-9,** Richard Megna/Fundamental Photographs, NYC; **13-10,** Carey B. Van Loon/Carey B. Van Loon; **p. 542,** Charles D. Winters/Photo Researchers, Inc.; **p. 543,** David Mechlin/Phototake NYC; **p. 547,** Ed Degginger/Color-Pic, Inc.; **13-16b,** Richard Megna/Fundamental Photographs, NYC; **p. 550** (left to right), © Dr. David Phillips/Visuals Unlimited; **p. 551,** © Katadyn North America. Used by permission; **p. 553,** J. Pat Carter/AP Wide World Photos; **p. 554** (top), Wayne Eastep/Getty Images Inc. – Stone Allstock; **p. 554** (bottom), Mark Joseph/Getty Images Inc. – Stone Allstock; **p. 555,** Library of Congress; **13-21,** © 2005 Richard Megna/Fundamental Photographs, NYC; **13-23** (left & right), Carey B. Van Loon/Carey B. Van Loon;

p. 559, Hank Morgan/Science Source/Photo Researchers, Inc.; **p. 560,** Hewlett Packard/Fundamental Photographs, NYC

CHAPTER 14 p. 572, Joseph P. Sinnot/Fundamental Photographs, NYC; **p. 595,** E.R. Degginger/Color-Pic, Inc.; **14-13,** James Blank/Getty Images, Inc. – Taxi; **14-15,** Robert Frerck/Getty Images Inc. – Stone Allstock; **p. 606** (top), Carey B. Van Loon/Carey B. Van Loon; **p. 606** (bottom), Oxford Molecular Biophysics Laboratory/Science Photo Library/Photo Researchers, Inc.; **p. 608,** NASA/Phototake NYC; **p. 619** (left & right), Richard Megna/Fundamental Photographs, NYC

CHAPTER 15 p. 622, Jim W. Grace/Photo Researchers, Inc.; **15-1,** Carey B. Van Loon/Carey B. Van Loon; **p. 623,** Alexandra Winkler/Reuters NewMedia Inc./Corbis/Bettmann; **643,** N.P. Alexander/Visuals Unlimited; **15-8a-b,** Richard Megna/Fundamental Photographs, NYC; **p. 652,** Grant Heilman/Grant Heilman Photography, Inc.; **p. 653,** Getty Images Inc. – Stone Allstock

CHAPTER 16 p. 663, FoodPix/Getty Images, Inc. – Foodpix; **p. 664,** Carey B. Van Loon/Carey B. Van Loon; **16-7,** Tom Pantages/Tom Pantages; **p. 681,** Carey B. Van Loon/Carey B. Van Loon; **p. 684,** Carey B. Van Loon/Carey B. Van Loon; **16-9,** Carey B. Van Loon/Carey B. Van Loon; **16-12,** Tom Pantages/Tom Pantages; **p. 698** (left), NYC Parks Photo Archive/Fundamental Photographs, NYC; **p. 698** (right), Kristen Brochmann/Fundamental Photographs, NYC

CHAPTER 17 p. 708, Richard Megna/Fundamental Photographs, NYC; **17-1,** Carey B. Van Loon/Carey B. Van Loon; **17-2,** Carey B. Van Loon/Carey B. Van Loon; **17-3,** Carey B. Van Loon/Carey B. Van Loon; **17-4,** Carey B. Van Loon/Carey B. Van Loon; **p. 721,** Tom Pantages/Tom Pantages; **17-8,** Carey B. Van Loon/Carey B. Van Loon; **p. 723,** Elena Rooraid/PhotoEdit; **p. 734,** John W. Finley/John W. Finley

CHAPTER 18 p. 747, China Tourism Press.Xu, Jin Yan/Getty Images Inc. – Image Bank; **p. 749,** Kalab/Custom Medical Stock Photo, Inc.; **p. 750,** Sovereign/ISM/Phototake NYC; **18-1,** Carey B. Van Loon/Carey B. Van Loon; **18-3a-b,** Carey B. Van Loon/Carey B. Van Loon; **p. 759,** Richard Megna/Fundamental Photographs, NYC; **18-5a-b,** Tom Pantages/Tom Pantages; **18-6,** Richard Megna/Fundamental Photographs, NYC; **p. 767a-b,** Carey B. Van Loon/Carey B. Van Loon; **18-8,** Carey B. Van Loon/Carey B. Van Loon; **p. 770,** Jane Burton/Bruce Coleman Inc.; **18-9,** Richard Megna/Fundamental Photographs, NYC; **p. 777,** Walter S. Clark/Photo Researchers, Inc.

CHAPTER 19 p. 780, Tony Wells/Mason Dixon Historical Society, Inc.; **p. 781** (top), Stockbyte; **p. 781** (bottom), Michael Dalton/Fundamental Photographs, NYC; **p. 783,** Central Library for Physics, Vienna, Austria; **p. 793,** © Bettmann/CORBIS; **p. 810,** P. Motta & T. Naguro/Science Photo Library/Photo Researchers, Inc.

CHAPTER 20 p. 822, Thomas Kienzle/AP Wide World Photos; **20-1,** Carey B. Van Loon/Carey B. Van Loon; **p. 832,** Bettmann/Corbis/Bettmann; **20-7,** Diane Schiumo/Fundamental Photographs, NYC; **p. 837,** Stamp from the private collection of Professor C.M. Lang, photography by Gary J. Shulfer, University of Wisconsin, Stevens Point. "1980, Sweden (Scott #1344);" Scott Standard Postage Stamp Catalogue, Scott Pub. Co., Sidney, Ohio; **20-12,** Tom Pantages/Tom Pantages; **p. 843,** Carey B. Van Loon/Carey B. Van Loon; **20-15,** Liz Strenk/SuperStock, Inc.; **p. 845,** Leonard Lessin/Peter Arnold, Inc.; **p. 846,** Courtesy of Toyota Motor Sales, U.S.A., Inc.; **20-19,** Carey B. Van Loon/Carey B. Van Loon; **p. 848** (top), Serge Kozak/Zefa/CORBIS- NY; **p. 848** (bottom), Robert Erlbacher/Missouri Dry Dock and Repair Company, Inc.; **p. 851,** Runk/Schoenberger/Grant Heilman Photography, Inc.; **p. 854** (top), Charles E. Rotkin/Corbis/Bettmann; **p. 854** (bottom), Richard Pasley/Stock Boston; **p. 858,** Kenneth Eward/BioGrafx; **p. 861,** Carey B. Van Loon/Carey B. Van Loon; **p. 864,** New York Convention & Visitors Bureau

CHAPTER 21 p. 870, SuperStock, Inc.; **p. 871** (top), Joel E. Arem/Joel E. Arem; **p. 871** (bottom), Ed Degginger/Color-Pic, Inc.; **p. 874,** Science Photo Library/Photo Researchers, Inc.; **p. 875,** Kevin Schafer/Corbis/Bettmann; **p. 876,** Ed Degginger/Color-Pic, Inc.; **p. 879,** Jeffrey A. Scovil/Jeffrey A. Scovil; **p. 883,** William E. Ferguson/William E. Ferguson; **21-9,** Harris Photographic/Tom Stack & Associates, Inc.; **p. 884,** SuperStock, Inc.; **p. 885** (top), Sheila Terry/Science Photo Library/Photo Researchers, Inc.; **p. 885** (bottom), Carey B. Van Loon/Carey B. Van Loon; **p. 890,** Richard Megna/Fundamental Photographs, NYC; **21-14a-c,** Carey B. Van Loon/Carey B. Van Loon; **p. 894** (top), Ed Degginger/Color-Pic, Inc.; **p. 894** (bottom), Tom Bochsler/Pearson Education/PH College; **p. 896,** Bruce Frisch/Photo Researchers, Inc.; **p. 897,** Gim Media/Gemological Institute of America; **p. 903,** Photo courtesy of Kyocera Industrial Ceramics Corp./Vancouver, WA; **p. 904,** Frank La Bua/Pearson Education/PH College; **p. 905,** Jan Halaska/Photo Researchers, Inc.; **p. 908,** Bruce Frisch/Photo Researchers, Inc.; **p. 915,** Rolf Hicker/Getty Images Inc. – Stone Allstock

CHAPTER 22 p. 917, Richard Megna/Fundamental Photographs, NYC; **p. 918** (top), John Coletti/Stock Boston; **p. 918** (bottom), © The Nobel Foundation; **p. 919** (top), Richard Megna/Fundamental Photographs, NYC; **p. 919** (center), The Goodyear Tire & Rubber Company; **p. 919** (bottom), Argonne National Laboratory; **p. 923** (top), Richard Dunoff/Corbis/Stock Market; **p. 923** (bottom), Tom Pantages/Tom Pantages; **p. 924,** Richard Megna/Fundamental Photographs, NYC; **p. 927,** Carey B. Van Loon/Carey B. Van Loon; **p. 930,** Bill Pierce/Rainbow; **p. 931,** DK Limited/CORBIS- NY; **22-9a,** Jeffrey A. Scovil/Jeffrey A. Scovil; **22-9b,** Tom Bochsler/Pearson Education/PH College; **22-9c,** Carey B. Van Loon/Carey B. Van Loon; **22-9d,** Stephen Frisch/Stock Boston; **p. 935a & b,** Tom Bochsler/Pearson Education/PH College; **p. 939,** Geoff Tompkinson/Science Photo Library/Photo Researchers, Inc.; **p. 941,** Stamp from the private collection of Professor C. M. Lang, photography by Gary J. Shulfer, University of Wisconsin, Stevens Point. "1978,

Sweden (Scott #1271);" Scott Standard Postage Stamp Catalogue, Scott Pub. Co., Sidney, Ohio; **p. 942** (top), Grant Heilman/Grant Heilman Photography, Inc.; **p. 942** (bottom), NASA Headquarters; **p. 943**, Tom Pantages/Tom Pantages; **p. 944** (top right), Michael Dalton/Fundamental Photographs, NYC; **p. 944** (center), Richard Megna/Fundamental Photographs, NYC; **p. 944** (bottom), Richard Megna/Fundamental Photographs, NYC; **p. 945** (center right), Ed Degginger/Color-Pic, Inc.; **p. 945** (bottom), Tom Bochsler/Pearson Education/PH College; **p. 948**, Charlie Ott/Photo Researchers, Inc.; **p. 949**, Richard Megna/Fundamental Photographs, NYC; **p. 950**, Richard Megna/Fundamental Photographs, NYC; **22-24a**, NASA/Goddard Space Flight Center; **22-24b**, NASA/Tom Pantages; **p. 956**, Carey B. Van Loon/Carey B. Van Loon; **p. 960**, Tom Pantages/Tom Pantages

CHAPTER 23 p. 964, Michael Dalton/Fundamental Photographs, NYC; **p. 968**, Reprinted with permission from M. Seul, L.R. Monar, L. O'Gorman and R. Wolfe, Morphology and local structure in labyrinthine stripe domain phase, Science 254:1616-1618, Fig. 3 (1991). Copyright 1991 American Association for the Advancement of Science; **23-4b**, Photo courtesy of Peter Bourke, Outokumpu, Perth, Australia, reproduced by permission of Outokumpu Mintec OY, Espoo, Finland; **23-5**, Sol Mednick Photography Gallery & Gallery; **p. 974** (top), Wah Chang; **p. 974** (bottom), Day Williams/Photo Researchers, Inc.; **p. 976**, Robert Semeniuk/Corbis/Stock Market; **p. 977**, Steven Weinberg/Getty Images Inc. – Stone Allstock; **p. 978** (center), PhotoLink/Getty Images, Inc.- Photodisc; **p. 978** (bottom), Rich Chisholm/Corbis/Stock Market; **23-10**, Richard Megna/Fundamental Photographs, NYC; **p. 981**, Phil Degginger/Color-Pic, Inc.; **23-11**, Carey B. Van Loon/Carey B. Van Loon; **23-12**, Carey B. Van

Loon/Carey B. Van Loon; **p. 984**, Tom Pantages/Tom Pantages; **p. 987**, Richard Megna/Fundamental Photographs, NYC; **p. 988**, NASA/Tom Pantages; **p. 989**, © National Maritime Museum Picture Library, London, England; **p. 990**, ™ Netscape® **23-15**, David Parker/IMI/University of Birmingham High TC Consortium/Science Photo Library/Photo Researchers, Inc.; **p. 992**, Reproduced with permission from figure: 4a Michalet et al., SCIENCE 307: 538-44. Copyright 2005 American Association for the Advancement of Science; **23-16**, Richard Vanduyne

CHAPTER 24 p. 1001, Karl Hartmann/Traudel Sachs/Phototake NYC; **p. 1002**, Science Photo Library/Photo Researchers, Inc.; **24-1**, Carey B. Van Loon/Carey B. Van Loon; **24-16a**, Fritz Goro/Getty Images/Time Life Pictures; **24-18**, Carey B. Van Loon/Carey B. Van Loon; **24-20**, Carey B. Van Loon/Carey B. Van Loon; **24-21**, Carey B. Van Loon/Carey B. Van Loon; **24-22**, Carey B. Van Loon/Carey B. Van Loon; **p. 1029**, Tom Pantages/Tom Pantages; **24-26b**, Richard Megna/Fundamental Photographs, NYC; **p. 1032**, Ed Degginger/Color-Pic, Inc.

CHAPTER 25 p. 1040, Celestial Image Co./Photo Researchers, Inc.; **p. 1041**, Science Photo Library/Photo Researchers, Inc.; **p. 1042**, Lawrence Berkeley National Laboratory/Science Photo Library/Photo Researchers, Inc.; **p. 1045**, Bettmann/Corbis/Bettmann; **p. 1046**, UPI/Corbis/Bettmann; **p. 1047**, David Parker/Photo Researchers, Inc.; **p. 1050**, Corbis/Sygma; **p. 1051**, Science VU/NASA-JMP/Visuals Unlimited; **p. 1058**, Yann Arthus-Bertrand/Photo Researchers, Inc.; **25-9b**, David M. Doody/Tom Stack & Associates, Inc.; **p. 1059** (a), Phil Degginger/Getty Images Inc. – Stone Allstock; **p. 1059** (b), Victoria Speransky/Ivleva/

Magnum Photos, Inc.; **p. 1059** (c), Esbin/Anderson/Omni-Photo Communications, Inc.; **p. 1060**, EFDA-JET/Photo Researchers, Inc.; **p. 1061**, Custom Medical Stock Photo, Inc.; **p. 1062**, Stephen Agricola/The Image Works; **p. 1063a & b**, Perrin/CNRI/Phototake NYC; **p. 1064** (middle), Gemaldegalerie, Dahlem-Berlin, Germany/A.K.G., Berlin/SuperStock; **p. 1064**, International Atomic Energy Agency; **p. 1066**, U.S. Department of Energy/Science Source/Photo Researchers, Inc.

CHAPTER 26 p. 1073, Greg Vaughn/PacificStock.com; **p. 1076**, Stamp from the private collection of Professor C.M. Lang, photography by Gary J. Shulfer, University of Wisconsin, Stevens Point. "1992, Switzerland (Scott #913);" Scott Standard Postage Stamp Catalogue, Scott Pub. Co., Sidney, Ohio; **p. 1084**, Ed Degginger/Color-Pic, Inc.; **p. 1087**, Ed Degginger/Color-Pic, Inc.; **p. 1089**, Stamp from the private collection of Professor C.M. Lang, photography by Gary J. Shulfer, University of Wisconsin, Stevens Point. "1966, Belgium (Scott #624);" Scott Standard Postage Stamp Catalogue, Scott Pub. Co., Sidney, Ohio; **p. 1093**, Pete Saloutos/Corbis/Stock Market; **p. 1095**, Science Photo Library/Photo Researchers, Inc.; **p. 1098**, Bill Ross/Corbis/Bettmann; **p. 1118**, Christopher Springmann/Corbis/Stock Market; **p. 1122**, David Young-Wolff/PhotoEdit

CHAPTER 27 p. 1135, Tom Pantages/Phototake NYC; **p. 1139**, Richard Megna/Fundamental Photographs, NYC; **p. 1142**, Bettmann/Corbis/Bettmann; **p. 1145**, Jerry Mason/Science Photo Library/Photo Researchers, Inc.; **p. 1147**, National Exposure Research Laboratory, EPA/Tom Pantages; **27-15**, Arthur Lesk/Science Photo Library/Photo Researchers, Inc.; **p. 1154**, Tom Pantages/Tom Pantages; **27-26b**, Dan McCoy/Dan McCoy

INDEX

Selected Physical Constants

Acceleration due to gravity	g	$9.80665 \text{ m} \cdot \text{s}^{-2}$
Speed of light (in vacuum)	c	$2.99792458 \times 10^8 \text{ m} \cdot \text{s}^{-1}$
Gas constant	R	$0.0820574 \text{ L} \cdot \text{atm} \cdot \text{mol}^{-1} \cdot \text{K}^{-1}$
		$8.314472 \text{ J} \cdot \text{mol}^{-1} \cdot \text{K}^{-1}$
Electron charge	e^-	$-1.602176462 \times 10^{-19} \text{ C}$
Electron rest mass	m_e	$9.10938188 \times 10^{-31} \text{ kg}$
Planck's constant	h	$6.62606876 \times 10^{-34} \text{ J} \cdot \text{s}$
Faraday constant	F	$9.64853415 \times 10^4 \text{ C} \cdot \text{mol}^{-1}$
Avogadro constant	N_A	$6.02214199 \times 10^{23} \text{ mol}^{-1}$

Some Common Conversion Factors

Length

1 meter (m) = 39.37007874 inches (in.)

1 in. = 2.54 centimeters (cm) (exact)

Mass

1 kilogram (kg) = 2.2046226 pounds (lb)

1 lb. = 453.59237 grams (g)

Volume

1 liter (L) = 1000 mL = 1000 cm³ (exact)

     1 L = 1.056688 quart (qt)

1 gallon (gal) = 3.785412 L

Force

1 newton (N) = $1 \text{ kg} \cdot \text{m} \cdot \text{s}^{-2}$

Energy

1 joule (J) = $1 \text{ N} \cdot \text{m} = 1 \text{ kg} \cdot \text{m}^2 \cdot \text{s}^{-2}$

1 calorie (cal) = 4.184 J (exact)

1 electronvolt (eV) = $1.602176462 \times 10^{-19} \text{ J}$

1 eV/atom = $96.485 \text{ kJ} \cdot \text{mol}^{-1}$

1 kilowatt hour (kWh) = 3600 kJ (exact)

Mass-energy equivalence:

   1 unified atomic mass unit (u)

   = $1.66053873 \times 10^{-27} \text{ kg}$

   = 931.4866 MeV

Some Useful Geometric Formulas

Perimeter of a rectangle = $2l + 2w$

Circumference of a circle = $2\pi r$

Area of a rectangle = $l \times w$

Area of a triangle = $\frac{1}{2}$ (base $\times$ height)

Area of a circle = πr^2

Area of a sphere = $4\pi r^2$

Volume of a parallelepiped = $l \times w \times h$

Volume of a sphere = $\frac{4}{3} \pi r^3$

Volume of a cylinder or prism = (area of base) $\times$ height

$\pi \approx 3.14159$